CONTENTS—1985 FUNDAMENTALS VO... W9-BSP-158

CONTENTS—1983 EQUIPMENT VOLUME

WITHDRAWAL

1987 ASHRAE HANDBOOK

Heating, Ventilating, and Air-Conditioning Systems and Applications

American Society of Heating, Refrigerating and Air Conditioning Engineers, Inc.
1791 Tullie Circle, N.E., Atlanta, GA 30329

Copyright © 1987 by the American Society of Heating, Refrigerating and Air-Conditioning Engineers, Inc. All rights reserved.

DEDICATED

TO THE ADVANCEMENT OF

THE PROFESSION

AND ITS ALLIED INDUSTRIES

No part of this book may be reproduced without permission in writing from ASHRAE, except by a reviewer who may quote brief passages or reproduce illustrations in a review with appropriate credit; nor may any part of this book be reproduced, stored in a retrieval system, or transmitted in any form or by any means — electronic, photocopying, recording, or other — without permission in writing from ASHRAE.

Although great care has been taken in the compilation and publication of this volume, no warranties, express or implied, are given in connection herewith and no responsibility can be taken for any claims arising herewith.

Comments, criticisms, and suggestions regarding the subject matter are invited. Any errors or omissions in the data should be brought to the attention of the Editor. If required, an errata sheet will be issued at approximately the same time as the next Handbook. Notice of any significant errors found after that time will be published in the ASHRAE JOURNAL.

ISBN: 0-910110-50-6

TH
7015
A74
1987

16127832

CONTENTS

PREFACE

This Handbook completes the reorganization of the ASHRAE Handbook series. Last year's 1986 REFRIGERATION Volume included the refrigeration-related chapters from both the 1982 APPLICATIONS and the 1984 SYSTEMS volumes. The remaining chapters, which are primarily related to heating, ventilating, and air conditioning systems and applications, have been revised and included in this volume.

The 61 chapters are divided into four major sections. The first of these sections describes various heating and air-conditioning systems. These chapters help the engineer in evaluating the systems and learning how they operate.

The second and third sections cover specific applications and describe the air conditioning of public and private buildings, various forms of transportation and their facilities, and several industrial and manufacturing applications. Both the practicing engineer and those looking for information about the heating, ventilating, and air conditioning of a wide variety of applications will find this section a valuable reference.

The last section includes several chapters principally for the design engineer, although building owners and operating engineers will also find several chapters of interest.

Three chapters in this volume (40, 42, and 46) are new to the handbook series. They include information on the heating, ventilating, and air conditioning of nuclear facilities; ventilating and air conditioning for underground mines; and thermal storage.

Over half of the chapters have been extensively revised by volunteers who work with ASHRAE'S Technical Committees. The Handbook Committee appreciates their efforts, for it is the expertise of these volunteers that makes the Handbook a respected and authoritative reference. The major contributors are listed in the front of the handbook.

In addition to the new and revised chapters, the following changes have been made to the format:

- Both Inch-Pound (I-P) and International System (SI) units of measurement are used in this volume. This decision to publish only one edition, instead of separate I-P and SI editions, required revising most chapters to clarify the tables, figures, and equations.

- References are now shown in the chapter by author and date of publication rather than as superscript numbers. Many people find this method of referencing easier to follow and it has the added advantage of being easier to revise.

- Major section headings for each chapter are now located in the Table of Contents instead of at the beginning of each chapter, which should make information easier to find.

Changes in technology have also helped in producing this year's Handbook. The word processor has given the editorial staff increased flexibility, as well as new challenges. The text from about a quarter of the chapters was received from authors on a microcomputer floppy disk.

Errata for the 1983, 1985, and 1986 volumes precede the Index. Errata for this volume will be included in the 1988 EQUIPMENT Volume.

The Handbook Committee welcomes reader input. If you have suggestions and comments on improving a chapter or would like more information on helping review a chapter, please write to Handbook Editor, ASHRAE, 1791 Tullie Circle, Atlanta, GA 30329.

Robert A. Parsons
Handbook Editor

CONTRIBUTORS

In addition to the Technical Committees, the following individuals contributed significantly
to this volume. The appropriate chapter numbers follow each contributor's name.

David M. Elovitz (1)
Energy Economics, Inc.

John J. Harmon (1)
H. C. Yu & Associates

Harvey Brickman (1)
Tishman Realty & Construction Co.

George A. Freeman (2)
G. A. Freeman Engineering Associates

Robert N. Kittrell (3)
Griffith C. Burr, Inc.

Dale S. Cooper (4)
D. S. Cooper & Associates

Arthur B. Sirjord, Jr. (4)
TRA

Stephen W. Trelease (5)
Command-Aire Corp.

Donald K. Miller (6, 9)
York International Corp.

Thomas R. Bergh (7)
Airtite, Inc.

James M. Calm (9, 17)
Institute Cerac S.A.

H. Michael Hughes (9)
Friedrich Air Conditioning
and Refrigeration Co.

Richard C. Niess (9)
Dames & Moore

John Tuzson (9)
GRI

Douglas W. DeWerth (10)
American Gas Association
Laboratories

Eugene E. O'Neil (11)
Dunham-Bush, Inc.

Lawrence R. O'Dell (11)
Armstrong Machine Works

Richard E. Batherman (11)
VICO, Inc.

Raymond J. Albrecht (11)
NYS ERDA

Allen J. Hanley (11, 15, 54)
ABBDL-TECSULT, Inc.

David W. Wade (12)
RDA Engineering

John I. Woodworth (13, 14)
The Hydronics Institute

John C. Glunt (13, 14)
Blackmore & Glunt

A. Pharo Gagge (16)
John B. Pierce Foundation

Larry Berglund (16)
John B. Pierce Foundation

Duane L. Lom (17)
The Trane Company

Joseph A. Pietsch (17)
ARCO Comfort Products Co.

Nancy J. Banks (18)
Cargocaire Engineering Corp.

Thomas A. Snyder (19)
Bovay Engineers, Inc.

Mark S. Lentz (20)
Donohue & Associates, Inc.

Donald M. Eppelheimer (20, 22)
The Trane Company

John E. Wolfert (21)
Melvin Simon & Associates

Thomas R. Kroeschell (21)
Commonwealth Edison Company

George E. Millard, Jr. (22)
Orleans Parish School Board

William A. Murray (23)
Ellerbe Associates, Inc.

John R. Lewis (23)
John Lewis & Associates

Martin Grossman (23)
Dept. of Health and Human Services

Mary Jane Phillips (23)
Naval Medical Command

Charles D. Orth (24-Auto)
Singer Controls Division

Robert Cummings (24-Railroad)
Cummings Engineering Service

James J. Bushnell (24-Bus)
General Dynamics, Convair

David C. Allen (24-Bus)
Allen Associates, Inc.

George C. Letton, Jr. (25)
Aeronautical Systems Division
Department of the Air Force

Ross H. Albright (26)
Ingalls Shipbuilding

Charles A. Madson (27)
Lester B. Knight & Associates

Ram T. Kohli (28, 40)
Stone and Webster Engineers

Frederick H. Kohloss (28, 34)
F.H. Kohloss & Associates

John F. Salsburg (28)
BEC Engineers, Inc.

Alfred W. Woody (28)
Strand Engineering Company

Norman I. Lesser (29)
Port Authority of
New York and New Jersey

Kenneth A. Brow (30)
National Institutes of Health

Larry E. Carnes (30, 32)
Eastman Kodak Company

Robert W. McKinney (30)
National Institutes of Health

William Duncan (30)
U.S. Public Health Service

Chris P. Rosseau (30)
Newcomb & Boyd
Consulting Engineers

Robert L. Frazier (30, 40)
Lawrence Livermore
National Laboratories

George M. Adams (31)
General Motors Corp.

Harold Twietmeyer (31)
Retired

Emerson L. Besch (32)
College of Veterinary Medicine
University of Florida

James E. Woods (32)
Dept. of Mechanical Engineering
Iowa State University

Griffith C. Burr, Jr. (33)
Office of Griffith C. Burr, Inc.

Norman Goldberg (33 OA)
Economides and Goldberg

William A. Kumpf (34)
H. K. Ferguson Company

Carl B. Miller (35)
Consultant

Robert C. Moyer (36)
Eastman Kodak Company

W. T. Colling (36)
Eastman Kodak Company

D. L. Cooper (36)
Eastman Kodak Company

Louis D. Albright (37)
Dept. of Ag Engineering
Cornell University

Michael B. Timmons (37)
Dept. of Ag Engineering
Cornell University

Lowell E. Campbell (37)
U.S. Dept. of Agriculture

Kenneth J. Hellevang (38)
Extension Ag Engineer
North Dakota State University

Blaine F. Parker (38)
Dept. of Ag Engineering
University of Kentucky

Roy V. Baker (38)
USDA-ARS

William E. Mortimer (39)
Stone & Webster Engineers

Stanley A. Slabinski (39)
Somerset Technologies, Inc.

Donald S. Smith (39)
CRS Sirrine

Thomas W. Parker (39)
Weyerhaeuser Paper Company

Robert E. Jensen (40)
LLNL/Rockwell

George J. Sestak (40)
DuPont Company

Hank Bennighoff (40)
TVA

Sven Agerbeck (40)
Bechtel

Richard A. Evans (40)
Kaiser Engineers

Philip W. Hufnell (40)
DuPont Company

Edgar L. Galson (41)
Galson & Galson

David M. Kohli (42)
Parrott Mechanical, Inc.

Floyd C. Bossard (42)
F.C. Bossard & Associates, Inc.

Richard M. Kelso (43)
University of Tennessee

R.E. Fink (44)
Proctor & Schwartz

J.R. Thygeson (44)
Proctor & Schwartz

Robert C. Moyer (44)
Eastman Kodak Company

Gordon M. Reistad (45)
Dept. of Mechanical Engineering
Oregon State University

Harold G. Lorsch (46)
Mechanical Engineering &
Mechanics Department
Drexel University

Robert T. Tamblyn (46)
Engineering Interface, Ltd.

Maurice W. Wildin (46)
University of New Mexico

Calvin D. MacCracken (46)
Calmac Manufacturing Corp.

George A. Lane (46)
Dow Chemical Company

Walter J. Schaetzle (46)
University of Alabama

Gene M. Meyer (47)
Extension Engineer
Kansas State University

William S. Fleming (47)
W.S. Fleming & Associates

Alwin B. Newton (47)
(deceased)

Joseph A. Orlando (48)
GKCO, Inc.

Alan J. Van den Berg (48)
Edison Electric Institute

Lawrence G. Spielvogel (48)
L.G. Spielvogel, Inc.

Thomas A. West (49, 59)
The Bank of Nova Scotia

Thomas D. Underwood (49, 59)
Isotherm Engineering, Ltd.

K. Michael McGrath (49)
Edison Electric Institute

Ronald N. Jensen (49)
NASA

Verle A. Williams (51)
V.A. Williams & Associates

David L. Johnson (51)
CERL-ES

Robert M. Hoover (52)
Hoover, Keith & Bruce, Inc.

Charles W. Barrow (52)
(deceased)

Warren E. Blazier (52)
Warren Blazier & Associates

William R. Hollingshead (53)
Calgon Corporation

Paul Puckoris (53)
Puckoris & Associates

Richard G. Tonkym (53)
Mogul Corporation

William H. Stephenson (54)
Columbia Gas of Ohio

Wilbur L. Haag, Jr. (54)
Rheem Manufacturing Company

Edwin A. Nordstrom (54)
Amtrol, Inc.

John A. Clark, Jr. (54)
Patterson-Kelley

Calvin H. McClellan (56)
cba

William M. Anderson (56)
Norsaire Corporation

Branislav Korenic (56)
Baltimore Air Coil Company, Inc.

Walter L. Lipski (57)
Engineered Air Balance Company

Earl S. Hadden (57)
Los Alamos National Lab

Gaylon Richardson (57)
Engineered Air Balance Company

Francis J. McCabe (58)
Prefco Products, Inc.

John H. Klote (58)
National Bureau of Standards

Albert W. Black, III (60)
MEDSI

ASHRAE HANDBOOK COMMITTEE

Gordon W. Root, Chairman

1987 HVAC Volume Subcommittee: **Donald E. Ross,** Chairman

Richard E. Batherman   **Byron A. Hamrick, Jr.**   **Peter Lujan**   **Marvin Thedford, Jr.**

ASHRAE HANDBOOK STAFF

W. Stephen Comstock, Director of Communications and Publications

Robert A. Parsons, Handbook Editor   **Kelley D. Alexander,** Assistant Editor

Carl W. MacPhee, Consultant   **Lori C. Conway,** Editorial Assistant

Stanley B. Beitler, Production Manager   **Brenda C. Magbee,** Typography

Roxanne Starr and **Becky Makla,** Graphics

ASHRAE TECHNICAL COMMITTEES AND TASK GROUPS

SECTION 1.0—FUNDAMENTALS AND GENERAL
1.1 Thermodynamics and Psychrometrics
1.2 Instruments and Measurements
1.3 Heat Transfer and Fluid Flow
1.4 Control Theory and Application
1.5 Computer Applications
1.6 Terminology
1.7 Operation and Maintenance
1.8 Owning and Operating Costs
1.9 Electrical Systems

SECTION 2.0—ENVIRONMENTAL QUALITY
2.1 Physiology and Human Environment
2.2 Plant and Animal Environment
2.3 Gaseous Air Contaminants and Gas Contaminant Removal Equipment
2.4 Particulate Air Contaminants and Particulate Contaminant Removal Equipment
2.5 Air Flow Around Buildings
2.6 Sound and Vibration Control
TG Safety
TG Halocarbon Emission

SECTION 3.0—MATERIALS AND PROCESSES
3.1 Refrigerant and Brines
3.2 Refrigerant System Chemistry
3.3 Contaminant Control in Refrigerating Systems
3.4 Lubrication
3.5 Sorption
3.6 Corrosion and Water Treatment
3.7 Fuels and Combustion

SECTION 4.0—LOAD CALCULATIONS AND ENERGY REQUIREMENTS
4.1 Load Calculation Data and Procedures
4.2 Weather Data
4.3 Ventilation Requirements and Infiltration
4.4 Thermal Insulation and Moisture Retarders
4.5 Fenestration
4.6 Building Operation Dynamics
4.7 Energy Calculations
TG Energy Resources
TG Indoor Environmental Calculations
TG Building Envelope Systems

SECTION 5.0—VENTILATION AND AIR DISTRIBUTION
5.1 Fans
5.2 Duct Design
5.3 Room Air Distribution
5.4 Industrial Process Air Cleaning (Air Pollution Control)
5.5 Air-to-Air Energy Recovery
5.6 Control of Fire and Smoke
5.7 Evaporative Cooling
5.8 Industrial Ventilation
5.9 Enclosed Vehicular Facilities

SECTION 6.0—HEATING EQUIPMENT, HEATING AND COOLING SYSTEMS AND APPLICATIONS
6.1 Hot Water and Steam Heating Equipment and Systems
6.2 District Heating and Cooling
6.3 Central Forced Air Heating and Cooling Systems
6.4 In-Space Convection Heating
6.5 Radiant Space Heating and Cooling
6.6 Service Water Heating
6.7 Solar Energy Utilization
6.8 Geothermal Energy Utilization
6.9 Thermal Storage

SECTION 7.0—PACKAGED AIR-CONDITIONING AND REFRIGERATION EQUIPMENT
7.1 Residential Refrigerators, Food Freezers and Drinking Water Coolers
7.2 Beverage Coolers
7.5 Room Air Conditioners and Dehumidifiers
7.6 Unitary Air Conditioners and Heat Pumps

SECTION 8.0—AIR-CONDITIONING AND REFRIGERATION SYSTEM COMPONENTS
8.1 Positive Displacement Compressors
8.2 Centrifugal Machines
8.3 Absorption and Heat Operated Machines
8.4 Air-to-Refrigerant Heat Transfer Equipment
8.5 Liquid-to-Refrigerant Heat Exchangers
8.6 Cooling Towers and Evaporative Condensers
8.7 Humidifying Equipment
8.8 Refrigerant System Controls and Accessories
8.10 Pumps and Hydronic Piping
8.11 Electric Motors—Open and Hermetic
TG Unitary Combustion-Engine-Driven Heat Pumps

SECTION 9.0—AIR-CONDITIONING SYSTEMS AND APPLICATIONS
9.1 Large Building Air-Conditioning Systems
9.2 Industrial Air Conditioning
9.3 Transportation Air Conditioning
9.4 Applied Heat Pump/Heat Recovery Systems
9.5 Cogeneration Systems
9.6 Systems Energy Utilization
9.7 Testing and Balancing
9.8 Large Building Air-Conditioning Applications

SECTION 10.0—REFRIGERATION SYSTEMS AND APPLICATIONS
10.1 Custom Engineered Refrigeration Systems
10.2 Automatic Ice-Making Plants and Skating Rinks
10.3 Refrigerant Piping
10.4 Ultra-Low Temperature Systems and Cryogenics
10.5 Refrigerated Distribution and Storage Facilities
10.6 Transport Refrigeration
10.7 Commercial Food Display and Storage Equipment
TG Refrigeration Load Calculations

SECTION 11.0—REFRIGERATED FOOD TECHNOLOGY AND PROCESSING
11.1 Meat, Fish and Poultry Products
11.3 Dairy Products
11.5 Fruits, Vegetables and Other Products
11.6 Prepared Food Products
11.9 Thermal Properties of Foods

CHAPTER 1

AIR-CONDITIONING SYSTEM SELECTION AND DESIGN

AN air-conditioning system maintains desired environmental conditions within a space. In almost every application, there are several ways these conditions may be maintained. Ideally, air-conditioning systems permit people or products to function within the structures at optimum level. Different systems approach this ideal with varying degrees of success.

Air-conditioning systems are categorized by how they control cooling in the conditioned area. They are also segregated to accomplish specific purposes by special equipment arrangement. This chapter considers procedures for selecting the appropriate system for a given application. It also describes and defines the design concepts and characteristics of the basic air-conditioning systems. Chapters 2 through 5 describe various systems and their attributes, based on their terminal cooling medium and their common variations.

SELECTING A SYSTEM

The designer has responsibility for considering various systems and recommending the one or two that will perform as desired, fit into the available space, and give the owner the best combination of first cost, operating cost, and reliability.

Those five factors are interrelated, so the owner and building designer must consider how each affects the other. The relative importance of these five factors differs with different owners and often changes from one project to another for the same owner.

SELECTION GOALS

An owner invests in air conditioning to achieve goals other than providing a desired environment. Goals may be: (1) to complete a process such as the operation of computer equipment, the infection-free implant of an artificial hip, the manufacture of semi-conductors, or any other task; (2) to provide a desirable environment for employees to reduce fatigue and errors and make the location a desirable place to work; (3) to increase the sale of goods or services; (4) to increase net rental income; or (5) to enhance the sale of the property soon after project completion.

The relative importance of first cost as compared to operating cost, the extent and frequency of maintenance and whether that maintenance requires entering the occupied space, how often a system may be expected to fail, how much of the project would be affected by a failure, and how long before the failure can be corrected are typical concerns of owners. Each of these concerns has a different priority, depending on the owner's goals.

The owner can only make appropriate value judgments if the designer provides complete information on the advantages and disadvantages of each option. Just as the owner does not usually

The preparation of this chapter is assigned to TC 9.1, Large Building Air-Conditioning Systems.

have the knowledge of the relative advantages and disadvantages of different systems, the designer rarely knows all the owner's financial and functional goals. Hence, it is important to involve the owner in selecting the system.

SYSTEM CONSTRAINTS

The first step in selecting a system is to determine and document constraints dictated by performance, capacity, available space, and any other factors important to the project.

Few projects allow detailed quantitative evaluation of all alternatives, and common sense and subjective experience narrow choices to two or three potential systems.

Cooling Loads

Establishing the cooling load often narrows the choice to systems that will fit within the available space and are compatible with the building architecture. The FUNDAMENTALS Volume covers how to determine the magnitude and characteristics of the cooling load and how it varies with time and operating conditions. By establishing the capacity requirement, the size of equipment can be estimated. Then, the number of options may be narrowed to those systems that work well on projects of certain broad size ranges.

Zoning Requirements

Loads vary over time in the various areas due to changes in weather, occupancy, activities, and solar exposure. Each space with a different exposure requires a different control zone to maintain constant temperature. Some areas with special requirements may need individual control, or individual systems, independent of the rest of the building. Variations in indoor conditions, which are acceptable in one space, may be unacceptable in other areas of the same building. The extent of zoning, the degree of control required in each zone, and the space required for individual zones will also narrow the system choices.

No matter how efficiently a particular system operates, or how economical it may be to install, it cannot be considered if it: (1) does not maintain the desired interior environment within an acceptable tolerance through all conditions and occupant activity, and (2) does not physically fit into the building without being objectionable.

Heating and Ventilation

Cooling and humidity control are often the basis of sizing air-conditioning components and subsystems, but the system may also provide other functions such as heating and ventilation. For example, if the system provides large quantities of outside air for ventilation or replaces air exhausted from the building, only systems that transport large air volumes need to be considered. In that situation, the ventilation system will require a large air-handling and duct-distribution system, so other means can be discarded.

Effectively delivering heat to an area may be an equally strong factor in system selection. A distribution system that offers high efficiency and high comfort for cooling may be a poor compromise for heating. That performance compromise may be small for one application and in one climate and be unacceptable in another that has more stringent heating requirements.

Architectural Constraints

Air-conditioning systems and the associated distribution systems often take substantial space. Major components may also require special support from the structure. The size and appearance of terminal devices, whether they are diffusers, fan coil units, or radiant panels, have an impact on the architectural design because they are visible from the occupied space.

Other factors that limit the selection of a system include (1) acceptable noise levels, (2) space available to house equipment and its location relative to the occupied space, (3) space available for distribution pipes and ducts, and (4) the acceptability of components obtruding into the occupied space—both physically and visually.

NARROWING THE CHOICE

Each of the succeeding system chapters includes an *Evaluation* section, which briefly summarizes the good and bad features of various systems. Comparing the features against the list of design factors and their relative importance will usually identify two or three approaches that most nearly meet the project criteria. In making subjective choices, it is helpful to keep notes on all systems considered and the reason for eliminating those that are unacceptable.

In most cases, two system selections will evolve: the *secondary* (or distribution) system delivers heating or cooling to the occupied space from a *primary* system, which converts energy from fuel or electricity. The two systems are, to a great extent, independent, so several secondary systems will work with different primary systems. In some cases, however, only one particular secondary system will work with a specific primary system.

Once subjective analysis has identified two or three systems—and sometimes only one choice may remain—detailed quantitative evaluations of each system must be made. All systems considered should provide satisfactory performance to meet the owner's essential goals. The owner then needs specific data on each system to make an informed choice. Chapter 28 in the 1985 FUNDAMENTALS Handbook, "Energy Estimating," outlines how to estimate annual energy costs. In this volume, Chapter 59 deals with mechanical maintenance, and Chapter 49 describes life-cycle costing, a method that compares overall economics of systems.

SELECTION REPORT

As the last step of system selection, the designer prepares a memorandum or report that summarizes the selection criteria, briefly outlines the systems considered inappropriate, and compares the systems selected for detailed study by answering the following questions.

1. Does the system fit in the available space, or does it require some architectural modification? Does the system use more floor space than others considered, or does it require construction of additional space for mechanical rooms or shafts?
2. Will the system deliver the desired uniform temperature under

varying weather and solar conditions? If compromises are made from the ideal control zoning, how much variation may be expected between spaces?
3. How much will the system cost to own compared to others considered? What is the recovery time of the initial investment, interest on investment, and the future cost of replacement equipment?
4. What are the operating costs of this system compared to others, including energy costs, maintenance, operating labor, and supplies?
5. What reliability can the owner expect compared to other systems? What component failures might affect the entire building, and which would affect only limited areas? How easily may the system be serviced? How quickly can the system be restored to operation after various equipment failures?
6. Is the system flexible enough to meet changes in the owner's needs? What is required to add a control zone? Can it meet the increased capacity requirements of a space when equipment is added? How will changes in the interior layout and arrangement affect performance?

The System Selection Report should conclude with a recommended system choice, along with reasons for the choice. The report should be discussed with the owner long enough to be sure the owner's goals have been recognized and the owner understands the reasons for the designer's recommendations.

THE BASIC CENTRAL AIR-CONDITIONING AND DISTRIBUTION SYSTEM

The basic secondary system is an all-air, single-zone, air-conditioning system. It may be designed to supply a constant air volume or a variable air volume and for low, medium, and high pressure air distribution. Normally, the equipment is located outside the conditioned area, in a basement, penthouse, or service area. It can, however, be installed within the conditioned area if conditions permit. The equipment can be adjacent to the primary heating and refrigeration equipment or at considerable distance from it by circulating refrigerant, chilled water, hot water, electricity, or steam for energy transfer.

APPLICATIONS

Some central system applications are: (1) spaces with uniform loads, (2) small spaces requiring precision control, (3) multiple systems for large areas, (4) systems for complete environmental control, and (5) a primary source of conditioned air for other subsystems.

Spaces with Uniform Loads

Spaces with uniform loads are generally those with relatively large open areas and small external loads, such as theaters, auditoriums, department stores, and the public spaces of many buildings. Here, the air-conditioning loads are fairly uniform, and adjustment for minor variations can be made by supplying more or less air in the original design and balance of the system.

In office buildings, the interior areas generally meet these criteria as long as local areas of relatively intense and variable heat sources, such as computers, are treated separately. In these applications, non-ceiling partitions allow wider diffusion of the conditioned air and equalization of temperatures. These areas usually require year-round cooling, and any isolated spaces with

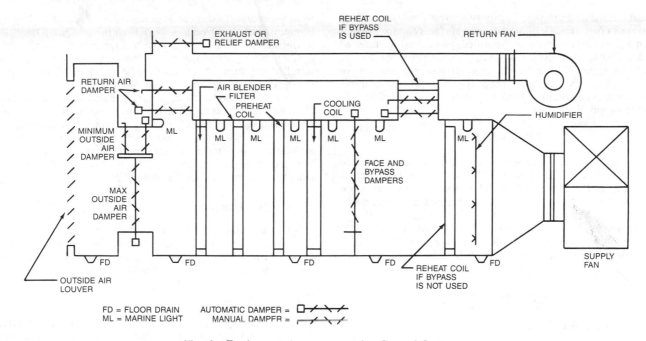

Fig. 1 Equipment Arrangement for Central Systems

limited occupancy may require special evaluation, as discussed in Chapter 19 in this volume.

The central system can also adapt to one-story buildings and top floors of single-occupancy spaces, if the exterior walls are part of the main conditioned areas and if the space has a uniform roof load.

In most single-room commercial applications, temperature variations of up to 4°F (2°C) at outside walls are usually considered acceptable for tenancy requirements. However, these variations should be carefully determined and limited during design. If people sit or work near the outside walls or if they are isolated by partitions, supplementary heating equipment may be required at the walls, depending on the outdoor design temperature in the winter.

Spaces Requiring Precision Control

These spaces are usually isolated rooms within a larger building and have stringent requirements for cleanliness, humidity, temperature control, and air distribution. Central system components can be selected and assembled to meet the exact requirements of the area.

Multiple Systems for Large Buildings

In large buildings such as hangers, factories, large stores, office buildings, and hospitals, practical considerations require installation of multiple central systems. The size of the individual system is usually limited only by the building's structural limitations.

Primary Source for Other Systems

Systems for controlling conditions in individual zones are described in the following chapters of this volume. These systems move a constant supply of conditioned air for ventilation and control some of the air-conditioning load. This air supply often reduces the amount of conditioned air handled by the central system and, consequently, the space required for ductwork. Ductwork size can be reduced further by moving air at high velocities.

However, high velocity system design must consider the resultant high pressure, sound levels, and energy requirements. Chapters 7 and 33 of the 1985 FUNDAMENTALS Volume, Chapter 3 of the 1983 EQUIPMENT Volume, and Chapter 52 of this volume give design procedures.

Environmental Control

All-air systems generally provide the necessary air supply to dilute the controlled space in applications requiring close aseptic or contamination control. These applications usually are combinations of supply systems and scavenging exhaust systems that circulate the diluting air through the space. Since establishing adequate dilution volumes is related to space configuration, occupancy type, air delivery, and scavenging methods, the designer must consider the terminal systems used.

The cleanliness of the air supply also relates directly to the level of environmental control desired. Suitable air filtration should be incorporated in the central system upstream from the air moving and tempering equipment. Some applications, such as hospitals, require downstream filtration as well.

These systems usually incorporate some form of energy recovery. Chapter 10 of the 1983 EQUIPMENT Volume has information on air cleaners, and Chapters 8, 11, and 12 of the 1985 FUNDAMENTALS Volume include data on physiological factors, contaminants, and odors.

CENTRAL SYSTEM PERFORMANCE

Figure 1 shows a typical draw-through central system that supplies conditioned air to a single zone or to another system. A blow-through configuration may also be used if space or other conditions dictate. The quantity and quality of this air is fixed by space requirements and determined, as described in Chapter 26 of the 1985 FUNDAMENTALS Volume. Air gains and loses heat by contacting the heat transfer surfaces and by mixing with air of another condition. Some of these mixtures are intentional, as at the outdoor air intake. Others are the result of the physical characteristics of a particular component, as when untreated air passes without contacting the fins of a coil.

All treated and untreated air must be thoroughly mixed for maximum performance of heat transfer surfaces and for uniform temperatures in the airstream. Stratified, parallel paths of treated and untreated air must be avoided, particularly in the vertical plane of systems using double inlet or multiple wheel fans. Because these fans do not completely mix the air, different temperatures can occur in branches coming from opposite sides of the supply duct.

LIFE SAFETY

Air-conditioning systems serve increasingly for smoke control during fires. Controlled air flow provides smoke-free areas for occupant evacuation and firefighter access. Space pressurization creates a low pressure area at the smoke source and surrounds it with high pressure spaces. The publication, "Design of Smoke Control Systems for Buildings," sponsored by the U.S. Veterans Administration, ASHRAE, and the U.S. Department of Commerce, National Bureau of Standards, has detailed information.

COMPONENTS

Air Conditioning Units

The designer considers the function and physical characteristics of the space to be conditioned and the air volume and thermal exchange capacities required to determine the system's air-handling requirement. Then, the various components may be selected and arranged by keeping the fundamental requirements of the central system in mind. These requirements are: equipment must be adequate, accessible for easy maintenance, and not too complex in arrangement and control to produce the required conditions.

Further, the designer considers economics in component selection. Both initial cost and operating costs bear on design decisions. The designer should not arbitrarily design for a 500 fpm (2.5 m/s) face velocity, which has been common for selection of cooling coils and other components. A 1977 study showed that filter and coil selection at 300 to 400 fpm (1.5 to 2.0 m/s), with its lower pressure loss, could pay back on constant volume systems. Chapter 49 in this volume has further energy and life-cycle cost details.

Figure 1 shows a general arrangement of the components of a single zone, all air, central system suitable for year-round air conditioning with close control of temperature and humidity. Seldom would all these components be used in a comfort application. Although Figure 1 indicates a built-up system, most of the components are available completely assembled by the manufacturer or in sub-assembled sections that can be bolted together in the field.

Factors to be considered when selecting central system components include evaluation of specific design parameters to balance cost, controllability, operating expense, maintenance, noise, and space. The sizing and selection of primary air-handling units substantially affect the results obtained in the conditioned space. See the 1983 EQUIPMENT Volume for a detailed discussion of each of the unit components.

Return Air Fan

A return air fan is optional on small systems but usually essential for the proper operation of large systems. It functions to provide a positive return and exhaust from the conditioned area, particularly when mixing dampers permit cooling with outdoor air in intermediate seasons.

The return air fan ensures that the proper volume of air returns from the conditioned space. It prevents excess pressure when the economizer cycle introduces more than the minimum quantity of outside air. It also reduces the resistance to the supply fan.

A damper controlled by a static pressure regulator should be installed in return air systems to offset stack effect in highrise buildings.

The supply fan(s) must be carefully matched with the return fan, particularly in variable air volume systems. The return air fan should handle a slightly smaller air quantity to account for fixed exhaust systems, such as the toilet exhaust, and to ensure a slight positive pressure in the conditioned space. Fan selection and control of variable volume systems is specialized. See Chapter 2 in this volume for design details.

Automatic Dampers

An air economizer with opposed blade dampers for the outdoor, return, and relief air streams provides the highest degree of control. The section under mixing plenums covers which conditions dictate the use of parallel blade dampers.

Relief Openings

Relief openings in large buildings should be constructed similarly to outdoor air intakes, but they should have motorized or self-acting backdraft dampers to prevent high wind pressures or stack action from causing the air flow to reverse when the automatic dampers are open. The pressure loss through relief openings should be 0.10 in. of water (25 Pa) or less. Low leakage dampers, like those for outdoor intakes, prevent rattling and minimize leakage.

Relief dampers sized for the same air velocity as the maximum outdoor air dampers facilitate control when an air economizer cycle is used. Power relief fans that are interconnected with outside air dampers can exhaust the area, especially when an economizer cycle is part of the system. The relief air opening should be located so that the exhaust air does not short-circuit to the outdoor air intake.

Return Air Dampers

The negative pressure in the outdoor air intake plenum is a function of the resistance or static pressure loss through the outside air louvers, damper, and duct. The positive pressure in the relief air plenum is, likewise, a function of the static pressure loss through the exhaust or relief damper, the exhaust duct between the plenum and outside, and the relief louver. The pressure drop through the return air damper must accommodate the pressure difference between the positive pressure-relief air plenum and the negative pressure outside air plenum. Proper sizing of this damper facilitates both air balancing and mixing. An additional manual damper may be required for proper air balancing.

Outdoor Air Intakes

Resistance through outdoor intakes varies widely, depending on construction. Frequently, architectural considerations dictate the type and style of louver. The HVAC engineer must see that the louvers selected offer a minimum pressure loss, preferably not to exceed in 0.10 in. of water (25 Pa). High efficiency, low pressure loss louvers that effectively limit carry-over of rain are available. Flashing installed at the outside wall and weep holes or a floor drain will carry away rain and melted snow entering the intake. Cold regions may require a snow baffle to direct fine snow particles to a low velocity area below the dampers. Outdoor dampers should be low leakage types with special gasketed edges and special end treatment. Separate damper sections for the minimum outdoor air needed for ventilation and the maximum outdoor air needed for economizer cycle are strongly recommended.

Mixing Plenum

If the equipment is next to outdoor louvers in a wall, the minimum outdoor air damper should be located at the return damper connection. An outside air damper sized for 1500 fpm (7.6 m/s) gives good control. The pressure difference between the relief plenum and outdoor intake plenum must be taken through the return damper section. A higher velocity through the return air damper, high enough to cause this loss at its full open position, will facilitate air balance and create good mixing. Return air dampers should be set so that any deflection of air is toward the outside air to create maximum turbulence and mixing.

Mixing dampers should be placed across the full width of the unit, even though the location of the return duct makes it more convenient to return air through the side. When return dampers are placed at one side, return air passes through one side of the fan, and cold outdoor air passes through the other. If the air return must enter the side, some form of air blender should be used.

While opposed blade dampers offer better control, properly proportioned parallel blade dampers are more effective than opposed blade dampers for mixing air streams of different temperatures. If parallel blades are used, each damper should be mounted so its partially opened blades direct the airstreams toward the other damper to obtain maximum mixing.

Baffles that direct the two airstreams to impinge on each other at right angles and in multiple jets create the turbulence required to mix the air thoroughly. In some instances, unit heaters or propeller fans have been used for mixing. Dampers must be sequenced and arranged to achieve proper mixing, regardless of the final type and configuration. Otherwise, the preheat coil will waste heat (if included) or the cooling coil may freeze. Low leakage outdoor air dampers minimize leakage during shutdown.

Coil freezing can be a serious problem with chilled water coils. Full flow circulation of chilled water during freezing weather, or even reduced flow with a small recirculating pump, discourages coil freezing and eliminates stratification. Further, it can provide a source of off-season chilled water in air-water systems. Antifreeze solutions or complete coil draining also prevent coil freezing.

Filter Section

A system's overall performance depends heavily on the filter. Unless the filter is regularly maintained, system resistance increases and air flow is diminished. Accessibility is the primary consideration in filter selection and location. In a built-up system, there should be a minimum of 3 ft. (1 m) between the upstream face of the filter bank and any obstruction. Other requirements for various types of filters can be found in the 1983 EQUIPMENT Volume and ASHRAE Standard 52-76.

Good mixing of outdoor and return air is also necessary for good filter performance. A poorly placed outdoor air duct or a bad duct connection to the mixing plenum can cause uneven loading of the filter and bad distribution of air through the coil section. Because of the low resistance of the clean areas, the filter gauge may not warn of this condition.

Preheat Coil

The preheat coil should have wide fin spacing, be accessible for easy cleaning, and be protected by filters. If the preheat coil is located in the minimum outdoor air stream rather than the mixed air stream as shown in Figure 1, it should not heat the air to an exit temperature above 35 to 45 °F (2 to 7 °C), and preferably become inoperative at outdoor temperatures of 45 °F (7 °C). Inner distributing tube or integral face and bypass coils are preferable with steam. Hot water preheat coils, if used, should have a constant flow recirculating pump and should be piped for parallel flow so that the coldest air will contact the warmest coil surface first.

Cooling Coil

In this section, sensible and latent heat are removed from the air. In all finned coils, some air passes through without contacting the fins or tubes. The amount of this bypass can vary from 30% for a four-row coil at 700 fpm (3.5 m/s) to less than 2% for an eight-row coil at 300 fpm (1.5 m/s).

The dew point of the air mixture leaving a four-row coil might satisfy a comfort installation with 25% or less outdoor air, a small internal latent load, and temperature control only. For close control of room conditions for precision work, a deeper coil with sprays or an air washer might be required. A copper tube, copper fin coil is required for sprays.

A central station unit that is the primary source of conditioned air for other subsystems, such as in an air-water system, does not need to supply as much air to a space. In this case, the primary air furnishes outdoor air for ventilation and handles space dehumidification and some sensible cooling; the room terminal then provides the balance of the sensible cooling. This application normally requires deeper coils with more fins and sprays. See the 1985 FUNDAMENTALS Volume and the 1983 EQUIPMENT Volume for further information.

Bypass Section

Air is mixed a third time in the bypass section, if used. At reduced internal loads, the room thermostat opens the bypass damper, which permits return air to enter the bypass section. At the same time, the face damper on the cooling section closes and reduces the flow of cooled and dehumidified air. The temperature of the mixture rises, and overcooling is prevented. The amount of heat available depends on the amount of return air. The outdoor air required for ventilation passes through the dehumidifier section, so this system will control room relative humidity better than any other constant volume system except a dew point control with reheat system.

Supplemental heat may be required to maintain room temperature in the event of a net heat loss. The relative humidity in the room will increase as the bypass opens under conditions of constant internal latent heat load. Chilled water at a constant flow and temperature will control the dew point. For more precise control, a space humidistat can control chilled water flow and reheat. The ASHRAE Psychrometric Charts in Chapter 6 of the 1985 FUNDAMENTALS Volume show the process.

Because the apparatus has a high air resistance compared to that of the bypass, the total resistance on the supply fan drops as the bypass opens, and the total volume of air delivered to the room increases. A supply fan with a steep and constantly rising pressure curve will limit this increased volume; otherwise, a constant volume control can be installed. Without a volume control, this system should only be applied where volume variations do not seriously affect occupant comfort.

Because there is a large pressure drop across the bypass damper, it has an abnormally high leakage when it is closed. This leakage must be considered in the system design, and the apparatus dew point should be lowered to compensate. For optimum psychrometric performace, a bypass should bypass only return air, as shown in Figure 1.

To maintain a fairly constant supply air volume, the pressure loss through the bypass at full flow must equal the pressure loss through all components from the outdoor air intake to the bypass mixing plenum at full cooling flow. The bypass requires a perforated plate to develop the pressure drop. Return air filters should also be used. Bypass dampers should be sized for a velocity of 2000 to 2500 fpm (10 to 13 m/s). Face dampers should match the coil face area, and low leakage, opposed-blade dampers must be used.

Reheat Coil Section

Reheat is strongly discouraged unless recovered from other energy sources (see ASHRAE Standard 90A-1980). Reheating is limited to a laboratory, health care, or similar applications where it is essential to control temperature and relative humidity accurately.

Heating coils located in the reheat position, as shown in Figure 1, are frequently used for warm-up, although a coil in the preheat position is preferable. The reheat coil may also be located in the bypass duct.

Hot water heating coils provide the highest degree of control. Oversized coils, particularly steam, can stratify the air flow, so inner distributing coils are preferable for steam applications. Electric coils may also be used.

Humidifier

For comfort installations in which close control is not essential, moisture can be added to the air by pan-type humidifiers with a heating coil and, in some instances, by mechanical atomizers. Proper location of this equipment will prevent stratification of moist air in the system. A pan-type humidifier should be centered on the airstream; two or more unit humidifiers should be simultaneously controlled and distributed across the airstream.

The capacity of the humidifying equipment should not exceed the expected peak load by more than 10%. If the humidity is controlled from the room or the return air, a limiting humidistat and fan interlock may be needed in the supply duct to prevent condensation when temperature controls call for cooler air.

Steam grid humidifiers or recirculating sprays with dew point control usually are used for accurate humidity control. These can be sprayed coils or air washers. In this application, the evaporation heat should be replaced by heating the recirculated water rather than by increasing the size of the preheat coil. The same precautions for pan humidifiers apply to the steam grid type. It is not possible to add moisture to saturated air, even with a steam grid humidifier. Air in a laboratory or other application that requires close humidity control must be reheated after leaving a dehumidifier coil before moisture can be added. This operation increases the air quantity required to cool the space.

Steam grid humidifiers, pan-type humidifiers, and spray water heaters add some sensible heat that should be accounted for in the psychometric evaluation.

Supply Air Fan

Either axial flow or centrifugal fans may be chosen as supply air fans for straight-through flow applications. In factory fabricated units, more than one centrifugal fan may be tied to the same shaft. If head room permits, a single-inlet fan should be chosen when air enters at right angles to the flow of air through the equipment. These arrangements will permit a direct flow of air from the fan wheel into the supply duct without abrupt change in direction and loss in efficiency. It will also permit a more gradual transition from the fan to the duct and increase the static regain in the velocity pressure conversion.

To minimize inlet losses, the distance between the casing walls and the fan inlet should be at least the diameter of the fan wheel. With a single-inlet fan, the length of the transition section should be at least half the width or height of the casing, whichever is longer.

If fans blow through the equipment, the air distribution through the downstream components needs analyzing, and baffles should be used to ensure uniform air distribution. See the 1983 EQUIPMENT Volume and the 1985 FUNDAMENTALS Volume for more information on fans.

AIR DISTRIBUTION

Ductwork

Ductwork should deliver conditioned air to an area as directly, quietly, and economically as possible. Structural features of the building generally require some compromise and often limit depth. The 1985 FUNDAMENTALS Volume explains ductwork design in detail and gives several methods of sizing duct systems.

Since ductwork is sold on a cost-per-unit-weight basis, a design with the lowest weight that will handle the required air quantities is the most cost effective. Table 1 shows that heat gains and losses is greater in ducts with high aspect ratios; thus, they require more insulation. Also, ducts with large panels radiate more noise and require greater stiffness.

On wide-bay buildings with deep girders, it is important to coordinate duct design with structural steel. Then, low aspect ratio ducts can be run through the reinforcing web of the girders instead of running ducts with high aspect ratios to accommodate normal ceiling heights.

When the duct layout has few outlets, conventional low-velocity design assumes a uniform resistance per 100 ft (30 m) of equivalent length of 0.08 or 0.10 in. of water (20 or 25 Pa). On complex systems with long runs and medium and high pressures of 1.5 to 8 in. of water (375 to 2000 Pa), the self-balancing and energy-saving features of the static pressure regain method of duct sizing should be considered. This method also produces the best results with a variable air volume duct distribution system.

Table 1 (I-P) Effect of Aspect Ratio on Duct Weight

Aspect Ratio	Standard Size, in.	Perimeter, in.	U. S. Std. Gauge Steel	Weight,[a] lb/linear ft
1 to 1	32 by 32	128	22	16.6
2 to 1	44 by 22	132	22	17.0
4 to 1	64 by 16	160	20	22.0
8 to 1	96 by 12	216	18	39.0

[a]Includes 10% for slips, angles, and scrap.

Table 1 (SI) Effect of Aspect Ratio on Duct Mass

Aspect Ratio	Size, mm	Perimeter, mm	U. S. Std. Gauge Steel	Mass per linear metre,[a] kg/m
1 to 1	810 by 810	3240	22	24.7
2 to 1	1120 by 560	3360	22	25.3
4 to 1	1600 by 400	4000	20	32.7
8 to 1	2400 by 300	5400	18	58.0

[a]Includes 10% for slips, angles, and scrap.

Room Terminals

In some instances, such as in low velocity, all-air systems, the air may enter from the supply air ductwork directly into the conditioned space through a grille or diffuser.

In high velocity air systems, an intermediate device normally controls air volume, reduces duct pressure, or both. Various devices are available, including: (1) an air-water induction terminal, which includes a coil or coils in the induced air stream to condition the return air before it mixes with the primary air and enters the space; (2) an all-air induction terminal, which controls the volume of primary air, induces ceiling plenum air, and distributes the mixture through low velocity ductwork to the space; (3) a fan-powered mixing box, which uses a fan to accomplish the mixing rather than depending on the induction principle; and (4) a VAV box, which varies the amount of air delivered with no induction. This air may be delivered to low pressure ductwork and then to the space, or the terminal may contain an integral air diffuser.

Insulation

Ductwork that runs outside the conditioned area should be insulated. Acoustical lining is often used for thermal insulation, if its overall heat transfer coefficient is low enough.

Insulation is seldom placed in hung ceilings that serve as return plenums. Exceptions are made when duct runs are so long that the heat pickup requires additional air to offset the temperature rise in the duct and when the duct surface temperature is low enough to cause condensation. The need for insulation should be checked for a ceiling hung below a flat roof, even though the roof load has been included in the system capacity.

Ceiling Plenums

The space between a hung ceiling and under the floor slab above is used frequently as a return plenum to reduce sheet metal work. Local and national codes should be checked before using this approach in new design. Most codes prohibit combustible material in a return air ceiling plenum. Ceiling plenums are not normally designed as supply plenums because the ceiling space is difficult to seal against leakage.

Lobby ceilings with lay-in panels do not work well as return plenums where negative pressures from high-rise elevators or an adjacent factory area may occur. If the plenum leaks to the low-pressure area, the tiles may lift and drop out when the outside door is opened and closed. Return plenums directly below a roof deck have substantially higher return air gain than a ducted return. This has the advantage of reducing the heat gain to or loss from the space.

Controls

Controls should be automatic and simple for best operating and maintenance efficiency. Operations should follow a natural sequence, so one controlling thermostat closes a normally open heating valve, opens the outdoor air mixing dampers, modulates the face and bypass dampers, or opens the cooling valve, depending on space need. In certain applications, an enthalpy controller, which compares the heat content of outdoor air to that of return air, may override the temperature controller. This control opens the outdoor air damper when conditions reduce the refrigeration load. On smaller systems, a dry-bulb control saves the cost of the enthalpy control and approaches these savings when an optimum change-over temperature, above the design dew point, is established.

A minimum outdoor air damper with separate motor, selected for a 1500 fpm (7.6 m/s) velocity, is preferred to one large outdoor air damper with minimum stops. A separate damper simplifies air balancing.

A mixed air temperature control can reduce operating costs and also reduce temperature swings from load variations in the conditioned space. Chapter 51 of this volume on "Automatic Controls" shows control diagrams for various arrangements of central system equipment.

Equipment Isolation

Vibration and sound isolation equipment is required for most central system fan installations. Standard mountings of fiberglass, ribbed rubber, neoprene mounts, and springs are available for most fans and prefabricated units.

In some applications, the fans may require concrete inertia blocks in addition to non-enclosed spring mountings. Steel springs require sound-absorbing material inserted between the springs and the foundation. Horizontal discharge fans operating at a high static pressure frequently require thrust arrestors.

Ductwork connections should be made with fireproof fiber cloth sleeves having considerable slack, but without offset between the fan outlet and rigid duct. Misalignment between the duct and fan outlet can cause turbulence, generate noise, and reduce system efficiency. Electrical and piping connections to vibration-isolated equipment should be made with flexible conduit and flexible connections.

Equipment noise transmitted through the ductwork can be reduced by sound-absorbing units, acoustical lining, and other means of attenuation. Sound transmitted through the return and relief ducts should not be overlooked. Acoustical lining sufficient to attenuate any objectionable system adequately or locally generated noise should be considered. Chapter 52 of this volume, Chapter 7 of the FUNDAMENTALS Volume, and ASHRAE Standard 68-78 have further information on sound and vibration control.

Space Heating

Steam is an acceptable media for central system preheat or reheat coils, while low temperature hot water permits a simple and more uniform means of perimeter and general space heating. Individual automatic control of each terminal provides the ideal space comfort. A control system that varies the water temperature inversely with the change in outdoor temperature provides water temperatures that produce acceptable results in some applications. The most satisfactory ratio to produce average results can be set after the installation is completed and actual operating conditions are ascertained.

Multiple perimeter spaces on one exposure served by a central system may be heated by supplying warm air from the central system. Areas that have heat gain from lights and occupants and no heat loss will require cooling in winter, as well as in summer.

In some systems, very little heating of the return and outdoor air will be required when the space is occupied. Local codes dictate the amount of outside air required. For example, with return air at 75°F (24°C) and outside air at 0°F (-18°C), the temperature of a 25% outdoor/75% return air mixture would be 56°F (13°C), which is close to the temperature of the air supplied to cool such a space in summer. A preheat coil installed in the minimum outdoor air stream to warm the outdoor air in this instance can produce overheating unless it is sized as previously recommended. A preheat coil located in the mixed air stream, assuming good mixing, avoids this problem. The outdoor air damper should be kept closed until room temperatures are reached during warm-up. A return air thermostat can terminate the warm-up period.

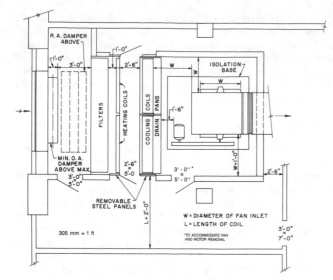

Fig. 2   Recommended Space Requirements and Clearances for Central System Fan Room

Where a central air-handling unit supplies both perimeter and interior spaces, the supply air must be cool to handle the interior zones. Additional control is needed to heat the perimeter spaces properly. Reheating the air is the simplest solution, but it is not acceptable by most energy codes. An acceptable solution is to vary the volume of air to the perimeter and combine it with a terminal heating coil or a separate perimeter heating system, either baseboard, overhead air heating system, or a fan-powered mixing box with supplemental heat. The perimeter heating should be individually controlled and integrated with the cooling control.

Resetting the supply water temperature downward when less heat is required will generally improve temperature control. Refer to Chapters 9 and 29 in the 1983 EQUIPMENT Volume and Chapters 13, 14, and 51 in this volume.

INSTALLATION

Prefabricated Units

Prefabricated units are frequently shipped subassembled for erection in the field. The following installation pointers will help in the maintenance and operation of the equipment:

1. Line up flanges and remove any dents or twists.
2. If gaskets are not provided, caulk or tape joints to prevent leakage.
3. Check each coil and filter section for any bypass leakage.
4. Seal all openings.
5. If the equipment room is not wide enough to permit coil removal, place the coil section opposite a door or a knock-out panel with a steel frame in the wall. Make similar provision for removing the fan shaft and wheels.
6. If space in the equipment room is limited, place piping, filter access, wiring, motor, and drive on the same side with a minimum 4 ft. (1.2 m) clearance between casing and wall.
7. Keep a minimum clearance of 18 in. (460 mm) on the opposite side for servicing the fan bearing and for painting.
8. Offset all piping branches and use ground joint unions or flanges to permit coil removal without disturbing the mains or control valves.
9. Be sure all pipe openings in the casing have airtight escutcheons.

Built-Up Units

Figure 2 shows minimum clearances for a large built-up unit operating at medium or high pressure. The unit should be installed as follows:

1. The casing may be insulated single-wall or double-wall sheet metal.
2. Install waterproof floor with floor drains as noted or as required.
3. Place a 0.25 in. (6 mm) gasket between all steel flanges of the casing and masonry.
4. Install gasketed access doors that are equipped with wedge-type locks that are operable from inside and hinged so that either positive or negative plenum pressure keeps them closed to prevent leakage.
5. Install light switch with a pilot light outside each casing section to control a vaporproof light with a wire guard.
6. Direct intake louver away from a residential building or quiet area unless baffled for equipment sound.
7. Install a properly drained space between the louver and outdoor air damper to collect rain water or fine snow that passes through the louvers.
8. Include generously sized mixing plenum to permit easy filter maintenance, maximum turbulence, and mixing of outdoor and return air and room to install baffles to prevent stratification.
9. Install an access door to the mixing plenum large enough to accommodate a standard package of filter media and, on large systems, a hand truck. This section is usually fabricated with sheet metal, but larger plenums are often built of masonry and have standard weatherstripped steel doors. Although it is desirable, it is not necessary to have access between the filter and heating coil, because, as a dry coil, it does not require frequent cleaning.
10. Place material to seal the openings between the coil and the casing on the exit side, so it is accessible if the heating coil needs to be removed.
11. Install drain pan for the cooling and dehumidifying section on a concrete pad or structural steel base at least 6 in. (150 mm) above the floor to facilitate connecting the piping to the coils and drains. If set on concrete, set the drain pan on heavy-density insulation and lay in mastic on heavy-density roofing felt to protect the underside from corrosion and absorb any irregularities in the concrete surface. If set on steel, insulate the underside with waterproof insulation.
12. Keep the pan level or pitched toward drain.
13. Place a drain pan under each coil bank stacked more than one high with a separate downspout to the main drain.
14. Trap all drains with a water seal at least 1 in. (25 mm) deeper than the pressure caused by the fan, and pitch 0.25 in. per foot (20 mm/m) to an indirect waste receptacle. Insulate drains if they pass through any space where damage from condensation drip might occur.
15. Use drainage fittings with cleanout plugs at each change of direction.
16. Locate floor drains in the inlet plenum, at the entrance and exit of the cooling coil, and in a humidifier plenum.
17. Place access on the entrance and exit of the cooling and humidifying section to allow for periodic cleaning of the coils and sprays, if they are used.
18. Install an access door in the fan section large enough for motor and fanwheel removal.
19. Build a masonry fan section, lined with acoustical panels, to lower sound levels in adjacent rooms. This should be a separate partition with air space between it and the equipment room walls. Heavy gauge sheetmetal with steel framework and external stiffeners, adequately insulated with rigid sound and heat insulation, may be less costly and offer more versatility for

internal component arrangement. Acoustical treatment on the fan section ceiling and on the floor under the spring-loaded fan base will reduce sound transmission to other floors.

20. Run piping mains parallel to major ductwork with hangers between the ducts and not through them.

21. Valve drop branches to equipment at the main and arrange them so they will not interfere with access doors or the removal of coils and other equipment.

22. Be sure final connections are removable without disturbing control valves or the drop branches.

23. Install all equipment piping after the ductwork so that ductwork dodging pipes will not compromise air handling efficiency.

24. Figure 2 shows the heating and cooling coils in banks split vertically to limit the size of the coils. Control the heating or cooling coils in one bank by one control valve assembly in the main piping.

25. In addition, install a balancing valve in the return branch piping from each individual coil to ensure uniform loading across the face of the coil banks to prevent stratification.

26. Plumb water coils (except hot water preheat coils) to run counter flow.

27. Provide preheat coils with individual control valves and thermostats to minimize freezing in the event of air stratification.

28. Run main electric feeder conduits across the ceiling perpendicular to main ducts and between beams and terminate in readily accessible pull boxes in a clear area of the room.

29. Run subfeeders and branch circuits beneath the floor, stubbing up through waterproof sleeves near the electrical equipment.

30. Run all final connections to moving equipment or vibration and sound isolated structures in a flexible cable with adequate slack.

31. Place the main electric distribution panel and motor control center near the main entrance of the room.

32. Mount the local automatic temperature control panel near the air-conditioning equipment to keep capillary tubing and control connectors as short as possible.

33. Be sure all electric and temperature control panels are well lighted.

Checking Installation and Balancing

After installation:

1. Check for air leaks in the casing and in the sealant around the coils and filter frames by moving a light source along the outside of the joint while observing the darkened interior of the casing. Caulk any leaks.

2. Note points where piping enters the casing to be sure that the escutcheons are tight. Do not rely on pipe insulation to seal these openings because, in time, it will shrink.

3. In prefabricated units, check that all panel fastening holes are filled to prevent whistling.

4. Make a final check for leaks after start-up. Chapter 57 of this Volume discusses procedures for both air and water systems.

MECHANICAL SUPPORT EQUIPMENT

The type of central heating and cooling equipment used for large building air-conditioning systems depends chiefly on economic factors, once the total required capacity has been determined. Component choice depends on such factors as the type of fuel available, environmental protection required, structural support, and available space.

Rising energy costs have fostered many designs to recover the internal heat from lights, people, and equipment to reduce the size of the heating plant. Chapter 6 describes several heat-recovery arrangements.

The search for energy savings has extended to total energy systems, in which on-site power generation has been added to the heating and air conditioning project. The economics of this function is determined by gas and electric rate differentials and the electric to heat demands for the project. In these systems, the waste heat from the generators can be input to the cooling equipment, either to drive turbines of centrifugal compressors or to serve absorption chillers. Chapter 8 of this Volume gives further details on total energy systems.

Among the largest installations of central mechanical equipment are the central cooling and heating plants serving groups of large buildings. These plants provide higher diversity and generally operate more efficiently and with lower maintenance and labor costs than individual plants.

The economics of these systems require extensive analysis. Boilers, gas and steam turbine-driven centrifugals, and absorption chillers may be installed in combination in one plant. In large buildings with core areas that require cooling while perimeter areas require heating, one of several heat reclaim systems could heat the perimeter to save energy. Chapter 33 in the EQUIPMENT Volume gives details of these combinations, and Chapter 12 in this volume gives design details of central plants.

Most large buildings, however, have their own central heating/cooling plant in which the choice of equipment depends on the following:

1. required capacity and type of usage
2. costs and kinds of available energy
3. location of the equipment room
4. the type of air distribution system
5. owning and operating costs

Many electric utilities impose severe penalties for peak summertime power use or, alternatively, offer incentives for off-peak use of power. This policy has renewed interest in thermal storage systems—both water and ice. The storage capacity paid for by summertime load leveling is now available for use in the winter, making heat reclaim a more viable option. With ice-storage systems, the low temperature ice water can provide colder air than is available from a conventional system. Use of high water temperature rise and lower temperature air results in lower pumping and fan energy and, in some instances, offsets the energy penalty due to the lower temperature required to make ice.

Heating Equipment

Steam and hot water boilers for heating are manufactured for high or low pressure and use coal, oil, electricity, gas, and sometimes, waste material for fuel. Low pressure boilers are rated for a working pressure of 15 psig (200 kPa) for steam, 160 psig (1200 kPa) for water, with a maximum temperature limitation of 250 °F (121 °C). Package boilers, with all components and controls assembled as a unit, are available. Electrode or resistance-type electric boilers are available in sizes up to 12,000 kW and larger for either hot water or steam generation. Chapter 24 in the 1983 EQUIPMENT Volume has further information.

Where steam or hot water is supplied from a central plant, as on university campuses and downtown areas of large cities, the service entrance to the building must conform to utility standards. The utility should be contacted at the beginning of the project to determine availability, cost, and the specific requirements of the service.

Fuels

Fuels must be considered, when the boiler system is selected, to ensure maximum efficiency. Chapter 15 of the 1985 FUNDAMENTALS Volume gives fuel types, properties, and proper combustion factors. Chapter 23 in the 1983 EQUIPMENT Volume includes information for the design, selection, and operation of automatic fuel-burning equipment.

Refrigeration Equipment

The major types of refrigeration equipment used in large systems are as follows:

1. Reciprocating— 1/16 to 150 hp (0.046 to 120 kW).
2. Helical rotary—100 to 750 tons (350 to 2600 kW).
3. Centrifugal—100 to 10,000 tons (350 to 35,000 kW).
4. Absorption—100 to 1600 tons (350 to 5600 kW).

Reciprocating, helical rotary, and centrifugal compressors have many types of drives—electric motors, gas and diesel engines, and gas and steam turbines. The compressors may be purchased as part of a refrigeration chiller consisting of compressor, drive, chiller, condenser, and necessary safety and operating controls. Reciprocating and helical rotary compressor units are frequently used in field assembled systems, with air-cooled or evaporative condensers arranged for remote installation.

Centrifugal compressors are usually included in packaged chillers. Most centrifugal chillers use water-cooled condensers. Air-cooled centrifugal packages are available in limited sizes.

Absorption chillers are water cooled. They use a lithium bromide/water or water/ammonia cycle and are generally available in the following three configurations: (1) direct fired, (2) indirect fired by low pressure steam or hot water, and (3) indirect fired by high pressure steam or hot water. Small, direct-fired chillers are single-effect machines with capacities from 3.5 to 25 tons (12 to 88 kW). Japan produces larger direct-fired, double-effect chillers in the 100- to 1500-ton (350 to 5250 kW) capacity range.

Low pressure steam at 15 psig (200 kPa) or hot water heats the generator of single-effect absorption chillers with capacities from 50 to 1600 tons (175 to 5600 kW). Double-effect machines use higher pressure steam up to 150 psig (1100 kPa) or hot water at an equivalent temperature. Absorption chillers of this type are available from 350 to 1100 tons (1225 to 3850 kW).

The absorption chiller is sometimes combined with steam turbine-driven centrifugal compressors in large installations. Steam from the noncondensing turbine is piped to the generator of the absorption machine. When a centrifugal unit is driven by a gas turbine or an engine, an absorption machine generator may be fed with steam or hot water from the jacket. A heat exchanger that will transfer the heat of the exhaust gases to a fluid medium may increase the cycle efficiency. Chapter 14 of the 1983 EQUIPMENT Volume gives details on "Absorption Air-Conditioning and Refrigeration Equipment."

Cooling Towers

Water is usually cooled by contact with the atmosphere to reject heat from the water-cooled condensers of air-conditioning systems. Either natural draft or mechanical draft cooling towers or spray ponds accomplish the cooling. Of these, the mechanical draft tower, which may be of the forced draft, induced draft, or ejector type, can be designed for most conditions because it does not depend on the wind. Air-conditioning systems use towers ranging from small package units of 5 to 500 tons (18 to 1800 kW) or field erected towers, with multiple cells in unlimited sizes.

The tower must be winterized if required for cooling at ambient outdoor dry-bulb temperatures below 35°F (2°C). Winterizing includes the capability of bypassing water directly into the tower return line (either automatically or manually, depending on the installation) and of heating the tower pan water to a temperature above freezing.

Heat may be added by steam or hot water coils or electric resistance heaters in the tower pan. Also, it is usually necessary to provide an electric cable on the condenser water and make up water pipe and to insulate these heat-traced sections to prevent the pipes from freezing. When it is necessary to operate the cooling tower at or near freezing conditions, the tower fan (or fans) should be cycled by an immersion thermostat in the basin water, or by a head pressure control on the compressor, to minimize freezing of the tower fill.

Where the cooling tower will not operate in freezing weather, provisions for draining the tower and piping are necessary. Draining is the most effective way to prevent tower and piping from freezing.

Careful attention must also be given to water treatment to keep maintenance required in the refrigeration machine absorbers and/or condenser to a minimum.

Cooling towers may also cool the building in off seasons by filtering and directly circulating the condenser water through the chilled water circuit, by cooling the chilled water in a separate heat exchanger, or by using the heat exchangers in the refrigeration equipment to produce thermal cooling. Towers are usually selected in multiples so they may be run at reduced capacity and shut down for maintenance in cool weather. Chapter 21 in the 1983 EQUIPMENT Volume includes further design and application details.

Air Cooled Condensers

Air cooled condensers pass outdoor air over a dry coil to condense the refrigerant. This results in a higher condensing temperature and, thus, a larger power input at peak conditions; however, this peak is short over 24 hours because the outdoor air normally has a large daily range. The air-cooled condenser is popular in small reciprocating systems because of its low maintenance requirements.

Evaporative Condensers

Evaporative condensers pass air over coils sprayed with water, thus taking advantage of adiabatic saturation to lower the condensing temperature. As with the cooling tower, freeze prevention and close control of water treatment are required for success. The lower power consumption of the evaporative versus the air-cooled condenser is gained at the expense of the water used and higher maintenance.

Pumps

Air-conditioning pumps are usually centrifugal pumps. Pumps for large and heavy-duty systems have a horizontal split case with double suction impeller for easier maintenance and high efficiency. End suction pumps, either close coupled or flexible connected, are used for smaller tasks.

Major applications for pumps in the equipment room are as follows: (1) primary and secondary chilled water, (2) hot water, (3) condenser water, (4) condensate pumps, (5) boiler feed pumps, and (6) fuel oil.

When the pumps handle hot liquids or have high inlet pressure drops, the required net positive suction head (NPSH) must not exceed the NPSH available at the pump. It is common practice to provide two identical pumps—one a spare, or each sized for 50% of the design flow at the design head, operating in parallel to maintain system continuity in case of a pump failure.

Sometimes the chilled water and condenser water system characteristics permit using one spare pump for both systems, with valved connections to the manifolds of each. Chapters 13 and 14 in this volume gives design recommendations, and Chapter 31 in the 1983 EQUIPMENT Volume gives information on selection of pumps.

Piping

Air-conditioning piping systems can be divided into two parts; the piping in the main equipment room and the piping required for the air-handling equipment throughout the building. The air-handling system piping follows procedures detailed in Chapters 5, 13, 14, and 15 in this volume.

The major piping in the main equipment room includes fuel lines, refrigerant piping, and steam and water connections. Chapter 34 in the 1985 FUNDAMENTALS Volume gives details for sizing and installing these pipes. Chapter 11 includes more information on piping for steam systems. Chapter 15 has information on chilled and dual water systems.

Instrumentation

All equipment must have adequate gauges, thermometers, flow meters, balancing devices, and dampers for effective system performance. In addition, capped thermometer wells, gage cocks, capped duct openings, and volume dampers should be at strategic points for system balancing. Chapter 57 on "Testing, Adjusting and Balancing" in this volume indicates the locations and types of fittings required.

Recent advances in electronic and computer technology are changing traditional control system architecture. Pneumatic and electric relay logic is being replaced by microprocessors and software programs to establish control sequences. Output signals are converted to pneumatic or electric commands to actuate HVAC hardware.

A central control console to monitor the many system points should be considered by any large, complex air-conditioning system. A control panel permits a single operator to monitor and perform functions, at any point in the building, to increase occupant comfort and free maintenance staff for other duties. Chapter 51 on "Automatic Control," in this volume, describes these systems in detail.

SPACE REQUIREMENTS

In the initial phases of building design, the engineer seldom has sufficient information, while the architect usually wants the design immediately. Most experienced engineers have developed rules of thumb to estimate the building space needed.

The air-conditioning system selected, the building configuration, and other variables govern the space required for the mechanical system. The final design is usually a compromise between what the engineer recommends and what the architect can accommodate.

Although few buildings are identical in design and concept, some basic criteria are applicable to most buildings and help allocate the space that approximates the final requirements. These space requirements are often expressed as a percentage of the total building floor area.

Mechanical, Electrical, and Plumbing Facilities

The total mechanical and electrical space requirements range from 4 to 9% of the gross building area, with the majority of buildings falling within the 6 to 9% range.

It is desirable to have most of the facilities centrally located to minimize long duct, pipe, and conduit runs and sizes; simplify shaft layouts; and centralize maintenance and operation. A central location also reduces pump and fan motor power, which may reduce building operating costs. But for many reasons, it is often impossible to centrally locate all the mechanical, electrical, and plumbing facilities within the building. In any case, the equipment should be kept together to minimize space re-

quirements, centralize maintenance and operation, and simplify the electrical distribution system.

Equipment rooms generally require clear ceiling heights ranging from 12 to 20 feet (3.7 to 6 m), depending on equipment sizes and the complexity of ductwork, piping, and conduit.

The main electrical transformer and switchgear rooms should be as close to the incoming electrical service as practical. If there is an emergency generator, it should be close to the switchgear room to keep interconnection costs to a minimum. Also, the emergency generator should be near a source of combustion air. There must be adequate noise control, and the exhaust gases must be vented to the outdoors.

The main plumbing equipment room usually contains gas and domestic water meters, the domestic hot water system, the fire protection system, and various other elements such as compressed air; special gases; and vacuum, ejector, and sump pump systems. Some water and gas utilities require a remote outdoor meter location.

The heating and air-conditioning equipment room houses the boiler or pressure-reducing station or both; the refrigeration machines, including the chilled water and condensing water pumps; converters for furnishing hot or cold water for air conditioning; control air compressors; vacuum and condensate pumps; and other miscellaneous equipment.

The HVAC equipment is flexible in that it is often economical to locate the refrigeration plant at the top or intermediate floors or on the roof. The electrical service and structural costs will rise, but these may be offset by reduced condenser and chilled water piping, energy consumption, and equipment cost because of lower operating pressure. Even the boiler plant may be placed on the roof, which eliminates a chimney through the building.

Gas fuel may be more desirable because oil storage and pumping present added design and operating problems. However, restrictions on gas as a boiler fuel may preclude this option. Heat-recovery systems, in conjunction with the refrigeration equipment, can drastically reduce the heating plant size in buildings with large core areas. With well-insulated buildings and electric utility rates structured to encourage a high use factor, even electric resistance heat can be attractive, which reduces space requirements even further.

Additional space might be needed for a telephone terminal room, a pneumatic tube equipment room, an incinerator, and similar areas.

Most buildings, especially larger ones, need cooling towers, which often present problems. If the cooling tower is on the ground, it should be at least 100 ft (30 m) away from the building for two reasons: to reduce tower noise in the building and to keep intermediate season discharge air from fogging the building's windows. Towers should be kept the same distance from parking lots to avoid staining car finishes with water treatment chemicals. When the tower is on the roof, its vibration and noise must be isolated from the building. Some towers are less noisy than others, and some have attenuation housings to reduce noise levels. These options should be explored before selecting a tower.

The bottom of many towers, especially larger ones, must be set on a steel frame 4 to 5 ft. (1.2 to 1.5 m) high to allow room for piping and proper tower and roof maintenance. Pumps below the tower will provide adequate net positive suction head, but they must be installed to prevent draining the piping on shutdown.

Fan Room Requirements

Fan rooms for the substructure block and main floor are usually placed in the lower level of the building—either in the basement or on the second floor. Second-floor mechanical rooms have the advantage of easy outdoor access for makeup air, exhaust, and equipment replacement.

Fan rooms on upper floors largely depend on the total area of the floor. Buildings with large floor areas often have multiple fan rooms on each floor. Many high-rise buildings, however, may have one fan room serving 10 to 20 floors—one serving the lower floors, one serving the middle of the building, and one at the roof serving the top quarter of the building.

Life safety is a very important factor in fan room location. Chapter 58 in this volume discusses principles of fire spread and smoke control.

Interior Shafts

Interior shaft space accommodates return and exhaust air; interior supply air; hot, chilled, and condenser water piping; steam and return piping; electric closets; telephone closets; plumbing piping; and possible pneumatic tubes and conveyer systems.

The shafts must be clear of stairs and elevators on at least two sides to allow maximum headroom when the pipes and ducts come out at the ceiling. In general, duct shafts having an aspect ratio of 2:1 to 4:1 are easier to develop than large square shafts. The rectangular shape also makes it easier to go from the equipment in the fan rooms to the shafts.

The size, number, and location of shafts is important in multistory buildings. Vertical duct distribution systems with little horizontal branch ductwork are desirable because they are usually less costly; easier to balance; create less conflict with pipes, beams, and lights; and enable the architect to design lower floor-to-floor heights.

The number of shafts is a function of building size and shape, but, in larger buildings, it is usually more economical, in cost and space, to have several small shafts rather than one large shaft. Separate supply and exhaust duct shafts may be desired to reduce the number of duct crossovers and to operate the exhaust shaft as a plenum. Ten to 15% additional shaft space should be allowed for future expansion and modifications. The additional space also reduces the initial installation cost.

Equipment Access

Properly designed mechanical equipment rooms must solve the problem of how and where to move large, heavy equipment in, out, and within the building. Equipment replacement and maintenance can be very costly if access is not planned properly.

Because systems vary greatly, it is difficult to estimate space requirements for refrigeration and boiler rooms without making block layouts of the system selected. Block layouts allow the engineer to develop the most efficient arrangement of equipment, with adequate access and serviceability. They further help in preliminary discussions with the owner and architect. Only then can the engineer obtain verification of the estimates and provide a workable and economical design.

REFERENCE

Wheeler, A.E. 1977. Air Handling Unit Design for Energy Conservation. *ASHRAE Journal*, June.

CHAPTER 2

ALL-AIR SYSTEMS

GENERAL

This chapter covers the design and use of all-air systems in single and multiple zone applications. An all-air system provides complete sensible and latent cooling capacity in the cold air supplied by the system. No additional cooling is required at the zone. Heating can be accomplished by the same airstream, either in the central system or at a particular zone.

In some applications, heating is accomplished by a separate heating system. The term *zone* implies the provision or the need for separate thermostatic control, while the term *room* implies a partitioned area that may or may not require separate control.

All-air systems are classified in two basic categories: (1) single-path systems and (2) dual-path systems. Single-path systems contain the main heating and cooling coils in a series flow air path; a common duct distribution system at a common air temperature feeds all terminal apparatus. Dual-path systems contain the main heating and cooling coils in parallel flow or series-parallel flow air paths with either: (1) a separate cold and warm air duct distribution system, which blends the air at the terminal apparatus (dual-duct systems) or (2) a separate supply duct to each zone, with air supplied to that zone at the air temperature controlled at the main supply fan (multi-zone).

These classifications may be divided as follows:

Single-Path Systems
  Single duct, constant volume
  Single-zone systems
  Reheat systems, single duct—variable air volume
  Simple variable air volume
  Variable air volume, reheat
  Single duct—variable air volume, induction
  Single duct—variable air volume, fan powered
  Constant fan, intermittent fan
Dual-Path Systems
  Dual duct, single fan—constant volume
  Single fan, constant volume—reheat

Variable Air Volume
Multi-zone

The all-air system adapts to many air-conditioning systems for comfort or process work. It is applied in buildings that require individual control of conditions and have multiple zones, such as office buildings, schools and universities, laboratories, hospitals, stores, hotels, and ships. All-air systems are also used in special applications for close control of temperature and humidity, including clean rooms, computer rooms, hospital operating rooms, and textile and tobacco factories.

SYSTEM CONSIDERATION

Duct Systems

All-air supply duct systems can be designed for high or low velocity. High velocity systems reduce duct sizes and save space, but they usually have higher friction losses and system pressures. For some low velocity systems, medium or high pressures may be desired for easy balancing or necessary because of the substantial pressure drop caused by flow control regulators.

On any variable flow systems, changing operating conditions create rates of air flow in the ducts different from those used in the design. This varying air flow in the supply duct requires careful analysis to ensure that the system will perform efficiently at all loads. This is particularly true with the wide use of high velocity systems in all-air designs. Chapter 33 of the 1985 FUNDAMENTALS Volume includes duct sizing and maximum velocity recommendations.

Return air ducts are usually sized by the equal friction method. In many applications, ceilings or corridors are used for return air plenums; the return air is then collected at a central point on each floor. This approach should be reviewed to be sure it meets local code requirements. For example, the National Electric Code requires either conduit or Teflon insulated wire installed in a return air plenum ceiling, which affects costs.

The preparation of this chapter is assigned to TC 9.1, Large Building Air-Conditioning Systems.

Heating

Heating requirements can be met in all-air systems by (1) the same air stream used for cooling; (2) a separate perimeter air system; or (3) a radiation system using water, steam, electric resistance, or radiant heating. The following factors affect the need or desirability of a separate perimeter heating system.

1. Severity of the heating load.
2. Nature and orientation of the building envelope.
3. Effects of downdraft at windows and the radiant effect of the cold glass surface.
4. Type of occupancy, i.e., sedentary versus transient.
5. Periods of occupancy, i.e., in buildings such as offices and schools, unoccupied for considerable periods; fan operating costs can be reduced by heating with perimeter radiation during unoccupied periods instead of with the fan system.

A perimeter heating system can operate with any of the all-air systems. However, its greatest application has been in conjunction with variable air volume (VAV) systems for cooling-only service. The section on "Variable Air Volume Systems" in this chapter has further details.

Heating and Cooling Loads

A proper design considers all load components and their effect on system operation. The 1985 FUNDAMENTALS Volume covers basic calculations for air system loads, flow rates, and psychrometrics based on mass flow and weight. Chapter 26 of the same volume gives equations based on volumetric flow of standard air at 13.33 ft^3/lb (830 L/kg) of dry air. The designers should understand their relationship to the psychrometric chart and the interaction among various heat load components in different air system designs.

Room Air Volume

Basic equations to determine the required air quantity, as a function of load, for individual rooms (zones) are the same for all systems. The air supplied to each room must meet the peak load condition. The peak may be determined by sensible or latent room cooling or heating loads.

The peak air quantity required for cooling must be compared to the air quantity required for ventilation.

Air Volume for Ventilation

These standards apply when the required supply air for these loads is deficient in any of the following ways:

1. If it does not contain adequate outside air for such a room, supply air for ventilation must be determined from the required room outdoor air, CFM_{Or}, as:

$$Q_{sRv} = Q_{Or}/X_O$$

where

Q_{sRv} = room supply air for ventilation requirements, cfm (L/s)
Q_{Or} = minimum outdoor air required in a particular room, cfm (L/s)
X_O = ratio of the systems total outdoor air to its total supply air, which satisfies outdoor air requirements in the majority of rooms

(ASHRAE Standard 62-1981 covers ventilation requirements.)

2. If the supply air is inadequate to makeup exhaust requirements in the room and only conditioned air is used as makeup (i.e., there is no supplementary ventilation supply system), it may be necessary to increase the total air to balance the exhaust air quantity. This presumes that there is no return air from the room. Moreover, the entire volume of makeup ventilation air becomes an outdoor air burden to the system in the form of a larger X_O distributed to all rooms, even though all the air supplied to this particular room is not outdoor air and:

$$Q_{sRv} = Q_{cR}$$

where

Q_{cR} = air exhausted or relieved from a room and not returned to the conditioned air system, cfm (L/s)

3. If the desired rate of air exchange in the room is not satisfied, rate of air change governs and:

$$Q_{sRv} = VN/F \text{ (No. of air changes per hour)}$$

where

V = Room volume, ft^3(m^3)
N = Number of air changes per hour
F = Units correction factor, 60 (3.6)

4. If air movement, as measured by an area index instead of an air change index, is not satisfied or:

$$Q_{sRv} = K \ Q/A$$

where

K = Constant multiplier
Q/A = Flow per unit area index, cfm/ft^2 [L/(s $\cdot$ m^2)]

The rate of air change and K are both empirical values without established or universally accepted standards. These values vary with the designer's experience and local building codes.

Temperature Versus Air Quantity

Designers have considerable latitude in selecting supply air temperatures and corresponding air quantities within the limitations of the procedures for determining heating and cooling loads outlined in the 1985 FUNDAMENTALS Volume. ASHRAE Standard 55-1981 also addresses the effect of these variables on comfort. In making a selection, the designer needs to consider the initial cost economies of lower air quantities and low air temperatures (smaller fan and duct sysem) against possible problems of distribution, odor, condensation, or air movement. Low air quantity and low supply air temperature may require increased refrigeration capacity and operating cost or an increase in the combined operating cost of the refrigeration equipment and fan system. In addition, cooling with the seasonal outside air must be evaluated.

Other Design Considerations

All-air systems operate with a low temperature differential between the supply air and the space, so any loads imposed by the system that affect the air temperature differential and required air quantities must be considered. These include the following:

1. Supply air fan heat gain. This includes total pressure heat gain when the supply fan is placed after the cooling coil in a draw-through configuration. It only includes the velocity pressure heat gain when the supply fan is placed before the cooling coil in a blow-through configuration.
2. Heat gain or loss in the supply duct system.

3. Heat gain or loss of return air in a ceiling plenum return. This is affected by air-handling lighting fixtures and roof load.
4. Duct leakage.
5. Equipment leakage—especially dual-duct mixing boxes.

PSYCHROMETRICS

Chapter 6 in the 1985 FUNDAMENTALS Volume describes the application of the psychrometrics chart to system design. Each of the major systems described in this chapter are presented on a psychrometric chart. Representation of the local components on the chart best illustrates the design parameters and operating characteristics of the all-air systems.

COMPONENTS AND CONTROLS

This chapter principally covers total systems designed to offset full-load and part-load conditions and the flexibility of the various components of a common air system under simultaneous heating and cooling loads. An adequate design can (1) maintain conditions in no-load zones during peak and off-peak system loads and (2) maintain them in zones with peak latent and off-peak sensible loads during mild weather with high ambient humidity. Therefore, these no-load and off-peak criteria must be considered when selecting the individual components for the total system.

The various components of an all-air system, such as air distribution duct design, automatic controls, control equipment, refrigeration systems, and others are covered in appropriate chapters in this volume and in the 1985 FUNDAMENTALS and 1983 EQUIPMENT volumes.

EVALUATION

Advantages

All-air systems have the following features and advantages:

1. The central location of major equipment consolidates operation and maintenance to unoccupied areas and permits maximum choice of filtration equipment, odor and noise control, and high quality, durable equipment.
2. Complete absence within the conditioned area of drain piping, electrical equipment wiring, and filters. This feature reduces possible damage to furnishings in occupied areas and minimizes service needs in these areas.
3. Allows the use of the greatest number of potential cooling season hours with outside air in place of mechanical refrigeration; cooling with outside air is recommended only when it is economical without excessive disadvantages.
4. Seasonal changeover is simple and readily adaptable to automatic control.
5. Gives a wide choice of zonability, flexibility, and humidity control under all operating conditions, with simultaneous heating and cooling available—even during off-season periods.
6. Heat-recovery systems may be readily incorporated.
7. Allows good design flexibility for optimum air distribution, draft control, and local requirements. Interferes least with draperies at windows.
8. Well suited to applications requiring unusual exhaust makeup.
9. Infringes least on perimeter floor space.
10. Adapts to winter humidification.

Disadvantages

All air systems have the following disadvantages:

1. Requires additional duct clearance, which can reduce the usable floor space and increase the building height.
2. In areas with low outside air temperatures where air (not radiation) is used for perimeter heating, fans must operate longer during unoccupied periods.
3. Air-balancing is difficult and requires great care. In systems without built-in zone self-balancing devices, air balancing may have to be done several times.
4. All-air perimeter systems are usually not available for use during building construction as soon as perimeter hydronic systems.
5. Accessibility to terminals demands close cooperation between architectural, mechanical, and structural designers.
6. Applications with high internal cooling loads require greater air flow, so the designer should work closely with the architect to solve possible architectural problems.

SINGLE-PATH SYSTEMS (PRIMARY AIR AND TERMINAL MIXING)

Single Duct, Constant Volume

Control of the dry-bulb temperature within a space requires a balance between the space load and the capacity of the supply air to offset the load. Single-duct, constant volume systems alter the supply air temperature while maintaining constant air volume. Both single-zone and constant-volume designs are used.

Single-Zone Systems

The simplest all-air system is a supply unit serving a single temperature-control zone. The unit can be installed either within or remote from the space it serves and may operate with or without distributing duct work. Ideally, this system responds completely to the space needs. Well-designed systems maintain temperature and humidity closely and efficiently. They can be shut down when desired without affecting the operation of adjacent areas.

Figure 1 shows a schematic of the single-zone central unit. The return fan may only be needed if 100% outdoor air is used for cooling at some time during the year. It can be eliminated if air is relieved from the space with very little pressure loss through a relief system.

Reheat Systems

The reheat system is a modification of the single-zone system. It provides (1) zone or space control for areas of unequal loading, (2) heating or cooling of perimeter areas with different exposures, or (3) close control for process or comfort applications. As the word "reheat" implies, heat is added as a secondary process to either preconditioned primary air or recirculated room air.

Relatively small, low-pressure systems have reheat coils in the duct at each zone. More sophisticated designs have higher pressure ducts and pressure reduction devices and maintain constant volume to balance the system at the reheat zone. The heating medium can be hot water, steam, or electricity. Figure 2 shows a schematic of a reheat system. The system obtains conditioned air from the central unit at a fixed cold air temperature.

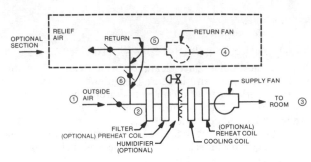

FIG. 1A...SINGLE-DUCT SYSTEM

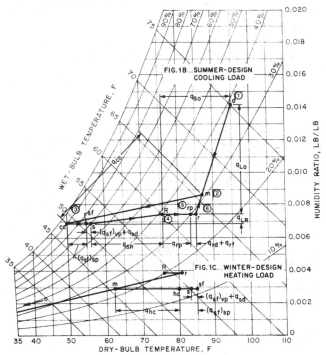

Fig. 1 Typical Arrangement of Components and Psychrometric Chart for a Single-Duct Single-Zone System

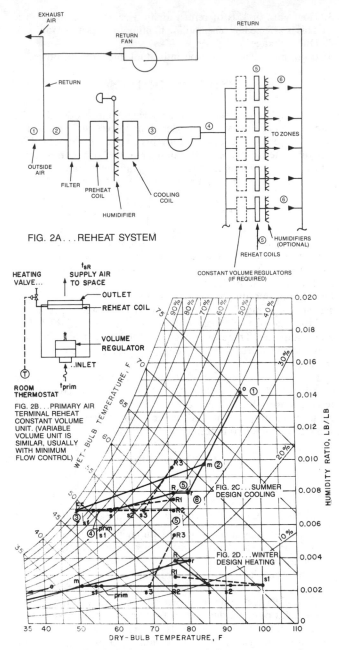

FIG. 2A...REHEAT SYSTEM

FIG. 2B...PRIMARY AIR TERMINAL REHEAT CONSTANT VOLUME UNIT. (VARIABLE VOLUME UNIT IS SIMILAR, USUALLY WITH MINIMUM FLOW CONTROL)

Fig. 2 Typical Arrangement of Components and Psychrometric Chart for a Reheat System

The air quantity is selected to offset the maximum cooling load in the space(s). The control thermostat calls for reheat when the cooling load in the space drops below the design value.

Constant volume reheat systems offer designers many options in the initial design stages. These can be revised during construction as zoning changes are made. Field changes to accommodate later zoning revisions can be made by adding a heating coil or terminal unit. Constant volume reheat systems can maintain close control of space humidity. Assuming reasonably close dew point control at the central apparatus, only variations in space moisture conditions will vary the relative humidity, *R*. Additional moisture, if needed, can be added at the terminal device, which is controlled by a space humidistat.

Design Considerations

Air Volume. A single-zone system is psychrometrically identical to one zone of a reheat system. Therefore, system air volume is equal to the sum of the individual peak air volumes for each zone.

Supply Air Conditions. In a constant volume reheat system, the supply air temperature is determined in conjunction with the air quantity. The procedure for these calculations can be found in the 1985 FUNDAMENTALS Volume.

Humidification. Reheat systems permit close control of the space dry-bulb temperature at all load conditions. Space humidities can be maintained between any selected high limit and the humidity ratio of the supply air, since supply air moisture level remains fixed under partial load conditions. During winter, the moisture level of the system is principally a function of the dew point of the outside supply air and the building latent load. As a result, a single-duct system without reheat offers cooling flexibility, but it cannot control summer humidity independent of temperature requirements. Chapter 51 of this volume has further information on humidity control.

Components and Controls

A single-zone system responds to only one set of space conditions. Thus, it is limited to spaces where variations occur almost uniformly throughout the zone or where the load is stable. Single-zone systems are applied to small department stores, small individual shops in a shopping center, individual classrooms of a small school, and computer rooms. For example, a rooftop unit with a refrigeration system that serves an individual space is a single-zone system. The refrigeration system, however, can be remote and serve several single-zone units in a larger installation.

A single-zone system can be controlled by varying the quantity of the cooling medium or by providing reheat, face and bypass dampers, or a combination of these. Single-duct systems with reheat satisfy variations in load by providing independent heating and cooling sources.

Evaluation

The advantages and disadvantages of single-duct, constant volume systems are as follows:

Advantages. The reheat system closely controls space conditions. It particularly applies to laboratories (high exhaust requirements) or to applications requiring close control of space conditions because of the product (textile mills) or occupants (hospitals—operating rooms, intensive care units, etc.)

Disadvantages. A reheat system is expensive to operate and does not meet most energy codes for ordinary comfort conditioning applications, unless heat recovery is available for heating or the variable air volume concept is applied.

Energy efficiency can be improved in a constant volume reheat system by the following methods:

1. Reset the central supply air temperature to allow the cooling coil to satisfy the zone with the greatest cooling requirements.
2. Use space thermostats with a "dead band" to reduce the amount of reheat energy used during the cooling cycle or use dual temperature heating/cooling thermostats and reset for lower temperature when running an air economizer instead of refrigeration.
3. Use an internal source, heat-recovery system to recover heat from the refrigeration cycle or an exhaust or relief air system.

SINGLE DUCT, VARIABLE AIR VOLUME

A Variable Air Volume (VAV) System controls the dry-bulb temperature within a space by varying the volume of supply air rather than the supply air temperature. VAV systems can be applied to interior or perimeter zones, with common or separate fan systems, common or separate air temperature control, and with or without auxiliary heating devices. The variable volume concept may apply to vary air volume in the main system and/or to the control zones. This section covers the application of variable volume to reheat, while later sections cover its relationship to dual-duct, induction, and fan-powered systems.

A space thermostat can control flow by varying the position of a simple damper or a volume regulating device in duct, a pressure-reducing box, or at the terminal diffuser or grille. Depending on the complexity of the air distribution system, initial cost considerations, the lowest throttling ratio expected at part load, and the complexity of the initial and part-load balancing problems, variable volume may or may not be combined with fan or system static pressure controls.

Simple Variable Air Volume (VAV)

Simple VAV systems typically cool only and have no requirement for simultaneous heating and cooling in various zones. Perimeter radiation, radiant heat, or an independent constant volume, variable temperature air system normally handles heating requirements.

The fan system is designed to handle the largest simultaneous block load, not the sum of the individual peaks. As each zone peaks at a different time of day, it borrows the extra air from off-peak zones. This transfer of air from low-load to high-load zones occurs only in a true variable volume system. A system that runs excess air into a return air ceiling or bypasses it to the return duct may use zone variable volume temperature control principles; but the total design air volume is the sum of the peaks, since it is circulated on a constant volume basis. Such systems do not permit smaller fans and duct mains.

Figure 3 shows a typical arrangement of a variable volume system with separate perimeter heating. The psychrometric chart (Figure 3A) shows typical performance for maximum and partial load for both summer and winter operation. In cooling-only applications, air is delivered to the space at a fixed temperature to offset maximum space heat gains. The space thermostat reduces the volume of supply air as the load decreases. The solid lines in Figure 3A represent average system conditions. Dotted lines represent individual room conditions as the air volume to the room varies.

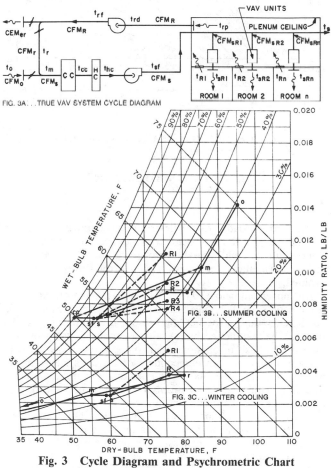

Fig. 3   Cycle Diagram and Psychrometric Chart
for a True Variable Air Volume (VAV) System
with Separate Perimeter Radiation

Variable Air Volume—Reheat

This simple Variable Air Volume System integrates heating at or near the terminal units. It is applied to systems requiring full heating and cooling flexibility in interior and exterior zones. The terminal units are set to maintain a predetermined minimum throttling ratio necessary to offset the heating load.

Variable volume with reheat permits flow reduction as the first step in control. Heat then turns on when the air flow reaches a predetermined minimum. When compared to a constant volume reheat system, this procedure reduces operating cost appreciably. A summer abort feature inactivates reheat during the summer, providing additional savings. When the minimum flow for the variable volume is reached and the reheat coil is maintaining conditions, the operation is identical to the psychrometric performance detailed in Figure 2A for the constant volume reheat system. Control, however, is at reduced air flow. Figure 4 shows the approximate performance of the variable volume reheat system for a complete season.

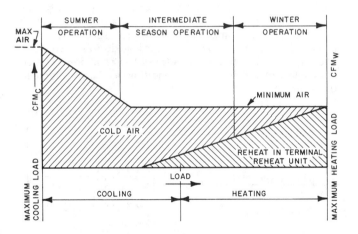

Fig. 4 Control Operation of VAV Terminal Reheat Units

DESIGN CONSIDERATIONS

Air Volume

If net room loads are not determined accurately, a variable volume system will have too much air flow, causing partial throttling at full load and excessive throttling at part loads. Oversizing of fans, ducts, terminals, and control valves should be avoided.

Air movement below 10 fpm (0.05 m/s) is uncomfortable for some people, so there has been concern over reduced air flow, particularly during the heating season. Minimum air circulation can be maintained by (1) raising supply air temperatures on a system basis or on a reheated zone-by-zone basis, (2) auxiliary heat in the room independent of the air system, (3) individual zone fan recirculation and blending of varying amounts of supply with room air or supply with ceiling plenum air, and (4) variable volume induction unit recirculation.

When variable volume is controlled by a constant volume fan that returns surplus air via a return air hung ceiling, the heat from lights and roof transmission becomes a room load. Constant air volume of this type requires each zone to satisfy the worst peak condition, and the benefit of variable volume is not realized.

Supply Air Conditions. When a common duct with temperature control feeds perimeter and interior spaces that require cooling during winter (i.e., with a separate perimeter radiation system), it is often advisable to reset the supply air temperature higher as the ambient temperature decreases, but only enough to avoid cold-draft sensations. The higher temperature does increase the fan energy required to move the greater volume of air, however.

For maximum heating and cooling flexibility, the supply air temperature must be low enough to handle the most severe winter cooling zone. The relationship between heater temperature and supply air temperature schedules is important for flexibility and operating economy.

Full shutoff terminals used with either radiation or transmission heating systems need no special provisions for variable volume terminals at the perimeter, since night setback or morning warm-up is performed by the perimeter heating system, independent of the variable volume terminal. The interior system VAV terminals will stay shut as long as room temperatures stay below the night setting, so the VAV fan system stays idle at night.

Following are several procedures for more positive warm-up:
1. Some variable volume terminals reverse the control sequence and permit the full volume of warm air to enter the space when heating is automatically or manually provided at the central equipment.
2. A dual-action, automatic changeover thermostat and the control supply pressure can be changed in conjunction with heating provided at the central equipment.
3. Normally open, variable volume terminals can be installed with a common main air pneumatic or electrical control line that shuts off and opens the terminal whenever the supply temperature is above room temperature.
4. During warm-up and before rooms are occupied, the fan system is generally run for a short time with outside air dampers closed. The length of the warm-up period depends on ambient conditions and length of shutdown.

Humidification. Whenever the supply air is throttled, its capacity to dehumidify air in the cooled zone decreases. Normally, this decrease is not a problem at minimum air volumes. For normal occupancy concentrations with normal, fairly constant, internal lighting loads, a small reduction in evaporator temperature and supply air will compensate for the reduced air volume.

However, spaces with high latent loads must be examined carefully on the psychrometric chart before variable air volume can be applied. Such spaces can often be treated economically in variable volume systems with a combination of variable volume and one of the several methods for maintaining minimum ventilation. In critical spaces, a humidistat may override the air volume reduction controlled by thermostat and control a reheat coil to maintain proper zone temperatures.

Components and Controls

Variable Air Volume Units. Variable air volume can be controlled by duct-mounted units serving air outlets in a control zone or by control units integral to each supply air outlet.

Pressure Independent Volume Regulator Units regulate the flow rate in response to the thermostat's call for heating or cooling. The required flow rate is maintained regardless of fluctuation of the VAV unit inlet or system pressure. These units can be field or factory adjusted for maximum and minimum (or shut off) cfm (m/s) settings. They will operate at inlet static pressures as low as 0.2 in. of water (50 Pa) at maximum system design volumes.

Pressure-Dependent, Air-Flow Limiting, Maximum-Volume Units regulate maximum volume, but the flow rate below maximum varies with the inlet pressure variation. Generally, air flow will oscillate when pressure varies. These units are less expensive than pressure-independent units and can be used where pressure independence is required only at maximum volume, where system pressure variations are relatively minor, and where some degree of "hunting" is tolerable.

Pressure Dependent Units. These units do not regulate the flow rate but position the volume regulating device in response to the thermostat. These units are the least expensive and should only be used where there is no need for limit control and the system pressure is stable.

Bypass (Dumping) Units. VAV room supply is accomplished in constant volume systems by returning excess supply air into the return ceiling plenum or return air duct, thus bypassing the room. However, this reduction of system volume is not energy efficient. Use is generally restricted to small systems where a simple method of temperature control is desired, initial cost is modest, and energy conservation is unimportant.

Supply Outlet Throttling Units. The area of the throat or the discharge opening of these supply outlets, usually linear diffusers, is thermostatically varied. The opening varies in approximate proportion to the air volume to maintain throw pattern stability, even with low air quantities. Since these units are pressure dependent, constant pressure regulators are usually required in the duct system. Noise is a particular concern when selecting outlets for occupied spaces.

Controls. The type of controls for variable volume units varies with the terminal device. Most use either pneumatic or electric control that may either be self-powered or system air actuated. Self-powered controls position the regulator with liquid-filled power elements. System air types use volume regulators to meter air from the system supplying air to the space. Components for both types are usually contained in the terminal device.

To conserve horsepower and limit system noise, especially in larger systems, fan-operating characteristics and system static pressure should be controlled. Many methods are available, including fan speed control, variable inlet vane control, fan bypass, fan discharge damper, and variable pitch fan control. These control methods are covered in the 1983 EQUIPMENT Volume.

The pressure-sensing location depends, to some extent, on the type of variable volume terminal. Pressure-dependent units without controllers should be near the static pressure midpoint of the duct run to ensure minimum pressure variation in the system. Where pressure independent units are installed, pressure controllers may be at the end of the duct run with highest static pressure loss. This sensing point ensures maximum fan-power savings while maintaining the minimum required pressure at the last terminal.

However, as the flow through the various parts of a large system varies, so do the static pressure losses. Some field adjustment is usually required to find the best location for the pressure sensor. In many systems, the first location is two-thirds to three-fourths the distance from the supply fan to the end of the main trunk duct. As the pressure at the system control point increases due to terminal units closing, the pressure controller signals the fan controller to position the fan volume control, which reduces flow and maintains constant pressure.

The fan power equation shows that the potential for fan energy savings with fan speed control is substantially greater than with variable inlet vanes (VIV). Power is directly related to both total pressure and air volume, and both methods effect the same energy saving when volume is reduced. However, VIV control only takes advantage of the portion of the system's pressure reduction that is not compensated for by throttling the fan, while variable speed control takes advantage of the full system pressure reduction, which is a square-root function of flow. The savings are analogous to those for variable speed pumping.

A velocity controller installed in the outside air intake ensures that dampers are open sufficiently to provide the minimum outside air flow desired when total flow is reduced. A less costly method is to schedule a variable minimum position of the outside air damper from the duct static pressure sensor or the fan control operator, either of which reacts directly to system volume reduction. Chapter 51 of this volume provides other applicable controls.

Advantages

Advantages of variable volume systems, in addition to those of all-air systems, are as follows:

1. The variable volume concept, when combined with one of the perimeter heating systems, offers inexpensive temperature control for multiple zoning and a high degree of simultaneous heating-cooling flexibility.

2. In true VAV systems, full advantage may be taken of changing loads from lights, occupancy, solar, and equipment; diversities of as much as 30%, compared with systems based on the sum of the peaks, are permitted. Consequently, the cost is lower for fans, refrigerations, heating, and associated plant auxiliaries, as well as for duct mains, insulation, and piping systems. This saving is usually much greater than the additional cost of variable volume terminal devices and fan control apparatus. This saving does not apply to return air systems. The fan energy wasted in all Constant Air Volume (CAV) systems and the additional cooling and heating waste in CAV reheat systems can be substantial.

3. True VAV air systems, except pressure-dependent systems, are virtually self-balancing, impaired only by inadequate static pressure control of volume regulation. The larger the network, the greater the need for these controls. This feature also makes it impossible to balance VAV systems with full load supply air quantities greater than actual load requirements.

4. It is easy and inexpensive to subdivide into new zones and to handle increased loads with new tenancy or usage if the overall system has the reserve for the load increase or if load does not exceed the original design simultaneous peak. Return air systems do not have this advantage, except as the distribution hardware might lend itself to subdivisions and partition changes (but not to load increases). Only the end duct variable volume unit might be limited by the size of the last branch. Joining duct ends from split runs around a building perimeter supplied by either a common fan or separate fans increases the diversity allowance for duct mains with the common fan and for ducts and fans with the case of separate fans. It also eliminates the end duct zone capacity limitation.

5. Operating cost savings are accrued from the following building characteristics. These savings do not apply to return air systems.
   a. Fans run long hours at reduced volumes, so, depending on the type of fan control, they use less energy. Also, the installed fan power is reduced.
   b. Refrigeration, heating, and pumping matches diversity of loads, so energy is saved.
   c. Outside air cooling, where applicable, gives better economy from (1) lower mixing temperatures at constant

minimum outdoor air with reduced supply air and (2) less parasitic reheat, since part-load zones may first be reduced to minimum supply air and the supply temperature may be raised before engaging reheat. This gives longer filter life, since less outside air is required for the same cold supply temperature.

  d. Unoccupied areas may be fully cut-off to decrease both refrigeration and ventilation requirements.

6. Insulation may be omitted from supply ducts in return air ceilings with less concern about the effect of a rise in supply air temperature (as long as final branches and terminals are sized for a higher air volume). The zone thermostat automatically increases the volume, as required. However, the most appreciable temperature rise occurs in the smaller duct; therefore, duct branches or end runs carrying small air quantities (under 1500 cfm or 700 L/s) should be insulated at the end of long trunk ducts. This first-cost savings of omitting insulation is offset by a minor increase in fan-energy cost resulting from the increase in the quantity of room supply air.

7. Maintaining lower-than-design air quantities during most of the operating time tends to reduce, rather than aggravate, draft problems. Tests by Straub (1969) on variable volume distribution systems, with ceiling outlets sized at less than 300 cfm (140 L/s) each, conclude that problems are more likely to exist at high air flow rates than at low ones. Also, slight adjustments in room temperature more effectively produced comfort than change in flow rates, even at low air movements in zones of 10 to 15 fpm (50 to 75 mm/s).

8. Assuming adequate attention has been given to the selection and static pressure control of fans and VAV devices, the VAV System operates at maximum noise level only at full load and is considerably quieter at off-peak loads.

9. VAV allows simultaneous heating and cooling without seasonal changeover.

10. No zoning is required in central equipment.

11. For internal source heat-recovery systems, the large surface, high-stack convectors required for radiation perimeter heating should be compared with the constant volume perimeter system's easier use of low level heat in central coils.

12. VAV and air perimeter systems that use a common central air apparatus and reheat for the perimeter exposures with overhead supply (mild climates) may be lower in initial cost than VAV and radiation designs, but at a considerable penalty in energy and operating costs.

Design Precautions

In applying this system, the designer should consider the following:

1. Air Distribution
   a. Install high entrainment types of outlets to achieve higher air velocity at minimum flow.
   b. Evaluate performance at minimum, as well as maximum flow.
   c. Evaluate the effect of minimum volume on space air movements.
   d. A single plane ceiling allows air to hug the ceiling at reduced volumes (Coanda effect). Ceiling breaks and obstructions should be at the end of the design throw of the air jet.
   e. Note that air troffer lighting may reduce design air volume to an undesirably low level with VAV terminals that only throttle the flow.

2. Fans and Controls
   a. Use fan controls to save power and to operate at minimum system pressure for noise control. They may not be economical for systems of 10,000 cfm (5 M³/s) and below.
   b. Note that on cooling start-up with all variable volume controls wide open, system static pressure will be abnormally low and system volume abnormally high. Limit-load fans are desirable in this case.
   c. Check supply and return fan operating characteristics at maximum and minimum flow.
   d. Provide minimum outside air volume to comply with ventilation codes.

3. System Operating Characteristics
   a. Determine the warm-up requirement after prolonged shutdown, particularly for systems using cold air bypass to plenums or if terminals do not close tightly at no load. Consider the possibility of overcooling if minimum settings are used on VAV units.
   b. In zones with highly fluctuating loads, determine the need for heating or reheat to prevent increased space humidity.
   c. Flow controllers require uniform entering air conditions to perform accurately, while volume regulators do not.
   d. In ceiling return air systems, consider the effect of interior space cooling loads during winter, if warm air is used on perimeter units. The higher ceiling temperature may increase the total ceiling load in the room and decrease the amount of ceiling plenum air induced, thus requiring a greater air volume for winter than for summer.
   e. Check system sound levels at maximum flow conditions. Assuming adequate selection and static pressure control for fans and variable volume devices are given, the variable volume system usually operates at maximum noise level at full load. Inlet vanes and fan discharge dampers must be checked for sound levels at maximum closed position. Adjustable outlets for volume control must also be checked to determine sound level at minimum flow position of the outlets. Except for low pressure systems, throttling devices must be located 5 to 10 diameters from the outlet in the occupied space.

4. VAV and Air Skin Systems
   a. The fan energy savings listed under advantages apply to interior VAV systems of duplex designs (separate skin air handler). A separate skin system requires more fan energy than the perimeter radiation system because it supplies a constant volume of air and fan-powered heating during unoccupied periods. The fan energy required by common-fan reheated skin designs is even higher, especially if VAV terminals in interior areas do not shut off completely at night.
   b. Carefully consider fire and smoke control with an under-window skin supply, since fire-rated floors are pierced with substantial openings.
   c. Recognize that the initial cost of a separate fan system is generally higher than VAV and radiation combinations for comparable skin zoning, unless expensive radiation enclosures are used. The margin of difference, however, is lower with overhead skin distribution (in milder climates) than for under-window air distribution.

5. VAV Bypass Systems
   a. Note that limited benefits result from variable volume ceiling bypass systems, as compared with true system throttling variable control and variable volume systems. Benefits are limited to simple temperature control and variable zone

flexibility at moderate initial cost with low noise levels and with the advantages attributed to air systems in general. Energy and operational economics possible with true variable volume systems and initial cost advantages resulting from the effects of load shifting and diversities on equipment and duct systems are not applicable to VAV systems.

SINGLE-DUCT VARIABLE AIR VOLUME—INDUCTION

The variable air volume induction system has a terminal unit to reduce cooling capacity by simultaneously reducing primary air and increasing induced room or ceiling air at a constant room supply volume.

Design Considerations

From both a calculation and psychrometric standpoint, VAV induction systems are a hybrid between VAV and dual-duct systems. The system primary air quantities reduce with load, thus retaining the diversity of VAV, while the individual room process blends cold primary air with recirculated ceiling plenum air (Figure 5).

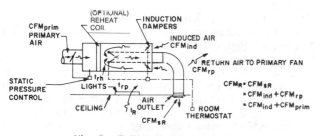

Fig. 5 Ceiling Induction Unit

The terminal device is usually located in the ceiling cavity above the conditioned space, but it is sometimes in the room. It is applied to systems with a return air drop ceiling for best use of available internal heat, but most of its reduction capability is independent of the ceiling temperature rise. (Figure 6, "Summer Design Cooling," shows the psychrometric process.) It can be used without reheat coils in spaces with internal loads only when provisions are made for morning warm-up and night heating. When there is insufficient heat gain in the room and ceiling to balance the transmission losses and primary air cooling capacity, either a reheat coil or auxiliary heating must be provided.

Air Volume. Damper leakage occurs through induction dampers during the 100% primary air mode, although the leakage factor is smaller for induction leakage than that from a dual-duct port under system pressure, assuming both dampers are of equal quality.

The primary air supply to off-peak rooms at peak system design conditions must be adequate to handle the room load, as well as neutralize the heat of lights in the induced air. Therefore, the instantaneous peak air volume is somewhat higher than required by a true variable air volume system.

The following precautions should be observed:

a. Each unit's ability to handle reduced loads without reheat is a function of its maximum induction ratio and the ceiling temperature. Manufacturer's data, installation conditions, and the ceiling temperature require careful analysis to develop the proper design.

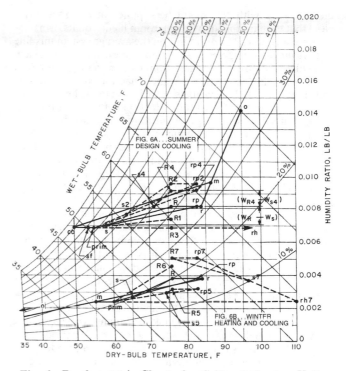

Fig. 6 Psychrometric Chart of a Ceiling-Induction Unit

b. High occupancy areas should be checked at full and part loads for reheat need. They should have separate units and shutoff features for economy during unoccupied periods.

c. Heating from lights in exposed areas must be carefully checked. The adequacy of heat, especially during unoccupied periods (even if lights will be on), must be checked. If lights will stay on, it is advantageous to coordinate air handlers and lighting circuits for maximum flexibility. The temperature control must override the master lighting switches for each module. Also, the shorter replacement period of lamping used for unoccupied period heating should be considered, even though total hours of life may be extended with continuous operation.

d. Separate heating systems should be considered (independent of induction unit reheat coils) to permit air system shutdown during unoccupied periods. Roof ceiling cavities can be heated in this way to maintain a high ceiling temperature, as an alternative to reheat coils and night fan operation.

e. Heat reclaim units should have the capacity to handle winter heating over extended unoccupied periods, such as during school vacations and work stoppages.

Supply Air Conditions. Figures 5 and 6 show the induction unit in a design using 100% return air light troffers. The solid lines represent average system conditions of all units at system peak, while dotted lines represent individual, simultaneous room cycles. During system peak, off-peak rooms induce ceiling air at state t_{rp} and blend it with the average primary air at t_{prim}, for average supply state t_s. (Peak rooms also suffer induction damper leakage.) The average room temperature t_r is produced at the system's average sensible heat factor for all rooms. The balance of the return air, not induced and recirculated, picks up the duct, and portion of the primary air cycle is that of a single-path system.

A peak-loaded room with a high sensible heat factor will take all primary air and yield t_{r1}. A fully-loaded conference room, blending t_{prim} with t_{rp2}, might be supplied at t_{s2} to yield t_{R2}. Note that each unit in an off-peak room blends on its own mixing line, such as $rp2$ to $prim$, not on the average system mix line rp to $prim$. This assumes that even in a free ceiling return, each unit collects almost all moisture from its own room in the return air because it is close to the room and it has limited static pressure capability. The unit's capacity is not sensitive to the heat of lights as only 15 to 30% of the total reduction comes from the heat of light (at a 7 °F or 4 °C rise), while most of its reduction comes from primary air volume reduction.

Winter Cooling (Figure 6A). If the perimeter and roof are heated by an auxiliary process, all-induction units can cool all year except for morning warm-up or during any unoccupied period. The average system cycle at design winter occupied condition might appear as *m-prim-sR-r-m*.

Warm-up and unoccupied period heating may be accomplished by various means without reversing thermostats, whether VAV controls are the full shutoff type or minimum primary air type. However, the minimum primary air type (without reheat coils) may overcool. Therefore, it may be desirable to increase the temperature of the primary air several degrees during the winter, even though this increases running costs.

Winter Heating (Figure 6A). The unit should have primary air reheat when (1) any room lacks adequate exposed surface heating, (2) lighting is off (during occupied periods), (3) dehumidification is required during any operating mode, or (4) any room overcools during periods with minimum cooling requirements. All such units will blend on their respective *rh-rp* lines, producing a room state at a moisture level described before. The room thermostat will control the reheat to any required relative humidity along line *prim-rh* in both the winter and summer modes.

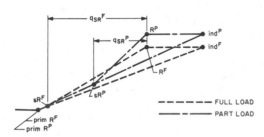

Fig. 7 Solution for Full-Load and Part-Load Room Primary Air Volumes at System Peak

Components and Controls

Where heating is provided with the terminal unit, the reheat coil operates in sequence when the room temperature drops. The coil does not usually turn on until the primary air dampers or regulators close, and the total supply air has been reduced to a minimum level. If the unit's primary air dampers cannot regulate volume, self-contained static pressure regulating devices can maintain a reasonable upstream pressure variation. Inlet static pressure to the terminal device in excess of 2 in. of water (500 Pa) should be checked carefully with manufacturers' sound ratings. Fan static pressure regulation is also recommended.

When the VAV induction units vary the room supply air, precautions for air distribution apply (although somewhat less stringently concerning cold air bypass). Conventional diffuser terminals without bypass may be used, but drafts and sufficient ventilation criteria must still be considered.

Terminal diffusers for the ceiling induction unit are usually installed overhead. Buildings in cold climates or buildings with large glass areas may require a separate perimeter heating system at temperatures of 40 °F (4 °C) and below. Heating loads above 40 °F (4 °C) can be handled by a heating coil in the ceiling induction unit.

Evaluation

1. The VAV induction unit waits to reduce the room air supply until it permits a substantial reduction in cooling capacity below 100% full load ratio. Ordinary VAV systems throttle room air immediately. Induction units can, therefore, maintain satisfactory air motion at a lower full load ratio than can ordinary VAV systems.
2. Because this system uses some of the heat from lights as a reheat substitute, it may be considered an internal source heat recovery system without the heat pump apparatus. However, only that portion of the return air heat that is induced (25 to 60%, depending on the induction ratio) can be used. The balance of the heat from lights and all the return fan and duct gains in the return air can only be recovered with a heat pump. The heat recovered from lights in interior areas is even smaller, since these areas have much lower full load ratio reductions.
3. The initial load reduction with induction blending, in contrast with initial air volume reduction for true single-duct VAV, requires a slightly larger air system.
4. Lights used to heat the perimeter area, or to avoid reheat, can save fuel. However, the physical design may prohibit or severely limit this benefit. For example, a common fan design for interior and perimeter areas, with separate perimeter radiation, dictates a primary air temperature between 55 to 60 °F (13 to 16 °C) for winter cooling of interior and sunlit zones. Even a maximum induction ratio prohibits any space heating, with the average room temperature unable to rise above 74 °F (23 °C) in such designs. Only a separate perimeter fan system can heat the perimeter if no reheat coil is used, and then only if no outside air is used, as with single-duct VAV systems.
5. Induction systems are not as economical as true variable air volume systems in terms of initial costs. Higher primary air static pressure is required for induction than for true VAV, thus increasing fan power and operating costs.
6. This design uses the available heat from lights but this advantage should be compared with less costly units required for other designs.
7. Plenum air is normally not filtered. As in all induction units, an induction nozzle produces air movement. To keep nozzle sounds at an acceptable level, static pressure should normally be kept below 2 in. (500 Pa) at the unit entrance.
8. System air balance, with respect to controlling fan static pressure and regulating the volume of the primary air at the unit, should be considered, as in any VAV system.
9. Extended supply and return paths downstream of the terminal unit are prohibitive, as are long, flexible air hose lengths, because of external static pressure availability.

SINGLE-DUCT VARIABLE AIR VOLUME—FAN POWERED

Fan-powered systems are available in parallel or series flow. In parallel units, the fan sits outside the primary airstream to allow *intermittent* fan operation. In series units, the fan sits in the primary airstream and runs *continuously* when the zone is occupied. Fan-Powered systems, both series and parallel, are often selected because they move more air through a room at low cooling loads and during reheating compared to VAV reheat or perimeter radiation systems.

Constant Fan—Series Arrangement

A constant volume fan-powered induction unit mixes primary air with induced air by using a continuously operating fan. It provides a relatively constant volume of air to the space. Constant fan, variable air volume terminals are used on pressure independent systems for interior or perimeter zones. They are supplied with or without an auxiliary heating coil. The constant fan VAV terminal will supply minimum (down to zero) air static pressure at the primary air inlet while also providing constant air discharge for heating and cooling. As more or less cold primary air flows through the unit, plenum return air is induced to mix with the primary air, providing enough total air flow for a constant discharge.

As the cold primary air valve modulates from maximum to minimum (or closed), the unit recirculates more plenum temperature air. When used in a perimeter zone, a hot water heating coil, electric heater, remote baseboard heater, or remote radiant heater is sequenced with the cooling to cover the heating load. Between heating and cooling operations, a dead band of fan recirculation only is desirable for maximum energy savings (Figure 8).

To avoid short circuiting of primary air through the fan terminal into the return air plenum, a balancing device permits the discharge to be adjusted so that total air delivery equals the maximum primary air load requirement. During unoccupied periods, the supply air-handling unit remains deenergized and individual heating zone terminals are cycled to maintain a reduced heating space temperature.

Intermittent Fan—Parallel Arrangement

An Intermittent Fan Terminal is also called a Variable Air Volume, Fan-Powered Induction Unit. It modulates primary air in response to cooling demand and energizes the integral fan in sequence to deliver induced air to meet heating demand.

Intermittent fan, variable air volume terminals are used with pressure-dependent and pressure-independent systems. They are primarily used in perimeter zones where auxiliary hot water or electric heating is required. The induction fan operating range normally overlaps the range of the primary air valve. A back draft damper on the terminal fan prevents conditioned air from escaping into the return air plenum when the terminal fan is off.

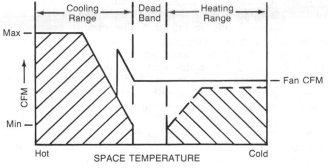

Fig. 9   Intermittent Fan Unit Cycle

As the cold primary air valve modulates from maximum to minimum (or closed), the induction fan starts at an adjustable starting point. This sequence provides an energy-saving dead band between cooling and heating modes (Figure 9). In the dead band mode, available heat from lighting or auxiliary sources may be reclaimed. The built-in heating element provides supplementary heat to satisfy the demands of the space thermostat.

The supply air-handling unit must handle the required cooling air delivery load with enough inlet static pressure at the terminal to meet the combined pressure drop requirements of terminal and downstream resistance. Intermittent fan terminals with a reduced air volume heating load should be sized for a reduced resistance downstream of the terminal unit. Constant volume fan terminals will have the terminal unit fan sized for the full air flow and downstream resistance.

During unoccupied periods, the supply air-handling unit remains off, and individual heating zone terminals are cycled to maintain a reduced heated space temperature. The primary air valve also remains closed during unoccupied periods.

Design Considerations

Air Volume. Primary air volumes for variable volume fan-powered systems should be designed with the same considerations described for VAV reheat systems. In addition, minimum ventilation requirements for the type of building must be considered both when the building is occupied and unoccupied.

Local fire protection codes and smoke control may require automatic dampers for terminal induction ports.

Minimum air circulation rates may be increased with intermittent fan terminals by selecting a larger fan to cover a larger percentage of the cooling air volume (60 to 90%) instead of 50% and by overlapping more fan operation in the cooling range.

Since fan terminals draw air from a common ceiling plenum, isolation of one zone from another is not normal practice. However, additional return air ducts may be required for balancing, particularly for perimeter zones located far from the main supply fans.

Air volume requirements may require separate supply systems for the perimeter heating zones and the interior cooling zones.

Air-handling units that supply primary air to *constant* fan terminals are sized *without* taking the static pressure drop through the terminal nor the downstream resistance into account.

Air-handling units that supply primary air to *intermittent* fan terminals are sized for the additional static pressure drop through the terminal, plus the downstream resistance.

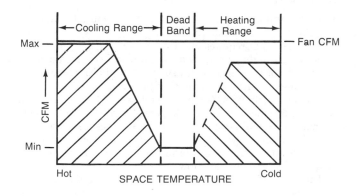

Fig. 8   Constant Fan Unit Cycle

Where a small volume of colder primary air (less than 55 °F or 13 °C) is mixed with a minimum variable amount of plenum air, the terminal must include a mixing plenum designed to eliminate downstream temperature stratification. Temperatures across the discharge duct should not vary more than 1° for each 10° difference between primary and induced air temperatures. Temperature differences from one diffuser to the next are minimized by proper mixing in the terminal unit. This uniformity may not be critical when all the air volume from a terminal serves the same room.

Series terminals generally produce slightly more noise in the occupied space than parallel units. Both the primary air valve and the fan act as sound sources in both units.

The radiated fan sound usually differs between series and parallel units due to the air volume requirements of each. Series fans deliver the total design cooling air volume, while parallel fans generally deliver 50 to 75% of that amount. As a result, series units normally require a larger fan or the same fan run at a higher speed. Thus, more sound radiates from series units than from parallel.

Because series air flow to the zone is constant, airborne or diffuser and fan-generated noise is constant. In parallel units, airborne or diffuser sound may change with the air flow. Also, intermittent fan operation may cause a noticeable change in radiated sound when the fan motor starts and stops.

Primary air introduced into series units should not exceed the delivered air volume. Overpressurizing the unit increases energy consumption because primary air spills into the return plenum and causes the series fan to run at a much higher speed.

Supply Air Conditions. Fan-powered induction systems combine the diversity of the VAV systems for throttling cooling air with the benefits of heat reclamation. Fan-powered induction units with a higher induction ratio (50% for intermittent to 100% for constant volume) are better for areas with a high percentage of internal heat gain.

On constant volume terminals that mix colder primary air with induced air, the dew point of the induced air is critical and controls the limits of the primary supply air temperature. A building that has been dormant for a long period, such as on weekends or during the summer, must start up with primary air at 55 °F (13 °C) to remove sufficient moisture at the central air-handling unit to prevent condensation at the terminals. The primary air temperature may be lowered once the relative humidity of the return air plenum has been reduced and the temperature of the resulting mixture is not below the dew point of the primary air.

Humidification. During the winter, pan, steam injection, or water spray humidifiers may be installed downstream of the heating coil to add moisture to the primary air system. The amount must be limited by the amount and temperature of the primary air, however. Larger ventilation load requirements may require a heating coil to maintain the supply air temperature.

To avoid muggy, humid, or damp conditions in the conditioned space, especially during mild weather or under high latent loads, dehumidification or precooling of the ventilation air may be justified. Spaces with insufficient air movement may require intermittent fan terminals with greater overlap of cooling and fan operating ranges. Constant fan terminals can mix subcooled primary air with induced air for improved space comfort conditions. Normally, the fan terminal has no provision for handling condensate, so all dehumidification must be done at the primary air-handling unit.

Components and Controls

The two fan-powered induction terminals use many similar components, including the following:

1. Primary air valve (pressure dependent or independent)
2. Blower/Motor assembly
3. Insulated casing with mixing plenum
4. Optional heating coil (hot water or electric)
5. Pneumatic, electric, or electronic controls

The main difference between the constant fan and intermittent fan units is the configuration of the components. The *Constant Fan Unit* has the fan located at the outlet of the insulated casing. It is in line and downstream of the primary air valve so that all conditioned air passes through the fan. The heating coil may be downstream or upstream of the fan. If upstream, the temperature rise must be limited to protect the fan motor. Constant fan terminals include a pressure independent, flow averaging controller and a fan adjustment feature that allows the fan to be matched to the maximum design primary air setting.

The *Intermittent Fan Unit* has the fan and heating coil section mounted beside or perpendicular to the primary air valve. The two sections then discharge into a common mixing plenum. The fan is sized for the smaller heating load (usually 50 to 75% of the cooling load). The fan is controlled through a PE switch or fan relay and is energized in sequence with the operating range of the primary air valve controller.

Evaluation

Advantages

1. The constant volume fan-powered induction unit provides most of the standard VAV air handling economies with a constant volume of air flow to the space.
2. By combining a heating coil with the fan, the constant volume fan terminal can provide overhead heating, cooling, and ventilating.
3. Primary air-handling units can remain off during unoccupied periods while terminal fans deliver heat, as required.
4. Primary air may be reduced from maximum to zero minimum without sacrificing air circulation.
5. Primary air temperature may be reduced before being mixed with induced air, which further reduces primary air volume requirements. This feature reduces the first cost by reducing duct and air-handling unit sizes, but it may require more refrigeration.

Disadvantages

1. Each terminal includes a fan motor that will ultimately require service or replacement.
2. Each terminal requires electrical power for the fan.
3. Terminals pulling air from a common ceiling return plenum should not be used in areas such as hospitals, where cross-contamination of air streams is possible.
4. Fan terminals with hot water coils should be fitted with disposable filters and an access panel for coil cleaning. Where inadequate maintenance personnel or procedures exist, the designer must review whether to provide filters on fan terminals above the ceiling. Terminals with electric heaters require unobstructed air flow for safe operation.
5. Fan-powered terminals must meet local code requirements for electrical, independent laboratory certification, wiring, and construction materials, as they apply to ceiling plenums.

DUAL-PATH SYSTEMS

DUAL DUCT

Dual-duct systems condition all the air in a central apparatus and distribute it to the conditioned spaces through two parallel mains or ducts. One duct carries cold air and the other warm air, providing air sources for both heating and cooling at all times. In each conditioned space or zone, a mixing valve responsive to a room thermostat mixes the warm and cold air in proper proportions to satisfy the prevailing heat load of the space.

Basic dual-duct cycles are shown in Figures 10, 11, and 12. Modifications to these cycles may be desirable for certain design or load conditions. When dual-duct systems are designed to satisfy the conditions of no-load zone, they will maintain acceptable room conditions at all times in actual operation.

Return fans shown may be eliminated on small installations if provisions are made to relieve the excess outdoor air from the conditioned spaces. They are generally required for economizer cooling cycles in systems with substantial return air duct work.

Dual-duct systems may be designed as either constant volume or variable volume.

Single Fan—Constant Volume

Figure 10 shows the simplest, least costly, and most compact apparatus for dual-duct conditioning. Thermodynamically, this cycle is equivalent to a single-duct system with face-and-bypass dampers at the coiling coil, arranged to bypass a mixture of outdoor and recirculated air in response to a zone thermostat as the internal heat load fluctuates. When the internal heat load falls during a period with a high outdoor dew point, the cycle will allow relative humidities to rise rapidly unless heat is added.

In dual-duct systems, heat is usually added to the warm airstream when internal cooling loads are light. Also, since the cold air t_c during the heating season is held constant at 55 to 60°F (13 to 16°C), raising the warm air t_w as the outdoor temperature t_o decreases permits better blending temperature at the zone mixing boxes, better humidity control, and better balancing between hot and cold ducts during all operating conditions.

Figure 10A shows several cold air and warm air conditions entering each mixing box, which actually occurs from an accumulated temperature change as heat is transferred to or from the duct. However, for clarity, Figures 10B and 10C show a single cold air temperature and warm air temperature, since the small differences cannot be distinguished on the psychrometric chart. The designer should remember that tail-end ducts with little air flow are influenced by duct transmission much more than are large trunks and, if uninsulated, may be distinctly different in temperature from the average warm air or cold air temperature.

The majority of dual-duct systems for comfort application are based on the cycle of Figure 10. These systems give good results when designed and operated under the following set of conditions:

1. In moderately humid climates, where outdoor design conditions do not exceed 78°F (25°C).
2. When minimum outdoor air does not exceed 35 to 40% of total air flow.
3. When heat is available under the guidelines of the energy codes and applied properly for partial summer load operation.
4. When summer cold-duct temperature does not exceed 55°F (13°C).

Single-Fan, Constant Volume—Reheat

Functionally, this cycle (Figure 11) is equivalent to a conventional reheat system. The only difference is that reheat is applied at a central point instead of at several stations close to points of distribution. All operational and cost penalties of conventional reheat systems apply to this cycle. A dual-duct reheat cycle on large installations in cold climates requires safety features for protection during breakdowns. When reheat is obtained from refrigeration hot gas rejection apparatus, much of the cost of prime fuel is eliminated, but refrigeration energy costs remain the same.

Variable Air Volume

Dual-duct variable volume systems blend cold and warm air in various volume combinations. These systems may include

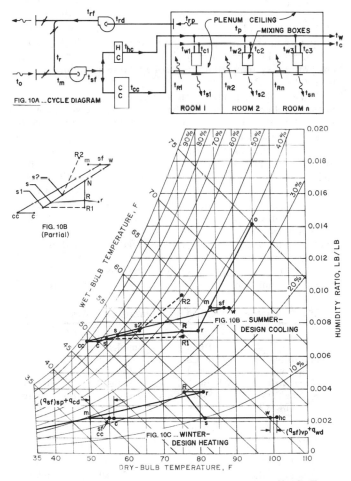

Fig. 10   Cycle and Psychrometric Chart for Single-Fan Dual-Duct System with Blow-Through Dehumidifier

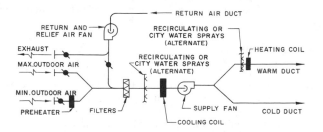

Fig. 11   Single-Fan Dual-Duct Hot Deck Reheat Cycle

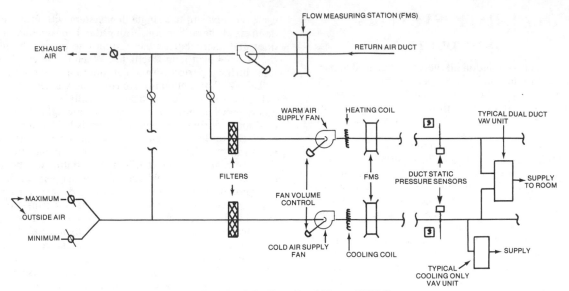

Fig. 12   Multiple Fan, Dual-Duct, VAV System

single-duct VAV units connected to the cold deck for cooling-only of interior spaces.

Various arrangements of components are possible. Figure 12 shows a typical dual-duct VAV system. This system uses two supply fans—one for the hot deck and one for the cold deck.

Each fan's volume is controlled independently by the static pressure in its respective duct. The return fan is controlled relative to the sum of the hot and cold fan volumes using flow measuring stations (FMS). Chapter 51 has details on control of this type.

Each fan is sized for the anticipated maximum coincident hot or cold volume, not the sum of the instantaneous peaks. The cold deck can be maintained at a constant temperature either by operating the cooling coil with a minimum of fresh air or with a cooling economizer when the outside air is below the cold deck set point. This operation does not affect the hot deck, which can recover heat from the internal load for hot deck heating. The heating coil only operates when heating requirements cannot be met with return air or when the hot deck air supply temperature is reset with the outside temperature to reduce the required size of the hot system fan and duct system. Outdoor air can provide ventilation air via the hot fan system when the outdoor air is warmer, but not more humid, than the system return air.

This system has the advantage of a true single-path VAV system, except for warm port leakage. When cold air is modulated for control before mixing, it operates similar to VAV induction (without constant air volume to the room) when mixing occurs without hot deck reheat. It is similar to a reheat system (but with less refrigeration penalty) when mixing occurs while the reheat coil operates in the hot deck. It uses more energy than a true VAV system but less than a constant volume dual-duct system.

Design Considerations

Air Volume. Peak zone air supply requirements are complicated because mixing dampers always leak from the closed portion (i.e., warm port at cooling peak; cold port at winter peak).

Either the cold deck temperatures must be reduced or the cold deck air volumes increased to compensate for the damper leakage

when operating at peak cooling load. Likewise, the hot deck temperature or the hot deck air volumes must be increased to compensate for this leakage in the peak heating mode.

The leakage ratio is expressed as a fraction of the total air handled by the damper assembly. It is a function of the system static pressure and the quality of the damper shutoff. For better quality mixing assemblies, the leakage ratio will vary from 0.03 to 0.07. Field constructed damper assemblies (common in low pressure systems) and multi-zone mixing assemblies range from 0.10 to 0.20.

Cold air volume and the refrigeration capacity handle the sum of the simultaneous peaks of the cold air requirements for all zones. All fresh air should enter the system through the cold deck for proper humidification.

The temperatures of cold, warm, and room air are needed to calculate winter design air quantities and to size the heating coil. The warm duct sizes are seldom derived by considering the warm air requirement under winter peak. The maximum flow in the warm duct ordinarily occurs during light summer loads or during intermediate season operation when warm duct temperatures are kept at a low level. For this reason, warm air duct sizes are fixed as a certain percentage of the cold air duct area, as shown in Table 1.

Cold duct connections to each mixing box are sized for the peak air volume that flows to each zone. Cold duct branches

Table 1   Factors for Constant Volume, Dual-Duct Design

Ratio of System Summer Cold Air to System Total Air = CFM_c/CFM_s	Ratio of Zone Cold Air to Total Zone Air for Purpose of Sizing Cold Duct	System with Supplementary Heating at Perimeter of Building	100% Air System
		Ratio of Warm Duct Area to Cold Duct Area	
1.0 to 0.9	1.0	0.70	0.80
0.89 to 0.85	0.95	0.70	0.80
0.84 to 0.80	0.90	0.75	0.85
0.79 to 0.75	0.85	0.75	0.85
0.74 or smaller	0.80	0.80	0.90

From *Air Conditioning, Heating and Ventilating*, December 1964.

that serve many zone mixing boxes that have little or no diversity between them (i.e., have the same exposure with identical lighting loads and solar conditions) should be sized for the sum of the peaks in each zone.

Trunks, mains, or branches that serve multiple exposures or zones with appreciable diversity between them (i.e., non-simultaneous peaks) may be sized according to Table 1, Column 2. This simplified procedure gives a greater safety factor than obtained with a more detailed study.

With variable volume, dual-duct designs, warm air no longer neutralizes the cold air at initial partial loads, because the flow is reduced first. Oversizing of warm ducts is not necessary if the terminal units accurately control minimum flow at varying system pressures. *Table 1 does not apply to variable volume systems.*

In dual-duct systems, where volume is controlled at terminal points, the duct-sizing technique becomes less critical than for other systems, and extreme precision in duct sizing becomes unnecessary. The cold ducts can be sized by equal friction, static regain, velocity methods, or a combination of all three. Volume regulators in mixing units absorb all pressure unbalance caused by the initial design, partial load operation, or future changes in load distribution. These regulators also produce a mechanically stable system under all normal operating conditions, irrespective of the procedure used in duct sizing, if the power needed in the longest duct is estimated correctly.

As pointed out previously, the maximum flow through the warm ducts may occur during intermediate season operation, if low temperatures are maintained in a warm chamber. For this reason, the warm duct sizes are usually determined as a ratio of area to cold duct sizes. The factors from Table 1 can be used for this purpose. However, air distribution costs and space requirements can be reduced by raising the intermediate season warm-duct temperature sufficiently to reduce the warm air demand so that it is equal to or less than that required for winter heating.

Supply Air Conditions. Uniform air temperatures are essential in cold and warm chambers upstream of heating cooling coils. Stratified air in cold climates, especially in large plants, may cause coil freeze-ups and control and operating difficulties. The following safety provisions for winter operation can protect against breakdowns on large installations:

1. Using two or more supply and return fans for each apparatus room
2. Supplying the air distribution system by two or more air-handling plants
3. Providing direct radiation on the building perimeter

The warm air temperature should not be very high at mild ambient conditions of 50 to 60°F (10 to 18°C). Otherwise, leakage from the warm duct in sunlit zones prevents the cold air from maintaining comfortable conditions. A poorly designed mixing box with a 10% leakage rate can raise the supply temperature as much as 4 to 5°F (2 to 3°C). A heavy energy consumption penalty also results when the warm air temperature is set higher than needed to satisfy heating requirements or, conversely, when cold air temperature is lower than needed to satisfy cooling requirements during the heating season. Automatic scheduling of these deck temperatures from the coldest winter zone and warmest summer zone is recommended where economically feasible.

Humidification. Room humidities at any operating condition, particularly at part load, during mild, muggy weather, or when a high ratio of outdoor air is used, may be improved by precooling the outdoor airstream with primary chilled water, tail-water

from the main cooling coil, or well water. If the moisture content of the mixed airstream passing into the warm duct could be lowered by dehumidifying the outside air, the room humidity would be improved. However, the minor benefit derived may not justify the initial cost or the added energy consumption.

When humidity must be kept below a specified design condition under all operating conditions and psychrometric studies rule out the cycle in Figure 10, the single fan reheat cycle and precooling of outside air should be examined. Figure 11 shows such an arrangement that limits relative humidities in the conditioned spaces through the entire range of operation. However, the energy use in this cycle is high because of the continuous reheat demand and the additional refrigeration most installations need to treat the air that is bypassed to the warm air duct under maximum load conditions. This cycle is not economical for most comfort installations and is restricted to special applications.

Components and Controls

Constant volume systems have two types of all-air mixing terminal units: those that merely control space temperature and those that maintain both the temperature and the desired air flow volume. An operator responds to a space thermostat that modulates the valving device to proportion the warm and cold air delivered to the space. Either type can be acoustically treated to attenuate noise.

Without volume regulation, the air flow to the conditioned spaces varies with pressure changes in the two ducts, which, in turn, vary with the relative demands for warm or cold air. The potential volume variation increases with the size and pressure of the distribution system and may vary as much as two to one. Some regulation can be effected by a system of static pressure regulators in the ducts. However, in larger systems, dual-duct units without volume regulation are not recommended.

The constant volume unit with thermostat mixing of the warm and cold air is the more common terminal device. This unit not only keeps the distribution system stable, but also simplifies the initial balancing of the system. Figures 13A and 13B show common methods of controlling this type of unit to satisfy both the temperature and volume requirements. The mixing is similar in each case, with operator-controlled valves positioned by a room thermostat.

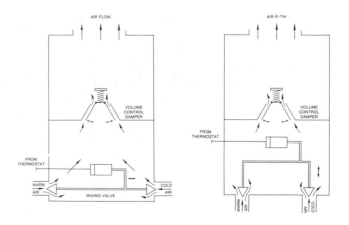

Fig. 13A & 13B   Mixing and Volume Control with a Self-Actuated, Spring-Loaded Volume Regulator for a Constant Volume System

In Figure 13A, air flow is controlled by a spring-loaded regulator that closes as the system pressure rises. The spring and movement may be calibrated and set to maintain constant flow at any prescribed volume. The bypassing of air from one duct to the other, while unequal pressures exist in the two ducts, is usually prevented by the space thermostat. However, this terminal device may require air check valves at the inlets under certain conditions.

In Figure 13C, the cold and warm air dampers have separate operators. The thermostat controls the flow of warm air and a static pressure regulator compensates for changes in the warm air supply by varying the cold air flow. When the static pressure regulator controls flow as shown, its required sensitivity depends on the permissible volume variations. To limit flow variations to ±5%, the regulator and operator combination must limit static pressure variations across the resistance plate to ±10%. With a normal control resistance of 0.5 in. of water (125 Pa), the permissible static pressure variation is ±0.05 in. of water (±12 Pa). Turbulence on either side of the controlling resistance could also shift the control volume. Constant volume units of Figure 13B should be carefully designed and operated to avoid excessively reducing warm air pressures at the inlet to the duct.

Variable volume dual-duct systems use the mixing unit with an adjustable volume control regulator, as shown in Figure 14. The two regulators control air volume at maximum and minimum flow. If space temperature falls, the room thermostat closes the motor-operated regulator. When this regulator is closed, the second or minimum position regulator maintains minimum volume at varying system pressures.

Each part of the double-volume regulator in Figure 14 is similar to the regulator in Figure 13A; that is, it is arranged for pneumatic sequencing of flow reduction down to a minimum air flow setting, followed by constant volume mixing. One thermostat serves the combined function. These terminal units can be applied to any dual-duct system, whether high, medium, or low pressure.

With greater control flexibility required under current energy codes, modern variable volume dual units use a combination

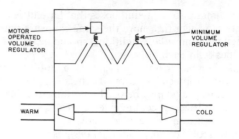

Fig. 14   Dual-Duct Variable Volume Mixing Unit

of two pressure-independent VAV regulating units—one for the hot deck and one for the cold deck. These units can be calibrated for many flow volume conditions. Several typical hot and cold flow volumes are indicated in Figure 15.

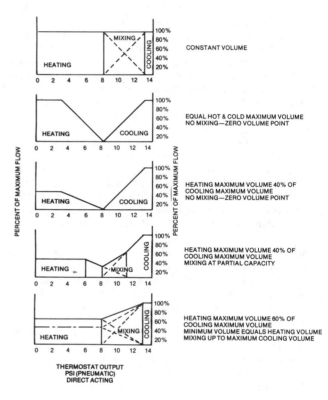

**Fig. 15   Typical Hot/Cold Flow Volumes
for VAV Dual-Duct Units**

Evaluation

The specific advantages of dual-duct systems, in addition to those common to all-air systems, are as follows:

1. When 100% air systems are used, there is complete absence of water, steam, and drain piping; electrical equipment; wiring; and filters in the conditioned spaces.
2. Flexibility is obtained to meet specified design or cost objectives in any installation.
3. The system can be combined with direct radiation or with other conditioning methods. Thus, no mechanical equipment is placed at the perimeter of the building, thereby saving valuable floor area. This feature is especially valuable in ex-

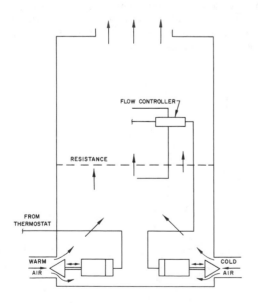

**Fig. 13C   Mixing and Volume Control with a Static
Pressure Flow Controller and Separate Warm and Cold Port
Controls for Constant Volume or VAV System**

isting buildings when removing the heating system is unnecessary or not otherwise justified. It reduces fan-operating costs by heating with the perimeter radiation during unoccupied periods instead of heating with the high pressure fan system.

4. Zoning of central equipment is seldom required. Under some design and operating conditions, however, it may be advantageous to provide separate air-handling equipment for exterior and interior zones.
5. Hot-deck heat is availabale year-round. It maintains temperature and humidity very well in lightly loaded and in no-load zones. It does not control humidity well in terminal reheat systems.
6. Systems with terminal volume regulation are self-balancing.

The main disadvantages in the design of a dual-duct system are as follows:

1. To make the system mechanically stable, the terminal units must adequately control volumetric delivery.
2. Because most installations have limited space, duct velocities and pressures are higher than in other installations.
3. The arrangement of two parallel ducts with cross overs to terminal points requires special attention, study, and technical knowledge by the designer and installer.
4. Dual-duct systems do not operate as economically as VAV dual-duct systems, which do not operate as economically as true VAV systems.
5. Initial cost is usually higher than for VAV systems.

MULTI-ZONE SYSTEMS

The multi-zone system applies to a relatively small number of zones served by a single, central air-handling unit. Different zone requirements are met by mixing cold and warm air through zone dampers at the central air handler in response to zone thermostats. The mixed, conditioned air is distributed throughout the building by a system of single-zone ducts. Packaged units, complete with all components, or field-fabricated apparatus casings may be used. The return air is handled in a conventional manner.

The multi-zone system is similar to the dual-duct system except for the differences described in this section. It can provide a smaller building with a wide variety of packaged equipment that has some of the advantages of dual-duct systems at lower initial cost. However, it is limited to smaller projects with multiple runs of single-zone ducts. It lacks the control sophistication for comfort and operating economy that can be built into the multi-zone system. Although all the basic cycle variations available for dual-duct may be built into multi-zone systems, the most common are the cycles of Figures 10 and 11.

From an economic and practical standpoint, multi-zone systems usually handle more than one room with a single duct. Although dual-duct systems often are similar, the incremental cost of room-by-room zoning (with parallel ducts already near all rooms) is appreciably lower and, therefore, easier to justify.

Multi-zone packaged equipment is usually limited to about 12 zones, while built-up systems can include as many as can be physically incorporated in the layout.

VAV may be applied to multi-zone systems with packaged or built-up systems that have the necessary zone volume regulation and fan controls. Separate, individually sequenced actuators for the hot and cold dampers are required instead of a common actuator with linked dampers.

Air volume and refrigeration capacities are treated mainly as described in the section on "Dual Path System." The air volume

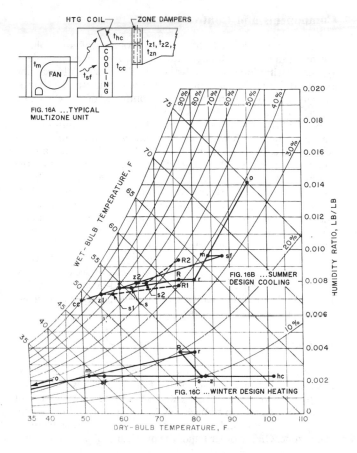

Fig. 16   Multizone System and Psychrometric Chart

may be somewhat higher or the total cooling coil load somewhat lower due to more damper leakage.

Design Consideration

Figure 16A schematically illustrates the most common multizone configuration and reveals the physical difference between the multi-zone and dual-duct systems; the zone mixing dampers are generally distributed horizontally along the hot and cold deck discharge plenums of the air handler. Each mixing box of Figure 10 is analogous to a section of multi-zone damper allocated to each zone. The psychrometric analyses and equations are identical to Figures 10A and 10B, except for the following:

1. The supply air blending occurs along line cc-sf for summer instead of c-w; and between states sf and hc during winter instead of between c and w.
2. The duct temperature rise with multi-zone occurs along each zone duct, instead of in the cold duct and warm duct, respectively.

Figure 11 shows a layout more commonly used for multi-zone than for dual-duct systems. The packaged rooftop units have hot-gas reheat coils to reduce fuel use during intermediate seasons, and supplemented with a steam, hydronic, direct electric, or direct fuel-fired exchanger. Supplementary heat is used when hot-gas reheat is inadequate above 40 to 45 °F (4 to 7 °C) ambient. It is also used below these ambient conditions when the hot-gas and refrigeration cycles are normally shut off in favor of economizer outdoor air cooling.

Components and Control

Just as with dual-duct, the potential problems of zone volume variation increase with larger variance in zone sizes, complexity, and distribution system pressure. The designer should examine the need for individual zone volume regulation and/or static pressure control, recognizing that uncontrolled design can cause volume variations of as much as 2:1.

Normal-quality manufactured dampers for built-up or packaged units, whether field or factory manufactured, have leakage factors X_{1k} as high as 0.10 to 0.20, especially if maintenance is poor. The effect of leakage is appreciable on the cooling coil temperature, room peak air volume, or both. Leakage must be considered based on field experience and on manufacturer's data. The designer can specify dampers fabricated for 0.03 to 0.05 leakage, because they are available from some package unit manufacturers or from control damper manufacturers for units built on site.

Multi-zone packaged equipment, using direct expansion cooling coils, hot-gas, electric, or direct fuel-fired hot deck exchanges, generally has step-controls for hot- and cold-deck capacity that may limit the quality of temperature and humidity control, unless specific controls are provided.

Evaluation

The multi-zone approach to dual-path systems has no specific advantages not already listed, since the dual-duct design can also be applied with packaged or central units, either with or without volume regulation. In some architectural situations, limited ceiling space might prohibit dual-duct crossovers, thereby favoring multi-zone. On the other hand, the physical problem of machine room egress for many small ducts might present more of a problem for multi-zone design than two larger mains for dual-duct designs.

The following design considerations are peculiar to multi-zone systems:

1. All rooms in the same zone should be similarly loaded so that all areas respond equally to internal load changes or external loads such as solar gain and thermal transmission (gain or loss).
2. Any zone thermostat handling more than one room can sense only one room's temperature.
3. Hot-deck temperature (including rescheduling) and cold-deck temperature should be adequately controlled to avoid wide fluctuations.
4. Several large zones should not be combined with a few small zones. This can cause erratic behavior in air flow to the small zones when the large zones are modulated.
5. Humidity control without hot-deck heat can be poor during high ambient wet bulb and high internal load conditions. Multi-zone units are not suitable for the southern United States. In this region, during most of the year, the high ambient wet-bulb fresh air make-up bypasses the cooling coil via the hot deck and causes humidity control problems in the occupied space.
6. The cycling, rather than modulating, of most multi-zone heating and cooling plants should be recognized.
7. Once the system is installed, it is uneconomical to add a zone-mixing damper control to any area whose load characteristics have changed relative to other areas on the original zone.
8. Multi-zone systems with high damper leakage and constant deck temperatures cost more to operate than those with tight dampers and deck temperature scheduling.

CHAPTER 3

AIR-AND-WATER SYSTEMS

AIR-AND-WATER systems conditon spaces by distributing air and water sources to terminal units installed in habitable space throughout a building. The air and water are cooled or heated in central mechanical equipment rooms. The air supplied is called primary air; the water supplied is called secondary water. Sometimes a separate electric heating coil is included in lieu of a hot water coil.

The section that covers secondary water distribution applies to fan-coil units, radiant panel systems, and induction systems. The discussion of exterior air-conditioning loads applies to any system serving the exterior zones of a building. This chapter is concerned primarily with air-and-water induction systems. Fan-coil units are discussed in Chapter 4, and radiant panels are discussed in Chapter 7.

Air-and-water systems apply primarily to exterior spaces of buildings with high sensible loads and where close control of humidity is not required. These systems work well in office buildings, hospitals, hotels, schools, apartment houses, research laboratories, and other buildings where their capabilities meet the performance criteria. In most climates, these systems are installed in exterior building spaces and are designed to provide (1) all required space heating and cooling needs and (2) simultaneous heating and cooling in different parts of the building during intermediate seasons.

EXTERIOR ZONE AIR-CONDITIONING LOADS

Before designing an air-conditioning system for exterior building spaces, it is necessary to understand the air-conditioning load variations in these spaces. These loads cause significant variations in space cooling and heating requirements, even when these rooms occupy the same exposure of the building. Accordingly, exterior building spaces require individual room control. Basic load components in exterior building spaces must be considered in the proper application of air-and-water systems.

Internal Loads

Heat gain from lights is always a cooling load, and, in most buildings (other than residential), it is relatively constant during the day. Increasing emphasis on energy conservation is causing lights to be turned off when not required, making lighting loads more variable. Heat gain from occupants is always a cooling load and is commonly the only room load that contains a latent component. Heat gain from equipment can vary from zero to maximum and is an important factor in office buiding design.

External Loads

Heat gain from the sun is always a cooling load. It is often the chief cooling load factor and is highly variable. For a given space, solar heat gain will always vary during the day. In addi-

---

The preparation of this chapter is asigned to TC 9.1, Large Building Air-Conditioning Systems.

tion to normal changes resulting from movement of the sun, solar gain can fluctuate greatly within minutes. The magnitude and rate of change of this load component depends on building orientation, glass area, cloud cover, and the building's capacity to store heat. Constantly changing shade patterns from adjacent buildings, trees, or exterior columns and nonuniform overhangs will cause significant variations in solar load between adjacent offices on the same solar exposure.

Transmission load can be either a heat loss or a heat gain, depending on the outdoor temperature.

Moderate pressurization of the building with ventilation air is normally sufficient to offset summer infiltration. In winter, however, infiltration can cause a significant heat loss, particularly on the lower floors of high-rise buildings. The magnitude of this component varies with wind and stack effect, as well as with the temperature difference across the outside wall.

The *maximum cooling load* in a particular space is a function of the magnitude of individual load components and the times at which they occur. The *maximum heating load* is a function of transmission and infiltration. Net load variations on a given day during summer or winter can result from variations in occupancy, or in equipment heat gain, and from irregular shadow patterns. During the winter, rooms that are shaded or have little internal heat gain may require cooling.

To perform successfully, an air-conditioning system must be capable of satisfying these load variations on a room-by-room basis while fulfilling all other performance criteria, such as humidity control, filtration, air movement, and noise.

SYSTEM DESCRIPTION

An air-and-water system includes central air-conditioning equipment, duct and water distribution systems, and a room terminal. The room terminal may be an induction unit, a fan-coil unit, or a conventional supply air outlet combined with a radiant panel. Generally, the air supply has a constant volume and, as noted earlier, is called primary air to distinguish it from room air or secondary air that has been recirculated. The primary air provides clean outside air for ventilation. In the cooling season, the air is dehumidified sufficiently in the central conditioning unit to achieve comfort humidity conditions throughout the spaces served and to avoid condensation resulting from normal room latent load on the room cooling coil. In winter, moisture can be added centrally, to limit dryness. As the air is dehumidified, it is also cooled to offset a portion of the room sensible loads. The air may be from outdoors, or a mixture of outdoor and return air. A preheater is usually required where freezing temperatures are found. Highly efficient filters will keep the induction unit terminal nozzles clean. Whether or not reheaters are included in the air-handling equipment depends on the type of system, as explained later.

The quantity of primary air supplied to each space is determined by (1) the ventilation requirement, (2) the required sensible cooling capacity at maximum room cooling load (for conventional induction units, this capacity will equal the room load minus the sensible capacity of the room coil, which will be a determinant only when the room coil capacity is limited by physical factors), (3) the maximum sensible cooling capacity following changeover to the winter cycle when chilled water is no longer circulated to the room terminal, and (4) the A/T ratio, which is discussed later in this chapter.

In the ideal air-and-water system design, the secondary cooling coil is always dry; this greatly extends terminal unit life and eliminates odors and the possibility of bacteria growth. The primary air normally controls the space humidity. Therefore, the moisture content of the supply air must be low enough to offset the room latent heat gain and to maintain a room dewpoint low enough to preclude condensation on the secondary cooling surface.

While some systems operate successfully without a secondary coil drain system, a condensate drain is recommended for all air-and-water systems. Most importantly, unlike fan-coil units, the induction unit is not designed or constructed to handle condensation. Therefore, it is critical that an induction terminal operate dry. It is even more critical that the primary air dehumidification be adequate to prevent condensation on the radiant panel.

The water side, in its basic form, consists of a pump and piping to convey water to the heat transfer surface within each conditioned space. The heat exchange coil may be an integral part of the air terminal (as with induction units), a completely separate component within the conditioned space (radiant panel), or either (as with fan-coil units). The water can be cooled by direct refrigeration, but is cooled more commonly by introducing chilled water from the primary cooling system or by heat transfer through a water-to-water exchanger. To distinguish it from the primary chilled water circuit, the water side is usually referred to as the secondary water loop or system.

Air-and-water systems are categorized as two-pipe, three-pipe, or four-pipe systems. They are basically similar in function and include both cooling and heating capabilities for year-round air conditioning. The name is derived from the water distribution system. In two-pipe systems, the water is distributed by one supply and one return pipe for either cold or warm water supply. The three-pipe system has a cold water supply, a warm water supply, and a common return. Because the cold and warm water blends, the three-pipe system has excessive energy waste and is not recommended. Existing three-pipe systems are ideal candidates for energy conservation retrofit. The four-pipe system distribution of secondary water has cold water supply, cold water return, warm water supply, and warm water return pipes. As discussed later in this chapter, the arrangements of the secondary water circuits and their control systems differ, depending on the type of secondary water category.

AIR-WATER INDUCTION SYSTEMS

Figure 1 shows a basic arrangement for an air-water induction terminal. Centrally conditioned primary air is supplied to the unit plenum at high pressure. The acoustically treated plenum attenuates part of the noise generated in the unit and duct system. A balancing damper adjusts the primary air quantity within limits.

The high-pressure air flows through the induction nozzles and induces secondary air from the room through the secondary coil. This secondary air is either heated or cooled at the coil, depending on the season, the room requirement, or both. Ordinarily, the room coil does no latent cooling, but a drain pan collects condensed moisture from unusual temporary latent loads. Primary and secondary air is mixed and discharged to the room.

A lint screen is normally placed across the face of the secondary coil. Induction units are installed in custom enclosures

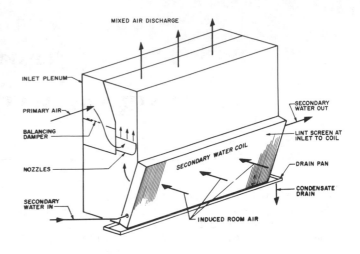

Fig. 1   Air-Water Induction Unit

designed for the particular installation or, in standard cabinets, provided by the unit manufacturer. These enclosures must permit proper flow of secondary air and discharge of mixed air without imposing excessive pressure losses. They also must allow easy servicing.

Induction units are usually installed under a window at a perimeter wall, although units designed for overhead installation are available. During the heating season, the floor-mounted induction unit can function as a convector during off-hours with hot water to the coil and without a primary air supply. A number of induction unit configurations are available, including units with low overall height or with larger secondary coil face areas to suit particular space or load needs.

Advantages of Induction Systems

1. Individual room temperature control with the capability of adjusting each thermostat for a different temperature at relatively low cost.
2. Separate heating and cooling sources in the primary air and secondary water gives the occupant a choice of heating or cooling.
3. Less space is required for the distribution system when the air supply is reduced by using secondary water for cooling and high velocity air design. The return air duct system is reduced in size and sometimes can be eliminated or combined with the return air system for other building areas, such as the interior spaces.
4. The size of the central air-handling apparatus is smaller than that of other systems, since little air must be conditioned.
5. Dehumidification, filtration, and humidification are performed in a central location remote from conditioned spaces.
6. Ventilation air supply is positive.
7. Space can be heated without operating the air system via the secondary water system. Nighttime fan operation is avoided in an unoccupied building. Emergency power for heating, if required, is much lower than for most all-air systems.
8. System components are long-lasting. Room terminals operated dry have an anticipated life of 15 to 25 years. The piping and ductwork longevity should equal that of the building.
9. Individual induction units do not contain fans, motors, or compressors. Routine service is generally limited to temperature controls, cleaning of lint screens, and infrequent cleaning of the induction nozzles.

Disadvantages of Induction Systems

1. Relatively low primary air quantities make the two-pipe changeover design for operating during intermediate seasons more critical than in alternate system types. The four-pipe changeover system overcomes this disadvantage.
2. The two-pipe changeover induction system has operating complexities not present in other systems. The operator must understand the system cycles and changeover procedures. This disadvantage, and the need for heating at one time of the day and cooling at another, has effectively ruled out the two-pipe changeover system for modern buildings.
3. For most buildings, these systems are limited to perimeter space; separate systems are required for other building areas.
4. Controls tend to be more complex than for many all-air systems.
5. Secondary air flow can cause the induction unit coils to become dirty enough to affect performance. Lint screens or low efficiency filters used to protect these terminals require frequent in-room maintenance and reduce unit thermal performance.
6. The primary air supply usually is constant with no provision for shutoff. This is a disadvantage in residential applications, where tenants or hotel room guests may prefer to turn off the air conditioning, or where management may desire to do so to reduce operating expense.
7. A low primary chilled water temperature is needed to control space humidity adequately.
8. The system is not applicable to spaces with high exhaust requirements (e.g., research laboratories), unless supplementary ventilation air is provided from other systems.
9. Central dehumidification eliminates condensation on the secondary water heat transfer surface under maximum design latent load. However, abnormal moisture sources (e.g., from open windows or people concentraion) can cause condensation that can have annoying or damaging results.
10. Energy consumption for induction systems is higher than for most other systems due to the increased power required by the primary air pressure drop in the terminal units.
11. The initial cost for four-pipe induction systems is greater than for most all-air systems.

AIR-WATER FAN-COIL SYSTEMS

The fan-coil system is similar to induction unit systems. The essential difference is the substitution of the fan-coil unit for the induction unit. The fan-coil system has most of the advantages of the induction system, plus the following:

1. System can be operated with the primary air turned off.
2. The air velocity rate is fairly constant regardless of the primary air quantity.
3. Requires less room maintenance than induction units.
4. Primary air can either connect directly to the fan-coil unit or supply the room separately.

Fan-coil systems are discussed in Chapter 4.

AIR-WATER RADIANT PANEL SYSTEMS

The advantages and disadvantages of radiant panels are discussed in Chapter 7.

PRIMARY AIR SYSTEMS

Figure 2 illustrates the primary air system for the air-water system. These conventional components are discussed in Chapter 2. Some primary air systems operate with 100% outdoor air at all times. Systems using return air should have provision for operating with 100% outdoor air to reduce operating cost during certain seasons. In some systems, when the quantity of the

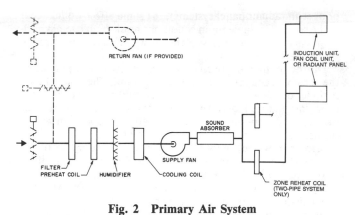

Fig. 2 Primary Air System

primary air supplied exceeds the ventilation or exhaust requirements, the excess air is recirculated by a return system common with the interior system. A quality filter is desirable in the central air treatment apparatus. If it is necessary to maintain a given humidity level in cold weather, a humidifier can usually be installed. Steam humidifiers have been used successfully. The water sprays must be operated in conjunction (1) with the preheat coil elevating the temperature of incoming air or (2) with heaters in the spray water circuit.

The cooling coil is usually selected to provide primary air at a dew point low enough to dehumidify the system totally. Hence, the temperature of the air leaving the cooling coil will be about 50 °F (10 °C) or less, and almost completely saturated. For these requirements, a deep coil (usually with six or eight rows) and a chilled water temperature of about 42 °F (5.5 °C) or less are needed.

The supply fan should be selected at a point near maximum efficiency to reduce power consumption, heating of the supply air, and noise. Sound absorbers are usually required at the fan discharge to attenuate fan noise.

Reheat coils are required in a two-pipe system. Reheat is not required for the primary air supply of four-pipe systems. Many primary air distribution systems for air-water induction units were designed with 8 to 10 in. of water (2.0 to 2.5 kPa) system static pressure. With the energy use restrictions of today, this is no longer economical. Careful selection of the primary air cooling coil and induction units for reasonably low air pressure drops is necessary to achieve a medium velocity and medium pressure primary air system. Distribution for fan coil and radiant panel systems may be low velocity or a combination of low and medium velocity systems. The duct system should be designed with the static regain method. Variations in pressure between the first and last terminals should be minimized to limit the pressure drop across balancing dampers.

Room sound characteristics vary depending on unit selection, air system design, and the manufacturer. Units should be selected by considering the unit manufacturer's sound power ratings, the desired maximum room noise level, and the acoustical characteristics of the room. Limits of sound power level can then be specified to obtain acceptable acoustical performance.

PERFORMANCE UNDER VARYING LOAD

Under peak load conditions, the psychrometrics of air-and-water systems are essentially identical for two- and four-pipe systems.

The primary air mixes with secondary air conditioned by the room coil within the induction unit prior to delivery to the room. Mixing also occurs within a fan-coil unit with a direct connected air supply. If the primary air is supplied to the space separately (as in fan coil systems with independent primary air supplies or as with radiant panel systems), the same effect would occur in the space. The same room conditions result from two physically independent processes as if the air was directly connected to the unit.

During cooling, the primary air system provides a portion of the sensible capacity and all of the dehumidification. The remainder of the sensible capacity is accomplished by cooling the room air induced over the secondary coil. The mixture of primary and secondary air is discharged to the room. In winter, primary air is provided at a low temperature, and if humidity control is provided, the air is humidified. All room heating is supplied by the room secondary coil. All factors that contribute to the cooling load of perimeter space in the summer, with the exception of the transmission, add heat in the winter. The transmission factor becomes negative when the outdoor temperature falls below the room temperature. Its magnitude is directly proportional to the difference between the room and outdoor temperatures.

For all air-water systems where primary air enters at the terminal unit, the primary air is provided at summer design temperature in winter. A limited amount of cooling can be accomplished by the primary air operating without supplementary cooling from the secondary coil. As long as internal heat gains are not high, this amount of cooling is usually adequate to satisfy east and west exposures during the fall, winter, and spring, since the solar heat gain is reduced during these seasons. The north exposure is not a significant factor, since the solar gain is very low. For the south, southeast, and southwest exposures, the peak solar heat gain occurs in winter, coincident with lower outdoor temperatures (Figure 3).

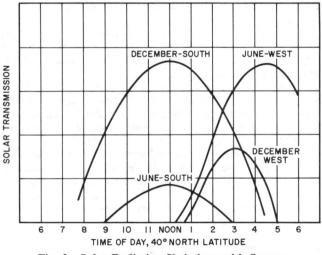

Fig. 3   Solar Radiation Variations with Season

In buildings with large areas of glass, the transmitted heat from indoors to the outside, coupled with the normal supply of cool primary air, will not balance internal heat and solar gains until an outdoor temperature well below freezing is reached. Double-glazed windows, with clear or heat-absorbing glass, aggravate this condition because this type of glass permits constant inflow of solar radiation during the winter. However, the insulating effect of the double glass reduces the reverse transmission, and thereby reduces the outdoor temperature to which cooling must be kept available. In buildings with very high internal heat gains from lighting or equipment, the need for cooling from the room coil, as well as from the primary air, can extend well into the winter. In any case, the changeover temperature at which the cooling capacity of the secondary water coil is no longer required is an important calculation.

CHANGEOVER TEMPERATURE

For all systems using outdoor air, there is an outdoor temperature at which secondary cooling is no longer required. The system can accomplish cooling by using outdoor air; at lower temperatures, heating rather than cooling is needed. With all-air systems operating with up to 100% outdoor air, mechanical cooling is seldom required at outdoor temperatures below 55 °F (12 °C). An important characteristic of air-water systems, however, is that secondary water cooling may continue to be needed, even when the outdoor temperature is considerably less than 50 °F (10 °C). This cooling may be provided by the mechanical refrigeration unit or by a thermal economizer cycle. Full-flow circulation of the primary air cooling coil at temperatures below 50 °F (10 °C) often provides all necessary cooling while preventing coil freeze-up and reducing preheat requirements. Alternatively, secondary water to condenser water heat exchangers function well. Some systems circulate condenser water directly. This system should be used with caution, recognizing that the vast secondary water system is being operated as an open recirculating system with the potential hazards that may accompany improper water treatment.

The outdoor temperature at which the heat gain to every space can be satisfied by the combination of cold primary air and the transmission loss is termed the changeover temperature. Below this temperature, refrigeration is no longer required for cooling primary air or chilling secondary water.

The following equation determines the temperature (Carrier 1965).

$$t_{co} = t_r - [q_{IS} + q_{ES} - cQ_p (t_r - t_p)]/\Delta q_{td} \qquad (2)$$

where

t_{co} = temperature of changeover point, °F (°C).
t_r = room temperature at time of changeover, normally taken as 76 °F (24 °C).
t_p = primary air temperature at the unit after the system is changed over, normally taken as 48 °F (9 °C).
Q_p = primary air quantity, cfm (L/s)
q_{IS} = internal sensible heat gain, Btu/h (W).
q_{ES} = external sensible heat gain, Btu/h (W).
Δq_{td} = heat transmission per degree of temperature difference between room and outdoor air.
c = 1.10 (1.229).

Since in two-pipe changeover systems the entire system is usually changed from winter to summer operation at the same time, the room with the lowest changeover point should be identified. In northern latitudes, this room usually has a south, southeast, or southwest exposure because the solar heat gains on these exposures reach their maximum during the winter months. However, since changeover is made at comparatively cool outdoor temperatures, substantially increased storage may be available. For buildings of moderate glass area with good room heat storage characteristics, a factor of 0.4 applied to the solar load accounts for the effects of storage and blinds.

If the calculated changeover temperature is below approximately 40 °F (4 °C), a thermal economizer cycle should operate in the winter to allow the refrigeration plant to shut down above freezing.

While the factors controlling the changeover temperature of air-water systems are understood by the design engineer, its basic principles are often more difficult for the system operators to understand. It is important that the concept and the calculated changeover point be clearly explained in operating instructions prior to operating the system. Some increase from the calculated changeover temperature is normal in actual operation. Also, a range or band of changeover temperatures, rather than a single value is a practical necessity to preclude frequent change in the seasonal cycles and to grant some flexibility in operating procedure. The difficulties associated with operator understanding and the need to change over several times a day in many areas has severely limited the acceptability of the changeover system.

REFRIGERATION LOAD

The design refrigeration load is determined by considering the entire portion of the building served by the air-and-water system at the same time. Because the load on the secondary water system depends on the simultaneous demand of all spaces, the sum of the individual room or zone peaks is not considered.

The peak load time is influenced by the relative amounts of the east, south, and west exposures; the outdoor wet-bulb temperature; and the period of building occupancy. Where the magnitude of the solar load is about equal for each of the above exposures, the building peak usually occurs in midsummer afternoon when the west solar load and outdoor wet-bulb temperature are at or near concurrent maximums.

The refrigeration load equals the primary air-cooling coil load plus the secondary system heat pickup.

$$q_{re} = q_s + c_1 Q_p (h_{ea} - h_{la}) - c_2 Q_p (t_r - t_s) \qquad (3)$$

where

q_{re} = refrigeration load, Btu/h(W).
q_s = room sensible heat for all spaces at time of peak, Btu/h(W).
h_{ea} = enthalpy of the primary air upstream of the cooling coil at time of peak Btu/lb (kJ/kg).
h_{la} = enthalpy of the primary air leaving the cooling coil, Btu/lb (kJ/kg).
Q_p = primary air quantity, cfm (L/s)
t_r = average room temperature for all exposures at peak time.
t_s = average primary air temperature at the point of delivery to the rooms.
c_1 = 4.5 (1.202).
c_2 = 1.10 (1.229).

The secondary water system cooling load may be determined by subtracting the primary air cooling coil load from the total refrigeration load.

TWO-PIPE SYSTEMS

Description

Two-pipe systems for induction fan-coil or radiant panel systems derive their name from the water distribution circuit, which consists of one supply and one return pipe. Each unit or conditioned space is supplied with secondary water from this distribution system and with conditioned primary air from a central apparatus. The system design and the control of the primary air and secondary water temperatures must be such that all rooms on the same system (or zone, if the system is separated into independently controlled air and water zones) can be satisfied during both heating and cooling seasons. The heating or cooling capacity of any unit at a particular time is the sum of the primary air output plus the secondary water output of that unit.

The primary air quantity is fixed, and the primary air temperature is varied in inverse proportion to outside temperature to provide the necessary amount of heating during summer and intermediate seasons. During winter cycle operation, the primary air is preheated and supplied at approximately 50°F (10°C) to provide a source of cooling. All units in a given primary air reheater zone must be selected to operate satisfactorily with the common primary air temperature.

The secondary water-coil output of each unit is controlled by a local space thermostat and can vary from zero to 100% of coil capacity, as required to maintain space temperature. The

secondary water is cold in summer and intermediate seasons and warm in winter. All rooms on the same secondary water zone must operate satisfactorily with the same water temperature.

Figure 4 shows the capactiy ranges available from a typical terminal unit. On a hot summer day, the unit can satisfy loads varying from about 25 to 100% of the design unit cooling capacity. On a 50°F (10°C) intermediate season day, the unit can satisfy a heating requirement by closing off the secondary coil and using only the output of the warm primary air. A lesser heating or net cooling requirement is satisfied by the cold secondary water coil output, which offsets the warm primary air to obtain cooling. In winter, the unit can provide a small amount of cooling by closing the secondary coil and using only the cold primary air. Smaller cooling loads and all heating requirements are satisfied by using the warm secondary water.

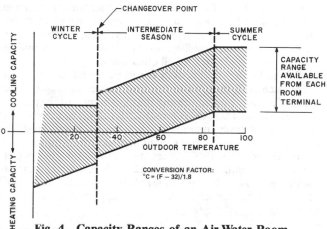

Fig. 4 Capacity Ranges of an Air-Water Room Terminal Operating on a Two-Pipe System

Critical Design Elements

The most critical design elements of a two-pipe system are the calculation of primary air quantities and the final adjustment of the primary air temperature reset schedule. All rooms require a minimum amount of heat during the intermediate season, available from a common primary air supply temperature. The A/T ratio concept to maintain a constant relationship between the primary air quantity and the heating requirements of each space fulfills this requirement. Understanding the ratio of primary air to transmission per degree (A/T ratio) determining the primary air temperature and changeover point, is fundamental to proper design and operation of a two-pipe system.

Transmission Per Degree

Calculating the transmission heat flow per degree temperature difference between space temperature and outside temperature, assuming steady-state heat transfer, determines the relative heating requirement of every space. This is the sum of (1) the glass heat transfer coefficient times glass areas, (2) wall heat transfer coefficient times wall area, and (3) roof heat transfer coefficient times roof area.

Air-to-Transmission Ratio

The A/T ratio is the ratio of the primary air flow to a given space divided by the transmission per degree of that space:

A/T ratio = Primary Air/Transmission Per Degree

All spaces on a common primary air zone must have approximately the same A/T ratios. The design base A/T ratio establishes the primary air reheat schedule during intermediate seasons. Spaces with A/T ratios higher than the design base A/T ratio will tend to be overcooled during light cooling loads at outdoor temepratures in the 70 to 90°F (21 to 32°C) range, while spaces with A/T ratios lower than the design ratio will lack sufficient heat during the 40 to 60°F (4 to 15°C) outdoor temperature range when the primary air is warm for heating and the secondary water is cold for cooling.

The minimum primary air quantity that will satisfy the requirements for ventilation, dehumidification, and both summer and winter cooling, as explained in the "System Description" section, is used to calculate the minimum A/T ratio for each space. If the system will be operated with primary air heating during cold weather, the heating capacity can also be the primary air quantity determinant for two-pipe systems.

The design base A/T ratio is the highest A/T ratio obtained, and the primary air flow to each space is increased, as required, to obtain a uniform A/T ratio in all spaces. An alternate approach is to locate the space with the highest A/T ratio requirement by inspection, establish the design base A/T ratio, and obtain the primary air flow for all other spaces by multiplying this A/T ratio by the transmission per degree of all other spaces.

For each A/T ratio, there is a specific relationship between the outdoor air temperature and the temperature of the primary air that will maintain the room at 72°F (22°C) or more during conditions of minimum room cooling load. Figure 5 illustrates this variation based on an assumed minimum room load, equivalent to 10°F (5°C) times the transmission per degree. Primary air temperatures over 122°F (50°C) at the unit are seldom used. The reheat schedule should be adjusted for hosptial rooms or other applications where a higher minimum room temperature is desired, or where there is no minimum cooling load in the space.

Deviation from the A/T ratio is sometimes permissible. A minimum A/T ratio equal to 0.7 of the maximum A/T is suitable, if the building is of massive construction with considerable heat storage effect (Carrier 1965). The heating performance when using warm primary air becomes less satisfactory than for systems with a uniform A/T ratio. Therefore, systems deigned for A/T ratio deviation should be suitable for changeover to warm secondary water for heating whenever the outdoor temperature falls below 40°F (4°C). A/T ratios should be more closely maintained on buildings with large glass areas, with curtain wall construction, or on systems with low changeover temperature.

Changeover Temperature Considerations

Transition from summer operations to intermediate season operation is done by gradually raising the primary air temperature as the outdoor temperature falls to keep rooms with small cooling loads from becoming too cold. The secondary water remains cold during both summer and intermediate seasons. Figure 6 illustrates the psychrometrics of summer cycle operation near the changeover temperature.

As the outdoor temperature drops further, the changeover temperature will be reached. The secondary water system can then be changed over to provide hot water for heating.

If the primary air flow is increased to some spaces to elevate the changeover temperature, the A/T ratio for the reheat zone will be affected. Adjustments in the primary air quantities to other spaces on that zone probably will be necessary to establish a reasonably uniform ratio.

System changeover can take several hours and usually temporarily upsets room temperatures. Good design, therefore, includes provision for operating the system with either hot or cold secondary water over a range of 15 to 20°F (8 to 11°C) below the changeover point. This range makes it possible to operate with warm air and cold secondary water when the outside temperature rises above the daytime changeover temperature. Changeover to hot water is limited to times of extreme or protracted cold weather.

Optional hot or cold water operation below the changeover point is provided by increasing the primary air reheater capacity to provide adequate heat at the colder outside temperatures.

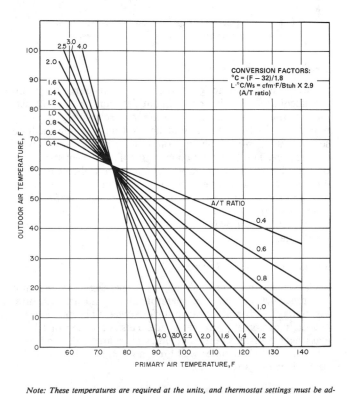

Note: These temperatures are required at the units, and thermostat settings must be adjusted to allow for duct heat gains or losses. Temperatures are based on:

1. Minimum average load in the space equivalent to 10 deg F (5°C) multiplied by the transmission per degree.

2. Preventing the room temperature from dropping below 72 F (22°C). These values compensate for radiation and convection effect of the cold outdoor wall.

Fig. 5　Primary Air Temperature vs. Outdoor Air Temperature

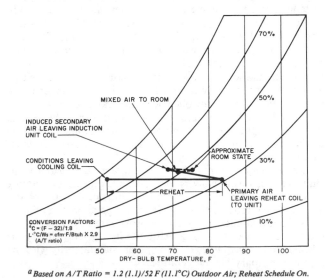

a Based on A/T Ratio = 1.2 (1.1)/52 F (11.1°C) Outdoor Air; Reheat Schedule On.

Fig. 6　Psychrometric Chart, Two-Pipe System, Off-Season Cooling[a]

Figure 7 shows temperature variations for a system operating with changeover. This indicates the relative temperature of the primary air and secondary water throughout the year and the changeover temperature range. The solid arrows show the temperature variation when changing over from summer to winter cycle. The open arrows show the variation when going from winter to summer cycle.

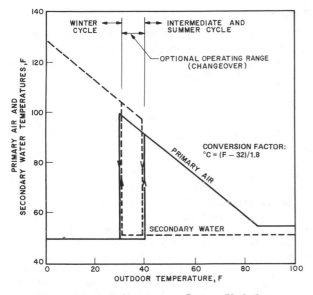

Fig. 7   Typical Changeover System Variations

Non-changeover Design

Non-changeover systems should be considered to simplify system operation for buildings with mild winter design climates, or for south exposure zones of buildings with large winter solar loads. A non-changeover system operates on intermediate season cycle throughout the heating season, with cold secondary water to the terminal unit coils and with warm primary air satisfying the entire heating requirements. Typical system temperature variations are shown in Figure 8.

Spaces may be heated during unoccupied hours by operating the primary air system with 100% return air. This feature is necessary, since the non-changeover design does not usually include the ability to heat the secondary water. In addition, cold secondary water must be available throughout the winter months.

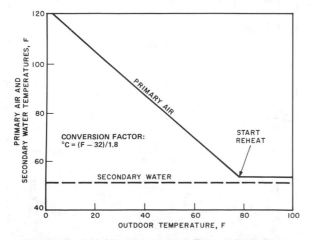

Fig. 8   Typical Non-changeover System Variations

Primary air duct insulation and observance of close A/T ratios for all units are essential for proper heating during cold weather.

Zoning

A properly designed single-zone, two-pipe system can provide good temperature control on all exposures during all seasons of the year. Initial cost or operating cost can be improved by zoning in several ways, such as the following:

1. Zoning primary air to permit different A/T ratios on different exposures.
2. Zoning primary air to permit solar compensation of primary air temperature.
3. Zoning both air and water to permit different changeover temperatures for different exposures.

All spaces on the same primary air zone must have the same A/T ratio. The minimum A/T ratios often are different for spaces on different solar exposures, thus requiring the primary air quantities on some exposures to be increased if they are placed on a common zone with other exposures. The primary air quantity to units serving the north, northeast, or northwest exposures can usually be reduced by using separate primary air zones with different A/T ratios and reheat schedules. Primary air quantity should never be reduced below minimum ventilation requirements.

The peak cooling load for the south exposure occurs during the fall or winter months when outside temperatures are lower. If present or future shading patterns from adjacent buildings or obstructions will not be present, primary air zoning by solar exposure can reduce air quantities and unit coil sizes on the south. Units can be selected for peak capacity with cold primary air instead of reheated primary air. Primary air zoning and solar compensators will save operating cost on all solar exposures by reducing primary air reheat and the secondary water refrigeration penalty.

Separate air and water zoning will save operating cost by permitting north, northeast, or northwest exposures to operate on winter cycle with warm secondary water at outdoor temperatures as high as 60°F (16°C) during winter months. Systems with a common secondary water zone must operate with cold secondary water to cool south exposures. Primary air flow can be lower because of separate A/T ratios, resulting in reheat and refrigeration cost savings.

Room Control

During summer, the thermostat must increase the output of the cold secondary coil when the room temperature rises. During winter, the thermostat must decrease the output of the warm secondary coil when the room temperature rises. Changeover from cold water to hot water in the unit coils requires changing the action of the room temperature control system. Room control for non-changeover systems does not require the changeover action, unless it is required to provide gravity heating during shutdown.

Evaluation

Characteristics of two-pipe air-and-water systems are as follows:

1. They are usually less expensive to install than four-pipe systems.
2. They are less capable of handling widely varying loads or providing widely varying choice of room temperatures than four-pipe systems.

3. They are cumbersome to change over, increasing the need for competent operating personnel.
4. They are more costly to operate than four-pipe systems.

Electric Heat for Two-Pipe Systems

Electric heat can be supplied with a two-pipe air-water system by using a central electric boiler and hot water terminal coils or by individual electric resistance heating coils in the terminal units.

One approach uses small electric resistance terminal heaters for the intermediate season heating requirements and a two-pipe changeover chilled-water/hot-water system. The electric terminal heater heats when outdoor temperatures are above 40°F (4°C), and cooling is available with chilled water in the chilled-water/hot-water system. System or zone reheating of the primary air is reduced greatly or eliminated entirely. When outdoor temperatures fall below this point, the chilled-water/hot-water system is switched to hot water, providing greater heating capacity. Changeover is limited to a few times per season, and simultaneous heating/cooling capacity is available, except in extremely cold weather, when little, if any, cooling is needed. If electric resistance terminal heaters are used in this type system, the heaters should be prevented from operating whenever the secondary water system is operated with hot water.

Another approach is to size electric resistance terminal heaters for the peak winter heating load, and to operate the chilled water system as a non-changeover cooling-only system. This system avoids the operating problem of chilled-water/hot-water system changeover. In fact, this approach functions like a four-pipe system, and, in areas where the electric utility establishes a summer demand charge and has a low unit energy cost for high winter consumption, can have a lower life cycle cost than hydronic heating with fossil fuel.

THREE-PIPE SYSTEMS

Three-pipe air-and-water systems for induction, fan-coil, and radiant panel systems have three pipes to each terminal unit. These pipes are a cold water supply, a warm water supply, and a common return. These systems are rarely used today because they consume excess energy. For a detailed discussion, refer to Chapter 4 of the 1973 SYSTEMS Volume and Chapter 4 of the 1976 SYSTEMS Volume.

FOUR-PIPE SYSTEMS

Description

Four-pipe systems have a cold water supply, cold water return, warm water supply, and warm water return. The terminal unit usually has two independent secondary water coils: one served by hot water, the other by cold water. The primary air is cold and remains at the same temperature year-round. During peak cooling and heating, the four-pipe system performs in a manner similar to the two-pipe system with essentially the same operating characteristics. Between seasons, any unit can be operated at any level from maximum cooling to maximum heating, if both cold water and warm water are being circulated. Any unit can be operated at or between these extremes without regard to the operation of other units.

All units are selected on the basis of their peak capacity. The A/T ratio design concept for two-pipe systems does not apply to four-pipe systems. There is no need to increase primary air quantities on north or shaded units beyond the amount needed for ventilation and to satisfy cooling loads. The available net cooling is not reduced by heating the primary air. Attention to the changeover point is still important, since cooling of spaces on the south side of the building may continue to require second-ary water cooling to supplement the primary air at low outdoor temperatures.

Since the primary air is supplied at a constant cool temperature at all times, it is sometimes feasible for fan-coil or radiant panel systems to extend the interior system supply to the perimeter spaces, eliminating the need for a separate primary air system. The type of terminal unit and the characteristics of the interior system are determining factors.

Zoning

Zoning of primary air or secondary water systems is not required. All terminal units can heat or cool at all times, as long as both hot and cold secondary pumps are operated and sources of heating and cooling are available.

Room Control

The four-pipe terminal usually has two completely separated secondary water coils—one receiving hot water and the second receiving cold water. The coils are operated in sequence by the same thermostat; they are never operated simultaneously. The unit receives either hot water or cold water in varying amounts or else no flow is present, as shown in Figure 9A. Adjustable, dead-band thermostats further reduce operating cost.

Figure 9B illustrates another unit and control configuration. A single secondary water coil at the unit and three-way valves located at the inlet and outlet admit water from either the hot or cold water supply, as required, and divert it to the appropriate return pipe. This arrangement requires a special three-way modulating valve, originally developed for one form of the three-pipe system. It controls the hot or cold water selectively and proportionally but does not mix the streams. The valve at the coil outlet is a two-position valve open to either the hot or cold water return, as required.

When all aspects are considered, the two-coil arrangement provides a superior four-pipe system. The operation of the induction unit controls is the same year-round. Units with secondary air bypass control are not applicable to four-pipe systems.

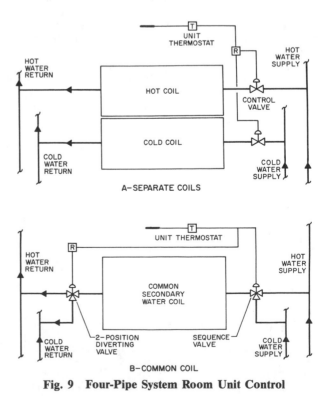

Fig. 9   Four-Pipe System Room Unit Control

Evaluation

Compared to the two-pipe system, the four-pipe air-and-water system has the following characteristics:

1. It is more flexible and adaptable to widely differing loads, responding quickly to load changes.
2. It is simpler to operate.
3. It operates without the summer-winter changeover and the primary air reheat schedule.
4. Efficiency is greater and operating cost is lower, though initial cost is generally higher.
5. The system can be designed with no interconnection of the hot and cold water secondary circuits, and the secondary system can be completely independent of the primary water piping.

SECONDARY WATER DISTRIBUTION

This discussion of secondary water system design is applicable to induction, fan-coil, and radiant panel systems. The secondary water system, as considered in this section, includes the portion of the water distribution system that circulates water to room terminal air-conditioning units (or radiant coils) when the cooling (or heating) of such water has been accomplished either by extraction from or heat exchange with another source in the primary circuit. In the primary circuit, water is cooled by flow through a chiller or is heated by a heat input source. Primary water is limited to the cooling cycle and is the source of the secondary water cooling. Heating applications of the primary-secondary concept are usually thought of in the primary-booster or main-zone relationship and are discussed in other chapters.

The term *secondary water* evolved as a part of the term to describe a component of the air-water system. The water flow through the unit coil performs secondary cooling when the room air (secondary air) gives up heat to the water. The design of the secondary water system differs for the two- and four-pipe systems.

Components

The components of a secondary water distribution system usually include the following items:

1. Secondary water pump.
2. Room terminal coils (secondary coil).
3. Terminal capacity control.
4. Piping and appurtenances.
5. Expansion tank.
6. Heat exchanger or blending control.

To cool the secondary water, chilled water is introduced into the secondary circuit directly through a blending control from the primary chilled water circuit, or alternatively, by a water-to-water heat exchanger. If the secondary circuit provides heat, a hot water, steam, or electric heat exchanger is incorporated into the loop. Hot water from a primary circuit is sometimes directly introduced, as is done with chilled water. However, careful designing is necessary to prevent mixing of the primary hot and primary cold circuits on two-pipe systems.

Design Considerations

Basic design procedures for the secondary water system in the two-pipe changeover system are no different from other dual-temperature piping systems and are covered in Chapter 4. The secondary water distribution system delivers a design flow of hot or chilled water to the secondary water coil of the room terminal unit so that the room unit has sufficient capacity for the space served.

In some systems, the room terminal units are applied without manual or automatic water control valves. In this design, the room unit capacity may be controlled by manual or thermostatic control of the fan speed for room fan-coil units or by control of a coil bypass damper. Since it is difficult to balance water flow accurately to each room unit after the water system has been installed, the piping must be sized carefully, using reversed return where possible.

Direct return riser or header layouts can be used if reversed return is not adaptable to the building. The direct return should have a sufficiently low pressure loss between the nearest and farthest subcircuits compared to the subcircuit pressure loss so that the imbalance will have negligible effect on the terminal coil capacity. This is practical if the terminal subcircuit pressure loss is fairly large, on the order of 10 to 15 ft of water (30 to 45 kPa) and is relatively constant for all terminals irrespective of their design flow. To assist the designer, some terminal unit manufacturers have incorporated resistance in the coil to achieve a uniform pressure drop. Fixed resistance or automatic flow regulators can also be installed in series with the terminal coil for this purpose. Most air-and-water systems include a large number of room terminals, making water balancing by individual adjustment of manual balancing fittings difficult. Therefore, it is necessary to ensure approximately the same pressure drop through all parallel circuits.

Correct water balance is less critical if the selected design temperature rise (or drop) through the terminal coil is fairly low, since capacity will not be significantly reduced by minor flow shortages. However, this may increase the initial cost.

Where the room units are applied with thermostatically controlled two-way water valves for capacity control, the layout and balancing of the water circuit are also less critical, since all units will not require the maximum flow simultaneously. When some control valves operate at throttled condition, additional water becomes available to those that are not throttled. This advantage does not apply to terminals using air flow control or manual control valves. In the latter case, occupants can allow the space to overcool or overheat by leaving their valves in the full open position.

Depending on operating temperatures of the secondary water and the condition of the air surrounding the piping, supply and return lines may require insulation to prevent sweating and to conserve energy. Frequently, perimeter pipe chases are subject to an influx of unconditioned air and should be sealed at points where the piping comes through the floor or wall to the conditioned space. Packing a suitable insulation material around the pipes will any openings. Sealing prevents humid air from entering the conditioned space, which can cause condensation on the room unit coil. Additional sealing prevents the spread of smoke or flame in the event of fire (the material chosen for sealing should meet fire codes) and reduces sound transmission between adjoining spaces.

Shutoff valves should be installed on each supply and return riser to isolate it from the rest of the system. An isolated riser is easy to maintain and permits part of the system to operate before completion of the total system. Each riser should have a drain valve. Air vents should be installed at the top of risers not vented into headers.

Shutoff valves should be installed at each unit, or in the lines serving two or three units, so that individual units can be isolated for maintenance without shutting down and draining an entire riser. A bypass valve is frequently installed on the system side of the unit shutoff valves, permitting the system to be flushed out prior to start-up without the risk that construction dirt will foul the control valves (if used).

The air-and-water system is usually designed so that latent cooling is not the normal function of the secondary water coil.

Condensation at the room coil is not desirable because it may generate odors and requires a full piping system to remove condensate.

If the system is designed for dry-room unit coil operation, the secondary water should be maintained at a temperature that provides maximum sensible cooling at the coil without being so cold that condensation occurs under normal operating conditions. If occupancy with higher latent heat gains is anticipated, the secondary water should be maintained at a higher temperature, and the reduction of cooling capacity should be accepted.

The secondary water supply temperature to induction units incorporating single row coils and water flow control should be maintained at no more than 3 °F (1.5 °C) below the normal maximum room dewpoint. The supply temperature to fan-coil units (with deeper cooling coils) or to any units with air flow control should not be below the normal maximum room dewpoint. The supply water temperature to ceiling radiant panel terminals should be not less than 3 °F (1.5 °C) higher than the anticipated maximum room dewpoint to avoid wet and possibly dripping ceilings.

If induction or fan-coil units are required to handle some latent load, a condensate return system must be installed. Drain pans beneath the coil are a standard accessory. Even if no drain piping is provided, these pans can serve as a reservoir for moisture resulting from short-term condensation on the coil, such as occurs on start-up. Subsequent reevaporation will dissipate the condensate.

Condensate lines should be installed in hotels and apartments in which it is difficult to predict accurately the latent loads that will be imposed by showers, cooking, or open windows. They should also be installed when such units are installed overhead. The horizontal runouts must be pitched to the condensate risers or mains. Insulation of the condensate piping is usually not necessary. When installed in existing buildings, an initial cost saving may be feasible by using old water or steam lines as part of the condensate system.

A room unit in its own factory-built enclosure has compact piping to allow installation of a minimum-sized cabinet. With furred-in installation, more space is often available for piping. Rarely is space abundant, and careful analysis of the physical

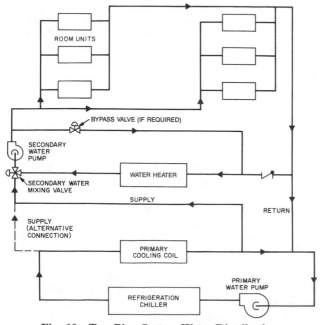

Fig. 10   Two-Pipe System Water Distribution with Mixing Control

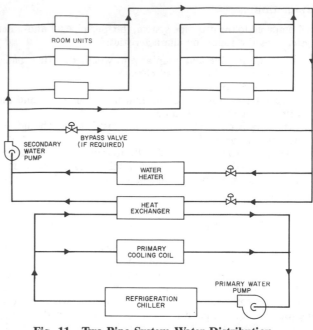

Fig. 11   Two-Pipe System Water Distribution with Separated Circuits

arrangement is advised. A mock-up of the unit, enclosure, piping, and air duct, if it is physically involved, will often reveal problems and solutions not otherwise discernible. Chilled water control valves and shutoff valves mounted over the unit condensate pan, or an extension of it, eliminates insulation expense.

Two-Pipe System Arrangement

Two secondary water system arrangements applicable to two-pipe systems are illustrated in Figures 10 and 11; both systems have separate primary and secondary water circuits and circulation pumps.

Mixing Control. In the mixing control system shown in Figure 10, the primary chilled water is circulated from the chiller to the primary cooling coil(s). A portion of the primary water is mixed through the secondary water three-way valve into the secondary circuit to maintain its design temperature. The quantity of primary water introduced is determined by its temperature, the design temperature of the secondary water system, and the load on the secondary water system. Since the water leaving the primary water coil under peak conditions may be within a few degrees of the secondary water design temperature, the proportion of water supplied to total the secondary system flow may be high. Water quantities are maintained in balance through the return connection, which returns to the primary system a water quantity equal to that taken through the mixing valve. A thorough analysis of the hydraulics should be made.

An alternative arrangement of the mixing control system is the introduction of primary water at the temperature leaving the chiller, as shown in Figure 10. The primary water temperature is low, and the water interchange between systems is reduced considerably. The alternative method permits the design of the primary cooling coil system with no effect on the secondary water.

Separated Circuits. Figure 11 shows primary and secondary water circuits completely separated hydraulically. Secondary water is cooled by a water-to-water heat exchanger, which receives primary water from the chiller to provide the secondary cooling. This arrangement makes it impossible for either the primary or secondary circuit to be affected hydraulically by the other circuit. In large buildings, where several secondary water circuits are served by a single primary system, there may be advantages to separating the water circuits. In high-rise buildings, the secondary water distribution should be divided horizontally into two or more zones to limit system pressures caused by height. The zones are isolated from each other hydraulically, with one or more using a primary-to-secondary heat exchanger for secondary cooling.

Heating. A heater in the piping circuit warms the secondary water. In the system with mixing control, the three-way valve is positioned to close flow from the primary system. In separate circuits, the branch to the heat exchanger is shut down. The heater is controlled to maintain the desired outlet water temperature, either constant or, if the design requires, scheduled in accordance with the outdoor air temperature. An overcall switch elevates the secondary water temperature during the off-hours for gravity heating or during the start-up period.

Water Flow. Secondary water is either constant or variable, depending on the control system. When secondary water flow is reduced by throttling, the pressure differential across the room unit control valves will increase. Control valves will not close above a definite maximum pressure differential. In some instances, they have a lower maximum pressure differential limit for satisfactory throttling without noise.

To ensure satisfactory control, quiet operation, and sufficient valve seat life when many room units are operating at part load, the system should be designed as follows:

1. Select a secondary pump with a flat characteristic curve so the pump head at minimum flow does not exceed the differential pressure recommended by the valve manufacturer.
2. Provide a gradually opening bypass valve or a main throttling valve regulated by a differential pressure controller to limit the pressure across the system.
3. As an alternative to (2), provide three-way valves on one-third to one-half of the terminal coils throughout the circuit so that there will be sufficient flow through these valves to limit the pressure buildup and to keep the supply water at a uniform temperature.
4. Evaluate variable speed pumping to reduce operating cost.

If unit capacity is controlled by regulating air through the secondary coil, water flow and pressures in the system will be the same during all load conditions. Where the system has variable flow and serves several exposures that are not likely to require simultaneous maximum water flow for cooling, the pump capacity can be reduced from the sum of the individual terminal design flows. Such reductions should be conservative, since the thermostats in rooms may be set at lower than design temperature under partial load, causing a greater total flow than anticipated from the building load calculation.

Four-Pipe System Arrangement

Figures 12 and 13 show two secondary water systems applicable to four-pipe systems. Both systems have separate secondary water pumps and piping. In the separated arrangement illustrated in Figure 12, not only are the two secondary circuits separated, but the secondary water is cooled in a water-to-water heat exchanger, normally served by the primary chilled water circuit (which may be connected to other sources of cooling for off-season operation).

The secondary water system shown in Figure 13 is similar to the one described for two-pipe systems. Primary chilled water is bled into the secondary chilled water circuit through a mixing valve controlled to maintain a constant secondary water temperature, and an equal quantity is returned to the primary water system. The secondary hot water is heated by a heat exchanger in that circuit. An overcall switch elevates the secondary water

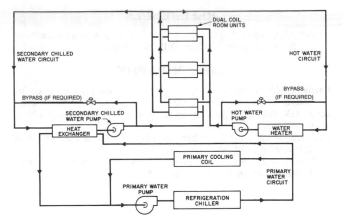

Fig. 12 Four-Pipe System Water Distribution with Separated Circuits

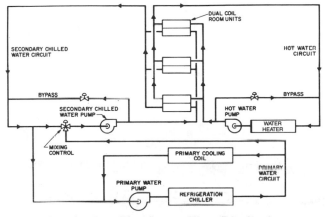

Fig. 13 Four-Pipe System Water Distribution with Mixing Control

temperature during start-up or during off-hours for gravity heating.

Water flow in the secondary circuits is highly variable throughout the season, and gradual acting bypass, main throttling valves, or speed control should be at both secondary water pumps. The control should maintain a relatively constant pressure differential across each system and within the limit set by control valve manufacturers. Terminal coil flow demand for chilled water in winter (or hot water in summer) may fall to zero in parts of the distribution system. Three-way valves are desirable for units at the extremities of the piping system, particularly at the top and bottom units on perimeter risers. They will provide some continuous flow through the pumps and exchangers and prevent damage from freezing of chilled water piping in exposed chases during very cold weather.

Standby Provision

Standby secondary water pumps and heat exchangers should be considered for systems serving critical applications, such as hospitals or apartments where winters are cold. However, on two-pipe systems, a substantial degree of standby protection for heating is afforded by operating the primary air system on its summer cycle if the secondary system equipment fails. In contrast with two-pipe systems, the loss of the secondary hot water pump or heat exchanger will deny the spaces served by a four-pipe system their only source of heat. Accordingly, the installation of standby equipment or stocking of critical spare parts is advisable for most buildings with four-pipe systems.

REFERENCES

Carrier Air Conditioning Company. 1965. *Handbook of Air Conditioning System Design*. McGraw-Hill, New York.

BIBLIOGRAPHY

Barnard, W.R. 1958. Which system is best for multi-room air conditioning, *Air Conditioning, Heating and Ventilating*. November.

Bond, G.V. 1960. Air conditioning for large office buildings. *Architectural Record*. October.

Menacker, R. 1977. Electric induction air-conditioning system. ASHRAE *Transactions*, Vol. 83, Part 1, p. 664.

McFarlan, A.I. 1967. Three-pipe systems: concepts and controls. ASHRAE *Journal*, Vol. 9, No. 8, August, p. 37.

Pannkoke, T. 1980. Air terminal devices, what's available? *Heat, Piping & Air Conditioning*. November.

Ross, D.E. 1974. Variable-air-volume system evaluation for commercial office buildings. ASHRAE *Transactions*, Vol. 80, Part I, p. 476.

Smith, L. 1958. How an office building's occupancy affects its air conditioning design. *Heating, Piping & Air Conditioning*. October.

Wilson, M.J. 1958. How to select right air-conditioning system for multistory building. *Heating, Piping & Air Conditioning*. August, October, and November.

Wilson, M.J. 1960. Selecting air-conditioning systems for specific applications. *Air Conditioning, Heating and Ventilating*. October.

York Corporation. 1961. *Three-Pipe Air Conditioning Systems*. York Corporation, Application Data, Yorkaire.

CHAPTER 4

ALL-WATER SYSTEMS

SYSTEM DESCRIPTION

Convective Radiation Heating

ALL-WATER systems heat and/or cool a space by direct heat transfer between water and circulating air. Hot water systems deliver heat to a space by water that is hotter than the air in contact with the heat transfer surface. Examples of such systems include the following:

1. Baseboard radiation
2. Free-standing radiators
3. Wall or floor radiant
4. Bare pipe (racked on wall)
5. Other configurations

These types may further be classified as gravity convection, where air moves past the transfer surface because of density differences caused by heating or cooling. These systems also lose large amounts of heat by radiation to colder surfaces.

Although these systems provide comfort during the heating season, they are not state-of-the-art, except in limited applications where spot heating may be required. This equipment is seldom seen in new buildings, except where large amounts of glass or high rates of infiltration are encountered in specific areas and then, mostly in cold climates.

Fan Coil Units

The Four Basic Principles of Air Conditioning listed below apply to heating, as well.

1. Temperature Control
2. Humidity Control
3. Air Movement
4. Air Purity (filtration and outside air make-up)

If all-water systems include cooling as well as heating, they must move air by forced convection through the conditioned space, filter the circulating air, and introduce outside ventilation air. Terminal units with cold water coils, heating coils, blowers, replaceable air filters, drain pans for condensate, etc., are designed for these purposes. Terminal units are available in various configurations to fit under windowsills, above furred ceilings, in vertical pilasters built into walls, etc. These units must be properly controlled by thermostats for heating and cooling temperature control, by humidstats for humidity control, by blower control or other means for regulating air quantity, and by a method for adding ventilation air into the system.

In applying all-water systems, the manufacturer's capacity ratings should be obtained to verify performance under actual operating conditions.

Basic elements of fan-coil units are a finned-tube coil, filter, and fan section (Figure 1). The fan recirculates air continuously from the space through the coil, which contains either hot or chilled water. The unit may contain an additional electric resistance, steam, or hot water heating coil. The electric heater is often sized for fall and spring to avoid changeover problems in two-pipe systems.

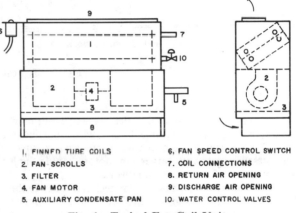

1. FINNED TUBE COILS	6. FAN SPEED CONTROL SWITCH
2. FAN SCROLLS	7. COIL CONNECTIONS
3. FILTER	8. RETURN AIR OPENING
4. FAN MOTOR	9. DISCHARGE AIR OPENING
5. AUXILIARY CONDENSATE PAN	10. WATER CONTROL VALVES

Fig. 1 Typical Fan-Coil Unit

A cleanable or replaceable low-efficiency filter, located upstream of the fan, prevents clogging the coil with dirt or lint entrained in the recirculated air. It also protects the motor and fan, and reduces the level of airborne contaminants within the conditioned space. The unit is equipped with an insulated drain pan. The fan and motor assembly is arranged for quick removal servicing. Most manufacturers furnish units tested and labeled by Underwriters' Laboratories, as required by some local codes, with cooling performance that is ARI certified.

Ventilation air boxes, with a dampered opening for connection to apertures in the outside wall, are optional. These units are not recommended because wind pressure allows no control over the amount of outside air that is admitted. Room fan-coil units for the domestic market are generally available in nominal sizes of 200, 300, 400, 600, 800, and 1200 cfm (95 to 570 L/s) often with multi-speed, high efficiency fan motors.

Types and Location

Room fan-coil units are available in many configurations. Figure 2 shows several vertical units. Low vertical units are available for use under windows with low sills; however, in some cases, the low silhouette is achieved by compromising such features as filter area, motor serviceability, and cabinet style.

Floor-to-ceiling, chase-enclosed units are available in which the water and condensate drain risers are part of the factory-furnished unit. Supply and return air systems must be isolated from each other to prevent air and sound interchange between rooms.

The preparation of this chapter is assigned to TC 9.1, Large Building Air-Conditioning Systems.

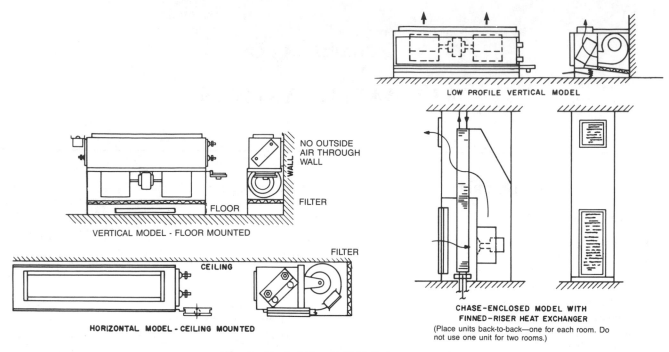

Fig. 2   Typical Fan-Coil Unit Arrangements

Horizontal overhead units may be fitted with ductwork on the discharge to supply several outlets. A single unit may serve several rooms, *e.g.,* in an apartment house where individual room control is not essential and a common air return is feasible. High static pressure units with larger fan motors handle the higher pressure drops of units with ductwork.

Central ventilation air may be connected directly to the inlet plenums of horizontal units or introduced directly into the space. If this concept is used, provisions should be made to ensure that this air is pretreated and held at a neutral temperature of 70 °F (21 °C) so as not to cause occupant discomfort when the unit is off. One way to prevent air leakage is to provide a spring-loaded motorized damper, which closes off the ventilation air whenever the units' fan is off. Coil selection must be based on the temperature of the entering mixture of primary and recirculated air, and the air leaving the coil must satisfy the room sensible cooling and heating requirements. Horizontal models conserve floor space and usually cost less, but when located overhead in furred ceilings, they create problems such as condensate collection and disposal, mixing of return air with other rooms, leakage of pans causing damaged ceilings, and difficulty of access for filter and component removal.

Vertical models give better results in climates or buildings with high heating requirements. Heating is enhanced by under-window or exterior wall locations. Vertical units can be operated as convectors with the fans turned off during night setback.

UNIT VENTILATORS

Unit ventilators are similar to fan-coil units, except they may serve a multiple fan coil system with pretreated ventilation air, which eliminates the problems of direct introduction of outside air.

WATER DISTRIBUTION

Chilled and hot water must run to the fan-coil units. The piping arrangement determines quality of performance, ease of operation, and initial cost of the system.

Two-Pipe Changeover

This low initial cost concept supplies either chilled water or hot water through the same piping system. The fan-coil unit has a single coil, and room temperature controls reverse their action, depending on whether hot or cold water is available at the unit coil. This system works well in warm weather when all rooms have a cooling requirement and in cold weather when all rooms have a heating requirement. *It does not have the simultaneous heating or cooling capability* that is required for most projects during intermediate seasons, i.e., when some rooms have a cooling requirement while others have a heating requirement. This problem can be especially troublesome if a single piping zone supplies the entire building. Zoning by solar exposure to permit operation of any zone on either heating or cooling, independent of the others, partly overcomes this difficulty. However, one room may still require cooling while another room on the same solar exposure requires heating—particularly if the building is partially shaded by an adjacent building.

Another difficulty of the two-pipe changeover system is the need for frequent changeover from heating to cooling, thus complicating the operation and increasing energy consumption *to the extent that it may become impractical.* For example, two-pipe changeover system hydraulics must consider water expansion (and relief) that occurs during the cycling from cooling to heating.

Psychrometric principles also show the loss of dehumidification capability throughout the system during the heating cycle.

Two-Pipe Changeover with Partial Electric Strip Heat. This arrangement provides simultaneous heating/cooling capability in intermediate seasons by using a small electric strip heater in the fan-coil unit. The unit can handle heating requirements in mild weather, typically down to 40 °F (4 °C), while continuing to circulate chilled water to handle any cooling requirements. When the outdoor temperature drops sufficiently to require heating in excess of electric strip heater capacity, the water system must be changed over to hot water.

The designer should consider the disadvantages of the two-pipe system carefully; many installations of this type waste energy and have been unsatisfactory in climates where frequent change-over is required and where interior loads require cooling simultaneously as exterior spaces require heat.

Two-Pipe Nonchangeover with Full Electric Strip Heat. This two-pipe system is not recommended for energy conservation, but it may be practical in areas with a small heating requirement. Any two-pipe system must be carefully analyzed. In any case, they are not recommended for commercial buildings.

Four-Pipe Distribution

The four-pipe concept generally has the highest initial cost, but it provides the best fan-coil system performance, such as (1) all season availability of heating and cooling at each unit, (2) no summer/winter changeover requirement, (3) simpler operation, and (4) use of any heating fuel, heat recovery, or solar heat. In addition, it can be controlled to maintain a "dead band" between heating and cooling so there is no possibility of simultaneous heating and cooling.

Central Equipment

Central equipment size is based on the block load of the entire building at the time of building peak load, not on the sum of individual fan-coil unit peak loads. Cooling load should include appropriate diversity factors for lighting and occupant loads. Heating load is based on maintaining the unoccupied building at design temperature, plus an additional allowance for pick-up capacity if the building temperature is set back at night.

If water supply temperatures or quantities are to be reset at times other than at peak load, the adjusted settings must be adequate for the most heavily loaded space in the building. An analysis of individual room load variations is required.

If the side exposed to the sun or interior zone loads require chilled water in cold weather, using condenser water with a water-to-water interchanger should be considered. Varying refrigeration loads require the water chiller to operate satisfactorily under all conditions.

The only reason to use central plant equipment in an all-water system is to provide correct amounts of ventilation or make-up air to the various spaces being served by terminal units. The disadvantages of providing direct injection of untreated outside air through apertures in outside walls have previously been mentioned.

Ventilation requires an outside air pre-treatment unit complete with sized heating and cooling coils, filters, fan, etc., to offset the ventilation load. An additional advantage of the ventilation unit is that, if it is sized for the internal latent load, the terminal cooling coil remains dry, which may eliminate the need for piped drains from the condensate pans. A dry system must be carefully designed to be sure no condensate leaks develop. Ventilation units should be sized to maintain the supply air temperature between 70 and 72°F (21 and 22°C). This neutral temperature removes the outside air load from the terminal unit, so it can switch from heating to cooling and vice-versa without additional internal or external heat loads.

APPLICATIONS

Fan-coil systems are best applied to individual space temperature control. Fan-coil systems also prevent cross-contamination from one room to another. Suitable applications are hotels, motels, apartment buildings, and office buildings. Fan-coil systems are used in a number of hospitals, but are less desirable because of the low efficiency filtration and difficulty in maintaining adequate cleanliness in the unit and enclosure.

Where internal sensible loads require heating and/or cooling simultaneously, both mediums must be provided continuously.

This practice should only be applied where humidity control is required.

ADVANTAGES

A major advantage of the all-water system is the delivery system (piping versus duct systems) requires less building space, a smaller or no central fan room, and duct space is needed. The system has all the benefits of a central water chilling and heating plant, while retaining the ability to shut off local terminals in unused areas. It gives individual room control with little cross-contamination of recirculated air from one space to another. Extra capacity for quick pull-down response may be provided. Since this system can heat with low temperature water, it is particularly suitable for solar or heat recovery refrigeration equipment. For existing building retrofit, it is often easier to install piping and wiring than the large ductwork required for all-air systems.

DISADVANTAGES

All-water systems require much more maintenance than central all-air systems, and this work must be done in the occupied areas. Units that operate at low dew points require condensate pans and a drain system that must be cleaned and flushed periodically. Condensate disposal can be difficult and costly. It is also difficult to clean the coil, if necessary. Filters are small, low in efficiency, and require frequent changing to maintain air volume. In some instances, drain systems can be eliminated if dehumidification is *positively* controlled by a central ventilation air system.

Ventilation is often accomplished by opening windows or by installing outside wall apertures. Ventilation rates are affected by stack effect and wind direction and velocity.

Summer room humidity levels tend to be relatively high, particularly if modulating chilled water control valves are used for room temperature control. Alternatives are two-position control with variable speed fan and the by-pass unit variable chilled water temperature control.

VENTILATION

Ventilation air is generally the most difficult factor to control and represents a major load component. To save energy, it should be reduced to a minimum. The designer should select the method that meets local codes, performance requirements, and cost constraints.

Central Ventilation Systems

A central ventilation system maintaining neutral air at about 70°F (21°C) best controls ventilation air with the greatest freedom from problems related to stack effect and infiltration. Ventilation air then may be introduced to the room through the fan-coil unit, as shown in Figure 3. Any type of fan-coil unit in any location may be used if the ventilation system has separate air outlets.

Ventilation air contributes significantly to the room latent cooling load, so a dehumidifying coil should be installed in the central ventilation system to reduce the room humidities during periods of high outside moisture content.

In buildings where fan-coil units serve exterior zones only and a separate all-air system serves interior zones, it is possible to provide exterior zone ventilation air through the interior zone system. This arrangement can provide desirable room humidity control, as well as temperature control of the ventilation air. In addition, ventilation air held in the "neutral zone" of 70°F (21°C)

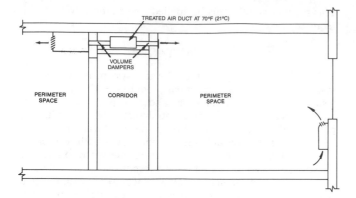

Fig. 3　Ventilation from Separate Duct System

at 50% rh can be introduced into any all-water system without affecting the comfort conditions being maintained by the terminal units.

CONTROL AND WIRING

Unit Capacity Controls

Fan-coil unit capacity can be controlled by coil water flow, air bypass, fan speed, or a combination of these. Water flow can be thermostatically controlled by either return air or wall thermostats.

Fan speed control may be automatic or manual. Automatic control is usually on-off with manual speed selection. Units are available with variable speed motors for modulated speed control. Room thermostats are preferred where fan speed control is used. Return air thermostats do not give a reliable index of room temperature when the fan is off.

On-off speed control is poor because (1) alternating shifts in fan noise level is more obvious than the sound of a constantly running fan, and (2) air circulation patterns within the room are noticeably affected.

Wiring

Fan-coil conditioner fans are driven by small motors generally of the shaded pole or capacitor type, with inherent overload protection. Operating wattage of even the largest sizes rarely exceeds 300 W at the high speed setting. Running current rarely exceeds 2.5 A.

Almost all the motors on units sold in the United States are wired for 115 V, single-phase, 60 Hz current, and they provide multiple (usually three) fan speeds and an off position. Other voltages and power characteristics may be encountered, depending upon location, and should be investigated before determining the fan motor characteristics.

In planning the wiring circuit, local and national electrical codes must be followed. Wiring methods generally provide separate electrical circuits for the fan-coil units and do not connect them into the lighting circuit.

Separate electrical circuits connected to a central panel allow the building operator to turn off unit fans from a central point during unoccupied hours. While this panel costs more initially, it can lower operating costs in buildings that do not have 24-hour occupancy. Use of separate electrical circuits is advantageous in applying a single remote thermostat mounted in a well-exposed perimeter space to operate unit fans.

Unit Selection

Some designers size fan-coil units for nominal cooling at the medium speed setting when a three-speed control switch is provided. This method ensures quieter operation within the space and adds a safety factor, in that capacity can be increased by operating at high speed. Sound power ratings are available from many manufacturers.

Only the internal space heating and cooling loads need to be handled by the terminal fan coil units when outside air is pretreated by a central system to a neutral air temperature of about 70°F (21°C). This pretreatment should reduce the size and cost of the terminal units.

Piping

Even when outside air is pretreated, a condensate removal system should be installed on the terminal units. This precaution ensures that moisture condensed from air from an unexpected open window that bypasses the ventilation system is carried away. Drain pans are an integral feature of all units. Condensate drain lines should be oversized to avoid clogging with dirt, etc., and provision should be made for periodic cleaning of the condensate drain system. Condensation may occur on the outside of the drain piping, which requires that these pipes be insulated. Many building codes have outlawed systems without condensate drain piping due to the damage they can cause under uncontrollable conditions.

Maintenance

Room fan-coil units are equipped with either cleanable or throwaway filters that should be cleaned or replaced when dirty. Good filter maintenance improves sanitation and full airflow, ensuring full capacity. The frequency of cleaning varies with the application. The presence of lint in apartments, hotels, and hospitals usually requires more filter service in those applications.

Fan-coil unit motors require periodic lubrication. Motor failures are not common, but when they occur, it is possible to replace the entire fan quickly with minimal interruption in the conditioned space. The defective motor can be repaired or replaced. The condensate drain pan and drain system should be cleaned or flushed periodically to prevent overflow.

CHAPTER 5

UNITARY REFRIGERANT-BASED SYSTEMS
FOR AIR-CONDITIONING

MULTIPLE-PACKAGED unit systems are applied to almost all classes of buildings. They are especially suitable where less demanding performance requirements, low initial cost, and simplified installation are important. These systems have been applied to office buildings, shopping centers, manufacturing plants, hotels, motels, schools, medical facilities, nursing homes, and other multi-occupancy dwellings. They are also suited for air conditioning existing buildings with limited life or income potential. Applications also include specialized facilities requiring high performance levels, such as computer rooms and research laboratories.

SYSTEM CHARACTERISTICS

These systems are characterized by many different air-conditioning units, each with an integral refrigeration cycle. The components are factory assembled into an integrated package, which includes fans, filters, heating coil, cooling coil, refrigerant compressor(s), refrigerant side controls, and air side controls. The equipment is manufactured in various configurations to meet a wide range of applications. Window air conditioners, through-the-wall room air conditioners, unitary air conditioners for indoor and outdoor locations, air source heat pumps, and water source heat pumps are examples. Specialized packages for computer rooms, hospitals, and classrooms are also available.

Components are matched and assembled to achieve specific performance objectives. Although available as large unitary equipment packages customized for specific requirements, the equipment is available only in pre-established increments of capacity with set performance parameters, such as sensible heat ratio at a given room condition, or cfm of air per ton of refrigeration (L/s per kW). These limitations make practical the manufacture of low cost, quality-controlled, factory-tested products. Performance characteristics vary among manufacturers for a particular kind and capacity of unit. All characteristics should be carefully assessed to ensure that the equipment performs as needed for the application. Several trade associations have developed standards by which manufacturers may test and rate their equipment. Chapters 42, 43, and 44 of the 1983 EQUIPMENT Volume describe the equipment used in multiple-packaged unitary systems and the pertinent industry standards.

Although this equipment can be applied in single units, this chapter covers the application of multiple units to form a complete air-conditioning system for a building. Multiple-packaged unit systems for perimeter spaces are frequently combined with a central all-air system. These combinations can provide better humidity control, air purity, and ventilation than packaged units alone. The all-air system may also serve interior building space that could not be conditioned by wall or window-mounted units.

Advantages

1. Individual room control is simple and inexpensive.
2. Each room has individual air distribution with simple adjustment by the occupant.
3. Heating and cooling capability can be provided at all times, independent of the mode of operation of other spaces in the building.
4. Individual ventilation air may be provided whenever the conditioner operates.
5. Manufacturer matched components have certified ratings and performance data.
6. Manufacturer assembly allows improved quality control and reliability.
7. Manufacturer instructions and multiple unit arrangements simplify the installation through repetition of tasks.
8. Only one unit conditioner and one zone of temperature control is affected if equipment malfunctions.
9. Readily available.
10. One manufacturer is responsible for the final equipment package.
11. For improved energy control, equipment serving vacant spaces can be turned off locally or from a central point, without affecting occupied spaces.
12. System operation is simple. Trained operators are not required.
13. Less mechanical and electrical room space is required than with central systems.
14. Initial cost is usually low.
15. Equipment can be installed to condition one space at a time as a building is completed, remodeled, or as individual areas are occupied, with favorable initial investment.
16. Energy can be metered directly to each tenant.

Disadvantages

1. Limited performance options are available because air flow and cooling coil and condenser sizing is fixed.
2. Not generally suited for close humidity control, except when using special purpose equipment such as packaged units for computer rooms.
3. Temperature control is usually two-position, which causes swings in room temperature.
4. Equipment life may be relatively short.
5. Energy use may be greater than for central systems, if efficiency of the unitary equipment is less than that of the combined central system components.
6. Low cost cooling by outdoor air economizers is not always available.
7. Air distribution control is limited.
8. Operating sound levels can be high.
9. Ventilation capabilities are fixed by equipment design.
10. Overall appearance can be unappealing.
11. Air filtration options are limited.

The preparation of this chapter is assigned to TC 9.1, Large Building Air-Conditioning Systems.

12. Maintenance may be difficult because of the many pieces of equipment and their location, frequently in occupied spaces.

WINDOW-MOUNTED AIR CONDITIONERS AND HEAT PUMPS

A window air conditioner (air-cooled room conditioner) is designed to cool/heat individual room spaces. Chapter 42 of the 1983 EQUIPMENT Volume and ANSI/AHAM Standard RAC-1, 1982, Room Air Conditioners, describe this equipment.

Design Considerations

Window units may be used as auxiliaries to a central heating or cooling system or to condition selected spaces when the main system is shut down. In such applications, the window units usually serve only part of the spaces conditioned by the basic system. Both the basic system and the window units should be sized to cool the space adequately without the other operating.

Window units are furnished with individual electric controls. However, when several units are used in a single space, the controls should be interlocked to prevent simultaneous heating and cooling. In commercial applications (e.g., motels), centrally operated switches can de-energize units in unoccupied rooms.

Window units are used where low initial cost, quick installation, and other operating or performance criteria outweigh the advantages of more sophisticated systems. Room units are also available in through-the-wall sleeve mountings. Sleeve-installed units are popular in low cost apartments, motels, and homes.

Applied in a system, window units usually supplement existing heating or cooling systems. As a supplement to cooling, they are most often added to an inadequate existing system and sized to meet the required capacity when both systems operate.

Advantages

1. Simple installation.
2. No mechanical equipment room space is required.
3. Low initial cost.

Disadvantages

1. Relatively short equipment life, typically 10 years; window units are built to appliance standards, rather than building equipment standards.
2. May have relatively high energy usage.
3. Requires outside air; thus, cannot be used for interior rooms.
4. Condensate removal can cause dripping on walls, balconies, or sidewalks.

THROUGH-THE-WALL MOUNTED AIR CONDITIONERS AND HEAT PUMPS

A through-the-wall air-cooled room air-conditioner is designed to cool or heat individual room spaces. Design and manufacturing parameters vary widely. Specifications range from appliance grade through heavy-duty commercial grade. The latter is called a *packaged terminal air conditioner*, in ANSI/ARI Standard 310-82. All others are covered in ANSI/AHAM Standard RAC/2-1982.

The through-the-wall conditioner system incorporates a complete air-cooled refrigeration and air-handling system in an individual package. Each room is an individual occupant, controlled zone. Cooled or warmed air is discharged in response to thermostatic control to meet room requirements. The section on controls summarizes how controls allow the use of individual room systems during out-of-schedule hours, yet return all systems automatically to normal schedule use.

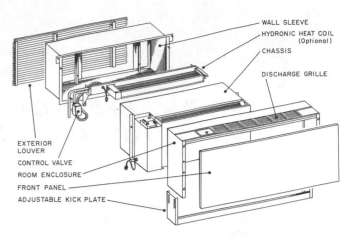

Fig. 1   Packaged Terminal Air Conditioner with Heat Section Separate From Cooling Chassis

Each packaged terminal air conditioner has a self-contained, air-cooled, direct-expansion cooling system; a heating system (electric, hot water, or steam); and controls. Two general configurations are shown: Figure 1 shows a wall box, an outdoor louver, heater section, cooling chassis, and cabinet enclosure. Figure 2 shows a combination wall sleeve cabinet, plus combination heating and cooling chassis with outdoor louver.

Through-the-wall air conditioner or heat pump systems are installed in buildings requiring many temperature control zones such as (1) office buildings, (2) motels and hotels, (3) apartments and dormitories, (4) schools and other education buildings, and (5) in zones of nursing homes or hospitals where air recirculation is allowed.

This system is applicable for renovation of existing buildings, since existing heating systems can still be used. The system lends itself to both low- and high-rise buildings. In buildings where a stack effect is present, this system should be limited to those areas that have dependable ventilation and a tight wall of separation between the interior and exterior.

Room air conditioners are often used in parts of buildings primarily conditioned by other systems. This application is desirable where spaces to be conditioned are (1) isolated physically from the rest of the building and (2) occupied on a different time schedule, e.g., clergy offices in a church and ticket offices in theaters.

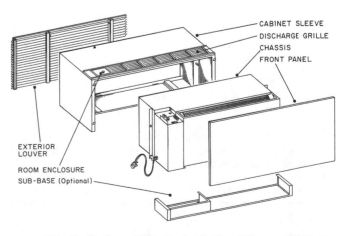

Fig. 2   Packaged Terminal Air Conditioner with Combination Heating and Cooling Chassis

Design Considerations

In choosing through-the-wall equipment adequate to meet the requirement of an application, the system designer should evaluate the following characteristics:

Sound Level. The noise levels of these units are not always satisfactory. Check that the noise level of the equipment meets sound level requirements.

Ventilation Air. Ventilation air through each terminal may be inadequate with many types of systems, particularly in high-rise structures because of the stack effect. Chapter 22 of the 1985 FUNDAMENTALS Volume explains combined wind and stack effects. Electrically operated outdoor air dampers, which close automatically when the equipment is stopped, reduce heat losses in winter.

Condenser Fan Operation. Some room air conditioners have only one motor to drive both the evaporator and condenser fans. These units circulate air through the condenser coil whenever the evaporator fan is running, even during the heating season. The annual energy consumption of systems having a single motor is generally higher than those with separate motors, even when Energy Efficiency Ratios (Coefficients of Performance) are the same for both types of equipment. The year round continuous flow of air through the condenser increases dirt accumulation on the coil and other components, which increases maintenance and reduces equipment life.

Condensate Disposal. Because through-the-wall conditioners are seldom installed with drains, they require a positive and reliable means of condensate disposal. Conditioners are available that spray the condensate in a fine mist over the condenser coil. These units can dispose of more condensate than can be developed, without any drip, splash, or spray from the equipment. In heat pump units, provision must be made for disposal of condensate generated from the outside coil during the heating mode.

Cold Weather Operation. Many air-cooled room conditioners experience evaporator icing and become ineffective when outdoor temperatures fall below about 65°F (18°C). With high lighting levels and high solar radiation often experienced in contemporary buildings, be certain that mechanical cooling can be provided at a low enough outdoor ambient temperature.

Life Expectancy. Manufacturers project a 10- to 15-year life expectancy for this type of equipment with proper maintenance.

Rainproof Louver and Wall Box. The louver and wall box must stop wind-driven rain from collecting in the wall box and leaking into the building. The wall box should drain to the outside.

Advantages

1. Initial cost is generally less than for a central system adapted to heat or cool each room under the control of the room occupants.
2. Because no energy is needed to transfer air or chilled water from mechanical equipment rooms, the energy consumption may be lower than central systems. However, this advantage may be offset by better efficiencies of central station equipment.
3. Building space is conserved because ductwork and mechanical rooms are not required.
4. Installation only requires a hole in the wall for unit mounting, and connection to electrical power.
5. Generally, the system is well-suited to spaces requiring many zones of individual temperature control.
6. Designer can specify electric, hydronic, or steam heat.
7. Service can be quickly restored by replacing a defective chassis with a spare.

Disadvantages

1. Humidification, when required, must be provided by separate equipment.
2. Packaged terminal air conditioners must be installed on the perimeter of the building.
3. Noise levels vary considerably and are not generally suitable for critical applications.
4. Routine unit maintenance is required to maintain capacity. Condenser and cooling coils must be cleaned, and filters must be changed regularly.

Controls

All controls for through-the-wall air conditioners are included as a part of the conditioner. The following control configurations are available:

Thermostat Control that is either unit mounted or remote wall-mounted.

Guest Room Control for Motels and Hotels with provisions for starting and stopping the equipment from a central point.

Office Building and School Controls (for use less than 24 h), through a time clock, start and stop the equipment at a preset time. The conditioners operate normally with the unit thermostat until the preset cutoff time. After this point, each conditioner has its own reset control, which allows the occupant of the conditioned space to reset the conditioner for either cooling or heating, as required.

Master/Slave Control is used when multiple conditioners are operated by the same thermostat.

Emergency Standby Control allows a conditioner to operate during an emergency, such as a power failure, so that the room-side blowers can operate to provide heating. Units must be specially wired to allow operation on emergency generator circuits.

AIR-TO-AIR HEAT PUMPS

The Air-to-Air heat pump cycle described in Chapter 44 of the 1983 EQUIPMENT Volume is available in through-the-wall room air conditioners. Application considerations are quite similar to conventional units without the heat pump cycle. The heat pump cycle is used for space heating above 35 to 40°F (2 to 5°C) outdoor temperature. Electric resistance elements supply heating below this level and during frost cycles.

The prime advantage of the heat pump cycle is the reduction in annual energy consumption for heating. Savings in heat energy over conventional electric heating range from 10 to 60%, depending on the climate of the location.

OUTDOOR UNITARY EQUIPMENT SYSTEMS

An outdoor unitary equipment system can be designed to cool or heat an entire building. The complete system includes unitary equipment, a ducted air distribution system, and a temperature control system. The equipment is generally mounted on the roof, but can also be mounted at grade level.

When a single unit application is required, the rooftop unit and associated ductwork constitute a central station all-air system, not a multiple unit system. Rooftop units are designed as central station equipment for single-zone, multi-zone, and variable air volume applications. These systems are described in Chapter 2.

Design Considerations

Location. Centering the rooftop unit over the conditioned space results in reduced fan power, ducting, and wiring.

Duct Insulation. All outdoor ductwork should be insulated. In addition, (1) the ductwork should be sealed to prevent condensation in the insulation during the heating season and (2) the ductwork insulation should be weatherproofed to keep it from getting wet.

Zoning. Use single-zone, not multizone, units where feasible. For large areas such as manufacturing plants, warehouses, gymnasiums, and so forth, single-zone units are less expensive and provide protection against total system failure.

Return Fans. Use units with return air fans whenever static pressure loss exceeds 0.25 in. of water (60 Pa) or the unit introduces a large percentage of outdoor air via an economizer.

Exhaust or Relief Fans. Units are also available with relief fans for use with an economizer in lieu of continuously running a return fan. Relief fans can be initiated by static pressure control.

Heating. Natural gas, propane, oil, electricity, hot water, steam, and refrigerant gas heating options are available.

Controls. Most operating and safety controls are provided by the equipment manufacturer. Although remote monitoring panels are optional, they are recommended to permit operating personnel to monitor system performance.

Mounting and Isolation. Rooftop units are generally mounted using integral support frames or lightweight steel structures. Integral support frames are designed by the manufacturer to connect to the base of the unit. No duct openings are required for the supply and return ducts. The completed installation must adequately drain condensed water. Lightweight steel support structures allow the unit to be installed above the roof using separate flashed duct openings. Any condensed water can be drained through the roof drains.

Vibration. Most unitary equipment is available with separate vibration isolation of the rotating equipment; isolation of the entire unit casing is not always required.

Noise. Outdoor noise from unitary equipment should be reduced to a minimum. Airborne noise can be attenuated by silencers in the supply and return air ducts or by acoustically-lined ductwork. Avoid installation directly above spaces where noise level is critical.

Special Considerations. In a rooftop application, the air handler is outdoors and needs to be weatherproofed against rain, snow, and, in some areas, sand. In cold climates, fuel oil does not atomize and must be warmed to burn properly. Hot water or steam heating coils and piping must be protected against freezing. In some areas, enclosures are needed to maintain units effectively during inclement weather. A permanent safe access to the roof is essential, as well as a roof walkway to protect against roof damage.

Accessories. Accessories such as economizers, special filters, and humidifiers are available. Factory-installed and wired economizer packages are also available. Other options offered are return and exhaust fans, variable volume controls with hot gas by-pass, smoke and fire detectors, portable external service enclosures, special filters, and microprocessor-based controls with various control options.

Multiple outdoor units are usually the single-zone type. The number of units is determined by the temperature control zoning; each zone has a unit. The zones are determined by the cooling and heating loads for the space served, occupancy, allowable roof loads, flexibility requirements, appearance, duct size limitations, or equipment size availability. Multiple unit systems have been installed in manufacturing plants, warehouses, schools, shopping centers, office buildings, and department stores. These units also serve core areas of buildings whose perimeter spaces are served by packaged terminal air conditioners. These systems are usually applied to low-rise buildings of one or two floors, but have been used for conditioning multi-story buildings, as well.

Advantages

1. Equipment location allows for shorter duct runs, reduced duct space requirements, lower initial cost, and ease of service access.
2. Installation is simplified.
3. Valuable building space for mechanical equipment is conserved.

Disadvantages

1. Maintenance or servicing of outdoor units is difficult during inclement weather.
2. Frequent removal of panels for access may destroy the weatherproofing of the unit, causing electrical component failures, rusting, and water leakage.
3. Rusting of casings is a potential problem. Many manufacturers prevent rusting by using vinyl coating and other protective measures.
4. Equipment life is reduced by outdoor installation.

INDOOR UNITARY EQUIPMENT SYSTEMS

System Description

Unitary equipment for indoor locations is designed to cool or heat entire buildings. The complete system consists of an indoor unit with either a water-cooled condenser or a remote air-cooled condensing unit, a duct distribution system, and a temperature control system. Equipment is generally installed in service areas adjacent to the conditioned space. When a single unit is required, the indoor unit and its related ductwork constitute a central all-air system, as described in Chapter 2. Figure 3 shows an indoor unit with some commonly used components.

Design Considerations

Multiple-unit systems generally use single-zone (including variable volume) unitary air conditioners with a unit for each zone (Figure 4). The zoning is determined by (1) the cooling and heating loads, (2) occupancy considerations, (3) flexibility requirements, (4) appearance considerations, and (5) equipment and duct space availability. Multiple-unit systems are popular air-conditioning approaches for office buildings, manufacturing plants, shopping centers, department stores, and apartment buildings.

Core Systems. Unitary systems can be used throughout a building, or to supplement perimeter area packaged terminal air-conditioning systems to serve interior spaces (Figure 5). Except for areas with heat loss through the floor or the roof, or where tempering of ventilation air would require it, no heating is required by the core area system.

Since core areas frequently have little or no heat loss, unitary

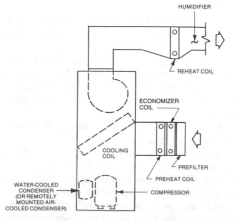

Fig. 3   Unitary Package with Accessories

equipment with water-cooled condensers can be applied with water-source heat pumps serving the perimeter.

Separate Unit for All Outdoor Air. In this multiple unit system, one all-outdoor air unit preconditions outside air for a group of units (Figure 6). This unit prevents hot, humid air from entering the conditioned space under periods of light loading. The outdoor unit should have sufficient capacity to cool the required ventilation air from outdoor design conditions to interior design dew point. Zone units are then sized to handle only the internal load for their particular area.

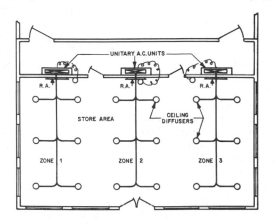

Fig. 4   Multiple Packaged Units

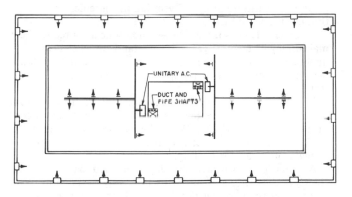

Fig. 5   Multiroom, Multistory Office Building with Unitary Core and Through-the-Wall Perimeter Air Conditioners

This preconditioned outdoor air feature can be incorporated into unitary systems for existing high-rise buildings to allow tenants to control their own systems (Figure 7).

Economizer Cycle. Energy use can be reduced in many locales by cooling with outdoor air in lieu of mechanical refrigeration when outdoor temperature permits. Units must be located close to an outside wall or outside air duct shaft. Where this is not possible, it may be practical to add an economizer cooling coil adjacent to the preheat coil (Figure 3). Cold water is obtained by cooling the condenser water through a winterized cooling tower. Chapter 21 of the 1983 EQUIPMENT Volume has further details.

Specialized Systems. Special purpose unitary equipment is frequently used to cool, dehumidify, humidify, and reheat to maintain close control of space temperature and humidity in computer areas. Chapter 33 includes more information about this system and its design.

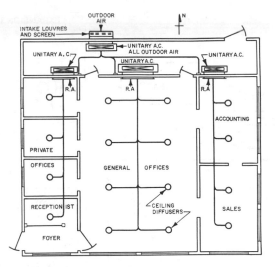

Fig. 6   Multiple Packaged Units with Separate Outdoor Air Makeup Unit

Advantages

1. Installation is simplified. Equipment is readily available and its size allows easy handling.
2. Relocation of units to other spaces or buildings is practical, if necessary.
3. Units are available with complete, self-contained control systems including variable volume control, economizer cycle, night set-back, and morning warm-up.

Disadvantages

1. Access to equipment is sometimes hindered because of its location.
2. Air distribution with a plenum discharge arrangement is limited.
3. Fans have limited static pressure ratings.
4. Air-cooled units must be located at outside walls.
5. Multiple units and equipment closets or rooms may occupy rentable floor space.

WATER-SOURCE HEAT PUMP SYSTEMS

Any number of water-to-air heat pumps may be installed in a closed loop system. Water circulates through each unit via two pipes connected in parallel to the closed loop.

Figure 8 shows a closed-loop water-source heat-pump system. It includes multiple direct-expansion water-cooled heat pumps

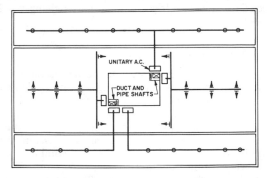

Fig. 7   Multiroom, Multistory Office Building with Unitary Air Conditioners

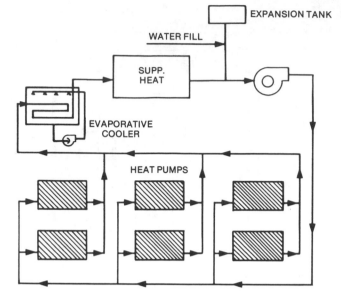

Fig. 8   Closed Loop Water Source Heat Pump System

serving both interior and perimeter zones. The water circuit should include two pumps—one is 100% stand-by, and a means for adding and rejecting heat to and from the loop. The loop temperature is maintained between 60 and 95 °F (16 and 35 °C). A supply water temperature in this range allows the heat pumps either to heat or cool and maintain temperature in each zone.

Units on the heating mode extract heat from the circulated water, while units on the cooling mode reject heat to the water. Thus, the system recovers and redistributes heat, where needed. Unlike air-source heat pumps, heat available for this system does not depend on outdoor temperature. The water loop is the primary source of heat, but a secondary source, typically a boiler, is usually provided.

Another version of the closed-loop water-source heat-pump system uses a coil buried in the earth as a heat source and heat sink. This "earth coupled" system does not normally need the boiler and cooling tower incorporated in other closed-loop systems to keep the circulating water within acceptable temperature limits. However, earth coupled heat pumps must operate at lower entering water (or antifreeze solution) temperatures.

When cooling, each heat pump operates as a water-cooled air conditioner. When heating, the evaporator and the condenser functions are reversed, and the equipment operates as a water chiller. Heat is removed from the water in the water-to-refrigerant heat exchanger. That heat, plus the heat from the compressor, is rejected through the refrigerant-to-air heat exchanger and heats the room.

Design Considerations

This semi-decentralized system has been successfully applied in many types of multi-room buildings. A popular application has been the office buildings, where heat gains from the interior can be redistributed to the perimeter during the winter. Other applications include hotels and motels, schools, apartment buildings, nursing homes, manufacturing facilities, and hospitals. Operating costs for this system are most favorable in applications where both heating and cooling is required.

Unit Types. Chapter 44 of the 1983 EQUIPMENT Volume describes various types and styles of units and the control options available.

Zoning. The multiple water-source heat pump system offers excellent zoning capability. Since equipment can be placed in interior areas, the system can accommodate the future relocation of partitions with minimum duct changes. Some systems use heat pumps for perimeter zones and the top floor, with cooling-only units serving interior zones; but all units connected into the same water circuit.

Heat Recovery and Heat Storage. This system lends itself well to heat storage. Installations that cool most of the day in winter and heat at night (such as a school) make excellent use of heat storage. The water may be stored in a large storage tank in the closed-loop circuit ahead of the boiler. In this application, the loop temperature is allowed to build up to 90 °F (32 °C) during the day. The stored water at 90 °F (33 °C) can be used during unoccupied hours to maintain heat in the building, with the loop temperature allowed to drop to 60 °F (16 °C). The water heater would not be used until the loop had dropped the entire 30 °F (17 °C). The storage tank operates as a flywheel to prolong the period of operation where neither heat makeup nor heat rejection is required.

Concealed Units. Equipment in the ceiling spaces must have access for maintenance and servicing filters, control panels, compressors, and so forth. The condensate drain lines also require space between the drain connection on the unit and the top of the ceiling.

Ventilation. Outdoor air for ventilation may be (1) ducted from a ventilation supply system to the units or (2) drawn in directly through a damper into the individual units. To operate satisfactorily, the air entering the water-source heat pumps should be above 60 °F (16 °C). In cold climates, the ventilation air must be preheated. Stack effect, wind, and balancing difficulties can greatly vary the quantity of ventilation air entering directly through individual units.

Secondary Heat Source. The secondary heat source for heat makeup my be electric, gas, oil, solar, and/or waste heat. Normally, a water heater or boiler is used; however electric resistance heat in the individual heat pumps, with suitable changeover controls, may also be considered.

The changeover control may be an aquastat set to switch from heat pump to resistance heaters when the loop water reaches the minimum 60 °F (16 °C). When the loop temperature reaches 70 °F (21 °C), the resistance heat is cut out and the heat pump is again operated for heating.

An electric water heater is readily controlled to provide 60 °F (16 °C) outlet water and can be used directly in the loop. With a gas or oil-fired combustion boiler, a heat exchanger may be used to transfer heat to the loop or, depending on the type of boiler used, a modulating valve may blend water from the boiler into the loop.

Solar energy can supply part of the secondary heat. Water or antifreeze solution circulated through collectors can add heat to the system loop via a heat exchanger.

Boiler Capacity. The boiler should have a capacity of 75% of the sum of the greatest block loads heated by heat pumps, plus the calculated heat loss from the heat rejector.

Night Setback. A building with night setback must have a boiler sized for the installed capacity, not the building heat loss, since the morning warm-up cycle will require every heat pump to operate at full heating capacity until the building is up to temperature. In this case, the boiler should be sized for 75% of the total heating capacity of all-water source heat pumps installed in the building, plus the heat rejector heat loss. Night setback must not allow temperatures in any spaces to fall below 55 °F (13 °C) to ensure proper restarting of the units.

Heat Rejector Selection. A closed-loop circuit requires a heat rejector that is either a heat exchanger (loop water to cooling tower water) or a closed-circuit evaporative cooler. The heat rejector is selected in accordance with manufacturer's selection curves, using the following parameters:

Water Flow Rates. Manufacturers' recommendations on water flow rates vary between 2 and 3 gpm/ton (0.04 and 0.05 L/s·kW) of installed cooling capacity. The lower flow rates are generally preferred in regions having a relatively low summer outdoor design wet-bulb temperature. In more humid climates, a higher flow rate will allow a higher water temperature to be supplied from the heat rejector to the heat pumps, without a corresponding increase in temperature leaving the heat pumps. Thus, cooling tower or evaporative cooler size and cost is minimized without penalizing performance of the heat pumps.

Water Temperature Range. Range (the difference between the leaving and entering water temperatures at the heat rejector) is affected by heat pump EER, water flow rate, and diversity. It will typically be between 10 and 15°F (6 and 8°C).

Approach. Approach is the difference between the water temperature leaving the cooler and the wet-bulb temperature of the outside air. The maximum water temperature expected in the loop supply is a function of the design wet-bulb temperature.

Diversity. Diversity is the maximum instantaneous cooling load of the building divided by the installed cooling capacity. Diversity times the average range of the heat pumps is the applied range of the total system (the rise through all units in the system and the drop through the heat rejector). Hence:

$$D = Q_m/Q_i$$

where

Q_m = maximum instantaneous cooling load.
Q_i = total installed cooling capacity.
D = diversity.

$$R_s = DR_p$$

where

R_s = range of system.
R_p = average range of heat pumps.

The average leaving water temperature of the heat pumps is the entering water temperature of the heat rejector. The leaving water temperature of the heat rejector is the entering water temperature of the heat pumps.

Winterization of the Heat Rejector. On buildings with some potential year-round cooling (i.e., office buildings), all loop water must circulate through the evaporative cooler at all times. This procedure reduces the danger of freezing. In addition, a standby pump in the system starts automatically in case the main loop pump fails. However, it is important to winterize the heat rejector to minimize the heat loss.

In northern climates, the most important winterization step is to install a discharge air plenum with positive closure, motorized, ice-proof dampers. The entire casing that houses the tube bundle and the discharge plenum may be insulated. The sump, if outside the heated space, should be equipped with electric heaters. The heat pump equipment manufacturer's instructions will help in the selection and control of the heat rejector.

If sections of the water circuit will be exposed to freezing temperatures, the addition of an antifreeze solution should be considered. In a serpentine pipe circuit having no automatic valves that might totally isolate individual components, ethylene glycol concentrations between 10 and 15% provide protection against bursting pipes, yet it has minimal effect on system performance (Trelease 1978).

An open cooling tower with a separate heat exchanger (Friedrich 1977) is a practical alternative to the closed water cooler (Figure 9).

An additional pump is required to circulate the tower water through the heat exchanger. In such an installation where no tubes are exposed to the atmosphere, it may not be necessary to provide freeze protection on the tower. The sump may be in-

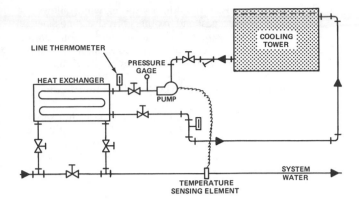

Fig. 9 Cooling Tower with Heat Exchanger

doors or, if outdoors, may be heated to keep the water from freezing. This arrangement allows the use of small, remotely located towers. Temperature control necessary for tower operation is maintained by a sensor in the water loop system controlling operation of the tower fan(s).

The combination of an open tower, heat exchanger, and tower pump frequently is lower in first cost than an evaporative cooler. In addition, operating costs are less because no heat is lost from the loop in the winter and, frequently, less power is required for the cooling tower fans.

Ductwork Layout. Often, the closed-loop water-to-air heat pump system has ceiling-concealed units and the ceiling area is used as the return plenum. Troffered light fixtures are a popular means of returning air to the ceiling plenum.

The air supply from the heat pumps should be designed for quiet operation. Heat pumps connected to ductwork require external static pressure. The heat pump manufacturers' recommendations should be consulted for the maximum and minimum external static pressure allowable with each piece of equipment.

Piping Layout. A reverse return piping system should be used wherever possible with the closed-loop water-to-air heat pump system. This is particularly true where all units are essentially the same capacity. Balancing is then minimized except for each of the system branches. If a direct return system is used, balancing the water flow is required at each individual heat pump. The entire system flow may circulate through the boiler and heat rejector in series, as shown in Figure 8. Water makeup should be at the constant pressure point of the entire loop water system. Piping system design is similar to the secondary water distribution of air-and-water systems. Chapter 3 has supplemental design information.

A clean piping system is vital to successful performance of the water source heat pump system. The pipe should be clean when installed, kept clean during construction, and thoroughly cleaned and flushed upon completion. Startup water filters in the system bypass (pump discharge to suction) should be included on large, extensive systems.

Advantages

1. Affords opportunity for energy conservation by recovering heat from interior zones and/or waste heat and by storing excess heat from daytime cooling for nighttime heating.
2. Allows recovery of solar energy at a relatively low fluid temperature where solar collector efficiency is likely to be greater.
3. The building does not require wall openings to reject heat from air-cooled condensers.

4. Units are not exposed to outdoor weather, which allows installation on the seacoast and in other corrosive atmospheres.
5. Units have a longer expected life than air-cooled heat pumps.
6. Noise levels can be lower than air-cooled equipment because condenser fans are eliminated and the compression ratio is lower.
7. Two-pipe fan coil systems are potentially convertible to this system.
8. Should a unit fail, the entire system is not shut down. However, loss of pumping capability, heat rejection, or secondary heating could affect the entire system.
9. Energy for the heat pumps can be metered directly to each tenant. However, this metering would not include energy consumed by the central pump, heat rejector, or boiler.
10. Total life cycle cost of this system frequently compares favorably to central systems when considering relative installed cost, operating costs, and system life.

Disadvantages

1. Space is required for boiler, heat exchangers, pumps, and heat rejector.
2. Initial cost is higher than for most other multiple-packaged unit systems.
3. Reduced airflow can cause the heat pump to cycle cutout. Good filter maintenance is imperative.

Controls

The closed-loop heat-pump system has simpler controls than those for other totally central systems. There are only two control points: one to add heat when the water temperature drops to 60°F (16°C) and the other to reject heat when the water temperature rises to 90°F (32°C).

The manufacturer includes thermostatic controls for the individual heat pumps. The boiler controls should be checked to be sure outlet water is controlled at 60°F (16°C), since controls normally supplied with boilers are in a much higher range. Some heat pump manufacturers provide a control and alarm panel that sounds an alarm when the loop water temperature exceeds recommended limits or if water flow stops completely.

An evaporative cooler should be controlled by increasing or decreasing heat rejection capacity in response to the loop water temperature leaving the cooler. A reset schedule that operates the system at lower water temperatures (to take advantage of lower outdoor wet-bulb temperatures) can save energy when heat from the loop storage is not likely to be used.

System abnormal condition alarms should operate as follows: (1) On a fall in loop temperature to 50°F (10°C), sound alarm horn. Open heat pump control circuits at 45°F (7°C). (2) On a rise in loop temperature to 105°F (41°C), sound alarm horn. Open heat pump control circuits at 115°F (46°C). (3) On sensing insufficient system water flow, flow switch sounds the alarm horn and opens heat pump control circuits.

An **outside ambient control** should be provided to prevent operation of the sump pump at freezing temperatures.

Optional system control arrangements include (1) night setback control, (2) automatic unit start-stop, with after-hour restart as a tenant option, (3) warm-up cycle, (4) pump alternator control, and (5) central no-flow control to de-energize heat pumps.

REFERENCES

CHP Company. 1985. *Selection Criteria, Closed Circuit Evaporative Water Cooler For Use With California Heat Pump Units and System.* Form CHP-H-070-85-18009.

Friedrich Co. 1977. *Engineering Handbook: Water Source Heat Pump Heat Recovery Systems.* Friedrich Air Conditioning and Refrigeration Co.

Trelease, S.W. 1978. Closed Loop Reverse Cycle Air Conditioning. *Building Operating Management.* January, p. 50.

CHAPTER 6

HEAT RECOVERY SYSTEMS

THIS chapter covers basic concepts of heat recovery for HVAC systems in commercial, institutional, and industrial (CII) buildings. The details of specific systems are limited only by economics and the designer's imagination. Optimum use of countercurrent heat exchange surfaces and innovative circuiting of chillers and condensers to reduce pumping pressure, optimum circuiting of storage tanks, and outside air exchange all improve efficiency and enhance processes.

Conceptually, the system designer must ask (1) whether the *total* heat energy entering and/or generated within the facility is fully used before it is rejected from the facility and (2) if it is not, what percentage of the total heat input is wasted, and what portion of this waste could be recovered to defer or reduce HVAC or water heating requirements cost effectively?

Comprehensive designs require (1) knowledge of the building, processes, operating patterns, available energy sources, and an economic analysis; (2) designers with an understanding of the material contained in this volume, particularly Chapter 49; and (3) specific performance data on primary HVAC equipment (many components are customized to meet specific job requirements).

This chapter concentrates on heat recovery for HVAC uses. Chapter 9 covers applied heat pumps, and Chapter 8 deals with cogeneration.

While first cost of equipment is important, payback to the owner in operating and maintenance cost savings should be a primary concern. Another concern is the volume and floor space required by air economizer units. An analysis of internal loads and available temperatures and appropriate scheduling of equipment operation during all seasons can help keep space requirements to a minimum.

DEFINITIONS

Internal heat is total passive heat generated within the conditioned space. It includes heat generated by lighting, computers, business machines, occupants, and mechanical and electrical equipment such as fans, pumps, compressors, and transformers. Normally, this heat must be removed to control the environment.

Internal process heat is from industrial activities and sources such as waste water, boiler flue gas, coolants, exhaust air, and some waste materials. This heat is normally wasted unless equipment is included to extract it for further use.

External heat is heat from sources outside the conditioned area. This heat from gas, oil, steam, electricity, or solar sources supplements internal heat and internal process heat sources. Recovered heat can reduce the demand for external heat.

Waste heat is heat rejected from the building because temperature is too low for economical recovery.

Recovered (or reclaimed) heat comes from internal heat sources. It is used for space heating, domestic or service water heating, air reheat in air-conditioning, or other similar requirements. Recovered heat may be stored for later use.

Stored heat from external or recovered heat sources is held in reserve for later use.

Usable temperature is the temperature or range of temperatures at which heat energy can be absorbed, rejected, or stored for use within the system.

Breakeven temperature (t_{be}) is the outdoor temperature at which the heat losses from the conditioned spaces and the internal spaces and the internal heat are equal.

Changeover temperature (t_{co}) is the outdoor temperature that the designer sets as the change from net cooling to net heating by the air-conditioning system.

Balanced heat recovery occurs when internal heat equals recovered heat and no external heat is introduced to the conditioned space. Maintaining balance may require raising the temperature of the recovered heat. The following section and Chapter 9 on "Heat Pumps" give more details.

BALANCED HEAT RECOVERY

In a balanced system, all components work year round to recover all the internal heat before adding external heat. Any excess heat is either stored, rejected, or both. The "Heat Storage" section includes more details.

When the outdoor temperature drops significantly, or on nights and weekends when the building is shut down, internal heat may be insufficient to meet space conditioning requirements. Then, a balanced system provides heat from storage or an external source. When internal heat is again generated, the external heat is automatically reduced to maintain proper temperature in the space. Some time occurs before equilibrium is reached.

The size of the equipment and the external heat source can be reduced in a storage balanced system. Regardless of the system, a heat balance analysis establishes the merits of balanced heat recovery at various outdoor temperatures.

Outdoor air that is less than 55 to 65°F (13 to 18°C) may be used to cool building spaces in an air economizer cycle. When considering this method of cooling the space required by ducts, air shafts, and fans, as well as the increased filtering requirements to remove contaminants and the hazard of possible freezeups of dampers and coils must be balanced against alternatives such as the use of deep row coils with anti-freeze fluids and efficient heat exchange. Innovative use of heat pump principles may give considerable energy savings and more satisfactory human comfort than an air economizer. In any case, hot and cold air should never be mixed to control zone temperatures because it is a waste of energy.

HEAT REDISTRIBUTION

Many building projects, especially those with computers or large interior areas, generate more heat than can be used for most of the year. Operating cost is kept to a minimum when the air-conditioning changes over from heating to cooling at the breakeven outdoor temperature at which external heat losses equal internal heat loads. If heat is unnecessarily rejected or added to the space, the changeover temperature will vary from the natural breakeven temperature and operating costs will increase. Heating costs can be reduced or eliminated if excess heat is stored for later distribution.

The preparation of this chapter is assigned to TC 9.4, Applied Heat Recovery/ Heat Pump Systems.

The various means of using internal heat provide additional criteria for selecting both equipment and the external heat source. The optimum selection is often discovered after the heat balance and its effect on operation is analyzed. Fuel or electric power costs may not be the dominant factor regarding operating costs until a proper changeover temperature is chosen. Equipment that substantially lowers the changeover temperature can cause higher operating costs than selections with higher fuel or power costs.

HEAT BALANCE CONCEPT

The *heat balance concept* in an overall building project or a single space requires that one of the following take place on demand:
1. Heat must be removed.
2. Heat must be added.
3. Heat generated must exactly balance the heat required, in which case heat should be neither added nor removed.

In small air-conditioning projects serving only one space, either cooling or heating satisfies thermostat demands. If humidity control is not required, the problem is simple. Assuming both heating and cooling are available, the automatic controls will respond to the thermostat to supply either. A system should *not* heat and cool the same space simultaneously.

Multi-room buildings commonly require heating in some rooms and cooling in others. Good design considers the building as a whole and transfers excess internal heat from one area to another, as required, without introducing external heat that would require waste heat disposal at the same time. The heat balance concept is violated when this occurs.

Humidity control must also be considered. Any system must add or remove only enough heat to maintain the desired temperature, plus any heat required for humidity control. Large percentages of outdoor air with high wet-bulb temperatures, as well as certain types of humidity control, may require reheat, which could upset the desirable balance. Usually, humidity control can be obtained without upsetting the balance. When reheat is unavoidable, internally transferred heat from heat recovery should always be used to the extent available before using an external heat source such as a boiler. However, the effect of the added reheat must be analyzed, since it affects the heat balance and may have to be treated as a variable internal load.

When a building requires heat and the refrigeration plant is not in use, dehumidfication is not usually required and the outdoor air is dry enough to compensate for any internal moisture gains. (This should be carefully reviewed for each design.)

HEAT BALANCE STUDIES

The following analytical methods illustrate situations that can occur in non recovery and unbalanced heat recovery situations. Figure 1 graphically shows the major components that comprise the total air-conditioning load of a building. Values above the zero line are cooling loads, and values below the zero line are heating loads. On an individual basis, the ventilation and conduction loads cross the zero line, which indicates that these loads can be a heating or a cooling load, depending on outdoor temperature. The solar load and internal loads are always a cooling load and are, therefore, above the zero line.

Figure 2 combines all the loads shown in Figure 1. The graph is obtained by plotting the conduction load of a building at various outdoor temperatures, and then adding or subtracting the other loads at each temperature. The project load lines with and without solar effect cross the zero line at 16 and 30°F (-9 and -1°C), respectively. These are the outdoor temperatures for the plotted conditions when the naturally created internal load exactly balances the losses.

It is important to emphasize that this heat balance diagram as plotted, includes only the building loads with no allowance

for addditional external heat from a boiler or other source. If external heat is necessary because of system design, the diagram should include the additional heat.

Figure 3 illustrates what happens when heat recovery is eliminated. Here, it is assumed that at a temperature of 70°F (21°C), heat from an external source is added to balance the perimeter loss in increasing amounts down to the minimum outdoor temperature winter design condition. Figure 3 also adds

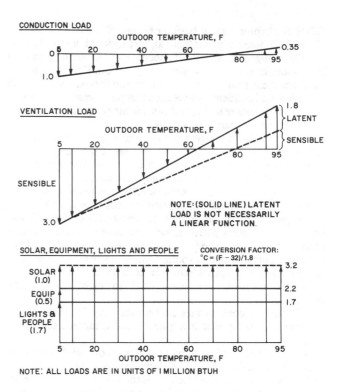

NOTE: ALL LOADS ARE IN UNITS OF 1 MILLION BTUH

Fig. 1   Major Load Components

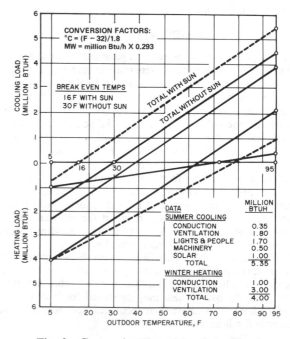

DATA	MILLION BTUH
SUMMER COOLING	
CONDUCTION	0.35
VENTILATION	1.80
LIGHTS & PEOPLE	1.70
MACHINERY	0.50
SOLAR	1.00
TOTAL	5.35
WINTER HEATING	
CONDUCTION	1.00
VENTILATION	3.00
TOTAL	4.00

Fig. 2   Composite Plot of Loads in Fig. 1
(adjust for internal motor heat)

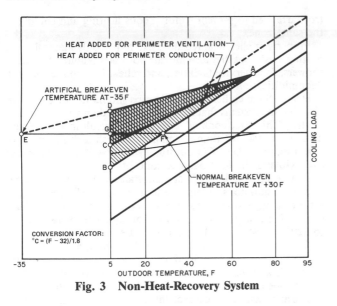

Fig. 3   Non-Heat-Recovery System

the heat required for the peripheral zone ventilation. The outdoor air comprising part or all of the supply air must be heated from outdoor to room temperature. Only the temperature range above the room temperature is effective for heating to balance the perimeter conduction loss.

These loads are plotted at the minimum outdoor winter design temperature, resulting in a new line ADE. This line crosses the zero line at $-35\,°F$ ($-37\,°C$), which becomes the artificially created breakeven temperature rather than $30\,°F$ ($-1\,°C$), when not allowing for solar effect. When the sun shines, the added solar heat at the minimum design temperature would further drop the $-35\,°F$ ($-37\,°C$) breakeven temperature.

Such a design adds more heat than the overall project requires and does not use a balanced heat recovery system to use the available internal heat. This problem is most evident during mild weather on systems not designed for year-round operation.

Two examples of situations that can be shown in a heat balance study are as follows:

1. As the outdoor air wet-bulb temperature drops, the total heat of the air falls. If a mixture of outdoor and recirculated air is cooled to $55\,°F$ ($13\,°C$) in the summer and the same dry-bulb temperature is supplied by an economizer cycle for interior space cooling in the winter, there will be an entirely different result. As the outdoor wet-bulb temperature drops below $55\,°F$ ($13\,°C$), each unit volume of air introduced does more cooling. To make matters more difficult, this increased cooling is latent cooling, which requires the addition of heat to prevent too low relative humidity, yet this air is intended to do cooling. The extent of this added external heat for free cooling is shown to be very large when plotted on a heat balance analysis at $0\,°F$ ($-18\,°C$) outside.

Figure 3 is typical for many current non-heat-recovery systems. There may be a need for cooling, even at the minimum design temperature, but it can be eliminated by using available internal heat. When this asset is thrown away, and external heat is added, operation is inefficient.

Some systems recover heat from exhaust air to heat the incoming air. When a system operates below its natural breakeven temperature (t_{be}) such as 30 or $16\,°F$ (-1 or $-9\,°C$) shown in Figure 2, the heat recovered from exhaust air is useful and beneficial. This assumes that only the available internal heat is used and that no supplementary heat is added at or above the t_{be}. Above the t_{be}, the internal heat is sufficient without the heat from the exhaust air, which would become excessive heat to be removed by more outdoor air or refrigeration.

If heat is added to create an artificial t_{be} of $-35\,°F$ ($-37\,°C$) as in Figure 3, any recovered heat above $-35\,°F$ ($-37\,°C$) requires an equivalent amount of heat removal elsewhere. If the project were in an area with a minimum design temperature of $0\,°F$ ($-18\,°C$), heat recovery from exhaust air would be a liability at all times for the conditions stipulated in Figure 2. This does not mean that the value of heat recovered from exhaust air should be forgotten. The emphasis should be on recovering heat from exhaust air rather than on adding heat from external sources.

Proprietary equipment with counterflow chiller and condenser circuits, as well as efficient exchange with exhaust or ambient air can often reduce operating costs without the large air volumes required by air economizers.

2. A heat balance shows that insulation, double glazing, and so forth can be extremely valuable on some projects. However, these practices may be undesirable during the heating season, when excess heat must usually be removed from CII buildings. For instance, for minimum winter design temperatures of approximately 35 to $40\,°F$ (2 to $4\,°C$), it is improbable that the interior core of a large office building will ever reach its breakeven temperature. The temperature lag for shutdown periods, such as nights and weekends, at minimum design conditions could never economically justify the added cost of double windows. Therefore, double windows merely require the amount of heat saved to be removed elsewhere.

These are only two of many factors that can be analyzed. A temperature-frequency scale superimposed on a properly constructed heat balance diagram can be another valuable analytical tool. It is possible to further superimpose a kilowatt-hour or steam consumption cost and integrate it with a time frequency scale to predict approximate operating cost with different types of power or fuel. Some computer programs with weather tapes are available for this type of analysis.

GENERAL APPLICATIONS

Applied Heat Pumps and Heat Recovery Chillers

A heat pump extracts heat from a substance (usually air or water) and transfers it to the same or a different substance at a *higher* temperature. In a physical sense, all refrigeration equipment, including air conditioners and chillers using the refrigeration cycle, are heat pumps. However, heat pump refers to equipment that *heats*, while chiller refers to equipment that *cools*. Dual-mode heat pump/chillers both heat and cool, either separately or simultaneously. Chapter 9 includes examples of applied heat pumps in energy-recovery systems that are not included here.

Heat pumps are available that transfer heat from water to air, air to water, water to water, and air to air. Some heat pumps can use waste heat to generate hot water up to $180\,°F$ ($82\,°C$) or higher to meet heating needs in retrofit projects, or up to $220\,°F$ ($104\,°C$) for industrial processes.

Systems

A properly applied heat reclaim system automatically responds to the balanced heat recovery concept. An example is a reciprocating water chiller with a hot gas diverting valve and both a water-cooled and an air-cooled condenser. Hot gas from the compressor is rejected to the water-cooled condenser. This hot water provides internal heat as long as it is needed. At a predetermined temperature, the hot gas is diverted to the air-cooled condenser, rejecting excess heat from the total building system. Larger projects with centrifugal compressors use double condenser chiller units, which are available from many manufacturers. For typical buildings, chillers normally provide hot water for space heating at 105 to $110\,°F$ (41 to $43\,°C$). Heat pump applications up to 160 or 180°F (71 to 82°C) are becoming common.

Chapter 9, which relates the closed-loop application of water-to-air unitary heat pumps, should be carefully reviewed. This system illustrates both the basic heat recovery concept and balanced heat recovery. It simultaneously heats and cools with heat rejected to and extracted from a common two-pipe water loop that is maintained at 60 to 90°F (16 to 32°C). External or stored heat enters the *total* building system only when the loop return temperature drops below 60°F (16°C), i.e., when the internal and/or stored heat has been used up by those units in the heat extraction mode. However, at approximately 90°F (32°C) loop supply temperature, the *total* building system has generated excess heat, which must be either rejected or stored.

Many equipment manufacturers have published application manuals for closed-loop water-to-air heat pump systems. The addition of water storage tanks and supplementary solar heating at a low (60°F or 16°C) water temperature makes this system an attractive, affordable heat-recovery system for various size projects.

Incorporating thermal storage on the water-cooled condenser loop can greatly reduce or even eliminate the need for external heat. The storage provision can range from a simple hot water storage tank to more sophisticated phase change materials, or to a combination high temperature heat pump/storage system. External heat should *not* be added at the storage vessel.

Many buildings that run chillers all or most of the year are reclaiming some of the condenser heat to provide domestic hot water. See Figure 4.

Designers should include a source of external heat for "back-up." The control system should ensure that back-up heat is not injected unless all internal heat has been used. For example, if electric back-up coils are in series with hot water coils fed from a hot water storage tank, they may automatically start when the system restarts after the building temperature has dropped to a "night low limit" setting. An adjustable time delay in the control circuit gives the stored hot water time to warm the building before energizing the electric heat.

This type of heat reclaim system is readily adaptable to smaller projects using a reciprocating chiller with numerous air terminal units or a common multi-zone air handler. The multi-zone air handler should have individual zone duct heating coils and controls arranged to prevent simultaneous heating and cooling in the same zone.

Properly applied heat reclaim systems not only meet all space heating needs, but they also provide hot water required for public showers, food service facilities, and reheat in conjunction with dehumidification cycles.

Heat reclaim chillers or heat pumps should not be used with air-handling systems that have modulating damper economizer control. This "free cooling" concept may result in a higher annual operating cost than a "minimum fresh air" system with a heat reclaim chiller. Careful study will show if the economizer cycle violates the heat balance concept.

Heat reclaim chillers or heat pumps are available in many sizes and configurations. Combinations include (1) centrifugal, reciprocating, and screw compressors; (2) single and double bundle condensers; (3) cascade design for higher temperatures [up to 220°F (104°C)]; and (4) air- or water-cooled or both.

The designer can make the best selection after making both a heating and cooling load calculation and a preliminary economic analysis, and after understanding the building, processes, operating patterns, and available energy sources.

The application of heat reclaim chillers or heat pumps ranges from simple systems with few control modes to complex systems having many control modes and incorporating two-, three-, or four-pipe circulating systems. Certain system concepts using double bundle condensers and single condenser bundles coupled with exterior closed circuit coolers have been patented. These patents may impose some constraints on design considerations, but royalties or other arrangements may be acceptable. Potential infringements should be checked early in the planning stage.

A successful heat-recovery design depends on the performance of the total *system*, not just the chiller or heat pump. A careful and thorough analysis is often time-consuming and requires more design time than a non-recovery system. The *balanced heat recovery* concept should guide all phases of planning and design, and the effects of economic compromise should be studied. There may be little difference between the initial cost (installed cost) of a heat-recovery system and a non-recovery system, especially in larger projects. Also, in view of energy costs, life cycle analysis usually shows dramatic savings when using balanced heat recovery.

MULTIPLE BUILDINGS

A multiple building complex is particularly suited to heat recovery. Variations in occupancy and functions provide an abundance of heat sources and uses. Applying the balanced heat concept to a large multi-building complex can result in large energy savings. Each building captures its own total heat by interchange. Heat rejected from one building could possibly heat adjacent buildings.

INDUSTRIAL HEAT RECOVERY

Unlimited opportunities for heat recovery exist in industrial facilities. Heat exchangers can be effective energy devices in individual plants. Chapter 35 of the 1983 EQUIPMENT Volume covers air-to-air recovery equipment, including guidance for economic evaluation. Chapter 9 of this volume gives further guidance on using applied heat pumps for heat recovery through temperature amplification.

Proximity of the *heat source* to the *heat use* is the most significant constraint when using heat-recovery equipment. The cost of transporting air over great distances can be prohibitive.

In many instances, a piping system coupled with a refrigeration compressor (heat transfer unit) can replace an expensive duct system. Figure 4 illustrates this concept and is intended to stimulate ideas. The primary compressor module can be

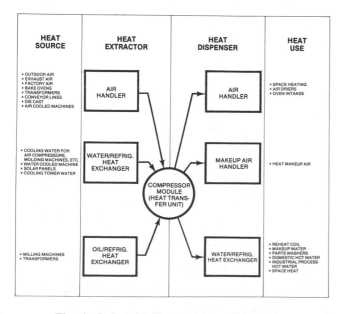

Fig. 4   Industrial Heat Recovery Schematic

reciprocating, centrifugal, or screw. The transfer fluid can be water, glycol, or refrigerant. The final selection and arrangement depends on several factors, including temperature, distances, total load, and configuration of the *heat sources*. For specific industrial processes, the application manuals and documented case histories available from manufacturers of recovery refrigeration machines should be consulted.

A variety of heat exchangers are available for heat recovery, especially for industrial applications. Both parallel and counterflow exchangers may be used, although counterflow is most commonly used for heat recovery. Tube-in-shell exchangers installed so the fluid most likely to cause fouling passes through the tubes are also common. Removable tube heads facilitate mechanical cleaning.

Appropriate materials that resist corrosion and fouling from the fluids should be specified for use. The supplier needs accurate information on fluid properties, flow rates, fouling factors, and pressure drops to furnish reliable and cost-effective exchangers. In some cases, intermediate heat exchangers are needed between a process fluid and the water or brine that passes through the chillers and condensers.

For good operating economy, plate-type heat exchangers permit very close temperature approaches in the range of 2 to 5 °F (1 to 3 °C). These exchangers are made with parallel corrugated titanium, stainless steel, or other appropriate material separated by gaskets and then clamped together. Because the plates can be easily separated for cleaning and inspection, they are commonly used in the food and dairy industry.

Spiral plate heat exchangers have the advantage of enabling close temperature approaches in a compact unit. Thus, they require less space than other exchangers.

Another type of heat exchanger consists of trombone shaped horizontal coils stacked in vertical rows. The coils are cooled by water or other fluids flowing over them. This exchanger requires more space than others, but has the advantage of easy access for cleaning and inspection during continuous operation.

HEAT STORAGE

Heat can be stored for later use in liquids and phase change materials. The demand for stored heat varies with the heating load profile versus the rejected heat available from various sources. The amount of rejected heat seldom matches the requirement; there is either a simultaneous excess or deficiency.

The designer must provide a cost-effective means of (1) accepting rejected heat, (2) storing it for a satisfactory time with minimal thermal losses, and (3) delivering it where needed at the proper temperature, consistent with the requirements for the flow and heat transfer capabilities of the devices demanding the heat. Supplemental heat sources are used to increase the amount of heat and/or boost the temperature of heat from storage. Suitable baffles and piping orientation reduces the need to boost the temperature.

ARI *Standard 410-81* lists entering fluid temperatures of 120 to 250 °F (49 to 121 °C) for air heating coils. Traditionally, 180 °F (82 °C) fluid with a 10 to 20 °F (6 to 11 °C) range has been used in coils for cost-effective air units, though special applications have been found for up to a 40 °F (22 °C) range. Heating coils usually cannot be used for fluids below 120 °F (49 °C), although entering fluids down to 105 °F (41 °C) temperature level have been used in areas where comfort is not critical.

Standard centrifugal units modified for heat recovery can supply 105 °F (41 °C) fluid, whereas special centrifugal units can routinely supply up to 120 °F (49 °C) fluid. Positive displacement compressor R-22 systems can provide up to 125 °F (52 °C) fluid; R-12 heat pump systems can provide up to 160 °F (71 °C) fluid for heating purposes with full heat rejection. Desuperheaters can provide less heat at higher temperatures. Temperatures of 220 °F (104 °C) can be reached by other halocarbon refrigerants. Beyond these temperatures, booster heaters are generally required to avoid exceeding the practical limits on compression equipment and lubricants.

Sensible Heat Storage

Sensible heat storage alternatives include (1) tank storage, (2) aquifer thermal energy storage (ATES), (3) cavern/mine storage, (4) earth storage, (5) lake and pond storage, and (6) rock bed storage.

Heat is stored sensibly by changing the temperature of the heat storage material (usually a liquid and/or a solid). The material's heat content changes without the material changing phase. In the cases of tank, lake, and pond storage, the storage material also serves as the heat transfer fluid. For other storage types, heat is also stored in the containment or matrix materials.

Size and economics dictate which storage is best suited to a given heat-recovery application. Storage size is determined by energy availability and demand profiles, storage losses, and storage temperature. During initial design phases, a storage efficiency is assumed, and preliminary sizing and costs are established. Storage alternatives for the project can then be compared.

Mixing the storage fluid reduces the "quality" of the stored heat because the difference between the usable temperature and storage temperature is increased. As this difference increases, so does the energy required by the heat-recovery heat pump to boost the temperature to a *usable temperature* high enough to heat the space effectively. Mixing is caused by thermal diffusion, buoyancy, and the inertia effect of the jets into or out of the store. In tank storage, thermal stratification of the stored fluid can be promoted by carefully designing the supply/return jets, by placing diaphragms or baffles between the liquid layers, or by segmenting the tank into compartments.

Stratification in heated stored fluids is assisted by the buoyancy differential to prevent temperature blending. Stratification is enhanced by tank height-to-diameter ratios above four and by using baffles and diffusers with proper nozzle orientations.

Heat-storage system designers have a wide choice of fluid and phase change materials, with each providing a specific need. The bibliography gives design parameters for various heat storage media. The temperatures available for consideration depend on the cooling and heating equipment chosen for the specific installation. The basic function of satisfying peak demand requirements at optimum owning and operating costs continues to justify the need for heat-storage systems.

BIBLIOGRAPHY

ASHRAE. 1981. *Industrial Heat Pump Systems.* ASHRAE Seminar, J.M. Calm, Chairman; Chicago, January 28.

ASHRAE. 1984. *Survey of Thermal Energy Installations in the United States and Canada.* ASHRAE, Inc., Atlanta, GA.

Bierwirth, H.C. 1982. Packaged heat pump primer. *Heating-Piping,* July.

Bryson, S. 1980. Warm up with your computer. *Data Processing,* Vol. 22, October, p. 38.

Carrier Corporation. 1977. *Engineering Guide for Reciprocating Chiller Heat Reclaim Systems.* Cat. No. 592-026.

Chemical Engineering Progress. 1979. Waste heat recovery: special report. Vol. 75, December, p. 25-42.

Commercial Remodeling. 1981. Hospital heat recovery system saves a bundle. August.

Curl, R.S. 1978. Cutting waste to reduce energy costs. *Heating-piping,* Vol. 50, August, p. 73-81.

Davis, N. 1982. Waste heat recovery the simple way. *Process Engineering,* Vol. 63, January, p. 51.

Energy Management. 1983. Heating with 55 °F water.

Engineering News. 1979. Industrial heat pump boosts fuel efficiency for users. Vol. 202, January 18.

Engineering News. 1981. Lab cages cast off heat. Vol. 206, June 8, p. 403-6.

Freedman, G.M. 1981. Strategy criterion for transition of a central system from heat recovery to conventional heating and refrigerating. ASHRAE *Journal,* Vol. 23, December, p. 27-30.

Heating/Piping/Air Conditioning. 1978. Heat recovery system saves money, saves problems. Vol. 50, August, p. 203.

Heating/Piping/Air Conditioning. 1980. Processing beer with waste heat. August.

Holland, F.A.; Watson, F.A.; and Devotta, S. 1982. *Thermodynamic Design Data for Heat Pump Systems.* Pergamon Press Ltd., Oxford, England.

Hoyos, G.H., and Muzzy, J.D. 1980. Use low-grade waste heat for refrigeration *Chemical Engineering,* Vol. 87, May 5, p. 140+.

Lane, G.A. 1982. Congruent-melting phase-change heat storage materials. ASHRAE *Transactions,* Vol. 88, Part 11.

LeMay, R.C. 1980. What 300 industrial surveys show. *Energy Engineering,* Vol. 53, April, p. 60.

Lieberman, L. 1981. Heat recovery system heats/cools huge complex. *Specified Engineering,* Vol. 45, March, p. 77-8.

Lloyd, A.S. 1983. Heat pump water heating systems. *Heating/Piping/Air Conditioning,* May.

Manning, E. 1980. Design plant-wide heat recovery. *Hydrocarbon Process,* Vol. 59, November, p. 245-7.

McFarlan, A.I. 1983. Late developments in the field of heat recovery. SAIRAC *Journal of Heating, Air Conditioning & Refrigeration,* Vol. 15, No. 7, July, p. 14+.

Mechanical Engineering. 1980. Waste heat recovery. Vol. 102, August, p. 51.

Merrill, R.F. 1979. Calculating heat-exchanger capacity for a heat recovery system. *Plastics Engineering,* Vol. 33, August, p. 30-2.

Miller, B. 1981. Tuning in to the fact of life: heat from cooling water, *Plastics World,* Vol. 30, September, p. 60-72.

Mueller, J.H. 1980. Energy savings of heat recovery equipment. *Iron & Steel Engineering,* Vol. 57, June, p. 64-6.

Niess, R.C. 1982. Simultaneous heating and cooling through heat recovery. *Specifying Engineer,* Vol. 48, August.

Palnchet, R.J., et.al. 1978. Method picks best heat recovery schemes. *Oil and Gas Journal,* Vol. 76, November 27, p. 51-4.

Plant Engineering. 1980. Computer system controls energy use. Vol. 34, July 10, p. 50.

Ross, J.L. 1983. Rooftop VAV vs water source heat pumps. *Heating/Piping/Air Conditioning,* Vol. 55, May.

Stamm, R.H. 1983. Energy pump. *Heating/Piping/Air Conditioning,* March.

Trelease, S.W. 1980. Water source heat pump evaluation. *Heating/Piping/Air-Conditioning,* October.

Truedsson, G.R. 1980. Industrial waste heat recovery: a case in point. *Energy Engineering,* Vol. 77, February, p. 14-16.

Whitehead, E.R., and Roley, Jr, R.D. 1976. The heat pump—a proven device for heat recovery systems. ASHRAE *Journal,* Vol. 18, May, p. 31.

Woods, D., and Ellis, R.F. 1983. Waste heat recovery system. *Food Processing,* August.

CHAPTER 7

PANEL HEATING AND COOLING SYSTEMS

RADIANT panel systems combine controlled temperature room surfaces with central station air conditioning. The controlled temperature surfaces may be in the floor, walls or ceiling, and the temperature is maintained by circulating water, air or electric resistance. The central station air system can be a basic, one-zone, constant temperature, constant volume system; or it can include some or all of the features of dual-duct, reheat, multizone or variable volume systems. A controlled temperature surface is referred to as a radiant panel if 50% or more of the heat transfer is by radiation to other surfaces seen by the panel. This chapter is concerned with surfaces whose temperatures are controlled and are the primary source of heating and cooling within the conditioned space.

High temperature surface radiant panels over about 300°F (150°C) energized by gas, electricity, or high temperature water are discussed in Chapter 16, "High Intensity Infrared Radiant Heating."

APPLICATIONS

Residences

Embedded pipe coil systems, electric resistance panels and forced warm air panel systems have all been used. The embedded pipe coil system is the most common, using grid coils in the floor slab or copper tubing systems in older plaster ceilings. These systems are well suited to normally constructed residences with normal glass areas. Lightweight hydronic metal panel ceiling systems have been applied to residences. Prefabricated electric panels have also proved advantageous, particularly in add-on rooms.

Office Buildings

The panel system is usually applied as a perimeter system providing heating, cooling, or both. A single-zone central air supply system provides ventilation air, dehumidification and usually some or all of the sensible cooling. Often, tempered air is supplied at a constant volume, and the room thermostat modulates the panel output. In some applications, the panels are arranged for zone control, and the air system is designed to provide individual room control. Water distribution systems using the two- or four-pipe concept may be used. Panel systems are readily adaptable to accommodate most changes in partitioning. Installations can be made where complete flexibility is on a modular basis. Electric panels in lay-in ceilings have been used for full perimeter heating.

Schools

Panels are usually selected for heating and cooling, or for heating only, in all areas except gymnasiums and auditoriums.

For heating only applications, the system may be used with any type of approved ventilation system. The panel system is usually sized to offset the transmission loads plus any reheating of the air required. If the school is air conditioned by a central air system and has perimeter heating panels, a single-zone piping system might be used to control panel heating output, and the room thermostat would modulate the supply temperature or supply volume of air delivered to the room. Heating and cooling panel applications are similar to office buildings. Another advantage of panel heating and cooling for classroom areas is that mechanical equipment noise does not interfere with instructional activities.

Hospitals

The principal application of radiant panel systems over the past 30 years has been for hospital patient rooms. This system is well suited because it: (1) provides a draft-free, thermally stable environment, (2) requires no mechanical equipment or bacteria and virus collectors in the space requiring maintenance and (3) does not take up space within the room. Individual room control is usually by throttling the water flow through the panel. The air supply system is often a 100% outdoor air system, and minimum air quantities delivered to the room are those required for ventilation and exhaust of the toilet room and soiled linen closet. The piping system may have a two- or four-pipe design. Water control valves should be in the corridor outside the patient room so that they can be adjusted or serviced without entering the room. All piping connections above the ceiling should be soldered or welded and thoroughly tested. If cubicle tracks are applied to the ceiling surface, track installation should be coordinated with the radiant ceiling. Security panel ceilings are often used in areas of the hospital occupied by mentally disturbed patients since no equipment is accessible to the occupant for destruction or self-inflicted injury.

Swimming Pools

Panel heating systems are well suited to swimming pools because the partially clothed body emerging from the water is very sensitive to the thermal environment. Floor panel temperatures are restricted so as not to cause foot discomfort. Ceiling panels are generally located around the perimeter of the pool, not directly over the water. Panel surface temperatures are higher to compensate for the increased ceiling height and to produce a greater radiant effect on the partially clothed body. Ceiling panels may be placed over windows to reduce condensation.

Apartment Buildings

For heating, pipe coils are embedded in the masonry slab. The coils must be carefully positioned so as not to overheat one apartment when maintaining desired temperatures in another. The slow response of embedded pipe coils in buildings with large

The preparation of this chapter is assigned to TC 9.1, Large Building Heating and Air Conditioning Systems.

glass areas may prove to be unsatisfactory. Installations for heating and cooling have been made with pipes embedded in a hung plaster ceiling. A separate minimum volume dehumidified air system provides the necessary dehumidification and ventilation for each apartment. In recent years, there has been an increased application of electric resistance elements embedded in the floor or behind a skimcoat of plaster at the ceiling. The electric panels are easy to install and have the advantage of simplified individual room control.

Industrial Applications

Panel systems have found wide application in general space heating for industrial buildings in Europe. However, there has been only a limited application of this type in the Western Hemisphere. With the increasing demand for worker comfort, panel systems should be considered. For example, one special application is an internal combustion engine test cell, where the walls and ceilings are cooled with chilled water. Although the ambient air temperature in the space ranges up to 95 °F (35 °C), the occupants work in relative comfort when 55 °F (13 °C) water is circulated through the ceiling and wall panels.

Other Building Types

Metal panel ceiling systems can be operated as heating systems at elevated water temperatures, and have been used in airport terminals, convention halls, lobbies, museums and especially where large glass areas are involved. Cooling may also be applied. Because radiant energy travels through the air without warming it, ceilings can be installed at any height and remain effective. The highest ceiling installed for a comfort application is 50 ft (15 m) above the floor with a panel surface temperature of approximately 285 °F (141 °C) for heating. The ceiling panels offset the heat loss from a single-glazed all-glass wall.

The high lighting levels in television studios make them well suited to panel systems. The panels are installed for cooling only and are placed above the lighting system to absorb the radiation and convection heat from the lights and normal heat gains from the space. Besides absorbing heat from the space, the panel ceiling also improves the acoustical properties of the studio.

Metal panel ceiling systems are also installed in minimum and medium security jail cells and other areas where disturbed occupants are housed. The ceiling construction is made more rugged by increasing the gauge of the ceiling panels and using security clips so that the ceiling panels cannot be removed. Part of the perforated metal ceiling can be used for air distribution.

EVALUATION

Principal advantages of panel systems are:
1. Comfort levels are better than those of other conditioning systems because radiant loads are treated directly and air motion in the space is at normal ventilation levels.
2. Mechanical equipment is not needed at the outside walls, simplifying the wall, floor and structural systems.
3. All pumps, fans, filters and so forth are centrally located, simplifying maintenance and operation.
4. Cooling and heating can be simultaneous, without central zoning or seasonal changeover, when four-pipe systems are used.
5. Supply air quantities usually do not exceed those required for ventilation and dehumidification.
6. The occupied space has no mechanical equipment requiring maintenance or repair.
7. Draperies and curtains can be installed at the outside wall without interfering with the heating and cooling system.

8. The modular panel concept provides flexibility to meet changes in partitioning.
9. A 100% outdoor air system may be installed with less severe penalties in terms of refrigeration load because of reduced air quantities.
10. No space is required within the air-conditioned room for the mechanical equipment. This feature is especially valuable when compared to other conditioning methods in existing buildings, hospital patient rooms and other applications where space is at a premium, where maximum cleanliness is essential or where dictated by legal requirements.
11. A common central air system can serve both the interior and perimeter zones.
12. Wet surface cooling coils are eliminated from the occupied space, reducing the potential for septic contamination.
13. The panel system can use the automatic sprinkler system piping. (See NFPA 13-1982, Chapter 5, Sections 5-6). The maximum water temperature must not fuse the heads.
14. Radiant cooling and minimum supply air quantities provide a draft-free environment.
15. Noise normally associated with fan coil or induction units is eliminated.

Disadvantages are similar to those listed in Chapter 3, "Air and Water Systems."

SYSTEM CONSIDERATIONS

All bodies with a surface temperature above absolute zero emit rays with wavelengths depending on the body surface temperature. Every facet of the surface emits rays in straight lines at right angles to the facet. When examined under a microscope, the surface of concrete or rough plaster is covered with numerous facets, each giving off radiant energy. Polished steel or similar polished surfaces show no such facets. Thus, a rough surface emits heat rays more efficiently than a polished surface.

The invigorating effect of radiant heat is experienced when the body is exposed to the sun's rays on a cool but sunny day in spring. Some of these rays impinging on the body come directly from the sun and include the whole range of ether waves. Other rays coming from the sun impinge on surrounding objects, where they are increased in wavelength and reradiated to the body as low temperature radiation, producing a comfortable feeling of warmth. Should a cloud pass over the sun, instantly there is a sensation of cold; although in such a short interval, the air temperature does not vary at all.

In searching for the correct conditions compatible with the physiological demands of the human body, no system can be rated as completely satisfactory unless it satisfies the three main factors controlling heat loss from the human body: radiation, convection and evaporation. It is sometimes thought that a radiant heat system is desirable only for certain buildings and only in some climates. However, wherever people live, these three factors of heat loss must be considered. It is as important to provide the correct conditions in very cold climates as it is in moderate climates. Maintaining the correct comfort conditions by low temperature radiation is possible for even the most severe weather conditions.

Panel heating and cooling systems function to provide a comfortable environment by controlling surface temperatures and minimizing excessive air motion within the space. Thermal comfort, as defined by ASHRAE *Standard 55-1981*, is "that condition of mind which expresses satisfaction with the thermal environment." A person is not aware that the environment is being heated or cooled. The mean radiant temperature (MRT) strongly influences the feeling of comfort. When the surface temperature of the outside walls, particularly those with large amounts of glass, begins to deviate excessively from the ambient air temperature of the space, it is increasingly difficult for convective systems to counteract the discomfort resulting from cold or hot walls. Heating and cooling panels neutralize these deficiencies and minimize excessive radiation losses from the body.

Unlike most heat transfer equipment where performance can be measured in specific terms, the performance of the radiant panel is related directly to the structure in which it is located, and an evaluation of this interrelationship is desirable. Research and testing of panel performance have been conducted by various independent researchers and manufacturers. Heat transfer between the radiant panel and the other room surfaces is well established in a boxlike room where the primary heat gains and losses are from the wall, floor or ceiling surfaces. The performance ratings presented in this chapter for radiation and convection can be applied directly to the calculated room heating and cooling loads. Various investigators and manufacturers report increased cooling performance because of solar effects and ceiling-mounted lighting fixtures. This empirical information, which has been developed as a result of field testing, should only be used in consultation with manufacturers experienced in this field.

Fortunately, most building surfaces have high emissivity factors and therefore absorb and reradiate energy from the active panels. This is significant because all surfaces within the room tend to assume an equilibrium temperature resulting in an even thermal comfort condition within the space. In much the same way that light energy from a lighting fixture illuminates the room so that all surfaces can be seen, a warm radiant panel emits energy that is absorbed and reradiated, and all surfaces become warm. Warm ceiling panels are effective for winter heating because they warm the floor and glass surfaces by direct transfer of radiant energy. The surface temperature of well constructed and properly insulated floors will be 2 to 3 °F (1 to 2 °C) above the ambient air temperature, and the inside surface temperature of glass is increased significantly. Inside single-glass surface temperatures 10 to 15 °F (5 to 8 °C) above those indicated in Figure 5 are commonly observed. As a result, downdrafts are minimized to the point where no discomfort is felt. Installation with ceiling heights of 50 ft (15 m) and single glass from floor to ceiling provide satisfactory results.

PSYCHROMETRIC AND SEASONAL CHANGEOVER

Chapter 3, "Air-and-Water Systems," covers year-round radiant panel heating and cooling systems.

HEAT TRANSFER BY PANEL SURFACES

A heated or cooled panel transfers heat to or from a room by convection and radiation. In the following section, the two transfer mechanisms are first considered separately and then combined to facilitate design calculations. See Chapter 3 in the 1985 FUNDAMENTALS Volume for more information.

Radiation Transfer

The basic equation for radiation exchange is the Stefan-Boltzmann equation (Chapter 3 of the 1985 FUNDAMENTALS Volume). This equation may be written as:

$$q_r = \varsigma F_a F_e + [(T_r/100)^4 - (T_p/100)^4] \qquad (1)$$

where

q_r = heat transferred by radiation, Btu/h · ft² (W/m²).
T_r = mean radiant temperature of unheated surface, °R (K).
T_p = average surface temperature of heated panel, °R (K).
F_a = configuration factor (dimensionless).
F_e = emissivity factor (dimensionless).
ς = 0.1713 Btu/h · ft² · °R (5.6697 W/m² · K).

Where several surfaces exposed to the panel have widely differing temperatures, it may be necessary to compute the area-weighted Average Unheated (or Uncooled) Surface Temperature (AUST) exposed to the panels. In confined situations or special applications, such as shipboard berthing spaces with an adjacent hot gas stack, or in situations where the emissivity of the surfaces is significantly different, each surface must be evaluated using the geometrical factors from the charts in Chapter 3 of the 1985 FUNDAMENTALS Volume. Fanger (1972) shows room related angle and shape factors or they may also be developed from algorithms in ASHRAE *Energy Calculations* 1 (1976).

Similarly, when considering spot cooling, it may be necessary to consider the influence of gaseous radiation (Hutchinson 1947). For normal application, these refinements are generally insignificant. The Hottel equation [Eq. (2)] is used frequently. This equation assumes a simple, boxlike room in which there is a uniformly heated ceiling, floor or wall; all other surfaces are at another temperature; and all surfaces are perfectly diffusing.

$$F_c = F_a F_e = \frac{1}{1/F_{1\text{-}2} + [(1/e_1) - 1] + A_1/A_2[(1/e_2) - 1]} \qquad (2)$$

where

F_c = combined configuration and emissivity factor.
$F_{1\text{-}2}$ = view factor = 1.0.
e_1 and e_2 = emissivities of the surfaces.
A_1 and A_2 = areas of the surfaces.

In practice, the emissivity of nonmetallic or painted metal nonreflecting surfaces is about 0.9. When this emissivity is used in Eq. (2), the combined factor is about 0.87 for most rooms. Substituting this value in Eq. (1), the constant becomes about 0.15, and the equation for heating can be rewritten:

$$q_r = 0.15 \left[\left(\frac{t_p + a}{100} \right)^4 - \left[\left(\frac{\text{AUST} + a}{100} \right)^4 \right] \right] \qquad (3)$$

or for cooling:

$$q_r = 0.15 \left[\left(\frac{\text{AUST} + a}{100} \right)^4 - \left(\frac{t_p + a}{100} \right)^4 \right] \qquad (3a)$$

where

q_r = heat transferred by the panel to or from the room surfaces by radiation, Btu/h · ft² (W/m²).
t_p = the average panel surface temperature, °F (°C).
AUST = area-weighted average temperature of the unheated surfaces in the room, °F (°C).
a = 460 (273).

The actual radiation transfer in a room may be somewhat different from that given by Eq. (3) or (3a) because of nonuniform temperatures, irregular room surfaces, variations in emissivity of materials and so forth. It is generally agreed, however, that the equation is accurate to within 10% when used in conventional heating and cooling calculations. Min *et al.* (1956) showed that the value of the constant of Eq. (3) and (3a) was 0.152 in the test room. The design information in this chapter is based on that constant value. Radiation exchange calculated from Eq. (3) is given in Figure 1. The values apply to ceiling, floor or wall panel output.

Radiation removed by a cooling panel for a range of normally encountered temperatures and as calculated from Eq. (3a), which is a variation of Eq. (3), is given in Figure 2. In many specific instances where normal multistory commercial construction and fluorescent lighting are used, the room temperature at the 5-ft (1.5-m) level will closely approach the AUST (Average Uncooled Surface Temperatures). In structures where the main heat gain is through the walls or where incandescent lighting is used, the wall surface temperatures tend to rise considerably above the room air temperature.

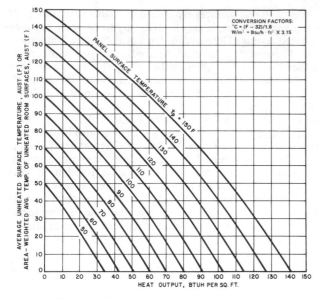

Fig. 1   Heat Transferred by Radiation from a Heated Ceiling, Floor, or Wall Panel

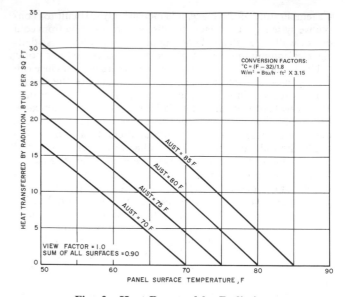

Fig. 2   Heat Removed by Radiation to a Cooled Ceiling or Wall Panel

Convection Transfer

The convection coefficient q_c is defined as the heat transferred by convection in Btu/h·ft²·°F (W/m²·K) difference between air and panel temperatures. Heat transfer convection values are not easily established. Convection in panel systems is usually considered to be natural; that is, air motion is generated by the warming or cooling of the boundary layer of air which starts moving as soon as its temperature rises above or drops below the surrounding air temperature. In practice, however, there are many factors that interfere with or affect natural convection. The configuration of the room and the spaces determines the natural convection. Infiltration, the movement of persons and mechanical ventilating systems can introduce some forced convection that will disturb the natural process.

Parmelee and Huebscher (1947) included the effect of forced convection on heat transfer from panels as an increment to be added to the natural convection coefficient. However, increased heat transfer from forced convection should not be used, because the increments are unpredictable in pattern and performance and do not significantly increase the total capacity of the panel system.

The convection in a panel system is a function of the panel surface temperature and the temperature of the airstream layer directly below the panel. The most consistent results are obtained when the air layer temperature is measured close to the region where the fully developed stream begins, usually 2 to 2.5 in. (50 to 65 mm) below the panels. Very little heat transfer literature describes experiences pertinent to this application, although some pioneer work by Wilkes and Peterson (1938) has been done.

Min et al. (1956) determined natural convection coefficients referred to the center of the space 5 ft (1.5 m) above the floor in a 12 by 24 ft (300 by 600 mm) room. Equations (4) to (9), derived from this research, can be used to calculate heat transfer from panels by natural convection.

Natural convection from a heated ceiling

$$q_c = 0.041 \ (t_p - t_a)^{1.25}/D_e^{0.25} \qquad (4)$$

$$q_c = 0.20 \ (t_p - t_a)^{1.25}/D_e^{0.25} \qquad (4 \ SI)$$

Natural convection from a heated floor or cooled ceiling

$$q_c = 0.39 \ (t_p - t_a)^{1.31}/D_e^{0.08} \qquad (5)$$

$$q_c = 2.42 \ (t_p - t_a)^{1.31}/D_e^{0.08} \qquad (5 \ SI)$$

Natural convection from a heated or cooled wall panel

$$q_c = 0.29 \ (t_p - t_a)^{1.32}/H^{0.05} \qquad (6)$$

$$q_c = 1.87 \ (t_p - t_a)^{1.32}/H^{0.05} \qquad (6 \ SI)$$

where

q_c = heat transfer by natural convection, Btu/h·ft² (W/m²).
t_p = temperature of panel surface, °F (°C).
t_a = temperature of the air, °F (°C).
D_e = equivalent diameter of panel (4 area/perimeter), ft (m).
H = height of wall panel, ft (m).

Schutrum and Humphreys (1954) measured panel performance in furnished test rooms that did not have uniform temperature surfaces and found no variations large enough to be significant in heating practice. Schutrum and Vouris (1954) established that the effect of room size was also usually insignificant. The convection equations can therefore be simplified to:

Natural convection from a heated ceiling

$$q_c = 0.021 \ (t_p - t_a)^{1.25} \qquad (7)$$

$$q_c = 0.138 \ (t_p - t_a)^{1.25} \qquad (7 \ SI)$$

Natural convection from a heated floor or cooled ceiling

$$q_c = 0.32 \ (t_p - t_a)^{1.31} \qquad (8)$$

$$q_c = 2.18 \ (t_p - t_a)^{1.31} \qquad (8 \ SI)$$

Natural convection from a heated or cooled wall panel

$$q_c = 0.26 \ (t_p - t_a)^{1.32} \qquad (9)$$

$$q_c = 1.78 \ (t_p - t_a)^{1.32} \qquad (9 \ SI)$$

Figure 3 shows heat output by natural convection from floor and ceiling heating panels as calculated from Eq. (7) and (8).

Figure 4 shows heat removed by natural convection by cooled ceiling panels as calculated by Eq. (8) and data from Wilkes and Peterson (1938) for specific panel sizes. An additional curve il-

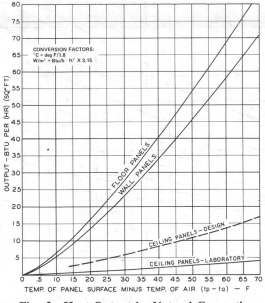

**Fig. 3   Heat Output by Natural Convection
from Floor and Ceiling Heating Panels**

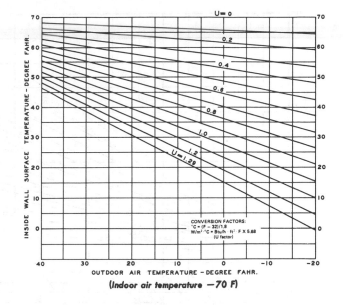

(Indoor air temperature —70 F)

**Fig. 5   Relation of Inside Surface Temperature
to Overall Coefficient of Heat Transfer**

lustrates the effect of forced convection on the latter data. Similar adjustment of the ASHRAE data is inappropriate, but the effects would be similar. For preliminary design 1 Btu/h · ft² · °F (5.7 W/m² · °C) between room design and panel temperature may be used.

Combined Heat Transfer (Radiation and Convection)

The combined heat transfer from a panel to a room can be determined by adding the radiant heat transfer from Figure 1

or 2 to the convective heat transfer from Figure 3 or 4, respectively . Figures 1 and 2 require calculating the AUST in the room. In calculating the AUST, the surface temperature of the inside walls is assumed to be the same as the room air temperature. The surface temperatures of outside walls and exposed floors or ceilings can be obtained from Figure 5 for a 70°F (21°C) room temperature. Figure 6 give corrections for other temperatures.

The combined heat transfer for ceiling and floor panels used to heat rooms in which the air temperature is 70 to 76°F (21 to 24°C) can be read directly from Figures 7 and 8, respectively. These diagrams apply to rooms in which the AUST does not differ greatly from room air temperatures. Tests by Schutrum et al. (1953a, 1953b) show that the temperatures are almost equal.

Figure 9 shows the combined radiation and convection transfer for cooling, as given in Figures 2 and 4. The data in Figure 9 do not include heat gains from sun, lights, people, or equipment: manufacturer's data includes these heat gains.

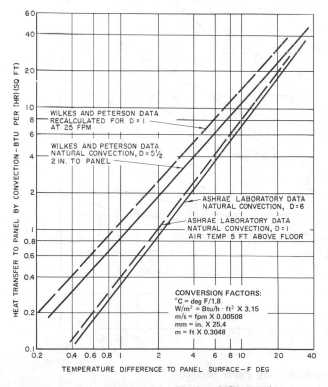

**Fig. 4   Heat Removed by National Convection
to Ceiling Cooling Panels**

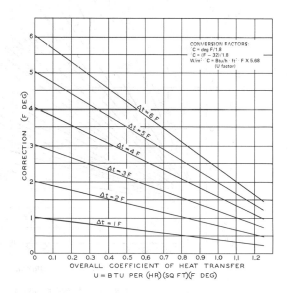

**Fig. 6   Inside Wall Surface Temperature Correction
for Air Temperatures Other Than 70°F (21°C)**

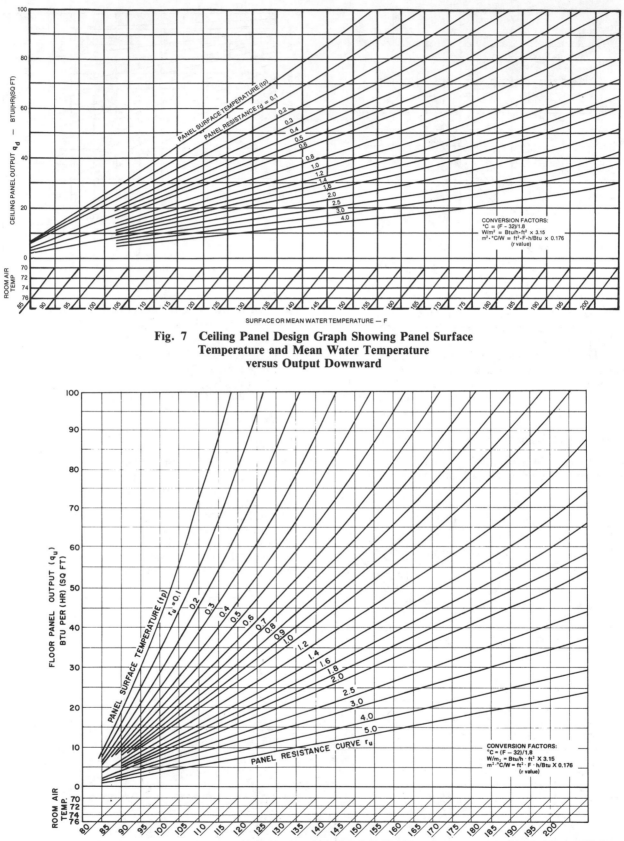

**Fig. 7   Ceiling Panel Design Graph Showing Panel Surface
Temperature and Mean Water Temperature
versus Output Downward**

**Fig. 8   Floor Panel Design Graph Showing Panel Surface
Temperature and Mean Water Temperature
versus Output Upward**

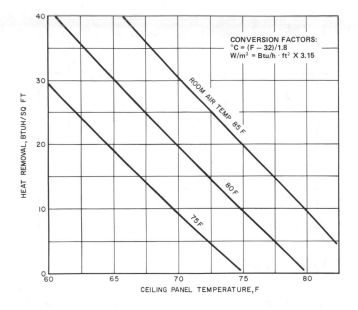

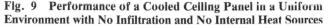

Fig. 9   Performance of a Cooled Ceiling Panel in a Uniform Environment with No Infiltration and No Internal Heat Sources

In suspended ceiling panel systems, heat transfers from the ceiling panel to the floor slab above (heating) and vice versa (cooling). The ceiling panel surface temperature is affected because of heat transfer to or from the panel and the slab by radiation and, to a much smaller extent, by convection. The radiation component can be approximated using Figure 1. The convection component can be estimated from Figure 3 or 4. In this case, the temperature difference is that between the top of the ceiling panel and the midspace of the ceiling. The temperature of the ceiling space should be determined by testing, since it varies with different panel systems. However, much of this heat transfer is nullified when insulation is placed over the ceiling panel, which, for perforated metal panels, also provides acoustical control.

If lighting fixtures are recessed into the suspended ceiling space, radiation from the top of the fixtures raises the overhead slab temperature and transfers heat to the space by convection. This energy is absorbed at the top of the cooled ceiling panels by radiation, as in Figure 2, and by convection, generally in accordance with Eq. (4). The amount the top of the panel absorbs depends on the system. Most manufacturers have information available. Similarly, panels installed under a roof absorb additional heat, depending on configuration and insulation.

HEATING AND COOLING SYSTEMS

Radiant panel systems are similar to other air-water systems in the arrangement of the system components (see Figure 10). Room thermal conditions are maintained primarily by direct transfer of radiant energy, rather than by convection heating and cooling. The room heating and cooling loads are calculated in the conventional manner. Manufacturers' ratings generally are for total performance and can be applied directly to the calculated room load.

Metal ceiling panels are usually integrated into a system that heats and cools. In such a system, a source of dehumidified ventilation air is required in summer, and the system is classed as one of the combination air-water systems. Also, various amounts of forced air are supplied year-round. When metal panels are applied for heating purposes only, a ventilation system may or may not be required, depending on local codes.

The ceiling panel systems commonly used today are an outgrowth of the perforated metal, suspended, acoustical ceiling. These radiant ceiling systems are usually designed into buildings where the features of the suspended acoustical ceiling can be combined with panel heating and cooling. The panels can be designed as small units to fit the building module and provide extensive flexibility for zoning and control; or the panels can be arranged as large continuous areas for maximum economy.

Metal ceiling panels can be perforated so that the ceiling becomes sound absorbent when acoustical material is installed on the back of the panels. The acoustical blanket is also required for thermal reasons, so that the reverse loss or upward flow of heat from the metal ceiling panels is minimized.

Some ceiling installations require active panels to cover only a portion of the room, and compatible matching acoustical panels are selected for the remaining ceiling area.

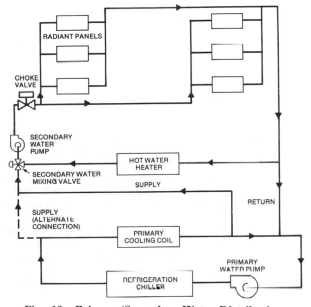

Fig. 10   Primary/Secondary Water Distribution System with Mixing Control

GENERAL DESIGN CONSIDERATIONS

Metal ceiling panels can be used with two- and four-pipe distribution systems. It is common to design for a 20°F (11°C) temperature drop for heating across a given grid and a 5°F (2.8°C) rise for cooling, but larger temperature differentials may be used, if applicable.

Panel design requires determining panel area, panel type, supply water temperature, water flow rate and panel arrangement. Panel performance is directly related to room conditions. Airside design also must be established. Heating and cooling loads may be calculated by procedures covered in Chapters 22 through 27 in the 1985 FUNDAMENTALS Volume. The procedure is as follows:

1. Determine room design dry-bulb temperature, relative humidity and dewpoint.
2. Calculate room sensible and latent heat gains.
3. Select mean water temperature for cooling.
4. Establish minimum supply air quantity.
5. Calculate latent cooling available from the air.
6. Calculate sensible cooling available from the air.
7. Determine panel cooling load.

8. Determine panel area for cooling.
9. Calculate room heat loss.
10. Select mean water temperature for heating.
11. Determine panel area for heating.
12. Determine water flow rate and pressure drop.
13. Design the panel arrangement.

The application, design, and installation of panel systems have certain requirements and techniques that should be recognized:

1. As with any hydronic system, look closely at the piping system design. Piping should be designed to assure that water of the proper temperature and in sufficient quantity will be available to every grid or coil at all times. Reverse-return systems should be considered to minimize balancing problems.

2. The apparatus dew point of the cooling coils in the air distributing system should be designed for full capacity plus a 10 to 15% safety factor, because most operational problems occur when the supply air is short on dehumidification capacity.

$$SHR = \frac{RSH - PC}{RTH} \qquad (10)$$

where

   SHR = sensible heat ratio
   RSH = room sensible heat
     PC = panel cooling
   RTH = room total heat

3. Individual ceiling panels can be connected for parallel flow using headers, or for sinuous or serpentine flow. To avoid flow irregularities within a header-type grid, the water channel or lateral length should be greater than the header length. If the laterals in a header grid are forced to run in a short direction, this problem can be solved by using a combination series-parallel arrangement.

4. Noises from entrained air, high velocity or high pressure drop devices or from pump and pipe vibrations must be avoided. Water velocities should be high enough to prevent separated air from accumulating and causing air binding. Where possible, avoid automatic air venting devices over ceilings of occupied spaces.

5. Design piping systems to accept thermal expansion adequately. Do not allow forces from piping expansion to be transmitted to ceiling panels. Thermal expansion of the ceiling panels must be considered.

6. In circulating water systems, both steel and copper pipe or tube are used widely in ceiling, wall or floor panel construction. Some types of plastic pipe also may be suitable where codes permit. Where coils are embedded in concrete or plaster, no threaded joints should be used for either pipe coils or mains. Steel pipe should be the all-welded type. Copper tubing should be soft-drawn coils. Fittings and connections should be minimized. Changes in direction should be made by bending. Solder-joint fittings for copper tube should be used with a medium temperature solder of 95% tin, 5% antimony or capillary brazing alloys. All piping should be subjected to a hydrostatic test of at least three times the working pressure, but not less than 150 psig (1100 kPa). Maintain adequate pressure in piping while pouring concrete.

7. Locate ceiling panels adjacent to the outside wall and as close as possible to the areas of maximum load. The panel area within 3 ft (1 m) of the outside wall should have a heating capacity equal to or greater than 50% of the wall transmission load.

8. Ceiling system designs based on passing return air through the panels into the plenum space above the ceiling are not recommended, because much of the panel heat transfer is lost to the return air system.

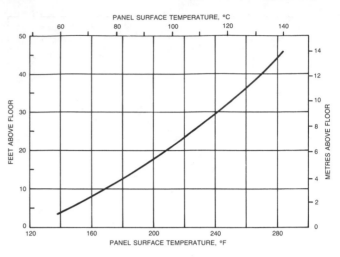

Fig. 11 Suggested Design Ceiling Surface Temperatures at Various Ceiling Heights

9. Allow sufficient space above the ceiling for installation and connection of the piping that forms the radiant panel ceiling.

10. Placing the thermostat on a side wall where it can see the outside wall and the warm ceiling should be considered. The normal thermostat cover reacts to the warm ceiling panel, and the radiant effect of the ceiling on the cover tends to alter the control point so that the thermostat controls 2 to 3 °F (1 to 2 °C) lower when the outdoor temperature is a minimum and the ceiling temperature is a maximum. Experience indicates that radiantly heated rooms are more comfortable under these conditions than when the thermostat is located on a back wall.

11. When selecting heating design temperatures for a ceiling panel surface, mean water temperature or watt density of an electric panel, the design parameters are:

   a. Excessively high temperatures over the occupied zone will cause the occupant to experience a "hot head effect."

   b. Temperatures that are too low can result in an oversized, uneconomical panel and a feeling of coolness at the outside wall.

   c. The technique in item 7 above should be given priority.

   d. With normal ceiling heights of 8 to 9 ft (2.4 to 2.7 m), panels less than 2 ft (0.6 m) wide at the outside wall can be designed for 235 F (113 °C) surface temperature. If panels extend beyond 2 ft (0.6 m) into the room, the panel surface temperature should be limited to the values as given in Figure 11. The surface temperature of concrete or plaster panels is limited by construction.

12. If throttling valve control is used, either the end of the main should have a fixed bypass, or the last one or two rooms on the mains should have a bypass valve to maintain water flow in the main. Thus, when a throttling valve modulates, there will be a rapid response.

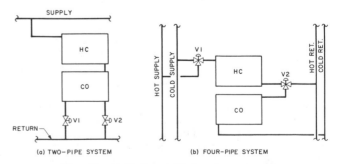

Fig. 12 Split Panel Piping Arrangement for Two-Pipe and Four-Pipe Systems

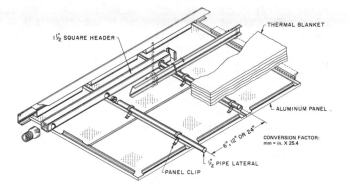

Fig. 13 Metal Ceiling Panels Attached to Pipe Laterals

13. When the panel chilled water system is started, the circulating water temperature should be maintained at room temperature until the air system is completely balanced, the dehumidification equipment is operating properly and building humidity is at design value.

14. When the panel area for cooling is greater than the area required for heating, a two-panel arrangement (Figure 12) can be used. Panel HC (heating and cooling) is supplied with hot or chilled water year-round. When chilled water is used, the controls function activate panel CO (cooling only), and both panels are used for cooling.

15. To prevent condensation on the room side of cooling panels, the panel water supply temperature should be maintained at least 1°F (0.6°C) above the room design dew point temperature. This minimum difference is recommended to allow for the normal drift of temperature controls for the water and air systems, and also to provide a factor of safety for temporary increase in space humidity.

16. Selection of summer design room dew point below 50°F (10°C) generally is not economical.

17. The most frequently applied method of dehumidification utilizes cooling coils. If the main cooling coil is six rows or more, the dew point of the air leaving will approach the temperature of the water leaving. The cooling water leaving the dehumidifier can then be used for the panel water circuit.

18. Several chemical dehumidification methods are available to control latent and sensible loads separately. In one application, cooling tower water is used to remove heat from the

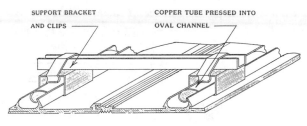

Fig. 15 Extruded Aluminum Panel with Integral Copper Tube

chemical drying process, and additional sensible cooling is necessary to cool the dehumidified air to the required system supply air temperature.

19. When chemical dehumidification is used, hygroscopic chemical-type dew point controllers are required at the central apparatus and at various zones to monitor dehumidification.

20. When cooled ceiling panels are used with a variable air volume (VAV) system, the air supply rate should be near maximum volume to assure adequate dehumidification before the cooling ceiling panels are activated.

Other factors to consider when using panel systems are:

1. Early evaluation is necessary to use the panel system to full advantage in optimizing the physical building design.

2. Recessed lighting fixtures, air diffusers, hung ceilings and other ceiling devices must be selected on the basis of providing the maximum ceiling area possible for use as radiant panels.

3. The air-side design must be able to maintain humidity levels at or below design conditions at all times to eliminate any possibility of condensation on the panels. This becomes more critical if space dry- and wet-bulb temperatures are allowed to drift as an energy conservation measure, or if duty cycling of the fans is used.

4. Cooling panels should not be used in or adjacent to high humidity areas.

5. Thermal expansion of the ceiling and other devices in or adjacent to the ceiling should be anticipated.

6. Operable sash should be designed to discourage unauthorized operation.

COMPONENTS

Three types of metal ceiling systems are available. The first consists of lightweight aluminum panels, usually 12 by 24 in. (300 by 600 mm), attached in the field to 0.5-in. (15-mm) galvanized pipe coils.

Figure 13 illustrates a metal ceiling panel system that uses 0.5-in. (15-mm) pipe laterals, on either 6-, 12- or 24-in. (150-, 300- or 600-mm) centers, hydraulically connected in a sinuous or parallel flow welded system. Aluminum ceiling panels are clipped to these pipe laterals, acting as a heating panel when warm water is flowing, or as a cooling panel when chilled water is flowing.

The second consists of a copper coil metallurgically bonded to the aluminum face sheet to form a modular panel. Modular panels are available in sizes up to about 36 by 60 in. (900 by 1525 mm) and are held in position by various types of ceiling suspension systems. Figure 14 illustrates a metal panel ceiling system using copper tubing, metallurgically bonded to an aluminum panel.

The third type is an aluminum extrusion face sheet with a copper tube pressed into an oval channel on the back of the face sheet. Extruded panels can be manufactured in almost any shape and size. Extruded aluminum-type panels are often used as long-narrow panels at the outside wall and are independent of the ceiling system. Panels 15 or 20 in. (380 or 510 mm) wide usually

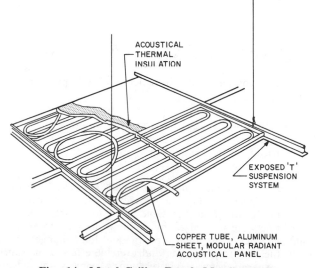

Fig. 14 Metal Ceiling Panels Metallurgically Bonded to Copper Tubing

Table 1   Thermal Resistance of Metal Ceiling Panels

Type of Panel	Thermal Resistance to Heat Flow ft² · °F · h/Btu (m² · K/w)		
	Spacing—Inches (mm)		

STEEL PIPE — PAN EDGE HELD AGAINST PIPE BY SPRING CLIP — ALUMINUM PAN 0.032 IN. THICK

	3 (75)	6 (150)	12 (300)
(steel pipe / aluminum pan)	—	0.31[a] (0.05)	0.61[a] (0.11)

TUBE SPACING — COPPER TUBE SOLDERED TO 0.040 IN. THICK ALUMINUM SHEET

	4 (100)		8 (200)
(copper tube soldered)	0.071[a] (0.01)		0.15[a] (0.03)

TUBE SPACING — COPPER TUBE PRESSED INTO ALUMINUM EXTRUSION, 0.050 IN. THICK

	5 (125)
(copper tube pressed)	0.071[a] (0.01)

[a]Manufacturer's data.

satisfy the heating requirements of a typical office building. Lengths up to 20 ft (6.1 m) are available. Figure 15 illustrates a metal panel using a copper tube pressed into an aluminum extrusion.

Hydronic ceiling panels have a low thermal resistance and respond quickly to changes in space conditions. Table 1 shows thermal resistance values for various ceiling constructions.

COOLING CONTROLS

Controlling the panel water circuit temperature by mixing, heat exchange, or using the water leaving the dehumidifier is typical. Other considerations are listed in the section, "General Design Conditions." It is imperative to dry out the building space before starting the panel water system, particularly after extended down periods, such as weekends. Such delayed starting action can be controlled manually or by device.

Panel cooling systems require the following basic areas of temperature control: (1) exterior zones, (2) areas under exposed roofs to compensate for transmission and solar loads, and (3) control of each typical interior zone to compensate for internal loads. For optimum results, each extrior corner zone and similarly-loaded face zone should be treated as a separate subzone. Panel cooling systems may also be zoned to control temperature in individual exterior offices, particularly in applications where there is a high lighting load, or for corner rooms with large glass areas on both walls.

The temperature control of the interior air and panel water supply should not be functions of the outdoor weather. The normal thermostat drift is usually adequate compensation for the slightly lower temperatures desirable during winter weather. This drift should be limited to result in a room temperature change of not more than 1.5°F (0.8°C). Control of the interior zones is best accomplished by devices that reflect the actual presence of the internal load elements. Frequently, time clocks and current sensing devices are used on lighting feeders.

Because air quantities are generally small, constant volume supply air systems should be used. With the apparatus arrang-

ed to supply air of appropriate apparatus dew point at all times, it is possible to avoid compromising indoor conditions with a panel cooling system throughout the year. As with all systems, to prevent condensation on window surfaces, the supply air dew point should be reduced during extremely cold weather according to the type of glazing installed.

Chapter 51 has general information on automatic controls. The section, "Panel Heating Systems" covers heating control.

DISTRIBUTION AND LAYOUT

Distribution

Chapter 3, "Air-and-Water Systems," and chapters covering hydronic systems apply to radiant panels.

Layout

Layout and design of metal radiant ceiling panels for heating and cooling begins early in the job. (See "Design Considerations.") The type of ceiling chosen influences the radiant design and conversely, thermal considerations may dictate what ceiling type to be used. Heating/cooling ceilings are usually the modular type and are used in all metal ceilings or in metal radiant panel plus acoustic tile ceilings. The ceiling type or location and size of ceiling penetrations may not be known. A reasonable design approach is to assume 80% of the floor area will be available for radiant panels. Heating panels should be located adjacent to the outside wall. Cooling panels may be positioned to suit other elements in the ceiling. In applications with normal ceiling heights, heating panels that exceed 160°F (71°C) should not be located over the occupied area. In hospital applications, valves should be located in the corridor outside patient rooms.

EVALUATION

Metal radiant-acoustic ceilings provide heating, cooling, sound absorption, insulation, and unrestricted access to the plenum space. They are easily maintained, can be repainted to look new, and have a life expectancy in excess of 30 years. The system is quiet, comfortable, draft-free, easy to control, and responds quickly. The system is a basic air-and-water system, and, as such, the design and application techniques are familiar. First costs are competitive with other systems and a life cycle cost analysis often shows that the long life of the equipment makes it the lowest cost in the long term. The system has been used in hospitals, schools, office buildings, colleges, airports, and exposition facilities.

PANEL HEATING SYSTEMS

The most common forms of panels applied in panel heating systems are as follows:

1. Metal ceiling panels
2. Embedded piping in ceilings, walls or floors
3. Air-heated floors
4. Electrically heated ceilings or floors
5. Electric ceiling panels

Residential heating applications usually consist of pipe coils or electric elements embedded in masonry floors or plaster ceilings. This construction is suitable where loads are stable and solar effects are minimized by building design. However, in buildings where glass areas are large and load changes occur faster, the slow response, lag and override effect of masonry panels are unsatisfactory. Lightweight metal panel ceiling systems respond quickly to load changes.

Warm air and electric heating elements are two design concepts used in systems influenced by local factors. The warm air system has a special cavity construction where air is supplied to a cavity behind or under the panel surface. The air leaves the cavity through a normal diffuser arrangement and is supplied to the room. Generally, these systems are used as floor radiant panels in schools and in floors subject to extreme cold, such as in an overhang. Cold outdoor temperatures and heating medium temperatures must be analyzed with regard to potential damage to the building construction. Electric heating elements embedded in the floor or ceiling construction and unitized electric ceiling panels are used in various applications to provide both full heating and spot heating of the space.

Radiant panels are often located in the ceiling because it is exposed to all other surfaces and objects in the room. It is not likely to be covered, as are the floors, and higher surface temperatures can be used. Also, its smaller mass enables it to respond more quickly to load changes.

DESIGN CONSIDERATIONS

Metal Ceiling Panels

Metal radiant panels can be used with any of the all-air cooling systems described in Chapter 2. Chapters 22 through 25 of the 1985 FUNDAMENTALS Volume describe how to calculate heating loads. The current use of double glazing and heavy insulation in outside walls has reduced transmission heat losses enough to make infiltration and reheat a major concern.

Additional design considerations are as follows:

1. Perimeter radiant heating panels, not extending more than 2 ft (0.6 m) into the room, may operate at higher temperatures, as described under "Design Considerations" in the Heating and Cooling Systems section.
2. Electric panel watt densities exceeding 95 W/ft² (1 kW/m²) cause local surface temperatures of 250°F (120°C). This high temperature is not recommended for comfort applications with normal ceiling heights.
3. Hydronic panels operate efficiently at low temperatures and are suitable for condenser water heat reclaim systems.
4. The National Electrical Code and Underwriter Laboratories listing requirements should be followed in the layout and arrangement of electric radiant panels.
5. The section on "Heating and Cooling Systems" gives additional information.

Embedded Piping in Ceilings, Walls, and Floors

Panel Thermal Resistance. The thermal resistance to heat flow may vary considerably among panel systems, depending on the type of bond between the water tube and the panel material. This bond may change with time, corrosion between lightly touching surfaces, method of maintaining contact and other factors. The actual thermal resistance of any proposed system should be verified by testing whenever practical. Tables 2 through 5 show some typical values for thermal resistance factors for various types of floor and ceiling panels.

The thermal resistance factors shown are for ferrous and nonferrous pipe and tube. Recently, the use of non-metallic, plastic tubing has increased. Long lengths are available in coils up to 1000 ft (305 m), which simplify installation. Resistance and performance data should be obtained from the manufacturer.

Effect of Floor Coverings. Floor coverings can have a pronounced effect on the performance of a floor heating panel system. The added thermal resistance of the floor covering reduces upward heat flow and increases the heat flow to the underside of the slab. To maintain a given upward heat flow after

a floor covering has been added, the temperature of the heating medium must be increased. Data on the thermal resistance of common floor coverings are given in Table 5.

Where covered and bare floor panels exist in the same system, it may be possible to maintain a high enough water temperature to satisfy the covered panels and balance the system by throttling the flow to the bare slabs. In some instances, however, the increased water temperature required when carpeting is applied over floor panels makes it impossible to balance floor panel systems in which only some rooms have carpeting, unless the pipe is arranged to permit zoning using more than one water temperature.

Panel Heat Losses. Heat transferred from the upper surface of ceiling panels, the back surface of wall panels, the underside of floor panels or the edges of any panel is considered a panel heat loss. Panel heat losses are part of the building heat loss if the heat is transferred outside of the building. If the heat is transferred to another heated space, the panel loss is a source of heat for the space and is not a part of the building heat loss. In either case, the magnitude of panel loss should be determined.

Panel heat loss to space outside the room should be kept to a reasonable amount by insulation. Panel heat loss to heated spaces may require reduction by insulation if the amount of heat transferred is excessive or if objectionable temperatures develop. For example, a floor panel may overheat the basement below and a ceiling panel may cause the temperature of a floor surface above it to be too high for comfort unless it is properly insulated.

The heat loss from most panels can be calculated by using the coefficients given in Chapter 20 of the 1985 FUNDAMENTALS Volume. These coefficients should not be used to determine the downward heat loss from panels built on grade because the heat flow from them is not uniform (Sartain and Harris 1956, ASHAE 1957). The heat loss from panels built on grade can be estimated from Figure 16.

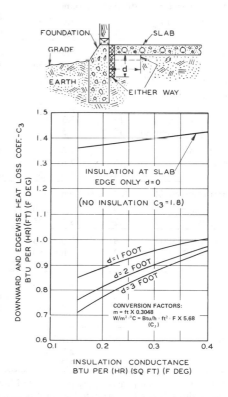

Fig. 16 Downward and Edgewise Heat Loss Coefficient for Concrete Floor Slabs on Grade

Table 2 Thermal Resistance of Bare Concrete Floor Panels (Heating)

Panel Construction	Spacing, in.	Heat Flow Ratio, q_u/q_d or q_u/q_{de}								Spacing, mm	Heat Flow Ratio, q_u/q_d or q_u/q_{de}							
		1		3		5		10			1		3		5		10	
		Panel Thermal Resistance, ft²·°F·h/Btu									Panel Thermal Resistance, m²·K/W							
		Up	Down	Up	Down	Up	Down	Up	Down		Up	Down	Up	Down	Up	Down	Up	Down
4-in. (100-m) Concrete Slab with 2-in. (50-mm) Cover																		
0.5-in. (15-mm) (nom.) nonferrous tube	9	0.57	0.52	0.46	0.84	0.43	1.17	0.42	1.97	230	0.10	0.09	0.08	0.15	0.08	0.21	0.07	0.34
	12	0.73	0.68	0.58	1.16	0.54	1.65	0.51	2.86	300	0.13	0.12	0.10	0.20	0.10	0.29	0.09	0.50
0.5-in. (15-mm) (nom.) ferrous or 0.75 in. (20-mm) (nominal) nonferrous tube	9	0.49	0.42	0.41	0.66	0.39	0.90	0.38	1.80	230	0.09	0.07	0.07	0.12	0.07	0.16	0.07	0.32
	12	0.63	0.55	0.50	0.93	0.48	1.30	0.46	2.35	300	0.11	0.10	0.09	0.16	0.08	0.23	0.08	0.41
6-in. (150-mm) Concrete Slab with 2-in. (50-mm) Cover																		
0.5-in. (15-mm) (nom.) nonferrous tube	9	0.59	0.70	0.47	1.05	0.45	1.39	0.43	2.25	230	0.10	0.12	0.08	0.18	0.08	0.24	0.08	0.40
	12	0.78	0.90	0.60	1.40	0.56	1.97	0.54	3.21	300	0.14	0.16	0.11	0.25	0.10	0.35	0.10	0.56
0.75-in. (20-mm) (nom.) nonferrous pipe	9	0.51	0.61	0.43	0.87	0.41	1.13	0.40	1.78	230	0.09	0.11	0.08	0.15	0.07	0.20	0.07	0.31
	12	0.68	0.78	0.54	1.23	0.51	1.63	0.49	2.61	300	0.12	0.14	0.10	0.22	0.09	0.29	0.09	0.46
0.75-in. (20-mm) (nom.) ferrous pipe	9	0.47	0.55	0.40	0.77	0.39	0.98	0.38	1.50	230	0.08	0.10	0.07	0.14	0.07	0.17	0.07	0.26
	12	0.63	0.71	0.50	1.07	0.48	1.44	0.46	2.36	300	0.11	0.12	0.09	0.19	0.08	0.20	0.08	0.42
1-in. (25-mm) (nom.) nonferrous tube or or ferrous pipe	12	0.59	0.66	0.48	0.98	0.46	1.30	0.45	2.11	300	0.10	0.12	0.08	0.17	0.08	0.23	0.08	0.37
	15	0.73	0.83	0.57	1.21	0.54	1.73	0.51	2.74	380	0.13	0.15	0.10	0.21	0.10	0.30	0.09	0.48

q_u = upward heat flow from panel
q_d = downward heat flow from panel
q_{de} = apportioned downward and edgewise heat flow from panel

Table 3 Thermal Resistance of Concrete Ceiling Panels (Heating)

Panel Construction	Spacing, in.	Heat Flow Ratio[a], q_u/q_d						Spacing, mm	Heat Flow Ratio, q_u/q_d					
		0		0.5		1.0			0		0.5		1.0	
		Panel Thermal Resistance, ft²·°F·h/Btu							Panel Thermal Resistance, m²·K/W					
		Up	Down	Up	Down	Up	Down		Up	Down	Up	Down	Up	Down
6-in. (150-mm) Concrete Slab with 1-in. (25-mm) Cover													
0.5-in. (15-mm) (nominal) nonferrous tube	9	3.6	0.30	0.9	0.35	0.7	0.45	230	0.63	0.05	0.16	0.06	0.12	0.08
	12	5.1	0.35	1.1	0.45	0.9	0.55	300	0.90	0.06	0.19	0.08	0.16	0.10
0.5-in. (15-mm) (nom.) ferrous or 0.75-in. (20-mm) (nominal) nonferrous tube	9	2.6	0.25	0.7	0.30	0.6	0.35	230	0.46	0.04	0.12	0.05	0.11	0.06
	12	4.0	0.30	0.9	0.40	0.8	0.50	300	0.70	0.05	0.16	0.07	0.14	0.08
0.75-in. (20-mm) (nominal) ferrous pipe or 0.75-in. (20-mm) (nom.) nonferrous tube	9	2.1	0.20	0.6	0.25	0.6	0.30	230	0.37	0.04	0.11	0.04	0.11	0.05
	12	3.3	0.30	0.8	0.35	0.7	0.40	300	0.58	0.05	0.14	0.06	0.12	0.07
	15	4.5	0.35	1.0	0.45	0.8	0.55	380	0.79	0.06	0.18	0.08	0.14	0.10
1-in. (25-mm) (nom.) ferrous pipe	9	1.6	0.20	0.5	0.25	0.5	0.25	230	0.28	0.04	0.09	0.04	0.09	0.04
	12	2.6	0.25	0.7	0.30	0.9	0.40	300	0.46	0.04	0.12	0.05	0.16	0.07
	15	3.6	0.30	0.9	0.40	0.7	0.45	380	0.63	0.05	0.16	0.07	0.12	0.08
8-in. (200-mm) Concrete Slab with 1-in. (25-mm) Cover													
0.5-in. (15-mm) (nom.) nonferrous tube	9	3.6	0.30	1.0	0.35	0.8	0.40	230	0.63	0.05	0.18	0.06	0.14	0.07
	12	5.2	0.35	1.2	0.45	1.0	0.55	300	0.92	0.06	0.21	0.08	0.18	0.10
0.5-in. (15-mm) (nominal) ferrous pipe or 0.75-in. (20-mm) (nom.) non-ferrous tube	9	2.9	0.25	0.9	0.30	0.8	0.35	230	0.51	0.04	0.16	0.05	0.14	0.06
	12	4.0	0.30	1.1	0.40	0.9	0.45	300	0.70	0.05	0.19	0.07	0.16	0.08
0.75-in. (20-mm) (nom.) ferrous pipe or 1-in. (25-mm) (nom.) nonferrous tube	9	2.2	0.20	0.8	0.30	0.7	0.30	230	0.39	0.04	0.14	0.05	0.12	0.05
	12	3.3	0.30	1.0	0.35	0.8	0.40	300	0.58	0.05	0.18	0.06	0.14	0.07
	15	4.3	0.35	1.1	0.40	0.9	0.50	380	0.76	0.06	0.19	0.07	0.16	0.09
1-in. (25-mm) (nom.) ferrous pipe	9	1.7	0.20	0.7	0.25	0.7	0.25	230	0.30	0.04	0.12	0.04	0.12	0.04
	12	2.7	0.25	0.9	0.30	0.8	0.35	300	0.48	0.04	0.16	0.05	0.14	0.06
	15	3.7	0.30	1.0	0.40	0.9	0.45	380	0.65	0.05	0.18	0.07	0.16	0.08

q_u = upward heat flow from panel q_d = downward heat flow from panel
[a]Any ceiling panel also acts as a floor panel to the extent of its upward heat flow. If the upward heat flow is high and the space above is occupied, check floor surface temperature for possible foot discomfort. Also check effect on heating requirements of the space above. It is not good practice to have the major portion of the upper room's heating requirements supplied by the upward heat flow of a ceiling panel below.

Table 4   Thermal Resistance of Plaster Ceiling Panels
(Heating or Cooling)

Panel Construction

Standard gypsum plaster (three coats) with 3/8-in. (10-mm) nominal nonferrous tube or 1/2-in. (15-mm) nominal ferrous pipe above metal lath tied at 8-in. (200-mm) intervals with good tube imbedment, or 3/8-in. (10-mm) nominal nonferrous tube below metal or gypsum lath.

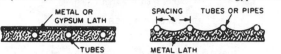

Spacing, in. (mm)	Thermal Resistance to Downward Heat Flow, r_d, ft$^2 \cdot$ °F $\cdot$ h/Btu (m$^2 \cdot$ K/W)					
	Heat Flow Ratio, q_u/q_d					
	0	0.2	0.4	0.6	0.8	1.0
4.5	0.30	0.34	0.38	0.42	0.46	0.50
(115)	(0.05)	(0.06)	(0.07)	(0.07)	(0.08)	(0.09)
6	0.45	0.51	0.57	0.63	0.69	0.75
(150)	(0.08)	(0.09)	(0.10)	(0.11)	(0.12)	(0.13)
9	0.75	0.85	0.95	1.05	1.15	1.25
(230)	(0.13)	(0.15)	(0.17)	(0.18)	(0.20)	(0.22)
16	1.15	1.29	1.43	1.57	1.71	1.85
(400)	(0.20)	(0.23)	(0.25)	(0.28)	(0.30)	(0.33)

NOTES: Any ceiling panel also acts as a floor panel to the extent of its upward heat flow. If the upward heat flow is high and the space above is occupied, check floor surface temperature for possible foot discomfort (see Schutrum *et al.* 1953). Also check effect on heating requirements of the space above. It is not good practice to have the major portion of the upper room's heating requirements supplied by the upward heat flow of a ceiling panel below.

Recommended maximum inlet water temperature (t_{max}) = 140 °F (60 °C).

Table 5   Thermal Resistance of Floor Coverings

Description	Resistance, r_{uc},	
	ft$^2 \cdot$ °F $\cdot$ h/Btu	m$^2 \cdot$ K/W
Bare concrete, no covering	0.00	0.00
Asphalt tile	0.05	0.01
Rubber tile	0.05	0.01
Light carpet	0.6	0.11
Light carpet with rubber pad	1.0	0.18
Light carpet with light pad	1.4	0.25
Light carpet with heavy pad	1.7	0.30
Heavy carpet	0.8	0.14
Heavy carpet with rubber pad	1.2	0.21
Heavy carpet with light pad	1.6	0.28
Heavy carpet with heavy pad	1.9	0.33

Electrically Heated Ceilings

Several different forms of electric resistance units are available for heating interior room surfaces. These include: (1) electric heating cables that may be embedded in concrete or plaster or laminated in drywall ceiling construction, (2) prefabricated electric heating panels to be attached to room surfaces and (3) electrically heated fabrics or other materials for application to, or incorporation into, finished room surfaces.

The spacing between adjacent runs of heating cable can be determined using Eq. (11):

$$s = 12 \, A_n/C \qquad (11)$$

$$s = 1000 \, A_n/C \qquad (11 \text{ SI})$$

where

s = cable spacing, in. (mm).
A_n = net panel heated area, ft^2 (m^2).
C = length of cable, ft (m).

For cable having a watt density of 2.75 W/ft (9 W/m), the minimum permissible spacing is 1.5 in. (40 mm) between adjacent runs. Some manufacturers recommend a minimum spacing of 2 in. (50 mm) for drywall construction.

Net panel area, A_n, in Eq. (11) is the net ceiling area available after deducting the area covered by the nonheating border, lighting fixtures, cabinets and other ceiling obstructions. Since, for simplicity, Eq. (11) contains a slight safety factor, small lighting fixtures are usually ignored in determining net ceiling area.

The 2.5-in. (65-mm) clearance required under each joist for nailing in drywall applications occupies one-fourth of the ceiling area, if the joists are 16 in. (400 mm) o.c. Therefore, for drywall construction, the net area, A_n, must be multiplied by 0.75. Many installations have a spacing of 1.5 in. (40 mm) for the first 2 ft (600 mm) from the cold wall. Remaining cable is then spread over the balance of the ceiling.

Electrically Heated Wall Panels

Cable embedded in walls similar to ceiling construction is occasionally found in Europe. Because of possible damage from nails driven for hanging pictures or from building alteration, most codes in the United States prohibit such panels. Some of the prefabricated panels described in the preceding section are also used for wall panel heating.

Electrically Heated Floors

For a given floor heating cable assembly, the required cable spacing is determined from Eq. (11). In general, cable watt density and spacing should be such that floor panel watt density is not greater than 15 W/ft^2 (160 W/m^2). Higher watt densities [up to 25 W/ft^2 (270 W/m^2)] are often specified for the 2-ft (0.6-m) border next to cold walls. It is important to check with the latest issue of the *National Electric Code* and other applicable codes to obtain information on maximum panel watt density and other required criteria and parameters.

Air-Heated Floors

Several methods have been devised to warm interior room surfaces by circulating heated air through passages in the floor. In some cases the heated air is recirculated in a closed system. In others, all or a part of the air is passed through the room on its way back to the furnace to provide supplementary heating and ventilation. Figure 17 indicates one common type of construction. Compliance with applicable building codes is important.

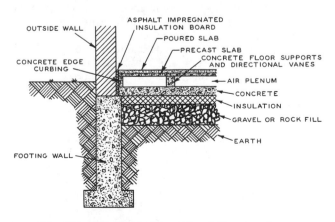

Fig. 17   Warm Air Floor Panel Construction

COMPONENTS

Hydronic Panels

Components of hydronic metal panels are described in the section "Heating and Cooling Systems."

Electric Metal Ceiling Panels

These panels are usually made for lay-in ceilings (Figure 18). Panels may also be (1) surface-mounted on gypsum board and wood ceilings or (2) recessed between ceiling joists. Panels range in size from 4-ft (1.2-m) wide to 8-ft (2.4-m) long. The maximum output is 95 W/ft^2 (1.0 W/m^2).

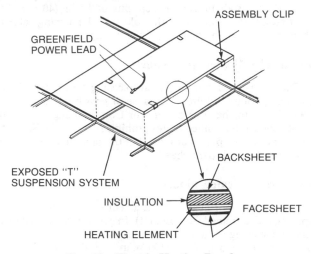

Fig. 18   Electric Heating Panel

Embedded Piping

Piping Embedded in Ceilings. One of the following types of construction is generally used.

1. Pipe or tube is embedded in the lower portion of a concrete slab, generally within an inch (25 mm) of its lower surface. If plaster is to be applied to the concrete, the piping may be placed directly on the wood forms. If the slab is to be used without plaster finish, the piping should be installed not less than 0.75 in. (19 mm) above the undersurface of the slab. Figure 19 shows this method of construction. The minimum coverage must comply with local building code requirements.
2. Pipe or tube is embedded in a metal lath and plaster ceiling. If the lath is suspended to form a hung ceiling, the lath and heating coils are securely wired to the supporting members so that the lath is below, but in good contact with, the coils. Plaster is then applied to the metal lath, carefully embedding the coil as shown in Figure 20.
3. Smaller diameter copper tube is attached to the underside of wire lath or gypsum lath. Plaster is then applied to the lath to embed the tube, as shown in Figure 21.
4. Other forms of ceiling construction are composition board, wood paneling, etc., with warm water piping, tube or channels built into the panel sections.

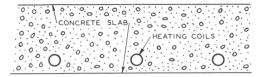

Fig. 19   Coils in Structural Concrete Slab

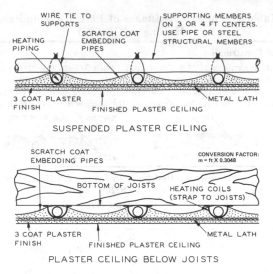

Fig. 20   Coils in Plaster Above Lath

Coils are usually the sinuous type, although some header or grid-type coils have been used in ceilings. Coils may be plastic, ferrous or nonferrous pipe or tube, with coil pipes spaced from 4.5 to 9 in. (115 to 230 mm) on centers, depending on the required output, pipe or tube size and other factors.

Where plastering is applied to pipe coils, a standard three-coat gypsum plastering specification is followed, with a minimum of 0.38 in. (10 mm) of cover below the tubes when they are installed below the lath. Generally, the surface temperature of plaster panels should not exceed 120°F (49°C). This can be accomplished by limiting the water temperature in the pipes or tubes in contact with the plaster to a maximum temperature of 140°F (60°C). Insulation should be placed above the coils to reduce *reverse loss,* the difference between heat supplied to the coil and net useful output to the heated room.

To protect the plaster installation and to assure proper air drying, heat must not be applied to the panels for two weeks after all plastering work has been completed. When the system is started for the first time, the water supplied to the panels should not be higher than 20°F (11°C) above the prevailing room temperature at that time and not in excess of 90°F (32°C). Water should be circulated at this temperature for about two days, then increased at a rate of about 5°F (2.8°C) per day to 140°F (60°C).

During the air-drying and preliminary warm-up periods, there should be adequate ventilation to carry moisture from the panels. No paint or paper should be applied to the panels before these periods have been completed or while the panels are being operated. After paint and paper have been applied, an additional shorter warm-up period, similar to first-time starting, is also recommended.

Embedded Piping in Walls and Floors. Although not as universally used as ceiling panels, wall panels can be constructed by any of the methods outlined for ceilings. The construction

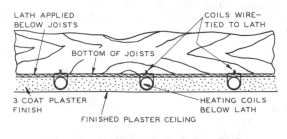

Fig. 21   Coils in Plaster Below Lath

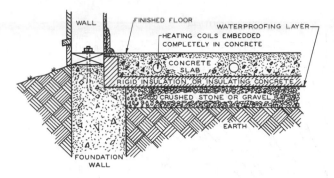

Fig. 22 Coils in Floor Slab on Grade

for piping embedded in floors depends on whether the floor is laid on grade or above grade.

1. Plastic, ferrous and nonferrous pipe and tube are used in floor slabs that rest on grade. The coils are constructed as sinuous-continuous pipe coils or arranged as header coils with the pipes spaced from 6 to 18 in. (150 to 450 mm) on centers. The coils are generally installed with 1.5 to 4 in. (40 to 100 mm) of cover above the coils. Insulation is recommended to reduce the perimeter and reverse losses. Figure 22 shows the application of pipe coils in slabs resting on grade. Coils should be embedded completely and should not rest on an interface. Any supports used for positioning the heating coils should be nonabsorbent and inorganic. It is suggested that reinforcing steel, angle iron, pieces of pipe or stone or concrete mounds be used. No wood, brick, concrete block or similar materials should be used for support of coils. A waterproofing layer is desirable to protect insulation and piping.
2. Where the coils are embedded in structural load-supporting slabs above grade, construction codes may affect their position. Otherwise, the coil piping is installed as described for slabs resting on grade.
3. A warm-up and start-up period for concrete panels should be similar to that outlined for plaster panels.

Embedded systems will likely fail sometime during their life. Adequate valves and properly labeled drawings will help to isolate the point of failure.

Electrically Heated Ceilings

Electric heating cables for embedded or laminated ceiling panels are factory-assembled units furnished in standard lengths of about 75 to 1800 ft (25 to 550 m). These cable lengths cannot be altered in the field. The cable assemblies are normally rated at 2.75 W per linear ft (9 W/m) and are supplied in capacities from 200 to 5000 W in roughly 200-W increments. Standard cable assemblies are available for 120, 208 and 240 V. Each cable unit is supplied with 7-ft (2-m) nonheating leads for connection at the thermostat or junction box.

Electric cables for panel heating have electrically insulated coverings resistant to medium temperature, water absorption, aging effects and chemical action with plaster, cement or ceiling lath material. This insulation is normally a polyvinylchloride (PVC) covering which may have a nylon jacket. The outside diameter of the insulation covering is usually about 0.12 in. (3 mm).

For plastered ceiling panels, the heating cable may be stapled to gypsum board, plaster lath or similar fire-resistant materials with rust-resistant staples. With metal lath or other conducting surfaces, a coat of plaster (brown or scratch coat) is applied to completely cover the metal lath or conducting surface before the cable is attached. After fastening on the lath and applying the first plaster coat, each cable is tested for continuity of cir-

cuit and for insulation resistance of at least 100,000 ohms measured to ground.

The entire ceiling surface is finished with a covering of thermally noninsulating sand plaster about 0.50 to 0.75 in. (13 to 19 mm) thick or other approved noninsulating material applied according to manufacturer's specifications. The plaster is applied parallel to the heating cable, rather than across the runs. While new plaster is drying, the system should not be energized and the range and rate of temperature change should be kept low by other heat sources or by ventilation until the plaster is thoroughly cured. Vermiculite or other insulating plaster causes cables to overheat and is contrary to code provisions.

For laminated drywall ceiling panels, the heating cable is placed between two layers of gypsum board, plasterboard or other thermally noninsulating fire-resistant ceiling lath. The cable is stapled directly to the first (or upper) lath, and the two layers are held apart by the thickness of the heating cable. It is essential that the space between the two layers of lath be *completely* filled with a noninsulating plaster or similar material. This fill holds the cable firmly in place and improves heat transfer between the cable and the finished ceiling. Failure to fill the space completely between the two layers of plasterboard may allow the cable to overheat in the resulting voids and cause cable failure. The plaster fill should be applied according to manufacturer's specifications.

Electric heating cables are ordinarily installed with a 6-in. (150-mm) nonheating border around the periphery of the ceiling. An 8-in. (200-mm) clearance must be provided between heating cables and the edges of the outlet or junction boxes used for surface-mounted lighting fixtures. A 2-in. (50-mm) clearance must be provided from recessed lighting fixtures, trim and ventilating or other openings in the ceiling.

Heating cables or panels must be installed only in ceiling areas which are not covered by partitions, cabinets or other obstructions. However, it is permissible for a single run of isolated embedded cable to pass over a partition.

The *National Electric Code* requires that all general power and light wiring be run above the thermal insulation or at least 2 in. (50 mm) above the heated ceiling surface, or that the wiring be derated.

In drywall ceiling construction, the heating cable is always installed with the cable runs parallel to the joist. A 2.5-in. (64-mm) clearance between adjacent cable runs must be left centered under each joist for nailing. Cable runs that cross over the joist must be kept to a minimum. Where possible, these crossings should be in a straight line at one end of the room.

Figure 23 shows details of ceiling cable installation practice for plastered construction.

Prefabricated Electric Ceiling Panels. A variety of prefabricated electric heating panels are available for either supplemental or full room heating. These panels are available in sizes from 2 by 4 ft (0.6 by 1.2 m) to 6 by 12 ft (1.8 by 3.6 m). They are constructed from a variety of materials such as gypsum board, glass, steel and vinyl. Different panels have rated inputs varying from 10 to 95 W/ft² (108 to 1023 W/m²) for 120, 208, 240 and 277 V service. Maximum operating temperatures vary from about 100 to about 300°F (38 to 149°C), depending on watt density. National and local codes should be followed when placing partitions, lights, and air grilles adjacent to or near electric panels.

Panel heating elements may be embedded conductors, laminated conductive coatings, or printed circuits. Nonheating leads are connected and furnished as part of the panel. Some panels can be cut to fit available space; others must be installed as received. Panels may be either flush or surface mounted and, in some cases, are finished as part of the ceiling. Rigid panels that are about 1-in. (25-mm) thick and weigh about 25 lb (11kg)

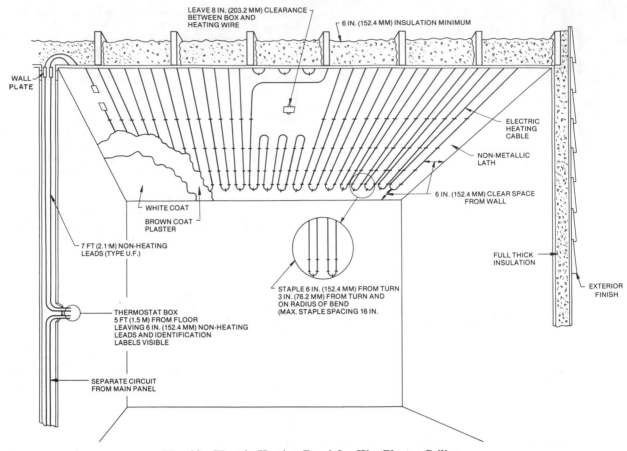

Fig. 23   Electric Heating Panel for Wet Plaster Ceiling

each are available to fit standard 2 by 4 ft (0.6 by 1.2 m) modular tee-bar ceilings. Always follow the installation instructions furnished by the manufacturer.

Electrically Heated Floors

Electric heating cable assemblies, such as those used for ceiling panels, are sometimes used for concrete floor heating systems. Since the possibility of cable damage during installation is greater for concrete floor slabs than for ceiling panels, these assemblies must be carefully installed. After the cable has been placed, all unnecessary traffic should be eliminated until the concrete covering has been poured and hardened.

Preformed mats are sometimes used for electric floor slab heating systems. These mats usually consist of PVC-insulated heating cable woven in, or attached to, metallic or glass fiber mesh. Such mats are available as prefabricated assemblies in many sizes from 2 to 100 ft² (0.18 to 9.3 m²) and with various watt densities.

Mineral-insulated (MI) heating cable is another effective method of slab heating. MI cable is a small-diameter, highly durable, flexible heating cable composed of solid electric-resistance heating wire or wires surrounded by tightly compressed magnesium oxide electrical insulation and enclosed by a metal sheath. MI cable is available in stock assemblies in a variety of standard voltages, watt densities and lengths. A cable assembly consists of the specified length of heating cable, waterproof hot-cold junctions, 7-ft (2-m) cold sections, UL-approved end fittings and connection leads. Several standard MI cable constructions are available, such as single conductor, twin conductor and double cable. Custom-designed MI heating cable assemblies can be ordered for specific installations.

Other outer-covering materials that are sometimes specified for electric floor heating cable include: (1) silicone rubber, (2) lead and (3) tetrafluoroethylene (Teflon).

Floor Heating Cable Installation. When PVC-jacketed electric heating cable is used for floor heating, the concrete slab is laid in two pourings. The first pour should be at least 3-in. (75-mm) thick and, where practical, should be insulating concrete to reduce downward heat loss. For a proper bond between the layers, the finish slab should be poured within 24 hours of the first pour, with a bonding grout applied. The finish layer should be at least 1.5 in. (38 mm) and not more than 2-in. (50-mm) thick. This top layer must not be insulating concrete (see Figure 21). At least 1 in. (25 mm) of perimeter insulation should be installed as shown in Figures 16 and 24.

The cable is installed on top of the first pour of concrete not closer than 2 in. (50 mm) from adjoining walls and partitions.

Methods of fastening the cable to the concrete include:

1. The cable is stapled to wood nailing strips fixed in the surface of the rough slab. The predetermined cable spacing is maintained by daubs of cement, plaster of paris or tape.
2. In lightweight or uncured concrete, the cable can usually be stapled directly to the slab using hand-operated or powered stapling machines.
3. Special anchor devices are available that are nailed to the first slab to hold the cable in position while the top layer is being poured.

Preformed mats can be embedded in the concrete in a continuous pour. The mats are positioned in the area between expansion and/or construction joints and electrically connected to a junction box. The slab is poured to within 1.5 to 2 in. (38 to 50 mm) of the finished level. The surface is rough screeded,

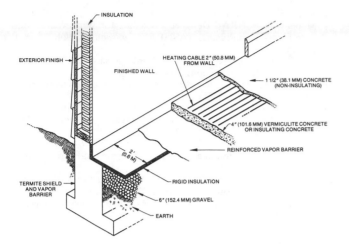

Fig. 24 Electric Heating Cable in Concrete Slab

and the mats placed in position. The final cap is applied immediately. Since the first pour has not set, there is no adhesion problem between the first and second pour, and a monolithic slab results. A variety of contours can be developed by using heater wire attached to glass fiber mats. Allow for circumvention of obstructions in the slab.

MI electric heating cable can be installed in concrete slab using either one or two pours. For single-pour applications the cable is fastened to the top of the reinforcing steel before the pour is started. For two-layer applications the cable is laid on top of the bottom structural slab and embedded in the finish layer. Proper spacing between adjacent cable runs is maintained by using prepunched copper spacer strips nailed to the lower slab.

CONTROLS

Automatic controls for panel heating differ from those for convective heating because of the thermal inertia characteristics of the panel heating surface and the increase in the mean radiant temperature within the space under increasing loads for panel heating, However, many of the control principles for hot water heating systems described in Chapters 14 and 15 also apply to panel heating. Chapter 51 has further information on automatic controls. Because radiant panels do not depend on air-side equipment to distribute energy, many control methods have been used successfully. However, a control interface between heating and cooling should be installed to prevent simultaneous heating and cooling.

Panels such as concrete slabs have large heat storage capacity and continue to emit heat long after the room thermostat has shut off the heting medium supply. In addition, there is a considerable time lag between thermostat demand and heat delivery to the space, since a large part of the heat must first be stored in the thermally heavy radiant surface. This inertia will cause uncomfortable variations in space conditions unless controls are provided to detect load changes early.

In general, the temperature of the heating medium supplied to the panel surface should be varied in accordance with outdoor temperature. However, for embedded pipe panels precautions must be taken to prevent the introduction of excessively hot water, which might damage the panels if controls failed. A manual boiler bypass or other means of reducing the water temperature may be necessary to prevent new panels from drying out too rapidly (see Embedded Piping for Ceiling Panels).

Because the mean radiant temperature (MRT) within a panel heated space must increase *as the heating load increases,* the air temperature during this increase should be lowered 1 or 2 °F (0.5 to 1 °C) to maintain comfort. In ordinary structures with normal infiltration loads, the required reduction in air temperature is small, enabling a conventional room thermostat to be used.

In panel heating systems, lowered night temperatures will produce unsatisfactory results with heavy panels such as concrete floors. These panels cannot respond to a quick increase or decrease in heating demand within the relatively short time required, resulting in a very slow reduction of the space temperature at night and a correspondingly slow pickup in the morning. Lightweight panels, such as plaster or metal ceilings and walls, may respond to changes in demand quickly enough for moderately satisfactory results from lowered night temperatures. Tests on a metal ceiling panel demonstrated the speed of response to be comparable to that of conventional environmental systems. However, very little fuel savings can be expected even with light panels unless the lowered temperature is maintained for long periods. If reduced nonoccupancy temperatures are employed, some means of providing a higher-than-normal rate of heat input for rapid warm-up is necessary, or a long warm-up period should be provided, as explained in Chapter 16.

Electric Heating Slab Controls

For comfort heating applications, the surface of a floor slab (t_s) is held to a maximum of 80 to 85 °F (26 to 29 °C). Therefore, when used as a primary heating system, thermostatic control devices sensing air temperature should not be used to control the slab temeprature, but should be wired in series with a slab-sensing thermostat. The remote sensing thermostat in the slab acts as a limit switch to control maximum surface temperatures allowed on the slab. The ambient sensing thermostat controls the comfort level. For supplementary slab heating, as in kindergarten floors, a remote sensing thermostat in the slab is commonly used to tune in the desired comfort level. Indoor-outdoor thermostats are used to vary the floor temperature inversely with the outdoor temperature. If the heat loss of the building is calculated for 70 to 0 °F (21 to −18 °C), and the floor temperature range is held from 70 to 85 °F (21 to 29 °C) with a remote sensing thermostat, the ratio of outdoor temperature to slab temperature is 70:15 (39:8), or approximately 5:1. This means that a 5 °F (2.8 °C) drop in outdoor temperature requires a 1 °F (0.6 °C) increase in the slab temperature. An ambient sensing thermostat is used to vary the ratio between outdoor and slab temperatures. A time clock is used to control each heating zone if off-peak slab heating is desirable.

DISTRIBUTION AND LAYOUT

Metal radiant heating panels, hydronic and electric, are applied to building perimeter spaces for heating in much the same way as finned tube convectors. Metal panels are usually installed in the ceiling and are integrated into the ceiling design. The layout and arrangement of panels usually considers architectural design.

Partitions may be erected to the face of hydronic panels but not to the active heating portion of electric panels because of possible element overheating and burnout. Electric panels are often sized to fit the building module with a small removable filler or dummy panel at the window mullion to accommodate future partitions. Hydronic panels can run continuously.

Field modification, by cutting and fitting, of hydronic panels is possible, but should be kept to a minimum to keep installation costs down. Electric panels cannot be modified in the field.

EVALUATION

Mean Radiant Temperature (MRT) has the greatest influence on body comfort. Comfort levels are better than those experienced with other air-conditioning systems because radiant loads are treated directly and air motion in the space is at normal ventilation levels.

Interest has developed in radiant floor heating with the introduction of polybutylene tubing and new design techniques. The systems are energy-efficient and use low water temperatures available from solar collector systems.

Metal radiant panels can be integrated into the ceiling design to provide a narrow band of radiant heating around the perimeter of the building. The radiant system offers advantages over baseboard or overhead air in appearance, comfort, operating efficiency and cost, maintenance, and product life.

REFERENCES

ASHAE. 1956. Thermal Design of Warm Water Ceiling Panels. ASHAE *Transactions,* Vol. 62, p. 71.

ASHAE. 1957. Thermal Design of Warm Water Concrete Floor Panels. ASHAE *Transactions,* Vol. 63, p. 239.

ASHRAE. 1981. Thermal Environmental Conditions for Human Occupancy. ASHRAE Standard 55-1981.

Bareither, H.D.; Fleming, A.N.; and Alberty, B.E. *Temperature and Heat-Loss Characteristics of Concrete Floors Laid on the Ground, Research Report* 48-1, Small Homes Council, University of Illinois.

Boyar, R.E. 1963. Room Temperature Dynamics of Radiant Ceilings and Air Conditioning Comfort Systems. ASHRAE *Transactions,* Vol. 69, p. 37.

Fanger, P.O. 1972. *Thermal Comfort Analysis and Applications in Environmental Engineering.* McGraw Hill, Inc., New York, NY.

Gagge, A.P.; Rapp, G.H.; and Hardy, J.D. 1967. The Effective Radiant Field and Operative Temperature Necessary for Comfort with Radiant Heating. ASHRAE *Journal,* May, p. 63.

Hogan, R.E., Jr., and Blackwell, B. 1986. Comparison of Numerical Model with ASHRAE Designed Procedure for Warm-Water Concrete Floor-Heating Panels (ASHRAE *Transactions,* Vol. 92, Part 1B, pp. 589-601).

Houghten, F.C. et al. 1942. Heat Loss Through Basement Floors and Walls. ASHVE *Transactions,* Vol. 48, p. 369.

Hutchinson, F.W. 1947. Influence of Gaseous Radiation in Panel Heating. ASHVE *Transactions,* Vol. 53, p. 285.

McNall, P.E., Jr.; and Biddison, R.E. 1970. Thermal and Comfort Sensations of Sedentary Persons Exposed to Asymmetric Radiant Fields. ASHRAE *Transactions,* Vol. 76, p. 123.

Min, T.C. et al. 1956. ASHAE Research Report No. 1576-Natural Convection and Radiation in a Panel Heated Room. ASHAE *Transactions,* Vol. 62, p. 337.

Parmelee, G.V.; and Huebscher, R.G. 1947. Forced Convection Heat Transfer from Flat Surfaces. ASHVE *Transactions,* Vol. 53, p. 245.

Sartain, E.L.; and Harris, W.S. 1956. Performance of Covered Hot Water Floor Panels, Part I-Thermal Characteristics. ASHAE *Transactions,* Vol. 62, p. 55.

Schlegel, J.C.; and McNall, P.E., Jr. 1968. The Effect of Asymmetric Radiation on the Thermal and Comfort Sensations of Sedentary Subjects. ASHRAE *Transactions,* Vol. 74, p. 144.

Schutrum, L.F.; and Huimphreys, C.M. 1954. ASHVE Research Report No. 1499—Effects of Non-Uniformity and Furnishings on Panel Heating Performance. ASHVE *Transactions,* Vol. 60, p. 121.

Schutrum, L.F.; Parmelee, G.V.; and Humphreys, C.M. 1953a. ASHVE Research Report No. 1473—Heat Exchanges in a Ceiling Panel Heated Room. ASHVE *Transactions,* Vol. 59, p. 197.

Schutrum, L.F.; Parmelee, G.V.; and Humphreys, C.M. 1953b. ASHVE Research Report No. 1490—Heat Exchanges in a Floor Panel Heated Room. ASHVE *Transactions,* Vol. 59, p. 495.

Schutrum, L.F.; and Vouris, J.D. 1954. ASHVE Research Report No. 1516—Effects of Room Size and Non-Uniformity of Panel Temperature on Panel Performance. ASHVE *Transactions,* Vol. 60, p. 455.

Wilkes, G.B.; and Peterson, C.M.F. 1938. Radiation and Convection from Surfaces in Various Positions. ASHVE *Transactions,* Vol. 44, p. 513.

CHAPTER 8

COGENERATION SYSTEMS

COGENERATION is the sequential use of energy from a primary source such as oil, coal, natural gas, or biomass fuels to produce two useful energy forms—heat and power. By capturing and applying heat that would otherwise be rejected, cogeneration systems operate at efficiencies greater than those achieved when heat and power are produced in separate or distinct processes.

Cogeneration systems produce mechanical and/or electrical power; the latter can be used at the cogeneration facility or transferred in part or whole to the electric utility grid. Isolated cogeneration systems, whose electrical output is used onsite to satisfy all site power requirements, are referred to as *total energy systems*. A cogeneration system that is actively tied to the utility grid can, on a contractual basis, exchange power with the public utility. This lessens the need for redundant onsite generating capacity and allows operation at maximum thermal efficiency.

Analysis of the magnitude, duration, and coincidence of electrical and thermal loads, and selection of prime movers and waste heat recovery determine system feasibility and design. Integrating the design of the project's electrical and thermal requirements with the energy plant is required for optimum economic benefit. The basic components of the cogeneration plant are (1) prime movers, (2) generators, (3) waste heat recovery systems, (4) control systems, (5) electrical and thermal transmission and distribution systems, and (6) connections to building mechanical and electrical services.

This chapter covers prime movers, generators, heat recovery, and control systems. Thermal transmission and distribution systems are discussed in Chapter 12.

PRIME MOVERS

The basic component in a cogeneration system is the prime mover, which converts fuel energy to shaft energy. The conversion devices normally used are reciprocating internal combustion engines, combustion gas turbines, expansion turbines, and steam boiler-turbine combinations. Engine and turbine drives are discussed in Chapter 33 of the 1983 EQUIPMENT Volume.

Reciprocating engines are the most common type of prime mover used in cogeneration plants. These engines are available in sizes up to 27,000 brake horsepower (20 MW) and use all types of liquid and gaseous fuels. Internal combustion engines that use the diesel cycle can be fueled by a wide range of petroleum products, although No. 2 diesel oil is most commonly used. Diesel cycle engines can also be fired with gaseous fuel in combination with the liquid fuel. Under these conditions, the liquid acts as the combustion ignitor and is called *pilot oil*.

Spark ignition Otto cycle engines are produced in sizes up to 18,000 bhp (13.5 MW) and can use natural gas, liquefied petroleum gases (LPG), and other gaseous and volatile liquid fuels. Engines usually operate in the range of 360 to 1200 rpm (6 to 20 r/s). The specific operating speed selected depends on the size of machine, characteristics of manufacturers, the generator, and the desired length of time between complete engine overhauls. Engines are usually selected to provide a minimum of 20,000 to 30,000 operating hours between minor overhauls.

The engine components include a fuel input system; fuel air mixing cycle; ignition system; combustion chamber; exhaust gas collection and removal system; lubrication system; and power transmission gear with pistons, connecting rods, crank shafts, and flywheel. Some engines also increase power output using turbochargers (combustion air compressors driven by exhaust gas turbines) that increase the amount of air delivered to the combustion chamber. The engines are generally from 20 to 40% efficient in converting fuel to shaft energy. Figure 1 is a typical fuel curve for a gas-fired internal combustion engine, based on the lower heating value of the fuel.

Combustion gas turbines, although used primarily for aircraft propulsion, have been developed for stationary use and are gaining acceptance as prime movers. Turbines are available in sizes from 50 to 173,000 bhp (37 kW to 130 MW) and can burn a wide range of liquid and gaseous fuels. They are capable of shifting from one fuel to another without loss of service.

Gas turbines consist of an air compressor section to boost combustion air pressure, a combination fuel air mixing and combustion chamber (combustor), and an expansion turbine section that extracts energy from the combustion gases. In addition to these components, some turbines use regenerators that are turbine discharge gas-to-combustion inlet air-heat exchangers to increase machine efficiency. Most turbines are the single-shaft type, i.e., air compressor and turbine on a common shaft. However, some split shaft machines that use one turbine stage

---

The preparation of the chapter is assigned to TC 9.5, Cogeneration Systems.

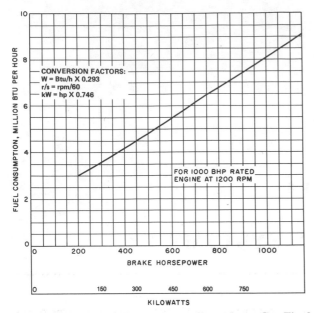

Fig. 1 **Typical Fuel Consumption Curve for a Gas-Fired Internal Combustion Engine**

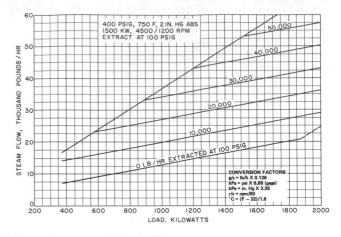

Fig. 2 **Effect of Extraction Rate on Total Steam Requirement for Condensing Turbine**

on the same shaft as the compressor and a separate power turbine driving the output shaft, are available.

Present turbines rotate at speeds varying from 3600 to 60,000 rpm (60 to 1000 r/s) and often need speed reduction gear boxes to obtain shaft speeds suitable for generators. Turbines are completely rotary in motion and relatively vibration-free. This feature, coupled with their lightweight and high power output, provides an advantage over reciprocating engines with regard to space and foundation requirements. However, in smaller sizes, the combustion gas turbine has a fuel-to-power efficiency of 12 to 20%, which is lower than efficiencies obtainable from reciprocating engines. Larger turbines approach a fuel-to-power efficiency of 30%. Expansion turbines are gas turbines that use compressed waste gases available from gas-producing processes.

There are two types of steam turbines: *condensing,* which operates at exhaust pressures below atmospheric and requires vacuum-type condensers and pumps; and the *noncondensing or backpressure* type, which operates at exhaust pressures of atmospheric to about 50 psia (345 kPa). Although the exhaust steam from backpressure turbines is available for further use, condensing-type turbines coupled to generators are often selected because of their lower steam rate.

Extraction turbines are not as simple as backpressure types but are more flexible in operation. The steam in an extraction turbine expands part of the way through the turbine until the pressure and temperature level required by the external thermal load are attained. The remaining steam continues through the low pressure turbine stages. However, it is easier to adjust for non-coincident electrical and thermal loads. Because steam cycles operate at pressures exceeding those allowed by ASME and local codes for unattended operation, their practical use in cogeneration plants is limited to large systems where attendants are required for other reasons or the labor burden of operating personnel does not seriously affect overall economics. Figure 2 is for a 1500-kW condensing turbine, indicating the effect of various extraction rates on total steam requirements.

GENERATORS

Generators are available in a wide range of sizes, speeds, types, and control options. Many engine manufacturers offer package

arrangements in which the generator and prime mover come as a unit on the same skid.

Criteria influencing the selection of alternating current (ac) generators for cogeneration systems are (1) machine efficiency in converting mechanical input into electrical output at various loads; (2) electrical load requirements, including frequency, power factor, and distortion requirements; (3) phase balance capabilities; (4) equipment cost; and (5) motor starting current requirements. Industrial generator manufacturers have detailed information available on their equipment.

Generator speed is a direct function of the number of poles and output frequency. For 60-Hz output, the speed can range from 3600 rpm (60 r/s) for a two-pole machine to 900 rpm (15 r/s) for an eight-pole machine. A wide latitude exists in matching generator speed to prime mover speed without reducing the efficiency of either unit. This range in speed and, by extension, frequency, suggests that electrical equipment, whose operation is improved at a special frequency might be accommodated. For example, on-site generation is a convenient way to supply high frequency power to fluorescent lighting systems, thus improving their efficiency.

Standard generators can be selected for a wide variety of voltages and frequencies. High frequency (420- or 840-Hz) lighting can be produced from one generator on a shaft, while standard frequency (60 Hz in North America and 50 Hz elsewhere) power is produced from another alternator on the same shaft. Direct current (dc) power also can be produced by itself or in tandem with ac power.

If the rotational speed of the prime mover allows for direct generator coupling, it is desirable to have direct drive between the generator and its prime mover to eliminate reduction gears.

Generator efficiency is a nonlinear function of the load and is maximum usually at or near the rated load (see Figure 3). The rated load estimate should include a safety factor to cover such transient conditions as short-term peaking and equipment start-up. Industrial generators are designed to handle a steady-state overload of 20 to 25% for several hours of continuous operation. If sustained overloads are possible, the generator ventilation system must be able to relieve the temperature rise of the windings. The prime mover must be able to accommodate the overload. Proper phase balance is extremely important. Driving three-phase motors from the three-phase generator presents the best phase balance, assuming that the power factor requirements have been met.

Driving single-phase motors and building-lighting or building-distribution systems may cause an unbalanced distribution of

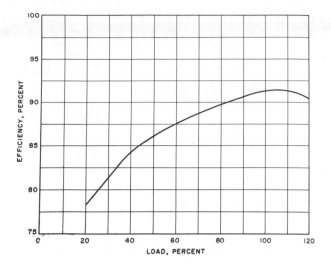

Fig. 3 Typical Generator Efficiency

the single-phase loads, leading to harmonic distortion, over-heating, and electrical imbalance of the generator. Practically, maximum-phase imbalance can be held within 5 to 10% by proper distribution system loading. Voltage is regulated by using static convertors or rotating dc generators to excite the alternator. Voltage regulation should be within 2% from full load to no load during static conditions. Good electronic three-phase voltage sensing is necessary to control the system response to load changes and the excitation of paralleled alternators to ensure reactive load division.

The system power factor is reflected to the generator and should be no less than 0.8 for generator efficiency. To fall within this limit, the planned electrical load may have to be adjusted so the combined leading power factor substantially offsets the combined lagging power factor. Although more expensive, individual power factor correction is preferred to total power factor correction on the bus.

Generation systems transfer considerable heat to the equipment space. It is necessary to remove this heat to provide acceptable working conditions and to protect the electrical systems from overloading because of high ambient conditions. Heat can be removed by outdoor air ventilation systems that include dampers and fans regulated to prevent overheating or excessively low temperatures in extreme weather.

GENERAL HEAT RECOVERY

On-site generation provides an opportunity to use the fuel energy that the prime mover does not convert into shaft energy. If the heat cannot be used effectively, the plant efficiency is limited to the prime mover thermal efficiency. However, if the site heat energy requirements can be met effectively by the normally wasted heat at the level it is available from the prime mover, this salvaged heat reduces the normal fuel requirements of the site and increases the total overall plant efficiency.

The prime mover furnishes two kinds of energy: (1) mechanical energy from the shaft and (2) unused heat energy remaining after the fuel or steam has acted on the shaft. Shaft loads (generators, centrifugal chillers, compressors, and process equipment) require a given amount of rotating mechanical energy. Once the prime mover is selected to provide the required shaft output, it has a fixed relationship to heat availability and system efficiency,

depending on the prime mover fuels versus heat balance curves. The ability to use the prime mover heat determines overall system efficiency and is one of the critical factors in economic feasibility.

Steam turbine drives can be arranged to extract steam at intermediate turbine stages. The heating value of the extracted steam is the difference between the enthalpy of the steam at the point it is removed from the turbine or at the turbine's exhaust and the enthalpy of the steam in its final state. This extracted steam, reduced from input conditions in both pressure and temperature by the amount of shaft work, is fed to the heat exchange equipment, absorption chillers and, steam turbine-driven centrifugal chillers. In Figure 2 at zero extraction and rated load, the turbine heat rate is about 11,000 Btu/kWh (3200 kJ/KJ). As the steam use exceeds the minimum flow required to drive the turbine and the total steam flow increases (turbine drive and steam extraction), the amount chargeable to drive the generator begins to decrease. In effect, when the turbine is acting both as a generator drive and pressure reducing station, the overall efficiency increases.

In the gas turbine cycle, the thermal to electrical efficiency is approximately 12 to 30%, with the remainder of the fuel energy discharged in the exhaust through radiation or through internal coolants in large turbines. A minimum exhaust temperature of about 300°F (150°C) is required to prevent condensation. Because of the lower fuel to power efficiency, the quantity of heat recoverable per unit of power is greater for the gas turbine than for a reciprocating engine. This heat is generally available at the higher temperature of the exhaust gas. The net result is an overall first law thermal efficiency of approximately 60% and higher. Since gas turbine exhaust contains a large percentage of excess air, it is possible to install afterburners or boost burners in the exhaust boiler system to supplement the heat recovered from the exhaust or to level out the steam production during reduced turbine loads. Boost burning can increase cycle efficiency to a maximum of 90%. Finally, absorption chillers capable of direct operation off of turbine exhausts are available, offering another design option.

The conventional method of controlling steam or hot water production is to bypass a portion of the exhaust gases around the boiler tubes and out the exhaust stack through a gas bypass valve assembly (see Figure 4).

In all reciprocating internal combustion engines, except small air-cooled units, heat can be reclaimed from the lubricating

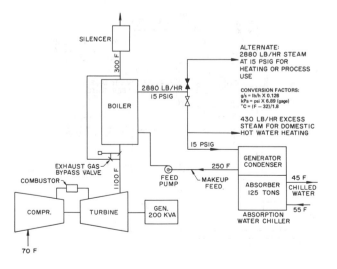

Fig. 4 Typical Heat Recovery Cycle for 200 kVA (160 kW) Gas Turbine

system, jacket cooling system, and the exhaust. These engines require extensive cooling of the machine to remove excessive heat conducted into the power train during combustion and the heat resulting from friction. Coolant fluids and lubricating oil are circulated to remove this engine heat. Some engines are also constructed to permit cooling water to change to steam within the engine.

Waste heat in the form of hot water or low-pressure steam is recovered from the engine jacket manifolds and exhaust, as shown in Figures 5 through 10. Additional heat can be recovered from the lubrication system. Provisions similar to those used with gas turbines are necessary if supplemental heat is required, except that exhaust heat-recovery equipment cannot be fuel-fired. If electric elements are used for supplemental heat, the additional electrical load is reflected back to the prime mover, which reacts accordingly by making additional waste heat, creating a feedback effect and stabilizing system operation.

The approximate distribution of input fuel energy for an engine operating at rated load is as follows:

| Shaft power | 33% |
| Convection and radiation | 7% |

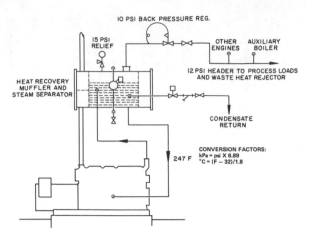

Fig. 7   Engine Cooling with Gravity Circulation and Steam Heat Recovery

| Rejected in jacket water | 30% |
| Rejected in exhaust | 30% |

These amounts vary with engine load and design.

Four-cycle engine heat balance for naturally aspirated (Figures 11 and 12) and turbocharged gas engines (Figure 13) show typical heat distribution. The exhaust gas temperature for these engines is about 1200°F (650°C) at full load and 1000°F (540°C) at 60% load.

Two-cycle engines operate at lower exhaust gas temperatures, particularly at light loads, because the scavenger air volumes remain high through the entire range of capacity. High volume, lower temperature exhaust gas offers less efficient exhaust gas heat recovery possibilities. The exhaust gas temperature is ap-

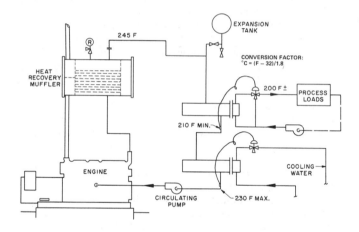

Fig. 5   Hot Water Heat Recovery System

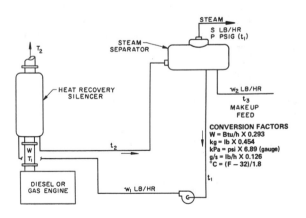

Heat Recovered from Exhaust, Btu/h (W):
$$Q_E = Wc_p\,(T_1 - T_2)$$
where c_p = specific heat of exhaust.

Water Temperature to Separator, °F (°C):
$$t_2 = (Q/w_1) + t_1$$

Steam Produced at P, psig (lb/h) [kPa gauge (g/s)]:
$$S = w_1(t_2 - t_1)/h$$

where h = latent heat of steam at P, psi (kPa) gauge (or t_1) plus heat per lb (kg) required to raise feed water from t_3 to t_1.

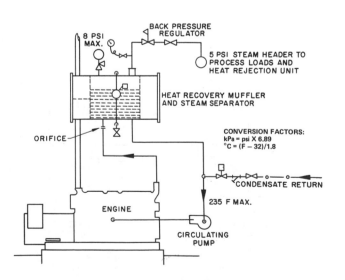

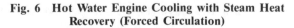

Fig. 6   Hot Water Engine Cooling with Steam Heat Recovery (Forced Circulation)

Fig. 8   Exhaust Heat Recovery System Using a Separate Steam Separator

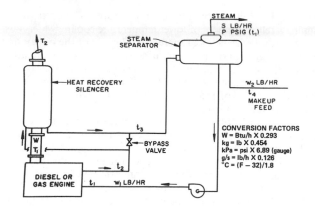

Heat Recovered from Exhaust, Btu/h (W):
$$Q_E = Wc_p(T_1 - T_2)$$
where c_p = specific heat of exhaust.
Heat Released to Jacket Water Btu/h (W):
$$Q_{jw} = w_1(T_2 - T_1)$$
Steam Produced at P, psig (lb/h) [kPa gauge (g/s)]:
$$S = w_1(t_3 - t_1)/h$$
where h = latent heat of steam at P, psi (kPa) gauge (or t_1) plus heat per lb (kg) to raise feed water from t_4 to t_1.

Fig. 9   High Temperature Cooling System with Exhaust Heat Recovery Using a Separate Steam Separator

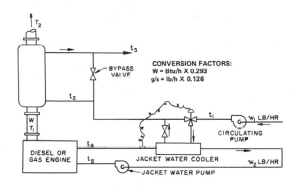

Heat Recovered from Exhaust, Btu/h (W):
$$Q_E = Wc_p(T_2 - T_1)$$
where c_p = specific heat of exhaust.
Temperature of Heat Recovered from Jacket Water
$$t_2 = (w_2/w_1)(t_4 - t_5) + t_1$$
Temperature of Heat Recovered (Expressed as Outlet Water Temp)
$$t_3 = (Q/w_1) + t_2$$

Fig. 10   Combined Exhaust and Jacket Water Heat Recovery System

proximately 700 °F (370 °C) at full load and drops below 500 °F (260 °C) at low loads.

When the equipment is part of a cogeneration system operating in parallel with the utility grid, the system may be operated in a manner that meets thermal demands. In eliminating the need for auxiliary heat sources and alternate heat disposal systems, and allowing the generator to meet the system electrical requirements by purchasing supplemental power or by selling excess power, the system operates at peak efficiency at all times.

LUBRICATING SYSTEM HEAT RECOVERY

All engine designs use the lubricating system to remove some heat from the machine. Some configurations use piston skirt cooling with oil; other designs remove more extensive engine heat with the lubricating system. The operating temperature of the engine may be significant in determining the proportion of engine heat the lube oil removes. Radiator-cooled units generally use the same fluid to cool the engine water jacket and the lube oil, so the temperature difference between the oil and the jacket coolant is not significant. If the oil temperature rises in one area (such as the piston cooling skirts), this heat might be given off

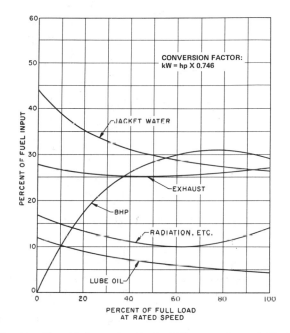

Fig. 11   Heat Balance for Typical Unsupercharged Engine with Hot Exhaust Manifold

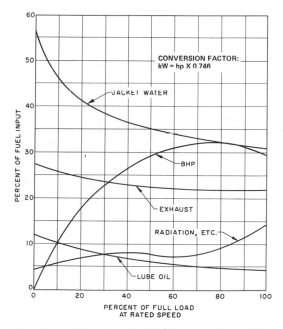

Fig. 12   Heat Balance for Typical Unsupercharged Engine with Water-Cooled Exhaust Manifold

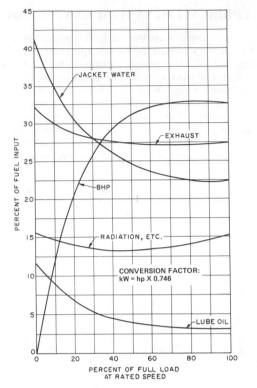

Fig. 13   Heat Balance for Typical Turbocharged Engine

to other engine oil passages and then removed by the jacket coolant.

When the engine jacket water temperatures are much higher than the lubricant temperatures, the reverse process occurs and the oil removes heat from the engine oil passages. Heat is dissipated to lube oil in a four-cycle engine with a high temperature [225 to 230 °F (107 to 110 °C)] jacket water coolant at a rate of about 7 or 8 Btu/bhp·min (0.188 or 0.165 W/kW); oil heat is rejected in the same engine at 3 to 4 Btu/bhp·min (0.071 to 0.094 W/kW). However, this engine uses more moderate [180 °F (82 °C)] coolant temperatures for both lube oil and engine jacket. Determining the lube oil cooling effect is necessary to design lube oil heat exchangers and coolant systems.

High quality lubricating oils are generally suitable for operation at temperatures between 160 and 200 °F (71 and 93 °C), with longer oil life expected at the lower temperatures. Condensation may occur in the crankcase if the oil is too cool, reducing its useful life about 20% for each 10 °F (5.5 °C) increase in operating temperature above 180 °F (80 °C). Each lubricant, engine, and application condition has individual characteristics, and only an appropriate laboratory analysis of periodic lube oil samples can establish optimum lubricant service periods. A typically shorter life at higher temperatures is one of the limitations. Between 5 and 10% of the total fuel input produces heat that must be extracted from the lube oil; this may warrant using oil coolant at temperatures high enough to permit economic use in a process such as domestic water heating. Avoid using copper in lube oil piping and oil side surfaces in coolers and heat exchangers to reduce the possibility of oil breakdown caused by contact with the copper.

Lube oil heat exchanger design should be able to maintain oil temperatures at 190 °F (88 °C) with the highest coolant temperature consistent with the economics of salvage heat value. Engine manufacturers usually size their oil cooler heat transfer surface on the basis of 130 °F (54 °C) entering coolant water, and without provision for additional lubricant heat gains that oc-

cur with high engine operating temperatures. The costs of obtaining a reliable supply of lower temperature cooling water must be compared with costs of increasing the size of the oil cooling heat exchanger and operating at a cooling water temperature of 165 °F (74 °C). In applications where engine jacket coolant temperatures are above 220 °F (104 °C) and where there is use for heat at a level of 155 to 165 °F (68 to 74 °C), the lube oil heat can be salvaged profitably.

The lube oil coolant should not foul the oil cooling heat exchanger. Do not use raw water unless it is free of silt, calcium carbonates, sand, and other contaminants. A good solution is a closed circuit, treated water system with an air-cooled transfer coil arranged to avoid freezing. A domestic water heater can be installed on this closed circuit to act as a reserve heat exchanger and to salvage some useful heat when needed. Diesel engine inlet air temperatures are not as critical as turbocharged natural gas engines, and the aftercooler water on diesel engines can be run in series with the lube oil cooler (see Figure 14).

Turbochargers on natural gas engines require medium fuel gas pressure [12 to 20 psi (80 to 140 kPa)] and rather low aftercooler water temperatures [90 °F (32 °C) or less] for high compression ratios and best fuel economy. Aftercooler water at 90 °F (32 °C) is a premium coolant in many applications since the usual sources are raw domestic water and evaporative cooling systems, such as cooling towers. Using a domestic water solution may be expensive because (1) the coolant is continuously needed while the engine is running and (2) the available heat exchanger designs require using a large amount of water even though the load is less than 200 Btu/h·bhp (80 W/kW). A cooling tower can be used, but will require winter freeze protection and water quality control, both of which increase initial costs. If a cooling tower is used, the lube oil coolant load can be included in the tower load when there is no use for salvage lube oil heat.

The turbocharger increases engine capacity and extends the optimum fuel consumption curve, because the usual limitation on larger gas-fueled engines is the volume of combustion air and fuel that can be inserted in the available combustion chamber. Most stationary reciprocating engines were developed for use with diesel fuel. The energy ratings with the liquid fuel are higher than with naturally aspirated gaseous fuel. Turbocharging on diesel service permits more air pressure to be applied in the cylinder so that larger quantities of the separately injected fuel can be burned efficiently.

In the gaseous fuel system, the fuel must always have a pressure high enough to enter the carburetor and mix with the boosted pressure of the combustion air. Since the gas and air mixture will ignite at a specific temperature-pressure relationship, the

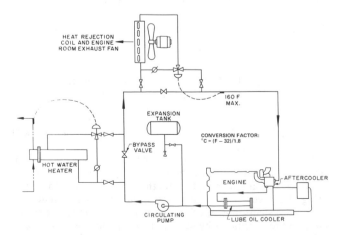

Fig. 14   Typical Lube Oil and Aftercooler System

lower the inlet air temperature is, the higher the compression ratio can go before spontaneous combustion (preignition) occurs.

JACKET HEAT RECOVERY

Engine jacket cooling passages for reciprocating engines, including the water cooling circuits in the block, heads, and exhaust manifolds, must remove about 30% of the heat input to the engine. If the machine operates at temperatures above 180°F (82°C) coolant temperature, condensation of combustion products should product no effect. Some engines have modified gasket and seal designs enabling satisfactory operation up to 250°F at 30 psi (121°C at 210 kPa) gauge. To avoid thermal stress, the maximum temperature rise through the engine jacket should not exceed 15°F (8.3°C). Flow rates must be kept within the engine manufacturers' design limitations to avoid erosion from excessive flow or inadequate distribution within the engine from low flow rates.

Engine-mounted, water circulating pumps driven from an auxiliary shaft can be modified with proper shaft seals and bearings to give good service life at the elevated temperatures. Configurations that have a circulating pump for each engine increase reliability because the remaining engines can operate if one engine pump assembly fails. An alternative design uses an electric-drive pump assembly to circulate water to several engines and has a standby pump assembly in reserve.

Forced circulation hot water, 250°F at 30 psi (121°C at 210 kPa) gauge, can be used for many process loads, including hot water heating systems for comfort and process, absorption refrigeration chillers, and domestic hot water heating. The distribution of engine jacket coolant must be limited to lessen the risk of leaks or other failures that would prevent the engines from cooling. One solution is to confine each engine circuit to its individual engine, using a heat exchanger to transfer the salvaged heat to another circuit that might serve several engines and an extensive distribution system. An additional heat exchanger is needed in each engine circuit to remove heat whenever the utilizing circuit did not extract all the heat produced (see Figure 5). The reliability of this approach is very high, but because the using circuit must be at a lower temperature than the engine operating level, it requires larger heat exchangers, piping and pumps.

The controls should include low temperature limits to prevent excessive heat loads from seriously reducing the operating temperature of the engines. Engine castings may crack if they are subjected sudden cooling when a large demand for heat a large heat utilization circuit is turned on and temporarily overloads the system. A heat storage tank is an excellent buffer for such occasions, since it can provide heat at a very high rate for short periods and protects the machinery serving the heat loads. The heat level can be controlled with supplementary heat input such as an auxiliary boiler to ensure adequate capacity in the system for any loads.

Another method of protecting the engine heat recovery system from instantaneous load is by flashing the recovered heat into steam and using the steam as the distribution fluid (see Figure 6). By using a back pressure regulator, the steam pressure on the engine can be kept uniform, and the auxiliary steam boilers can supplement the distribution steam header. The same engine coolant system using forced circulation water at 235°F (113°C) entering and 250°F (121°C) leaving the engine can produce steam at 235 F, 8 psi (113°C, 55 kPa) gauge. The engine cooling circuit is the same as in other high temperature water systems. This is accomplished by maintaining a static head above the circulating pump inlet adequate to avoid cavitation at the pump, and restricting the flow rate at the entrance to the steam flash chamber. This causes a change in pressure and prevents flash steam from occurring within the engine.

A steam distribution system through heat exchangers permits using the salvaged heat without contaminating the engine cooling system from downstream piping systems. The salvage heat temperature is kept high enough for most low-pressure steam loads. Returning condensate must be treated to prevent engine oxidation. The flash tank system can be the sediment accumulator for the treatment chemicals.

Some engines use natural convection, ebullient cooling (see Figure 7) with water circulated by a gravity head into the bottom of the engine where it is heated by the engine to form steam bubbles. This lowers the density of the fluid, which then rises to a separating chamber, or flash tank, where the steam is released and the water is recirculated to the engine. By maintaining the flash tank at a static head of several feet above the highest part of the engine, a rapid flow of coolant circulates through the engine, and there is a very small temperature difference between inlet and outlet. It is necessary to maintain a constant back pressure at the steam outlet of the flash chamber to prevent sudden lowering of the operating pressure. If the operating pressure changes rapidly, the steam bubbles in the engine quickly expand and probably interfere with fluid circulation, permitting overheating at the most critical points in the engine. This method of engine cooling is suitable for operation at up to 15-psi (100-kPa) steam, 225°F (124°C), using components built to meet Section VIII of the ASME *Boiler and Pressure Vessel Code, Unfired Pressure Vessels*.

The engine coolant passages must be designed for gravity circulation and must eliminate steam bubbles freely. It is important to consider how coolant is allowed to flow out of the engine heads and exhaust manifolds. Each coolant passage must vent upward to encourage gravity flow and the free release of steam toward the steam separating chamber. Engine heat removal is most satisfactory when these circuits are used because fluid temperatures are uniform throughout the machine. The free convection cooling system depends less on mechanical accessories and is more readily arranged for completely independent assembly of each engine with its own coolant system than other engine cooling systems.

EXHAUST GAS RECOVERY

Almost all of the heat transferred to the engine jacket cooling system can be reclaimed in a standard jacket cooling process or in combination with exhaust gas heat recovery. However, only part of the exhaust heat can be salvaged. This is because of the practical limitations of heat transfer equipment and the prevention of flue gas condensation. Energy balances are often based on standard air at 60°F (16°C); however, it is not practical to reduce the exhaust temperature to this level. A recommended minimum exhaust temperature of 250°F (121°C) has been established by the Diesel Engine Manufacturers Association. Many heat recovery boiler designs are based on a minimum exhaust temperature of 300°F (150°C) to avoid water vapor condensation and acid formation in the exhaust piping. Final exhaust temperature at part-load is important on generator sets that operate at part-load most of the time. Depending on the initial exhaust temperature, approximately 50 to 60% of the available exhaust heat can be recovered.

A complete heat recovery system, including jacket water, lube oil, and exhaust, can increase the overall cycle thermal efficiency to approximately 75%. Many types of exhaust heat-recovery equipment are available in the same categories as standard firetube and water-tube boilers. Because engine exhaust must be muffled to reduce ambient noise levels, most recovery units also act as silencers. Figure 15 illustrates a typical noise curve. Figure 16 shows typical attenuation curves for various types of silencers. Table 1 gives design criteria.

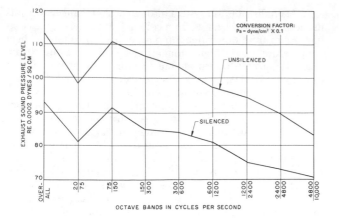

Fig. 15   Typical Reciprocating Engine Exhaust Noise Curve

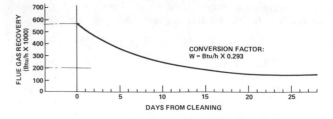

Fig. 17   Thermal Energy Recovered from 600 kW Diesel Engine, Flue-Gas Heat Recovery Unit

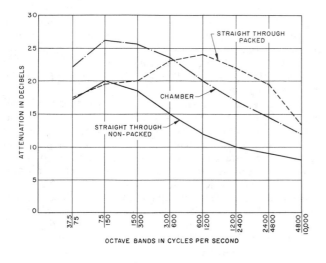

Fig. 16   Typical Attenuation Curves for Engine Silencers

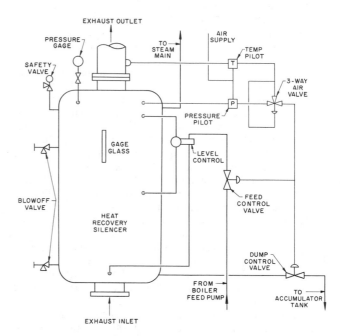

Fig. 18   Automatic Boiler System with Overriding Exhaust Temperature Control

Other heat recovery silencers and boilers include coil-type hot water heaters with integral silencers, water-tube boilers with steam separators for gas turbine, and engine exhausts and steam separators for high-temperature cooling of engine jackets. Recovery boiler design should facilitate inspection and cleaning of the exhaust gas and water sides of the heat transfer surface. Diesel engine units should have a means of soot removal. Soot deposits can quickly reduce the heat exchanger effectiveness (see Figure 17). These same recovery boilers can also serve other requirements of the heat-recovery system, such as surge tanks, steam separators, and fluid level regulators.

In many applications of heat-recovery equipment, the varied demand for heat requires some method of automatic control.

In vertical recovery boilers, control can be achieved by varying the water level in the boiler. Figure 18 shows a control system using an air-operated pressure controller with diaphragm or bellows control valves. When steam production begins to exceed the demand, the feed control valve begins to close, throttling the feed supply. Concurrently, the dump valve begins to open, and the valves reach an equilibrium position that maintains a level in the boiler to match the steam demand. This system can be fitted with an overriding exhaust temperature controller that regulates the boiler output to maintain a preset minimum exhaust temperature at the outlet. This type of automatic control is limited to vertical boilers, since the ASME *Boiler and Pressure Vessel Code* does not permit horizontal boilers to be controlled

Table 1   Noise Criteria in Decibels for Typical Areas

Octave Bands, Hz:	37.5 to 75	75 to 150	150 to 300	300 to 600	600 to 1200	1200 to 2400	2400 to 4800	4800 to 10 000
Highly critical hospital or residential zone	70	49	38	35	34	33	33	33
Night, residential	72	57	47	40	38	38	38	38
Day, residential	75	62	52	45	43	43	43	43
Commercial	78	68	60	55	51	47	44	43
Industrial—commercial	78	73	65	60	58	57	54	54
Industrial	85	82	76	72	70	68	66	66
Ear damage risk	110	102	96	94	94	94	94	94

by varying the water level. With the latter type, a control condenser, radiator, or thermal storage can be used to absorb excess steam production.

In hot water units, a temperature-controlled bypass valve can be used to divert the water or the exhaust gas to achieve automatic modulation with heat load demand (see Figure 10). The heat-recovery equipment should not adversely affect the primary function of the engine to produce work. Therefore, the design of waste-heat recovery boilers should begin by determining the back pressure imposed on the engine exhaust. Limiting back pressures vary widely with the make of engine, but the general range is 6 in. water (1.5 kPa) gauge. The next step is to calculate the heat transfer area that gives the most economical heat recovery without reducing the final exhaust temperature below 300°F (140°C).

Heat recovery silencers are designed to adapt to all engines, and efficient heat recovery depends on the initial exhaust temperature. Most designs can be modified by adding or deleting heat transfer surface to suit the initial exhaust conditions and to maximize heat recovery down to the minimum temperature of 300°F (150°C). Figure 19 illustrates the effect of lowering the exhaust temperature below 300°F (150°C). This curve is based on a specific heat recovery silencer design with an initial exhaust temperature of 1000°F (538°C). Lowering the final temperature from 300 to 200°F (150 to 93°C) increases heat recovery 14% with a 38% surface increase. Similarly, a reduction from 300 to 100°F (150 to 38°C) increases heat recovery 29% but requires a 130% surface increase. Therefore, the cost of heat transfer surface is a factor that must be considered when setting the final temperature.

The other factor to consider is the problem of water vapor condensation and acid formation when the exhaust gas temperature passes through the dew point. This point varies with fuel and atmospheric conditions, and usually is in the range of 125 to 150°F (52 to 66°C). This gives an adequate margin of safety for the 250°F (121°C) minimum temperature recommended by DEMA. Also, it allows for other conditions that could cause condensation, such as an uninsulated boiler shell or other cold surface in the exhaust system, or part loads on an engine.

Little data have been published on the effect of water vapor in exhaust gas. The quantity varies with the fuel type and the intake air humidity. The standard combustion equation for methane fuel, with the correct amount of air for complete combustion, gives a relationship of 5 lb (2.25 kg) of water vapor in the exhaust for every 0.45 lb (kg) of fuel burned. Similarly,

for diesel fuel, the ratio is 3 lb (1.38 kg) of water vapor per 0.45 lb (kg) of fuel. In the gas turbine cycle, these relationships would not hold true because of the large quantities of excess air. The condensates formed at low exhaust temperatures can be highly acidic, such as sulfuric acid from diesel fuels and carbonic acid from natural gas fuels, both of which can cause severe corrosion in the exhaust stack.

There are several heat recovery equations and rules that can be applied quantitatively to determine the feasibility of a heat recovery application. If engine exhaust flow and temperature data are available, and maximum recovery to 300°F (150°C) final exhaust temperature is desired, the basic equation is:

$$Q = \dot{m}(C_p)_g(T_1 - T_2)$$

where

Q = heat recovered, Btu/h (W)
$\dot{m}$ = exhaust flow, lb/h (kg/s)
T_1 = exhaust temperature,°F (°C)
T_2 = final exhaust temperature,°F (°C)
$(C_p)_g$ = specific heat of gas, 0.25 Btu/lb • °F (1.05 kJ/kg • °C)

This equation applies to both steam and hot water units. To estimate the quantity of steam obtainable, divide the total heat recovered (Q) by the latent heat of steam at the desired pressure. The latent heat value should include an allowance for the temperature of the feedwater return to the boiler. The basic equation is:

$$Q = \dot{m}(h_s - h_f)$$

where

$\dot{m}$ = mass flow rate
h_s = enthalpy of steam
h_f = enthalpy of feedwater

Similarly, the quantity of hot water can be determined by:

$$Q = \dot{m}(C_p)_w(T_1 - T_2)$$

where

$(C_p)_w$ = specific heat of water, 1 Btu/lb • °F (4.17 kJ/kg • °C)
T_1 = temperature of water out
T_2 = temperature of input water

If the shaft power is known but engine data is not, the heat available from the exhaust can be estimated at about 1000 Btu/h per hp or 1 lb/h steam per hp (393 W/kW). The exhaust recovery equation is also applicable to gas turbines, although the quantity of flow will be much greater. The estimating figure for gas turbine boilers is 8 to 10 lb/h of steam per hp (1.35 to 1.69 g/s of steam per kW). These factors are reasonably accurate for steam pressures in the range of 15 to 150 psi (103 to 1034 kPa) gauge.

The normal procedure is to design and fabricate heat recovery boilers to the ASME *Code (Section VIII, Unfired Pressure Vessels)* for the working pressure required. Since the temperature levels in most exhaust systems are not excessive, it is common to use flange or firebox quality steels for the pressure parts and low carbon steels for the nonpressure components. Wrought iron or copper can be used for extended-fin surfaces to improve the heat transfer capacities. In special applications such as sewage gas engines, where exhaust products are highly corrosive, wrought iron or special steels are used to improve corrosion resistance.

GENERAL INSTALLATION PROBLEMS

The circulating fluid systems must be kept clean because the internal coolant passages of the engine are not readily accessible for service. The installation of piping, heat exchangers, valves, and accessories must include provisions for internal cleaning of

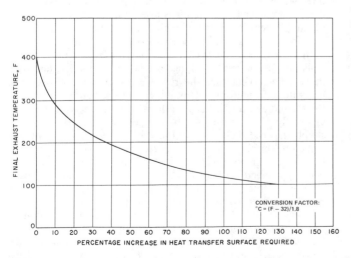

Fig. 19   Effect of Lowering Exhaust Temperature Below 300°F (150°C)

these circuits before they are placed in service. Coolant fluids must be noncorrosive and free from salts, minerals, or chemical additives that can deposit on hot engine surfaces or form sludge in relatively inactive fluid passages. Generally, engines cannot be drained and flushed effectively without major disassembly, making any chemical treatment of the coolant fluid that produces sediment or sludge undesirable.

An initial step toward maintaining clean coolant surfaces is to limit fresh water makeup. The coolant system should be tight and leak-free. Softened water or mineral-free water is effective for initial fill and makeup. Forced circulation hot water systems may require only minor corrosion-inhibiting additives to ensure long, trouble-free service; this feature is one of the major assets of hot water heat-recovery systems.

The ebullient cooling method presents some special hazards for water treatment. Evaporation takes place in the engine, and the concentration of dissolved minerals increases at this critical location. This problem can be minimized by using gravity or forced circulation to encourage high flow rates and by reducing minerals added to the system to a negligible amount. Elevating the fask tank or using pumps to maintain a high static head also reduces the tendency for engine fouling. The water treatment must be adequate to prevent corrosion from free oxygen brought in with returned condensate and makeup water. Additional treatment should control corrosion in the heat recovery muffler and steam separator and in the condensate system. If the cost of pumping the water and the discount in utilization temperature can be absorbed in the system design, a hot water system is preferred. Most available engines are designed for forced circulation of the coolant.

Where several engines are used in one process, independent coolant systems for each machine will avoid a complete plant shutdown from a common coolant system component failure. Such independence can be a disadvantage in that the unused engines are not maintained at operating temperature, as they are when all units are in a common circulating system. If the idle machine temperature drops below the dew point of the combustion products, corrosive condensate will form in the exhaust gas passages each time the idle machine is started.

When substantial water volume and machinery weight must be heated up to operating temperature, the condensate volume is quite significant and must be drained. Some contaminants will get into the lube oil and reduce the service life. If the machinery gets very cold, it may be difficult to start. Units that are started and stopped frequently require an off-cycle heating sequence to lessen the exposure to corrosion. Forced lubrication by an auxiliary externally powered lubricating oil pump is beneficial to the engine when the unit is off. Continuously bathing the engine parts in oil and maintaining engine temperatures near their normal operating temperature improves engine life and lowers the engine maintenance costs. This should be weighed against the pumping losses and the radiation heat losses to the engine room environment.

Water level control of separate steam-producing engine cooling systems is needed to prevent back flow through the steam nozzle of idle units. Using a back pressure regulating valve, a steam check valve, or equalizing line can prevent this problem.

Analysis of the installation costs, available product designs, and operating experience indicates that forced circulation hot water heat recovery systems are best suited to installations of about 1000 kW or smaller total capacity and where future expansion is limited by other design considerations. In projects of much larger capacity, the fluid pumping systems become unwieldy, and future capacity increase becomes difficult. Larger projects are better served with free convection, ebullient-cooled packages for each engine, with a low-pressure steam header connecting various sources of heat input to utilization loads. Larger

projects can have special water conditioning and testing apparatus. The added complexity of coolant quality control in the steam systems can be justified by the greater reliability of the independent engine coolant systems.

CONTROL SYSTEMS

Controls for cogeneration systems are required for (1) system output, (2) safety, (3) prime mover automation, and (4) waste heat recovery and disposal.

Building requirements determine the level of automation. Every system must have controls to regulate the output energy and to protect the equipment. Independent power plants require constantly available control energy to actuate cranking motors, fuel valves, circuit breakers, alarms, and emergency lighting. Battery systems are generally used for these functions, since stored energy is available if the generating system malfunctions. Automatic chargers maintain the energy level with minimum battery maintenance.

Generators operating in parallel with utility system grids have different control requirements than those that operate isolated from the utility grid. A system that operates in parallel and provides emergency standby power if a utility system source is lost must also be able to operate in the same control mode as the system that normally operates isolated from the electric utility grid.

Control requirements for systems that provide electricity and heat for equipment and processors differ, depending upon the number of energy sources and the type of operation relative to the electric utility grid. Isolated systems generally use more than one prime mover during normal operation to allow for load following and redundancy.

Table 2 shows the control functions required for systems operating isolated from the utility grid and systems operating in parallel with the grid with single and multiple prime movers. Frequency and voltage are directly controlled in a single-engine isolated system. The power is determined by the load characteristics and is met by automatic adjustment of the throttle. Reactive power is also determined by the load and is automatically met by the exciter in conjunction with voltage control.

The heat output to the primary process is determined by the load on the engine. It must be balanced with actual requirements by being supplemented or by having excess heat rejected through peripheral devices such as cooling towers. Similarly, if more than one level of heat is required, controls are needed to (1) reduce it from a higher level when it is available at the primary level, (2) supplement it if it is not available, or (3) provide for its rejection when availability exceeds the requirements.

In an isolated plant with more than one prime mover, controls must be added to balance the power output of the prime movers and to balance the reactive power flow between the generators. Synchronizing equipment must be added to parallel the second and any other additional generators with the first. Generally, an isolated system requires that the prime movers supply the needed electrical output with the heat availability controlled by the electrical output requirements. Any imbalance in heat requirements results in burning supplemental fuels or wasting recoverable heat through the heat rejection system.

Supplemental firing and heat rejection can be eliminated by parallel operation of the generators and the electric utility system grid and by adjusting the throttle for the required amount of heat. The electric generation then depends on heat requirements; imbalances between the heat and the electrical load are carried by the electric utility system, either through absorption of excess generation or through the delivery of supplemental electrical energy to the electrical system. In parallel operation, both

Table 2   Generator Control Functions

	Isolated		Parallel	
	One Engine	Two or more Engines	One Engine	Two or more Engines
Frequency (Hz)	Yes	Yes	No	No
Voltage (V)	Yes	Yes	No	No
Power kW	No (Load Following)	Yes (Division of Load)	No	Yes (Division of Load)
Reactive kVAR	No (Load Following)	Yes (Division of kVAR)	Yes	Yes
Heat T_1 Btu or Joules	Supplement only	Supplement only	Load Following	Load Following
Heat $T_2 - T_x$ Btu or Joules	Reduce from T_1 or Supplement	Reduce from T_1 or Supplement	Reduce from T_1 & Load Following	Reduce from T_1 & Load Following
Cooling Btu or Joules	Remove excess heat (Tower, Fan, etc.)	Remove excess heat (Tower, Fan, etc.)	Normally No (Emergency Yes)	Normally No (Emergency Yes)
Synchronizing	No	Yes	Yes	Yes
Black start	Yes	Yes (one engine)	Emergency Use	Emergency Use (one engine)

frequency and voltage are determined by the utility service. The power output is determined by the throttle setting, which responds to the system heat requirements. Only the reactive power flow is independently controlled by the generator controls. When additional generators are added to the system, there must be a means for controlling the power division between multiple prime movers and to continue to divide and control the reactive power flow. All units require synchronizing equipment.

Additional electric utility interface requires safety on the electric grid and the ability to meet the operating problems of the electric grid and the generating system. Additional control functions depend on the desired operating method during loss of interconnection. For example, the throttle setting on a single generator operating in parallel with the utility is determined by the heat recovery requirements and its exciter current, which is set by the reactive power flow through the interconnection. When the interconnection with the utility is lost, the generator control system must detect that loss, assume voltage and frequency control, and immediately disconnect the intertie to prevent an unsynchronized reconnection. With the throttle control now determined by the electric load, the heat produced may not match the requirements for supplemental or discharge heat from the system. When the utility source is reestablished, the system must be manually or automatically synchronized and the control functions restored to normal operation.

Loss of the source may be sensed by one or more of the following factors: overfrequency, underfrequency, overcurrent, overvoltage, undervoltage, or any combination of these factors. The most severe condition occurs when the generator is delivering all electrical requirements of the system up to the point of disconnection, whether it is on the electric utility system or at the plant switchgear. Under such conditions, the generator tends to operate until the load changes. At this time, it either speeds up or slows down, allowing the over or underfrequency device to sense loss of source and to reprogram the generator controls to isolated system operation. The interconnection is normally disconnected during such a change and automatically prevented from reclosing to the electric system until the electric source is reestablished and the generator is brought into synchronism.

The start-stop control may include manual or automatic activation of the engine fuel supply, engine cranking cycle, and establishment of the engine heat removal circuits. Stop circuits always shut off the fuel supply and, for spark-ignited engines, the ignition system is generally grounded as a precaution against incomplete fuel valve closing.

The prime mover must be protected from malfunction by alarms that warn against unusual conditions and by safety shutdown under unsafe conditions. The control system must protect against failure of (1) speed control (overspeed), (2) lubrication (low oil pressure, high oil temperature), (3) heat removal (high coolant temperature or lack of coolant flow), and (4) combustion process (fuel, ignition).

The generator system must be protected from overload, overheating, and short circuit faults. The minimum protection is a properly sized circuit breaker with a shunt-trip coil for immediate automatic disconnect in the event of low voltage, overload, or reverse power. The voltage regulation control must prevent overvoltage.

Generally, a simple control system is adequate where labor is available to make minor adjustments and to oversee system operation. Fully automatic, completely nonattended systems have the same advantages as automatic temperature control systems and are gaining in acceptance.

Fully automated generator controls should be considered for office buildings, hotels, motels, apartments, large shopping centers, some schools, and manufacturing plants, where there is the need for closely controlled frequency and voltage. The control system must be highly reliable, regardless of load change or malfunction, and protect the system equipment from transients and malfunctions. To do this, each generator must be controlled. Generators that operate in parallel require interconnecting controls. The complete system must be integrated to the building use, give properly sequenced operation and provide overall protection. In addition to those controls required for a single prime mover installation, the following further controls are required for multiple generator installations:

1. Simultaneous regulation of fuel or steam flow to each prime mover to maintain required shaft output.

2. Load division and frequency regulation of generators by a signal to the fuel controls.
3. System voltage regulation and reactive load division by maintaining the generator output at the required level.
4. Automatic starting and stopping of each unit for protection in the event of a malfunction.
5. Load demand and unit sequencing by determining when a unit should be added or taken off the bus as a function of total load.
6. Automatic paralleling of the oncoming unit to bus after it has been started and reaches synchronous speed.
7. Safety protection for prime movers, generators, and waste heat recovery equipment in the event of overload or abnormal operation, including a means of load dumping (automatic removal of building electrical loads) in case the prime mover overloads of fails.

When the system is operated in isolation of the utility grid, the engine speed control must maintain frequency within close tolerances, both at steady-state and transient conditions. Generators operating in parallel require a speed control to determine frequency and to balance real load between operating units. To obtain precise control, an electronic governing system is generally used to throttle the engine; the engine responds quickly and is capable of responding to control functions as follows:

1. Engine speed sensing and controlling to operating frequency, i.e., 60 cps.
2. Synchronizing the oncoming generating unit to the bus so it can be paralleled.
3. Sensing true real load rather than current to divide real load between parallel units. (This must be done through the speed control to the throttle.)
4. Proper throttle operation during start-up to ensure engine starting and prevention of overspeed as the engine approaches rated speed.
5. Time reference control is desirable to maintain clock accuracy to within 60 s per month.

Voltage must be held to close tolerances by the voltage regulator from no load to full load. A tolerance of $\pm 1\%$ is realistic for steady-state conditions from no load to full load. The voltage regulator must allow the system to respond to load changes with minimum transient voltage variations. During parallel operation, the reactive load must be divided through the voltage regulator to maintain equal excitation of the alternators connected to the bus. True reactive load sensing is of prime importance to good reactive load division; current sensing is not adequate. An electronic voltage control responds rapidly and, if all three phases are sensed, better voltage regulation is obtained even if the loads are unbalanced on the phases. The alternator construction of a well-designed voltage regulator dictates the voltage transient variation.

Engine sizing can be influenced by the control system's accuracy in dividing real load. If one engine lags another in carrying its share of the load, the capacity that it lags is never used. Therefore, if the load sharing tolerance is small, the engines can be sized more closely to the power requirements. A load sharing tolerance of less than $\pm 5\%$ of unit rating is necessary to use the engine capacity to good advantage.

This is also true for reactive load sharing and alternator sizing. If reactive load sharing is not close, a circulating current results between the alternators. The circulating current uses up alternator capacity, which is determined by the heat generated by the alternator current. The heat generated, and therefore the alternator capacity, is proportional to the square of the current. Therefore, it is advisable to install a precise control system. The added cost is justified by the possible installation of smaller engines and alternators.

When starting a unit, the following must be performed in sequence: (1) initiate engine crank, (2) open fuel valve and throttle, (3) when engine starts, terminate cranking, (4) when desired speed is reached, eliminate overshoot, (5) if the engine refuses to start in a given period of time, register a malfunction and start the next unit in sequence, and (6) on reaching the desired speed, synchronize the started engine-alternator to the bus to be paralleled without causing mechanical and electrical severe transients. A time period should be allowed for synchronization; if it does not occur during the allotted time, a malfunction should register and the next unit in sequence should start.

Once a unit is on the line, real and reactive load division should be effective immediately. The throttle of the unit coming on the line must be advanced so that it will accept its share of the load. The unit or units that were carrying all the load will have their throttle(s) retarded so that they will give up load to the oncoming unit until all units share equally, or in proportion to the unit size if they are sized differently. During the load-sharing process, control frequency must be maintained and, once paralleled, the load-sharing control must correct continuously to maintain the load balance. Reactive load sharing is similar but is done by the voltage regulator varying the excitation of the alternator exciter field.

Problems that will increase installation cost can arise during installation. These can be minimized by carefully checking out the cogeneration system, particularly the engine-alternator units. Typical problems arising during installation include: (1) engine actuators placed too near exhaust pipes, causing excessive wear of actuator bearings and loose parts in the engine actuator, (2) improper wiring, and (3) sloppy linkage between engine actuator and carburetor. Sensors used to send a malfunction signal to the control system can also cause trouble when not properly installed. It is practical to use two sensors, one for alarm indication of an abnormal condition and the other for shutdown malfunction.

ENERGY USER INTERCONNECTIONS

A cogeneration system provides both power and thermal energy. Depending on the design and operating decisions, the users can intertie with the electric utility with energy delivered to the utility grid. For the cogeneration system to operate thermally and be economically efficient, the energy delivered by the system must be at the levels required by the energy users.

The selection of the prime movers is partially based on user thermal requirements. Internal combustion reciprocating engines have the lowest ratio of thermal to electric energy with low temperature heat at a maximum of 200°F (93°C) and 250°F (121°C) available from lube oil and jacket water, respectively. This heat can be used to supply thermal energy to applications requiring low temperature heat or where the low temperature heat can be used effectively for preheat. In addition, for maximum heat recovery, the building thermal application must take sufficient energy from the recovered heat stream to lower its temperature to that required to cool the prime mover effectively. A supplementary means for rejecting prime mover heat may be required if the thermal load does not provide adequate cooling or as a backup to thermal load loss.

Gas turbines can provide higher quantities and better qualities of heat per unit of power, while extraction steam turbines can provide even greater flexibility in both the quantity and quality (temperature and pressure) of heat delivered. Externally fired prime mover cycles, such as the Stirling Cycle, are also flexible in quantity and quality of thermal energy.

In selecting prime movers and evaluating cogeneration economics, consider the amount of thermal energy available, its quality, and the degree to which this recovered energy can satisfy user requirements. Also, consider the degree to which the user's energy systems provide necessary cooling to the cogeneration facility.

Electrical energy can be delivered to the utility grid, directly to the user, or both. Generators for on-site power plants can deliver electrical energy at levels equal in quality to those provided by the electric utility for voltage regulation, frequency control, harmonic content, reliability, and phase balance. They are also capable of satisfying stringent requirements imposed by user computer applications, medical equipment, high frequency equipment, and emergency power supplies. The cogenerator's electrical interface should be designed according to user or utility electrical characteristics.

GLOSSARY

Avoided Cost: The decremental cost for the electric utility to generate or purchase electricity that is avoided through the purchase of power from a cogeneration facility.

Back-up Power: Electric energy available from or to an electric utility during an unscheduled outage to replace energy ordinarily generated by the facility or the utility. Frequently referred to as standby power.

Base Load: The minimum electric or thermal load generated or supplied continuously over a period of time.

Bottoming-Cycle: A cogeneration facility in which the energy input to the system is first applied to another thermal energy process; the reject heat that emerges from the process is then used for power production.

Capability: The maximum load that a generating unit, generating station, or other electrical apparatus can carry under specified conditions for a given period of time, without exceeding approved limits of temperature and stress.

Capacity: The load for which a generating unit, generating station, or other electrical apparatus is rated.

Capacity Credits: The value included in the utility's rate for purchasing energy, based on the savings accrued through the reduction or postponement of new generation capacity that results from purchasing power from cogenerators.

Capacity Factor: The ratio of the actual annual plant electricity output to the rated plant output.

Central Cooling: The same as central heating except that cooling (heat removal) is supplied instead of heating; usually a chilled water distribution system and return system for air conditioning.

Central Heating: Supply of thermal energy from a central plant to multiple points of end-use, usually by steam or hot water, for space and/or service water heating; central heating may be large-scale as in plants serving university campuses, medical centers, and military installations or in central buildings systems serving multiple zones; also district heating.

Cogeneration: The sequential production of electrical or mechanical energy and useful thermal energy from a single energy stream.

Coproduction: The conversion of energy from a fuel (possibly including solid or other wastes) into shaft power (which may be used to generate electricity) and a second or additional useful form. The process generally entails a series topping and bottoming arrangement of conversion to shaft power and either process or space heating. Cogeneration is a form of coproduction.

Demand: The rate at which electric energy is delivered at a given instant or averaged over any designated time period.

Annual Demand—The greatest of all demands that occurred during a prescribed demand interval in a calendar year.

Billing Demand—The demand upon which customer billing is based, as specified in a rate schedule or contract. It can be based on the contract year, a contract minimum, or a previous maximum and does not necessarily coincide with the actual measured demand of the billing period.

Coincident Demand—The sum of two or more demands occurring in the same demand interval.

Instantaneous Peak Demand—The maximum demand at the instant of greatest load.

Demand Charge: The specified charge for electrical capacity on the basis of the billing demand.

Energy Charge: That portion of the billed charge for electric service based on the electric energy (kilowatt-hours) supplied, as contrasted with the demand charge.

Grid: The system of interconnected transmission lines, substations, and generating plants of one or more utilities.

Grid Interconnection: The intertie of a cogeneration plant to an electric utility's system to allow electricity flow in either direction.

Harmonics: Waveforms whose frequencies are multiples of the fundamental (60 Hz) wave. The combination of harmonics and fundamental wave causes a nonsinusoidal, periodic wave. Harmonics in power systems are the result of non-linear effects. Typically, harmonics are associated with rectifiers and inverters, are furnaces, arc welders, and transformer magnetizing current. There are voltage and current harmonics.

Heat Rate: A measure of generating station thermal efficiency, generally expressed in Btu per net kilowatt-hour.

Heating Value: The energy content in a fuel that is available as useful heat.

Interruptible Power: Electric energy supplied by an electric utility subject to interruption by the electric utility under specified conditions.

Load Factor: The ratio of the average load supplied or required during a designated period to the peak or maximum load occurring in that period.

Maintenance Power: Electric energy supplied by an electric utility during scheduled outages of the cogenerator.

Off-Peak: Time periods when power demands are below average; for electric utilities, generally nights and weekends; for gas utilities, summer months.

Power Factor: The ratio of real power (kW) to apparent power (kVA) for any given load and time; generally expressed as a decimal.

Selective Energy Systems: A form of cogeneration in which part, but not all, of the site's electrical needs are met with on-site generation, with additional electricity purchased from a utility as needed.

Supplemental Thermal: The heat required when recovered engine heat is insufficient to meet thermal demands.

Supplementary Firing: The injection of fuel into the recovered heat stream to raise its energy content (heat).

Supplementary Power: Electric energy supplied by an electric utility in addition to the energy the facility generates.

Thermal Capacity: The maximum amount of heat that a system can produce.

Topping-Cycle: A cogeneration facility in which the energy input to the facility is first used to produce useful power, with the reject heat from power production then used for other purposes.

Total Energy Systems: A form of cogeneration in which all electrical and thermal energy needs are met by on-site systems; a total energy system can be completely isolated or switched over to a normally disconnected electrical utility system for back-up.

Voltage Flicker:　Term commonly used to describe a significant fluctuation of voltage.

Wheeling:　The use of the transmission facilities of one system to transmit power for another system.

BIBLIOGRAPHY

Internal Combustion Engine Institute. 1962. *Engine Installation Manual.*
National Engine Use Council. 1967. *NEUC Engine Criteria.*

CHAPTER 9

APPLIED HEAT PUMP SYSTEMS

A HEAT pump is a device that extracts heat from one substance and transfers it to another portion of the same substance or to a second substance at a higher temperature. In a physical sense, all refrigeration equipment, including air conditioners and chillers with refrigeration cycles, are heat pumps. In engineering, however, the term "heat pump" is reserved for equipment that heats for beneficial purposes, rather than that which removes heat for cooling only. Dual-mode heat pumps provide separate heating and cooling, while heat reclaim heat pumps provide heating or simultaneous heating and cooling. An applied heat pump requires application engineering as opposed to the direct use of a manufacturer-designed unitary product, although many applied systems incorporate unitary equipment. Applied systems can include built-up (field- or custom-assembled from components) and industrial heat pumps. Almost all modern heat pumps use a vapor compression (modified Rankine) cycle. Any of the other refrigeration cycles discussed in Chapter 1 of the 1985 FUNDAMENTALS Volume are also suitable, and their use is currently being researched and developed. While most modern heat pumps are powered by electric motors, limited use is being made of engine and turbine drives and very limited use of heat-actuated equipment. Applied heat pump systems are most commonly used for heating and cooling buildings but are gaining popularity for efficient domestic and service water, pool, and process heating.

Modern large central heat pumps having capacities from 20 to 2200 hp (15 kW to 16 MW) of compressor-motor rating operate in many facilities. Some of these machines are capable of output water temperatures of 220°F (104°C) and up to 60 psi (400 kPa) gauge steam.

Compressors in large central systems vary from one large centrifugal unit to as many as eight multicylinder reciprocating units. A single or central system is generally used throughout the building, but in some instances, the total capacity is divided among several separate heat pump systems to facilitate zoning. Well water, solar, air, and internal building heat are used as heat sources. Compression can be one- or multi-stage. Frequently, heating and cooling are supplied simultaneously to separate zones.

Decentralized systems with water loop heat pumps are commonly used. These systems employ multiple water-source heat pumps connected by a water loop. They can also include heat rejectors (cooling towers and dry coolers), supplementary heaters (boilers and steam heat exchangers), loop reclaim heat pumps, solar collection devices, and thermal storage. Initial costs are relatively low, and building reconfiguration is flexible.

Community and district heating systems based on both centralized and distributed heat pump systems are being researched. A few prototypes are in use.

HEAT PUMP TYPES

Several types of applied heat pumps (both open and closed cycle) are available; some reverse their cycle for both heating and cooling in HVAC systems, while others are for heating only in HVAC and industrial process applications. The basic types are as follows:

The preparation of this chapter is assigned to TC 9.4, Applied Heat Recovery/ Heat Pump Systems.

Closed Vapor Compression Cycle (Figure 1). Using a conventional, separate refrigerant cycle, this is the most common type for both HVAC and industrial process use. It may use a compound, multi-stage, or cascade refrigeration cycle.

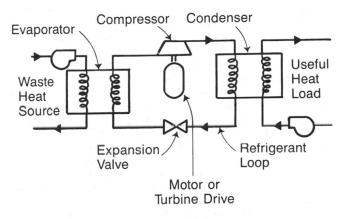

Fig. 1   Closed Vapor Compression Cycle

Mechanical Vapor Recompression (MVR) Cycle with Heat Exchanger (Figure 2). Process vapor is compressed to a temperature and pressure sufficient for reuse directly in a process. Energy consumption is minimum, since temperature levels are optimum for the process. Typical applications for this cycle include evaporators (concentrators) and distillation columns.

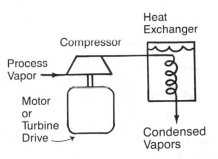

Fig. 2   Vapor Recompression Cycle with Heat Exchanger

Open Vapor Recompression Cycle (Figure 3). A typical application for this cycle is in an industrial plant with a series of steam pressure levels and an excess of steam at a lower-than-desired pressure level. The heat is pumped to a higher pressure by compressing the lower pressure steam.

Waste Heat Driven Rankine Cycle (Figure 4). This cycle is useful where large quantities of heat are wasted and where energy costs are high. The heat pump portion of the cycle may be either open or closed, but the Rankine cycle is usually closed.

Heat pumps are classified by (1) heat source and sink, (2) heating and cooling distribution fluid, (3) thermodynamic cycle, (4) building structure, (5) size and configuration, and (6) limitation of the source and the sink. Table 1 shows the more

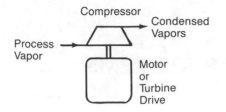

Fig. 3   Open Vapor Recompression Cycle

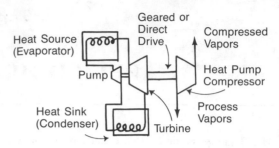

Fig. 4   Waste Heat Driven Rankine Cycle

common types of closed cycle heat pumps for air-conditioning service.

The *air-to-air* heat pump is the most common type and is particularly suitable for factory-built unitary heat pumps. It is widely used in residential and commercial applications. (See Chapter 44 of the 1983 EQUIPMENT Volume and Chapter 5 of this volume.) The first diagram in Table 1 is typical of the refrigeration circuit used. A few installations have been made in which the forced-convection indoor heat transfer surface has been replaced by a radiant panel.

In air-to-air heat pump systems, as shown in the second diagram of Table 1, the air circuits can be interchanged by motor-driven or manually operated dampers to obtain either heated or cooled air for the conditioned space. In this system, one heat-exchanger coil is always the evaporator and the other is always the condenser. The conditioned air passes over the evaporator during the cooling cycle, and the outdoor air passes over the condenser. The positioning of the dampers causes the change from cooling to heating.

A **water-to-air** heat pump relies on water as the heat source and sink, and uses air to transmit heat to or from the conditioned space.

Air-to-water heat pumps are commonly found in large buildings where zone control is necessary. They are also used to produce hot or cold water in industrial applications.

Earth-to-air heat pumps can use the direct expansion of the refrigerant in an embedded coil, as presented in Table 1, or they can be indirect, described under the earth-to-water type.

A **water-to-water** heat pump uses water as the heat source and sink for both cooling and heating. Heating-cooling changeover can be done in the refrigerant circuit, but it is often more convenient to perform the switching in the water circuits, as shown in Table 1. Although the diagram shows direct admittance of the water source to the evaporator, in some cases, it may be necessary to apply the water source indirectly through a heat exchanger (or double wall evaporator) to avoid contaminating the water source into the normally treated closed chilled water system. Another method is to use a closed-circuit condenser water system.

An **earth-to-water** heat pump may be like the earth-to-air type shown but may have a refrigerant-water heat exchanger like the water-to-air type shown in Table 1. Ground (earth) coupled heat pumps use the earth as a heat source or sink and are coupled to the evaporator or condenser by a secondary fluid circuit. An anti-freeze solution is pumped through the horizontal or vertical pipes embedded in the earth. Soil, moisture, composition, density, and uniformity close to the surrounding field areas affect the success of this method of heat exchange. The materials of construction for the pipe and the corrosiveness of the local soil and underground water affect the heat transfer and the service life. A variation of this cycle could transfer heat from the evaporator, plus the heat of compression to a water cooled condenser. The condenser heat would then be available for heating air, domestic hot water, or other items. A further variation could use refrigerant in DX, flooded, or recirculation evaporator circuits for the earth pipe coils or for an above-ground exchanger for air or other fluids.

Internal source, including water-loop, heat pumps use the high internal cooling load generated in modern buildings either directly or with storage.

Solar heat pumps rely on stored low temperature solar heat as the heat source. Solar heat pumps may resemble water-to-air, or other types, depending on the form of solar heat collector and type of heating and cooling distribution system.

Waste heat pump installations have been made that use sanitary sewage waste heat or laundry waste heat as a heat source. The waste fluid can be introduced directly into the heat pump evaporator after waste filtration, or it can be taken from a storage tank, depending on the application.

Refrigerant-to-Water Heat Pumps condense a refrigerant by the cascade principle shown on Page 4.15 of the 1986 REFRIGERATION Volume. Cascading pumps the heat to a higher level, where it is rejected to water or another liquid. This type of heat pump can also serve as a condensing unit to cool almost any fluid or process. More than one heat source can be used to offset those times when insufficient heat is available from the primary source.

HEAT SOURCES AND SINKS

Table 2 shows the principal media as heat sources and heat sinks. The choice for an application is influenced primarily by geographic location, climatic conditions, initial cost, availability, and type of structure. Table 2 presents the various factors to be considered for each type. A discussion of design and selection factors for each source and sink follows.

Air

Outdoor air is a universal heat-source, heat-sink medium for the heat pump. Extended-surface, forced-convection heat-transfer coils transfer the heat between the air and the refrigerant. Typically, these surfaces are 50 to 100% larger than the corresponding surface on the indoor side of heat pumps that use air as the distributive medium. The volume of outdoor air handled is also greater in about the same proportions. The temperature difference during the heating operation between the outdoor air and the evaporating refrigerant is generally from 10 to 25 °F (6 to 14 °C). The performance of air heating and cooling coils is given in more detail in Chapters 6 and 9 of the 1983 EQUIPMENT Volume.

When selecting or designing an air-source heat pump, two factors in particular must be considered: (1) the temperature variation in a given locality and (2) frost formation.

As the outdoor temperature decreases, the heating capacity of an air-source heat pump decreases. Selecting equipment for a given outdoor heating design temperature is therefore more critical than for a fuel-fired system. Consequently, the equipment must be sized for as low a balance point as is practical

Table 1 Common Heat Pump Types

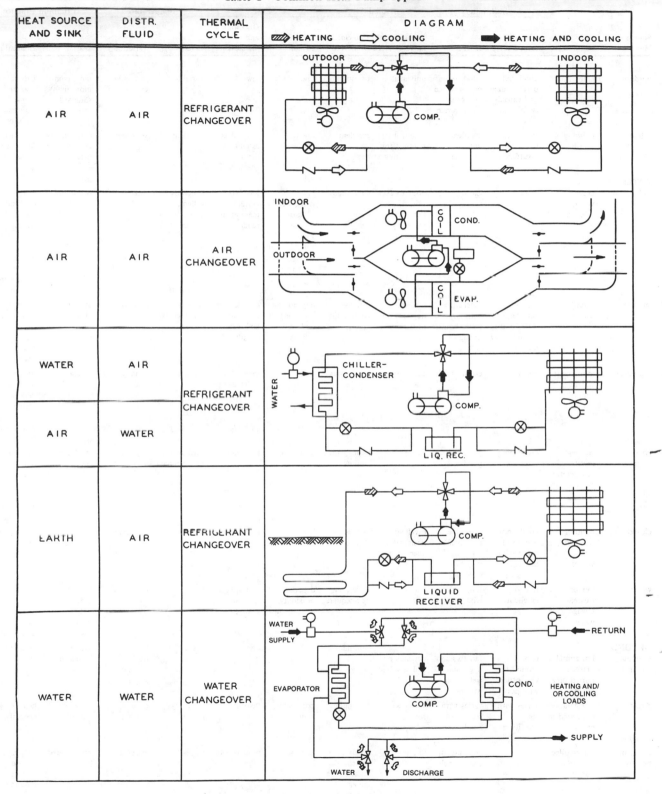

HEAT SOURCE AND SINK	DISTR. FLUID	THERMAL CYCLE	DIAGRAM
AIR	AIR	REFRIGERANT CHANGEOVER	
AIR	AIR	AIR CHANGEOVER	
WATER	AIR	REFRIGERANT CHANGEOVER	
AIR	WATER		
EARTH	AIR	REFRIGERANT CHANGEOVER	
WATER	WATER	WATER CHANGEOVER	

for heating without having excessive and unnecessary cooling capacity during the summer. The procedure for finding this balance point, which is defined as the outdoor temperature at which capacity matches heating requirements, is given in Chapter 44 of the 1983 EQUIPMENT Volume.

When the surface temperature of an outdoor air coil is 32°F (0°C) or lower, frost may form, and can, if allowed to continue, interfere with heat transfer. A nominal amount of frost deposit of about 2 to 3 lb/ft² of coil face area (10 to 15 kg/m²) does not substantially affect the heat transfer capacity of the coil. The number of defrosting operations are influenced by the climate, air-coil design, and the hours of operation. Experience shows that little defrosting is generally required below 20°F (−7°C) and below 60% rh. This can be confirmed by psychro-

Table 2 Heat Pump Sources and Sinks

Source or Sink	Examples	Suitability		Availability		Cost		Temperature		Common Practice	
		Heat Source	Heat Sink	Location Relative to Need	Coincidence with Need	Installed	Operation and Maintenance	Level	Variation	Use	Limitations
AIR outdoor	ambient air	good, but performance and capacity fall when very cold	good, but performance and capacity fall when very hot	universal	continuous	low	low	variable	generally extreme	most common, many standard products	defrosting and supplemental heat usually required
exhaust	building ventilation	excellent, but insufficient	excellent, but insufficient	excellent if planned for in building design	excellent	low to moderate	low unless exhaust is dirt or grease laden	excellent	very low	emerging as conservation measure	insufficient for typical loads
WATER well	groundwater, well often shared with potable water source	excellent	excellent	poor to excellent, practical depth varies by location	continuous	low if existing well used or shallow wells suitable, can be high otherwise	low, but periodic maintenance required	generally excellent, varies by location	extremely stable	common	water disposal and required permits may limit, double wall exchangers may be required, may foul or scale
surface	lakes, rivers, ocean	excellent with large water bodies or high flow rates	excellent with large water bodies or high flow rates	limited, depends on proximity	usually continuous	depends on proximity and water quality	depends on proximity and water quality	usually satisfactory	depends on source	available, particularly for fresh water	often regulated or prohibited; may clog, foul, or scale
tap (city)	municipal water supply	excellent	excellent	excellent	continuous	low	low unless water use or disposal is charged	excellent	usually very low	excellent	use or disposal may be regulated or prohibited, may corrode or scale
condensing	cooling towers, refrigeration systems	excellent	poor to good	varies	varies with cooling loads	usually low	moderate	favorable as heat source	depends on source	available	suitable only if heating need is coincident with heat rejection
closed loops	building water-loop heat pump systems	good, loop may need supplemental heat	favorable, loop heat rejection may be needed	excellent if designed as such	as needed	low	moderate	as designed	as designed	very common	may be impractical as retrofit
waste	raw or treated sewage, grey water	fair to excellent	fair, varies with source	varies	varies, may be adequate	depends on proximity, high for raw sewage	varies, high for raw sewage	good	usually low	uncommon, practical only in large systems	usually regulated; may clog, foul, scale, or corrode
GROUND ground-coupled	horizontal or vertical buried pipe loops	good if ground is wet, otherwise poor	fair to good if ground is wet, otherwise poor	depends on soil suitability	continuous	high	low	usually good	low, particulary for vertical systems	available, increasing	high initial costs
direct	refrigerant circulated in ground	varies with soil conditions	varies with soil conditions	varies with soil conditions	continuous	extremely high	favorable	varies by design	generally low	extremely limited	leaks very expensive
SOLAR direct or heated water	solar collectors and panels	fair	poor, usually unacceptable	universal	highly intermittent, night use requires storage	extremely high	moderate to high	varies	extreme	very limited	supplemental source or storage required
INDUSTRIAL process heat or exhausts	distillation, molding, refining, washing	fair to excellent	varies, often impractical	varies	varies	varies	generally low	varies	varies	varies	often impractical unless heat used in same plant as obtained

metric analysis using the principles given in Chapter 6 of the 1983 EQUIPMENT Volume. However, under very humid conditions when small suspended water droplets are present in the air, the rate of frost deposit can be about three times as great as predicted from psychrometric theory. Then, a heat pump may require defrosting after as little as 20 minutes of operation. The effect of this condition on loss of available heating capacity should be taken into account in applying an air-source heat pump.

The early application of air-source heat pumps followed commercial refrigeration practice and used relatively wide fin spacing, i.e., 4 to 5 fin/in. (5 to 6 mm fin spacing), on the theory that this would minimize the frequency of defrosting. However, experience has proven that effective hot gas defrosting permits much closer fin spacing and reduces the size and bulk of the system. In current practice, fin spacings of 8 to 13 per inch (2 to 3 mm) are widely used.

In many institutional and commercial buildings, some air must be continuously exhausted year-round. This exhaust air can be used as a heat pump air source, although supplemental heat is generally added.

The high humidity in indoor swimming pools causes condensation on ceiling structural members, walls, windows, and floors and causes discomfort to spectators. Traditionally, outside air and dehumidification coils with reheat from a boiler that also heats the pool water are used. This application is ideal for air-to-air and air-to-water heat pumps because energy costs can be reduced. Suitable materials must be chosen to resist corrosion from chlorine and high humidity.

Water

Water can be a satisfactory heat source, subject to the considerations listed in Table 2. City water is seldom used because of cost and municipal restrictions. Geothermal water is an innovative heat source in some areas. Well water is particularly attractive because of its relatively high and nearly constant temperature, generally about 50°F (10°C) in northern areas and 60°F (16°C) or higher in the south. Frequently, sufficient water is available from wells where the water is reinjected into the aquifer. The use is non-consumptive and, with proper system design, only the temperature changes. The water quality should be analyzed, and the possible effect of scale formation and corrosion should be minimized. In some instances, it may be necessary to separate the well fluid from the system equipment with an additional heat exchanger. Special consideration must also be given to filtering and settling ponds for specific fluids. Other considerations are the costs of drilling, piping, pumping, and means for disposal of used water. Information on well water availability, temperature, and chemical and physical analysis is available from U.S. Geological Survey offices located in many major cities.

Interest in geothermal energy has led to the identification of many geothermal energy sources with temperatures compatible with heat pump systems. They range from the typical shallow well temperatures mentioned above to temperatures where direct use for heating is possible. When using temperatures higher than typical ground water temperatures, special attention should be given to designing the system for the proper fluid temperature drop. This is necessary, since increasing the temperature drop decreases the fluid flow requirements for a specified heating rate. When the available temperature is high enough for direct use, but the available water resource flow is insufficient to satisfy the heating load, the heat pump can be used to meet the load by achieving a greater drop in the resource temperature than the temperature necessary for direct use. Geothermal system designs are presented in more detail in Chapter 45.

Surface or stream water may be used; but under reduced winter temperatures, the cooling spread between inlet and outlet must be limited to prevent freezeup in the evaporator absorbing the heat.

Under industrial conditions, waste process water (e.g., spent warm water in laundries, plant effluent, and warm condenser water) may be a source for heat pump operations.

Use of water during cooling operations follows the conventional practice for water-cooled condensers.

Water-refrigerant heat exchangers are generally direct-expansion or flooded water coolers, either shell-and-coil or shell-and-tube type. In small capacity refrigerant change-over systems, they are connected as refrigerant condensers during the heating cycle and as refrigerant evaporators during the cooling cycle. In applied heat pumps, the water is reversed instead of the refrigerant and the heat pump is used for heating only.

Earth

Earth as a heat source and sink, by heat transfer through buried coils, has not been used extensively. Soil composition varies widely from wet clay to sandy soil, and has a predominant effect on thermal properties and expected overall performance. The heat-transfer process in soil is primarily one of bulk temperature change with time (e.g., transient heat flow). Thermal diffusivity (α), the ratio of thermal conductivity to the product of unit density and specific heat, $\alpha = k/\rho c$, is a dominant factor and is difficult to determine at different building sites. The moisture content is also an influence, since energy in the ground also can be transported via moisture travel in the soil.

Earth coils are one of two basic types. The first is single, serpentine heat exchanger pipes buried 3 to 6 ft (0.9 to 1.8 m) apart in a horizontal plane at a depth of 3 to 6 ft (0.9 to 1.8 m) below grade. Pipes may be buried deeper, but excavation costs must be considered. The second type of coil is a vertical concentric tube or U-tube heat exchanger. A vertical coil may consist of one long or several shorter exchangers.

Solar

The use of solar energy as a heat source, either on a primary basis or in combination with other sources, has attracted interest but has not emerged as an economical system. Air, surface water, shallow groundwater and shallow ground-source systems all use solar energy indirectly. The principal advantage of using solar radiation as a heat pump heat source is that, when available, it provides heat at a higher temperature level than other sources, resulting in an increase in coefficient of performance. Compared to a solar heating system without a heat pump, the collector efficiency and capacity are materially increased because of the lower collector temperature required.

Research and development in the solar-source heat pump field has been concerned with two basic systems—direct and indirect. The direct system places refrigerant evaporator tubes in a solar collector, usually a flat-plate type. Research shows that a collector without glass cover plates can also extract heat from the outdoor air. The same surface may then serve as a condenser using outdoor air as a heat sink for cooling. The refrigeration circuit resembles the earth-to-air heat pump shown in Table 1.

An indirect system circulates either water or air through the solar collector. When air is used, the first system shown in Table 1 for an air-to-air heat pump may be selected, the collector is added in such a way that (1) the collector can serve as an outdoor-air preheater, (2) the outdoor-air loop can be closed so that all source heat is derived from the sun, or (3) the collector can be disconnected from the outdoor air serving as the source or sink. When water is circulated through the collector, the heat pump circuit may be either water-to-air or water-to-water, as illustrated in Table 1.

All heat pump systems using solar energy as the only heat source require either an alternate heating system or a means of storing heat during periods of insufficient solar radiation. Heat storage is discussed in the section on "Auxiliaries" and in Chapter 46.

HEAT PUMP COMPONENTS

For the most part, the components and practices involved with heat pumps relate directly to the art of low temperature refrigeration. This section outlines the major components used and points out characteristics or special considerations that apply to heat pumps in combined room heating and air-conditioning applications or higher temperature industrial applications.

Compressors

Centrifugal Compressors. Centrifugal compressor characteristics essentially do not readily meet the needs of air-source heat pumps. High pressure ratios or high lifts, associated with low gas volume resulting from low load conditions, cause the centrifugal to surge. Therefore, most centrifugal applications in heat pumps have been limited to water-to-water or refrigerant-to-water heat pump systems, heat transfer systems, storage systems, and hydronically-cascaded systems (see the section on "Operating Cycles"). With these applications, the centrifugal compressor enables heat pumps to enter the field of industrial plants, as well as large multistory buildings; and installations with double-bundle condensers up to 512,000 Btu/h (150 MW) have been made. The transfer cycles permit low pressure ratios, and many single- and two-stage units with various refrigerants are operational with high COPs.

Reciprocating compressors are used more than any other type on systems in the range of 0.5 to 100 tons (1.8 to 350 kW) and larger. A brief description of this compressor is given in Chapter 12 of the 1983 EQUIPMENT Volume. For the most economical concept applied to combined heating and cooling, it is general practice to select the compressor for the heating duty and a separate, high efficiency chiller for the remaining cooling duty. When heating, the capacity of a particular compressor is the sum of the evaporator capacity (i.e., heat-source coil capacity) and the heat equivalent of the compressor work minus heat losses outside the conditioned space. Some machines are designed for heating only and others for dual heating and cooling.

A compressor used for comfort cooling has a medium clearance volume (ratio of gas volume remaining in cylinder after compression to the total swept volume is about 0.05). For an air-source heat pump, a compressor with a small clearance volume ratio, e.g., 0.025, is more suitable for low temperature operation and provides, for example, about 15% greater refrigerating capacity at an evaporator temperature of 0°F (−18°C) and a condenser temperature of 110°F (43°C). However, this compressor has somewhat more power demand under maximum cooling load conditions than does one of medium clearance.

More total heat capacity can be obtained at low outdoor temperatures by deliberately oversizing the compressor. When this is done, some capacity reduction for operation at higher outdoor temperatures can be provided by multi- and variable-speed drives, cylinder cutouts, or other methods.

The disadvantage of this arrangement is that the greater number of operating hours that occur at the higher suction temperatures must be served with the compressor in the unloaded condition, which generally causes lower efficiency and higher annual operating cost. The additional initial cost of the oversized compressor must be economically justified by the gain in

heating capacity. One method proposed for increasing the heating output at low temperatures uses *staged compression,* in which one compressor may compress from −29°F (−34°C) saturated suction temperature to 40°F (4°C) saturated discharge temperature (DTP), and a second compressor compresses the vapor from 40°F (4°C) STP to 120°F (49°C) DTP. In this arrangement, any two compressors may be interconnected in parallel, with both pumping from about 45°F (7°C) STP to 120°F (49°C) at the normal cooling rate point. Then at some predetermined outdoor temperature on heating, they are reconnected in series and compress in two successive stages.

Figure 5 shows the performance of a pair of compressors for units of both medium and low clearance volume. At low suction temperatures, the reconnection in series adds some capacity. However, the motor for this case must be selected for the maximum loading conditions for summer operation, even though the low stage compressor has a greatly reduced power requirement under the heating condition.

Rotary vane compressors, which can be used for the low stage of multi-stage plants, have a high capacity but are generally limited to less than seven pressure ratios. They also have limited means for capacity reduction.

Screw compressors offer high pressure ratios at low to high capacities and have fixed or variable slide-valve action to reduce capacity. Generally, large oil separators are required, since currently available compressors have oil injection. They are less susceptible to damage from liquid spillover and have fewer parts than do reciprocating compressors.

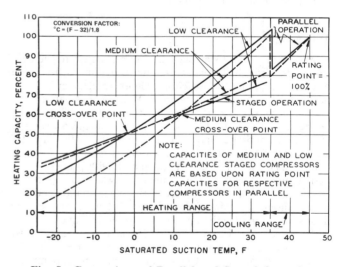

Fig. 5   Comparison of Parallel and Staged Operation for Air-Source Heat Pumps

Heat Transfer Components

Refrigerant-to-air and refrigerant-to-water heat exchangers, as previously described in the section "Heat Sources and Sinks," are similar to heat exchangers currently used in air-conditioning refrigeration. A refrigerant subcooler coil can be paired with an indoor air coil or used to preheat ventilation air on systems with a ventilation air supply. A substantial gain in capacity and coefficient of performance can result.

VESSELS AND PIPING COMPONENTS

Refrigeration Components

Refrigerant piping, receivers, expansion devices, and refrigeration accessories in heat pumps are usually the same as components found in other types of refrigeration and air-conditioning systems.

A **reversing valve** changes the system from the cooling to the heating mode. This changeover requires the use of a valve(s) in the refrigerant circuit, except where the change occurs in fluid circuits external to the refrigerant circuit (see Table 1). Reversing valves are usually pilot-operated by solenoid valves, which admit head and suction pressures to move the operating elements.

Expansion devices for controlling the refrigerant flow are normally thermostatic expansion valves, as described in Chapter 20 of the 1983 EQUIPMENT Volume. The control bulb must be located carefully. If the circuiting is arranged so that the refrigerant line on which the control bulb is placed can become the compressor discharge line, the resulting pressure developed in the valve power element may be excessive, requiring a special control charge or pressure-limiting element. When a thermostatic expansion valve is applied to an outdoor air coil, it is desirable to have a special *cross-charge* to limit the superheat at low temperatures for better use of the coil. When an expansion valve is attached to a coil operated as a condenser, a bypass with a check valve is normally provided, as indicated in Table 1.

On an air-source heat pump that operates over a wide range of evaporating temperatures, a capillary tube passes refrigerant at an excessive rate at low back pressures, causing liquid flood back to the compressor. In some cases, suction line accumulators or charge-control devices are added to minimize this effect.

A **refrigerant receiver,** which is commonly used as a storage place for liquid refrigerant, is particularly useful in a heat pump to take care of the unequal refrigerant requirements of heating and cooling. The receiver is usually omitted on heat pumps used for heating only.

Defrost Control (Air Source)

A variety of **defrosting control** schemes sense the need for defrosting air-source heat pumps, and initiate and terminate the defrost cycle.

A timer is sometimes set to start defrosting at predetermined intervals, e.g., about every 1.5 hours. The defrost cycle can be terminated either by a control sensing the coil pressure or a thermostat that measures the temperature of the liquid refrigerant in the outdoor coil. When the temperature (or corresponding saturation pressure) of the liquid leaving the outdoor coil rises to about 70°F (21°C), the completion of defrosting is ensured.

Another means of starting the defrost cycle is with a pressure control that reacts to the air pressure drop across the coil. Under conditions of frost accumulation, the airflow is reduced and the increased pressure drop across the coil initiates the defrost cycle. Again, the preferred method of terminating the defrost cycle is by using a refrigerant temperature control that measures the temperature of the liquid refrigerant in the coil.

A third method for defrosting involves a temperature differential control and two temperature-sensing elements. One element is responsive to outdoor-air temperature and the other to the temperature of the refrigerant in the coil. As frost accumulates, the differential between the outdoor temperature and the refrigerant temperature increases, initiating a defrost cycle. The system is restored to operation when the refrigerant temperature in the coil reaches a specified temperature, indicating that defrosting has been completed. When the outdoor air temperature decreases, the differential between outdoor air temperature and refrigerant temperature decreases, initiating the defrost cycle with greater frost buildup, unless compensation is provided.

Auxiliaries

Supplementary heaters may be included either within the heat pump package or external in the system. When installed in the distribution ductwork, they are frequently controlled to temper the air during defrost operation on units using *reverse-cycle* defrost. They are required for start-up where the heat source and sink are the same (e.g., heating process water using process effluent as the source).

Thermal storage in a heat pump system can improve its performance characteristics and is essential where the heat source and heating loads do not occur simultaneously. All materials have thermal storage properties to a greater or lesser degree. In buildings, the structural materials are almost always either absorbing heat from or delivering heat to the interior space. This effect is more pronounced in the cooling operation where greater air temperature variation is tolerated. Storage tends to reduce the rate of temperature change and helps to reduce the peak equipment requirements. In this sense, every heating and cooling system can be said to involve heat storage.

Many attempts have been made, particularly in recent years, to increase the heat-storage effect by using special heat-storage materials as part of the heating or cooling system. The result has been a reduction in the size of the heating or cooling equipment necessary to take care of peak demands.

In the case of the heat pump, a provision for heat storage not only reduces the size of the heat pump necessary for a given load, but it also provides a more desirable electrical load by shifting part of the load to the time of day when the cost of power is least. The off-peak electric hot water heater is a common example of such a heat storage application.

STRUCTURAL EFFECT ON SYSTEM DESIGN

Modern buildings use double-glazed windows and better insulation, as well as more internal areas with considerably higher internal heat gain from lights, people, computers, and other heat dissipating equipment. Systems for such buildings are normally required, particularly during mild weather, to supply heating to the exterior zones and cooling to the interior zones, simultaneously. In many instances, these systems may have to change daily or even hourly between the heating and cooling cycle to maintain the required indoor conditions.

The heat pump is exceptionally qualified for such applications and frequently shows a considerable saving in operating cost over other systems, because of its inherent ability to transfer heat from an interior zone, where cooling may be desired, to the exterior, where heating may be needed.

OPERATING CYCLES

Figures 6, 7, and 8 show three of the several possible operating cycles for simultaneously providing heating and cooling. Figure 6 illustrates one method of using water as the heat source or sink and as the heating and cooling medium. The compressor, evaporator, condenser, refrigerant piping, and accessories are essentially standard and are available as a factory-packaged water-to-water heat pump.

The cycle is flexible, and the heating or cooling medium is instantly available at all times. Heating can be provided exclusively to the zone conditioners by closing valves 2 and 3 and opening valves 1 and 4. With the valves in these positions, the water is divided into two separate circuits. The warm water circuit consists of the condenser (where the heat is supplied by the high temperature refrigerant), valve 1, zone conditioners, and a circulating pump. The cold water circuit consists of the evaporator (where heat is taken from the water by the low temperature refrigerant), valve 4, exchanger (where heat is taken from the source water), valve 1, and a circulating pump. The refrigerating compressor operates to maintain the desired leaving water temperature from the condenser.

Similarly, cooling can be exclusively obtained in the cycle of Figure 6 by opening valves 2 and 3 and closing valves 1 and 4.

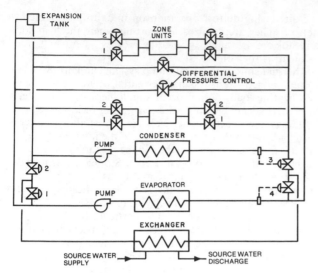

Fig. 6   Water-to-Water Heat Pump Cycle

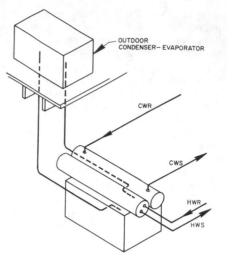

Fig. 7   Air-to-Water Single-Stage Heat Pump

With this arrangement, the cold water circuit consists of the evaporator (where heat is removed from the water by the low temperature refrigerant), valve 2, zone conditioners, and a circulating pump. The warm water circuit consists of the condenser (which receives the heat from the refrigerant), valve 3, exchanger (where heat is rejected to the source water), valve 2, and a circulating pump. The refrigerating compressor operates to maintain the desired water temperature leaving the evaporator.

During the intermediate season, simultaneous heating and cooling can be provided by the cycle shown in Figure 6. Valves 3 and 4 are modulated when valves 1 and 2 are open. Valve 3 is adjusted to maintain 85 to 140°F (30 to 60°C) water in the condenser circuit and valve 4 to maintain 45 to 50°F (7 to 10°C) in the evaporator circuit. The excess heating or cooling effect is wasted to the exchanger, which passes it on to the source water.

The source or sink water, if of suitable quality, can be supplied directly to the condenser and evaporator instead of by an exchanger, as illustrated by Figure 6, eliminating one heat transfer surface and its performance.

Figure 7 shows an air-source, air-to-water, single-stage heat pump working with a four-pipe system for simultaneous heating and cooling. The refrigerant cycle of this package is factory pre-assembled. However, the outside summer condenser or winter evaporator must be field connected to the compressor unit. In such heat pumps, which are available in packages to 150 tons (528 kW) of cooling, the only operational reversal takes place in the outdoor condenser-evaporator. The shell-and-tube evaporator and condenser remain as cooler and heater throughout, respectively. Most commercial units of this type use the flooded principle.

The air-to-air heat pump (Figure 8) is somewhat more efficient than the air-to-water system, since the conditioned air is heated or cooled directly by the refrigerant without the addition of another media. No shell-and-tube heat exchangers are required, which reduces the initial costs. All previously described heat pumps are also available without the simultaneous feature. Careful evaluation of each application permits the designer to select the best system for each particular case.

Systems for Heat Recovery

Many commercial structures require simultaneous heating and cooling for prolonged periods during occupancy. Frequently, the mechanical cooling equipment and the heating equipment must be operated jointly to provide the necessary comfort. Many cycles

have been developed to permit the transfer of heat from areas of heat surplus in the building to areas requiring heat. The double-bundle condenser working with a reciprocating or centrifugal compressor is most often used in this application. Figure 9 shows the basic configuration of this system, which makes heat available in the range of 100 to 130°F (38 to 54°C). The warm water is supplied as a secondary function of the heat pump and represents recovered heat.

Figure 10 shows a similar cycle, except that a storage tank has been added, enabling the system to store heat during the occupied hours by raising the temperature of the water in the tank. During the unoccupied hours, water from the tank is gradually fed to the evaporator providing load for the compressor and condenser that heats the building during the off hours.

Figure 11 is another transfer system capable of generating 130 to 140°F (54 to 60°C) or warmer water whenever there is a cooling load by cascading two compressors hydronically. In this configuration, one chiller can be considered as a chiller only and the second unit as a heating only heat pump.

Water-Loop System

Figure 12 illustrates a water-loop heat pump system with a storage tank and solar collectors. All the heat pumps installed

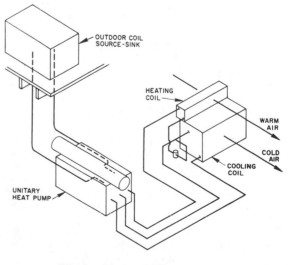

Fig. 8   Air-to-Air Heat Pump

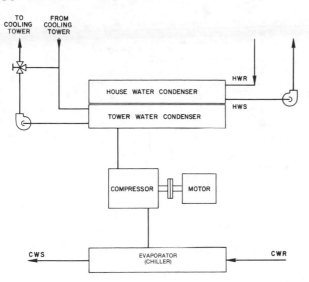

Fig. 9   Heat Transfer Heat Pump with Double-Bundle Condenser

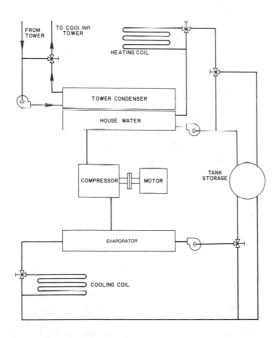

Fig. 10   Heat Transfer System with Storage Tank

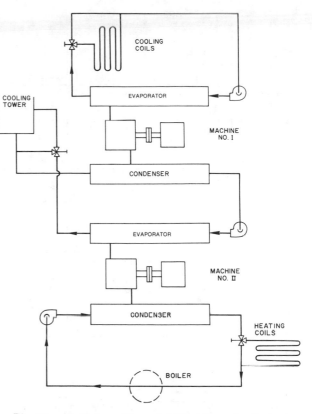

Fig. 11   Multistage (Cascade) Heat Transfer System

ing the heat removed to the two-pipe system by a shell-and-tube condenser. The total heat gathered by the two-pipe system is rejected to an evaporative cooler usually mounted on the roof. If and when some of the modules, particularly on the northern side, require heat, the individual units switch (by means of four-way refrigerant valves) into the heating cycle. The units derive their heat source from the two-pipe water loop, basically obtaining heat from a relatively high source; i.e., the condenser water of the other units. When only heating is required, all units are in the heating cycle and, consequently, a boiler is needed to provide 100% heating capability. The water loop is usually

in the perimeter of a building can instantly give either heating or cooling by absorbing or rejecting heat from the closed loop. The storage tank in the condenser circuit can store the excess heat during occupied hours and provide heat to the loop during unoccupied hours. During this process of storing and draining heat from the tank, solar heat can also be added within the limitations of the temperatures of the condenser system. The solar collectors are more effective and efficient under these circumstances because of the temperature ranges involved. The system can easily switch to either the chilled water or condenser water side and virtually eliminates the need for a boiler in the water-loop heat pump system.

Another cycle that combines transfer characteristics with water-to-air heat pump units is shown in Figure 13. Each module has one or more water-to-air heat pumps. The units are connected hydronically with a two-pipe system. Each unit cools conventionally, supplying air to the individual module and reject-

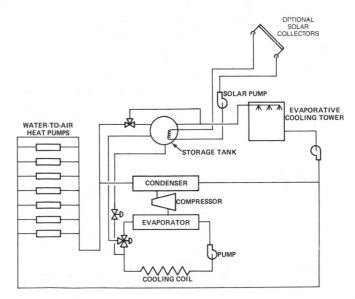

Fig. 12   Closed Loop Solar Heat Pump System

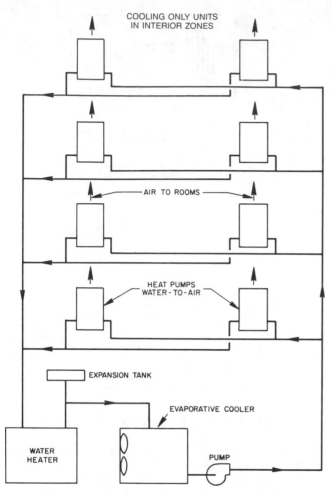

Fig. 13   Heat Transfer System Using Water-to-Air Unitary Heat Pump

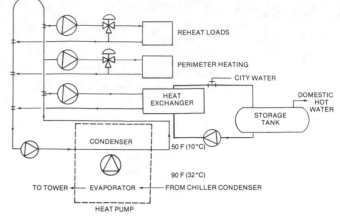

Fig. 14   Typical Waste Heat-Recovery System

Industrial Process Heat Pumps

Heat recovery in industrial plants offers numerous opportunities for applied heat pumps. Factory-packaged machines can produce condenser water temperatures up to 220 °F (104 °C) on special order, and steam can also be delivered.

Heat pumps are generally used in industrial applications for other than room heating and air conditioning. These applied heat pump systems are specifically engineered for the intended applications. Many such applications are found in the process industries. The operating principles and equipment are the same as discussed above, but the economic trade-offs are different from room heating and air conditioning and must be specifically investigated for each case. Guidelines provided should be reconsidered in view of the operating economics and technical issues involved for industrial process applications.

Two major classes of industrial heat pump systems can be distinguished: *closed* and *open* systems.

Closed cycle systems use a suitable working fluid, usually a refrigerant in a sealed system. They can use either the absorption or the vapor compression principle, depending on the temperature levels, and process economics. Heat is transferred to and from the system through heat exchangers similar to refrigeration system exchangers. Closed cycle heat pump systems are often classed with industrial refrigeration systems with operation occurring at higher temperatures. Refrigerant and oil choices must be consistent with available component and material restraints and limits, as well as mutual compatibilities at the expected operating temperatures. In addition, the viscosity and foaming characteristics of the oil and refrigerant mixtures must be consistent with the lubrication requirements at the specific mechanical load imposed on the equipment. Proper oil return and heat transfer at the evaporators and condensers must be considered (see Figure 15).

Open cycle systems use the process fluid to raise the temperature of the available heat energy by vapor compression. The most important class of applications is steam process fluid. Compression can be provided with a mechanical compressor or by a thermocompression ejector driven by the required quantity of high pressure steam. A distinction must be made between systems compressing relatively clean, process quality steam as opposed to contaminated steam from evaporation processes.

Boiler-generated process steam usually conforms to cleanliness standards that ensure corrosion-free operation of the compression equipment. However, boiler treatment chemicals often prevent the use of process steam in direct contact with food or potable water. An open cycle heat pump compressing process steam can provide exceptional steam energy management flex-

60 to 90 °F (16 to 32 °C) temperature and, therefore, needs no insulation.

A water-to-water heat pump can be added in the closed water loop before the heat rejection device (evaporative cooler) for further heat reclaim. This heat pump reuses the heat and provides domestic hot water or elevates water temperatures in a storage tank to be bled back into the loop.

Some aspects of these cycles may be proprietary and are covered by patents, and should not be used without appropriate investigation. Illustrations and their description are not meant to imply any endorsement of the cycles by ASHRAE but are used to illustrate the variations made in practical applications.

Waste Heat Recovery

In many large buildings, internal heat gains require year-round chiller operation. This internal heat is often wasted through a cooling tower. Figure 14 illustrates a heat pump installed in the water line from the chiller's condenser before rejection at the cooling tower. This arrangement uses the otherwise wasted heat to provide heat at the higher temperatures required for space heating, re-heat, and domestic water heating.

Prudent design may dictate cascade systems with chillers in parallel or series. Manufacturers can assist with custom components to meet a wide range or load and temperature requirements.

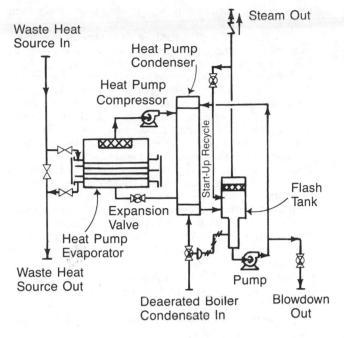

Fig. 15 Water-to-Steam Heat Pump

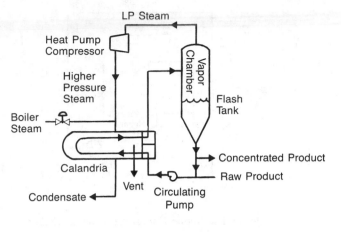

Fig. 16 Open Cycle Single-Effect Evaporator

porarily overspeeding the driver, while optimal efficiency is retained by sizing for nominal operating conditions. Proper integration of heat pump controls and process system controls is essential.

EQUIPMENT SELECTION

The heat source and heat sink surfaces, heating and cooling surfaces, heat pumps, and accessory equipment are sized and selected in accordance with current refrigeration and air-conditioning practices addressed in other chapters of this volume. The capacity of the system must meet the design heating and cooling requirements.

ibility to a process with variable steam demand, if the heat pump controls are integrated properly with the process controls.

Application of open cycle heat pumps to evaporation is exceptionally important (see Figure 16). The most frequent applications are in the dairy, food, paper, and chemical industries. The water vapor from the evaporator is compressed to higher pressure and temperature and is condensed at the heat transfer surface of the evaporator liberating its heat of condensation. An equivalent of 25 multiple effects can be realized. Depending on the temperature differential required for heat transfer in the evaporator [as low as 4°F (2°C)], the compression work required is a small fraction of the heat energy recovered. A separate condenser for "waste" steam is eliminated, and cooling water consumption is greatly reduced. However, the vapors from the evaporator may contain contaminants from the materials being concentrated and fouling, corrosion, or erosion of the compression system can take place. Adequate separators, baffles, and flow path must be provided with proper attention given to the materials and equipment selected. Coefficients of performance in excess of 25 are common. When process vapors are incompatible with compressor materials, or when low temperature evaporation is desired, a closed cycle evaporator, such as shown in Figure 17, can be used.

Vapor compositions can be different than liquid compositions and boiling point rise results. Mechanical vapor compression heat pumps can be applied to distillation columns (Figure 18). The overhead vapors are compressed to a higher pressure and temperature and then condensed in the reboiler. This eliminates the need for boiler steam in the reboiler and reduces overall energy consumption. After the pressure of condensed vapor as liquid from the reboiler is reduced through the expansion valve, some of the liquid at a lower temperature is returned to the column as reflux and the balance forms the overhead product, both as liquid and vapor. Vapor is recycled as necessary. Distillation processes attractive for this application include ethanol-water, methanol-water, and mixed hydrocarbon splitters.

An added benefit is obtained when capacity control is provided using a variable speed driver such as an engine, gas or steam turbine, or electric motor with variable speed provisions. Additional capacity for emergencies is also available by tem-

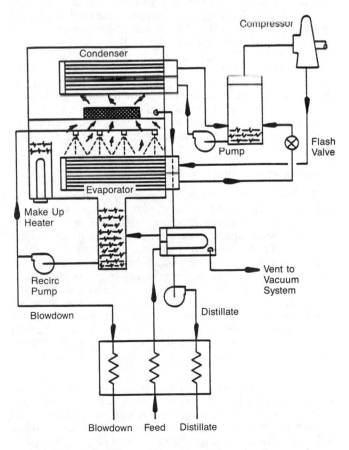

Fig. 17 Closed Cycle Vapor Compression

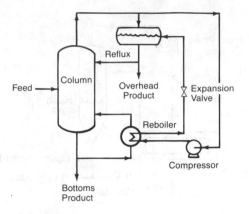

Fig. 18 Mechanical Vapor Compression for Distillation

Supplemental Heating

Heating needs may exceed the capacity available from equipment selected for the cooling load, particularly if outdoor air is used as the heat source. When this occurs, supplemental heating or additional compressor capacity should be considered. The additional compressor capacity or the supplemental heat is generally used only in the severest winter weather and, consequently, has a low usage factor. Both possibilities must be evaluated to determine the most economical selection.

When supplemental heaters are used, the elements should always be located in the air or water circuit downstream from the heat pump condenser. This permits the heat pump system to operate at a lower condensing temperature, increasing the system heating capacity, and improving the coefficient of performance. The controls should sequence the heaters so they are energized after all heat pump compressors are fully loaded. An outdoor thermostat is recommended to limit or prevent energizing of heater elements during mild weather when they are not needed. Where 100% supplemental heat is provided for emergency operation, it may be desirable to keep one or more stages of the heaters de-energized whenever the compressor is running. In this way, the cost of electrical service to the building is reduced to meet the maximum coincidental demand.

A flow switch should be used to prevent operation of the heating elements and the heat pump unless there is air or water flow.

Heating and Cooling Load Estimates

Realistic winter outdoor design temperatures should be selected to obtain authentic heating requirements and prevent installation of oversized supplemental heating equipment.

The winter design temperatures given in Table 1 of Chapter 24 in the 1985 FUNDAMENTALS Volume should be used, unless experience and more authentic data for the particular locality are available. The local utility company may have such data.

Conservative heating requirements and lower nightly indoor temperatures are not recommended, because the resulting additional heating capacity would unnecessarily increase both the initial and operating cost of the system. Instead, consider operating cycles using auxiliary equipment to provide higher operating efficiencies and load reduction, including the following:

1. Using the maximum, practical amount of insulation with proper vapor barrier in sidewalls, ceilings, and floors of a structure. Windows and doors should at least be weatherstripped and properly caulked; in most areas of the country, storm windows and doors (or the equivalent) can be justified.
2. Use of available, dependable heat sources within the struc-

tures, such as lights, motors, heat-producing machinery, and people.
3. Automatically closing the outdoor air intakes during nights, weekends, and other unoccupied periods, so that the heat loss will be limited to transmission and infiltration.
4. Proper selection of the ventilation air. Because the ventilation air load is an appreciable part of the total, reasonable ventilation quantities, without sacrificing a healthy environment, should be selected. Minimum quantities of outdoor air may even be unacceptable, because of objectionable, irritable, and toxic odors in the atmosphere due to a high percentage of hydrogen sulfide, smog, and other chemical effluences from industrial processes. Physical and chemical odor removal units, such as activated charcoal in combination with a conventional or electric air filter, are effective in purifying and removing odor-causing substances (see Chapter 12 in the 1985 FUNDAMENTALS Volume and Chapter 7 in the 1986 REFRIGERATION Volume). The quantity of ventilation air can often be reduced considerably, resulting in savings in both initial and operating cost.

For buildings with highly variable occupancies, the ventilation air quantity might be reduced at lower outdoor temperatures because the building is occupied by fewer people. This is particularly true in retail stores where fewer people shop during extremely cold weather. However, code requirements should be checked for restrictions on ventilating requirements before this principle is applied.

Reciprocating or Centrifugal Compressors

While most air-source installations for combined heating and cooling incorporate single-stage reciprocating compressors, the use of multistage compressors has increased. The two-stage compression system is particularly applicable in the extreme northern climate where the frequent occurrence of low outdoor temperatures makes the single-stage system impractical. In two-stage systems, the compressors can be used in parallel during the cooling cycle and in series during the heating cycle. The main advantages of staging are the increased capacity per unit of compressor displacement and increased compressor efficiency, which results in proportionally smaller (or perhaps eliminates) auxiliaries needed to provide a given heating effect at the lower outdoor temperatures. Whether these improvements in efficiency will outweigh the disadvantages of the higher initial cost of staging depends on the requirements of a particular installation.

Centrifugal compressors for larger capacity applications are primarily used on water-source heat pumps but also are readily applicable to air-source systems, particularly those using the reclaiming cycle (Figure 9). Multistaging of the centrifugal machines, similar to that described for the reciprocating units, can be prescribed using a brine when low temperature outdoor air is used as the heat source. Centrifugal assemblies normally use water as the heat transfer fluid on both the high and low sides of the refrigerating machine. When the unit is exposed to temperatures below 30 °F (−1 °C), an antifreeze liquid or brine with a suitable viscosity, corrosiveness and initial cost, is required.

Compressor Floodback Protection

On the more recent air source-sink (central plant type installations) a suction line separator, similar to that shown in Figure 19, has been used successfully. This separator, in combination with a liquid-gas heat exchanger, is a protection against migration and harmful liquid floodbacks to the compressor. The solenoid valve should be wired to open when the compressor is operating, and the hand valve should then be adjusted to provide an acceptable bleed rate into the suction line.

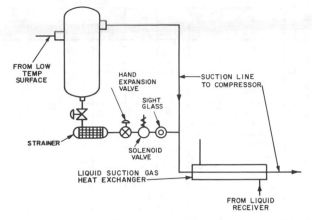

Fig. 19   Suction Line Separator for Protection Against Liquid

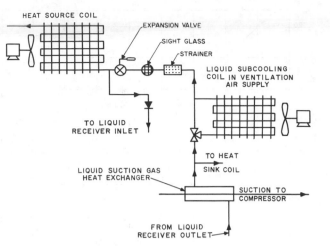
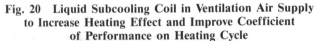
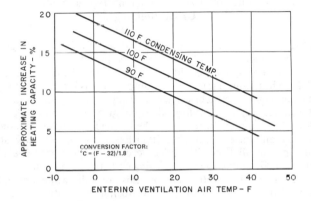

**Fig. 20   Liquid Subcooling Coil in Ventilation Air Supply
to Increase Heating Effect and Improve Coefficient
of Performance on Heating Cycle**

Liquid Subcooling Coils

A refrigerant subcooling coil can be added to the heat pump cycle, as illustrated by Figure 20, to preheat the ventilation air during the heating cycle and, at the same time, lower the temperature of the liquid refrigerant. Depending on the refrigerant circulation rate and the quantity and temperature of ventilation air, the heating capacity can be increased as much as 15 to 20%, as indicated by Figure 21.

Similarly, a source water coil can be incorporated in the water-to-water systems (Figure 6) to either preheat or precool the ventilation air, depending on the operating cycle, and thereby improve the performance. Means must be provided to prevent freezing of the water within the coil when exposed to ventilation air temperatures below 32 °F (0 °C).

Water Temperatures for Heating

A realistic warm water temperature should be selected for the design condition on all systems using water as the heat transfer fluid. Designing for water temperatures higher than actually required results in not only higher initial cost, but higher operating cost as well. When the same air coil is used for both heating and cooling, a coil selected for the summer cooling design load is generally sufficient to use heating water temperatures from 95 to 110 °F (35 to 43 °C).

When a building contains areas that must be heated but not cooled, it may be necessary to select a slightly deeper coil to satisfy the heating load with relatively low temperature water. The additional coil cost is relatively small and easily justified in comparison with the operating cost in raising the warm water temperature schedule of the entire building to meet requirements of several small areas for a few hours per year. Another alternative for these critical areas is to use direct electric heat, either as a supplement or as the total heating source.

The objection that low heating water temperatures result in drafty conditioned spaces is a misconception. Where a building is air conditioned both in summer and winter, the air quantities circulated are based on the design summer cooling load. Consequently, if sufficient heat is provided to spaces to offset any winter losses, the air temperature entering the space will be the same, regardless of the water temperature supplied to the coil. In fact, the lower water temperatures are more advantageous from the control standpoint, since the throttling water valve, bypass water valve or face-and-bypass dampers need not throttle through such an extreme range.

Defrosting of Heat Source Coils

Frost accumulates rather heavily on outdoor heat source coils when the temperature reaches approximately 40 °F (4 °C), but

**Fig. 21   Anticipated Increase in Heating Capacity Resulting
from Use of Liquid Subcooling Coil**

lessens somewhat with the simultaneous decrease in outdoor temperature and moisture content.

Occupants are not disturbed by automatic defrosting that uses hot gas in the indirect system because of the relatively short cycle (usually less than 10 minutes) and the thermal storage in the conditioned space. In most cases, the defrost cycle consists of changing the equipment to the cooling cycle where the outdoor coil becomes the condenser, and the indoor coil becomes the evaporator. In instances where discomfort is experienced because of the type of distribution, the supplemental heating can be used to offset the cooling effect.

Another method of defrosting is by spraying heated water over an outdoor coil. The water can be heated by the refrigerant or by auxiliaries.

Draining of Heat Source and Sink Coils

Direct expansion indoor and outdoor heat transfer surfaces serve as condensers and evaporators. Both surfaces, therefore, must have proper refrigerant distribution headers to serve as evaporators and have suitable refrigerant drainage while serving as condensers.

In a flooded system, the normal float control to maintain the required refrigerant level is used.

CONTROLS

The control system should provide flexible and effective heat pump operation. Capacity modulation, a convenient method of

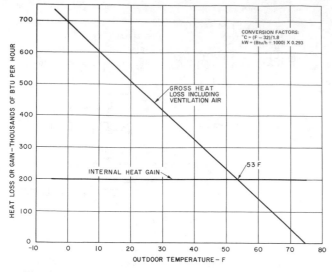

Fig. 22   Heat Loss and Heat Gain at Various Outdoor
Temperatures for Exterior Zone of Typical Multistory
Office Building

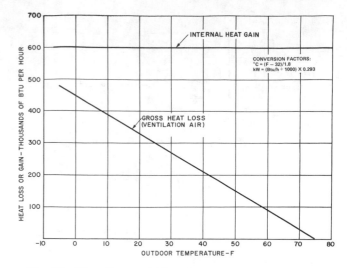

Fig. 23   Heat Loss and Heat Gain at Various Outdoor
Temperatures for Interior Zone of Typical Multistory
Office Building

switching from heating to cooling, and automatic defrosting of
the air source heat surfaces should be provided.

The control system should prevent energizing the supplemental
electric heater until (1) the heat pump system is unable to satisfy
the heating requirement when operating at full capacity and (2)
the source water or outdoor air is below a predetermined outdoor temperature. In this way, the coincident energy demand
will be minimized with a resulting lower average energy cost. In
some installations, it may be necessary to energize the supplemental heat during the defrosting cycle to minimize any cooling effect within the structure, but this normally will not exceed
the maximum coincident demand during the heating cycle.

On air-to-water and water-to-water systems, an outdoor reset
control of the hot water temperature may be desirable for improved economy. During milder weather, the warm water
temperature is rescheduled to a lower level, since less heat dissipation is required; this permits the compressor to operate at a lower
condensing temperature.

The following controls may be used to change from heating
to cooling.

1. A **conditioned space thermostat** on residences and small commercial applications.
2. An **outdoor air thermostat** (with provision made for manual
   overriding for variable solar and internal load conditions) can
   reverse the cycle on larger installations, where it may be difficult to find a location in the conditioned space, which
   reflects the desired operating cycle for the total building.
3. **Manual changeover.**
4. A **sensing device**, which responds to the greater load requirement, heating or cooling, is generally applied on simultaneous
   heating and cooling systems.
5. **Dedicated microcomputer** controls to automate changeover
   and perform all of the other control functions needed, as well
   as to simultaneously monitor the performance of the system.
   This may be a stand-alone device or incorporated as part of
   a larger building automation system.

On the heat pump system, it is important that space thermostats are interlocked with ventilation dampers so that both
operate on the same cycle. During the heating cycle, the fresh
air damper should be positioned for minimum ventilation air,
with the space thermostat calling for increased ventilation air
only if the conditioned space becomes too warm. Fan and/or

pump interlocks are generally provided to prevent the heat pump
system from operating if the use of the accessory equipment is
not available. On commercial and industrial installations, some
form of heat pressure control is required on the condenser at
outdoor air temperatures from 60 to 0°F (16 to −18°C).

Industrial process controls may have combinations of electrical and pneumatic controls with proportional auto reset and
batch modifications to prevent temperature drifts. Chapter 51
has further information.

HEAT RECLAIMING CYCLE

The heat pump adapts readily to installations requiring
simultaneous heating and cooling by transferring heat from the
interior of a structure (e.g., where cooling is desired) to the exterior, where heating is needed. This type of application frequently results in a considerable cost saving compared with other
designs, because of the resulting relatively high operating efficiency of the equipment under these conditions. An indication

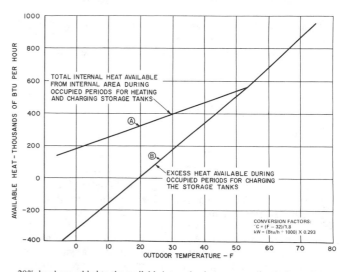

20% has been added to the available internal gain to account for the heat of compression added with the air-conditioning compressor.

Fig. 24   Quantity of Internal Heat Available to External
Areas and Storage Tank at Various Outdoor Temperatures
During Occupied Periods

of the magnitude of the recoverable heat in a modern multistory office building is given by Figures 23 and 24. Figures 22 and 23 show the day gross heat loss and the internal heat gain of the exterior and interior zones. Figure 24 shows the result of transferring this internal excessive heat gain to the exterior zone by means of a heat pump. Curve A of Figure 24 is the total internal heat available, and curve B is excess heat (above that needed by the exterior zone), which can be kept in a storage tank (using a cycle similar to that shown by Figure 10) for future particular installation. During the occupied periods, no outside heat source or supplemental heat is needed at outdoor temperatures of 19°F (−7°C) or above.

Chapter 6 covers other types of heat-recovery cycles.

BIBLIOGRAPHY

Airesearch Manufacturing Company. 1979. Cycle Selection of a High-Temperature Heat Pump. NTIS, PC AO6/MF AO1, DOE/CS/40005—T3.

Airesearch Manufacturing Company. 1984. Open Cycle Centrifugal Vapor Compression Heat Pump. Annual Report March 1983-February 1984. GRF-84/0085. NIIS PB85-113405.

Arnold, H.C.; Grossman, G.; and Blanco, Perez H. Investigations of Advanced Industrial Heat Pumps and Chillers for Low Grade Heat Recovery. Oak Ridge National Laboratory, TN.

Bard Manufacturing Company. Air Source Heat Pump Operation and Components. Manual No. 2100-059. Bard Manufacturing Company. Heat Pump Sizing (air-to-air and water-to-air). Manual No. 2100-057.

Bard Manufacturing Company. Operation and Troubleshooting Water-to-Air Heat Pumps. Manual No. 2100-054.

Bard Manufacturing Company. Water Systems and Well Pump and Pipe Sizing for Water Source Heat Pumps. Manual 2100-078.

Bard Manufacturing Company. Dual Fuel Add-On Heat Pump Guide for Operational Cost Savings for Regions 2 through 5. Manual No. 2100-070 (Region 2); No. 2100-071 (Region 3); No. 2100-072 (Region 4); No. 2100-073 (Region 5).

Beesley, A.H., and Rhinesmith, R.D. 1980. Energy Conservation by Vapor Compression Evaporation. Chemical Engineering Progress, August, pp. 37-41.

Becker, F.E., and Zakak, A.I. 1985. Recovering Energy by Mechanical Vapor Recompression. Chemical Engineering Progress, July, pp. 45-49.

Berntsson, T., et al. 1980. The Use of the Ground as a Heat Source for Heat Pumps in Urban Areas. An Overall Review of Technical-Economic Aspects. (English/Swedish). Doc. D39: Swed. Counc. Bldg. Res., Stockholm, (Available from Svensk Byggtjanst, Box 7853, S-103 99 Stockholm.)

Berutti, A. 1979. Saving Energy by Using Electricity. Electrical Construction and Maintenance, June.

Boland, D., and Hill, J.C. Heat Pumps Application in an Energy Integrated Process. ICI Petrochemicals Ltd., UK.

Booth, B. 1982. Industrial and Commercial Applications—Heat Pumps. Electricity Council, London. Paper presented at Electrotechnologies in Industry Conference, May 25-27, at Montreal.

Braham, G.D. Heat Recovery Technology for Swimming Pools by the Application of Heat Pumps. Electricity Council, London.

Bschorr, O. 1979. Heat Pump for Air Heating and Air Drying. (in German) Brennst.-Waerme-Kraft 31:483-85.

Burton, D.C., and Chaudoir, D.W. 1980. Industrial Heat Pumps for the Manufacture of Power Alcohol (Ethanol). Paper presented at 3rd World Energy Engineering Conference, October, Atlanta, GA.

Calm, J.M. 1981. The DOE Heat-Pump-Centered Integrated Community Energy Systems Project. Argonne National Laboratory.

Carrier Corp. 1982. Water Source Heat Pump System Design Guide for Commercial Systems. Catalog No. 592-045.

Cerina, A.; Portoso, D.; and Reali, A. 1981. Tests on the Industrial Application of the Heat Pump in the Testing Room for Engines of an Italian Firm (in Italian). Cond. Aria, IT. 25:390-95.

Christodonlou, P. Experiences with the Application of a Heat Pump System in the Evaporation Station of Platy Sugar Factory. VDI Berichte p. 1017-1037.

Clark, E.C. 1984. Chemical Heat Pumps Drive to Upgrade Waste Heat. Chemical Engineering, Feb. 20, p. 50-51.

Curis, O., and Laine, J.D. Gas Motors Driving Heat Pumps in the Malting Industry. Cie Electro-Mechanique, France.

Degueurce, B., and Tersiquel, C. Problems Encountered and Results Obtained in the Application of Compressors in Industrial Processes for Energy Conservation. Electricite de France, France.

Dizier, M. 1982. Recompression de Vapeur Dans Une Sucerie. Paper presented at Electrotechnologies in Industry Conference, May 25-27, Montreal.

Duane, B.P. 1982. Vapour Recompression—A Case Study. Paper presented at Electrotechnologies in Industry Conference, May 25-27, Montreal.

Edison Electric Institute. Application Handbook—Electric Heat Pumps in Waste Heat Recovery Systems. Washington, DC.

Ekroth, I.A. 1979. Thermodynamic Evaluation of Heat Pumps Working with High Temperatures. Proceedings, Inter-Society Energy Conversion Engineering Conf. 2:1713-19.

Fischer, H.C. 1981. Seasonal Ice Storage for Domestic Heat Pumps. Review, Intl. Froid/Intl. J. of Refrigeration, GB 4, No. 3:135-138.

Forwalter, J. 1979. Waste Heat from Refrigeration System Provides Energy for 140°F Hot Water. Food Processing, December.

Friedrich Air Conditioning & Refrigeration Co. Engineering Handbook: Water Source Heat Recovery System. FCM-EH4/77.

Garcia, P. 1981. Use of the Heat Pump in Wine-Making (in French). Rev. Prat. Froid Cond. Air, FR 36, No. 504:43-46.

Gilbert, J.S. 1983. Industrial Heat Pumps...Concepts, Energy Savings, and Cost Guidelines. Plant Engineering, November, pp. 74-77.

Gilbert, J.S. 1983. Heat Pump Strategies and Payoffs. Paper presented at the Industrial Energy Conservation Technology Conference, April, Houston, TX.

Guarino, L.J. 1982. Application of The Refrigeration Cycle for Distilling Liquids Compared with Conventional Evaporators. ASHRAE Journal, February, pp. 32-36.

Hagstedt, B.; Helland, P.; and Rosberg, K. Evaluation and Measurement of Existing Large Refrigeration and Heat Pump Installations Operated by the Swedish Cooperative Association (in Swedish). (Available from Byggdok, Halsingegatan 49, S-113 31 Stockholm.)

Heat Pump Cuts Industrial Energy Use. 1979. Power Engineering, February.

Heiburg, O. 1978. Heat Pump Installation with Gas Engine Drive-Design and Operational Experience (in German). Klima Kaelte Ing. 6, No. 7-8:261-64.

Hoffman, D. 1981. Low Temperature Evaporation Plants. Chemical Engineering Progress, October, pp. 59-62.

Hospital Heat Recovery System Saves a Bundle. 1980. Commercial Remodeling, August, pp. 50 and 51.

Hughes, C.H., and Emmermann, D.K. 1981. VTE/VC for Sea Water. Chemical Engineering Process, July, pp. 72 and 73.

Kearney, D.W. 1981. Industrial Applications of Vapor Compression Heat Pumps. International Gas Research Conference. pp. 1123-1133.

King, R.J. 1984. Mechanical Vapor Recompression Crystallizers. Chemical Engineering Progress, July, pp. 63-69.

Koebbeman, W.F. 1982. Industrial Applications of a Rankine-Powered Heat Pump for the Generation of Process Steam. Paper presented at the 1st International Symposium on the Industrial Application of Heat Pumps, March 24-26, Coventry, United Kingdom.

Koebbeman, W.F. 1981. Mechanical Technology Incorporated. High COP Rankine-Driven Heat Pump for the Generation of Process Steam. Latham, NY.

Krueger, W. 1979. Optimierung Der Waermeruechegewinnung Mit Kompressions-Waermepumpen (Application of Heat Pumps in Heat Recovery Loops) (in German). Waerme, 85, No. 2:27-30.

Leatherman, H.R. 1983. Cost Effective Mechanical Vapor Recompression. Chemical Engineering Progress, January, pp. 40-42.

Legendre, E.; and Bonduelle, F. 1977. Application of the Heat Pump for Concentration by Evaporation and for Drying in Agricultural Foodstuffs Industries. Comite Francais d'Electrothermie Versailles Symposium, Paper II, 4 April 21-22.

Liebowitz, H.M.; and Chaudoir, D.W. 1981. Design of an Open Rankine-Cycle Industrial Heat Pump. Paper presented at the Industrial Energy Conservation Technology Show, April, Houston, TX.

Liebowitz, H.M.; and Colosimo, D. 1981. Evaluation of Industrial Heat Pumps for Effective Low-Temperature Heat Utilization. Paper presented at the Industrial Energy Conservation Technology Show, April, Houston, TX.

Limberg, G.E. Brayton-Cycle Heat Pump for Solvent Recovery. AiResearch Mfg. Co., Torrance, CA.

McFarlan, A.I. 1983. Late Developments in the Field of Heat Recovery. SAIRAC *Journal*, July.

McGuigan, D. 1981. *Heat Pumps.* Garden Way Publishing. Charlotte, Vermont.

McQuay-Perfex Inc. Templifier Industrial Heat Pumps. Bulletins TP, TP-AL, TPB-Al. Staunton, VA.

Michel, J.W.; Lyon, R.N.; and Chen, F.C. 1978. Low-Temperature Heat Utilization Program. ORNL-5513, pp. 218-44, September 30.

Moreland, W.C., and Rolfe, R.W. 1982. Development and Design of an Electric Heat Pump for the Generation of Process Steam.

Nakanishi, T. *et al.* 1981. Industrial High-Temperature Heat Pump. *Hitachi Zosen Tech Rev.* 42(1):7-13.

Newbert, G.J. 1982. Industrial Heat Pump Demonstrations. ETSU, Harwell, United Kingdom.

Niess, R.C. 1978. How to Recycle Low-Grade Process Heat. *Electrical World.*

Niess, R.C. 1978. Putting the Squeeze on BTU's. Proceedings of the 4th Annual Heat Pump Technology Conference, pp. 4-1/6, April.

Niess, R.C. 1979. The Case for High Temperature Heat Pumps. Proceedings of the 5th Annual Heat Pump Technology Conference, April.

Niess, R.C. 1979. Utilization of Geothermal Energy with an Emphasis on Heat Pumps. Paper presented at the Symposium on Geothermal Energy and Its Direct Use in the Eastern U.S., April 5-7.

Niess, R.C. 1980. High Temperature Heat Pumps Can Accelerate the Use of Geothermal Energy. ASHRAE *Transactions*, Vol. 86, Part 1, pp. 755-762.

Niess, R.C. 1980. High-Temperature Heat Pumps Make Waste Heat Profitable. *Electrical Energy Management*, April.

Niess R.C. 1980. Industrial Heat Pump Applications for Waste Heat Recovery. Proceedings of the EPRI/RWE Heat Pump Conference at Dusseldorf, W. Germany, June.

Niess, R.C. 1981. Effluents and Energy Economics. *Water/Engineering and Management,* August.

Niess, R.C. 1981. High Temperature Heat Pump Applications. Proceedings of the 4th World Energy Engineering Congress, October, Atlanta, GA.

Niess, R.C. 1982. Simultaneous Heating and Cooling through Heat Recovery. *Specifying Engineer,* pp. 96-99, August.

Niess, R.C. 1982. Geothermal Heat Pump Systems are Competing Today. *Geothermal Resources Council Bulletin,* December.

Niess, R.C.; and Weinstein, A. 1982. Cutting Industrial Solar System Costs in Half. Paper presented at the Industrial Energy Conservation Technology Conference, April, Houston, TX.

Norelli, P. 1980. Industrial Heat Pumps. *Plant Engineering*, August/September.

North, C.D.R. Large Gas Engine Driven Heat Pumps. GEA Airchangers Ltd., United Kingdom.

Ober, A. 1980. Chilled Water Supply and Distribution for Large Air Conditioning Installations (in German). *Heiz. Luft. Haustech.*, DE. 31(12):452-458.

Oklahoma State University. 1979. Proceedings of the 4th Annual Heat Pump Technology Conference—A University Extension Program of the OSU Division of Engineering, Technology and Architecture, April 9-10, at Oklahoma State University, Stillwater.

Oklahoma State University. 1980. Proceedings of the 5th Annual Heat Pump Technology Conference—A University Extension Program of the OSU Division of Engineering, Technology and Architecture, April 14 and 15, Oklahoma State University, Stillwater.

Oliver, T.N. 1982. Process Drying with a Dehumidifying Heat Pump. Westair Ltd., United Kingdom.

Parker, J.D. 1975. Heat Pump Can Recycle Industrial Heat. *Electric World*, May, pp. 69-80.

Perez-Blanco, H. 1981. Heat Pump Concepts for Industrial Use of Waste Heat. NTIS, PC A04/MF A01, ORNL/TM-7655.

Podhoreski, A. 1979. Improving the Efficiency of Refrigeration Systems. Paper presented at Ontario Hydro Seminar on Energy Management in the Food and Beverage Industry, October 10 and 17.

Process Steam Generation: A Look at an Alternative Energy Source. 1983. *Energy Management Technology*, May/June. pp. 24-27.

Reay, D.A. 1977. *Industrial Energy Conservation—A Handbook for Engineers and Managers.* Pergamon Press, Toronto.

Reay, D.A. 1980. Industrial Applications of Heat Pumps. *Chemical and Mechanical Engineers*, Vol. 27, No. 4:86-93; No. 5:73-78.

Reistad, G.M.; and Means, P. 1980. Heat Pumps for Geothermal Applications: Availability and Performance. Report DOE/ID/12020-TI.

Reynaud, J.F. 1982. Development of Heat Pumps in Industrial Processes in France. Paper presented at the Electrotechnologies in Industry Conference, May 25-27, Montreal. .

Robb, G.A. 1978. Electric Heat Pumping and Co-Generation Economic Considerations by Regions. Paper presented at 64th Annual Meeting of Canadian Pulp and Paper Assoc., Montreal.

Rogers, J.T. 1975. Industrial Use of Low Grade Heat in Canada. Energy Research Group, Carleton University, Report ERG 75-4.

Shah, S.A.; Short, T.H.; and Fynn, R.P. 1980. Solar Pond-Assisted Heat Pump Heating System for Commercial Greenhouses. Proceedings of the Annual Meeting American Section Intl. Solar Energy Society, 3(1):67-71.

Smith, I.E.; and Carey, C.O.B. Thermal Transformers for Up-Grading Industrial Waste Heat. Cranfield Institute of Technology, United Kingdom.

Solar Heat Pumps: Solution for Cold Climates. 1979. *Electric Comfort Conditioning News*, pp. 16-17, June.

Svedinger, B.; *et al.* 1981. Heat from Earth, Rock and Water (in English). Summary S2, 1981 Report T1: Swed. Counc. Bldg. Res., Stockholm.

Strack, J.T. 1982. Heat Pumping in Industry—A State-of-the-Art Study. Ontario Hydro Research Division, Toronto, Report to Canadian Electrical Association, Contract 130 U Soa, September.

Stucki, A. 1979. Heat Pump Cuts Oil Use by 40,000 Gallons/Year. *Contractors Electrical Equipment*, November.

Swearingen, J.S.; and Ferguson, J.E. 1983. Optimized Power Recovery from Waste Heat. *Chemical Engineering Progress*. August, pp. 66-70.

Tabb, E.S.; and Kearney, D.W. An Overview of the Industrial Heat Pump Applications Assessment and Technology Development Programs of the Gas Research Institute. Gas Research Institute and Insights West, Inc.

Timm, M.L. 1985. Economics of Compressor Selection for Open and Closed Cycle Vapor Compression Evaporators. Master's Thesis, University of Wisconsin-Milwaukee, December.

Trane Co. 1981. Water Source Heat Pump System Design. *Applications Engineering Manual*, AM-SYS7.

Trelease, S.W. 1978. Closed-Loop Reverse Cycle Air-Conditioning Weather-Proofing. *Building Operating Management*, January.

U.S. Patent 4,344,828. 1982. Energy Efficient Distillation Apparatus. Inventor: J.D. Melton. Assignee: None. Issued August 17.

U.S. Patent 4,345,971. 1982. Distillation Employing Heat Pump. Inventor: W.K.R. Watson. Assignee: None. Issued August 24.

U.S. Patent 4,390,396. 1983. Apparatus for the Distillation of Vaporizable Liquids. Inventor: H. Koblenzer. Assignee: Langbein-Phanhauser Werke AG. Issued June 28.

U.S. Patent 4,461,675. Energy Efficient Process for Vaporizing a Liquid and Condensing the Vapors Thereof. Inventors: H.F. Osterman, G.C. Nylen. Assignee: Allied Corp.

Vacuum-Evaporator System Cuts Energy Costs. *Chemical Engineering*, pp. 43 and 45, August 23, 1983.

Villadsen, V. 1983. Oil in Refrigeration Plants. *Papers Referaat*, Frigair '83.

Villaume, M. 1981. Use of the Heat Pump in Apartment Buildings (in French). Rev. Gen. Froid, FR, 71, No. 4:217-29.

Weinstein, A., *et al.* 1979. Applying Heat Pump Engineering to Industrial Hot Water Needs. *Solar Engineering*, March, pp. 24-26.

Weinstein, A.; Sero, S.; and Niess, R.C. 1981. Solar Assisted Domestic Hot Water Heat Pump System. Paper presented at Annual Meeting of American Section of International Solar Energy Society, May 28, Philadelphia, PA.

Weinstein, A.; and Van Zuiden, G.J. 1979. Reducing Solar Costs with Solar-Assisted Templifier. Proceedings of International Solar Energy Society.

Wise, J.L. 1982. Energy Pumps—Closing the Energy Cycle. TAPPI *Proceedings*, pp. 211-216.

Wood, C. 1981. Heat Pumps Key to Highly Efficient Dryer. *Canadian Renewable Energy News*.

York Div., Borg-Warner Corp. 1981. High-Level Heat Pumps. An Equipment Brochure.

Yundt, B. 1984. Troubleshooting VC Evaporators. *Chemical Engineering,* December, pp. 46-55.

CHAPTER 10

AIR DISTRIBUTION DESIGN FOR SMALL HEATING AND COOLING SYSTEMS

THIS chapter describes the design of small forced air heating and cooling systems, covers system component selection, and explains their importance. Residential and certain small commercial systems may be designed using this procedure, but large commercial systems are beyond this chapter's scope.

SYSTEM COMPONENTS

Forced air systems are heating and/or cooling systems that use motor-driven blowers to distribute heated, cooled, and otherwise treated air for the comfort of individuals within confined spaces. A typical residential or small commercial system includes: (1) a heating and/or cooling unit, (2) accessory equipment, (3) ductwork, (4) supply and return grilles, and (5) controls. These components are described briefly in the following sections.

Heating and Cooling Units

There are three main types of forced air heating and cooling devices: (1) furnaces, (2) air conditioners, and (3) heat pumps.

Furnaces are the basic component of most forced air heating systems. They are augmented with an evaporator coil when cooling is included in the system, and they are manufactured to use all available common fuels. The fuel type dictates installation requirements, safety considerations, and so forth. (See Chapter 25 of the 1983 EQUIPMENT Volume.)

Air conditioners come in various configurations for forced air systems. (See Chapter 43 of the 1983 EQUIPMENT Volume.) The most common application uses a split-system air conditioner with a furnace. In this application, the air-conditioning evaporator coil is installed on the discharge air side of the furnace. The compressor and condensing coil are located outside the structure, and refrigerant lines connect the outdoor and indoor units.

Self-contained air conditioners (split or packaged systems) are another type of forced air system. These units contain all necessary air-conditioning components, including the circulating air blowers, and may or may not include fuel-fired heat exchangers or electric heating elements.

The heat pump cools and heats by reverse cycle operation of the refrigeration system. It is available in split-system and packaged (self-contained) configurations. Since the heat pump requires supplemental heating in most areas of the country, electric heating elements are usually included with the heat pump as part of the forced air system. Heat pumps are also combined with fossil fuel furnaces to take advantage of their high efficiency at mild temperatures. (See Chapter 44 of the 1983 EQUIPMENT Volume.)

The preparation of this chapter is assigned to TC 6.3, Central Forced Air Heating and Cooling Systems.

Accessory Equipment

Forced air systems enable users to humidify the environment, clean contaminants from recirculated air, and provide for economizer operation. They may include supplemental methods such as solar heating.

Humidifiers. Structures with complete vapor barriers (walls, ceilings, and floors) normally require no supplemental moisture during the heating season, since internally generated moisture maintains an acceptable relative humidity of 20 to 60%. Also, structures with vapor barriers maintain lower relative humidity during the cooling season. Properly sized and operated cooling systems should maintain a nominal 50% rh.

Several types of humidifiers are available, including self-contained steam, atomizing, evaporative, and heated pan. Chapter 5 of the 1983 EQUIPMENT Volume describes the units in detail. The Air Conditioning and Refrigeration Institute (ARI) rates various humidifiers in ARI Standard 610-82.

Humidifiers must match the heating unit. Discharge air temperatures on heating systems vary, and some humidifiers do no provide their own heat source for humidification. Some humidifiers should be applied with caution to heat pumps because of the low temperature of air delivered on heating (Chapter 5 of the EQUIPMENT Volume).

Electronic Air Cleaners. These units attract oppositely charged particles, fine dust, smoke, and other particulates to collecting plates in the air cleaner. While these plates remove finer particles, larger particles are trapped in an ordinary throwaway or permanent filter. A nearly constant pressure drop and efficiency can be expected, unless the cleaner becomes severely loaded with dust.

Custom Accessories. The many variations in solar, off-peak storage, and other custom systems are not covered specifically in this chapter. However, their components may be classified as duct system accessories if proper allowances are made for static pressure drops. If the accessories require the entire static pressure drop for the desired air flow, no air-moving capability would remain for a duct system.

Economizer Control. This device monitors outdoor temperature and humidity and automatically shuts down the air-conditioning unit when a preset outdoor condition is met. Damper motors open outdoor return air dampers, letting outside air enter the system to provide comfort cooling. When outdoor air conditions are no longer acceptable, the outdoor air dampers close and the air-conditioning unit comes back on.

All of these accessories affect system air flow and pressure requirements. Losses must be taken into account when selecting the heating and cooling equipment and sizing the ductwork.

Ducts

Many forced air systems have minimum ductwork discharging directly into large spaces. With minimum duct resistance, the blower can operate at lower speeds, reducing the power required to move the correct quantity of air over heat exchangers. Most systems require ducts composed of manufactured components or on-site constructed air passages. A properly designed duct system and its interconnection with air-moving equipment and other accessories is the heart of a good forced air system.

In large forced air systems for commercial and industrial work, the duct system is usually designed within such constraints as space, costs, code requirements, and so forth. The air-moving equipment and power requirements are selected after the duct system has been designed. In small commercial applications and residential work, ductwork design depends on the air-moving characteristics of the blower included with the selected equipment. It is important to recognize this difference between small commercial or residential systems and large commercial and industrial systems. The designer of smaller systems must determine resistances to the movement of air and adjust the ductwork size to limit the static pressure against which the blower operates. Manufacturers publish static pressure versus flow rate information for the blower so the designer can determine the maximum static pressure against which the blower will operate while delivering the proper volume of air. (See Chapter 3 of the 1983 EQUIPMENT Volume.)

Supply Outlets and Return Grilles

A forced air system is as efficient as its air delivery component. The quantity and velocity of air movement within the space and the proper mixing of supply air with space air affect comfort levels. Supply air should be directed to the sources of greatest heat loss and/or heat gain to offset their effects. Registers and grilles for the supply and return systems should accommodate all aspects of the supply air distribution patterns such as throw, spread, and drop; also, the outlet and return grille velocities must be held within reasonable limits. Any noise generated at the grille is of equal or greater importance than duct noise. (See Chapter 32 of the 1985 FUNDAMENTALS Volume.)

Controls

Forced air heating and/or cooling systems may be adequately controlled in several ways. High quality devices that control heating and/or cooling to spaces with minimum temperature variation should be provided. Spaces with large variations in load requirements may require very sophisticated devices to provide good temperature control. Systems with minimal variations in load requirements in the space may function adequately with one central wall thermostat or a return air thermostat. Residential conditioning systems of 60,000 Btu/h (18 kW) capacity or less are typically operated with one central thermostat.

Forced air system control may require several devices, depending on the sophistication of the system and the accessories used (Chapter 51). Energy conservation has increased the importance of control systems, so now methods that were considered too expensive for small systems may be cost effective.

Temperature control, the primary consideration in forced air systems, may be accomplished by a *single-stage thermostat*. When properly located with properly set anticipators, this device will accurately control temperature. *Multistage thermostats* are required on many systems (e.g., a heat pump with auxiliary heating) and may improve temperature regulation. *Outdoor thermostats*, in series with indoor control, can stage heating increments adequately. They also control economizer systems in lieu of the more expensive enthalpy control for operating dampers in the economizer.

Indoor thermostats may include many control capabilities within one device, including continuous or automatic fan control and automatic or manual changeover between heating and cooling. Where more than one system conditions a common space, manual control is preferred to prevent simultaneous heating and cooling.

Thermostats with programmable temperature controls allow the occupant to vary the temperature setpoint for different periods. These devices save substantial energy by applying automatic night setback and/or daytime temperature setback on fossil-fueled or electric resistance heating equipment, but they should be used with caution on heat pumps.

Two-speed fan control may be desirable for fossil-fueled systems but should not be applied to heat pump systems unless recommended by the manufacturer. Humidistats should be specified for humidifier control.

When applying unusual control schemes, manufacturer recommendations should always be observed to guard against equipment damage or misuse.

SYSTEM DESIGN

All components described in this section must be considered equally in the design of a forced air heating and/or cooling system. Satisfactory design involves more than the layout and sizing of the ductwork. The size and performance characteristics of system components are interrelated, and the overall system design should proceed in the organized manner described. For example, furnace selection depends on the heat gain and loss; however, the sizing will also be affected by ductwork location (attic, basement, and so forth), night setback, and humidifier usage. Following is the recommended procedure:

1. Determine preliminary supply and return grille locations.
2. Determine preliminary ductwork location.
3. Determine heating and cooling unit location.
4. Select accessory equipment. Frequently, air-conditioning and accessory equipment is not provided with initial construction; however, the system may be designed to add these components later.
5. Select control components.
6. Determine heating and cooling loads.
7. Select equipment.
8. Determine air flow requirements for each supply and return location.
9. Finalize ductwork design (determine duct sizes).
10. Select supply and return grilles.

This procedure requires certain preliminary information such as location, weather conditions, and architectural considerations. The following sections cover the preliminary considerations and discuss how to follow this recommended procedure.

Locating Outlets, Ducts, and Equipment

A residence's characteristics determine the location and the type of forced air system that can be installed. The presence or absence of particular areas within a residence has a direct influence on equipment and ductwork location. The structure's size, room or area use, and air distribution system determine how many central systems will be needed to maintain comfort temperatures in all areas.

A full basement is an ideal location to install equipment and ductwork. If a residence has a crawl space, the ductwork and equipment can be located there, or the equipment can be placed in a closet or utility room. When the equipment is within the conditioned space, a non-ducted return air system may be adequate. The equipment's enclosure must meet all fire and safety code requirements; adequate service clearance must also be provided. In a home built on a concrete slab, the equipment should

Table 1 General Characteristics of Supply Outlets

Group	Outlet Type	Outlet Flow Pattern	Most Effective Application	Preferred Location	Size Determined by
1	Ceiling and high sidewall	Horizontal	Cooling	Not critical	Major application—heating or cooling
2	Floor registers, baseboard and low sidewall	Vertical, nonspreading	Cooling and heating	Not critical	Maximum acceptable heating temperature differential
3	Floor registers, baseboard and low sidewall	Vertical, spreading	Heating and cooling	Along exposed perimeter	Minimum supply velocity differs with type and acceptable temperature differential
4	Baseboard and low sidewall	Horizontal	Heating only	Long outlet—perimeter; Short outlet—not critical	Maximum supply velocity should be less than 300 fpm (1.5 m/s)

be located in the conditioned space (for systems that do not require combustion air), an unconditioned closet, an attached garage, the attic space, or outdoors. The ductwork normally is located in a furred-out space, in the slab, or in the attic.

Construction materials for a slab duct system must meet specific corrosion, fire resistance, crushing and bending strength, deterioration, odor, delamination, and moisture absorption requirements specified by *Federal Specifications SS-A-701* of the Federal Housing Administration and *Standard 90B* of the National Fire Code (NFPA No. 90B-84).

Weather conditions should be considered when locating heating and air-conditioning equipment, as well as ductwork. Packaged outdoor units for houses in severely cold climates must be carefully installed according to manufacturer recommendations to operate satisfactorily. Most houses in cold climates have basements, making them well suited for indoor furnaces and split-system air conditioners or heat pumps. In mild and moderate climates, the ductwork is frequently in the attic or crawl space. Ductwork located outdoors, in attics, crawl spaces, and basements must be insulated, as outlined in Chapter 33 of the 1985 FUNDAMENTALS Volume.

Although the principles of air distribution discussed in Chapter 32 of the 1985 FUNDAMENTALS Volume apply in forced air system design, simplified methods of selecting outlet size and location are generally used.

Supply outlets fall into four general groups, defined by their air discharge patterns: (1) horizontal high, (2) vertical nonspreading, (3) vertical spreading, and (4) horizontal low. Straub and Chen (1957) and Wright et. al. (1963) describe these types and their performance characteristics under controlled laboratory and actual residence conditions. Table 1 lists the general characteristics of supply outlets. It includes the performance of various outlet types for cooling, as well as heating, since one of the advantages of forced air systems is that they may be used for both heating and cooling. However, as indicated in Table 1, no single outlet type is best for both heating and cooling.

The best outlets for heating are located near the floor at outside walls and provide a vertical spreading air jet, preferably under windows, to blanket cold areas and counteract cold drafts. Called perimeter heating, this arrangement mixes the warm supply air with both the cool air from the area of high heat loss and the cold air from infiltration, preventing drafts.

The best outlet types for cooling are located in the ceiling and have a horizontal air discharge pattern. NFPA 90B-84 provides the following summary regarding outlet type:

"For year-round operation the correct choice of a system depends on the principal application. If heating is of major or equal importance, perimeter diffusers (the floor diffuser is but one type of perimeter diffuser) should be selected. The system should be designed for the optimum

supply velocity during cooling. If cooling is to be the primary application and heating is of secondary importance because of the relatively mild outdoor conditions, ceiling diffusers will perform most satisfactorily."

Determining Heating and Cooling Loads

Design heating loads can be calculated by following the procedures outlined in Chapters 22 to 25 of the 1985 FUNDAMENTALS Volume. Design cooling loads can be calculated by the procedures presented in Chapters 26 and 27 of the 1985 FUNDAMENTALS Volume.

When calculating design loads, heat losses or gains from the air distribution system must be included in the total load for each room. Losses from ducts can be calculated by following the procedures in Chapter 33 of the 1985 FUNDAMENTALS Volume.

Many designers assume that a minimum number of air recirculations per hour is required to provide comfort at design conditions, causing them to oversize the cooling system and/or the the air handler to maintain the minimum recirculation rate. The air circulation system's ability to perform, however, is more a function of proper register selection and placement than of a specific, historically accepted recirculation level.

Selecting Equipment

Heating and cooling equipment should be selected after considering capacity, efficiency, configuration, quality, and so forth. Many manufacturers offer forced air furnaces fueled by natural gas, liquefied petroleum gas, fuel oil, or electricity. The configuration or type of furnace selected is determined by factors such as furnace location, type of duct system, and fuel being considered. Standard forced air furnace configurations are:

1. *Low Boy (Upflow)*—Used where low furnace height is required, such as in a basement with a low ceiling.
2. *High Boy (Upflow)*—Used where furnace height is not a problem, such as in basements, utility rooms, or closets.
3. *Counterflow (Downflow)*—Used where supply ducts are located beneath the furnace, e.g., in a concrete slab floor or in a crawl space. The counterflow furnace is usually located in a utility room or closet.
4. *Horizontal*—Used where horizontal air flow and low furnace height are required, such as in a crawl space or attic area.
5. *Outdoor*—Used where space inside the home is a problem. Insulated supply and return ducts must be connected to the outside unit.

A furnace or boiler's output heating capacity should match or slightly exceed the calculated load. Note that the calculated load must include duct losses, humidification load, night set-back recovery load, as well as building conduction and infiltration heat losses. Chapter 25 of the 1983 EQUIPMENT Volume has detailed information on how to size and select a furnace properly.

Many manufacturers offer extra features, which may increase the efficiency of forced air furnaces. Electric ignition systems are replacing standard pilot lights. Vent dampers stop the flow of heated air up the chimney when the furnace burner is not operating. Permanent split capacity motors operate more efficiently than shaded pole motors.

When a system both heats and cools, the cooling equipment should be carefully selected to match the design load as closely as possible. Minimum sizing should not be less than 95% of the design, with maximum oversizing not more than 115% of design cooling requirements.

Air Flow Requirements

After equipment selection and prior to duct design, the following decisions must be made:

1. Determine the air quantities required for each room or space during heating and cooling. The air quantity selected should be the greater of the heating or cooling requirement.
2. Determine the number of supply outlets needed for each space to supply the selected air quantity, giving detailed consideration to discharge velocity, spread, throw, terminal velocity, occupancy patterns, location of heat gain and heat loss sources, and register or diffuser design.
3. Determine the return system type (multiple or central), the availability of space for the grilles, the filtering system (return air filter grilles or electronic filtration), maximum velocity limitations for sound, efficient filtration velocity, and space use limitations.

This required air flow rate, along with the static pressure limitation of the blower, is the hub around which the duct system is designed. The total air flow selected must be proportioned to the room or space load requirements. The heat loss or gain for each space determines the proportion of the total air flow supplied to each space.

The static pressure drop in supply registers should be limited to about 0.03 in. water (7.5 Pa). The required pressure drop must be deducted from the static pressure available from the system for duct design.

The flow rate delivered by a single supply air delivery point should be determined by considering: (1) the space limitations for duct and register installation, (2) the pressure drop for the register considered at the flow rate selected, (3) the adequacy of the air delivery patterns for offsetting heat losses or gains, and (4) the space use patterns.

Manufacturer's specifications provide blower air flow rates for each blower speed and external static pressure combination. Determining static pressure available for duct design should include the possibility of adding accessories in the future, e.g., electronic air cleaners or humidifiers. Therefore, it is recommended that the highest available fan speed not be used for design. The following air flow rates are recommended for air conditioners and heat pumps:

Air flow	cfm/ton	(L/(s · kW)
Typical*	400	(54)
Some Heat Pumps	450	(60)
Humid Areas	360	(49)
Dry Areas	429	(57)

*For normal residential cooling (70% sensible and 30% latent heat)

For heating-only systems, an air temperature rise of 40 to 80 °F (22 to 47 °C) is recommended (Table 2).

Table 2 Blower Speeds vs External Static Pressure

| External Static Pressure, in. water (Pa) | Blower Speeds, cfm (L/s) | | | | |
	Low	Medium Low	Medium	Medium High	High
0.2	900	1100	1250	1350	—
(50)	(424)	(519)	(590)	(637)	—
0.4	700	950	1100	1300	1450
(100)	(330)	(448)	(519)	(613)	(684)
0.6	—	650	900	1150	1300
(150)	—	(307)	(425)	(543)	(613)

Example: Design conditions are:
  Room heat loss—5000 Btu/h (1.5 kW)
  Room heat gain—3800 Btu/h (1.1 kW)
  Total air flow rate—1000 cfm (470 L/s)
  Total heat gain—30,000 Btu/h (8.8 kW)
  Total heat loss—45,000 Btu/h (13.2 kW)

Solution in inch-pound units:

$$\text{Heating air flow rate} = \frac{5000}{45,000} \cdot 1000 = 111 \text{ cfm}$$

$$\text{Cooling air flow rate} = \frac{3800}{30,000} \cdot 1000 = 127 \text{ cfm}$$

In SI units:

$$\text{Heating air flow rate} = \frac{1.5}{13.2} \cdot 470 = 53 \text{ L/s}$$

$$\text{Cooling air flow rate} = \frac{1.1}{8.8} \cdot 470 = 59 \text{ L/s}$$

The supply outlet should handle the larger 127 cfm (59 L/s) flow rate for cooling. If both heating and cooling are required, the air quantity delivered to the room must satisfy the largest air flow rate required.

Duct Design Recommendations

Because of the competitive nature of the residential construction business and the practical necessity of using less sophisticated design techniques for these systems, the modified equal-friction duct loss calculation method is recommended. This method is satisfactory as long as the designer understands its strengths and weaknesses. It should be applied only to those systems requiring less than a normal air-moving capacity of 2250 cfm (1060 L/s) or a 60,000 Btu/h (18 kW) cooling requirement.

With this procedure, the pressure available for supply and return duct losses is found by deducting coil, filter, grille, and accessory losses from the manufacturer's specified blower pressure. The remaining pressure is divided between the supply and return system. Multiplying the supply pressure by 100 and then dividing it by the duct run having the longest equivalent length gives the design friction-loss value per 100 ft length of duct. Using duct calculators and the friction chart simplifies the calculations, but pressures must be in proper units. Branch ducts are sized to balance the available pressure without exceeding recommended maximum velocities. Low resistance duct runs may require dampering.

The ductwork proportions the total air supplied by the system to spaces according to the space heating and/or cooling requirements. The return air systems may be single, multiple, or any combination that will return air to the equipment within design static pressure and with satisfactory air movement patterns.

Following are some general rules in duct design:

1. Keep main ducts as straight as possible.
2. Streamline transitions.

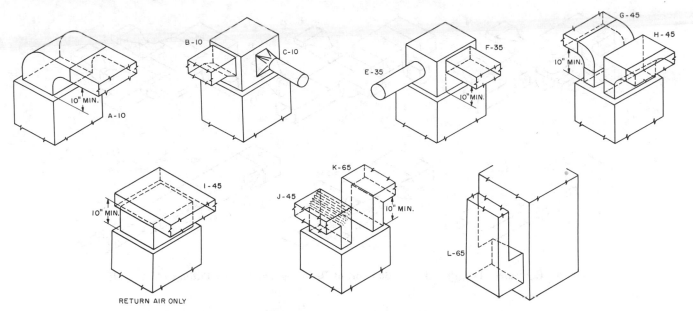

Fig. 1   Equivalent Length in Feet (0.3048 m) of Supply and Return Air Plenum Fittings (ACCA 1984)

3. Design elbows with an inside radius of at least one-third the duct width. If this inside radius is not possible, include turning vanes.
4. Make ducts tight and properly sealed to limit air loss.
5. Insulate and/or line ducts well, where necessary, to conserve energy and limit noise.
6. Locate branch duct takeoffs at least 4 ft (1.2 m) downstream from a fan or transition, if possible.
7. Isolate the air-moving equipment from the duct system flexible connectors to isolate noise.

Another aspect to consider in ductwork design is noise. Designing as closely as practical to the following recommended air flow velocities will minimize noise:

Main Ducts:	700 to 900 fpm	(3.6 to 4.6 m/s)
Branch Ducts:	600 fpm	(3.0 m/s)
Branch Risers:	500 fpm	(2.5 m/s)

Considerable difference may exist between the cooling and heating flow rate requirements. Since many systems cannot be rebalanced seasonally, a compromise must be made in the duct design to accommodate the most critical need. For example, a kitchen may require 165 cfm (78 L/s) for cooling but only 65 cfm (31 L/s) for heating. Since the kitchen may be used heavily during design cooling periods, the cooling flow rate should be used. Normally, the maximum design flow rate should be used, since register dampers do allow some optional reduction in air flows.

Duct Design Procedure

1. Determine the heating and cooling load to be supplied by each outlet using the previously outlined ASHRAE or ACCA procedure. Include duct losses or gains.
2. Make a single-line diagram of the supply and return duct systems—at least one outlet in a room or area for each 8000 Btu/h (2.3 kW) loss or 4000 Btu/h (1.2 kW) gain, whichever is greater.
3. Label all fittings and transitions to show equivalent lengths on the single-line drawing. (Refer to Figures 1 to 7 for approximate equivalent lengths of fittings.)

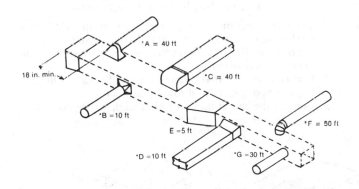

Branch	Basic Equiv. Length, ft.	No. of Downstream Branches	Added Equiv. Length, ft.	Final Equiv. Length, ft.
G	30	0	0	30
F	50	1	10	60
D	10	2	20	30
C	40	0	0	40
B	10	1	10	20
A	40	2	20	60

*Values shown above apply only when the branch is at the end of the trunk duct (ex. G above). For all other branches, add to the equivalent length shown ten feet (10 ft) times the number of branches downstream between the takeoff being evaluated and the end of the trunk duct.

Fig. 2   Example Duct System and Equivalent Length of Extended Plenum Fittings (ACCA 1984)

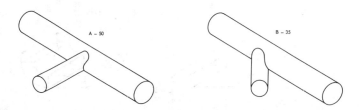

Fig. 3   Equivalent Length in Feet (0.3048 m) of Round Trunk Duct Fittings (ACCA 1984)

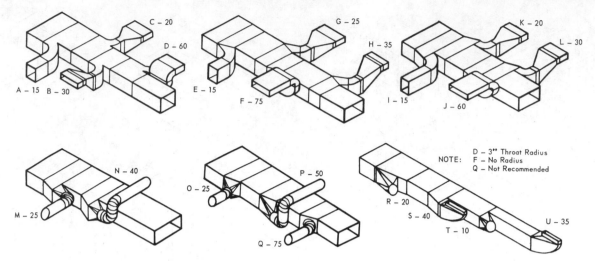

Fig. 4 Equivalent Length in Feet (0.3048 m) of Reducing Trunk Duct Fittings (ACCA 1984)

4. Show measured lengths of ductwork on the single-line drawing.
5. Determine the total effective length of each branch supply. (Begin at the air handler and add all equivalent lengths and measured lengths to each outlet: Effective length = Equivalent length + Measured length.)
6. Proportion the total air flow rate to each supply outlet for both heating and cooling.
   Example: Supply outlet flow rate =

   $$\frac{\text{Outlet heat loss (gain)}}{\text{Total heat loss (gain)}} \cdot \text{Total system flow rate}$$

7. The flow rate required for each supply outlet is equal to the heating or cooling flow rate requirement (normally the larger of the two rates).
8. Label the supply outlet flow rate requirement on the single-line drawing for each outlet.
9. Determine the total external static pressure available from the unit at the selected air flow rate.
10. Subtract the supply and return register pressure, external coil pressure, filter pressure, and so forth, from the available static pressure to determine the static pressure available for the duct design.

11. Proportion the available static pressure between the supply and return systems. *Example:*

Supply (75%)	0.15 in. water	(37 Pa)
Return (25%)	0.05 in. water	(13 Pa)
Total	0.20 in. water	(50 Pa)

Sizing the Branch Supply Air System

12. Use the supply static pressure available to calculate each branch design static pressure for 100 ft (or m) of equivalent length.
    Example: Branch design static pressure =

    $$\frac{\text{Supply static pressure available} \cdot 100}{\text{Effective length of each branch supply}}$$

13. Enter the friction chart (Chapter 33 of the 1985 FUNDAMENTALS Volume) at the branch design static pressure opposite the flow rate for each supply, and read the round duct size and velocity.
14. If velocity exceeds maximum recommended values, increase the size and specify and runout damper.
15. Convert the round duct to rectangular, where needed.

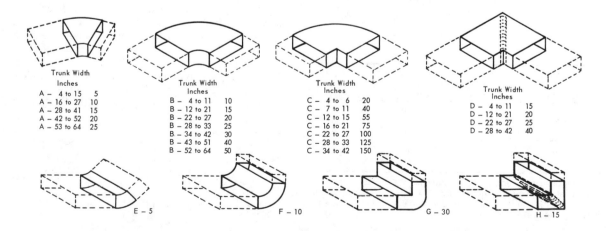

Fig. 5 Equivalent Length in Feet (0.3048 m) of Angles and Elbows for Trunk Ducts (ACCA 1984)

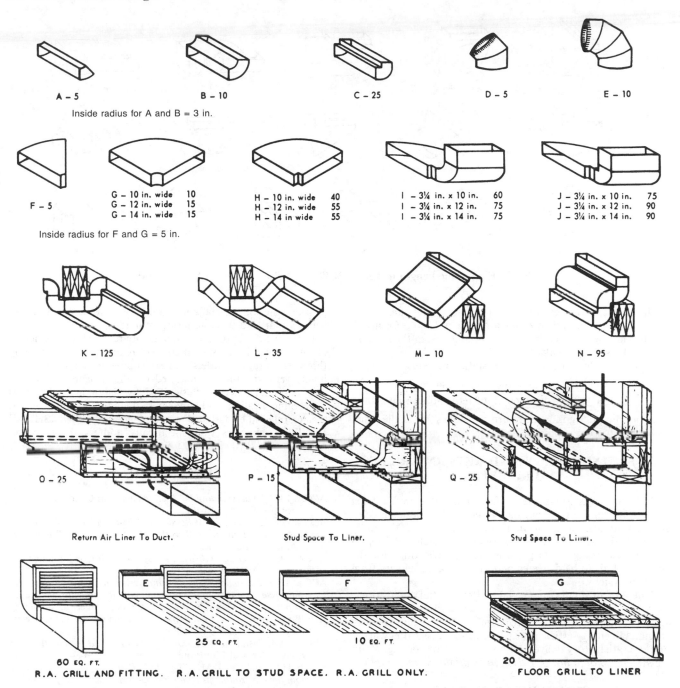

Fig. 6   Equivalent Length in Feet (0.3048 m) of Angles and Elbows for Individual and Branch Ducts (ACCA 1984)

Sizing the Supply Trunk System

16. Determine the branch supply with the longest total effective length and, from this, determine the static pressure to size the supply trunk duct system.
Example: Supply trunk design static pressure =

$$\frac{\text{Total supply static pressure available} \cdot 100}{\text{Longest effective length of branch duct supplies}}$$

17. Total the heating air flow rate and the cooling air flow rate for each trunk duct section. Select the larger of the two flow rates for each section of duct between runouts or groups of runouts.

18. Design each supply trunk duct section by entering the friction chart at the supply trunk static pressure and sizing each trunk section for the appropriate air volume handled by that section of duct.
Trunks should be checked for size after each runout and reduced, as required, to maintain velocity above branch duct design velocity.

19. Convert round duct size to rectangular, where needed.

Sizing the Return Air System

20. Select the number of return air openings to be used.
21. Determine the volume of air that will be returned by each of the return air openings.

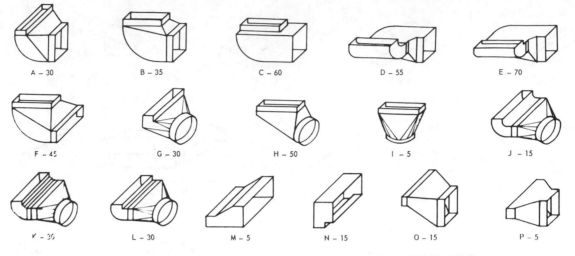

Fig. 7 Equivalent Length in Feet (0.3048 m) of Boot Fittings (ACCA 1984)

22. From Step 11, select the return air static pressure.
23. Determine the static pressure available per 100 ft (or m) effective length for each return run, and design the same as for the supply trunk system.
    Example: Return trunk design/static pressure =

$$\frac{\text{Total return static pressure available} \cdot 100}{\text{Longest effective length of return duct runs}}$$

24. The trunk design for the return air is the same as the trunk design for the supply system.

SELECTING SUPPLY AND RETURN GRILLES AND REGISTERS

Grilles and registers are selected from a manufacturer's catalog with appropriate engineering data after the duct design is completed. Rule-of-thumb selection should be avoided. Carefully determine the suitability of the register or grille selected for each location according to its performance specifications for the quantity of air to be delivered and the discharge velocity from the duct system.

Generally, in small commercial and residential applications, the selection and application of registers and grilles is highly important, especially since system size and air-handling capacity are small in energy-efficient structures. Proper selection will ensure the satisfactory delivery of heating and/or cooling. *Cooling systems should not be oversized to attain air recirculation.*

COMMERCIAL SYSTEMS

The duct design procedure described in this chapter can be applied to small commercial systems using residential equipment, provided the commercial application does not include moisture sources that lead to large moisture loads.

In commercial applications that do not require low noise levels, air duct velocities may be increased, reducing duct size. Long throws from supply outlets are also required for large areas, and higher velocities may be required for that reason.

Commercial systems with significant variation in air flow rates for cooling, heating, and large internal loads (e.g., kitchens and theaters) should be designed in accordance with other ASHRAE Handbook chapters that specifically address these combinations.

REFERENCES

ACCA. 1967. *Understanding the friction chart.* Air Conditioning Contractors of America TT-102.

ACCA. 1984. *Duct Design for Residential Winter and Summer Air Conditioning and Equipment Selection.* Air Conditioning Contractors of America, Manual D.

ACCA. 1963. *Selection of distribution systems.* Air Conditioning Contractors of America, Manual G.

ACCA. 1977. *Equipment selection and system design procedures for commercial summer and winter air conditioning (using unitary equipment).* Air Conditioning Contractors of America, Manual Q.

ARI. 1982. *Central system humidifiers.* Air-Conditioning and Refrigeration Institute Std. 610-82, 22 pp.

NFPA. 1984. *Installation of warm air heating and air conditioning systems.* National Fire Protection Assn. No. 90B-84.

Straub, H.E.; and Chen, M. Ming. 1957. *Distribution of air within a room for year-round air conditioning-part II.* University of Illinois Engr. Exp. Sta. Bull. No. 442, March.

Wright, J.R.; Bahnfleth, D.R.; and Brown, E.J. 1963. *Comparative performance of year-round systems used in air conditioning research no. 2.* Univ. of Illinois Engr. Exp. Sta. Bull. No. 465, January.

CHAPTER 11

STEAM SYSTEMS

A STEAM system uses the vapor phase of water to supply heat or kinetic energy through a piping system. As a source of heat, steam can heat a conditioned space with suitable terminal heat transfer equipment such as fan coil units, unit heaters, radiators, and convectors (fin tube or cast iron), or through a heat exchanger that supplies hot water or some other heat transfer medium to the terminal units. In addition, steam is commonly used in heat exchangers (shell-and-tube, plate or coil types) to heat domestic hot water and supply heat for industrial and commercial processes such as laundry and kitchen equipment. Steam is also used as a heat source for certain cooling processes such as single- and two-stage absorption refrigeration machines.

STEAM SYSTEM ADVANTAGES

Steam offers the following advantages:

1. Steam flows through the system unaided by external energy sources such as pumps.
2. Because of its low density, steam can be used in tall buildings where water systems create excessive pressure.
3. Terminal units can be added to or removed from the system without making basic changes to the system design.
4. Steam components can be repaired or replaced by closing the steam supply without the difficulties associated with draining and refilling a water system.
5. Steam is pressure-temperature dependent; therefore, the system temperature can be controlled by varying either steam pressure or temperature.
6. Steam can be distributed throughout a heating system with little change in temperature.

In view of the above advantages, steam is applicable for the following facilities:

1. Where heat is required for processes and comfort heating, such as in industrial plants, hospitals, restaurants, dry cleaning plants, laundries, and commercial buildings.
2. Where the heating medium must travel great distances, such as in facilities with scattered building locations, or where the building height would result in excessive pressures in water systems.
3. Where intermittent changes in heat load occur.

The preparation of this chapter is assigned to TC 6.1, Hot Water and Steam Heating Equipment and Systems.

FUNDAMENTALS

Steam is the vapor phase of water generated by adding more heat than required to maintain its liquid phase at a given pressure, causing the liquid to change to vapor without any further increase in temperature. Table 1 illustrates the pressure-temperature relationship and various other properties of steam.

Temperature is the thermal state of both liquid and vapor at any given pressure. The figures shown are for *dry saturated steam.* The vapor temperature can be raised by adding more heat, resulting in *superheated steam,* which is used (1) where higher temperatures are required, (2) in large distribution systems to compensate for heat losses and ensure that steam is delivered at the desired saturated pressure and temperature, and (3) to ensure that the steam is *dry* and does not contain entrained liquid that could damage the turbine in some turbine-driven equipment.

Enthalpy of the Liquid, h_f, (Sensible Heat) is the amount of heat in Btu (kJ) required to raise the temperature of a pound (kg) of water from 32°F (0°C) to the boiling point at the pressure indicated.

Enthalpy of the Evaporation (Latent Heat of Vaporization) is the amount of heat required to change a lb (kg) of boiling water at a given pressure to a lb (kg) of steam at the same pressure. This same amount of heat is released when the vapor is condensed back to a liquid.

Enthalpy of the Steam, h_g, (Total Heat) is the combined enthalpy of liquid and vapor and represents the total heat above 32°F (0°C) in the steam.

Specific Volume, the reciprocal of density, is the volume of unit mass and indicates the volumetric space that 1 lb (1 kg) of steam or water will occupy.

An understanding of the above helps explain some of the following unique properties and advantages of steam:

1. Most of the heat content of steam is stored latent heat that permits large quantities of heat to be transmitted efficiently with little change in temperature. Since the temperature of saturated steam is pressure-dependent, a negligible temperature reduction occurs from a reduction in pressure caused by pipe friction losses as steam flows through the system, regardless of the insulation efficiency, as long as the boiler maintains the initial pressure and the steam traps remove the condensate. Conversely, in a hydronic system, inadequate insulation can significantly reduce fluid temperature.

2. Steam, as all fluids, flows from areas of high pressure to areas of low pressure and is able to move throughout a system without an external energy source. Heat dissipation causes the

Table 1   Properties of Saturated Steam[a]

Pressure			Saturation Temperature °F	Specific Volume ft³/lb		Enthalpy Btu/lb		
Gauge		Absolute psia		Liquid V_f	Steam V_g	Liquid h_f	Evap. h_{fg}	Steam h_g
25	in. Hg	2.4	134	.0163	146.4	101	1018	1119
9.56	Vac.	10	193	.0166	38.4	161	982	1143
0		14.7	212	.0167	26.8	180	970	1150
2		16.7	218	.0168	23.8	187	966	1153
5		19.7	227	.0168	20.4	195	961	1156
15		29.7	250	.0170	13.9	218	946	1164
50		64.7	298	.0174	6.7	267	912	1179
100		114.7	338	.0179	3.9	309	881	1190
150		164.7	366	.0182	2.8	339	857	1196
200		214.7	388	.0185	2.1	362	837	1179

[a]Values shown are rounded off or approximate and are provided to illustrate the various properties discussed in the text. For calculation and design purposes, use values of thermodynamic properties of water shown in Chapter 6 of the 1985 FUNDAMENTALS Volume or a similar table.

Table 1 (SI)   Properties of Saturated Steam[a]

Pressure, kPa	Saturation Temperature °C	Specific Volume, L/kg		Enthalpy, kJ/kg		
		Liquid V_f	Steam V_g	Liquid h_f	Evap. h_{fg}	Steam h_g
19.9	60	1.02	7669	251	2358	2609
47.4	80	1.03	3405	335	2308	2643
101	100	1.04	1672	419	2256	2775
199	120	1.06	891	504	2202	2706
362	140	1.08	508	589	2144	2733
618	160	1.10	307	676	2082	2758
1003	180	1.13	194	763	2015	2778
1555	200	1.16	127	852	1941	2793

[a]Values shown are rounded off or approximate and are provided to illustrate the various properties discussed in the text. For calculation and design purposes, use values of thermodynamic properties of water shown in Chapter 6 of the 1985 FUNDAMENTALS Volume or a similar table.

vapor to condense, creating a reduction in pressure caused by the dramatic change in specific volume (1600:1 at atmospheric pressure).

3. As steam gives up its latent heat at the terminal equipment, the condensate that forms is initially at the same pressure and temperature as the steam. When this condensate is discharged to a lower pressure (as when a steam trap passes condensate to the return system), the condensate contains more heat than necessary to maintain the liquid phase at the lower pressure; this excess heat causes some of the liquid to vaporize or "flash" to steam at the lower pressure. The amount of liquid that flashes to steam can be calculated by Equation (1).

$$\% \text{ Flash Steam} = \frac{100 \times (h_{f1} - h_{f2})}{h_{fg2}} \qquad (1)$$

where

h_{f1} = Enthalpy of liquid at P_1
h_{f2} = Enthalpy of liquid at P_2
h_{fg2} = Latent heat of vaporization at P_2

Flash steam contains significant and useful heat energy that can be recovered and used, as explained in the "Heat Recovery" section. This re-evaporation of condensate can be controlled (minimized) by subcooling the condensate within the terminal equipment before it discharges into the return piping. The amount of subcooling should not be so large as to cause a significant loss of heat transfer (condensing) surface.

EFFECTS OF WATER, AIR, AND GASES

The enthalpies shown in Table 1 are for *dry saturated steam*. Most systems operate near these theoretically available values, but the presence of water and gases can affect enthalpy, as well as have other adverse operating effects.

Dry saturated steam is pure vapor without entrained water droplets. There is usually some amount of water present as the result of carryover as condensate forms because of heat losses in the distribution system. *Steam quality* describes the amount of water present and can be determined by calorimeter tests.

While steam quality might not have a significant effect on the heat transfer capabilities of the terminal equipment, the *backing up* or presence of condensate can be significant because the enthalpy of condensate h_f is negligible compared with the enthalpy of evaporation h_{fg}. If condensate does not drain properly from pipes and coils, the rapidly flowing steam can push a slug of condensate through the system. This can cause water hammer and result in objectionable noise and damage to piping and system components.

The presence of air also reduces the steam temperature. Air reduces heat transfer because it migrates to and insulates heat transfer surfaces. Further, oxygen in the system causes pitting of iron and steel surfaces. Carbon dioxide (CO_2) traveling with steam dissolves in condensate forming carbonic acid, which is extremely corrosive to pipes and heat-transfer equipment.

The combined adverse effects of water, air, and CO_2 necessitate their prompt and efficient removal.

HEAT TRANSFER

The quantity of steam that must be supplied to a heat exchanger to transfer a specific amount of heat is a function of (1) the steam temperature and quality, (2) the character and entering and leaving temperature of the medium to be heated, and (3) the heat exchanger design. For a more detailed discussion of heat transfer, see Chapter 3 of the 1985 FUNDAMENTALS Volume.

BASIC STEAM SYSTEM DESIGN

Because of the various codes and regulations governing the design and operation of boilers, pressure vessels, and systems, steam systems are classified according to operating pressure. Low pressure systems operate at 15 psig (100 kPa above atmospheric) and under, and high pressure systems operate at 15 psig (100 kPa above atmospheric) and over. There are many sub-classifications within these broad classifications, especially for heating systems such as one- and two-pipe, gravity, vacuum, or variable vacuum return systems. However, these sub-classifications relate to the distribution system or temperature-control method. Regardless of classification, all steam systems include a source of steam, a distribution system, and terminal equipment, where steam is used as the source of power or heat.

STEAM SOURCE

Steam can be generated directly by boilers using oil, gas, coal, wood, and waste as a fuel source or solar, nuclear, and electrical energy as a heat source, and indirectly by recovering heat from processes or equipment such as gas turbines and diesel or gas engines. The cogeneration of electricity and steam should always be considered for facilities that have steam requirements throughout the year. Where steam is used as a power source (such as in turbine driven equipment), the exhaust steam may be used in heat-transfer equipment for process and space heating.

Steam can be provided by a facility's own boiler or cogeneration plant or can be purchased from a central utility serving a city or specific geographic area. This distinction can be very important. A facility with its own boiler plant almost always has a *closed loop* system and requires that the condensate be as hot as possible when it returns to the boiler. Conversely, condensate return pumps require a few degrees (temperature) of sub-cooling to prevent cavitation or flashing of condensate to vapor at the suction eye of pump impellers. The degree of subcooling will vary, depending upon the hydraulic design or characteristics of the pump in use.

Central utilities often do not take back condensate, so it is discharged by the using facility and results in an *open loop* system. If a utility does take back condensate, it rarely gives credit for its heat content. Since steam is almost always purchased by the pound cost based on 1000 lb or 1 Mlb (454 kg) of steam, any heat recovered from the condensate in once-through or open-loop systems reduces the net cost per thermal unit. Except for losses to the atmosphere, which for the most part can be eliminated, every pound of steam eventually becomes a pound of condensate. If condensate is returned at 180°F (82°C) and a heat-recovery system reduces this temperature to 80°F (27°C), 100,000 Btu's (233 000 kJ) is recovered from every 1000 lb (454 kg) of steam purchased. The heat remaining in the condensate represents 10 to 15% of the heat purchased from the utility. Using this heat effectively can reduce steam and heating costs by 10% or more. This is discussed further in the "Heat Recovery" section.

Boilers

Fired and waste heat boilers should be constructed and labeled according to the ASME *Boiler and Pressure Vessel Code*. Details on design, construction and application can be found in Chapter 24 of the 1983 EQUIPMENT Volume. Boiler selection is based on the combined loads, including heating processes and equipment that use steam, hot water generation, piping losses, and pickup allowance.

The Hydronics Institute codes are used to test and rate most low pressure heating boilers that have net and gross ratings. In smaller systems, selection is based on a net rating. Larger system selection is made on a gross load basis. The occurrence and nature of the load components with respect to the total load determines the number of boilers used in an installation.

Heat Recovery and Waste Heat Boilers

Steam can be generated by waste heat, such as exhaust from fuel-fired engines and turbines. Figure 1 schematically shows a typical exhaust boiler and heat-recovery system used for diesel engines. A portion of the water used to cool the engine block is diverted as preheated make-up water to the exhaust heat boiler to obtain maximum heat and energy efficiency. Where the quantity of steam generated by the waste heat boiler is not steady or ample enough to satisfy the facility's steam requirements, a conventional boiler must generate supplemental steam.

Heat Exchangers

Heat exchangers are used in most steam systems. Steam-to-water heat exchangers (sometimes called converters) are used to heat domestic hot water and to supply the terminal equipment in hot-water heating systems. These heat exchangers are usually the shell-and-tube type, where the steam is admitted to the shell and the water is heated as it circulates through the tubes. Condensate coolers (water-to-water) are sometimes used so to subcool the condensate while reclaiming the heat energy.

Water-to-steam heat exchangers (steam generators) are used in HTW systems to provide process steam. Such heat exchangers generally consist of a U-tube bundle, through which the HTW circulates, installed in a tank or pressure vessel.

All heat exchangers should be constructed and labeled according to the ASME *Boiler and Pressure Vessel Code*.

BOILER CONNECTIONS

Recommended boiler connections for Pumped and Gravity

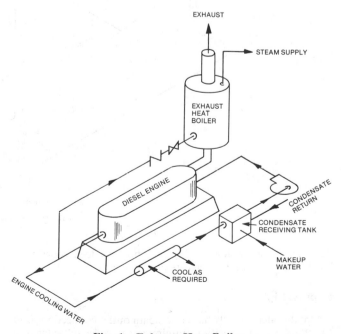

Fig. 1 Exhaust Heat Boiler

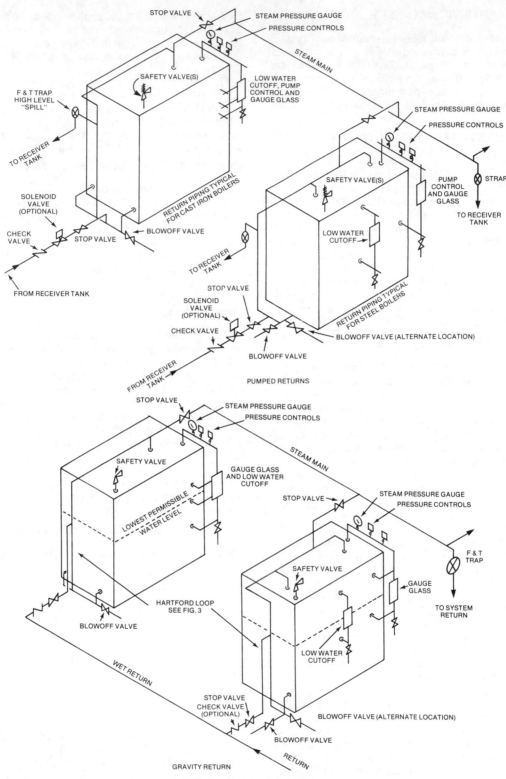

Fig. 2 Boiler Connections

Return Systems are shown in Figure 2; however, local codes must be checked for specific legal requirements.

Supply Piping

Small boilers usually have one steam outlet connection sized to reduce steam velocity to minimize carryover of water into supply lines. Large boilers can have several outlets that minimize boiler water entrainment.

Figure 2 shows piping connections to the steam header. Although some engineers prefer to use an enlarged steam header for additional storage space, there usually is not a sudden demand for steam, except during the warmup period, so an oversized header is a disadvantage. The boiler header can be the same size as the boiler connection or the pipe used on the steam main. The horizontal runouts from the boiler (or boilers) to the header should be sized by calculating the heaviest load that will be placed on the boiler. The runouts should be sized on the same basis as the building mains. Any change in size after the vertical uptakes should be made by reducing elbows.

Return Piping

Cast iron boilers have return tappings on both sides, while steel boilers have only one return tapping. Where two tappings are provided, both should be used to effect proper circulation through the boiler. Condensate in boilers can be returned by a pump or a gravity return system.

Recommended return piping connections for systems using gravity return are detailed in Figure 3. Dimension "A" must be a minimum of 28 in. for each 1 psig maintained at the boiler (100 mm/kPa) to provide the hydraulic head required to return the condensate to the boiler. To provide a reasonable safety factor, make dimension "A" a minimum of 14 in. (355 mm) for small systems with piping sized for pressure drop of 1/8 psi (0.9 kPa), and a minimum of 28 in. (710 mm) for larger systems with piping sized for a pressure drop of 1/2 psi (3.5 kPa). The Hartford Loop protects against a low water condition, which can occur if a leak develops in the wet return portion of the piping system. The Hartford Loop takes the place of a check valve on the wet return; however, certain local codes require check valves. Because of hydraulic head limitations, gravity return systems are only suitable for systems operating at a boiler pressure between 1/2 to 1 psig (3.5 to 6.9 kPa above atmospheric). However, since these systems have minimum mechanical equipment and low initial installed cost, they are appropriate for many small systems. Kremers (1982) and Stamper and Koral (1979) provide additional design information on piping for gravity return systems.

Recommended piping connections for steam boilers with pump-returned condensate are shown in Figure 2. It is common practice to provide an individual condensate or boiler feed-water pump for each boiler. Pump operation is controlled by the boiler water level control on each boiler. However, one pump may be connected to supply the water to each boiler from a single manifold by using feedwater control valves regulated by the individual boiler water level controllers. When such systems are used, the condensate return pump runs continuously to pressurize the return header.

Return piping should be sized based on total load. The line between the pump and boiler should be sized for a very small pressure drop and the maximum pump discharge flow rate.

DESIGN STEAM PRESSURE

One of the most important decisions in the design of a steam system is the selection of the generating, distribution, and utilization pressures. Considering investment cost, energy efficiency, and control stability, the pressure should be held to the minimum values above atmospheric pressures that are practical to accomplish the required heating task, unless detailed economic analysis indicates advantages in higher pressure generation and distribution.

The first step in selecting pressures is to analyze the load requirements. Space heating and domestic water heating can best be served, directly or indirectly, with low pressure steam less than 15 psig or 250°F (100 kPa above atm. or 121°C). Other systems that can be served with low pressure steam include absorption units (10 psi or 70 kPa above atm.), cooking, warming, dishwashers, and snow-melting heat exchangers. Thus, from the standpoint of load requirements, high pressure steam (above 15 psi or 100 kPa above atm.) is required only for loads such as dryers, presses, molding dies, power drives, and other process-

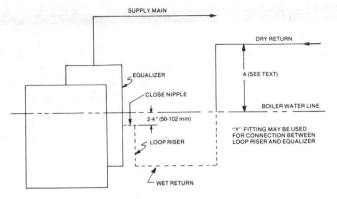

Fig. 3   Boiler with Gravity Return

ing, manufacturing, and power requirements. The load requirement establishes the pressure requirement.

When the source is close to the load(s), the generation pressure should be high enough to provide the (1) load design pressure, (2) friction losses between the generator and the load, and (3) control range. Losses are caused by flow through the piping, fittings, control valves, and strainers. If the generator(s) is located remotely from the loads, there could be some economic advantage in distributing the steam at a higher pressure to reduce the pipe sizes. When this is considered, the economic analysis should include the additional investment and operating costs associated with a higher pressure generation system. When an increase in the generating pressure requires a change from below to above 15 psi (100 kPa), the generating system equipment changes from low pressure class to high pressure class and there are significant increases in both investment and operating cost.

Where steam is provided from a non-fired device or prime mover such as a diesel engine cooling jacket, the source device can have an inherent pressure limitation.

STEAM SYSTEM PIPING

The piping system distributes the steam, returns the condensate, and removes air and non-condensable gases. In steam heating systems, it is important that the piping system distribute steam, not only at full design load, but at partial loads and excess loads that can occur on system warmup. The usual average winter steam demand is less than half the demand at the lowest outdoor design temperature. However, when the system is warming up, the load on the steam mains and returns can exceed the maximum operating load for the coldest design day, even in moderate weather. This load comes from raising the temperature of the piping to the steam temperature and the building to the indoor design temperature. Supply and return piping should be sized according to Chapter 34 of the 1985 FUNDAMENTALS Volume.

Supply Piping Design Considerations

1. Size pipe according to Chapter 34 of the 1985 FUNDAMENTALS Volume, taking into consideration pressure drop and steam velocity.
2. Piping should be pitched uniformly down in the direction of steam flow at 1/4 in. in 10 ft (2 mm/m). If piping cannot be pitched down in the direction of the steam flow, refer to Chapter 34 of the 1985 FUNDAMENTALS Volume for rules on pipe sizing and pitch.
3. Piping should be well insulated to avoid unnecessary heat loss. (See Chapter 20 of the 1985 FUNDAMENTALS Volume.)
4. Condensate from unavoidable heat loss in the distribution system must be removed promptly to eliminate water hammer and degrading steam quality and heat transfer capability.

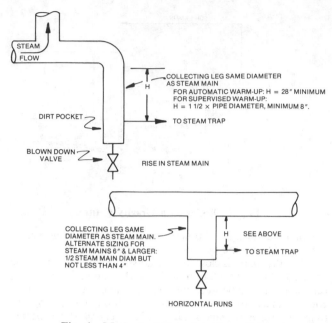

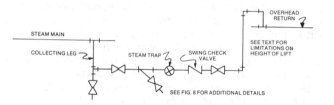

Fig. 4 Method of Dripping Steam Mains

Fig. 5 Trap Discharging to Overhead Return

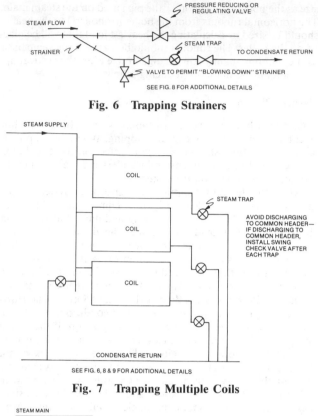

Fig. 6 Trapping Strainers

Fig. 7 Trapping Multiple Coils

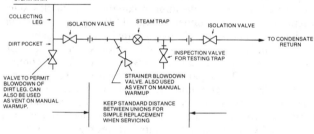

Fig. 8 Recommended Steam Trap Piping

Drip legs must be installed at all low points and natural drainage points in the system, such as at the ends of mains, bottoms of risers, and ahead of the pressure regulators, control valves, isolation valves, pipe bends, and expansion joints. On straight horizontal runs with no natural drainage points, drip legs should be spaced at intervals not exceeding 300 ft (90 m) when the pipe is pitched down in the direction of the steam flow and a maximum of 150 ft (45 m) when the pipe is pitched up so that condensate flow is opposite of steam flow. These distances should be reduced by about half in systems that are warmed up automatically rather than in a system where valves are opened manually to remove air and excess condensate that forms during warmup conditions.

5. Where horizontal piping must be reduced in size, use eccentric reducers that permit the continuance of uniform pitch along the bottom of piping (in downward pitched systems). Concentric reducers must be avoided on horizontal piping, since they can cause water hammer.

6. All branch lines from the steam mains should be taken off the top, preferably at a 45° angle, although vertical 90° connections are acceptable.

7. Where the length of a branch takeoff is less than 10 ft (3 m), the branch line can be pitched back ½ in. per 10 ft (4 mm/m) providing drip legs as described in (4) above.

8. Drip legs must be sized properly to separate and collect the condensate. Drip legs at vertical risers should be full and extend beyond the rise, as shown in Figure 4. Drip legs at other locations should be the same diameter as the main. In steam mains 6 in. (150 mm) and over, this can be reduced to half the diameter of the main, but to not less than

4 in. (100 mm). Where warmup is supervised, the length of the collecting leg is not critical. However, the recommended length is one and a half times the pipe diameter and not less than 8 in. (200 mm). For automatic warmup, collecting legs should always be the same size as the main and be at least 28 in. (710 mm) long to provide the hydraulic heat for the pressure differential necessary for the trap to discharge before a positive pressure is built up in the steam main.

9. Condensate should flow by gravity from the trap to the return piping system. Where the steam trap is located below the return line, the condensate must be lifted. In systems operating above 40 psi (275 kPa above atm.), the trap discharge can usually be piped directly to the return system as shown in Figure 5. However, back pressure at the trap discharge (return line pressure plus hydraulic head created by height of lift) must not exceed steam main pressure, and the trap must be sized after considering back pressure. In systems operating under 40 psi (275 kPa above atm.), drip legs must be installed on equipment where the temperature is regulated by modulating the steam control valves and where the back pressure at the trap exceeds or is close to system pressure. The trap discharge should flow by gravity to a vented condensate receiver from which it is pumped to the overhead return.

10. Strainers installed before the pressure reducing and control valves are a natural water-collection point. Since water carry-over can erode the valve seat, a trap should be installed at the strainer blow-down connection as shown in Figure 6.

Terminal Equipment Piping Design Considerations

1. Piping should be the same size as the supply and return connections of the terminal equipment.
2. Equipment and piping should be accessible for inspection and maintenance of the steam traps and control valves.
3. The terminal units should be piped to minimize strain caused by expansion and contraction of piping. This can be done with pipe bends, loops, or three elbow swings to take advantage of piping flexibility, or with expansion joints or flexible pipe connectors.
4. In multiple coil applications, each coil should be separately trapped for proper drainage as shown in Figure 7. Piping two or more coils to a common header served by a single trap can cause condensate backup, improper heat transfer, and inadequate temperature control.
5. Terminal equipment, where temperature is regulated by a modulating steam control valve, requires special consideration. Refer to the section on "Condensate Removal from Temperature Regulated Equipment."

Return Piping Design Considerations

1. Flow in the return line is two-phase, consisting of steam and condensate. See Chapter 34 of the 1985 FUNDAMENTALS Volume for sizing considerations.
2. The return lines should be pitched downward in the direction of the condensate flow at ½ in. per 10 ft (4 mm/m) to ensure prompt condensate removal.
3. The return line should be well insulated, especially where the condensate is returned to the boiler or the condensate enthalpy is recovered.
4. Where possible and practical, heat-recovery systems should use the condensate enthalpy. See the section on "Heat Recovery."
5. The dirt pockets of the drip legs and strainer blowdowns should be equipped with valves to remove dirt and scale.
6. Steam traps should be installed close to drip legs and should be accessible for inspection and repair. Servicing is simplified by making the pipe sizes and configuration identical for a given type and size of trap. The piping arrangement shown in Figure 8 facilitates inspection and maintenance of steam traps.
7. When elevating condensate to an overhead return, consider the pressure at the trap inlet and the fact that it requires approximately 1 psi to elevate condensate 2 ft (10 kPa/m). See (9) of "Supply Piping Design Considerations" for complete discussion.

CONDENSATE REMOVAL FROM TEMPERATURE REGULATED EQUIPMENT

When air, water, or another product is heated, the temperature or heat transfer rate can be regulated by a modulating steam pressure control valve. Since pressure and temperature do not vary at the same rate as load, the steam trap capacity, which is determined by the pressure differential between the trap inlet and outlet, may be adequate at full load, but not at some lesser load.

Analysis shows that steam pressure must be reduced dramatically to achieve a slight lowering of temperature. In most applications, this can result in sub-atmospheric pressure in the coil, while as much as 75% of full condensate load has to be handled by the steam trap. This is especially important for coils

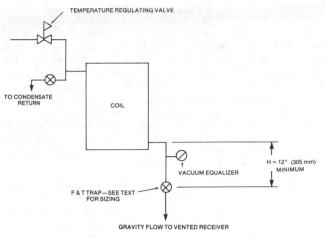

Fig. 9 Trapping Temperature Regulated Coils

exposed to outside air, since sub-atmospheric conditions can occur in the coil at outside temperatures below 32°F (0°C) and the coil will freeze if the condensate is not removed.

There are detailed methods for determining condensate load under various operating conditions (Kremers 1982). However, in most cases, this load does not need to be calculated if the coils are piped as shown in Figure 9 and this procedure is followed:

1. The steam trap should be 1 to 3 ft (0.3 to 0.9 mm) below the bottom of the steam coil to provide a hydraulic head of approximately 0.5 to 1.5 psig (3.5 to 10.3 kPa above atm.). Location of the trap at less than 12 in. (300 mm) minimum usually results in improper drainage and operating difficulties.
2. Vacuum breakers must be installed between the coil and trap inlet to ensure that the hydraulic head can drain the coil when it is at atmospheric or sub-atmospheric pressure. The vacuum breaker should respond to a differential pressure of no greater than 3 in. of water (750 Pa). For atmospheric returns, the vacuum breaker should be opened to the atmosphere, and the return system must be designed to ensure no pressurization of the return line. In vacuum return systems, the vacuum breaker should be piped to the return line.
3. Discharge from the trap must flow by gravity, without any lifts in the piping, to the return system, which must be vented properly to the atmosphere to eliminate any back pressure that could prevent the trap from draining the coil. Where the return main is overhead, the trap discharge should flow by gravity to a vented receiver, from which it is then pumped to the overhead return.
4. Traps must be designed to operate at maximum pressure at the control valve inlet and sized to handle the full condensate load at a pressure differential equal to the hydraulic head between the trap and coil. Since the actual condensate load can vary from the theoretical design load because of the safety factors used in coil selection and the fact that condensate does not always form at a uniform steady rate, steam traps should be sized according to the following:
   a. 0-15 psig (0 to 100 kPa above atm.) at the control valve inlet: size the trap for twice the full condensate load (coil condensing rate at maximum design conditions) at 0.5 psi (3.5 kPa) pressure differential.
   b. 16-30 psig (110 to 200 kPa above atm.) at the control valve inlet: size the trap for twice the full condensate load at 2 psi (14 kPa) pressure differential.
   c. 31 psig (210 kPa above atm.) and over at the control valve inlet: size the trap to handle triple the full condensate load at a pressure differential equal to half the control valve inlet pressure.

STEAM TRAPS

Steam traps are an essential part of all steam systems, except one-pipe steam heating systems. Traps discharge condensate, which forms as steam gives up some of its heat, and direct the air and noncondensable gases to a point of removal. This occurs in steam mains and distribution piping because of unavoidable heat losses through less-than-perfect insulation, as well as in terminal equipment such as radiators, convectors, fan coil units, and heat exchangers, where steam gives up heat during normal operation. Condensate is a by-product of a steam system and must always be removed from the system as soon as it accumulates due to the following:

1. The available enthalpy of a pound of condensate is negligible compared with a pound of steam. Every pound of steam that condenses becomes a pound of condensate. Although the condensate still contains some valuable heat content, using this heat by holding the condensate in the terminal equipment reduces the heat transfer surface. It also causes other operating problems because of air retention, which further reduces heat transfer, and noncondensable gases such as CO_2, which cause corrosion problems. As discussed in "Basic Steam System Design," using condensate heat is usually only desirable when the condensate is not returned to the boiler. Methods for this are discussed in the "Heat Recovery" section.
2. Because steam moves rapidly in mains and supply piping, if condensate accumulates to the point where the steam can push a slug of it, serious damage can occur from the resulting water hammer.

Ideally, the steam trap should remove all condensate promptly, along with air and noncondensable gases that might be in the system, with little or no loss of live steam. A steam trap is an automatic valve that can distinguish between steam and condensate or other fluids. Traps are classified as follows:

1. *Thermostatic traps* react to the difference in temperature between steam and condensate.
2. *Mechanical traps* operate by the difference in density between steam and condensate.
3. *Kinetic traps* rely on the difference in flow characteristics of steam and condensate.

The following points apply to all steam traps:

1. There is no single type of steam trap best suited to all applications, and most systems require more than one type of trap.
2. Steam traps, regardless of type, should be carefully sized for the application and condensate load to be handled, since both undersizing and oversizing can cause serious problems. Undersizing can result in undesirable condensate backup and excessive cycling that can cause premature failure. Oversizing might appear to solve this problem and make selection much easier because fewer different sizes are required, but if the trap fails, excessive steam can be lost.

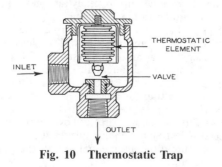

Fig. 10   Thermostatic Trap

Thermostatic Traps

In thermostatic traps, as shown in Figure 10, a bellows or bimetallic element operates a valve that opens in the presence of condensate and closes in the presence of steam. Because condensate is initially at the same temperature as the steam from which it was condensed, the thermostatic element must be designed and calibrated to open at a temperature below the steam temperature; otherwise, the trap would blow live steam continuously. Therefore, the condensate must be sub-cooled by allowing it to *backup* in the trap and a portion of the upstream drip leg piping, both of which are left uninsulated. Some thermostatic traps operate with a continuous water leg behind the trap so there is no steam loss; however, this prohibits the discharge of air and noncondensable gases, and can cause excessive condensate to back up into the mains or terminal equipment and cause operating problems. Devices that operate without significant backup can lose steam before the trap closes.

Although both bellows and bimetallic traps are temperature sensitive, their operations are significantly different. The *bellows thermostatic trap* has a lower boiling point than water. When the trap is cold, the element is contracted and the discharge port is open. As hot condensate enters the trap, it causes the bellows contents to boil and vaporize before the condensate temperature rises to steam temperature. Because the bellows' contents boil at a lower temperature than water, the vapor pressure inside the bellows element is greater than the steam pressure outside, causing the element to expand and close the discharge port.

Assuming the contained liquid has a pressure-temperature relationship similar to that of water, the balance of forces acting on the bellows element remains relatively constant, no matter how the steam pressure varies. Therefore, this is a balanced-pressure device that can be used at any pressure within the operating range of the device. However, this device should not be used where superheated steam is present, since the temperature is no longer in step with the pressure and damage or rupture of the bellows element can occur.

Bellows thermostatic traps are best suited for steady light loads on low pressure service. They are most widely used in radiators and convectors in HVAC applications.

The *bimetallic thermostatic trap* has an element made from metals with different expansion coefficients. Heat causes the element to change shape, permitting the valve port to open or close. Because a bimetallic element responds only to temperature, most traps have the valve on the outlet so that steam pressure is trying to open the valve. Therefore, by properly designing the bimetallic element, the trap can operate on a pressure-temperature curve approaching the steam saturation curve, but not as closely as with a balanced pressure bellows element.

Unlike the bellows thermostatic trap, bimetallic thermostatic traps are not adversely affected by superheated steam or subject to damage by water hammer, so they can be readily used for high pressure applications. They are best suited for steam tracers, jacketed piping, and heat-transfer equipment, where some condensate backup is tolerable. If they are used on steam main drip legs, the element should not back up condensate.

Mechanical Traps

Mechanical traps are buoyancy operated, depending on the difference in density between steam and condensate. The *float and thermostatic trap,* commonly called the F & T trap (Figure 11), is actually a combination of two types of traps in a single trap body: (1) a bellows thermostatic element operating on temperature difference, which provides automatic venting and (2) a float portion, which is buoyancy operated. Float traps without automatic venting should not be used for steam systems.

On startup, the float valve is closed and the thermostatic element is open for rapid air venting, permitting the system or

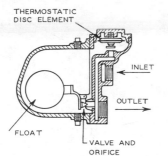

Fig. 11   F & T Trap

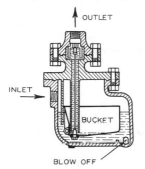

Fig. 12   Open Bucket Trap

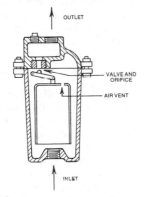

Fig. 13   Inverted Bucket Trap

equipment to rapidly fill with steam. When steam enters the trap body, the thermostatic element closes and, as condensate enters, the float rises and the condensate discharges. The float regulates the valve opening so it continuously discharges the condensate at the rate at which it reaches the trap.

The F & T trap has large venting capabilities, continuously discharges condensate without backup, handles intermittent loads very well, and can operate at extremely low pressure differentials. F & T traps are suited for use with temperature-regulated steam coils. They also are well suited for steam main and riser drip legs on low pressure steam-heating systems. Although F & T traps are available for pressure to 250 psig (1700 kPa above atm.) or higher, they are susceptible to water hammer, so other traps are usually a better choice for high pressure applications.

Bucket traps operate on buoyancy, but they use a bucket that is either open at the top or inverted instead of a closed float. *Open bucket traps* are shown in Figure 12. Initially, the bucket is empty and rests on the bottom of the trap body with the discharge vented, and, as condensate enters the trap, the bucket floats up and closes the discharge port. Additional condensate overflows into the bucket causing it to sink and open the discharge port, allowing steam pressure to force the condensate out of the bucket. At the same time, it seals the bottom of the

discharge tube, prohibiting air passage. Therefore, to prevent air binding, this device has an automatic air vent, as does the F & T trap.

Inverted bucket traps (Figure 13) eliminates the size and venting problems associated with open bucket traps. Steam or air entering the submerged inverted bucket causes it to float and close the discharge port. As more condensate enters the trap, it forces air and steam out of the vent on top of the inverted bucket into the trap body where the steam condenses by cooling. When the weight of the bucket exceeds the buoyancy effect, the bucket drops, opening the discharge port, and steam pressure forces the condensate out, and the cycle repeats.

Unlike most cycling-type traps, the inverted bucket trap continuously vents air and noncondensable gases. Although it discharges condensate intermittently, there is no condensate backup in a properly sized trap. Inverted bucket traps are made for all pressure ranges and are well suited for steam main drip legs and most HVAC applications. Although they can be used for temperature regulated steam coils, the F & T trap is usually better because it has the high venting capability desirable for such applications.

Kinetic Traps

Numerous devices operate on the difference between the flow characteristics of steam and condensate and on the fact that condensate discharging to a lower pressure contains more heat than necessary to maintain its liquid phase. This excess heat causes some of the condensate to flash to steam at the lower pressure.

Thermodynamic traps, (Figure 14) are simple devices with only one moving part. When air or condensate enters the trap on start-up, it lifts the disk off its seat and is discharged. When steam or hot condensate (some of which "flashes" to steam upon exposure to a lower pressure) enters the trap, the increased velocity of this vapor flow decreases the pressure on the underside of the disk and increases the pressure above the disk, causing it to snap shut. Pressure is then equalized above and below the disc, but since the area exposed to pressure is greater above than below it, the disk remains shut until the pressure above is reduced by condensing or bleeding, permitting the disk to snap open and repeat the cycle. This device does not cycle open and shut as

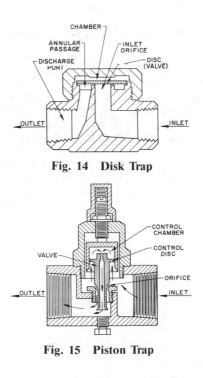

Fig. 14   Disk Trap

Fig. 15   Piston Trap

a function of condensate load; it is a time cycle device that opens and shuts at fixed intervals as a function of how fast the steam above the disk condenses. Since disk traps require a significant pressure differential to operate properly, they are not well suited for low pressure systems or for systems with significant back pressure. They are best suited for high pressure systems and are widely applied to steam main drip legs.

Impulse traps, also called **piston traps** (Figure 15), continuously pass a small amount of steam or condensate through a "bleed" orifice, changing the pressure positions within the piston. When live steam or very hot condensate that flashes to steam enters the control chamber, the increased pressure closes the piston valve port. When cooler condensate enters, the pressure decreases, permitting the valve port to open. Most impulse traps cycle open and shut intermittently, but some modulate to a position that passes condensate continuously.

Impulse traps can be used for the same applications as disk traps; however, because they have a small "bleed" orifice and close piston tolerances, they can stick or clog if dirt is present in the system.

Orifice traps (Figure 16) have no moving parts. All other traps have discharge ports or orifices, but in the traps described above, this opening is oversized, and some type of closing mechanism controls the flow of condensate and prevents the loss of live steam.

The orifice trap has no such closing mechanism, and the flow of steam and condensate is controlled by two-phase flow through an orifice. A simple explanation of this theory is that an orifice of any size has a much greater capacity for condensate than it does for steam because of the significant differences in their densities and because "flashing" condensate tends to choke the orifice. An orifice is selected larger than required for the actual condensate load; therefore, it continuously passes all condensate along with the air and noncondensable gases, plus a small controlled amount of steam. The steam loss is usually comparable to that of most cycling type traps.

Orifice traps must be sized more carefully than cycling-type traps. On light condensate loads, the orifice size is small and, like impulse traps, tends to clog. Orifice traps are suitable for all system pressures and can operate against any back pressure. They are best suited for steady pressure and load conditions such as steam main drip legs.

PRESSURE-REDUCING VALVES

Where steam is supplied at pressures higher than required, one or more pressure-reducing valves (pressure regulators) are required. The pressure-reducing valve reduces pressure to a safe point and regulates pressure to that required by the equipment. The district heating industry refers to valves according to their functional use. There are two classes of service: (1) where the steam must be shut off completely (dead end valves) to prevent buildup of pressure on the low pressure side during no load (single-seated valves should be used) and (2) where the low pressure lines condense enough steam to prevent buildup of pressure from valve leakage (double-seated valves can be used). Valves available for either service are direct-operated, or spring,

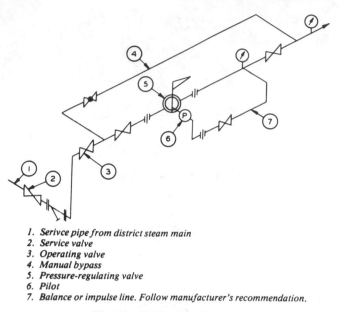

1. Serivce pipe from district steam main
2. Service valve
3. Operating valve
4. Manual bypass
5. Pressure-regulating valve
6. Pilot
7. Balance or impulse line. Follow manufacturer's recommendation.

Fig. 17   PRV—Low Pressure

weight, air-loaded, or pilot-controlled, using either the flowing steam or auxiliary air or water as the operating medium. The direct-operated, double-seated valve is less affected by varying inlet steam pressure than the direct-operated, single-seated valve. Pilot-controlled valves, either single- or double-seated, tend to eliminate the effect of variable inlet pressures.

Installation

Pressure-reducing valves should be readily accessible for inspection and repair. There should be a bypass around each reducing valve equal to the area of the reducing-valve seat ring. The globe valve in a bypass line should have plug disk construction and must have an absolutely tight shutoff. A steam pressure gauge, graduated up to the initial pressure, should be installed on the low pressure side. The gauge should be ahead of the shutoff valve because the reducing valve can be adjusted with the shutoff valve closed. A similar gauge should be installed downstream from the shutoff valve for use during manual operation. Typical service connections are shown in Figure 17 for low pressure service and Figure 18 for high pressure service. In the smaller sizes, the pressure-regulating valve can be removed, a filler installed, and the inlet stop valves used for manual pressure regulation until repairs are made.

Strainers should be installed on the inlet of the primary pressure-reducing valve and before the second-stage reduction if there is considerable piping between the two stages. If a two-stage reduction is made, it is advisable to install a pressure gauge

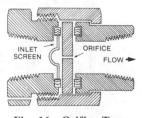

Fig. 16   Orifice Trap

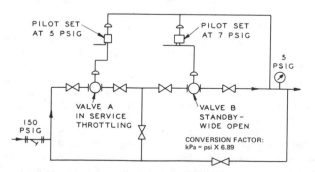

Fig. 18   PRV—High Pressure

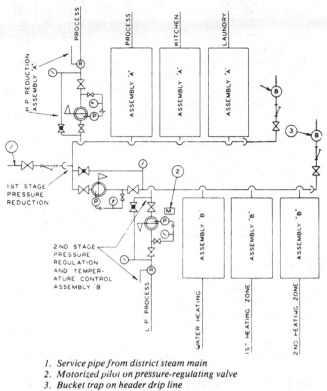

1. *Service pipe from district steam main*
2. *Motorized pilot on pressure-regulating valve*
3. *Bucket trap on header drip line*

Note: Where process equipment is individually controlled, temperature control on header may be omitted. All fittings should be American Standard Class 250 cast iron or 300 lb steel in both reduction and regulation assemblies.

Fig. 19   Steam Supply

immediately before the reducing valve of the second-stage reduction to set and check the operation of the first valve. A drip trap should be installed between the two reducing valves.

Where pressure-reducing valves are used, one or more relief devices or safety valves must be provided, and the equipment on the low pressue side must meet the requirements for the full initial pressure. The relief or safety devices are adjoining or as close as possible to the reducing valve. The combined relieving capacity must be adequate to avoid exceeding the design pressure of the low pressure system if the reducing valve does not open.

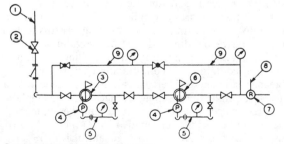

1. *Service pipe from district steam main*
2. *Service valve*
3. *Pressure-reducing valve*
4. *Pilot*
5. *Balance line*
6. *Pressure-regulating valve*
7. *Safety relief valve*
8. *Relief valve discharge to outside*
9. *Bypass, one size smaller than pressure-reducing valve*

Note: All fittings should be American Standard Class 250 cast iron and/or 300 lb steel.

(Used Where High-Pressure Steam is Supplied for Low-Pressure Requirements)

Fig. 20   Two Stage PRV

Local codes in most areas dictate the safety relief valve installation requirements.

Safety valves should be set at least 5 psi (35 kPa) higher than the reduced pressure when the reduced pressure is under 35 psig (240 kPa above atm.) and at least 10 psi (70 kPa) higher than the reduced pressure, if the reduced pressure is above 35 psig (240 kPa above atm.) or the first-stage reduction of a double reduction. The outlet from relief valves should not be piped to a location where the discharge can jeopardize persons or property or is a violation of local codes.

Figure 19 shows a typical service installation, with a separate line to various heating zones and process equipment. If the initial pressure is below 50 psig (340 kPa above atm.), the first-stage pressure-reducing valve can be omitted. In Assembly A (Figure 19), the single-stage pressure-reducing valve is also the pressure-regulating valve.

When making a two-stage reduction, e.g., 150 to 50 psig (1030 to 340 kPa above atm.) and then 50 to 2 psig (340 to 14 kPa above atm.), allow for the expansion of steam on the low pressure side of each reducing valve by increasing the pipe area to about double the area of a pipe the size of the reducing valve. This also allows steam to flow at a more uniform velocity. It is recommended that the valves be separated by a distance of at least 20 ft (6 m) to reduce excessive hunting action of the first valve.

Figure 20 shows a typical double-reduction installation where the pressure in the district steam main is higher than can safely be applied to building heating systems. The first or pressure reducing valve effects the initial pressure reduction. The pressure-regulating valve regulates the steam to the desired final pressure.

Pilot-controlled or air-loaded direct-operated reducing valves can be used without limitation for all reduced-pressure settings for all heating, process, laundry, and hot water services. Spring-loaded direct-operated valves can be used for reduced pressures up to 50 psig (340 kPa above atm.), providing they can pass the required steam flow without excessive deviation in reduced pressure.

Weight-loaded valves are used for reduced pressures below 15 psig (100 kPa above atm.) and for moderate steam flows.

Pressure-equalizing or impulse lines must be connected to serve the type of valve selected. With direct-operated diaphragm valves having rubber-like diaphragms, the impulse line should be connected into the bottom of the reduced-pressure steam line to allow for maximum condensate on the diaphragm and in the impulse or equalizing line. If it is connected to the top of the steam line, a condensate accumulator should be used to reduce variations in the head of condensate on the diaphragm. Equalizing or impulse lines for pilot-controlled and direct-operated reducing valves using metal diaphragms should be connected into the expanded outlet piping approximately 2 to 4 ft (0.6 to 1.2 m) from the reducing valve and pitched away from the reducing valve to prevent condensate accumulation. Pressure impulse lines for externally pilot-controlled reducing valves using compressed air or fresh water should be installed according to manufacturer's recommendations.

Valve Size Selection

Pressure-regulating valves should be sized to supply the maximum steam requirements of the heating system or equipment. Consideration should be given to rangeability, speed of load changes, and regulation accuracy required to meet system needs, especially with temperature control systems using intermittent steam flow to heat the building.

The reducing valve should be selected carefully. The manufacturer should be consulted. Piping to and from the reducing valve should be adequate to pass the desired amount of steam at the desired maximum velocity. A common error is to make the size of the reducing valve the same as the service or outlet pipe size;

this makes the reducing valve oversized and causes wiredrawing or erosion of the valve and seat because of the high velocity flow caused by the small lift of the valve.

On installations where the steam requirements are large and variable, wiredrawing and cycling control can occur during mild weather or during reduced demand periods. To overcome this condition, two reducing valves are installed in parallel, with the sizes selected on a 70 and 30% proportion of maximum flow. For example, if 10,000 lb of steam per hour (2840 kW) is required, the size of one valve is based on 7000 lb of steam per hour (1988 kW), and the other is based on 3000 lb of steam per hour (744 kW). During mild weather (spring and fall), the larger valve is set for slightly lower reduced pressure than the smaller one and remains closed as long as the smaller one can meet the demand. During the remainder of the heating season, the valve settings are reversed to keep the smaller one closed, except when the larger one is unable to meet the demand.

TERMINAL EQUIPMENT

A variety of terminal units are used in steam-heating systems. All are suited for use on low pressure systems. Terminal units used on high pressure systems have heavier construction, but are otherwise similar to those on low pressure systems.

Terminal units are usually classified as follows:

1. *Natural convection units* transfer some heat by radiation. The equipment includes cast-iron radiators, finned-tube convectors, and cabinet and baseboard units with convection-type elements. See Chapter 28 of the 1983 EQUIPMENT Volume.
2. *Forced convection units* employ a forced air movement to increase heat transfer and distribute the heated air within the space. The devices include unit heaters, unit ventilators, induction units, fan-coil units, the heating coils of central air-conditioning units, and many process heat exchangers. When such units are used for both heating and cooling, there is a steam coil for heating and a separate chilled water or refrigerant coil for cooling. See Chapters 6, 9, and 27 of the 1983 EQUIPMENT Volume and Chapters 1 through 4 of this volume.
3. *Radiant panel systems* transfer some heat by convection. Because of the low temperature and high vacuum requirements, this type of unit is rarely used on steam systems.

Selection of Terminal Equipment

The primary consideration in selecting terminal equipment is comfortable heat distribution. The following briefly describes suitable applications for specific types of steam terminal units.

Natural Convection Units

Radiators, convectors, and convection-type cabinet units and baseboard convectors are commonly used for (1) facilities that require heating only, rather than heating and cooling, such as factories, warehouses, schools, and apartment houses, and (2) in conjunction with central air-conditioning systems as a source of perimeter heating or for localized heating in spaces such as corridors, entrances, halls, toilets, kitchens, and storage areas.

Forced Convection Units

Forced convection units can be used for the same types of applications as natural convection units but are primarily used for facilities that require both heating and cooling, as well as spaces that require localized heating.

Unit heaters are often used as the primary source of heat in factories, warehouses, and garages and as supplemental freeze protection for loading ramps, entrances, equipment rooms, and fresh air plenums.

Unit ventilators are forced convection units with dampers that introduce controlled amounts of outside air. They are used in spaces with ventilation requirements not met by other system components.

Cabinet heaters are often used in entrance ways and vestibules that can have high intermittent heat loads.

Induction units are similar to fan coil units, but the air is supplied by a central air system rather than individual fans in each unit. Induction units are most commonly used as perimeter heating for facilities with central systems.

Fan coil units are designed for heating and cooling. On water systems, a single coil can be supplied with hot water for heating and chilled water for cooling. On steam systems, single- or dual-coil units can be used. Single-coil units require steam-to-water heat exchangers to provide hot water to meet heating requirements. Dual-coil units have a steam coil for heating and a separate coil for cooling. The cooling media for dual-coil units can be chilled water from a central chiller or refrigerant provided by a self-contained compressor. Single-coil units require the entire system to be either in a heating or cooling mode and do not permit simultaneous heating and cooling to satisfy individual space requirements. Dual-coil units can eliminate this problem.

Central air-handling units are used for most larger facilities. These units have a fan, heating and cooling coil, and a compressor if chilled water is not available for cooling. Multi-zone units are arranged so that each air outlet has separate controls for individual space heating or cooling requirements. Large central systems distribute either warm or cold conditioned air through dual-duct systems and employ separate terminal equipment such as mixing boxes, reheat coils, or variable volume controls to control the temperature to satisfy each space. Central air-handling systems can be factory assembled, field erected, or built at the job site from individual components.

CONVECTION-TYPE STEAM-HEATING SYSTEMS

Any system that uses steam as the heat transfer medium can be considered a steam-heating system; however, the term "steam-heating system" is most commonly applied to convection-type systems using radiators or convectors as terminal equipment. Other types of steam-heating systems use forced convection, in which a fan or air-handling system is used with a convector or steam coil such as unit heaters, fan coil units, and central air conditioning and heating systems.

Convection-type steam-heating systems are used in facilities that have a heating requirement only, such as factories, warehouses, and apartment buildings. They are often used in conjunction with central air-conditioning systems to heat the perimeter of the building. Also, steam is commonly used with incremental units that are designed for cooling and heating and have a self-contained air-conditioning compressor.

Steam-heating systems are classified as one-pipe or two-pipe systems, according to the piping arrangement that supplies steam to and returns condensate from the terminal equipment. These systems can be further sub-divided by (1) the method of condensate return (gravity flow or mechanical flow by means of condensate pump or vacuum pump) and (2) by the piping arrangement (up-feed or down-feed and parallel or counter flow for one-pipe systems).

One-Pipe Steam-Heating Systems

The one-pipe system (Figure 21) has a single pipe through which steam flows to and condensate is returned from the terminal equipment. These systems are designed as gravity return, although a condensate pump can be used where there is insufficient height above the boiler water level to develop enough pressure to return condensate directly to boiler.

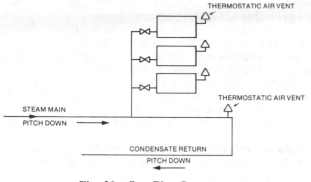

Fig. 21   One-Pipe System

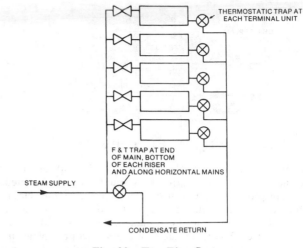

Fig. 22   Two-Pipe System

A one-pipe system with gravity return does not have steam traps; instead it has air vents at each terminal unit and at the ends of all supply mains to vent the air so the system can fill with steam. There must be an air vent at each terminal unit and steam traps at the ends of each supply main in systems with a condensate pump.

The one-pipe system with gravity return has low initial cost and is simple to install, since it requires a minimum of mechanical equipment and piping. One-pipe systems are most commonly used in small facilities such as small apartment buildings and office buildings. In larger facilities, the larger pipe sizes required for two-phase flow, problems of distributing steam quickly and evenly throughout system, inability to zone the system, and difficulty in controlling the temperature make the one-pipe system less desirable than two-pipe systems.

The heat input to the system is controlled by cycling the steam on and off. In the past, temperature control in individual spaces has been a problem. Many systems have adjustable vents at each terminal unit to help balance the system, but these are seldom effective. A practical approach is to use a *self-contained thermostatic valve* in series with the air vent (as explained in the "Temperature Control for Steam Heating Systems" section) that provides individual thermostatic control for each space.

Many designers do not favor one-pipe systems because of their distribution and control problems. However, when a self-contained thermostatic valve is used to eliminate the problems, one-pipe systems can be considered for small facilities, where initial cost and simple installation and operation are prime factors.

Most one-pipe gravity return systems are in facilities that have their own boiler, and, since returning condensate must overcome boiler pressure, these system usually operate from a fraction of a psi to a maximum of 5 psi. The boiler hook-up is critical and the Hartford Loop (described in the section on "Boiler Connections") is used to avoid problems that can occur with boiler low-water condition. Stamper and Koral (1979) and Hoffman give piping design information for one-pipe systems.

Two-Pipe Steam-Heating Systems

The two-pipe system (Figure 22) uses separate pipes to deliver the steam and return the condensate from each terminal unit. Thermostatic traps are installed at the outlet of each terminal unit to keep the steam in the unit until it gives up its latent heat, at which time the trap cycles open to pass the condensate and permits more steam to enter the radiator. If orifices are installed at the inlet to each terminal unit, as discussed in the "Steam Distribution" and "Temperature Control" sections below, and if the system pressure is precisely regulated so only the amount of steam is delivered to each unit that it is capable of condens-

ing, the steam traps can be omitted. However, omitting steam traps is generally not recommended for initial design.

Two-pipe systems can have either gravity or mechanical returns; however, gravity returns are restricted to use in small systems and are generally outmoded. In larger systems that require higher steam pressures to distribute steam, some mechanical means, such as a condensate pump or vacuum pump, must return condensate to the boiler. A vacuum return system is used on larger systems and has the following advantages:

1. The system fills quickly with steam. The steam in a gravity return system must "push" the air out of the system, resulting in delayed heatup and condensate return that can cause low-water problems. A vacuum return system can eliminate these problems.
2. The steam supply pressure can be lower, resulting in more efficient operation.

Variable vacuum or sub-atmospheric systems are a variation of the vacuum return system in which a controllable vacuum is maintained in both the supply and return sides. This permits using the lowest possible system temperature and prompt steam distribution to the terminal units. The primary purpose of variable vacuum systems is to control temperature as discussed in the "Temperature Control" section.

Unlike one-pipe systems, two-pipe systems can be simply zoned where piping is arranged to supply heat to individual sections of the building that have similar heating requirements. Heat is supplied to meet the requirements of each section without overheating other sections. The heat also can be varied according to hours of use, type of occupancy, sun load, and similar factors.

STEAM DISTRIBUTION

Steam supply piping should be sized so that the pressure drops in all branches of the same supply main are nearly uniform. Return piping should be sized for the same pressure drop as supply piping for quick and even steam distribution. Since it is impossible to size piping so that pressure drops are exactly the same, the steam flows first to those units that can be reached with the least resistance, resulting in uneven heating. Units furthest from the source of steam will heat last, while other spaces are overheated. This problem is most evident when the system is filling with steam. It can be severe on systems in which temperature is controlled by cycling the steam on and off. The problem can be alleviated or eliminated by balancing valves or inlet orifices.

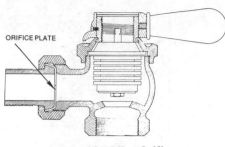

Fig. 23 Inlet Orifice

Balancing valves are installed at the unit inlet and contain an adjustable valve port to control the amount of steam delivered. The main problem with such devices is that they are seldom calibrated accurately, and variations in orifice size that are as small as .003 in.² (1.9 mm²) can make a significant difference.

Inlet orifices (Figure 23) are thin brass or copper plates installed in the unit inlet valve or pipe unions. Inlet orifices can solve distribution problems, since they can be drilled for appropriate size and changed easily to compensate for unusual conditions. Properly sized inlet orifices can compensate for oversized heating units, reduce energy waste and system control problems caused by excessive steam loss from defective steam traps, and provide a means of temperature control and balancing within individual zones.

Table 2 shows suggested orifice sizes that were determined experimentally for a gravity return (vented condensate receiver) system. Since the table only shows a maximum pressure differential of 6 in. Hg (20 kPa) and most systems operate at higher pressure differentials and/or with a vacuum return, more accurate sizing can be determined by calculating the required sizes from the appropriate data provided by the manufacturers of orifice plates.

If orifices are installed in valves or pipe unions that are conveniently accessible, minor rebalancing among individual zones can be accomplished through replacement of individual orifices.

TEMPERATURE CONTROL

All heating systems require some means of temperature control to achieve desired comfort conditions and operating efficiencies. In convection-type steam-heating systems, the temperature and resulting heat output of the terminal units must be increased or decreased. This can be done by (1) permitting the steam to enter the heating unit intermittently, (2) varying the steam temperature delivered to each unit, and (3) varying the amount of steam delivered to each unit.

There are two types of controls: those that control the temperature or heat input to the entire system and those that control the temperature of individual spaces or zones. Often, both types are used together for maximum control and operating efficiency.

Intermittent flow controls, commonly called heat timers, control the temperature of the system by cycling the steam on and off during a certain portion (or fraction) of each hour as a function of the outdoor and/or indoor temperature. Most of these devices provide for night setback, and newer "computer-style" models optimize morning startup as a function of outdoor and indoor temperature and make anticipatory adjustments. Used independently, these devices do not permit varying heat input to various parts of the building or spaces, so they should be used with zone control valves or individual thermostatic valves for maximum energy efficiency.

Zone control valves control the temperature of spaces with similar heating requirements as a function of outdoor and/or indoor temperature, as well as permit duty cycling. These intermittent flow control devices operate full open or full closed. They are controlled by an indoor thermostat and are used in conjunction with a heat timer, variable vacuum, or pressure differential control that controls heat input to the system.

Individual thermostatic valves installed at each terminal unit can provide the proper amount of heat to satisfy the individual requirements of each space and eliminate overheating. Valves can be actuated electrically, pneumatically, or by a self-contained mechanism that has a wax or liquid filled sensing element requiring no external power source.

Individual thermostatic valves can be and are often used as the only means of temperature control. However, these systems are always "on," resulting in inefficiency and no central control of heat input to the system or to the individual zones. Electric and pneumatic operators allow centralized control to be built into the system. However, it is desirable to have a supplemental system control with self-contained thermostatic valves in the

Table 2 Orifice Capacities for Low Pressure Steam Systems in lb/h

Orifice Diameter 64th of an Inch	6 in. Hg Differential	5 in. Hg Differential	4 in. Hg Differential	2 in. Hg Differential	1 in. Hg Differential
7	4.5- 5.8	4.0- 5.3	3.8- 4.8	2.5- 3.3	
8	5.8- 7.3	5.3- 6.8	4.8- 6.3	3.3- 4.3	2.0- 2.8
9	7.3- 9.0	6.8- 8.3	6.3- 7.5	4.3- 5.3	2.8- 3.5
10	9.0-11.0	8.3-10.0	7.5- 9.3	5.3- 6.5	3.5- 4.3
11	11.0-13.0	10.0-12.0	9.3-11.0	6.5- 7.8	4.3- 5.0
12	13.0-15.5	12.0-14.3	11.0-12.8	7.8- 9.3	5.0- 6.0
13	15.5-18.0	14.3-16.5	12.8-14.8	9.3-10.8	6.0- 7.0
14	18.0-20.8	16.5-19.0	14.8-16.8	10.8-12.3	7.0- 8.0
15	20.8-23.5	19.0-21.5	16.8-19.0	12.3-14.0	8.0- 9.3
16	23.5-26.5	21.5-24.3	19.0-21.5	14.0-16.0	9.2-10.5
17	26.5-29.8	24.3-27.3	21.5-24.3	16.0-18.0	10.5-11.8
18	29.8-33.3	27.3-30.5	24.3-27.0	18.0-20.0	11.8-13.0
19	33.3-37.0	30.5-33.8	27.0-30.0	20.0-22.0	13.0-14.5
20	37.0-40.8	33.8-37.3	30.0-33.3	22.0-24.5	14.5-16.0
21	40.8-44.8	37.3-41.0	33.3-36.3	24.5-26.8	16.0-17.8

Note—The radiator orifice plates in this table are cup-shaped brass stampings 0.023 in. thick, which are made to be inserted in radiator valve unions. Based on tests by Sanford and Sprenger (1931). SI Conversion Factors: 1 in. = 25.4 mm; 1 in. Hg. = 3.38 kPa; 1 lb/h = 0.1 g/s.

Table 3 Pressure Differential Temperature Control[a]

Outdoor Temperature		Required Pressure Differential	
F	(°C)	in. Hg.	(kPa)
0	(−18)	6.0	(20.3)
10	(−12)	4.5	(15.2)
20	(−7)	3.2	(10.8)
30	(−1)	2.1	(7.1)
40	(4)	1.2	(4.1)
50	(10)	0.5	(1.7)
60	(16)	0.1	(0.34)

[a]To maintain 70°F (21°C) indoors for 0°F (−18°C) outdoor design.

form of zone control valves, or a system that controls the heat input to the entire system, relying on self-contained valves as a local high temperature shutoff only.

Self-contained thermostatic valves can also be used to control temperature on one-pipe systems that cycle on and off when installed in series with the unit air vent. On initial startup, the air vent is open, and inherent system distribution problems still exist. However, on subsequent on-cycles where the room temperature satisfies the thermostatic element, the vent valve remains closed preventing the unit from filling with steam.

Variable vacuum or sub-atmospheric systems control the temperature of the system by varying the steam temperature through pressure control. These systems differ from the regular vacuum return system in that the vacuum is maintained in both supply and return lines. Such systems usually operate at a pressure range from 2 psig to 25 in. Hg vacuum (85 to 115 kPa). Inlet orifices are installed at the terminal equipment for proper steam distribution during mild weather.

Since design-day conditions are seldom encountered, the system usually operates at a substantial vacuum. Because the specific volume of steam increases as the pressure decreases, it takes less steam to fill the system and operating efficiency results. The variable vacuum system can be used in conjunction with zone control valves or individual self-contained valves for increased operating efficiency.

Pressure differential control (two-pipe orifice) systems provide centralized temperature control with any system that has properly sized inlet orifices at each heating unit. This method operates on the principle that flow through an orifice is a function of the pressure differential across the orifice plate. The pressure range is selected to fill each heating unit on the coldest design day; on warmer days, the supply pressure is lowered so that heating units are only partially filled with steam, thereby reducing their heat output. An advantage of this method is that it virtually eliminates all heating unit steam trap losses because the heating units are only partially filled with steam on all but the coldest design days.

The required system pressure differential can be achieved manually with throttling valves or with an automatic pressure differential controller. Table 3 shows the required pressure differentials to maintain 70°F (21°C) indoors for 0°F (−18°C) outdoor design, with orifices selected according to Table 2. Required pressure differential curves can be established for any combination of supply and return line pressures by sizing orifices to deliver the proper amount of steam for the coldest design day, calculating the amount of steam required for warmer days using Equation (2) and then selecting the pressure differential that will provide this flow rate.

$$\text{Required Flow Rate} = \text{Design Day Flow Rate} \times$$
$$\frac{\text{Outside Temp.}}{\text{Design Indoor Temp.} - \text{Design Outdoor Temp.}} \quad (2)$$

Pressure differential systems can be used with zone control valves or individual self-contained thermostatic valves to achieve increased operating efficiency.

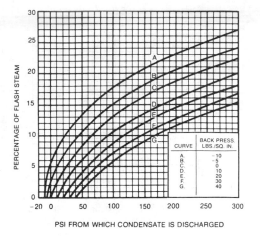

Fig. 24 Flash Steam

HEAT RECOVERY

Because enthalpy is available in the condensate discharged to the return system, it may be worthwhile to recover this enthalpy to the maximum extent possible. Two methods are generally employed: (1) the enthalpy of the liquid condensate (*sensible heat*) can be used to vaporize or "flash" some of the liquid to steam at a lower pressure or (2) it can be used directly in a heat exchanger to heat air, fluid, or a process.

The particular methods used vary with the type of system. As explained in the "Basic Steam System Design" section, facilities that purchase steam from a utility generally do not have to return condensate and, therefore, can recover heat to the maximum extent possible. On the other hand, facilities with their own boiler generally want the condensate to return to the boiler as hot as possible, limiting heat recovery since any heat removed from condensate has to be put back at the boiler to generate steam again.

Flash Steam

Flash steam is an effective use for the enthalpy of the liquid condensate. It can be used in any facility that has a requirement for steam at different pressures, regardless of whether steam is purchased or generated by a facility's own boiler. Flash steam

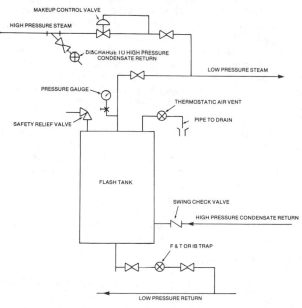

Fig. 25 Vertical Flash Tank

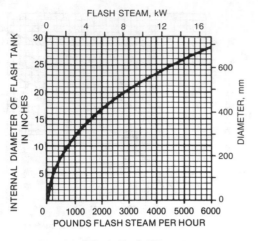

Fig. 26 Flash Tank Diameters

can be used in any heat-exchange device to heat air, water, or other liquids or directly in processes with lower pressure steam requirements.

Equation 1 (p. 11.2) may be used to calculate the amount of flash steam generated, and Figure 24 provides a graph for calculating the amount of flash steam as a function of system pressures.

Although flash steam can be generated directly by discharging high pressure condensate to a lower pressure system, most designers prefer a *flash tank* to control flashing. Flash tanks can be mounted either vertically or horizontally, but the vertical arrangement shown in Figure 25 is preferred beause it provides better separation of steam and water, resulting in the highest possible steam quality.

The most important dimension in the design of vertical flash tanks is the internal diameter, which must be large enough to ensure low upward velocity of flash to minimize water carryover. If the upward velocity is low enough, the height of the tank is not important, but it is good practice to use a minimum height of 2 or 3 ft (0.6 to 0.9 m). The chart in Figure 26 can be used to determine the internal diameter and is based on a steam velocity of 10 ft/s (3 m/s), which is the maximum velocity in most systems.

Installation is important for proper flash tank operation. Condensate lines should pitch towards the flash tank. If more than one condensate line discharges to the tank, each line should be equipped with a swing check valve to prevent back flow. Condensate lines and the flash tank should be well insulated to prevent any unnecessary heat loss. A thermostatic air vent should be installed at the top of the tank to vent any air that accumulates. The tank should be trapped at the bottom with an inverted bucket or float and thermostatic (F & T) trap sized to triple the condensate load.

The demand load must always be greater than the amount of flash steam available or the low pressure system can be over-pressurized. A safety relief valve should always be installed at the top of the flash tank to preclude such a condition.

Since the flash steam available is generally less than the demand for low pressure steam, a makeup valve ensures that the low pressure system maintains design pressure.

Flash tanks are considered pressure vessels and must be constructed in accordance with ASME and local codes.

Direct Heat Recovery

Direct heat recovery that uses the enthalpy of the liquid in some type of heat exchange device is appropriate when condensate is not returned to a facility's own boiler; any lowering of condensate temperature below 212 °F (100 °C) requires reheating at the boiler to regenerate steam.

The enthalpy of the condensate can be used in fan coil units, unit heaters, or convectors to heat spaces where temperature control is not critical such as garages, ramps, loading docks, and entrance halls or in a shell-and-tube heat exchanger to heat water or other fluids.

In most HVAC applications, the enthalpy of the liquid condensate most effectively and efficiently used to heat *domestic hot water* with a shell-and-tube or plate-type heat exchanger, commonly called an *economizer*. Many existing economizers do not use the enthalpy of the condensate effectively because they are designed only to preheat makeup water flowing directly through the heat exchanger at the time of domestic hot water usage. Hot water use seldom coincides with condensate load, and most of the enthalpy is wasted in these preheat economizer systems. Heat recovery can only be effective with a storage type hot water heater. This can be a shell-and-tube heat exchanger for a condensate coil for heat recovery and a steam or electric coil when the condensate enthalpy cannot satisfy the demand, or a storage-type heat exchanger incorporating only a coil for condensate with a supplemental heat exchanger to satisfy peak loads. Chapter 34 provides useful information on determining hot water loads for various facilities, but in general the following provides optimum heat recovery.

1. Install the greatest storage capacity in the available space. Although all systems must have supplemental heaters for peak load conditions, with ample storage capacity these heaters may seldom function if all the necessary heat is provided by the enthalpy of the condensate.
2. For maximum recovery, permit stored water to heat to 180 °F (82 °C) or higher, using a mixing valve to temper the water to the proper delivery temperature.

COMBINED STEAM AND WATER SYSTEMS

Combined steam and water system are often used to take advantage of the unique properties of steam, described in the "Advantages of Steam Systems" and "Fundamentals" sections.

Combined systems are used where a facility must generate steam to satisfy the heating requirements of certain processes or equipment. They are usually used where steam is available from a utility and economic considerations of local codes preclude the facility from operating its own boiler plant. There are two types of combined steam and water systems: (1) where steam is used directly as a heating medium; the terminal equipment must have two separate coils, one for heating with steam and one for cooling with chilled water and (2) where steam is used indirectly and is piped to heat exchangers that generate the hot water for use at terminal equipment; the exchanger for terminal equipment may use either one coil or separate coils for heating and cooling.

Combined steam and water systems may be two-, three-, or four-pipe systems. Chapters 2, 3, and 4 have further descriptions.

REFERENCES

Hoffman Steam Heating Systems Design Manual. Bulletin No. TES-181, Hoffman Specialty ITT Fluid Handling Div., Indianapolis, IN.

Kremers, J.A. 1982. Modulating Steam Pressure in Coils Compound Steam Trap Selection Procedures. Armstrong *Trap Magazine,* Volume 50, Number 1. Available from Armstrong Machine Works, Three Rivers, Michigan 49093.

Power Piping. ANSI/ASME *B31.1-1980.*

Sanford, S.S; and Springer, C.B. 1931. Flow of Steam Through Orifices. ASHVE *Transactions,* Vol. 37, pp. 371-394.

Stamper, E.; and Koral, R.L. 1979. *Handbook of Air Conditioning, Heating and Ventilating.* Third Edition. Industrial Press, New York, NY.

CHAPTER 12

HEATING AND COOLING FROM A CENTRAL PLANT

CENTRAL heating plants and distribution systems have been in service in many cities, universities, and industrial facilities for more than 70 years (NBS 1975). The current emphasis on energy conservation, new technology, and more demanding standards in controlling the building interior environment are responsible for the rapid increase in the number of central plants for heating and cooling with associated distribution systems.

PIPING DISTRIBUTION SYSTEM

Economic justification for central plant and distribution systems for two or more buildings requires an analysis of the possible alternatives, including (1) direct construction costs of the installations, (2) operating expenses, (3) maintenance and replacement budgets, and (4) the value of such indirect factors as aesthetics, noise, air pollution, safety, future flexibility, reliability, and convenience. Cost and value comparisons are complex and result from carefully considering many details of each alternative design possibility. Some positive features of central plant over individual building design are as follows:

1. The central plant has greater flexibility to use alternative energy sources as availability and technological change cause reevaluation of energy conversion systems.
2. The central plant and distribution system uses less space in the buildings served.
3. Energy is converted to a usable form for conventional heating and cooling systems often more efficiently in larger capacity apparatus.
4. Large energy conversion apparatus is generally constructed for longer service life with reduced life-cycle cost.
5. Central plants usually require less total installed capacity than dispersed because peak demand usually occurs at different times in several terminal loads.
6. Central plants can provide reserve capacity of standby service at a lower cost because a spare machine can serve several loads. This feature improves reliability and service continuity.
7. Partial load performance of central plants might be more efficient than many isolated small systems, since the larger plant can operate one or more capacity modules as the combined load requires. Central plants may have very efficient base load units plus less costly, less efficient peaking equipment for use in extreme loads or emergency.
8. Central plant system instrumentation and control systems are generally of better quality and are more comprehensive than the comparable systems commonly applied to isolated systems, thereby improving performance efficiency and reliability.

9. Maintenance activities are concentrated in central heating and cooling systems and might economically justify employing skilled operators and technicians at a central location.
10. Central plants enhance safety in the energy conversion process. Fuel systems, combustion processes, large electrical loads, and chemical treatment are better controlled in the central plant with skilled operators and with physical isolation from public spaces.

The piping distribution system that delivers the desired cooling and heating to the point of use is a sizable burden that must be included in the comparative analysis of design alternatives. Factors influencing the economic comparison are (1) initial cost, (2) service life and maintenance costs, (3) heat loss or gain in the piping system, (4) costs of pumping the fluids, (5) dependability, (6) accessibility, and (7) adaptability for future changes.

The initial stage of developing a central plant and distribution system is a major investment that often requires additional development and expansion to prove economically attractive. The planning for central facilities accounts for the ultimate growth of the area served; all of the apparatus selections, pipe sizing, fuel supply, electric entrance, and space allocations must provide for the eventual maximum plant development.

TYPES OF INSULATED PIPING SYSTEMS

As the use and size of central systems increase and the operating conditions vary more widely, it becomes increasingly important to design suitable safety factors into new systems. Design criteria, application procedures, and performance results (including safety factors) for the strength, corrosion protection, fluid flow, and thermal properties of underground piping systems can be obtained from piping system manufacturers. These requirements must apply to all components of the underground piping system, since the proper functioning and life of the system depend on the combined performance of all the materials. This is important because of the high failure rate experienced in underground systems and the fact that repairs to underground systems are more difficult to handle than in aboveground conditions.

Industry agreement has evolved three temperature ranges for distribution systems and related equipment: (1) steam and water, at 250°F (121°C) and higher; (2) water and steam, from 180 to 250°F (82 to 121°C); and (3) chilled water and dual-temperature water, 35 to 180°F (1.7 to 82°C). Chilled water systems and dual-temperature systems are quite similar in most respects to low temperature systems. For additional information on the performance and interrelation of components of underground systems, see Chapter 20 of the 1985 FUNDAMENTALS Volume. Distribution piping systems can be categorized as (1) tunnels and con-

The preparation of this chapter is assigned to TC 6.1, Hot Water and Steam Heating Equipment and Systems.

crete trenches, (2) factory-fabricated systems (air-space and non-air-space), (3) field-fabricated systems, and (4) poured envelope systems.

Tunnels

Functional requirements of the distribution piping system are best served by completely accessible piping in a reinforced concrete tunnel. The tunnel should be sized to accommodate predictable load growth and have piping available for inspection, repair, modification, replacement, addition of new services, and protection from most hazards. Tunnels require adequate ventilation, service openings for personnel and equipment, illumination, and drainage, and must be arranged to permit installation and maintenance of required valves, anchors, guides, and expansion loops and joints.

Personnel safety must include isolation barriers to localize hazards from escaping high pressure steam or other high temperature fluids. Piping practices in tunnels are the same for conventional buildings. See Chapters 11, 13, 14, and 15 of this volume as they apply to particular services.

Concrete Trenches

These reinforced concrete structures are designed just large enough to contain the desired pipe systems; a removable top on the trench at ground level permits service to the contents. As in the tunnel, provision must be made for draining. The top should be designed to prevent surface water from entering. There should be adequate slope and space between the trench floor and the insulation to prevent seepage and leaks from wetting the insulation. Since an air space is advantageous for draining water and for drying the insulation, do not fill the trench with bulk insulation. Piping practices in concrete trenches are the same as for piping in buildings. See Chapters 11, 13, 14, and 15 of this volume as they apply to particular services.

Factory-Fabricated Systems, Air-Space

These conduit systems consist of a carrier pipe, insulation, an annular air space between the insulation and outer conduit, and the conduit itself (usually steel), all assembled with internal supports. There can be one or more carrier pipes in a single conduit, but separate conduits provide greater reliability in systems having one pipe with a shorter life expectancy than the others, such as condensate return lines. Hot water lines can be either single or multiple pipe. Expansion loops, bends, tees, and anchor sections are factory fabricated for field assembly. Insulation is usually either calcium silicate or fiberglass. To date, calcium silicate is the only insulation that has passed the boiling and drying test criteria established by the National Academy of Sciences.

The variations available in this type of system differ primarily in the casings and the corrosion protection materials used. Steel casings with various protective coatings are generally selected. Cast iron and fiberglass reinforced plastic (FRP) materials have been used but are now infrequently specified.

The system manufacturer supplies the installer with the joining materials and complete installation instructions. These systems are designed so that the air space is continuous throughout the line from one manhole to the next. If water enters the conduit, this feature allows water to be drained from the system. Once the water has been drained and any required repairs have been made, the insulation can be dried in place and restored to its original efficiency by blowing air through the conduit.

As part of their design, these systems accommodate expansion by the inherent pipe flexibility at changes of direction or expansion loops. If required, the conduit is oversized at these points to allow the piping to move. Inverts of all conduits are in direct alignment and pitched to permit drainage. Since these systems are confirmed to be airtight when installed, a positive pressure of 5 to 8 psi (35 to 55 kPa) can be maintained in the air space. This pressure is then monitored with a device that signals when the pressure drops, alerting operating personnel to a possible conduit leak.

Factory-Fabricated Systems, Non-Air-Space

These systems consist of a carrier pipe, insulation, and an outer casing or jacket in contact with the insulation. This system has no air space.

The carrier pipe can be of any suitable material. Examples are steel, copper, epoxy-lined asbestos cement, PVC, or FRP. It is important that the carrier pipe be selected for the operating pressure and temperature, as well as its compatibility with the fluid carried.

The insulation used is usually foamed-in-place polyurethane if the operating temperatures are within its limits. Some systems for high temperature service use calcium silicate, fiberglass, cellular glass, or combinations of these with urethane. Where urethane is used with other insulations in high temperature applications, the thickness of the high temperature insulation must be selected to prevent the interface temperature of the insulations from exceeding the temperature limits of the urethane. Table 1 lists physical properties.

When joints for metallic carrier pipes are welded, the system must provide for pipe movement. The expansion can be absorbed by movement within the insulation casing, expansion joints or ball joints, or preferably with expansion loops or changes in the direction of the piping.

If expansion joints or ball joints are used, they must be located in manholes or buildings for accessibility. As part of the system design, proper anchorage must be provided to control movement. When joints are made with suitable slip-type couplings, expansion and contraction can be accommodated without loops or other expansion devices. With slip-type couplings, proper thrust blocks must be provided to control pipe movement at fittings and dead ends.

When non-air-space systems are used for underground service, materials must be carefully selected for heat resistance and to prevent water from entering. One technique is to compartmentalize these systems so that the spread of water is limited to a single-pipe length. Thermoplastic materials used for the casing should be carefully evaluated, since relatively small heat leaks might damage the casing to the detriment of the entire system.

In recent years, European underground piping system manufacturers have developed a "bonded" system. The bonded system differs principally from "sliding" systems in that the polyurethane foam insulation is approximately twice the insulation density and is always foamed in place in the annular space between the steel carrier pipe and plastic outer casing. Foam materials and densities are chosen to ensure that forces resulting from the thermal expansion of the steel carrier pipe are transmitted through the urethane foam and outer plastic casing to the surrounding soil. Test results indicate that a safety factor greater than five exists when considering the sheer stress of the bond between piping system components and the friction forces normally encountered between the plastic casing and surrounding soil. Two major advantages attributed to this system are as follows:

1. Actual piping movement can be restrained (within acceptable stress limitations) by the friction forces of the surrounding soil.
2. The complete bond between insulation and steel pipe retards

Table 1 Comparison of Commonly Used Insulations in Underground Piping Systems[a]

Item	Calcium Silicate	Urethane Foam	Cellular Glass	Preformed Glass Fiber	Loose Glass Fiber	Insulating Concrete	Hydrocarbon Powder	Hydrophobic Powder
Thermal conductivity, Btu · in./ft^2 · h · °F (W · mm/m^2 · °C)								
at 100°F(37.8°C)	0.33 (47.5)	0.15 (21.6)	0.39 (56.2)	0.26 (37 .4)	0.32 (46.1)	0.6-4 (86.4-576)	0.6-0.8 (86.4-115.2)	0.53-0.8 (76.3-115.2)
at 200°F(93.3°C)	0.37 (53.3)	0.17 (24.5)	0. 47 (67.7)	0.30 (43.2)	—	—	—	0.6-0. 81 (86.4-116.6)
at 300°F(148.9°C)	0.41 (59.0)	—	0.55 (79.2)	0.33 (47.5)	—	—	—	0.66-0.85 (95-1 22.4)
at 400°F(204.4°C)	0.46 (66.2)	—	0.64 (92.2)	—	—	—	—	
Density, lb/ft^3(kg/m^3)	10-14 (160-224)	1.5-4 (24-64)	9-10 (144-160)	3-7 (48-112)	2-11 (32-176)	20 -30 (320-480)	45-55 (720-880)	35-65 (560-1040)
Max. temperature, °F(°C)	1200 (649)	260 (127)	800 (427)	370-500 (188-260)	1000 (538)	1800 (982)	300-450 (149-232)	500 (260)
Compressive strength, psi (Pa)	75-165 (517-1137)	20-50 (138-345)	1 00 (689)	5 (34)	0 (0)	100-150 (689-1034)	70-85 (482-586)	70-85 (482-586)
@% compression	5%	5%	—	—	—	—	5%	5%
Moisture absorption	Great	Slight	Nil	Gr eat	Great	Moderate	Moderate	Nil
Effect on k factor	Large	Slight	Slight	Large	Large	Slight	Large	Slight
Resistance to boiling	Good	Poor	Fair	Go od	Good	Good	Poor	Poor
Recovery-drying	Good	Poor	Good	Good	Good	Good	Poor	Poor
Resistance to abrasion	Fair	Fair	Fair	P oor	Nil	Good	Poor	Good
Resistance to vibration	Fair	Good	Poor	Good	Poor	Fair	Fair	Good
Stability: shrink, shock	Good	Good	Fair	Excellent	Excellent	Good	Good	Good
Combustible	No	Yes	No	Yes	No	No	Yes	No

[a]The descriptive terms in this table are only approximations because any insulation and the conditions under which it is used vary.
   The thermal conductivities for these materials, and for urethane foam used in the trench, are for dry material. Since foam may absorb ground water, and water vapor may eventually enter the interstices between powder particles, the eventual k values are difficult to estimate.

moisture propagation should the underground piping system outer casing break.

Field-Fabricated Systems

In these systems, the carrier pipe, insulation, and casing are assembled on-site and are built in several ways. The most common design consists of a concrete slab base with embedded supports for the insulated pipe. The system is protected by half-rounds of clay or concrete pipe placed over the carrier pipe and resting on the slab. Caulking and other construction methods prevent ground water entrance. The slab must be poured to grade, and adequate drainage is essential to minimize corrosion of the carrier pipes.

Formed insulation placed on the pipe or a bulk insulation placed inside the casing fill as much of the system around the carrier pipe as possible. However, bulk insulation may restrict drainage and is subject to wetting, which can reduce thermal efficiency and promote corrosion. A second type of system temporarily supports the assembled pipe off the trench bottom to allow the application of insulation and waterproof coverings over the insulation. It is imperative to have supplemental drainage systems outside the enclosed pipe structure to keep ground water away from the structure.

Poured Envelope Systems

These systems are constructed by assembling the pipe in the trench, supporting it on blocks above the trench bottom, and then pouring the insulation material into the trench to encase the pipe completely. The supporting blocks should be removed as the pouring progresses down the trench to achieve complete encasement and to prevent concentrated corrosion at the point of contact with the pipe, or the supports must be bitumastic coated to prevent capillarity between support and insulation. Poured envelope systems are initially less expensive than other types of systems.

In all other systems, there is a specific barrier to the entrance of ground water, and the system need only be designed and installed properly to maintain the integrity of that barrier. Poured envelope systems depend on using the insulation itself as a water barrier. In low temperature applications, poured envelopes may lose thermal efficiency because of moisture migration and condensation.

A good drainage system is recommended to minimize deterioration of the insulating quality. The four types of envelope materials are (1) insulating concrete, (2) hydrocarbon powder, (3) hydrophobic powder, and (4) polyurethane foam.

Insulating concrete is a Portland cement-bound, lightweight aggregate with additives, which gives the designer substantial latitude in selecting the desirable degree of structural strength and thermal efficiency. This system resists superimposed loads and gives continuous support and alignment for the piping. Concrete encasement should not be used with any piping system jointed with rubber ring couplings because the concrete may interfere with rubber ring operation.

In welded systems, a parting agent is placed around the piping to allow free longitudinal movement. Anchors are steel plates embedded in the thickened and reinforced concrete base slab and welded to the piping. Expansion voids are built into the conduit at corners and loops, using internal blockouts to provide the space for pipe movements. Anchoring is the same as for any other welded steel system. A properly designed system must have internal emergency drains and vents to remove accidental and residual construction water and serve as leak detectors.

Any crack that develops in the concrete endangers the entire system. Once ground water gets to the pipe, the water follows the pipe-concrete interface and can eventually cause corrosion anywhere along the pipeline.

Hydrocarbon powders are thermoplastic materials composed of lightweight aggregate with asphalt binders. These can be poured directly into the trench; but it is better to pour the hydrocarbon powders over a structural concrete base pad with either temporary or permanent pipe support. A continuous waterproof membrane covering the entire system keeps water away from the system. These materials should never be used with any rubber ring jointing system since the hydrocarbons harm the rubber rings. Provision for thermal expansion and anchoring should be the same as for other welded steel systems. Expansion is limited because repeated cycling hardens the mass and causes additional resistance to transverse pipe movements.

Hydrophobic powders are treated to be water repellent. The non-wettability characteristic prevents water from dampening the powder, causing loss of thermal efficiency. The installation methods are identical for hydrocarbon powders, except that compaction of the material is required only for chilled water and cryogenic applications.

Polyurethane foam insulation efficiency may vary considerably over a long time span with the amount and pressure of the moisture, temperature, age, density, and cell size. Density and cell size vary with the control of conditions under which the foaming took place. Foam in trenches should have a density high enough to provide a parallel compressive strength of 40 psi (267 kPa) and should never be used at temperatures over 240 to 250 °F (116 to 121 °C), or 210 °F (99 °C) if any ground moisture is present. A combination of water and temperature above 210 °F (99 °C) quickly destroys the urethane.

Froth-pour or direct spray are the two application methods. For froth-pour techniques, simple forms are erected to contain the foam, which has a final density of about 2.0 to 2.5 lb/ft^3 (32 to 40 kg/m^3) and compressive strength after 24 hours from 25 to 40 psi (172 to 275 kPa). The direct spray method is more rapid, eliminates the need for side forms, and usually provides a denser material, from 2.2 to 3.0 lb/ft^3 (35 to 48 kg/m^3), with somewhat greater compressive strength. Voids are required for expansion-contraction movement of the spray material.

INSULATED PIPING SYSTEM DESIGN

General Considerations

An underground heat or chilled-water distribution piping system should provide efficient long-term operation (25 to 40 years) through structural soundness and protection from corrosion and other deterioration. To achieve this goal, it is necessary to design a system with the following characteristics:

1. Protection of a metallic carrier pipe from corrosion by cathodic protection or other means.
2. An insulation of the required thermal efficiency that is durable and can accommodate expansion of the piping system, and can tolerate occasional contact with the fluid being piped or ground water.
3. A protective casing that resists ground water infiltration, mechanical or structural damage, and corrosion, as well as other causes of deterioration.
4. A system that can be restored to its original condition by drying in the event of occasional flooding, or limits flooding to one pipe length.

HEAT TRANSFER COMPUTATIONS

Heat transfer in a piping system is not related to the load factor and can be a large part of the total load. Several factors affect the heat transfer, the main one being the difference between earth and fluid temperatures. For example, the extremes might be a 6 in. (150 mm) insulated 400 °F (204 °C) water line in 40 °F (4.4 °C) earth with 100 to 200 Btu/h·lin ft (96 to 192 W/m) loss, and a 6 in. (150 mm) uninsulated 55 °F (12.8 °C) chilled water return in 60 °F (15.6 °C) earth with 10 Btu/h·lin ft (9.6 W/m) gain. The former requires analysis to determine the insulation needs and effect on the total heating system; the latter suggests analysis and insulation needs might be minimal. Other factors that affect heat transfer, but to a lesser extent than soil temperature are (1) depth of burial, which is related to the earth temperature, (2) soil conductivity, which is related to moisture content, and (3) distance between adjacent pipes.

There are several methods to compute heat gains or losses in underground piping systems. Since the heat transfer process from underground heat distribution systems is a transient phenomenon, the best method is a computerized, iterative process and finite difference or finite element technique that calculates thermal conductivity and thermal gradient as each changes with respect to the other. Simple analytical equations are available, however, to determine pipe-ground heat exchange under steady-state conditions. Steady-state calculations for a one-pipe system can be done without a computer, but it becomes increasingly difficult for a two-, three- or fourpipe system unless a computer is used.

The following computation methods developed by the Federal Construction Council (1975) and Kusuda and Powell (1970) provide a steady-state heat transfer analysis of simple underground systems. The magnitude of error depends on the difference between the chosen parameters (such as temperatures and thermal conductivity of surrounding soil and insulation materials) and the actual values. Since the earth around the pipe is heterogeneous, its thermal properties and temperature are difficult to define. The handbook data is more useful for a consistent comparative analysis rather than for absolute accuracy of computation. Earth temperatures and earth thermal conductivity factors are listed immediately after the computation methods.

Required Data for Figure 1:

   d = depth of burial, in. (mm).
   r = radius of the system (to the exterior surface of the system), in. (mm).
   T_G = earth temperature, °F (°C).
   K_s = earth thermal conductivity, Btu·in./h·ft^2·°F (W/m^2·K).
   C = system thermal conductance, Btu/h·°F·ft (W/°C·m) of pipe.
   t_f = temperature of fluid being distributed, °F (°C).

Calculations (Figure 1):

1. System or Pipe Heat Transfer Factor:

$$\frac{1}{k_p} = \frac{1}{C} + \frac{12}{2\pi K_s} \ln \left\{ \frac{d}{r} + \sqrt{\left(\frac{d}{r}\right)^2 - 1} \right\}$$

or, when $\dfrac{d}{r} \gg 1$

$$\frac{1}{k_p} = \frac{1}{C} + \frac{12}{2\pi K_s} \ln \left(\frac{2d}{r}\right)$$

2. *System or Pipe Heat Loss:*

$$C = K_p (T_f - T_G)$$

Required Data for Figure 2:

   d_1 = depth of burial, Pipe No. 1, in. (mm).
   d_2 = depth of burial, Pipe No. 2, in. (mm).
   r_1 = radius of the system, Pipe No. 1, in. (mm).
   r_2 = radius of the system, Pipe No. 2, in. (mm).
   T_G = earth temperature, °F (°C).
   K_s = earth thermal conductivity, Btu·in./h·ft^2·°F (W/m^2·K).
   C = system thermal conductance, Btu/h·°F·ft (W/°C·m) of pipe.
   T_{f1} = temperature of fluid being carried in Pipe No. 1, °F (°C).
   T_{f2} = temperature of fluid being carried in Pipe No. 2, °F (°C).
   a = center distance between pipes (No. 1 and 2), in. (mm).

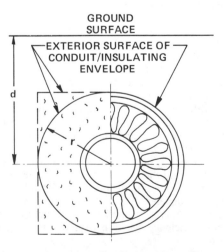

Fig. 1   Heat Loss from Single-Pipe System

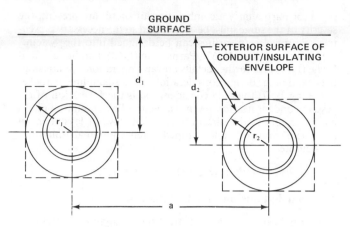

Fig. 2   Heat Loss from Two-Pipe System with Pipes in Separate Conduit/Envelope

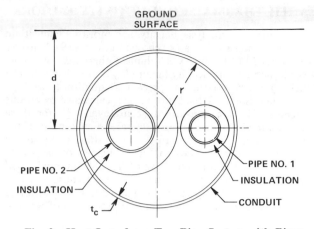

Fig. 3   Heat Loss from Two-Pipe System with Pipes in Same Conduit/Envelope

Calculations (Figure 2):

1. *Let:*

$$P_{11} = 1 + \frac{12C_1}{2\pi K_s} \ln\left(\frac{2d_1}{r_1}\right)$$

$$P_{12} = 1 + \frac{12C_2}{2\pi K_s} \ln\sqrt{\frac{a^2 + (d_1 + d_2)^2}{a^2 + (d_1 + d_2)^2}}$$

$$P_{21} = 1 + \frac{12C_1}{2\pi K_s} \ln\sqrt{\frac{a^2 + (d_1 + d_2)^2}{a^2 + (d_1 + d_2)^2}}$$

$$P_{22} = 1 + \frac{12C_2}{2\pi K_s} \ln\left(\frac{2d_2}{r_2}\right)$$

and

$$\Delta = P_{12}\,P_{21} - P_{11}\,P_{22}$$

2. *Pipe Heat Transfer Factors:*

$$K_{p1} = \frac{C_1}{\Delta}(P_{12} - P_{22})$$

and

$$K_{p2} = \frac{C_2}{\Delta}(P_{21} - P_{11})$$

3. *Equivalent Pipe Temperatures:*

$$T_{p1} = \frac{P_{12}\,T_{f2} - P_{22}\,T_{f1}}{P_{12} - P_{22}}$$

and

$$T_{p2} = \frac{P_{21}\,T_{f1} - P_{11}\,T_{f2}}{P_{21} - P_{11}}$$

4. *Pipe Heat Loss, Btu/h • ft (W/m):*

$$Q_1 = K_{p1}(T_{p1} - T_G)$$

and

$$Q_2 = K_{p2}(T_{p2} - T_G)$$

Required Data for Figure 3:

    d = depth of burial, in. (mm).
    r = radius of the system (to the exterior surface of the system), in. (mm).
    T_G = earth temperature, °F (°C).
    K_s = earth thermal conductivity, Btu/h • in. • °F (W/mm • °C).
    C_a = thermal conductance of conduit air space, Btu/h • °F • ft (W/°C • m) of pipe, normally 3.0 (0.42).

C_1 = thermal conductance of Pipe No. 1 plus insulation, Btu/h • °F • ft (W/°C • m) of pipe.
C_2 = thermal conductance of Pipe No. 2 insulation, Btu/h • °F • ft (W/°C • m) of pipe.
t_c = conduit wall thickness, in. (mm).
K_c = conduit wall thermal conductivity, Btu/h • in. (W/mm).
T_{f1} = temperature of fluid being carried in Pipe No. 1, °F (°C).
T_{f2} = temperature of fluid being carried in Pipe No. 2, °F (°C).

Calculations (Figure 3):

1. *Let:*

$$\frac{1}{P_0} = \frac{12}{2\pi}\left[\frac{1}{K_c}\ln\left(\frac{r}{r - t_c}\right) + \frac{1}{K_s}\ln\left\{\frac{d}{r} + \sqrt{\left(\frac{d}{r}\right)^2 - 1}\right\}\right]$$

$$\frac{1}{P_1} = \frac{1}{C_1} + \frac{1}{C_a}$$

$$\frac{1}{P_2} = \frac{1}{C_2} + \frac{1}{C_a}$$

or, when $\dfrac{d}{r} \gg 1$

$$\left\{\frac{d}{r} + \sqrt{\left(\frac{d}{r}\right)^2 - 1}\right\} = \left(\frac{2d}{r}\right)$$

2. *Pipe Heat Transfer Factors:*

$$K_{p1} = \frac{P_1\,P_0}{P_0 + P_1 + P_2}$$

and

$$K_{p2} = \frac{P_2\,P_0}{P_0 + P_1 + P_2}$$

3. *Equivalent Pipe Temperatures:*

$$T_{p1} = \left(1 + \frac{P_2}{P_0}\right)T_{f1} - \frac{P_2}{P_0}T_{f2}$$

and

$$T_{p2} = \left(1 + \frac{P_1}{P_0}\right)T_{f2} - \frac{P_1}{P_0}T_{f1}$$

4. *Pipe Heat Loss:*

$$Q_1 = K_{p1}(T_{p1} - T_G)$$

and

$$Q_2 = K_{p2}(T_{p2} - T_G)$$

EARTH THERMAL CONDUCTIVITY FACTORS

If soil type, sieve analysis, density, and moisture content are known, soil conductivities can be chosen from Table 9 of Chapter 23 of the 1985 FUNDAMENTALS Volume. Otherwise, the following earth thermal conductivity factor (K_S) in Btu $\cdot$ in./h $\cdot$ ft^2 $\cdot$ °F (W/m^2 $\cdot$ K) can be used in the preceding equations.

The values listed in Table 2 are averages calculated by various researchers. The are considered accurate enough for these calculation methods. Dry soil is very rare in most parts of the United States, and a low moisture content should be assumed only where it can be proven valid. Values of 10 to 12 Btu $\cdot$ in./h $\cdot$ ft^2 $\cdot$ °F (0.14 to 0.17 W/m^2 $\cdot$ K) are commonly used where soil moisture content is not known. Because moisture migrates toward chilled pipe, it is suggested that a K_s factor of 15 (0.22) be used as an average value for these types of systems.

HEAT LOSS FROM PIPES IN NONCIRCULAR SYSTEMS

Many underground systems install non-circular insulations and casings that complicate the heat transfer analysis. For a first order assumption, these non-circular systems might be simplified by an equivalent circular envelope concept. The assumed circular structure should have a circumference equal to the total length of the enclosing sides of the non-circular structure. The heat loss can then be approximated using the methods described above. An additional complication arises if the enclosing structure is of two different materials or of varying thicknesses. Finding a circular conduit of equivalent size and equivalent conductivity is more difficult, and increases the potential inaccuracy of the final results.

Among other methods is field potential plotting or heat flux plotting. This involves plotting a two-dimensional system of isotherms and adiabatics intersecting orthogonally to form, in the case of heat flow through the ground, a network of curvilinear squares. The rate of heat flow between isothermal boundaries can be obtained directly from the network.

None of the suggested calculation procedures except that of finite differences deals with the transient aspect of heat transfer to consider the changing pipe, climatic and soil conditions. The soil temperature data to be used for the calculations of underground systems (Table 3) are important. Although it is recommended that average surface temperatures be used for the calculations, the best temperature data consistent with the steady-state heat transfer theory are the average, normal, undisturbed earth temperatures surrounding the pipe.

WATER HAMMER SURGE

In most small hot water or chilled water systems, the potential for excessive surge is usually negligible. However, the designer should be aware of the factors contributing to an excessive surge, which can rupture the pipeline or damage connected equipment. These factors are: unusually long pipelines, more like transmission than distribution lines; higher-than-normal flow velocities; high operating pressures; rapid valve closing operations; air pockets in pipelines; and improper filling of pipeline. If any of

these (or particularly a combination of these) are present, the severity of the surge must be ascertained so the necessary preventive or protective measures can be designed into the system.

Crocker and King (1967), Parmakian (1963), and Streeter and Wylie (1967) give further details on valve operations, pump stoppage, and other design considerations. In a steam line, (Crocker and King 1967) the only consideration is the formation of excessive condensate. To prevent surge, the line should be pitched, preferably in the direction of steam flow, at least 1 in. in 50 ft (1.67 mm/m), and trapped often enough to minimize condensate.

PIPE SYSTEM MOVEMENT

Thermal Expansion and Contraction

Thermal expansion and contraction cause piping systems to move. Similar movement can also occur in attached machinery and structures. This movement must be accommodated to prevent damage to structures and system elements. The movement can be accommodated by using the inherent flexibility of the piping system as laid out, by designing loops into the system where needed, by expansion joints, or by special couplings. The method or devices selected depend on force limitations, available space, installed cost, serviceability, maintenance cost, length of life, and type of system selected.

Couplings

Many systems have couplings that absorb expansion and contraction. Elastomer-gasketed couplings or those applied to grooved end pipe are commonly used in systems operating within the temperature and pressure limits of the elastomer selected. When these are used, no other expansion devices are needed. However, pressure can force these joints to separate longitudinally near a change of direction. Controlling this movement is discussed in the section "Pipe Anchors."

Inherent Piping Flexibility

The Code for Power Piping (ANSI/ASME B31.1) states that thermal expansion and contraction should be provided for by pipe bends, elbows, offsets, or changes in direction of the pipeline. If a line is routed with enough changes of direction to provide pipe flexibility, no additional accommodation for expansion is needed. For long straight lines of pipe, expansion loops or a combination of loops and changes of direction must be added.

Pipe Bends and Loops

In the simplest case, axial movement in each of two pipe segments connected through a 90° elbow is accommodated by bending in each segment (Figure 4A). The addition of pipe segments results in a Z-bend (Figure 4B), and ultimately in a loop (Figure 4C). Various charts and calculation methods are available to simplify the design of these three basic pipe configurations. It is important that the method selected recognizes the restraints on the system. For complicated piping arrangements in a two-plane configuration, many commercial computer programs are available that give accurate design information such as stresses and deflections at any point in the line, as well as anchor forces.

Stresses on the pipe, amount of pipe movement, anchor forces, and available expansion space dictate acceptable design. As a general rule, anchor forces from flexible piping systems are lower than any other type of expansion compensation. It is important to provide space for lateral and longitudinal pipe move-

Table 2 Soil Conductivities

Soil Moisture Content, % by weight (mass)	Conductivity, Btu $\cdot$ in./h $\cdot$ ft^2 $\cdot$ °F (W/m^2 $\cdot$ K)		
	Sand	Silt	Clay
Low, <4%	2 (0.29)	1 (0.14)	1 (0.14)
Medium, 4 to 20%	13 (1.87)	9 (1.30)	7 (1.01)
High, >20%	15 (2.16)	15 (2.16)	15 (2.16)

Table 3   Average Earth Temperature from 0 to 10 ft (0 to 3 m) Below Surface

Location	Winter °F (°C)	Spring °F (°C)	Summer °F (°C)	Autumn °F (°C)	Annual °F (°C)
Alabama					
Birmingham	54 (12.2)	58 (14.4)	71 (21.7)	68 (20.0)	63 (17.2)
Mobile	61 (16.1)	63 (17.2)	74 (23.3)	71 (21.7)	67 (19.4)
Montgomery	58 (14.4)	61 (16.1)	73 (22.8)	70 (21.1)	65 (18.3)
Arizona					
Flagstaff	35 (1.7)	39 (3.9)	54 (12.2)	50 (10.0)	45 (7.2)
Phoenix	60 (15.6)	64 (17.8)	79 (26.1)	75 (23.9)	69 (20.6)
Tucson	59 (15.0)	62 (16.7)	76 (24.4)	73 (22.8)	68 (20.0)
Yuma	65 (18.3)	69 (20.6)	84 (28.9)	80 (26.7)	75 (23.9)
Arkansas					
Little Rock	53 (11.7)	57 (13.9)	72 (22.2)	68 (20.0)	62 (16.7)
Texarkana	56 (13.3)	60 (15.6)	74 (23.3)	61 (16.1)	65 (18.3)
California					
Eureka	50 (10.0)	51 (10.6)	54 (12.2)	54 (12.2)	52 (11.1)
Fresno	54 (12.2)	58 (14.4)	72 (22.2)	68 (20.0)	63 (17.2)
Los Angeles	58 (14.4)	59 (15.0)	64 (17.8)	63 (17.2)	61 (16.1)
Sacramento	53 (11.7)	56 (13.3)	67 (19.4)	64 (17.8)	60 (15.6)
San Diego	59 (15.0)	60 (15.6)	66 (18.9)	65 (18.3)	62 (16.7)
San Francisco	53 (11.7)	54 (12.2)	59 (15.0)	57 (13.9)	56 (13.3)
Colorado					
Denver	39 (3.9)	43 (6.1)	60 (15.6)	56 (13.3)	50 (10.0)
Grand Junction	39 (3.9)	44 (6.7)	65 (18.3)	60 (15.6)	52 (11.1)
Pueblo	41 (5.0)	45 (7.2)	62 (16.7)	58 (14.4)	51 (10.6)
Connecticut	40 (4.4)	44 (6.7)	61 (16.1)	57 (13.9)	50 (10.0)
Delaware	44 (6.7)	48 (8.9)	64 (17.8)	60 (15.6)	54 (12.2)
Washington, DC	47 (8.3)	51 (10.6)	66 (18.9)	63 (17.2)	57 (13.9)
Florida					
Fort Myers	70 (21.1)	71 (21.7)	78 (25.6)	76 (24.4)	74 (23.3)
Jacksonville	63 (17.2)	66 (18.9)	75 (23.9)	73 (22.8)	69 (20.6)
Key West	74 (23.3)	75 (23.9)	80 (26.7)	79 (26.1)	77 (25.0)
Miami	72 (22.2)	74 (23.3)	79 (26.1)	78 (25.6)	76 (23.9)
Orlando	68 (20.0)	70 (21.1)	77 (25.0)	75 (23.9)	72 (22.2)
Tallahassee	61 (16.1)	64 (17.8)	74 (23.3)	72 (22.2)	68 (20.0)
Tampa	68 (20.0)	69 (20.6)	77 (25.0)	75 (23.9)	72 (22.2)
Georgia					
Albany	60 (15.6)	63 (17.2)	75 (23.9)	72 (22.2)	67 (19.4)
Atlanta	54 (12.2)	57 (13.9)	70 (21.1)	67 (19.4)	62 (16.7)
Augusta	56 (13.3)	59 (15.0)	72 (22.2)	69 (20.6)	64 (17.8)
Savannah	60 (15.6)	63 (17.2)	74 (23.3)	71 (21.7)	67 (19.4)
Idaho					
Boise	40 (4.4)	44 (6.7)	62 (16.7)	58 (14.4)	51 (10.6)
Idaho Falls	28 (−2.2)	33 (0.6)	54 (12.2)	49 (9.4)	41 (5.0)
Illinois					
Cairo	49 (9.4)	53 (11.7)	70 (21.1)	66 (18.9)	60 (15.6)
Chicago	38 (3.3)	43 (6.1)	62 (16.7)	57 (13.9)	50 (10.0)
Peoria	39 (3.9)	44 (6.7)	63 (17.2)	58 (14.4)	51 (10.6)
Springfield	41 (5.0)	45 (7.2)	64 (17.8)	60 (15.6)	52 (11.1)
Indiana					
Evansville	47 (8.3)	51 (10.6)	67 (19.4)	63 (17.2)	57 (13.9)
Indianapolis	41 (5.0)	46 (7.8)	64 (17.8)	59 (15.0)	52 (11.1)
South Bend	38 (3.3)	42 (5.5)	61 (16.1)	56 (13.3)	49 (9.4)
Iowa					
Davenport	39 (3.9)	44 (6.7)	64 (17.8)	59 (15.0)	51 (10.6)
Des Moines	37 (2.8)	42 (5.5)	63 (17.2)	58 (14.4)	50 (10.0)
Waterloo	35 (1.7)	40 (4.4)	61 (16.1)	56 (13.3)	48 (8.9)
Kansas					
Wichita	45 (7.2)	50 (10.0)	68 (20.0)	64 (17.8)	57 (13.9)
Kentucky					
Lexington	44 (6.7)	48 (8.9)	65 (18.3)	61 (16.1)	54 (12.2)
Louisiana					
Baton Rouge	61 (16.1)	63 (17.2)	74 (23.3)	72 (22.2)	67 (19.4)
New Orleans	63 (17.2)	65 (18.3)	75 (23.9)	73 (22.8)	69 (20.6)
Shreveport	58 (14.4)	61 (16.1)	75 (23.9)	72 (22.2)	66 (18.9)
Maine					
Caribou	24 (−4.4)	29 (−1.7)	50 (10.0)	45 (7.2)	37 (2.8)
Portland	33 (0.6)	38 (3.3)	56 (13.3)	51 (10.6)	44 (6.7)

Table 3   Average Earth Temperature from 0 to 10 ft (0 to 3 m) Below Surface (Continued)

Location	Winter °F (°C)	Spring °F (°C)	Summer °F (°C)	Autumn °F (°C)	Annual °F (°C)
Maryland	45 (7.2)	49 (9.4)	65 (18.3)	61 (16.1)	55 (12.8)
Massachusetts					
Boston	41 (5.0)	44 (6.7)	61 (16.1)	57 (13.9)	51 (10.6)
Worcester	36 (2.2)	40 (4.4)	58 (14.4)	54 (12.2)	47 (8.3)
Michigan					
Alpena	33 (0.6)	37 (2.8)	54 (12.2)	50 (10.0)	43 (6.1)
Detroit City	38 (3.3)	43 (6.1)	60 (15.6)	56 (13.3)	49 (9.4)
Escanaba	30 (−1.1)	35 (1.7)	53 (11.7)	49 (9.4)	42 (5.5)
Grand Rapids	36 (2.2)	40 (4.4)	58 (14.4)	54 (12.2)	47 (8.3)
Minnesota					
Duluth	25 (−3.9)	30 (−1.1)	52 (11.1)	47 (8.3)	38 (3.3)
Minneapolis	32 (0.0)	37 (2.8)	60 (15.6)	54 (12.2)	46 (7.8)
Mississippi	57 (13.9)	61 (16.1)	73 (22. 8)	70 (21.1)	65 (18.3)
Missouri					
Kansas City	44 (6.7)	49 (9.4)	68 (20.0)	64 (17.8)	56 (13.3)
Saint Louis	45 (7.2)	49 (9.4)	67 (19.4)	63 (17.8)	56 (13.3)
Springfield	45 (7.2)	49 (9.4)	66 (18 .9)	62 (16.7)	56 (13.3)
Montana					
Billings	35 (1.7)	40 (4.4)	59 (15.0)	55 (12.8)	47 (8.3)
Butte	27 (−2.8)	31 (−0.6)	50 (10.0)	45 (7.2)	38 (3.3)
Great Falls	34 (1.1)	38 (3.3)	56 (13.3)	52 (11.1)	45 (7.2)
Nebraska					
North Platte	37 (2.8)	42 (5.5)	62 (16.7)	57 (13.9)	49 (9.4)
Omaha	39 (3.9)	44 (6.7)	65 (18.3)	60 (15.6)	52 (11.1)
Scotts Bluff	36 (2.2)	41 (5.0)	60 (15.6)	56 (13.3)	48 (8.9)
Nevada					
Las Vegas	56 (13.3)	60 (15.6)	78 (25.6)	74 (23.3)	67 (19.4)
Reno	40 (4.4)	44 (6.7)	58 (14.4)	55 (12.8)	49 (9.4)
Winnemucca	38 (3.3)	42 (5.5)	60 (15.6)	56 (13.3)	49 (9.4)
New Hampshire	33 (0.6)	38 (3.3)	56 (13.3)	52 (11.1)	45 (7.2)
New Jersey					
Atlantic City	45 (7.2)	49 (9.4)	63 (17.2)	60 (15.6)	54 (12.2)
Newark	43 (6.1)	47 (8.3)	63 (17.2)	59 (15.0)	53 (11.7)
New Mexico					
Albuquerque	46 (7.8)	50 (10.0)	67 (19.4)	63 (17.2)	57 (13.9)
Raton	38 (3.3)	42 (5.5)	58 (14.4)	54 (12.2)	48 (8.9)
Roswell	51 (10.6)	54 (12.2)	69 (20.6)	66 (18.9)	60 (15.6)
New York					
Albany	36 (2.2)	40 (4.4)	59 (15.0)	54 (12.2)	47 (8.3)
Buffalo	37 (2.8)	41 (5.0)	58 (14.4)	54 (12.2)	47 (8.3)
New York	44 (6.7)	47 (8.3)	63 (17.2)	59 (15.0)	53 (11.7)
North Carolina					
Asheville	48 (8.9)	51 (10.6)	64 (17.8)	61 (16.1)	56 (13.3)
Raleigh	51 (10.6)	55 (12.8)	69 (20.6)	65 (20.0)	60 (15.6)
North Dakota	26 (−3.3)	32 (0.0)	56 (13.3)	50 (10.0)	41 (5.0)
Ohio					
Cincinnati	45 (7.2)	49 (9.4)	65 (18.3)	61 (16.1)	55 (12.8)
Cleveland	40 (4.4)	44 (6.7)	61 (16.1)	57 (13.9)	51 (10.6)
Columbus	41 (5.0)	46 (7.8)	62 (16.7)	59 (15.0)	52 (11.1)
Toledo	38 (3.3)	43 (6.1)	60 (15.6)	56 (13.3)	49 (9.4)
Oklahoma	50 (10.0)	54 (12.2)	71 (21.7)	67 (19.4)	60 (15.6)
Oregon					
Baker	36 (2.2)	40 (4.4)	56 (13.3)	52 (11.1)	46 (7.8)
Eugene	46 (7.8)	48 (8.9)	59 (15.0)	47 (8.3)	52 (11.1)
Portland	46 (7.8)	49 (9.4)	60 (15.6)	57 (13.9)	53 (11.7)
Pennsylvania					
Erie	38 (3.3)	42 (5.5)	58 (14.4)	55 (12.8)	48 (8.9)
Philadelphia	44 (6.7)	48 (8.9)	64 (17.8)	61 (16.1)	54 (12.2)
Pittsburgh	40 (4.4)	44 (6.7)	61 (16.1)	57 (13.9)	51 (10.6)
Scranton	40 (4.4)	44 (6.7)	61 (16.1)	57 (13.9)	50 (10.0)
Rhode Island	39 (3.9)	43 (6.1)	59 (15.0)	56 (13.3)	49 (9.4)
South Carolina					
Charleston	58 (14.4)	61 (16.1)	72 (22.2)	70 (21.1)	65 (18.3)
Columbia	56 (13.3)	59 (15.0)	72 (22.2)	69 (20.6)	64 (17.8)
South Dakota	32 (0.0)	37 (2.8)	60 (15.6)	55 (12.8)	46 (7.8)

Table 3 Average Earth Temperature from 0 to 10 ft (0 to 3 m) Below Surface (Concluded)

Location	Winter °F (°C)	Spring °F (°C)	Summer °F (°C)	Autumn °F (°C)	Annual °F (°C)
Tennessee					
Knoxville	50 (10.0)	54 (12.2)	68 (20.0)	65 (18.3)	59 (15.0)
Memphis	52 (11.1)	56 (13.3)	71 (21.7)	68 (20.0)	62 (16.7)
Texas					
Amarillo	47 (8.3)	50 (10.0)	67 (19.4)	63 (17.2)	57 (13.9)
Brownsville	68 (20.0)	60 (15.6)	79 (26.1)	77 (25.0)	74 (23.3)
Dallas	47 (8.3)	61 (16.1)	76 (24.4)	72 (22.2)	66 (18.9)
El Paso	54 (12.2)	58 (14.4)	72 (22.2)	69 (20.6)	63 (17.2)
Houston	62 (16.7)	65 (18.3)	76 (24.4)	73 (22.8)	69 (20.6)
San Angelo	58 (14.4)	61 (16.1)	74 (23.3)	71 (21.7)	66 (18.9)
San Antonio	61 (16.1)	64 (17.8)	77 (25.0)	74 (23.3)	69 (20.6)
Utah					
Salt Lake City	40 (4.4)	44 (6.7)	63 (17.2)	59 (15.0)	51 (10.6)
Vermont	32 (0.0)	37 (2.8)	57 (13.9)	52 (11.1)	44 (6.7)
Virginia					
Lynchburg	48 (8.9)	51 (10.6)	66 (18.9)	62 (16.7)	57 (13.9)
Norfolk	51 (10.6)	54 (12.2)	68 (20.0)	64 (17.8)	59 (15.0)
Washington					
Seattle-Tacoma	44 (6.7)	47 (8.3)	57 (13.9)	55 (12.8)	51 (10.6)
Spokane	37 (2.8)	41 (5.0)	58 (14.4)	54 (12.2)	47 (8.3)
Yakima	40 (4.4)	44 (6.7)	61 (16.1)	57 (13.9)	50 (10.0)
West Virginia					
Charleston	47 (8.3)	50 (10.0)	65 (18.3)	61 (16.1)	56 (13.3)
Wisconsin					
Green Bay	31 (−0.6)	36 (2.2)	56 (13.3)	51 (10.6)	44 (6.7)
La Crosse	32 (0.0)	38 (3.3)	60 (15.6)	55 (12.8)	46 (7.8)
Milwaukee	35 (1.7)	40 (4.4)	58 (14.4)	54 (12.2)	47 (8.3)
Wyoming					
Cheyenne	35 (1.7)	39 (3.9)	55 (12.8)	51 (10.6)	44 (6.7)
Rock Springs	31 (−0.6)	35 (1.7)	54 (12.2)	50 (10.0)	42 (5.5)
Sheridan	33 (0.6)	37 (2.8)	56 (13.3)	52 (11.1)	44 (6.7)
Hawaii					
Hilo	72 (22.2)	72 (22.2)	74 (23.3)	74 (23.3)	73 (22.8)
Honolulu	74 (23.3)	75 (23.9)	77 (25.0)	77 (25.0)	76 (24.4)
Alaska					
Anchorage	25 (−3.9)	29 (−1.7)	46 (7.8)	42 (5.5)	35 (1.7)
Fairbanks	14 (−10.0)	19 (−7.2)	38 (3.3)	34 (1.1)	26 (−3.3)
Juneau	34 (1.1)	36 (2.2)	47 (8.3)	45 (7.2)	41 (5.0)

ment. This space can be provided in tunnels, trenches, and conduits. When direct burial of bare or insulated pipe is used, any pipe movement must be accommodated by the distortion of the insulation or by a separate structure that guarantees voids for unrestricted movement. Such a structure may be an oversized casing, or additional insulation around the elbow and connecting pipe, or a boxed-in area or mineral wool blankets around the pipe in the case of a poured envelope insulation. Safe and satisfactory designs do not assume that the plasticity of the soil or other surrounding materials will accommodate the movement.

Cold springing of the pipe is a technique in which an elbow leg designed to bend in a positive direction due to expansion is pulled half of the designed movement in a negative direction. The pulled leg is then connected to the piping run that has been shortened by the amount of cold spring. Cold springing of pipe during installation reduces stress within a piping system. The Power Piping Code (ANSI/ASME B31.1-1983), however, does not permit credit for cold springing in calculating the piping stress. This is because sufficiently large stresses caused by thermal expansion relax in the hot condition due to local yielding or creep. The stress is reduced (and usually appears as a stress of reversed sign) when the pipe returns to the cold condition. Credit for cold springing is allowed in the calculation of thrusts and movements acting on equipment, provided an effective method of obtaining the designed cold spring is specified and

used. Cold springing of loops and Z-bends is relatively easy in the field. Single elbows are very difficult to cold spring.

Other Expansion Devices

Using the inherent flexibility of the piping system as designed, is the preferred method of accommodating pipe movement. However, it may be necessary to use other expansion devices if there is a lack of space for expansion loops or changes of direction. Expansion joints, when used with an underground system, should be installed in manholes or buildings where they are accessible for maintenance or replacement. They must be insulated to prevent heat loss and excessive temperatures in manholes that operating personnel must enter. Expansion joints in manholes should be protected from corrosive ice-melting highway salts and chemicals.

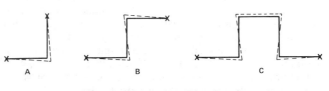

Fig. 4 Expansion Pipe Bends

Bellows expansion joints use the accordion action of the corrugations to permit movement. Conventional free-flexing joints are most frequently applied to axial movements. Other designs use restraining devices for safe multiple movements. Bellows material must be protected for external and internal corrosion. Where chlorides may be present or inadvertently added to boiler water, most manufacturers recommend Monel bellows. Joints to be insulated should have insulating covers. Stress corrosion possibilities must be considered.

Sliding joints such as piston or sleeve expansion joints require accurate installation, very close alignment of piping, and frequent inspection. Packed and packless styles are differentiated, although their functions and principles are similar. Recent developments in higher temperature-resistant, low friction plastic materials for packings and gaskets have improved the service of these joints. This style of joint is well-suited to systems that cycle frequently.

Ball or swivel joints are spherically gasketed pipe connectors that permit angular and torsional rotation of the two connecting pipes. By combining two joints in a piping system, large amounts of expansion can be accommodated in a short offset. As with other restrained joints, pipe guides must be applied properly to limit pipe movement to the design capacity of the joint. Deflection forces are minimal and anchor forces are relatively small. As with all restrained joints, the connecting pipe between joints imposes a weight load that must be supported separately if not within the joint manufacturer's design load carrying capacity.

Other variations include hinged joints that permit an elbow to act as a hinge on one plane. Gimbal joints permit an elbow to act as a hinge on all planes. Universal joints can absorb axial movement and permit lateral offset in any direction. Cyclic life, joint design, and individual manufacturing techniques can be predicted by manufacturers for specific applications.

For either free flexing or restrained joints, carefully planned guides and anchors must be designed to keep pipe movements within the movement capacity of the joints. Restrained joints can assume some guiding and will reduce anchor loads in some cases. Normally for free-flexing joints, anchors divide pipe into straight sections with only one joint between anchors. Joint manufacturers have information on product use in varying pressures, temperatures, and velocities, as well as for the required pipe guides and supports.

PIPE ANCHORS

Anchors are necessary for all piping systems. They serve the following purposes:

1. For those systems using flexible piping or expansion joints in manholes, anchors control the direction and amount of pipe movement.
2. For those systems using gasketed couplings to accommodate expansion, anchors prevent separation of the pipe from hydraulic pressure.

When using flexible piping to accommodate expansion, the location of the anchor is important, since it controls the direction and amount of movement into the pipe elbows. The system should be analyzed to determine the amount of flex a particular element can accommodate. The anchor is then positioned to limit it to this amount. When possible, anchors should be located on main lines at branch connections. When using expansion joints or ball joints, anchors are located on the straight lengths of pipe to limit the amount of movement to avoid exceeding the capacity of the device. Systems using gasketed couplings require anchors (sometimes referred to as thrust blocks) at (1) all changes of direction, such as at elbows and tees, (2) changes in size, and (3) terminals, as at dead ends or closed valves.

Particular consideration should be given to the pipe forces acting on connecting equipment. The forces must be within the design limits of the equipment, and in the case of floating machinery, must not result in harmful movement. To prevent harmful forces on equipment, the pipe can be anchored at the point of connection. Interrelated floating machinery installation with vibration absorption joints is covered in Chapter 52. Anchor forces should be analyzed as part of the system design. Unless the anchor is located within a manhole, the system anchor is placed within a concrete block with sufficient bearing area on undisturbed earth to resist axial forces, and of sufficient mass to resist the overturning moment.

Forces Affecting Anchors

Each anchor experiences one or a combination of the following forces:

1. Forces required to deflect pipe bends in flexible piping systems.
2. Thrust caused by internal pressure that occurs with expansion joints or gasketed couplings in lines with valves, caps, pipe reduction, and elbows at anchors. It often reaches maximum when the system is hydrostatically tested.
3. Friction resistance of guides or rollers.
4. Any unusual forces such as hydraulic surge or centrifugal thrust.

Vector addition of the forces acting at each anchor yields a basic force value for the design of that anchor. Since the movement of the anchor or fitting encased in a concrete block is prevented by bearing against the soil in which it is buried, the soil must be undisturbed or satisfactorily tamped. The bearing area of the anchor equals the total force of thrust divided by the bearing value of the soil:

Anchor Bearing Area, ft^2 (m^2) =

$$\frac{\text{Total Thrust, lb (kg)}}{\text{Bearing Value Soil, lb/ft}^2 \text{ (kg/m}^2)}$$

Pipe supports and guides are needed to center the carrier pipe in the conduit and prevent sag caused by the weight of the pipe and fluid. Generally, these restrict the carrier pipe to axial movement only. Guides are needed to allow axial movement, maintain column action, and limit lateral movement, when using expansion joints, and for pipe in poured envelope systems. Only pipe supports are needed in those systems in which thermal expansion is absorbed in the couplings, if the trench is prepared and backfilled properly. Guides are not needed because lateral movement is not induced. In other types of systems, improperly controlled movement (both axial and lateral) can damage the casing. Therefore, the supports, guides, and conduit must all be of sufficient size to accommodate the movement.

For tunnel or trench systems, special styles of supports and guides are commercially available to protect the insulation and provide small friction forces. Industry standards for pipe support spacing are usually met or exceeded by proprietary conduit systems. Supports with conduit systems must be designed to permit drainage and ventilation of the system. They must also support, but permit free movement of, the pipe axially, as well as laterally at changes of directions where expansion occurs.

Loads on Pipe and Pipe-Supporting Strength

The structural design of underground systems requires that the supporting strength of the casing pipe, as installed, must equal or exceed the loads imposed on it by the weight of earth and any superimposed surface loads. Where a rigid pipe is subjected to both internal pressure loads and crushing loads, added stresses from both types of loads may require the reduction of load conditions and/or the use of a higher strength pipe to maintain desired safety factors.

Load calculations should include both earth load and superimposed surface loads. In the case of rigid pipe, the pipe load should be compared to the pipe strength, converting the actual loads to an equivalent ASTM three-edged bearing load, since that is the way pipe strength is determined and listed. For flexible pipes, the actual loads should be used to determine pipe deflection, which should be held within 5% of the diameter (Uni-Bell Plastic Pipe Assoc. 1977). The design should include proper safety factors. The specifications should indicate the bedding class required, and the job should be inspected to ensure that the pipe is being installed according to the class requirements specified to prevent failure.

The casing pipe should always be designed on the basis of crush strength if it is a rigid material. In this instance, the carrier pipe can be designed for pressure only, since the casing will absorb all crush load without deformation. The casing or conduit design of a flexible material is different from that of rigid casings. Within limits, a flexible conduit will deflect without damage when loads are applied. As the load is applied, the top of the conduit deflects downward and the sides outward. The passive pressure of the soil surrounding it resists the lateral movement to help increase the load-carrying capacity of the pipe. However, the deflection of the casing transmits part of the crushing load to the foam and carrier or core pipe. This is not usually a problem in small diameter pipe but should be investigated for casings 18 in. (450 mm) and larger, and in all cases where loads may be excessive.

Drainage Systems

Proper drainage should be a part of the design of systems that cannot be dried if the insulation becomes wet, or that do not limit water spread if localized casing damage occurs. The drainage system should be designed with considerable safety factors and carrying capacity on the assumption that soil intrusion eventually will render it less effective. All precautions should be taken to prevent this deterioration, and field construction should be carefully inspected to assure fulfillment of the specification requirements. The drainage lines should consist of the necessary perforated pipelines laid to grade and slightly below the main piping system. French drains are generally ineffective and should be used only when there is proper construction and operation. In some soils, the excavated trench will collect water from other areas, resulting in an abnormal water condition around the system. This makes drainage even more imperative.

Branch Connections

Service lines from a main to a building may be provided in any type of system. In welded or flanged systems, these takeoffs should be located as close as possible to a main line anchor to minimize transverse movement of the branch pipe. When this is not feasible, adequate space must be provided for the induced lateral movement of the branch line. In a welded system the main line will generally act as an anchor for the branch pipe, therefore its axial expansion must be determined and accommodated within the building or by other means. In conduits with an air-space, concepts such as tightness, drainage, and vent continuity must be maintained in the branches. Branches for systems using gasketed couplings must be anchored at the main line connection.

Manholes

Manholes provide direct access to underground piping at suitable intervals. They may also serve as a monitor of the ad-

jacent underground conduit system. Frequency of access for operation or maintenance is affected by the terrain and type of institutions served. Examples of manhole locations are as follows:

1. Vertical changes in elevation in a steam distribution system require steam traps for condensate removal. Space must be provided for trap maintenance.
2. Expansion joints and pertinent anchors are placed in manholes because of occasional service or replacement needs.
3. Service lines or branches, equipped with control or shutoff valves, serving present or planned buildings are contained in a manhole. The difference in elevation for a service line can be readily accommodated.
4. System isolation or divider valves, while rarely used, do require ready access during emergencies.

Manholes must be adequate to fulfill their function. Inspection of valves and traps is easier and more reliable when there is adequate space to move around. As the pressures and temperatures increase, more clearance should be provided. A space of 18 to 24 in. (450 to 600 mm) on the working side is minimal. Service of the equipment in a manhole, including the removal and replacement of valves, expansion joints, and pumps affect size. Overhead room must be available to swing out the equipment, including the necessary rigging. Installed clearance alone may not be adequate, and the style and arrangement of the valves govern the clearances. Expansion joints may be staggered in an elongated manhole for closer pipe spacing or a reduced number of fittings.

Material selected for manholes should suit the ground exposure. Reinforced concrete is commonly used, although masonry units or prefabricated pressure-tight steel chambers are feasible. Structural strength must be adequate for the soil conditions plus possible superimposed loads by vehicles. Watertight construction is necessary when ground or surface water is a possibility, with concrete walls and floors poured monolithically or with a dumbbell-type vinyl water stop installed at the joint.

When design criteria allow, the manhole walls and top seal should extend 6 in. (150 mm) above grade to protect against rain or snow melt. Earth is graded away from a manhole to facilitate drainage. When design allows for only a manhole cover to be above grade, the top slabs underground should be sloped-to-drain and contain a waterproofing admixture; otherwise, surface coatings of high-temperature-resistant, waterproofing materials should be applied.

Walls or floors of manholes can be designed to anchor the piping. Structural analysis must anticipate forces from expansion and contraction. Anchors are discussed elsewhere in this chapter. The manhole access opening should be installed in a corner of the top, opposite the sump or drain connection in the floor. Safety-type ladder rungs should be cast in the concrete, or an equivalent steel ladder with side rails should be provided. There should be an 18-in. (450-mm) clearance between the wall and the piping on the access side.

Manhole drainage is important in all installations. Manhole flooding has been reported as a contributing cause of underground failures. In free-draining soil, a sump at the bottom connected to an open-joint tile drain field can be used when storm sewers are unavailable. However, these are not entirely satisfactory and are used infrequently. When gravity drainage is not practical, reliable electric sump pumps should be installed. The switch components must be selected to withstand both high temperature and humidity. Steam ejectors are not suitable because of poor reliability and open-blow problems.

Manhole ventilation is next to drainage in importance in ensuring proper system operation and service life. Steam or water vapor leads and piping system venting or draining bring water vapor into the manhole. Ventilation requires a hot-air exhaust opening to the atmosphere at ceiling level and a cold-air input pipe from the atmosphere ending just above the floor, both of which must be protected from surface water entry. When design criteria permit, a 4-in. (100-mm) or 6-in. (150-mm) thin wall pipe, ending with a mushroom cap or a 180° bend about 18 in. (450 mm) above the manhole, provides effective ventilation.

In some applications, the vent piping extends to an adjacent building. The vents also signal when a problem develops in the manhole, making inspection easier. Piping insulation in manholes should be as complete as possible to minimize heat loss and temperature buildup. It is necessary to waterproof the insulation to prevent moisture absorption and loss of thermal efficiency. Valve bodies and flanges should be covered. Mechanical protection of the insulation is desirable and often necessary to withstand foot traffic when the piping is adjacent to the access ladder. Auxiliary equipment (steam traps, flash tanks, condensate receivers and pumps, pressure reducing valves, and flow meters) can be installed in manholes as an operating requirement or convenience.

CORROSION

Underground distribution systems are subjected to external and internal corrosion. The two primary solutions are using noncorrodible materials or adequate corrosion control. External corrosion is controlled with protective coatings that withstand the soil environment and the operating conditions of the piping system and, where proper investigation dictates, cathodic protection. Some consultants feel that cathodic protection is advisable because corrosion can occur at any breaks in the coating. Internal corrosion is controlled by fluid treatment or special piping materials.

Causes of Corrosion

Most corrosion of ferrous metals is an electrochemical reaction caused by a difference in electrical potential caused by nonhomogeneous conditions in the soil or in the pipe wall. This nonhomogeneity can be from oxygen differences (loose soil at top of pipe versus packed soil in trench bottom), soil differences (clay at bottom versus loam at top, or sand backfill versus normal soil), moisture differences, new pipe versus old, organic matter in the trench, or microdifferences in the pipe wall structure.

The interconnection of dissimilar metals encourages corrosion. For example, if steel pipe is connected to copper pipe, the steel pipe will corrode. Road de-icing salts and some fertilizers make soil very corrosive. Bacteria in some organic soils create strong corrosion cells. An additional source of corrosion is stray direct currents in the ground; these may originate from industrial welding operations, high voltage dc transmission lines, foreign cathodic protection installations, and various other causes. Internal corrosion (Chapter 53) is affected by the chemistry of the fluid carried. Oxygen and carbon dioxide content are important factors. Internal corrosion is often a problem in steel condensate lines. Moody (1973), Vanderweil and Donahue (1978), Hort (1975), and Lauderbaugh give further information.

Determination of Corrosion Possibility

Several tests can help determine to what degree corrosion might occur in the soil. A corrosion survey should be made by a corrosion engineer before designing the piping. This should include an evaluation of soil conditions and the chemistry of the water or other fluid to be carried in the piping. The design engineer can then choose proper materials, external corrosion control, fluid treatment, and inhibitors or internal lining to minimize costs and maximize system life and reliability.

One test that is helpful and almost universally used is the resistivity test. This measures the soil's electrical current carrying capacity. Since corrosion produces a small current flow in the soil from a corroding point on the metal pipe to a noncorroding point on the pipe, that current flow will be inversely proportional to the soil's resistivity. The lower the soil resistivity, the greater the current flow and the faster corrosion proceeds. Resistivity often directly indicates the rate of corrosion, and soils are often rated by their resistivity, as described below.

Classification of Corrosive Soil

The U.S. Federal Construction Council Building Research Advisory Board suggests the following soil classifications:

Corrosive
1. Soil resistivity of 10 000 ohm·cm (100 Ω·m) or less
2. Detection of any stray current in the soil
3. Where the water table is frequently above the bottom of the piping system
4. Where the water table is occasionally above the bottom of the system and surface water is expected to accumulate and remain for long periods in the soil surrounding the system

Mildly Corrosive
Soil resistivity is between 10 000 and 30 000 ohm·cm (100 and 300 Ω·m).

Noncorrosive
Soil resistivity is 30 000 ohm·cm (300 Ω·m) or greater.

Corrosive conditions may also be aggravated by pH, sulfates, chlorides, bacteria, and possible stray current.

Corrosion Protection

Chapter 53 of this volume and National Association of Corrosion Engineers Standard RP-01-690 give guides to the choice, application, requirements and testing of coatings. There are two basic types of cathodic protection systems; both are used in conjunction with proper pipe coating materials. The two basic types are the galvanic anode system and the impressed current system. ASME (1983), NACE, and Fitzgerald (1974) describe the design, use, and periodic testing of cathodic protection systems. Cathodic protection systems should be tested annually to ensure maintenance of protection. They should be designed for each application by specialists in corrosion protection in accordance with prevailing standards. A corrosion specialist should evaluate the soil to determine whether cathodic protection should be used for ferrous metal piping, conduits, and manholes.

Using nonmetallic pipe or conduit is often a good means of combating corrosion. Some asbestos cement is subject to possible deterioration in soils with high sulfate content. Asbestos cement manufactured to AWWA Standards to Type II pipe (under 1% free-lime content) is resistant to sulfate reaction in any concentration found in any soils around the world. Asbestos cement pipe should be used with caution in soils with a pH below 4.5.

OPERATING GUIDELINES

Inspection

Regular periodic inspection of manholes, building entrances, and drain and vent connections for water alerts maintenance personnel when leaks develop. Manholes, pump pits, valve boxes, and conduit vents and drains should be inspected to determine if water is or has been present. The condition of the insulation jackets, expansion joints, valves, steam traps, sump pumps, conduit entrances, ventilation ducts, and safety ladders should be noted and recorded. Evidence of water or corrosion should lead to prompt corrective action before minor difficulties become a major repair item. A warm, wet environment is most conducive to rapid deterioration of manhole equipment.

Locating Leaks

General evaluation of heat leakage from buried lines can be done with infrared scanning equipment. More detailed location is often made with temperature probes in the earth overburden to develop a profile of temperature changes. Checking for hot spots and observation of test excavations are practical solutions generally used for non-pressure-tight systems.

Leaks in air-space systems can often be found by introducing an odorant into the conduit. The conduit is pressurized and the line is walked to detect the specific location of the leak. Another method is to inject either refrigerant gas or helium into the system under air pressure. When using a refrigerant, leaks are located by applying a halide torch to the surface. With helium, a probe is inserted into the ground along the length of the system to find the leak. Without such equipment, a systemized search can be made by excavation, starting at the middle of the line to determine the direction of the leak from that point. The suspected section is inspected beginning at its mid-point. This is continued until the leak is found. Vapor emission from the conduit vent indicates whether there is a leak in a particular segment or run of pipe.

Temporary Repairs

A quick response to a leak in underground systems is necessary from both operational and economical standpoints. The insulation and piping deteriorates rapidly when small leaks are not repaired. Temporary repairs should be made permanent as soon as possible, and not forgotten because operations have been restored.

Rehabilitation

Condensate return lines are most frequently subject to internal deterioration. Frequently, after years of service, it is necessary to replace the return piping. Procedures vary with the type of system installed. Usually, the existing piping is abandoned and replaced with new piping in a parallel trench. Copper pipe and glass fiber filament-wound epoxy resin pipe have been used successfully as a substitute for ferrous pipe in condensate service.

CENTRAL CHILLING PLANT

Multiple air-conditioning loads interconnected with a central chilled water system have some important economic advantages and energy conservation opportunities. The size of air-conditioning loads served and their distances from the chilling plant are principal factors in determining the feasibility of central plants. The distribution system pipe capacity requirement is sensitive to the design temperature difference between the supply and return lines. Usually, the terminal air-conditioning equipment is selected for a chilled water temperature rise of 16 to 20°F (9 to 11°C) and occasionally as high as 24°F (13°C).

It is usually more economical to select air quantities and the heat exchange surface in the terminal units for the maximum possible temperature rise. Supply water temperatures are limited to about 38°F (3°C) minimum to prevent the chiller from freezing. If supply water temperatures are normally carried at somewhat higher settings and are reduced only in periods of high loading, the increased power required to produce low water temperatures is kept to a minimum.

An economic evaluation of piping and pumping costs versus chiller power requirements can establish the most suitable supply water temperature, provided the process requirement does not dictate the supply water temperature. It is often more efficient to use isolated auxiliary equipment for special process requirements and allow the central plant supply water temperature to float upward with higher chiller efficiency at decreased system loads.

Design Considerations

Most central water chilling systems are designed in phases; it is important that design integration between the central plant and its connected load be maintained when the system is extended. The primary plant designer must provide design criteria concerning the base design and establish design guidelines for building chilled water systems to be connected to the primary distribution system. Secondary system designers must meet the established standards for operating pressure, supply and return water temperature, system cleanliness, air elimination, and initial fill and makeup water procedure.

Primary water distribution systems are designed either to a constant flow (variable return temperature) or to a variable flow (constant return temperature) base. The design decision between constant or variable volume flow has a significant bearing on the design of the primary distribution system, on the methods of building load connection to the primary system, and on the selection and arrangement of the chillers.

The constant volume primary system is generally applied to the smaller system where simplicity of design and operation are extremely important and where primary distribution pumping costs are insignificant. A series arrangement of chillers is used because of the variable return temperature.

The full-load primary flow volume depends on the type of constant volume distribution system used. The first type connects the building and its terminals across the primary distribution system, using the primary pumps to drive chilled water through wild-flowing or three-way valve-controlled terminals. There can be a particularly difficult full-load flow balance problem because of the interconnection of many separate flow circuits.

Constant volume flow distribution is also applied with separately pumped building circuits. The primary-secondary isolation pumping isolates the flow balance problem between buildings. In this case, the primary flow volume can be significantly less than the summation flow needed by the terminals if the secondary circuit supply temperature is higher than the primary circuit supply temperature.

Figure 5 illustrates a central system with a constant flow rate in the secondary and primary circuits. The secondary circuit return water temperature approaches its supply water temperature as the load decreases. The return water temperature in the primary loop is always between the primary supply water temperature and the summary effect of all the connected secondary returns. One result of this constant flow design is that the chillers have decreased entering water temperatures; as a consequence, it may be necessary to run several machines simultaneously, each at reduced load, rather than one unit at full load. Under such circumstances, the auxiliary burdens of condenser water pumps, tower fans, and added chiller water pressure drop may become significant portions of the total energy input.

The variable water flow rate can improve energy use and even expand the capacity of the piping system. Design temperature rise is seldom reached in the total system because of the diverse performance of many secondary circuits. Each secondary circuit must be designed for two-way throttling valve control so that leaving water temperatures are as high as the process can tolerate. Constant flow three-way control valves should be limited to a few loads that avoid deadhead flow in long circuits.

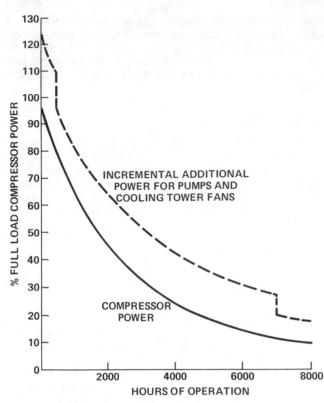

Chiller #1 and #2 can be operated individually or in series (#2 following #1).

Fig. 5   Chilled Water System with Constant Flow Rate[a]

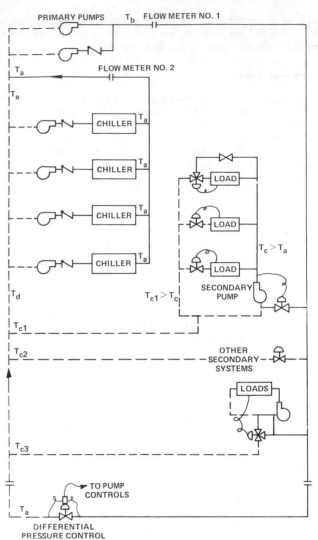

$T_e = T_a$, when flow M2 > M1; $T_e = T_d$, when flow M2 < M1.
$T_d = \Sigma T_a + T_{c1} + T_{c2} + T_{c3}$.

   Constant flow branch may serve in lieu of ΔP control valve systems with loop head primary pumps.

Fig. 6   Temperature-Actuated Diversity Control Valves

If the primary chilled water system return temperature is to be kept high in part-load conditions, it is necessary for the flow rate to be reduced correspondingly. Multiple parallel pumps or variable speed pumps can be installed to reduce flow and head, with important savings in pumping energy. With an assured specific temperature differential across the chillers, the refrigeration equipment can be selected to ensure high efficiency at predominant part-load conditions. The need for two-way terminal control cannot be overemphasized if variable volume system objectives are to be met. Flow-throttling valves provide the continuous high return temperature necessary if the system load change is to be correlated with a corresponding system flow change.

Secondary systems are usually two-pipe, with individual secondary pumping for the building piping system. However, in some cases, the differential pressure of the central system may be sufficient to cause flow through the building system without secondary pumping. The maximum differential pressure that can be applied to the secondary circuit control valves must be limited by design or fail-safe automatic pressure controls. Pressure differential control can be applied to the building circuit to prevent exorbitant differential pressures across the two-way terminal control valves. When the buildings are separately circulated, isolating primary-secondary piping and pumping techniques are used. This ensures that the two-way valves are subjected only to the differential pressure head established by the secondary pump.

Where the water temperature in a given building does not need to be as low as the water from the primary loop system, temperature-actuated diversity control valves can be applied in the primary loop crossover bridge, as shown in Figure 6. This valve admits only the required amount of chilled water from the primary loop system to mix with the secondary return water to deliver the required supply water temperature to the secondary

circuit. When the secondary circuit supply temperature must be at or near primary flow temperature, the diversity control valve can be operated as a function of the variation in secondary system flow rate by using sophisticated flow-measuring controllers in the secondary circuit. Flow regulators in the crossover bridge prevent an excess demand of primary chilled water. Excessive differential pressure in the primary loop can be controlled by judiciously locating differential control valves, as shown in Figure 6.

When secondary building pumps are used, it is necessary to remove any possibility of series interconnections between the primary loop pump and the secondary pumps. A series connection can cause the primary return to operate at a higher pressure than the supply and disrupt normal system flow patterns. Series operation is usually caused by the improper use of three-way bypass or mix valves in the primary to secondary connection.

The total height of the system, which is the distance between the highest and lowest points in the system, must be considered for a district cooling system. Because the temperature range for a chilled water cooling system is relatively small, heat exchangers between the distribution system and building system are not usually used at the individual buildings. They are frequently used with steam and HTW distribution systems to limit system static heads. In tall buildings all piping, valves, coils, and other equipment installed in the chilled water system may be required to withstand higher pressures than steam or hot water heating systems. Where system static pressure exceeds safe or economical operating pressure for control valves and other equipment, cascade pumping systems are needed to achieve separate pressure zones.

Pipes expand less in chilled water distribution systems than in heating distribution systems because the pipe experiences a smaller temperature range. For direct-burial distribution systems, this reduces or eliminates manholes that would normally be required for expansion joints in the heating system and reduces the number of anchor structures. Expansion cannot be disregarded entirely; if expansion joints are used, the anchor structures and anchoring forces can become formidable, particularly on large-diameter pipe with high internal pressures.

For underground buried piping, insulation values are less critical with chilled water than with HTW and steam, since the temperature of the chilled water is usually much closer to ground temperatures. Many installations have insulation on the supply main only.

Equipment Arrangement

Variations in central chilled water system designs are required for each project to reflect the unique circumstances of geography, existing facilities, space availability, source energy availability, budget constraints, construction scheduling, and provision for expansion. Many design concepts, other than those described in this chapter, have been developed for particular projects.

Metering

Central plants often charge as a function of energy delivered to each customer. In steam systems, the positive displacement condensate meter, especially built for high temperature and available for application in vacuum return systems, is an accepted measuring device. The meter totals the amount of condensate with high accuracy. Although steam flow meters are more complex and subject to error caused by the variation in steam density as steam pressure varies, they are the only suitable device if condensate is not returned from the process.

Hot and chilled water heat meters are required to measure changes in flow and differences in temperature change between inlet and outlet from the system, and to calculate the volume of heat change. Displacement-type water meters with differential-temperature measuring bulbs and capillaries, which are linked to a water-driven mechanical computer and totalizer, are available to read energy delivered. When applied to reasonably constant flow rates and where temperature differences are significant, these meters are sufficiently accurate. However, many sophisticated systems require flow rate adjustment from 0 to 100%, and it is not uncommon to see a low load temperature difference of only 1 or 2 °F (0.5 or 1 °C) between in and out. Such applications require a precision orifice-type flow meter with electronic or pneumatic temperature-sensing and -transmitting. The signals from the flow transmitter and the temperature differential transmitter are then fed to an integrating calculator for energy totalizing. Such instrumentation depends highly on skilled installation and continuing maintenance.

Rate Schedules for Heating and Cooling

Where central plants serve several commercial customers, a two-element system of charges similar to other utility rate schedules is used. There is usually a demand charge based on the maximum load the customer will impose on the system; this charge is designed to offset the investment expense of the central plant and distribution system. Energy consumption is metered and its charge is applied on a stepped rate, with gradually lower unit costs at higher use of the contract demand. The energy charge is usually subject to price escalation as a function of the changes in fuel cost, power cost, labor rates, and property or use taxes. Twenty-year service contracts are not uncommon.

Domestic customers, for whom the metering investment would be disproportionate to annual charges, are charged differently. Energy use is projected, using computerized calculation techniques to account for normal weather experience, occupancy schedules, building design loads, system operating characteristics and customer apparatus efficiency. The calculated use is made on the basis of an annual cost per unit area of floor served, with defined limits concerning hours of operation, permissible lighting levels, and ventilation air quantities. Elapsed-time hour meters on customer equipment (such as fans and pumps) are effective in relating energy use to charges for heating and cooling services.

Expansion Tanks, Relief Valves and Water Makeup

It is essential to allow for volumetric change in the fluid as a function of temperature. The expansion tank must be in one location and can be at a high point in the piping system if that location is always common to the distribution system. Multiple air-filled tanks in several locations cause erratic and possibly harmful movement of air through the piping system and can cause serious hydraulic surges. Although diaphragm expansion tanks eliminate the air movement, the possibility of hydraulic surge should be considered. It is important that the expansion tank becomes the single point of no pressure change as a function of circulating pump operation. The addition of several pumps in auxiliary circuits inside buildings served by the distribution loop can severely complicate the pressure shown at the other points. See Chapter 13 for an analysis of expansion tank location and sizing.

Many distribution systems for chilled or hot-chilled water serve several large buildings. Each building subsystem requires service and repair and usually has isolation valving. When a repair is made in a water system, the fluid lost must be replaced and the air that entered the piping system must be vented. The isolated segment should be filled and vented before the isolation valves are opened, to eliminate the possibility of a sudden change in system pressure and accumulation of air in the distribution loop. All high points must have air eliminators.

Relief valves for protection against high hydraulic pressure should be provided at each section of the system that can be isolated. For instance, where large chillers are frequently valved off at both ends from the common expansion tank and relief valve, each unit must have relief valves to expel the volume of water that will grow from the 45 °F (7 °C) operating temperature to the idle machine temperature of 85 to 110 °F (29 to 43 °C.)

Most large water systems are equipped with automatic fill valves that add water when the static pressure drops lower than is necessary to maintain fluid at the high point. It is most desirable to account for water lost in a closed system. This can be done by a conventional water meter on the makeup line that also provides necessary data for water treatment of makeup. The fill valve should be controlled to open or close and not modulate to very low flow, so that the water meter can detect all makeup.

REFERENCES

ASME. 1983. Power Piping. ANSI/ASME *Standard* B31.1-1983, American Society of Mechanical Engineers.

AWWA. 1980. Asbestos-Cement Distribution Pipe, 4 in. Through 16 in. (100 mm Through 400 mm) NPS, for Water and Other Liquids. AWWA *Standard* C400-80, American Water Works Association, Denver.

Coad, J. 1977. Investment Optimization, A Methodology for Life-Cycle Cost Analysis. ASHRAE *Journal*, January.

Colorado State University and Johns-Manville Corp. Concepts of Water Hammer and Air Entrapment in the Filling and Testing of Pipelines. Available from Johns-Manville.

Crocker, S. and King, R.C. 1967. *Piping Handbook*. McGraw-Hill, New York. (Water Hammer, p. 15; Design for Thermal Expansion, Ch. 4 and 5; and Insulation, Ch. 6.)

DeGarmo, E.D. 1967. *Engineering Economy*. McMillan, New York.

Eckert, E.R.G. and Drake, R.M. 1972. *Analysis of Heat and Mass Transfer* McGraw-Hill, New York, p. 98.

Federal Construction Council. Field Investigation of Underground Heat Distribution Systems. Technical Report No. 47, NAS Publication No. 1144.

Federal Construction Council. 1975. Criteria for Underground Heat Distribution Systems. Technical Report No. 66.

Federal Construction Council. Evaluation of Components for Underground Heat Distribution Systems. Technical Report No. 39-64, NAS Publication No. 1196.

Fitzgerald, J.H. 1974. Engineering Data File, Corrosion Control for Buried Piping. *Heating, Piping, Air Conditioning*, March.

Fitzgerald, J.H. and Moody, K.J. Design Criteria of Underground Heat and Chilled Water Distribution Systems for Corrosion Protection.

Hort, P. 1975. Case History, Lack of Predesign Survey Proves Costly. *Materials Performance*, January.

Joy, F.A. 1957. Thermal Conductivity of Insulation Containing Moisture. American Society for Testing Materials, Philadelphia, *ASTM Special Technical Publication No. 217*, p. 65.

Kellogg Company. 1956. *Design of Piping Systems*. John Wiley and Sons, New York.

Kusuda, T. and Powell, F.J. 1970. Heat Transfer Analysis of Underground Heat Distribution Systems. National Bureau of Standards, Washington, D.C., NBS Report 10194, April.

Kusuda, T. and Achenbach, P.R. 1965. Earth Temperature and Thermal Diffusivity at Selected Stations in the United States. ASHRAE *Transactions*, Vol. 71, Part 1, p. 61.

Kusuda, T. 1968. Least Squares Analysis of Annual Earth Temperature Cycles for Selected Stations in the Contiguous United States. National Bureau of Standards, Washington, D.C., NBS Report 9493, January.

Lauderbaugh, A. *The Fundamentals of Galvanic Corrosion Manufacturers*. Light & Heat Co., Pittsburgh, PA.

Lehmann, D.C. 1976. Evaluating Energy Savings Measures. ASHRAE *Journal*, June.

Malloy, J.F. 1969. *Thermal Insulation*. Van Nostrand-Reinhold.

McAdams, W.H. *Heat Transmission*. McGraw-Hill, New York, p. 19.

Meador, J.T. 1976. MIUS Technology Evaluation-Thermal Energy Conveyance. Oak Ridge National Laboratory, ORNL/HUD/MEUS-22, May.

Mesko, J. 1975. Economic Advantages of Central Heating and Cooling Systems. Underground Heat and Chilled Water Distribution Systems. Center for Building Technology, National Bureau of Standards, NBS Building Science Series 66.

Moody, K.J. 1973. Corrosion Case Histories; Two Steam Distribution System Failures. *Heating, Piping, Air Conditioning*, November.

NACE. Recommended Practice: Control of External Corrosion on Underground or Submerged Metallic Piping Systems. Standard RP-01-690, National Association of Corrosion Engineers.

NBS. 1978. Economic Effects of Metallic Corrosion in the U.S. Report to Congress by National Bureau of Standards. Also reported in *Iron Age*, April 3.

NBS. 1977. Technical Guidelines for Energy Conservation. Center for Building Technology, National Bureau of Standards, Washington, D.C.

Parmakian, J. 1963. *Water Hammer Analysis*. Dover Publications.

Rawly, F.B. and Algren, A.B. 1937. Thermal Conductivity of Building Material. University of Minnesota Bulletin No. 12, p. 131, St. Paul, MN.

Rohsenow, W.M.; Hartnett, J.P.; and Ganic, E.N. 1986. *Handbook of Heat Transfer* (2nd Ed.), McGraw-Hill, New York, p. 2-4.

Standards of Expansion Joint Manufacturers' Association.

Streeter, V. and Wylie, E. 1967. *Hydraulic Transients*. McGraw-Hill, New York.

Uni-Bell Plastic Pipe Association. 1977. *Handbook of PVC Pipe Design and Construction*. Library of Congress 77-88369.

Vanderweil, G. and Donahue, J. 1978. In-Place Testing of Thermal Distribution Systems. *Heating, Piping, Air Conditioning*, April.

WPCF. *Design and Construction of Sewers*. WPCF Manual of Practice.

CHAPTER 13

BASIC WATER SYSTEM DESIGN

WATER systems use hot or chilled water to convey heat to or from a conditioned space or process through piping connecting a boiler, water heater or chiller; suitable terminal heat transfer units are located at the space or process. Hot water heating and chilled water cooling systems are frequently called *hydronic* systems.

Water systems can by classified by (1) temperature, (2) flow generation, (3) pressurization, (4) piping arrangement, and (5) pumping arrangement.

There are two types of hot water heating systems classified by flow generation: (1) the *gravity* system, which uses the difference in weight between the supply and return water columns of a circuit or system to circulate water, and (2) the *forced* system, in which a pump, usually driven by an electric motor, maintains the flow.

Water systems are either once-through or recirculating systems. This chapter describes *forced recirculating systems*.

TEMPERATURE CLASSIFICATIONS OF WATER SYSTEMS

Water system classifications by operating temperature are:

Low Temperature Water System (LTW). A hot water heating system operating within the pressure and temperature limits of the ASME boiler construction code for low pressure heating boilers. The maximum allowable working pressure for low pressure heating boilers is 160 psi (1100 kPa) with a maximum temperature limitation of 250°F (121°C). The usual maximum working pressure for boilers for LTW systems is 30 psi (200 kPa), although boilers specifically designed, tested and stamped for higher pressures may frequently be used with working pressures to 160 psi (1100 kPa). Steam-to-water or water-to-water heat exchangers are also used often.

Medium Temperature Water System (MTW). A hot water heating system operating at temperatures of 350°F (175°C) or less, with pressures not exceeding 150 psi (1030 kPa). The usual design supply temperature is approximately 250 to 325°F (120 to 160°C), with a usual pressure rating for boilers and equipment of 150 psi (1030 kPa).

High Temperature Water System (HTW). A hot water heating system operating at temperatures over 350°F (175°C) and usual pressures of about 300 psi (2100 kPa). The maximum design supply water temperature is 400 to 450°F (200 to 230°C), with a pressure rating for boilers and equipment of about 300 psi (2100 kPa). The pressure-temperature rating of each component must be checked against the system's design characteristics.

Chilled Water System (CW). A chilled water-cooling system operating with a usual design supply water temperature of 40 to 55°F (4.4 to 13°C), and normally operating within a pressure range of 125 psi (860 kPa). Antifreeze or brine solutions may be used for systems (usually process applications) that require temperatures below 40°F (4.4°C). Well water systems can use supply temperatures of 60°F (15°C) or higher.

Dual-Temperature Water System (DTW). A combination water heating and cooling system that circulates hot and/or chilled water to heat or cool with common piping and terminal heat transfer apparatus. They operate within the pressure and temperature limits of LTW systems, with usual winter design supply water temperatures of about 100 to 150°F (38 to 66°C) and summer supply water temperatures of 40 to 55°F (4.4 to 13°C).

Condenser water systems remove the heat from water-cooled refrigerant condensers, usually in connection with cooling towers or city or well water services.

Low temperature water (LTW) systems operate below allowable maximum limits of 160 psig (1100 kPa) pressure and 250°F (120°C) water temperature. Modern LTW systems are of the *forced* type and use a pump to circulate water. *Gravity* systems, which use the difference in temperature and weight between supply and return columns of water to create the thermal head, are seldom used today. See the *Heating, Ventilating and Air Conditioning Guide* issued prior to 1957 for detailed information on gravity systems. Figure 1 shows heads obtained at various supply-return temperature differences. These data may be useful

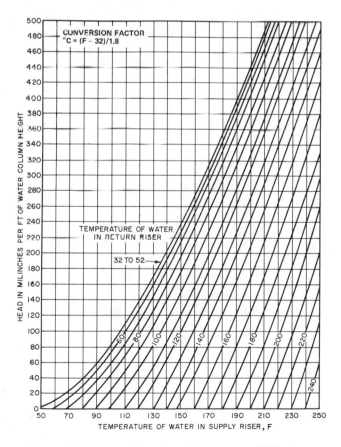

Fig. 1 Heads Resulting from Temperature Difference (Gravity Systems)

The preparation of this chapter is assigned to TC 6.1, Hot Water and Steam Heating Equipment and Systems.

in determining thermal effects of high elevation or temperature difference on head in forced circulation systems and in gravity circulation solar heating applications.

LTW systems are used in buildings ranging in size from small single dwellings to very large and complex structures. Terminal heat transfer units include convectors, cast iron radiators, baseboard and commercial finned-tube, fan-coil units, unit heaters, unit ventilators, multizone air-handling units, and snow-melting panels. A heat transfer coil inside or outside of the boiler is often used to supply hot water directly to the domestic water system or to a storage tank. A large storage tank may be included in the system to store energy to use when such heat input devices as the boiler or a solar energy collector are not supplying energy.

This chapter covers procedures for designing and selecting piping and components applying particularly to LTW systems. Simplified design methods based on a 20 °F (11 °C) temperature drop in the system have been eliminated. Although such methods are widely used and generate satisfactory system performance when applied properly, they do not determine the system operating point. The pipe size is often uneconomically large, and the actual system flow rate is likely to be much higher than intended. Such design methods seldom consider temperature drops higher than 20 °F (11 °C), which results in overdesign.

FUNDAMENTALS

The design of effective and economical water systems is affected by complex relationships between the various system components. The design water temperature, flow rate, piping layout, pump selection, terminal unit selection, and control method are all interrelated. The size and complexity of the system determines the importance of these relationships in affecting the total system operating success. Present hot water heating system design practice originated in residential heating applications where a 20 °F (11 °C) temperature drop (TD) was used to determine flow rate. Besides producing satisfactory operation and economy in small systems, this TD enabled simple calculations because 1 gpm (0.063 L/s) conveys 10,000 Btu/h (2.93 kW).

Heat Transfer

Sensible Heating or Cooling. The quantity of sensible heat transferred to the heated or cooled medium in a specific heat exchanger is a function of the surface area, the mean temperature difference between the water and the medium, and the overall heat transfer coefficient (which is a function of the fluid velocities, character of heated medium, construction of the heat transfer element, and other factors). It may be expressed by:

$$q = UA\Delta t_m \qquad (1)$$

where

q = heat transfer rate, Btu/h (W).
U = overall coefficient of heat transfer, Btu/h • ft^2 • °F (W/m^2 • °C).
A = surface area, ft^2 (m^2).
Δt_m = logarithmic mean temperature difference, heated medium to water, °F (°C).

Cooling and Dehumidification. The quantity of heat removed from the cooled medium when both sensible cooling and dehumidification are present is expressed by:

$$q_t = W\Delta h \qquad (2)$$

where

q_t = heat transfer rate, Btu/h (W).

W = mass flow rate of cooled medium, lb/h (kg/s).
Δh = enthalpy difference between entering and leaving conditions of cooled medium, Btu/lb (J/kg).

Heat Transferred from the Water. The quantity of heat transferred from the water is a function of the flow rate, the specific heat, and the temperature drop or rise of the water as it passes through the heat exchanger. The heat transferred from the water, which for all practical purposes must equal the heat transmitted to the conditioned medium by the heat exchanger, is expressed by:

$$q_w = Wc\ (t_1 - t_2) \qquad (3)$$

where

q_w = heat transfer rate from water, Btu/h (W).
W = mass flow or weight of water, lb/h (kg/s).
c = specific heat of water, Btu/lb • °F (J/kg • °C).
t_1 = temperature of water entering unit,°F (°C).
t_2 = temperature of water leaving unit,°F (°C).

For convenience, Eq. (3) may be rewritten as follows with water flow rates in gpm (L/s).

$$q_w = 60\ Gwc\ (t_1 - t_2) \qquad (4)$$

or in SI $q_w = Gwc\ (t_1 - t_2)/1000 \qquad (4\ SI)$

where

G = water flow rate, gpm (L/s).
w = density, lb/gal (kg/m^3).

The value of w should be obtained for the temperature at which the flow rate is determined; the value of c should be determined for the average water temperature.

Heat Conveyed by Piping. The quantity of heat conveyed by the piping is established in the same manner, where the value of W is the total flow through the piping rather than to a specific heat exchanger.

Pressure Drop

For any specific system, the pressure drop varies as the square of the flow as:

$$H_2/H_1 = (W_2/W_1)^2 \qquad (5)$$

where

H_2 = pressure drop at final conditions, ft head (kPa).
H_1 = pressure drop at initial conditions, ft head (kPa).
W_2 = mass flow rate, lb/h (kg/s), or volume flow rate, gpm (L/s), at final conditions.
W_1 = mass flow rate, lb/h (kg/s), or volume flow rate, gpm (L/s), at initial conditions.

DESIGN WATER TEMPERATURE

Design water temperature is the maximum (heating) or minimum (cooling) water temperature supplied to the system at design operating conditions. This design water temperature should be determined as a result of economic analysis of system requirements unless it is dictated by process load requirements.

Selecting Temperature Range

Operating temperature and range are selected by (1) whether the system is for heating and/or cooling, (2) the type and pressure rating of the primary heat source, and (3) the types of terminal units, pumps and accessories.

Low temperature water systems are the most widely used heating systems for virtually all residential and many commercial and institutional systems where loads consist primarily of space heating and domestic water heating and do not exceed 5000 MBh (1.5 MW) total (1 MBh = 1000 Btu/h).

Medium temperature water systems are most commonly used for space heating in large commercial and institutional buildings or in industrial applications with process loads, and where total loads range from 5000 to 20,000 MBh (1.5 to 6 MW).

High temperature water systems are generally limited to campus-type district heating installations and to applications requiring process heating temperatures of 325 °F (163 °C) or higher. Such systems usually have loads greater than 10,000 to 20,000 MBh (3 to 6 MW).

Chilled water systems usually are installed in comfort air conditioning or process cooling applications where water temperatures below 40 °F (4.4 °C) are not required and where a separate heating source is available.

Dual-temperature water systems are installed principally for year-round comfort air-conditioning applications where both heating and cooling are required and where the comfort load is the major portion of the total load.

The designer may combine several systems to achieve the most satisfactory and economical design. An HTW distribution system might be selected to serve several process loads directly with high temperature water. Space heating zones in some areas might be handled with low or medium temperature water through a water-to-water heat exchanger, while another zone might be treated as a dual-temperature system with the chilled water source serving only in that zone.

The design water temperature is determined differently than the heating design where common terminal heat transfer elements both heat and cool. In heating, the design flow rate is selected to meet the heating requirement after the design water temperature has been arbitrarily established. In most dual-temperature water system designs, the flow rate is determined by the chilled water capacity requirement. The hot water supply temperature must be selected at that chilled water flow rate to provide the required heating capacity. Because of the large heat transfer surface and the relatively high flow rates required to meet the chilled water capacity requirements, supply temperatures for heating in these systems are usually low. In many cases, the hot water supply temperature in dual-temperature systems will be about 130 °F (54 °C) or below, and may be below 100 °F (37 °C) at design outdoor temperatures. For system balance, power consumption may be reduced by using a smaller heating pump for lower flow rate and greater water temperature drop.

Outdoor reset of hot water temperatures in two-pipe hot and chilled water systems minimizes overheating during mild weather and the time required for changeover. Very low supply temperatures for heating are also essential in three-pipe systems to minimize the quantity of heat that must be extracted from the return water by the chiller, especially at light load. Heating design water temperatures in four-pipe systems are determined conventionally and frequently use water temperatures in the range of 200 to 240 °F (93 to 115 °C), especially where there are separate heat transfer elements at the terminal.

The design water temperature for cooling applications usually has a narrow range because of the limitations imposed by dehumidification and by eliminating freeze-up in the chiller. Water temperatures from 42 to 50 °F (6 to 10 °C) are used in comfort applications. In well water systems, design supply temperatures as high as 60 °F (15 °C) can be used, although temperatures in this range are suited principally for sensible cooling applications. Where water temperatures below 40 °F (5 °C) are required, antifreeze or brine solutions are usually used.

DESIGN FLOW RATES

The required water flow rate is the total of the flow rates required by the individual terminal units to provide the rated heating or cooling capacity at design conditions. Flow rates are determined basically by (1) assigning an arbitrary system temperature difference or (2) finding a minimum system flow rate by summing flow rates to individual terminals or zones.

Using an arbitrary system temperature difference (TD) has been common, and is well-suited to small system design. Using a minimum system flow rate is recommended for large systems, as it usually results in the least overall cost and best performing system. In large systems, the design TD should be the result, not the base point, of the design.

In small buildings, flow rates to all terminal units are frequently based on an assumed overall system TD, i.e., 20 °F (11 °C) for heating or 8 °F (4.5 °C) for cooling. This has proven to provide sound economy and satisfactory performance in small systems.

Minimum System Flow Rate

For large systems, a minimum system flow rate should provide the lowest cost and maximum control. Several methods are used to determine minimum flow rate to the individual terminals and, by summation, the total system flow rate.

1. Various basic terminal units are capable of producing full capacity at specific temperature drops. For example, baseboard and finned-tube units are selected frequently for 20 to 50 °F (11 to 28 °C) drop, unit heaters for 50 °F (28 °C) and extended surface coils in air systems for 100 °F (56 °C).

2. Manufacturers' catalogs list capacity ratings at various flow rates and entering temperatures. Engineers can select units for minimum flow rate (or maximum TD) to produce desired capacities.

3. Another method is to assume a constant temperature approach (leaving water temperature minus final heated medium temperature) for each class of equipment. For example, this approach might be 20 °F (11 °C). Thus, for an air handler with 120 °F (49 °C) final air temperature, the leaving water would be at 140 °F (60 °C). Similarly, a domestic water heater might have a final temperature of 180 °F (82 °C), which would indicate a leaving system water of 200 °F (93 °C). Assuming a constant supply water temperature, the TD and flow rate for each terminal is determined. Flow rates determined in this manner are usually stated in gpm (L/s) or mass flow in lb/h (kg/s). Mass flow rates are established by dividing capacity by temperature difference and specific heat. For example: Mass flow rate for 100 MBh (29.3 kW) at 100 °F TD 100,000/100 °F = 1000 lb/h. [Mass flow rate for 30 kW at 50 °C TD with specific heat = 4.18 kJ/(kg·°C) is 30/(4.18·50) = 0.144 kg/s].

Mass flow rate is being used as a design criterion, since it simplifies calculations and eliminates many problems associated with previous approaches. Specific heat may be taken into account when calculating flow rate, especially for HTW design where the change in specific heat is important. Flow rate for 100 MBh at 100 °F TD and for 350 °F mean water temperature ($c_p = 1.050$) follows:

$$100,000/(100 \times 1.050) = 952 \text{ lb/h}$$

Figure 2 illustrates relationships between temperature, specific heats, and mass flow rates per gpm (L/s).

Design flow rates for dual-temperature systems are usually based on an estimated system temperature rise, depending on the type of terminal apparatus and the supply temperature. The maximum hot water temperature is established at a value high enough to provide the necessary heating capacity in the units with the greatest heating requirement at the summer flow rate, which are usually in the perimeter zone. In general, higher temperature rises reduce the pump and distribution system cost, and increase chiller efficiency. Therefore, it is more economical in large systems to select the air quantities and heat exchange surface in the terminal heat transfer units for the maximum possible temperature rise at the available supply temperature, so the least quantity of water is circulated to handle the load.

The selections of the design flow rate and the supply temperature are closely related. Generally, lower supply chilled water temperatures permit higher rises but result in lower chiller efficiencies, unless higher rises are used concurrently to increase the mean temperature difference between the chilled water temperature and the evaporator refrigerant temperature.

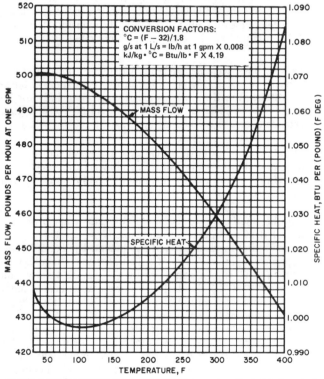

CONVERSION FACTORS:
$°C = (F - 32)/1.8$
g/s at 1 L/s = lb/h at 1 gpm X 0.008
$kJ/kg • °C = Btu/lb • F X 4.19$

Specific heat is for pressure at saturated liquid temperature. Basic data for calculation and construction of curves from Keenan and Keyes.

Fig. 2 Mass Flow and Specific Heat of Water

PIPING SYSTEM DESIGN

After the comfort or process heating or cooling load calculations have been made for the system and all the various terminal heat transfer units have been selected and located, a tentative piping layout for the system can be made. An engineering analysis of the spaces or processes being served, zoning, available space, and relative cost is required to determine the piping arrangement, or combinations of piping arrangements, that will best meet the system's needs. After selecting the arrangement,

the piping system can be designed to connect generators with terminal equipment.

Generally, the most economical distribution system layout results from running the mains by the shortest and most convenient route to the terminal equipment having the largest flow rate requirements, and then laying out the branch or secondary circuits to connect with these mains.

Water distribution mains are most frequently located in corridor ceilings, above hung ceilings, wall-hung along a perimeter wall, in pipe trenches, in crawl spaces, or in basements. Water system piping need not be run at a definite level or pitch, but may change up or down as architectural or structural needs require. Water system piping can be divided into the following two arbitrary classifications:

1. Pipe circuits suitable for complete small systems or for terminal or branch circuits on large systems.
   a. Series loop.
   b. One-pipe.
   c. Two-pipe *reverse*-return.
   d. Two-pipe *direct*-return.
2. Main distribution piping used to convey water to and from the terminal units or circuits in a large system.
   a. Two-pipe *direct*-return.
   b. Two-pipe *reverse*-return.
   c. Three-pipe.
   d. Four-pipe.

The application usually dictates the distribution system. In small buildings, a specific piping system arrangement can normally be used throughout. In large buildings, combinations of several arrangements are usually best.

Figure 3 compares a reverse-return circuit with a direct-return circuit. In the direct-return system, the length of supply and return piping through the several subcircuits are unequal. This may cause unbalanced flow rates and require careful balancing to provide each subcircuit with design flow. The reverse-return system provides nearly equal total lengths for all terminal circuits.

Direct return piping has been successfully applied where the designer has guarded against major flow unbalance by the following:

1. Providing for pressure drops in the subcircuits or terminals that are significant percentages of the total head, usually establishing *close* subcircuit pressure drops at higher values than the far subcircuits.

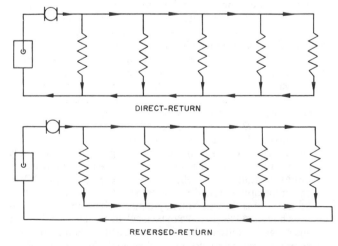

DIRECT-RETURN

REVERSED-RETURN

Fig. 3 Direct- and Reverse-Return Two-Pipe Systems

2. Minimizing distribution piping pressure drop, especially in the prime generators.
3. Using pumps with flat head characteristics selected to the *left of center* to minimize changes in available head with system flow reductions.
4. Including balancing devices and/or flow measuring devices at each terminal or branch circuit.
5. Using control valves with a high head loss at the terminals.

Branch Circuits

Two-pipe reverse-return branch piping (or risers) is usually desirable if low pressure drop terminals are used. Direct-return branch piping should be considered when it is possible to have minimum branch pressure drop and maximum heat terminal element pressure drop.

SELECTING THE PIPING ARRANGEMENT

The characteristics of the building to be heated determine the pipe routing; the system design depends on load, control and installation requirements, and on operating cost. To meet these requirements, basic piping arrangements such as (1) series loop, (2) one-pipe, (3) two-pipe reverse-return, and (4) two-pipe direct-return are selected. The four basic systems can also be combined in various ways to use the advantages of each.

Series Loop Arrangement

A series loop is a continuous run of pipe or tube from a supply connection to a return connection. Terminal units are a part of the loop. Figure 4 shows a system of two series loops on a supply and return main (*split series loop*). One or many series loops can be used in a complete system. Loops may connect to mains, or all loops may run directly to and from the boilers.

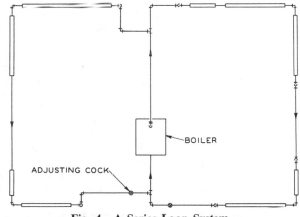
Fig. 4   A Series Loop System

The water temperature drops progressively as each radiator transfers heat to the air; the amount of drop depends on the radiator output and water flow rate. For economical design, particularly at high design temperature drop, it may be necessary to adjust the size of each unit on the loop according to the average water temperature (AWT) in each. True system operating water temperature and flow rate must be known to calculate AWT for each unit on the loop. If all terminal units in series on one loop are in one zone of interconnecting air space, the entire set of units can be considered *one radiator,* and all units can be sized at the AWT of the loop. If individual units on a loop are in separate enclosed spaces, each unit must be sized to its own actual AWT.

A decrease in the loop water flow rate increases the temperature drop in each unit and in the entire loop. The average water temperature shifts downward progressively from the first to last radiator in series. Unit output gradually lowers from the first to last on the loop. Consequently, comfort cannot be maintained in separate spaces heated with a single series loop if the water flow rate is varied. Controlling the output from individual terminal units on a series loop is impractical except by controlling heated air flow. Manual dampers can be used on natural convection units; automatic fan or face-and-bypass damper control can be used on forced air units.

A series loop system often needs short mains or no mains. In occupied spaces, a loop may be run entirely above the floor, eliminating pipe trenches, insulation, and furring. Therefore, a series loop may be the only possible water heating method in an existing building. Installation cost is low.

All loop circuit water flows through all pipes and each terminal unit, and all pressure drops are added. Loop length is limited by the total pressure drop the available pump head must meet. The length can be increased by increasing operating temperature drop and decreasing flow rate. Loop length is seldom a design limitation if the limitations of space temperature control with the series loop are recognized.

When series loop circuits are used as subcircuits of a larger two-pipe direct-return system, flow balance must be maintained as with any direct-return system. Flow balancing valves should be installed on the subcircuits. A pumped series loop can be connected to a two-pipe supply main by using a primary-secondary connection. It is usually impractical to add a series loop to a one-pipe main because diverted flow to the loop circuit is low.

One-Pipe (Diverting Fitting) Arrangement

One-pipe circuits (Figure 5) use a single loop main. For each terminal unit, a supply and a return tee are installed on the main. One of the two tees is a special diverting tee, which creates a pressure drop in the main flow to divert part of it to the unit. One (supply) diverting tee is usually sufficient for upfeed (units above the main) systems. Two special fittings (supply and return tees) are usually required to overcome thermal head in downfeed units. Special tees are proprietary; consult manufacturer's literature for flow rates and pressure drop data. Unit selection can be only approximate without these data.

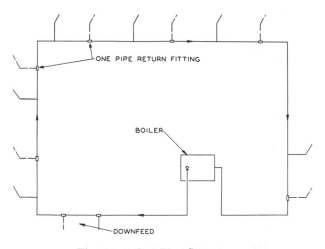
Fig. 5   A One-Pipe System

One-pipe circuits allow manual or automatic control of flow to individual connected heating units. On-off rather than flow modulation control is advisable because of the relatively low pressure and the low diverted flow. Cost is likely to be greater than for the series loop because of extra branch pipe and fittings, including special tees. A manual air vent in each unit is usually required because of the low water velocity through the unit. The length and load imposed on a one-pipe circuit are usually small because of these limitations.

Since only a fraction of the main flow is diverted in a one-pipe circuit, the flow rate and pressure drop as unit water flow is controlled are less variable than in some other circuits. One-pipe circuits can therefore be useful in large systems that cannot tolerate large, uncontrolled changes in pump head and flow. (Primary-secondary connections used on any type of circuit provide superior isolation of pump pressure change.) When two or more one-pipe circuits are connected to the same two-pipe mains, the circuit flow may need to be mechanically balanced, as in other types of circuits. After balancing, sufficient flow must be maintained in each one-pipe circuit to ensure adequate flow diversion to the units.

Two-Pipe Arrangement

Two-pipe circuits can be direct-return or reverse-return. In direct-return circuits, the return main flow direction is opposite the supply main flow, and the return water from each unit takes the shortest path back to the boiler. In reverse-return circuits, the return main flow is in the same direction as the supply main flow, and the return main returns all water to the boiler after the last unit is fed. The direct-return system is popular because it requires less main pipe length. However, it usually requires circuit balancing valves on units or subcircuits. Reverse-return systems seldom need balancing valves, as the water flow distance to and from the boiler is virtually the same through any unit. The cost of installing a direct-return compared to a reverse-return system must be evaluated for each design. Direct-return systems usually have a higher operating (pumping) cost because of the added balancing fitting pressure drops at the same flow rate. Figure 6 illustrates a reverse-return system for a small building.

Combination Piping Arrangement

The four basic piping arrangements exist only to describe function; one type can grade into another, and a piping system can contain from one to all four types of piping arrangements.

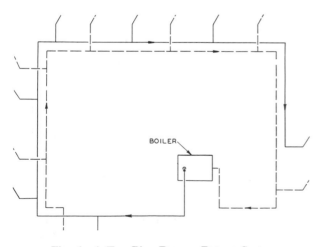

Fig. 6   A Two-Pipe Reverse-Return System

Figure 4 illustrates a *split series loop* system. If the mains were very short, it would be *two separate series loops*. If each loop contained only one radiator, it would be a two-pipe direct-return system. If the returns (or supplies) from the radiators were reversed on the main, it would be a two-pipe reverse-return system. As pipe lengths and number of units vary, and as circuit types are combined, basic names for piping circuits become meaningless; flow, temperature, and head must be determined for each circuit and for the complete system.

Figure 7 illustrates LTW circuits as components of medium temperature systems (see Chapter 15). Different temperatures and temperature drops can be combined in a system; the main and subcircuits can be designed for the temperature drop needed. Heat exchangers and primary-secondary connections are useful in isolating one circuit from other circuits at different temperature drops. Multiple pumps and different circuit pressure drops can also be used to obtain different temperature drops within the overall system. Figure 8 shows basic boiler connections for a hot-water system.

CHILLED WATER AND DUAL TEMPERATURE SYSTEMS

The selection of a particular type of chilled or dual-temperature water system for a specific application should be based on a careful analysis of several factors: (1) the nature of the loads involved, (2) the characteristics and layout of the building, (3) the comfort and control requirements, and (4) an economic analysis of the complete system.

Generally, two-pipe chilled water systems are used only in applications where heating is not required, where a heating system exists or where another medium is tapped for heating.

With a two-pipe dual-temperature system, the possibility of satisfying the constantly changing heating and cooling requirements of the individual spaces, and the cost of providing the additional zoning, increases with the number of zones provided. For this reason, in applications where the load analysis indicates that a large number of zones is required, the alternatives available in two-pipe natural cooling systems (discussed later in this chapter) or in three- or four-pipe systems should be considered.

However, in applications where temperature variations do not fluctuate rapidly and where loads in adjacent spaces are predictable and similar, the two-pipe dual-temperature system provides economical and satisfactory performance. Much of the success in such a system lies in the proper system zoning and in the changeover method that minimizes the time required for changeover to be completed.

In applications requiring both heating and cooling, the choice between using a single or multiple zone two-pipe system and either a three- or four-pipe system must be made by weighing the initial and operating costs of the various systems against comfort and control requirements.

Two-pipe dual-temperature systems have low initial cost and are generally preferred where: (1) initial cost is a primary consideration, (2) loads throughout the system or zone can be expected to be reasonably similar, and (3) rapid or frequent changeover from heating to cooling is not likely to be required regularly.

Three- and four-pipe systems have the advantage of providing instantaneous selective heating or mechanical cooling in any space, independent of any other space requirements. This is particularly advantageous in systems where (1) individual room control has been provided, (2) heating and cooling may be required in different spaces simultaneously in the same zone during the intermediate season, and (3) rapid changeover is required as a

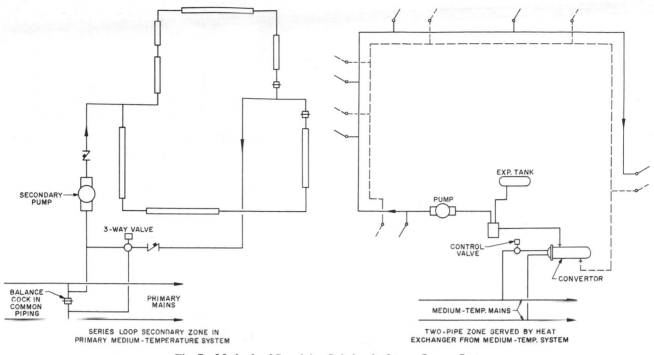

Fig. 7   Methods of Supplying Subcircuits from a Larger System

result of wide variations in outdoor temperature during a 24-hour period. Three- and four-pipe systems are often used with heat pumps, but also can be used in systems with conventional boilers and chillers, in which lack of access or the class of terminal equipment installed makes it impracticable to use outdoor air for cooling during the intermediate season.

Compared with two-pipe systems, three- and four-pipe systems have the disadvantage of higher initial cost for the distribution system and associated pumps and controls. They also have the disadvantage, as opposed to a two-pipe natural cooling system, of higher energy costs because of the additional pump power required and the longer operating hours for the chiller. In a three- or four-pipe system, the chillers must run whenever any space

in the building requires cooling; while in a system that can cool with outdoor air, the chillers do not run unless the outdoor temperature exceeds 55 to 60°F (13 to 16°C). The energy used by auxiliary equipment must be included in comparisons.

Schematic diagrams of elementary two-, three-, and four-pipe systems are shown in Figure 9.

PRESSURE DROP

Data on pressure drop and pipe sizing is in Chapter 34 of the 1985 FUNDAMENTALS Volume. Data on pressure drop through fittings and valves also are contained in that chapter.

Energy Relationship in Piping Circuits

The energy required to force water through a closed loop hydronic system is unaffected by static pressure because the energy required to force water up a supply riser is completely regained as the water falls through the return riser. Thus, only the friction loss in the system determines the energy requirement for a closed loop system. The total energy requirement of a system comprising several branch circuits is determined by the circuit having the highest pressure drop.

Figure 10 shows a typical direct-return closed loop system. If the pump develops sufficient energy to cause design flow rate through the longest circuit, A-B-C-D-G-H-I-J, through valve (V), terminal (HT), and balance fitting (BC), more than sufficient head is available to produce design flow through the other branch circuits, B-I, C-H, and K-L. It may be necessary to provide balance fittings in these circuits.

The same analysis applies to the reverse-return system in Figure 11. Whichever of the terminal circuits, B-I, C-H, D-G, or K-L, has the highest pressure drop determines the path governing the total pressure drop for the system A through J. The other terminals may require balancing.

Both Figures 10 and 11 include a side circuit, A-K-L-J, that

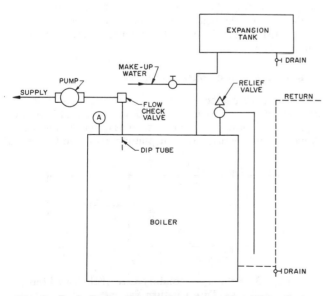

Fig. 8   Basic Boiler Connections for a Hot Water System

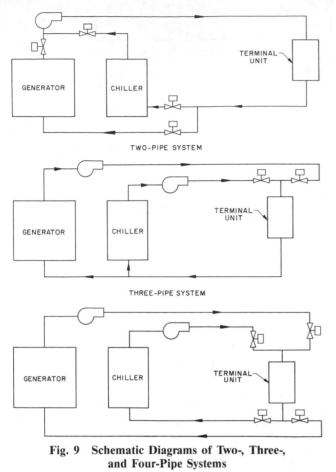

Fig. 9   Schematic Diagrams of Two-, Three-,
and Four-Pipe Systems

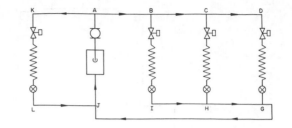

Fig. 11   Typical Reverse-Return Closed Loop Piping Circuit
(A to J through B, C, and D)

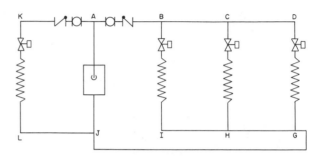

Fig. 12   Zone Pump in Reverse-Return Circuit

Open Circuits. The open loop piping circuit differs from the closed loop circuit in that the piping is broken and is open to the atmosphere at the break, as in cooling tower piping. Required energy differs for the supply and return piping because the pump must raise supply water to a higher elevation (distribution header) than that of the return main in the tower basin. Required energy is thus established by friction, plus the static height, which is the difference in elevation between the tower distribution and basin. Chapter 14 shows cooling tower circuit designs.

PUMP SELECTION

Circulating pumps used in water systems can vary in size from small in-line circulators delivering 5 gpm at 6 or 7 ft head (4 L/s at 18 to 20 kPa above atm.) to base-mounted pumps handling hundreds or thousands of gpm with heads limited only by the pressure characteristics of the system. Pump operating characteristics must be carefully matched to system operating requirements.

Pump Curves and Water Temperature

Performance characteristics of centrifugal pumps are described by *pump curves,* which plot flow versus head or pressure together with other information such as efficiency and power. A more complete discussion of pump curves is in Chapter 31

is shorter than the others and requires severe balancing. Frequently, a separate (or zone) pump can be installed in such a circuit, as shown in Figure 12, to eliminate these problems and to save pumping power. Each of the pumps in Figure 12 operates against only the head of its own circuit plus that common to both circuits, J-A, through the chiller or boiler and its accessory equipment.

The branch circuits may also be connected to the distribution system through a primary-secondary relationship (Figure 13). Since this type of connection provides hydraulic isolation between the primary and secondary, the primary circuit or distribution system does not include any pressure losses from any of the terminal branch circuits. Thus, for branch circuit D-G, the primary system pressure drop is the friction loss through A-B-C-D-G-H-I-J only. The pressure drop in each of the secondary circuits affects only its own pump and not the primary pump.

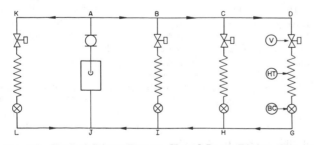

Fig. 10   Typical Direct-Return Closed Loop Piping Circuit

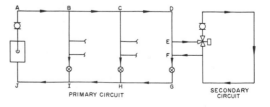

Fig. 13   Primary-Secondary Circuits in Two-Pipe
Direct-Return System

of the 1983 EQUIPMENT Volume. Using volume such as gpm for flow rate and feet for head yields a pump curve unaffected by water temperature.

Many engineers design systems based on mass flow rate (lb per h) rather than gpm. Mass flow on a pump curve may be converted to volume flow by dividing by the density of the fluid at the design operating temperature. For example:

100,000 lb/h at 40 °F water temperature =
100,000 lb/h /500 lb/h per gpm = 200 gpm

100,000 lb/h at 400 °F water temperature =
100,000 lb/h /432 lb/h per gpm = 232 gpm

In SI units a pump curve of flow rate is L/s versus the ratio of fluid pressure over fluid density is unaffected by temperature.

When the design is based on mass flow, pressure drop (energy head) requirements for the supply and return piping do not require correction for temperature.

A complete piping system follows the same water flow-pressure drop relationships as any component of the system [see Eq. (5)]. Thus, the energy head required for any proposed flow rate through the system may be determined and a system curve constructed. The system curve is important in pump selection and is determined by using calculated system head at the design flow rate as the *known* base point value.

The system curve can be most easily constructed from data obtained from solving a rearrangement of Eq. (5) as follows:

$$(H_1)^{0.5}/W_1 = (H_2)^{0.5}/W_2 \qquad (6)$$

where

H_1 = known (or calculated) head, ft
W_1 = design flow rate, gpm
H_2 = system curve head point, ft of head
W_2 = system curve flow rate point, gpm

In SI units H_1 and H_2 are the fluid pressure divided by density. This rearrangement permits the pressure drops of selected flow rates to be determined and a typical system curve to be plotted (Figure 14). Intersection of the system curve with any pump curve defines the point of operation for that pump in that system, because the First Law of Thermodynamics states the pump energy input must equal the system energy loss from fluid friction. Note that in Figure 14 the operating points of the two pumps do not yield markedly different system flow rates because of the squared relationship between head and flow rate.

Figure 15 illustrates how a shift to the right of the system curve affects system flow rate. This shift can be caused by incorrectly calculating the system pressure drop by using arbitrary safety factors or overstated pressure drop charts. Variable system flow caused by control valve operation or improperly balanced systems with subcircuits having substantially lower pressure drops than the longest circuit can also cause a shift to the right.

As described in Chapter 31 of the 1983 EQUIPMENT Volume, pumps applied to closed loop piping systems should have a *flat head* characteristic and should operate slightly to the left of the peak efficiency point on their curves. This permits some degree of pump shift to the right without causing undesirable pump operation, overloading, or reduction in available head across maximum pressure drop circuits. Pumps with steep curves should not be used since they tend to limit system flow rates.

Many dual-temperature systems are designed so that the chillers are bypassed during the winter months. The chiller pressure drop, which may be quite high, is thus eliminated from the system pressure drop, and the pump shift to the right may be quite large. For such systems, system curve analysis should be used to check the actual winter pump operation points.

Variable flow usually occurs in water systems where control valves are used at the terminal heat transfer elements. Control is established by operating the valve to direct water either to the terminal heat transfer element or to the bypass. A complete system design using this control has relatively fixed flow characteristics, provided the balance fitting has been adjusted so that the bypass and terminal unit pressure drops are equal. When balance fittings are not provided, or the bypass is unbalanced, a flow shift to the right will occur. The modulating three-way valve application introduces a right shift at a 50-50 flow position.

Systems designed using single-seated valves have highly variable characteristics. Such systems can operate under conditions ranging from an all-valves-opened operating position, to a dead-end, virtually no-flow condition. Pump shutoff heads in these systems must not be large enough to force valves open or to interfere with their operation.

When selecting hydronic system pumps, consider (1) that the

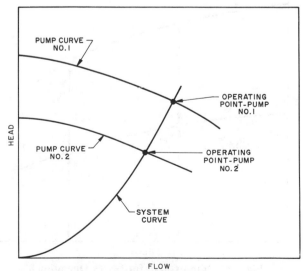

Fig. 14 Typical System Curve

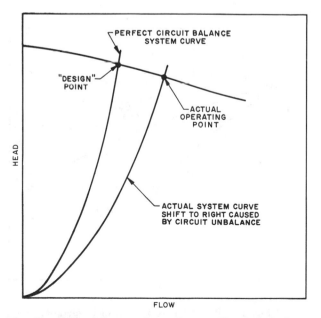

Fig. 15 Shift of System Curve Due to Circuit Unbalance

operating points may be highly variable, depending on load conditions, (2) the types of control valves used, and (3) the piping circuitry and heat transfer elements. The best selection generally will be:

1. For design flow rates and made using pressure drop charts that illustrate actual closed loop hydronic system piping pressure drops.
2. To the left of the center of the pump curve to allow shifts to the right caused by system circuit unbalance, direct-return circuitry applications and modulating three-way valve applications.
3. A flat pump curve to compensate for unbalanced circuitry and to provide a minimum pressure ratio increase across two-way control valves.

Pump Zoning

Small residential and commercial systems are often pump zoned for temperature control. Larger systems are also pump zoned to reduce operating pump power, eliminate excessive energy requirements in controlled circuits close to the boiler room, or to provide separate reset temperature control for various building zones.

Regardless of the reason for pump zoning, the circuit head used to select the pump must include the individual circuit pressure drop for which the pump is to be applied plus the pressure drop through the common piping and equipment (boiler, chiller and so forth) through which all pumps circulate.

All zone pumps must have check valves at the discharge to prevent excessive start-up load and reverse flow through the pump under a nonoperating condition. Do not apply a *safety factor* when determining required pump head.

Improper evaluation of zone circuit requirements may cause excessive common piping flows and pressure drop to the point of back checking, and flow through zones with low head pumps may stop. This can be especially serious for zones exposed to freezing possibilities. Similar troubles can occur when single fine-mesh strainers are used, and allowed to plug up, in the header piping common to all zone pumps.

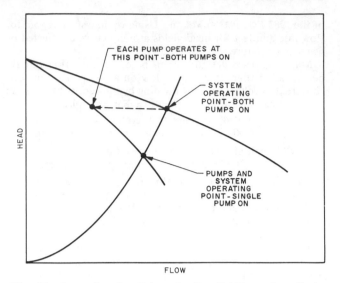

Fig. 17   Operating Conditions for Parallel Pump Installation

Parallel Pumping

Pumps are often applied in parallel (Figure 16). In parallel, each pump operates at the same head and provides its share of the system flow at that head. Generally, pumps of equal size are used and the parallel pump curve is established by doubling the flow of the single pump curve (Figure 17).

Plotting a system curve across the parallel pump curve shows the operating points for both single and parallel pump operation (Figure 18). Note that single pump operation does not yield 50% flow. The system curve crosses the single pump curve considerably to the right of its operating point when both pumps are running. This leads to two important considerations: (1) the pumps must be powered to prevent overloading during single pump operation and (2) single pump operation permits standby service up to as much as 80% of design flow.

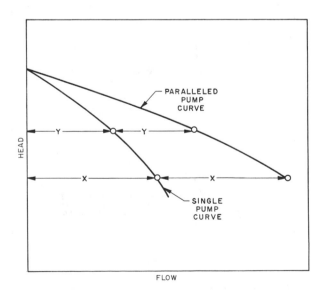

Fig. 16   Pump Curve for Parallel Operation

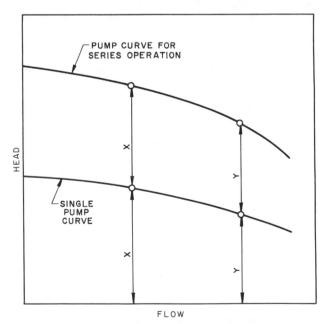

Fig. 18   Pump Curve for Series Operation

Series Pumping

When operated in series, each pump operates at the same gpm flow and provides its share of the total head at that flow (Figure 18). A system curve plotted across the series pump curve shows the operating points for both single and series pump operation (Figure 19). Note that single pump operation provides flow up to about 80% standby and at a lower power requirement.

Series pump installations are often used in heating and cooling systems so that both pumps operate during the cooling season to provide maximum flow and head while only a single pump operates during the heating season. Note that both parallel and series pump applications require that the *actual* pump operating points be used to accurately determine the *actual* pumping points. Adding artificial safety factor head, using improper pressure drop charts or incorrectly calculating pressures drop may lead to an unwise selection.

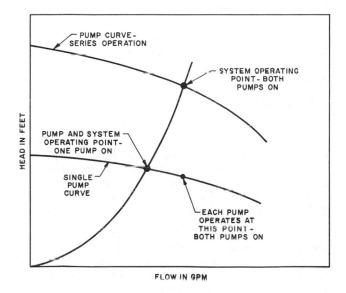

Fig. 19   Operating Conditions for Series Pump Installation

Standby Pump Provision

The simplest and most common standby provision is to install a properly valved equal-capacity standby pump to be used when operating pump service is required. Also, a single standby may be provided for several similarly sized zone pumps. As noted, parallel or series pump installation can provide up to 80% standby, which often is sufficient.

SYSTEM PRESSURIZATION

The objectives of system pressure control are to (1) limit the pressure at all system equipment to its allowable working pressure, (2) maintain minimum pressure for all normal operating temperatures to vent air and prevent cavitation at the pump suction and boiling of system water, and (3) to accomplish these objectives with a minimal addition of new water.

An expansion tank is the primary device used for system pressure control. The excess water volume in the system, resulting from increased temperature, is stored in the expansion tank during periods of high operating temperatures and is returned to the system when the system water temperature is lower. The expansion tank must be able to store the required volume of water

during maximum design operating temperatures without exceeding the maximum allowable operating pressure, and to maintain the required minimum pressure when the system is cold. Some designers provide an automatic fill valve to maintain the minimum system pressure by supplying water to make up for leakage. Others supply additional system water by using a manually operated valve.

The safety relief valve installed on a hot water boiler in accordance with the ASME *Boiler and Pressure Vessel Code* limits the maximum pressure at the boiler. Since it is a safety device, it should not be considered an operating control.

Requirements and Methods

When choosing a method to maintain the pressure above saturation, consider the following factors:

1. The pressurization system should be relatively simple and reliable. Loss of pressurization causes flashing within the system, which can lead to problems within pumps, generators, heat exchange devices and the piping system.
2. Oxygen should be excluded from the system to maintain corrosion-free characteristics, both in pressurization and in the operating cycle. This precludes the use of air in direct contact with the water as a pressurizing means. Do not use cycles that periodically withdraw and reintroduce water.
3. The control of the pressurization system should maintain the inherently stable conditions of the hot water cycle. Fluctuations in system pressure or temperature should be minimized by taking advantage of the thermal storage of the cycle. This will improve combustion efficiency through relatively steady firing rates.

Available fundamental methods for keeping pressure in a hydraulic system at or above a desired minimum level include using:

1. An elevated storage tank.
2. A hydraulic pump. However, the large pressure changes encountered with small changes in volume make this method relatively impractical.
3. An expansion tank sized to accommodate the volume of water expansion, with sufficient gas space to keep the pressure range within the design limits of the system. Where air is used as the initial gas, the system should be kept tight because every recharging cycle introduces additional oxygen with the air and thus promotes system corrosion. The initial oxygen during start-up will react with the system components, leaving a basically nitrogen atmosphere in the expansion tank. The initial fill pressure sets the minimum level, while the compression of the gas space caused by water expansion determines the maximum system pressure.
4. A diaphragm expansion tank precharged to the system fill pressure and sized to accept the expansion of the water. The air charge and the water are permanently separated by a diaphragm that eliminates corrosion and noise caused by air in the system.
5. Steam pressurization and inert gas pressurization for MTW and HTW cycles, as described in Chapter 15.

Systems with expansion tanks are either open or closed. The *open tank* system (Figure 20) is vented to the atmosphere and is generally limited to installations having operating temperatures of 180°F (82°C) or less because of system boiling and tank water evaporation problems. The tank should be at least 3 ft (1 m) above the high point of the system and connected to the suction side of the pump to prevent subatmospheric system pressures

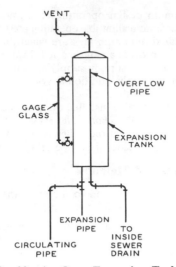

Fig. 20   An Open Expansion Tank

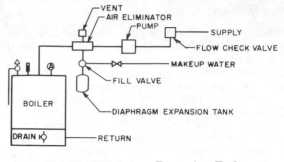

Fig. 22   Diaphragm Expansion Tank

caused by pump operation. The system should have an internal overflow drain. As required by the ASME *Boiler and Pressure Vessel Code,* water must be prevented from freezing in the tank, the tank vent, and the pipe leading to the tank. The minimum tank volume should equal 6% of the total system water volume. Note that continuous oxygen contamination (absorption) occurs at the exposed water surface, making the system less corrosion-free than the closed design.

The *closed system* (Figures 21 and 22) uses an airtight tank to pressurize the system for operation over a wide range of conditions. As the excess water caused by thermal expansion moves into the expansion tank, it compresses the trapped air inside and increases the pressure on the system. If the tank, or the amount of air in it, is too small, the pressure on the system will exceed the maximum allowable and cause the safety relief valve to waste water from the system. When the system cools, the pressure will drop to a value less than minimum, making air venting impossible, or drawing air into the system if automatic air vent valves are located at a high point of the piping. If the tank is too large, it will cost more and require more space.

In small systems having small water volumes and low pressures from the pump and elevation, expansion tanks are small and

problems are not critical. In large systems, the size of the expansion tank and pressure control problems can be critical. The following are ways to reduce expansion tank size and satisfactorily control pressure.

1. A compressed gas, if available, can be admitted to the expansion tank to obtain the desired pressure.
2. The additive pressure of the pump can be reduced by the use of larger pipe sizes or greater design temperature drop.
3. The boiler can be constructed for pressures higher than 30 psig (200 kPa).
4. The steam boiler can be used with a steam-to-water heat exchanger to heat the water circulated.

The point where the expansion tank is connected should be carefully selected to avoid the possibility that normal operation of automatic, check or manual valves will isolate the tank from a hot boiler or any other part of the system.

Effect of Pump Location

The location of the pump in relation to the expansion tank connection determines whether the pump pressure is added to or subtracted from the system static pressure. This is because the junction of the tank with the system is a point of *no pressure change* whether or not the pump operates.

In Figure 23, Diagram A, the pump is discharging away from the boiler and expansion tank, full pump pressure will appear as an increase at the pump discharge, and all points downstream will show a pressure equal to the pump pressure minus the friction loss from the pump to that point. The fill pressure need be only slightly higher than the system static pressure.

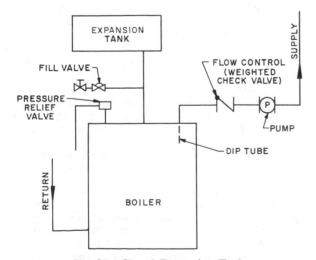

Fig. 21   Closed Expansion Tank

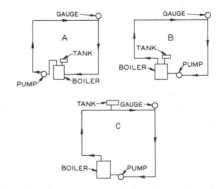

Note: Net expansion of water equals expansion of water less volumetric expansion of metal system.

Fig. 23   Effect of Pump Location and
Expansion Tank Connection

When the pump discharges into the boiler and expansion tank (Figure 23, Diagram B) full pump pressure appears as a decrease below the system fill pressure. Thus, unless the fill pressure is higher than the pump pressure, a vacuum can be created within the system. This arrangement is not generally used, except in small systems or systems in low-rise buildings where pumps have a low total head capability.

Attic tanks (Figure 23, Diagram C) are often used to reduce expansion tank size. Points between the pump discharge and the tank will show a pressure increase when the pump operates and points between the tank and the pump suction will show a pressure decrease. The required fill pressure no longer needs to include system static pressure. See the examples of expansion tank sizing (following) for details of the effect of these changes.

Calculation of Water Expansion

A system's water volume is determined from heating unit water capacities, obtained from manufacturers, and pipe or tube volume (see Table 1).

Effect of Increased Temperature Difference

At any given average system operating temperature, an increase in the design temperature drop can result in a smaller expansion tank, since the lower circulating rate reduces pipe sizes. For example, if the design range is changed from 170 to 190 °F (77 to 88 °C) or 180 °F (82 °C) average to 150 to 210 °F (66 to 99 °C) or 180 °F (82 °C) average, the water circulation rate will be reduced to one-third of its original value. The actual reduction in water quantity, and therefore in water expansion, for any given change in water temperature difference varies with the amount of piping in the system. The water content of the hot water generator, radiation and other heat-exchange components may or may not change in size. On larger systems, an economic study of the effects of various operating temperature ranges is often warranted.

Sizing Expansion Tanks

The size of a closed expansion tank is determined by (1) the volume of the water in the system, (2) the range of water temperatures normal to system operation, (3) the air pressure in the expansion tank when the fill water first enters it, (4) the relationship of the height of the boiler, which is usually the item with the lowest working pressure, to the expansion tank and the high point of the system, (5) the pressure caused by the circulating pump, (6) the location of the circulating pump with respect to the expansion tank connection, and (8) the boiler. The expansion tank size for a closed system can be determined from the following ASME formula, which should be used only for operating temperatures between 160 and 280 °F (70 to 140 °C).

$$V_t = (0.00041t - 0.0466)V_s/[(P_a/P_f) - (P_a/P_o)] \qquad (7)$$

$$V_t = (0.000738t - 0.03348) V_s/[(P_a/P_f) - (P_a/P_o)] \qquad (7\ SI)$$

where

V_t = minimum volume of the expansion tank, gal (m^3)
V_s = system volume, gal (m^3)
t = maximum average operating temperature, °F (°C)
P_a = pressure in expansion tank when water first enters, ft of water (kPa), absolute
P_f = initial fill or minimum pressure at tank, ft of water (kPa), absolute
P_o = maximum operating pressure at tank, ft of water (kPa), absolute

A widely used formula recommended for temperatures below 160 °F (70 °C) is:

$$V_t = E/[(P_a/P_f) - (P_a/P_o)] \qquad (8)$$

where

E = net expansion of the water in the system when heated from minimum temperatures to maximum temperature, gal (m^3) (Figure 24).

Examples. The system for the following examples has (1) a water volume of 1000 gal, (2) a high point of the system at the top of a return riser 25 ft from the top of the boiler directly above the boiler room, (3) a circulating pump having a 20-ft head, and (4) a 30-psi boiler with an ASME rated safety relief valve as the item of equipment having the lowest pressure rating. The P_a is atmospheric pressure, 34 ft of water absolute, in all examples. The design average water temperature is 200 °F. Friction losses between the high point of the system and the boiler are assumed to be negligible.

Table 1   Volume of Water in Standard Pipe and Tube

Nominal Pipe Size		Schedule No.	Standard Steel Pipe				Type L Copper Tube			
			Inside Diameter		Volume		Inside Diameter		Volume	
in.	(mm)		in.	(mm)	gal/ft	(L/m)	in.	(mm)	gal/ft	(L/m)
3/8	(10)	—	—	—	—	—	0.430	(1.09)	0.0075	(0.09)
1/2	(15)	40	0.622	(1.58)	0.0157	(0.19)	0.545	(1.38)	0.0121	(0.15)
5/8	(16)	—	—	—	—	—	0.666	(1.69)	0.0181	(0.22)
3/4	(20)	40	0.824	(2.09)	0.0277	(0.34)	0.785	(1.99)	0.0251	(0.31)
1	(25)	40	1.049	(2.66)	0.0449	(0.56)	1.025	(2.60)	0.0429	(0.53)
1 1/4	(32)	40	1.380	(3.50)	0.0779	(0.97)	1.265	(3.21)	0.0653	(0.81)
1 1/2	(40)	40	1.610	(4.09)	0.106	(1.32)	1.505	(3.82)	0.0924	(1.15)
2	(50)	40	2.067	(5.25)	0.174	(2.16)	1.985	(5.04)	0.161	(2.00)
2 1/2	(65)	40	2.469	(6.27)	0.249	(3.09)	2.465	(6.26)	0.248	(3.08)
3	(80)	40	3.068	(7.79)	0.384	(4.77)	2.945	(7.48)	0.354	(4.40)
3 1/2	(90)	40	3.548	(9.01)	0.514	(6.38)	3.425	(8.70)	0.479	(5.95)
4	(100)	40	4.026	(10.23)	0.661	(8.21)	3.905	(9.92)	0.622	(7.73)
5	(125)	40	5.047	(12.82)	1.04	(12.92)	4.875	(12.38)	0.970	(12.05)
6	(150)	40	6.065	(15.41)	1.50	(18.63)	5.845	(14.85)	1.39	(17.26)
8	(200)	30	8.071	(20.50)	2.66	(33.03)	7.725	(19.62)	2.43	(30.18)
10	(250)	30	10.136	(25.75)	4.19	(52.04)	9.625	(24.45)	3.78	(46.95)
12	(300)	30	12.090	(30.71)	5.96	(74.02)	11.565	(29.38)	5.46	(67.81)

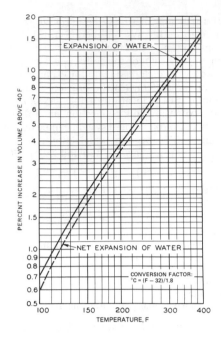

Fig. 24   Expansion of Water Above 40°F (4.4°C)

Example 1: Determine the size of expansion tank required when connected, as shown in A, Figure 23.

Solution: Installation is as shown in A, Figure 23, with the expansion tank at the same level as the safety relief valve. The net expansion of the water in the system is represented by the term $(0.00041t - 0.0466)$ V_s from Eq. (7):

$$[(0.00041)(200) - 0.0466] (1000) = 35.4 \text{ gal}$$

As stated, P_a is 34 ft of water, absolute. Referring to the discussion for A, Figure 23, the minimum pressure, P_f, is equal to the height of the system above the expansion tank, 25 ft, plus 4 ft for positive venting, a total of 29 ft of water gauge, or 63 ft of water absolute. P_o is equal to the safety relief valve setting minus 5 psi or 10%, whichever is larger (and which gives the lowest P_o). Thus, (30 psi − 5 psi) 2.31 = 57.8 ft water gauge, or 91.8 ft of water absolute. Substituting in Eq. (7)

$$V_t = 35.4/[(34/63) - (34/ 91.8)] = 209.1 \text{ gal}$$

Example 2: Determine the size of expansion tank required when connected as shown in B, Figure 23.

Solution: All conditions remain the same, except the expansion tank is connected at the discharge of the pump rather than at the suction. When the pump operates, the pressure at the top of the return riser is reduced by an amount equal to the head of the pump. Therefore, to maintain a positive pressure at the top of the system, the minimum pressure must be increased an amount equal to the head of the pump, 20 ft of water (the pressure developed by the pump). P_f, the minimum pressure, equals 29 + 20, or 49 ft of water gauge, or 83 ft of water absolute. The required volume by Eq. (7) is:

$$V_t = 35.4/[(34/83) - 34/91.8)] = 901.5 \text{ gal}$$

Example 3: Determine the size of expansion tank required when it is connected as shown in C, Figure 23.

Solution: The expansion tank is located at the top of the system with the result that the height of the system has no effect on the required minimum pressure, P_f. However, the tank is located far enough from the pump to consider friction loss in the piping between the pump and the tank in determining how pump operation affects system pressures. Assume that the tank is located at such a point that the friction loss between the tank connection to the system and the suction of the pump is 8 ft, with the resistance in the return riser to the boiler still considered negligible.

The pressure in the expansion tank remains the same whether or not the pump runs. Therefore, since 8 ft of friction loss exists between the expansion tank and the pump suction at the top of the return riser, the pressure in the expansion tank must be increased by that amount to maintain a positive air-venting pressure at that point.

The minimum pressure in the tank, P_f, should be the sum of 4 ft for positive venting pressure and 8 ft for pump effect, or 12 ft water gauge, which is 46 ft of water absolute. Since the pump is located between the expansion tank connection and the boiler, P_o, the maximum pressure in the tank must be less than the maximum operating pressure of the relief valve by an amount equal to the effect of pump operation on the boiler pressure. In this case, the effect of the pump is reduced by the friction loss between the expansion tank and the boiler. The head of the pump, 20 ft less friction as discussed, 8 ft, is equal to 12 ft. The pressure caused by the height of the system is 25 ft. The sum of the pump head and the building height effect is 37 ft.

P_o, then, is 57.8 − 37 = 20.8 ft of water gauge, or 54.8 ft of water absolute. Other factors remain as discussed in the other examples. Substituting in Eq. (7), the required expansion tank size is:

$$V_t = 35.4/[(34/46) - (34/ 54.8)] = 298.2 \text{ gal}$$

In **Examples 1, 2 and 3,** the calculated size of the expansion tank has been indicated; usually a standard tank size should not be smaller than that calculated.

For diaphragm expansion tanks, the ASME formula for minimum tank volume can be restated as:

$$V_t = (0.00041t - 0.0466)V_s/[1 - (P_f/P_o)] \qquad (9)$$

$$V_t = (0.000738t - 0.003348)V_s/[1 - (P_f/P_o)] \quad (9 \text{ SI})$$

where

P_f = fill pressure, which is equal to the precharge pressure.

The numerator of Eq. (9) is the net expansion of the water in the system and is the minimum required acceptance volume of the diaphragm expansion tank.

The following examples illustrate the principles applying in sizing diaphragm expansion tanks for the same systems described in **Examples 1, 2** and **3**.

Example 4: $V_t = 35.4/[1 - (63/91.8)] = 112.8 \text{ gal}$

Example 5: $V_t = 35.4/[1 - (83/91.8)] = 369.1 \text{ gal}$

Example 6: $V_t = 35.4/[1 - (46/54.8)] = 220.4 \text{ gal}$

The two following important factors in tank sizing have not been illustrated in **Examples 1** to **3:**

1. *Using compressed air to increase the amount of air in the tank.* This factor affects the value of P_a by increasing it above atmospheric pressure. Using compressed air to *charge* the expansion tank reduces the required tank volume.

2. *The effect of a design maximum temperature substantially higher than 212°F (100°C).* It is possible for the expansion tank to operate properly without adding the pressure required to maintain liquid water at temperatures exceeding 212°F (100°C). This basis of design requires: (a) pressure increase in the system as the temperature increases from 40°F (4.4°C) to the final design temperature must be sufficient to keep the pressure above that corresponding to the temperature of the water to prevent boiling and (b) system operating personnel must told the proper pressure for various system temperatures so they can maintain proper system pressure control. An automatic fill valve cannot be used to maintain the minimum pressure for such a system.

For further data relating to pressurization and tank sizing, see Chapter 15. These data may be used for all hot water systems, regardless of operating temperatures.

Chilled Water System—Closed Tank Sizing

Closed tanks are used often on chilled water and dual-temperature systems to maintain the closed, corrosion-free characteristics of the hydronic system. Tank sizing by Eq. (6) results in tanks of very small size because of low expansion coefficients [40 to 90°F and 70 to 140°F (4.5 to 32°C and 21 to 60°C)]. For this reason, closed compression tanks applied to chilled water systems are sized to half the equivalent hot water size, considering the piping system as operating from 70 to 200°F (21 to 93°C).

The following formula can be used for diaphragm expansion tanks:

$$V_t = eV_s/[1 - (P_f/P_o)] \qquad (10)$$

where:

e = net expansion factor for water (see Table 2).

The lowest temperature equals the minimum design temperature. In a chilled water system, the highest temperature is the highest anticipated ambient temperature during summer shutdown. In a dual temperature system, the highest temperature is the maximum average operating temperature.

Example 7: A system has 10,000 gal. The lowest temperature is 40°F; the highest, 90°F.

From Table 2 the expansion factor is 0.0041. Using the pressure factor in the denominator from **Example 6** above, 1 − (46/54.8) = 0.161, Eq. (10) will read:

$$V_t = (0.0041)(10\ 000)/0.161 = 254.7\ \text{gal}$$

ADVANTAGES OF WATER SYSTEMS FOR HEATING

Forced circulation of water used as a heating medium is economical because it (1) provides heat along entire outdoor exposures by using baseboard, finned radiation, or radiant panels; (2) responds quickly but uniformly to load changes using minimum pipe sizes; (3) permits piping to run at any pitch or level, up or down, to match building or site configuration; (4) provides in the total water mass the desirable inertia effect, which helps balance diverse system load requirements with uniform input at fuel burners; (5) requires fewer specialties; and (6) permits practical air elimination to minimize corrosion and maintenance.

Table 2   Net Expansion of Water in Chilled and Dual-Temperature Systems with Lowest Temperature of 40°F (4°C)

Highest Temperature, °F	Factor e	Highest Temperature, °C	Factor e
90	0.0041	30	0.0034
100	0.0058	35	0.0048
110	0.0077	40	0.0065
120	0.0100	45	0.0084
130	0.0124	50	0.0104
140	0.0150	55	0.0126
150	0.0179	60	0.0150
160	0.0209	65	0.0176

Resetting system supply water temperatures with respect to outdoor air temperature or load provides (1) an economical way to match system heat output to load requirements to minimize overheating, pipe losses and fuel waste; (2) increased comfort produced by uniform heating equipment surface temperatures, which are made possible by maintained water flow rates at varying temperatures; (3) improved automatic control valve operation, since nearly closed port positions are minimized, and (4) possible reductions in piping insulation otherwise needed to prevent overheating caused by pipe losses.

DESIGN CONSIDERATIONS

The water system for a specific building application should be selected after carefully analyzing the nature of the loads involved, the building's characteristics and layout, the comfort and control requirements, and the economics of the complete system.

Nature of Loads

Central water systems may serve a wide variety of heating and cooling loads in a building. Commonly encountered loads are: comfort heating and cooling, domestic water heating, process heating and cooling, and steam generation for process or power use. The proportion and duration of these loads can be a major factor in determining the type of water system design for the building. In comfort heating applications, where the entire load consists of space heating and domestic water heating requirements, the designer can select the type of system and its operating temperature range solely on the basis of economic factors. Where process loads are added, particularly the need for process steam, the system operating temperature will depend on these requirements.

Comfort or process cooling requirements normally dictate the use of a chilled or dual-temperature water system with a separate system for domestic hot water supply. In large distribution systems that require chilled water in only a portion of the system, however, hot water may be supplied throughout the building and chilled water may be generated only within the zone where it is to be used.

Systems in which a major portion requires both heating and cooling should be analyzed to determine whether to install a two-, three-, or four-pipe dual-temperature system. The correct determination of heat losses and gains for the comfort and process loads is the first factor affecting the adequacy and proper distribution of heating and cooling in buildings served by water systems.

Building Characteristics

The size, complexity, and function of the building must be considered in determining the water system to install. Many applications require some zones to be heated at the same time others are cooled. Others may require flexibility so that partitions can be moved in the future to change space size and arrangements. All of these occupancy and comfort requirements must be considered when selecting the system, the distribution piping layout, the terminal heating and cooling units, and the control methods.

Local codes or statutes may require the services of a full-time licensed operating engineer for any system using temperatures and pressures outside the low temperature range. The number and capability of the operating and maintenance personnel may dictate to some degree the system design.

ECONOMICS IN WATER SYSTEM DESIGN

The principal economic consideration in any water system design is the balance of initial and operating costs. Initial cost includes generating and terminal equipment and the distribution system. Generator and terminal cost is dictated by the load requirements and temperature range selected, and the cost of the distribution system by the water quantity circulated to handle the design load. The higher the temperature drop of a hot water system or the temperature rise of a chilled water system at design conditions, the more economical the distribution system.

For a specific system, both initial and operating costs will be lower with reductions in water quantity circulated. Initial cost reductions result from the smaller and less expensive piping system, the reduced requirement for secondary building space and smaller pumps. Reduced operating costs result from lower pump power needed. Much depends on the techniques used to make smaller flow rates possible.

Heating Systems (Nonresidential)

Three approaches are possible for large heating systems: (1) higher supply temperatures, (2) primary-secondary pumping, and (3) terminal equipment designed for smaller flow rates. All three may be used, either singly or in combination, to achieve the desired result.

Using higher supply water temperatures is an obvious way to achieve higher temperature drops and smaller flow rates. Terminal units with a reduced heating surface can be used. These smaller terminals are not necessarily less expensive, however, because their required operating temperatures and pressures may increase manufacturing cost and the problems of pressurization, corrosion, expansion, and control. System components may not increase in cost uniformly with temperature, but may increase in steps conforming to the three major temperature classifications. Within each classification, the most economical design uses the highest temperature within that classification.

Primary-secondary pumping reduces the size and cost of the distribution system, and also uses larger flows and lower temperatures in the terminal or secondary circuits. A primary pump circulates water in the primary distribution system while one or more secondary pumps circulate the terminal circuits. The connection between primary and secondary provides complete hydraulic isolation of both circuits and permits a controlled interchange of water between the two. Thus, a high supply water temperature can be used in the primary at a low flow rate and high temperature drop, while lower temperature and conventional temperature drops can be used in the secondary.

For example, a system could be designed with primary-secondary pumping in which the supply temperature from the boiler was 300 °F (150 °C), the supply temperature in the secondary was 200 °F (93 °C), and the return temperature was 180 °F (82 °C). This would result in a conventional 20 °F (11 °C) TD in the secondary zones, but would permit the primary circuit to be sized on the basis of a 120 °F (67 °C) drop. The primary-secondary pumping arrangement is most advantageous with terminal units such as convectors and finned radiation, which are generally unsuited for small flow rates design.

Many types of terminal heat transfer units are being designed to use smaller flow rates with temperature drops up to 100 °F (56 °C) in low temperature systems and up to 150 °F (83 °C) in medium temperature systems. Fan apparatus, the heat transfer surface used for air heating in fan systems, and water-to-water heat exchangers are most susceptible to such design.

Cooling Systems

Designers have less latitude in selecting supply water temperatures for cooling applications because there is only a narrow range of water temperatures low enough to provide adequate dehumidification and high enough to avoid chiller freezeup. Circulated water quantities can be substantially reduced by selecting proper air quantities and heat transfer surface at the terminals. Using terminals suited for a 12 °F (6.5 °C) rise, rather than an 8 °F (4.5 °C) rise, reduces circulated water quantity and pump power by one-third, and increases chiller efficiency.

A proposed system should be economically evaluated to achieve the desired balance between installation cost and operating cost. In many cases, the factors that determine water quantity can be varied for a better economic balance. Table 3 shows the effect of coil circuiting and chilled water temperature on the water quantity and rise. The coil rows, fin spacing, air-side performance, and cost are identical for all selections. Morabito (1960) showed how such changes affect the overall system. Considering the investment cost of piping and insulation versus the operating cost of refrigeration and pumping motors, higher temperature rises, i.e., about 1.0 to 1.5 gpm/ton at 16 to 24 °F temperature rise (18 to 27 mL/s · kW at 9 to 13 °C) are preferred on chilled water systems with long distribution piping runs; larger flow rates should be used only where practical in close-coupled systems.

For the most economical design, the minimum flow rate to each terminal heat exchanger is calculated. For example, if one terminal can be designed for a 18 °F (10 °C) rise, another for 14 °F (8 °C), and others for 12 °F (7 °C), the highest rise to each terminal should be used, rather than designing the system for an overall temperature rise based on the least capabilities. The control system selected also influences the design water quantity. For systems using multiple terminal units, diversity factors can be applied to water quantities before sizing pump and piping mains if exposure or usage prevents the unit design loads from

Table 3　Chilled Water Coil Performance[a]

Coil Circuiting	Chilled Water Inlet Temp, °F (°C)	Coil Pressure Drop, psi (kPa)	Chilled Water Flow gpm/ton (mL/s · kW)	Chilled Water Temp Rise, °F (°C)
Full[b]	45 (7.2)	1.0 (6.9)	2.2 (39)	10.9 (6.1)
Half[c]	45 (7.2)	5.5 (37.9)	1.7 (31)	14.9 (8.3)
Full[b]	40 (4.5)	0.5 (3.4)	1.4 (25)	17.1 (9.5)
Half[c]	40 (4.5)	2.5 (17.2)	1.1 (20)	21.8 (12.1)

[a]Based on cooling air from 81 °F (27 °C) db, 67 °F (20 °C) wb to 58 °F (14 °C) db, 56 °F (14 °C) wb.
[b]Full circuiting (also called single circuit). In this circuit arrangement, water at the inlet temperature flows simultaneously through all tubes in a plane transverse to air flow; it then flows simultaneously through all tubes, in unison, in successive planes (i.e., rows) of the coil.
[c]Half circuiting. Tube connections are arranged so there are half as many circuits as there are tubes in each plane, or row, thereby using higher water velocities through the tubes. This circuiting is used with small water quantities.

occurring simultaneously, and if water flow control using two-way valves is used. If air-side control (e.g., face-and-bypass or fan cycling) or three-way valves on the water side are used, diversity should not be a consideration in pump and piping design, although it should be considered in the chiller selection.

HEAT SOURCES AND CHILLERS

The heat source for the several hot water heating systems discussed previously may be a boiler, a heat exchanger (or converter), or a direct-contact heater. (See Chapter 24 of the 1983 EQUIPMENT Volume for information on boilers.)

Heat Exchangers

Heat exchangers or converters are used as heat sources for many hot water systems, and are of three general types: (1) steam-to-water, (2) water-to-water, or (3) water-to-steam (generators).

Steam-to-water heat exchangers are usually shell-and-tube units. Steam is admitted to the shell, and water is heated as it circulates through the tubes. Steam-to-water converters are useful where an addition is to be made to an existing steam system and where hot water heating is desired. They are also widely used in areas where district steam is available and individual buildings are to be heated with a hot water system. High-rise buildings can be zoned vertically by using steam distribution and installing converters at various levels to serve several floors, thus limiting maximum operating pressures in the zone. Water-to-water heat exchangers (generally shell-and-tube units) are used in process or domestic water services or in HTW systems to lower the water temperature for certain zones. Water-to-steam heat exchangers generally consist of a U-tube bundle installed in a tank or pressure vessel to provide space for the release of steam. They are used in HTW systems to provide process steam where required. Heat exchangers should be constructed and labeled according to the ASME *Boiler and Pressure Vessel Code*.

Direct Contact Heaters

High temperature water can be obtained from direct contact heaters, as described in Chapter 15.

Water Chillers

Water chillers are the cooling source for chilled water or dual-temperature systems. There are three general types of water chillers: (1) reciprocating, (2) centrifugal, and (3) absorption. For further information, see Chapters 12, 14, and 18 of the 1983 EQUIPMENT Volume.

Heat Pumps

A heat pump may provide both hot and chilled water in a dual-temperature system. Heat pumps are described in Chapter 44 of the 1983 EQUIPMENT Volume and Chapter 9 of this volume. Water temperatures available are generally low in winter [about 90 to 130°F (32 to 55°C)] and terminal heat transfer must be designed to operate under these conditions. In some cases, a supplementary heat source is used to raise temperature levels.

TERMINAL HEATING AND COOLING UNITS

Many types of terminal units are available for central water systems. Some are suited to only one type of system and others may be used in all types of systems. Terminal units may be classified in several ways:

1. *Natural convection units,* which include cast-iron radiators, cabinet convectors and baseboard and finned-tube radiation, are used in heating systems. See Chapter 29 of the 1983 EQUIPMENT Volume.
2. *Forced convection units* include unit heaters, unit ventilators, fan-coil units, induction units, air handling units, heating and cooling coils in central station units, and most process heat exchangers. Fan-coil units, unit ventilators, and central station units can be used for heating, ventilating, and cooling. For further information, see Chapters 9 and 28 of the 1983 EQUIPMENT Volume and Chapters 1 to 4 of this volume.
3. *Radiation* includes panel systems, unit radiant panels, and certain special types of cast-iron radiation. All transfer some heat by convection, and are generally used for heating in LTW systems. However, special designs of both tubular and panel overhead radiant surfaces are being used in medium and high temperature water systems to take advantage of the lowered surface requirements achieved by using high surface temperatures. Panel cooling is applied in conjunction with space humidity control to maintain the space dew point below the panel surface temperature. See Chapter 7 for further information on radiant cooling and heating.

SELECTING TERMINAL UNITS

Terminal units must be selected for sufficient capacity to match the calculated heating and cooling (sensible and latent) loads. Manufacturers' catalog ratings should be used for actual operating conditions. Ratings indicate water temperature, temperature drop or rise, entering air temperature, water velocity, and air flow. They are usually given for standard test conditions with correction factors; otherwise, curves and rating tables covering a range of operating conditions are given.

In any single circuit having similar loads and a single control point, the terminal units should be of similar response types. Cast iron radiators should not be installed in the same controlled circuit as baseboard or convector units. Use caution when including fan-operated units with natural convection units on the same pumping circuit.

Radiators and Convectors

Cast-iron radiation and cabinet convectors were widely used in LTW systems. Ceiling-hung radiators are sometimes used where floor space may not be available for other units. Pressure limitations must be considered for cast iron radiation. Convectors are used extensively in areas where high output is needed and limited space is available, and where linear heat distribution is not desired. Typical areas heated include corridors, entries, toilet rooms, storage areas, work rooms, and kitchens.

Baseboard and Finned-Tube Radiation

Baseboard and finned-tube radiation permits the blanketing of exposed surfaces for maximum comfort. Enclosures can be selected to blend with the architectural treatment. Baseboard and finned-tube elements are generally rated at various average water temperatures and at one or more water velocities. Velocity corrections can be applied. These units are not limited to systems designed to a 20°F (11°C) TD, and can be used with temperature drops up to 50°F (28°C) (Pierce 1963).

Unit Ventilators

Unit ventilators, originally developed for specific application in school classrooms, may be used in a much wider range of applications. Unit ventilators consist of a forced convection heating or cooling unit with dampers permitting introduction of controlled amounts of outdoor air to provide a complete cycle of heating, ventilating, ventilation cooling or mechanical cooling as required. Condensation may be a problem during summer operation unless chilled water flow is stopped when fans are not operating; condensate drains are necessary. Comparatively low supply temperature and rise may be required.

Fan-Coil and Induction Units

Fan-coil units are generally used, with or without outdoor air, in dual-temperature water systems. The same coil is often used for both heating and cooling. Intermittent or multispeed fan operation or valves usually provide individual control. Hot water ratings are usually based on flow rates or temperature drops at various entering water and air temperatures. Temperature drops of 40 to 60 °F (22 to 33 °C) are frequently used. Induction units are similar to fan-coil units, except that air circulation is provided by a central air system that handles part of the load, instead of by a blower in each cabinet.

Unit Heaters

Unit heaters are available in several types: (1) horizontal propeller fan, (2) downblow, and (3) cabinet. They are used where high output in a small space is required, and where no cooling is to be added. Cabinet units are frequently applied in corridors and at entrances to blanket doors that are frequently opened. They normally do not provide ventilation air.

Central Station Units

Central station units have chilled water coils and/or hot water coils, and are available in a variety of sizes and types. Air capacities can range from a few hundred to many thousand cfm (L/s) delivery. Single zone units can be used for heating, ventilating, or cooling from a single dual-temperature system with a single-duct air distribution system. (Heating and cooling coils for central station units are selected and applied, as described in Chapters 6 and 9 of the 1983 EQUIPMENT Volume.)

Multizone units use separate heating and cooling coils discharging air simultaneously through separate duct systems. Temperature in each system is separately controlled. Central station units may be complete factory-assembled units or may be built up on the job from components selected and matched by the designer.

Process Heat Exchangers

Process heat exchangers are frequently used in water systems to provide other water temperatures, to generate steam, or to heat or cool some other process fluid. A process heat exchanger is often used to produce domestic hot water and may be the instantaneous or the storage type (see Chapter 54). Steam generators are usually used in medium or high temperature systems because of temperature requirements. Heat exchangers may also be used for process applications or for isolating portions of the system. Process heat exchangers must be selected according to the process requirement and available water temperature.

SELECTING AND LOCATING TERMINAL HEATING UNITS FOR LTW SYSTEMS

All types of hot water terminal units can be used in LTW systems. Before using a unit, consult the manufacturer's literature to determine the pressure drop and energy output compared to the design average water temperature and flow rate. The pressure drop and water capacity of finned pipe or tube in enclosures (baseboard and fin tube) are usually the same as the equivalent diameter pipe or tube used in piping the system. By LTW definition, maximum water temperature available in the boiler is 250 °F (120 °C): the boiler high limit control commonly limits this to 240 °F (116 °C). To prevent cycling on high limit at maximum heat demand, a practical design limit for maximum temperature is 230 to 235 °F (110 to 113 °C).

A terminal unit's output is rated at each of various average water temperatures. As flow rate through the unit decreases, temperature drop increases; larger design temperature drops are achieved by reducing flow rate. Since the maximum entering water temperature is fixed, an increase in temperature drop or the equivalent decrease in flow rate lowers the available average water temperature and reduces the unit's energy output. Therefore, the terminal unit size should be chosen only after determining the operating flow rate and temperature drop using the methods covered previously.

Terminal units should be located at points of maximum heat loss. When possible, units in living spaces should be under windows and on outside walls to counteract downdrafts and warm otherwise cold surfaces. Units in entries and other points of high infiltration should be located so that their air discharge counteracts cold drafts. See Chapter 29 of the 1983 EQUIPMENT Volume.

Mechanical Considerations

Air Elimination. If air and the other gases are not eliminated from the flow circuit, they may cause binding in the terminal heat transfer elements, noise, and loss of hydraulic stability. A closed tank without a diaphragm can be installed at the point of the lowest solubility (air in water) in the system, which will divert gas bubbles into the tank with an air separator or boiler dip tube. A diaphragm tank contains a properly sized, permanent, sealed air cushion, so all air in the system can be removed by an air separator and air elimination valve installed at the point of lowest solubility. Manual vents should be installed at high points to remove all trapped air during initial operation and ensure that the system is tight. Shut-off valves should be installed on any automatic air removal device to permit servicing without draining the system.

Drain and Shutoff. All low points should have drains. Separate shutoff and draining of individual equipment and circuits should be possible so that the entire system does not have to be drained to service a particular item.

Balance fittings should be applied as needed to permit balancing of individual terminals and major subcircuits. These fittings should be at the circuit return when possible.

Pitch. Piping need not pitch but can run level, providing flow velocities exceeding 1.5 ft/s (0.5 m/s) are maintained.

Strainers should be used where necessary to protect the system elements. Strainers in the pump suction need to be analyzed carefully to avoid cavitation. Large separating chambers can serve as main air venting points and dirt strainers ahead of pumps. Automatic control valves or spray nozzles operating with small clearances require protection from pipe scale, gravel and welding slag, which may readily pass through the pump and its protective separator. Individual fine mesh strainers may therefore be required ahead of each control valve. Condenser water systems without water regulating valves do not always require a strainer. If a cooling tower is used, the strainer provided in the tower basin will be usually adequate.

Thermometers or thermometer wells should be installed to assist the system operator on routine operation and trouble-shooting. Permanent thermometers with the correct scale range and separable sockets should be used at all points where temperature readings are needed regularly. Thermometer wells should be installed where readings will be needed only during start-up and infrequent troubleshooting.

Flexible connectors are sometimes installed at pumps and machinery to reduce pipe vibration. Vibrations are transmitted through the water column across a flexible connection and reduce the effectiveness at the connector. Flexible connectors, however, prevent damage caused by misalignment of equipment piping flanges. See Chapter 52 for vibration isolation information. Expansion and flexibility and hanger and support information is in Chapter 34 of the 1983 EQUIPMENT Volume.

Gauge cocks should be installed at points requiring pressure readings. Note that gauges permanently installed in the system will deteriorate because of vibration and pulsation and will be unreliable. It is good practice to install gauge cocks and provide the operator with several quality gauges for troubleshooting.

Insulation should be applied to minimize pipe loss and to prevent condensation during chilled water operation (see Chapter 20 of the 1985 FUNDAMENTALS Volume).

Condensate drains from dehumidifying coils should be trapped and piped to an open-sight plumbing drain. Traps should be deep enough to overcome the air pressure differential (between drain inlet and room), which ordinarily will not exceed 2 in. of water (0.5 kPa). Pipe should be copper or galvanized steel, and insulated to prevent moisture condensation. Depending on the quantity and temperature of condensate, plumbing drain lines may require insulation to prevent sweating.

Automatic fill valves should be connected to the pipe between the expansion tank and the system, which is the point of no pressure change, regardless of whether or not the system pump is operating.

Controllability

The sensible heat transfer characteristics of heat exchangers are generally nonlinear with changes in flow. Figure 25 shows that for a 20°F (11°C) design TD, a 50% decrease in flow changes the overall heating element output by only 10%, and that flow must be reduced to about 10% of design to effect a 50% change in output. With higher design TD's, however, the curve becomes more linear, as shown for 60°F (33°C) TD. Higher design TDs thus improve controllability, although the nonlinearity must always be considered in the valve selection. Figure 26 illustrates that heat transfer varies almost directly with average water temperature, assuming constant flow and entering air temperature. This relationship for a 20°F (11°C) TD unit applies to all hot water heat transfer and to all sensible cooling using chilled water.

Figures 25 and 26 illustrate several points:

1. Supply water temperature and heat transfer surface area are the most important factors in determining capacity when small design TDs are used.
2. If flow is controlled, appropriate valves must be used to compensate for the nonlinear relationships shown in Figure 25.

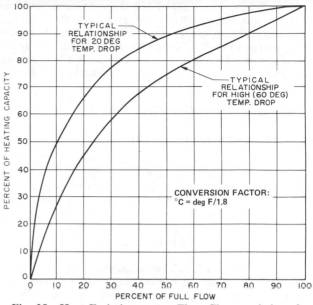

Fig. 25   Heat Emission versus Flow Characteristics of Typical Hot Water Heating Coil

3. Heat loss or gain must be calculated accurately because oversized terminal units increase control problems, such as: (a) a modulating valve or damper may use a major portion of its *stroke* just to reduce capacity to design, leaving only a short stroke for part-load control, and (b) with on-off control, oversized terminals may lead to wide temperature fluctuations and to inadequate dehumidification in chilled water units.
4. Reset control compensates for many control variables and should be used whenever possible. It is advantageous because heat transfer is governed more by water temperature than by any other factor.

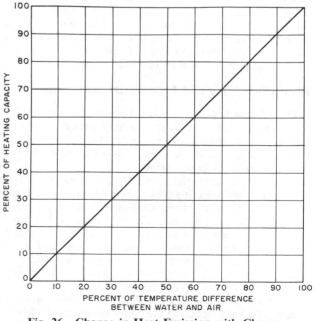

Fig. 26   Change in Heat Emission with Change in Water Temperature

5. Using a higher design TD tends to decrease control problems.
6. The relative insensitivity of heat transfer to flow change is an important reason for not oversizing the pump. An increase in flow rate to 150% of design, for example, will increase heat transfer only a few percent, but may cause a large increase in pumping power and aggravate the control problems noted previously.

DESIGN PROCEDURE

Preliminary Equipment Layout

Determining Flows in Mains and Laterals. Regardless of the method used to determine the flow through each item of terminal equipment, the desired result should be listed in terms of mass flow in lb/h (kg/s) on the preliminary plans or in a schedule of flow rates for the piping system. Note that in the design of small systems, or in chilled water systems, the determination may be made in terms of gpm (L/s), instead of lb/h (kg/s).

In an equipment schedule or on the plans, starting from the most remote terminal and working back towards the pump, progressively list the cumulative flow in each of the mains and branch circuits in the entire distribution system.

Preliminary Pipe Sizing. For each portion of the piping circuit, a tentative pipe size is selected from the unified flow chart (Figure 1, Chapter 34 of the 1985 FUNDAMENTALS Volume), using a value of pipe friction loss ranging from 0.75 to 4 ft per 100 ft or approximately 100 to 500 mil in./ft (80 to 400 Pa/m).

Residential piping size is often based on pump preselection, using pipe sizing tables, which are available from the Hydronics Institute or from manufacturers.

Preliminary Pressure Drop. Using the preliminary pipe sizing indicated above, determine the pressure drop through each portion of the piping. Determine the total pressure drop in several of the longest circuits to determine what maximum pressure drop through the piping, including the terminals and control valves, must be available in the form of pump head.

Preliminary Pump Selection. The preliminary selection should be based on the pump's ability to fulfill the determined capacity requirements. It should be selected at a point left-of-center on the pump curve, and should not overload the motor. Because of the squared relationship between flow and head, the flow capacity variation between a next-closest stock selection and an exact point selection will be relatively minor.

Final Pipe Sizing and Pressure Drop Determination

Final Piping Layout. The overall piping layout should be examined to determine if pipe sizes in some areas need to be readjusted. Several principal circuits should have approximately equal pressure drops so that excessive heads are not needed to serve a small portion of the building.

Consider both the initial costs of the pump and piping system and the pump's operating cost when determining final system friction loss. Generally, lower heads and larger piping are more economical when longer amortization periods are considered, especially in larger systems. However, in small systems such as in residences, it may be most economical to select the pump first and design the piping system to meet the available head. In all cases, the piping system design and pump selection should be adjusted until the optimum design is found.

When the final piping layout has been established, the friction loss for each section of the piping system can be determined by reading directly from the pressure drop charts (Chapter 34 of the 1985 FUNDAMENTALS Volume) for the mass flow rate in each portion of the piping system.

After calculating the friction loss at design flow for all sections of the piping system, all fittings, terminal units, and control valves, summarize them for several of the longest piping circuits to determine the precise head against which the pump must operate at design flow.

Final Pump Selection. After completing the final pressure drop calculations, select the final pump by plotting a system flow and pump curve and selecting the pump that operates closest to the actual calculated design point.

AUTOMATIC TEMPERATURE CONTROL

The basic principles of automatic temperature control are discussed in Chapter 51. The control of many equipment components is discussed in this volume, in the chapters dealing with the respective components. The following sections relate to water systems in general, and include only those control considerations that are specific to water system design. The automatic temperature control requirements in a water system vary widely with system size and complexity and with the equipment used. The controls that may be required are *system controls* and *zone* (or *individual*) *controls* for terminal heat transfer equipment.

System Control

Where space heating is the principal load, outdoor reset of supply temperature with outdoor temperature change is almost always desirable. Outdoor reset may provide all the necessary control in small systems or may be used in combination with zone or individual room control in larger systems. Outdoor reset can be achieved in hot water boilers by varying the boiler water temperature or by varying the flow from the boiler to the system. Variable water flow may be accomplished with a three-way valve as in Figure 27 or with a primary-secondary pumping arrangement as in Figure 28.

Zone Control

Zone temperature control is frequently used in space heating or cooling applications with zoning requirements established by exposure, occupancy or other factors. Individual zones can be controlled by intermittent circulator operation or through single-seated or three-way valves, often combined with outdoor reset. In large buildings, continuous water circulation usually is needed to minimize the hazard of freezing. In such systems, secondary pumping, not intermittent operation should be used for control. Zone control is most applicable to convection heating ter-

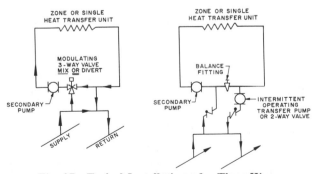

Fig. 27　Typical Installation of a Three-Way, Two-Position Valve

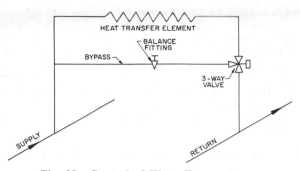

Fig. 28   Control of Water Temperature

minals and in spaces with similar occupancies and loads. In small buildings, on-off control is usually used, with simple zone valves in each zone.

Individual Control

Individual control of each terminal heat exchanger is usually used with fan equipment or in any space heating or cooling application where there are large fluctuations in occupancy or other load factors. Individual terminal control may be achieved by varying (1) water flow, (2) conditioned medium flow, and (3) water temperature. Combinations of these may be used in some cases.

Control of Water Flow

Valve control, either single-seated or three-way, is the most common means of varying the water flow to terminals. Single-seated valves vary the flow by throttling. Three-way valves control the flow by diverting water around the terminal. Both produce the same result within the terminal: reduction in capacity by reducing flow within the terminal. They differ, however, in their effects on system flow rates and pressures.

Control of Conditioned Medium Flow

Variable flow of a conditioned medium across a terminal heat exchanger may be obtained in several ways:

Face and bypass control is often used in chilled water applications and in outdoor preheaters. However, it has some disadvantages because it is incapable of 100% shutoff, is unstable at low loads, and often requires outdoor reset or supplementary valve control for best results.

Intermittent fan operation is generally limited to unit heaters, fan coil units, and similar fan-operated equipment where proportioning control is not warranted.

Variable air volume is most commonly achieved by varying fan speed, by volume dampers, or by variable inlet guide vanes.

A proper balance of the relationships between the various components in a water system is most important in the area of control performance. For optimum performance, carefully consider the mutual influence of several factors, including: (1) control methods, (2) system flow relief, and (3) selection of control valve, pump, and piping.

Control Valve Selection

The proper selection and application of control valves in water systems is essential to good performance. Such control valves must meet two minimum requirements: (1) they must be

specifically characterized for water service and (2) they must be sized for a pressure drop, at design flow rate, that is a significant portion of the maximum available head. Proportioning valves must have equal percentage characteristics, and the valve pressure drop at design flow should be no less (and preferably more) than 5 psi (35 kPa), or 25% of the maximum pump head, whichever is greater. The higher the design water temperature, the more critical such requirements for valve selection become.

Effect of Flow Variations

Control valve performance may be affected adversely by wide variations in differential pressure. Sluggish circulation may reduce capacity due to increased pipe losses and lead to air binding or deposit of solids in various parts of the system. Consequently, it is important to maintain flows in the system as part loads, which are comparable to design flow conditions. Since the capacity of hot water heat exchangers is nonlinear to flow, little capacity reduction occurs until temperature difference between the supply water and the heated medium are reached. The control valve, for optimum stability, must have the opposite characteristic (equal percentage).

Proper control performance requires that the valve provide an initial pressure drop high enough to ensure that control is not destroyed by the increased pressure differential due to flow reduction. Also, the valve must have a relatively high turn-down ratio (ratio of maximum usable flow to minimum controllable flow) and a minimum leakage in its closed position. The valve must also be designed to meet the temperature and pressure requirements of the system in which it is being used.

Minimizing Pressure Variations in System Design

Not all systems require special precautions to avoid large piping flow variations. In many cases, selecting a high pressure drop for the control valves at design flow and using a flat-head pump sufficiently stabilizes flow. Other factors that make special precautions unnecessary may be present in the system, such as:

Uncontrolled Terminals. Most large systems, especially those designed for space heating, usually have many heating terminals, such as unit heaters, that are not valve controlled. The flow through these may be adequate to keep the water hot in the system and prevent cavitation at the pump.

Reset Water Temperature. Using an outdoor reset control improves flow characteristics. Good reset water temperature design establishes a correlation between water temperature and load, so that many of the control valves will remain in an open and controlling position.

Open Flow Circuit Design. Many systems are designed for continuous flow through all or several subcircuits as established by face-and-damper control or three-way valve usage. For continuous primary bypass flow, primary-secondary design methods are used. When a minority of the circuits are continuous flow (the majority being two-way), they should permit flow through long sections of main to allow the greatest pipe friction loss.

Open Piping Circuits. Open piping connections are often applied at circuit ends to maintain pipe temperatures and permit bleed-flow, thus preventing pump casing temperature increase at dead shutoff valve operation. Piping size is usually nominal, i.e., 0.5 in. (12 mm). A typical application in MTW and HTW systems is a small bypass line connected across supply and return riser piping at the control point.

Primary-Secondary Pumping. This can cause smaller potential variations in available head, since the control valve is usually located so that only the secondary pump (often an in-line low head circulator) influences its flow. This hydraulic isolation from the higher-head primary pump can do much to eliminate the control problem in large systems. Primary-secondary pumping also provides a way to improve control valve performance quality. With the control valve in the secondary circuit, hydraulic isolation from primary pump pressures is provided, and available pressure drop across the valve is limited to that developed by the secondary pump, which usually has a comparatively low head characteristic.

Flat-Head Pumps. Using pumps with flat-head characteristics improves control performance by limiting the variations in pump pressure available as flow in the system is reduced.

System Flow Relief

Controlling system flow is desirable both from a control standpoint and to avoid dead-end service. For best control, minimize the variations in pump delivery pressure and system pressure drop. Special system design precautions may be necessary to provide flow relief. Large fluctuations in pressure drop through the piping can be controlled by several means:

Three-way valves on the terminal equipment theoretically bypass water to maintain piping flow. In actual practice, the amount of water bypassed varies with the pressure drop in the bypass line. System flows and pressure drops may vary widely, and even increase significantly, at part load.

System bypass may be used in various forms, such as a manual bypass, a bypass-relief valve, or a differential pressure controller. The bypass should be at the end of the main to maintain relatively constant flow and pressure drop throughout the distribution piping, and to hold a more or less constant pressure differential between the supply and return.

Both arrangements have the advantages of maintaining hot water flow in the system and of holding the pressure drop through the piping fairly constant, regardless of flow variations in the terminals. On the other hand, because they maintain the flow through the pump at a consistently high level, they tend to increase the system's operating power requirements, since power input to a pump is essentially proportional to the flow. This may become an important consideration in large distribution systems.

Pressure Differential Valves

Pressure differential valves are actuated by differential pressures, and are sometimes applied across the pump, in a bypass between the pump discharge and suction. This arrangement is recommended for extremely steep-curve pumps only, since differential bypass valves applied across a flat-curved pump provide no services the pump does not. Pump bypass differential valve application does not affect dead-end operation.

Differential pressure control valves are useful, however, when applied in the distribution piping circuit, preferably at remote locations and across the supply and return mains. This permits flow through the piping circuit, thus permitting pipe friction loss to be deducted from the valve differential pressures without decreasing the temperatures in the mains.

Pump Throttle (Differential-Operated) Valves

Differentially-operated throttle valves are sometimes placed at the pump discharge while the differential controller is placed in the system across *representative riser* supply and return connections. Valve throttling action substitutes for reduced pipe friction loss, thereby maintaining a relatively constant control valve differential pressure. Note, however, that under a light load flow

can be reduced to a point where throttling action is relatively ineffective. The throttle control is best applied under *reset* control conditions or when some *open flow circuitry* is introduced.

Variable speed pumps change delivery pressure and capacity according to requirements established by differential pressure controllers, which are located in the system at *representative risers* (across supply and return connections). Variable speed pump application is costly, but has very desirable results.

Paralleled and Series Pumping. Pressure can also be reduced by staged operation of parallel or series pumps.

Effect of Temperature Drop on Control Performance

The design temperature drop can have a profound effect on control valve performance. In heating systems, the higher the design water TD and the lower the design water temperature, the more nearly linear the capacity-flow characteristic of the terminal heat transfer element becomes and the better the control performance at reduced loads. Using higher design water temperature drops at lower supply temperatures can best be achieved by using terminal heat exchangers specifically designed to handle the heating capacity requirement at the smallest possible flow.

While smaller design water quantities improve control performance, this consideration alone is not sufficient to assure good control performance. Other considerations are: (1) properly characterized valves and a pressure drop through the valve, at design flow rate, which is a significant percentage of the maximum available head; (2) outdoor reset of water temperature improves control and should be used wherever possible; and (3) secondary pumping provides hydraulic isolation of the terminal and improves the control quality.

Single-Seated versus Three-Way Valves

The choice between two-way (single-seated) and three-way valves must always be made in terms of the specific system in question. Single-seated valves have the advantages of lower cost and better flow-lift characteristics, and can be obtained with equal-percentage-characteristic plugs. Three-way valves are difficult to characterize properly for more than linear characteristics. Single-seated valves are available in smaller port sizes and are, therefore, more readily selected for the proper pressure drops at small design flow rates. These factors tend to improve the control performance of single-seated valves as far as controlling the terminal heat transfer element is concerned.

However, three-way valves have the advantages of maintaining a generally constant flow in the system, thus minimizing variations in developed pump pressure and system resistance with load variations, and of maintaining flow through the pump. Single-seated valves with other provisions for maintaining flow, such as differential pressure controllers, are usually preferred, especially in MTW or HTW systems or in process applications where control is critical.

Dual-temperature system control can be diverse, depending on the control requirement and the terminal heat exchange unit being used. For chilled water, face-and-bypass control can be selected for dehumidification at reduced loads. Flow control, using either two- or three-way valves, is often used, especially in applications where sensible cooling is the predominant requirement. Other control methods, including on-off fan control and variable fan speed, are selected for fan-coil and similar units to reduce initial cost.

Two-pipe hot and chilled water systems are frequently zoned to minimize the problem at changeover. Outdoor reset control is normally applied only on the heating side with a constant temperature supply used for chilled water, except in systems where the terminal units are designed for sensible cooling only. Such systems eliminate the need for condensate drain lines from the terminal units, or where dehumidification is handled separately. The chilled water temperature is controlled by a three-way valve, or a pair of two-way valves, modulated to maintain the chilled water supply temperature above the dew point. Typical installations include air-water induction systems in which the dehumidification occurs in the primary air, and fan-coil applications with a separate ventilation air system for dehumidification.

When two- or three-way valves are operated simultaneously or in sequence for a changeover, the precautions regarding selections for high pressure drops do not apply. These valves should be sized for comparatively low pressure drops because they are normally two-position valves, which do not require proportioning control between the two end points.

Freeze Prevention

All circulating water systems require precautions to prevent freezing, particularly in makeup air applications where coils are exposed to 100% outdoor air, where undrained chilled water coils are in the winter airstream, or where piping passes through unheated spaces. Freezing will not occur as long as flow is maintained and the water is at least warm. Unfortunately, during extremely cold weather or in the event of a power failure, water flow and temperature cannot be guaranteed. Additionally, continuous pumping can be energy intensive and cause system wear. Precautions to avoid flow stoppage follow:

1. If intermittent pump operation is used as an economy measure, use an automatic override to operate the pump in below freezing weather.
2. Pump starters should automatically restart after power failure.
3. Select nonoverloading pumps.
4. Custodians should be clearly instructed never to shut down pumps in subfreezing weather.
5. Do not use aquastats, which can stop a pump, in boilers.
6. Avoid sluggish circulation, which may cause air binding or dirt deposit. Systems should be properly balanced and cleaned and proper air control must be provided.

In fan equipment handling outdoor air, precautions must be taken to avoid stratification of air entering the coil. The best methods for proper mixing of indoor and outdoor air follow:

1. Blow-through design ensures mixing within the fan before the air enters the coil.
2. Intake and approach duct systems should be designed to promote natural mixing.
3. Coils should be circuited to allow parallel flow of air and water.

Freezeup may still occur with any of these precautions. If a glycol is not used, water should circulate at all times. Valve-controlled elements should have low limit thermostats and sensing elements should be located to assure accurate air temperature readings. Primary-secondary pumping of coils with three-way valve injection (as in Figure 28) is advantageous. Outdoor reset of water temperature should be used wherever possible. MTW or HTW should not be used directly for outdoor air preheating. Ideally, preheaters should be selected so that they are fully on at all times during subfreezing temperatures.

ANTIFREEZE SOLUTIONS

Water solutions of ethylene glycol and propylene glycol are

Table 4 Freezing Points for Solutions of Ethylene Glycol and Propylene Glycol

Glycol, % by mass	Ethylene Glycol		Propylene Glycol	
	°F	°C	°F	°C
10	26	−3	26	−3
15	22	−6	22	−6
20	18	−8	18	−8
25	13	−11	12	−11
30	7	−14	6	−14
40	−8	−22	−9	−23
50	−29	−34	−34	−37
60	−55	−48	<−60	<−51

commonly used in hot water heating systems and chilled water cooling systems when there is a danger of freezeup. This use may be needed: (1) in snow-melting applications (see Chapter 55), (2) in systems supplying heating coils subjected to 100% outdoor air where the methods outlined above may not be able to provide absolute antifreeze protection, (3) in isolated parts or zones of a heating system where intermittent operation or long runs of exposed piping increase the danger of freezing, or (4) in process cooling applications requiring temperatures below 40°F (4.4°C). While using ethylene glycol or propylene glycol is comparatively expensive and tends to create corrosion problems unless suitable inhibitors are used, it may be the only practical solution in many cases.

Solutions of triethylene glycol, as well as certain other heat transfer fluids, may also be used. However, ethylene glycol and propylene glycol are the most common materials used in hydronic systems.

Heat Transfer and Flow

Figures 13 through 18 in Chapter 18 of the 1985 FUNDAMENTALS Volume show specific heat, specific gravity, and viscosity of various aqueous solutions of ethylene glycol and propylene glycol. Table 4 lists freezing points for the two solutions.

System flow rate is affected by specific gravity or density and specific heat according to the following equation:

$$q_w = 500 \, G(\text{sp. gr.}) \, c_p \, (t_1 - t_2) \qquad (11)$$

or in SI units

$$q_w = G \varrho \, c_p \, (t_1 - t_2) \qquad (11 \text{ SI})$$

where

q_w = total heat transfer rate, Btu/h (kW)
G = water, or solution flow rate, gpm (m³/s)
sp. gr. = specific gravity
ϱ = density, kg/m³
c_p = specific heat, Btu/lb · °F (kJ/kg · °C)
t_1 = entering temperature, °F(°C)
t_2 = leaving temperature, °F(°C)

Effect on Heat Source or Chiller

Generally, it is not good practice to use ethylene glycol solutions directly in a boiler because of the danger of chemical corrosion caused by glycol breakdown on direct heating surfaces. However, properly inhibited glycol solutions can be used in LTW systems and directly in the heating boiler. Automobile antifreeze solutions are not recommended because the silicate inhibitor can cause fouling, pump seal wear, fluid gelation, and reduced heat transfer. It is possible to isolate the area or zone requiring the antifreeze protection in a separate zone with a heat exchanger

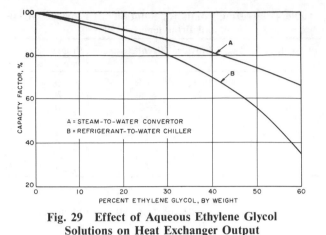

Fig. 29   Effect of Aqueous Ethylene Glycol Solutions on Heat Exchanger Output

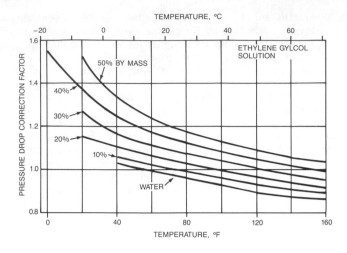

Fig. 31   Pressure Drop Correction for Ethylene Glycol Solutions

or converter. Glycol solutions are used directly in water chillers in many cases.

The use of glycol solutions affects the total output of a heat exchanger by changing the film coefficient of the surface contacting the solution. This change in film coefficient is primarily caused by viscosity changes. Figure 29 illustrates typical changes in output for two types of heat exchangers, a steam-to-liquid converter and a refrigerant-to-liquid chiller. The curves are plotted for one set of operating conditions only and reflect the change in ethylene glycol concentration as the only variable. Propylene glycol has similar effects on heat exchanger output.

Since many other variables, such as liquid velocity, steam or refrigerant loading, temperature difference, and unit construction, affect the overall coefficient of a heat exchanger, designers should consult manufacturers' ratings when selecting such equipment. The curves only indicate the magnitude of these output changes.

Effect on Terminal Units

Since the effect of glycol on the capacity of terminal units may vary widely with temperature, the manufacturer's rating data should be consulted when selecting heating or cooling units in glycol systems.

Effect on Pump Performance

Centrifugal pump characteristics are affected to some degree

by glycol solutions because of viscosity changes. Figure 30 shows these effects on pump capacity, head, and efficiency. Figure 15 and 16 in Chapter 18 of the 1985 FUNDAMENTALS Volume plot the dynamic viscosity of ethylene glycol and propylene glycol. Water viscosity is also shown in the figures. Centrifugal pump performance is normally catalogued for water at 60 to 80 °F (15 to 27 °C). Hence, absolute viscosity effects below 1.1 centipoises (1.1 mPa·s), which is the absolute viscosity of water at 60 °F (16 °C), can safely be ignored as far as pump performance is concerned. In intermittently operated systems, such as snow-melting applications, viscosity effects at start-up may decrease flow enough to slow pick up.

Effect on Piping Pressure Loss

The friction loss in piping also varies with viscosity changes. Figures 31 and 32 give correction factors for various ethylene glycol and propylene glycol solutions from 0 to 160 °F (−20 to 70 °C). These factors are applied to the calculated pressure loss for water, as determined previously. Ethylene glycol and propylene glycol solutions need no correction above 160 °F (70 °C).

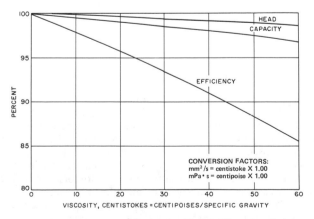

Fig. 30   Effect of Viscosity on Pump Characteristics

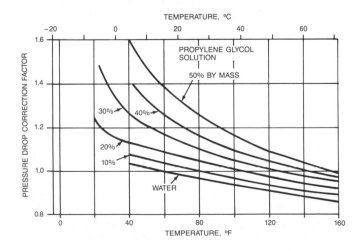

Fig. 32   Pressure Drop Correction for Propylene Glycol Solutions

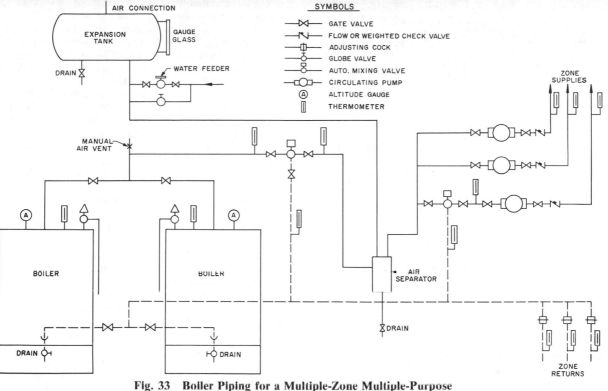

Fig. 33   Boiler Piping for a Multiple-Zone Multiple-Purpose Heating System

Installation and Maintenance

Since glycol solutions are comparatively expensive, the smallest possible concentrations to produce the desired antifreeze properties should be used. The total water content of the system should be calculated carefully to determine the required amount of glycol. The solution can be mixed outside the system in drums or barrels and then pumped in. Air vents should be watched during filling to prevent loss of solution. The system and the cold water supply should not be permanently connected; so automatic fill valves are not used.

Ethylene glycol and propylene glycol normally include an inhibitor to help prevent corrosion. Solutions should be checked each year using a suitable refractometer to determine glycol concentration.

Certain precautions regarding the use of inhibited ethylene glycol solutions should be taken to extend their service life and to preserve equipment:

1. Before installing the glycol solution, thoroughly clean and flush the system.
2. It is preferable to use waters that are classified as soft and are low in chloride and sulfate ions to prepare the solution.
3. Limit the maximum operating temperature to 250°F (120°C) in a closed hydronic system. In a heat exchanger, limit glycol film temperatures to 300 to 350°F (150 to 175°C) to prevent deterioration of the solution.
4. Check the concentration of inhibitor periodically, following procedures recommended by the glycol manufacturer.

BOILER ROOM PIPING, COMPONENTS AND CONTROLS

Figure 17 illustrates typical piping connections and com-

ponents, and Figure 33 illustrates those for a more elaborate system. This section covers only a few possibilities or installation requirements. Follow the boiler manufacturer's recommendations for individual boiler models. The ASME *Boiler Code* lists specific requirements; insurance and governmental codes and standards require additional items and practices. Regulatory bodies are generally concerned most with safety and efficiency. Requirements include a high limit control, a safety relief valve, and other safety controls and devices on the boiler, and a boiler efficiency within an accepted test rating. For boiler details, see Chapter 24, 1983 EQUIPMENT Volume.

Multiple Boilers

Two or more boilers can be used to supply energy to a system in several ways:

1. The set of boilers can be piped and controlled to operate as *one boiler* with an output equal to the sum of all the outputs. Total boiler output is selected to meet design load.
2. Additional boilers can be connected to a system of one or more boilers sized to the load. The additional boilers are standby for emergency use, and are unfired and valved off from system water flow. Figure 33 illustrates two boilers on a piping system, and can represent items (1) or (2).
3. The set of boilers can be piped to the mains and controlled so that one, two, three or more boilers fire as demand increases and fewer boilers fire as demand drops. The entire set is sized to the load (additional boilers may be connected but closed off, as standby). This arrangement is called *modular,* since each boiler is a module of energy, independently controlled. When useful, two or more boilers can be piped and controlled to fire in unison; this subset of boilers is a module of energy.

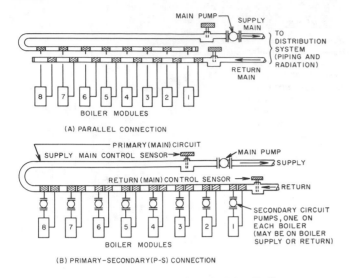

Fig. 34 Typical Piping for Modular Boilers

The firing sequence of modules typically is controlled by a change in main water temperature; a minimum continuous main water flow is required for good control response. Outside air temperature change may also be used to control the number of modules firing. Since a drop in the main water or outside air temperature is required to turn on an additional module, the supply main temperature is lowest at maximum load, unless outdoor reset is used. Many types of control are possible; consult control and boiler manufacturers for available control models and systems.

Minimizing standby loss minimizes energy waste. When possible, unfired boilers should cool to room temperature; cycling boilers should not be at a temperature higher than demand requires. Standby loss can be minimized by having outdoor reset of water temperature and by preventing water flow in unfired boilers. This can be done by using automatic water shutoff valves on modules piped in parallel to the mains, or by using a primary-secondary connection to the supply main. There are no shutoff valves in parallel piping; water at return main temperature flows continuously through all unfired boilers.

Other methods for piping and controlling modular boilers are possible. Using a set of boilers to heat domestic water, alone or in addition to the heating load, is common.

STANDBY AND OTHER LOSSES

Standby loss usually is defined as the loss of heat energy from a heating device that is hot but not being fired, as air flows through the unit and out the chimney. No loss occurs if the unit is at room temperature, since there is no heat transfer; standby loss does not occur during firing, since the heat flow through the chimney (called *stack loss*) is accounted for in overall efficiency. A minimum stack loss of about 15% of input during firing is required to produce adequate chimney operation and prevent water vapor condensation from flue gases.

Standby loss from a given installation is highest when the heating unit temperature is the highest and air flow through the unit and chimney is not restricted during the unfired periods. Standby loss decreases with the heating unit temperature. Any single boiler, alone or part of a multiple boiler system, is required to cycle on and off at times, at a water temperature (during off as well as on cycle) required by the load and the control system.

A control system for a hot water heating system that: (1) allows boilers that are unfired for long periods to cool to room temperature and/or (2) reduces boiler and system water temperature during mild weather when loads are lower, will minimize standby loss. *Outdoor reset* of water temperature can be used to accomplish item (2); simple single-thermostat control of the fuel burner (when the system design allows such control) also resets water temperature lower in mild weather. Controlling water temperature during long unfired periods is discussed under "Multiple Boilers".

Various testing, rating, and installation codes have been developed and applied for automatic stack dampers. These are designed to reduce standby loss by reducing gas flow to the chimney during unfired periods. Such dampers are primarily for residential-size heating systems.

Boilers used to maintain a supply of domestic water at a fixed temperature will have appreciable standby loss unless a storage tank and a means for valving the boiler off from the hot stored water are provided, or unless stack dampers are used.

Energy losses other than standby are common. Water leaks from the system waste energy. Firing rates substantially higher than needed reduce efficiency and increase energy waste. Radiant and convective heat losses from heating units and piping are not recovered if the heat is delivered to outside spaces rather than to where heat is desired. Energy is saved by insulating all heating system component surfaces that are appreciably above the surrounding air temperature and that do not contribute heat to design load.

REFERENCES

Morabito, B.P. 1960. How Higher Cooling Coil Differentials Affect System Economics. ASHRAE *Journal,* Vol. 2, No. 8, August, p. 60.

Pierce, J.D. 1963. Application of Fin Tube Radiation to Modern Hot Water Heating Systems. ASHRAE *Journal,* Vol. 5, No. 2, February, p. 72.

CHAPTER 14

CHILLED AND DUAL-TEMPERATURE WATER SYSTEMS

THE design considerations in the preceding chapter are general, and apply to all system types. The following material applies to specific systems.

Chilled Water Systems

Chilled water systems are two-pipe systems that connect the chiller or cooling source directly with a heat transfer unit equipped with a cooling coil. Heating is independent. Chilled water systems are frequently used (1) for the cooling coils in central station air handling units, (2) for systems in which separate hot water, steam or electric resistance sources are used for heating, (3) in remodeling work where a cooling system is added to a building with an existing heating system, or (4) in process applications.

Two-Pipe Chilled Water Systems

Two-pipe chilled water systems are installed where heating is not required or where heating is supplied independently.

Chilled water systems can be applied in any building, but are normally confined to applications such as cooling coils in central air handling apparatus and in air handling, fan coil or induction units for interior zones not requiring heating.

The general principles and design procedures described in Chapter 13 apply to chilled water systems. Since no water temperature changeover is involved, the layout of a chilled water system consists of little more than connecting the chiller with the terminal heat transfer elements or units in the conventional manner. Figures 1 and 2 show schematic diagrams of typical chilled water systems. If the terminals have air-side or three-way valve control, flow through the system will be relatively constant and the arrangement in Figure 1 can be used. If two-way valves are used for terminal control and a system bypass has not been provided, system flow will vary and the arrangement

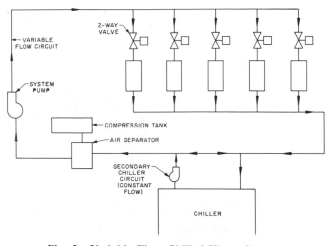

Fig. 2   Variable Flow Chilled Water System

in Figure 2 may be preferred to maintain constant flow in the chiller. The procedures for pump selection, pressurization, piping design, expansion tank sizing and other factors are described in Chapter 13 (see Chapters 3 and 4 for more information).

Brine Systems

Brine systems are normally selected for comfort applications where the nature of the loads or other factors may require temperatures below 40 °F (5 °C), or in 100% outdoor air systems to protect coils against freezing. Since the principles involved in dual-temperature water can be applied to sophisticated lower temperature process applications, brines other than conventional water solutions are discussed here.

Brine type selection is based on (1) the freezing point—suitable for the lowest operating temperatures, (2) the process— open or closed piping system, danger of product contamination by brine, (3) cost and availability—quantity of makeup required, (4) safety to operating personnel—toxic, poisonous, explosive, flammable effect on operating pressures, (5) thermal performance—specific heat, density, viscosity and film coefficient, (6) chemical—stability and corrosion suitablity for use with piping and system equipment material, and (7) acceptance by codes, ordinances, regulatory agencies and the insurer.

Calcium chloride, sodium chloride and ethylene glycol brines are commonly used in open systems. Volatile brines, such as methylene chloride (Refrigerant 30), methanol, trichloroethylene and trichloromonofluoromethane (Refrigerant 11) are usually used with closed piping systems to prevent brine evaporation. The above brines are generally suited to applications between −30 and 30 °F (−34 and −1 °C). Volatile refrigerants such as Refrigerant 30 or Refrigerant 11 are used for temperatures below this range.

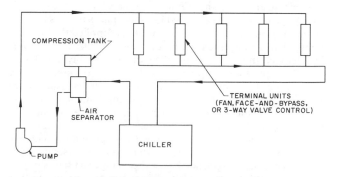

Fig. 1   Constant Flow Chilled Water System

The preparation of this chapter is assigned to TC 6.1, Hot Water and Steam Heating Equipment and Systems.

All materials in the piping system, including flange gaskets, valve seats and packing, pump seals and other specialities must be compatible with the brine. Thermal expansion and contraction must be provided for.

The space around the piping and equipment should be adequate for proper insulation. Extensions of valve bonnets, thermometer wells and other items, along with an adequate vapor seal, are usually necessary. Special efforts should be made to obtain an adequate seal around valve bonnets, thermometer wells and other items that pierce the vapor barrier.

Piping for volatile refrigerant brines should be installed similarly to conventional refrigerant piping, kept as clean as possible and dehydrated by evacuation before brine is charged into the system. A closed expansion tank pressurized with dry nitrogen permits the brine to expand on system warm-up and maintains suitable operating pressures in the system at design temperature.

The pumping head is determined by calculating the total equivalent length of piping in the system and multiplying this value by the friction rate for the brine type and temperature. The correct friction rate for a specific application can be obtained from brine or equipment manufactures, or can be calculated from the Reynolds number and D'Arcy equation. Pipe friction, equipment pressure drop, expressed in feet of brine, and hydrostatic lift, if applicable, are added to obtain total system pumping head. The pump rating and motor power should be based on the brine being used and the actual operating temperature.

Further information on brines is contained in Chapter 16 of the 1985 FUNDAMENTALS Volume and in Chapter 5 of the 1986 REFRIGERATION Volume.

Two-Pipe Dual-Temperature Water Systems

In dual-temperature applications, two-pipe systems are frequently used to convey either hot water for heating or chilled water for cooling through common piping to the terminal heat transfer elements. In these systems both the hot water generator and the chiller are connected through valves or other means to the distribution piping, and the system water changes over from hot to chilled as the heating or cooling requirement changes.

Two-pipe dual-temperature water systems have the lowest cost and have been the most commonly applied types of hot and chilled water systems. During cold weather, hot water is circulated to all units or terminals in the circuit or zone. During hot weather, chilled water is circulated to all units. Changeover from heating to cooling may be for the entire circuit, or for a single zone in

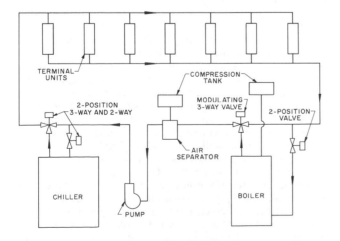

Fig. 3 Two-Pipe Dual-Temperature System

zoned systems. Changeover occurs at a central location, either manually by the operating engineer or automatically by an outdoor thermostat that is frequently solar-compensated.

Two-pipe dual-temperature systems are often applied to the secondary water piping, to the induction units in air-water induction systems, to fan-coil units and to year-round unit ventilators. A typical two-pipe dual-temperature system is shown in Figure 3. This arrangement, in which flow through the chiller depends on system flow, is selected when the air-side or threeway valve control is on the terminal units. A system bypass or an arrangement using a secondary pump at the chiller (Figures 2 and 5) may be preferred.

Two-Pipe Natural Cooling Systems

Two-pipe dual-temperature natural cooling systems have air handling units arranged to use up to 100% outdoor air. In these systems, cooling is accomplished during the summer season using chilled water and during intermediate seasons by introducing outdoor air while hot water is supplied to the system. This makes simultaneous heating or cooling possible, as long as the outdoor temperature is equal to or below the summer cooling supply air design temperature selected for the air handling units. This provides individual unit changeover that approaches, but does not equal in all applications, the changeover achieved by the three- or four-pipe system.

Two-pipe natural cooling systems generally have the advantage of lower operating costs and lower initial cost when compared with either conventional two-, three- or four-pipe systems. Disadvantages are that (1) the class of terminal units and the individual control systems required for the units can be more expensive than conventional fan-coil or induction terminals, (2) access to sufficient quantities of outdoor air can be difficult in some applications, particularly in interior zones, (3) relatively large quantities of outdoor air may be required to achieve maximum operating economies depending on the switchover temperature, and (4) the indoor humidity is usually higher when the system is on natural cooling.

These systems are most commonly found in classroom buildings and laboratories where large amounts of outdoor air are required for ventilation. They are most often applied in perimeter zones or on the top floors of buildings where outdoor air is accessible through sidewall or roof intakes.

In two-pipe natural cooling systems, the changeover temperature is determined solely by the summer design temperature differential. Therefore, comparatively small design temperature differentials and large air quantities maximize operation economy. If the cooling supply temperature is 65 °F (18 °C), cooling for a space with a cooling design temperature of 78 °F (26 °C) can be achieved selectively by supplying up to 100% outdoor air at any time the outdoor temperature is below 65 °F (18 °C). Heating can be achieved in other spaces in the same circuit at the same time, because hot water is supplied through the piping. This arrangement limits the band of *intermediate* outdoor temperatures to a very narrow range, possibly 2 to 3 °F (1 to 2 °C) of outdoor temperature or less. It also makes zoning for separate changeover of individual zones unnecessary, since the entire system can be changed over simultaneously. At any temperature below the changeover temperature, either heating or cooling is available in any space.

The operating economies of the two-pipe natural cooling system are significant compared with most other systems, since chillers never need to operate below the changeover temperature, usually 60 to 65 °F (16 to 18 °C). This compares with most other system types that require chiller operation at temperatures of 50 or 40 °F (10 or 5 °C) or below and, in some previously noted cases, at temperatures below freezing.

Piping design, pump selection, pressurization and other design elements are similar to those previously described for two-pipe systems and all dual-temperature systems. Changeover is the same as in two-pipe dual-temperature systems, except that multiple circuit zoning is not required and the entire system changeover can occur at a single outdoor temperature.

Changeover Temperature

The changeover temperature is the temperature at which the water in the circuit or zone changes from hot to chilled. It is determined by a number of factors, the most significant of which is the changeover temperature in the space itself, which determines when cooling capacity is required instead of heating capacity. This space requirement can vary widely in different applications and within the same building. It is a function of the balance of the heat gains from occupants, lights, solar radiation or other heat sources, against the heat losses from transmission, infiltration and ventilation. Some spaces, such as interior zones, may never need heating.

On the other hand, spaces with exposed walls or roofs and especially those with large glass areas, low lighting loads and occupancy densities, may need heating even when outdoor temperatures are 65 °F (18 °C) or higher. Spaces with large proportions of exposed glass can have widely varying heating and cooling requirements, depending on whether the glass is sunlit or not and on the exposure. Densely occupied spaces, such as restaurants, auditoriums and classrooms, can have widely varying load requirements, especially if occupancy is intermittent. Widely varying conditions can occur at the same time in different portions of the same building. Changeover temperature in the space (T_{CO}) can be determined by the following equation:

$$T_{CO} = T_R - \Sigma H_C - a\, Q_S\, (T_R - T_S)/\Sigma H_H \qquad (1)$$

where

T_{CO} = changeover temperature, °F (°C)
T_R = room temperature, °F (°C)
Q_S = primary supply air quantity, cfm (L/s)
T_S = primary supply air temperature, °F (°C)
ΣH_C = sensible cooling load, Btu/lb (kJ/kg)
ΣH_H = heat loss per °F (°C) temperature change
a = 1.08 (1.2)

In buildings where humidity control is a prime concern, the changeover temperature is dictated by the dew point temperature required to maintain the indoor design relative humidity.

In addition to the space load requirements for heating or cooling, the changeover temperature is also dictated by the type of system used and by the heating or cooling available from sources other than the circulating water system. For example, the availability of heating or cooling capacity in the primary air system can greatly modify the changeover temperature required in the secondary water circuits of an air-water induction system. In all-water systems, the availability of outdoor air for cooling can raise the temperature at which heat is supplied to all units. Even when limited quantities of outdoor air are available, as is the case in some fan-coil applications, the outdoor air can provide some cooling in spaces requiring it when hot water is being supplied to the entire zone circuit.

Depending on the particular space requirements, and the amount of heating or cooling capacity that can be provided by the primary air system or the ventilating air, each zone can have a changeover temperature that best meets its average needs. In many cases where changeover is manual, the building custodian determines when changeover is required by observing the temperature conditions in the space. Automatic changeover is accomplished either by an outdoor thermostat that can be solar-compensated, by a master thermostat in the space, or both.

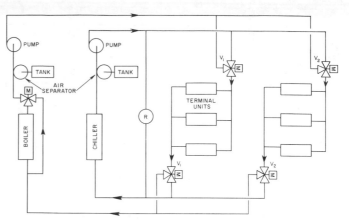

Fig. 4 Two-Pipe Multiple-Zone Dual-Temperature System Using Zone Valves

A typical system might have a changeover temperature of 50 °F (10 °C). At an outdoor temperature of 50 °F (10 °C), the system changes from cooling to heating if the outdoor temperature drops, or from heating to cooling if the outdoor temperature rises. In many cases, especially in sun-exposed perimeter zones with large glass areas, much lower changeover temperatures may be required.

The changeover from hot to chilled water in the system piping is generally related to, and coincidental with, the starting of the refrigeration equipment. This is not necessarily true in all types of air-water systems. For example, in an air-water induction system, when outdoor temperatures are sufficiently low, it may be possible to chill the secondary water circulated to the induction terminals sufficiently by passing it through the primary dehumidifier, making chiller operation unnecessary. This arrangement is economical for preheating outdoor primary air and reduces chiller operating costs.

Two-pipe dual-temperature systems, which do not have access to outdoor air for cooling, perform very adequately during those periods when only cooling or only heating is required in all the spaces on the circuit or zone. Whenever internal loads fluctuate over a wide range or some perimeter spaces require heating while others require cooling, the system fails. In most buildings, this latter condition occurs when the outdoor temperature falls below 65 to 70 °F (18 to 21 °C). During these periods, unoccupied shaded exposures frequently require heating while sunny exposures require cooling. This problem is accentuated in glass-walled or curtain-walled buildings where varia-

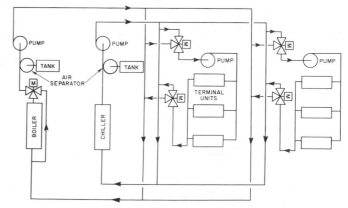

Fig. 5 Two-Pipe Multiple-Zone Dual-Temperature System Using Zone Pumps

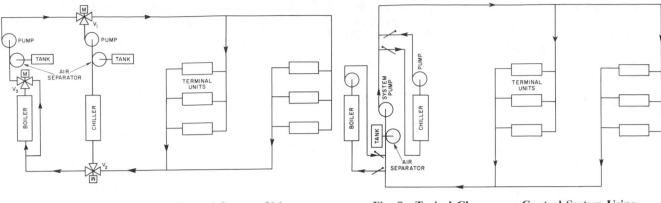

Fig. 6 Typical Changeover Control Systems Using Three-Way Valves and Separate Pumps

Fig. 8 Typical Changeover Control System Using Primary-Secondary Pumps

tions in solar and transmission loads are felt almost immediately in the perimeter spaces.

To provide a degree of flexibility, the two-pipe dual-temperature system is often zoned so that hot water can be supplied to units in one zone, while chilled water is supplied to units in another zone (see Figures 4 and 5). The greater the number of zones provided, the more flexible the system will be in meeting changing loads and maintaining design conditions in the spaces. It is frequently possible to divide the building into two or four zones according to exposure. Buildings in large cities frequently require vertical zoning so that lower floors that are shaded by other buildings are on a separate zone than the upper floors exposed to the sun. The number of zones varies from building to building. The final decision on the number of zones used depends on initial cost and space limitations. Figures 4 and 5 show two possible arrangements of multiple-zone systems. In Figure 4, there are only two pumps, and the flow of hot or chilled water in each zone depends on the positions of valves V-1 and V-2. In Figure 5, separate pumps maintain flow in each zone regardless of whether heating or cooling is required.

Changeover

Changeover of either mechanical or natural cooling two-pipe dual-temperature systems can be accomplished in various ways. The most common use two- or three-way valves to change the system circuit over to either the boiler or chiller, depending on the requirement. Primary-secondary pumping can also be used for changeover.

Figure 6 shows a typical changeover control system in which three-way valves and separate hot and chilled water pumps are installed. During chilled water operations, valves V-1 and V-2 are open to the chiller and closed to the boiler, and pump P-2 operates. During hot water operations, V-1 and V-2 are closed to the chiller and open to the boiler and pump P-1 operates. Valve V-3 is a blending valve for varying the hot water supply temperature with changing outdoor temperatures. Because of the isolation of the respective circuits, separate expansion tanks and relief valves are used on both the boiler and chiller.

Figure 7 shows a typical changeover control using three-way valves and a single system pump. Pump P-1 operates during both seasons, and valves V-1 and V-2 are open to the chiller during chilled water operation and to the boiler during hot water operation. Valve V-3 modulates the system water temperature during the heating period. Again, two tanks and relief valves are required, since the separate portions of the circuit are isolated during some portion of the season.

Figure 8 shows a typical changeover control using primary-secondary pumps. System pump P-1 operates continuously. When cooling is required, chilled water pump P-2 operates. When heating is required, hot water pump P-3 operates intermittently as required to vary the system water temperature as the outdoor temperature changes.

Figure 9 shows another variation, in which a two-way valve is installed on the boiler and water is permanently bypassed through the chiller. Pump P-1 operates continuously. When chilled water is required, the chiller operates and valve V-1 remains closed. When heating is required, the chiller is shut down and

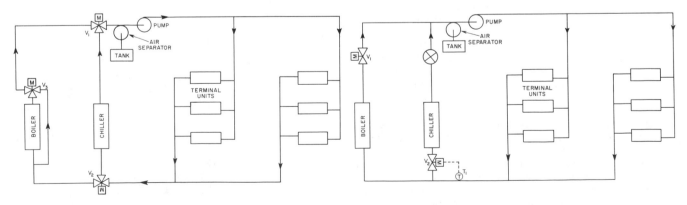

Fig. 7 Typical Changeover Control System Using Three-Way Valves and a Single Pump

Fig. 9 Changeover Control Using Two-Way Valve on Boiler

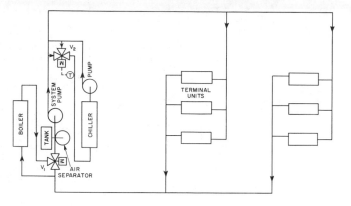

Fig. 10 Changeover Control With Blending Circuit on Chiller

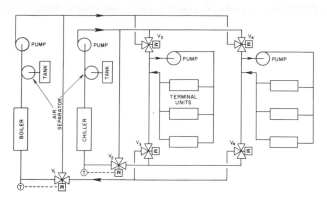

Fig. 12 Changeover Control Using Blending Circuits for Multiple Zones

valve V-1 is positioned to vary the flow from the boiler to vary the system water temperature as the outdoor temperature changes. Valve V-2 is a safety control that closes to prevent flow into the chiller if the return water becomes too hot. The arrangement shown in Figure 9 is most applicable in mild climates where the heating season is relatively short and hot water supply temperatures below 100 °F (38 °C) are used.

Other arrangements are possible that have advantages or disadvantages in specific applications. However, precautions must always be taken. During chilled water operation, the flow through the chiller must be maintained at a value fairly close to the design flow rate to avoid reduced water temperatures and freezeup. In any arrangement where the chiller is connected to a system in which flows can be significantly reduced, a bypass, either in the system or around the chiller, is necessary to maintain such flows. The arrangements shown in Figure 5 and 8 eliminate this difficulty.

In addition, the changeover can result in a sudden influx of hot water into the chiller or cold water into the hot water generator. In either case, the system design must minimize the rate at which this water is introduced or absorb the thermal shock imposed on the equipment by the sudden temperature change. *In the chiller, it is necessary to assure that the temperature of the water introduced is not high enough to cause excessive refrigerant pressures in the evaporator.* Normally a maximum temperature of 80 °F (27 °C) is recommended for water entering the chiller. For this reason, it is necessary to apply the minimum practical supply temperatures during winter operation and to decrease the system water temperature as outdoor temperatures increase. This assures that water temperatures returned from the

system at changeover are suitable for introduction into the chiller. Particular attention must be given to part-load conditions in which the return water temperature can be close to the supply temperature if three-way valves or system bypass control are used.

In addition, pressurization must be adequate throughout the system, and large portions of the system, particularly the boiler, must not be isolated from the compression tank during any portion of the seasonal operation.

Changeover of a zone or the complete system can be either manual or automatic. Manual changeover is uncomplicated but can be burdensome in climates where daily changeover is required during some seasons. Automatic changeover frees the operating personnel for other duties and equipment failure can be avoided with sufficient safety controls. Semi-automatic changeover, in which all changeover becomes automatic by manually positioning a switch, is a frequent compromise.

An outdoor thermostat is used for automatic changeover. When the outdoor temperature rises, the thermostat bypasses enough system water around the boiler to permit the system to cool down. When the system water has cooled, the thermostat introduces it to the chiller and starts the compressors. The sequence is reversed when the outdoor temperature falls.

Whether changeover from winter to summer operation is manual or automatic, the system water must cool to about 80 °F (27 °C) before it can be introduced into the chiller. It may be several hours before chilled water is available, especially if too high a supply temperature has been used in mild weather. Changeover arrangements that use loop zones or blending circuits (e.g., in Figures 10, 11, and 12) provide some advantage, since the chiller can be operated to help reduce the system water temperature and accelerate changeover. Valve V-2 is positioned by the thermostat in the chiller return to blend chilled water with system water until the system has been brought down to temperature.

Conversely, large quantities of cold water cannot be introduced into most hot boilers without risking damage. In some hot water generators, chilled water should be allowed to warm up or be fed in gradually to avoid thermal shock to the generator from the temperature change. This can be done automatically by a low-limit aquastat in the boiler that controls the three-way valve and bypasses most of the system water around the boiler until the burner increases the water temperature. The net effect is that of gradually warming the system without introducing large quantities of cold water into the hot water generator. Another arrangement is shown in Figures 11 and 12 in which a blending circuit is also installed on the hot water generator. Note that while V-1 in the figures is located differently from conventional control valves for varying system water temperature, it can also be used for this purpose if properly controlled.

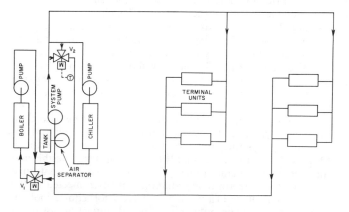

Fig. 11 Changeover Control With Blending Circuits on Boiler and Chiller

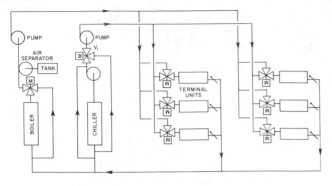

Fig. 13 Typical Three-Pipe System

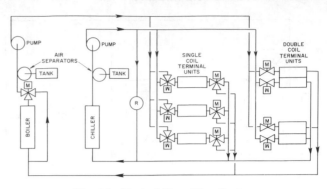

Fig. 14 Typical Four-Pipe System

Whether the central changeover is manual or automatic, changeover at the terminal units is usually automatic. Controls are arranged so that all units are simultaneously changed over by a manual or automatic switch from the central equipment room, or by a strap-on aquastat in the unit, which senses the supply water temperature and indexes the controls accordingly.

Outdoor reset control, in which the system water temperature is continuously varied according to the outdoor temperature, should be used during all heating operation. Using a linear variation in water temperature from design water temperature [usually as low as possible, about 120 to 150 °F (49 to 66 °C) maximum] at design outdoor temperature to 80 °F (27 °C) water temperature at the changeover temperature [determined by load, usually 40 to 60 °F (5 to 16 °C)] is recommended. This reset schedule minimizes the time delay and the risk of shock to the chiller and boiler during changeover.

Three-Pipe Systems

The three-pipe system in Figure 13 has separate hot and chilled water pumps and supply mains; a single pump can be installed in the common return main. The return runouts from all terminal units are connected to a common return line, and all water is returned through the same return main after it flows through the terminal equipment. Certain aspects of three-pipe systems are proprietary; patents should be investigated before finalizing system design. Chapters 3, 4, and 9 have further details.

Four-Pipe Systems

Figure 14 shows a typical four-pipe system, in which separate supply and return mains for both hot and chilled water are run to the same terminal equipment. The heat transfer element in the terminal may be a single element that can be supplied with either hot or chilled water, depending on the individual requirements, or separate heating and cooling elements may be selected. Separate pumps are used for hot and chilled water, and the mains can be arranged in either a direct or reversed return.

Four-pipe systems consist of a two-pipe heating sytem plus a two-pipe cooling system. The terminal unit controls are arranged to accommodate either heating or cooling water. Where a single terminal heat transfer element is selected, a four-pipe valve (or sequenced two-way throttling valves) is used on the inlet to the heat transfer element to modulate from full hot water flow, to no flow, and then to full chilled water flow, depending on the requirements. A two-position changeover diverting valve in the return from the heat transfer element is operated in sequence with the supply valve to return water to the chilled water return main when chilled water is being supplied, or to the hot water return main when hot water is being supplied.

In another variation, the terminal unit has two heat transfer elements, one for heating and one for cooling. Separate two-way valves are inserted in the supply of each, and the valves are controlled in sequence by the room thermostat to provide heating or cooling to meet space requirements. The control system can be arranged either for sequence control to provide heating or cooling, or for reheat control. The control valves may be pneumatic, electric, or electronic.

Both types of four-pipe systems completely isolate the chilled and the hot water systems, except for the small amount of water that can be in the coil at changeover. Units requiring hot water receive water from the hot water pump and the boiler or generator. Much higher hot water supply temperatures are possible with four-pipe systems than are practicable with three-pipe systems, especially where separate heating coils are used. Outdoor reset of the system water temperature is recommended to compensate for changes in outdoor temperature. Generally, it is not necessary to circulate hot water to the units until the outdoor ambient temperature drops below the temperatures within the space. The exact requirement for providing hot water may vary with the application and with the system to which the four-pipe heat exchanger is being applied. For example, if the primary air temperature is lower than the room temperature, it may be desirable to provide hot water even when the outdoor ambient temperature is above the desired maximum indoor space temperature, to counteract the cooling effect of the primary air in shaded exposures.

Chilled water is supplied to the terminal units exactly as described for chilled water systems. Again, it is necessary to supply chilled water only when the space temperature is above the changeover temperature, which is determined as described previously for two-pipe systems. However, the chillers must be operated whenever any space needs chilled water for cooling, unless an outdoor air cooling cycle is applied.

Three-pipe systems provide the same flexibility to meet changing room loads as do four-pipe systems, while permitting some initial cost savings by using the common return system instead of two separate return systems. One valve instead of two is installed at each terminal unit. The most common valves are pneumatic, electric or electronic, or self-contained. They all are nonmixing, which selects and modulates water from either the hot or chilled water supply.

Four-pipe systems have somewhat lower operating costs than three-pipe sytems and since the hot and chilled water systems are entirely separate, pressure regulation is far less critical. Moreover, because higher supply temperatures are possible and the systems are separate, other types of heating equipment, such as convectors and fin-tube radiation can be connected to the hot water circuit for heating spaces that do not require cooling. Four-pipe systems have the additional advantage of not being proprietary.

Piping layout, pump selection, expansion tank sizing and location and similar considerations are the same for each portion of the four-pipe system as they are for any hot water heating system described in Chapter 13, and for the chilled water systems described in this chapter.

Four-pipe systems can be used with certain heat pumps to transfer heat from a zone that requires cooling to a zone that requires heating. This can be done by condenser water reheat or a variety of other low energy cost arrangements.

Condenser Water Systems

Condenser water systems for refrigerant compressors are classified as *cooling tower systems,* or as *once-through systems,* such as city water, well water or pond or lake water systems. They are usually open systems, in which air is continuously in contact with the water, and require a different approach to pump selection and sizing than do closed heating and cooling systems. Exceptions occur when closed-circuit towers or plate-type heat exchangers are used. Some heat conservation systems rely on a split condenser heating system that includes a two-section condenser. Heat from one section of the condenser is used for heating in closed circuit systems, and is occasionally interconnected with chilled water systems. The other section of the condenser serves as a heat-reject circuit, which is an open system connected to a cooling tower.

In selecting a pump for a condenser water system, consideration must be given to the static head and the system friction loss. The pump inlet must have an adequate net positive suction head.

In addition, continuous contact with air in an open system introduces impurities that can cause scale and corrosion on a continuing basis. Fouling factors and an increased pressure drop caused by aging of the piping must be included in the condenser design. See Chapter 16 of the 1983 EQUIPMENT Volume. The water flow quantity required depends on the refrigeration unit used and on the available temperature of the condenser water.

Cooling tower water is available at a temperature several degrees above the design wet-bulb temperature, depending on tower performance. In city, lake, river or well water systems, the maximum water temperature that occurs during the operating season must be used for equipment selection.

From manufacturers' performance data with a known condenser water temperature, the required flow rate may be determined for any condensing temperature and capacity. A condensing temperature and corresponding flow rate can then be selected to produce the required capacity with minimum energy input and purchased water within the load capability of the driver.

Once-Through Systems

Figure 15 shows a water-cooled condenser using city, well or river water. The return is run higher than the condenser so that the condenser is always full of water. Water flow through the condenser is modulated by a control valve in the supply line, usually actuated from condenser head pressure to maintain a constant condensing temperature with load variations. City water systems should always include approved back flow prevention devices and open sight drains, as shown. When more than one condenser is used on the same circuit, individual control valves are used to avoid balance problems.

Piping should be sized according to the principles outlined in Chapter 54, with velocities of 5 to 10 fps (1.5 to 3.0 m/s) for flow rates. A pump is not required where city water is used. Pumps may be necessary for well or river water, in which case the procedure for pump sizing is the same as for cooling tower systems.

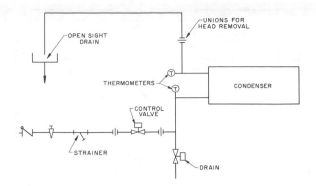

Fig. 15 Water-Cooled Condenser Connections for City Water

Cooling Tower Systems

Figure 16 illustrates a typical cooling tower system for a refrigerant condenser. Water flows to the pump from the tower basin and is discharged under pressure to the condenser and then back to the tower. Since it is desirable to maintain condenser water temperature above a predetermined minimum, water is diverted through a control valve to maintain minimum sump temperature. Piping from the tower sump to the pump requires some cautions. Sump level should be above the top of the pump casing for positive prime, and piping pressure drop should be minimized. All piping must pitch up either to the tower or the pump suction to eliminate air pockets. Suction strainers should be equipped with inlet and outlet gauges to indicate when cleaning is required. Vortexing in the tower basin is prevented by piping connections at the tower according to the manufacturer's specification and by limiting flow to the maximum allowed by the sump design. Pump performance is enhanced by a straight section of suction pipe five times the diameter in length.

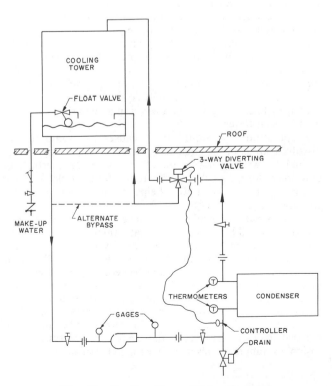

Fig. 16 Cooling Tower Piping Systems

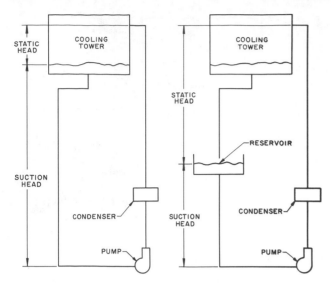

**Fig. 17   Schematic Piping Layout Showing Static
and Suction Head**

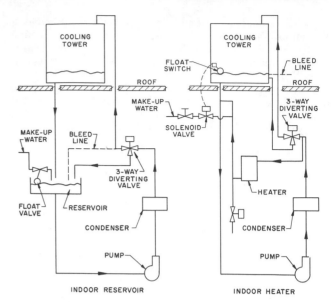

Fig. 18   Cooling Tower Piping to Avoid Freezeup

The elements of required pump head are illustrated in Figure 17. Since there is an equal head of water between the level in the tower sump or interior reservoir and the pump on both the suction and discharge sides, these heads cancel each other and can be disregarded. The elements of pump head are: (1) static head from tower sump or interior reservoir to the tower header, (2) friction loss in suction and discharge piping, (3) pressure loss in condenser, (4) control valves and (5) strainer and tower nozzles if used. These elements added in feet of water determine the required pump total dynamic head.

Normally, piping is sized to yield water velocities between 5 and 12 fps (1.5 and 3.7 m/s). Friction factors for 15-year-old pipe are commonly used. The manufacturers' data contains pressure drops for condenser, cooling tower, control valves and strainers. If condensers are installed in parallel, only the one with the highest pressure drop is counted. Combination flow measuring and balancing valves can be used to equalize pressure drops.

If multiple cooling towers are to be connected, the piping should be designed so that the pressure loss from the tower to the pump suction is approximately equal for each tower. Large equalizing lines or a common reservoir maintain the same water level in each tower.

Evaporation in a cooling tower causes a concentration of dissolved solids in the circulating water. This concentration is limited by wasting a portion of the water as overflow or blowdown. Also, the drift loss that results from droplets of water drifting out of the tower helps to maintain a limited concentration.

Makeup water is required to replace the water lost by drift, evaporation and blowdown. Automatic float valves are usually installed to maintain a constant water level.

Depending on the chemistry of the water available for the cooling tower, water treatment may be necessary to prevent scaling, corrosion or biological fouling of the condenser and circulating system. On large systems, fixed continuous feeding chemical treatment systems are frequently installed in which chemicals, including acids for pH controls, must be diluted and blended and then pumped into the condenser water system. Corrosion resistant materials may be required for surfaces that come

in contact with these chemicals. For further information on water treatment, refer to Chapter 33.

Special precautions are required if cooling towers are to operate in subfreezing weather. Ice formation can hinder the performance of the tower by obstructing air flow, and periodic manual shutdown of the tower fan may be necessary for de-icing. Operating periods in cold weather can be longer if the tower fan is thermostatically controlled with the bypass, so that gravity air flow is achieved and larger water quantities are circulated through the tower. The diverting valve that bypasses the tower should have a wide throttling range from 12 to 15 °F (7 to 9 °C) to avoid cycling, since periodic flow into the tower can cause rapid icing in subfreezing weather.

Exposed piping must be protected or drained when a tower operates intermittently during cold weather. The most satisfactory arrangement is to provide an indoor receiving tank into which the cold water basin drains by gravity. The makeup line, overflow and pump suction are then connected to the reservoir tank rather than to the tower basin. This leaves only the warm discharge line exposed to the weather; it can be drained by a small bleed line connected to the tower basin or reservoir (see Figure 18).

Tower basin heaters or heat exchangers connected across the supply and return line to the tower can also be selected, although their cost can be high. Steam or electric basin heaters are most commonly used. An arrangement incorporating an indoor heater is also shown in Figure 18.

Cooling towers that are unused for considerable periods of time should be drained. Using glycol solutions in cooling towers is not recommended.

City water is occasionally piped to condenser cooling systems for wintertime use. Whenever such connections are made, effective back flow preventer equipment that may be required by plumbing codes must be installed.

Temperature Controls

Chapter 51 includes automatic control information.

CHAPTER 15

MEDIUM AND HIGH TEMPERATURE WATER HEATING SYSTEMS

HIGH temperature water systems are classified as those operating with supply water temperatures above 350 °F (177 °C) and designed to a pressure rating of 300 psi (2 MPa) gage. Medium temperature water systems have operating temperatures below 350 °F (177 °C) and permit design to a pressure rating of 125 to 150 psig (960 to 1130 kPa). The usual practical temperature limit is about 450 °F (232 °C) because of pressure limitations on pipe fittings, equipment and accessories. The rapid rate of pressure rise (see Figure 1) that occurs over 450 °F (232 °C) increases system cost since higher pressure rated components are required. The design principles for both medium temperature and high temperature systems are basically the same. In this chapter, *HTW* refers to both systems.

This chapter presents the general principles and practices that apply to HTW and distinguishes them from low temperature water systems operating below 250 °F (120 °C). Refer to Chapter 13 for basic design considerations applicable to all hot water systems.

SYSTEM CHARACTERISTICS

The following characteristics distinguish HTW systems from steam distribution or low temperature water systems:

1. The system is a completely closed circuit with supply and return mains maintained under pressure. There are no losses from flashing, and heat not used in the terminal heat transfer equipment is returned to the HTW generator. Tight systems have minimal corrosion.
2. Mechanical equipment that does not control the performance of individual terminal units is concentrated at the central station.
3. Piping can slope up or down or run at a variety of elevations to suit the terrain and the architectural and structural requirements without provision for trapping at each low point. This may reduce the amount of excavation required and eliminate drip points and return pumps required with steam.
4. Considerably greater temperature drops are used and less water is circulated than in low temperature water systems.
5. The pressure in any part of the system must always be well above the pressure corresponding to the temperature at saturation in the system to prevent flashing of the water into steam.
6. Terminal units requiring different water temperatures can be served at their required temperatures by: regulating the flow of water, modulating the water supply temperature, placing some units in series, using heat exchangers or other methods.
7. The high heat content of the water in the high temperature water circuit acts as a thermal flywheel, evening out fluctuations in the load. The heat storage capacity can be fur-

ther increased by adding heat storage tanks or by increasing the temperature in the return mains during periods of light load.
8. The high heat content of the heat carrier makes high temperature water unsuitable for two-pipe dual temperature (hot and chilled water) applications and for intermittent operation if rapid start-up and shutdown are desired, unless the system is designed for minimum water volume and is operated with rapid response controls.
9. Higher engineering skills are required to design a HTW system that is simple, yet safer and more convenient to operate than a comparable steam or low temperature water system.
10. HTW system design requires careful attention to basic laws of chemistry and physics as these systems are less forgiving than standard hydronic systems.

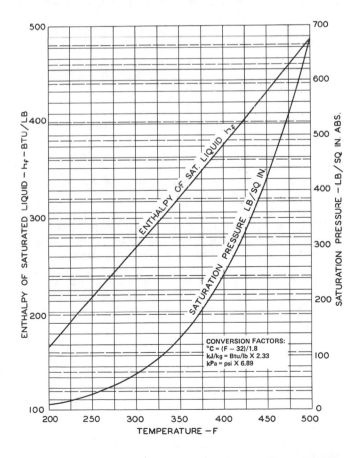

**Fig. 1   Relation of Saturation Pressure and Enthalpy
to Water Temperature**

The preparation of this chapter is assigned to TC 6.1, Hot Water and Steam Heating Equipment and Systems.

THE BASIC SYSTEM

High temperature water systems are similar to conventional forced hot water heating systems. They require a heat source, which can be a direct-fired HTW generator, a steam boiler, or an open or closed heat exchanger, to heat the water. The expansion of the heated water is usually taken up in an expansion vessel, which simultaneously pressurizes the system. Heat transport depends on circulating pumps. The distribution system is closed, comprising supply and return pipes under the same basic pressure. Heat emission at the terminal unit is indirect by heat transfer through heat transfer surfaces. The basic system is shown in Figure 2.

The principal differences from low temperature water systems are the higher pressure used, the consequently heavier equipment, the generally smaller pipe sizes and the manner in which water pressure is maintained.

Most systems are either (1) a saturated steam cushion system, in which the high temperature water develops its own pressure or (2) a gas- or pump-pressurized system, in which the pressure is imposed externally.

HTW generators and all auxiliaries (such as water makeup and feed equipment, pressure tanks and circulating pumps) are usually located in a central station. Cascade HTW generators sometimes use an existing steam distribution system and are installed remote from the central plant.

DESIGN CONSIDERATIONS

Selection of the system pressure, supply temperature, temperature drop, type of HTW generator and the pressurization method are the most important initial design considerations. Some determining factors are:

1. Type of load (space heating and/or process). Load fluctuations during a 24-hour period and a one-year period. Process loads might require water at a given minimum supply temperature continuously, while space heating can permit temperature modulation as a function of outdoor temperature or other climatic influences.
2. Terminal unit temperature requirements.
3. Distance between heating plant and space or process requiring heat.
4. Quantity and pressure of steam used for power equipment in the central plant.
5. Elevation variations within the system and the effect of the basic pressure distribution.

Usually, distribution piping is the major investment in an HTW system. A distribution system with the widest temperature spread (ΔT) between supply and return will have the lowest initial and operating costs. Economical designs have a ΔT of 150 °F (65 °C) or higher.

The requirements of terminal equipment or user systems determine the system selected. For example, if the users are 10 psig (170 kPa) steam generators, the return temperatures would

be 250 °F (121 °C). A 300 psig (2 MPa) rated system operated at 400 °F (204 °C) would be selected to serve the load. In another example, where the primary system serves predominantly 140-180 °F (60-82 °C) hot water heating systems, an HTW system that operates at 325 °F (162 °C) could be selected. The supply temperature is reduced by blending with 140 °F (60 °C) return water to the desired 180 °F (82 °C) hot water supply temperature in a direct-connected hot water secondary system. This highly economical design has a 140 °F (60 °C) return temperature in the primary water system and a ΔT of 185 °F (82 °C).

Because the danger of waterhammer is always present if flashing occurs when the pressure drops to the point when pressurized hot water flashes to steam, the primary HTW system should be designed with steel valves and fittings of 150 psi (1.0 MPa). The secondary water, which operates below 212 °F (100 °C) and is not subject to flashing and waterhammer, can be designed for 125 psi (860 kPa) and standard HVAC equipment.

Theoretically, water temperatures up to about 350 °F (177 °C) can be provided using equipment suitable for 125 psi (860 kPa). But in practice, unless *push-pull* pumping is used, maximum water temperatures will be limited by the system design, pump heads, and elevation characteristics to values between 300 and 325 °F (150 and 163 °C).

Many systems designed for self-generated steam pressurization have a steam drum through which the entire flow is taken, and which also serves as an expansion vessel. A circulating pump in the supply line takes water from the tank. The temperature of the water from the steam drum cannot exceed the steam temperature in the drum that corresponds to its pressure at saturation. The point of maximum pressure is at the discharge of the circulating pump. If, for example, this pressure is to be maintained below 125 psig (960 kPa), the pressure in the drum that corresponds to the water temperature cannot exceed 125 psig (960 kPa) minus the sum of the pump head and the pressure head that is caused by of the difference in elevation between the drum and the circulating pump.

Most systems are designed for inert gas pressurization. In most of these systems, the pressurizing tank is connected to the system by a single balance line on the suction side of the circulating pump. The circulating pump is located at the inlet side of the HTW generator. There is no flow through the pressurizing tank, and a reduced temperature will normally establish itself inside. A special characteristic of the gas-pressurized systems is the apparatus that creates and maintains gas pressure inside the tank.

In designing and operating an HTW system, it is important to maintain a pressure that always exceeds the vapor pressure of the water, even if the system is not operating. This may require limiting the water temperature and thereby the vapor pressure, or increasing the imposed pressure.

Elevation and the pressures required to prevent water from flashing into steam in the supply system can also limit the maximum water temperature that may be used, and must therefore be studied in evaluating the temperature-pressure relationships and method of pressurizing the system.

The properties of water that govern design are as follows:

1. Temperature versus pressure at saturation (Figure 1).
2. Density or specific volume versus temperature.
3. Enthalpy or sensible heat versus temperature.
4. Viscosity versus temperature.
5. Type and amount of pressurization.

The relationships among temperature, pressure, specific volume, and enthalpy are all available in the steam tables. The properties of water for the range 212 to 400 °F (100 to 204 °C) are summarized in Table 1. Figure 2 of Chapter 13 indicates mass flow and specific heat for water temperatures to 400 °F (204 °C).

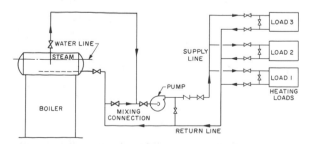

Fig. 2   Elements of a High Temperature Water System

Table 1   Properties of Water—212 to 400°F (100 to 204°C)

Temperature		Pressure		Density		Specific Heat		Total Heat Above 32°F (0°C)				Dynamic (absolute) Viscosity
°F	(°C)	psia[a]	(kPa)	lb/ft³	(kg/m³)	Btu/lb · F	(kJ/kg · °C)	Btu/lb[a]	(kJ/kg)	Btu/ft³	(kJ/m³)	Centipoise (mPa · s)
212	(100.0)	14.70	(101.3)	59.81	(957.0)	1.007	(4.219)	180.07	(419.6)	10,770	(401 721)	0.2838
220	(104.4)	17.19	(118.4)	59.63	(954.1)	1.009	(4.228)	188.13	(438.3)	11,216	(418 357)	0.2712
230	(110.0)	20.78	(143.2)	59.38	(950.1)	1.010	(4.232)	198.23	(461.9)	11,770	(439 021)	0.2567
240	(115.6)	24.97	(172.0)	59.10	(945.6)	1.012	(4.240)	208.34	(485.4)	12,313	(459 275)	0.2436
250	(121.1)	29.83	(205.5)	58.82	(941.1)	1.015	(4.253)	218.48	(509.1)	12,851	(479 342)	0.2317
260	(126.7)	35.43	(244.1)	58.51	(936.2)	1.017	(4.261)	228.64	(532.7)	13,378	(498 999)	0.2207
270	(132.2)	41.86	(288.4)	58.24	(931.8)	1.020	(4.274)	238.84	(556.5)	13,910	(518 843)	0.2107
280	(137.8)	49.20	(339.0)	57.94	(927.0)	1.022	(4.282)	249.06	(580.3)	14,430	(538 239)	0.2015
290	(143.3)	57.56	(396.6)	57.64	(922.2)	1.025	(4.295)	259.31	(604.2)	14,947	(557 523)	0.1930
300	(148.8)	67.01	(461.7)	57.31	(917.0)	1.032	(4.324)	269.59	(628.1)	15,450	(576 285)	0.1852
310	(154.4)	77.68	(535.2)	56.98	(911.7)	1.035	(4.337)	279.92	(652.2)	15,950	(594 935)	0.1779
320	(160.0)	89.66	(617.8)	56.66	(906.6)	1.040	(4.358)	290.28	(676.4)	16,437	(613 100)	0.1712
330	(165.6)	103.06	(710.1)	56.31	(901.0)	1.042	(4.366)	300.68	(700.6)	16,931	(631 526)	0.1649
340	(171.1)	118.01	(813.1)	55.96	(895.4)	1.047	(4.387)	311.13	(724.9)	17,409	(649 356)	0.1591
350	(176.7)	134.63	(927.6)	55.59	(889.4)	1.052	(4.408)	321.63	(749.4)	17,879	(666 887)	0.1536
360	(182.2)	153.04	(1054.5)	55.22	(883.5)	1.057	(4.429)	332.18	(774.0)	18,343	(684 194)	0.1484
370	(187.8)	173.37	(1194.5)	54.85	(877.6)	1.062	(4.450)	342.79	(798.7)	18,802	(701 315)	0.1436
380	(193.3)	195.77	(1348.9)	54.47	(871.5)	1.070	(4.483)	353.45	(823.5)	19,252	(718 100)	0.1391
390	(198.9)	220.37	(1518.4)	54.05	(864.8)	1.077	(4.513)	364.17	(848.5)	19,681	(734 101)	0.1349
400	(204.4)	247.31	(1704.0)	53.65	(858.4)	1.085	(4.546)	374.97	(873.7)	20,117	(750 364)	0.1308

[a]Reprinted by permission from *Thermodynamic Properties of Steam*, J. H. Keenan and F. G. Keyes, published by John Wiley and Sons, Inc., 1936 edition.

Direct-Fired High Temperature Water Generators

In direct-fired HTW generators, the central stations are comparable to steam boiler plants operating within the same pressure range. The generators should be selected for size and type in keeping with the load and design pressures, as well as the circulation requirements peculiar to high temperature water. In some systems, both steam for power or processing and high temperature water are supplied from the same boiler; in others, steam is produced in the boilers and used for generating high temperature water; and in many others, the burning fuel directly heats the water.

The HTW generators can be the water-tube or fire-tube type, and can be equipped with any conventional fuel firing apparatus. The water-tube type can have either forced circulation, gravity circulation or a combination of both. The recirculating pumps of forced circulation generators must operate continuously while the generator is being fired. Steam boilers relying on natural circulation might require internal baffling when used for HTW generation. In Scotch Marine boilers, thermal shock may occur, caused by a sudden drop in the temperature of the return water or when the ΔT exceeds 40°F (22°C). Forced circulation HTW generators are usually the once-through type and rely solely on pumps to achieve circulation. Depending on the design, internal orifices in the various circuits might be required to regulate the water flow rates in proportion to the heat absorption rates. Circulation must be maintained at all times while the generator is being fired, and the flow rate must never drop below a minimum indicated by the manufacturer.

Where gravity circulation steam boilers are used for HTW generation, the steam drum usually serves as an expansion vessel. In steam pressurized forced circulation HTW generators, a separate vessel is commonly used for maintaining the steam pressure cushion and for expansion. A separate vessel is always used when the system is cushioned by an inert gas or auxiliary steam. Proper internal circulation is essential in all types of boilers to prevent tube failures from overheating or unequal expansion.

In early HTW systems, the generator is a steam boiler with an integral steam drum used to absorb the expansion of the water level and for pressurization. A dip pipe removes water below the water line (see Figure 3) (Applegate 1958). This dip pipe should be installed so that it picks up water at or near the satura-tion temperature, without too many steam bubbles. If a pipe breaks somewhere in the system, the boiler must not empty to a point where heating surfaces are bared and the danger of a boiler explosion results. The same precautions must be taken with the return pipe. If the return pipe is connected in the lower part of the boiler, a check valve should be placed in the connecting line to the boiler to preclude the danger of emptying the boiler.

When two or more such boilers supply a common system, the same steam pressure and water level must be maintained in each. Water and steam balance pipes are usually installed between the drums (see Figure 4). These should be liberally sized. The table below shows recommended sizes.

Boiler Rating, million Btu/h (kW)		Balance Pipe Dia, in. (mm)	
2.5	(733)	3	(80)
5	(1465)	3.5	(90)
10	(2930)	4	(100)
15	(4395)	5	(125)
20	(5860)	6	(150)
30	(8790)	8	(200)

A difference of only 0.25 psi (1.7 kPa) in the system pressure between two boilers operated at 100 psig (790 kPa) would cause a difference of 9 in. (230 mm) in the water level. The situation

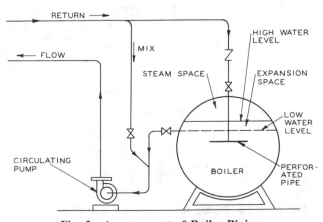

Fig. 3   Arrangement of Boiler Piping

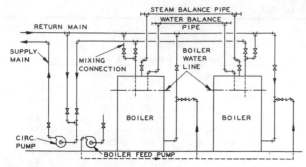

Fig. 4   Piping Connections for Two or More Boilers in HTW Systems Pressurized by Steam

is further aggravated because an upset is not self-balancing. Rather, when too high a heat release in one of the boilers has caused the pressure to rise and the water level to fall in this boiler, the decrease in the flow of colder return water into it causes a further pressure rise, while the opposite happens in the other boiler. It is therefore important that the firing rates match the flow through each boiler at all times. Modern practice is to use either flooded HTW heaters with a single external pressurized expansion drum common to all the generators, or the combination of steam boilers and direct contact (cascade) heater.

Expansion and Pressurization

In addition to the information in Chapter 13, the following factors should be considered:

1. The connection point of the expansion tank used for pressurization greatly affects the pressure distribution throughout the system and the avoidance of HTW flashing.
2. Proper safety devices for high and low water levels and ex-

cessive pressures should be incorporated in the expansion tank and interlocked with combustion safety and water flow rate controls.

The following fundamental methods, in which pressure in a given hydraulic system can be kept at a desired level, amplify the discussion in Chapter 13 (Blossom and Ziel 1959, National Academy of Sciences 1959).

1. An elevated storage tank is a simple pressurization method, but because of the great heights required for the pressure encountered, is generally impractical.
2. Steam pressurization requires the use of an expansion vessel separate from the HTW generator. Since firing and flow rates can never be perfectly matched, some steam is always carried. Therefore, the vessel must be above the HTW generators and connected in the supply water line from the generator. This steam, supplemented by flashing of the water content in the expansion vessel, provides the steam cushion that pressurizes the system.

The expansion vessel must be equipped with steam safety valves capable of relieving the steam generated by all the generators. The generators themselves usually are designed for a substantially higher working pressure than the expansion drum, and their safety relief valves are set for the higher pressure to minimize their lift requirement.

The basic HTW pumping arrangements can be either single-pump, in which one pump handles both the generator and system loads or two-pump, in which one pump circulates high temperature water through the generator and a second pump circulates high temperature water through the system. (See Figures 5 and 6.) The circulating pump moves the water from the expansion vessel to the system and back to the generator. The vessel must be elevated to increase the net positive suction head to prevent cavitation or flashing in the pump suction. This arrangement is critical. A bypass from the HTW system return

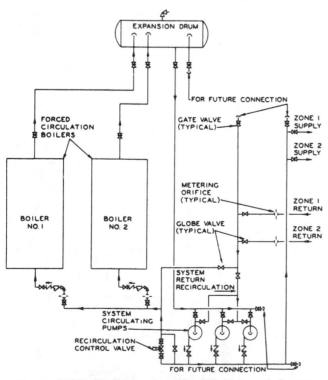

Fig. 5   HTW Piping for Combined (One-Pump) System (Steam Pressurized)

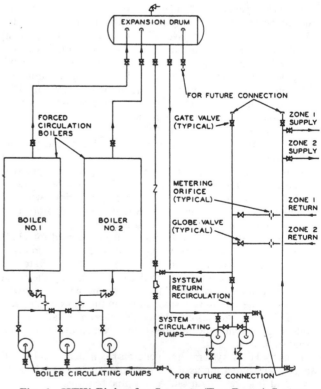

Fig. 6   HTW Piping for Separate (Two-Pump) System (Steam Pressurized)

line to the pump suction helps prevent flashing. Cooler return water is then mixed with hotter water from the expansion vessel to give a resulting temperature below the corresponding saturation point in the vessel.

In the two-pump system, the boiler recirculation should always exceed the system circulation, since excessive cooling of the water content of the drum by the cooler return water entering the drum, in case of overcirculation, can cause pressure loss and flashing in the distribution system. Back flow into the drum can be prevented by installing a check valve in the balance line from the drum to the boiler recirculating pumps. Higher cushion pressures may be maintained by auxiliary steam from a separate generator.

Sizing. Steam-pressurized vessels should be sized for a total volume V_T, which is the sum of the volume V_1 required for the steam space, the volume V_2 required for water expansion and the volume V_3 required for sludge and reserve. An allowance of 20% of the sum of V_2 and V_3 is reasonable for the volume V_1, required for the steam space.

The volume V_2 required for water expansion is determined from the change in water volume from the minimum to the maximum operating temperatures of the complete cycle. It is not necessary to allow for expansion of the total water volume in the system from a cold initial start. It is necessary during a start-up period to bleed off the volume of water caused by expansion from the initial starting temperature to the lowest average operating temperature.

The volume V_3 for sludge and reserve varies greatly depending on the size and design of system and generator capacity. An allowance of 40% of the volume V_2 required for water expansion is reasonable.

3. Nitrogen, the most commonly used inert gas, is used for gas pressurization. Air is not recommended because the oxygen in air contributes to corrosion in the system.

The expansion vessel is connected as close as possible to the suction side of the HTW pump by a balance line. The inert gas used for pressurization is fed into the top of the cylinder, preferably through a manual fill connection using a reducing station connected to an inert gas cylinder. Locating the relief valve below the minimum water line is advantageous, since it is easier to keep it tightly sealed with water on the pressure side. If the valve is located above the water line, it is exposed to the inert gas of the system.

To reduce the area of contact between gas and water and the resulting absorption of gas into the water, the tank should be installed vertically. It should be located in the most suitable place in the central station. Similar to the steam-pressurized system, the pumping arrangements can be either one- or two-pump. (See Figures 7 and 8.)

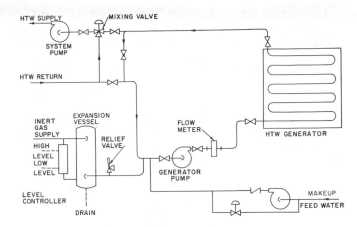

Fig. 8   Inert Gas Pressurization for Two-Pump System

The ratings of fittings, valves, piping and equipment are considered in determining the maximum system pressure. A minimum pressure of about 25 to 50 psi (170 to 340 kPa) over the maximum saturation pressure can be used. The imposed additional pressure head above the vapor pressure must be large enough to prevent steaming in the HTW generators at all times, even under conditions when flow and firing rates in generators operated in parallel, or flow and heat absorption in parallel circuits within a generator, are not evenly matched. This is critical since gas-pressurized systems do not have steam separating means and safety valves to evacuate the steam generated.

The simplest type of gas pressurization system uses a variable gas quantity with or without gas recovery (see Figure 9) (National Academy of Sciences 1959). In this system, the inert gas is relieved from the expansion vessel when the water rises and is wasted, or it is recovered in a low-pressure gas receiver from which the gas compressor pumps it into a high pressure receiver for storage. When the water level drops in the expansion vessel, the control cycle adds inert gas from bottles or from the high pressure receiver to the expansion vessel to maintain the required pressure.

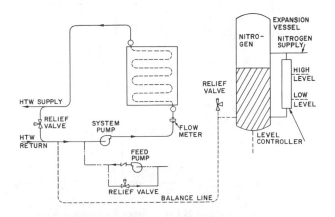

Fig. 7   Inert Gas Pressurization for One-Pump System

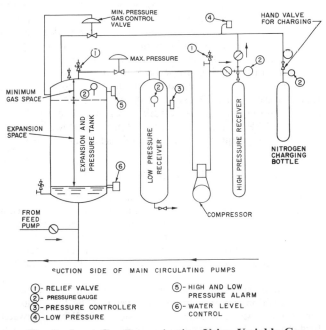

Fig. 9   Inert Gas Pressurization Using Variable Gas Quantity with Gas Recovery

Gas wastage can significantly affect the operating cost. The gas recovery system should be analyzed based on the economics of each application. It is generally more applicable to larger systems.

Sizing. The vessel should be sized for a total volume V_T, which is the sum of the volume V_1 required for pressurization, the volume V_2 required for water expansion and the volume V_3 required for sludge and reserve.

Calculations made on the basis of pressure-volume variations following Boyle's Law are reasonably accurate, assuming that the tank operates at a relatively constant temperature. The minimum gas volume can be determined from the expansion volume V_2 and from the control range between the minimum tank pressure P_1 and the maximum tank pressure P_2. The gas volume varies from the minimum (V_1) to a maximum, which includes the water expansion volume V_2.

The minimum gas volume V_1 can be obtained from:

$$V_1 = P_1 V_2/(P_2 - P_1)$$

where P_1 and P_2 are units of absolute pressure.

An allowance of 10% of the sum of V_1 and V_2 is reasonable for the sludge and reserve capacity, V_3. The volume V_2 required for water expansion should be limited to the actual expansion that occurs during system operation through its minimum to maximum operating temperatures. It is necessary to bleed off water during a start-up cycle from a cold start. It is practicable on small systems, e.g., under 1,000,000 Btu/h to 10,000,000 Btu/h (290 to 2900 kW) to size the expansion vessel for the total water expansion from the initial fill temperature.

4. Pump pressurization in its simplest form consists of a feed pump and a regulator valve. The pump operates continuously, introducing water from the makeup tank into the system. The pressure regulator valve bleeds continuously back into the makeup tank. This method is usually restricted to small process heating systems. However, it can be used to temporarily pressurize a larger system to avoid shutdown during inspection of the expansion tank.

In larger central HTW systems, pump pressurization is combined with a fixed quantity gas compression tank that acts as a buffer. When the pressure rises above a preset value in the buffer tank, a control valve opens to relieve water from the balance line into the makeup storage tank. When the pressure falls below a preset second value, the feed pump is started automatically to pump water from the makeup tank back into the system. The buffer tank is designed to absorb only the limited expansion volume that is required for the pressure control system to function properly; it is usually small.

To prevent corrosion-causing elements, principally oxygen, from entering the HTW system, the makeup storage tank is usually closed and a low-pressure nitrogen cushion of 1 to 5 psi (7 to 35 kPa) gage is maintained. The gas cushion is usually the variable gas quantity type with release to the atmosphere.

Direct Contact Heaters (Cascades)

High temperature water can be obtained from direct contact heaters in which steam from turbine exhaust, extraction or steam boilers is mixed with return water from the system. The mixing takes place in the upper part of the heater where the water cascading from horizontal baffles comes in direct contact with steam (Hansen 1966). The basic systems are shown in Figures 10 and 11.

The steam space in the upper part of the heater serves as the steam cushion for pressurizing the system. The lower part of the heater serves as the system's expansion tank. Where the water heater and the boiler operate under the same pressure, the surplus water is usually returned directly into the boiler through a pipe

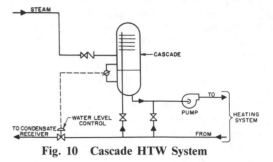

Fig. 10   Cascade HTW System

connecting the outlet of the high temperature water circulating pump to the boiler.

The cascade system is also applicable where both steam and HTW services are required (Hansen and Liddy 1958). Where heat and power production is combined, the direct contact heater becomes the mixing condenser (Hansen and Perrsall 1960).

System Circulating Pumps

Forced circulation boiler systems can be either *one-pump* or *two-pump*. These terms do not refer to the number of pumps, but to the number of groups of pumps installed. In the former (see Figure 5), a single group of pumps assures both generator and distribution system circulation. In this system, both the distribution system and the generators are in series (Carter and Sturdevant 1958).

However, to ensure the minimum flow through the boiler at all times, a bypass around the distribution system must be provided. The one-pump method usually applies only to systems in which the total friction head is relatively low, since the energy loss of available circulating head from throttling in the bypass at times of reduced flow requirements in the district can substantially increase the operating cost.

In the two-pump system (see Figure 6), an additional group of recirculating pumps is installed solely to provide circulation for the generators (Carter and Sturdevant 1958). One pump is often used for each generator to draw water either from the expansion drum or the system return and pump it through the generator into the expansion drum. The system circulating pumps draw water from the expansion drum and circulate it through the distribution system only. The supply temperature

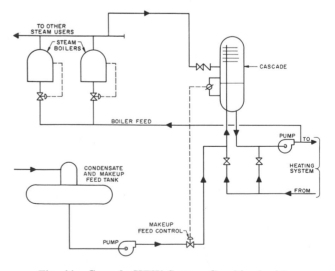

Fig. 11   Cascade HTW System Combined with Boiler Feedwater Preheating

to the distribution system can be varied by mixing water from the return into the supply on the pump suction side. Where zoning is required, several groups of pumps can be used with a different head and different temperature in each zone. The flow rate can also be varied without affecting the generator circulation, and without using a system bypass.

In steam-pressurized systems, the circulating pump is installed in the supply line to maintain all parts of the distributing system at pressures exceeding boiler pressure. This minimizes the danger of flashing into steam.

It is common practice to install a mixing connection from the return to the pump suction that bypasses the HTW generator. This connection is used for start-up and for modulating the supply temperature; it should not be relied on for increasing NPSH at the pump inlet. Where it is impossible to provide the required submergence by proper design, a separate small bore premixing line should be provided.

Hansen (1966) describes *push-pull* pumping, which divides the circulating head equally between two pumps in series. One is placed in the supply and is sized to overcome frictional resistance in the supply line of the heat distribution system. The second pump is in the return and is sized to overcome frictional resistance in the return. The expansion tank pressure is impressed on the system between the pumps. The HTW generator is either between the pumps or in the supply line from the pumps to the distribution system (see Figure 12).

In the push-pull system, the pressures in the supply and the return mains are symmetrical in relation to a line representing the pressure imposed on the system by the pressurizing source (expansion tank). This pressure becomes the system pressure when the pumps are stopped. The heat supply to using equipment or secondary circuits is controlled by two equal regulating valves, one on the inlet and the other on the outlet side, instead of the customary single valve on the leaving side. Both valves are operated in unison from a common controller; there are equal frictional resistances on both sides. Therefore, the pressure in the user circuits or equipment is maintained at all times halfway between the pressures in the supply and return mains. Since the halfway point is located on the symmetry line, the pressure in the user equipment or circuits is always equal to that of the

pressurizing source (expansion tank) plus or minus static heads caused by elevation differences. In other words, no system distribution head is reflected against the user circuit or equipment.

While the pressure in the supply system is higher than that of the expansion tank, the pressure in the return system, being symmetrical to the former, is lower. Therefore, the push-pull method is applicable only in systems where the temperature in the return is always significantly lower than that in the supply. Otherwise, flashing could occur. This is critical and requires careful investigation of the temperature-pressure relationship at all points. The push-pull method is not applicable in reverse-return systems.

The particular feature of push-pull pumping is the overall pressure reduction, permitting use of standard 125 psi (860 kPa) fittings and equipment in many MTW systems. Such systems, combined with secondary pumping, can be connected directly to low temperature terminal equipment in building radiation. Temperature drops normally obtainable only in HTW systems can be achieved with MTW.

For example, 330 °F (166 °C) water can be generated at 90 psig (720 kPa) and distributed at less than 125 psig (960 kPa). Its temperature can be reduced to 200 °F (93 °C) by secondary pumping. The pressure in the terminal equipment then is 90 psig (720 kPa) and the MTW is returned to the primary system at 180 °F (82 °C). The temperature difference between supply and return in the primary MTW system is 150 °F (66 °C), which is comparable to that of an HTW system. In addition, conventional heat exchangers, expansion tanks and water makeup equipment are eliminated from the secondary systems.

DISTRIBUTION PIPING DESIGN

Data for pipe friction are in Chapter 34 of the 1985 FUNDAMENTALS Volume. These pipe friction and fitting loss tables are for a 60 °F (16 °C) water temperature. When applied to HTW systems, the values obtained are excessively high. The data should be used for preliminary pipe sizing only. Final pressure drop calculations should be made using the fundamental *Darcy-Weisbach* equation (on page 34.1 of the 1985 FUNDAMENTALS Volume) in conjunction with friction factors, pipe roughness and fitting loss coefficients presented on page 2.10 of the 1985 FUNDAMENTALS Volume.

The conventional conduit or tunnel distribution systems are used with similar techniques for installation (see Chapter 12). A small valved bypass connection between the supply and the return pipe should be installed at the end of long runs to maintain a slight circulation in the mains during periods of minimum or no demand.

All pipe, valves, and fittings used in HTW systems should comply with the requirements of the ANSI/ASME Standard B-31.1-85, *Power Piping*, and ANSI/ASME Standard B-31.2-68, *Fuel Gas Piping*. These codes state that hot water systems shall be designed for the highest pressure and temperature actually existing in the piping under normal operation. This pressure equals cushion pressure plus pump head plus static pressure. Schedule 40 steel pipe is applicable to most HTW systems with welded steel fittings and steel valves. A minimum number of joints should be used. In many installations, all valves in the piping system are welded or brazed. Flange connections used at major equipment can be serrated, raised flange facing or ring joint. It is desirable to have backseating valves with special packing suitable for this service.

The ratings of valves, pipe and fittings must be checked to determine the specific rating point for the given application. The *pressure* rating for a standard 300 psi (2 MPa) steel valve operating at 400 °F (204 °C) is 665 psi (4.6 MPa). Therefore, it

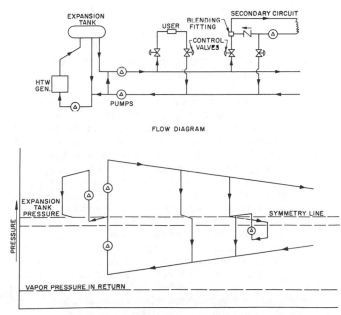

FLOW DIAGRAM

PRESSURE - LOCATION DIAGRAM

Fig. 12 Typical MTW System with Push-Pull Pumping

is generally not necessary to use steel valves and fittings over 300 psi (2 MPa) ratings in HTW systems.

Since high temperature water is more penetrating than low temperature water, leakage caused partly by capillary action should not be ignored because even a small amount of leakage vaporizes immediately. This slight leakage becomes noticeable only on the outside of the gland and stem of the valve where thin deposits of salt are left after evaporation. Avoid screwed joints and fittings in HTW systems. Pipe unions should not be used in place of flange connections, even for small bore piping and equipment.

Individual heating equipment units should be installed with separate valves for shutoff. These should be readily accessible. If the unit is to be isolated for service, valves will be needed in both the supply and return piping to the unit. Valve trim should be stainless steel or a similar alloy. Do not use brass and bronze.

High points in piping should have air vents for collecting and removing air and low points should have provision for drainage. Loop-type expansion joints, in which the expansion is absorbed by deflection of the pipe loop, are preferable to the mechanical type. Mechanical expansion joints must be properly guided and anchored.

HEAT EXCHANGERS

Heat exchangers or converters commonly use steel shells with stainless steel, admiralty metal or cupro-nickel tubes. Copper should not be used in HTW systems above 250°F (121°C). Material must be chosen carefully, considering the pressure-temperature characteristics of the particular system. All connections should be flanged or welded. On larger exchangers, water-box-type construction is desirable to remove the tube bundle without breaking piping connections. Normally, HTW is circulated through the tubes, and because the heated water contains dissolved air, the baffles in the shell should be constructed of the same material as the tubes to control corrosion.

AIR HEATING COILS

In HTW systems over 400°F (204°C), coils should be cupro-nickel or all-steel construction. Below this point, other materials (e.g., red brass) can be used after determining their suitability for the temperatures involved. Coils in outdoor air connections need freeze protection by damper closure or fan shutdown controlled by a thermostat. It is also possible to set the control valve on the preheat coil to a minimum position. This protects against freezing, as long as there is no unbalance in the tube circuits where parallel paths of HTW flow exist. A better method is to provide constant flow through the coil and control heat output with face and bypass dampers or by modulating the water temperature with a mixing pump.

SPACE HEATING EQUIPMENT

In industrial areas, space heating equipment can be operated with the available high temperature water. Convectors and radiators may require water temperatures in the low and medium temperature range [120 to 180°F or 200 to 250°F (49 to 82°C or 93 to 121°C)], depending on their design pressure and proximity to the occupants. The water velocity through the heating equipment affects its capacity. This must be considered in selecting the equipment because, if a large water temperature drop is used, the circulation rate is reduced and consequently the flow velocity may be reduced enough to appreciably lower the heat transfer rate.

Convectors, specially designed to provide low surface temperatures, are now available to operate with water temperatures from 300 to 400°F (149 to 204°C).

These high temperatures are suitable for direct use in radiant panel surfaces. Since radiant output is a fourth-power function of the surface temperature, the surface area requirements are reduced over low temperature water systems. The surfaces can be flat panels consisting of a steel tube, usually 0.38 or 0.5 in. (10 or 13 mm), welded to sheet steel turned up at the edges for stiffening. Several variations are available. Steel pipe can also be used with an aluminum or similar reflector to reflect the heat downward and to prevent smudging the surfaces above the pipe.

Instrumentation and Controls

Pressure gauges should be installed in the pump discharge and suction and at locations where pressure readings will assist operation and maintenance. Thermometers (preferably dial type) or thermometer wells should be installed in the flow and return pipes, the pump discharge and at any other points of major temperature change or where temperatures are important in operating the system. It is desirable to have thermometers and gauges in the piping at the entrance to each building converter.

On steam-pressurized cycles, the temperature of the water leaving the generator should control the firing rate to the generator. A master pressure control operating from the steam pressure in the expansion vessel should be incorporated as a high limit override. Inert-gas-pressurized systems should be controlled from the generator discharge temperature. Combustion controls are discussed in detail in Chapter 23 of the 1983 EQUIPMENT Volume.

In the water-tube generators most commonly used for HTW applications, the flow of water passes through the generator in seconds. The temperature controller must have a rapid response to maintain a reasonably uniform leaving water temperature. In steam pressurized units, the temperature variation must not exceed the anti-flash pressure margin. At 300°F (149°C) a 5°F (3°C) temperature variation corresponds to a 5 psi (35 kPa) variation in the vapor pressure. At 350°F (177°C) the same temperature variation results in a vapor pressure variation of 10 psi (70 kPa). At 400°F (204°C) the variation increases to 15 psi (100 kPa) and at 450°F (232°C) to 22 psi (150 kPa). The permissible temperature swing must be reduced as the HTW temperature increases or the pressure margin must be increased to avoid flashing.

Keep the controls simple. The rapid response through the generator makes it necessary to modulate the combustion rate on all systems with a capacity of over a few million Btu/h (thousands of kW). In the smaller size range, this can be done by high-low firing. In large systems, particularly those used for central heating applications, full modulation of the combustion rate is desirable through at least 20% of full capacity. On-off burner control is generally not used in steam-pressurized cycles because the system loses pressurization during the *off* cycle, which can cause flashing and cavitation at the HTW pumps.

All generators should have separate safety controls to shut down the combustion apparatus when the system pressure or water temperature is high. HTW generators require a minimum water flow at all times to prevent tube failure. Means should be provided to measure the flow and to stop combustion if the flow falls below the minimum value recommended by the generator manufacturer. For inert-gas-pressurized cycles, a low pressure safety control should be included to shut down the combustion system if pressurization is lost. Figure 13 shows the basic schematic control diagram for a HTW generator.

Valve selection and sizing are very important because of relatively high temperature drops and smaller flows in HTW

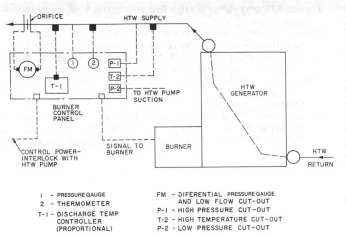

Fig. 13   Control Diagram for HTW Generator

systems. The valve must be sized so that it is effective over its full range of travel. The valve and equipment must be sized to absorb, in the control valve at full flow, not less than half the available pressure difference between supply and return mains where the equipment is served. A valve with equal percentage flow characteristics is needed. Sometimes two small valves provide better control than one large valve. Stainless steel trim is recommended, and all valve body materials and packing should be suitable for high temperatures and pressures. The valve should have a close-off rating at least equal to the maximum head produced by the circulating pump. Generally, two-way valves are more desirable than three-way because of equal percentage flow characteristics and the smaller capacities available in two-way valves. Single-seated valves are preferable to double-seated valves since the latter do not close tightly.

Control valves are commonly located in the return lines from heat transfer units to reduce the valve operating temperature and to prevent plug erosion caused by high temperature water flashing to steam at lower discharge pressure. A typical application is to control the temperature of water being heated in a heat exchanger where the heating medium is high temperature water. The temperature measuring element of the controller is installed on the secondary side and should be located where it can best detect changes to prevent overheating of outlet water. When the measuring element is located in the outlet pipe, there must be a continuous flow through the exchanger and past the ele-

ment. The controller regulates the HTW supply to the primary side by means of the control valve in the HTW return. If the water leaving the exchanger is used for space heating, the set point of the thermostat in this water can be readjusted according to outdoor temperature.

Another typical application is to control a low- or medium-pressure steam generator, usually less than 50 psi (350 kPa) gage, using high temperature water as the heat source. In this application, a proportional pressure controller measures the steam pressure on the secondary side and positions the HTW control valve on the primary side to maintain the desired steam pressure. For general information on automatic controls refer to Chapter 31.

Where submergence is sufficient to prevent flashing in the *vena contracta,* control valves can be in the HTW supply instead of in the return to water heaters and steam generators (see Figure 14). When used in conjunction with a check valve in the return, this arrangement shuts off the high temperature water supply to the heat exchangers if a tube bundle leaks or ruptures.

WATER TREATMENT

Water treatment for HTW systems should be referred to a specialist. Oxygen introduced in makeup water immediately oxidizes steel at these temperatures, and over a period of time the corrosion can be substantial. Other impurities can also harm boiler tubes. Solids in impure water left by invisible vapor escaping at packings increase maintenance requirements. The condition of the water and the steel surfaces should be checked periodically in systems operating at these temperatures.

HEAT STORAGE

The high heat storage capacity in water produces a flywheel effect in most HTW systems that evens out load fluctuations. Systems with normal peaks can obtain as much as 15% added capacity through such heat storage. Excessive peak and low loads of a cyclic nature can be eliminated by a HTW accumulator, based on the principle of stratification. Heat storage in an extensive system can sometimes be increased by bypassing water from the supply into the return at the end of the mains, or by raising the temperature of the returns during periods of low load.

SAFETY CONSIDERATIONS

A properly engineered and operated HTW system is safe and dependable. Careful selection and arrangement of components and materials are important. Piping must be designed and installed to prevent undue stress. When HTW is released to atmospheric pressure, flashing takes place, which absorbs a large portion of the energy. Turbulent mixing of the liquid and vapor with room air reduces the temperature well below 212 °F (100 °C). With low mass flow rates, the temperature of the escaping mixture can fall to 125 to 140 °F (52 to 60 °C) within a short distance, compared with the temperature of the discharge of a low temperature water system, which remains essentially the same as the temperature of the working fluid (Hansen 1959, Armstrong and Harris 1966).

When large mass flow rates of HTW are released to atmospheric pressure in a confined space, e.g., rupture of a large pipe or vessel, a very hazardous condition could exist, similar to that occurring with the rupture of a large steam main. Failures of this nature are rare if good engineering practice is followed in system design.

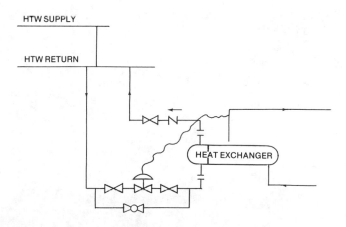

Fig. 14   Heat Exchanger Connections

REFERENCES

Applegate, G. 1958. British and European Design and Construction Methods. ASHRAE Journal Section, *Heating, Piping and Air Conditioning,* March, p. 169.

Armstrong, C.P.; and Harris, W.S. 1966. Temperature Distributions in Steam and Hot Water Jets Simulating Leaks. ASHRAE *Transactions,* Vol. 72, Part I, p. 147.

Blossom, J.S.; and Ziel, P.H. 1959. Pressurizing High-Temperature Water Systems. ASHRAE *Journal,* November, Vol. 1, p. 47.

Carter, C.A.; and Sturdevant, B.L. 1958. Design of High Temperature Water Systems for Military Installations. ASHRAE Journal Section, *Heating, Piping, and Air Conditioning,* February, p. 109.

Hansen, E.G. 1959. Safety of High Temperature Hot Water. *Actual Specifying Engineer,* July.

Hansen, E.G. 1966. Push-pull Pumping Permits Use of MTW in Building Radiation. *Heating, Piping & Air Conditioning,* May, p. 97.

Hansen, E.G.; and Liddy, W. 1958. A Flexible High Pressure Hot Water and Steam Boiler Plant. *Power,* May, p. 109.

Hansen, E.G.; and Perrsall, N.E. 1960. Turbo-Generators Supply Steam for High-Temperature Water Heating. *Air Conditioning, Heating and Ventilating,* June, p. 90.

National Academy of Sciences. 1959. *High Temperature Water for Heating and Light Process Loads. Federal Construction Council Technical Report* No. 37. National Research Council Publication No. 753.

CHAPTER 16

INFRARED RADIANT HEATING

HIGH intensity infrared radiant heating systems use compact self-contained heaters to obtain high radiant energy output. Infrared radiant heaters operate at source temperatures from 500 to 5000 °F (260 to 2760 °C) (see Chapter 30 of the 1983 EQUIPMENT Volume for available infrared heaters.)

High intensity radiant heating systems can be designed as *spot heating* systems for selective heating of individuals or, more commonly, for *total building heating*. Complete systems have been applied to industrial, commercial, and school buildings and use energy for space heating effectively. They can also be used in loading docks, grandstands, theaters, and store marquees.

When infrared comfort heating is used, the environment is characterized by (1) a high-temperature, strongly directional radiant field created by the infrared heaters, (2) a low-temperature radiant field represented by the walls or enclosing surfaces, and (3) ambient air temperatures, often lower than those found with conventional convective heating systems.

In room installations where heater mounting heights are low, the floor may be strongly irradiated, adding substantially to (2) above. The convected heat loss from the radiant heater will increase ambient temperatures. Ultimately, the combined action of these factors determines occupant comfort and the thermal acceptability of the environment.

ELEMENTARY DESIGN RELATIONSHIPS

When using radiant heating for human comfort, four simplifying concepts are used to describe the temperature and energy characteristics of the total radiant environment. They are as follows:

1. *Mean Radiant Temperature* ($\bar{t}_r$) is the temperature of an imaginary isothermal *black* enclosure in which an occupant would exchange the same amount of heat by radiation as in an actual nonuniform environment.
2. *Ambient Air Temperature* (t_a) is the temperature of the air surrounding the occupant.
3. *Operative Temperature* (t_o) is the temperature of a uniform isothermal black enclosure in which the occupant exchanges the same amount of heat by radiation and convection as in an actual nonuniform environment.
4. *Effective Radiant Flux* (ERF) is defined as the *net radiant heat exchanged* at the ambient temperature t_a between an occupant, whose surface is hypothetical, and all enclosing surfaces and directional heat sources and sinks. In other words, ERF is the net radiant energy received by the occupant from all surfaces and sources, whose temperatures *differ* from the ambient air t_a. This concept is particulary useful in high intensity radiant heating applications.

The preparation of this chapter is assigned to TC 6.5, Radiant Space Heating and Cooling.

The relationship between the above factors is shown for an occupant, at surface temperature t_{sf}, exchanging sensible heat (H_m) in a room with ambient air temperature (t_a) and mean radiant temperature ($\bar{t}_r$). The linear radiative and convective heat transfer coefficients are h_r and h_c, respectively; the latter coefficient is a function of the air movement (v) present. The heat balance equation is:

$$H_m = h_r(t_{sf} - \bar{t}_r) + h_c(t_{sf} - t_a) \qquad (1)$$

During thermal equilibrium, H_m is metabolic heat less work less evaporative cooling by sweating. By definition of Operative Temperature,

$$H_m = (h_r + h_c)(t_{sf} - t_o) \qquad (1a)$$

Thus

$$t_o = (h_r \cdot \bar{t}_r + h_c t_a)/(h_r + h_c) \qquad (2)$$

where the sum ($h_r + h_c$) is the combined heat transfer coefficient (h). In other words, t_o is an average of $\bar{t}_r$ and t_a weighted by their respective heat transfer coefficients and represents how people sense the thermal level of their total environment as a single temperature.

By rearranging Equation (1),

$$H_m + h_r(\bar{t}_r - t_a) = h(t_{sf} - t_a) \qquad (3)$$

where $h_r(\bar{t}_r - t_a)$ is, by definition, the Effective Radiant Field (ERF) and represents the *radiant energy absorbed by the occupant from all temperature sources different from the ambient t_a*.

The principal relationships between $\bar{t}_r$, t_a, t_o, and ERF follow:

$$\text{ERF} = h_r(\bar{t}_r - t_a) \qquad (4)$$

$$\text{ERF} = h(t_o - t_a) \qquad (5)$$

$$\bar{t}_r = t_a + \text{ERF}/h_r \qquad (6)$$

$$t_o = t_a + \text{ERF}/h \qquad (7)$$

$$\bar{t}_r = t_a + (h/h_r)(t_o - t_a) \qquad (8)$$

$$t_o = t_a + (h_r/h)(\bar{t}_r - t_a) \qquad (9)$$

In Equations 1 through 9, the radiant environment is treated as a black body with temperature $\bar{t}_r$. The effect of the emissivity of the source, radiating at absolute temperature in degrees Rankine (Kelvin), and the absorptance of the skin and clothed surfaces is reflected in the effective values of $\bar{t}_r$ or ERF and not in the linear radiation exchange coefficient h_r, which is given in general by:

$$h_r = f_{eff} \cdot 4\sigma[(\bar{t}_r + t_a)/2 + \underline{T}]^3 \qquad (10)$$

where f_{eff} is the ratio of the radiating surface of the human body to its total *DuBois surface area* (A_D) and is 0.71 (see Equation 15 and discussion); σ is the *Stefan-Boltzmann Constant*, which is 0.1713×10^{-8} Btu/h·ft^2 R^4 or 5.67×10^{-8} W/(m^2·K^4), and $\underline{T} = 460$ when temperatures are in °F and $\underline{T} = 273$ when temperatures are in °C.

The convection coefficient for an occupant is:

$$h_c = C_1 v^{0.5} \tag{11}$$

where

h_c = convection coefficient, Btu/h · °F [W/(m² · k)]
v = air movement, fpm (m/s)
C_1 = constant, 0.107 (8.5)

When $\bar{t}_r > t_a$, the radiant flux ERF adds heat to the body system; when $t_a > \bar{t}_r$, heat is lost from the body system by radiant cooling. ERF is independent of the surface temperature of the occupant and can be measured directly by a black Globe Thermometer or any blackbody radiometer or flux meter using the ambient air (t_a) as its heat sink.

In the above definitions, the body clothing and skin surface have been treated as a black body, exchanging radiation with an imaginary blackbody surface at temperature $\bar{t}_r$. However, the effectiveness of any individual radiating source on human occupants is governed by the absorptance (α) of the skin and clothing surface for the color temperature in °R (K) of the radiating source. The relationship between α and temperature is illustrated in Figure 1. The values for α are those expected relative to a matte-black surface normally used on the Globe Thermometer or any radiometer for measuring radiant energy. For radiators below 1700 °F (1200 K), skin and clothing surfaces may be considered essentially black bodies for design purposes. A gas radiator usually operates at 1700 °F (1200 K); a quartz lamp, for example, radiates at 4000 °F (2500 K) with 240 volts; the sun's radiating temperature is 10,000 °F (5800 K). The use of α in estimating the ERF and t_o caused by sources radiating at temperatures above 1700 °F (1200 K) is discussed later in this chapter.

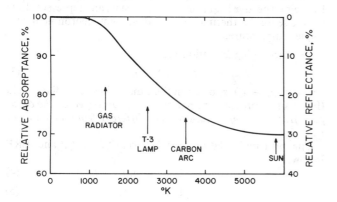
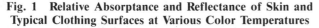

Fig. 1   **Relative Absorptance and Reflectance of Skin and Typical Clothing Surfaces at Various Color Temperatures**

DESIGN CRITERIA FOR ACCEPTABLE RADIANT HEATING

Perceptions of comfort, temperature, and thermal acceptability are related to activity, the transfer of body heat from the skin to the environment, and the resulting physiological adjustments and body temperatures. Heat transfer is affected by the ambient air temperature, thermal radiation, air movement, humidity, and clothing worn. Thermal sensation is described by feelings of *hot, warm, slightly warm, neutral, slightly cool, cool,* and *cold*. An acceptable environment is one in which at least 80% of the occupants would perceive a thermal sensation between "slightly cool" and "slightly warm." Comfort is associated with a neutral thermal sensation during which the human body regulates its internal temperature with a minimum of physiological effort in the activity concerned. Warm discomfort, in contrast, is related primarily to *physiological strain*

necessary to maintain the body's thermal equilibrium rather than to the temperature sensation experienced. For a full discussion on the interrelation of the above physical, psychological, and physiological factors involved, refer to Chapter 8 of the 1985 FUNDAMENTALS Volume.

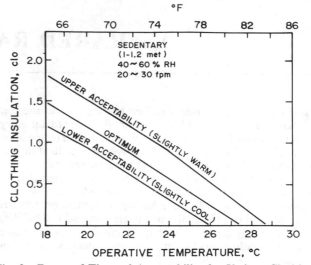

Fig. 2   **Range of Thermal Acceptability for Various Clothing Insulations and Operative Temperatures**

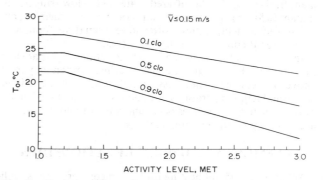

Fig. 3   **Optimum Operative Temperatures for Active People in Low Air Movement Environments**

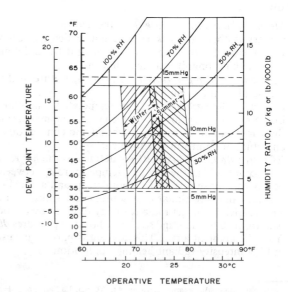

Fig. 4   **ASHRAE Comfort Chart Modified for Radiant Heating**

ASHRAE studies show a linear relationship between the clothing insulation worn and the t_o for comfort. This is illustrated for a sedentary subject in Figure 2. Figure 3 shows how activity and clothing together affect the t_o for comfort. Both figures use a constant humidity at 40 to 60% RH. Figure 4 shows the effects of high and low humidity for a sedentary person wearing average clothing and how t_o and humidity combine to form loci of constant Effective Temperature (ET*), which is indexed on an imaginary 50% RH curve on a psychrometric chart with ambient temperature P_a and t_o. Figure 4 also shows how, at a given ET* level for comfort, the corresponding t_o lowers slightly as humidity increases above 50% RH or increases slightly as humidity decreases below 50% RH. In other words, a comfortable t_o at 50% RH would become slightly warmer as humidity rises or slightly cooler as humidity lowers below the 50% level. Changes in humidity have a much greater effect on "warm" and "hot" discomfort. In contrast, cold discomfort is only slightly affected by humidity and is very closely related to a "cold" thermal sensation. Figures 2, 3, and 4 are adapted from those in ANSI/ASHRAE *Standard 55-1981, Thermal Environmental Conditions for Human Occupancy*.

In summary, the desired specifications for any radiant heating installation designed for human occupancy and acceptability must involve the following primary steps:

1. Define the probable activity (metabolism and clothing worn by the occupant and the air movement in the occupied space. Two examples are the following:

   Case 1: Sedentary (1.1 met) 0.6 clo; air movement 0.15 m/s;
   Case 2: Light work (2 met); 0.9 clo; 0.5 m/s;

2. Select from either Figure 2 or Figure 3 the optimum t_o for comfort and acceptability:

   Case 1: $t_o = 23\,°C$;   *Case 2:* $t_o = 17\,°C$

3. For the ambient air temperature (t_a) concerned, calculate the mean radiant temperature ($\bar{t}_r$) and/or ERF necessary for comfort and thermal acceptability.

   Case 1: For $t_a = 15\,°C$
   From (10), $h_r = 0.71(6.0) = 4.3\ \mathrm{W/(m^2 \cdot K)}$

   From (11), $h_c = 3.3$; $h = 7.6$
   By Eq. (8) and (4), ERF for comfort equals
   7.6(23 − 15) or 61 W/m²;
   $t_r = 15 + 61/4.3 = 29.2\,°C$.

   Case 2: For $t_a = 10\,°C$ at 50% RH;
   $h_r = 0.71(5.5) = 3.9$
   $h_c = 7.1$; $h = 11\ \mathrm{W/(m^2 \cdot K)}$
   For comfort, ERF = 11(17 − 10) or 77 W/m²
   $\bar{t}_r = 10 + 77/3.9 = 29.7\,°C$

4. The t_o for comfort, predicted by Figure 2, falls on the "slightly cool" side when humidity is low; for very high humidities, the predicted t_o for comfort appears to be "slightly warm." This small effect on comfort may be seen in the modified ASHRAE Comfort Chart (Figure 4).

   For example: for high humidity at $t_{dp} = 13\,°C$, the t_o for comfort is:
   Case 1: $t_o = 25\,°C$, compared with 23 °C at 50% RH.
   Case 2: $t_o = 15.2\,°C$, compared with 17 °C at 50% RH.

For installations where thermal acceptability is the primary consideration, humidity can be ignored in preliminary design specifications. However, for many conditions where radiant heating and the work level cause sweating and high heat stress, humidity is a major consideration.

GENERAL DESIGN CONSIDERATIONS FOR BEAM RADIANT HEATERS

Spot beam radiant heat conveniently and economically improves comfort and acceptability at a specific location in a large, poorly heated work area. The design problem is specifying the type, capacity, and orientation of the beam heater. The parameters that must be considered are discussed below.

Using the same reasoning for Equations 1 through 9, the radiant flux (ΔERF), which must be added to an unheated work space having operative temperature t_{uo} that results in a t_o for comfort (given by Figure 2 or 3), is:

$$\Delta ERF = h(t_o - t_{uo}) \tag{12}$$

or

$$t_o = t_{uo} + \Delta ERF/h \tag{12a}$$

This equation is unaffected by air movement. The heat transfer coefficients h_r and h for the occupant in Equation (12) and (13) are always those given by Equation (10) and (11).

The radiant field term ERF is, by definition, the energy absorbed *per unit total body surface* (A_D), known as the *DuBois Area*, and *not* the total effective radiating area (A_{eff}) of the body.

Simple Geometry of Beam Heating

Figure 5 illustrates the parameters that must be considered in specifying a beam radiant heater designed to produce the ERF (or $\bar{t}_r$) necessary for comfort at the occupant's work station. They are as follows:

I_K = irradiance from beam heater, Btu/h · sr (W/sr)
K = absolute irradiating temperature of beam heater, °R, (K)
β = elevation angle of heater in degrees (at 0°, the beam is horizontal)
Φ = azimuth angle of heater in degrees (at 0°, the beam is facing the subject)
d = distance from beam heater to center of occupant, ft (m)
A_p = projected area of occupant on a plane normal to direction of heater beam (Φ, β), ft² (m²)
α_K = absorptance of skin-clothing surface at emitter temperature °F (K) (see Figure 1)
Ω = solid angle of heater beam, steradians

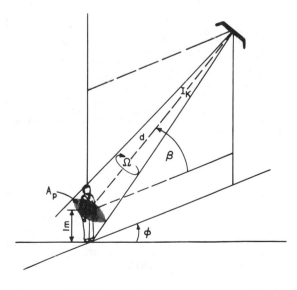

Fig. 5   Geometry and Symbols for Describing Beam Heaters

ERF may also be measured as the heat absorbed at the clothing and skin surface of the occupant from a beam heater at absolute temperature and given in Btu/h·ft² (W/m²) by:

$$ERF = [\alpha_K \cdot I_K \cdot (A_p/d^2)]/A_D \qquad (14)$$

where (A_p/d^2) is the solid angle subtended by the projected area of occupant from the radiating beam heater I_K, which is treated here as a point source. A_{Du} is the *DuBois Area*, which is $0.0621\ W^{0.425}\ H^{0.725}$ in lb and ft ($0.202\ W^{0.425}\ H^{0.725}$ in kg and m).

Two radiation area factors are defined as:

$$f_{eff} = A_{eff}/A_D \qquad (15)$$

$$f_p = A_p/A_{eff} \qquad (16)$$

where A_{eff} is the effective radiating area of the total body surface. Equation (14) becomes:

$$ERF = \alpha_K \cdot f_{eff} \cdot f_p \cdot I_K/d^2 \qquad (17)$$

Fanger (1973) developed precision optical methods to evaluate the angle factors (f_{eff} and f_p) over the range of Φ and β angles, covering 4π steridians for both sitting and standing positions and for males and females. An average value for f_{eff} of 0.71 for both sitting and standing is accurate within ±2%. The variations in angle factor (f_p) over various azimuths and elevations while seated or standing are illustrated in Figures 6 and 7 and, according to Fanger, they apply equally to males and females.

Infrared heating equipment manufacturers usually supply performance specifications for their equipment (Gagge, et al. 1967). The relation between color temperature of heaters and the applied voltage or wattage is also available. Gas-fired radiators usually operate at constant emitting temperatures of 1340 to 1700°F (1000 to 1200 K). Figure 1 relates the absorptance (α_K) to the radiating temperature of the radiant source. Manufacturers also supply the radiant flux distribution of beam heaters with and without reflectors. Figures 8 through 11 illustrate the radiant flux distribution for four typical electric and gas-fired radiant heaters. In general, electrical beam heaters produce as much as 70 to 80% of their total energy output as radiant heat in contrast to 40% for gas-fired types. In practice, the designer

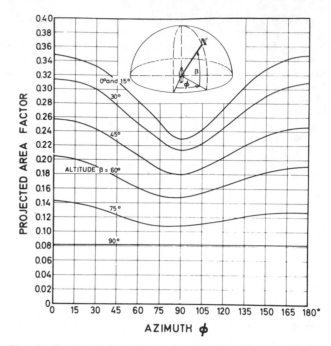

Fig. 7   Projected Area Factor for Standing Persons, Nude and Clothed (Fanger 1973)

should choose a beam heater that will "illuminate" the subject with acceptable uniformity. Even with complete "illumination" by a beam 0.609 sr (21.6°) wide, Figure 8 shows that only 8% (100% · 1225 · 0.109/1620) of the initial input wattage to the heater is usable for specifying the necessary I_K in Eq. (17). The corresponding percentages for Figures 9, 10, and 11 are 5%, 4%, and 2%. The last two are for gas-fired beams. Finally, the balance of the input energy to the beam heater not used for irradiating the occupant directly will ultimately increase the t_{uo} or t_a and $\bar{t}_{ru}$ of the room environment. This increase will reduce the original ERF required for comfort and acceptability. The continuing reradiation and convective heating of surrounding walls and the presence of air movement ultimately make precise calculations of radiant heat exchange difficult.

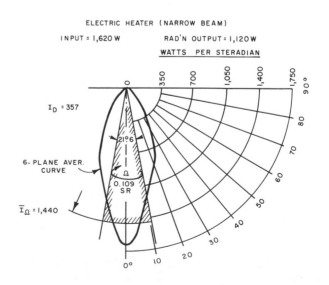

Fig. 8   Radiant Flux Distribution Curve of Typical Narrow-Beam High Intensity Electric Infrared Heaters

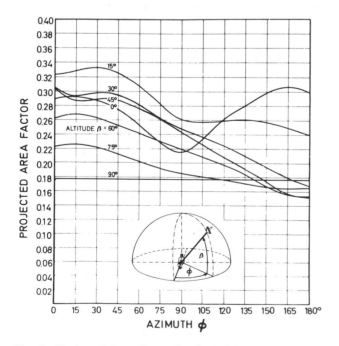

Fig. 6   Projected Area Factor for Seated Persons, Nude and Clothed (Fanger 1973)

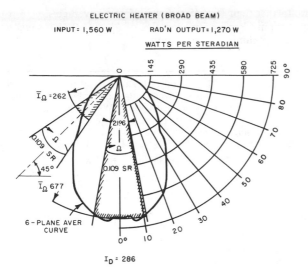

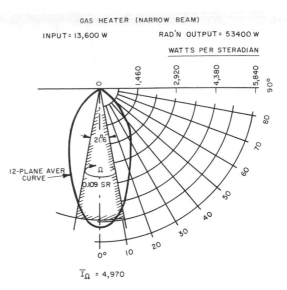

Fig. 9 Radiant Flux Distribution Curve of Typical Broad-Beam High Intensity Atmospheric Gas-Fired Infrared Heaters

Fig. 10 Radiant Flux Distribution Curve of Typical Narrow-Beam High Intensity Atmospheric Gas-Fired Infrared Heaters

The above basic principles are illustrated by the following examples:

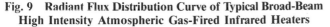

Example 1: Determine the beam radiation intensity required for comfort from a quartz lamp (Figure 8) when the worker is sedentary, lightly clothed (0.5 clo), and seated. The ambient t_a is 15 °C, with air movement 0.15 m/s. The lamp is mounted on the 2.4 m-high ceiling and is directed at the back of the seated person so that the elevation angle β is 45° and the azimuth is 180°. Assume $t_a = t_{uo} = \bar{t}_{ru}$.

Answer. From Figure 3, the required t_o for comfort is 24.6 °C (for 1.1 met, 0.5 clo). $h = h_r + h_c = 4.4 + 3.3$ or 7.6 [from Eq. (10) and (11)]. From Eq. (5), ERF for comfort = 7.6(24.6 − 15) or 73 W/m². The ($\bar{t}_r - t_a$) difference would be 73/4.4 or 17 °C from Eq. (4).

At 240 volt operation, $\alpha_K = 0.85$ at 2200 K (from Figure 1); $f_{eff} = 0.71$; $f_p = 0.17$ (Figure 7); $d = (2.4 - 0.6)$ or 1.8 m; where 0.6 is sitting height of occupant.

By Eq. (17), the irradiation (I_K) from the beam heater necessary for comfort is:

$$I_K = \mathrm{ERF} \cdot d^2/(\alpha_K \cdot f_{eff} \cdot f_p) \qquad (17a)$$
$$= 73(1.8)^2/(0.85 \cdot 0.71 \cdot 0.17)$$
$$= 2305 \text{ W/sr}$$

Example 2: For the same occupant in **Example 1**, when two beams located on the ceiling are directed downward at the subject at 45° and at azimuth angle 90° on each side, what would be the I_K required from each heater?

The ERF for comfort from each beam is 73/2 or 36.5 W/m² · f_p is 0.25 (from Figure 6). Hence, the required irradiation from each beam is:

$$I_K = 36.5(1.8)^2/(0.9 \cdot 0.71 \cdot 0.25)$$
$$= 740 \text{ W/sr (at half power } V = 155V, K \cong 2000, \alpha_K \cong 0.9.)$$

This estimate indicates that two beams similar to Figure 9, each operating at half rate of voltage, can produce the necessary ERF for comfort. A comparison between the I_K-requirements in **Examples 1** and **2** shows that irradiating the back while sitting is much less efficient than irradiating from the side.

Example 3: A broad beam gas-fired radiator is mounted 5 m above the floor. The radiator is directed 45° downward toward a standing subject 4 m away (see Heater #1 in Figure 12).

Question (a): What is the resulting ERF from the beam acting on subject? By Eq. (21) ERF = $\alpha_K \cdot f_{eff} \cdot f_p \cdot I_K/d^2$; $\alpha_K = 0.97$ (Figure 1); $f_{eff} = 0.71$; $f_p = 0.26$ (at $\beta = 45°$; $\Phi = 0°$) (Figure 7); $d^2 = 4^2 + 4^2$, here the center of the standing man is 1 m off the floor; $I_K = 2340$ W/sr (Figure 11).

Answer: By Eq. (17), ERF at position C = 13.1 W/m². If the heater was 2 m from the subject instead of 5.7, ERF would be 23.3.

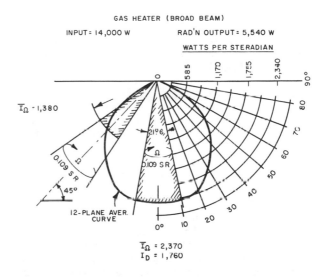

Fig. 11 Radiant Flux Distribution Curve of Typical Broad-Beam High Intensity Atmospheric Gas-Fired Infrared Heaters

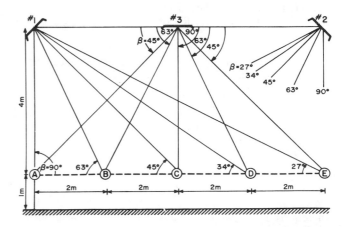

Fig. 12 Calculation of Total ERF From Three Gas-Fired Heaters on a Worker Standing at Positions A through E

Question (b): How does the ERF vary along the 0° azimuth, every 2 m beginning at a point directly under the heater (#1 in Figure 12) and for elevations $\beta = 90°$ at A, 63.4° at B, 45° at C, 33.6° at D and 26.6° at E. The values for f_p for the five positions are (A) 0.08, (B) 0.19, (C) 0.26, (D) 0.30, and (E) 0.33.

Answer: Since the beam is directed 45° downward, the deviation from the beam center for a person standing at the five positions (A-E) are respectively 45°, 18.4°, 0°, 11.4°, and 18.4°; the corresponding I_K values from Figure 12 are 1450, 2340, 2340, 2340, and 2340. The respective d^2 are 16, 16 + 4, 16 + 16, 16 + 36, 16 + 64. The ERF for a person standing in the five positions are (A) 5; (B) 14; (C) 13; (D) 9.5; and (E) 6.5 all in W/m^2 (rounding to nearest 0.5 W).

Question (c): How will the total ERF at each of the five locations A-E vary if two additional heaters (#2 and #3 in Figure 12) are added 5 m above the floor over positions C and E? The center heater is directed downward, the outer one directed as above, 45° towards the center of the room.

At each of five room locations (A, B, C, D, E), the ERF from each of the three radiators are added to determine the total ERF affecting the person standing.

From the symmetry for the three positions, the total field ERF for the five is ERF$_1$ + ERF$_2$ + ERF$_3$

(A) 5 + 8 + 6.5		or	19.5
(B) 14 + 13.5 + 9.5		or	37
(C) 13 + 8 + 13		or	34
(D) 9.5 + 13.5 + 14		or	37
(E) 6.5 + 8 + 5		or	19.5

Average ΣERF over positions B, C, and D = 36 W/m^2.

Question (d): What would be the lowest acceptable t_a for a standing normally clothed worker in the B-D area?

From Eq. (5), the lowest t_a is:

$$t_a = t_o(\text{for comfort}) - \frac{\Sigma ERF}{h}$$

Answer: For a standing person, $h \cong 7.5$ W/(m$^2 \cdot$ k) and the value for ΣERF/h is now 36/7.5 or almost 5 K. Since the t_o for comfort is in range 22-23 °C, the minimum acceptable t_a would be 17-18 °C.

FLOOR RERADIATION

In most radiant heater installations, local floor areas are strongly irradiated. Within these areas, the floor absorbs most of this energy and warms to an equilibrium temperature (t_f) higher than that of the ambient air (t_a) and the unheated room enclosure surfaces. The temperature of the unheated areas (walls, ceiling, and floor distant from heaters) can be assumed to be the same as the air temperature. Part of the energy directly absorbed by the floor is transmitted by conduction to the cooler underside (or, for slabs-on-grade, to the ground), part is convected to room air, and the remainder is reradiated. The warmer floor will raise effective ERF or $\bar{t}_r$ over that caused by the heater alone.

For a person standing on a large flat floor area, raised to temperature t_f by direct radiation, the linearized $\bar{t}_r$, caused by the floor and unheated walls, on the occupant is:

$$\bar{t}_{rf} = F_{p-f} t_f + (1 - F_{p-f})t_a \qquad (18)$$

where all unheated walls, ceiling, and ambient air are assumed to be t_a, and F_{p-f} is the angle factor governing the radiation exchange between the heated floor and the person.

The ERF$_f$ from the floor affecting the occupant, caused by the ($t_f - t_a$) difference, is:

$$ERF_f = h_r(\bar{t}_{rf} - t_a) \qquad (19)$$
$$= h_r F_{p-f}(t_f - t_a) \qquad (19a)$$

where h_r is again the linear radiation transfer coefficient for a person as given by Eq. (10). Figures 50 or 53 in Fanger (1973) shows F_{p-f} is 0.44 for a standing or sitting subject when walls

are farther than 16 ft (5 m) away. For an average size 16 ft by 16 ft room (5 m by 5 m), a value of $F_{p-f} = 0.35$ is suggested for this preliminary estimation.

Example 4: If the floor temperature of a room fitted with radiant heaters is raised 10° above t_a, what is the expected increase in radiant field (ERF$_f$) affecting a standing occupant? With air movement of 0.15 m/s, what increase in $t_o - t_a$ for comfort can be expected?

Answer: Using average values for $h_r = 4.4$ W/(m$^2 \cdot$ K) and a combined coefficient for man = 7.7, from Eq. (19) the radiant field is:

$$ERF_f = 4.4 \cdot 0.35 \cdot 10 = 15.4 \text{ W/m}^2$$

and the difference

$$t_o - t_a = 15.4/7.7 \text{ or } 2 \text{ K from Eq. (7)}.$$

In other words, raising the floor 10 °C, the operative temperature affecting the occupant is 2 K above the ambient t_a.

Example 5: For the three gas-fired heaters shown in Figure 12 and described in Questions (a), (b), and (c) of Example 3, what would be the expected rise in the floor temperature above t_a, and how would it affect the lowest acceptable t_a in the working area B-D?

Answer: Assuming that α_K for the floor is unity for the gas heaters, that the equivalent I_K in B-D area for three heaters directed downward to the floor is 2340 W/sr, that the value for d^2 from heater to floor is 25 m^2, that each unit floor area in the B-D area is evenly illuminated, and that there is *no heat conduction* through the floor to the ground or space below, the equilibrium heat balance per unit area of the floor is:

$$J_K/d^2 = (h_{cf} + h_{rf})(t_f - t_a)$$

or

$$2340/25 = (1.5 + 5.4/2)(t_f - t_a)$$

where
     $h_{cf} = 1.5$ (estimated)
     $h_{rf} = 4\sigma (273 + t_f)^3 \cdot f_{f-room}$

Hence $t_f - t_a = 21.3$ °K

Hence from Eq. (19)

$$ERF_f = 4.4 \cdot 0.35 \cdot 21.3 = 33 \text{ W/m}^2$$

The total ERF, acting on the occupant, is now 36 W/m^{-2} for direct radiation from heaters (see Question c) *plus* the 33 W/m^{-2} from the floor itself. The acceptable $t_o - t_a$ difference would be (36 + 33)/7.8 or 9 °K. For a comfortable t_o or 23 or 24 °C, the lowest acceptable t_a is 14 or 15 °C.

The above example illustrates a significant design problem. Here the floor was assumed to be "adiabatic." For this *ideal* floor, its reradiation would be as effective for warming the occupant as the direct radiation from the gas-beam heaters.

In reality, the absorbed radiation heat lost by conduction through each unit area of floor is a function of the product $(k_f/d_f)(t_f - t_{gr})$ where k_f is the average specific conductivity for floor thickness d_f, and t_{gr} is the temperature of the ground or surface below the floor.

For total space heating, especially during heating and cooling cycles, the factor describing the *thermal inertia* of the floor is $(k\varrho c)^{-0.5}$, where k is the specific conductivity, ϱ is the density, and c is the specific heat.

In summary, when radiant heaters warm occupants in a selected area of a poorly heated space, the radiation heat necessary for comfort consists of two additive components: (1) the ERF directly caused by the heater and (2) reradiation ERF$_f$ from the floor. The effectiveness of floor reradiation can be improved by choosing flooring with a low specific conductivity. Flooring with high thermal inertia may be desirable during radiant transients, which may occur as the heaters are cycled by a thermostat set at the desired operative temperature t_o in the work area.

Asymmetric Radiant Fields

In the past, comfort heating has required that flux distribution in occupied areas be uniform, which is not possible with beam radiant heaters. The phrase "reasonable uniform radiation distribution" is used as a practical design requirement. There are many asymmetric radiation fields that are very pleasant, such as lying in the sun on a cool day or standing in front of a warm fire. While common sense suggests not to place a radiant beam heater too close to the subject, a limited amount of asymmetry is allowable for comfort heating. However, there are no fully satisfactory criteria for judging what degree of asymmetry is allowable.

For this purpose, Fanger (1980) proposed that a "Radiant Temperature Asymmetry" be defined as the difference between the plane radiant temperature of two opposing surfaces. "Plane radiant temperature" is the equivalent $\bar{t}_{r1}$, caused by radiation on one side of the subject, compared with the equivalent $\bar{t}_{r2}$, caused by radiation on the opposite side. For a subject sitting in a chair and heated by two lamps oriented as in Example 2, a $(\bar{t}_r - t_a)$ asymmetry as high as 31 °F (17 °C) has been observed as comfortable for normally clothed subjects but only as high as 20 °F (11 °C) for unclothed subjects (Gagge et al. 1967). Both values applied to eight subjects. For an unclothed subject lying on an insulated bed under a horizontal level bank of lamps, neutral temperature sensation occurred at a 72 °F (22 °C) t_o, which corresponded to a $t_o - t_a$ of 20 °F (11 °C) or $\bar{t}_r - t_a$ of 27 °F (15 °C), both averaged for eight subjects (Stevens et al. 1969). In studies on heated ceilings, the asymmetry, when 80% of eight male and eight female clothed subjects voted conditions to be comfortable and acceptable, was 20 °F (11 °C). The latter case compared the floor and heated ceilings. In Example 3, Question (c) above, for the combined direct versus floor reradiation, the resulting $(\bar{t}_{rh} - \bar{t}_{rf})$ is about 1 °F (0.5 °C), which indicates negligible asymmetry. In general, the human body has a great ability to sum sensations spatially caused by radiant heat from many hot and cold sources on the skin surface. For example, Australian aborigines sleep unclothed next to open fires in the desert at night, where t_a is 43 °F (6 °C), the $\bar{t}_r$ caused directly by the three fires alone is 171 °F (77 °C), by the cold sky, $\bar{t}_r$ is 30 °F (−1 °C); the resulting t_o during sleep is 82 °F (28 °C), a value acceptable for human comfort when the subject is unclothed and acclimatized to cold (Scholander 1958).

From the limited field and laboratory data available, an allowable design radiant asymmetry of 22 ± 5 °F (12 ± 3 K) should cause little discomfort over the comfortable t_o range used by ANSI/ASHRAE *Standard* 55-1981 in Figures 2 and 3 above. Clothing insulation tends to raise the acceptable asymmetry, while increasing air movement reduces it. Increased activity also reduces human sensitivity to changing $\bar{t}_r$ or t_o and, consequently, increases the allowable asymmetry. In conclusion, radiant asymmetry caused by high intensity IR heaters is not a major cause of discomfort. However, the design engineer should use caution whenever asymmetry, either measured by a direct beam radiometer or estimated by calculation, causes a greater $\Delta \bar{t}_r$ than 27 °F (15 K) from two opposing directions.

SYSTEM DESIGN

Figure 13 indicates the basic radiation patterns commonly used in design for radiation from point or line sources (Boyd 1962). The area radiated by a point source varies as the square of the distance from the source. The area from a (short) line source also varies substantially as the square of distance with about the same area as the circle actually radiated at that distance. For line sources, the width of the pattern is determined by the reflector shape and position of the element within the reflector. The

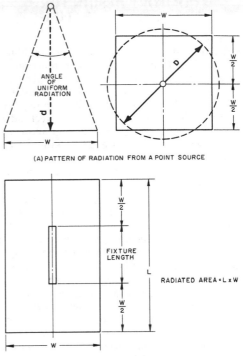

(A) PATTERN OF RADIATION FROM A POINT SOURCE

(B) PATTERN OF RADIATION FROM A LINE SOURCE

The projected area (W^2) normal to a beam Ω sr wide at distance d is $\Omega \cdot d^2$. The floor area irradiated by a beam heater at an angle elevation β is $W^2/\sin \beta$. Fixture length (L) increases the area irradiated by the factor $(1 + L/W)$.

Fig. 13 Basic Radiation Patterns Used in System Design (Boyd 1962)

rectangular area used for installation purposes as the pattern of radiation from a line source assumes a length equal to the width plus the fixture length. Although the length is often two or three times the pattern width, the assumed basis is satisfactory for design.

Electric infrared fixtures are often identified by their beam pattern (Rapp and Gagge 1967). The beam referred to is the radiation distribution normal to the line source element. The following definition is suggested for identifying beam characteristics:

The beam of a high intensity infrared fixture is that area in which the intensity is at least 80% of the maximum intensity encountered anywhere within the beam when measured in the plane in which maximum control of energy distribution is exercised.

The extent of the beam is usually designated in angular degrees and may be symmetrical or asymmetrical in shape. For adaptation to their design specifications, some manufacturers indicate beam characteristics based on 50% maximum intensity.

The control contemplated for an electric system affects the desirable maximum end-to-end fixture spacing. Since *actual* length of pattern is about three times the *design* pattern length, control in three equal stages is made by placing every third fixture on the same circuit. Where all fixtures are controlled by input controllers or variable voltage to electric units, end-to-end fixture spacing can be nearly three times the design pattern length. Side-to-side minimum spacing is determined by the distribution pattern of the fixture and is not influenced by the method of control.

COMFORT DESIGN FOR TOTAL SPACE HEATING

Where radiant equipment is applied to total building heating, the conditions differ from conventional heating only slightly by a moderately elevated ERF, $\bar{t}_r$, or t_o, over the ambient t_a. Relatively standard methods of design can be used, although informal studies indicate that radiant heating requires a lower heating capacity than convection heating. Direct radiation and reradiation from warm floors on personnel allow air temperatures to be lower than with convection heating. Some electric radiant heaters emit a significant amount of visible light. In some cases, these systems then serve the combined purpose of heating and illumination.

Most gas radiation systems for full building heating concentrate the bulk of capacity at mounting heights of 10 to 16 ft (3 to 5 m) at the perimeter, directed at the floor near the walls. Mounting of units at considerably greater heights is not unusual. In any event, successful application depends upon supplying the proper amount of heat in the occupied area. Heaters should be located to take maximum advantage of the pattern of radiation produced. Exceptions to perimeter placement include walls with high transmission losses and extreme height, as well as large roof areas where roof heat losses exceed perimeter and other heat losses.

Electric infrared systems installed indoors for complete building heating have used layouts in which radiation is uniformly distributed throughout the area used by people, as well as layouts emphasizing perimeter placement, such as in ice hockey rinks.

For general area heating (large areas within larger areas), the orientation of equipment and people is less important than in spot heating. With reasonably uniform radiation distribution provided in work or living areas, exact orientation of the units can be ignored. To compensate for cold walls, higher intensities of radiation may be desirable near those walls with outside exposure. For frequently occupied work locations close to outside walls, radiation shields (preferably reflective to infrared), fastened a few inches from the wall and allowing for free air circulation between the wall and shield, often prove effective.

In full building heating, unit orientation is of concern where radiant and convective output best overcome the structure's heat losses. The objective of a complete heating system should be to provide a warm floor with low conductance to the heat sink beneath the floor. This thermal storage may permit cycling of units with standard controls.

TEST INSTRUMENTATION FOR RADIANT HEATING

Accurate calculation of radiant heat exchange may involve some untested assumptions. Ultimately the design engineer must test and readjust the installation in the field and evaluate it for human acceptability. The following elementary instruments are suggested for this purpose.

The Black Globe Thermometer

The simplest physical instrument available, which can directly measure $\bar{t}_r$, ERF, and t_o, is the classic (Bedford) globe thermometer, a thin-walled, matte-black, hollow sphere with a thermocouple, thermister, or thermometer placed at the center. When a black globe is in thermal equilibrium with its radiant environment, the gain in radiant heat from various heated sources is balanced by the convective loss to ambient air. Thus, in terms

of the globe's linear radiation (h_{rg}) and convection (h_{cg}) transfer coefficients, the heat balance after equilibrium is:

$$h_{rg}(\bar{t}_{rg} - t_g) = h_{cg}(t_g - t_a) \tag{20}$$

where $\bar{t}_{rg}$ is the mean radiant temperature "seen" and measured by the globe.

In general, the $\bar{t}_{rg}$, as measured by Eq. (20), also equals the $\bar{t}_r$ affecting man when the globe is placed at the center of the occupied space and when the radiant sources are distant from the globe.

The ERF$_g$, as measured by a black globe is,

$$\text{ERF}_g = (h_{rg} + (\bar{t}_{rg} - t_a) \tag{21}$$

which is analogous to Eq. (4) for humans. From Eq. (20) and (21), it follows that

$$\text{ERF}_g = (h_{rg} + h_{cg})(t_g - t_a) \tag{22}$$

The ERF$_g$, as measured by Eq. (22), must be modified by two factors that describe the shape and skin-clothing absorptance of an occupant relative to the black sphere. The corresponding ERF affecting the occupant is

$$\text{ERF (for man)} = f_{eff} \cdot \alpha_K \cdot \text{ERF}_g \tag{23}$$

where f_{eff} is the effective radiating area of the human body (~ 0.71) and also equals the ratio (h_r/h_{rg}) [see Eq. (10)]. The definition of t_o affecting man, in terms of t_g and t_a, is given by:

$$t_o = \underline{K}t_g + (1 - \underline{K})t_a \tag{24}$$

where the weighting coefficient $\underline{K}$ is:

$$\underline{K} = \alpha_K \cdot f_{eff} \cdot (h_{rg} + h_{cg})/(h_r + h_c) \tag{25}$$

Ideally, when K is unity, the t_g of the globe would equal the t_o affecting man.

For an average equilibrium temperature of 77°F (25°C) ($\sim$ comfort), from Eq. (10) and noting that the "f_{eff} for globe" is unity,

$$h_{rg} = 1.06 \text{ Btu/h} \cdot \text{ft}^2 \cdot °F \quad [h_{rg} = 6.01 \text{ W/(m}^2 \cdot \text{K)}] \tag{26}$$

and

$$h_{cg} = 0.345 \, D^{-0.4} v^{0.5} \tag{27}$$

$$h_{cg} = 6.32 \cdot D^{-0.4} \cdot v^{0.5} \tag{27SI}$$

where

D = globe diameter, in. (m)
v = air velocity, fpm (m/s)

Equation (27) is *Bedford's* convective heat transfer coefficient for the 6 in. (150 mm) globe's convective loss, modified for *D*. For any radiating source below 1700°F (1200 K), it can be shown that the ideal diameter of a sphere to make $\underline{K}$ = unity and to be *independent* of air movement is a sphere 8 in. (200 mm) in diameter. For example, Table 1 shows the value of $\underline{K}$ for various values of globe diameter D and ambient air movement V.

Table 1 shows that the uncorrected temperature of the traditional 6 in. (150 mm) globe would overestimate the true $t_o - t_a$ difference by 6% in V values up to 200 fpm (1 m/s), and the probable error of overestimating t_o by t_g uncorrected would be

Table 1   K Value for Various Air Velocities and Globe Diameters, $\alpha_g = 1$

Air Velocity fpm	m/s	D = 0.05 m ~2 in.	0.01 m ~4 in.	0.15 m ~6 in.	0.20 m ~8 in.
50	0.25	1.35	1.15	1.05	0.99
100	0.5	1.43	1.18	1.06	0.99
200	1.0	1.49	1.21	1.07	1.00
400	2.0	1.54	1.23	1.08	1.00
800	4.0	1.59	1.26	1.09	1.00

less than 0.9°F or 0.5°C. Globe diameters between 6 to 8 in. (150 to 200 mm) are optimum for using the uncorrected t_g measurement for t_o. The exact value for $\underline{K}$ may be used for the smaller sized globes when estimating for t_o from t_g and t_a measurement. $\bar{t}_r$ may be found by substituting Eq. (26) and (27) in Eq. (20), since $\bar{t}_r$ (man) $= \bar{t}_{rg}$. The smaller the globe, the greater the variation in $\underline{K}$ caused by air movement. Globes with $D > 8$ in. (200 mm) will overestimate the importance of radiation gain versus convection loss.

For sources radiating at a high temperature (1340 to 10,000°F or 1000 to 5800 K), the ratio α_m/α_g may be set near unity by using a "pink" colored globe surface for α_g, whose absorptance for the sun is 0.7, a value similar to that of human skin and normal clothing (Madsen 1976).

In summary, the black globe thermometer, which is simple and inexpensive, may be used to measure $\bar{t}_r$ [Eq. (20)] and ERF [Figure 1 and Eq. (22) and (23)]. The uncorrected t_g of a 6 to 8 in. (150 to 200 mm) diameter black globe is an accurate measure of the t_o affecting occupants when the radiant heater temperature is less than 1700°F (1200 K). A "pink" globe extends its usefulness to sun temperature (10,000°F or 5800 K). The globe is more useful when it is lightweight with low thermal capacity, since its time to thermal equilibrium would be shortened.

Many instruments of various shapes, heated and unheated, have been designed using the above heat exchange principles. Madsen (1976) developed an instrument that can measure the predicted mean vote (PMV) from the $t_g - t_a$ difference, as well as correct for clothing insulation, air movement, and activity (ISO 1984). All such instruments measure acceptability in terms of the t_o, $\bar{t}_r$, and ERF, as sensed by their own geometric shape.

The Directional Radiometer

There are many commercial radiometers whose angle of acceptance (in steradians) allows the engineer to point directly at a wall, floor, or high-temperature source and read the average temperature of the surface it "sees." They are calibrated to measure either the radiant flux accepted by the radiometer or the equivalent blackbody radiation temperature (usually in °F or °C rather than K) of the emitting surface. Many are collimated to "see" small areas of either body, clothing, wall, or floor surface. A directional radiometer allows rapid surveys and analyses of the important radiant heating factors in an installation such as temperature of skin, clothing surface, and walls and floors, as well as the radiation intensity (I_K) directed from heaters on the occupant. One radiometer for direct measurement of the equivalent radiant temperature has an angle of acceptance of 2.8° or 0.098 sr, i.e., at 1 ft it would measure the average temperature over a projected circle about 3/8 in. in diameter (30 mm in 1 m).

APPLICATION CONSIDERATIONS

1. Use of both gas and electric high-temperature infrared heaters in applications where there is any danger of igniting inflammable dust or vapors or of decomposing vapors forming toxic gases must be avoided. Lower temperature vented heaters require the same consideration as convective unit heaters.
2. Fixtures must be located with recommended clearances to ensure proper heat distribution. Piling stored materials too close to the fixture, which causes hot spots to develop, must also be avoided. Manufacturers' recommendations must be observed.
3. Unvented gas heaters used inside tight, poorly insulated buildings may cause excessive humidity with condensation on cold surfaces. Proper use of insulation, vapor barriers, and ventilation prevents these problems.
4. Combustion-type heaters in tight buildings may require makeup air to ensure proper venting of combustion gases. Some infrared heaters are equipped with induced draft fans to relieve this problem.
5. Some partially transparent materials may be sensitive to uneven application of high intensity infrared. Infrared energy is transmitted without loss from the radiator to the absorbing surfaces. The system must produce the proper temperature distribution at the absorbing surfaces. Problems are rarely encountered with glass 0.25 in. (6 mm) or less in thickness.
6. Comfort heating with infrared heaters requires a reasonably uniform flux distribution in the occupied area. While thermal discomfort can be relieved in warm areas with high air velocity, such as on loading docks, the full effectiveness of a radiant heater installation is reduced by the presence of high air velocity. At specific locations in large working areas, direct radiant heating may be one practical means of gaining acceptability by the occupant.

LETTER SYMBOLS

A_{DU} Area, total surface of man, as measured by DuBois, ft² (m²)

A_{eff} Area, effective radiating of man, ft² (m²)

A_p Area, projected normal to the beam, ft² (m²)

clo Unit of clothing insulation and equal to 1.137 ft²·°F·h/Btu (0.200 m²·K/W)

D Diameter of Globe Thermometer, in., m

ERF   Effective radiant flux (man), Btu/h·ft² (W/m²)

ERF_f Radiant flux caused by heated floor on occupant, Btu/h·ft² (W/m²)

F_{p-f} Angle factor between person and heater floor

F_{f-room} Shape factor between floor and surrounding room

H_m Net metabolic heat loss from body surface, Btu/h·ft² (W/m²)

I_K Irradiance from beam heater, Btu/h·sr (W/sr)

$\underline{K}$ Coefficient that relates t_a and t_g to t_o [Eq. (27)]

L Fixture length, ft (m)

Met Unit of metabolic energy equal to 18.4 Btu/h·ft² (58 W/m²)

W Width of a square equivalent to the projected area of a beam Ω sr and d, distance, ft² (m²)

c Specific heat, Btu/lb·°F (J/kg·K)

d Distance of beam heater from occupant, ft (m)

d_f Average floor thickness, ft (m)

F_{eff} Ratio, radiating surface (man) to its total area (DuBois)

f_p Fraction, total body surface irradiated by heater beam

h Combined heat transfer coefficient (man), Btu/h·ft²·°F [W/(m²·K)]

h_c Convective transfer coefficient for man, Btu/h·ft²·°F [(W/(m²·K)]

h_{cf} Convection coefficient between floor and air, Btu/h·ft²·°F [(W/(m²·K)]

h_{cg} Convection coefficient for globe, Btu/h·ft²·°F [(W/(m²·K)]

h_r Linear radiation transfer coefficient (man), Btu/h·ft²·°F [(W/(m²·K)]

h_{rf} Linear radiation transfer coefficient from floor surface over 2π sr, Btu/h·ft²·°F [(W/(m²·K)]

h_{rg} Linear radiation transfer coefficient for globe, Btu/h·ft²·°F [(W/(m²·K)]

k Conductivity in Btu/h·ft·°F [(W/(m·K)] (floor)

k_f Average conductivity of flooring material, Btu/h·ft·°F [(W/(m·K)]

t_a Ambient air temperature (near occupant), °F (°C)

t_f Temperature, floor, °F (°C)

t_{gr} Temperature, ground or surface below floor, °F (°C)

t_o Operative temperature, °F (°C)

$\bar{t}_r$ Mean radiant temperature affecting occupant, °F (°C)

t_{sf} Exposed surface temperature of occupant, °F (°C)

t_{uo} Operative temperature of unheated work space °F (°C)

v air velocity, fpm (m/s)

α	Relative absorptance of skin clothing surface to that of matte black surface
α_f	Absorptance of floor surface
β	Elevation angle of beam heater, degs.
Ω	Radiant beam width, sr
Φ	Azimuth angle of heater, degs.
ϱ	Density (floor), lb/ft^3 (kg/m^3)
σ	*Stefan-Boltzmann Constant* and equal to 0.1713×10^{-8} $Btu/h \cdot ft^2 \cdot °R^4$ $[0.0567 \ \mu W/(m^2 \cdot K^4)]$

REFERENCES

Boyd, R.L. 1962. Application and Selection of Electric Infrared Comfort Heaters. ASHRAE *Journal,* Vol. 4, No. 10, p. 57.

Fanger, P.O. 1973. *Thermal Comfort.* McGraw Hill Book Co., New York, NY.

Fanger, P.O.; Banhidi, L.; Olesen, B.W.; and Langkilde, G. 1980. Comfort Limits for Heated Ceiling. ASHRAE *Transactions,* Vol. 86, Part II, pp. 141-156.

Gagge, A.P.; Rapp, G.M.; and Hardy, J.D. 1967. The Effective Radiant Field and Operative Temperature Necessary for Comfort with Radiant Heating. ASHRAE *Transactions,* Vol. 73, Part I and ASHRAE *Journal,* Vol. 9, pp. 63-66.

Hardy, J.D.; Gagge, A.P. and Stolwijk, J.A.J. (Ed.). 1970. *Physiological and Behavioral Temperature Regulation.* C.C. Thomas, Springfield, IL.

ISO. 1984. Moderate Thermal Environments—Determination of the PMV and PPD Indices and Specifications of the Conditions for Thermal Comfort. ISO *Standard* 7730-1984. International Standard Organization, Geneva.

Madsen, T.L. 1976. Thermal Comfort Measurements. ASHRAE *Transactions,* Vol. 82, Part I, pp. 60-70.

Rapp, G.M.; and Gagge, A.P. 1967. Configuration Factors and Comfort Design in Radiant Beam Heating of Man by High Temperature Infrared Sources. ASHRAE *Transactions,* Vol. 73, Part III, pp. 1.1-1.8.

Scholander, P.E. 1958. Cold Adaptation in the Australian Aborigines. *J. Appl. Physiology,* Vol. 13, pp. 211-18.

Stevens, J.C.; Marks, L.E.; and Gagge, A.P. 1969. The Quantitative Assessment of Thermal Comfort. *Environmental Research,* Vol. 2, pp. 149-165.

BIBLIOGRAPHY

AGA. 1960. *Literature Review of Infra-Red Energy Produced with Gas Burners.* Research *Bulletin* 83, Catalog No. 35/IR, American Gas Association.

Boyd, R.L. 1964. Beam Characteristics of High Intensity Infrared Heaters. *IEEE Paper CP 64-123,* Institute of Electrical and Electronics Engineers, February.

Boyd, R.L. 1963. Control of Electric Infrared Energy Distribution. *Electrical Engineering,* February, p. 103.

Boyd, R.L. 1959. High Intensity Infrared Radiant Heating. *Heating, Piping and Air Conditioning,* November, p. 140.

Boyd, R.L. 1961. How to Apply High Intensity Infrared Heaters for Comfort Heating. *Heating, Piping and Air Conditioning,* January, p. 230.

Frier, J.P.; and Stephens, W.R. 1962. Design Fundamentals for Space Heating with Infrared Lamps. *Illuminating Engineering,* December.

Griffiths, I.S.; and McIntyre, D.A. 1974. Subjective Response to Overhead Thermal Radiation. *Human Factors,* Vol. 16, No. 3, pp. 415-422.

Hardy, J.S.; Gagge, A.P.; and Stolwijk, J.A.J. (Ed.). 1970. *Physiological and Behavioral Temperature Regulation.* CC. Thomas, Springfield, IL.

McIntyre, D.A. 1974. The Thermal Radiating Field. *Building Science,* Vol. 9, pp. 247-262.

McNall, P.E., Jr.; and Biddison, R.E. 1970. Thermal and Comfort Sensations of Sedentary Persons Exposed to Asymmetric Radiant Fields. ASHRAE *Transactions,* Vol. 76, Part I.

Olesen, S.; Fanger, P.O.; Jensen, P.B.; and Nielsen, O.J. 1972. Comfort Limits for Man Exposed to Asymmetric Thermal Radiation. Building Research Est. Report: *Thermal Comfort and Moderate Heat Stress.*

Walker, C.A. 1962. Control of High Intensity Infrared Heating. ASHRAE *Journal,* Vol. 4, No. 10, October, p. 66.

CHAPTER 17

RESIDENCES

THE space conditioning systems selected for residential use vary with both local and application factors. Among the local factors are fuel availability (both present and projected), fuel prices, climate, and socioeconomic circumstances. Application factors include type of housing, construction characteristics, building codes, and the availability of both installation and maintenance skills. As a result, many different systems are selected to provide combinations of heating, cooling, humidification, dehumidification, and air filtering. This chapter emphasizes the more common systems for space conditioning of both single and multifamily residences. Generally, however, low-rise multifamily buildings (e.g., duplexes and townhouses of three or less stories) follow single-family practice. Retrofit and remodeling construction also adopt the same systems as those for new construction, but site-specific circumstances may call for unique designs.

Table 1 lists the common residential heating and cooling systems. Three groups generally recognized are central forced air, central hydronic, and zonal. System selection and design involves four key decisions: (1) the services provided, (2) distribution and delivery means, (3) source(s) of energy, and (4) conversion device(s).

Climate dominates the services provided. Heating, cooling, or both are generally required. Air cleaning (by filtration or electrostatic devices) can be added to most systems. Humidification is generally provided only with heating when psychrometric conditions make it necessary for comfort (see Chapters 6 and 8 of the 1985 FUNDAMENTALS Handbook) and also can be added to most systems. Cooling generally dehumidifies; the combination of cooling and dehumidification, commonly with air cleaning, is generally called air conditioning.

Central forced air systems predominate in North America, largely because cooling can be easily included. Figure 1 and Figure 2 show two typical residential installations.

Figure 1 includes a gas furnace, a split system cooling unit, a central system humidifier, and an electronic air filter. The system (referring to the numbers in the figure) functions as follows: Air returns to the equipment through a return air duct (1). It passes initially through the electronic air filter (2). The circulating blower (3) is an integral part of the gas furnace (4) that supplies heat during winter. The humidifier (10) adds moisture to the heated air, which circulates throughout the home through the supply duct (9). When cooling is required, the circulating air passes through the evaporator coil (5) that absorbs heat and cools the air. Refrigerant lines (6) connect the evaporator coil to a remote air-cooled condensing unit (7) located outdoors. Condensate collected by the evaporator drains away through the pipe (8).

Figure 2 includes a heat pump, electric furnace, a central system humidifier, and an electronic air filter. The system functions as follows: Air returns to the equipment through the return air duct (1) and passes through the electronic air filter (2). The circulating blower (3) is an integral part of the heat pump (4) that supplies heat via the indoor coil (6) during the heating

---

season. Electric heaters (5) supplement heat from the heat pump or during the defrost cycle. The humidifier (10) adds moisture to the heated air, which circulates throughout the home through the supply duct (9). When cooling is required, the circulating air passes through the indoor coil (6), which absorbs heat and cools the air. Refrigerant lines (11) connect the indoor coil to the outdoor unit (7). Condensate collected by the indoor coil is drained away through the pipe (8).

Central hydronic systems are popular both in Europe and installations in North America where central cooling is not provided; central air-conditioning is generally impractical in hydronic systems for single-family houses with conventional equipment. Zonal systems are often applied in building additions and retrofits but have limited acceptance in new construction.

Semicentralized systems (e.g., two or more central systems that serve individual floors or separately serve the sleeping and com-

Table 1 Residential Heating Systems

	Forced Air	Hydronic	Zonal
Source of Energy	Gas Oil Electricity Resistance Heat pump	Gas Oil Electricity Resistance Heat pump	Gas Electricity Resistance Heat pump
Heat Distribution Medium	Air	Water Steam	—
Heat Distribution System	Ducting	Piping	—
Terminal Devices	Diffusers Registers Grilles	Radiators Fan-coil units	Included with product

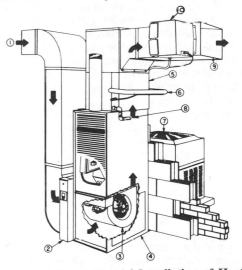

Fig. 1 Typical Residential Installation of Heating, Cooling, Humidifying and Air-Filtering

The preparation of this chapter is assigned to TC 7.6, Unitary Air Conditioners and Heat Pumps.

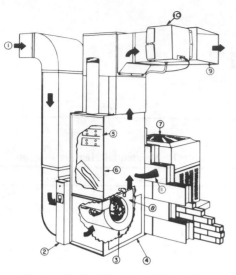

**Fig. 2   Typical Residential Installation
of a Heat Pump System**

munal portions of a home) are also widely installed, particularly in large single-family houses.

The source of energy is a major consideration in system selection. Gas and electricity are dominant followed by oil, wood, district thermal, solar, coal, and others. Local availability and assurance of future availability are the most limiting factors. Relative energy prices, safety, and environmental (both indoor and outdoor) concerns are further factors. Where various energy sources are available, economics generally govern the selection.

SINGLE-FAMILY RESIDENCES

HEATING EQUIPMENT

Heat Pumps

Heat pumps heat and cool approximately one-third of new single-family houses in the United States. Heat pumps may be classified by their respective thermal source and distribution medium in the heating mode. The most common equipment is air-to-air, followed, in order of declining application, by water-to-air, air-to-water, and water-to-water. The thermal sink for cooling is generally assumed to be the same as the thermal source.

Heat pump systems, as contrasted to the actual heat pump equipment, are generally described as air-source or ground-source. Ground-source systems may employ water-to-air or water-to-water heat pumps to extract heat from the ground either via groundwater or from a ground-coupled system. Ground coupling circulates brine or water to transfer heat from the ground via a buried heat exchanger.

Contrasted to these two indirect systems, direct ground-source systems use ground-to-air heat pumps with direct expansion evaporators buried in the ground, but they are very rare. Water-source systems that extract heat from surface water (e.g., lakes or rivers) or city (tap) water are also used. Heat pump systems that use water as a distribution medium are identified as air-source hydronic, water-source hydronic, or ground-source hydronic systems.

Heat pumps for single-family houses are normally of the unitary type; that is, they consist of one or more factory assembled modules designed to be connected and used together. Unitary systems contrast to applied and built-up heat pumps, which require field engineering to select compatible components and to design a complete system.

Virtually all current heat pumps commercially available (particularly in North America) are electrically powered. As discussed in Chapter 44 of the 1983 EQUIPMENT Handbook, supplemental heat is generally required during peak or defrost modes of operation; likewise, backup heat may be added as insurance against equipment failure. Although supplemental and backup heat are generally electrical resistance heat, add-on and unitary bivalent heat pumps combine heat pumps with fuel-fired devices instead.

In add-on systems, a heat pump is added—often as a retrofit—to a furnace or boiler. The heat pump and combustion device operate alternately, each when most cost effective, or in parallel in specifically designed systems. The unitary bivalent heat pump, by contrast, combines the heat pump and combustion device into a common chassis and cabinets to provide similar benefits at lower installation costs.

Ground water as a heat source/sink for heating and cooling with water source heat pumps has recently attracted attention because it offers the following advantages compared to air source heat pumps: (1) the capacity is independent of ambient temperature, thus reducing supplementary heating requirements; (2) no defrost cycle is required, which simplifies the controls and reduces machine complexity; and (3) the seasonal efficiency is usually higher in both the heating and cooling modes.

The idea of community wells with untreated water kept separate from the potable water system has been proposed. This water could be supplied as a utility and individually metered to the dwelling unit.

Water supply, quality, and disposal must also be considered for ground-water systems. The ASHRAE publication *Design Manual on Closed Loop and Ground Coupled Heat Pumps* provides detailed information on these subjects. The number of ground-coupled heat pump systems with brines or water in buried plastic heat exchangers is growing. Brines are discussed in the above reference and in Chapter 18 of the 1985 FUNDAMENTALS Handbook.

The principal heat exchanger designs are horizontal and vertical, with the vertical including both multiple shallow and single deep well configurations. Ground-coupled systems avoid the water quality, quantity, and disposal concerns but are usually more expensive and slightly less efficient than ground-water systems. Table 2 in Chapter 9 of this volume summarizes common sources and sinks for heat pumps.

Solar-assisted and solar-source heat pumps have been proposed and attempted in limited applications. Although extensive research and development has been conducted to develop gas and oil-fired heat pumps, they are not presently marketed for residential use in North America.

Heat pumps may be equipped with desuperheaters (either integral or field added) to reclaim heat for domestic water heating. Likewise, integrated space-conditioning and water-heating heat pumps are also available. These include a full-condensing mode to heat water either by heat reclaim from the condenser or via a dedicated heat pump.

Furnaces

As indicated in Table 1, furnaces are fueled by gas (natural or propane), electricity, oil, or wood (wood products). High efficiency models, generally fueled by natural or liquid propane (LP) gas, are now available on the market. These models obtain high efficiencies by added heat exchanger surface areas and by reducing heat loss during furnace off times. Some high efficiency furnaces condense water vapor from the flue products, which additionally increases the furnace efficiency.

Recent findings indicate that the indoor air of many households contains chemicals from cleaning fluids and the like that may cause early corrosion failures in certain furnace heat exchanger materials. Because of this problem, high efficiency models may require ducting outdoor air to the combustion chamber. High efficiency models that condense flue products also require plumbing to drain the condensate.

Wood fueled furnaces are used in selected areas that have an adequate wood supply for fuel. A recent advance in wood furnaces has been the addition of catalytic materials to enhance the combustion process and, therefore, increase furnace efficiency.

Hydronic Heating Systems—Boilers

With the growth of demand for central cooling systems, hydronic systems have declined in popularity in new construction, but still account for a significant portion of existing systems in the northern climates. Both steam and hot water are in use. The fluid is heated in a central boiler and distributed via a system of piping to individual fan-coil units or baseboard convectors located in each room.

Most recent residential systems use a forced circulation, multiple zone, hot water system with a series loop piping arrangement. The equipment is described in Chapters 24 and 29 of the 1983 EQUIPMENT Handbook. Hot water and steam heating systems are described in Chapters 11 and 13 of this volume. A number of industry-developed procedures in common use are adaptations of the design information contained in Chapter 13.

Design water temperature is based on economic and comfort considerations. In general, higher temperatures result in lower first costs because smaller distribution units are needed, but losses tend to be greater, which results in higher operating costs, and comfort is less because the heat source is concentrated. Typical design temperatures range from 180 to 200°F (82 to 93°C). The preferred control system allows the water temperature to decrease in response to warmer outdoor temperatures. Provisions for expansion and contraction of the piping and heat distributing units and the elimination of air from the system are essential for leak-tight and quiet systems.

Systems with condensing boilers must be designed for return water temperatures in the range of 120 to 130°F for most of the heating season. Systems with non-condensing boilers must maintain high enough water temperatures in the boiler to prevent condensation of water vapor in the flue gases.

If rapid heating is required, both the radiation and boiler size must be increased, but gross oversizing of boilers and radiation should be avoided.

Zonal Heating Systems

Zonal heating systems consist of individual heaters located in each living space. These heaters are usually gas-fired or have an electrical input. Electrical heaters are available in the following types: baseboard free-convection, wall insert free-convection, forced-fan, and radiant panels for walls and ceilings, as well as radiant cables and inserts for walls, ceilings, and floors.

Another form of zonal electric heating is the use of individual heat pumps in each living space. These heat pumps are of either the air-to-air, water-to-air, or hydronic types.

A recent addition to the zonal heat pump group is the multizone heat pump, which uses a central compressor and outdoor heat exchanger to service up to five indoor zones. Each zone consists of one or more fan coils with separate thermostatic control for each zone. Such systems are used both in new and retrofit construction.

The matching of equipment heating capacity to heating requirements for each room is very critical for zonal systems. Heating delivery cannot be adjusted by adjusting air flow, as in ducted systems, so greater precision on room-by-room sizing is needed.

Individual zonal systems offer the potential for operating economies, since unoccupied areas can be kept at lower temperatures. So, for example, communal areas can be maintained at lower temperatures at night and sleeping areas kept at lower temperatures during the day.

Solar Heating

Both active and passive solar energy systems are used to heat residences. In a typical active system, flat plate collectors heat either air or water. Air systems then distribute the heated air either to the heated space for immediate use or to mass storage such as a rock pile. Water systems pass the heated water through a secondary heat exchanger and store extra heat in a water tank.

Passive systems include a number of approaches, most commonly trombe walls and sunspaces. South facing glazing (with overhanging eaves to reduce solar gains in the summer) and movable insulating panels reduce heating requirements. Like active systems, however, supplementary and backup heating ability is generally needed. Chapter 47 of this volume has detailed information on sizing solar heating equipment.

AIR CONDITIONERS

Nearly all residential structures are heated; about 50% of all existing residences have some form of cooling, and 70% of all new residential units include cooling.

Unitary Air Conditioners

In forced air systems, the same air distribution duct system can be used for both heating and cooling. The split central cooling system is most widely used. It consists of an evaporator coil mounted in the indoor circulating air system and a remote air-cooled condensing unit. Coils are available for upflow, downflow, and horizontal air flow patterns, corresponding to the type of furnace.

The condensing units contain an electric motor-driven compressor, condenser, condenser fan and fan motor, and electrical controls. These units are normally installed on outside pad, but some models are installed through-the-wall. The condensing unit and evaporator coil are connected by refrigerant tubing that may be field-supplied, but precharged, factory-supplied tubing with quick-connect couplings is common where the distance between components is not excessive.

A distinct advantage of this type of system is that it can readily be added to existing forced air heating systems. Air flow rates may need to be increased to achieve good performance, but most existing heating duct systems are adaptable to cooling.

Air flow rates of 350 to 450 cfm per nominal ton of refrigeration (47 to 60 L/S per kw) are normally recommended to achieve good performance of cooling systems.

Some forced air-heating equipment includes cooling as an integral part of the product. Year-round heating and cooling packages with a gas, oil, or electric furnace for heating and an electric motor-driven vapor-compression system for cooling are available. Also, air-to-air and water source heat pumps provide cooling and heating by reversing the flow of refrigerant.

Distribution systems. Duct systems for cooling should be designed and installed in accordance with accepted practice. Useful information is found in ACCA (Air-Conditioning Contractors of America) Manuals D and G, and Chapter 11 of the 1983 EQUIPMENT Handbook. The duct sizes of year-round air-conditioning systems are usually larger than those of equivalent winter heating systems, since cooling air is supplied at only 15 to 25°F (8 to 14°C) below room temperature.

Reliable methods of duct design that consider the specific air flow and static pressure characteristics of the systems should be used. The type and size of supply and return inlets and their locations to effect satisfactory room air distribution must be considered. The usual practice is to calculate both cooling and heating air flow requirements and design an air distribution system for the larger air quantity required. This is usually the cooling air flow. Multispeed fans are sometimes included to reduce the higher air flow when heat is delivered.

In one- or two-story homes, heating and cooling loads are not the same for all rooms. Generally, separate preliminary calculations are made for the heating and cooling air distribution requirements, and then adjustments are made to achieve a compromise solution. For example, it may be necessary to include additional cooling outlets in one or more of the upstairs rooms, in rooms that have large glass areas facing south or west, or in rooms with unusually high internal heat loads such as kitchens.

Both technical and economic aspects of residential cooling should be considered. An elaborately zoned air distribution system is rarely economical. However, because external weather primarily influences the load, the cooling load in each room changes from hour to hour. To obtain ultimate comfort, therefore, the owner should be able to make seasonal or more frequent adjustments to the air distribution system.

Such adjustments may involve the opening of additional outlets in second-floor rooms during the cooling cycle and throttling or closing of heating outlets in some rooms during the winter. On deluxe applications, additional refinements may be economically justified. One such refinement could be the installation of a heating and cooling system based primarily on heating requirements, with additional independent cooling ducts or self-contained units serving some or all of the second-floor rooms. Another solution would be the inclusion of zone controls for rooms that have unusual load variations or high internal heat gains during the summer.

Operating characteristics of both heating and cooling equipment must be considered when zoning is used. For example, a reduction in the air quantity to one or more rooms may reduce the air flow across the evaporator to such a degree that frost forms on the fins. Reduce air flow on heat pumps during the heating season, as it can overload if air flow across the indoor coil is not maintained at 350 to 450 cfm per nominal ton of refrigeration (47 to 60 L/S per kW). A reduced air volume to a given room could reduce the air velocity from the supply outlet and cause unsatisfactory air distribution in the room, as well.

When multiple split-system units are applied to zones, the way space is divided must be considered. First- and second-floor zones or communal- and sleeping-area zones could be established. Factors such as physical layout and the amount of load in each area will affect the decision on how to divide the floor space.

Special considerations. In split-level houses, the cooling and heating are complicated by the internal gravity circulation that takes place through the large openings between the various levels. In many split-level houses, the upper bedrooms tend to overheat in the winter and undercool in the summer. Multiple outlets, some near the floor and others near the ceiling on all levels, have been used with some success. The owner opens some outlets and closes others from season to season to control air flow. Gravity circulation between floors can be reduced by locating returns high in each room and by keeping doors closed.

In existing homes, the amount of cooling that can be added is limited by the air-handling capacity of the existing furnace and duct system. While this is usually satisfactory for normal occupancy, it may not be adequate where large-party entertainment is frequent.

In all cases where cooling is added to existing homes, the supply-air outlets must be checked for acceptable cooling air distribution. Upward airflow at an effective velocity is impor-

tant to consider when converting existing heating systems with floor or baseboard outlets to both heat and cool. It is not necessary to change the deflection from summer to winter for registers located at the perimeter of a residence. Registers located at the inside walls of rooms also operate satisfactorily without changing of deflection from summer to winter.

Owners of residential air-conditioning systems usually prefer minimum perceptible air motion. Perimeter baseboard outlets with multiple slots or orifices effectively meet these requirements. Ceiling outlets with multidirectional vanes are also satisfactory in warm climates.

A residence without a forced air-heating system may be cooled by a central cooling system with a separate duct system or by zonal cooling units. The central system may be a single-package with all refrigeration components in one unit, or it may be a split system with an outdoor condensing unit (such as that used with an evaporator coil and a furnace) connected by refrigerant tubing to an evaporator coil in an indoor blower unit. Individual room units mounted through-the-wall may also be used.

Cooling equipment must be located carefully. Because cooling systems require higher indoor air flow rates than most heating systems, the generated indoor sound levels are usually higher. Thus, indoor air-handling units should be placed far from sleeping areas.

Outdoor noise levels should also govern the location of the equipment. Many communities have ordinances regulating the sound level of mechanical devices, including cooling equipment. Many manufacturers of unitary air conditioners certify the sound level of their products in an ARI program (ARI Standard 270). ARI Standard 275 tells how to predict the dBA sound level when the ARI sound rating number, the equipment location relative to reflective surfaces, and the distance to the listener are known.

An effective and often the least expensive way to reduce noise is to put distance and natural barriers, such as walls or corners, between the sound source and the listener. Outdoor units should be placed as far as practical from porches and patios, which may be used when the house is being cooled. Locations near bedroom windows should also be avoided. Neighbors should also be considered when locating the unit. Neighbors may want to open their windows while the unit is operating. Therefore, the rear of residences are usually preferred locations. Proper acoustical barriers, such as walls and fences, can also reduce radiated sound levels.

There should be no obstructions to airflow to air-cooled condensing units. The hot air from the unit should not discharge toward walkways, shrubbery, house overhang, or open windows.

Zonal Cooling Systems

The window air conditioner, installed in one or more rooms, is the most common zonal cooling device for single-family houses. Through-the-wall models and, infrequently, package terminal air conditioners (PTACs) are also used. Zonal heat pumps, previously discussed, can and are also used for zonal cooling. Window evaporative coolers are common in parts of the southwestern and western United States.

Capacity Selection

The heat loss, heat gain, or both of each conditioned room, crawl space, and basement in the structure must be accurately calculated to select the proper equipment with the proper output and to design the duct or piping system. To determine heat loss and heat gain accurately, the floor plan and details of the construction must be known. The plan should include information on the wall, ceiling, and floor construction and the type and thickness of insulation. Details of the design of windows and external doors are also needed. To conserve energy, it is recommended that the building be designed to meet or preferably to exceed the requirements identified in ASHRAE Standard 90A-1980, *Energy Conservation in New Building Design.*

With this information, the heat loss and heat gain can be calculated by using the basic data in Chapters 22 through 27 of the 1985 FUNDAMENTALS Handbook, and by using *Air-Conditioning Contractors of America Manual J* or other similar calculation procedures.

Proper matching of equipment capacity to the design heat loss and heat gain is essential. The heating capacity of air source heat pumps is usually supplemented by auxiliary heaters, most often of the electric resistance type; in some cases, however, fossil fuel furnaces or solar-input systems are used.

Insufficient capacity results in inability to hold indoor design temperatures when outdoor design temperatures occur. Grossly oversized equipment can cause discomfort due to short on-times and wide indoor temperature swings. Gross oversizing will also contribute to higher energy use due to an increase in starting thermal transient losses, stopping thermal transient losses, and off-cycle losses. Recent trends toward heavily insulated, tightly constructed buildings with continuous vapor barriers and very little infiltration can cause high indoor humidity conditions, and dehumidification may become necessary during the winter months. Air-to-air heat-recovery equipment is being used to provide ventilation air to some tightly constructed houses.

Evaporative Coolers

In arid climates such as the southwestern United States, evaporative coolers are used to cool residences. Further details on evaporative coolers can be found in Chapter 4 of the 1983 EQUIPMENT Volume and Chapter 56 of this volume.

HUMIDIFIERS

For better winter comfort, a growing number of residences install equipment to increase relative humidity levels. In a ducted heating system, a central system humidifier can be attached to or installed within a supply plenum or a main supply duct or installed between the supply and return duct systems. Caution should be exercised when applying supply-to-return duct humidifiers on heat pump systems. Air flow across the indoor coil should be maintained at 350 to 450 cfm per ton (47 to 60 L/s per kW). If the heating system is not ducted, a self-contained humidifier can be used. Even though this type introduces all the moisture to one area of the home, moisture will migrate and raise humidity levels in other rooms.

Central system humidifiers are rated in accordance with ARI Standard 610. This rating is expressed in the number of gallons (litres) per day evaporated by $140\,°F$ $(60\,°C)$ entering air. Some manufacturers certify the performance of their product to the ARI standard, and these products are listed in the *ARI Directory of Certified Central System Humidifiers.*

Selecting the proper size humidifier is important and is outlined in ARI Standard 630, *Selection, Installation and Servicing of Humidifiers.* Since the maximum level of relative humidity that can be maintained without condensation forming is a function of the coldest surface in the living space, usually windows, double-pane glass, or storm windows must be installed. The low inside surface temperature of single-pane glass, $27\,°F$ $(-3\,°C)$ when outdoor air is $0\,°F$ $(-18\,°C)$, causes condensation at even low humidity levels, thus limiting humidity below the preferred comfort level. With single-pane glass, the humidifier becomes ineffective and condensed moisture can damage windows, sills, and walls.

A humidifier should always be installed with a humidistat that can be set to prevent condensation on windows. Failure to do so may cause structural damage due to excessive condensation. Humidistats also save energy by preventing overhumidification. The main load on a humidifier is infiltrated air that enters through cracks in the structure and improperly sealed doors and windows. Caulking and weatherstripping significantly increases the effectiveness of a humidifier.

Since moisture migrates through porous structural materials, insulated walls, ceilings, and floors should have a vapor barrier installed on the inside surface of the insulation. Improper attention to this construction detail allows moisture to migrate from inside to outside. If excessive migration occurs, paint on the exterior may blister, insulation may become damp and loose its effectiveness, and the structure may be damaged. Chapter 5 of the 1983 EQUIPMENT Handbook has more information on residential humidifiers.

AIR FILTERS

Most comfort conditioning systems that circulate air incorporate some form of air filtration device. Usually, this consists of disposable filters having relatively low air-cleaning efficiency. The comfort and cleanliness level of the residential system can be easily improved by adding high efficiency air-filter equipment, such as the electronic air filter, which uses electrostatic principles.

Air filters are mounted in the return air duct or plenum and operate whenever air circulates through the duct system. Electronic air filters are rated in accordance with ARI Standard 680, *Air Filter Equipment,* which is based on ASHRAE Standard 52-76, *Method of Testing Air Cleaning Devices Used in General Ventilation for Removing Particulate Matter.* Atmospheric dust spot efficiency levels are generally less than 20% for disposable filters and will vary from 60 to 90% for electronic air filters.

To maintain a high level of performance, the collectors of electronic air filters must be cleaned periodically. To warn of the need for cleaning, indicators that signal the need for cleaning are often used. Electronic air filters have higher initial costs than disposable, throwaway filters, but generally they will last for the life of the air-conditioning system. Chapter 10 of the 1983 EQUIPMENT Handbook covers the design of residential air filters in more detail.

CONTROLS

Historically, residential heating and cooling equipment has been controlled by a wall thermostat. Today, the simple wall thermostat with bimetallic strip is being replaced by a microelectronic thermostat that can control heating and cooling equipment at different levels, depending upon the time of day. This has led night setback control to reduce energy demands and the cost of operation. For heat-pump equipment, electronic thermostats can incorporate night setback with an appropriate recovery scheme, again to control the cost of operation.

Control of each zone is important to lower heating and cooling costs. Sophisticated controls feed back the individual zone demand to the central station unit for more precise matching of the central station output to the load.

MOBILE HOMES

Most mobile homes are usually heated by forced air. Heating equipment is generally located in a closet adjacent to a hallway. The heated air discharges to a duct system located beneath the floor. Floor supply outlets are located throughout the home. Return air ducts are not used, so the air returns down the hallway to the closet containing the heating equipment. Most forms of conventional heating equipment are used, including furnaces (gas, oil, or electric) and heat pumps.

Gas and oil furnaces for mobile home application are of the sealed combustion type. This type of furnace draws all combustion air from outside and discharges the combustion products outside through windproof venting. Gas-fired equipment is field-convertible for either natural gas or LPG. Cooling can be added to most mobile home duct systems by using an evaporator coil-condensing unit split system or by ducting the output of a single-package cooling unit into the main under-the-floor trunk duct.

MULTIFAMILY RESIDENCES

Attached homes and low-rise multifamily apartments generally use heating and cooling equipment comparable to that used in single-family dwellings. Separate systems for each apartment allows individual control to suit the tenant and facilitate individual metering of energy use.

Central Forced Air Systems

High-rise multifamily structures may also use unitary heating and cooling equipment comparable to that used in single-family dwellings. Equipment for this system may be installed in a separate mechanical equipment room in the apartment or it may be placed in a furred soffit or above a hung ceiling over a corridor or closet. Access to the equipment should be through a service corridor or entrance.

Small residential warm air furnaces may also be used, but a method of venting the combustion products from gas- or oil-fired furnaces is required. It may be necessary to use a multiple-vent chimney or a manifold-type vent system. Local codes should be consulted. Sealed combustion furnaces that are placed near or on an outside wall are also available for apartments.

Hydronic Central Systems

Individual heating and cooling units are not always possible or practical in high-rise structures; in this case, applied central systems are used. Hydronic central systems of the two or four-pipe type are widely used in high-rise apartments. Each dwelling unit has individual room units, located at the perimeter or interior, valance systems, or ducted fancoil units.

The most effective hydronic system is the four-pipe type. It provides complete flexibility for heating or cooling for each apartment dweller and generally has the most favorable operating costs. The two-pipe system is somewhat less effective and costs more to operate, since it cannot provide heating and cooling simultaneously. This limitation causes problems during the spring and fall when some apartments in a complex require heating, while others require cooling due to solar or internal loads. This is overcome in some systems by operating the two-pipe system in a cooling mode and providing the relatively low amount of heating that may be required by individual electric resistance heaters. Chapter 4 of this volume has additional information on hydronic systems.

Through-the-Wall Units—Zonal

The through-the-wall room air conditioner and the packaged terminal air conditioner (PTAC) and heat pump (PTHP) versions of these products provide the highest room-by-room flexibility in low-rise and high-rise apartments. In this application, each apartment room with an outside wall has a through-the-wall unit.

These units are used extensively when renovating old apartment buildings because they are self-contained and do not require complex renovation for ductwork.

Room air conditioners have integral controls and may include resistance heating or reverse cycle heating. Packaged terminal air conditioners have special indoor and outdoor appearance treatments, which make these units adaptable to a wider range of architectural needs. They are available with gas heat, electric resistance heat, hot water heat, steam heat, or as a reverse cycle heat pump. The controls may be integral or remote wall-mounted. Useful information may be found in Chapter 42 of the 1983 EQUIPMENT Handbook and ARI Standards 310 and 380.

Water Loop Heat Pump Systems

Any mid-rise and high-rise apartment structure that has a core generating heat and, therefore, requires cooling on a year-round basis can be very efficiently adapted to water loop heat pump systems. These systems have the flexibility and control of a four-pipe system. Water source heat pumps allow for individual metering of each apartment with the owner paying only the utility cost for the circulating pump, cooling tower, and supplemental boiler heat, which can be prorated.

Refer to Chapter 5 for additional information on water loop heat pump systems. In addition, solar energy can be used as a supplementary energy source if supplementary energy is required.

Special Concerns for Apartment Buildings

There are many types of ventilation systems used in apartment buildings. Local building codes may govern quantities. Average values are normally 35 to 50 cfm (16.5 to 23.6 L/s) for bathrooms and 1 to 2 cfm per ft^2 (5 to 10 L/s per m^2) but not less than 50 cfm (24 L/s) for kitchens. Tempered outdoor air, usually slightly in excess of the exhaust quantities to pressurize the building, is generally introduced into the corridors.

Some buildings, with centrally controlled exhaust and supply systems, operate the systems on time clocks for certain periods of the day. In other cases, it is common practice to reduce or shut off the outside air during extremely cold periods. If known in advance, these factors should be considered when estimating heating load.

Buildings using exhaust and supply air systems 24 hours a day may benefit from air-to-air heat recovery devices (see Chapter 35 of the 1983 EQUIPMENT Handbook). Such recovery devices can reduce energy consumption by capturing 60 to 80% of the sensible and latent heat extracted from the air source.

Infiltration loads in high-rise buildings without ventilation openings for perimeter units are not controllable on a year-round basis by general building pressurization. When outer walls are pierced to supply outdoor air to unitary or fan-coil equipment, combined wind and thermal stack effects create added problems.

Interior public corridors in apartment buildings should have positive ventilation with at least two air exchanges per hour. Conditioned supply and exhaust air is preferable, but some designs transfer air into the apartments, if necessary, through acoustically lined transfer louvers to provide kitchen and toilet makeup air. Supplying air into, instead of exhausting air from, corridors minimizes the drawing of odors from apartments into corridors.

Air-conditioning equipment must be isolated to reduce noise generation or transmission. The design and location of cooling towers must be chosen to avoid disturbing not only occupants within the building but also their neighbors in adjacent buildings. An important load, frequently overlooked in apartment buildings, is heat gain from piping for hot water services. In large apartment houses, a central panel allows individual apartment air-conditioning systems or units to be supervised for maintenance and operating purposes.

RETAIL FACILITIES

THIS chapter covers the design and application of air-conditioning and heating systems for various retail merchandising facilities. Refer to other handbooks for load calculations, systems, and equipment.

SMALL STORES

LOAD DETERMINATION

To apply equipment properly, it is necessary to know the construction of the space to be conditioned, as well as the use and occupancy. The time of day in which greatest occupancy occurs, the physical building characteristics, and lighting layouts should be obtained.

The following must also be considered.

Electric power: size of existing service.
Heating: availability of steam, hot water, gas, oil, or electricity.
Cooling: availability of chilled water, well water, city water, and water conservation equipment.
Rigging and Delivery of Equipment—access for equipment delivery.
Structural Considerations.
Existing Obstructions—removed or relocated.
Ventilation—opening through roof or wall for outside air duct, number of doors to sales area, and exposures.
Orientation of Store.

Specific design requirements must be considered, such as the increased outdoor air required for exhaust systems where lunch counters exist. Heavy smoking and objectionable odors may require special filtering in conjunction with outdoor air intake. Load calculations should be made with the procedure outlined in Chapters 25 and 26 of the 1985 FUNDAMENTALS Volume.

Table 4 presents typical factors that can be used as check figures and field estimates. However, Table 4 should not be used for final determination of load, since the values are only averages.

DESIGN CONSIDERATIONS

Small stores are often constructed with large glass areas in front, which may result in high peak solar heat gain, except for northern exposures. High heat loss may be experienced on cold, cloudy days. This portion of the small store should be designed to offset the greater cooling and heating requirements. Entrance heaters may be needed in cold climates.

Many new small stores are part of a shopping center. While exterior loads will differ in these stores, the internal loads will be similar, and the need for proper design is equally important.

System Design

Single-package rooftop equipment is common in store air conditioning. Units are factory-assembled in a weathertight case;

the refrigerant system is factory-charged and sealed, and internally wired; thus, installation is simplified. The use of multiple units to condition the store can mean less ductwork and can maintain comfort in the event of equipment failure. Prefabricated and matching curbs simplify installations and ensure compatibility with roof materials.

The heat pump, offered as packaged equipment, readily adapts to small-store applications and has an economical first cost, if the heating equipment is the responsibility of the owner or tenant. Winter design conditions and utility rates should be compared against operating costs of conventional heating systems before deciding on this type of equipment.

Water-cooled unitary equipment is available in all capacities required for small-store air conditioning, but many communities in the United States have restrictions on the use of city water for condensing purposes and require installation of a cooling tower system. Water-cooled equipment generally operates efficiently and economically.

Air Distribution

External static pressures available in small-store air-conditioning units are limited, and duct systems should be designed to keep duct resistances low. Duct velocities should range between 800 to 1200 fpm (4.1 to 6.1 m/s) and pressure drops between 0.07 to 0.10 in. of water per 100 ft (0.6 to 0.8 Pa/m) of duct run. Average air quantities range from 350 to 450 cfm per ton (47 to 60 L/s per kW) refrigeration in accordance with the calculated internal sensible heat load.

Attention should be paid to suspended obstacles such as lights and displays, which will interfere with proper air distribution.

The duct system should contain enough dampers for air balancing. Dampers in the return duct and outdoor air duct should be installed for proper outdoor air-return air balance. Volume and splitter dampers should be installed in takeoffs from the main supply duct for air balance into branch ducts.

Control System

Controls for small-store systems should be kept simple and yet perform the required functions. Unitary equipment generally has factory-installed cooling controls with terminal boxes for external installation of power and control wiring by the electrician. Provisions also are made for heating controls.

Automatic dampers should be placed in the outdoor air duct to prevent outdoor air from entering the area when the fan is turned off.

Heating controls vary with the nature of the heating medium. Duct heaters generally are furnished with safety controls installed by the manufacturer. Space thermostats can control the heater through a summer-winter switch. All control circuits should be actuated through the load side of the fan circuit.

Maintenance

Air-conditioning units in small stores should be assigned to a reliable service company on a yearly contract to protect the

The preparation of this chapter is assigned to TC 9.8, Large Building Air-Conditioning Applications.

initial investment and maintain maximum efficiency. The contract should clearly state the responsibility for filter replacements or cleaning, repair and adjustment of controls, oil and grease, compressor maintenance, replacement of refrigerant, pump repairs, electrical maintenance, winterizing and startup of system, and replacement of materials and extra labor required for repairs.

Improving Operating Costs

Outdoor air economizers can improve the operating cost of cooling systems in most climates. These are generally available as factory options or accessories with roof mounting unitary units.

Night setback should be evaluated for stores with more than 8 hours of operation. The lights, heating, and cooling would be sources of potential savings. This can be incorporated with economizer controls. Increased exterior insulation will generally reduce operating energy requirements and may, in some cases, allow for a reduction in the size of equipment to be installed. Many types of insulation are now available for roofs, ceilings, masonry walls, frame walls, slabs, and foundation walls. Many codes now have minimum requirements for insulation and fenestration materials.

VARIETY STORES

The variety store features a wide range of merchandise, often including a large lunch counter or a separate restaurant, auto service area, and garden shop. Some stores sell pets, including monkeys, fish, and birds. This variety of merchandise must be considered in designing an air-conditioning system for such a store.

In addition to the sales area, such areas as stock rooms, rest rooms, offices, and special storage rooms for perishable merchandise may require air conditioning or refrigeration.

The design and application suggestions for small stores apply also to variety stores. The following design and application information should be considered additional to that applying to small stores.

LOAD DETERMINATION

The heating and cooling loads should be calculated in accordance with the methods discussed in the 1985 FUNDAMENTALS Volume. However, some of the design data for the major sources of load will be discussed briefly in this section.

Operating economics and the spaces served often dictate the indoor design conditions for variety store air conditioning. Some variety stores may base summer load calculations on higher inside temperatures, such as 80 °F db (27 °C db), while the thermostats are set to control to 72 to 75 °F db (22 to 24 °C db). This reduces the installed equipment size while providing the desired inside temperature most of the time.

Special rooms for candy storage, if required, are usually designed for a room temperature of 70 °F (21 °C), with a separate unitary air conditioner.

The heat gain from lighting will not be uniform throughout the entire area, with some areas such as jewelry and other specialty displays having as high as 6 to 8 watts per ft² (65 to 86 W/m²) of floor area. For the entire sales area, an average value of 2 to 4 watts per ft² (20 to 40 W/m²) may be used. For stock rooms, receiving, marking, toilet, and rest room areas, a value of 2 watts per ft² (20 W/m²) may be used. When available, actual lighting layouts should be used for load computation rather than average values.

The store owner usually will establish the population density for a variety store, based on the location and size of the store and past experience.

The food preparation and service areas in a variety store range from small lunch counters with heat-producing equipment (ranges, griddles, ovens, coffee urns, toasters) in the conditioned space to large deluxe installations with separate kitchens beyond the conditioned space. See Chapter 19 for more specific information on HVAC for kitchen and eating spaces.

The heat released from special merchandising equipment, such as amusement rides for children or equipment used for preparing such items as popcorn, pizza, frankfurters, hamburgers, doughnuts, roasted chickens, and cooked nuts, should be obtained from the manufacturer's data.

Minimum outdoor air generally is based on 5 cfm (2.4 L/s) per person in sales areas and 15 cfm (7.1 L/s) per person for a separate restaurant area. A positive pressure should be maintained in the building.

DESIGN CONSIDERATIONS

Variety stores are generally constructed with a large open sales area and a partial glass storefront. The installed lighting is usually sufficient to offset the design roof heat loss. Therefore, the interior portion of these stores needs cooling during business hours throughout the year. The perimeter areas and especially the storefront and entrance areas may have a highly variable heating and cooling requirement.

Proper zone control and HVAC design are essential to meet the variable requirements of the storefront and entrance areas. Checkout lanes, entrances, and exits are generally located in this area, making proper environmental control even more important.

System Design

The important factors in selection of a variety store air-conditioning system are (1) life cycle costs, (2) floor space required for equipment, (3) maintenance requirements and equipment reliability, and (4) simplicity of control. Roof-mounted unitary units are the most common type used for variety store air conditioning.

Air Distribution

The air supply for the large sales area can generally be designed for the primary cooling requirement. Air distribution for the perimeter areas must consider the variable heating and cooling requirements.

Control System

The control system should be simple, dependable, and fully automatic, since it normally will be operated by store personnel who have little knowledge of the air-conditioning system. Many types of automatic control are used in chain stores. The system should be designed so the store operator is only required to turn a switch to start or stop the system, or to change to night operation.

Maintenance

Most variety stores do not employ trained maintenance personnel, but rely instead on service contracts with either the installer or a local service company. For improving operating costs, see information for small stores.

SUPERMARKETS

LOAD DETERMINATION

Heating and cooling loads usually may be calculated by the methods given in the 1985 FUNDAMENTALS Volume. Data for calculating the loads from people, lights, motors, and special heat-producing equipment should be obtained from the store owner or manager or the equipment manufacturer. Space conditioning in a supermarket is required for two reasons: human comfort and proper operation of the refrigerated display cases. A minimum quantity of outdoor air should be introduced through the air-conditioning unit. The amount of outside air is the larger of the volume required for ventilation or to maintain slightly positive pressure in the space.

Many supermarkets are units of a large chain owned or operated by one company. Standardized construction, layout, and equipment used in designing many similar stores simplifies the load calculations.

It is important that the final air-conditioning load be correctly determined. Table 1 shows most general classifications of refrigerated display cases and tabulates the total heat extraction, sensible heat, latent heat, and the percentage of latent to total load. These data have been calculated from condensing unit data for actual operating conditions and from observed defrost water. Engineers report considerable fixture heat removal (case load) variation as the relative humidity and temperature vary in relatively small increments. Increases in relative humidity above 55% add substantial load, while reduced relative humidity substantially decreases the load, as shown in Figure 1.

The refrigerating effect, imposed by the display fixtures in the store, must be subtracted from the gross air-conditioning requirements for the building to produce a new total load and percentage of latent and sensible heat, which the air conditioning must handle.

Table 1 Refrigerating Effect Produced by Open Refrigerated Display Fixtures

Display Fixture Types	Refrigerating Effect (RE) on Building, Btu/h·ft (W/m) of Fixture*			
	Latent Heat, Btu/h·ft (W/m)	%Latent to Total RE	Sensible Heat, Btu/h·ft (W/m)	Total RE, Btu/h·ft (W/m)
Low temperature				
Frozen food				
Single deck	38(36)	15	207(199)	245(236)
Single deck-double island	70(67)	15	400(384)	470(452)
2 deck	144(138)	20	576(554)	720(692)
3 deck	322(310)	20	1288(1238)	1610(1540)
4 or 5 deck	400(384)	20	1600(1538)	2000(1923)
Ice cream				
Single deck	64(62)	15	366(352)	430(413)
Single deck-double island	70(67)	15	400(384)	470(452)
Standard temperature				
Meats				
Single deck	52(50)	15	298(286)	350(336)
Multideck	219(211)	20	876(842)	1095(1053)
Dairy				
Multideck	196(188)	20	784(754)	980(942)
Produce				
Single deck	36(35)	15	204(196)	240(231)
Multideck	192(184)	20	768(738)	960(923)

*These figures are general magnitudes for fixtures adjusted for today's average desired product temperatures and apply to store ambients in front of the display cases of 72 to 74°F (22.2 to 23.3°C) with 50 to 55% rh. Raising the dry bulb only 3 to 5°F (2 to 3°C) and the humidity 5 to 10% can increase loads (heat removal) 25% or more. Equally lower temperatures and humidities, as found in stores in winter, have an equally marked effect on lowering loads and heat removal from the space. Consult display case manufacturer's data for the particular equipment to be used.

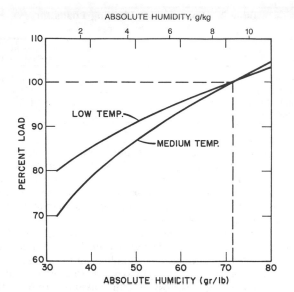

Fig. 1 Refrigerated Case Load Variation with Store Air Humidity

DESIGN CONSIDERATIONS

In recent years, store owners and operators have frequently complained about cold aisles in stores, heating systems that operate even when the outdoor temperature is 78°F (26°C), and air-conditioning systems that operate infrequently. The reason for such complaints is usually attributed to spillover of cold air from open refrigerated display equipment.

Although refrigerated display equipment may be the cause of cold stores, the problem is not that of excessive spillover or improperly operating equipment. To provide proper comfort and performance conditions, the design of heating and air-conditioning systems must compensate for the following effects caused by open refrigerated display equipment.

1. The increased heating requirements due to removal of large quantities of heat, even in summer, when only dehumidification is required.
2. The net air-conditioning load after deducting the latent and sensible refrigeration effect (Item 1). The load reduction and change in sensible-latent load ratio have a major effect on the equipment selection.
3. The need for special air circulation and distribution to offset the localized removal of large quantities of heat by open equipment.
4. Independent temperature and humidity control.

Each of these problems is present, to some degree, in every supermarket, although variations exist due to climate and store layout. The following sections discuss how to overcome these problems. Some of the instances may appear unusual but may cause extremely high energy bills if the year-round air-conditioning system has not been designed to compensate for the effects of open equipment.

Heat Removed by Refrigerated Display Equipment

The display refrigerator not only cools a displayed product but envelopes it in a blanket of cold air, which absorbs heat from the room air in contact with it. Approximately 80 to 90% of the heat removed from the room by vertical refrigerators is absorbed through the display opening. The open refrigerator thus acts as a large air cooler, absorbing heat from the room and rejecting it via the condensers outside the building. Occasionally,

Table 2   Approximate Lighting Loads for Department Stores

Area	Watts per ft² (W/m²)
Basement	3-5 (32-54)
First floor	4-7 (43-75)
Upper floors, women's wear	3-5 (32-54)
Upper floors, house furnishings	2-3 (22-32)

this conditioning effect can be more than the design air-conditioning capacity required by the store. *The heat removed by the refrigerated equipment must be considered in the design of the air-conditioning and heating systems,* because this heat is being removed constantly, day and night, summer and winter, *without regard for the store temperature.*

The display cases increase the heating requirement of the building and *heat will often be required at times when not normally expected.* The following example is an indication of the extent of this cooling effect. The desired store temperature is 75°F (24°C). Stored heat loss or gain is assumed to be 15,000 Btu/h per deg F of temperature difference between outdoor and store temperature (7.9 kW/°C). (This value will vary with store size, location, exposure, etc.) The heat removed by refrigerated equipment is 190,000 Btu/h (55.7 kW). (This will vary with the number of refrigerators.) The latent heat removed is assumed to be 19% of the total (see Table 2), leaving 81% sensible or 154,000 Btu/h (45.1 k/W), which will cool the store 154,000/15,000 = 10°F (5.5°C).

Therefore, by its constant sensible heat removal from its environment, the refrigerated equipment in this store will cool the store 10°F (5.5°C) below outdoor temperature in winter and summer. Thus, in mild climates, heat must be added to the store to maintain comfort conditions.

The designer has the choice of discarding the heat removed by refrigeration or reclaiming it. If economies and store heat data indicate that the heat should be discarded, *this heat extraction from the space must be added to the heating load calculations.* If not, the heating system may not have sufficient capacity to maintain the design temperature under peak conditions.

The additional sensible heat removed by the cases may raise the air conditioning latent load from 32% to as much as 50% of the net heat load. Removal of a 50% latent load by means of refrigeration alone is very difficult. Normally, it requires reheat or chemical adsorption.

Multishelf refrigerated display equipment today requires 55% rh or less. In the dry-bulb ranges of average stores, humidity in excess of 55% can cause heavy coil frosting, product zone frosting with low temperature cases, fixture sweating, and substantial increased power consumption for refrigeration.

Simple control systems can closely control humidity. This is accomplished by using a humidistat during summer cooling, which transfers heat from the standard condenser to the heating coil. The store thermostat maintains proper summer temperature conditions and the humidistat maintains proper humidity conditions. Override controls prevent a runaway situation between the humidstat and thermostat.

The equivalent result can be accomplished with a conventional air-conditioning system by using three- or four-way valves and reheat condensers in the ducts. This system borrows heat from the standard condenser and is controlled by a humidistat. More recently, desiccant dehumidifiers have been used.

Humidity

The cooling from the refrigeration equipment does not preclude the need for air conditioning. On the contrary, it increases *the need for humidity control.*

With increases in humidity in the store, heavier loads are imposed upon the refrigeration equipment, operating costs increase, more defrost periods are required, and display life of products is decreased. The dew point rises with the relative humidity, and sweating can become profuse—to the extent that even non-refrigerated items such as shelving superstructures, canned products, mirrors, and walls may sweat.

There are two different methods to achieve humidity control. One is an electric vapor compression air conditioner, which cools air to a temperature below its dew point to remove moisture. This means overcooling the air to condense the moisture and then reheating it to a temperature suitable to maintain comfort. Condenser waste heat is often used. Vapor compression holds humidity levels at 50 to 55% rh. The trends in store design, which include more food refrigeration and more efficient lighting, reduce the sensible component of the load even further.

The second method of dehumidification uses desiccant dehumidifiers. A desiccant absorbs or adsorbs moisture directly from air to its surface. The moisture trapped by the desiccant material is reactivated, passing hot air at 180°F to 230°F through the desiccant base. Condenser waste heat can provide as much as 40% of the heat required. Desiccant systems in supermarkets hold humidity levels between 30 and 40% rh. This results in significant savings in the refrigerated cases' operation.

System Design

The same air-handling equipment and distribution system generally are used for both cooling and heating. The entrance area of a supermarket is the most difficult section to heat. Many stores in the northern United States are built with vestibules provided with separate heating equipment to temper the cold air entering from outdoors. Auxiliary heat may also be provided at the checkout area, which is usually close to the front entrance.

Other methods used to heat entrance areas include (1) air curtains, (2) gas-fired or electric infrared radiant heaters, and (3) the use of waste heat from the refrigeration condensers. Air-cooled condensing units are most commonly used in supermarkets. Typically, a central air handler conditions the entire sales area. Specialty areas like bakeries, computer rooms, or warehouses are better seved with a separate air handler. The loads in these areas vary and don't require the same control as the sales area. Most installations are made on the roof of the supermarket. If air-cooled condensers are located at ground level outside the store, they must be protected against vandalism, as well as truck and customer traffic. If water-cooled condensers are used on the air-conditioning equipment and a cooling tower is required, provisions should be made to prevent freezing during winter operation.

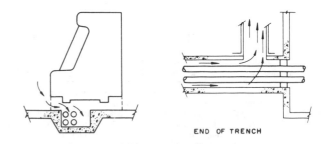

Fig. 2   Floor Return Ducts

Air Distribution

Many designers overcome the concentrated load at the front of the supermarket by discharging at least 60% of the total air supply into the front third of the sales area.

The volume of air supply to the space with the vapor compression system has been typically 1 cfm/ft² (5 L/s per m²) of sales area. This should be calculated based on both the sensible and latent internal loads. The desiccant system typically requires 0.5 cfm/ft² (2.5 L/s per m²) and is determined by the sensible load. This is due to the high moisture removal rate of a desiccant system and, in most cases, only about 40% of the circulation rate passes through the dehumidifier.

The air cooled by the refrigerators, being more dense, settles to the floor and becomes increasingly colder. The major effect is in the first 36 in. (915 mm) above the floor. If this cold air remains still, it will cause discomfort and serve no purpose, even though other areas of the store may need more cooling at the same time. To take advantage of the cooling effect of the refrigerators and provide an even temperature in the store, *the cold air must be mixed with the entire store air.* Cold floors or areas of the store cannot be eliminated by the addition of heat alone, and any reduction of air-conditioning capacity without circulation of the localized cold air would be analogous to installing an air conditioner without a fan.

To accomplish the necessary mixing, air returns should be located at the floor level and strategically placed to remove the cold air near concentrations of refrigerated fixtures. The returns should be designed and located to avoid creating drafts.

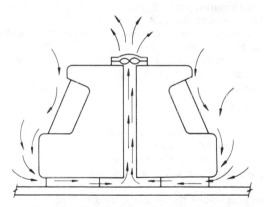

Fig. 3   Air Mixing Using Fans Behind Cases

Two general solutions are:

1. **Return Ducts in Floor.** This is the preferred method and can be accomplished in two ways. The floor area in front of the refrigerated display cases is the coolest area. All these cases have refrigerant lines run to them, usually in tubes or trenches. By enlarging the trenches or size of the tubes and having them open under the cases for air return, the air can be drawn in from the cold area (see Figure 2). The air is returned to the air-handling unit through a tee connection to the trench before it enters the back room area. The opening where the refrigerant lines enter the back room should be sealed.

   If refrigerant line conduits are not used, the air can be returned through inexpensive underfloor ducts.

   Where fixtures do not have sufficient undercase air passage, check with the manufacturer. Often they can be raised off the floor approximately 1.5 in. (40 mm).

   Floor trenches can also be used as a duct for tubing, electrical supply, etc.

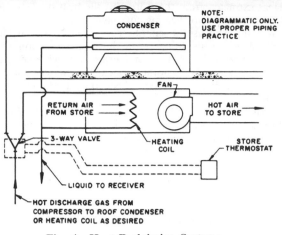

Fig. 4   Heat Reclaiming Systems

Floor level return relieves the problem of localized cold areas and cold aisles and uses the cooling effect for store cooling, or increases by the heating efficiency distributing the air in areas where most needed.

2. **Fans behind Cases.** If ducts cannot be placed in the floor, circulating fans can draw the air from the floor and discharge it into the upper levels (see Figure 3).

   However, while this approach will prevent objectionable cold aisles in front of the refrigerated display cases, it will often allow the area with a concentration of refrigerated fixtures to be colder than the rest of the store.

Control Systems

The control system should be as simple as practicable so that store personnel are required only to change the position of a selector switch in order to start, stop, or change the system from heating to cooling or from cooling to heating. Control systems for heat recovery applications become more complex and should be coordinated with the equipment manufacturer.

Maintenance, Heat Reclamation

Most supermarkets, except the large chains, do not employ trained maintenance personnel but rely on service contracts with either the installer or a local service company. This method relieves the store management of the personal responsibility of keeping the air-conditioning system in proper operating condition.

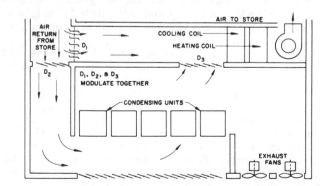

Fig. 5   Machine Room with Automatic Temperature Control Interlocked with Store Temperature Control

Heat extracted from the store plus the heat of compression may be reclaimed for heating cost savings. One way to reclaim the rejected heat uses a separate condenser located in the air conditioner's air-handling system alternately or in conjunction with the main refrigeration condensers to provide heat, as required (see Figure 4). Another system uses water-cooled condensers and delivers its rejected heat to a water coil in the air handler.

The heat rejected by conventional machines using air cooled condensers may be reclaimed by proper duct and damper design (see Figure 5). Automatic temperature controls can either reject this heat outdoors, recirculate it through the store, or store it in water tanks for future use.

DEPARTMENT STORES

Department stores vary in size, type, and area of location so that the design of an air-conditioning system requires an individual solution for each store. An ample minimum quantity of outdoor air reduces or eliminates odor problems. Essential features of the quality system include (1) an automatic control system properly designed to compensate for load fluctuations, (2) zoned air distribution to maintain uniform conditions under shifting loads, and (3) use of outdoor air for cooling during intermediate seasons and peak season sales periods. It is also desirable to adjust indoor temperatures for variations in outdoor temperatures. While the control of humidity to close tolerances is not necessary, the properly designed system should operate to maintain relative humidity not over 50% with a corresponding dry-bulb temperature of 78°F (26°C). This humidity limit eliminates musty odors and retards perspiration, particularly in fitting rooms.

LOAD DETERMINATION

Because the occupancy (except for store personnel) is transient, indoor conditions are commonly established not to exceed 78°F (25.6°C) dry-bulb and 50% rh at design outdoor summer design conditions, and 70°F (21°C) db at design outdoor winter conditions. Winter humidification is seldom used in store air conditioning.

The number of customers and store personnel normally found on each conditioned floor must be ascertained. Particular attention should be paid to specialty departments or other areas having a greater-than-average concentration of occupants. Lights should be checked for wattage and types. Table 2 gives approximate values for lighting in various areas; Table 3 gives approximate occupancies.

Other sources of load, such as motors, beauty parlor and restaurant equipment, and any special display or merchandising equipment, should be determined.

The minimum outside air requirement is 0.5 air change per hour—enough to overcome infiltration by producing a slight positive pressure within the structure. The minimum outdoor air standard is 5 cfm (2.4 L/s) per person, but 7.5 cfm (3.6 L/s) per person is preferred. These standards have been found generally acceptable and adequate for removing odors and keeping the building atmosphere fresh. However, local ventilation ordinances may require greater quantities of outdoor air.

Paint shops, alteration rooms, restrooms, eating places, and locker rooms should be provided with positive exhaust ventilation, and their requirements must be checked against local codes.

Table 3   Approximate Occupancy for Department Stores

Area	Ft²(m²) per person
Basement, metropolitan area	25-100 (2-9)
Basement, other with occasional peak	25-100 (2-9)
First floor, metropolitan area	25- 75 (2-7)
First floor, suburban	25- 75 (2-7)
Upper floors, women's wear	50-100 (4.6-9)
Upper floors, house furnishings	100 or more (9 or more)

DESIGN CONSIDERATIONS

Before making load calculations, the designer should examine the store arrangement to determine the various items that will affect the load, as well as the system design. For existing buildings, a survey can be made of actual construction, floor arrangement, and load sources. For new buildings, examination of the drawings and discussion with the architect or owner will be required.

Larger stores may have beauty parlors, restaurants, lunch counters, or auditoriums. These special areas may operate during all store hours. Where the load from one of these areas is small in proportion to the total, this load may be included in the portion of the air-conditioning system serving the same floor. If, for any reason, present or future operation may be compromised by such a method, a separate air-conditioning system should serve this space. A separate air distribution system should be provided for the beauty parlor because of the concentrated load in this area.

The restaurant, because of the required service facilities, is generally centrally located. It is often used only during the noon hours. For control of odors, a separate air-handling system should be considered. Future plans for the store must be established, since they can have a great effect on the type of air-conditioning and refrigeration systems to be used.

System Design

Air-conditioning systems for department stores may be of the unitary or central-station type. Heat pumps, either water- or air-source, are also used where favorable load conditions are available and elimination or reduction in size of a boiler plant is feasible.

The selection of the system should be based on owning and operating costs, as well as any other special considerations for the particular store. The store hours, load variations, and size of load will affect the final selection of equipment and system.

Larger department stores often use central station systems consisting of air-handling units with chilled water cooling coils, hot water heating coils, fans, and filters. Air systems must have adequate zoning for varying loads, occupancy, and usage. The wide variations in people loads that occur may permit consideration of variable volume air-distribution systems. The water chilling and heating plants must distribute water to the various air-handling systems and zones and may take advantage of some diversity of loads in the total building.

The sales area should not be used for air-conditioning equipment; ceiling, roof, and mechanical equipment room locations should be used instead wherever practicable. In selecting locations for equipment, the maintenance and operation of the system after installation are important factors.

Air Distribution

All buildings must be studied for orientation, wind exposure, construction, and floor arrangement. These factors not only affect load calculations but also zone arrangements and duct locations. In addition to planning for entrances, wall areas with significant glass, roof areas, and population densities, the expected locations of various departments (such as the lamp department) should be considered. Certain flexibility must be left in the duct design to allow for future movement of various departments. The preliminary duct layout should also be checked from the standpoint of winter heating to determine any special situations to be considered. In the case of entrances, it usually is necessary to design for separate air systems, particularly in northern areas. This would also be true for storage areas where cooling is not contemplated.

Air curtain installations may be used at entrance doorways to limit or prevent infiltration of unconditioned air, while providing greater ease of entry. For further information on air curtains, see Chapter 29 of the 1985 FUNDAMENTALS Volume.

Control Systems

The extent of automatic control will depend on the type of installation and the extent to which it is zoned. The central station supplying air to the zones must be controlled so that air of the correct condition is delivered to the zones. Outdoor air should be automatically controlled to operate at minimum cost.

Partial or full automatic control should be placed on the refrigeration system to compensate for load fluctuations. Completely automatic refrigeration plants are now practical and should be considered carefully.

Maintenance

Most department stores employ operating personnel for routine operating and maintenance requirements. However, these stores normally rely on service and preventive maintenance contracts for the specialized requirements of refrigeration cycles, chemical treatment, central plant systems, and major repairs.

Improving Operating Costs

Outdoor air economizer systems can reduce the operating cost of the cooling system in many climates. These are generally available as factory options or accessories with the air-handling units or control systems. Heat recovery and thermal storage systems should also be analyzed.

CONVENIENCE CENTERS

Many small stores, variety stores, supermarkets, drug stores, theaters, and even department stores are located in convenience centers normally owned by a developer. The space for an individual store is usually leased. Arrangements for installing air-conditioning systems in leased space will vary. In a typical arrangement the developer has a shell structure built and provides the tenant an allowance for a typical heating and cooling system, and other minimum interior finish work. The tenant must install the HVAC system under this leasing arrangement.

LOAD DETERMINATION

The heating and cooling loads should be calculated for the individual spaces in accordance with the methods discussed in Chapter 25 and 26 of the 1985 FUNDAMENTALS Volume. Lease requirements may limit maximum cooling available for tenants.

DESIGN CONSIDERATIONS

The developer or owner may establish standards for typical heating and cooling systems that may or may not be sufficient for the specified space requirements. Therefore, a tenant may have to install systems of different sizes and types than originally allowed for by the developer. The tenant must ascertain that power and other services will be available for its total intended requirements.

The use of party walls in convenience centers tends to reduce heating and cooling loads. However, the partition load while an adjacent space is unoccupied must be considered.

REGIONAL SHOPPING CENTERS

The regional shopping center generally incorporates a heated and air-conditioned mall. The regional shopping center is normally owned by a developer who may be an independent party or one of the major tenants in the center.

The major department stores are generally considered to be separate buildings, although they are attached to the mall. The space for individual stores is usually leased. Arrangements for installing air-conditioning systems in the individual leased spaces will vary. Typically, a developer will have a completely finished mall and a shell strucure built for the individual stores. An allowance is provided to the tenant for a typical heating and cooling system and other minimum interior finish.

LOAD DETERMINATION

The heating and cooling loads should be calculated for the individual spaces in accordance with the methods discussed in the 1985 FUNDAMENTALS Volume and the maximum loads permitted by the lease.

DESIGN CONSIDERATIONS

The owner provides the air-conditioning system for the enclosed mall. The mall system may use a central plant or individual unitary units. The owner will generally require that the individual tenant stores connect to a central plant system and include charges in the rent for heating and cooling. Where unitary systems are used, the owner generally requires that the individual tenant install a unitary system of similar design.

The owner may establish standards for typical heating and cooling systems that may or may not be sufficient for the specific space requirements. Therefore, a tenant may have to install systems of different sizes than originally allowed for by the developer.

Leasing arrangements may include language that has a detrimental effect on conservation (such as allowing excessive lighting and outdoor air or deleting requirements for economizer systems). The designer of HVAC systems for tenants in a shopping center must be fully aware of the lease requirements and work closely with leasing agents to guide these systems toward better energy efficiency.

System Design

Regional shopping centers vary widely in physical arrangements and architectural design. The single level and smaller malls usually use unitary systems for mall and tenant air conditioning. The larger and multilevel malls usually use central plant systems. The owner sets the design of the mall system and generally requires that similar systems be installed for tenant stores.

A typical central plant system may distribute chilled water to the individual tenant stores and the mall air-conditioning system and use electric heating at the local use point. Some systems distribute both hot and chilled water. All-air systems have been used, which distribute chilled or heated air to the individual tenant stores and the mall air-conditioning system and use variable volume control or electric heating at the local use point.

Table 4 Typical Installed Capacity and Energy Usage Enclosed Mall Centers[a]
Based on 1979 Data—Midwestern U.S.

Type of Space	Installed Cooling[b] Btu/h·ft^2	Annual Consumption kWh/ft^{2c}			
		Lighting[d]	Cooling[e]	Heating[f]	Misc.
Candy store	44.8 to 78.0	23.9 to 29.6	7.8 to 23.5	9.6 to 5.7	2.4 to 70.1
Clothing store	37.3 to 45.5	14.1 to 24.9	8.0 to 9.6	8.9 to 5.1	1.2 to 6.7
Fast food	48.2 to 78.0	16.7 to 32.4	9.8 to 23.5	9.6 to 3.8	38.1 to 70.0
Game room	33.8 to 44.5	6.8 to 12.5	7.2 to 7.3	13.8 to 4.7	0.2 to 13.8
Gen. merchandise	32.9 to 43.6	13.2 to 23.3	6.3 to 9.7	6.3 to 5.6	1.4 to 9.3
Gen. service	39.3 to 50.3	15.7 to 17.4	7.8 to 9.2	12.0 to 5.9	7.6 to 8.2
Gift store	36.4 to 51.1	12.8 to 22.9	6.3 to 10.0	7.1 to 4.9	0.4 to 2.2
Grocery	69.5 to 86.2	10.9 to 19.3	5.3 to 8.9	6.0 to 7.0	18.6 to 21.0
Jewelry	53.5 to 66.1	37.2 to 44.9	10.6 to 12.3	5.6 to 3.6	7.6 to 9.3
Mall	30.0 to 48.0	5.4 to 12.0	8.3 to 13.7	11.5 to 5.6	0.2 to 1.5
Restaurant	40.0 to 53.0	5.0 to 22.0	7.8 to 12.3	19.0 to 16.7	17.2 to 21.0
Shoe store	36.9 to 50.6	20.4 to 32.1	7.4 to 11.4	7.2 to 4.6	1.0 to 2.3
Center average	30.0 to 48.0	18.0 to 28.0	8.0 to 15.0	6.0 to 3.0	1.0 to 3.0

[a]Operation of center assumed to be 12 h/day and 7 days/week.
[b]Multiply Btu/h · ft^2 by 3.15 to convert to W/m^2
[c]Multiply kWh/ft^2 by 10.76 to convert to kWh/m^2

[d]Lighting includes miscellaneous and receptacle loads.
[e]Heating includes blower and is for electric resistance heating.
[f]Cooling includes blower motor and is for unitary-type system.

Air Distribution

The air distribution for individual stores should be designed for the particular space occupancy. Some tenant stores maintain a negative pressure relative to the mall for odor control.

The air distribution system should maintain a slight positive pressure relative to atmospheric and a neutral pressure relative to most of the individual tenant stores. Smoke removal for fire protection should be considered. Exterior entrances should have vestibule entrances with independent heating systems.

Maintenance

The center may employ operating personnel for routine operating and maintenance requirements of the mall. However, these centers normally rely on service and preventive maintenance contracts for the specialized requirements of refrigeration cycles, chemical treatment, central plant systems, and major repairs. The individual tenant stores may have to provide their own maintenance.

Improving Operating Costs

Outdoor air economizer systems can improve the operating cost of the cooling system in many climates. These are generally available as factory options or accessories with the air-handling units or control systems. Heat recovery and thermal storage systems should also be analyzed. Some shopping centers have successfully employed cooling tower heat exchanger or strainer cycle economizers.

MULTIPLE-USE COMPLEXES

Multiple-use complexes are being developed in most metropolitan areas. These complexes generally combine the retail facilities with other functions such as office space, hotel space, residential space, or other commercial space into a single site. The combining of functions into a single site or structure provides benefits such as improved land use; structural savings; more efficient parking; utility savings; and opportunities for more efficient electrical, fire protection, and mechanical systems.

LOAD DETERMINATION

The HVAC loads should be determined for the individual occupancies by the methods outlined in the 1985 FUNDAMENTALS Volume. The various occupancies may have peak HVAC demands that occur at different times of the day and even at different times of the year. Therefore, the various occupancies should have HVAC loads determined independently. Where a combined central plant is to be considered, a block load should also be determined.

DESIGN CONSIDERATIONS

The retail facilities are generally located on the lower levels of multiple-use complexes, and other commercial facilities are on upper levels. Generally, the perimeter loads of the retail portion difffers from the other commercial space. The greater lighting and population densities also make the HVAC demands different for the retail space than for the other commercial space.

The differences in HVAC characteristics for the various occupancies within a multiple-use complex indicate that separate air handling and distribution should be used for the separate functions. However, combining heating and cooling units into a central plant can achieve substantial savings.

A combined central heating and cooling plant for a multiple-use complex also provides good opportunities for heat recovery, thermal storage, and other similar sophistificaton that may not be economical in a single-use facility.

System Design

Individual air-handling and distribution systems should be designed for the various occupancies. The central heating and cooling plant may be sized for the block load requirements, which may be less than the total of each occupancy's demand.

Control Systems

The multiple-use complex typically has a requirement for a centralized type of control system. This may be dictated by requirements for fire and smoke control, security, remote monitoring, billing for central facilities use, maintenance control, building operations control, and energy management.

CHAPTER 19

COMMERCIAL AND PUBLIC BUILDINGS

CHAPTERS 18 through 25 of this volume cover common commercial and public buildings. Places of assembly, dwellings (except multifamily housing, which is covered in Chapter 17), hospitals, health centers, educational facilities, laboratories, industrial buildings, stores, shopping centers, and survival shelters are discussed in separate chapters.

This chapter is organized into eight sections. The first section, "General Criteria" applies to all buildings. It includes information on load characteristics, design concepts, and design criteria. Design criteria address such items as comfort level; costs; local conditions and requirements; and fire, smoke, and odor control that may apply to all building types.

The remaining sections present information applicable to the following specific buildings:

Dining and Entertainment Centers
Office Buildings
Libraries and Museums
Bowling Centers
Communication Centers
Transportation Centers
Warehouses

These sections include information on load characteristics, design concepts and criteria, special considerations, and systems applicability, as appropriate.

GENERAL CRITERIA

Every system discussed in this volume can, if properly applied, be successful in any building. However, such parameters as initial and operating costs, space allocation, architectural design, and the consulting engineer's evaluation and experience limits the proper system choices for a given building type and location.

Heating and air-conditioning systems that are simple in design and of the proper size for a given building generally have fairly low maintenance and operating costs. For optimum results, it is desirable to build as much inherent thermal control into the

basic structure as is economically possible. Such control might include high thermal characteristic materials, insulation, and multiple or special glazing and shading devices. Owners and architects must consider all aspects of a structure's design that interface with building systems, and the entire scope of the project, not just the mechanical equipment, that may be designed into the building.

Another design consideration, not always recognized, is the relationship between building shape and orientation and air-conditioning capacity. Since the exterior load may vary from 30 to 60% of the total air-conditioning load when the fenestration area ranges from 25 to 75% of the floor area, it may be desirable to minimize the perimeter area. For example, a rectangular building with a four-to-one aspect ratio requires substantially more refrigeration than a square building with the same floor area.

Retrofitting of existing buildings continues to be an important part of the construction industry, because of increased costs of construction and the necessity of reducing energy consumption. The design criteria found in the ASHRAE *Handbooks* pertain to retrofit designs, as well as to new designs.

Many factors affect the system selected; some relate to specific building types, others relate to all building types. Table 1 lists parameters to consider before selecting a system for any building. The system choice, often made by the owner, may not be based on a value engineering study. It is decided, to a great degree, by the engineer's ability to relate those factors involving higher first cost or lower life-cycle cost and benefits that have no calculable dollar value (Chapter 1 in this volume, "Air-Conditioning System Selection and Design").

Proper design also considers controlling noise and minimizing pollution of the atmosphere and water into which the system will discharge.

Some buildings are constructed with only heating and ventilating systems. If such buildings provide for future cooling, humidification, or both, the design principles are the same as for a fully air-conditioned building. For these buildings, greater design emphasis should be placed on natural or forced ventilation systems to minimize occupant discomfort during hot weather.

The general responsibility for this chapter is assigned to TC 9.8, Large Building Air-Conditioning Applications.

Table 1   General Design Criteria[a]

| General Category | Specific Category | Inside Design Conditions | | Air Movement | Circulation Air Changes per Hour |
		Winter	Summer		
Dining and Entertainment Centers	Cafeterias and Luncheonettes	70 to 74 °F (21 to 23 °C) 20 to 30% rh	78 °F (26 °C)[e] 40% rh	50 fpm (0.25 m/s) @ 6 ft (1.8 m) above Floor	12 to 15
	Restaurants	70 to 74 °F (21 to 23 °C) 20 to 30% rh	74 to 78 °F (23 to 26 °C) 55 to 60% rh	25 to 30 fpm (0.13 to 0.15 m/s)	8 to 12
	Bars	70 to 74 °F (21 to 23 °C) 20 to 30% rh	74 to 78 °F (23 to 26 °C) 50 to 60% rh	30 fpm (0.15 m/s) @ 6 ft (1.8 m) above Floor	15 to 20
	Night Clubs	70 to 74 °F (21 to 23 °C) 20 to 30% rh	74 to 78 °F (23 to 26 °C) 50 to 60% rh	below 25 fpm (0.13 m/s) at 5 ft (1.5 m above Floor)	20 to 30
	Kitchens	70 to 74 °F (21 to 23 °C)	85 to 88 °F (29 to 31 °C)	30 to 50 fpm (0.15 to 0.25 m/s)	12 to 15[m]
Office Buildings		70 to 74 °F (21 to 23 °C) 20 to 30% rh	74 to 78 °F (23 to 26 °C) 40 to 50% rh	25 to 45 fpm (0.13 to 23 m/s) 0.75 to 2 cfm/sq. ft (4 to 10 L/s • m²)	4 to 10
Libraries And Museums	Average	68 to 72 °F (20 to 22 °C) 40 to 55% rh		below 25 fpm (0.13 m/s)	8 to 12
	Archival	See Special Considerations		below 25 fpm (0.13 m/s)	8 to 12
Bowling Centers		70 to 74 °F (21 to 23 °C) 20 to 30% rh	75 to 78 °F (24 to 26 °C) 50 to 55% rh	50 fpm (0.25 m/s) @ 6 ft (1.8 m) above Floor	10 to 15
Communication Centers	Telephone Terminal Rooms	72 to 78 °F (22 to 26 °C) 40 to 50% rh	72 to 78 °F (22 to 26 °C) 40 to 50% rh	25 to 30 fpm (0.13 to 0.15 m/s)	8 to 20
	Teletype Centers	70 to 74 °F (21 to 23 °C) 40 to 50% rh	74 to 78 °F (23 to 26 °C) 45 to 55% rh	25 to 30 fpm (0.13 to 0.15 m/s)	8 to 20
	Radio and Television Studios	74 to 78 °F (23 to 26 °C) 30 to 40% rh	74 to 78 °F (23 to 26 °C) 45 to 55% rh	below 25 fpm (0.13 m/s) @ 12 ft (3.7 m) above Floor	15 to 40
Transportation Centers	Airport Terminals	70 to 74 °F (21 to 23 °C) 20 to 30% rh	74 to 78 °F (23 to 26 °C) 50 to 60% rh	25 to 330 fpm (0.13 to 0.15 m/s) @ 6 ft (1.8 m) above Floor	8 to 12
	Ship Docks	70 to 74 °F (21 to 23 °C) 20 to 30% rh	74 to 78 °F (23 to 26 °C) 50 to 60% rh	25 to 30 fpm (0.13 to 0.15 m/s) @ 6 ft (1.8 m) above Floor	8 to 12
	Bus Terminals	70 to 74 °F (21 to 23 °C) 20 to 30% rh	74 to 78 °F (23 to 26 °C) 50 to 60% rh	25 to 30 fpm (0.13 to 0.15 m/s) @ 6 ft (1.8 m) above Floor	8 to 12
	Garages	40 to 55 °F (4 to 13 °C)	80 to 100 °F (26 to 36 °C)	30 to 75 fpm (0.15 to 0.38 m/s)	4 to 6 Refer to NFPA
Warehouses		k	k		1 to 4

Minimum[b] Outdoor Air	Noise[c]	Filtering[d] Efficiencies	Energy Budget 10^3 Btu/sq ft/yr	Load Profile	General
10 cfm (5 L/s) per Person	NC 40 to 50[f]	35% or Better	50 to 400	Peak @ 1 to 2 P.M.	Prevent Draft Discomfort for Patrons Waiting in Serving Line
5 cfm (2.5 L/s) per Person	NC 35 to 40	35% or Better	50 to 500	Peak @ 1 to 2 P.M.	
100% or 10 cfm (5 L/s) Per Person w/Odor Control	NC 35 to 50	Use Charcoal for Odor Control with Manual Purge Control for 100% outside air to exhaust +35% Prefilters	50 to 400	Peak @ 5 to 7 P.M.	
25 cfm (12 L/s) per Person	NC 35 to 45[g]	Use Charcoal for Odor Control with Manual Purge Control for 100% outside air to exhaust ±35% Prefilters	20 to 250	Peak after 8 P.M. off 2 A.M. to 4 P.M.	Provide Good Air Movement but Prevent Cold Draft Discomfort for Dancing Patrons
100%	NC 40 to 50	10 to 15% or Better	100 to 400	h	Negative Air[i] Pressure Required for Odor Control
0.05 to 0.25 cfm/ft² (0.3 to 1.3 L/s·m²) or 5 cfm (2.5 L/s) per Person	NC 30 to 45	35 to 60% or Better	25 to 300	Peak @ 4 P.M.	
5 cfm (2.5 L/s) per Person	NC 35 to 40	35 to 60% or Better	150 to 250	Peak @ 3 P.M.	
5 cfm (2.5 L/s) per Person	NC 35	35% Prefilters + Charcoal Filters 85-95% Final[j]	25 to 100	Peak @ 3 P.M.	
20 to 30 cfm (9 to 14 L/s) per Person	NC 40 to 50	10 to 15%	100 to 200	Peak @ 6 to 8 P.M.	
5 cfm (5 L/s) per Person	to NC 60	85% or Better	150 to 500	Varies with Location and Use	Constant Temperature and Humidity Required
10 cfm (5 L/s) per Person	NC 40 to 50	85%	50 to 150	Varies with Location and Use	
10 cfm (5 L/s) per Person	NC 15 to 25	35% or Better Better	100 to 200	Varies Widely from Changes in Lighting and People	
5 cfm (2.5 L/s) per Person	NC 35 to 50	35% or Better + Charcoal	100 to 150	Peak @ 10 A.M. to 9 P.M.	Positive Air Pressure Required in Terminal
5 cfm (2.5 L/s) per Person	NC 35 to 50	10 to 15%	25 to 100	Peak @ 10 A.M. to 5 P.M.	Positive Air Pressure Required in Waiting Area
5 cfm (2.5 L/s) per Person	NC 35 to 50	35% with Exfiltration	150 to 250	Peak @ 10 A.M. to 5 P.M.	Positive Air Pressure Required in Terminal
1.5 cfm/ft² (7.5 L/s·m²)	NC 35 to 50	10 to 15%	20 to 200	Peak @ 10 A.M. to 5 P.M.	Negative Air Pressure Required to Remove Fumes
0.01 cfm/ft² (0.05 L/s·m²) or 5 cfm (2.5 L/s) per Person	up to 75	10 to 35%	20 to 350[l]	Peak @ 10 A.M. to 3 P.M.	

Notes to Table 1 General Design Criteria

[a]This table shows design criteria differences between various commercial and public buildings. It should not be used as the sole source for design criteria. Each type of data contained here can be determined with much greater meaning from other chapters in the ASHRAE *Handbooks* and from ASHRAE *Standards.*

[b]Governing codes should be consulted to determine minimum allowable requirements. Outdoor air requirements may often be reduced if high efficient adsorption or other odor- or gas-removal equipment is used, but never below 5 cfm (2.5 L/s) per person. (See Chapter 50, "Control of Gaseous Contaminants," in this volume. Also, see Chapter 12, "Odors," 1985 FUNDAMENTALS, and ASHRAE *Standard* 62-1981.)

[c]Refer to Chapter 52, "Sound and Vibration Control," in this volume.

[d]Average Atmospheric Dust Spot Efficiency. (See ASHRAE *Standard,* 52-76 for method of testing.)

[e]Food in these areas is often eaten more quickly than in a restaurant, so the turnover of diners is much faster. Since diners seldom remain as long, they don't require the degree of comfort necessary in restaurants. Thus, it may be possible to lower design criteria standards and still provide reasonably comfortable conditions. Although space conditions of 80°F (26.7°C) and 50% rh may be satisfactory for patrons when it is 95°F (35°C) and 50% rh outside, indoor conditions of 78°F (25.6°C) and 40% rh is better.

[f]Cafeterias and luncheonettes usually have some or all of the food preparation equipment and food trays in the same room with the diners. These eating establishments are generally noisier than restaurants, so noise transmission from the air-conditioning equipment is not as critical a factor.

[g]In some nightclubs, the noise from the air-conditioning system must be kept low so that all patrons can hear the entertainment.

[h]Peak kitchen heat load does not generally occur at peak dining load, although in luncheonettes and some cafeterias where cooking is done in the dining areas, peaks may be simultaneous.

[i]NFPA National Fire Code 96-84 defines requirements for hood, fan, ducts, and fire protection.

[j]Methods for removal of chemical pollutants must also be considered.

[k]Inside design temperatures for warehouses often depend on the materials stored inside.

[l]Also includes service stations.

[m]Usually determined by kitchen hood requirements.

LOAD CHARACTERISTICS

Any building analyzed for heat recovery or total energy systems requires sufficient load-profile and load-duration information on all forms of building input to perform the following:

1. Properly evaluate the instantaneous effect of one upon the other when no energy storage is contemplated.
2. Evaluate short-term effects (up to 48 hours) when energy storage is used. Chapter 6, "Heat Recovery Systems," and Chapter 9, "Applied Heat Pump Systems" have further information.

Load-profile curves consist of appropriate energy loads plotted against the time of day. Load-duration curves indicate the accumulated number of hours, at each load condition, from the highest to the lowest load for a day, a month, or a year. The area under load profile and load-duration curves for corresponding periods will be equivalent to load *x* time. These calculations must consider the type of air and water distribution systems in the building.

Comparison of load profiles for two or more energy forms during the same operating period permits determining load-matching characteristics under diverse operating conditions. For example, when the thermal energy is recovered from a diesel-electric generator at a rate equal to or less than the thermal energy demand, the energy can be used instantaneously, avoiding waste. But it may be worthwhile to store thermal energy when it is generated at a greater rate than demanded at the same time. A load profile study helps determine the economics of thermal storage.

Similarly, with internal source heat-recovery systems, load studies show the degree simultaneous or 48-hour cooling and heating loads match one another. Load matching must be integrated over the operating season with the aid of load-duration curves for overall feasibility studies.

These curves are useful with any energy consumption analysis calculations as a basis for hourly input values in computer programs (see Chapter 28, 1985 FUNDAMENTALS).

Economic feasibility of district heating and cooling systems (aside from environmental considerations) are influenced by load density and diversity factors for branch feeds to buildings along distribution mains. For example, the load density or energy per unit length of distribution main can be small enough in a complex of low-rise, lightly-loaded buildings, located at considerable distance from one another, to make a central heating, cooling, or heating and cooling plant uneconomic (see Chapter 12, "Heating and Cooling from a Central Plant").

Concentrations of internal loads peculiar to each application are covered later in this chapter and in Chapters 22 through 27 of the 1985 FUNDAMENTALS Volume.

DESIGN CONCEPTS

When a structure is characterized by several exposures and multipurpose use, especially with wide load swings and non-coincident energy use in certain areas, multi-unit or unitary systems may be considered for such areas; but not necessarily for the entire building (see Chapter 6). The benefits of transferring heat, absorbed by cooling from one area to other areas, processes, or services that require heat, may enhance the selection of such systems. This is especially true if the systems have closed water loop heat pumps or other equipment. Limitations in availability and relative costs of the various energy sources will also influence the system selection.

When the cost of energy is included in rent with no means for permanent or check-metering, tenants tend to consume excess energy. This energy abuse raises operating costs for the owner, decreases profitability, and affects the environment detrimentally. Design features can minimize excess energy penalties but seldom eliminate abuse. For example, HUD field records in total-electric housing show that nationwide rent-included dwellings use approximately 20% more energy than those directly metered by a public utility company.

Diversity factor benefits for central heating and cooling in rent-included buildings may result in lower building demand and connected loads. However, energy abuse may easily result in load factors and annual energy consumption exceeding that of buildings where the individual has a direct economic incentive to reduce energy consumption.

DESIGN CRITERIA

In many applications, design criteria are fairly evident, but in all cases, the engineer should understand the owner's and user's intent, since any one factor may influence system selection. The engineer's personal experience and judgment in the projection of future needs may be a better criterion for system design than any other single factor.

Comfort Level

Comfort, as measured by temperature, humidity, air motion, air quality, noise, and vibration, is not identical for all buildings, activities of occupants, or use of space.

For spaces with a high population density, or with a sensible heat factor less than 0.75, lower dry-bulb temperature (db) reduces the generation of latent heat. Reduced latent heat may further reduce the need for reheat and save energy. Therefore, finding an optimum temperature should be the goal of a detailed design analysis.

Costs

Owning and operating costs can affect system selection and seriously conflict with other criteria. The engineer, therefore, must help the owner resolve such conflicts (see Chapter 1). The cost and availability of different fuels must also receive attention.

Local Conditions

Local and national codes and regulations, and environmental concerns must be included in the design. The "Load and Energy Calculation" section (Chapters 22 through 31) in the 1985 FUNDAMENTALS Handbook gives information on calculating the effects of weather in specific areas.

Automatic Temperature Control

Proper automatic temperature control is essential to maintain occupant comfort during the varying occupant loads that occur. Improper temperature control may mean a loss of customers in restaurants and other public-occupied buildings. Opportunities exist for energy management due to varying hours of operations, different occupant loading during the day, and the need for management control of the building. An energy management control system can be combined with a building automation system to allow the owner to control energy management, lighting, security, fire protection, and other similar systems from one central control system. Chapter 51, "Automatic Control," and Chapter 48, "Energy Management," include more details.

Fire, Smoke, and Odor Control

Fire and smoke can easily spread by elevator shafts, stairwells, and other means. Although an air-conditioning system can spread fire and smoke by fan operation, penetrations required in walls or floors, or by stack effect without fan circulation, a properly designed and installed system may be a positive means of fire and smoke control.

Knowledge of effective techniques for positive control after fire startup is limited (see Chapter 58, "Fire and Smoke Control"). Effective attention to fire and smoke control will also help prevent odor migration to unventilated areas (see Chapter 50, "Control of Gaseous Contaminants").

DINING AND ENTERTAINMENT CENTERS

LOAD CHARACTERISTICS

Air conditioning of restaurants, cafeterias, bars, and nightclubs presents common load problems encountered in comfort conditioning, with additional factors pertinent to dining and entertainment applications. Such factors include the following:

1. Extremely variable loads, with high peaks, in many cases occurring twice daily.
2. High sensible and latent heat gains because of gas, steam, electric appliances, people, and food.
3. Localized high sensible and latent heat gains in dancing areas.
4. Unbalanced conditions in restaurant areas adjacent to kitchens that, although not part of the conditioned space, still require special attention.
5. Heavy infiltration of outdoor air through doors during rush hours.

Internal heat and moisture loads come from occupants, motors, lights, appliances, and infiltration. Separate calculations should be made for patrons and employees. The sensible and latent heat load must be proportioned in accordance with the design temperature selected for both sitting and working people, because latent to sensible heat ratio decreases as room temperature decreases for each category.

Hoods required to remove heat from appliances may also substantially reduce the space latent loads.

Infiltration is a considerable factor in many restaurant applications because of short occupancy and frequent door use. Infiltration is increased by the need for large quantities of air to replace air exhausted through hoods and for smoke removal. Wherever possible, vestibules or revolving doors should be installed to reduce such infiltration.

DESIGN CONCEPTS

Some of the factors that influence system design and equipment selection are as follows:

1. High concentration of food, body, and tobacco-smoke odors require adequate ventilation with proper exhaust facilities.
2. Step control of refrigeration plants to give satisfactory and economical operation under reduced loads.
3. Air exhausted at the ceiling removes smoke and odor.
4. Building design and space limitations often favor one equipment type over another. For example, in a restaurant having a vestibule with available space above it, air conditioning with condensers and evaporators remotely located above the vestibule may be satisfactory. Such an arrangement saves valuable space, even though self-contained units located within the conditioned space may prove somewhat lower in initial cost. In general, small cafeterias, bars, and the like, with loads up to 10 tons (35 kW) can be most economically conditioned with packaged units, while larger and more elaborate establishments require central plants.
5. If not required for kitchen exhaust, air required by an air-cooled or evaporative condenser may be drawn from the conditioned space. This eliminates the need for operating additional exhaust fans and also improves overall plant efficiency because of the lower temperature air entering the condenser. Proper water treatment is necessary if an evaporative condenser is used. Also, it may be necessary to bypass air when air is not required.
6. The usual practice for the smaller restaurant with an isolated plant has been to use direct-expansion systems.

7. Some air-to-air heat recovery equipment can reduce the energy required for heating and cooling ventilation air. Chapter 35, "Air-to-Air Energy Recovery Equipment" in the 1983 EQUIPMENT Volume, includes details.

Since eating and entertainment centers generally have low sensible heat factors and require high ventilation rates, fan-coil and induction systems are usually not applicable. All-air systems are more suitable. Space must be established for ducts, except for small systems with no ductwork. Large establishments are often served by centrally chilled water systems.

In cafeterias and luncheonettes, the air-distribution system must keep food odors from the serving counters away from areas where patrons are eating. This usually means heavy exhaust air requirements at the serving counters, with air supplied into and induced from eating areas. Exhaust air must also remove the heat from hot trays, coffee urns, ovens, etc., to minimize patron and employee discomfort and reduce air-conditioning loads. These factors often create greater air-conditioning loads for cafeterias and luncheonettes than for restaurants.

Odor Removal

Air transferred from dining areas into the kitchen keep odors and heat out of dining areas and cool the kitchen. Outdoor air intake and kitchen exhaust louvers should be located so that exhaust air is neither drawn back into the system, nor causes discomfort to passersby.

Where odors may possibly be drawn back into dining areas, activated charcoal filters, air washers, or ozonators may be used to remove odors. No kitchen, locker room, toilet, or other odiferous air should be recirculated unless air purifiers are used.

Hood Types

The air quantity for proper ventilation is a function of kitchen equipment heat release and kitchen hood size. The heat release factor is the more important criterion, but canopy-type hoods do not operate at maximum efficiency unless entrance air face velocity is at least 75 fpm (0.4 m/s). Face velocities of 75 to 100 fpm (0.4 to 0.5 m/s) should be used for design, with 60 fpm (0.3 m/s) as an absolute minimum.

Slot-type exhaust hoods are more efficient than overhead hoods, but they are more costly and may diminish valuable work area unless properly applied. Slot hoods require 150 to 200 cfm per linear foot (230 to 310 L/(s • m)) for proper operation but may substantially reduce kitchen exhaust air requirements (see Chapter 43, "Industrial Exhaust Systems"). Slot hoods may also reduce overall kitchen ventilation system cost by obviating an additional makeup air system and related energy cost.

Push-pull exhaust hoods similar to the slot-type hoods reduces the kitchen air-conditioning load. Outside air is supplied at the hood's perimeter or at the ceiling near the hood through slot diffusers. The exhaust hood then exhausts the supplied outside air plus approximately 15% additional air from the kitchen. Air colder than 60°F (16°C) entering the hood may coagulate grease on the grease filters, thus causing a high static pressure drop, unless they are regularly maintained. In addition, kitchen personnel may be uncomfortable if untempered outside air is directed from the hood toward their work stations.

Exhaust hoods incorporating water-wash cleaning systems can recover heat from hot kitchen exhaust air (see Chapter 35 of the 1983 EQUIPMENT Volume for heat recovery equipment).

Hood Fire Protection

In the past, carbon dioxide (CO_2), water sprinklers, and steam-smothering systems have been used. Most systems today use water spray hoods or dry chemical extinguishing agents.

Provisions should be made to disconnect and isolate the fuel source from the kitchen cooking equipment under the exhaust hood and shut off the hood exhaust fan if the hood's fire protection system is activated.

Hood Duct Construction

Some local codes require a refractory-type exhaust duct that allows grease fires to burn themselves out (see NFPA National Fire Code No. 96-84).

In multistory structures, a significant problem is the space required for the range hood exhaust duct, which is considered a low-temperature chimney. The duct usually rises to the roof to prevent odor spread, grease streaking of walls, and to eliminate fire hazards. Chimney size and space should be determined early during building design (see NFPA National Fire Code No. 96-84).

Hood Exhaust System Design

Ductwork should be designed for a velocity of 1800 to 2200 fpm (9 to 11 m/s) to minimize the settling of grease particles. All turns should be made with elbows that have a minimum centerline radius of 1.5 times duct dimension in the turning direction. Where this is not possible, grease traps and cleanout panels may be provided in the ducts.

In case of fire, the design should not allow the flames to go through the fan. Heat produced provides enough energy for smoke to rise because of stack effect. Therefore, a thermally actuated bypass should be furnished around the fan to close off the fan motor. This arrangement is mandatory in New York City and Chicago. Other hood exhaust system designs may be used if they are reviewed and approved by local code officials.

Wherever possible, the fan should be located at the discharge end of the duct run to offset ductwork leads, which could cause odor problems.

Ductwork design must allow for sufficient expansion caused by high temperatures during a fire. NFPA National Fire Code 96-84 and Chapter 1 ("Duct Construction") of the 1983 EQUIPMENT Volume has detailed design criteria.

Kitchen Air Conditioning

Kitchens can often be air conditioned effectively, without excessive cost, if planned in the initial design phases. It is not necessary to meet the same design criteria as for dining areas, but kitchen temperatures can be reduced significantly. The relatively large people and food loads in dining and kitchen areas produce a high latent load. Additional cooling required to eliminate excess moisture increases refrigeration plant, cooling coils, and air-handling equipment size.

Self-contained units, advantageously located, with air distribution designed not to produce drafts off hoods and other equipment, can be used to spot cool intermittently. The costs are not excessive, and kitchen personnel efficiency can be improved greatly.

SPECIAL CONSIDERATIONS

In establishing design conditions, duration of individual patron occupancy should be considered, since patrons entering from outdoors are more comfortable in a room of high temperature than those who remain long enough to become acclimated. Nightclubs and deluxe restaurants should usually be operated at a lower effective temperature than cafeterias and luncheonettes.

Very often, the ideal design condition must be rejected for an acceptable condition because of equipment cost or performance limitations. Restaurants are frequently affected in this way, since ratios of latent to sensible heat may result in uneconomical equipment selection, unless a combination of lower design dry-bulb temperature and higher relative humidity (giving equal effective temperature) is selected.

In severe climates, entrances and exits in any dining establishment should be completely shielded from diners to prevent drafts. Vestibules provide a measure of protection. However, both vestibule doors are often open simultaneously. Revolving doors or local means for heating or cooling infiltration air may be provided to offset drafts.

Employee comfort is difficult to maintain at a uniform level because of temperature differences between kitchen and dining room and partly because employees are constantly in motion while patrons are seated. Since customer satisfaction is essential to a dining establishment's success, patron comfort is the primary consideration. However, maintenance of satisfactory temperature and atmospheric conditions for customers also helps to alleviate employee discomfort.

One problem in dining establishments is the use of partitions to separate areas into modular units. Partitions create such varied load conditions that individual modular unit control is generally necessary.

Baseboard radiation or convectors, if required, should be located so as not to overheat patrons. This is difficult to achieve in some layouts because of movable chairs and tables. For these reasons, it is desirable to enclose all dining room and bar heating elements in insulated cabinets with top outlet grilles and baseboard inlets. With heating elements located under windows, this practice has the additional advantage of directing the heat stream to combat window downdraft and air infiltration.

Restaurants

In restaurants, people are seated and served at tables, while food is generally prepared in remote areas. This type of dining is usually enjoyed in a leisurely and quiet manner, so the ambient atmosphere should be such that the air conditioning is not noticed.

Bars

Bars are often a part of a restaurant or nightclub. Where they are establishments on their own, they often serve food, as well as drinks and they should be classified as restaurants, with food preparation in remote areas. Alcoholic beverages produce pungent vapors, which must be drawn off. In addition, smoking at bars is generally considerably heavier than in restaurants. Therefore, outdoor air requirements are relatively high by comparison.

Nightclubs

Nightclubs may include a restaurant, bar, stage, and dancing area. The bar should be treated as a separately zoned area, with its own supply and exhaust system. People in the restaurant area who dine and dance may require twice the air changes and prob-

ably a large air-conditioning unit than patrons who dine and then watch a show. The length of stay in nightclubs generally exceeds that encountered in most eating places. In addition, eating in nightclubs is usually secondary to drinking and smoking. Patron density will usually exceed that of conventional eating establishments.

Kitchens

The kitchen has the greatest concentration of noise, heat load, smoke, and odors; ventilation is the chief means of removing them and preventing these objectionable elements from entering dining areas. Kitchen air pressure should generally be kept negative, relative to other areas, to ensure odor control. Maintenance of reasonably comfortable working conditions is becoming increasingly important.

OFFICE BUILDINGS

LOAD CHARACTERISTICS

Office buildings usually include both peripheral and interior zone spaces. The peripheral zone may be considered as extending from 12 to 18 ft (3.7 to 5.5 m) inward from the outer wall toward the interior of the building and frequently has a large window area. These zones may be extensively subdivided. Peripheral zone areas have variable cooling loads in summer because of changing sun position and weather. These zone areas also require heating in winter. During intermediate seasons, one side of the building may require cooling, while another side simultaneously requires heating. However, the interior zone spaces whose thermal loads are derived almost entirely from lights, office equipment, and people requires a fairly uniform cooling rate throughout the year. Often, interior space conditioning is done by an independent system, which has variable air volume control for low or no-load conditions.

Most office buildings are occupied from approximately 8:00 A.M. to 6:00 P.M., although many are occupied by some personnel from as early as 5:30 A.M. to as late as 7:00 P.M. Some tenants' operations may require night work schedules, usually not to extend beyond 10:00 P.M. Office buildings may contain printing plants, communications operations, broadcasting studios, and computing centers, which could operate 24 hours a day. Therefore, for economical air-conditioning design, the intended usages of an office building must be reasonably well established before design development.

Occupancy will vary considerably. In accounting or other sections where clerical work is done, the maximum density is approximately one person per 75 ft^2 (7 m^2) of floor area. Where there are private offices, the density may be as little as one person per 200 ft^2 (18.6 m^2). The most serious cases, however, are the occasional waiting rooms, conference rooms, or director's rooms where occupancy may be as high as one person per 20 ft^2 (1.9 m^2).

The lighting load in an office building constitutes a sizable part of the total heat load. Lighting and normal equipment electrical loads average from 2 to 5 W/ft^2 (21 to 54 W/m^2), but may be considerably higher, depending on lighting type and the extent of equipment. Buildings with computer systems and other electronic equipment can have electrical loads as high as 5 to 10 W/ft^2 (54 to 108 W/m^2). Accurate appraisal should be made of the amount, size, and type of computer equipment anticipated for the life of the building to size the air-handling equipment properly and provide for future installation of air-conditioning apparatus.

Where electrical loading is 6 W/ft^2 (65 W/m^2) or more, an effort should be made to withdraw heat from the source by exhaust air or water tubing. About 30% of the total lighting heat output from recessed fixtures can be withdrawn by exhaust or return air and, therefore, will not enter into space conditioning supply air requirements. By connecting a duct to each fixture, the most balanced air system can be provided. However, this method is expensive, so the suspended ceiling is often used as a return air plenum with the air drawn from the space to above the suspended ceiling through the lights.

Miscellaneous allowances (for fan heat, duct heat pickup, duct leakage, and safety factors) should not exceed 12% of the total.

Building shape and orientation are often determined by the building site, but variations in these factors can produce increases of 10 to 15% in refrigeration load. Shape and orientation should, therefore, be carefully analyzed in the early design stages.

DESIGN CONCEPTS

The variety of functions and range of design criteria applicable to office buildings have allowed the use of almost every available air-conditioning system. Multistory structures are discussed here; however the principles and criteria are similar for all sizes and shapes of office buildings.

Attention to detail is extremely important, especially in modular buildings. Each piece of equipment, duct and pipe connections, and the like may be duplicated hundreds of times. Thus, seemingly minor design variations may substantially affect construction and operating costs. In initial design, each component must be analyzed not only as an entity, but as part of an integrated system. This systems design approach is essential to achieve optimum results.

There are several classes of office buildings; classes are determined by the type of financing required and the tenants who will occupy the building. Design evaluation may vary considerably, based on specific tenant requirements; it is not enough to consider just typical floor patterns. Included in many larger office buildings are stores, restaurants, recreation facilities, radio and television studios, and observation decks.

Built-in system flexibility is essential for office building design. Business office procedures are constantly being revised; therefore, basic building services should be able to meet changing tenant needs.

The type of occupancy may have an important bearing on the selected air-distribution system. For buildings with one owner or lessee, operations may be defined clearly enough so that a system can be designed without the degree of flexibility needed for a less well-defined operation. However, owner-occupied buildings may require considerable design flexibility, since the owner will pay for all alterations. The speculative builder can generally charge alterations to tenants. When different tenants occupy different floors, or even parts of the same floor, the degree of design and operation complexity increases to ensure proper environmental comfort conditions to any tenant, group of tenants, or all tenants at once. This problem is more acute where tenants have seasonal and variable overtime schedules.

Stores, banks, restaurants, and entertainment facilities may have hours of occupancy or design criteria that differ substantially from those of office buildings; therefore, they should have their own air-distribution systems and, in some cases, their own refrigeration equipment.

Main entrances and lobbies are sometimes served by a separate system because they buffer the outside atmosphere and the building interior. Some engineers prefer to have a lobby summer temperature of 4 to 6°F (2.3 to 3.4°C) above office temperature to reduce thermal shock to people entering or leaving the building.

The unique temperature and humidity requirements of data processing system installations, and the fact that they often run 24 hours daily for extended periods, generally warrant separate refrigeration and air-distribution systems. Separate backup HVAC systems may be required for data processing areas in case the main building HVAC system should fail. Chapter 33, "Data Processing System Areas," has further information.

The degree of air filtering required should be determined. The service cost and the effect air resistance has on energy costs should be analyzed for various types of filters. Initial filter cost and air pollution characteristics also need to be considered. Activated charcoal filters for odor control and reduction of outdoor air requirements is another option to consider.

There is seldom justification for 100% outdoor air systems for office buildings; therefore, most office buildings are designed to minimize outdoor air usage. Dry bulb or enthalpy controlled economizer cycles should be considered for reduction of energy costs.

When an economizer cycle is used, systems should be zoned so that energy abuse will not occur by having to heat outside air. This is often accomplished by a separate air distribution system for the interior and each major exterior zone.

Office buildings have used dual-duct, induction, or fan-coil systems. More recently, variable air-volume systems and deluxe self-contained perimeter-unit systems have become more common. Where fan-coil or induction systems have been installed at the perimeter, separate all-air systems have been generally used for the interior.

Many office buildings without an economizer cycle have a bypass multizone unit installed on each floor, with a heating coil in each exterior zone duct. Variable air volume variations of the bypass multizone and other floor-by-floor, all-air systems are also increasingly being used. These systems are popular because of low fan horsepower, low initial cost, and energy savings. Energy savings can result from independent operating schedules, which are possible between floors occupied by tenants with different operating hours.

It may be more economical for smaller office buildings to have perimeter radiation systems with conventional, single-duct, low velocity air-conditioning systems furnishing air from packaged air-conditioning units or multizone units. The need for a perimeter system should be carefully analyzed, since this system is a function of exterior glass percentage, external wall thermal value, and climate severity.

Interior space usage usually requires that interior air-conditioning systems allow modification to handle all load situations. Variable air volume systems have often been used. When using variable air volume systems, a careful evaluation of low load conditions should be made to determine if adequate air movement, air changes, and fresh air can be provided without overcooling at the proposed supply air temperature. Increases in supply air temperature tend to nullify energy savings in fan horsepower, which are characteristic of variable air volume systems.

In small to medium office buildings, air source heat pumps may be chosen. In larger buildings, internal source heat pump systems (water-to-water) are feasible with most types of air-conditioning systems. Heat removed from core areas is either rejected to a cooling tower or perimeter circuits. The internal source heat pump can be supplemented by a boiler on extremely cold days or over extended periods of limited occupancy. Removed excess heat may also be stored in hot water tanks.

Many heat recovery or internal source heat pump systems exhaust air from conditioned spaces through lighting fixtures. Approximately 30% of lighting heat can be removed in this manner. One design advantage is a reduction in required air quantities. In addition, lamp life is extended by operation in a much lower ambient temperature.

Suspended ceiling return-air plenums eliminate sheet metal return-air ductwork to reduce floor-to-floor height requirements. However, suspended-ceiling plenums may increase the difficulty of proper air balancing throughout the building. Problems often connected with suspended-ceiling return plenums are as follows:

1. Air leakage through cracks, with resulting smudges.
2. Tendency of return-air openings nearest shaft opening or collector duct to pull too much air, thus creating uneven air motion and possible noise.
3. Air in suspended-ceiling plenum may be blocked from return-air shaft by beams or partitions.
4. Effect on building structure fireproofing.
5. Noise transmission between office spaces.

Air leakage can be minimized by proper workmanship. To overcome drawing too much air, return air ducts can be run in the suspended ceiling pathway from the shaft, often in a simple radial pattern. The ends of the ducts can be left open or dampered. Generous sizing of return air grilles and passages will lower the percentage of circuit resistance attributable to the return-air path. This will bolster effectiveness of supply air-balancing devices and reduce the significance of air leakage and drawing too much air. Structural blockage can be solved, in coordination with the structural engineer and architect, by locating openings in beams or partitions with fire dampers, where required.

Total office building electro-mechanical space requirements are approximately 8 to 10% of gross area. Clear height required for fan rooms will vary from approximately 10 to 18 ft (3 to 5.5 m), depending on involved distribution system and equipment complexity. On typical office floors, perimeter units require approximately 1 to 3% of floor area, whereas interior shafts require 3 to 5%. Therefore, ducts, pipes, and equipment require approximately 3 to 5% of each floor's gross area. Electrical and plumbing space requirements per floor average an additional 1 to 3% of gross area.

Where large central HVAC units supply multiple floors, shaft space requirements depend on the number of fan rooms. In such cases, one mechanical equipment room usually furnishes air requirements for 8 to 20 floors (above and below for intermediate levels), with an average of 12 floors. The more floors served, the larger the duct shafts and equipment required. This results in higher fan room heights, greater equipment size and weight, and higher operating costs due to increased fan motor horsepower.

The fewer floors served by an equipment room, the more equipment rooms will be required to serve the building. This axiom allows greater flexibility in serving changing floor or tenant requirements. Often, one mechanical equipment room per floor and complete elimination of vertical shafts requires no more total floor area than a few larger mechanical equipment rooms, especially when there are many small rooms and they are often the same height as typical floors. Equipment can also be smaller, although maintenance costs will be higher. Energy costs may be reduced, with more equipment rooms serving fewer

areas, because the equipment can be shut off in unoccupied areas.

Equipment rooms on upper levels generally cost more to install because of rigging and transportation logistics, but this cost must be balanced against lower level revenue and desirability of space by tenants.

In any case, mechanical equipment rooms must be thermally and acoustically isolated from office areas.

Cooling towers are the largest single piece of equipment required for air-conditioning systems. Cooling towers require approximately 1 ft^2 of floor area per 400 ft^2 (1 m^2/400 m^2) of total building area and are from 13 to 40 ft (4 to 12 m) high. When towers are located on the roof, the building structure must be capable of supporting the cooling tower and dunnage, full water load (approximately 120 to 150 lb/ft^2 or 590 to 730 kg/m^2), and wind load stresses.

Where cooling tower noise may affect neighboring buildings, towers should be designed to include sound traps or other suitable noise baffles. This may affect tower space, weight requirements, and motor horsepower.

Cooling towers are sometimes enclosed in a decorative screen for aesthetic reasons; therefore, calculations should ascertain that the screen has sufficient free area for the tower to obtain its required air quantity.

If the tower is placed in a rooftop well, near a wall, or split into several towers at various places or levels, design becomes more complicated and tower initial and operating costs increase substantially. Also towers should not be split and placed on different levels because hydraulic problems increase. Finally, the cooling tower should be built high enough above the roof so the bottom of the tower and the roof can be maintained properly.

SPECIAL CONSIDERATIONS

Office building areas with special ventilation requirements include elevator machine rooms, electrical, and telephone closets, electrical switchgear, plumbing rooms, refrigeration rooms, and mechanical equipment rooms. The high heat loads in some of these rooms may require air-conditioning units for spot cooling.

In larger buildings having intermediate elevator, mechanical, and electrical machine rooms, it is desirable to have these rooms on the same level or possibly on two levels. This may simplify the horizontal ductwork, piping, and conduit distribution systems and permit more effective ventilation and maintenance of these equipment rooms.

LIBRARIES AND MUSEUMS

In general, libraries have stack areas, working and office areas, a main circulation desk, reading rooms, rare book vaults, and small study rooms. Many libraries also contain seminar and conference rooms, audio-visual rooms, record and tape listening rooms, special exhibit areas, computer rooms, and perhaps an auditorium. This wide diversity of functions requires careful analysis to provide proper environmental conditions.

Museums fall into several categories:

1. Art museums and galleries.
2. Natural and social history.
3. Scientific.
4. Specialized topics.

In general, museums have exhibit areas, work areas, offices, and storage areas. Some of the larger museums may have shops, a restaurant, etc., but these areas are not basic to this type of building and are discussed in other sections.

Specialized topic museums, such as reconstructed or preserved residences or industrial museums showing product development and growth, usually have less complex air-conditioning requirements. In some scientific museums, the necessity for reproducing the results of various exhibits or experiments may require close environmental control.

Most art museums and galleries, and some natural history museums, have their exhibits exposed within the viewing area. However, some exhibits are kept in enclosed cases, cubicles, or rooms. The latter exhibits may require special conditions that differ markedly from human comfort requirements. In this case, separate systems may be set up for maintaining the proper temperature and humidity.

Work areas in art museums consist of rooms for restoration and touch-up, picture framing, sculpture mounting, and repair. Paints, chemicals, plaster of Paris, and other materials requiring special temperature, humidity, and air circulating conditions are used. Noise level is not critical but should not be objectionable to occupants.

A greater variety of functions, such as animal stuffing and reconstruction of fossils or cultural exhibits, may be performed in the work areas of natural and social history museums. Some museums have research facilities and laboratories, and odors and chemicals in these areas may require larger exhaust air quantities. Individual room or area zone control will generally be necessary.

Storage areas in most museums often contain large numbers of articles for which exhibit space is not available, or articles that must be repaired. These storage areas may have to be kept within fairly close environmental conditions.

LOAD CHARACTERISTICS

Many libraries, especially college libraries, operate up to 16 hours a day and may run the air-conditioning equipment about 5,000 hours a year. Such constant usage requires the selection of heavy duty, long life equipment that requires little maintenance. Museums are generally open about 8 to 10 hours a day, 5 to 7 days a week, and many people who visit museums do not remove their outer clothing.

The ambient conditions should not vary in temperature or relative humidity. The conditions should remain constant 24 hours a day year-round. Cold or hot walls and windows and hot steam or water pipes should be avoided. Object humidity may cause destructive effects, even if the ambient relative humidity is under control. If the ambient dry-bulb temperature varies or the collection is subjected to radiant effects, the temperature of objects will vary, always lagging behind the atmospheric changes.

Some of the specific factors of particular importance in determining the heating and cooling loads are as follows:

1. *Sun Gain.* Libraries and museums usually have windows, sometimes of stained glass, and skylights—more in traffic areas, than in book stacks or storage areas. Care must be taken to minimize the effects of sun; shortwave (actinic) rays are particularly injurious. Heat gain from skylights, often over artificially lighted frosted-glass ceilings, can be reduced by a separate forced ventilation system.
2. *Transmission.* In winter, effects on objects located close to outside walls and possible condensation of moisture on the objects and the surface of outside walls must be evaluated. In summer, possible radiant effects from exposure should be considered.
3. *People.* Some areas may have concentrations as high as 10

ft^2 (0.9 m^2) per person, while office space will have closer to 100 or 120 ft^2 (9 to 11 m^2) per person and book stack areas up to 1000 ft^2 (93 m^2) per person.

When smoking is permitted, return air should be contained, and the recirculated part of the air should be deodorized with activated charcoal and similar odor-removal devices.
4. *Lights.* A detailed examination should be made of wattage provided in various rooms and the length of operation of the lights. In book stacks, various storage rooms, and vaults, lights may be discounted completely because of occasional use.
5. *Stratification.* The main reading rooms, large entrance halls, and large art galleries often have high ceilings that may allow the air temperature to stratify.

After individual room loads are evaluated at their optimum values to determine air requirements, the instantaneous refrigeration load should be calculated using proper diversity and storage factors.

DESIGN CONCEPTS

All-air systems are preferred in library areas where steam or water damage may ruin rare books, manuscripts, tapes, etc. This is also true for museums because exhibit items are generally irreplaceable. However, there are many libraries that have used air-water systems with satisfactory results.

In some libraries with auditoriums, it is possible to use the spaces under the seats and behind the backs of the seats for handling the supply and return-air distribution. In picture galleries, the wall space below the rail height may be made available. Under some circumstances the space above and below the wall cases may be used. In book stacks, each tier or deck should have individual air supply and return. Newly constructed book stacks would probably be interior spaces, with air ductwork and other services worked into the steel shelf-supporting structure. The most important consideration in designing air distribution should be to avoid stagnant spaces in all exhibits, especially in storage rooms and vaults. Steam or water piping should not run through exhibit or storage rooms, to avoid possible damage by accidental leaks and radiation.

Patron traffic in museums may follow a planned or random pattern, depending on the size of the museum, the number of exhibits and people, or the organization of the exhibits. The pattern may affect the type of air-conditioning system. People loads vary, depending on whether there is a new exhibit, the time of day, weather, and other factors. Thus, individually controlled zones are required to maintain optimal environmental conditions.

The most difficult problem encountered in designing an air-conditioning system for a museum is that partitioned areas may be radically changed from one exhibit to another. Attempts to establish a modular system for partitions have been only partially successful because of the wide range of sizes of items in the exhibits. Air distribution and lighting systems must be set up in the most flexible manner possible to minimize problems.

In art museums, particularly, partitions may create local pockets with hot air supply or exhaust; transfer grilles may be placed in the partitions to obtain some air movement.

Another problem is the location of room thermostats and humidistats. Sometimes it is not practicable to locate them either in the room or in the common return—air duct because conditions indicated may be typical of only a small area. One solution is to have the basic floor set up with small, individual zones. This, of course, is one of the most costly solutions. Other potential solutions are to locate the thermostats in return-air ducts and on aspirating diffusers.

SPECIAL CONSIDERATIONS

Many old manuscripts, books, museum exhibits, and works of art have been damaged or destroyed because they were not kept in a properly air-conditioned environment. The need for better preservation of such valuable materials, plus a rising popular interest in using libraries and museums, requires that most of them, whether new or existing, be air conditioned.

Air-conditioning problems for these buildings are generally similar, but differ in areas of design concepts and application. The temperature and humidity ranges that are best for books, museum exhibits, and works of art do not usually fall within the human comfort range. Thus, compensations must be made to balance the value of preserving contents against human comfort, as well as initial and operating costs of air-conditioning.

Design Criteria

In the average library or museum, less stringent design criteria are usually provided than for archives because the value of the books and collections does not justify the higher initial and operating costs. Low efficiency air filters are often provided. Relative humidity is held below 55% rh. Room temperature are held within the 68 to 72°F (20 to 22°C) range.

Archival libraries and museums should have 85% or better air filtration, a relative humidity of 35% for books, and temperatures of 55 to 65°F (13 to 18°C) in book stacks and 68 F (20°C) in the reading room. Canister-type filters or spray washers should be installed if chemical pollutants are present in the outdoor air.

Art storage areas are often maintained at 60 to 72°F (18 to 22°C) or lower, and 50% rh (±2%). Stuffed, fur-bearing animals should be stored at about 40 to 50°F (4 to 10°C) and 50% rh for maximum preservation; fossils and old bones will keep better at higher humidities. Museum authorities should be consulted to ensure optimal conditions for specific collections.

Building Contents

Because preservation of the collections housed within these buildings is so important, the reaction of each of the materials in the collections to room conditions should be carefully considered.

Paper used in books and manuscripts before the eighteenth century was very stable and not significantly affected by room environment. Paper, produced by a cottage industry, was made in small lots by breaking down the wood fibers by stamping, by using naturally alkaline water from mountain streams, and by applying a gelatin sizing. Industrialized production, in which wood fibers were cut with steel knives, ordinary water was used, and rosin sizing was substituted for gelatin, made a paper that is susceptible to deterioration because of the acid content in the paper and sizing. For archival preservation, this paper should be stored at very low temperatures. It is estimated that for each 10°F (5.5°C) dry-bulb that the room temperature is lowered, the life of the paper will double, and that any humidity reduction will also lengthen the life of paper.

Libraries, however, house more than books: they are media centers which also store and use films and tapes. The dessication point for microfilm and magnetic tape is below 35% relative humidity. This, then, is the lower limit for relative humidity in libraries, with the optimum humidity just above this point to minimize paper deterioration. The upper limit for humidity when the room dry-bulb temperature exceeds 65°F (18.3°C) is 67% rh because mold forms above this point.

Many materials housed in museums are organically based and also benefit from lower room temperatures. Museums that display only part of their collection at one time and keep the rest in storage rooms should consider reducing storage temperature to a point below the comfort chart to lengthen the life of organic materials.

Chemical pollutants and dirt are other factors that affect the preservation of books and organic materials. Chemical pollutants causing the greatest concern are sulfur dioxide, the oxides of nitrogen, and ozone. Electrostatic filtration of the air is not recommended because it can generate ozone. Sulfur dioxide combines with water to form sulfuric acid. In the past, sulfur dioxide was removed from outdoor air by using a washer in which the spray water was kept at a pH value between 8.5 and 9.0. Some newer museum and library system designs use special canister-type filters to remove sulfur dioxide.

Effect of Ambient Atmosphere

The temperature and, particularly, the relative humidity (not humidity ratio) of the air have a marked influence on the appearance, behavior, and general quality of hygroscopic materials such as paper, textiles, wood, and leather. This influence is caused because the moisture content of these substances comes into equilibrium with the moisture content of the surrounding air.

This process is of particular importance because it can multiply the destructive effect of changes in the ambient atmosphere. If any object in a collection (such as a book, painting, tapestry, or other article on exhibit) is at a temperature higher or lower than that of the air in the museum or library, the relative humidity of the air close to the object will differ considerably from that of the ambient room air.

The Object Humidity is the relative humidity of the thin film of air in close contact with the surface of an object and at a temperature cooler or warmer than the ambient dry-bulb (Banks 1974). Object Humidity differs from that of the ambient air because the dry-bulb temperature of various layers of the air film approaches that of the object while the dew point temperature remains constant.

If objects in a museum are permitted to cool overnight, the next day they will be enveloped by layers of air having progressively higher relative humidities. These may range from the ambient of 45 to 60% to 97% immediately next to the object surface, thus effecting a change in material regain or even condensation. This, combined with the hygroscopic or salty dust often found on objects recovered from excavations, can produce a destructive effect. If the particular material is warmed, however, the object's humidity will be lower than the humidity of the surrounding space. This warming may be caused by spotlights or any hot, radiating surface.

Sound and Vibration

Air conditioning should be treated with sound and vibration isolation to ensure quiet comfort for visitors and staff. Acoustical isolation is also necessary to avoid transmitting or setting up resonant (sympathetic) vibration within objects on exhibit, which may be damaged by such motion. Sound level should be low, but not so low as to produce an environment where normal sounds will be objectionable. It should also be noted that exhibit spaces tend to be acoustically reverberant (see Chapter 52, "Sound and Vibration Controls").

Case Breathing

Many objects and exhibits are housed in cases, and unless they are sealed tightly, the cases tend to breathe (Banks 1974). (The Declaration of Independence and the U.S. Constitution are inscribed on sheepskin parchment and enclosed within sealed receptacles filled with helium.) The air in a case expands and contracts as air temperature is changed by variation in ambient temperature, lights, and atmospheric pressure. Consequently, the air within the case will change more or less frequently. The worst offender in this instance may be a spotlight thought to be installed far enough from the case as to have no effect.

Special Rooms

When the library or museum contains seminar and conference rooms, audiovisual, record and tape listening rooms, and special exhibit areas, individual environmental room control is needed. Seminar and conference rooms may be exposed to heavy smoking, so auxiliary 100% exhaust should be provided. The other rooms listed may require a slightly quieter environment. Separate temperature and humidity controls should be provided for record and tape storage rooms.

Location of mechanical equipment rooms and air-handling equipment should be as remote as possible from the reading and exhibit areas to minimize the need for expensive sound and vibration isolation measures.

BOWLING CENTERS

Bowling centers may also contain a bar, restaurant, children's play area, offices, locker rooms, and other types of facilities. Such auxiliary areas will not be discussed in this section, except as they may affect design criteria for the bowling alley, which will consist of alleys and bowlers' and spectators' areas.

LOAD CHARACTERISTICS

Bowling alleys usually have their greatest period of use in the evenings, but weekend daytime use may also be heavy. This means that when designing for the peak air-conditioning load on the building, it is necessary to compare the day load and its high outside solar and off-peak people loads, with the evening peak people load with no solar loads. Since bowling areas generally have little fenestration, the solar load may not be an important factor.

If the building contains auxiliary areas, these areas may be included in the refrigeration and air-distribution systems for the bowling alleys, with suitable provisions for zoning the different areas, as load analysis may dictate. Alternatively, separate systems may be established for each area having different load operation characteristics.

Heat build-up due to lights, external transmission load, and pin-setting machinery in front of the foul line can be reduced by exhausting some air above the alleys or from the area of the pin-setting machines. In the calculation of the air-conditioning load, a portion of the unoccupied alley space load is included. Since this consists mainly of lights and some transmission load, about 15 to 30% of this heat load may have to be taken into account. The higher figure may apply when the roof is poorly insulated, no exhaust air is taken from this area, or no vertical baffle is used at the foul line. One estimate is 5 to 10 Btu/h • ft^2 (16 to 32 W/m^2) of vertical surface at the foul line, depending mostly on the type and intensity of the lighting.

The heat load from bowlers and spectators is found in Chapter 26, "Air-Conditioning Cooling Load," of the 1985 FUNDAMENTALS Volume. The proper heat gain should be applied for each person to avoid too large a design heat load.

DESIGN CONCEPTS

As with other building types having high occupancy loads, heavy smoke and odor concentration, and low sensible heat factors, all-air systems are generally the most suitable for bowling alley areas. Since most bowling alleys are almost windowless structures except for such areas as entrances, exterior restaurant, and bar, it is not economical to use terminal unit systems because of the small number required. Where required, radiation is generally placed at perimeter walls and entrances.

It is not necessary to maintain normal indoor temperatures down the length of the alleys; temperatures may be graded down to the pin area. Unit heaters are often used at this location.

Air Pressurization

Spectator and bowling areas must be well shielded from entrances so that no cold drafts are created in these areas. To minimize infiltration of outdoor air into the alleys, the exhaust and return-air system should handle only 85 to 90% of the total supply air, thus maintaining a positive pressure within the space.

Air Distribution

Packaged units without ductwork produce uneven space temperatures, and unless they are carefully located and installed, they may cause objectionable drafts. Central ductwork systems are recommended for all but the smallest buildings, even where packaged refrigeration units are used. Since only the areas behind the foul line are air conditioned, the ductwork should provide comfortable conditions within this area.

The return and exhaust air systems should have a large number of small registers uniformly located at high points, or pockets, to draw off the hot, smoky, and odorous air. In some parts of the country and for larger bowling alleys, it may be desirable to use all outdoor air to cool during intermediate seasons.

SPECIAL CONSIDERATIONS

People in sports and amusement centers often engage in a high degree of physical activity, which makes them feel warmer and increases their rate of evaporation. In these places, odor and smoke control often are important environmental considerations.

Bowling alleys are characterized by the following:

1. A large number of people concentrated in a relatively small area of a very large room. A major portion of the floor area is unoccupied.
2. Heavy smoking, high physical activity, and high latent heat load.
3. Greatest use from about 6:00 to 12:00 P.M.

The first two items make it mandatory that large amounts of outdoor air be furnished to minimize odors and smoke in the atmosphere.

The area between the foul line and the bowling pins need not be air conditioned or ventilated. Transparent or opaque vertical partitions are sometimes installed to separate the upper portions of the occupied and non-occupied areas so that air-distribution is better contained within the occupied area.

COMMUNICATION CENTERS

Communication centers include telephone terminal buildings, teletype centers, radio stations, television studios, and transmitter and receiver stations.

Most telephone terminal rooms are air conditioned because constant temperature and relative humidity helps prevent breakdowns and increases equipment life. In addition, air conditioning permits the use of a lower number of air changes, which, for a given filter efficiency, decreases the chances of damage to relay contacts and other delicate equipment.

Teletype centers are similar to telephone terminal rooms except, since people operate the teletype machines, more care is required in the design of the air-distribution systems.

Radio and television studios require critical analysis for the elimination of heat buildup and control of noise. Television studios have the added problem of air movement, lighting, and occupancy load variations. This section deals with television studios, since they encompass most of the problems found in the radio studios.

LOAD CHARACTERISTICS

The air-conditioning load for telephone terminal rooms is primarily equipment heat load, since human occupancy is limited. Teletype centers are similar, except for the load from people who operate the teletype machines.

Television studios have very high lighting capacities, which may fluctuate considerably in intensity over short periods. The operating hours may vary every day. In addition, there may be from one to several dozen people on stage for short times. The air-conditioning system must be extremely flexible and capable of handling wide load variations quickly, accurately, and efficiently, similar to the conditions of a theater stage. The studio may also have an assembly area with a large number of spectator seats. Generally, studios are located so that they are completely shielded from external noise and thermal environments.

DESIGN CONCEPTS

The critical areas of a television studio consist of the performance studio and control rooms. The audience area may be handled in a manner similar to that for a place of assembly. Each area should have its own air-distribution system or at least its own zone control that is separate from the studio system. The heat generated in the studio area should not be allowed to permeate the audience atmosphere.

The air-distribution system selected must have the capabilities of a dual duct, single duct with cooling and heating booster coils, variable air volume, or multizone system to satisfy the design criteria. The air-distribution system should be designed so that simultaneous heating and cooling cannot occur, unless such heating is achieved solely by heat-recovery methods.

Studio loads seldom exceed 100 tons (350 kW) of refrigeration. Even if the studio is part of a large communications center or building, it is desirable for the studio to have its own refrigeration system in case of emergencies. In this size range, the refrigeration machine may be of the reciprocating-piston type. This type requires a remote location so that machine noise is isolated from the studio.

SPECIAL CONSIDERATIONS

On-Camera Studio

This is the stage of the television studio and requires the same general considerations as a concert hall stage. Air movement must be uniform and since scenery, cameras, and equipment may be moving during the performance, ductwork must be planned carefully to avoid interference with proper studio functioning.

Control Rooms

Each studio may have one or more control rooms serving different functions. The video control room, which is occupied by the program and technical directors, contains monitoring sets and picture effect controls. The room may require up to 30 air changes per hour to maintain proper conditions. The large number of air changes required and the low sound level that must be maintained require that special analysis be given to the air-distribution system.

If a separate control room is furnished for the announcer, the heat load and air-distribution problems will not be as critical as those for the program, technical, and audio directors.

Thermostatic control should be furnished in each control room, and provisions should be made to enable occupants to turn air conditioning on and off.

Noise Control

Studio microphones are moved throughout the studio during a performance, so they may be moved past or set near air outlets or returns. These microphones are considerably more sensitive than the human ear; therefore, air outlets or returns should be located away from areas where microphones are likely to be used.

Air Movement

It is essential that air movement within the stage area, which often contains scenery and people, be kept below 25 fpm (0.13 m/s) within 12 ft (3.7 m) from the floor. The scenery is often fragile and will move in air velocities above 25 fpm (0.13 m/s); also, actors' hair and clothing may be disturbed.

Air Distribution

Ductwork must be fabricated and installed so that there are no rough edges, poor turns, or improperly installed dampers to cause turbulence and eddy currents within the ducts. Ductwork should contain no holes or openings that might create whistles. Air outlet locations and the distribution pattern must be carefully analyzed to eliminate turbulence and eddy currents within the studio that might cause noise that could be picked up by studio microphones.

At least some portions of supply, return, and exhaust ductwork will require acoustical material to maintain NC 20 to 25. Any duct serving more than one room should acoustically separate each room by means of a sound trap. All ductwork should be suspended by means of neoprene or rubber in shear-type vibration mountings. Where ductwork goes through wall or floor slabs, the openings should be sealed with acoustically deadening material. The supply fan discharge and the return and exhaust fan inlets should have sound traps; all ductwork connections to fans should be made with non-metallic, flexible material. Air distribution for control rooms may require a perforated ceiling outlet or return-air plenum system.

Piping Distribution

All piping within the studio, as well as in adjacent areas that might transmit noise to the studio, should be supported on suitable vibration mountings. To prevent transmission of vibration, piping should be supported from rigid structural elements to maximize absorption.

Mechanical Equipment Rooms

These rooms should be located as remotely from the studio as possible. All equipment should be selected for very quiet operation and should be mounted on suitable vibration-eliminating supports. Structural separation of these rooms from the studio is generally required.

Offices and Dressing Rooms

The functions of these rooms are quite different from each other and from the studio areas. It is recommended that such rooms be treated as separate zones, with their own controls.

Air Return

Whenever practicable, the largest portion of studio air should be returned over the banks of lights. This is similar to theater stage practice. Sufficient air should also be removed from studio high points to prevent heat buildup.

Testing

All television and radio studios must have complete sound-measuring equipment on hand to search quickly for and find all unwanted sources of noise.

TRANSPORTATION CENTERS

The major transportation facilities are airports, ship docks, bus terminals, and passenger car garages. Airplane hangars and freight and mail buildings are also among other types of buildings found at airports. Freight and mail buildings are usually handled as standard warehouses.

LOAD CHARACTERISTICS

Airports, ship docks, and bus terminals operate on a 24-hour basis, although on a reduced schedule during late evening and early morning hours.

Airports

Terminal buildings consist of large, open circulating areas, one or more floors high, often with high ceilings, check-in counters, and various types of stores, concessions, and convenience facilities. Lighting and equipment loads are generally average, but occupancy varies substantially. Exterior loads are, of course, a function of architectural design. The largest single problem often results from thermal drafts created by large entranceways, high ceilings, and the long passageways, which have many openings to the outdoors.

Ship Docks

Freight and passenger docks consist of large, high-ceilinged structures with separate areas for administration, visitors, passengers, cargo storage, and work. The floor of the dock is usually exposed to the outdoors just above the water level. Portions of the side walls are often open while ships are in port. In addition, the large portion of ceiling (roof) area presents a large heating and cooling load. Load characteristics of passenger dock terminals generally require that the roof and floors be well insulated. Occasional heavy occupancy loads in visitor and passenger areas must be considered.

Bus Terminals

This building type consists of two general areas: the terminal building, which contains passenger circulation, ticket booths, and stores or concessions, and the bus loading area. Waiting rooms and passenger concourse areas are subject to a highly variable people load. Occupancy density could reach 10 ft^2 (1 m^2) per person, and, at extreme periods, 3 to 5 ft^2 (0.3 to 0.5 m^2) per person.

DESIGN CONCEPTS

Since heating and cooling plants may be centralized or provided for each building or group in a complex, these will not be discussed. In large, open circulation areas of transportation centers, any all-air system can be adapted, including zoning as required. Where ceilings are high, air-distribution will often be along the side wall to concentrate the air conditioning, where desired, and avoid disturbing stratified air. Perimeter areas may require heating by radiation, fan-coil system, or hot air blown up from the sill or floor grilles, particularly in colder climates.

Airports

Airports generally consist of one or more central terminal buildings connected by long passageways to rotundas containing departure lounges for airplane loading. Most terminals have portable telescoping-type loading bridges connecting departure lounges to the airplanes. These passageways eliminate the heating and cooling problems attendant with traditional permanent structure passenger loading.

Because of difficulties in controlling the air balance resulting from the many outside openings, high ceilings, and long, low passageways (which often are not air conditioned), the terminal building (usually air conditioned) should be designed to maintain a substantial positive pressure. Zoning will generally be required in passenger waiting areas, departure lounges, and at ticket counters to take care of the widely variable occupancy loads.

Main entrances may be designed with air curtains, vestibules, and properly designed windbreaker partitions to minimize undesirable air currents within the building.

Hangars must be heated in cold weather, and ventilation may be required to eliminate possible fumes (although fueling is seldom permitted in hangars). Gas-fired radiant panel heating is being used more extensively in hangars because it provides comfort for employees at relatively low operating costs.

Hangars may also be heated by large air blast heaters or floor-buried heated liquid coils. Local exhaust air systems may be used to evacuate fumes and odors that result in smaller ducted systems. Under some conditions, exhaust systems may be portable and may possibly include odor-absorbing devices.

Ship Docks

In severe climates, occupied floor areas may contain heated floor panels. The roof should be well insulated and, in appropriate climates, evaporative spray cooling will substantially reduce the summer load. Freight docks are usually heated and well ventilated but seldom cooled.

High ceilings and openings to the outdoors may present serious draft problems unless the systems are designed properly. Vestibule entrances or air curtains will help minimize cross drafts. Air door blast heaters at cargo opening areas may be quite effective.

Ventilation of the dock terminal should prevent noxious fumes and odors reaching occupied areas. Therefore, occupied areas should be under a positive pressure and the cargo and storage areas exhausted to maintain a negative air pressure. Occupied areas should be enclosed to simplify the possibility of local air conditioning.

In many respects, these are among the most difficult buildings to heat and cool because of their large open areas. If each function is properly enclosed, then any commonly used all-air or large fan-coil system could be suitable. If areas are left largely open, the best approach is to concentrate on proper building design and the heating and cooling of the openings. High intensity infrared spot heating can often be advantages. (For further information, see Chapter 30, "High-Intensity Infrared Heaters," of the 1983 EQUIPMENT Volume). Exhaust ventilation from tow truck and cargo areas should be exhausted through the roof of the dock terminal.

Bus Terminals

Conditions are similar to those for airport terminals, except that all-air systems are more practical since ceiling heights are often lower and perimeters are usually flanked by stores or office areas. The same types of systems are applicable as for airport terminals, but ceiling air distribution will generally be feasible.

Properly designed metal pan radiant ceiling systems may be used if high occupancy latent loads are fully considered. This may result in smaller duct sizes than are required for all-air systems and may be advantageous where bus loading areas are above the terminal and require structural beams. This heating system reduces the volume of the building.

The terminal area air-supply system should be under a high positive pressure to assure that no fumes and odors infiltrate from bus areas. Positive exhaust from bus-loading areas is essential for a properly operating total system. (See Chapter 29, "Enclosed Vehicular Facilities").

SPECIAL CONSIDERATIONS

Airports

Filtering of outdoor air with activated charcoal filters should be considered for areas subject to excessive noxious fumes from jet engine exhausts.

Ship Docks

Ventilation design must ensure that fumes and odors from fork trucks and cargo in work areas do not penetrate occupied and administrative areas.

Bus Terminals

The primary concerns with enclosed bus loading areas are health and safety problems, which must be handled by proper ventilation (see Chapter 29).

Although diesel engine fumes are generally not as noxious as gasoline fumes, bus terminals often have many buses loading and unloading at the same time, and the total amount of fumes and odors may be quite disturbing.

Enclosed Garages

From a health and safety viewpoint, enclosed bus loading areas and car garages present the most serious problems in these building types (see Chapter 29).

Three major problems are encountered. The first and most serious is carbon monoxide gas (CO) emission by cars and buses, which can cause serious illness and possibly death. The second problem is oil and gasoline fumes, which may cause nausea and headaches and can also create a fire hazard. The third involves lack of air movement and the resulting stale atmosphere that develops because of the increase in the carbon dioxide (CO_2) content in the air. This condition may cause headaches or grogginess.

Most codes require a minimum of four to six air changes per hour. This is predicated on maintenance of a maximum safe CO concentration in the air, assuming short periods of occupancy in the garage.

All underground garages should have facilities for testing the CO concentration or should have the garage checked periodically by a competent organization that performs such tests. Clogged duct systems, improperly operating fans, motors or dampers, clogged air intake or exhaust louvers, etc., may not allow proper air circulation. Proper maintenance is required to minimize any operational defects.

Carbon Monoxide Criteria

Minimum ventilation requirements, as set up by the *National Bureau of Standards* and ASHRAE, as examples, are primarily concerned with preventing buildup of noxious concentrations of carbon monoxide (CO).

However, keeping the CO level within safe limits is no guarantee that patrons or employees in the garage will not experience discomfort. The air furnished will probably be sufficient to eliminate any atmospheric staleness, but the greatest discomfort can be caused by oil and gasoline fumes. These fumes are particularly noticeable in areas with poor air circulation and at poorly ventilated ramps. Therefore, a properly designed air-distribution system is essential to a comfortable and safe human environment.

WAREHOUSES

Warehouses are used to store merchandise and may be open to the public at times. They are also used to store equipment and material inventories as part of an industrial facility. The buildings are generally not air conditioned, but often have heat and ventilation sufficient to provide a tolerable working environment. Facilities such as shipping, receiving, and inventory control offices, associated with warehouses and occupied by office workers, are generally air conditioned.

LOAD CHARACTERISTICS

Internal loads from lighting, people, and miscellaneous sources, as a rule, are very low. Most of the load is thermal transmission and infiltration. An air-conditioning load profile would tend to flatten where materials stored are massive enough to cause the peak load to lag.

DESIGN CONCEPTS

Most warehouses are only heated and ventilated. Forced flow unit heaters may, in many instances, be located to heat entrances and work areas. Even though comfort for warehouse workers may not be desired, it may be necessary to keep the temperature above 40°F (4°C) to protect sprinkler piping or stored materials from freezing.

Thermal qualities of the building, which would be included if the building might later be air conditioned, also minimizes required heating and aids in comfort. For maximum summer comfort without air conditioning, excellent ventilation with noticeable air movement in work areas is necessary. Even greater comfort can be achieved in appropriate climates by adding roof spray cooling. This can reduce the roof's surface temperature by 40 to 60°F (20 to 30°C), thereby reducing ceiling radiation inside.

SPECIAL CONSIDERATIONS

Powered forklifts and trucks using gasoline, propane, and other fuels are often used inside warehouses. Proper ventilation is necessary to alleviate the buildup of CO and other noxious fumes. Proper ventilation of battery-charging rooms for electrically powered forklifts and trucks is also required.

REFERENCES

Banks, P.N. 1974. Environmental standards for storage of books and manuscripts. *The Library Journal*, Vol. 99, No. 3, February).

HUD *Bulletin LR-11.* Housing and Urban Development Agency, Washington, DC.

Library of Congress. 1975. Environmental Protection of Books and Related Material. Washington, DC: *Library of Congress Preservation Leaflet* No. 2. February.

Smith, R. 1969. Paper impermanence as a consequence of pH and storage conditions. *Library Quarterly*, Vol. 39, No. 2, April.

CHAPTER 20

PLACES OF ASSEMBLY

THIS chapter covers the air-conditioning design problems associated with enclosed public assembly buildings. Federal, state, and local guides relating to energy conservation have a major impact on system design and performance and require consideration for every place of assembly. The first part of Chapter 19 covers general criteria that also apply to public assembly buildings.

COMMON CHARACTERISTICS

Assembly rooms are generally large, have relatively high ceilings, and are few in number for any given facility. They generally have a periodically high density of occupancy per unit floor area, as compared to other buildings, and thus have a relatively low design sensible heat ratio. Space volume per person is usually high, thus allowing fewer air changes than for many other building types.

LOAD CHARACTERISTICS

Assembly buildings have relatively few actual hours of use per week. They may seldom be in full use when maximum outdoor temperatures or solar effects occur. The designer must obtain as much information as possible regarding the anticipated hours of use, particularly the times of full seating, so that simultaneous loads may be considered to obtain optimum air-conditioning loads and operating economy. These buildings often are fully occupied for as little as 1 to 2 hours, and the load may be materially reduced by precooling. Latent cooling requirements should be considered before reducing equipment size. The infrequent nature of the cooling loads allows these buildings to benefit from thermal storage systems.

The occupants usually generate the major room cooling load. The number of occupants is best determined from the seat count, but when this is not available, it can be estimated at 7.5 to 10

ft^2 (0.7 to 1.0 m^2) per person for the entire seating area, including exit aisles but not the stage or performance areas or entrance lobbies.

Ventilation

Ventilation is a major contributor to total load. ASHRAE Standard 62 lists outdoor air requirements for various occupancies. Typical minimum ventilation rates range from 20 to 35 cfm (9.4 to 16.5 L/s) per person. These rates may be reduced somewhat if the facility is used for only short periods and where it can be *flushed out* between performances. Some building codes may require higher ventilation rates.

Assembly buildings lend themselves to automatic recirculation and outdoor air control so that preoccupancy warm-up or cooling can be accomplished with low ventilation loads and light occupancy use can be handled with a reduced outdoor air loads.

The evaluation of ventilation loads is important to consider the effect of infiltration in any structure. Generally, sufficient outside air should be introduced into the air-handling system to offset the effect of infiltration and keep the structure under positive pressure.

Lighting Loads

Lighting loads are one of the few major loads that vary from one type of assembly building to another. Lighting may be at the level of 150 ft candles (1600 lux) in convention halls where color television cameras are expected to be used, but lighting is virtually absent during a presentation in a motion picture theater. In many assembly buildings, lights are controlled by dimmers or other means to present a suitably low level of light during performances, with much higher lighting levels during clean-up, when the house is nearly empty. The designer should ascertain what light levels will be associated with maximum occupancies. This is not only in the interest of economy but also to determine the proper room sensible heat ratio.

The preparation of this chapter is assigned to TC 9.8, Large Building Air-Conditioning Applications.

Indoor Air Conditions

The indoor air temperature and humidity should parallel the ASHRAE comfort recommendations (see Chapter 8 of the 1985 FUNDAMENTALS Volume), but the following should be considered:

1. In sports arenas, gymnasiums, and some motion picture theaters, people generally dress informally in summer. The summer indoor conditions may favor the warmer end of the thermal comfort scale with no major ill effect. By the same reasoning, the winter indoor temperature may favor the cooler end of the scale.
2. In churches, concert halls, and legitimate theaters, people tend to be fairly well dressed, with most men wearing jackets and ties and women often wearing suits. The temperature should favor the middle range of design, and there should be little summer-to-winter variation.
3. In convention and exhibition centers, the visiting public is more or less continually walking. Here the indoor temperature should favor the lower range of comfort conditions both in summer and in winter.
4. For spaces of high population density or sensible heat factors of 0.75 or less, a lower dry-bulb temperature results in less latent heat from people, thus reducing the need for reheat and resulting in energy saving. Therefore, the optimum space dry-bulb temperatures should be the result of detailed design analysis.
5. Restrictions of energy-conserving codes must be considered in system design and operation.

Because of their low room sensible heat ratio, assembly rooms generally require some form of reheat to maintain the relative humidity at a suitably low level during periods of maximum occupancy. Use of refrigerant hot gas or condenser water reject heat is frequently justifiable for this purpose. Face and bypass control of low temperature cooling coils is also effective. In colder climates, it may also be desirable to provide humidification. Chapter 15 of the 1985 FUNDAMENTALS Volume addresses the effect of mid-range humidity on decreasing the life of airborne organisms and the increased susceptibility of people to infection in a low humidity environment. High rates of internal gain may make evaporative humidification attractive during economizer cooling.

Precooling

Cooling the building mass several degrees below the desired indoor temperature several hours before it is occupied allows it to absorb a portion of the peak heat load. This precooling reduces the equipment size needed to meet short-term loads. The effect can be used if precooling time (at least 1 hour) is available prior to occupancy, and then only when the period of peak load is relatively short (2 hours or less).

The designer must advise the owner that the space temperature is cold to most people as occupancy begins, and then continues to climb as the performance progresses. This may be satisfactory, but it should be understood by all concerned before proceeding with a precooling design concept. Precooling is best applied when the space is used only occasionally during the hotter part of the day and when provision of full capacity for that occasional purpose is not economically justifiable.

Stratification

Because most applications involve relatively high ceilings, some of the heat may stratify above the occupied zone, thereby reducing the equipment load. Heat gain from lights can be stratified, except for the radiant effect (about 50% for fluorescent and 65% for incandescent or mercury-vapor fixtures). Similarly, only the radiant effect of upper wall and roof load (about 33%) reaches the occupied space. Stratification can be achieved only when air is admitted and returned at a sufficiently low elevation so that it does not mix with the upper air.

SYSTEM CONSIDERATIONS

Ancillary Facilities

Ancillary facilities are generally a part of any assembly building. Almost all have some office space. Convention centers and many auditoriums and sports arenas have restaurants and cocktail lounges. Churches may have a religious school or apartments for the clergy. Many have parking structures. These varied facilities are mentioned individually in other chapters of this volume. However, for reasonable operating economy, these facilities should be served by separate systems when their hours of use are quite different from the main assembly areas.

Air-Conditioning Systems

Because of their characteristic large size and the need for considerable ventilation air, assembly buildings are generally served by all-air systems, usually of the single-zone or variable-volume type (see Chapter 2 of this volume). Separate air-handling units usually serve each zone, although multizone, dual-duct, or reheat types can also be applied with lower operating efficiency. In larger facilities, separate zones are generally provided for the entrance lobbies and arterial corridors that surround the seating space. In some assembly rooms, folding or rolling partitions divide the space for different functions, so a separate zone of control for each resultant space is best. In extremely large facilities, several air-handling systems may serve a single space, simply because of the limits of equipment size that can fit into the structure and also for energy and demand considerations.

Filtration

Most places of assembly will be minimally filtered with filters rated at 30 to 35% efficiency, as tested in accordance with ASHRAE *Standard* 52-76. Where smoking is permitted, however, filters with a minimum rating of 80% are required before any effective amount of tobacco smoke is removed. Filters with 80% or higher efficiency are also recommended for those facilities having particularly expensive interior decor. Higher efficiency filters last long, due to the few operating hours of these facilities, and sometimes can be demonstrated to be economically justifiable for that reason alone. Low efficiency prefilters are usually included with high efficiency filters to extend their useful life.

Air Distribution

In assembly buildings, people generally remain in one place throughout a performance and cannot avoid drafts. Good air distribution is essential to a successful installation.

Heating is seldom a major problem except at entrances or during pre-occupancy warm-up. Generally speaking, the seating area is isolated from the exterior by lobbies, corridors, and other ancillary spaces. It is practical to supply cooled air from the overhead space, where heat from lights can be directly absorbed and where much of the occupant heat can be aspirated and mixed with the supply air above the occupied zone. Return air openings can also aid air distribution. Air returns located below seating or at a low level around the seating can effectively distribute air with minimum drafts. Where returns are below the seats, register velocities in excess of 275 fpm (1.4 m/s) may cause objectionable drafts and noise.

It is sometimes necessary, due to the configuration of these spaces, to install jet-type nozzles with long throw requirements of 50 to 150 ft (15 to 45 m) for sidewall supplies. For ceiling distribution, downward throw is not critical. This approach has been successful in applications that are not particularly noise-sensitive, but the designer needs to secure the best possible advice on the selection and application of air-distribution nozzles. The application data must also be verified to ensure proper performance for specific projects.

The air-conditioning systems must be quiet. This requirement is difficult to achieve if the air supply is expected to travel 30 ft (9 m) or more from sidewall outlets to condition the center of the seating area. The large size of most houses of worship, theaters, and halls require high air discharge velocities from the wall outlets, which would create objectionable noise to those sitting near the outlets. Therefore, the concept of *making the return air system do some of the work* must be adopted, which means that the supply air is discharged from the air outlet (preferably at the ceiling) at the highest velocity consistent with an acceptable noise level. This velocity does not allow the conditioned air to reach the furthest portions of the audience. Therefore, return air registers, located in the vicinity of those not reached by the conditioned air, pull the air and cool or heat the audience, as required. In this way, the supply air blankets the seating area and is pulled down uniformly by the return air registers under or beside the seats.

A certain amount of exhaust air should be taken from the ceiling of the seating area, preferably over the balcony (when there is one) to prevent formation of pockets of hot air, which can produce a radiant effect and cause discomfort, as well as increase the cost of air conditioning. Where the ceiling is close to the audience (*e.g.*, below balconies and mezzanines), specially designed plaques or air-distributing ceilings should be provided to absorb noise.

Regular ceiling diffusers placed more than 30 ft (9 m) apart normally give acceptable results if careful engineering is applied in the selection of diffusers. Because large air quantities are generally involved and because the building is large, it is common to select fairly large capacity diffusers, which tend to be noisy due to the energy involved. In recent years, linear diffusers have been found to be more acceptable architecturally. These also perform well if selected properly. Integral dampers in diffusers should not be used as the sole means of balancing the system. These dampers, particularly in larger diffusers, generate intolerable amounts of noise.

Noise Control and Vibration

The desired noise criteria (NC) vary with the type and quality of the facility. The need for noise control is minimal in a gymnasium or swimming amphitheater, but it becomes very important in a quality concert hall. Some facilities are used for varied functions and require noise control evaluation over the entire spectrum of use.

In most cases, sound and vibration control is required for both equipment and duct systems, as well as in the selection of diffusers and grilles. When engaged on a project like a theater or concert hall, consultation with an experienced acoustics engineer is recommended. In these projects, the quantity and quality or characteristic of the noise becomes important.

The following NC values for air-conditioning equipment noise audible in the space are offered as a guide:

	Desired	Acceptable	Maximum
1. Churches	NC30	NC35	NC40
2. Auditoriums			
a. Motion Picture Theater	NC30	NC35	NC40
b. Concert Hall	NC20	NC25	NC30
c. Legitimate Theater	NC20	NC25	NC30
3. Convention Halls	NC30	NC35	NC40
4. Exhibition Centers	NC35	NC40	NC45
5. Gymnasiums	NC40	NC45	NC50
6. Swimming Amphitheaters	NC40	NC45	NC50
7. Sports Arenas	NC40	NC45	NC50
8. Casinos	NC40	NC45	NC50

Transmission of vibration and noise can be decreased by mounting pipes, ducts, and equipment on a separate structure independent of the music hall. If the mechanical equipment space is close to the music hall, it may be necessary to float the entire mechanical equipment room on isolators, including the floor slab, structural floor members, and other structural elements, supporting pipes, or similar materials that can carry vibrations. Properly designed inertia pads are often used under each piece of equipment, which is mounted on vibration isolators.

Manufacturers of vibration isolating equipment have devised methods to float large rooms and entire buildings on isolators. Where subway and street noise may be carried into the structure of the music hall, it is necessary to float the entire music hall on isolators. When the music hall is isolated from outside noise and vibration, it is necessary to isolate it from mechanical equipment and other internal noise and vibrations.

External mechanical equipment noise from equipment such as cooling towers should not be allowed to enter the building. Shielding of these noise generators is required.

Noise levels in music halls should not be greater than NC20 to NC25. When the hall is used for recording music, the noise levels from mechanical equipment and the sound coming into the space from outdoors or from adjacent spaces must not exceed NC15. Achieving a sound level of NC15 is difficult unless all mechanical equipment can be located far from the music hall.

Mechanical Equipment Rooms

The location of the mechanical and electrical equipment rooms affects the degree of sound attenuation treatment required. Mechanical equipment rooms located near the seating area are more critical because of the normal attenuation of sound through space. Mechanical equipment rooms located near the stage area are critical because the stage is designed to project sound to the audience. If possible, mechanical equipment rooms should be located in an area separated from the main seating or stage area by buffers such as lobbies, service areas, etc. The economies of the structure, attenuation, equipment logistics, and site must be considered in the selection.

At least one mechanical equipment room is placed near the roof to house the toilet, general exhaust, cooling tower, kitchen, and emergency stage exhaust fans, if any. Individual roof-mounted exhaust fans may be used, thus eliminating the need for a mechanical equipment room. However, to reduce sound problems, mechanical equipment should not be located on the roof over the music hall or stage but over offices, storerooms, or auxiliary spaces.

CHURCHES

The principle characteristics of assembly buildings generally apply to churches. The seating capacity of churches is usually well defined, except in those cases where a *social hall* is separated from the main auditorium by a movable partition to form a single large auditorium for special holiday services. It is important to know when and how often this sort of maximum use is expected.

Churches seldom have full or near-full occupancy more than once a week, but they have considerable use for smaller functions (weddings, funerals, christenings, daycare, etc.) throughout the balance of the week. It is important to determine how the building will be used, because this use varies considerably. When thermal storage systems are used, longer operation of equipment prior to occupancy may be required due to the high thermal mass of the structure.

Because the design of many churches is inspired by the classic Gothic cathedral, the resultant high vaulted ceiling creates thermal stratification. Where stained glass is used, it is assumed to have a shade coefficient approximately equal to solar glass (S.C. = 0.70).

Churches represent a severe test of designers' ingenuity to secure an architecturally acceptable solution to the problem of locating equipment and air-diffusion devices. Desired results are obtained with maximum coordination between disciplines. When the occupants are seated, drafts and cold floors should be avoided.

Houses of worship may also have auxiliary rooms that should be air conditioned. The manner in which this is done is dependent on the relationship of the architectural layout and the systems selected to furnish the air conditioning. Privacy between adjacent areas is important in the air distribution scheme. Diversity in the total air-conditioning load requirements should be evaluated to take full advantage of the characteristics of each building.

In houses of worship and auditoriums, it is desirable to provide some degree of individual control for the platform, sacristy, and bema or choir area.

AUDITORIUMS

The types of auditoriums considered are the motion picture theater, the playhouse, and the concert hall. All follow the general pattern discussed previously as common to all assembly buildings. Other types of auditoriums, in elementary schools and the large auditoriums found in some convention centers, follow the same principles, with varying degrees of complexity.

Motion Picture Theaters

Motion picture theaters are the simplest of the auditorium structures mentioned here. They run continuously for periods of 4 to 8 hours and, thus, are not a good choice for precooling techniques, except for the first matinee peak. They operate frequently at low occupancy levels, and low-load performance must be considered.

Motion picture sound systems make noise control less important than in other kinds of theaters. The lobby and exit passageways in the motion picture theater are seldom densely occupied, although some light to moderate congestion can be expected for short times in the lobby area. A reasonable design for the lobby space would be one person per 20 to 30 ft² (2.0 to 2.8 m²).

The lights are dimmed, since, at most times, the house is occupied; full lighting intensity is used only during cleaning. A reasonable judgment on lamp watts above the seating area during a performance would be 5 to 10% of the installed wattage. Designated smoking areas should be handled with separate exhaust or air-handling systems to avoid contamination of the entire facility.

Projection Booths

The projection booth represents the major problem in motion picture theater design. For large theaters using high intensity lamps, projection room design must follow applicable building codes. If no building code applies, the projection equipment manufacturer usually has specific requirements. The projection room may be air conditioned, but it is normally exhausted or operated at negative pressure. Exhaust is normally taken through the housing of the projectors. Additional exhaust is required for the projectionist's sanitary facilities. Other heat sources include the sound and dimming equipment. This equipment requires a continuously controlled environment, necessitating a separate system.

Smaller theaters, using 16-mm *safety* film, have fewer requirements for projection booths. It is a good idea to condition the projection room with filtered supply air to avoid soiling lenses. Heat sources in the projection room include, in addition to the projector light, the sound equipment heat, as well as the dimming equipment heat—all of which are frequently located in the projection booth.

Legitimate Theaters

The legitimate theater differs from the motion picture theater in the following ways:

1. Performances are seldom continuous. Where more than one performance occurs in a day, the performances are separated by a period of 2 to 4 hours. Accordingly, precooling techniques are applicable, particularly for afternoon performances.
2. Legitimate theaters seldom play to houses that are not full or near full.
3. Legitimate theaters usually have intermissions, and the lobby areas are used for drinking and socializing. Periods of occupancy are relatively short, however, seldom exceeding 15 to 20 minutes. During occupancy, the load may be as dense as one person per 5 ft² (0.5 m²)
4. Because sound amplification is less used than in a motion picture house, background noise control is more important.
5. Stage lighting contributes considerably to the total cooling load in the legitimate theater. Lighting loads can vary from performance to performance.

Stages

The stage presents the most complex problem. It consists of the following loads:

1. A heavy, mobile lighting load
2. Intricate or delicate stage scenery, which varies from scene to scene and presents difficult air-distribution requirements
3. Actors performing tasks that require exertion

Approximately 40 to 60% of the lighting heat load can be negated by exhausting air around the lights. This procedure works for lights around the proscenium, but, for the light strips over the stage, it is more difficult to locate ducts directly over the lights because of the scenery and light drops. Careful coordination is required to achieve an effective and flexible design layout.

The conditioned air should be introduced from the low side and back stages and returned or exhausted around the lights. Some exhaust air must be taken from the top of the tower directly over the stage containing lights and equipment (fly). The air distribution design is further complicated because pieces of scenery consist of light materials that flutter in the slightest air current. Even the vertical stack effect created by the heat from lights causes this motion. Therefore, low air velocities are required. The air must be distributed over a wide area with many supply and return registers.

Due to the scenery changes, low supply or return registers from the floor of the stage are almost impossible to provide. However, some return air at the footlights and for the prompter should be considered. Air conditioning should also be provided for the stage manager and the control board area.

One phenomenon encountered in many theaters with overhead flies is the billowing of the stage curtain when it is down. This problem is due to the stack effect created by the height of the main stage tower, the heat from the lights, and the temperature difference between the stage and seating areas. Proper air distribution and balancing can minimize this phenomenon. Bypass damper arrangements with suitable fire protection devices may be feasible.

Loading docks adjacent to stages located in cold climates should be heated. The doors to this area may be open for long periods while scenery is being loaded or unloaded for a performance.

On the stage, local code requirements must be followed for emergency exhaust ductwork or skylight (or blow-out hatch) requirements, which are often sizable and should be incorporated in the earliest designs. Skylights may not be architecturally desirable, but the emergency exhaust fans often require as much space and are usually higher.

Concert Halls

Concert halls and music halls are similar to the legitimate theater in many ways. They normally have a full stage, complete with fly gallery, for presentation of operas, ballet, and musical comedy shows. There are dressing areas for performers. The only differences between the two are size and decor, with the concert hall being larger and more plushly finished.

Air-conditioning design must consider that the concert hall is used frequently for special charity and civic events, which may be preceded by or followed by parties held in the lobby area and may include dancing. Concert halls often have cocktail lounge areas, which become very crowded, with heavy smoking during intermissions. These areas should be equipped with flexible exhaust-recirculation systems. Concert halls may also have full restaurant facilities.

Noise control is important. The design must avoid characterized or narrow-band noises in the level of audibility. Much of this noise is structure-borne resulting from inadequate equipment and poor piping vibration isolation. An experienced acoustical engineer is essential for help in the design of these applications. The building will usually be designed to screen outside noise from adjacent streets or aircraft. Care should be taken to avoid air-conditioning designs that permit noises to enter the space through air intakes or reliefs or carelessly designed duct systems.

SPORTS ARENAS

Functions performed in sports arenas may be quite varied, so the air-conditioning loads will vary. They are not only used for sporting events such as basketball, ice hockey, boxing, track meets, etc., but may also house circuses, rodeos, convocations, rock concerts, and special exhibitions such as home, animal, or sports shows or industrial exhibitions. For a multipurpose operation such as this, the designer must provide mechanical systems having a high degree of flexibility. High volume ventilation systems may be satisfactory in many instances, depending on load characteristics and outside air conditions.

Load Characteristics

Depending on the degree of flexibility intended in the project's use, the load may vary from a very low sensible heat ratio for events such as boxing to a relatively high sensible heat ratio for industrial exhibitions. Often multispeed fans improve the performance at these two extremes and can aid in sound control for special events such as concerts or convocations. When using multispeed fans, the designer should consider the performance or air distribution devices and cooling coils when the fan is operating at lower speeds.

The designer must determine the degree of imperfection that can be tolerated in an all-purpose facility, or at least the kind of performances for which the facility is primarily intended.

As with other assembly buildings, seating and lighting combinations are the most important load considerations. Boxing, for example, may have the most seating, since the arena area is very small. For the same reason, however, the area that needs to be intensely illuminated is also small. Thus, boxing matches may represent the worst latent load situation. Other events that present latent load problems are rock concerts and large-scale testimonial dinner dances. The rock concert may be the worst latent load problem, but the audience is generally less concerned with thermal comfort. A good exhaust ventilation system is a must, however, since the audience at rock concerts eats and smokes during the performance to a much greater degree than is experienced at pop concerts. Circuses, basketball, and hockey have a much larger arena area and less seating. The sensible load from lighting the arena area does improve the sensible heat ratio. The large expanse of ice in hockey games represents a considerable reduction in both latent and sensible loads. High latent loads caused by occupancy or ventilation will create severe problems in ice arenas such as condensation on interior surfaces and fog. Special attention should be paid to this phenomenon when designing facilities with this function.

Enclosed Stadiums

The enclosed stadium may have either an operable or fixed roof. When the roof is open, mechanical ventilation is not required. However, when it is closed, ventilation is needed. Ductwork must be run in the permanent sections of the stadium. The large air volumes required and the long air throws make proper air distribution difficult to achieve; thus, the duct distribution systems must be capable of substantial flexibility and adjustment.

Some open stadiums have radiant heating coils in the floor slabs of the seating areas for use during cold weather. Another means of providing warmth is the use of gas-fired, electric, or infrared radiant heating panels located above occupants.

Open racetrack stadiums present a ventilation problem if the outside of the grandstand area is enclosed. The grandstand area may have multiple levels and be 1320 ft (400 m) long and 200 ft (65 m) deep. The interior areas must be ventilated because of toilets, concession odors, and high population density. General practice is to provide about four air changes per hour for the stand seating area and exhaust the air through the rear of the service areas. More efficient ventilation systems may be selected if architectural considerations permit.

Air-supported structures require the continuous operation of a fan to maintain the structure in a properly inflated condition. The possibility of condensation on the underside of the air bubble should be considered. The U value of the roof should be sufficient to prevent condensation at the lowest expected ambient temperature.

Heating and air-conditioning functions can be incorporated into the inflating system or they can be separately furnished. Applications, though increasing rapidly, still require working closely with the enclosure manufacturer to achieve proper and integrated results. Solar and radiation control is also possible through the structure's skin.

Ancillary Spaces

The concourse areas of sports arenas contain concession stands that are heavily populated during entrance, exit, and intermission periods. Considerable odor is generated in these areas by food, drink, and smoke, which require considerable ventilation. Where energy conservation is an important factor, carbon filters and controllable recirculation rates should be considered.

Ticket offices, restaurants, and similar facilities are often expected to be operative during hours that the main arena is closed, and, therefore, separate systems should be considered for these areas.

Locker rooms require little treatment other than excellent ventilation, not less than 2 or 3 cfm/ft^2 (10 to 15 L/s per m^2). To reduce the outdoor air load, excess air from the main arena may be transferred into the locker room areas, with reheat or recooling by water or primary air, as required, to maintain the locker room temperature. To maintain proper air balance under all conditions, locker room areas require separate supply and exhaust systems.

Concourse area air systems should be considered for their flexibility of returning or exhausting air, since these areas are subject to heavy smoking between periods of sports events. Economics of this type of flexibility should be evaluated with regard to the associated problem of air balance and freeze-up in cold climates.

When an ice skating rink is designed into the structure, the problems of ground water conditions, site drainage, structural foundations, insulation, and waterproofing become even more important. The rink floor may have to be strong enough to support heavy trucks. The floor insulation also must be strong enough to take this load. Ice-melting pits of sufficient size with steam pipes, may have to be furnished. If the arena is to be air conditioned, the possibility of combining the air-conditioning system with the ice rink system should be analyzed. The radiant effect of the ice on the people and the roof heat and light heat on the ice must be considered in the design and operation of the system. Also, low air velocity at the floor is related to minimizing refrigeration load. High air velocities will cause moisture to be drawn from the air by the ice sheet. Fog is caused by the uncontrolled introduction of airborne moisture through ventilation with warm, moist outside air. Fog can be controlled by reducing outdoor air ventilation rates and appropriate air velocities bringing the air in contact with the ice or with air conditioning.

The type of lighting used over ice rinks must be carefully considered when precooling is used prior to hockey games and between periods. Main lights should be capable of being turned off, if feasible. Incandescent lights require no warm-up time and are more applicable than types that require warmup.

Gymnasiums

Smaller gymnasiums, such as those found in school buildings, are miniature versions of sports arenas and often incorporate many multipurpose features.

Many school gymnasiums are not air conditioned. Most have a perimeter radiation system and either a central ventilation system with four to six air changes or unit heaters located in the ceiling area. High intensity infrared heating is appearing more frequently in gymnasiums.

Most gymnasiums are located in schools. Public and private organizations and health centers may also have gymnasiums. During the day, most gymnasiums are used for physical culture activities, but in the evening and weekends, they may be used for sports events, social affairs, or meetings. Therefore, their activities fall within the scope of a civic center. More gymnasiums are being considered for air conditioning to make them more suitable for extracurricular activities.

The design criteria are similar to sports arenas and civic centers when used for nonstudent training activities. However, for schooltime use, space temperatures are often kept between 65 and 68 °F (18 and 20 °C), when weather permits. Occupancy and degree of activity during daytime use does not usually require high quantities of outdoor air, but if used for other functions, system flexibility will be required.

CONVENTION AND EXHIBITION CENTERS

The convention-exhibition center performs more diverse functions than any building type and it presents a unique challenge to the designer. The center generally is a high-bay, long-span space in which many varied functions take place. With interior planning, and depending on the product type being exhibited, it can be changed weekly from an enormous computer room into a gigantic kitchen, a large machine shop, department store, automobile showroom, or miniature zoo, to name just a few. It can also be the site of a gala banquet or a major convention meeting room.

The income earned by the facility is a direct function of the time it takes to change over from one activity to the next, so a highly flexible utility distribution system and air-conditioning system is needed.

Ancillary facilities include restaurants, bars, concession stands, parking garages, offices, television broadcasting rooms, and multiple meeting rooms varying in capacity from small (10 to 20 people) to large (hundreds or thousands of people). Often, an appropriately sized full-scale auditorium or sports arena will also be incorporated.

By their nature, the facilities are much too large and diverse in usage to be served by a single air-handling system, so situations previously noted may be accommodated as indicated here and in other chapters of this volume.

Load Characteristics

The main exhibition room undergoes a variety of loads, depending on the type of activity in progress. Industrial shows provide the highest sensible loads, which may have a connected capacity of 20 W/ft² (215 W/m²) along with one person per 40 to 50 ft² (3.7 to 4.6 m²). Loads of this magnitude are seldom considered because large power-consuming equipment is seldom in continuous operation at full load. An adequate design accommodates (in addition to lighting load) about 10 W/ft² (108 W/m²) and one person per 40 to 50 ft² (3.7 to 4.6 m²) as a maximum continuous load.

Alternative loads may be encountered that will be very different in character. When the main hall is used as a meeting room, the load will be much more latent in character. Thus, multispeed fans or variable volume systems may provide a better balance of load during these high latent, low sensible periods of use. The determination of accurate occupancy and usage information is critical in any plan to design and operate such a facility efficiently and effectively.

System Applicability

The main exhibition hall would normally be handled by one or more all-air systems. These systems should be capable of operating on all outdoor air, because, during set-up time, the main hall will contain a number of highway-size trucks bringing in or removing exhibit material. There are also occasions when the space is used for equipment that produces an unusual amount of fumes or odors, such as restaurant or printing industry displays. It is helpful to build some flues into the structure to duct noxious fumes directly to the outside.

The groups of smaller meeting rooms are best handled with either separate individual room air-handling systems, or with variable-volume central systems, because these rooms have very high individual peak loads but are in infrequent use. Constant volume systems of the dual- or single-duct reheat type waste considerable energy when serving empty rooms, unless special design features are incorporated.

The offices and restaurant spaces often operate for many more hours than the meeting areas or exhibition areas and should be served from separate systems. Storage areas generally can be conditioned by exhausting excess air from the main exhibit hall through these spaces.

SWIMMING POOLS

Swimming pool design requires good cooperation between the architect and consulting engineer. The materials to be used in the construction of the walls, floors, and roof, and their method of application, must be carefully analyzed and selected to ensure that the building will not be damaged by the humid, corrosive environment or by condensation. The careful selection of materials for the heating, ventilating, and/or air-conditioning systems and their controls is important for the same reason. The importance of energy conservation has emphasized the costs of ventilating the pool enclosure to control corrosion and condensation. In many cases, ventilation is the dominant source of heat loss.

The design of the heating and air-conditioning or ventilation systems must be carefully planned to provide comfort for spectators and swimmers, in or out of the pool. Excessive air motion or drafts in the pool area must be avoided.

Pools located in the interior of a building may provide less of a design problem than pools with wall and roof exposures. The use of glass on pool exposures complicates the design problem and adds cost, expecially in cold climates. Glass walls or exposures make cold draft conditions and condensation difficult and expensive to eliminate. The pool area should be isolated from adjacent building areas, if possible, by providing a negative pressure at the pool.

Load Characteristics

Swimming pools are characterized by high latent loads that should be controlled to minimize corrosion and condensation on the building construction. Outdoor air of proper moisture content may be used for this purpose. During periods when outdoor humidity is high, it may be necessary to provide some form of reheat for humidity control. When applicable, using rejected heat from the refrigeration cycle should be considered for this purpose.

Pools used for open or free swimming have a large number of people engaged in fairly strenuous physical activity. Air must be introduced to the space without causing discomfort to occupants, in and out of the pool.

Design Concepts

The following three basic types of pools are discussed in this section:

1. Swimming pools with no spectator facilities
2. Swimming pools with spectator facilities
3. Therapeutic pools

Pools require humidity control to maintain comfort conditions. Pool air-handling systems are designed to use up to 100% outdoor air for cooling and/or dehumidification. On a winter cycle, when outdoor temperature and humidity are below pool design conditions, the amount of outdoor air can be controlled by a humidistat to maintain the desired humidity level. On a summer cycle, when outdoor temperature and humidity are above pool design conditions, minimum outdoor air is used. A sophisticated means of control during the summer cycle would employ a enthalpy controller to use either outdoor air or return air, whichever has the lower enthalpy.

Spectator areas should have their own air supply, and pool air should not return or exhaust through the spectator area because of its high moisture content and chlorine odor.

System Applicability

All-air systems are required to remove the large quantities of moisture in the air. Warm wall and floor surfaces increase occupant comfort and can be accomplished by application of insulation in walls, heating the perimeter tunnel where available, warm air curtains on perimeter walls and glass, and radiation and radiant panels.

Close attention should be given to latent chlorine and moisture levels. High levels of humidity and corrosive elements are more likely to occur during non-use hours of the pool area. The architect/engineer has little or no control over the building operation after occupancy, so building material selection is extremely critical.

Design Criteria

Design conditions for pools are:

Indoor Air:	
Pleasure Swimming	75 to 85°F (24 to 29°C), 50 to 60% rh
Therapeutic	80 to 85°F (27 to 29°C), 50 to 60% rh
Pool Water:	
Pleasure Swimming	75 to 85°F (24 to 27°C)
Therapeutic	85 to 95°F (29 to 35°C)
Competitive Swimming	72 to 75°F (22 to 24°C)
Whirlpool/Spa	97 to 102°F (36 to 39°C)

Relative humidities should not be maintained below recommended levels because of the evaporative cooling effect on a person emerging from the pool. Humidities higher than recommended encourage corrosion and condensation problems, as well as occupant discomfort. Lower-than-necessary relative humidity increases the rate of pool evaporation and pool heating requirements.

Air velocity at any point 8 ft (2.4 m) above the walking deck of the pool should not exceed 25 fpm (0.13 m/s). In a diving area, air velocity around the divers should be below this level.

In spectator seating areas, air velocity may be increased to 40 to 50 fpm (0.2 to 0.25 m/s), unless seats are located in an area also occupied by swimmers.

Calculation for Minimum Air Requirements. The air supplied to the pool must be sufficient to remove the water that evaporates from the surface of the pool. The rate of evaporation can be found from empirical Equation 1:

$$w_p = \frac{A(95 + 0.425v)}{Y} [p_w - p_a] \qquad (1)$$

In SI units Eq. (1) is:

$$w_p = \frac{A(0.0887 + 0.07815v)}{Y} [p_w - p_a] \qquad (1 \text{ SI})$$

where

w_p = evaporation of water, lb/hr (kg/s)
A = area of pool surface, ft^2 (m^2)
v = air velocity over water surface, fpm (m/s)
Y = latent heat required to change water to vapor at surface water temperature, Btu/lb (kJ/kg)
p_a = saturation pressure at room air dew point, in. Hg/(kPa)
p_w = saturation vapor pressure taken at the surface water temperature, in. Hg/(kPa)

For values of Y about 1000 Btu/lb (2330 kJ/kg) and values of v ranging from 10 to 30 fpm (0.05 to 0.15 m/s), Equation 1 can be reduced to:

$$w_p = 0.1\, A(p_w - p_a) \qquad (2)$$

or in SI units

$$w_p = 4.0 \cdot 10^{-5} \cdot A(p_w - p_a) \qquad (2 \text{ SI})$$

The minimum air quantity required to remove this evaporated water can be found from Equation 3:

$$Q = \frac{w_p/C}{\varrho(W_i - W_o)} \qquad (3)$$

where

Q = quantity of air, cfm (m^3/s)
C = units conversion, 60 min/hr
ϱ = standard air density, 0.075 lb/ft^3 (1.204 kg/m^3)
W_i = humidity ratio of pool air at design criteria, lb/lb (kg/kg)
W_o = humidity ratio of outdoor air at design criteria, lb/lb (kg/kg)

The values of W can be obtained from the ASHRAE psychrometric charts.

Design outdoor conditions should be reviewed carefully in cold climates, because this optimum condition for moisture removal occurs infrequently, and several outdoor conditions should be reviewed and calculated before establishing the minimum air volumes.

This calculated quantity of air often produces only one or two air changes per hour—a low rate of air movement. The following air flow rates are recommended, assuming the minimum air requirement from the previous calculation falls below the minimum recommendations. Most codes require six air changes per hour, except where air conditioning is furnished.

Pools with no spectator facilities	4 to 6 air changes
Spectator facilities............................	6 to 8 air changes
Therapeutic pools	4 to 6 air changes

Air volume above the minimum calculated value is recirculated, but the fan system incorporates return-exhaust fans and outdoor air, exhaust air, and return air controls to enable larger amounts (up to 100%) of outdoor air to be introduced during milder weather for temperature and humidity control. The return-exhaust fan facilitates the introduction of outdoor air and the maintenance of recommended pressure. Terminal reheat may be needed to maintain space control of relative humidity conditions where air conditioning, especially DX, processes are used. Otherwise, relative humidities will rise, fostering growth of molds and mildew and attacking building materials.

Heating elements should be large enough to handle more than design amounts of outdoor air to control humidity during periods of heavy pool use. High levels of activity increase the total wetted surface exposed to ventilation, resulting in high evaporation rates.

Air Distribution and Filtering

The type of air distribution system influences the amount of air introduced into the pool area. Air volume above the minimum calculated value may be recirculated, provided the recirculated air is dehumidified and filtered to reduce air contaminants to safe levels. Care should be taken in the choice of filtration used, especially where filter media may react with chlorine in the air. The air-handling system should have filters of 45 to 60% (based on ASHRAE Filter Test *Standard* 52-76) for occupant comfort and protection and to minimize streaking of walls and floors from dirt contacting moist surfaces.

Noise Level

Pool air system noise levels may be designed for NC45 to 50 without causing discomfort or annoyance.

Special Considerations

Condensation and corrosion from the humid, corrosive atmosphere of the pool can cause damage and even failure of materials and equipment within or serving a swimming pool. Ferrous metals should be eliminated from all areas of pool construction. Insulation on roofs or walls must be protected by a vapor barrier. Suspended ceilings should be discouraged because they provide a high humidity enclosure that requires separate ventilation. Despite such ventilation, the ceiling and appurtenances, such as lights, supports, etc., are subject to hidden corrosion.

All components of the pool-heating, air-handling, and air-distribution systems exposed directly or indirectly to the moist, corrosive pool atmosphere should be noncorrosive, or, where it is economically unfeasible to do so, they should be protected with a high quality corrosion-resistant coating.

All ductwork serving pool areas should be constructed of aluminum, coated steel, or other rust-resistant material. The high moisture content of the pool air being conveyed in ductwork requires extra design considerations. Return or exhaust ductwork located above ceilings should be waterproofed and pitched to drains and insulated if passing through cool areas.

The pool should be maintained at a slightly negative pressure of 0.05 to 0.15 in. of water (12 to 37 Pa) to prevent moisture and chlorine odors from migrating to other areas of the building. Pool air may be used as make-up for showers and toilet rooms, but a separate system is more desirable. Locker rooms and offices should have separate supplies and a positive pressure relationship with respect to the pool. Openings from the pool to other areas should be minimized, and passageways should have a vestibule (air lock) or some other arrangement to discourage the passage of air and moisture.

A properly designed air-distribution system is essential for uniform, draft-free conditions. Side wall distribution is generally less costly than overhead supply, but it is more difficult to design to provide draft-free conditions. Any air outlet over the pool is difficult to adjust manually and may increase air motion over the water surface, thus increasing the rate of evaporation. It is not necessary for return and/or exhaust outlets to be located low to pick up the moisture, since the water vapor tends to rise.

In cold climates, the combination of high humidities and the use of glass requires careful design and engineering to avoid condensation problems. Double or triple glazing combined with radiation is relatively ineffective where ceiling air is directed toward high glass areas. This results in a forced downdraft condition, which will quickly overwhelm the natural convection caused by radiation. It is far more noticeable in pool areas than other occupancies due to the evaporative cooling that occurs on a body in conjunction with the relatively low dew point conditions incident with cold weather. Blanketing the glass with an air stream from below is another method of avoiding condensation and eliminating downdrafts.

Where radiation from cold glass is not desirable, a radiant panel floor or high intensity infrared system may be used but supplemented with supply air to eliminate downdrafts, since radiant floors alone may not be sufficiently effective against large glass areas. Locating the return slots at the bottom of the glass reduces draft effects away from the wall.

Pool water-filtering equipment and chemical gases require special ventilation rates for occupational safety. This requirement is the decisive factor in the design of the pool equipment room air-handling system.

WORLD FAIRS AND OTHER TEMPORARY EXHIBITS

At frequent intervals, large-scale exhibits are constructed throughout various parts of the world to stimulate business, present new ideas, and provide cultural exchanges. Fairs of this type take years to construct, are open from several months to two years, and are sometimes designed with the thought of future use of some of the buildings, either at the fair site or elsewhere. Fairs, carnivals, exhibits, etc., which may consist of prefabricated shelters and tents that are moved from place to place and remain in a given location for only a few days or weeks, will not be covered here because they seldom require the involvement of architects and engineers.

DESIGN CONCEPTS

One consultant or agency should be responsible for setting uniform utility service regulations and practices to ensure proper organization and operation of all exhibits. Exhibits that remain open only during the intermediate spring or fall months require a much smaller heating or cooling plant than for peak summer or winter design conditions. This information is required in the earliest planning stages so proper analysis of system and space requirements can be established accurately.

Occupancy

Fair buildings have heavy occupancy during visiting hours, but patrons seldom stay for long periods in any one building. The approximate length of time that patrons stay in the building determines design of the air-conditioning system. The shorter the anticipated stay, the greater the leeway in designing for less-than-optimum operating design conditions, equipment, and duct layout. If patrons are wearing outer garments while in the building, this will affect operating design conditions.

Equipment and Maintenance

Heating and cooling equipment used solely for maintaining proper comfort conditions and not for exhibit purposes may be second-hand or leased equipment, if it is available and of the proper capacities.

Another possibility is to rent all air-conditioning equipment to reduce the exhibitors' capital investment and eliminate disposal problems when the fair is over.

Depending upon the size of the fair, the length of time it will operate, the types of exhibitors, and the policies of the fair sponsors, it may be desirable to analyze the potential for a centralized heating and cooling plant versus individual plants for each exhibit. The proportionate cost of a central plant to each exhibitor, including utility and maintenance costs, may be considerably less than having to furnish space and plant utility and maintenance costs. The larger the fair, the more it appears that savings may result. It also makes it practical to consider making the plant a showcase, suitable for exhibit and possibly added revenue. Another feature of a central plant is that it may form the nucleus for the commercial or industrial development of the area after the fair is over.

If each exhibitor furnishes their own air-conditioning plant, it is advisable to analyze short-cuts that may be taken to reduce equipment space and maintenance aids. For a six-month to two-year maximum operating period, for example, tube pull or equipment removal space is not needed or may be drastically reduced. Higher fan and pump motor horsepowers and smaller equipment is permissible to save on initial costs. Ductwork and piping costs should be kept as low as possible because these are usually the most difficult items to salvage; cheaper materials may be substituted wherever possible. The job must be thoroughly analyzed to eliminate all unnecessary items and reduce all others to bare essentials.

The central plant may be designed for short-term use as well. However, if the plant will be used after the fair closes, the central plant should be designed in accordance with the best practice for long-life plants. It is difficult to determine how much of the piping distribution system can be used effectively for permanent installations. For that reason, piping should be initially designed in a simple manner, preferably in a grid, loop, or modular layout, so that future additions can be made simply and economically.

Air Cleanliness

The efficiency of the filters for each exhibit is determined by the nature of the area served. Since the life of an exhibit is very short, it is desirable to furnish the least expensive filtering system. If possible, one set of filters should be selected to last for the life of the exhibit. In general, the filtering efficiencies do not have to exceed 30%. See ASHRAE *Standard* 52-76 on atmospheric air.

SYSTEM APPLICABILITY

If a central air-conditioning plant is not built, the systems installed in each building should be the least costly to install and operate for the life of the exhibit. These units and systems should be designed and installed to occupy the minimum usable space.

Whenever feasible, heating and cooling should be performed by one medium, preferably air, to avoid running a separate piping and radiation system for heating and a duct system for cooling. Air curtains used on an extensive scale may, upon analysis, simplify the building structure and lower total costs.

Another possibility when both heating and cooling is required is a heat pump system, which may be less costly than separate heating and cooling plants. Economical operation may be possible, depending on the building characteristics, light, and people load. If well or other water is available, it may produce a more economical installation than an air source heat pump.

Since exhibits and buildings can serve many varied functions, when specific problems or applications arise, reference should be made to the building type most closely resembling the exhibit building.

CHAPTER 21

DOMICILIARY FACILITIES

GENERAL

ALL structures in this group are single-room or multi-room, long- or short-term dwelling (or residence) units that are stacked sideways or vertically. Ideally, each room or unit should have equipment, distribution, and/or control that allows it to be cooled or heated and ventilated independently of any other room. If this ideal is not available, optimum air conditioning for each room will be compromised.

The group consists of apartment houses (high- and low-rise rental, cooperative, and condominium, either as single-purpose structures or as a portion of a multipurpose building), dormitories, hotels, motels, nursing homes, and similar building types. They have many common characteristics. Apartment houses are discussed in Chapter 17. Chapter 19 covers general criteria and characteristics common to these types of buildings.

LOAD CHARACTERISTCS

1. Constantly operational but not necessarily occupied at all times. It is desirable to design adequate flexibility into each unit's HVAC system so that cooling and ventilation may be shut off and heating shut off or turned down.
2. Low lighting and occupancy concentrations; generally sedentary or light activity. Transient in nature with greater night use of bedrooms. Occasionally heavy occupancy; smoking and physical activity in dining rooms, living rooms, and other areas used for entertaining.
3. Potentially high appliance load, odor generation, and exhaust requirements in kitchens, whether integrated with or separated from residential quarters.
4. Generally, exterior rooms, except sometimes for kitchens, toilets, and dressing rooms; usually multiple exposure for the building as a whole and frequently for many individual dwelling units.
5. Toilet, washing, and bathing facilities almost always incorporated within dwelling units for hostelries and nursing homes; only occasionally in dormitories. With public toilet and bathing facilities, lavatories are sometimes provided within dwelling units.
6. Relatively high domestic hot water building demands, generally over short periods of an hour or two, several times a day. This can vary from a fairly moderate and level daily load profile for senior citizens buildings, to sharp, unusually high peaks at about 6:00 P.M. in dormitories. Chapter 54 includes details on service hot water systems.
7. Load characteristics of rooms, dwelling units, and buildings can be well defined without the need for any substantial future design load changes other than the addition of a service such as cooling, which may not have been originally incorporated.

The predominance of exterior exposures with glass and shifting, transient, interior loads results in low diversity factors, while the long-hour usage results in fairly high load factors. Numerous tables showing an approximate range of load characteristics have been prepared by various agencies, both private and public,

---

The preparation of this chapter is assigned to TC 9.8, Large Building Air-Conditioning Applications.

throughout the United States. However, such tables are only a guide and must be qualified by the actual local data collected by the engineer.

DESIGN CONCEPTS AND CRITERIA

Wide load swings and diversity in and between rooms require great care in designing a flexible system for 24-hour comfort. Besides opening windows (available in all dwelling units), the only positive technique for flexible temperature control is individual room components, under individual room control, which can cool, heat, and ventilate independently of the equipment in any other room.

In some climates, summer humidity levels become objectionable because of the low internal sensible loads when cooling is on-off controlled. Modulated cooling and/or reheat may be required to achieve satisfactory comfort. The use of reheat should be avoided whenever possible.

Odor control is impractical and uncontrollable within any single dwelling unit. Most designers simply strive to confine odors within the dwelling unit. Systems with pressurized public corridors from which makeup air is drawn into the dwelling unit are most successful. Because of the high operating cost of providing makeup air, high local odor concentrations, and codes that prohibit centralized air return from dwelling units to common supply air fans, all-air systems are not in common use.

The noise threshold for some people is low enough that certain types of equipment disturbs their sleep; however, even unitary systems of poor quality (as long as they are not in need of repair) are acceptable to most people, especially if they must choose between a fairly steady noise (which effectively masks extraneous, intermittent noises) and no air conditioning at all. Poor noise levels may be acceptable in areas where there are low cooling degree days. Medium and better quality equipment is available with NC35 levels at 10 to 14 ft (3 to 4 m) distances in medium to soft rooms, with little sound change when the compressor cycles.

Perimeter fan-coil systems are usually quieter than unitary systems. However, many occupants are more disturbed by equipment with wide changes in noise levels than in a continuous higher level. Fan-coil units often cycle the fans for thermostat control, and a high enough noise level evident during *on* cycles can be more objectionable than the compressor cycling of a through-the-wall unit masked by its continuously operating fan.

SYSTEMS

ENERGY EFFICIENT SYSTEMS

Whenever possible, energy efficient systems should be applied in this type occupancy. These systems include water source heat pumps and air source heat pumps. Water source heat pumps may be solar assisted in areas with ample solar radiation. Energy efficient equipment generally has the lowest operating cost and is relatively simple, an important factor in multiple dwelling and domiciliary facilities, where skilled operating personnel are unlikely to be available. Most systems allow individual operation and thermostatic control. The standard system allows individual metering so that most, if not all, of the cooling and heating costs can be metered directly to the occupant. In existing buildings, individual metering can be done by BTU measuring, meters, and timers for fan motors. Chapter 9 has information regarding the design and operation of heat pumps. Chapter 6 describes more complex heat recovery systems that may be practical in large installations.

The water loop heat pump system has favorable operating costs compared with air-cooled unitary equipment, especially where electric heat is used. Favorable installed cost encourages use of this system in mid-rise and high-rise buildings, where individual dwelling units have floor areas 800 ft^2 (74 m^2) or larger.

Except for a central circulating pump, heat rejector fans, and a supplementary heater, the system is predominantly decentralized; individual metering allows most of the HVAC operating costs to be paid by the occupants. A wide selection of air conditioner sizes and equipment styles is available to meet various space requirements. System life should be longer than for other unitary systems because most of the mechanical equipment is protected within the building and not exposed to outdoor conditions; also, the refrigeration circuit is not subjected to as severe an operating duty because system water temperatures are controlled to operate under optimum conditions. Low operating costs are possible from inherent energy conservation as excess heat may be stored from daytime for the following night, and heat is transferred from one part of the building to another.

Simultaneous heating and cooling occurs during cool weather because heating is required in many areas, but cooling becomes necessary in some rooms because of solar or internal loads. Frequently, surplus heat throughout the building on a mild day is transferred into the hot water loop by air condensers on cooling cycle so that water temperature rises. The heat remains stored in water where it can be extracted at night without operating a water heater. This heat storage is improved by having a greater mass of water in the pipe loop; some systems include a storage tank for this purpose. Because the system is designed to operate during the heating season with water supplied at temperatures as low as 60°F (15°C), the water loop heat pump lends itself to solar assist with relatively high solar collector efficiencies resulting from the low water temperature.

Installed cost of the water loop heat pump system becomes higher in very small buildings. Where natural gas or fossil fuels are available at reasonable cost, the operating cost advantages of this system may diminish in severe cold climates with prolonged heating seasons, unless heat can be recovered from some source such as solar collectors or internal heat loads from a commercial area also served by the same system.

ENERGY NEUTRAL SYSTEMS

Energy neutral systems do not allow simultaneous cooling and heating. Systems of these types include Packaged Terminal Air Conditioners (PTAC) (through-the-wall units), window units for cooling (combined with finned or baseboard radiation for heating), unitary air conditioners with an integrated heating system, fan coils with remote condensing units, and variable air volume (VAV) systems with baseboard heating. To qualify as energy neutral systems, controls must prevent simultaneous operation of the cooling and heating cycles. In unitary equipment, this may be as simple as a heat-cool switch. In other types, dead-band thermostatic control may be required to separate cooling and heating.

PTAC are frequently applied in buildings where most of the individual units are relatively small, consisting of one or two rooms. A common arrangement for two rooms adds a supply plenum to the discharge of the PTAC unit so that some portion of the conditioned air can be diverted into the second, usually smaller, room. Multiple PTAC units are used in larger areas with more rooms, providing for additional zoning within the area. Additional radiation heat is sometimes specified in cold climates, where needed, to distribute heat around the perimeter.

The PTAC system can have electric resistance heat, for lowest initial cost, and a decentralized HVAC system, or have hot water or steam heating coils, where combustion fuels are available to provide lower operating costs. Despite relatively inefficient refrigeration circuits, operating costs of PTAC systems are quite reasonable because of the individual thermostatically controlled operation of each machine, which eliminates the use of reheat while still avoiding overheating or overcooling the space. Also, very little power is devoted to circulating the room air, since the equipment is located in the space being served. Servicing is simple—a spare chassis replaces a defective machine, which can then be forwarded to a qualified service organization for repair. Thus, building maintenance requires relatively unskilled personnel.

Noise levels are generally no higher than NC40, but some units are noisier than others. Installations near a seacoast should be carefully considered and specified with special construction (usually stainless steel) to avoid accelerated corrosion to aluminum and steel components caused by salt from the sea water. Installation in high-rise buildings above 12 stories requires special care, both in the design and construction of outside partitions and in the installation of the air conditioners to avoid operating problems associated with leakage around and through the machines caused by *stack effect*.

This system offers reasonable operating costs and noise levels within the occupied space, which are tolerable but somewhat higher than those of the concealed water source heat pump system. The system may be affected by legislation prescribing maximum acceptable outdoor equipment noise levels. Fan coil units with remote condensing units are used in smaller buildings. Units are located in closets, and ductwork distributes air to the rooms in the unit. Condensing units can be located on roofs, at ground level, or on balconies.

Frequently, the least expensive system to install is finned or baseboard radiation for heating and window-type room air conditioners for cooling. Often, the window units are purchased individually by the building occupants. This system offers reasonable operating costs and is relatively simple to maintain. Window units have the shortest equipment life, the highest operating noise level, and the poorest distribution of conditioned air of any of the systems compared in this section. This system may cause air and dirt leakage around window units.

Low capacity residential warm air furnaces may be used for heating only, but they require some method of venting the products of combustion. In a one- or two-story structure, it is possible to use individual chimneys or flue pipes, but in a high-rise structure, it is necessary to use a multiple vent chimney or a well-designed manifold vent system. Local codes should be consulted.

Sealed combustion furnaces have been developed for domiciliary use. These units draw all the combustion air from outside and discharge the flue products outside through a windproof vent. The unit must be located near an outside wall and exhaust gases must be directed away from windows and intakes. One- or two-story structures may also use outdoor units mounted on the roof or on a pad at ground level. All of these heating units can be obtained with cooling coils, either built-in or add-on. Evaporative-type cooling units are popular in motels, low-rise apartments, and residences of the Southwest. Chapter 5 refers to unitary equipment, and Chapter 2 covers VAV designs for central buildings.

INEFFICIENT ENERGY SYSTEMS

Inefficient energy systems allow simultaneous cooling and heating. Examples of these systems are terminal reheat, two-, three-, and four-pipe fan coil units, and induction systems. Some systems, such as the four-pipe fan coil, can be controlled so that they are energy neutral. However, their primary use is for humidity control.

The four-pipe system and two-pipe systems with electric heaters can be designed with complete temperature and humidity flexibility during summer and intermediate season weather, although none provides winter humidity control. Each of these systems provide full dehumidification and cooling with chilled water, reserving the other two pipes or electric coil for space heating or reheat. The systems and controls needed are expensive, and only the four-pipe system, with an internal-source heat-recovery design for the warm coil energy, can operate at low cost.

TOTAL ENERGY SYSTEMS

Any multiple housing facility with high year-round domestic hot water requirements is one of the more attractive applications for total energy. The thermal profiles for HVAC and service hot water can match the electrical generating profile better than many other applications, and the 24-hour loads permit higher load factors and better equipment use. However, a detailed load profile must be analyzed before this application is recommended. Reliability and safety must also be considered with heat-recovery systems.

Any system described previously can provide the HVAC portion of total energy. The major considerations for choice of system as they apply to total energy are as follows:

1. Optimum use must be made of the thermal energy recoverable from the prime mover during all operating modes, not just during maximum HVAC design conditions.
2. Heat recoverable via the heat pump cycles may become less useful, since many of its potential operating hours will be satisfied with some or all of the heat recovered from the prime mover. It becomes more difficult, therefore, to justify the additional investment for heat pump or heat recovery cycles because operating savings are lower.
3. The best use for recovered waste heat is for those services using only heat (*i.e.,* domestic hot water and space heating).

SPECIAL CONSIDERATIONS

Many types of ventilation systems are installed in domiciliary buildings. Local building codes govern air quantities. Where they do not, average values are about 35 to 50 cfm (16.5 to 23.6 L/s) for bathrooms and 1 to 2 cfm per ft^2 (163 to 326 L/s per m^2) but not less than 75 cfm (35.4 L/s) for kitchens. Outdoor air, usually slightly in excess of the exhaust quantities to pressurize the building, is introduced into the corridors.

Buildings using centrally controlled exhaust and supply systems operate the systems on time clock for certain periods of the day. In other cases, it is common practice to reduce or shut off the outside air during extremely cold periods, although this practice is not recommended. If known in advance, these factors should be considered when estimating heating load.

Buildings using exhaust and supply air systems on a 24-hour basis may merit consideration of air-to-air heat recovery devices (see Chapter 35 of the 1983 EQUIPMENT Volume). Such recovery devices can reduce the consumption of energy by capturing 60 to 80% of the sensible and latent heat extracted from the air source.

Infiltration loads in high-rise buildings without ventilation openings for perimeter units are not controllable on a year-round basis by general building pressurization. When outer walls are pierced for outdoor air to unitary or fan-coil equipment, combined wind and thermal stack-effect forces create problems. These factors must be considered for high-rise buildings (see Chapter 22 of the 1985 FUNDAMENTALS Volume).

Interior building public corridors should have tempered supply air with transfer into individual area units, if necessary, through suitable acoustically lined transfer louvers to provide kitchen and toilet makeup air requirements. Corridors, stairwells, and elevators should be pressurized for fire and smoke control (see Chapter 58).

Kitchens should not be exhausted but recirculated through activated charcoal. Toilet exhaust can be VAV with installation of a damper operated by light switch. A controlled source of supplementary heat in each bathroom is recommended to ensure comfort while bathing.

Care must be taken to isolate air-conditioning equipment to reduce noise generated or transmitted. The design and location of the cooling tower is important to avoid disturbing occupants within the building and neighbors in adjacent buildings.

An important load, frequently overlooked, is heat gain from piping for hot water services. More insulation should be used than is currently considered normal practice. In large, luxury-type buildings, a central panel allows supervision of the individual air-conditioning unit(s) for operation and maintenance.

Some domiciliary facilities achieve energy conservation by reducing indoor temperatures. A reduction of indoor temperatures should be pursued with caution, however, if there are aged occupants because they are susceptible to hypothermia.

DORMITORIES

Dormitory buildings frequently have large commercial dining and kitchen facilities, laundering facilities, and common areas for interior recreation and bathing. Such ancillary loads improve the economic feasibility of heat pump or total energy systems—especially on campuses with year-round activity.

When dormitories are shut down during cold weather, the heating system must supply sufficient heat to prevent freezeup. If the dormitory contains administrative offices, eating facilities, etc., these facilities should be designed as a separate zone or system for optimum flexibility and economy.

Subsidiary facilities should be controlled independently for flexibility and shutoff capability, but they may share common refrigeration and heating plants. With internal source heat pumps, such interdependence of unitary systems permits reclamation of all possible internal heat that is usuable for building heating, domestic water preheating, snow melting, etc. It is easier and less expensive to use heat reclaim coils in air exhausted from the building than to use air-to-air heat-recovery devices. Also, heat reclaim can be easily sequence-controlled to add heat to the building's chilled water systems, when required.

HOTELS AND MOTELS

Both hotel and motel accommodations are usually single room with toilet and bath adjacent to a corridor, flanked on both sides by guest rooms. They may be single-story, low-, or high-rise. Multipurpose subsidiary facilities range from stores and offices to ballrooms, auditoriums, and meeting halls. Luxury motels may be built with similar facilities. Occasional variations are seen, with kitchenettes and, more frequently than for apartments, outside doors to patios and balconies, as well as multiroom suites.

LOAD CHARACTERISTICS

Guest rooms are more frequently unoccupied than apartments, tending toward lower diversity factors; however, because occupied apartments may involve some unoccupied rooms, the situation tends to reverse. Therefore, diversity factors for hostelries may be higher or lower than for apartment buildings within the same residential area.

Hostelries without guest room cooking facilities usually peak an hour or two earlier in the morning than apartment houses and have lower noon and evening peaks. Electrical and cooling peaks for hostelries are highest between 6:00 and 8:00 P.M.

Because of the lower guest room peaks, substantial use of subsidiary facilities with non-coincident peaks, and more concentrated living areas, load factors for hostelries are higher than for apartment buildings.

The diversity of use for all areas of hostelries makes load profile studies the key to minimum selection requirements, avoidance of unnecessary oversizing and duplication, and low operating cost designs.

DESIGN CONCEPTS AND CRITERIA

Air conditioning in hotel rooms should be quiet, easily adjustable, and draft-free. It must also provide ample fresh air. The hotel business is competitive, and space is at a premium, so systems that require the least space and have low total owning and operating costs should be selected.

Imaginative use of energy profiles for each auxiliary area can lead to major investment savings due to common central plant and air distribution systems. When odor generation is common to the facilities on one air system, or when diverse odors are generated but controlled in a common apparatus, a VAV system with zone reheat sequencing can offer many advantages over the unitary system approach for each zone. Chapters 19 and 20 of this volume provide information on various public and assembly areas, and Chapter 12 details VAV design.

Systems must be trouble-free and allow easy maintenance because shutdown of systems will often cause loss of revenue. Installation of multiple heating and refrigeration plant units ensures continuity of services. Emergency generators are required for protection against electrical power outages. Many utilities provide dual service and transfer devices to prevent long power outages.

The ballroom is the showplace of a hotel, and it requires special attention to include a satisfactory air-distribution system within the interior design concept. Most ballrooms do not provide proper comfort for the functions they serve. Ballrooms generally have more odors and smoke than other places of assembly when used for banquets. Most ballrooms are designed as multipurpose rooms, and often the peak loads occur when they are used as meeting rooms.

Economies in initial and operating costs are possible by proper transfer of air from air-conditioned areas to service areas such as kitchens, workshops, and laundry and storage rooms. Smaller air quantities may achieve satisfactory results and eliminate the need for separate supply systems.

In hotel guest wing towers, space is at a premium, so means of heat and odor removal should be considered that do not run kitchen range hood flues and boiler and emergency generator exhaust stacks (which take away potential guest room space) to the top of the building. Such discharges should be located at least 100 ft (30 m) away from the nearest outside air intake. Hotels require good instrumentation for all major systems and services so that accurate operating data may be analyzed to ensure economy of operation.

Well-designed instrumentation, control, and flexibility of shutoff in all areas have potential for operating savings. A good maintenance staff and well-instructed cleaning staff can regulate or shut off energy services in unoccupied areas. Virtually all new hotels and motels incorporate some type of guest room energy management system so units can be shut off in unoccupied rooms, temperature can be reset, or all functions can be controlled from the front desk and overridden by the occupant.

APPLICABILITY OF SYSTEMS

For guest rooms, most hotels use fan coil systems or *deluxe* self-contained unit systems. Depending on the architectural design and climate, the units may be located under the exterior windows, in the hung ceiling over the bathroom or vestibule, or vertically in the wall between the bathroom and bedroom.

Hotels lend themselves to VAV systems because they have simple room layouts and no guest cooking facilities. This is particularly true in tropical or high humidity climates and when doors open to the outside, creating condensation problems on exposed casings of fan-coil units.

Each bathroom requires an average of 75 cfm (35.4 L/s) of design exhaust air. This air usually comes from the ventilation air delivered to each room. Some systems supply outdoor air to the corridors, and this air is transferred into each room by the bathroom exhaust; however, this does not control odor and smoke. In tropical climates and where outdoor air supplied to the corridors has not been previously treated, this indirect method provides poor humidity control; in many instances, controlled air supply systems are added.

Great latitude is available in system selection for other hotel areas, as long as the systems satisfy the space and hotel operating requirements. These systems are predominantly all-air because of high ventilation requirements, possibly with reheat or recool devices, as required.

With substantial public area cooling required during the heating season, as well as large heat sources from kitchens and laundries, internal source heat pumps with storage should be considered for hostelries. They can also be attractive for total energy systems because of their constant thermal demand.

SPECIAL CONSIDERATIONS

In some climates, guest bathrooms should have supplementary heat available to the guests. Guest rooms opening to the outdoors should have self-closing doors, so excess condensation does not form on the cooling coils within room units.

If the fan in fan coil units is shut off, the cooling coil control valve should also close to prevent possible damage from excess condensation.

Design information for administration, eating, entertainment, assembly, and other areas will be found in Chapters 3 and 4. In tropical climates, special design techniques must be used to prevent excess moisture buildup in closets and storage areas and to avoid mildew and resultant damage to clothing and other materials. An effective device is to maintain a light in the closet.

MULTIPLE-USE COMPLEXES

Multiple-use complexes are developed in most metropolitan areas. These complexes combine the retail facilities, office space, hotel space, residential space, or other commercial space into a single site. The various occupancies may have peak HVAC demands occuring at different times of the day and year. HVAC loads should be determined independently for each occupancy. Where a combined central plant is considered, a block load should also be determined.

The difference in HVAC characteristics for the various occupancies indicates that separate air handling and distribution should be used for the separate functions. However, substantial economics can be achieved by combining the heating and cooling units into a single central plant. A central plant provides good opportunities for heat recovery, thermal storage, and other similar sophistication that may not be economical in a single-use facility. The multiple-use complex requires a central control system for fire and smoke control, security, remote monitoring, billing for central facility use, maintenance control, building operations control, and energy management.

REFERENCES

McClelland, L. 1983. Tenant Paid Energy Costs in Multi-Family Rental Housing. DOE, University of Colorado, Campus Box 108, Boulder, CO 80309.

CHAPTER 22

EDUCATIONAL FACILITIES

ENERGY use has become increasingly important in educational facilities in relation to other goods and services. As a result, energy will account for a larger percentage of school budgets and receive increased attention from school boards and admnistrators. Compliance with ASHRAE *Standard* 90A-80 and various state and local energy codes will become mandatory.

The need to acquire new knowledge promises adult education an increasing role in our society; this will cause extended use of educational facilities. Such post-school instruction takes place in evenings, over weekends, and during summers. Also, schools are not always fully occupied during the normal daytime school period. Thus, occupancy may vary from full occupancy during the morning hours to one or two rooms at night or during weekends; buildings frequently are virtually empty at lunchtime.

Remodeling existing schools poses a more difficult problem than designing new schools, but it is becoming relatively more important. Equipment has to be adapted to existing building conditions, and ingenuity and careful planning are required to keep costs low and keep the buildings in operation.

The problems and requirements of secondary and elementary schools are sufficiently different from those of universities and colleges to warrant treatment as two separate subjects. Prior to any design, close consultation and cooperation between school boards, school administration, architects, and engineers is of vital importance.

GENERAL DESIGN CONSIDERATIONS

Environmental factors have a significant impact on teaching and learning. Design for the best indoor environment for learning must consider heat loss, heat gain, air movement, ventilation means, and ventilation rates. Space temperature requirements and lighting are also important for an efficient teaching environment. Variations and times of occupancy require a flexible means of heating, cooling, and automatic control to conserve energy and reduce operating costs.

Comfort is a necessity for efficient teaching. Excessive variations in temperature may cause more discomfort than maintenance of slightly higher or lower temperatures with reasonable variations of $\pm 3\,°F$ ($\pm 1.7\,°C$).

Automatic control of system operation and temperature is a necessity if comfortable conditions and efficient operation are to be obtained. Proper application of controls may return the investment within a year or two through savings in labor and fuel. Such controls must change from heating to cooling in a few minutes when a class is occupied after morning warm-up because of the heat suddenly supplied by lights and students. This heating-cooling cycle may also occur several times during the day if the school has an energy management system.

Some odors can be tolerated, but when they are disagreeable and distracting, they interfere with learning. Therefore, odors should be controlled by proper ventilation (see Table 1). The required air quantities are for acceptable outdoor air or for a combination of acceptable outdoor air and recirculated air with adequate temperature control and filtration. To conserve energy, outdoor air may be reduced to 33% of specified, but not less than 5 cfm (2.4 L/s) per person. An additional reason for good ventilation is the prevention of respiratory ailments and their rapid spread.

Simple and minimal maintenance, combined with sturdiness of the equipment, is an important requirement in educational facilities. Equipment must absorb a great deal of abuse from students with only perfunctory attention from custodians. Also, possible damage to the building due to maintenance and service operations should be considered. Service of roof-mounted equipment may cause roof damage. Provisions should be made for some protection to minimize this problem.

Systems for educational facilities should be evaluated on a *life cycle cost* basis, which attempts to consider operating, maintenance, replacement, and recoverability (obsolescence) costs, along with system performance. A life cycle analysis requires experience and good judgment.

Although climate control systems for educational facilities may be similar to systems applied to other types of buildings, it is necessary to understand the operation of the various systems, as well as the school operations, to suit the mechanical systems to the special educational facilities. Year-round school programs, adult education, night classes, and community functions put

Table 1   Ventilation Requirements for Various School Spaces

	Estimated Persons per 1000 ft^2 (100 m^2) of Floor Area	Required Ventilation Air cfm (L/s) per Occupant	
		Minimum	Recommended
Classrooms	50	10 (4.7)	10-15 (4.7- 7.8)
Multiple-Use Rooms	70	10 (4.7)	10-15 (4.7- 7.8)
Laboratories[a]	30	10 (4.7)	10-15 (4.7- 7.8)
Craft Shops, Vocational Training Shops[a]	30	10 (4.7)	10-15 (4.7- 7.8)
Music, Rehearsal Rooms	70	10 (4.7)	15-20 (7.8- 9.4)
		5 (2.4)	5- 7.5 (2.4- 3.5)
Gymnasiums	70	20 (9.4)	25-30 (11.8-14.2)
Libraries	20	7 (3.3)	10-12 (4.7- 5.7)
Common Rooms, Lounges	70	10 (4.7)	10-15 (4.7- 7.8)
Offices	10	7 (3.3)	10-15 (4.7- 7.8)
Lavatories	100	15 (7.8)	20-25 (9.4-11.8)
Locker Rooms[b]	20	30 (14.2)	40-50 (18.9-23.6)
Lunchrooms, Dining Halls	100	10 (4.7)	15-20 (7.8- 9.4)
Corridors	50	15 (7.8)	20-25 (9.4-11.8)
Utility Rooms	3	5 (2.4)	7-10 (3.3- 4.7)
Dormitory Bedrooms	20	7 (3.3)	10-15 (4.7- 7.8)

[a]Special contaminant control systems may be required.
[b]Cfm/locker.

The preparation of this chapter is assigned to TC 9.8, Large Building Air-Conditioning Applications.

ever-increasing demands on these facilities and require that the environmental control system be designed carefully to meet varying needs. Classrooms, lecture rooms, and assembly rooms have uniformly dense occupancies. Gymnasiums, cafeterias, laboratories, shops, and similar functional spaces have lighter occupancies and also have different and varying ventilation and temperature requirements. Many schools include multipurpose rooms serving as auditoriums, gymnasiums, and community meeting rooms. System flexibility is more important because of this wide variation in use and occupancy.

In most cases, the installed cost of an effective heating and ventilating system will approach the cost of a complete air-conditioning system. Generally, a well-designed heating and ventilating system will contain all the fans, dampers, controls, etc., necessary for air conditioning, except for the refrigeration cycle. Since school buildings almost always need cooling when occupied—not just during the summer months—the additional cost will improve the usefulness and efficiency and prevent premature obsolescence.

Table 2 indicates recommended winter and summer design dry-bulb temperatures for various types of spaces in schools. These values should be evaluated in individual applications to avoid energy waste but not at an excessive sacrifice of comfort. Reduction in winter design may cause discomfort at the perimeter. Perimeter walls need to be designed to reduce uncomfortable radiation transfer to occupants.

ENVIRONMENTAL AND REGULATORY CONSIDERATIONS

There are many different climate zones, and a system that is optimal for one may not be the best choice in another. Since climate affects energy consumption, the effect of the average temperature should be considered carefully in selecting energy sources, equipment, and the design of the entire building for optimum life cycle cost; average temperature is a more important consideration for energy consumption than the extremes.

Many states have special regulations for school buildings. Fire, building, ventilation, and noise control codes all may have a great effect on design; ventilation requirements vary in different states and different localities. If the regulations are poor or nonexistent, good design practice generally dictates the minimum air

Table 2 Recommended Winter and Summer Design Dry-Bulb Temperatures for Various Types of Spaces Common in Schools[a]

Space	Winter Design, °F (°C)	Summer Design, °F (°C)
Classrooms, Laboratories, Lecture Halls, Library, Administration Areas, etc.	72 (22)	78 (26)[b]
Multipurpose Rooms, Lunchrooms, Shops	72 (22)	78 (26)
Gymnasiums	65-70 (18-21)	—[c]
Natatoriums	80 (27)[d]	—[c,d]
Kitchen	68 (20)	—[c]
Locker, Shower Rooms	75 (24)[d]	—[c,d]
Toilets	72 (22)	—[c]
Storage	65 (18)	—[c]
Mechanical	60 (16)	—[c]
Corridors	68 (20)	80 (27)[b]

[a]For spaces of high population density and where sensible heat factors are 0.75 or less, lower dry-bulb temperatures will result in generation of less latent heat, which may reduce the need for reheat and thus save energy. Therefore, optimum dry-bulb temperatures should be the subject of detailed design analysis.
[b]Frequently not air conditioned.
[c]Usually not air conditioned.
[d]Provide ventilation for humidity control.

change required and the outdoor air quantity. In more severe climates, consideration may be given to treatment of the return air to reduce odors and fumes. However, since schools need cooling much of the time (even in cold climates), reduction in ventilating air may not save substantial amounts of energy and should be analyzed carefully.

Energy studies also are becoming a legal requirement in many states. Computer programs are available to prepare such studies. (See Chapter 28 of the 1985 FUNDAMENTALS Volume.)

CONTROLS

The ideal climate-control system for educational facilities should serve diverse areas, regardless of the use of the various spaces involved. For example, when showing movies or video tapes with the lights turned off, heating may be required, while a nearby area may require cooling. During evenings and weekends, some areas may be used for special events or instructions while other rooms are unoccupied. These varying and often unpredictable conditions are best met by separate control of each space. Equipment should be capable of efficient operation at extremely low and variable loads. It may be desirable to design for future expansion with minimal investment.

Since most heat is required at night and weekends when buildings are at least partially unoccupied, *night set-back* becomes virtually mandatory.

A central control system is also desirable, especially one that ensures equipment is turned either to night set-back or off when not in use. Because of the large portion of both the heating and cooling load that can be attributed to the required ventilation, provision should be made in the control system to close the outside air dampers when the space is not occupied. Central monitoring and control systems, as described under the "College and University" section of this chapter, can often be justified for a larger elementary or secondary school.

FINANCIAL AND SPACE CONSIDERATIONS

Educational facility planners and owners generally agree that the highest quality construction that can be afforded should be built, since these facilities must serve 20 to 40 years or more. The taxpayers pay for all costs of public schools—initial, operating, and maintenance—simultaneously. Thus, schools pay no taxes, which make life cycle costs the only valid criteria as far as taxpayers are concerned, although many schools still use the *most square feet (metres) per dollar* criteria.

Equipment requires building space, which may increase the cost of the usable floor space. Building costs are usually described in dollars per gross area. A better measure is the cost per 'usable' area per student or per classroom. The equipment selected should occupy minimum floor space in relatively inactive areas. This requirement has led to increasing use of roof-mounted equipment. Central equipment rooms are commonly large installations where the equipment is easily supervised, and a great deal of the maintenance is concentrated in one area. The engineer must evaluate these and other factors to arrive at an optimum choice for the particular project. Adequate all-year maintenance and service capability must be provided for all systems.

Protection of equipment from vandalism should be considered. All items accessible to students should be of heavy construction and resistant to tampering.

Flexibility of the mechanical system may be an important consideration. New classes and teaching methods may be adopted, requiring changes in ductwork, diffusers, temperature control zones, etc. The open classroom layout is an example; it may later be partitioned into conventional classroom spaces.

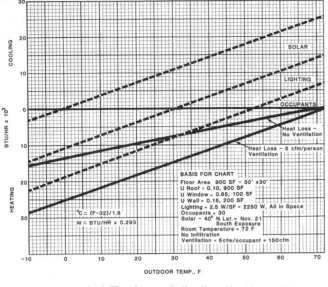

Fig. 1 Typical Heating and Cooling Requirements for Exterior Classrooms

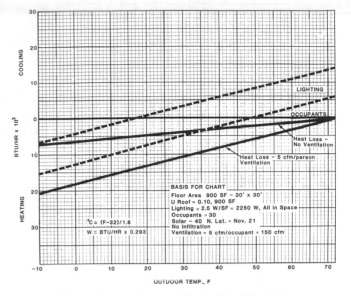

Fig. 2 Typical Heating and Cooling Requirements for Interior Classrooms

CLASSROOM LOAD PROFILE

When an interior room is occupied and the lights are on, some cooling will usually be required all year. This may be accomplished, at least partially, by use of outdoor air, if the outdoor temperature is 60 °F (16 °C) or less.

In general, the heat flow characteristics of exterior classrooms without windows are similar to interior rooms, as shown in Figures 1 and 2. Exterior rooms with less than conventional window areas (strip windows, for example) will have thermal characteristics somewhere between those shown in the charts for the inside and the exterior rooms.

The time of occupancy of educational facilities may be irregular. It has been a widespread assumption that schools are fully occupied from 8:00 A.M. to 3:30 P.M. and then vacant. School custodians, adult education, and civic affairs such as band practice and scout meetings make the total occupancy time far longer than the normal school year of 1400 to 1500 h. Surveys show anywhere from 2000 to 3300 h of occupancy with *equivalent full occupancy* (EFO) of about 50%. Similar to equivalent full load, equivalent full occupancy is a mathematical integration of the total number of classroom hours per year divided by the number of rooms in the building. EFO is a measure of potential energy saving by turning off lights and using climate-control equipment in the unoccupied parts of the building.

ENERGY CONSIDERATIONS

Most new buildings have to meet ASHRAE *Standard* 90A-80 and other federal or state codes. Usage patterns must be considered carefully in design selection of high efficiency equipment, proper insulation, and reduced fenestration, which are other ways to reduce energy consumption. In some cases, energy studies must be submitted. Simulated computer programs for energy studies are the most accurate for evaluating alternatives, if performed properly.

Outdoor air economizer cycle, which uses cool outdoor air during many hours of the year, can handle much of the high internal load. Proper sizing of the outdoor air dampers to balance the pressure loss between the indoor air return system and the outdoor air supply system is imperative for proper control of the economizer cycle. Low leakage outdoor air dampers should be used.

Night set-back, activated by a central control system, conserves energy by locking out mechanical cooling and lowering the heating requirement during unoccupied periods. Since approximately 90% of the heat requirement in a school occurs when the building is unoccupied, this often represents a substantial saving. Intermittent use of the building at night may make individual area night set-back more economical.

Water-to-air heat pumps may conserve energy if the school has interior spaces. Excess heat generated during the day may be stored in water tanks to provide heating at night. Some large package water-to-air heat pumps now have built-in air economizer cycles.

Solar energy can supplement other energy sources. Air-to-air heat recovery devices should be considred for those areas that require substantial exhaust and outdoor air makeup.

Air-to-air heat pumps may make electrical heating costs competitive with fossil fuels. Life cycle costs of air-to-air heat pumps are generally comparable with other systems.

Proper cooling requires the distribution of relatively large amounts of air—substantially more air than is generally needed for heating—which may cause severe discomfort at temperatures around 55 °F (13 °C). Therefore, this air must be distributed evenly to eliminate drafts and excessive air noise.

In extremely cold areas, care also must be taken to heat window areas, although, with the trend to more insulation and smaller windows, the problem of downdrafts is less critical.

EQUIPMENT AND SYSTEM SELECTION

Architectural planning of educational facilities varies greatly and has considerable influence on the building's heating and cooling load and on the selection of equipment. The use of ASHRAE *Standard* 90A-80 can lead to sufficient reduction in loads to allow year-round air-conditioning systems to be installed at costs that compare favorably to systems only for heating and ventilating.

No trends in educational facility design as related to heating, ventilating, and air-conditioning systems are evident. In smaller single-building facilities, centralized systems are often applied.

These systems, discussed in Chapter 5 of this volume, include unit ventilator, rooftop, and single and multizone-type units. Central station equipment, especially variable volume systems, continues to have wide application in larger facilities; water-to-air heat pumps have been used.

Recent studies indicate that control of temperature is a more significant comfort factor than control of humidity, providing the latter is maintained within reasonable limits. A methodology is being developed to rate various HVAC systems under consideration in terms of their relative efficacy in meeting various design parameters (see Chapter 1 of this volume).

Life cycle costs should be considered in the selection of the mechanical system; however, other considerations may preclude selection of the system with the lowest life cycle cost. Chapter 49 of this volume has more details on life cycle costs. The *systems approach* is another method applied to educational facility construction. This method establishes a performance specification as the basis for bidding for a complete facility. Many of the building components are prefabricated in the factory, thereby reducing construction time on the job site. This allows a bidder greater latitude in selecting individual systems, as long as the overall performance requirement is met. However, close coordination of all systems proposed for the facility is required to ensure compatibility.

There are many factors to be considered in selecting equipment, and the variety of equipment is such that analysis is becoming increasingly difficult. A matrix, such as that shown in Figure 3, may aid in selection. Each factor may be rated to give the designer a figure of merit for systems, fuels, etc. Examples of systems are in Chapters 1 through 6 and Chapter 10 of this volume.

Single Duct With Reheat

For energy conservation, reheat systems have been restricted by ASHRAE *Standard* 90A-80 and usually cannot be justified for schools, unless recovered energy is used for reheat.

Dual-conduit and dual-duct systems are recommended, if they are designed to minimize air quantities to those required and incorporate adequate energy conservation features to make them as economical as other systems.

Multizone

Reset controllers should be used to receive signals from zone thermostats and maintain hot deck and cold deck at optimum temperatures, which will minimize mixing of air streams. For energy conservation, it is important to select similar exposures for multizone units to minimize mixing of hot and cold air streams. Multizone units with a neutral zone that mix either heated or cooled air with return air, but do not mix heated and cooled air, will eliminate the energy-wasting practice of blending heated and cooled air streams.

Factory-assembled units for rooftop installation are available in capacities from about 10 to 80 tons (35 to 282 kW) in multizone, dual duct, and single-zone configurations. Options are offered for type of filtration, refrigerant reheat, heating source, return air fan, and control cycles. Routine servicing features may have to be added. Life expectancy may be less than for indoor equipment. However, some school districts have successfully operated rooftop units for over 15 years, with maintenance costs significantly less than schools with other systems.

Single Duct With Variable Volume

Supply air capacity is adjusted to space load by automatic volume control. Systems for exterior rooms are usually zoned by exposure.

SYSTEM LIFE CYCLE COST CONSIDERATIONS

CHECK APPLICABLE
Elementary School ☐
Secondary School ☐
College and University ☐

	Operating Cost	Energy Cost	Maintenance Cost	Life Expectancy	Suitability	Controllability	Availability	First Cost	Noise
Heating									
Direct Fired Air:									
Gas									
Oil									
Electric									
Solar									
Steam:									
Gas									
Oil									
Coal									
Solar									
Hot Water:									
Gas									
Oil									
Electric									
Solar									
Heat Pump, Electric:									
Air to Air									
Water to Air									
Water to Water									
Cooling									
Chilled Water:									
Absorption									
Steam									
Gas									
Oil									
Centrifugal									
Steam									
Electric									
Reciprocating									
Cooling Air DX Electric:									
Central-Variable Volume									
Multizone									
Modular, Rooftop									
SC Unit Ventilator									
Unitary									
Rooftop Variable Volume									

Fig. 3 Matrix for Relative Cost Comparison of Various HVAC Systems for Educational Facilities

A variable volume, single-duct system may be used in conjunction with reheat units at each single-duct unit. Control of this arrangement is in two steps; the first step reduces volume and the second step brings on reheat, where required, to maintain minimum ventilation rates.

The method of control for variable air volume systems should maintain minimum ventilation rates to provide comfort in an economical manner.

Package Units

Package units contain either split or single direct expansion air-conditioning units, generally serving a single room. Resistance electric heating elements, hot water, or steam coils are used to supply heat. Temperature controls in each unit permit automatic individual room heating and cooling, as desired.

Another type of packaged unit is the water-to-air (unitary or single package) heat pump. An uninsulated, constant flow unzoned water circuit serves each unit, which extracts or rejects heat in accordance with the room requirement. The closed loop incorporates a heat rejector (tower) and heat source (boiler). Certain operating conditions balance the loop; therefore, no heat should be added or rejected. Units simultaneously heat and cool according to room need. A water storage tank added to the circulating system can accumulate excess heat during the day for use at night.

Air-to-air heat pumps are also applicable to schools. Small rooftop and self-contained unit ventilators, featuring heat pump cycle, are also available.

SOUND LEVELS

Typical ranges of design levels are given below. The lower end of the range of each room type is justifiable for buildings—either in quiet locations or where provisions have been made for reducing sound transmission through exterior walls. The upper end of the range is appropriate for buildings in relatively noisy locations, without adequate exterior wall sound transmission loss, or where the owner's requirements and budget indicate lower costs are desirable.

	A-Sound Levels Decibels	Desired NC (Noise Criteria)
Libraries, classrooms	35-45	30-40
Labs, shops	40-50	35-45
Gyms, multipurpose corridors	40-55	35-50
Kitchens	45-55	40-50

For further information, see Chapter 52 of this volume.

REMODELING

To the consulting engineer, remodeling consists of two phases. First the engineer must ascertain what type of equipment is installed in the existing building, what should be reused or replaced, the overall facilities, possible space for future equipment, etc. Existing drawings, if available, may not reflect the current building because of changes after construction. Second the engineer must design a system that is compatible with the contemplated changes to this building in terms of time, cost, energy consumption, and appearance. Remodeling is frequently attempted during normal vacation shutdowns and after school hours to keep the facilities available for service.

Central systems, rooftop equipment, window units, unitary systems, and self-contained unit ventilators have all been used successfully. The matrix (Figure 3) may facilitate a quick, cost-effective selection evaluating the many variables involved, in conjunction with Chapter 1 of this volume. Life cycle cost analysis, in general, shows that lowest equipment cost does not result in the lowest total cost.

PRIMARY, MIDDLE, AND SECONDARY SCHOOLS

Load Characteristics

Primary and secondary schools are characterized by relatively small buildings, with the exception of some high schools, which may be large and approach the size and complexity of a small college. Most secondary school facilities, however, are low-rise structures of medium to small size.

Changes in teaching methods have affected educational facilities. Double-loaded corridor designs of individual classrooms have given way to open plan layouts and back again. Even open plan schools frequently have numerous portable partitions that are frequently changed. The more flexible the HVAC system, the less chance for obsolescence and the easier it is to adapt to changing requirements.

Design Criteria

Design criteria are the same as those mentioned under "General Design Considerations," except that for kindergarten to fourth grade, special care must be taken to have warm floors.

Equipment

Equipment for the small buildings should be simple to operate and require no skilled personnel. Specialized, trained operating personnel are often not available, and small schools usually find it necessary to hold down operating costs. Since the buildings are usually smaller and less elaborate in the lower grades, less elaborate HVAC systems are usually indicated.

Regional schools, on the other hand, may house large office areas, auditoriums, laboratories, shops, computer rooms, dispensaries, pools, gymnasiums, maintenance shops, cafeterias, etc., approaching the complexity of large institutions. Usually more and better skilled operating personnel are available, and systems can be more sophisticated and varied.

These larger buildings present many specialized problems (such as swimming pools), which are covered individually in other ASHRAE Handbook volumes.

COLLEGES AND UNIVERSITIES

The variety of buildings found on the campuses of colleges and universities resembles that of a small city. Consequently, the problems and requirements of colleges and universities are different from those found in secondary schools. Many colleges and universities have satellite campuses dispersed within the city or throughout the entire state. Therefore, the design requirements for campus buildings are influenced by many factors. Specific and special requirements for such buildings are established by the Planning Office or the Department of Physical Plant, also known as the Department of Buildings and Grounds.

The HVAC load for a given building on campus depends on the specific building use and the geographical location of the campus. The design criteria for a given campus building is established by the requirements of the users. For detailed discussion of a specific building type, refer to applicable chapters and integrate these with specific usage criteria.

Types of Campus Buildings

College and university campuses consist of various types of buildings; following is a list of major building types:

1. Administrative buildings
2. Buildings housing animal colonies
3. Auditoriums and theaters
4. Computer sites
5. Classroom buildings
6. Dormitory buildings
7. Garages and auto repair shops
8. Gymnasiums
9. Freight handling and storage buildings
10. Ice rinks
11. Museums
12. Stores (book, gift, clothing, restaurants, and cafeterias)
13. Student and faculty apartment buildings
14. Natatoriums
15. Tennis pavilions
16. Laboratory buildings
17. Maintenance and repair shops
18. Central plants
    a. Boiler
    b. Refrigeration
    c. Power generation
19. Barns
20. Poultry housing
21. Television studios
22. Radio stations
23. Hospitals
24. Chapels
25. Student unions

Although the college or university campus may consist of any combination of the building types listed, seldom is an entire campus constructed on a new location. This is unlike the secondary schools, where a new complex is erected to meet the needs of a new or expanding community. However, clusters of similar use are buildings such as research centers and dormitories, generally erected on central locations. These clusters may have individual heating-cooling equipment or may be connected to the central plant designed for the particular center.

Central heating and refrigeration plants on existing campuses dictate the type of heating-cooling system and equipment to be installed in the new buildings.

Central Heating and Refrigeration Plants

When planning a central heating and/or refrigeration plant for an existing college or university, various factors should be considered. In general, cost per given unit of energy is lower when it comes from the central plant. However, cost of distribution, piping (either direct, buried, or in utility tunnels), and pumping may offset the savings offered by a central plant. Detailed analyses of several central versus individual plant schemes, based on accurate long-term projections for the institution, are essential for the most desirable solution. These will include such factors as the following:

1. Central maintenance versus individual building maintenance
2. Pollution and noise control
3. Topography and easement characteristics
4. Type of central distribution such as steam, high temperature water, bleed versus convertor takeoffs, etc.
5. Types of fuel and HVAC equipment available or projected
6. Schedules of operations for the various buildings including diversity factors
7. Future expansion

It is important to evaluate all factors peculiar to a particular campus before selecting and designing a heating-cooling system, whether for a single building or a cluster of the entire campus.

The uncertainty of fuel prices and potential unavailability of certain fuels mandate investigation of alternate energy sources for central plants and individual buildings, where feasible. One such source is solid waste, which could be used in central plants of larger campuses. Solar energy should also be considered.

Central Monitoring and Control System

The multi-building campus requires constant monitoring of the various systems within these buildings. Manual operation of these systems requires large staffs and, consequently, becomes uneconomical. Central monitoring and control systems can often be justified on the basis of savings in labor. (See Chapter 31 of the 1984 SYSTEMS Volume.) In addition, central monitoring and control systems offer some means of controlling energy costs by the use of such methods as *scheduling* (which remotely shuts off equipment when it is not needed), *demand limiting* (which selectively switches off electric loads when demand limit is approached), and *duty cycling* (which cycles constant volume equipment during part-load operation).

The central monitoring and control systems can perform other functions, such as the following:

1. Monitoring and control of various accesses (building security)
2. Fire alarm system monitoring
3. Lighting control and maintenance scheduling
4. Optimization of operating equipment
5. Improved control system operation
6. More complete and accurate record-keeping of building, equipment, systems, and energy use information

REFERENCES

ASHRAE. 1980. *Energy Conservation in New Building Design.* ASHRAE Standard 90A-1980.

ASHRAE. 1981. *Thermal Environmental Conditions for Human Occupancy.* ASHRAE Standard 55-1981.

ASHRAE. 1981. *Ventilation for Acceptable Indoor Air Quality.* ASHRAE Standard 62-1981.

CHAPTER 23

HEALTH FACILITIES

CONTINUOUS advances in medicine and technology require constant reevaluation of the air-conditioning needs of hospitals and medical facilities. While there is medical evidence that proper air conditioning is beneficial in the prevention and treatment of many conditions, the relatively high cost of air conditioning demands efficient design and operation to ensure economical energy management.

The general hospital was selected as the basis for the fundamentals outlined in the first section of this chapter because of the variety of services it provides. Environmental conditions and design criteria apply to comparable areas in other health facilities. Nursing homes are addressed separately in the second section, since their fundamental requirements differ to a great extent from those of other medical facilities. "Outpatient Surgical Facilities" are addressed in the last section.

The specific environmental conditions required by a particular medical facility may vary from those in this chapter, depending on the agency responsible for the medical facility environmental standard. Among the agencies that may have standards are: state and local health agencies, Department of Health and Human Services, Indian Health Service, Public Health Service, Medicare/Medicaid, Department of Defense (Army, Navy, Air Force), the Veterans Administration, and the Joint Commission on Accreditation of Hospitals (JCAH). It is sometimes advisable to discuss infection control objectives with each hospital's infection control committee.

AIR CONDITIONING IN THE PREVENTION AND TREATMENT OF DISEASE

Dry conditions constitute a hazard to the ill and debilitated by contributing to secondary infection or infection totally unrelated to the clinical condition causing hospitalization. Clinical areas devoted to upper respiratory disease treatment, acute care, as well as the general clinical areas of the entire hospital, should be maintained at a relative humidity of 30% to 60%.

Patients with chronic pulmonary disease often have viscous respiratory-tract secretions. As these accumulate and increase in viscosity, the exchange of heat and water dwindles. Warm, humidified, inspired air is essential to prevent dehydration under these circumstances.

Patients requiring oxygen therapy or those with a tracheotomy (an artificial opening into the windpipe) require special attention to ensure a warm humid supply of inspired air. Cold, dry oxygen or the bypassing of the nasopharyngeal mucosa presents an extreme situation. Rebreathing techniques for anesthesia and enclosure in an incubator are special means of treating the impaired heat loss that must be considered under therapeutic environments.

Hospital air conditioning assumes a more important role than just the promotion of comfort. In many cases, proper air conditioning is a factor in the therapy of the patient, and, in some instances, it is the major treatment.

Studies show that patients in fully air-conditioned rooms generally have more rapid physical improvement than those in hot and humid rooms. Patients with thyrotoxicosis do not tolerate hot, humid conditions or heat waves very well. A cool, dry environment favors the loss of heat by radiation and evaporation from the skin and may save the life of the patient.

Cardiac patients may be unable to maintain the circulation necessary to ensure normal heat loss. The importance of air conditioning hospital wards and rooms of cardiac patients, particularly those with congestive heart failure, has been stressed as a therapeutic measure; it is also important in tropical or subtropical climates. Individuals with head injuries, those subjected to brain operations, and those with barbiturate poisoning may have hyperthermia, especially in a hot environment because of a disturbance in the heat regulatory center of the brain. Obviously, one important factor in recovery is an environment in which the patient can lose heat by radiation and evaporation—namely, a cool room with dehumidified air.

A hot, dry environment of 90°F (32°C) db and 35% relative humidity has been used over an extended period for the treatment of patients with rheumatoid arthritis, with reported improvement.

Burn patients need a hot environment and high relative humidity. A ward for severe burn victims should have temperature controls that permit adjusting the room temperature up to 90°F (32°C) db and the relative humidity up to 95%.

HOSPITALS

Although proper air conditioning is beneficial in the prevention and treatment of disease, the application of air conditioning to health facilities presents many problems not encountered in the usual comfort conditioning system.

The basic differences between air conditioning for hospitals (and related health facilities) and other building types stem from (1) the need to restrict air movement in and between the various departments; (2) the specific requirements for ventilation and filtration to dilute and remove contamination in the form of odor, airborne microorganisms and viruses, and hazardous chemical and radioactive substances; (3) the need for different temperature and humidity requirements for various areas; and (4) the need for sophistication in design to permit accurate control of environmental conditions.

Infection Sources and Control Measures

Bacterial Infection. Examples of bacteria that are highly infectious and transported within air or air and water mixtures are *Mycobacterium Tuberculosis* and *Legionalla pneumophilia* (Legionnaire's disease). Wells (1934) showed that droplets (or in-

---

The preparation of this chapter is assigned to TC 9.8, Large Building Air-Conditioning Applications.

fectious agents) that are 5 microns (μm) or less in size can remain airborne indefinitely. Isoard et al. (1980) and Luciano (1984) have shown that 99.9% of all bacteria present in the hospital are removed by 90 to 95% efficient (ASHRAE *Standard* 52-76) filters. This is because bacteria are typically present in colony-forming units that are larger than 1 micron. Some authorities recommend that HEPA filters having DOP Test filtering efficiencies of 99.97% be used in certain areas (see footnote *a* in Table 1).

Viral Infection. Examples of viruses that are transported by and virulent within air are *Varicella* (Chicken Pox/Shingles), *Rubella* (German Measles), and *Rubeola* (regular Measles). Epidemiological evidence and other studies indicate that the airborne viruses that transmit infection are so small that no known filtering technique is effective. Attempts to deactivate viruses with ultraviolet light and chemical sprays have not proven to be reliable and effective enough to be recommended by most codes as a primary infection control measure for viruses or bacteria. Therefore, isolation rooms and isolation anterooms with appropriate ventilation-pressure relationships are the primary infection control method used to prevent the spread of airborne viruses in the hospital environment.

Outside Air Ventilation. If outside air intakes are properly located (see "Air Quality" section below) and areas adjacent to outside air intakes are maintained properly, outside air is almost free of bacteria and viruses in comparison to room air. Infection control problems frequently involve a bacterial or viral source within the hospital. Ventilation air is a dilutant of the viral and bacterial contamination within a hospital. Ventilation systems also remove airborne infectious agents from the hospital environment if the systems are properly designed, constructed, and maintained to preserve the correct pressure relations between functional areas.

Temperature & Humidity conditions can inhibit or promote the growth of bacteria and activate or deactivate viruses. Some bacteria such as *Legionella pneumophilia* are basically water-borne and survive more readily in a humid environment. Codes and guidelines specify temperature and humidity range criteria in some hospital areas as an infection control measure, as well as a comfort criteria.

Table 1   Filter Efficiencies for Central Ventilation and Air-Conditioning Systems in General Hospitals

Minimum Number of Filter Beds	Area Designation	Filter Efficiencies, % (based on ASHRAE Std. 52-76)	
		Filter Bed No. 1	Filter Bed No. 2
2	Operating Rooms Delivery Rooms Nurseries Intensive Care Units	25	90
	Bone Marrow Transplant Organ Transplant Room	25	90[a]
	Patient Care Treatment Diagnostic and Related Areas	25	90[b]
1	Food Preparation Areas Laundries	80	—
	Administrative Bulk Storage Soiled Holding Areas	25	—

[a]HEPA filters at air outlets
[b]May be reduced to 80% for systems using all-outdoor air

AIR QUALITY

Systems must also provide air virtually free of dust, dirt, odor, and chemical and radioactive pollutants. In some instances, outside air quality is hazardous to patients suffering from cardiopulmonary conditions or respiratory or pulmonary conditions. In such instances, systems that intermittently provide 100% recirculated air should be considered, when justified and approved on a case-by-case basis by all parties having jurisdiction or interest.

Outdoor Intakes should be located as far as practical (on directionally different exposures whenever possible) but not less than 30 ft (9.1 m) from exhaust outlets of combustion equipment stacks, ventilation exhaust outlets from the hospital or adjoining buildings, medical-surgical vacuum systems, plumbing vent stacks, or from areas that may collect vehicular exhaust and other noxious fumes. The bottom of outdoor air intakes serving central systems should be located as high as practical but not less than 6 ft (1.8 m) above ground level, or if installed above the roof, 3 ft (0.9 m) above the roof level (DHHS 1984a).

Air Filters. A number of methods are available for determining the efficiency of filters in removing particulates from an air stream (See Chapter 10, 1983 EQUIPMENT Volume). All central ventilation or air-conditioning systems should be equipped with filters having efficiencies no less than those indicated in Table 1. Where two filter beds are indicated, Filter Bed No. 1 should be located upstream of the air-conditioning equipment, and Filter Bed No. 2 should be downstream of the supply fan, any recirculating spray water systems, and water-reservoir type humidifiers. Appropriate precautions should be observed to prevent wetting of the filter media by free moisture from humidifiers. Where only one filter bed is indicated, it should be located upstream of the air-conditioning equipment. All filter efficiencies are based on ASHRAE *Standard* 52-76.

The following are guidelines for filter installations.

1. HEPA filters having DOP test efficiencies of 99.97% should be used on air supply systems serving rooms used for clinical treatment of patients with a high susceptibility to infection from leukemia, burns, bone marrow transplant, organ transplant, or Acquired Immune Deficiency Syndrome. They should also be used on the exhaust discharge air from fume hoods or safety cabinets in which infectious or highly radioactive materials are processed and should be designed and equipped to permit safe removal, disposal, and replacement of contaminated filters.

2. All filters should be installed to prevent leakage between the filter segments and between the filter bed and its supporting frame. A small leak that permits any contaminated air to escape through the filter can destroy the usefulness of the best air cleaner.

3. A manometer should be installed in the filter system to provide a reading of the pressure drop across each filter bank. This precaution furnishes a more accurate means of knowing when filters should be replaced than by relying on visual observation.

4. High-efficiency filters should be installed in the system with adequate facilities provided for maintenance without introducing contamination into the delivery system or the area served.

5. Because high-efficiency filters are expensive, the hospital should project the filter bed life and replacement costs, and incorporate these into their operating budget.

6. During construction, openings in ductwork and diffusers should be sealed to prevent intrusion of dust, dirt, and hazardous materials. Such contamination is often permanent and provides a medium for the growth of infectious agents. Existing or new filters may rapidly become contaminated by construction dust.

Air Movement

The data given in Table 2 illustrate the degree of contamination that can be dispersed into the air of the hospital environment by one of the many routine activities for normal patient care. The bacterial counts in the hallway also clearly indicate the spread of this contamination.

Because of these necessary activities and the resultant dispersal of bacteria, air-handling systems should provide air movement patterns that minimize the spread of such contamination.

The laminar airflow concept developed for industrial clean room use has attracted the interest of some medical authorities. There are advocates of both the vertical and horizontal laminar airflow systems with and without fixed or movable walls around the surgical team (Pfost 1981). Many medical authorities do not advocate laminar airflow for surgeries but encourage air systems similar to those in this chapter.

Laminar airflow in surgical operating rooms is defined as airflow that is predominantly unidirectional when not obstructed. The unidirectional laminar airflow pattern is commonly attained at a velocity of 90 $\pm$20 fpm (0.46 $\pm$0.10 m/s).

Michaelson et al. (1966) reported that laminar airflow systems have shown promise for rooms used for the treatment of patients who are highly susceptible to infection. Among such patients would be the badly burned and those undergoing radiation therapy, concentrated chemotherapy, organ transplants, amputations, and joint replacement. Bench-type units may be used to a great extent in such areas as pharmacy, tissue banks, and laboratories.

Controlling airflow in hospitals and other health facilities to minimize the spread of contaminants is desirable in design and operation. Undesirable flow of air between rooms and floors is often difficult to control because of open doors, movement of staff and patients, temperature differentials, and stack effect accentuated by vertical openings such as chutes, elevator shafts, stairwells, and mechanical shafts common to hospitals. While some of these factors are beyond practical control, the effect of others may be minimized by terminating shaft openings in enclosed rooms and by designing and balancing air systems to create positive or negative air pressure within certain rooms and areas.

Systems serving highly contaminated areas such as contagious isolation rooms and autopsy rooms should maintain a negative air pressure within these rooms relative to adjoining rooms or the corridor. The negative pressure is obtained by supplying less air to the area than is exhausted from it. This induces a flow of air into the area around the perimeters of doors and prevents an outward airflow. The operating room offers an example of an opposite condition. This room, which requires air that is free of contamination, must be pressurized relative to adjoining rooms or corridors to prevent any air movement into the operating room from these relatively highly contaminated areas.

Differentials in air pressure can be maintained only in an entirely closed room. Therefore it is important to obtain a reasonably close fit of all doors or closures of openings between pressurized areas. This is best accomplished by use of weatherstripping and drop bottoms on doors. The opening of a door or closure between two such areas instantaneously reduces any existing pressure differential between them to such a degree as to nullify the effectiveness of the pressure. When such openings occur, a natural interchange of air will take place because of thermal currents resulting from temperature differences between the two areas.

For critical areas requiring the maintenance of pressure differentials to adjacent spaces while providing for personnel movement between the spaces and areas, the use of appropriate air locks or anterooms, is indicated.

Figure 1 shows the bacterial count in a surgery room and its adjoining rooms during a normal surgical procedure. These bacterial counts were taken simultaneously in each of the rooms. The relatively low bacteria counts in the surgery room, compared with those of the adjoining rooms, are attributed to less activity within operating rooms and to higher air pressure.

In general, it is recommended that air supply outlets to sensitive ultraclean areas, as well as highly contaminated areas, be located on the ceiling with perimeter or several exhaust inlets near the floor. This provides a downward movement of clean air through the breathing and working zones to the contaminated floor area for exhaust. In this respect, the bottoms of return or exhaust openings should not be below 3 in. (75 mm) above the room floor.

The hospital departments cited are examples of a few of the areas that require specific air movement patterns. A thorough knowledge of the procedures in the many hospital areas and the effects of air contamination upon them, therefore, are important to the designer of air-handling systems.

DESIGN CRITERIA FOR PRINCIPAL AREAS OF AN ACUTE GENERAL HOSPITAL

These criteria do not cover engineering fundamentals or problems common to building construction, but rather present special conditions peculiar to health facilities and of interest to the engineer. Federal, state, and local codes should be consulted to determine requirements that may vary from normal standards.

Temperature and Humidity

Specific recommendations for design temperatures and humidities are given in the next section, "Specific Design Criteria by Department." Temperature and humidity requirements for other in-patient areas not covered should be 72 °F (22 °C) or less.

Table 2   Influence of Bedmaking on Airborne Bacterial Count of Hospitals

Item	Count Per Cubic Foot (Cubic Metre)	
	Inside Patient's Room	Hallway Near Patient's Room
Background	34 (1200)	30 (1060)
During bedmaking	140 (4940)	64 (2260)
10 min after	60 (2120)	40 (1470)
30 min after	36 (1270)	27 (950)
Background	16 (560)	
Normal bedmaking	100 (3520)	
Vigorous bedmaking	172 (6070)	

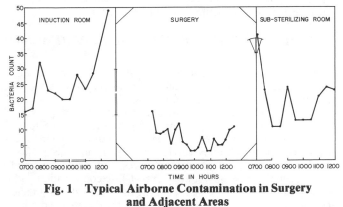

Fig. 1   Typical Airborne Contamination in Surgery and Adjacent Areas

For spaces of high population density or sensible heat factors of 0.75 or less, lower dry-bulb temperature results in generation of less latent heat, which may reduce the need for reheat and thus save energy. Optimum dry-bulb analysis should be the subject of detailed design analysis.

Pressure Relationships and Ventilation

Table 3 covers ventilation standards for comfort, as well as for asepsis and odor control, in areas of acute care hospitals that directly affect patient care. Table 3 does not necessarily reflect the criteria by DHHS or any other group. If specific organizational criteria must be met, refer to that organization's literature. Areas where specific standards are not given shall be ventilated in accordance with ASHRAE *Standard* 62-1981, "Ventilation for Acceptable Air Quality Including Requirements for Outside Air." Specialized patient care areas including organ transplant units, burn units, etc., shall have additional ventilation provisions for air quality control as may be appropriate (see the next section, "Specific Design Criteria by Department.")

Design of the ventilation system must, as much as possible, provide air movement that is from "clean to less clean" areas. However, continuous compliance may be impractical with the full use of some forms of variable air volume and load shedding systems used for energy conservation. In Table 3, those areas that require continuous control are noted with "P" or "N" for positive or negative pressure. Where ± is used, there is no requirement for continuous directional control.

The number of air changes may be reduced to 25% when the room is unoccupied if provisions are made to ensure that the number of air changes indicated is reestablished any time the space is occupied, and providing the pressure relationship to the surrounding rooms is maintained when the air changes are reduced.

Areas not indicated as requiring continuous directional control may have ventilation systems shut down when space is unoccupied and ventilation is not otherwise needed.

Because of the cleaning difficulty and potential for buildup of contamination, recirculating room units must not be used in areas marked "no". Note that the standard type recirculating room unit may also be impractical for primary control where exhaust to the outside is required. However, these may supplement the temperature controls unless otherwise prohibited. Isolation and Intensive Care rooms may be ventilated by reheat induction units in which only the primary air supplied from the central system passes through the reheat unit.

In rooms having hoods, extra air must be supplied for hood exhaust so that the designated pressure relationship is maintained.

For maximum energy conservation, use of a recirculated system is preferred. If an all-outdoor air system is used, an efficient heat recovery method should be considered.

SPECIFIC DESIGN CRITERIA BY DEPARTMENT

The environmental requirements of each of the departments/spaces within the five (chosen to organize discussion and not for definition) principal functions of an acute care general hospital, which include (1) Surgery and Critical Care, (2) Nursing, (3) Diagnostic and Treatment, (4) Sterilizing and Supply, and (5) Service, differ to some degree according to their function and the procedures carried out in them. This section describes how these departments/spaces are actually used and covers details of design requirements. Close coordination with health care planners is essential in the (mechanical) design and construction of health facilities to achieve the desired conditions.

Surgical Department

No area of the hospital requires more careful control of the aseptic condition of the environment than does the surgical suite. The systems serving the operating rooms, including cystoscopic and fracture rooms, require careful design to reduce to a minimum the concentration of airborne organisms. The greatest amount of the bacteria found in the operating room comes from the surgical team and as a result of their activities during an operation.

During an operation, most members of the surgical team are in the vicinity of the operating table, which creates the undesirable situation of concentrating contamination in this highly sensitive area.

Studies of operating room air-distribution systems and observation of installations in industrial clean rooms indicate that delivery of the air from the ceiling, with a downward movement to several exhaust inlets located on opposite walls, is probably the most effective air movement pattern for maintaining the concentration of contamination at an acceptable level. Completely perforated ceilings, partially perforated ceilings, and ceiling-mounted diffusers have been applied successfully (Pfost 1981).

Operating rooms. In the average hospital, operating rooms are not in use more than 8 to 12 hours per day, except on an emergency basis that may occur after normal hours. For this reason, and the need to conserve energy, the air-conditioning system should allow a reduction of air supplied to all or a portion of the operating rooms. However, positive space pressure should be maintained at reduced air volumes to ensure sterile conditions. Consultation with the hospital surgical staff will determine the feasibility of providing this feature.

A separate air-exhaust system or special vacuum system should be provided for removal of anesthetic trace gases (NIOSH 1975). One or more outlets in each operating room located to permit connection of the anesthetic machine scavenger hose may be used.

Although good results from air disinfection of operating rooms by irradiation have been reported, this method of disinfection is seldom used. The reluctance to use irradiation may be attributed to factors such as special designs required for installation, protective measures necessary for patients and personnel, constant vigilance relative to lamp efficiency, and the required maintenance.

The following conditions are recommended for operating, catheterization, cystoscopic, and fracture rooms:

1. Variable temperature range capability of 68 to 76 °F (20 to 24 °C).
2. Relative humidity of 50% minimum and 60% maximum.
3. Positive air pressure within the operating rooms relative to the pressure of any adjoining rooms by supplying 15% excess air.
4. Manometers installed to permit air pressure readings of the rooms. Thorough sealing of all wall, ceiling, and floor penetrations and tight-fitting doors are essential to maintain readable pressue.
5. Humidity indicator and thermometers located for easy observation.
6. Filter efficiencies in accordance with Table 1.
7. Entire installation to conform to the requirements of NFPA Standard 99-87, "Health Care Facilities."
8. Supply all air at or near the ceiling and exhaust air from at least two locations near the floor (see Table 3 for minimum ventilating rates). Bottom of exhaust outlets should be not less than 3 in. (75 mm) above the floor.
9. Acoustical materials should not be used as duct linings unless 90% efficient minimum terminal filters are installed downstream of the linings.

Table 3 General Pressure Relationships and Ventilation of Certain Hospital Areas

FUNCTION Area	Pressure Relationship to Adjacent Areas	Minimum Air Changes of Outdoor Air per Hour Supplied to Room	Minimum Total Air Changes per Hour Supplied to Room	All Air Exhausted Directly to Outdoors	Recirculated within Room Units
SURGERY AND CRITICAL CARE					
Operating Room (all-outdoor-air system)	P	15	15	Yes[1]	No
Operating Room (recirculating-air system)	P	5	25	Optional	No[2]
Recovery Room	P	2	6	Optional	No[2]
X-Ray	P	3	15	Optional	No
Delivery & Birthing	P	5	12	Optional	No[2]
Nursery Suite	P	5	12	Optional	No[2]
Trauma Room[3]	P	5	12	Optional	No[2]
Anesthesia Storage (see code requirements)	±	Optional	8	Yes	No
NURSING					
Patient Room	±	2	2	Optional	Optional
Toilet Room[4]	N	Optional	10	Yes	No
Intensive Care	P	2	6	Optional	No
Isolation[5]	±	2	6	Yes	No
Isolation Alcove or Anteroom[5]	±	2	10	Yes	No
Patient Corridor	±	2	4	Optional	Optional
DIAGNOSTIC AND TREATMENT					
Examination Room	±	2	6	Optional	Optional
Medication Room	P	2	4	Optional	Optional
Pharmacy	P	2	4	Optional	Optional
Treatment Room	±	2	6	Optional	Optional
X-Ray	±	2	6	Optional	Optional
Physical Therapy and Hydrotherapy	N	2	6	Optional	Optional
Soiled Workroom or Soiled Holding	N	2	10	Yes	No
Clean Workroom or Clean Holding	P	2	4	Optional	Optional
Autopsy	N	2	12	Yes	No
Darkroom	N	2	10	Optional	No
Nonrefrigerated Body Holding Room[6]	N	Optional	10	Yes	No
Laboratory, general					
Bacteriology	N	2	6	Yes	No
Biochemistry	P	2	6	Optional	No
Cytology	N	2	6	Yes	No
Glasswashing	N	2	10	Yes	Optional
Histology	N	2	6	Yes	No
Nuclear Medicine	N	2	6	Yes	No
Pathology	N	2	6	Yes	No
Serology	P	2	6	Optional	No
Sterilizing	N	Optional	10	Yes	No
Laboratory, media transfer	P	2	4	Optional	No[2]
STERILIZING AND SUPPLY					
Sterilizer Equipment Room	N	Optional	10	Yes	No
Linen and Trash Chute Room	N	Optional	10	Yes	No
Laundry, General	±	2	10	Yes	No
Soiled Linen Sorting and Storage	N	Optional	10	Yes	No
Clean Linen Storage	P	2 (Optional)	2	Optional	Optional
Central Medical & Surgical Supply					
Soiled or Decontamination Room	N	2	6	Yes	No
Clean Workroom and Sterile Storage	P	2	4	Optional	Optional
Equipment Storage	±	2 (Optional)	2	Optional	Optional
SERVICE					
Food Preparation Centers[7]	±	2	10	Yes	No
Warewashing	N	Optional	10	Yes	No
Dietary Day Storage	±	Optional	2	Optional	No
Bedpan Room	N	Optional	10	Yes	No
Bathroom	N	Optional	10	Optional	No
Janitors Closet	N	Optional	10	Optional	No

P = Positive   N = Negative   ± = Continuous Directional Control Not Required

Notes for Table 3

[1]For operating rooms, use of 100% outside air should be limited to those cases where local codes require it, only if heat recovery devices are used.

[2]Recirculating room units meeting the filtering requirement for the space may be used.

[3]The term "trauma room" used here is the operating room space in the trauma center that is routinely used for emergency surgery. The first air room and/or "emergency room" used for general initial treatment of accidental victims may be ventilated as noted for the "treatment room."

[4]Most existing governmental agency design criteria and codes require all air from toilet rooms to be exhausted directly outdoors. This requirement appears to be based on odor control. Practical experience has shown that health facilities, with the possible exception of nursing homes, having central toilet exhaust systems generally have sufficient dilution to render the toilet exhaust air practically odorless. For this reason, plus the need to conserve energy, it is recommended that consideration be given, with agency approval, to recirculation of up to 50% of toilet room air where central systems with appropriate conditioning and filtering equipment are employed.

[5]The isolation rooms described in these standards are those that might be used in the average community hospital. The assumption is made that the isolation procedures will be for infectious patients and that the room should also be suitable for normal private patient use when not needed for isolation. This compromise does not provide for ideal isolation. The designer should consider types and numbers of patients that might need this separation within the facility. When need is indicated by program, it may be desirable to provide more complete control with a separate ante-room as an air lock to minimize potential for airborne particulates from the patients' area reaching adjacent areas. Certain types of patients such as organ transplants, burn victims, etc., will require special considerations, including reverse isolation. Where these are part of the anticipated patient load, ventilation shall be modified, as necessary. *Variable exhaust that allows maximum room space flexibility with reversible airflow direction would be useful only if appropriate adjustments can be ensured for different types of isolation procedures.*

[6]The non-refrigerated body-holding room would be applicable only for facilities that do not perform autopsies on site and use the space for short periods while waiting for body transfer to be completed.

[7]Food Preparation Centers shall have ventilation systems that have an excess of air supply for positive pressure when hoods are not in operation. The number of air changes may be reduced or varied to any extent required for odor control when the space is not in use.

---

10. Any spray-applied insulation and fire proofing should be treated with fungi growth inhibitor.

Control centers that monitor and permit adjustment to temperature, humidity, and air pressure may be located at the surgical supervisor's desk.

Recovery Rooms. Postoperative recovery rooms used in conjunction with the operating rooms should be maintained at a temperature of 75 °F (24 °C) and a relative humidity of 50% minimum and 60% maximum. Because residual anesthesia odor and nausea resulting from anesthesia sometimes create an odor problem in recovery rooms, ventilation is important, and a balanced air pressure relative to the air pressure of adjoining areas should be provided.

Anesthesia Storage Room. The anesthesia storage room must be ventilated in conformance with NFPA Standard 99-87, "Health Care Facilities." However, mechanical ventilation only is recommended.

Obstetrical Department

The systems designed for the delivery suite should conform to the requirements for surgical suites, except that ventilation rates may vary.

Nursery

Air conditioning is essential for nurseries to provide the constant temperature and humidity conditions essential to care of the newborn in a hospital environment. The air movement patterns in nurseries should be carefully designed to reduce the possibility of drafts.

All air supplied to nurseries should be at or near the ceiling and all air should be removed near the floor with bottom of openings located not less than 3 in. (75 mm) above the floor. Air system filter efficiencies should conform to Table 1.

Full-term Nursery. A temperature of 75 °F (24 °C) with relative humidity from 30% minimum to 60% maximum is recommended for the full-term nursery, examination room, and work space. The maternity nursing section should be treated similarly to protect the infant during visits with the mother. The nursery should have a positive air pressure relative to the work space and examination room, and the rooms usually interposed between the nurseries and the corridor should be similarly pressurized relative to the corridor. This will prevent the infiltration of contaminated air from outside areas.

Special Care Nursery. The design conditions for this nursery require a variable range temperature capability from 75 to 80 °F (24 to 27 °C) and relative humidity from 30% minimum to 60% maximum. This nursery is usually equipped with individual incubators to regulate temperature and humidity. It is desirable to maintain these same conditions within the nursery proper to accommodate infants removed from the incubators, as well as those not placed in incubators. The pressurization of these nurseries should correspond to that of the regular nurseries.

Observation Nursery. Temperature and humidity requirements for this nursery are similar to those for the full-term nursery. Because infants in these nurseries have unusual clinical symptoms, the air from this area should not enter other nurseries. A negative air pressure relative to the air pressure of the workroom should be maintained in the nursery, and the workroom usually interposed between the nursery and the corridor should be pressurized relative to the corridor.

Emergency Department

This department, in most instances, will be the most highly contaminated area in the hospital, as a result of the soiled condition of many patients upon arrival and the relatively large numbers of persons accompanying them. Table 3 gives the ventilation requirements of the trauma rooms in this department. The temperature and humidity requirements of the trauma room are the same as those of the operating rooms in the surgical suites. Waiting rooms require a minimum ventilation rate of 10 air changers per hour. Temperatures and humidities of offices and waiting spaces should be within the comfort range. A negative air pressure should be maintained in the waiting room.

Nursing Department

Patient Rooms. The recommendations given in Tables 1 and 3 for air filtration and air change rates should be followed closely when using central systems for air conditioning patients' rooms to reduce cross-infection and for odor control. Rooms used for isolation of infected patients should have all air exhausted directly to outdoors. A winter design temperature of 75 °F (24 °C) and 30% relative humidity is recommended; 75 °F (24 °C) and 50% relative humidity is recommended for summer.

Where room-unit-type systems are used, it is common practice to exhaust an amount of air equal to the amount of outdoor air brought into the room for ventilation through the adjoining toilet room. The ventilation of toilets, bedpan closets, bathrooms, and all interior rooms should conform to applicable codes.

Intensive Care Unit. This unit will serve seriously ill patients with a variety of clinical conditions ranging from the postoperative to the coronary patient. A variable range temperature capability of 75 to 80 °F (24 to 27 °C) and a relative humidity of 30% minimum and 60% maximum with a positive air pressure is recommended.

Immunely Suppressed Patient Units. (This includes Bone Marrow or Organ Transplant, Leukemia, Burn, Acquired Immune

Deficiency Syndrome Patients, etc.) Such patients are highly susceptible to diseases. Some physicians prefer an isolated laminar airflow unit to protect the patient. Others are of the opinion that the conditions of the laminar cell have psychologically harmful effects upon the patient and prefer flushing out the room and reducing spores in the air. An air distribution of 15 air changes supplied through a nonaspirating diffuser is often recommended. The sterile air is drawn across the patient and returned near the floor, at or near the door to the room.

In cases where the patient is only immunely suppressed, a positive pressure should be maintained between the patient room and adjacent area. Some jurisdictions may require an anteroom, which maintains a negative pressure relationship with respect to the adjacent isolation room and an equal pressure relationship with respect to the corridor, nurse's station, or common area. Exam and treatment rooms should be treated in the same manner. A positive pressure should also be maintained between the entire unit and the adjacent areas to maintain a high sterile condition.

When a patient is both immunely suppressed and contagious, isolation rooms within the unit may be permanently designed and balanced to provide an equal or negative pressure relationship with respect to the adjacent area or anteroom. Alternatively, when permitted by the jurisdictional authority, such isolation rooms may be equipped with controls to enable the room to be either positive, equal, or negative in relation to the adjacent area. However, in such instances, controls in the adjacent area or anteroom must maintain the correct pressure relationship with respect to the other adjacent room(s).

A separate, dedicated air-handling system to serve the Immunely Suppressed Patient Unit simplifies pressure control and quality of air.

Isolation Unit. The isolation room, unless located in a strictly contagious disease ward, should be designed for a two-fold purpose. When occupied by an infectious disease patient, as those in a contagious disease ward, it should protect other patients from the disease. When occupied by a patient with very low resistance to infection such as burn, leukemia, bone marrow or organ transplant, or Acquired Immune Deficiency Syndrom patients, it should protect the occupant from the normal bacterial flora of the remainder of the hospital. To accomplish the dual purpose, it is necessary that an anteroom, to serve as an airlock, be interposed between the patient room and the hospital corridor. For reverse isolation, an alternative to an airlock is an open-wall-type patient isolator with an integral recirculating fan and HEPA filters. Also, there should be a procedure for safe removal and replacement of contaminated filters.

Filters of 90% efficiency should be used in the system serving the isolation room with all exhaust air discharged to the outdoors. The air pressure of the dual-purpose room should be maintained at the same air pressure as its anteroom and the corridor. The air pressure of isolation rooms used solely for infectious disease patients should be maintained at a negative air pressure relative to the air pressure of adjoining areas. Temperatures and humidities should correspond to those specified for patient rooms.

Treatment Rooms. Patients are brought to these rooms for special treatments that cannot be conveniently performed in the patient rooms. To accommodate the patient who may be brought from bed, the rooms should have individual temperature and humidity control. Temperatures and humidities should correspond to those specified for patients' rooms. The air pressure of the room should be maintained at the same pressure as that of the corridor.

Clean Workrooms. The clean workroom serves as a storage

and distribution center for clean supplies and should be maintained at a positive air pressure relative to the corridor.

The soiled workroom serves primarily as a collection point for soiled utensils and materials. It is considered a contaminated room and should have a negative air pressure relative to the air pressure of adjoining areas. Temperatures and humidities should be provided within the comfort range.

Floor Pantry. Ventilation requirements of this area depend upon the type of food service adopted by the hospital. Where bulk food is dispensed and dishwashing facilities are provided in the pantry, the use of hoods over equipment, with exhaust to the outdoors, is recommended. Small pantries used for between-meal feedings require no special ventilation. The air pressure of the pantry should be in balance with that of adjoining areas to reduce the movement of air into or out of it.

Diagnostic and Treatment Facilities

This area includes the following departments: (1) laboratory, (2) pathology, (3) radiology, (4) physical therapy, (5) occupational therapy, and (6) inhalation therapy.

Laboratories. Air conditioning for comfort and safety of the technicians is necessary in the laboratories (Degenhardt and Pfost 1983). Chemical fumes, odors, vapors, heat from the equipment, and the undesirability of open windows all contribute to this need.

Particular attention should be given to the sizes and types of equipment used in the various laboratories. The heat gain from equipment usually constitutes the major portion of the cooling load.

The general air-distribution and return systems should be constructed of conventional materials following standard designs for the type of systems used. Exhaust ducts serving hoods in which radioactive materials, volatile solvents, and strong oxidizing agents such as perchloric acid are used, should be fabricated of stainless steel for a minimum distance of 10 ft (3 m) from the hood outlet. Washdown facilities should be provided for hoods and ducts handling perchloric acid.

Hood use may dictate other duct materials. Hoods in which radioactive or infectious materials are to be used must be equipped with ultrahigh-efficiency filters at the exhaust outlet of the hood and have equipment and a procedure for the safe removal and replacement of contaminated filters. Exhaust duct routing should be as short as possible with a minimum of horizontal offsets. This is especially true for perchloric acid hoods because of the extremely hazardous explosive nature of this material.

Determining the most effective, economical, and safest system of laboratory ventilation requires considerable study. Where the laboratory space ventilation air quantities approximate the air quantities required for ventilation of the hoods, the hood exhaust system may be used to exhaust all ventilation air from the laboratory areas. In situations where hood exhaust exceeds air supplied, a supplementary air supply for hood make-up may be used.

This supplementary air supply, which need not be completely conditioned, should be provided by a system which is independent of the normal ventilating system. The individual hood exhaust system should be interlocked with the supplementary air system. However, should failure of the supplementary air system occur, the hood exhaust system should not shut off. Chemical storage rooms must have an individual exhaust air system with terminal fan.

Exhaust fans serving hoods should be located at the discharge end of the duct system to prevent any possibility of exhaust products entering the building. For further information on laboratory air conditioning and hood exhaust systems, see Chapter 30 of this volume, NFPA Standard 99-87, "Health Care

Facilities," and "Control of Hazardous Gases and Vapors in Selected Hospital Laboratories," by Hagopian and Doyle (1984).

The exhaust air from the hoods in the unit for biochemistry, histology, cytology, pathology, glass-washing-sterilizing, and serology-bacteriology should be discharged to the outdoors with no recirculation. The serology-bacteriology unit should be pressurized relative to the adjoining areas to reduce the possibility of infiltration of aerosols that might contaminate the specimens being processed. The entire laboratory area should be under slight negative pressure to reduce the spread of odors or contamination to other hospital areas. Temperatures and humidities should be within the comfort range.

Bacteriology Units should not have undue air movement, and care should be exercised to limit air velocities to a minimum. The sterile transfer room, which may be within or adjoining the bacteriology laboratory, is a room where sterile media are distributed and where specimens are transferred to culture media. To maintain a sterile environment, an ultrahigh-efficiency HEPA filter should be installed in the supply air duct near the point of entry to the room. The media room, essentially a kitchen, should be ventilated to remove odors and steam.

Infectious Disease and Virus Laboratories, found only in large hospitals, require special treatment. A minimum ventilation rate of six air changes per hour or make-up equal to hood exhaust volume is recommended for these laboratories, which should have a negative air pressure relative to any other area in the vicinity to prevent the exfiltration of any airborne contaminants from them. The exhaust air from fume hoods or safety cabinets in these laboratories require sterilization before being exhausted to the outdoors. This may be accomplished by the use of electric or gas-fired heaters placed in series in the exhaust systems, and designed to heat the exhaust air to 600 °F (315 °C). A more common and less expensive method of sterilization of exhaust is to use ultrahigh-efficiency filters in the system. Sterilization of hoods is also accomplished with integral steam formaldehyde spray systems.

Nuclear Medicine Laboratories administer radioisotopes to patients orally, intravenously, or by inhalation to facilitate diagnosis and treatment of human disease. There is little opportunity in most cases for airborne contamination of the internal environment, but exceptions warrant special consideration.

One important exception involves use of iodine-131 solution in vials or capsules to diagnose disorders of the thyroid gland (among occasional uses). Another involves use of xenon-133 gas via inhalation to study patients with reduced lung function. Capsules of iodine-133 occasionally leak part of their contents prior to use. Vials emit airborne contaminants when opened for preparation of a dose.

It is apparently common practice for vials to be opened and handled in a standard laboratory fume hood. A minimum face velocity of 100 fpm (0.5 m/s) should be adequate for this purpose. This recommendation applies only where the stated quantities are handled in simple operations. Other circumstances may warrant provision of a glovebox or similar confinement.

Use of xenon-133 for patient study involves a special instrument that permits the patient to inhale the gas and to exhale back into the instrument. The exhaled gas is passed through a charcoal trap mounted in lead and then often (but not always) vented outdoors. The process suggests some potential for escape of the gas into the internal environment.

Due to the uniqueness of this operation and the specialized equipment involved, it is recommended that system designers determine the specific instrument to be used and contact the manufacturer for guidance. Other guidance is available in the U.S. Nuclear Regulatory Commission (USNRC) Regulatory Guide 10.8 (1980). In particular, emergency procedures to be followed in case of accidental release of xenon-133 should include such considerations as temporary evacuation of the area and/or increasing the ventilation rate of the area.

Prior recommendations concerning pressure relationships, supply air filtration, supply air volume, no recirculation, and other attributes of supply and discharge systems for histology, pathology, and cytology laboratories are also relevant to nuclear medicine laboratories. There are, however, some special general ventilation system requirements imposed by the USNRC where radioactive materials are used. For example, USNRC Regulatory Guide 10.8 (1980) provides a computational procedure to estimate the airflow necessary to maintain xenon-133 gas concentration at or below specified levels. It also contains specific requirements as to the amount of radioactivity that may be vented to the atmosphere (with the disposal method of choice being adsorption onto charcoal traps).

Pathology Department. The areas of the pathology section that require special attention are the autopsy room and, in larger hospitals, the animal quarters.

Autopsy Rooms are subject to heavy bacterial contamination and odor. The exhaust system should discharge the air above the roof of the hospital. A negative air pressure relative to the air pressure of adjoining areas should be provided in the autopsy room to prevent the spread of this contamination. For smaller hospitals where the autopsy room is used infrequently, it may be desirable to provide local control of the ventilation system and odor control system with either activated charcoal or potassium permanganate impregnated activated alumina.

Animal Quarters, principally because of odor, require a mechanical exhaust system that discharges the contaminated air above the hospital roof. To prevent the spread of odor or other contaminants from the animal quarters to other areas, a negative air pressure of not less than 0.1 in. of water (25 Pa), relative to the air pressure of adjoining areas, must be maintained. Chapter 30 has further information on animal room air conditioning.

Radiology Department. The fluoroscopic, radiographic, therapy, and darkroom areas require special attention. Among conditions that make positive ventilation mandatory in these areas are the odorous characteristics of certain clinical conditions treated, special construction designed to prevent ray leakage, and lightproof window shades that reduce any natural light infiltration to the fluoroscopic area.

Fluoroscopic, Radiographic, and Deep Therapy Rooms require temperatures of 75 to 80 °F (24 to 27 °C) and humidity of 40 to 50%. Depending on the location of air supply outlets and exhaust intakes, lead lining may be required in supply and return ducts at the points of entry to the various clinical areas to prevent ray leakage to other occupied areas.

The darkroom normally is in use for longer periods than the X-ray rooms and should have an independent system to exhaust the air to the outdoors. The exhaust from the film drier may be connected into the darkroom exhaust. To maintain the integrity of the film during processing, a 90% efficiency filter should be installed in the air supply system for this area.

Physical Therapy Department. The cooling load of the electrotherapy section will be affected by the shortwave diathermy, infrared, and ultraviolet equipment used in this area.

Hydrotherapy Section. This section, with its various water treatment baths, generally is maintained at temperatures up to 80 °F (27 °C). The potential latent heat buildup in this area should not be overlooked. The exercise section will require no special treatment, and temperatures and humidities may be within the comfort zone. The air of these areas may be recirculated within the areas, and an odor-control system is suggested.

Occupational Therapy Department. In this department, spaces for activities such as weaving, braiding, artwork, and sewing require no special ventilation treatment. Recirculation of air of these areas using medium-grade filters in the system is permissible.

Larger hospitals or those specializing in rehabilitation have a greater diversification of skills and crafts such as carpentry, metalwork, plastics, photography, ceramics, and painting.

The air-conditioning and ventilation requirements of the various sections should conform to normal practice for such areas and to the code requirements relating to them. Temperatures and humidities should be maintained within the comfort zone.

Pharmacy. The pharmacy should be treated for comfort and will require no special ventilation. Laminar airflow benches may be needed in pharmacies that prepare intravenous solutions.

Inhalation Therapy Department. Inhalation therapy is for treatment of pulmonary and other respiratory disorders. The air must be very clean and the area should have a positive air pressure relative to adjacent areas.

Central Sterilizing and Supply

Used and contaminated utensils, instruments, and equipment are brought to this unit for cleaning and sterilization prior to reuse. The unit usually consists of a cleaning area, a sterilizing area, and a storage area where supplies are kept until requisitioned. Where these areas are in one large room, it is desirable to maintain an airflow from the clean storage and sterilizing areas toward to contaminated cleaning area for exhaust. The air pressure relationships should conform to those indicated in Table 3. Temperature and humidity within the comfort range is recommended.

The following guidelines are important in the central sterilizing and supply unit:

1. Insulate sterilizers in these areas to reduce heat load.
2. Amply ventilate sterilizer equipment closets to remove excess heat.
3. Where ethylene oxide gas sterilizers are used, provide a separate exhaust system with terminal fan (Samuals and Eastin 1980). Provide adequate exhaust capture velocity in the vicinity of sources of ethylene oxide leakage. Install an exhaust at sterilizer doors and over sterilizer drain. Exhaust aerator and service rooms. Also, ethylene oxide concentration, exhaust flow sensors, and alarms should be provided (OSHA).
4. Maintain storage areas for sterile supplies at a relative humidity of not more than 50%.

Service Department

Service areas include dietary, housekeeping, mechanical, and employee facilities. Whether these areas are air conditioned or not, adequate ventilation is important to provide sanitation and a wholesome environment. Ventilation of these areas cannot be limited to exhaust systems only; provision for supply air must be incorporated in the design. Such air must be filtered and delivered at controlled temperatures. The best design exhaust system may prove ineffective without an adequate air supply. Experience has shown that reliance on open windows results only in dissatisfaction, particularly during the heating season. The incorporation of air-to-air heat exchangers in the general ventilation system offers possibilities for economical operation in these areas.

Dietary Facility. This area usually includes the main kitchen, bakery, dietitian's office, dishwashing room, and dining space. Because of the various conditions encountered (*i.e.,* high heat and moisture production and cooking odors), special attention in design is needed to provide an acceptable environment. Kitchen ventilation should conform to local codes. In many in-

stances, hood exhaust quantities may dictate the quantity of supply air required.

Cooking equipment is usually grouped in one or more locations within the kitchen for efficient use. Hoods are provided over the equipment for removal of heat, odors, and vapors in accordance with code requirements. The entire system shall conform to the requirements of NFPA *Standard* 96-84, "Installation of Equipment for the Removal of Smoke and Grease-Laden Vapors from Commercial Cooking Equipment."

The dietitian's office is often located within the main kitchen or immediately adjacent to it. It is usually completely enclosed to ensure privacy and noise reduction. Air conditioning is recommended for the maintenance of normal comfort conditions.

The dishwashing room should be enclosed and ventilated at a minimum rate to equal the dishwasher hood exhaust. It is not uncommon for the dishwashing area to be divided into a soiled area and a clean area. When this is done, the soiled area should be kept negative to the clean area.

Depending on the size of the area, all or the greatest part of exhaust air may be taken off through the dishwasher hood. Exhaust ductwork should be noncorrosive and watertight to handle condensation of steam and should be graded to drip into a convenient drain.

Kitchen Compressor/Condenser Space. Ventilation of this space should conform to all codes with the following additional considerations: (1) Use 350 cfm of ventilating air per compressor horsepower (220 L/s per kW) for units located within the kitchen; (2) Condensing units should operate optimally at 90 °F (32.2 °C) maximum ambient temperature; and (3) Where air temperature or air circulation is marginal, combination air and water-cooled condensing units should be specified. It is often worthwhile to use condenser water coolers or remote condensers.

Dining Space. The ventilation of this space should conform to local codes. The reuse of dining space air for ventilation and cooling of food preparation areas in the hospital is suggested, providing the reused air is passed through 80% efficient filters. Where cafeteria service is provided, serving areas and steam tables are usually hooded. The air-handling capacities of these hoods should be at least 75 cfm/ft² (380 L/s per m²) of the perimeter area.

Housekeeping Facilities. Of these facilities, the soiled linen storage room, soiled linen sorting room, soiled utility room, and laundry processing area only require special attention.

The *soiled linen storage room,* provided for storage of soiled linen prior to pickup by commercial laundry, will be odorous and contaminated and should be well ventilated and maintained at a negative air pressure.

The *soiled linen storage and sorting room* provides in-house laundry service. The activities associated with sorting linen are reported to add heavily to the contamination of the laundry air, which, in turn, recontaminates the processed linens during the folding prior to return to the patient floors. To reduce this contamination, linen should be sorted in a room completely separated from the laundry processing area. The sorting room should be maintained at a negative air pressure relative to adjoining areas with all exhaust air discharged outdoors. The soiled utility room is provided for in-patient services and is normally contaminated with noxious odors. This room should be exhausted directly outside by mechanical means.

In the *laundry processing area,* the washers, flatwork ironers, tumblers, etc., should have direct overhead exhaust to reduce humidity. Such equipment should be insulated or shielded whenever possible to reduce the high radiant-heat effects. A canopy over the flatwork ironer and exhaust air outlets near other heat-producing equipment capture and remove heat best. The air supply inlets should be located to move air through the processing area toward the heat-producing equipment. The exhaust system from flat work stoners and from tumblers should be independent of the general exhaust system and should be equipped with lint filters. Air should exhaust above the roof or where it will not be obnoxious to other areas. Heat reclamation of the laundry exhaust air may be desirable and practicable.

Where air conditioning is contemplated, a separate supplementary air supply, similar to that recommended for kitchen hoods, may be located in the vicinity of the exhaust canopy over the ironer, or spot cooling for the relief of personnel confined to specific areas should be considered.

Mechanical Facilities. The air supply to boiler rooms should provide both comfortable working conditions and the air quantities required for maximum combustion rates of the particular fuel used. Boiler and burner ratings establish maximum combustion rates, so the air quantities can be computed according to the type of fuel. Sufficient air must be supplied to the boiler room to supply the exhaust fans, as well as boilers.

At working stations, the ventilation system should limit temperatures to 90 °F (32 °C) effective temperature (see the 1986 ASHRAE *Terminology of HVAC&R*) for a definition of effective temperature. When ambient outside air temperature is higher, maximum temperature may be that of outside air up to a maximum of 97 °F (36 °C).

Maintenance Shops, such as carpentry, machine, electrical, and plumbing shops, present no unusual ventilation requirements. Proper ventilation of paint shops and paint storage areas is important because of fire hazard and should conform to all applicable codes.

Employees' Facilities. These rooms should be treated to provide comfort and to conform to local codes.

Administration Department

This department includes the main lobby, admitting and business offices, and medical records. This area requires no unusual treatment and should be conditioned for occupant comfort. A separate air-handling system is considered desirable to segregate this area from the hospital proper.

CONTINUITY OF SERVICE AND ENERGY CONCEPTS

Zoning

Zoning of the air-handling systems may be desirable to compensate for exposures due to orientation or for other reasons imposed by a particular building configuration. Zoning—using separate air systems for different departments—may be indicated to minimize recirculation between departments, provide flexibility of operation, simplify provisions for operation on emergency power, and conserve energy.

By manifolding the air supply from several air-handling units, central systems can achieve a measure of standby capacity. To accommodate critical areas, which must operate continuously, air is diverted from noncritical or intermittently operated areas when one unit is shut down. Such provision or other means of standby protection is essential if the air supply is not to be interrupted by routine maintenance or component failure.

Separation of supply, return, and exhaust systems by department is often desirable; particularly for surgical, obstetrical, pathological, and laboratory departments. The desired relative balance within critical areas should be maintained by interlocking the supply and exhaust fans. For example, the surgical department exhaust should cease when the supply airflow is stopped.

Heating and Hot Water Standby Service

The number and arrangement of boilers should be such that when one boiler breaks down or routine maintenance requires that one boiler be temporarily taken out of service, the capacity of the remaining boilers is sufficient to provide hot water ser-

vice for clinical, dietary, and patient use; steam for sterilization and dietary purposes; and heating for operating, delivery, birthing, labor, recovery, intensive care, nursery, and general patient rooms. However, reserve capacity is not required in areas where a design dry-bulb temperature of 25 °F (−4 °C) represents no less than 99% of the total hours in any one heating period as noted in the Table of Climatic Conditions of the United States in Chapter 24 of the 1985 FUNDAMENTALS Volume.

Boiler feed pumps, heating circulating pumps, condensate return pumps, and fuel oil pumps should be connected and installed to provide normal and standby service. Supply and return mains and risers of cooling, and heating and process steam systems should be valved to isolate the various sections. Each piece of equipment should be valved at the supply and return ends.

Insulation

All hot piping, ducts, and equipment exposed to contact by the building occupants should be insulated to maintain the energy efficiency of all systems. To prevent condensation, ducts, casings, piping, and equipment with outside surface temperature below ambient dew point should be covered with insulation with an external vapor barrier. Insulation, including finishes and adhesives, on the exterior surfaces of ducts, pipes, and equipment, should have a flame spread rating of 25 or less and a smoke developed rating of 50 or less, as determined by an independent testing laboratory in accordance with NFPA National Fire Code 255-84 as required by NFPA 90A-85. Smoke development rating for pipe insulation should not exceed 150 (DHHS 1984a).

Linings in air ducts and equipment should meet the Erosion Test Method described in Underwriters' Laboratories Inc., Standard 181-81. These linings, including coatings and adhesives, and insulation on exterior surfaces of pipes and ducts in building spaces used as air supply plenums, should have a flame spread rating of 25 or less and a smoke developed rating of 50 or less, as determined by an independent testing laboratory in accordance with ASTM Standard E 84.

Duct linings should not be used in systems supplying operating rooms, delivery rooms, recovery rooms, nurseries, burn care units, and intensive care units, unless terminal filters of at least 90% efficiency are installed downstream of linings.

When modifying existing systems, asbestos materials should be handled and disposed of in accordance with applicable regulations.

Energy

Health care is an energy-intensive, energy-dependent enterprise. Hospital facilities are different from other structures because they are in operation 24 hours a day year-round, require sophisticated backup systems in case of utility shutdowns, use large quantities of outside air to combat odors and dilute microorganisms, and must deal with problems of infection and solid waste disposal. Similarly, large quantities of energy power the diagnostic, therapeutic, and monitoring equipment, and the support services (food storage, preparation and service, laundry facilities, etc.) that are essential to the efficient functioning of a major hospital.

Many hospitals conserve energy in various ways such as larger energy storage tanks, energy-saving measures, and energy conversion devices that transfer energy from hot or cold exhaust air from the building to heat or cool incoming air. Heat pipes, runaround loops, and other forms of heat recovery are receiving increased attention. A common project is a solid waste incinerator, which generates exhaust heat to develop steam for laundries and hot water for patient care.

The construction design of new facilities, including alterations of, and additions to, existing buildings, has a major influence on the amount of energy required to provide such services as heating, cooling, and lighting. The selection of building and system components for effective energy use requires careful planning and design. Integration of building waste heat into systems and with renewable energy sources such as solar under some climatic conditions will provide substantial savings (Setty 1976). ASHRAE *Standard* 90A-1980 should also be considered for applicability.

NURSING HOMES

Nursing homes may be classified as follows:

Extended Care Facilities for recuperation of hospital patients who no longer require hospital facilities but do require therapeutic and rehabilitation services by skilled nurses. This type is either a direct hospital adjunct or a separate facility having close ties with the hospital. Clientele may be any age, usually stay from 35 to 40 days, and usually have only one diagnostic problem.

Skilled Nursing Homes for care of people who require assistance in daily activities, many of whom are incontinent and nonambulatory, and some of whom are disoriented. These homes may or may not offer skilled nursing care. Clientele come directly from home or residential care homes, generally are elderly (average age of 80), stay an average of 47 months, and frequently have multiple diagnostic problems.

Residential Care Homes are generally for the elderly who are unable to cope with regular housekeeping chores but are able to care for all their personal needs, lead normal lives, have no acute ailments, and move freely in and out of the home and the community. These homes may or may not offer skilled nursing care. The average length of stay is four years or more.

Functionally, these buildings have five types of areas that are of concern to the designer: (1) administrative and supportive areas, inhabited by the staff; (2) patient areas that provide direct normal daily services; (3) treatment areas that provide special medical-type services; (4) clean work rooms for storage and distribution of clean supplies; and (5) soiled work rooms for collection of soiled and contaminated supplies and for sanitization of non-laundry items.

DESIGN CONCEPTS AND CRITERIA

Bacteria level in nursing homes does not command the same level of concern as it does in the acute care hospital. Nevertheless, the designer should be aware of the necessity for odor control, filtration, and airflow control between certain areas.

Table 4 lists recommended filter efficiencies for air systems serving specific nursing home areas. Table 5 lists recommended

Table 4 Filter Efficiencies for Central Ventilation and Air-Conditioning Systems in Nursing Homes[a]

Area Designation	Minimum Number of Filter Beds	Filter Efficiences (Percent) Main Filter Bed
Patient Care, Treatment, Diagnostic and Related Areas	1	80
Food Preparation Areas and Laundries	1	80
Administrative, Bulk Storage, and Soiled Holding Areas	1	30

[a]Ratings based on ASHRAE *Standard* 52-76.

Table 5 Pressure Relationships and Ventilation of Certain Areas of Nursing Homes

FUNCTION Area	Pressure Relationship to Adjacent Areas	Minimum Air Changes of Outdoor Air per Hour Supplied to Room	Minimum Total Air Changes per Hour Supplied to Room	All Air Exhausted Directly to Outdoors	Recirculated within Room Units
PATIENT CARE					
Patient Room	±	2	2	Optional	Optional
Patient Area Corridor	±	Optional	2	Optional	Optional
Toilet Room	N	Optional	10	Yes	No
DIAGNOSTIC AND TREATMENT					
Examination Room	±	2	6	Optional	Optional
Physical Therapy	N	2	6	Optional	Optional
Occupational Therapy	N	2	6	Optional	Optional
Soiled Workroom or Soiled Holding	N	2	10	Yes	No
Clean Workroom or Clean Holding	P	2	4	Optional	Optional
STERILIZING AND SUPPLY					
Sterilizer Exhaust Room	N	Optional	10	Yes	No
Linen and Trash Chute Room	N	Optional	10	Yes	No
Laundry, General	±	2	10	Yes	No
Soiled Linen Sorting and Storage	N	Optional	10	Yes	No
Clean Linen Storage	P	Optional	2	Yes	No
SERVICE					
Food Preparation Center	±	2	10	Yes	Yes
Warewashing Room	N	Optional	10	Yes	Yes
Dietary Day Storage	±	Optional	2	Yes	No
Janitor Closet	N	Optional	10	Yes	No
Bathroom	N	Optional	10	Yes	No

P = Positive   N = Negative   ± = Continuous Directional Control Not Required

minimum ventilation rates and desired pressure relationships for certain areas in nursing homes.

Recommended interior winter design temperature for areas occupied by patients is 75 °F (24 °C) and 70 °F (21 °C) for non-patient areas. Provisions for maintenance of minimum humidity levels for winter depend upon the severity of the climate and is best left to the judgment of the designer. Where air conditioning is provided, the recommended interior summer design temperature and humidity is 75 °F (24 °C), and 50% rh.

The general design criteria under the subheadings, "Heating and Hot Water Standby Service," "Insulation," and "Energy" for the acute care general hospital apply equally to nursing.

APPLICABILITY OF SYSTEMS

System applicability for nursing homes should be determined largely by analysis of the following items:

1. The nature and condition of the occupants
2. The required environment
3. The local climatic conditions
4. Energy conservation
5. System and operational costs

The occupants are usually frail, and many are incontinent. They may be ambulatory, but some are bedridden, with illnesses in advanced stages. The selected system must dilute and control odors and should be free of drafts. Local climatic conditions, costs, and designer judgment determine the extent and degree of air conditioning and humidification. Odor control may indicate either relatively large volumes of outside air with heat-recovery provisions or other air treatment conditioning, including activated carbon or potassium permanganate impregnated activated alumina, in the interest of energy conservation and reduced operating costs.

Temperature control should be on an individual room basis. Patients' rooms should have supplementary heat along exposed walls in geographical areas with severe climates. In moderate climates, *i.e.,* where outside winter design conditions are 30 °F (−1 °C) or above, heating from overhead may be used.

The following systems may be designed to satisfy the preceding design criteria and conditions:

1. VAV with reheat with radiation
2. VAV with reheat
3. Constant volume reheat with heat recovery
4. Constant volume reheat with heat recovery and radiation
5. Radiant ceiling with constant volume air
6. Under window or ceiling induction with reheat and heat recovery
7. Fan coil with primary air
8. Unitary heat pump with primary air

OUTPATIENT SURGICAL FACILITIES

Outpatient surgical facilities may be defined as follows:

1. Surgery is performed without anticipation of overnight stay of patients (*i.e.,* the facility operates 8 to 10 hours daily).
2. The facility may be a free-standing unit, part of an acute care facility, or part of a medical facility such as a medical office building (clinic).

DESIGN CRITERIA

The system designer should refer to the following paragraphs from the section on "Hospitals":

1. Infection Sources & Control Measures
2. Air Quality
3. Air Movement
4. Zoning

The air-cleaning requirements are taken from Table 1 for "operating rooms." A "recovery lounge" need not be considered a sensitive area. The bacteria concern is the same as for an acute-care hospital.

The minimum ventilation rates, desired pressure relationships, desired relative humidity, and design temperature ranges are similar to the requirements for hospitals shown in Table 3, except for the operating rooms, which may meet the criteria for "Trauma Rooms."

The design criteria for insulation applies equally to these facilities. Heating, air conditioning, and domestic hot water systems should have standby or emergency service capability. The system should be able to function after a natural disaster.

The following functional areas in an outpatient facility have similar design criteria as hospitals:

1. Administration
2. Surgical—operating rooms, recovery rooms, and anesthesia storage room
3. Diagnostic and Treatment—generally a small radiology area
4. Sterilizing and Supply
5. Service—soiled workroom, mechanical facilities, and locker rooms.

To reduce utility costs, facilities should include energy conserving procedures such as recovery devices, variable air volume, load shedding, or systems to shut down or reduce ventilation of certain areas when unoccupied. Mechanical ventilation should take advantage of the outside air by using an economizer cycle, when appropriate, to reduce heating and cooling loads.

REFERENCES

ASHRAE. 1986. Terminology of Heating, Ventilation, Air Conditioning, and Refrigeration. ASHRAE. Atlanta.

DHHS. 1984a. Guidelines for Construction & Equipment of Hospital and Medical Facilities. Department of Health and Human Services, Publication No. (HRS-M-HF) 84-1.

DHHS. 1984b. Energy Considerations for Hospital Construction & Equipment. U.S. Department of Health and Human Services, Publication No. (HRS-M-HF) 84-1A.

Degenhardt, R.A.; and Pfost, J.F. 1983. Fume Hood Design and Application for Medical Facilities. ASHRAE *Transactions*, Vol. 89, Part 2A & 2B.

Hagopian, J.H.; and Hoyle, E.R. 1984. Control of Hazardous Gases and Vapors in Selected Hospital Laboratories. ASHRAE *Transactions*, Vol. 90, Part 2B.

Isoard, P.; Giacomoni, L.; and Payronnet, M. 1980. Proceedings 5th International Symposium on Contamination Control. Munich, September.

Luciano, J.R. 1984. New Concept in French Hospital Operating Room HVAC Systems. ASHRAE *Journal,* February.

Michaelson, G.S.; Vesley, D.; and Halbert, M.M. 1966. The Laminar Air Flow Concept for the Care of Low Resistance Hospital Patients. Paper presented at the annual meeting of American Public Health Association, San Francisco, CA, November.

NIOSH. 1975. Elimination of Waste Anesthetic Gases and Vapors in Hospitals. U.S. Department of Health, Education, and Welfare, Publication No. NIOSH 75-137, May.

OSHA. Occupational Exposure to Ethylene Oxide. U.S. Department of Labor, OSHA 29 CFR, Part 1910.

Pfost, J.F. 1981. A Re-Evaluation of Laminar Air Flow in Hospital Operating Rooms. ASHRAE *Transactions,* Vol. 87, Part 2.

Samuals, T.M.; and Eastin, M. 1980. ETO Exposure Can Be Reduced by Air Systems *Hospitals,* July.

Setty, B.V.G. 1976. Solar Heat Pump Integrated Heat Recovery. *Heating, Piping and Air Conditioning,* July.

Wells, W.F. 1934. On Airborne Infection, Study II, Droplets and Droplet Nuclei. American Journal of Hygiene, 20:611.

CHAPTER 24

SURFACE TRANSPORTATION

AUTOMOBILE AIR CONDITIONING

WITH the increased ease of operation, comfortable ride, and lower noise levels of the modern automobile, driver and passenger have become conscious of their environment inside the car. The use of truck cab air conditioning is increasing for long-distance haulage.

All passenger cars sold in the United States must meet federal defroster requirements, so ventilation systems and heaters are included in the basic vehicle design. Trucks are excluded from federal requirements, but all manufacturers include heater/ defrosters as standard equipment. Air conditioning remains an extra cost option on nearly all vehicles.

ENVIRONMENTAL CONTROL

The environmental control system of modern automobiles consists of one or more of the following: (1) heater-defroster, (2) ventilation, and (3) cooling (air-conditioning) systems. The integration of the heater-defroster and ventilation systems is common. On factory-installed air-conditioning systems, the evaporator-blower system is also included in the heater package.

Heating

Outdoor air passes through a heater core, using engine coolant as a heat source. Interior air should not recirculate through the heater because of the danger of the occupants raising the interior air dew point above the temperature of the car's glass, which would cause visibility-reducing condensation.

Control of the heater capacity is achieved by either water flow regulation or control of the amount of outdoor air that is passed through the heater core. In the latter system, the remainder of the air, which does not pass over the heater core, is mixed with heated air to produce the desired temperature. A combination of ram effect from forward movement of the car and the electrically driven blower moves the air through the core.

Heater air is generally distributed into the lower forward compartment, along the floor under the front seat, and then up into the rear compartment. Heater air exhausts through body leakage points. The increased heater air quantity at higher vehicle speeds (ram assist through the ventilation system) compensates for an increase in drafts caused by the increase in ambient velocity. Air exhausters are sometimes installed to increase airflow and reduce the noise of air escaping from the car.

The heater air-distribution system is often nonadjustable. Supplementary ducts are sometimes required when consoles, panel-mounted air conditioners, or rear seat heaters are installed. Supplementary heaters are frequently available for third-seat passengers in station wagons and for limousine and luxury sedan rear seats.

The preparation of this chapter is assigned to TC 9.3, Transportation Air Conditioning.

Defrosting

A portion of the heated air from the heater core passes through ducts to defroster outlets situated at the bottom of the windshield. The heated air absorbs moisture from the windshield interior surface and raises the temperature of the glass above the car interior dew point. Furthermore, the induced outdoor air has a lower dew point than the air inside the vehicle, which is of higher humidity because of the moisture from the occupants and car interior. The defroster air-distribution pattern on the windshield is developed by test to provide the most satisfactory distribution system, fastest overall defrost, and assurance of conformity with federal standards.

Some systems operate the air-conditioning compressor to reduce the dew point, prevent the evaporator from increasing the dew point, or both. Some vehicles are equipped with side window demisters that direct a small amount of heated air and/or air with low dew point to the front side windows. Rear windows are primarily defrosted by heating wires embedded in the glass.

Ventilation

Fresh air ventilation is achieved by one of two systems: (1) ram air or (2) forced air. In both systems, air enters the vehicle through a screened opening in the cowl just forward of the base of the windshield. The cowl plenum is usually an integral part of the vehicle structure. Air entering this plenum can also supply the heater and evaporator cores.

In the ram air system, ventilation air flows aft and up toward the front-seat occupants' laps, and then over the remainder of their bodies. Additional ventilation occurs through turbulence and air exchange through open windows. Directional control of ventilation air is frequently not available with ram systems. Quantity is a function of vehicle velocity, though exhaust and air turbulence may be adjusted by opening windows or vents.

Forced air ventilation is available on many automobiles. The cowl inlet plenum and heater/air-conditioning blower are used together with instrument panel outlets for directional control. On air-conditioned vehicles, the forced air ventilation system uses the air-conditioning outlets. Vent windows and body air exhausts assist ventilation and exhaust air from the vehicle. Because of the increasing popularity of air conditioning and forced ventilation, most late model vehicles are not equipped with vent windows.

Air Conditioning

There are two basic types of systems: combination evaporator-heater and dealer-installed systems.

The **combination evaporator-heater system** is almost always used on factory-installed air conditioning, in conjunction with the ventilation system. This system is popular because (1) it permits dual use of components such as blower motors, outside air ducts, and structure; (2) it permits compromise standards where space considerations dictate (ventilation reduction on air-conditioned cars); (3) it generally reduces the number and complexity of driver controls; and (4) capacity control innovations such as reheat are possible.

Outlets in the instrument panel distribute air to the car interior. These are individually adjustable and some have individual shutoffs. The outside spot coolers are for the driver and front-seat passenger. Center outlets are primarily for rear-seat passengers.

The **dealer-installed system** is normally available only as a service or after-market installation. In recent designs, existing air outlets, blower, and controls are used. Evaporator cases are styled to look like factory-installed units. These units are integrated with the heater as much as possible to provide outside air and to take advantage of existing air-mixing dampers. Where it is not possible to use existing air ducts, custom ducts distribute the air in a manner similar to factory-installed units.

Because the most of the air for the rear-seat occupants flows through the center outlets of the front evaporator unit, a passenger in the center of the front-seat impairs rear-seat cooling. Supplemental trunk and roof units, for luxury sedans and station wagons, respectively, improve the cooling of those passengers located behind the front seat.

The trunk unit consists of a blower-evaporator unit, complete with expansion valve, installed in the trunk of limousines and premium line vehicles. The unit uses the same high side components as the front evaporator unit. It cools and recirculates air drawn from the base of the rear window (back-light) of the car, improves cooling of the rear seat passengers, and increases the system's overall capacity.

The roof-mounted unit is similar to the trunk unit, except that is it intended for station wagon use and is attached to the inside of the roof, toward the rear of the wagon. The advantages of the trunk unit apply here.

GENERAL CONSIDERATIONS

General considerations include ambient temperatures and contaminants, vehicle and engine concessions, flexibility, physical parameters, durability, electrical power, refrigeration capacity, occupants, infiltration, insulation, solar effect, and noise.

Ambient and Vehicle Criteria

Ambient Temperature. Heaters are evaluated for performance from −40 to 70°F (−40 to 16°C). Air-conditioning systems with reheat are evaluated from 30 to 110°F (−1 to 43°C). Add-on units are evaluated from 50 to 100°F (10 to 38°C), although ambient temperatures above 125°F (52°C) are occasionally encountered. Because the system is an integral part of the vehicle detail, factors resulting from vehicle heat and local heating must be considered.

Ambient Contaminants. Air and temperature resistance must be considered when selecting materials for seals and heat exchangers.

Vehicle Concessions. Vehicle performance standards must be observed. Proper engine coolant temperature, freedom from gasoline vapor lock, adequate electrical charging system, acceptable vehicle ride, minimum surge due to compressor clutch cycling, and handling must be maintained.

Flexibility. Engine water pressures range from 0 to 40 psig (0 to 280 kPa gauge pressure) and 55 psig (380 kPa) on trucks at the heater core inlet. The engine coolant thermostats remain closed until 160 to 205°F (71 to 96°C) coolant temperature is reached. Water flow is a function of pressure differential and system restriction but ranges from 0.6 gpm (0.04 L/s) at idle

to 46 gpm (2.9 L/s) at 60 mph (100 km/h) (lower for water valve regulated systems because of the added restriction).

Present antifreeze coolant solutions have specific heats from 0.65 to 1.0 Btu/lb · °F (2.7 to 4.2 kJ/kg · K) and boiling points from 250 to 272°F (121 to 133°C) (depending on concentration) when a 15 psi (100 kPa) radiator pressure cap is used.

Multiple speed blowers (usually four-speed) supplement the ram air effect through the ventilation system and produce the necessary velocities for distribution. Heater air quantities range from 125 to 190 cfm (60 to 90 L/s). Defroster air quantities range from 90 to 145 cfm (42 to 68 L/s). Other considerations are (1) compressor speed-engine speed, from 500 to 5500 rpm (8.3 to 92 r/s); (2) drive ratio, from 0.89:1 to 1.41:1; (3) condenser air from 50 to 125°F (10 to 52°C) and from 325 to 3000 cfm (150 to 1400 L/s) (corrected for restriction and distribution factors); and (4) evaporator air quantity from 100 to 300 cfm (47 to 140 L/s) (limits established by design but selective at operator's discretion) and from 35 to 150°F (2 to 66°C).

Physical Parameters

Parameters include engine rock, proximity to adverse environments, and durability.

Engine Rock. The engine moves relative to the rest of the car both fore and aft because of inertia and in rotation because of torque. Rotational movements at the compressor may be as much as 0.75 in. (20 mm) due to acceleration and 0.5 in. (13 mm) because of deceleration; fore and aft movement may be as much as 0.25 in. (6 mm).

Proximity to Adverse Environments. Wiring, refrigerant lines, hoses, vacuum lines, etc., must be protected from exhaust manifold heat and sharp edges of sheet metal. Accessibility to the normal service items such as oil filler caps, power steering filler caps, transmission dip sticks, etc., cannot be impaired. Removal of air-conditioning components should not be necessary for servicing other components.

Durability. Hours of operation are short compared to commercial systems (4000 h · 40 mph = 160,000 miles or 256,000 km) but all the shock and vibration the vehicle receives or produces must not cause a malfunction or failure.

Systems are designed to meet the recommendations of SAE *Safe Working Practice J639,* which states that the burst strength of those components subjected to high side refrigerant pressure is at least 2.5 times the venting pressure or pressure equivalent to venting temperature of the relief device. Components for the low-pressure side frequently have burst strengths in excess of 300 psi (2.1 MPa). The relief device should be located as close to the discharge gas side of the compressor as possible, and, preferably, in the compressor itself.

Power and Capacity

Fan size is kept to a minimum, not only for space and weight effect, but because of power consumption. If a standard vehicle has a heater that draws 10-A current and the air-conditioning system requires 20-A, an alternator and wiring system must be redesigned to supply this additional 10-A, with obvious cost and weight penalties.

The refrigeration capacity of a system must be adequate to reduce the vehicle interior temperature to the comfort temperature quickly and then maintain the selected temperature at reasonable humidity during all operating conditions and environments. A design is established by empirically evaluating all the known and predicted factors.

Occupancy per unit volume is high in automotive applications. The system must accommodate the heat load from the number of passengers for which the vehicle is designed. Either the prime system or a combination of the prime and an auxiliary system may be used.

Other Considerations

Infiltration varies as a function of the vehicle speed (absolute air velocity). It also varies from vehicle to vehicle. The body sealing requirements are a definite part of air-conditioning design for automobiles. Occasionally, seals beyond those required for dust, noise, and draft control are required.

Due to cost, insulation is seldom added to a vehicle to facilitate air conditioning. Insulation for sound control is generally considered adequate. Roof insulation is of questionable benefit because it retains heat that would be conducted to the outside skin of the vehicle during the nonoperating or soak periods. Additional dash and floor insulation is beneficial. Typical maximum ambient temperatures are 200°F (90°C) above mufflers and catalytic converters, 120°F (65°C) for other floor areas, 145°F (63°C) for dash and toe board, and 110°F (43°C) for sides and top. Solar effects must be added to the sides and top.

Solar effects must be considered in the following three separate phases:

Vertical. Maximum intensity occurs at or near the noon position of the sun. Windshield and backlight vertical projections and angles are considered as substantial additions.

Horizontal and Random Radiation. The intensity is significantly less, but the glass area is large enough to merit consideration.

Surface Heating. The temperature of the surface is a function of the solar energy absorbed, the interior and ambient temperatures, and velocity.

The temperature control system should not produce objectionable sounds. During maximum heating or cooling operation, a slightly higher noise level is acceptable. Thereafter, it should be possible to maintain comfort at a lower blower speed and at an acceptable noise level.

In air-conditioning systems, compressor-induced vibrations, gas pulsations, and noise must be kept to a minimum. Suction and discharge mufflers are often used to reduce noise. Belt-induced noises, engine torsional vibration, and compressor mounting all require particular attention.

COMPONENTS

The basic automobile air-conditioning system consists of the following key components.

Compressors

Much development has been carried out in the past several years to make compressors suitable for car cooling use.

Displacement. Today's compressors have displacements of 6.1 to 12.6 in.[3] (100 to 207 mL/rev). They are belt driven from the crankshaft at ratios ranging from 0.89:1 to 1.41:1.

Physical Size. With increasing engine size, number of accessories, and lower hoods, compressor size is most important. Length and height are particularly limited.

Speed Range. Since compressors are belt driven directly from the engine, they must withstand speeds over 6000 rpm (100 rev/s) and must be smooth and quiet down to 500 rpm (8.3 rev/s). Unless some means of varying the compressor drive ratio is developed, the top speeds may go even higher to improve low speed performance.

Torque Requirements. Because torque and vibration problems are so closely tied together, they impose difficult design problems. This does not preclude an economical single-cylinder compressor to reduce cost; however, any design must reduce peak torques and belt loads, which would normally be at a maximum in a single-cylinder design.

Refrigerant. Systems today use Refrigerant 12. Refrigerant 22 was used in the past to gain additional refrigerating effect for a given displacement, but the high discharge pressures up to 650 psi (4.5 MPa) at idle and slow car speeds were undesirable, and pressure pulses, that generate vibration, were more severe. Higher pressures and temperatures also accentuated compressor seal problems. With Refrigerant 12, the pressures at idle conditions seldom reach 400 psig (2.8 MPa).

Compressor Drives. A magnetic clutch, energized by dc power from the car engine electrical system, drives the compressor. The clutch is always disengaged when air conditioning is not required. The clutch can also be used to control evaporator temperature. (See the section on "Controls.")

Variable Displacement Compressors. Variable displacement compressors for automobile air conditioning are wobble-plate compressors. The angle of the wobble plate is changed in response to the suction and discharge pressure to achieve a constant suction pressure just above freezing regardless of load. A bellows valve or electronic sensor-controlled valve control the wobble plate.

Condensers

Condensers must be sized adequately. High discharge pressures reduce the compressor capacity and increase power requirements. Condenser air restriction must be compatible with the engine cooling fan and engine cooling requirements when the condenser is in series with the radiator. Generally, the most critical condition occurs at engine idle under high load conditions. An undersized condenser can raise head pressures sufficiently to stall small displacement engines.

Condensers are manufactured from copper or aluminum tubes with fins, or fins are skived from the aluminum tube. Aluminum is popular because of the lower cost and reduction in weight.

An oversized condenser may produce condensing temperature significantly below the engine compartment temperature. This can result in reevaporation of refrigerant in the liquid line when the liquid line passes through the engine compartment (the condenser is ahead of the engine and the evaporator is behind it). Engine compartment air has not only been heated by the condenser but by the engine and radiator. Typically, this establishes a minimum condensing temperature of 30°F (17°C) above ambient.

As refrigeration capacity is reduced by lower loads, the problem becomes more apparent because the liquid line velocity decreases. This is more apparent on cycling systems than on systems that have a continuous liquid flow. The effect is audibly detectable as gas entering the expansion valve. This problem can be reduced by adding a subcooler to the condenser.

Condensers are generally large enough to cover the entire radiator surface to prevent air bypass. Accessory systems designed to fit several different cars occasionally compromise by adding depth. Internal pressure drop should be as low as possible to reduce power requirements. Condenser to radiator clearances as low as 0.25 in. (6 mm) have been used, but 0.5 in. (13 mm) is considered preferable. Primary to secondary ratios vary from 8:1 to 16:1. Condensers are normally painted black so they will not be visible through the vehicle grille.

A condenser ahead of the engine cooling radiator not only restricts air but also heats the air entering the radiator. The addition of air conditioning requires supplementing the engine cooling system. Radiator capacity is increased by adding fins, depth, or face area. It can also be increased by increasing water flow by increasing water pump speed. Pump cavitation at high speeds is the limiting factor. Increasing the speed of the water pump increases the engine cooling fan speed, which not only supplements the engine cooling system but also provides more air for the condenser. Fan size, number of blades, and blade width and pitch are frequently increased and fan shrouds are often added when air conditioning is installed in an automobile.

Fan speed, diameter, and pitch increases mean a corresponding increase in noise and power consumption.

Temperature and torque sensitive drives (viscous drives or couplings), or flex-fans reduce these increases in noise and power. They rely on ram air produced by forward motion of the car to reduce the amount of air the radiator fan must move to maintain adequate coolant temperatures. As vehicle speed increases, fan requirements drop.

Front-wheel-drive vehicles typically have electric motor-driven cooling fans. Some vehicles also have side-by-side condenser and radiator designs, each with its own motor-driven fan.

Evaporator Systems

Current materials and construction are copper tube and aluminum fin, aluminum fin and tube, and aluminum plate and fin. Design parameters include air pressure drop, capacity, and condensate carryover. Fin spacing must permit adequate condensate drainage to the drain pan below the evaporator. Condensate must drain outside the vehicle. The vehicle exterior is generally at a higher pressure than the interior at road speeds [1 to 2 in. of water (250 to 500 Pa)]. Drains are usually on the high pressure side of the blower, sometimes incorporate a trap, and are as small as possible. Drains can be plugged not only by contaminates but also by road splash.

Vehicle attitude (slope of the road and inclines), acceleration, and deceleration must be considered when designing condensate systems. High pressure drops require externally equalized expansion valves. A bulbless expansion valve, which provides external pressure equalization without the added expense of the external equalizer, is available. The evaporator must provide stable refrigerant flow under all operating conditions and have sufficient capacity to ensure rapid cooldown of the vehicle after standing in the sun.

The conditions affecting evaporator size and design are different from residential and commercial installations in that the average operating time, from a hot-soaked condition, is less than 20 min. Inlet air at the start of the operation can be as high as 150°F (65°C), and it decreases as the duct system is ventilated. In a recirculating system, it decreases as the car interior temperature decreases. In a system using outdoor air, it decreases to a few degrees above ambient (perpetual heating by the duct system). During longer periods of operation, the system is expected to cool the entire vehicle interior, rather than just produce a flow of cool air.

During sustained operation, vehicle occupants want less air noise and velocity, so the air quantity must be reduced but sufficient capacity preserved to maintain satisfactory car interior temperatures. Ducts must be kept as short as possible and should preferably be insulated from engine compartment and solar-ambient heat loads. Thermal lag resulting from added heat sink of ducts and housings increases cooldown time.

Filters, Hoses, and Heater Cores

Air filters are not generally used. Some coarse screening prevents such objects as facial tissues, insects, and leaves from entering fresh air ducts. Studies have proved that wet evaporator surfaces reduce the pollen count appreciably. In one test an ambient of 23 to 96 mg/mm^2 showed 53 mg/mm^2 in a non-air-conditioned car and less than 3 mg/mm^2 in an air-conditioned car.

Rubber hose assemblies are used where flexible refrigerant transmission connections are needed due to relative motion between components or because stiffer connections cause installation difficulties and noise transmission problems. Refrigerant effusion through the hose wall is a design consideration. Effusion occurs at a reasonably slow and predictable rate, which in-

creases as pressure and temperature increase. A hose with a nylon core is less flexible (pulsation dampening), has a smaller O.D., is generally cleaner, and has practically no effusion.

The heat transfer surface in an automotive heater is usually cellular. It is a copper-brass assembly with lead-tin solder. The water course is brass (0.006 to 0.016), and the air course is copper (0.003 to 0.008). The tanks and connecting tubes are brass (0.026 to 0.034). Both U-flow and straight-through flow are used. Capacity is adjusted by varying face area [up to 120 in.^{2} (77 000 mm^2)], depth 2.5 in. (65 mm), and air side surface (for turbulence and air restriction) (see Figure 1).

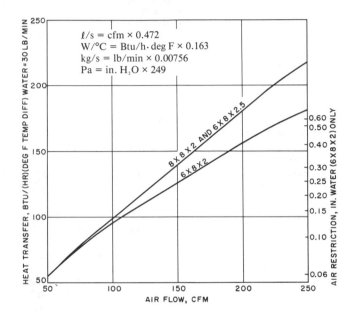

Fig. 1 Typical Heater Core Capacity

Receiver-Drier Assembly

The receiver-drier assembly accommodates charge fluctuations from changes in system load (refrigerant flow and density). It accommodates an *overcharge* of refrigerant [usually about 1 lb (0.5 kg)] to compensate for system leaks and hose effusion. The assembly houses the high side filter and desiccant. Several types of desiccant are used, the most common of which are activated alumina, silica gel, and molecular sieves in the granular or spherical form. Mechanical integrity (freedom from powdering) is important because of the vibration to which the assembly is exposed. For this reason, molded desiccants have not obtained wide acceptance.

Moisture retention at elevated temperatures is also important. The rate of release with temperature increase and the reaction while accumulating high concentration should be considered. Design temperatures of at least 140°F (60°C) should be used.

The receiver-drier often houses a sight glass to provide a visual indication of the sufficiency of the refrigerant charge in the system. It houses safety devices such as fusible plugs, rupture discs, or high pressure relief valves. The latter are gaining increasing acceptance, because they do not vent the entire charge. Location of the relief devices is important. Vented refrigerant should be directed in such a manner that it does not endanger personnel.

Receivers are usually (though not always) mounted on or near the condenser. They should be located so that ambient air ventilates them. Pressure drops should be minimum.

Expansion Valves

Thermostatic Expansion Valves (TXV) control the flow of refrigerant through the evaporator. These are applied as shown in Figures 4, 5, and 6. Both liquid and gas charged power elements are used. Also, internally and externally equalized valves are used as dictated by system design. Externally equalized valves are necessary where high evaporator pressure drops exist. A bulbless expansion valve, which senses evaporator outlet pressure without the need for an external equalizer, is now widely used.

Orifice Tubes

The use of an orifice tube instead of an expansion valve to control refrigerant flow through the evaporator has come into widespread use in original equipment installations. The components of the system must be carefully matched to obtain proper performance. Even so, there is some floodback of liquid refrigerant to the compressor under some conditions with this system.

Suction Line Accumulators

A suction line accumulator is required with an orifice tube system to ensure uniform return of refrigerant and oil to the compressor to prevent slugging and to cool the compressor. A typical suction line accumulator is shown in Figure 2. A bleed hole at the bottom of the standpipe meters oil and liquid refrigerant back to the compressor. The filter and desiccant are contained in the accumulator because no drier-receiver is used with this system. The amount of refrigerant charge is more critical when a suction line accumulator is used than it is with a dryer-receiver.

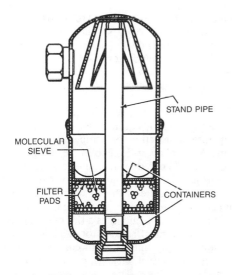

Fig. 2   Typical Suction Line Accumulator

Refrigerant Circuits

The cycling clutch refrigerant systems shown in Figures 3 and 4 are common in late model cars for both factory- and dealer-installed units. The clutch is cycled by a thermostat sensing evaporator temperature or by a pressure switch sensing evaporator pressure. Some dealer-installed units use an adjustable thermostat, which controls car temperature by controlling evaporator temperature. The thermostat also prevents evaporator icing. Most units use a fixed thermostat or pressure switch set to prevent evaporator icing. Temperature is then controlled by blending air with warm air coming through the heater core.

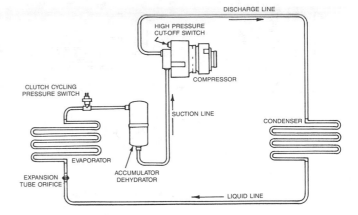

Fig. 3   Clutch Cycling Orifice Tube Air-Conditioning System Schematic

Cycling the clutch sometimes causes noticeable surges as the engine is loaded and unloaded by the compressor. This is more evident in cars with smaller engines. Reevaporation of condensate from the evaporator during the off cycle may cause objectionable temperature fluctuation or odor. This system cools faster and at lower cost than a continuous running system.

In orifice tube-accumulator systems, the clutch cycling switch disengages at about 25 psig (170 kPa) and cuts in at about 45 psig (310 kPa). Thus, the evaporator defrosts on each off-cycle. The flooded evaporator has enough thermal inertia to prevent rapid clutch cycling. It is desirable to limit clutch cycling to a maximum of 4 cycles per minute because heat is generated by the clutch at engagement.

The pressure switch can be used with a TXV in a dry evaporator if the pressure switch is damped to prevent rapid cycling of the clutch.

Continuous running systems, as shown in Figures 5 and 6, have also been widely used. An evaporator pressure regulator (EPR) keeps the evaporator pressure above the condensate freezing level. Temperature is controlled by reheat or air blending with warm air from the heater core. The valve, which is located on the downstream side of the evaporator, may be self-contained in its own housing and installed in the compressor suction line or may be placed in the suction cavity of the compressor. The device is pressure sensitive and operates to maintain a minimum evaporator pressure (saturation pressure). The setting depends on minimum airflow across the evaporator, the condensate draining ability of the evaporator coil, and the lowest ambient temperature at which it is anticipated that the system will be operated.

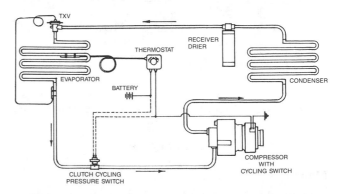

Fig. 4   Clutch Cycling System with Thermostatic Expansion Valve (TXV)

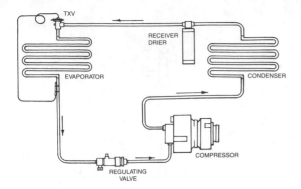

Fig. 5 Suction Line Regulation System

This system possesses neither of the disadvantages of the cycling clutch system mentioned previously, but it does increase the suction line pressure drop; hence, a slight reduction in system performance at maximum capacity. A solenoid version of this valve has also been used, which is controlled by an antifreeze switch, which senses evaporator fin temperature. The switch closes the valve electrically when the fin temperature drops to the control point.

Two basic refrigeration circuits use the evaporator pressure regulator (EPR). These are shown in Figures 5 and 6. Figure 5 shows the conventional dry-type system. Figure 6 shows a flooded evaporator system. This system uses a plate-and-separator type of evaporator with a tank at the top and bottom. It is also a unique piping arrangement. The TXV external equalizer line is connected downstream of the evaporator pressure regulator valve. Also, a small oil return line containing an internal pressure relief valve is connected downstream of the EPR. These two lines may be connected to the housing of the EPR valve downstream of its valve mechanism. This piping arrangement causes the TXV to open wide when the EPR throttles, thus flooding the evaporator and causing the EPR to act as an expansion valve. The system allows the air conditioner to be run at ambients as low as 35 °F (2 °C) to defog windows while maintaining adequate refrigerant flow and to ensure oil return to the compressor.

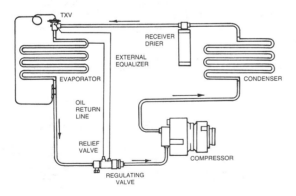

Fig. 6 Flooded Evaporator Suction Line Regulation System

CONTROLS

Manual

The fundamental mechanism is the flexible bowden-type control cable, which transmits linear motion with reasonable effi-

ciency and little hysteresis. Rotary motion is obtained by crank mechanisms. Common applications are (1) movement of damper doors, which control discharge air temperature in blend air systems; (2) regulation of the amount of defrost bleed; and (3) regulation of water valves to control the flow of engine coolant through the heater core.

Vacuum

This control method provides a silent, powerful method of manual control, requiring only the movement of a lever or a switch by the operator. Vacuum is obtained from the engine intake manifold. A vacuum reservoir [25 to 250 in³ (0.4 to 4 L)] may be used to ensure an adequate source. Most systems are designed to function at minimum vacuum of 5 to 6 in. of Hg (17 to 20 kPa), even though as much as 26 in. of Hg (88 kPa) may be available at times.

Linear or rotary slide valves select functions. Vacuum modulating, temperature compensating (bimetal) valves control thermostatic water valves. Occasionally, solenoid valves are used, but they are generally avoided because of their cost and associated wiring.

Electrical

Electrical controls regulate blower motors. Blowers have three or four speeds. The electrically operated compressor clutch frequently sees service as a secondary system control, operated by function (mode) selection integration, or evaporator temperature-sensing thermostats.

Temperature Control

Air-conditioning capacity control to control car temperature is achieved in one of two ways. The clutch can be cycled in response to an adjustable thermostat sensing evaporator discharge air, or the evaporator discharge air can be blended with or reheated by airflow through the heater core. The amount of reheat or blend is usually controlled by driver adjusted damper doors.

Solid-state logic interprets system requirements and automatically adjusts to heating or air conditioning, depending on the operator's selection of temperature and on ambient temperature. Manual override enables the occupant to select the defrost function. The system regulates not only this function but also controls capacity and air quantity. An in-car thermistor measures the temperature of the air within the passenger compartment and compares it to the setting at the temperature selector. An ambient sensor, sometimes a thermistor, senses ambient temperature to prevent offset or droop. These elements, along with a vacuum supply line from an engine vacuum reservoir, are coupled to the control package, consisting of an electronic amplifier and a transducer. The output is a vacuum or electrical signal regulated by the temperature inputs.

This regulated signal is supplied to servo units that control the quantity of water flowing in the heater core, the position of the heater blending door, or both; the air-conditioning evaporator pressure; and the speed of the blower. This same regulated signal controls sequencing of damper doors, resulting in the discharge of air on the occupant's feet or at waist level, or causing the system to work on the recirculating of outdoor air. A number of interlocking assurance devices are usually required. They prevent blower operation before engine coolant is up to temperature, prevent the air-conditioning compressor clutch from being energized at low ambient temperatures, and provide other features for passenger comfort.

BUS AIR CONDITIONING

Bus air conditioning design must consider highly variable loads, both from the standpoint of passenger load and of climate. It is usually not cost effective to design for a specific climate. Therefore, the design should consider all likely climates, from the high ambient temperatures of the dry southwest to the high humidity of the cooler east. Units should operate satisfactorily in ambient conditions up to 120°F (50°C). The quality of the ambient air must also be considered. Frequently, intakes are subjected to thermal contamination either from road surfaces, condenser air recirculation, or radiator air discharge. Vehicle motion also introduces pressure variables that affect condenser fan performance. A unit designed for both extremes has a greater sensible cooling capacity in hot, dry climates than in humid climates.

Bus air-conditioning units are generally tested as single units in climate controlled test cells. Testing of the vehicle in a large climate is now possible and a better measurement of installed performance can be obtained.

INTERURBAN BUSES

The following conditions have been adopted as a standard for interurban vehicles:

1. Capacity of 39 passengers
2. Insulation thickness of 1 to 1.5 in. (35 to 38 mm)
3. Double-pane tinted windows
4. Outdoor air intake of 400 cfm (190 L/s)
5. Road speed of 60 mph (100 km/h)
6. Inside design temperatures of 80°F (27°C) dry-bulb and 67°F (19.5°C) wet-bulb

Outside conditions typical of the United States give loads from 3.5 to 6.5 tons (12 to 23 kW). Unless a specific area requires a custom design, the designer should consider extreme conditions. The design should size the unit for standby conditions. Using the engine as the compressor drive for standby results in excessive capacity over the road, so appropriate unloading devices are necessary. A standby idle RPM increase can increase capacity and reduce compressor oversizing. Some interurban buses have a separate engine-driven air conditioner to give more constant performance; however, the space required, complexity, cost, and maintenance requirement is greater than for other units. Figure 7 shows a typical arrangement of equipment. A winter feature, which includes warm sidewalls and window diffusers, is important to offset down drafts. The return air openings near the floor help reduce stratification. These features, while desirable, are not as important on urban buses because passengers are exposed for only a short time and have appropriate clothing. Some additional thermal losses occur with sidewall distribution and underside ducting; therefore, effective insulation and avoidance of thermal short circuits is necessary. Placing the condenser in back of the front axle has been satisfactory. The condenser should not be placed low and near the rear axle on rear engine-driven buses because hot air [up to 140°F (60°C)] from the radiator reduces the condenser capacity.

Shock and Vibration

Most transport air-conditioning manufacturers design components for a shock loading between 3 and 5 G's. Vibration eliminators, flexible lines, and other shock cushioning devices interconnect the various air-conditioning components. The vibration characteristics of each component is different. On a direct, engine-connected compressor, whether the connection is made by belts, flexible drives, gearing, or clutches, relative motion occurs between the main engine and compressor. This motion may

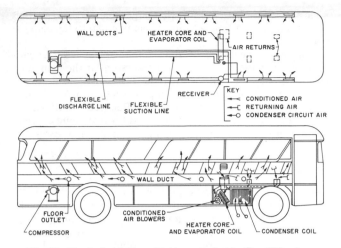

Fig. 7 Typical Airflow Pattern and Air-Conditioning Equipment Location in an Interurban Bus

be taken care of by shock arms, vibration dampening devices, or by automatic belt-tensioning devices. It is good practice to tie the compressor onto the engine by bracket extensions or other mounting devices so that the engine and compressor have no relative motion.

The relative motion between a compressor and other air-conditioning components is usually taken care of by flexible refrigerant hoses. The permeability of flexible lines have presented some difficulty with Refrigerant 22, so Refrigerant 12, because it operates at lower pressures, is usually chosen as the refrigerant.

URBAN BUSES

Urban bus heating and cooling loads are greater than those of the interurban bus. A city bus may seat up to 50 people and carry a crush load of standees. The fresh air load is greater because of the number of door openings and infiltration around doors. Table 1 shows the results of a test that recorded door openings. An urban bus stops frequently and may open both front and rear doors to take on or discharge passengers. Entering passengers bring with them the conditions existing outside, which could be considerably different than the stabilized conditions for which data is readily available.

The cooling capacity required for the typical 50 seat urban bus is from 6 to 10 tons of refrigeration (20 to 35 kW). The equipment must be flexible enough to range from low capacity to maximum capacity promptly because the passenger load varies greatly. Buses with engine-driven compressors suffer a loss of compressor capacity at idle. This loss is compensated for by sizing

Table 1 Door Operation of a City Bus[a]

	Front Entrance Door		Center Exit Door	
Door open				
Times per mile (km)	7.5	(4.7)	5.5	(3.4)
Times per hour	70		44	
% of operating time	35		15	
Longest time open	55	sec	34	sec
Shortest time open	3	sec	3	sec
Average time open	13.5 sec		12.5 sec	

[a]Observed during the rush period on a 35-passenger bus in San Antonio, Texas.

other parts of the system somewhat larger than the load analysis indicates to meet a time average capacity equal to the comfort goal.

At maximum engine speed, the compressor may have a capacity in excess of the cooling load or the rating of the remainder of the system—a condition that must also be considered. In general, the amount of power available is a limiting factor and, more recently, fuel consumption has influenced specifications. Therefore, equipment must be designed for maximum efficiency and the vehicle designed for minimum thermal losses.

System Types

Air-conditioning systems for urban buses generally fall into three categories. The newer, advanced design buses are usually equipped with either a roof-mounted or rear-mounted package unit similar to Figures 8 and 9, which includes all system components except the compressors. The compressor is usually belt or shaft driven from the main traction engine.

The heater is located just down stream of the evaporator. Hot water from the engine cooling system provides sufficient heat for most operations; however, additional sources may be required in colder climates for long durations of idle. Additional floor heaters may also be required to reduce effects of stratification. Air distribution for these systems is either through linear diffuser(s) in the ceiling fed from a duct concealed in the space between the roof and ceiling panels, or by longitudinal ducts concealed in the sidewalls above the windows behind the lighting fixtures.

Many older urban buses, similar to Figure 9 have an evaporator/blower unit mid-mounted below the bus floor, which feeds conditioned air through sidewall voids to slotted or perforated diffusers at the window sills. These systems have either an upper, rear-mounted condenser, or the condenser is mounted in tandem with the engine radiator. The tandem installations are susceptible to recirculation of radiator discharge air, which can severely reduce capacity, especially at idle. Compressors are either shaft-driven from the transmission auxiliary power take-off or belt driven directly from the engine. In either case, a clutch connects or disconnects the drive for system control. The wide separation of components in this design, require considerable lengths of interconnecting piping and many fittings and joints that are susceptible to leakage from vibration and physical damage. In addition, the air distribution systems, located in the lower sidewalls of the coach, are easily damaged during a traffic accident and are most difficult to repair and keep airtight.

Retrofit Systems

As the public has demanded a more comfortable riding environment, there has been an upsurge in retrofitting older buses with air-conditioning systems and in replacement of older systems with newer, more efficient designs. Available systems follow the configuration of systems supplied for new buses in that roof- and rear-mount units can be fitted into old coaches. Some manufacturers also offer a simple system of interior evaporator/blower units, using two to four units per bus, depending on the bus size and operating environment. These units are installed over the windows along one side of the bus. They sometimes replace the original lighting fixtures formerly at that location and provide the needed cooling without the need for ductwork installation. Refrigerant piping in these systems is somewhat more extensive than in packaged units, but the overall installation can be made faster, and at lower cost. In addition, the renovations to the bus interior are kept to a minimum, and the structural concern of cutting an opening in the roof is eliminated.

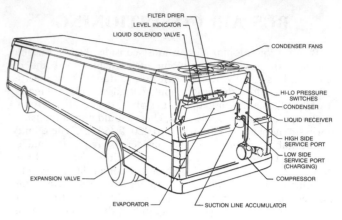

Fig. 8 Typical Mounting Location of Urban Bus Air-Conditioning Equipment

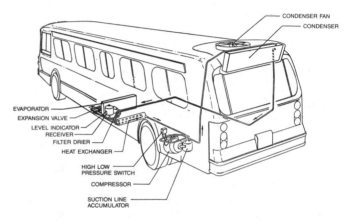

Fig. 9 Mounting Location of Air-Conditioning Equipment in Older Urban Buses

Compressors and Drives

Several different types and styles of compressors and drives are seen on urban buses. The four- or six-cylinder reciprocating compressor, which has some cylinders equipped with unloaders, is popular. The compressor is driven either from an auxiliary shaft extending from the transmission or mounted so that it can be directly belt-driven from the engine. In both cases, it is fitted with a clutch, either pneumatically or electrically actuated, by the temperature control system. Several designs have one or more high-speed, axial piston, or rotary compressors that are belt-driven and electric-clutch controlled. Helical screw compressors on urban transit busses also have been successfully demonstrated.

Articulated Coaches

Several urban transit authorities operate articulated buses in which each of the two sections is equipped with a separate roof-mount or rear-mount package unit. Each section has its own belt-driven compressor, and both units are usually located in the rear-section engine compartment. The package for the rear section has a dual condenser, while the package for the forward section has no condenser. Long runs of flexible refrigerant piping connect the front section to its compressor at the extreme rear of the rear section.

System Maintenance

Due to the extremely adverse operating environment of the urban transit bus, far more will be spent on inspection and repairs than on the initial cost of the system. For this reason, it is generally cost-effective to arrange the system for ease of access to the repairable parts and provide convenient points for checking the critical pressures, fluid levels, and temperatures. Ease of access to the air filters for replacement or cleaning is essential, since this is the most often performed maintenance task. Refrigerant piping joints should be kept to a minimum, and all controls, safety devices, and accessory items should be heavy-duty and able to withstand the extreme punishment and environments to which the bus will be subjected.

Controls

The typical urban transit coach is relatively simply controlled. Cooling thermostats for full- and part-capacity and a heating thermostat to operate the pump or valve serving the heating core are usually included. Many current systems use solid-state control modules to interpret the bus interior and outside ambient temperatures and generate signals to operate the full- or part-cooling or heating functions. In these systems, thermister temperature sensors are used, which usually give more stable and reliable operation than electro-mechanical controls.

Control systems also include a ventilation of outside air cycle. This mode of operation maintains the coach interior comfort level using 100% outside air. The system is used during the mild temperature zone between heating and air conditioning. The ventilation cycle permits longer compressor off-cycle time, which benefits the coach operator in both fuel economy and compressor life.

RAILROAD AIR CONDITIONING

The railroad air-conditioning system uses electro-mechanical equipment with refrigerants R-22 and R-12. Electronic solid-state automatic controls are common with a trend towards microprocessor control. Electric heating coils installed in the air-conditioning unit temper outside air brought for ventilation. Part of these coils are often used as reheat for humidity control.

Passenger Car Construction

Passenger car design has emphasized lighter car construction to lower costs of building and to decrease operating and maintenance cost. This drive to reduce weight and cost has also reduced the size and weight of air-conditioning equipment and other auxiliaries.

Vehicle Types

Mainline railroads operate single and bilevel cars, hauled by a locomotive. Three-phase AC power generated by alternators or static invertors in the locomotive operate the air-conditioning system, which typically consists of two, three, or four components or a single packaged unit.

Commuter cars operating around large cities are similar in size to mainline cars and carry similar types of air conditioning. However, in addition to locomotive hauled, they are often self-propelled by high voltage DC or AC power supplied from an overhead catenary or from a DC-supplied third rail system. On such cars, the air conditioning may operate on AC or DC power. Diesel-driven vehicles still operate in a few areas.

Subways usually operate on a third rail DC power supply. The car air conditioning operates on the normal DC supply voltage or on three-phase AC supply from an alternator or inverter mounted under the car. Split air-conditioning systems are common with evaporators at roof level and condensing section.

Street cars and downtown people movers usually run on the city AC or DC power supply and have air conditioners of similar design to subway car equipment. During rush hours, interior space is at a premium on these cars, so roof mounted packages are used more often than split systems.

Equipment Selection

The source and type of power dictate the type of air-conditioning equipment installed on a railroad car. Weight is also a major consideration, so AC powered semi-hermetic compressors, which are lighter than open machines with DC motor drives, are a common choice. Each car design must be carefully examined in this respect, since DC/AC invertors may increase the total system weight.

Other aspects of equipment selection include space requirements, location, accessibility, reliability, and maintainability. Interior and exterior equipment noise levels must be considered during the early stages of design and later when coordinating the equipment with the car-builder's ductwork and grilles.

Design Limitations

Space underneath and inside a railroad car is at a premium. This lack of space is even more pronounced on subway and commuter cars. This problem generally rules out floor-mounted units. Usually, the components of the system are built to fit the configuration of the available space. The curvature of the roof and the clearance beneath the car are two major factors that determine the shape and size of equipment.

A mainline railroad car must operate in various parts of the country, so air conditioning must handle the maximum outdoor air dry-bulb and wet-bulb design temperatures for all operating areas. Commuter cars and subway cars operate in a small geographical area, and only the local design temperatures and humidities need be considered.

Dirt and corrosion is an important design factor, especially if the equipment is beneath the car floor where it is subject to all types of weather, as well as very severe dirt conditions. For this reason, corrosion-resistant materials and coatings must be selected wherever possible. Aluminum has not proved durable enough because the sandblasting effect destroys any surface treatment on aluminum installed beneath the car.

Since dirt cannot be eliminated, the equipment must be designed for quick and easy cleaning. Access doors are needed to get inside or behind coils to blow out the dirt. Fin spacing on condenser and evaporator coils is limited to 8 to 10 fins per inch (2.5 to 3 mm) compared to 18 fins per inch (1.4 mm) on commercial and industrial equipment. Closer fin spacing causes more rapid dirt buildup and costs more to clean. Dirt, as well as other severe environmental conditions, must be considered in selecting motors and controls.

Railroad equipment requires considerably more maintenance and servicing than stationary units. A modern railroad car with sealed windows and a well-insulated structure becomes almost unusable if the air conditioning fails. For this reason, the equipment has many additional components to permit quick determination and correction of the failure. Motors, compressors, valves, etc., must be easily accessible for inspection or repair. The liquid receiver should have sight glasses so the amount of refrigerant can be quickly checked. Likewise, a readily accessible liquid charging valve should be available. Pressure gauges and test switches allow a fast check of the system while the train is stopped at intermediate stations.

Safety must be considered, especially on equipment located beneath the car. Supports should be failsafe in case a mounting bolt shears or a nut comes loose. A piece of equipment that hangs down or drops off could cause a train wreck. All belt drives or other revolving items must be safety guarded. High voltage controls and equipment must be labeled by approved warning signs. All pressure vessels and coils must meet ASME test specifications for protection of the passengers and maintenance people.

Interior Comfort

Air-conditioning and heating comfort conditions may be selected in accordance with ASHRAE *Standard* 55-1981. However, the selected temperature and humidity levels must consider the passenger's metabolic rate upon entry, clothing insulation, and journey time. Chapter 8 of the 1985 FUNDAMENTALS Volume has more details.

Vibration and dusty conditions preclude the use of commercial humidity controllers. Fan and compressor speed variation and reheat are used to provide humidity control during the cooling season. Normally a maximum relative humidity for optimum comfort is specified. In winter, humidity control is usually not necessary.

The dominant summer cooling load is due to the passengers. It is followed by ventilation, internal heat, car body transmission, and solar gain. Heating loads consist of car body losses and ventilation. The load calcuation does not credit heat from passengers and internal sources. Comfortable internal conditions in ventilated non air-conditioned cars can only be maintained when ambient conditions permit.

Due to the continuous variation in passenger and solar loads in mass-transit cars, the interior conditions are difficult to hold, and variation from the desired level of maximum acceptance occurs. Air-conditioning systems in North American cars are selected to maintain 75 to 80 °F (24 to 27 °C), with a maximum relative humidity of 55 to 60%. In Europe and elsewhere, the conditions are usually set at a dry-bulb temperature from 0 to 10 °F (0 to 5 °C) below the ambient, with a coincidental 50 to 66% relative humidity. In the heating mode, the car interior is kept in the 65 to 70 °F (18 to 21 °C range). Outdoor conditions are chosen from Chapter 24 of the 1985 FUNDAMENTALS Volume and local climatic data.

System Requirements

Most cars are equipped with overhead heat and floor heat. The overhead heat raises the temperature of the recirculated and ventilation air mixture to a temperature slightly above the car design. The floor heat offsets the heat loss through the car body.

Cooling and heating loads are calculated in accordance with Chapters 25 and 26 of the 1985 FUNDAMENTALS Volume. The times of maximum occupancy, outdoor ambient, and solar gain must be ascertained. For cooling loads on urban transit cars, this peak load usually coincides with the evening rush hour, and on intercity railroads, around mid afternoon.

Heating capacity for the car depends upon car body construction, and the car and wind velocity. In some instances, minimum car warmup time may be the governing factor. In long-distance trains, the toilets, galley, and lounges often have exhaust fans. The makeup air for such fans also adds to the air heating and cooling loads, unless the ventilation airflow exceeds the exhaust rate. Fresh air ventilation rates of 5.3 to 7.4 cfm (2.5 to 3.5 L/s) per occupant are desirable. Ventilation air pressurizes the car and reduces infiltration. On railroad cars with kitchen or toilet exhaust systems, care must be taken to ensure an excess of ventilation air over exhaust air.

Air Distribution

The most common type of air distribution system is a center line supply duct running the length of the car and located in the space between the ceiling and roof. The air outlets are usually ceiling mounted linear slot air diffusers. Egg crate recirculation grilles are positioned in the ceiling beneath the evaporator units. The main supply duct must be insulated on three sides because of the high temperatures in the space above the ceiling. The ventilation air should be taken from both sides of the roof line to overcome the effect of wind. Adequate snow and rain louvers must be installed on the outdoor air intakes. Separate outdoor air filters are usually paired with a return air filter. Disposable media or permanent cleanable air filters are used and they are normally serviced every month.

Piping Design

Standard refrigerant piping practice is followed for components. Pipe joints should be accessible for inspection and not concealed in car walls. When the complete system and piping has been installed, evacuation, leak testing, and dehydration must be completed successfully prior to charging. Piping should be supported adequately and installed without traps that could retard flow of oil back to the compressor. Pipe sizing and arrangement should be in accordance with Chapter 3 of the 1986 REFRIGERATION Volume. Evacuation, dehydration, charging, and testing should be performed as described in Chapter 22 of the 1983 EQUIPMENT Volume. Piping on packaged units should also conform to these standards.

Control Requirements

Car HVAC systems are automatically controlled for year-round comfort. In the cooling mode, load variations are handled by two-stage, direct expansion coils and compressors equipped with suction pressure unloaders or speed control. During low load conditions, cooling is provided by outdoor air supplied through the ventilation system. When low loads are combined with high humidity, a reheat cycle is activated.

A pump-down cycle and low ambient lockout protect the compressor from damage caused by liquid slugging. In addition, the compressor may be fitted with a crankcase heater that is energized during the compressor off cycle. During the heating mode, floor and overhead heaters are staged to maintain the car interior temperature.

Today's control systems use thermisters and solid-state auxiliary electronics instead of electro-mechanical devices. The control circuits are normally powered by low voltage DC or, occasionally, by single-phase AC.

Future Trends

The demand for lighter, more efficient railway cars remains strong. The use of rooftop packaged air-conditioning units has reduced weight and improved reliability by eliminating long piping runs. Most manufacturers offer hermetic compressors, which are isolated to withstand the shock and vibration normally encountered. Some manufacturers market heat pump units. Neither hermetic compressors or heat pumps have been fully field tested in North America. However, some operating authorities are looking toward them to reduce costs. Other major costs include maintenance and replacement parts. Recent specifications stipulate high reliability combined with low maintainance.

CHAPTER 25

AIRCRAFT

AIRCRAFT air-conditioning equipment must meet additional requirements beyond those for air conditioning of buildings, although basic principles are applicable. It must be compact, lightweight, accessible for quick inspection and servicing, highly reliable, and unaffected by airplane vibration and landing impact. The temperature control and pressure control systems must be capable of responding to rapid changes of ambient temperature and pressure as the airplane climbs and descends.

DESIGN CONDITIONS

The aircraft air-conditioning and pressurization system primarily maintains an aircraft environment that ensures the safety and comfort of passengers and crew and proper operation of on-board electronic equipment. The system must maintain this environment through the wide range of aircraft ambient temperatures and pressures. The effects of system and component failures must be accounted for in maintaining passenger and crew safety and operation of flight critical electronic equipment.

Ambient Temperature, Humidity, and Pressure

Figure 1 gives typical design ambient temperature profiles. The figure shows variations of ambient temperature for hot, standard, and cold days. The ambient temperatures used for the design of a particular aircraft may be higher or lower than those shown by Figure 1, depending on the regions in which the airplane may be operated. A recommended design ambient moisture variation with altitude for commercial aircraft is shown in Figure 2. Moisture content as high as 204 grains per lb of dry air (29.2 g/kg) at sea level are considered for military aircraft. The variation in ambient pressure with altitude is shown by Figure 3.

Air Conditioning Performance

Air conditioning for passenger and crew compartments and cargo compartments should provide the following performance.

Cooling. During cruise, the system should maintain an average cabin temperature of 75°F (24°C) with full passenger load. During ground operations, the system should be capable of maintaining an average cabin no higher than 80°F (27°C) with full passenger load and all external doors closed. It should be capable of cooling the cabin on the ground to an average temperature of 80°F (27°C) within 30 minutes starting with a cabin temperature of 115°F (46°C), no passengers or other heat loads, and all external doors closed.

Heating. During cruise, the system should maintain an average cabin temperature of 75°F (24°C), with 20% passenger load. During ground operations, the system should be capable of heating the cabin on the ground to an average temperature of 70°F (21°C) within 30 minutes, starting with a cold soaked airplane at a temperature of −25°F (−32°C) and an ambient temperature of −40°F (−40°C) with no passengers or other in-

ternal heat loads and with all external doors closed. The system should maintain the cargo compartment bulk air temperature above 40°F (4.4°C). Cargo floor temperatures should be above 32°F (0°C) to prevent freezing of cargo. These temperatures should be attainable during all cruise conditions.

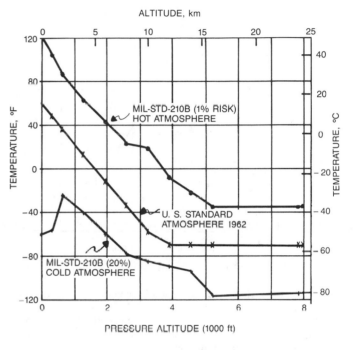

Fig. 1 Typical Ambient Temperature Profiles

Pressurization Performance

Figure 3 shows typical cabin pressure control operating range. Generally, aircraft designed for airline service are capable of maintaining a cabin altitude of 5000 to 7000 ft (1.5 to 2.1 km) at typical operating altitudes and limit cabin altitude to a maximum of 8000 ft (2.4 km) at maximum cruise altitudes. Typically, cabin altitude rate of change is limited for passenger comfort to 500 ft/min (2.5 m/s) for increasing altitude and 300 ft/min (1.5 m/s) for decreasing altitude. Military fighter aircraft are normally designed to maintain a 5 psi differential at altitudes above approximately 23,000 ft (7.0 km).

Airplanes flying above 10,000 ft (3.0 km) must be equipped with an oxygen system for use in case of loss of pressurization. To maintain cabin pressure control, air inflow to the pressurized cabin must exceed airflow leaking from the pressurized cabin. Leakage areas include controlled vents for the galley, toilets, and electronic equipment; and uncontrolled leakage through door seals and structural joints.

Ventilation

Crew and passenger compartments should be ventilated whenever the aircraft is in operational service. Actual ventilation rates in commercial aircraft range from 15 to 25 cfm/per-

The preparation of this chapter is assigned to TC 9.3, Transportation Air Conditioning.

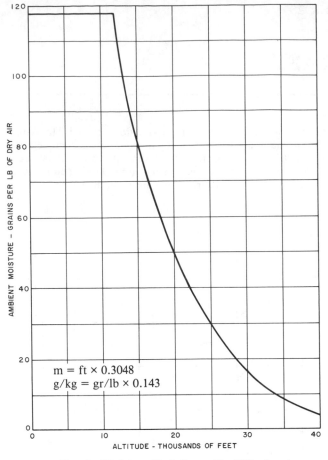

Fig. 2   Moisture Variation with Altitude

son based on a 100% passenger load. Generally, much higher ventilation rates are provided in the cockpit primarily to cool all the surrounding electrical and electronic equipment. A portion of the cabin ventilation air may be recirculated, but it should be filtered before reintroduction into the occupied areas. A ram air (outside air) or auxiliary ventilation source should be considered if reasonably probable failures could result in the loss of all ventilation. This auxiliary ventilation could consist of a ram air circuit supplying outside air through the normal distribution system, or provisions for manipulating cabin pressure control valves to draw ambient air through the cabin and flight deck, through door seals, negative relief valves, hatches, etc.

Air Quality

The quality of air in crew and passenger compartments depends on the quantity of fresh air supplied, contaminants that may be present in the air source, and the contamination generated within the aircraft compartments. Federal aviation requirements (FAR Part 25) stipulate that crew and passenger compartment air be free from harmful or hazardous concentrations of gases or vapors. For military aircraft, air contaminant level within occupied compartments should not exceed the threshold limit values established by the American Conference of Governmental Industrial Hygienists and published in AFOSH Standard 161-8.

An important aspect to air quality in many commercial aircraft applications is the dilution of tobacco smoke to acceptable levels. A number of tests have been run, in which smoker and non-smoker response to various dilution indices was obtained. The dilution index (D.I.) is defined as the liters of fresh air per

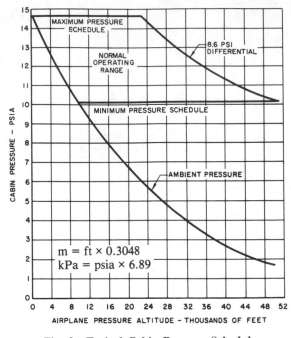

Fig. 3   Typical Cabin Pressure Schedule

mg. of tobacco burned. Figure 4 show how irritation varies with dilution index and Figure 5 shows the percentage of smokers and non-smokers who reported the irritation levels as acceptable.

Smoking Zones. The data of Figure 5 may be used, along with an estimated smoking rate of 17 mg/min per smoker to calculate the ventilation required to obtain any desired acceptance rate in a smoking zone.

Ventilation should be at a level so that at least 80% acceptance by smokers is achieved in smoking zones. For an 80% acceptance level, the dilution index is 240 L/mg for smokers in a smoking zone. At a smoking rate of 17 mg/min, a ventilation rate of 6.8 L/s per smoker is required (14.4 cfm).

Non-Smoking Zones. The minimum fresh air ventilation rate to limit CO_2 levels and control odors is 5 cfm per occupant; however, temperature control and distribution requirements may establish higher ventilation rates. If air is recirculated from smoking zones into non-smoking zones, it should be filtered to remove gaseous contaminants and aerosols or it should be diluted with enough fresh air to achieve a dilution index (D.I.) of 60 L/mg, which would be acceptable to 90% of the non-smokers. Equa-

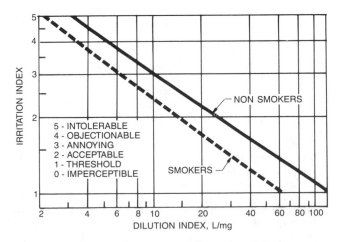

Fig. 4   Irritation versus Dilution of Smoke

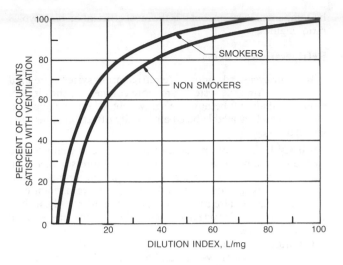

Fig. 5   Effect of Dilution Index on Occupant Satisfaction

tion (1) shows how the recirculation and fresh air requirements may be established in a non-smoking zone.

$$\text{Fresh Air} = (\text{Recir. Air.}) \, (k)$$

$$k = \left[\frac{\text{D.I. Required}}{\text{D.I. Smoking Zone}} - 1 \right] \tag{1}$$

Thus, if a 60 L/mg D.I. is required and the smoking zone D.I. is 24 L/mg, then 1.5 cfm of fresh air is required for every cfm of recirculated air.

Aircraft Without Designated Smoking Zones. Smaller aircraft, such as business and executive aircraft, commuters, and small and large military transports, may not have designated smoking zones. The dilution index for these aircraft is based on the total smoke generated and total fresh air supplied. To achieve a 90% acceptance of ventilation by non-smokers, a 60 L/mg D.I. is required for the entire cabin. The air distribution system for these types of aircraft should ensure good mixing to achieve a uniform D.I.

Ozone. Aircraft operating at altitudes above approximately 30,000 ft (9 km) may encounter atmospheric ozone concentrations of sufficient magnitude to affect cabin air quality adversely. Physiologically, ozone affects the soft tissues of the lung, causing pulmonary edema, dyspnea, and reduced lung capacity.

The effects of ozone are a function of ozone concentration and time of exposure. Currently, Federal Aviation Regulations (Part 25) set the following concentration and time of exposure limits for ozone in the cabins of transport aircraft:

1. 0.25 ppm (mg/kg) by volume, sea level equivalent, at any time above 32,000 ft (9.8 km)
2. 0.1 ppm (mg/kg) by volume, sea level equivalent, time-weighted average during any 3-hour interval above 27,000 ft (8.2 km)

Ozone concentration in an airstream can be reduced by an absorption process, a chemical reaction with a filter surface, or a catalytic decomposition process.

Ozone decomposes at a rate determined by the temperature. Thermal decomposition can be increased by allowing the air-ozone mixture to come in contact with metals or other materials that act as catalysts in decomposition reactions. Manganese dioxide, activated charcoal, stainless steel, and other common metals enhance the thermal decomposition of ozone.

Load Determination

The cooling and heating loads for a particular airplane must be determined from a heat transfer study and from an analysis of the solar and internal heat from occupants and electrical equipment. The study should consider all possible flow paths through the usually complex aircraft structure. Air film coefficients vary with altitude and should also be considered. For high-speed aircraft, the increase in air temperature and pressure due to ram effects is appreciable and may be calculated from Equations (2) and (3).

$$T_r = 0.2M^2 T_a F_r \tag{2}$$

$$P_r = (1 + 0.2M^2)^{3.5} P_a - P_a \tag{3}$$

where

F_r = Recovery factor, dimensionless.
T_r = increase in temperature due to ram effect, °F (°C).
M = Mach number, dimensionless.
T_a = absolute static temperature of ambient air, °R (K).
P_r = increase in pressure due to ram effect, kPa.
P_a = absolute static pressure of ambient air, kPa.

The average increase in airplane skin temperature for subsonic flight is generally based on a recovery factor, F_r of 0.9.

Ground and flight requirements may be quite different. An aircraft sitting on the ground in bright sunlight will have local skin temperatures considerably higher than the ambient, where the surface is painted a dark color or unpainted and perpendicular to the sun's rays. Painting the upper portion of the fuselage with white paint will reduce this effect considerably, as will a breeze blowing across the airplane.

Other considerations for ground operations are: cooldown or warmup requirements, time that doors are open for loading, and whether ground heating and cooling are provided from the installed equipment or from an external source.

DESIGN APPROACHES

A trade study of all possible state-of-the-art approaches should be conducted when establishing the air conditioning and pressurization system design for a particular aircraft. The design that meets performance requirements and is overall best from the standpoint of aircraft penalty, life cycle cost, and development risk should then be selected.

Air Distribution

The design should ensure air supply to, and exhaust from, the occupied compartments. The location of inlets is usually decided from previous experience and confirmed by quantified and subjective testing. Generally, passenger compartment air is introduced at high level and exhausted at floor level. The design of air exhausts should preclude the possibility of blockage by luggage, clothing, or litter. The overall flow pattern should keep contaminated air generated by failures under the floor, behind furnishings, or in electronic equipment from entering occupied compartments. Air from toilets and galleys should not be exhausted into other occupied areas.

The flight crew should have means to direct and vary airflow. Such adjustment should not significantly affect the overall balance of air distribution nor allow complete shut-off of air supply to the flight compartment.

With individual air supplies closed and the air conditioning system operating normally, the air velocity, in the vicinity of seated occupants, should not exceed 60 fpm (0.3 m/s) and should be between 20 and 40 fpm (0.1 to 0.2 m/s) for optimum comfort. To avoid the sensation of no air flow, air velocities should not be less than 10 fpm (0.05 m/s) at seated head height. Where individual air supplies are provided, the flow should be adjustable. The recommended jet velocity at seated head level should be at least 200 fpm (1 m/s). Cabin distribution ducting and air inlets should be sized to limit air velocities so air noise levels are not objectionable to occupants. Longitudinal movement of air in the passenger cabin should be minimized.

Compartment air distribution should be such that, in stabilized temperature control system phases, the variation in temperature should not exceed 5 °F (2.8 °C), measured in a vertical plane from 2 in. (50 mm) above floor level to seated head height.

The temperature of air entering occupied compartments should, in normal operation, be not less than 35 °F (2 °C) nor more than 160 °F (71 °C). Where cabin air supplies combine, or where cold or hot air is added for temperature control, the various supplies should be effectively mixed to achieve uniform temperature distribution, prior to distribution in occupied compartments.

Free water present in the air supply system should be removed to prevent it being discharged onto passengers or equipment. Any drainage facilities should ensure that the water presents no hazards to equipment or airplane structure.

Air Source

Engine compressor bleed air is the source of cabin pressurization and ventilation air on most current aircraft. Normally, bleed air contamination problems do not exist with current aircraft turbine engines. In most aircraft applications, the available compressor bleed air is more than adequate to meet the air conditioning and pressurization requirement throughout the ground and flight operating envelope. Under many operating conditions, the bleed air temperature and pressure are higher than required and must be regulated to lower values. Use of engine compressor bleed air can be a significant penalty to the aircraft, and this penalty should be considered when conducting trade studies to select the system approach.

Auxiliary compressors can be used in lieu of engine bleed. These compressors can be shaft driven off the engine gearbox or a remote gear box. Auxiliary compressors may also be driven by pneumatic, hydraulic, or electrical power.

Use of engine bleed air is a convenient means to obtain pressurized air. However, as a power source, bleed air use is generally not as efficient as other alternatives, in part because power often is dissipated by regulation to acceptable pressure levels. Electrical and hydraulic power can be provided at relatively high efficiencies but are limited by available sources or increase weight substantially. Direct mechanical power use is restricted

by component location, but it is the most efficient on high bypass ratio engines.

Refrigeration Systems

Both air cycle and vapor cycle refrigeration systems are used on aircraft. Air cycle systems are more common in the air conditioning of aircraft because the lightweight, compact equipment and the readily available bleed air usually offsets its inherently low efficiency.

Air Cycle. The conventional open air cycle is characterized by the continuous extraction of engine compressor bleed air, which is processed by the air cycle system and dumped overboard after its use for cabin and avionics environmental control. Most current aircraft use ram air as the primary heat sink. In most cases, an air cycle machine turbine provides the required cooling capacity.

On most current aircraft, fuel is generally used as a heat sink for secondary power systems and engine oil but it is not used as a heat sink for the Environmental Control System (ECS). The operating penalties of the open air cycle result from the cost of bleeding a large amount of air from the engine, from use of ram air as a heat sink and from the weight of the system hardware.

In the air cycle system, compressed air is cooled by expanding it through a turbine, which performs work. The turbine may drive a fan, which draws cooling air across an air-to-air heat exchanger (simple cycle), a compressor which raises the pressure of the air before it enters the turbine (bootstrap cycle), or both (simple/bootstrap or three-wheel bootstrap cycle). Figures 6, 7, and 8 show simplified schematics of each of these types of air cycle refrigeration systems.

The advantages of an air cycle refrigeration system are its light weight, compact size, and high reliability, while the disadvantages are low efficiency and poorer ground cooling. Ground cooling can be provided by an external air conditioning cart. Cooling with the installed equipment can be obtained by an auxiliary power unit, usually a gas turbine engine, to supply large quantities of high pressure air. The auxiliary power unit (APU) is carried aboard the aircraft. It is not practical to run the jet engines of an airplane on the ground to obtain cooling because of the higher power required, associated noise, and high rate of fuel consumption.

The newest open air cycle systems use high pressure water removal, cabin air recirculation, and air bearing cooling turbines, and they are discussed below:

Water Separation. The heart of a conventional low pressure water separator in an air cycle system is a cloth bag interposed

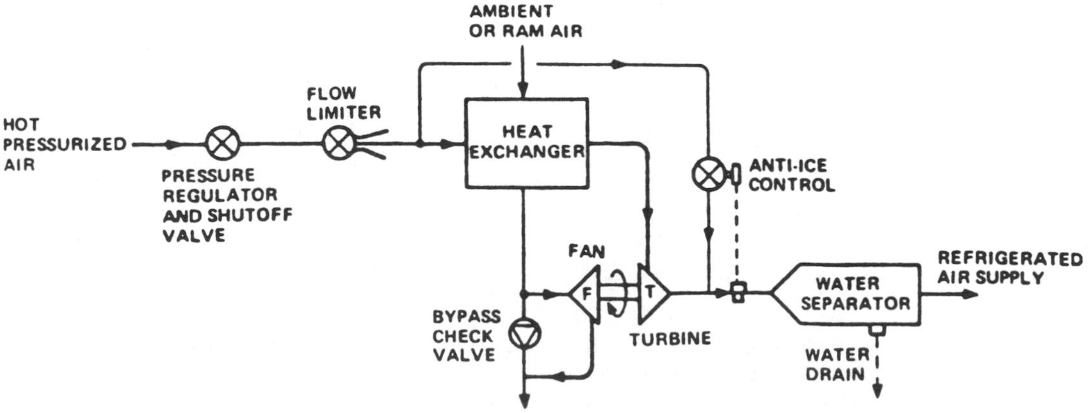

Fig. 6 Basic Simple Cycle

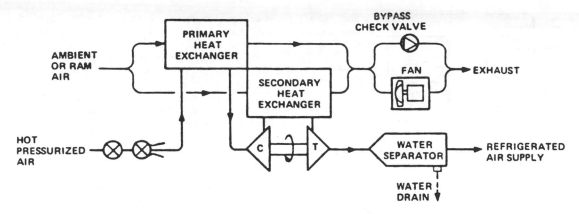

Fig. 7 Basic Bootstrap Cycle

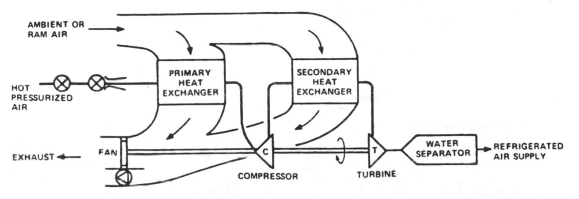

Fig. 8 Basic Three-Wheel Bootstrap Cycle

in the air-stream at the turbine discharge. This bag coalesces the water particles formed in the turbine as the air is cooled. The resulting large droplets are separated from the airstream by centrifuge baffles and traps and is either drained overboard or re-evaporated in the ram air heat sink supply to enhance the cycle efficiency.

The high-pressure water removal system condenses water at the turbine inlet. A large amount of the moisture for high humidity conditions may be condensed and removed at this point primarily because of the higher dew point temperature associated with the high pressures. Condensation is enhanced by cooling the turbine inlet temperature below the dew point temperature in a small heat exchanger using turbine discharge air. The velocity is low and the water may be induced to separate from the airstream and drain away. This scheme has the virtue of being maintenance free, whereas the coalescer bag of a low-pressure separator must be periodically cleaned. Figure 9 schematically shows a low-pressure water separator and a high-pressure separator.

Recirculation. Conventional air cycle systems are handicapped by their inability to use below-freezing turbine discharge temperatures effectively, since the frozen water particles would quickly block either a low-pressure water separator or the cabin supply duct system. If cabin air is returned to the turbine discharge and mixed with the turbine air, however, it has no influence on cooling capacity but raises the temperature of the air supply. By performing the anti-icing function with recirculated cabin air rather than hot bleed air, a greater amount of cooling can be achieved with a given quantity of bleed air.

Figure 10 shows this technique in conjunction with high pressure water separation. The recirculation could be achieved with a jet pump or a motor-driven fan.

Air Bearing Cooling Turbine. The air bearing cooling turbine is a recent innovation in the aircraft conditioning area. In this device, the oil-lubricated ball bearings of the cooling turbine are replaced by a type of journal and thrust bearing lubricated by air. Figure 11 shows the bearings for an air bearing turbine. This advancement not only eliminates the maintenance associated with the oil lubrication system, but it also improves the reliability.

Air bearings and high-pressure water separation are responsible for totally eliminating the requirement for periodic maintenance of an air cycle environmental control system.

Vapor Cycle. The vapor cycle system has a higher efficiency than the air cycle system, but it is generally heavier. It has the additional advantage of providing ground cooling with just an electrical power source. The vapor compressor and fans also may be driven by air turbines, but lesser quantities of high pressure air are required than for the air cycle system.

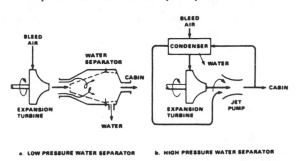

Fig. 9   Sketch of Low-Pressure Water Separator
and High-Pressure Water Separator

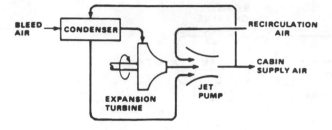

Fig. 10　Recirculation Technique as Implemented With High-Pressure Separation

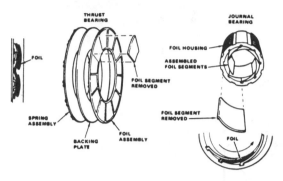

Fig. 11　Self-Acting Compliant Foil Air Bearing

Several of the early jet transports had vapor cycle refrigeration systems with a cooling capacity of approximately 20 tons. Small capacity vapor cycle units are currently used on commercial aircraft for galley refrigerators. Vapor cycle systems are widely used on general aviation aircraft and as supplementary systems for cooling electronic equipment on commercial and military aircraft.

Figure 12 shows a typical aircraft vapor cycle system. In this system, cabin air is normally recirculated by an electric fan through the evaporator when the airplane is on the ground. Capacity is modulated by an evaporator pressure regulator that raises or lowers the temperature level at which the refrigerant is evaporated. The expansion valve is thermostatic and must control to superheat sufficiently to ensure that no liquid enters the compressor. As flow is throttled at the evaporator pressure regulator or expansion valve, the surge control valve must open to bypass refrigerant and keep a minimum flow through the compressor. Since the position of each valve depends on the other valves in the loop, such a control system may be unstable.

Other methods of capacity modulation include bypassing air around the evaporator, throttling refrigerant at the evaporator inlet, varying compressor speed, or unloading the compressor. Motor speeds can be controlled by solid-state variable frequency drives where voltage is also varied accordingly. For evaporator inlet throttling with a motorized expansion valve and a centrifugal compressor, the function of the valve may be combined with the surge control on the same shaft. As the expansion valve closes, the bypass circuit opens.

Turbo-compressor air from outside or engine compressor bleed air may be manually selected after engines are started. It then switches on automatically at takeoff for cabin pressurization. The hot turbo-compressor or engine bleed air is first passed through an air-to-air heat exchanger, where it is partially cooled before entering the evaporator. Precooling is used to match the required in-flight capacity to that required on the ground and to improve system reliability.

The condenser fan provides cooling air on the ground and can also be turned on in flight to supplement ram air at low speeds and low altitude. In this system, the fan windmills in flight when turned off, but a separate circuit is provided for ram air on some airplanes. The cooling air is automatically modulated to maintain a minimum condensing pressure, both to reduce drag and to maintain pressure across the expansion valve at the low ambient encountered at high altitude.

The refrigerant must be non-toxic, odorless, and non-flammable. Refrigerants 11, 12, and 114 have been used in airplane systems, and other refrigerants may have specific advantages.

Temperature Control System

Independent, automatic temperature controls should be provided for the flight crew and passenger compartments. In large airplanes, additional temperature controls should be provided, on a zonal basis, to cater for uneven thermal loading due, for example, to mixed cargo/passenger configuration or non-uniform occupancy. Flight crew compartment temperature control should not be affected significantly by these other compartment controls. Each compartment or zone air temperature should be selectable within the range 65 to 85°F (18 to 30°C). The resultant temperature should be maintained within ±1°F (0.5°C) at the compartment sensor, when stabilized following initial switch-on or temperature re-selection. Means should be provided for temperature sensors to sample compartment air at a rate compatible with control sensitivity requirements. The air sample should be taken from a location representative of average compartment temperature. Following re-selection, compartment temperature should not overshoot the newly selected value by more than 3°F (1.5°C). Compartment supply temperature should be controlled within limits appropriate to required heating and cooling rates and with consideration to occupant safety.

Figure 13 shows a basic temperature control system for a source of cold air either from an air cycle refrigeration unit or from a ram air-cooled heat exchanger, as with a vapor cycle refrigeration system. Hot bleed air is added to the cold air source

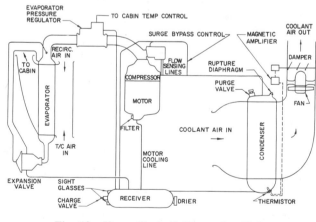

Fig. 12　Vapor-Cycle Refrigeration Unit

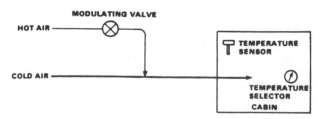

Fig. 13　Basic Temperature Control System

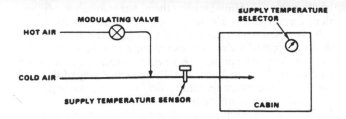

**Fig. 14   Duct Control System That Controls
Air Temperature in the Cabin Before It Enters the Cabin**

in response to the commands of a control system. The bleed air control system will hold the total flow delivered to the cabin to a fixed value no matter what the position of the modulating valve may be.

Basically, the crew selects a knob position that represents a desired cabin temperature. A sensor located at some point in the cabin measures the actual cabin temperature. The associated control equipment then compares these inputs and moves the valve to the position that will bring the cabin temperature to the selected value.

Figures 14 and 15 show variations of the basic concept and show a duct control system (which, instead of controlling the temperature in the cabin, controls the temperature of the air entering the cabin) and a two-compartment system, where the temperature of the cockpit and the cabin is controlled independently.

Cabin Pressurization Control System

The cabin pressurization control system must meter the exhaust cabin ventilating air to maintain the selected low altitude cabin against the variables of airplane altitude and variable cabin inflow air. Both pneumatic and electronic systems have been used.

Cabin pressure control systems maintain the pressure in the cabin at levels acceptable to humans, change pressure levels during climb and descent at rates that are acceptable, and limit transient pressure changes, commonly called bumps, to magnitudes that are not annoying.

Reactions in the human ear cause the initial complaints about pressure changes. Stretching of the ear drum is the major factor causing unpleasant sensations that make pressure changes objectionable. Contraction of the eustachian tube dilator muscles, as from swallowing or yawning, aids in opening the tube and equalizing pressure. A positive pressure within the middle ear is easier to neutralize as it helps force the air through

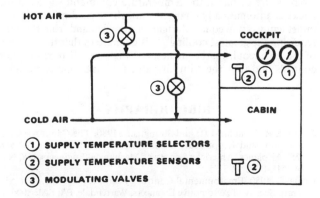

**Fig. 15   Duct Control System That Controls Air
Temperature in the Cabin and in the Cockpit Separately**

the tube. A negative pressure tends to collapse and seal the tube, hindering relief. For this reason, a lower rate of sustained pressure change is used for increasing ambient pressure than for decreasing it. Rates of 500 ft/min (2.5 m/s) ascending and 300 ft/min (1.5 m/s) descending have been the industry accepted maximums for a number of years.

Positive pressure relief at some maximum pressure must be provided to protect the airplane in the event of a pressure control system failure. A negative (vacuum) pressure relief mechanism to let air in when outdoor pressure exceeds cabin pressure must also be provided.

Other desirable features are a barometric correction selector to help select the proper landing field altitude so that the pressure differential at landing may approach zero, and a limit control to maintain a maximum cabin altitude if other control components fail. An indicating system should be provided, including a rate of climb indicator, and altitude warning horn, an altimeter, and a differential pressure indicator.

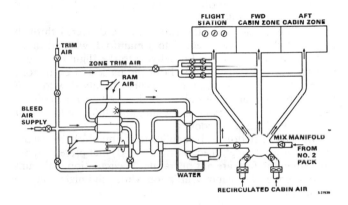

**Fig. 16   Air-Conditioning Schematic
for Commercial Airliner**

TYPICAL SYSTEM

Figure 16 shows the air cycle air-conditioning system for a current commercial transport aircraft. It operates from a source of preconditioned engine bleed air, creating a supply of conditioned air controlled to maintain the selected temperatures and ventilation rates within two passenger zones and the flight station. The various automatic temperature control functions are accomplished with electronic controllers and electric valve actuation. The two refrigeration packs are installed in the unpressurized area beneath the wing center section and are supplied with preconditioned bleed air from the two main engines or from the tail-mounted auxiliary power unit (APU). An underfloor distribution bay mixes conditioned air from the two packs with filtered recirculated cabin air and distributes it throughout the pressurized areas.

Preconditioned bleed air enters each of the two parallel air-conditioning packs through a flow control valve (Item 1), which also functions as a pack shutoff valve. Most of the basic refrigeration equipment is assembled into a package ready for installation into the aircraft. Each of the two packs includes a three-wheel air cycle machine (ACM), four heat exchangers, and the pack temperature control valves, as well as protective devices and all necessary ducting and hardware.

The ACM (Item 2) has three rotating wheels—a compressor, a turbine, and a fan—that are mounted on a common shaft supported by air bearings. After the bleed air passes through the primary heat exchanger (Item 3), where it is cooled by ram air, it enters the compressor section of the ACM, where it is compressed to a higher pressure and temperature. The bleed air is cooled again by ram air in the secondary heat exchanger (Item 4) and, after passing through the reheater (Item 5), enters the condenser (Item 6). The air discharging from the condenser contains free moisture that is removed in the extractor (Item 7) before the air enters the other side of the reheater. The function of the reheater is to cool the air on the first pass, thereby reducing the amount of cooling required of the condenser, and to reheat the air before it enters the turbine. This reheating process evaporates small amounts of entrained moisture that may still be present and creates a higher temperature at the turbine inlet with an attendant increase in turbine power. The energy removed from the turbine airflow causes a substantial temperature reduction, permitting a turbine discharge temperature well below the ram temperature.

Ram cooling air for the heat exchangers enters through a variable area ram inlet scoop, passes through the secondary and primary heat exchangers in series, and exhausts through a variable-area exhaust door. Operation of the ram inlet and exhaust door actuators (both Item 8) is under control of the pack temperature controller.

Conditioned air from the two packs is delivered through bulkhead check valves (Item 9) to a manifold, where it mixes with recirculated cabin air for delivery to the flight deck zone and the two passenger zones. Both the pack and cabin zone temperature controls limit the total cabin supply flow to 35°F (2°C) minimum at all altitudes. Conditioned air for the flight deck is removed upstream of the mix manifold, and fresh air is used for flight deck cooling.

Cabin recirculation air is supplied to the manifold by electric fans (Item 10) through check valves (Item 11) that prevent reverse flow when the fans are not operating. Recirculation maintains the desired level of cabin ventilation while minimizing the use of bleed air.

Air Conditioning Controls

Flow Control Operation. Maximum pack airflow is limited by flow control valves at the pack inlets. A dual flow schedule capability allows a pack flow to be increased 65% over normal flow schedule. With the high flow schedule, one pack will maintain approximately 80% of normal cabin airflow. The high flow schedule is automatically selected through aircraft wiring circuits whenever a cooling pack or cabin recirculating air fan is shut off.

Pack Temperature Control. When the air conditioning system is operating at maximum refrigeration capacity, the pack outlet temperature is determined by either the capabilities of the system or by the action of the low-limit controls. The maximum cooling capacity is necessary only for extremely hot conditions or to cool a heat-soaked aircraft. For most operating conditions, a warmer air supply is needed to satisfy the actual cabin cooling or heating demands, and the pack refrigeration capacity must be modulated.

The actual pack supply temperature requirement is determined by the zone controller and satisfies the cabin zone requiring the most cooling. Both packs are controlled to produce the required supply temperature. Each pack is operated independently by its own controller and temperature sensor, but both operate at the same condition and produce the same outlet temperature due to the single commanded temperature from the zone system. This results in the temperature control valve and ram doors operating at approximately the same relative position for both packs.

To adjust pack outlet temperature, the controller modulates the temperature control valve (Item 12) and the ram inlet and outlet actuators (both Item 8). Although each of these devices is independently actuated, the controller maintains a definite positional relationship between them. For maximum refrigeration, the ram doors are positioned fully open and the bypass valve is closed. To increase pack discharge temperature, the ram doors are partially closed, thus reducing cooling airflow while the bypass valve simultaneously begins opening to divert warm air around the air cycle machine. Proper scheduling of this pack control scheme minimizes ram air drag without exceeding equipment maximum temperature limitations.

The cabin air supply temperature leaving the mix manifold is limited to 35°F (2°C) minimum at all conditions. The temperature is measured by the duct air temperature sensor at the mix manifold outlet. The pack controller overrides the normal control schedule and modulates the temperature control valve and the ram air door actuators, as required.

An all-pneumatic backup control protects against icing that might occur during automatic control system failures. The pneumatic actuator of the low-limit valve (Item 13) is connected to sense the pressure difference across the condenser. The normal pressure drop across these items has no effect on the valve, but if an ice buildup starts, the increased pressure drop forces the low-limit valve open. Warm air then enters the turbine exit and stabilizes the ice accumulation at a low level. This feature also provides icing protection during manual mode of operation of the pack temperature control.

Cabin Zone Temperature Control. The cabin zone control subsystem incorporates a programmed duct air temperature control that accurately regulates during aircraft transient conditions. An inherent feature of the control is zone inlet duct temperature limitation, which results from electronic damping of the inlet temperature demand reference signal within predetermined limits.

Temperature is independently controlled in the flight station zone and in the forward and aft passenger zones by full-automatic feedback controls. The flight crew selects the desired temperature for each zone on selector units mounted in the flight station. Signals from each selector and corresponding zone temperature sensor are processed in the cabin zone controller, which produces a zone supply air temperature demand signal for each zone according to a predetermined schedule. That demand signal for each zone is appropriately supplied to each trim air control loop to provide the demanded temperature at each zone inlet.

The cabin zone controller also includes a discriminator function that selects the lowest of these demand signals and passes it to the pack controllers at the pack temperature command. Both packs are then modulated to provide this temperature. Thus, both packs are operated at the same supply duct temperature, which, when mixed with the cabin recirculation air, will satisfy the zone requiring the lowest inlet temperature. When the mix manifold outlet sensed temperature differs from the temperature demand, the temperature command signal to the packs is automatically changed until the sensed mix manifold outlet temperature equals the temperature demand from the zone requiring the greatest cooling. This guarantees that the demand of the zone requiring the greatest cooling is satisfied by the pack controls and that the trim air valve for that zone is closed.

BIBLIOGRAPHY

Crabtree, R.E; Saba, M.P.; and Strang, J.E. 1980. The Cabin Air Conditioning and Temperature Control System for the Boeing 767 and 757 Airplanes. American Society of Mechanical Engineers, NY, NY. ASME-80-ENAS-55.

Payne, G. 1980. Environmental Control Systems for Executive Jet Aircraft. Society of Automotive Engineers, Warrendale, PA, SAE 800607.

SAE. 1976. Aircraft Cabin Pressurization Control Criteria. Society of Automotive Engineers. Warrendale, PA. SAE Standard ARP 1270.

CHAPTER 26

SHIPS

THIS chapter covers air conditioning for oceangoing surface vessels including luxury liner, tramp steamer, or naval vessel. The general principals of air conditioning that apply to land installations also apply to marine installations, if all factors affecting the construction, purpose, and operation of a ship are considered. Most of the system designs discussed in this Handbook can, if properly applied, be used on ships. However, some systems are not suitable due to excessive first cost or inability to meet shock and vibration requirements for naval ships.

GENERAL CRITERIA

The following reasons for air conditioning ships are:

1. To provide an environment in which personnel can live and work without heat stress.
2. To increase crew efficiency, particularly during operation in the tropics.
3. To increase the reliability of electronic and similar critical equipment.
4. To prevent rapid deterioration of special weapons equipment aboard naval ships.

Factors to consider in the design of an air-conditioning system for shipbourd use are as follows:

1. The system should function properly under conditions of roll and pitch to which a ship is normally subjected.
2. The materials of construction should withstand the corrosive effects of salt air and sea water.
3. The system should be designed for uninterrupted operation during the voyage and continuously all year round. Since ships en route cannot be easily serviced, some standby capacity, spare parts of all essential items, and extra refrigerant charges should be carried.
4. The system should have no objectionable noise or vibration. The systems must meet the noise criteria required by the shipbuilding specification.
5. In view of the high premium for space on shipboard, the equipment should occupy a minimum of space commensurate with cost and reliability. Weight should be held to a minimum.
6. Since a ship may pass through one or more complete cycles of seasons on a single voyage and experience a change from winter operation to summer operation in a matter of hours, the system should be flexible enough to compensate for these climatic changes with a minimum of attention by the ship's operating personnel.
7. Infiltration through weather doors is generally disregarded. However, occasionally, specifications for merchant ships may require an assumed infiltration load for heating steering gear rooms and the pilot house.

8. Sun load must be considered on all exposed surfaces above the water line. If a compartment has more than one exposed surface, the surface with the greatest sun load is used, and the other exposed boundary is calculated at outside ambient temperature.
9. Cooling load inside design conditions are given as a dry bulb with a maximum rh. Cooling coil leaving air temperature for merchant ships is assumed to be 49°F (9°C) dry bulb. For naval ships, it is assumed to be 51.5°F (10.8°C) dry bulb; in both cases, the wet bulb is consistent with 95% rh. This off-coil air temperature is changed only in cases where humidity control is required in the cooling season.
10. In calculating winter heating loads, heat transmission through boundaries of machinery spaces in either direction is not considered.
11. The Society of Naval Architects and Marine Engineers bulletin, *Calculations for Merchant Ship Heating, Ventilation, and Air Conditioning Design*, gives sample calculation methods and estimated values.

MERCHANT SHIPS

Design Criteria

Outdoor Ambient Temperatures. The service and type of vessel determines the proper outdoor design temperature. Some luxury liners make frequent off-season cruises where more severe heating and cooling loads may be encountered. The selection of the ambient design should be based on the temperatures prevalent during the voyage. In general, for the cooling cycle, outdoor design conditions for North Atlantic runs are 95°F (35°C) dry bulb and 78°F (25.5°C) wet bulb; for semitropical runs 95°F (35°C) dry bulb and 80°F (26.5°C) wet bulb, and for tropical runs 95°F (35°C) dry bulb and 82°F (28°C) wet bulb. For the heating cycle, 0°F (−18°C) is usually selected as the design temperature, unless the vessel will always operate in higher temperature climates. The design conditions for seawater is 85°F (29.5°C) summer and 28°F (−2°C) winter.

Indoor Temperatures. Effective temperatures from 71°F (21.5°C) to 74°F (23°C) ET generally are selected as inside design conditions for commercial ocean going surface ships.

Inside design temperatures range from 76°F (24.5°C) to 80°F (26.5°C) dry bulb and approximately 50% rh for summer and 65°F (18°C) to 75°F (24°C) dry bulb for winter.

Consideration in the design of the air-conditioning system should be given to maintaining more comfortable room conditions during intermediate outside ambient conditions. Quality systems are designed to provide optimum comfort when outdoor ambient conditions of 65°F (18°C) to 75°F (24°C) dry bulb and 90 to 100% rh exist, and to ensure that proper humidity and temperature levels are maintained during periods when sensible loads are light. Some system types require more analysis and controls than others to achieve this goal.

The preparation of this chapter is assigned to TC 9.3, Transportation Air Conditioning.

Ventilation Requirements

Air Conditioned Spaces. In public spaces, i.e., messrooms, dining rooms, lounges, and similar spaces, a minimum of 12 cfm (5.7 L/s) of outdoor air per person or 0.33-h air change is required. In all other spaces, a minimum of 15 cfm (7.1 L/s) or 0.5-h air change of outside air must be provided. However, the maximum outside air for any air conditioned space is 50 cfm (23.6 L/s) per person.

Ventilated Spaces. The fresh air to any space is determined by the required rate of change or the limiting temperature rise. The minimum quantity of air supplied to any space is limited to 30 cfm (14.2 L/s) per occupant or 35 cfm (16.5 L/s) minimum per terminal. In addition to these requirements, exhaust requirements must be balanced.

Load Determination. The cooling load estimate for air conditioning consists of those factors discussed in Chapter 26 of the 1985 FUNDAMENTALS Volume, including the following:

1. Solar radiation.
2. Heat transmission through hull, decks, and bulkheads.
3. Heat (latent and sensible) dissipation of occupants.
4. Heat gain due to lights.
5. Heat (latent and sensible) gain due to ventilation air.
6. Heat gain due to motors or other electrical heat-producing equipment.
7. Heat gain from piping and other heat-generating equipment.

The cooling effect of adjacent spaces is not considered unless temperatures are maintained with refrigeration or air-conditioning equipment. The latent heat from the scullery, galley, laundry, washrooms, and similar ventilated spaces is assumed to be fully exhausted overboard.

The heating load estimate for air conditioning should consist of the following:

1. Heat losses through decks and bulkheads.
2. Ventilation air.
3. Infiltration (when specified).

No allowances are made for heat gain from warmer adjacent spaces.

Heat Transmission Coefficients

The overall heat transmission coefficient, U, between the conditioned space and the outside of the boundary in question, depends on the construction, material, and insulation. The composite structures common to shipboard construction do not lend themselves to theoretical derivation of such coefficients. They are most commonly obtained from full-scale panel tests. The Society of Naval Architects and Marine Engineers (SNAME) Bulletin 4-7, however, gives a method to determine coefficients, which may be used where tested data is unavailable. SNAME Bulletin 4-7 and SNAME (1971) are two sources of heat transfer coefficients to use in calculating heating and cooling loads.

Heat Dissipation From People

The rate at which heat and moisture are dissipated from people depends on the ambient dry-bulb temperature and their state of activity. The following gives values that can be used at 80°F (27°C) room dry bulb. For values at other room temperatures, see "References" section and Chapter 26 of the 1985 FUNDAMENTALS Volume.

Heat Gain From Sources Within the Space

The heat gain from motors, appliances, lights, and other equipment should be obtained from the manufacturer. Data

Degree of Activity at 80°F (27°C)	Heat Rate, Btu/h (W)		
	Sensible	Latent	Total
Dancing	245(72)	605(177)	850(249)
Persons eating (mess rooms and dining rooms	220(64)	330(97)	550(161)
Waiters	300(88)	700(205)	1000(293)
Moderate activity (lounge, ship's office, chart rooms, etc.)	200(59)	250(73)	450(132)
Light activity (staterooms, crew's berthing, etc.)	195(57)	205(60)	400(117)
Workshops	250(73)	510(149)	760(222)

found in Chapter 26 of the 1985 FUNDAMENTALS Volume may be used when manufacturer's data is unavailable.

EQUIPMENT SELECTION

General

The principal equipment required for an air-conditioning system can be divided into the following four broad categories:

1. the central station air-handling portion consisting of fans, filters, central heating and cooling coils, and sound treatment
2. the distribution network including air ductwork, and water and steam piping, as required
3. the required terminal treatment consisting of heating and cooling coils, terminal mixing units, and diffusing outlets
4. the refrigeration equipment

Factors to be considered in the selection of equipment are as follows:

1. Installed initial cost
2. Space available in fan rooms, passageways, machinery rooms, and staterooms
3. Operation costs including system maintenance
4. Noise levels
5. Weight

High velocity air distribution, which is now possible as a result of advanced techniques in noise attenuation, offers many advantages to the naval architect, shipbuilder, and shipowner. The use of unitary (factory-assembled) central air-handling equipment and prefabricated piping, clamps, and fittings facilitates the installation for both new construction and conversions. Substantial space saving is possible as compared to the conventional low velocity sheetmetal duct system. Maintenance is also reduced.

The greater use of factory-assembled central equipment also has reduced required fan room floor space, operating noise levels, and installation costs. Fans must be selected for stable performance over their full range of system operation and should have adequate isolation to prevent transmission of vibration to the deck. Effective sound treatment is essential, since fan rooms are often located adjacent to or near living quarters.

In general, all equipment is considerably more rugged than equipment for land applications, and it must withstand the corrosive environment of the salt air and sea. Materials such as stainless steel, nickel-copper, copper-nickel, bronze alloys, and hot-dipped galvanized steel are used extensively.

Fans

The Maritime Administration has a family of standard Vaneaxial, Tubeaxial, and Centrifugal fans. Selection curves found on the standard drawings are used in selecting fans. (Standard Plans S38-1-101, S38-1-102, S38-1-103). Belt-driven centrifugal fans must conform to these requirements, except for speed and drive.

Cooling Coils

1. They must have a maximum face velocity of 500 fpm (2.5 m/s).
2. They must have at least six rows of tubes and 25% more rows than required by the manufacturer's published ratings.
3. They must be based upon 42°F (5.6°C) inlet water temperature with a temperature rise of about 10°F (5.5°C).
4. Construction and materials are as specified (USMA 1965).

Heating Coils

1. They must have a maximum face velocity of 1000 fpm (5 m/s).
2. Preheaters for supply systems are selected for a final design temperature between 55°F (13°C) and 60°F (16°C) with outside air at 0°F (−18°C).
3. Preheaters for air-conditioning systems are selected to suit design requirements but with discharge temperature not less than 45°F (7°C) with 100% outside air at 0°F (−18°C).
4. Tempering heaters for supply systems are selected for a final design temperature between 50°F (10°C) and 70°F (21°C), with outside air at 0°F (−18°C).
5. Pressure drop for preheater and reheater in series, with full fan volume, must not exceed 0.5 in. of water (125 Pa).
6. The capacity of steam heaters is based on a steam pressure of 35 psi (240 kPa) gage, less an allowed 5 psi (35 kPa) gage line pressure drop and the design pressure drop through the control valve.

Filters

1. All supply systems fitted with cooling and/or heating coils must have manual roll, renewable marine-type air filters.
2. Filter face velocity must not exceed 500 fpm (2.5 m/s).
3. Filters must be protected from the weather.
4. Filters must be located so that they are not bypassed when the fan room door is left open.
5. Clean, medium rolls must either be fully enclosed or arranged so that the outside surface of the clean roll becomes the air entering side as the medium passes through the air stream.
6. The dirty medium must be wound with the dirty side inward.
7. Medium rolls are 65-ft (18.8-m) long and are readily available as standard factory-stocked items in nominal widths of 2, 3, 4, or 5 ft (0.6, 0.9, 1.2, or 1.5 m).
8. A permanently installed, dry-type filter gage, graduated to read from 0 to 1 in. of water (0 to 250 Pa), is installed on each air filter unit.

Air-Mixing Boxes

1. These boxes, if available, should fit between the deck beams.
2. Volume regulation over the complete mixing range must be within +5% of the design volume, with static pressure in the hot and cold ducts equal to at least the fan design static pressure.
3. The leakage rate of the hot and cold air valve(s) in their closed positions must not exceed 2%.
4. Calculations for space air quantities should allow for leakage through the hot air damper.
5. Box sizes are based upon manufacturer's published data, as modified above.

Air Diffusers

1. Air diffusers ventilate the space involved properly without creating drafts.

2. Diffusers serving air-conditioned spaces should be a high induction type and constructed so that moisture will not form on the cones when a temperature difference of 30°F (17°C) is used with the space dew point at least 9°F (5°C) above that corresponding to summer inside design conditions. Compliance with this requirement should be demonstrated in a mock-up test, unless previously tested and approved.
3. The volume handled by each diffuser should not, in general, exceed 500 cfm (240 L/s).
4. Diffusers used in supply ventilation systems are of the same design, except with adjustable blast skirts.
5. Manufacturer's published data is used in selecting diffusers.

Air-Conditioning Compressors

Insofar as practicable, compressors should be the same as those used for ship's service and cargo refrigeration, except as to the number of cylinders or speed. (See Chapter 30, "Marine Refrigeration," in the 1986 REFRIGERATION Volume.)

TYPICAL SYSTEMS

General

Comfort air-conditioning systems installed on merchant ships are classified as (1) those serving passenger staterooms, (2) those serving crew's quarters and similar small spaces, and (3) those serving public spaces. A brief description of the types of systems used is given in the following sections. Direct expansion or chilled water may be used for central station cooling coils. Recirculation exhaust fans, while not shown, are provided for many systems.

Single-Zone Central System

Public spaces are treated as one zone and are handled effectively by this simple arrangement. Exceptionally large spaces may require two systems. Generally, either built-up or factory-assembly fan coil central station systems are selected for large public spaces. Figure 1 shows a schematic of a typical system, which also is known as the *Type A* system. Under certain conditions, it is desirable to use all outdoor air, avoid the use of return ducts, and penalize the refrigeration plant accordingly. Outdoor air and return air are both filtered before being preheated, cooled, and reheated as required at the central station unit. A room thermostat maintains the desired temperature by modulating the valve regulating the flow of steam to the reheat coil. Humidity control is often provided. During mild weather, the dampers frequently are arranged to admit 100% outdoor air automatically.

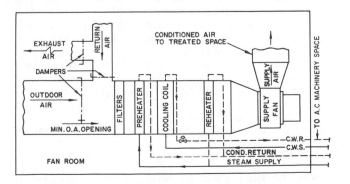

Fig. 1   Single-Zone Central (Type A) System

Multizone Central System

The system (Figure 2), also known as the *Type C* system, usually is confined to crew's and officers' quarters. Spaces are divided into zones in accordance with similarity of loads and exposures. Each zone has a reheat coil to supply air at temperature adequate for all spaces served. These coils, usually steam, are controlled thermostatically. Manual control of air volume is the only means for occupant control of conditions. Filters, cooling coils, and dampers are essentially the same as *Type D* systems.

Each internal sensible heat load component, particularly solar and lights, varies greatly. The thermostatic control methods cannot compensate for these large variations; therefore, this system cannot always satisfy individual space requirements. Volume control is conducive to noise, drafts, and odors.

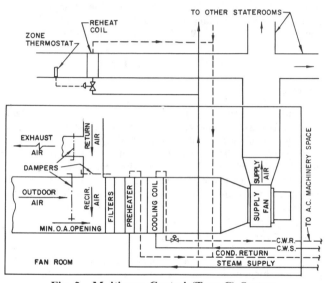

Fig. 2   Multizone Central (Type C) System

Terminal Reheat System

The terminal reheat system, or *Type D* system, is generally used for passengers' staterooms, officers' and crew's quarters, and miscellaneous small spaces (Figure 3). In this system, conditioned air is supplied to each space in accordance with its maximum design cooling load requirements. The room dry-bulb temperature is controlled by a reheater. A room thermostat automatically controls the volume of hot water passing through the reheat coil in each space. In this system, a mixture of outdoor and recirculated air circulates through the ductwork to the conditioned spaces. A minimum of outdoor air mixes with return or recirculated air in a central station system where it is filtered, dehumidified, and cooled by the chilled water cooling coils, and distributed by the supply fan through conventional ductwork to the spaces treated.

Dampers, controlled automatically in most instances, control the volume of outdoor air. No recirculated air is permitted for operating rooms and hospital spaces. When heating is required, the conditioned air is preheated at the control station to a predetermined temperature, and the reheat coils provide additional heating to maintain rooms at the desired temperature.

Air-Water Induction System

A second type of system for passenger staterooms and other small spaces is the air-water induction system (see Chapter 3) designated as the *Type E* system. This system normally is used

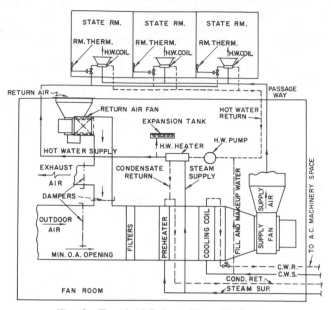

Fig. 3   Terminal Reheat (Type D) System

for the same spaces as for the Type D, except where the sensible heat factor is low, such as in mess rooms. In this system, shown in Figure 4, a central station dehumidifies and cools the primary outdoor air only.

The primary air is distributed to induction units located in each of the spaces to be conditioned. Nozzles in the induction units, through which the primary air passes, induce a fixed ratio of room (secondary) air to flow through a water coil and mix with the primary air. The mixture of treated air then is discharged to the room through the supply grille. The room air is either heated or cooled by the water coil. The flow of water to the coil (chilled or hot) can be controlled either manually or automatically to maintain the desired room conditions.

In this system, no return or recirculated air ducts are required, since only a fixed amount of outdoor (primary) air need be conditioned at the central station equipment. This relatively small amount of conditioned air must be cooled to a sufficiently low

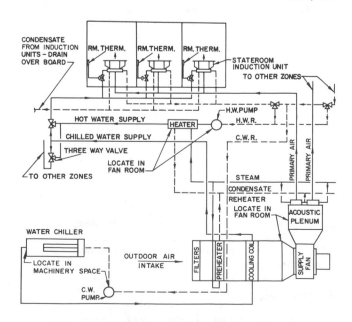

Fig. 4   Air-Water Induction (Type E) System

dew point to take care of the entire latent load (outdoor air plus room air). It is distributed at high velocity and pressure and thus requires relatively little space for air distribution ducts. However, this space saving is offset by the additional space required for water piping, secondary water pumps, induction cabinets in staterooms, and drain piping.

Space design temperatures are maintained during intermediate conditions (outdoor temperature above changeover point, and chilled water at the induction units), with primary air heated at the central station unit according to a predetermined temperature schedule. Unit capacity in spaces requiring cooling must be sufficient to satisfy the room sensible heat load plus the load of the primary air.

When outdoor temperatures are below the changeover point (chiller secured), space design temperatures are maintained by circulating hot water to the induction units. Preheated primary air provides cooling for spaces that have a cooling load. Unit capacity in spaces requiring heating must be sufficient to satisfy the room heat load plus the load of the primary air. Detailed analysis is required to determine changeover point and temperature schedules for water and air.

High Velocity Dual-Duct System

This system, also known as the *Type G* system, has gained considerable popularity in the marine field. It is normally used for the same kinds of spaces as Type D and E. In this system, all air is filtered, cooled, and dehumidified in the central units (see Figure 5). Blow-through coil arrangements are usually essential to ensure efficient design. A high-pressure fan circulates air through two ducts or pipes at high velocities approaching 6000 fpm (30 m/s). One duct (or pipe) carries cold air while the other handles warm air. A steam reheater in the central unit heats the air according to requirements of the outdoor air temperature.

The supply of warm and cold air flows to an air-mixing unit in each space served. Each mixing unit has a control valve that proportions hot and cold air from the two ducts to satisfy the demand of the room thermostat. Any desired temperature, within the limits of the capacity of the equipment, can quickly be obtained and maintained with this arrangement, regardless

of load variations in adjacent spaces. The air-mixing units incorporate self-contained regulators, which maintain a constant volume of total air delivery to the various spaces, regardless of adjustments in the air supplied to rooms down the line.

Some of the advantages of this system, compared with others that simultaneously heat and cool the spaces served, are as follows:

1. All conditioning equipment is centrally located, simplifying maintenance and operation.
2. The system can heat and cool adjacent spaces simultaneously without cycle changeover and with a minimum of automatic controls.
3. Since only air is distributed from fan rooms, no water or steam piping, electrical equipment, or wiring appear in conditioned spaces.
4. With all conditioning equipment centrally located, direct expansion cooling using halocarbon refrigerants is possible, eliminating all intermediary water-chilling equipment.

AIR DISTRIBUTION METHODS

Good air distribution in staterooms and public spaces is particularly difficult because of low ceiling heights and compact space arrangements. The design should consider the following conditions: room dimensions, ceiling height, volume of air handled, air temperature difference between supply and room air, location of berths, and allowable noise level. On major installations, mockup tests are often used to establish the exacting design criteria required for satisfactory performance.

Air usually returns from individual small spaces like staterooms either by a sight-tight louver mounted in the door or by an undercut in the door leading to the passageway. An undercut door is confined to small air quantities of 75 cfm (35 L/s) or less. Louvers are most commonly sized for a velocity of 400 fpm (2.0 m/s) based on net area.

Ductwork

Ductwork on merchant ships is constructed of steel. Ducts, other than those requiring heavier construction because of susceptibility to damage or corrosion, usually are made with riveted seams sealed either with hot solder or fire-resistant duct sealer, welded seams, or hooked seams and laps. They are fabricated of hot-dipped, galvanized, copper-bearing sheet steel, suitably stiffened externally. The minimum thickness of material is determined by the diameter for round ducts or the largest dimension of the rectangular ducts as follows:

All vertical exposed ducts	16 USSG 0.0598 in. (1.52 mm)
Horizontal or concealed vertical ducts less than 6 in. (150 mm)	24 USSG 0.0239 in. (0.61 mm)
Horizontal or concealed vertical ducts 6.5 in. (160 mm) to 12 in. (300 mm)	22 USSG 0.0299 in. (0.76 mm)
Horizontal or concealed ducts ducts 12.5 in. (310 mm) to 18 in. (460 mm)	20 USSG 0.0359 in. (0.91 mm)
Horizontal or concealed vertical ducts 18.5 in. (470 mm) to 30 in. (760 mm)	18 USSG 0.0476 in. (1.21 mm)
Horizontal or concealed vertical ducts over 30 (760 mm)	16 USSG 0.0598 in. (1.52 mm)

The increased application of high-velocity, high-pressure systems has resulted in a greater use of prefabricated round pipe and fittings, including spiral formed sheet metal ducts. It is im-

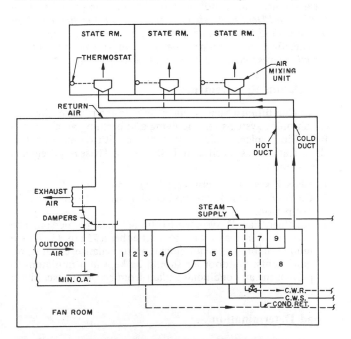

Fig. 5 Dual-Duct (Type G) System

portant that the field fabrication of the ducts and fittings be such that all are airtight. The use of factory fabricated fittings, clamps, and joints is effective in minimizing air leakage for these high pressure systems.

In addition to the usual space advantage, small ductwork saves weight, also an important consideration for this application.

CONTROLS

The conditioning load, even on a single voyage, varies over a wide range in a short period. Not only must the refrigeration plant meet these variations in load, but the controls must readily adjust the system to sudden climatic changes. Accordingly, it is the general practice to equip the plant with automatic controls. Since comfort is a matter of individual taste, room thermostats are placed in living spaces, such as staterooms, which can be adjusted by the occupant to suit personal comfort.

Manual volume control has also been used to regulate temperatures in cabins and staterooms. On the low velocity air-distribution system, however, manual volume control tends to disturb the air balance of the remainder of the spaces served. Manual controls are also applied on high velocity single-duct systems where a constant volume regulator is installed in the terminal box.

Design conditions in staterooms and public spaces can be controlled by any one or a combination of the following:

Volume Control (Used In Type C Systems). This is the least expensive and simplest control. Basic disadvantages are a lack of ability to meet simultaneous heating and cooling demands in adjacent spaces, unsatisfactory air distribution, objectionable noise, and inadequate ventilation because of reduction in air delivery.

Reheater Control. Zone reheaters of Type C systems are controlled by regulating the amount of steam to the zone coils by one of two methods. One method uses a room thermostat in a *representative* space with other spaces in the zone using manual dampers. Spaces served by this type of control do not always develop the desired comfort conditions. A second method uses a master-submaster control, which adjusts the reheater discharge temperature according to a predetermined schedule, so that full heat is applied at the design outside heating temperature and less heat as the temperature rises. This control also does not adjust to meet variations in individual room loads. However, it is superior to the *representative room thermostat* method because it is more foolproof.

Preheater Control. A duct thermostat, which modulates steam through the valve, controls the preheaters. The set point usually is a few degrees below the design cooling off-coil setting, to prevent bucking.

Coil Control. Except for Type A systems with humidity control and Type E system primary air coils, cooling coils (water) are controlled by a dew point thermostat to give a constant off-coil temperature during the entire cooling cycle. No control is provided for coils of Type E systems, because they are in series with the flow-through induction units, and maximum dehumidification must be accomplished by the primary coil to maintain dry coil operation in the room units.

Damper Control. Outdoor, return, and exhaust dampers are either manually (as a group) or automatically controlled. If automatic, one of two methods is used. One controls the damper settings by thermostats exposed to weather air. A second method uses a duct thermostat that restricts the outdoor air flow only when the design temperature leaving the cooling coil cannot be achieved with full flow through the coil.

For general information on automatic control, refer to Chapter 51.

REGULATORY AGENCIES

Merchant vessels that operate under the United States flag come under the jurisdiction of the U.S. Coast Guard. Accordingly, the installation and components must conform to the Marine Engineering Rules and Marine Standards of the Coast Guard. The design of the equipment and the installation must also comply with the requirements of the U.S. Public Health Service and Department of Agriculture. This involves, principally, ratproofing.

Comfort air conditioning installations do not primarily come under the American Bureau of Shipping. However, equipment should be manufactured, wherever possible, to comply with the American Bureau of Shipping Rules and Regulations. This is important when the vessels are equipped for carrying cargo refrigeration, since the air conditioning compressors may serve as standby units in the event of a cargo compressor failure. This compliance eliminates the necessity of a separate spare cargo compressor.

NAVAL SURFACE SHIPS

DESIGN CRITERIA

Outdoor Ambient Temperatures

Design conditions for naval vessels have been established as a compromise, considering the large cooling plants required for internal heat loads generated by machinery, weapons systems, electronics, and personnel. Temperatures of 90 °F (32 °C) dry bulb and 81 °F (27 °C) wet bulb are used as design requirements for worldwide applications, together with 85 °F (29.5 °C) sea water temperatures. Heating season temperatures are assumed to be 10 °F (−12 °C) for outdoor air and 28 °F (−2 °C) for sea water.

Indoor Temperatures

Naval ships are generally designed for space temperatures of 80 °F (26.5 °C) dry bulb with a maximum of 55% rh for most areas requiring air conditioning. The *Air Conditioning, Ventilation and Heating Design Criteria Manual for Surface Ships of the United States Navy* gives design conditions established for specific areas. *Standard Specification for Cargo Ship Construction* gives temperatures for ventilated spaces (USMA 1965).

Ventilation Requirements

Air Conditioned Spaces. Naval ship design requires that air-conditioning systems serving living and berthing areas on surface ships replenish air in accordance with damage control classifications, as specified in USN (1969). These requirements are as follows:

1. Class Z systems: 5 cfm (2.4 L/s) per person.
2. Class W systems for troop berthing areas: 5 cfm (2.4 L/s) per person.
3. All other Class W systems: 10 cfm (4.7 L/s) per person. The flow rate is increased only to meet either a 75 cfm (35.4 L/s) minimum branch requirement or to balance exhaust requirements. Outdoor air should be kept at a minimum to prevent the air-conditioning plant from becoming excessively large.

Load Determination

The cooling load estimate consists of coefficients from Design

Data Sheet DDS511-2 or USN (1969) and includes allowances for the following:

1. Solar radiation
2. Heat transmission through hull, decks, and bulkheads
3. Heat (latent and sensible) dissipation of occupants
4. Heat gain due to lights
5. Heat (latent and sensible) gain due to ventilation air
6. Heat gain due to motors or other electrical heat-producing equipment
7. Heat gain from piping, machinery, and other heat-generating equipment

Loads should be derived from requirements indicated in USN (1969).

The heating load estimate for air conditioning should consist of the following:

1. Heat losses through hull, decks, and bulkheads
2. Ventilation air
3. Infiltration (when specified)

Some electronic spaces listed in USN (1969) require 15% to be added to the cooling load for future growth and that one-third of the cooling season equipment heat dissipation (less the 15% added for growth) be used as heat gain in the heating season.

Heat Transmission Coefficients. The overall heat transmission coefficient U, between the conditioned space and adjacent boundary, should be from Design Data Sheet DDS 511-2. Where new materials or constructions are used, new coefficients may be used from SNAME or calculated using methods found in DDS 511-2 and SNAME.

Heat Dissipation from People. USN (1969) gives heat dissipation values for people in various activities and room conditions.

Heat Gain from Sources Within the Space. USN (1969) gives heat gain from lights and motors driving ventilation equipment. Heat gain and use factors for other motors and electrical and electronic equipment may be obtained from the manufacturer or Chapter 26 of the 1985 FUNDAMENTALS Volume.

EQUIPMENT SELECTION

The equipment described for merchant ships also applies for Naval vessels, except as follows:

Fans

The Navy has a family of standard vancaxial, tubeaxial, and centrifugal fans. Selection curves used for system design are found on NAVSEA standard drawings 810-921984, 810-925368, and 803-5001058. Manufacturers are required to furnish fans dimensionally identical to the standard plan and within ±5% of the delivery. No belt-driven fans are included in the fan standards.

Cooling Coils

The Navy uses eight standard sizes of direct expansion and chilled water cooling coils. All coils have 8 rows in the direction of air flow, with a range in face area of 0.6 to 10.0 square feet (0.06 to 0.93 m²).

The coils are selected for a face velocity of 500 fpm (2.5 m/s) maximum, but sizes 54 DW to 58 DW may have a face velocity of up 620 fpm (3.2 m/s) if the bottom of the duct on the discharge is sloped up at 15 degrees for a distance equal to the height of the coil.

Chilled water coils are most commonly used and are selected using 45 °F (7.2 °C) inlet water temperature with approximately 6.7 °F (3.74 °C) rise in water temperature through the coil.

This is equivalent to 3.6 gpm per ton [65 m/(s·kW)] of cooling.

Cfm quantity is based upon lowest leaving air temperature from each size cooling coil at design entering air temperature. Construction and materials are specified in MIL-C-2939.

Heating Coils

The Navy has standard steam and electric duct heaters with specifications as follows:

Steam Duct Heaters
1. Maximum face velocity is 1800 fpm (9.1 m/s).
2. Preheaters leaving air temperature is 42 to 50 °F (5.5 to 10 °C).
3. Steam heaters are served from the 50 psi (350 kPa) gage steam system.

Electric Duct Heaters
1. Maximum face velocity is 1400 fpm (7.11 m/s).
2. Temperature rise through the heater is per MIL-H-22594A, but in no case more than 48 °F (26.5 °C).
3. The power supply for the smallest heaters is 120 V, 3 phase, 60 hz. All remaining power supplies are 440 V, 3 phase, 60 hz.
4. The pressure drop through the heater must not exceed 0.35, in. of water (87 Pa) at 1000 fpm (5.1 m/s). Manufacturers tested data should be used in design of systems.

Filters

The Navy uses seven standard filter sizes with the following characteristics:

1. Filters are available in steel or aluminum.
2. Filter face velocity is between 375 and 900 fpm (1.9 and 4.6 m/s).
3. A filter cleaning station on board ship includes facilities to wash, oil, and drain filters.

Air Diffusers

The Navy has standard diffusers for air-conditioning systems, but generally it uses a commercial type similar to those for merchant ships.

Air Conditioning Compressors

The Navy uses R-12 reciprocal compressors up to approximately 150 tons (53 KW). For larger capacities open, direct-drive centrifugal compressors using R-114 are used. Seawater is used for condenser cooling at the rate of 5 gpm per ton [90 mL/(s·kW)] for reciprocal compressors and 4 gpm per ton [72 mL/(s·kW)] for centrifugal compressors.

Typical Systems

On Naval ships, zone reheat systems are used for most applications. Some ships with sufficient electric power have used low velocity terminal reheat systems with electric heaters in the space. Some newer ships have used a fan coil unit with fan, chilled water cooling coil, and electric heating coil in spaces with low to medium sensible heat per unit area of space requirements. The unit is supplemented by conventional systems serving spaces with high sensible or high latent loads.

Air Distribution Methods

Methods used on Navy ships are similar to those discussed in the section for merchant ships. The minimum thickness of materials for ducts are listed in Table 1.

Table 1 Minimum Thickness of Materials for Ducts

Sheet for Fabricated Ductwork (Dimensions in inches)

Diameter or Longer side	Non-Watertight Galvanized Steel	Aluminum	Watertight Galvanized Steel	Aluminum
Up to 6	0.018	0.025	0.075	0.106
6.5 to 12	0.030	0.040	0.100	0.140
12.5 to 18	0.036	0.050	0.118	0.160
18.5 to 30	0.048	0.060	0.118	0.160
Above 30	0.060	0.088	0.118	0.160

Sheet for Fabricated Ductwork (Dimensions in mm)

Diameter or Longer side	Non-Watertight Galvanized Steel	Aluminum	Watertight Galvanized Steel	Aluminum
Up to 150	0.46	0.64	1.90	2.69
160 to 300	0.76	1.02	2.54	3.56
310 to 460	0.91	1.27	3.00	4.06
470 to 760	1.22	1.52	3.00	4.06
Above 760	1.52	2.03	3.00	4.06

Welded or Seamless Tubing

Tubing Size Inches	(mm)	Non-Watertight Aluminum Inches (mm)	Watertight Aluminum Inches (mm)
2 to 6	(50 to 150)	0.035 (0.89)	0.106 (2.70)
6.5 to 12	(160 to 300)	0.050 (1.27)	0.140 (3.56)

Spirally Wound Duct (Non-Watertight)

Diameter Inches	(mm)	Steel Inches (mm)	Aluminum Inches (mm)
Up to 8	(200)	0.018 (0.46)	0.025 (0.64)
Over 8	(200)	0.030 (0.76)	0.032 (0.81)

Controls

The Navy's principal air-conditioning control uses a two-position dual thermostat that controls a cooling coil and an electric or steam reheater. This thermostat can be set for summer operation and does not require resetting for winter operation.

Steam preheaters use a regulating valve with a weather bulb controlling approximately 25% of the valves capacity to prevent freezeup, and a line bulb in the duct downstream of the heater to control the temperature between 42°F (5.5°C) and 50°F (10°C).

Other controls are used to suit special system types, such as pneumatic/electric controls when close tolerance temperature and humidity control is required, i.e. operating rooms. Thyristor controls are sometimes used on electric reheaters in ventilation systems (see Chapter 51).

REFERENCES

SNAME. Calculations for Merchant Ship Heating, Ventilation and Air Conditioning Design, Society of Naval Architects and Marine Engineers, Technical and Research Bulletin No. 4-16.

SNAME. Thermal Insulation Report, the Society of Naval Architects and Marine Engineers, Technical and Research Bulletin No. 4-7.

SNAME. 1971. *Marine Engineering.* Chapter 19 by J. Markert. Society of Naval Architects and Marine Engineers.

USMA. 1965. Standard Specification for Cargo Ship Construction. U.S. Maritime Adminstration, Washington, D.C.

USMA. Standard Plan S38-1-101, Standard Plan S38-1-102, and Standard Plan S38-1-103. U.S. Maritime Administration, Washington, D.C.

USN. 1969. The Air Conditioning, Ventilation and Heating Design Criteria Manual for Surface Ships of the United States Navy.

USN. NAVSEA Drawing No. 810-921984, NAVSEA Drawing No. 810-925368, and NAVSEA Drawing No. 803-5001058. Naval Sea Systems Command, Dept. of the Navy, Washington, D.C.

USN. *General Specifications for Building Naval Ships.* Naval Sea Systems Command, Dept. of the Navy, Washington, D.C.

Note: MIL specifications are available from Commanding Officer, Naval Publications and Forms Center, ATTN: NPFC 105, 5801 Tabor Ave., Philadelphia, PA 19120.

CHAPTER 27

ENVIRONMENTAL CONTROL FOR SURVIVAL

DOMINANT considerations in the design of most heating, ventilating, and air-conditioning systems relate either to maintaining comfort for occupants in enclosed spaces or to creating favorable environments for commercial processes. There are, in addition, special applications in which survival, not comfort, is the dominant concern. This chapter gives background information, parameters, and requirements relating to control of the physical and chemical environment for survival of people in enclosed spaces, when adjacent areas may be neither safe nor habitable.

The original version and subsequent revisions of this chapter focused on shelters intended for protection against effects that might develop during or after an attack with modern weapons (Glasstone 1962). Although the effects to be averted have included blast, fire, nuclear and thermal radiations, and contamination by chemical or biological agents, some emphasis has been given to the widespread and persistent effects of radioactive fallout, which could necessitate prolonged occupancy of many shelters (OCD 1962).

The primary source of information presented is based on theoretical and experimental data developed in connection with the design and use of structures as protective shelters, both above and below ground. Important contributions were also derived from evaluations of physiological stresses resulting from short- and long-term confinement of people in marginal environments. Becoming more familiar are such applications as underwater habitats; protected control centers or shelters for personnel in the nuclear and chemical industries; refuges for protection in the aftermath of explosion, fire, flooding, entrapment, or interruption of power in mines and high-rise buildings; and various means for improving survival during natural disasters.

The information in this chapter is general in context, and the term *shelter* is synonymous with any room, chamber, or enclosed space constructed and equipped to protect the health, safety, and lives of the occupants against certain hazards that may exist in the surroundings. Shelter requirements based on weapon effects remain, however, as a source and potential application for reliable design data.

FACTORS AFFECTING THE PHYSICAL ENVIRONMENT

With no planned control for the physical environment, the transient conditions in a shelter either approach a safe state of equilibrium or become intolerable. The intolerable condition might be due to either a high carbon dioxide concentration, accompanied by a low oxygen content, or to an excessive effective temperature. A progressive deterioration of the environmental conditions can be a physiological hazard, and remedial action would be needed before the individuals succumb to the extreme effects of vitiated air, elevated body temperature, organic strain,

or dehydration. Some factors that influence or reflect the physical environment in any occupied shelter are as follows:

1. Number of occupants and duration of occupancy.
2. Metabolic traits of the people: energy expenditure, sensible and latent heat transfer, oxygen consumed, and carbon dioxide produced.
3. Physiological and psychological reactions of people to the situation: environmental stresses, deprivation, states of health, dehydration effects, and tolerance limits.
4. Clothing (insulating properties, absorptivity, porosity).
5. Diet (solid and liquid, including drinking water).
6. Air and mean radiant temperatures, humidity, and air motion in all spaces (effective temperature of environment).
7. Inside surface areas and temperatures and moisture condensation.
8. Interior heat and moisture sources other than people, such as lights, motors, engines, and appliances (continuous or intermittent).
9. Heat exchange with adjacent structures or heat sources.
10. Thermal properties of the shelter and surrounding materials: conductivity, density, specific heat, diffusivity, and moisture content.
11. Thickness and mass shielding properties of the shelter enclosure for protection from nuclear radiation.
12. Weather conditions regarding variations in temperature, humidity, solar radiation, wind, and precipitation.
13. Initial conditions of the shelter environment and its surroundings (temperature distribution and moisture).
14. Temperature, humidity, quality, quantity, and distribution of air supplied to shelter spaces from a safe source.
15. Versatility and reliability of environmental control systems (ventilation, cooling, heating, air conditioning, power supply).
16. Protection in adapted places of refuge from fire and smoke effects; exclusion of fumes by interspace pressure differentials.
17. Ability of the structure to resist applied loads.

PHYSIOLOGICAL ASPECTS

The physiological factors of concern in the design of environmental control systems for survival shelters arise from metabolic heat; moisture and carbon dioxide generated by the occupants; and the human tolerance limits for cold, heat, humidity, CO, CO_2, and O_2. Response to heat or cold is essentially determined by ability to dissipate metabolic energy by the combined mechanisms of evaporation, convection, and radiation (see Chapter 8 of the 1985 FUNDAMENTALS Volume). A rise or fall from normal body temperature may be caused by physical hazards associated with heat stress or cold stress. Removal of clothing and suppression of activity are guards against heat stress in shelters; increasing the metabolic output through exercise and providing extra, dry clothing are guards against cold stress.

The preparation of this chapter is assigned to TC 9.8, Large Building Air-Conditioning Applications.

Metabolic heat production combined with warm climates and low air flow rates is a primary source of heat stress in the shelter environment. Since metabolic heat production is principally a function of activity, sedentary activity level is desirable. A sedentary person must dissipate energy at the rates shown in Figure 1 to maintain thermal equilibrium in a shelter environment. The value for a standard population sample is 275 Btu/h (80 W). The common value for sedentary metabolism in shelters is 400 Btu/h (117 W), the higher value providing an allowance for other than average groups and for increased metabolism for some working occupants (Pefley, Cull, and Sekins 1969).

Heat stress causes increased blood flow through the skin, and thus a rise in skin temperature. Heat transfer by radiation, convection, and evaporation then proceeds at an increased rate until thermal balance is restored, if possible. The nude skin temperature rises until the onset of perspiration stabilizes the skin temperature at approximately 95 °F (35 °C). Further rise in heat stress expands the role of evaporative cooling by increasing the perspiring area of the skin at about 95 °F (35 °C) until the entire body area is moist. Since the preferred mechanism for heat is sensible (convective and radiative) cooling, the body resorts to sweating only if sensible cooling is inadequate. Sensible cooling is the net effect of convection and radiation, which largely depends on the differences between the skin temperature and air dry-bulb temperature and the mean radiant temperature of the surroundings.

The effects of temperature, humidity, and clothing on the transfer of metabolic heat and moisture to the environment are shown graphically in Figure 2, which is based on a computational model, using physiological data and heat-mass transfer coefficients derived from several sources. (Chapter 8, 1985 ASHRAE Handbook, Pefley et al. 1969, Humphreys et al. 1965, Fanger et al. 1968, Allen 1972, Pefley et al. 1972.) In the model, mean skin temperature, T_s, is a function of air temperature, T_a.

Within the range of temperatures included in Figure 2, the value of T_s varies from a median of 93.2 °F (34 °C) when $T_a = 87.8$ °F (31 °C) through a range of about 3.6 °F (2 °C) above and below the median (Allen 1972). Air and skin temperatures are equal at 95 °F (35 °C), and evaporation is then the only effective process for transfer of metabolic heat. Values along the steep, solid line associated with minimal clothing with a value of 0.1 clo (0.02 K · m²/W) are proportional to the rate of sensible heat loss or gain ($R + C$), as well as the rate of latent heat loss (E) required for thermal equilibrium. Values along the broken lines that intersect the solid line are proportional to the maximum evaporative cooling effect ($\overline{E}$) attainable at various

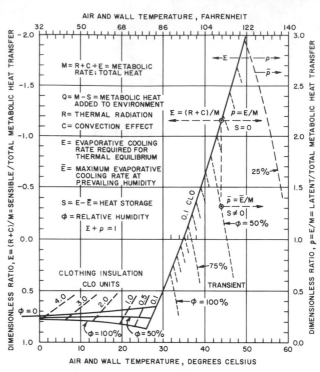

ᵃClothing is assumed to be permeable to water vapor.

Air velocity, $v = 30$ fpm (0.15 m/s).

A value often used for the metabolic rate of sedentary persons is M = 400 Btu/h (117.2 W) (100.8 kcal/h). For more definitive values, see Fig. 1.

The mass rate of water loss by evaporation, ω, is proportional to the rate of latent heat transfer, E or $\overline{E}$. If the units of E are Btu/h, then $\omega = E/1040$ lb/h. If the units of E are J/s or W, then $\omega = E/672$ kg/h. If the units of E are kcal/h, then $\omega = E/578$ kg/h. Equivalent values: 1.000 kg/h = 2.2046 lb/h.

At air temperature, T_a, model skin temperature, T_s, is:

$$T_s = 34 + 1.5 \text{ arc tan } [0.1967 \, (T_a - 31)].°C.$$

**Fig. 2   Model for Partition of Metabolic Heat Losses
from Sedentary Persons in Optimum Clothingᵃ**

relative humidities from 25 to 100%. Thus, metabolic equilibrium is not possible when the required rate exceeds the maximum rate of evaporative cooling. Under this transient condition, an increase in body temperature is inevitable.

Points of intersection for the lines that represent required and maximum rates of evaporative cooling are shown at intervals of 5% rh. At these points, skin surfaces are presumed to be completely wet, profuse sweating is necessary, and rapid dehydration occurs unless water losses are replaced occasionally. Such a situation is precarious and is tolerable for only a short time. If the metabolic rate for a man is 400 Btu/h (117 W), the maximum sweat rate required for evaporative cooling within the range of temperatures covered by Figure 2 is about 1.15 lb/h (145 mg/s).

If the metabolic rate of a sedentary person is 325 Btu/h (95 W), the air temperature is 111 °F (44 °C), and the relative humidity is 50%. The related points encircled on Figure 2 correspond to the values, $\varrho = 2.16$ and $\overline{\varrho} = 1.32$, for the required and maximum latent/total heat ratios. Thus, the required and maximum values for the rate of latent heat transfer are:

$$E = 2.16 \times 325 = 702 \text{ Btu/h}$$
$$= 2.16 \times 95 = 205 \text{ W}$$

and

$$\overline{E} = 1.32 \times 325 = 429 \text{ Btu/h}$$
$$= 1.32 \times 95 = 125 \text{ W}$$

The transient rate of heat storage is, then: $S = E - \overline{E} = 273$ Btu/h (80 W). If the mass of the person is 150 lb (68 kg), this rate of heat storage would cause the average body temperature to increase at a rate of about 2.2 °F (1.2 °C) per hour.

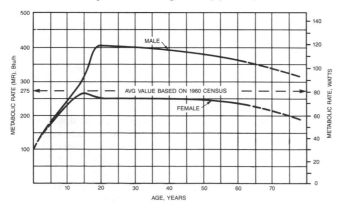

A typical sedentary metabolic rate per unit area of skin surface = 1 Met = 50 kcal/h · m² = 58.15 W/m² = 18.43 Btu/h · ft²

Chapter 8 of the 1985 FUNDAMENTALS Volume lists metabolic rates at various levels of physical activity.

**Fig. 1   Sedentary Metabolic Rates
as Functions of Ageᵃ**

If thermal equilibrium with a totally wet skin at about 95 °F (35 °C) is not achieved, the skin temperature will rise as will the deep body temperature, resulting in severe heat strain associated with further dilation of large vascular areas. The blood volume must increase or vasoconstriction must occur in other areas to maintain adequate blood flow and blood pressure. Maintenance of a high sweat rate also becomes critical.

Ability to cope with this severe environment is a function of available drinking water, salt, acclimatization, age (the very youngd and old being weakest), and health. Deficiencies in any of these factors in an extreme heat stress environment can trigger failure of the thermo-regulatory system and onset of heat stroke. At rest, body temperatures of 108 °F (42 °C) are fatal within minutes. Prolonged (one or two hours) temperatures of 106 °F (41 °C) will result in permanent damage to the liver and brain. A body temperature rise of 2 to 3 °F (1 to 1.7 °C) over a longer period would be hazardous. The values in Table 1 indicate limits beyond which the physiological strains resulting from heat stress or dehydration may be irreversible (Chapter 8, 1985 ASHRAE Handbook, Pefley et al. 1972, Blockley 1968).

Water Requirements

In a warm or hot environment, the problems of heat stress and metabolic equilibrium may be compounded by the effects of dehydration, if water losses cannot be replaced. Figure 2 shows that the requirement for latent (evaporative) cooling, and hence the need for water replacement, increases rapidly with dry-bulb temperature of the air in a warm environment. In a hot environment, the sensible heat component tends to warm the body and increase the latent cooling load to a value much greater than the actual metabolic rate.

The amount of potable water needed daily to avoid dehydration in a sedentary man are shown in Figure 3 for conditions under which sweat can be freely and completely evaporated from body surfaces. If the ambient air is humid and hot, more sweat may be excreted than can be evaporated, and the requirement for replacement water is increased. These effects have been noted at effective temperatures greater than 85 °F (30 °C). Women and children generally require less amounts of drinking water because their metabolic rates tend to be lower (Figure 1).

Analyses of data from some tests in which air motion around the subject was at a comparatively high and controlled level have indicated a strong correlation of water intake with effective temperature (ET), as well as dry-bulb temperature. Tests conducted under typical shelter conditions with young, healthy men showed a fresh water intake of 2.7 quarts (2.6 litres) per man-day at an ET of 85 °F (30 °C) (Blockley 1968). Other tests under simulated conditions at the same effective temperature indicated the same per capita rate of fresh water intake, but an intake slightly over 3 quarts (2.8 litres) per man-day with stored water (McNall and Ryan 1968). At an ET of 82 °F (28 °C), test results reported by both sources of data indicated a per capita range of 2.1 to 2.4 quarts (2.0 to 2.3 litres) per day for water usage.

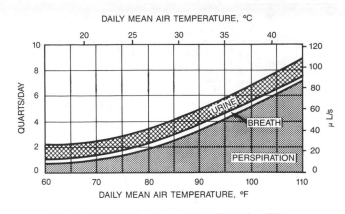

Fig. 3   Daily Requirement for Drinking Water to Avoid Dehydration in Men at Rest

The results of a long-term test indicated that healthy males under 50 years old can survive for 10 days at an ET of 82 °F (28 °C) when the dry-bulb temperature is 86 °F (30 °C), with a daily ration of 1.25 quarts (1.2 L) per person (Gorton 1972). During this deprivation test, the daily dietary allowance was 1000 kilocalories (4200 kJ) of OCD rations per person. The weight loss, attributed to both dehydration effects and deficient diet, was about 7% of initial body weight (mass).

In addition to adequate water and salt supply to minimize heat stroke hazard, well-ventilated body support, prone resting position, and minimum clothing will aid in suppressing its onset. Perspiration-wiping cloths and fanning by others effectively provide comfort to those experiencing extreme strain from the hot humid environment.

Cold stress causes the body to compensate by cutaneous vascular contraction, which reduces skin temperature and restores equilibrium between metabolic output and heat loss. This suppression of skin temperature also reduces evaporative loss from the skin to a minimum (Figure 2).

If vasoconstriction fails to maintain a heat balance through reduction in skin temperature, shivering will occur with a resulting increase in metabolism. If the environment is not too cold, the increased heat production will arrest the lowering of body temperature. As the rectal temperature falls below 90 °F (32.2 °C), the shivering mechanism begins to fail and may cease at rectal temperatures below 80 to 86 °F (27 to 30 °C). Exercising, putting on additional dry clothing, eating, and bringing people into close proximity to each other and away from low temperature zones are effective ways of combating cold stress.

Time-Temperature Tolerance

Predicted tolerance time limits are indicated in Table 2 for the exposure of properly clothed, healthy subjects at rest in a wide range of environments, from cold to hot (Chapter 8, 1985 ASHRAE Handbook, Pefley et al. 1972, Lind 1955). An effec-

Table 1   Physiological Limits for Healthy Male Subjects

Parameter	Conservative Values	Maximum Values
Sweat rate and heat of vaporization	1.06 quart/h(1.0 L/h)	Slightly higher than conservative values during moderate to strenuous work
Increase in body temperature	2 to 3 °F (1.1-1.7 °C)	4 to 5 °F (2.2 to 2.8 °C) [rectal, esophageal, and tympanic membrane], within four hours during moderate work
Pulse rate	130 beats per min	150 to 190 beats per min within four hours
Skin temperature		102 to 103 °F (38.9 to 39.4 °C) within four hours while standing at ease
Cardiac output (estimated)		Slightly over 25.4 quarts per min (0.4 L/s) within four hours while standing at ease
Dehydration limit		6% of body weight (mass)

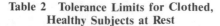

Table 2   Tolerance Limits for Clothed, Healthy Subjects at Rest

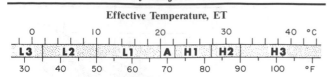

Effective Temperature Ranges:

A = 68 to 72°F (20.0 to 22.2°C)

This is the desirable range for long-term comfort of normally clothed persons when air motion is minimal and the mean radiant temperature does not differ greatly from air temperature.

L1 = 68 to 50°F (20.0 to 10.0°C)

H1 = 72 to 82°F (22.2 to 27.8°C)

Most people will tolerate environmental conditions within these ranges for periods of 14 days or more.

L2 = 50 to 35°F (10.0 to 1.7°C)

H2 = 82 to 90°F (27.8 to 32.2°C)

The physiological stresses associated with these ranges can be tolerated by most people for several hours and by motivated hardy individuals for 24 hours or longer.

L3 = Less than 35°F (1.7°C)

H3 = More than 90°F (32.2°C)

The severe physiological stresses associated with these ranges can be tolerated without injury for only a few hours at the threshold or a few minutes in extremely cold or hot- humid environments. Special consideration should be given to the procedures or control system needed for health, safety, and survival in situations under which the precarious conditions in ranges L3 or H3 might develop.

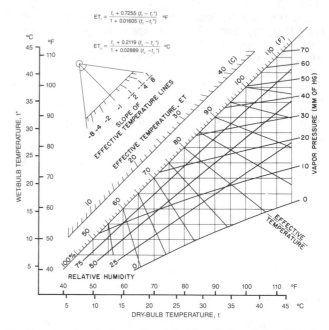

Chart based on approximate equations derived from the formulation of Effective Temperature (ET) Index with an air velocity of 20 fpm (0.1 m/s). See Figure 7 in Chapter 8 of the 1985 FUNDAMENTALS Volume. All ET lines pass through point in upper left.

Vapor pressure: 1 mm Hg = 133 Pa

Fig. 4   Still-Air Effective Temperature

tive temperature (ET) can be related to dry-bulb and wet-bulb temperatures by means of Figure 4. Conditions in range A, the comfort zone, do not impose any limits on the duration of occupancy.

Near the outer bounds of ET ranges L1 and H1, susceptible individuals (including infants, the aged, and persons afflicted with arthritis, heart disease, or metabolic disorders) may experience difficulties (Lee and Henschel 1963, Henschel et al. 1968). At low temperatures in range L1, chilblains may appear. At higher temperatures in range H1, anxiety, sleeplessness, nausea, and heat rash will probably occur during prolonged exposure.

If exposure to the moderate cold stress in ET range L2 or heat stress in ET range H2 is likely to be extended beyond a few hours, special care should be taken to maintain safe body temperatures. An adequate diet and multilayered clothing adaptable to the prevailing temperature level are essential during prolonged exposure to conditions in ET range L2. Reliance on the warming effects of increased physical activity or shivering is not a desirable alternative.

Minimal clothing is appropriate in ET range H2, and, to avoid dehydration, potable water should be available for replacing metabolic losses. The ability to cope with heat stress varies among individuals; persons having subnormal sweat response are inherently susceptible. A posture that affords maximum opportunity for evaporation from skin surfaces is desirable in a hot environment; impermeable clothing and furnishings that impede evaporation should be avoided.

Exposure to the severe cold stress in ET range L3 and heat stress in ET range H3 cannot be safely prolonged beyond limits determined by body temperatures, dehydration, and individual sensitivities. With subfreezing temperatures, the fingers and toes of sedentary persons are most susceptible to frostbite, even with protective clothing. Exposure to relatively high dry-bulb temperatures can be endured for significant periods if the partial pressure of water vapor in the air is low. An environmental

temperature of 176°F (80°C) is tolerable for about an hour if the air is virtually dry. However, breathing is slightly painful in air having a dew point of 122°F (50°C), and such a condition is endurable for only a few minutes (Lind 1955).

Vitiation Factors

Carbon dioxide concentration should not exceed 3% by volume and preferably should be maintained below 0.5%. For a sedentary person, 3 cfm (1.4 L/s) per person of fresh air will maintain a CO_2 concentration of 0.5%. At concentrations of 3% and above, performance deteriorates and basic physiological functions are affected. At 1.5%, basic performance and physiological functions are not affected, but slow adaptive processes have been observed that might induce pathophysiological states on long exposure. At 0.5 to 0.8%, no significant physiological or adaptive changes occur.

Oxygen level in a shelter is generally less critical than CO_2 levels in the absence of life-support systems. Oxygen concentration in normal air is about 21%; 17% is frequently taken as a limit for shelters.

An approximate relationship between physical activity, energy expenditure, oxygen consumption, carbon dioxide production, and rate of breathing is shown in Table 3. The respiratory quotient (RQ) is the volumetric ratio of carbon dioxide production to oxygen consumption. A value of 0.84 may be used for the conditions in Table 3. This is a representative value; the actual RQ largely depends on diet and body chemistry. In the absence of metabolic disorders, values of RQ associated with the oxidation of carbohydrates, proteins, and fats are about 1.0, 0.8, and 0.7, respectively (Allen 1972, Harrow and Mazur 1958).

The effects of carbon monoxide must be considered, even though the amount of this gas produced by the body is negligibly small. In confined shelter spaces, the prime source of CO would be tobacco smoking, with pipes producing five times and cigars almost 20 times as much as cigarettes. It can also come from fuel-burning devices in the shelter, from the exhaust gases of

Table 3 Per Capita Rates of Energy Expenditure, Oxygen Consumption, Carbon Dioxide
Production, and Pulmonary Ventilation for Man

Level of Physical Activity	Energy Expenditure; Metabolic Rate Btu/h	(W)	Oxygen Consumption ft³/h	(mL/s)	Carbon Dioxide Production ft³/h	(mL/s)	Rate of Breathing ft³/h	(mL/s)
Exhausting effort	3600	(1055)	6.66	(52.4)	5.7	(44.5)	146	(1150)
Strenuous work or sports	2400	(703)	4.44	(35.0)	3.8	(29.5)	97	(760)
Moderate exercise	1600	(469)	2.96	(23.3)	2.5	(19.7)	64	(500)
Mild exercise; light work	1000	(293)	1.84	(14.5)	1.55	(12.2)	40	(315)
Standing; desk work	600	(176)	1.10	(8.6)	0.93	(7.3)	24	(190)
Sedentary, at ease	400	(117)	0.74	(5.8)	0.62	(4.9)	16	(125)
Reclining, at rest	300	(88)	0.56	(4.4)	0.47	(3.7)	12	(95)

internal combustion engines, or through the ventilation intake from smoldering fires outside the shelter.

Carbon monoxide is invisible, odorless, tasteless, and non-irritating, and the human tolerance for CO is very slight. For industrial purposes, the allowable concentration is considered to be 50 ppm (50 mg/kg), which is equivalent to 0.005% by volume. This limit is based on an 8-hour workday, five days per week. For exposure over longer sustained periods, lower limits are used. For submarines, the limit is 50 ppm (50 mg/kg) or 0.005%, and for space cabins the design level is 10 ppm (10 mg/kg) or 0.001%. Increased levels of carbon dioxide can increase the toxic effect of CO. The increased CO_2 results in deeper and more rapid breathing, which, in turn, increases the absorption of CO into the body (OCD 1969).

Odorous substances arising from activities within the shelter, as well as other toxic or explosive gases, should also be considered. In connection with austere shelters, minimal rates of air replacement are generally sufficient to dilute odors associated with human occupancy. Hydrocarbons from fuel leakage, hydrogen from batteries being discharged, and ingress of radioactive particulates, pathogenic organisms, or chemical agents are all possible hazards.

CLIMATE AND SOILS

Heat loss calculations for underground shelters require values of thermal conductivity and thermal diffusivity of earth. Information on earth temperature is also required, which is related to the thermal and physical properties of soil, as well as to the climatic conditions. Table 4 illustrates thermal conductivity and diffusivity of various types of soil with respect to moisture content. Earth temperature may be estimated from the soil temperature data at several selected stations throughout the United States, published in Climatological Data of the U.S. Weather Record Center, Asheville, NC.

Earth temperature beyond a depth of 3 ft (0.9 m) is seldom affected by diurnal cycle of air, temperature, and solar radiation. The annual fluctuation of earth temperature, however, extends to a depth of 30 to 40 ft (9 to 12 m). The integrated monthly average earth temperature from surface to a depth of 10 ft (3 m) is insensitive to the thermal diffusivity of soil, as long as the diffusivity is larger than 0.02 ft²/h (0.5 mm²/s). Table 5 presents annual maximum and minimum earth temperature averaged over the surface to a depth of 10 ft (3 m) for 47 stations throughout the United States, which may be used for an approximate calculation of underground heat transfer (ASHRAE 1965).

Other useful references on the subject of earth temperature and thermal and physical properties are listed in the bibliography section of this chapter. Summer and winter design weather data from Chapter 24 of the 1985 FUNDAMENTALS Volume may be used as a guide in selecting design outdoor conditions for shelters.

CONTROL OF CHEMICAL ENVIRONMENT

Control of the physical environment may be regarded as two independent problems—control of the chemical environment and control of the thermal environment. Closed (buttoned-up) shelters without any replacement of the air from outside sources would remain habitable only for a few hours, unless a life-support system is used. The permissible *stay time* (period of occupancy) is determined by the net volume of space per person, and has been defined as the time required to raise the carbon dioxide concentration to 3% by volume. This is expressed as:

$$T_3 = 0.04V_c = 1.4V_m \qquad (1)$$

where

T_3 = time to reach 3% carbon dioxide, hours.
V_c = unit volume of space, ft³ per person.
V_m = unit volume of space, m³ per person.

Table 4 Thermal Properties of Soils, Rocks, and Concrete

Material Descriptor	Thermal Conductivity Btu/h · ft · °F	(W/m · K)	Thermal Diffusivity ft²/h	(mm²/s)	Density lb/ft³	(kg/m³)	Specific Heat Btu/lb · °F	(kJ/kg · K)
Dense Rock	2.00	(3.46)	0.050	(1.29)	200	(3200)	0.20	(0.84)
Average Rock	1.40	(2.42)	0.040	(1.03)	175	(2800)	0.20	(0.84)
Dense Concrete	1.00	(1.73)	0.033	(0.85)	150	(2410)	0.20	(0.84)
Solid Masonry / Heavy Soil, Damp	0.75	(1.30)	0.025	(0.65)	143 / 131	(2290) / (2100)	0.21 / 0.23	(0.88) / (0.96)
Heavy Soil, Dry / Light Soil, Damp	0.50	(0.865)	0.020	(0.52)	125 / 100	(2000) / (1600)	0.20 / 0.25	(0.84) / (1.05)
Light Soil, Dry	0.20	(0.346)	0.011	(0.28)	90	(1440)	0.20	(0.84)

Table 5 Annual Maximums and Minimums for Integrated Average Earth Temperatures[a]

| | Earth Temperatures | | | | | Earth Temperatures | | | |
| | Maximum | | Minimum | | | Maximum | | Minimum | |
Location	°F	(°C)	°F	(°C)	Location	°F	(°C)	°F	(°C)
Auburn, AL	74	(23.3)	56	(13.3)	Bozeman, MT	56	(13.3)	32	(0.0)
Decatur, AL	71	(21.7)	48	(8.9)	Huntley, MT	64	(17.8)	36	(2.2)
Tempe, AR	81	(27.2)	59	(15.0)	Lincoln, NB	69	(20.6)	39	(3.9)
Tucson, AR	85	(29.4)	65	(18.3)	Norfolk, NB	66	(18.9)	40	(4.4)
Brawley, CA	90	(32.2)	68	(20.0)	New Brunswick, NJ	65	(18.3)	42	(5.6)
Davis, CA	76	(24.4)	56	(13.3)	Ithaca, NY	59	(15.0)	39	(3.9)
Ft. Collins, CO	64	(17.8)	36	(2.2)	Raleigh, NC	73	(22.8)	52	(11.1)
Gainesville, FL	80	(26.7)	69	(20.6)	Columbus, OH	65	(18.3)	41	(5.0)
Athens, GA	77	(25.0)	57	(13.9)	Coshocton, OH	64	(17.8)	40	(4.4)
Tifton, GA	80	(26.7)	62	(16.7)	Lake Hefner, OK	77	(25.0)	51	(10.6)
Moscow, ID	57	(13.9)	37	(2.8)	Pawhuska, OK	74	(23.3)	50	(10.0)
Lemont, IL	65	(18.3)	39	(3.9)	Ottawa, Ont., Canada	59	(15.0)	36	(2.2)
Urbana, IL	68	(20.0)	42	(5.6)	Corvallis, OR	66	(18.9)	46	(7.8)
West Lafayette, IN	66	(18.9)	38	(3.3)	Pendleton, OR	67	(19.4)	39	(3.9)
Burlington, IA	71	(21.7)	38	(3.3)	Calhoun, SC	76	(24.4)	52	(11.1)
Manhattan, KS	69	(20.6)	41	(5.0)	Union, SC	70	(21.1)	48	(8.9)
Lexington, KY	70	(21.1)	46	(7.8)	Madison, SD	61	(16.1)	33	(0.6)
Upper Marlboro, MD	70	(21.1)	42	(5.6)	Jackson, TN	71	(21.7)	49	(9.4)
East Lansing, MI	63	(17.2)	37	(2.8)	Temple, TX	83	(28.3)	59	(15.0)
St. Paul, MN	62	(16.7)	34	(1.1)	Salt Lake City, UT	63	(17.2)	40	(4.4)
State Univ., MS	79	(26.1)	55	(12.8)	Burlington, VT	63	(17.2)	35	(1.7)
Faucett, MO	65	(18.3)	43	(6.1)	Pullman, WA	60	(15.6)	36	(2.2)
Kansas City, MO	66	(18.9)	42	(5.6)	Seattle, WA	61	(16.1)	45	(7.2)
Sikeston, MO	71	(21.7)	43	(6.1)					

[a]Earth temperatures are integrated averages from surface to a depth of 10 ft (3 m) derived to simulate observed phenomena, each for average amplitude and phase angle with earth thermal diffusivity, $\alpha = 0.025$ ft^2/h (0.645 mm^2/s or 0.00232 m^2/h).

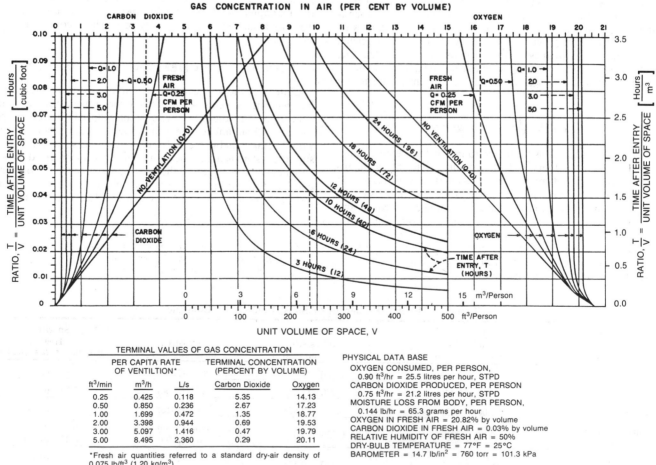

TERMINAL VALUES OF GAS CONCENTRATION				
PER CAPITA RATE OF VENTILTION*			TERMINAL CONCENTRATION (PERCENT BY VOLUME)	
ft³/min	m³/h	L/s	Carbon Dioxide	Oxygen
0.25	0.425	0.118	5.35	14.13
0.50	0.850	0.236	2.67	17.23
1.00	1.699	0.472	1.35	18.77
2.00	3.398	0.944	0.69	19.53
3.00	5.097	1.416	0.47	19.79
5.00	8.495	2.360	0.29	20.11

*Fresh air quantities referred to a standard dry-air density of 0.075 lb/ft³ (1.20 kg/m³)

PHYSICAL DATA BASE

OXYGEN CONSUMED, PER PERSON, 0.90 ft³/hr = 25.5 litres per hour, STPD
CARBON DIOXIDE PRODUCED, PER PERSON 0.75 ft³/hr = 21.2 litres per hour, STPD
MOISTURE LOSS FROM BODY, PER PERSON, 0.144 lb/hr = 65.3 grams per hour
OXYGEN IN FRESH AIR = 20.82% by volume
CARBON DIOXIDE IN FRESH AIR = 0.03% by volume
RELATIVE HUMIDITY OF FRESH AIR = 50%
DRY-BULB TEMPERATURE = 77°F = 25°C
BAROMETER = 14.7 lb/in² = 760 torr = 101.3 kPa

Fig. 5 Carbon Dioxide and Oxygen in Occupied Spaces

Thus, people can safely stay for 20 hours in a closed shelter having a net volume of 500 cu ft (14.2 m³) per person. The stay time can also be determined from Figure 5 for various conditions.

Figure 5 shows the relationship between the concentrations of carbon dioxide and oxygen in occupied spaces, the rate of ventilation per person, the net volume of space per person, and the time after entry. The terminal values of carbon dioxide and oxygen concentration are tabulated for various rates of ventilation. Figure 5 is based on rates of oxygen consumption and carbon dioxide production representative of people in confined quarters (Allen 1960).

The example shown by dotted lines indicates that a carbon dioxide concentration of 3.5% by volume will develop in 10 hours in an unventilated shelter having a net volume of 235 ft³ (6.65 m³) per person, and that the oxygen content of the air will then be 16.25% by volume. Ventilation with pure outdoor air is the most economical method for maintaining the necessary chemical quality of air in a shelter. The recommended minimum ventilating rate of 3 cfm (1.4 L/s) per person of fresh air will maintain a carbon dioxide concentration of about 0.5% and an oxygen content of approximately 20%, by volume, in a shelter occupied by sedentary people. However, an air replacement rate of 3 cfm (1.4 L/s) per person is not in itself sufficient to limit the resultant effective temperature to 85 °F (29.4 °C), under many conditions, unless the supply temperature is less than about 45 °F (7.2 °C). A ventilation capability for maintaining a low concentration of carbon dioxide and a correspondingly safe concentration of oxygen in a shelter has several advantages, including one or more of the following:

1. A longer stay time is gained for continued occupancy after shutdown of a ventilating system due to fire or for repair of disabled equipment.
2. Intermittent operation of a manual ventilating blower may become practicable.
3. Greater physical activity in the shelter becomes permissible.
4. Environmental conditions, such as temperature, humidity, moisture condensation, air distribution, air motion, and odors, as well as oxygen and carbon dioxide, may be improved without supplementary apparatus.

THERMAL ENVIRONMENT

Underground Shelters

As previously indicated, the thermal environment in a shelter depends on occupancy, construction features, climatic and soil conditions, and conditions of use. The internal environment represents a balance between heat generated inside the shelter, the heat conduction into the materials surrounding the shelter, and the heat exchange with the ventilating air. Because each of the heat exchanges include latent and sensible components that vary with time, computation of the temperature and humidity, for short periods of occupancy, is very complex.

The problem of keeping warm in shelters during winter conditions has not been considered acute inasmuch as normal, healthy people can tolerate temperatures as low as 50 °F (10 °C) for several days, if properly clothed. However, since people of all ages and in varying degrees of health will require shelter, and because it cannot be assumed that, on short warning, people will take adequate clothing into a shelter, the heating requirements of shelters should not be ignored. Generally, the need for heating will be greater in family-size shelters than in group or community shelters because of the greater surface area per occupant in the smaller shelters.

Because the steady-state rates of conducted heat are characteristically small for underground shelters, environmen-

tal temperatures less than 50 °F (10 °C) can usually be avoided by arranging the ventilating system to use metabolic heat generated by the occupants. During cold weather, a mixture of fresh and recirculated air in varying proportions then can be supplied to occupied spaces at a temperature of 50 °F (10 °C) or more. This procedure is less effective if the shelter were only partially occupied (Allen 1972).

During the summer, the maintenance of suitable environmental conditions in a shelter is, in most instances, a question of survival rather than comfort. From considerations of survival, the environmental criterion for 14 days' duration has been selected at 83 °F (28.3 °C) effective temperature, although higher or lower values may be used for different segments of the population.

Experimental measurements have been made in various family and group shelters with real or simulated occupants to determine the temperature and humidity that would develop after one to two weeks in various climates, and with various ventilation rates and occupancies. However, because of the time and expense required to cover a suitable range of all the important variables experimentally, both computer and analytical solutions of heat conduction have been applied. All of these methods involve simplifying assumptions, so they only yield approximate results for a specific situation.

Determination of shelter environment by analytical solution and by numerical analysis has been carried out by the National Bureau of Standards, together with comparisons of computed and experimental results in a few shelters (Achenbach et al. 1962, Kusuda and Achenbach 1963).

Prediction of shelter environment for a range of climatic and soil conditons, ventilation rates, and shelter sizes has been performed by computer techniques in ASHRAE and DCPA (Defense Civil Preparedness Agency, formerly Office of Civil Defense) sponsored research projects (Drucker and Cheng 1962, Drucker and Haines 1964, Baschiere et al. 1965).

Figures 6 and 7 show the relative effects of ventilation rate, earth conductivity, and shelter size, as determined in the ASHRAE study. The effect of initial earth temperature is small in magnitude, averaging about 0.2 °F (0.1 °C) shelter temperature per degree of earth temperature. The analog computer studies disclosed that after the tenth day, the temperature in the shelter would approximate 95% of the ultimate temperature rise.

Simplified Analytical Solutions

The thermal environment in a shelter is determined by the following energy balance relation:

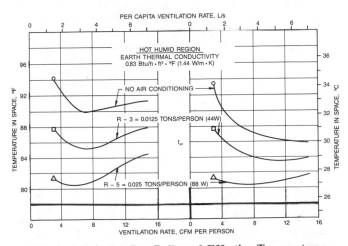

Fig. 6   Maximum Dry-Bulb and Effective Temperatures as Functions of Ventilation Rate

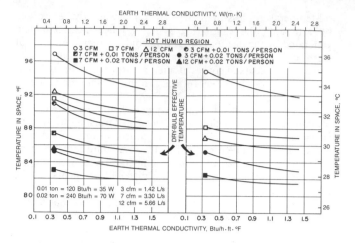

Fig. 7   Maximum Dry-Bulb and Effective Temperatures as Functions of Earth Thermal Conductivity

$$q_m + q_i = q_v + q_w + q_r \qquad (2)$$

where

q_m = human metabolic heat

q_i = heat generated by lights, cooking appliances, motor-driven equipment, and auxiliary power apparatus.

q_v = heat carried out by ventilation air.

q_w = conduction heat loss to the surrounding media.

q_r = heat absorbed by cooling equipment.

Both the sensible and latent portions of the human metabolic heat, q_m are functions of shelter temperature, although the sum of the two remains practically constant and varies in the range of from 300 to 600 Btu/h (88 to 176 W) per person, depending on activity levels. (See Chapter 8 of the 1985 FUNDAMENTALS Volume.) Table 1 illustrates the relationship between air temperature, and heat losses and moisture evaporated for an average sedentary man with optimum clothing. The internal heat generated by lights, cooking, etc. (q_i), is usually equal to only a small fraction of the human metabolic heat. Under emergency conditions, illumination can, if necessary, be reduced to a low level, with a resultant heating effect of about 10 to 20 Btu/h (3 to 6 W) per person (Allen 1962).

Unless heat and water vapor generated in the shelter is properly removed, shelter temperature and humidity increase to a point where basic metabolic heat balance of the human body will be disturbed, resulting in deep body temperature rise and, ultimately, in death. The currently accepted criterion for the tolerance limit for prolonged shelter occupancy is the effective temperature of 83 °F (28.3 °C).

Three possible modes of heat dissipation for the shelter can be considered: (1) cooling by forced or natural ventilation with outdoor air (corresponding to q_v); (2) cooling by the effect of heat conduction into the surrounding media (corresponding to q_w); and (3) mechanical cooling and dehumidifying with refrigeration or well water (corresponding to q_r). Adsorption or absorption of humidity by desiccant or hygroscopic fluid has been considered, but it usually tends to increase, rather than decrease, the effective temperature.

In general, shelters do not have apparatus to maintain a preselected state point, and the environment depends on prevailing conditions for thermal equilibrium. Temperature and humidity of the environment, therefore, varies or tends to rise progressively as a result of diurnal variations in outdoor air conditions, attenuation of conductive heat transfer in surrounding masses of initially cool materials, and temperature-dependent changes in the sensible/latent ratio for metabolic heat.

Comprehensive analyses of the heat-mass transfer problem have been made for selected configurations and conditions, and many tests have been performed with simulated and human occupants. From these studies, approximate techniques have been derived for three representative cases suitable for design and estimating purposes as follows:

Case 1 considers a ventilated shelter with insulated boundaries; that is, no heat is transmitted through walls, ceiling, or floor, and heat-moisture loads are removed only by ventilating air.

Case 2 considers short-term occupancy of an unventilated underground shelter (sealed or buttoned-up for a week or less) from which all heat is removed by conduction effects in surrounding masses of materials having an initially uniform temperature, and moisture is removed by condensation on relatively cool surfaces.

Case 3 considers a ventilated underground shelter from which heat and moisture are removed by the combined effects of ventilation and heat conduction.

The Case 1 solution, which requires a minimum of data, applies to any shelter in which solar radiation has little effect and is recommended for identified fallout shelters in normally heated basements and in aboveground core areas of buildings. Cases 2 and 3 include the cooling effects of earth conduction and inherently lead to a more economical system or a better environment in underground shelters, when earth properties, initial temperature, and shelter configuration are favorable. Case 2 or Case 3 shelters rely, to a minimum extent, on the ambient atmosphere for environmental control. Earth conduction alone may satisfy requirements for removal of metabolic heat in underground gallery-type shelters, which have a relatively low initial soil temperature, favorable thermal properties, and a large ratio of interior surface to floor area. Case 2 and Case 3 represent shelters having widely different shapes or sizes: the plane model for large chambers that are quite square in plan, the spherical model for small or cubical chambers, and the cylindrical model for elongated rectangular or gallery-type shelters.

Repeated trial solutions are necessary for determining the minimum ventilating rate for meeting stated effective temperature criteria. In most climatic areas, it may not be practical or even possible to prevent excessive effective temperatures, and ventilation system design should be based on coincident climatic data that may be exceeded during an acceptable portion of the year. If greater reliability is considered essential, apparatus for cooling may be indicated.

Ventilated and Insulated Shelters (Case 1)

Case 1 applies to an occupied space with insulated (adiabatic) boundaries; that is, the effects of heat transmitted by conduction through walls, floor, and overhead cover are virtually negligible relative to the thermal effects of internal loads associated with metabolic processes, lighting, and appliances that emit heat.

Ventilation with ambient air is the only means for removal of heat and moisture, and the system is presumed to create a uniform environment throughout the space. The method estimates capacities required for ventilation systems in shelters occupied during warm weather, when outside-inside temperature differentials may be minimal. The method is also useful for predicting the environmental conditions that might develop under various ambient conditions.

The Case 1 solution is based on the two sets of equations that follow. The first set, Equation 3 through 6a, uses the Inch-Pound system of units. The second set, Equation 3 SI through 6a SI, uses SI units and is equivalent to the first set. Ventilation rates are referred to standard dry air having a density of 0.75 lb/ft³ (1.201 kg/m³) and a specific heat of 0.24 Btu/lb • °F (1005

J/kg • °C). Ventilation rates, metabolic parameters, and all internal heat exchangers are reduced to quantities per person.

The metabolic rate or total heat transferred to the environment from each occupant is assumed to be 400 Btu/h (117 W), which is representative for sedentary adult males. The partition of metabolic heat (q_m) emitted by a normally clothed occupant into sensible (q_s) and latent (q_e) components can be adequately expressed as linear functions of dry-bulb temperature (t_a) of air in the space, as follows:

$$q_s = 10\,(100 - t_a) \qquad (3)$$

Btu/h, when t_a is 68°F or more. When t_a is 68°F or less, $q_s = 320$ Btu/h, a constant.

$$q_e = 10\,(t_a - 60) \qquad (4)$$

Btu/h, when t_a is 68°F or more, when t_a 68°F or less, $q_e = 80$ Btu/h, a constant.

Equations 3 and 4 can be used in conjunction with Equation 2, with $q_w = q_r = 0$, to derive the following relationships for the temperature (t_a) and humidity ration (W_a) of environmental air, thus:

$$t_a = \frac{q_i + 1.08 G t_v + 1000}{1.08G + 10} \qquad (5)$$

Fahrenheit, when t_a is 68°F or more, or

$$t_a = t_v + \frac{q_i + 320}{1.08G} \qquad (5a)$$

Fahrenheit, when t_a is 68°F or less, Also,

$$W_u = W_v + \frac{t_a - 60}{470G} \qquad (6)$$

pounds of moisture per pound of dry air, when t_a is 68°F or more, or

$$W_a = W_v + \frac{0.01702}{G} \qquad (6a)$$

pounds of moisture per pound of dry air, when t_a is 68°F or less.

where

G = ventilating rate, per person, cfm.
q_i = lighting load, per person, Btu/h.
t_v = dry-bulb temperature of supply air, °F.
W_v = humidity ratio of supply air, pounds of moisture per pound of dry air.

Example 1 (I-P Units): Determine the environmental conditions in an occupied chamber ventilated with fresh air at the rate of 15 cfm per person. Air is supplied to the space at a dry-bulb temperature of 77°F, wet-bulb temperature of 68°F, humidity ratio of 0.01265 unit mass of moisture per unit mass of dry air, and a still-air effective temperature of 73°F ET. The heat emitted by lights and equipment is 7.5 W (25.59 Btu/h) per person.

Solution: The temperature of air in the space is higher than 68°F. Then, from Equation 5,

$$t_a = \frac{25.59 + (1.08)(15)(77) + 1000}{(1.08)(15) + 10} = 86.76\,°F$$

and from Equation 6,

$$W_a = 0.01265 + \frac{86.76 - 60}{(470)(15)}$$

$$= 0.01645 \text{ lb of moisture per lb or dry air}$$

From ASHRAE Psychrometric Chart No. 1, at $W_a = 0.01645$ and $t_a = 86.76\,°F$, the wet-bulb temperature is 75.4°F. From Figure 4, the effective temperature is 80.4°F with slow movement of air in the space.

Equations 5 SI through 6a SI, based on SI units, are sequential counterparts for Equations 3 through 6a:

$$q_s = 5.275\,(37.78 - t_a) \qquad (3\ SI)$$

watt, when t_a is 20°C or more. When t_a is 20°C or less, $q_s = 93.78$ W, a constant.

$$q_e = 5.275\,(t_a - 15.56) \qquad (4\ SI)$$

watt, when t_a is 20°C or more, When t_a is 20°C or less, $q_e = 23.45$ W, a constant.

$$t_a = \frac{q_i + 1207 G t_v + 199.3}{1207G + 5.275} \qquad (5\ SI)$$

Celsius, when t_a is 20°C or more, or

$$t_a = t_v + \frac{q_i + 93.78}{1207G} \qquad (5a\ SI)$$

Celsius, when t_a is 20°C or less.

$$W_a = W_v + \frac{t_a - 15.56}{553.26G} \qquad (6\ SI)$$

grams of moisture per kilograms of dry air, when t_a is 20°C or more, or

$$W_a = W_v + \frac{1}{124.48G} \qquad (6a\ SI)$$

grams of moisture per kilogram of dry air, when t_a is 20°C or less.

where

G = ventilating rate, per person, m^3/s.
q_i = *lighting* load, per person, W.
t_v = dry-bulb temperature of supply air, °C.
W_v = humidity ratio of supply air, g of moisture per kg of dry air.

Example 1 (SI Units): Determine the environmental conditions in an occupied chamber ventilated with fresh air at the rate of 7 L/s per person. Air is supplied to the space at a dry-bulb temperature of 25°C, wet-bulb temperature of 20°C, humidity ratio of 12.65 g of moisture per kilogram of dry air, and a still-air effective temperature of 23°C ET. The heat emitted by lights and equipment is 7.5 W per person.

Solution: From Equation (5 SI),

$$t_a = \frac{7.5 + (1207)(7)(10^{-3})(25) + 199.3}{(1207)(7)(10^{-3}) + 5.275} = 30.46\,°C$$

and from Equation (6 SI),

$$W_a = 12.65 + \frac{30.46 - 15.56}{(553.26)(7)(10^{-3})}$$

$$= 16.50 \text{ g of moisture per kg of dry air}$$

From ASHRAE Psychrometric Chart No. 1 (SI) at $W_a = 16.50$ and $t_a = 30.46\,°C$, the wet bulb temperature is 24.2°C. From Figure 4, the effective temperature is 27.0°C with slow air movement in the space.

Curves showing the results of equations similar to Case 1 calculations made to determine ventilation requirements to maintain various effective temperature rises are shown in Figure 8. Figure 9 shows the relationship of shelter and outdoor dry-bulb temperature with ventilation rate.

When earth is below the shelter temperature, Case 1 solutions tend to overestimate the effective temperature as long as heat gain due to the solar heat load is negligible. Heat conduction loss to the surrounding media plays a significant role is dissipation of shelter heat during the sealed-up condition. Heat conduction to the surrounding media also helps decrease the shelter effective temperature or the ventilation air requirement during the normal shelter occupancy period.

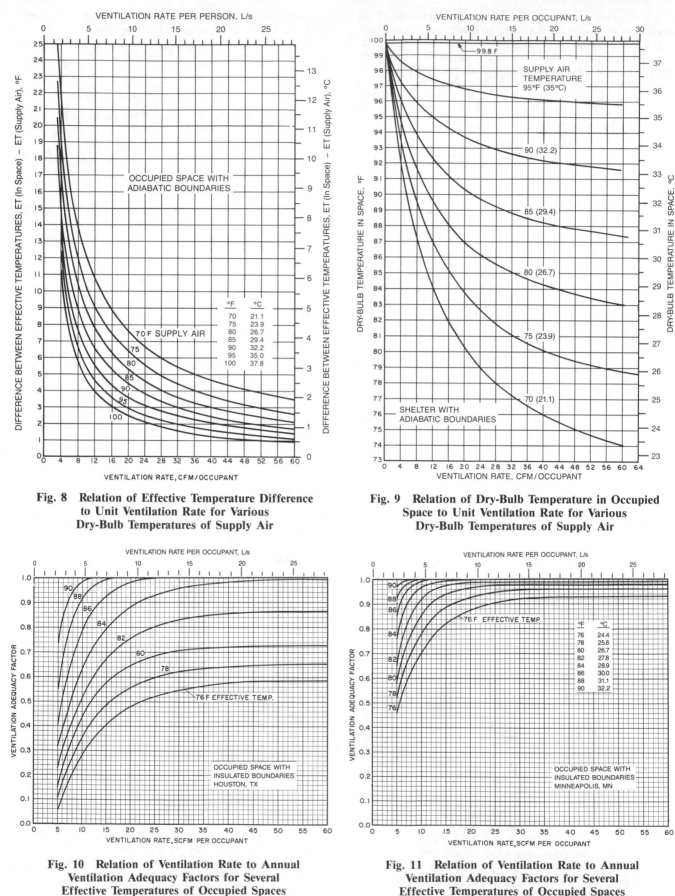

Fig. 8   Relation of Effective Temperature Difference to Unit Ventilation Rate for Various Dry-Bulb Temperatures of Supply Air

Fig. 9   Relation of Dry-Bulb Temperature in Occupied Space to Unit Ventilation Rate for Various Dry-Bulb Temperatures of Supply Air

Fig. 10   Relation of Ventilation Rate to Annual Ventilation Adequacy Factors for Several Effective Temperatures of Occupied Spaces in Houston, Texas

Fig. 11   Relation of Ventilation Rate to Annual Ventilation Adequacy Factors for Several Effective Temperatures of Occupied Spaces in Minneapolis, Minnesota

The Case 1 solution is useful in estimating the ventilation air requirement for a given outdoor air condition to maintain the shelter effective temperature below the tolerance limit during the summer. Since the summer shelter thermal environment is affected as strongly by wet-bulb temperature as by the dry-bulb temperature of the ventilation air, a coincident design criterion of these two temperatures is needed for selecting the ventilation equipment for a given climatic zone. Summer design weather data from Chapter 24 of the 1985 FUNDAMENTALS Volume do not meet this coincident requirement.

Ventilation adequacy factor accounts for the coincident occurences of dry- and wet-bulb temperatures for a specified shelter effective temperature and a per capita ventilation air rate. The ventilation adequacy factor is defined as the percentage of annual hourly coincident occurrences of dry- and wet-bulb temperatures of outdoor air that could maintain the shelter effective temperature below a specified level for a specific per shelter occupant ventilation rate. Ventilation adequacy factors have been calculated using a modified Case 1 solution for several cities, two of which are illustrated in Figures 10 and 11 for Houston, Texas and Minneapolis, Minnesota.

From Figure 10, for Houston, it is seen that an annual ventilation adequacy factor of 95% is obtained at a ventilation rate

of 28 cfm (0.013 m³/s) per person for an effective temperature of 84°F (28.9°C). In Houston, the outdoor air ventilation rate of 28 cfm (0.013 m³/s) per person is adequate for protecting the shelter occupant from effective temperatures exceeding 84°F (28.9°C) for 95% of the hours in the year. Conversely, for 5% of the year, 438 hours out of a total 8760 hours per year, which may or may not occur consecutively, the ventilation rate as large as 28 cfm (0.013 m³/s) per person is still inadequate to maintain the shelter effective temperature at 84°F (28.9°C) or lower.

Therefore, the ventilation adequacy factor is a useful index in evaluating the cost effectiveness of the ventilating, as well as cooling, facilities from the standpoint of survival in protective shelters. Since such curves have not been developed for many areas, the shelter designer can use weather bureau data (Monthly Local Climatological Data Supplement), along with Figures 8 and 9, to develop local ventilation adequacy factors. The use of 24-hour wet- and dry-bulb averages simplifies these compilations and introduces little error on actual daily average shelter conditions.

Weather Bureau records for 91 weather stations for a 10-year period were analyzed to determine ventilation rates required for specific ventilation adequacy factors, and shelter effective temperatures were calculated. Maps with isoventilation lines were

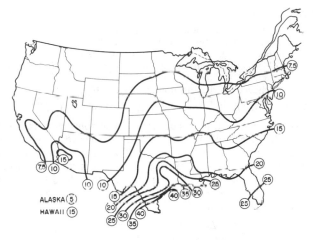

Fig. 12   Per Capita Rate of Ventilation Required to Maintain an Effective Temperature of 83°F (28.3°C) in an Occupied Space with 90% Adequacy During a Normal Year

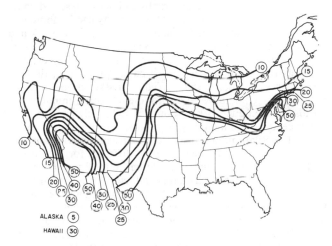

Fig. 14   Per Capita Rate of Ventilation Required to Maintain an Effective Temperature of 80°F (26.7°C) in an Occupied Space with 95% Adequacy During a Normal Year

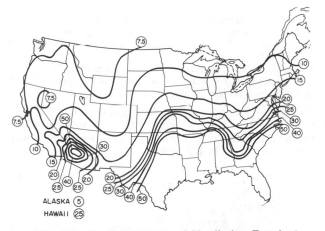

Fig. 13   Per Capita Rate of Ventilation Required to Maintain an Effective Temperature of 80°F (26.7°C) in an Occupied Space with 90% Adequacy During a Normal Year

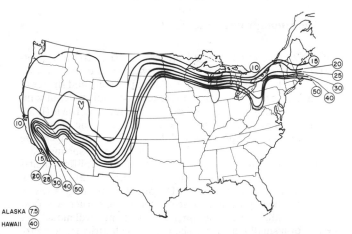

Fig. 15   Per Capita Rate of Ventilation Required to Maintain an Effective Temperature of 80°F (26.7°C) in an Occupied Space with 99% Adequacy During a Normal Year

developed for ventilation adequacy factors of 80, 85, 90, 95, and 99%, and for effective temperatures of 80, 83, 85, and 90°F (26.7, 28.3, 29.4, and 32.2°C).

Figure 12 shows the map for 83°F ET (28.3°C ET) and 90% adequacy. At any point on an isoventilation line [for instance, the line for 15 cfm (7.1 L/s) per person], an effective temperature of 83°F ET (28.3°C ET) would not be exceeded in an occupied shelter more than 10% of the time in a normal year. This map serves as the basis for design criteria recommended by DCPA for the ventilation of protective shelters. However, DCPA applies a standard adjustment of −1°F ET (0.6°C ET), and refers to this set of data (Figure 12) as the map for 82°F ET (27.8°C ET).

This downward adjustment is the result of observations made during simulated shelter occupancy tests. Figures 13, 14, and 15 show maps for 80°F ET (26.7°C ET), and for 90, 95, and 99% adequacy, respectively. A comparison of data from these maps shows that a substantial increase in the ventilation rate is needed to obtain a moderate improvement in the probable environment.

Ventilating systems for shelters can be simulated by either of two analytical models. The first, the isostate model, is based on the assumption that the environment is spatially uniform. This model is the basis for the graphs and maps presented under the Case 1 solutions. This state of uniformity can be approached only with a system that includes distribution ductwork and diffusion outlets. The second, the nonisostate or varistate model, is based on the incremental transfer of metabolic heat and moisture to the ventilating air as it passes in sequence through one or more occupied spaces. The varistate model is more realistic in the nonuniform environments with a minimum of air distribution ductwork and outlets. Relatively large changes in temperature and humidity are associated with low per capita rates of ventilation, and the predicted psychrometric states of air leaving such spaces may be quite different for the isostate and varistate models because the latent to total metabolic heat transfer is a function of environmental temperature (Allen 1970).

The degree of uniformity in the environment will depend on the size and shape of the space, the arrangement of the air distribution system, the locations of heat loads and obstructions to air flow, and the unit rate of ventilation. Since the environment at one end of the space corresponds to the initial state of the air, it is beneficial to ventilate an unheated shelter with a mixture of fresh and recirculated air during cold weather (Allen 1970).

Sealed Underground Shelters (Case 2)

Case 2 (sealed underground shelter with earth conduction effects) and Case 3 (ventilated shelter with earth conduction effects) have both been analyzed for deep underground shelter in which heat exchange near the surface does not materially influence the shelter thermal environment. Pratt and Davis (1958) and the Corps of Engineers (1959) calculated the change of shelter dry-bulb temperature and the inner surface temperature from the initially uniform earth temperature by solving transient heat conduction equations for three simplified shelter models: (1) one-dimensional plane wall model, (2) cylindrical model, and (3) spherical model. The one-dimensional plane wall model can be applied to a large shelter where corner heat flow effect is small, whereas the spherical and cylindrical models are better for a small family-size shelter. The cylindrical model provides a good approximation for long underground tunnels.

Functions for the approximate mathematical analysis for Case 2 are shown in Figure 16. Figure 16, f_1, f_2, and f_3 represent temperature rise functions for a plane wall, cylindrical, and spherical shelter model, respectively. Dimensionless time function, T, is computed by:

$$T = \frac{\alpha\theta}{(a_j)^2} \qquad (7)$$

where

α = thermal diffusivity of soil, ft²/h (m²/s).
θ = elapsed time, hours (s).
a = equivalent radius of the shelter, ft (m).

The subscript j refers to the model type, e.g., 1, 2, or 3.

The equivalent radius of the shelter may be approximated by the following equations:

(Plane Wall Model)	$a_1 = S_i^{0.5}$	(8)
(Cylindrical Model)	$a_2 = (S_c/\pi)^{0.5}$	(9)
(Spherical Model)	$a_3 = (S_i/4\pi)^{0.5}$	(10)

where

S_i = total inner surface area, ft² (m²).
S_c = cross-sectional area, ft² (m²).

The rise in temperature of the inner surface of the shelter is found from Equation 11.

$$\Delta t_w = t_w - t_0 = \frac{qa_j}{S_i k} f_j \qquad (11)$$

where

t_w = dry-bulb temperature of air in space, °F (°C).
t_0 = initial temperature of inner surface °F (°C).
q = total heat generated in the sealed-up shelter, Btu/h (W).
k = thermal conductivity of surrounding earth, Btu/h·ft·°F (W/m·K).
f_j = temperature rise function (see Figure 16).

For $T < 0.001$, f_1, f_2, f_3 may be calculated by $f_i = 1.13\,(T)^{0.5}$.

For the buttoned-up condition, the dew point temperature of air in the space is approximately equal to the average inner surface temperature (Achenbach et al. 1962). The small difference, Δt_x, between average air and inner surface temperatures depends on the ratio of the per capita rate of heat transfer by convection, q_c, to the per capita area of inner surfaces, S_p, as expressed in Equation 12:

$$\Delta t_x = t_a - t_w = q_c/h_c S_p \qquad (12)$$

and, with the assumption that the convective part of the internal heat loads is one-half the entire sensible heat load, in Equation 13:

$$q_c = (q_s + q_i)/2 \qquad (13)$$

where

t_a = dry-bulb temperature of air in space, °F (°C).
q_c = convective heat transfer at inner surfaces, Btu/h (W).
h_c = coefficient for convective heat transfer, Btu/h·ft²·°F (W/m²·k).
S_p = unit area of inner surfaces, ft² (m²) per person.
q_s = sensible part of metabolic heat, as defined by Equation 3 or 7.
q_i = lighting load, per person, Btu/h (W).

The approximate temperature difference needed to maintain the rate of convective heat transfer to inner surfaces of the enclosure can be found by combining Equations 12 and 13 with Equation 3 or 3 SI. In I-P units,

$$\Delta t_x = t_a - t_w = \frac{10(100 - t_w) + q_i}{2h_c S_p + 10} \qquad (14)$$

or using SI units,

$$\Delta t_x = \frac{5.275(37.78 - t_w) + q_i}{2h_c S_p + 5.275} \qquad (14\ SI)$$

In some cases, this temperature difference may be quite significant.

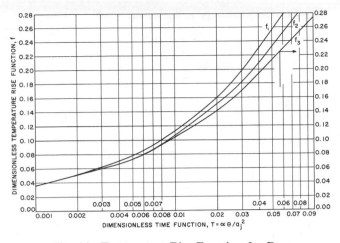

Fig. 16 Temperature Rise Function for Deep Underground Sealed Chambers

Example 2 (I-P Units): Determine the effective temperature in a sealed underground chamber after two days of occupancy. The space is 12.5 ft long and 10 ft wide, with a ceiling height of 8 ft. There are 12 occupants, each having a metabolic heat rate of 400 Btu/h. Two 40-W lights in the space together contribute 22.7 Btu/h per person to the heat load. The earth has an initial temperature of 68 °F, a thermal diffusivity of 0.025 ft²/h, and a thermal conductivity of 0.75 Btu/h · ft · °F. The convection coefficient, h_c, is 0.70 Btu/h · ft² · °F.

Solution: Because the space is small and somewhat cubical, the spherical model is most applicable. The total inner surface area is,

$$S_i = 2[(10)(12.5) + (8)(10) + (8)(12.5)] = 610.0 \text{ ft}^2$$

and the unit area is $S_p = 50.83$ ft² per person.
From Equation 10,

$$a_3 = (610/4\pi)^{0.5} = 6.967 \text{ ft}$$

From Equation 7, when $\theta = 48$ hours,

$$T = \frac{(0.025)(48)}{(6.967)^2} = 0.0247$$

From Figure 16, $f_3 = 0.153$. From Equation 11,

$$\Delta t_w = \frac{(12)(400 + 22.7)(6.967)}{(610)(0.75)} (0.153) = 11.82 °F$$

Then, the final temperature of inner surfaces is,

$$t_w = 68 + 11.82 = 79.82 °F$$

This value, the inner surface temperature, is also the dew point of air in the room. The difference between air and boundary surface temperatures can be estimated by Equation 14,

$$t_a - t_w = \frac{(10)(100 - 79.82) + 22.7}{(2)(0.7)(50.83) + 10} = 2.77 °F$$

and the temperature of air in the space is

$$t_a = 79.82 + 2.77 = 82.6 °F$$

Using ASHRAE Psychrometric Chart No. 1, with a dry-bulb temperature of 82.6 °F and a dew point of 79.8 °F, the wet-bulb temperature is 80.4 °F. From Figure 4, the effective temperature is 81.3 °F ET.

Since the space is sealed (not ventilated), vitiation of the air may impose the most restrictive limit on stay time. The volume of space is 1000 ft³, and with 12 occupants, the unit volume is 83.3 ft³ per person. From Figure 5, for a carbon dioxide concentration of 3% by volume, the time/volume ratio is about 0.037 man-hours per ft³. For this criterion, the stay time is (0.037 × 83.3) = 3.08 h.

Therefore, the sealed chamber in Example 2 can be safely occupied by 12 people for two days, but only if appropriate means are provided to revitalize and replace polluted air in the space.

Example 2 (SI Units): Determine the effective temperature in a sealed underground chamber after two days of occupancy. The space is 3.8 m long and 3.0 m wide, with a ceiling height of 2.4 m. There are 12 occupants, each having a metabolic heat rate of 117 W. Two 40-W lights in the space together contribute 6.67 W per person to the heat load. The earth has an initial temperature of 20 °C, a thermal diffusivity of 0.645 mm²/s, and a thermal conductivity of 1.3 W/(m · k). The convection coefficient, h_c, is 4.0 W/(m² · k).

Solution: Because the space is small and somewhat cubical, the spherical model is most applicable. The total inner surface area is,

$$S_i = 2[(3.0)(3.8) + (2.4)(3.0) + (2.4)(3.8)]$$
$$= 55.44 \text{ m}^2$$

and the unit area is 55.44/12 = 4.62 m² per person. From Equation (10 SI),

$$a_3 = (55.44/4\pi]^{0.5} = 2.100 \text{ m}$$

From Equation (7), when $\theta = 48$ h,

$$T = \frac{(0.645)(10^{-6})(48)(3600)}{(2.100)^2} = 0.0253$$

a dimensionless number. From Figure 16, $f_3 = 0.154$. From Equation (11),

$$\Delta t_w = \frac{12(117 + 6.6)(2.100)}{(55.44)(1.3)} (0.154) - 6.66 °C$$

Then the final temperature of inner surfaces is,

$$t_w = 20 + 6.66 = 26.66 °C$$

This value, the inner surface temperature, is also the dew point of air in the room. The difference between air and boundary surface temperatures can be estimated by Equation (14 SI),

$$t_a - t_w = \frac{5.275(37.78 - 26.66) + 6.67}{2(4.0)(4.62) + 5.275} = 1.55 °C$$

and the temperature in the space is,

$$t_a = 26.66 + 1.55 = 28.2 °C$$

Using ASHRAE Psychrometric Chart No. 1 (SI), with a dry-bulb temperature of 28.2 °C and a dew point of 26.7 °C, the wet-bulb temperature is 27.0 °C. From Figure 4, the effective temperature is 27.4 °C ET.

Since the space is sealed (not ventilated), vitiation of the air may impose the most restrictive limit on stay time. The volume of space is 27.36 m³ per person. From Figure 5, for a carbon dioxide concentration of 3% by volume, the time/volume ratio is about 1.31 man-hours per m³. For this criterion, the stay time is 1.31 × 2.28 = 3.0 h. Therefore, this sealed chamber could be safely occupied by 12 people for two days, but only if appropriate means were provided for revitalizing or replacing polluted air in the space.

Ventilated Underground Shelters (Case 3)

While the previous Case 2 solution example is useful in estimating shelter temperature rise during a relatively short period of buttoned-up condition, shelter thermal environment during the normal operation (where ventilation air is being introduced from outside) can be approximated as follows. Temperature rise of shelter air dry-bulb and shelter interior surface temperature can be calculated by ϕ_1 of Figure 17, ϕ_2 of Figure 18, and ϕ_3 of Figure 19, corresponding respectively to the plane wall, cylindrical, and spherical shelter models.

Equations 15 through 19 may be used with figures 17, 18, and 19 to calculate shelter air temperature. Equations 15 SI through 19 SI, are the SI unit counterparts.

In Figures 17, 18, and 19, parameter N is evaluated by the following expression for a 400 Btu/h occupant:

$$N = h \left(\frac{a_j}{k}\right) \left(\frac{1.08G + 10}{1.08G + 10 + hS_p}\right) \quad (15)$$

where

h = surface heat transfer coefficient, Btu/h · ft³ · °F
S_p = inner surface area per person, ft².

The temperature rise function ϕ_j (where $j = 1$, 2, or 3) can be used to calculate the temperature rise of the inner surface.

$$\Delta t_w = t_w - t_o = U_o \phi_j \tag{16}$$

where

$$u_o = \frac{q_i + 10(100 - t_o) + 1.08G(t_v - t_o)}{1.08G + 10} \tag{17}$$

By denoting that

$$n = \frac{hS_p}{1.08G + 10 + hS_p} \tag{18}$$

the rise in dry-bulb temperature of air in the occupied space can be calculated with

$$\Delta t_a = t_a - t_o = [(1 - n) + n\phi_j] \, U_o \tag{19}$$

With the resultant value of t_a, the effective temperature in the space can then be determined if the humidity ratio of the air is known. By assuming that latent heat removed from the space by condensation of moisture on inner surfaces is a small part of the heat removed by conductive effects at inner surfaces, the humidity ratio can be estimated by means of Equation 6.

Example 3 (I-P units): Determine the effective temperature at the end of a 14-day period of occupancy by 50 people in a ventilated underground chamber that is 25 ft long and 21 ft wide, with a ceiling height of 8 ft. Ventilation air having a dry-bulb temperature of 81.5 °F and a dew point of 68 °F is supplied to the space at a rate of 16 cfm per person. Per capita heat loads in the space are 400 Btu/h for metabolic effects, and 20.5 Btu/h for lighting. The adjacent earth has an initial temperature of 72.5 °F, a thermal diffusivity of 0.022 ft^2/h, and thermal conductivity of 0.63 Btu/h·ft·°F. The surface coefficient of heat transfer is about 1.5 Btu/h·ft^2·°F.

Solution: From an ASHRAE psychrometric chart, the humidity ratio of air supplied to the space is $W_v = 0.01475$ mass units of moisture per unit mass of dry air, and the wet-bulb temperature is 72 °F. From Figure 4, the apparent effective temperature of supply air is 76.7 °F ET. The total inner surface area is,

$$S_i = 2[(21)(25) + (8)(21) + (8)(25)] = 1786 \text{ ft}^2$$
$$S_p = 1786/50 = 35.7 \text{ ft}^2 \text{ per person}$$

The plane semi-infinite model is most applicable. From Equation (8)

$$a_1 = (1786)^{0.5} = 42.3 \text{ ft}$$

From Equation 15

$$N = \left[\frac{(1.5)(42.3)}{0.63} \right] \left[\frac{(1.08)(16) + 10}{(1.08)(16) + 10 + (1.5)(35.7)} \right]$$

$$= (100.62)(0.33737) = 33.94$$

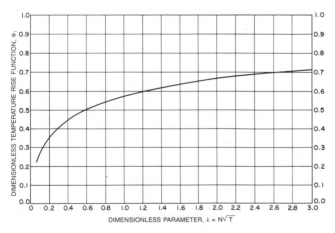

Fig. 17 Temperature Rise Chart for a Ventilated Deep Underground Chamber Using a Plane Semi-Infinite Model

a dimensionless number. From Equation (7)

$$T = \frac{(0.022)(14)(24)}{1786} = 0.00414$$

Then, $N(T)^{0.5} = 33.94(0.00414)^{0.5} = 2.18$
and, from Figure 17, $\phi_1 = 0.68$.

From Equation (17),

$$U_o = \frac{20.5 + 10(100 - 72.5) + (1.08)(16)(81.5 - 72.5)}{(1.08)(16) + 10} = 16.5 \text{ °F}$$

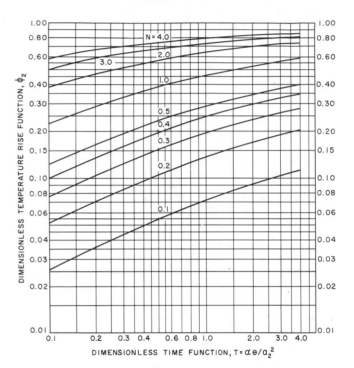

Fig. 18 Temperature Rise Chart for a Ventilated Deep Underground Chamber Using a Cylindrical Model

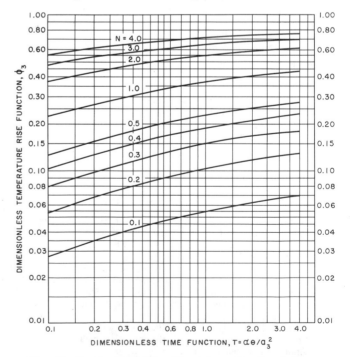

Fig. 19 Temperature Rise Chart for a Ventilated Deep Underground Chamber Using a Spherical Model

From Equation (18)

$$n = \frac{(1.5)(35.7)}{(1.08)(16) + 10 + (1.5)(35.7)} = 0.663$$

From Equation (16)

$$\Delta t_w = (16.5)(0.68) = 11.2\,°F$$
$$\text{and } t_w = 72.5 + 11.2 = 83.7\,°F,$$

From Equation (19)

$$\Delta t_a = [(1 - 0.663) + (0.663)(0.68)]\,(16.5) = 13.0\,°F$$
$$\text{and } t_a = 72.5 + 13.0 = 85.5\,°F$$

From Equation (6),

$$W_a = 0.01475 + \frac{85.5 - 60}{(470)(16)}$$

$$= 0.01814 \text{ lb of moisture per lb of dry air}$$

From ASHRAE Psychrometric Chart No. 1, at the end of the 14-day period, the predicted dew point of air in the space is 73.8 °F and the wet-bulb temperature is 77 °F. From Figure 4, the effective temperature will then be 80.7 °F.

In SI units, parameter N is evaluated for a 117 W occupant as follows:

$$N = h\left(\frac{a_j}{k}\right)\left(\frac{1207G + 5.275}{1207G + 5.275 + hS_p}\right) \qquad \text{(15 SI)}$$

where

h = surface heat transfer coefficient, $(W/m^2 \cdot K)$
S_p = inner surface area per person, m^2

The temperature rise function ϕ_j (where $j = 1, 2, \text{ or } 3$) can be used to calculate the temperature rise of the inner surface.

$$\Delta t_w = t_w - t_o = U_o\phi_j \qquad \text{(16 SI)}$$

where

$$U_o = \frac{q_i + 5.275(37.8 - t_o) + 1207G(t_v - t_o)}{1207G + 5.275} \qquad \text{(17 SI)}$$

By denoting that:

$$n = \frac{hS_p}{1207G + 5.275 + hS_p} \qquad \text{(18 SI)}$$

the rise in dry-bulb temperature of air in the occupied space can be calculated as:

$$\Delta t_a = t_a - t_o = [(1 - n) + n\phi_j]\,U_o \qquad \text{(19 SI)}$$

With the resultant value of t_a, the effective temperature in the space can then be determined if the humidity ratio of the air is known. By assuming that latent heat removed from the space by condensation of moisture on inner surfaces is a small part of the heat removed by conductive effects at inner surfaces, the humidity ratio can be estimated by means of Equation (6 SI).

Example 3 (SI units): Determine the effective temperature at the end of a 14-day period of occupancy by 50 people in a ventilated underground chamber that is 7.62 m long and 6.40 m wide, with a ceiling height of 2.44 m. Ventilation air having a dry-bulb temperature of 27.5 °C and a dew point of 20 °C is supplied to the space at a rate of 7.55 L/s per person. Per capita heat loads in the space are 117.2 W for metabolic effects, and 6 W for lighting. The adjacent earth has an initial temperature of 22.5 °C, a thermal diffusivity of 0.568 mm²/s, and thermal conductivity of 1.09 W/(m · K). The surface coefficient of heat transfer is about 8.52 W/(m² · K).

Solution: From an ASHRAE psychrometric chart, the humidity ratio of air supplied to the space is $W_v = 14.75$ g moisture per kg of dry air, and the wet-bulb temperature is 22.2 °C. From Figure 4, the apparent effective temperature of supply air is 24.8 °C ET.

The total inner surface area is,

$$S_i = 2[(6.4)(7.62) + (2.44)(6.4) + (2.44)(7.62)] = 165.9 \text{ m}^2$$
$$S_p = 165.9/50 = 3.32 \text{ m}^2 \text{ per person.}$$

The plane semi-infinite model is most applicable. From Equation (8),

$$a_1 = (165.9)^{0.5} = 12.88 \text{ m}$$

From Equation (15 SI),

$$N = \left[\frac{(8.52)(12.9)}{1.09}\right]\left[\frac{(1207)(0.00755) + 5.275}{(1207)(0.00755) + 5.275 + (8.52)(3.32)}\right]$$

$$= (100.68)(0.33716) = 33.94$$

a dimensionless number.

From Equation (7),

$$T = \frac{(0.568)(10^{-6})(14)(24)(3600)}{165.9} = 0.00414$$

Then, $N(T)^{0.5} = 33.94(0.00414)^{0.5} = 2.18$ and, from Figure 17, $\phi_1 = 0.68$.

From Equation (17 SI),

$$U_o = \frac{6 + 5.275(37.8 - 22.5) + (1207)(0.00755)(27.5 - 22.5)}{(1207)(0.00755) + 5.275}$$

$$= 9.2\,°C.$$

From Equation (18 SI),

$$n = \frac{(8.52)(3.32)}{(1207)(0.00755) + 5.275 + (8.52)(3.32)} = 0.663$$

From Equation (16 SI),

$$\Delta t_w = (9.2)(0.68) = 6.3\,°C$$
$$\text{and } t_w = 22.5 + 6.3 = 28.8\,°C.$$

From Equation (19 SI),

$$\Delta t_a = [(1 - 0.663) + (0.663)(0.68)]\,(9.2) = 7.2\,°C$$
$$\text{and } t_a = 22.5 + 7.2 = 29.7\,°C.$$

From Equation (6 SI),

$$W_a = 14.75 + \frac{29.7 - 15.6}{(553.26)(0.00755)}$$

$$= 18.14 \text{ g of moisture per kg of dry air}$$

From ASHRAE Psychrometric Chart No. 1 (SI) at the end of the 14-day period, the predicted dew point of air in the space is 23.2 °C, and the wet-bulb temperature is 25 °C. From Figure 4, the effective temperature will then be 27 °C.

These examples show that the thermal properties of the soil, the initial earth temperature, and the stay time in the shelter have an important effect on the interior surface required for the adequate removal of heat from underground shelters by earth heat conduction. The conductive cooling effect in shelter roofs having shallow earth cover would be reduced in warm weather, and reduced to an even greater degree if the upper surface were exposed to solar radiation. This condition was not considered in the previous examples. In locating underground shelters, available shade and grass cover should be taken advantage of to minimize the heat gain from the earth surface.

Since the shelter interior surface area per person (s_p) tends to decrease as the size of a shelter increases, the cooling by earth heat conduction becomes proportionately less in large shelters. However, earth conduction in conjunction with adequate ventilation air may be sufficient to maintain a habitable thermal environment in an underground fallout shelter located in relatively cool earth temperature regions. Under favorable conditions, an expensive mechanical cooling system can be avoided.

When earth temperature and the outdoor ventilation air can not alone maintain a habitable thermal environment, supplementary cooling must be used. The previous method of estimating the shelter thermal environment can still be applied if supply air temperature and humidity ratio are at the design exit conditions of the air-cooling systems.

The previous discussions for shelter thermal environment are all based on very simplified models. More rigorous calculations considering more complicated heat and vapor transfer models, which are closer to the actual underground shelter than those used in this chapter, have been performed with reasonable success by several investigators (Achenbach et al. 1962, Kusuda and Achenbach 1963, Drucker and Cheng 1962, Baschiere et al. 1965). These models can generally estimate transient shelter conditions to within 2 °F (1.1 °C) of observed temperatures. However, the method shown in this chapter can give approximate solutions that do not differ considerably from the actual thermal environment studied in experimental shelters containing simulated occupants.

Aboveground Shelters

The aboveground shelter is a more complicated structure to analyze than an underground shelter because of the variety of surroundings with which the shelter can transfer energy. The shelter can be exposed to the ambient weather, other spaces within the structure, and to the soil, if the shelter is at grade level or partially below grade. In some respects, calculating the loads transmitted between the shelter and its surrounding is no more involved than determining the heating or cooling loads present in any conventional structure. The difference is that the shelter interior will not be maintained at constant dry- and wet-bulb temperatures as in conventional structures. Thus, the standard procedures of estimating transmission loads must be applied carefully.

Several computer programs have been developed that can evaluate a shelter's ventilation requirements (Drucker and Cheng 1962, Baschiere et al. 1965). These computational aids require complete knowledge of the construction details of a shelter, which, at times, may be lacking. Evaluation of a shelter's ventilation requirements can be performed if the transmission loads are neglected and the equations and procedures given in Case 1 are used.

Neglecting the transmission loads in calculating the ventilation requirements of aboveground shelters is generally a valid assumption because (1) as the ambient temperature rises, the inside to outside temperature differential becomes small and (2) as the shelter temperature rises, a smaller portion of the metabolic energy is given off as sensible heat. Therefore, in extreme hot weather, the transmission energy loss is a small percentage of the total energy to be eliminated from the shelter. In addition, the absorption of solar radiation will reduce the transmission of energy from the shelter, sometimes to the point of eliminating the transmission loss and creating a heat flow into the shelter. Heat storage within the shelter structure and its contents would also be expected to reduce the shelter environmental conditions to a lower level than calculated by Case 1. However, studies have shown that these effects are present only during the first week of shelter occupancy. In the second week, the heat storage effects are reduced considerably, if not eliminated.

NATURAL VENTILATION

Infiltration and natural ventilation are similar in that both move air by using air density differences and wind forces rather than fans driven by some source of power. The distinction is that infiltration makes use of random openings and cracks, whereas natural ventilation is planned to take advantage of building configuration, orientation, circulation paths, and openings. Natural ventilation is most applicable in aboveground fallout shelter spaces in existing buildings that have large openings or passageways necessary for moving large quantities of air by small

pressure differentials. Since in most conceivable attacks almost all of the high-rise buildings will be exposed to a positive pressure sufficient to break out all windows, thermal forces will be quite weak compared with wind forces and generally will not provide adequate natural ventilation. Therefore, wind force is the only source of natural ventilation that can be considered. Since fallout particles descend after the blast wave has broken the windows, some fallout will be deposited on the floor adjacent to the openings. Although this source will make a relatively minor contribution to the total radiation received, the material shuld be removed as soon as possible to minimize the cumulative radiation dose.

An underground shelter having relatively cool walls may remain at a lower temperature than the outdoor air. This results in a stable condition that virtually eliminates air circulation or the effects of thermally induced natural ventilation (Ducar and Engholm 1965). However, under favorable conditions of orientation of shelter openings respective to adjacent structures, there may be a substantial natural ventilation effect due to kinetic wind forces.

An estimate of the magnitude of natural ventilation through an aboveground fallout shelter may be made by using the procedure in the section on natural ventilation in Chapter 22 of the 1985 FUNDAMENTALS Volume. However, these methods cannot be considered completely accurate. Because of the variable and complex post attack environment, it is difficult to evaluate natural ventilation accurately.

VENTILATION SYSTEMS

Mechanical Ventilation

Mechanical ventilation applies to all types and sizes of shelters and is not subject to the uncertainties associated with natural ventilation. The major limitation is that the maintenance of a safe, effective temperature, such as 83 °F (28.3 °C), is not practicable when the effective temperature of the outdoor air approaches the safe value. This method is most suitable for fallout shelters, in which there is no impelling reason to minimize the size of openings or to provide extensive purification treatment for the fresh air supplied to the shelter.

Fans or blowers for a forced ventilation system require an energy source for operation. A first step in designing a ventilating system for a shelter is to select a reliable source of power. The possible choices include auxiliary electric power and muscle power. In general, commercial electric power should not be relied on as the sole source, since the supply may be disrupted when needed. The use of auxiliary electric power implies that the blowers would be driven by an electric motor with power supplied by an auxiliary engine-generator. Waste heat from an engine-generator can often be used in a shelter for tempering air in winter or heating domestic water. *Manual drive* includes various types of drives that make use of arm or leg muscles. Fans or blowers with manual drives are limited in capacity by human factors and multiple units would be required in large shelters.

The system components for a shelter should be selected and arranged in accordance with the following objectives, wherever practicable:

1. Maintain a tolerable physical environment in the shelter.
2. Prevent or minimize the condensation of moisture on interior surfaces.
3. Facilitate operation, maintenance, and repair of all equipment.
4. Avoid awkward duct connections and the resultant noise and head losses.
5. Reuse waste air from the ceiling level of occupied spaces for

scavenging service spaces such as equipment rooms, toilets, and entryways.
6. Protect people and equipment from effects of weapons and fire to a degree consistent with potential capabilities of the shelter.
   a. Maintain radiation barriers inviolate by shielding at points where ducts penetrate the structural shell.
   b. Provide a weatherproof air intake fixture or hood that tends to exclude particulates, and locate this fixture at a safe distance from combustible materials and above levels of ground turbulence and flood water.
   c. Avoid contamination of interior spaces, equipment rooms, and entryways by radioactive particles and combustion gases from fires or fuel-burning equipment.
   d. Provide blast closures or attenuators for blast-resistant shelters.
   e. Provide filters for purifying fresh air to a degree consistent with the intended use of the shelter. Shield occupied spaces from air filters.
   f. Consider use of a life-support system for suitable closed shelters located in a potential fire area.
   g. Consider requirements for shock-mounting equipment in blast-resistant shelters.
7. Provide system flexibility to accommodate seasonal changes and variations in physical activity.
   a. Reduce the quantity of fresh air in cold weather or temper the fresh air with waste heat to avoid overcooling.
   b. Provide mixing dampers and plenum for partial recirculation of the air. This maintains air motion and tempers the air supplied to occupied spaces.
   c. Provide means for adjustment of air distribution to correct objectionable drafts and to balance the system in accordance with space usage—that is, for sleeping or recreation.
8. Anticipate and facilitate probable future improvements or changes in shelter capabilities.
9. Achieve optimum cost-effectiveness—minimum cost consistent with adequate performance.

An Environmental Control System

Figure 20 shows an environmental control system in an underground shelter. The various components are identified by numbers that correspond to the following itemized nomenclature,

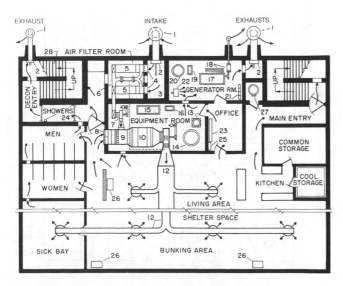

Fig. 20   Environmental Control System for an Underground Community Shelter

with brief comments. In general, blast-resistant shelter systems should have adequate provisions for shock mounting of components. Any equipment, such as heat-transfer apparatus, installed outside the protective structure must be blast-resistant.

1. **Weatherproof hoods** of the mushroom type for intake and exhaust air. Particle sizes having characteristic terminal velocities greater than the vertical component of the entering air velocity are not likely to be drawn into the ventilating system. Stormproof louvers in wall openings may also be used but are less effective in excluding particulates.
2. **Automatic blast closures.** Use of blast valves is consistent only in structures having appreciable blast resistance. Pressure-actuated blast valves close in a few milliseconds to prevent a destructive pressure rise within the shelter. Sensor-operated valves close before arrival of the shock wave and can be used when increased costs can be justified.
3. **Fresh air intake plenum.** This plenum serves as a settling chamber for coarse particles that may be radioactive and as an expansion chamber to limit pressure rise due to leakage during closure of blast valves. Intervening concrete walls provide shielding from this secondary source of radiation.
4. **Particulate filters or prefilters** for fresh air. Panel-type filters with dry, pleated, glass-fiber media supported on both sides by pleated wire screens would be most suitable for service in blast-resistant structures.
5. **Gas-particulate filter units.** Each unit consists of an extreme-efficiency particulate filter and a special activated-charcoal filter mounted and sealed in a rectangular frame. These units can be used effectively only in tight shelters planned or adapted for protection against biological and chemical warfare agents.
6. **Fresh air ductwork.** For normal operation, a bypass duct with two open dampers may be provided for gas-particulate filter units. When these filter units are in service, the two bypass dampers are closed, and the length of duct between the two dampers can be pressurized by a pipe connection to the main-fan discharge transition to ensure that any damper leakage is uncontaminated air.
7. **Fresh air blower** with electric motor drive. If the shelter is cooled by means *other* than ventilation with outdoor air, the capacity of the blower can be 3 cfm (1.4 L/s) per person, and this amount provides for some emergency overloading of the shelter. Since this blower pressurizes the shelter space and must operate against a rather high system resistance, if air flow is restricted by gas-particulate filters and blast valves, Class II construction may be indicated. Class I construction is adequate for fans in fallout shelters.
8. **Grilled opening** for recirculated air. Optional prefilters and activated-carbon filters may be provided, as shown behind the grille, for odor control. Alternatively, portable activated-carbon filter units may be used for this purpose.
9. **Mixing plenum** for fresh and recirculated air. Air quantities can be adjusted by changing damper positions or motor speeds.
10. **Air conditioning or heat-exchanger unit** with extended-surface cooling and heating coils. Cooling coils can use well water or chilled water, and heating coils can use waste heat from the engine generator.
11. **Main fan** with electric motor drive. Required capacity of this fan depends upon system design parameters. Adequate air distribution can be obtained with 10 to 15 cfm (4.7 to 7.1 L/s) per person.
12. **Air distribution ductwork** with diffusion outlets. Although design of the duct system may be dictated by requirements for normal uses of the structure, a simple low-cost system that distributes all of the air along the remote end of the occupied space may be quite adequate for survival shelters.

13. **Well and pump** for potable and cooling water. A charging well for waste water may be desirable. If well water is not available, other means must be substituted for removal of excess heat.

14. **Hydropneumatic tank** for pressure water system.

15. Optional **unitary water chiller** for alternative or supplementary use. This item may be needed for absolute control of the environment in hot humid climates where cool well water is not available. The system could be arranged for use of a unitary conditioner, which also avoids refrigerant lines between separated components.

16. **Circulating pump** for chilled water. This item may be an integral part of the package water chiller.

17. **Emergency engine-generator set.** The engine may be cooled by a heat exchanger using well water or, alternatively, by a remote radiator. The storage tank for fuel oil or gasoline, not shown, may be buried adjacent to the shelter if provisions are made for differential movements of tank and structure.

18. **Heat exchanger and muffler** for engine cooling and waste heat recovery.

19. **Hot water circulating pump.**

20. **Hot water storage tank.** Hot water can be used to advantage for tempering fresh air or for showers.

21. **Batteries** for cranking engine or for emergency lighting.

22. **Recirculating fan-coil unit** for cooling the generator room with well water.

23. **Control cabinet** for functional control apparatus.

24. **Decontamination facility.** Showers are provided for personnel entering from contaminated areas and to promote welfare of occupants.

25. **Cabinet** for detection or test instruments and special tools.

26. **Portable manually operated life-support packages.** These optional units should provide for about 24 hours of sealed operation during which the shelter may be subject to the effects of adjacent fires. Alternatively, a static life-support system using bottled oxygen and soda lime could be provided.

27. **Incinerator** for combustible waste materials.

28. **Sewage sump and pump** beneath the stairway.

The environmental control system (shown in Figure 20) has capabilities that are not likely to be essential for survival in most situations, and costs for a less comprehensive system are more acceptable. Minimum requirements for environmental control could be provided at much lower cost. In general, the nature of the environmental control system and its components will be determined after considering several factors, including the probability that the threat will materialize, the cost of protective features needed to avert specific hazards, the consequences of direct exposure to those hazards, alternative uses for the space, and the level of comfort required by expected occupants.

Air-Intakes

During an emergency, the ambient atmosphere may be contaminated with noxious gases, fumes, or particulate matter that must be partially or completely removed from any ventilating air supplied to occupied spaces in a protective structure. This can be accomplished by gas and/or particulate filters that have the necessary efficiencies and specific capabilities, if the attendant costs are not prohibitive. These costs include not only the cost of the filter installation and maintenance, but also the additional costs for air-moving apparatus and power needed to accommodate the flow resistance of the filters.

When radioactive, irritant, toxic, or pathogenic particulates are removed, air-intake facilities designed to use gravitational or inertial forces may be advantageous. If the hazardous particles are relatively coarse and/or dense, a properly designed air-intake facility may meet the requirement adequately without filters. If the installation includes particulate filters, the removal of coarse particles at the air intake facility would probably extend the service life of the filter elements. Particles having a mean diameter of 0.002 in. (50 μm) or more are considered coarse in these applications.

Air-intakes effective in removing particulates from ventilating air are grouped as (1) those that prevent the entry of particles into a fixture located outside the structure and (2) those that separate and collect the particles in a sump or chamber contained within the enclosed space.

External fixtures for intake air include gooseneck, mushroom, and sidewall types with projecting canopy. These share the characteristic that air from the atmosphere must enter the fixture in an upward direction with a vertical component of velocity low enough to capture only fine particles, while coarse particles fall to the ground.

Internal facilities for intake air include (1) vertical U-shaped vent shafts, in which the air changes direction abruptly and deposits coarse particles in a sump or basin from which they can occasionally be flushed with water down a drain pipe; and (2) gravity-separation chambers or passageways, through which the ventilating air flows horizontally at a low velocity so that coarse particles settle to the floor and accumulate until removed. Underground passageways may also moderate the temperature of outside air supplied to occupied spaces. In any case, air intakes should be located above the level of ground turbulence and above the high water mark of any anticipated flood. Screens that serve to exclude birds and vermin are desirable.

Gravity separation techniques relate to the fact that a free particle falls vertically downward in still air and accelerates to a terminal velocity (rate of settling) at which dynamic drag forces are equal to the gravitational force on the particle. The drag forces are determined by the relative velocity, size, and, to a lesser degree, shape of the particle, as well as the physical properties (density and viscosity) of the air.

In general, particles fall obliquely at an angle determined by the vector sum of terminal and wind velocities. The terminal velocities of spherical particles falling through standard air are shown in Figure 21 (Lapple and Shepherd 1940). Thus, the terminal velocity of nearly spherical particles having a mean

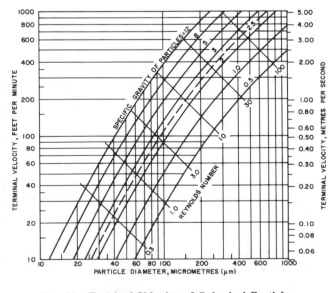

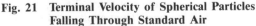

**Fig. 21 Terminal Velocity of Spherical Particles
Falling Through Standard Air**

diameter of 0.0059 in. (150 μm) and a specific gravity of 2.6 would be about 200 fpm (1.02 m/s). Then, an air-intake for a ventilating system arranged to admit air in an upward direction at a velocity of 200 fpm (1.02 m/s) would tend to separate particles having diameters greater than 0.0059 in. (150 μm) from the air stream.

EVAPORATIVE COOLING

Evaporative cooling either reduces the effective temperature or lowers the required ventilation rate in a shelter. The rate of change of effective temperature, with respect to dry-bulb temperatures, is positive over the ranges of dry- and wet-bulb temperatures that may be expected in shelters. Lowering the dry-bulb temperature through evaporative cooling lowers the effective temperature of the shelter for a fixed ventilation rate and inlet air condition. These trends have been verified by calculation of shelter conditions by a modified Case 1 solution.

Assuming that the evaporative cooler is at the inlet to the shelter, the adequacy of forced ventilation with evaporative cooling can be established for any evaporative cooler efficiency. Tests on an evaporative cooler with a 4-in. (100-mm) aspen wood pad have shown efficiencies as high as 97%. Commercially available units generally operate at about 80% efficiency. Tests with evaporative coolers with efficiencies of 80% show the possibility of reducing the required ventilation rates within a range of 2 to 83% (Figure 22). The greatest reductions are in the regions that are unventilatable by natural means, or those in which extremely high ventilation rates are required (Baschiere, Rathmann, and Lokmanhekim 1968).

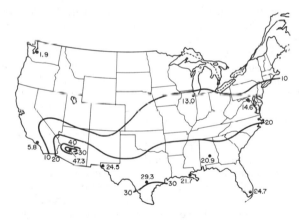

Fig. 22   Percent Reduction in Ventilation System Capacities Enabled by Use of Evaporative Coolers Having an Efficiency of 80% for Limiting Effective Temperatures in Occupied Spaces to 83°F (28.3°C) with 90% Adequacy During a Normal Year

Increasing evaporation efficiency from 80 to 85% increases the percent reductions an average of 2 to 3%, with a maximum of 5.3%. Therefore, evaporative coolers with efficiencies as low as 80% can be considered without significantly affecting the ventilation rate reductions below those associated with the 95% efficiency level.

MOISTURE IN ENCLOSED SPACES

During standby or unoccupied periods, moisture may have to be controlled; if shelters are located in areas having a high water table, complete water-proofing is necessary.

As in all facilities unoccupied for long periods without lighting or other heat sources, mildew and other moisture effects are likely to occur. Conventional methods such as mechanical dehumidifiers, silica gel, and calcium chloride can control the standby environment. Conventional, residential-type mechanical package dehumidifiers are generally unsuited for operation at temperatures below 60°F (16°C) due to frosting on the evaporator coils. Additional heat or alternate methods may have to be employed where colder temperatures are likely to occur.

Computer studies and actual shelter tests have shown that condensation on walls or ceilings is more likely to occur during a summer period, but, under certain conditions, may also occur in winter. The tendency to condense will be most pronounced in areas where the outside air dew point is high and ground temperature is low.

The interior surface temperatures of the shelter, as calculated in the Case 3 analysis, are helpful in predicting possible water vapor condensation along shelter walls.

For small shelters in moderate climatic regions, the condensation of water usually takes place during the initial phase of shelter occupancy while the soil temperature adjacent to the walls is relatively low. Drip from the ceiling is particularly objectionable. This may be prevented by suspending metal pans under the ceiling to carry the condensed moisture into containers or a sump. Dehumidification by use of sorbent materials or mechanical dehumidifiers adds heat to the space as water is being removed, and the resultant effect is an increase in effective temperature.

FIRE EFFECTS

Fires ignited by thermal radiation from a nuclear weapon or by normal causes may occur in all types of shelters. External fires could result where there is burning or smoldering material around or over a shelter or an intake opening. Basement shelters are vulnerable to fire and questionable in areas where direct or secondary fire effects are probable.

The probability of drawing in superheated air and toxic gases during a fire is reduced if the air intake opening is located at a distance from combustible buildings or other materials. Intakes at two different points with dampers reduce risk further. The most positive protection against fire effects can be provided by temporarily closing off the shelter openings, shutting down the ventilating system, and putting a life-support system into operation.

There is little evidence that oxygen is drawn from a shelter by a nearby fire, or that the oxygen in the area would be depleted to the point where life could not be sustained. If fire will burn, there is enough oxygen to breathe. The main danger comes from carbon monoxide and heated gases entering the air intake. Carbon monoxide and heated gases can also enter the shelter through porous walls and cracks in the shelter construction. The presence of hot air and toxic gases such as carbon monoxide would probably necessitate shutdown of the ventilation system. While there is sufficient air in a shelter to support life for a few hours without air replacement or revitalization, the attendant increase in carbon dioxide and decrease in oxygen concentration eventually requires that the shelter either be evacuated or have a life-support system placed in operation. For example, according to Figure 5, carbon dioxide concentration in an unventilated shelter having 100 ft³ (2.83 m³) of free space per person would increase to 3% by volume in 3.7 hours and to 5% in 6.1 hours.

When the top of the slab or overburden above an underground shelter is blanketed with burning or smoldering material, the shelter may experience intense heat flux from the flame above, resulting in a peak surface temperature near 2000°F (1100°C). The pattern of the surface temperature and heat flux in the shelter roof region, however, depends upon the characteristics of burning, heat content, and collapsing sequence of the burn-

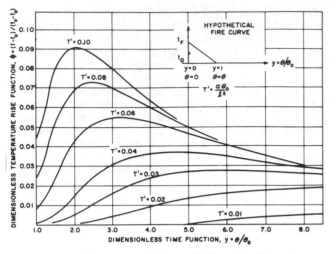

Fig. 23   Temperature Rise at Ceiling of a Chamber Caused by an Overhead Fire

ing structure. After the structure starts to cave in, the surface temperature may decrease, because the collapsed burn pile shields the shelter from the high temperature flame, and the air that had been feeding the fire from beneath the suspended burn pile is restricted. This high surface temperature, however, will cause the shelter roof near the fire to rise in temperature during the fire and continue to rise for some time after the fire subsides. An analysis of heat conduction in the shelter roof is complex because the thermal properties depend on temperature and moisture content for large temperature change, and because some of the conducted heat is absorbed by vaporization of the water contained in the earth or slab.

An estimate of the temperature rise at the ceiling of the shelter can be obtained from Figure 23. The assumed fire model for these curves is based upon sudden outside surface temperature rise to fire temperatures (t_F) at time = 0, followed by a linear return to the initial top slab surface temperature before the fire (t_o), as indicated in the insert of Figure 23. The elapsed time is designated as the fire period, θ_o. The temperature (t) of the lower surface of the slab continues to rise for a time during the post-fire period and can be computed from the temperature rise function ϕ_F at any time (θ) after the start of the fire. The crest of each curve occurs at the time when the temperature of the lower surface is maximum.

Equations 20, 21, and 22 may be written to express these relationships.

$$T' = \frac{\alpha\phi_o}{l^2} \qquad (20)$$

$$\phi_F = \frac{t - t_o}{t_F - t_o} \qquad (21)$$

$$T = \frac{\theta}{\theta_o} \qquad (22)$$

where

α = thermal diffusivity ft²/h (m²/s)
θ_o = fire period, h (s)
l = slab thickness, ft (m)
t = temperature of the slab lower surface, °F (°C)
t_F = fire temperature, °F (°C)
t_o = initial top slab surface temperature, °F (°C)
θ = time after start of fire, h (s)

Example 4: The structural roof slab over an underground chamber is covered with a layer of mineral fill to make a total thickness of l = 2 ft (0.61 m). The thermal diffusivity, α, of overhead materials is 0.030 ft²/h (0.774 mm²/s). The upper surface is covered with burning debris

from a collapsed building. During the fire, the temperature of the upper surface of cover materials increases suddenly from a normal of t_o = 80°F (26.7°C) to a maximum of t_F = 1500°F (816°C), and then decreases linearly to normal over a fire period of θ_o = 8 h. Determine the maximum temperature of the ceiling surface in the chamber and the time after ignition at which the maximum temperature occurs.

Solution A (I-P units):
From Equation 20,

$$T' = \frac{(0.03)(8)}{(2)^2} = 0.06$$

From Figure 23 at the peak of the 0.06 curve, ϕ_F is found to be 0.055. From Equation 21,

$$t - 80 = (0.055)(1500 - 80) = 78°F$$
$$t = 158°F = \text{maximum ceiling temperature.}$$

Noting that on Figure 23 the peak of the curve occurs at Y = 3.25, the value of θ is determined from Equation 22.

$$\theta = (8)(3.25) = 26 \text{ h to maximum ceiling temperature}$$

Solution B (SI units):
From Equation 20,

$$T' = \frac{(0.774)(10^6)(8)(3600)}{(0.61)^2} = 0.06$$

From Figure 23, at the peak of the T' = 0.06 curve, read ϕ_F = 0.055. Then, from Equation 21, $t - 26.7 = (0.055)(816 - 26.7) = 43.4°C$ and the maximum ceiling temperature, t = 70°C. On Figure 23, note that the peak of the curve occurs at dimensionless time, Y = 3.25. Then, the value of θ, the elapsed time to develop the maximum ceiling temperature, is determined from Equation 22, $\theta = (8)(3.25) = 26$ h, which is long after the end of the 8-h fire period.

Example 4 points out the importance of shelter location with regard to combustible structures or materials. A similar computation with increased overhead thickness would show the benefits to be derived from heavy earth cover.

The dosage of radiation received from a deposit of radioactive particulates decreases rapidly with increasing distance. For this reason, the mid-floors of a high-rise building afford substantial protection from exposure to radioactive fallout that may be deposited on the roof and surrounding ground surfaces. The degree of protection would be increased by absorption of nuclear radiations in any intervening walls and slabs of dense materials such as concrete. However, if a fire occurs, continued occupancy of the building would be hazardous—unless areas of protection against the lethal effects of fire and smoke have been provided. In general, fire-safe refuges or sanctuaries can be established on each floor of noncombustible structures. Fire-safe refuges are conceived as a viable alternative that can be used in conjunction with, not as a replacement for, the sprinkler systems and escape routes that are commonly associated with fire protection in buildings. The ventilating system often provided for pressurizing a stairwell can be increased in capacity and extended to serve also as a source of pure air for pressurizing fire-safe refuges to exclude toxic gases and smoke. Potentially, the best spaces for secondary use as places of refuge are rest rooms, service corridors, and elevator lobbies in a building core that also includes a pressurized stairwell.

The design and use of environmental control systems for fire safety may be restricted by conventional requirements of local building or fire codes, unless variances are approved.

SELECTION OF APPARATUS

The cost of virtually complete protection against all conceivable hazards is prohibitive. Therefore, the nature of the threat and the specific hazards against which protection is contemplated should be evaluated during preliminary planning. The system configuration and the components to be included can then be designed in accord with such guidance. Essential information on hazards and recommended or mandatory requirements for protective capabilities can be obtained from a cognizant government agency.

The need for air purification apparatus varies greatly among protective facilities, and the method selected can affect the system resistance to air flow, the power to drive air movers, and the capacity of any auxiliary power supply that may be needed. High efficiency air filters that remove fine particles would be needed if the threat included pathogenic organisms or irritant fumes. On the other hand, the acute hazard of radioactive fallout from nuclear explosions is associated with large particles that can be adequately separated from ventilating air by a suitable intake fixture. Many toxic gases can be removed from an air stream by activated charcoal impregnated with reactive or catalytic agents (Viessman 1954).

For survival under some unusual situations, a completely isolated environment with a self-sufficient life-support system may be necessary, including appartus for limiting carbon dioxide concentration, for replacing the oxygen consumed, and for controlling the effective temperature in the space (Gates 1960). For more detailed information on air-filtering apparatus, see Chapters 10 and 11 of the 1983 EQUIPMENT Volume.

REFERENCES

ACGIH. 1968. Threshold Limit Values of Air-borne Contaminants.

Achenbach, P.R.; Drapeau, F.J.J.; and Phillips, C.W. 1962. Environmental Characteristics of a Small Underground Fallout Shelter. ASHRAE Journal, January, p. 21.

Achenbach, P.R.; Kusuda, T.; and Drapeau, F.J.J. 1962. Mathematical Analysis of Thermal Environment in Underground Shelters. ASHRAE Symposium on Survival Shelters, p. 9.

Allen, F.C. 1960. Control of Shelter Environment. Proceedings, Environmental Engineering in Protective Shelters, NAS-NRC, February, p. 297

Allen, F.C. 1962. Mechanical Equipment Requirements. ASHRAE Symposium on Survival Shelters, p. 131.

Allen, F.C. 1970. Ventilating and Mixing Processes in Nonuniform Shelter Environments. Stanford Research Institute for OCD, AD 708-574.

Allen, F.C. 1972. Parametric Study of Thermal Problems in Densely Populated Shelters. Stanford Research Institute for Defense Civil Preparedness Agency, Menlo Park, CA, AD 749-796.

Baschiere, R.J.; Lokmanhekim, M.; Moy, H.C.; and Engholm, G. 1965. Analysis of Aboveground Fallout Shelter Ventilation Requirements. ASHRAE Transactions, Vol. 71, Part 1, p. 101.

Baschiere, R.J.; Rathmann, C.E.; and Lokmanhekim, M. 1968. Adequacy of Evaporative Cooling and Shelter Environmental Prediction. General American Research Division, GATX, OCD, AD 679-874.

Blockley, W.V. 1968. Dehydration and Survivability in Warm Shelters. Webb Associates, Malibu, CA, Office of Civil Defense, AD 673-857.

Buettner, K. 1957. Heat Transfer and Safe Exposure Time for Man in Extreme Thermal Environment. Mechanical Engineering. Vol. 79, November, p. 1031.

Dasler, A.R.; and Minard, D. 1965. Environmental Physiology of Shelter Habitation. ASHRAE Transactions, Vol. 71, Part 1, p. 115.

Drucker, E.E.; and Cheng, H.S.Y. 1962. Analog Study of Heating in Survival Shelters. ASHRAE Symposium on Survival Shelters, p. 35.

Drucker, E.E.; and Haines, J.T. 1964. A Study of Thermal Environment in Underground Survival Shelters Using an Electronic Analog Computer. ASHRAE Transactions, Vol. 70, p. 7.

Ducar, G.J. and Engholm, G. 1965. Natural Ventilation of Underground Fallout Shelters. ASHRAE Transactions, Vol. 71, Part 1, p. 88.

Fanger, P.O.; Nevins, R.G.; and McNall, P.E. 1968. Predicted and Measured Heat Losses and Thermal Comfort Conditions for Human Beings. Thermal Problems in Biotechnology. ASME, New York, NY, p. 61.

Gates, A.S. 1960. Submarine Atmosphere Control Problems and Methods. Proceedings, Environmental Engineering in Protective Shelters, NAS-NRC, p. 179.

Glasstone, S. 1962. Effects of Nuclear Weapons. Prepared by Dept. of Defense and published by Atomic Energy Commission.

Gorton, R.L. 1972. Response of Human Subjects to Reduced Levels of Water Consumption under Simulated Civil Defense Shelter Conditions. Kansas State University, Manhattan, KS, Office of Civil Defense, AD 739-562.

Harrow, B.; and Mazur, A. 1958. Textbook of Biochemistry. W.B. Saunders Co., Philadelphia, PA, p. 314.

Humphreys, C.M.; Henschel, A.; and Lee, D.H.K. 1965. Sensible and Latent Heat Losses from Occupants of Survival Shelters. Division of Occupational Health, Public Health Service, DHEW.

Kusuda, T.; and Achenbach, P.R. 1965. Earth Temperature and Thermal Diffusivity at Selected Stations in the United States. ASHRAE Transactions, Vol. 71, Part 1, p. 76.

Kusuda, T.; and Achenbach, P.R. 1963. Numerical Analysis of the Thermal Environment of Occupied Underground Spaces with Finite Cover Using a Digital Computer. ASHRAE Transactions, Vol. 69, p. 439.

Kusuda, T.; and Achenbach, P.R. 1965. Outdoor Air Psychrometric Criteria for Summer Ventilation of Protective Shelter. ASHRAE Transactions, Vol. 71, Part 1, p. 76.

Lapple, C.E.; and Shepherd, C.B. 1940. Calculation of Particle Trajectories. Industrial and Engineering Chemistry, Vol. 32, No. 5, p. 605.

Lee, D.H.K.; and Henschel, A. 1963. Evaluation of Thermal Environment in Shelters. Division of Occupational Health, Public Health Service, DHEW.

Lind, A.R. 1955. The Influence of Inspired Air Temperature on Tolerance to Work in the Heat. British Journal of Industrial Medicine, Vol. 12, p. 126.

McNall, P.E.; and Ryan, P.W. 1968. Water Consumption during 24-Hour Exposure to Hot Humid Environments. ASHRAE Journal, Vol. 10, March, p. 51.

Nevins, R.G.; and McNall, P.E. 1967. Human Physiological Responses to Shelter Environment. Institute for Environmental Research, Kansas State University, KS, Office of Civil Defense, AD 659-403.

Newburgh, L.H. (Ed). 1949. Physiology of Heat Regulation and the Science of Clothing. W.B. Saunders Company, Philadelphia and London.

OCD. 1962. Shelter Design and Analysis, Vol. 1. Fallout Protection. Office of Civil Defense. 1969. Shelter Design and Analysis. Environmental Engineering for Shelters, TR-20, Vol. 3. Office of Civil Defense.

OCD. 1971. Design Considerations for Fallout Shelter Ventilating Air Intake Systems. Technical Memorandum 71-1, Office of Civil Defense.

Pefley, R.K.; Abel, J.F.; and Dutton, J.S. 1972. Physiological Effects of Low Ventilation Rates, High Temperatures and High Humidities. University of Santa Clara, Santa Clara, CA, Civil Defense Preparedness Agency, AD 753-843.

Pefley, R.; and Allen, F.C. 1982. Fire-Safe Sanctuaries: A Viable Alternative for Life Safety in High-Rise Buildings. ASHRAE Transactions, Vol. 88, Part 2, Paper #2729, RP-211.

Pefley, R.K.; Cull, E.T.; and Sekins, K.M. 1969. Monoman Calorimeter Project. University of Santa Clara, Santa Clara, CA, Office of Civil Defense, AD 685-878

Pratt, A.W.; and Davis, L.F. 1958. Heat Transfer in Deep Underground Tunnels. National Building Studies Research, London.

U.S. Army. 1959. Heating and Air Conditioning of Underground Installations. Corps of Engineers, Manual EM 1110-345-450.

Viessman, W. 1954. How to Plan Air Conditioning for Protective Shelters. Heating, Piping, and Air Conditioning, Vol. 26.

Winslow, C.E.A.; and Herrington, L.P. 1949. Temperature and Human Life. Princeton University Press, Princeton, NJ.

Yaglou, C.P. 1960. Tolerance Limits of People for Cold, Heat, and Humidity in Underground Shelters. Proceedings, Environmental Engineering in Protective Shelters, NAS-NRC February, p. 31

BIBLIOGRAPHY

ASHRAE. 1978. Fire and Smoke Technology. ASHRAE Journal, July.

Blockley, W.V.; McCutchan, J.W.; and Taylor, C.L. 1954. Prediction of Human Tolerance for Heat in Aircraft. A Design Guide, WADC Technical Report 53-346.

Everetts, John; Witt, D.R.; and McLaughlin, E.R. 1970. The Feasibility of Augmenting Below-Grade Shelter Habitability with Conditioned Air. The Pennsylvania State University Report to Office of Civil Defense.

Hummell, J.D.; Bearint, D.E.; and Flanigan, L.J. 1964. Methods for Disposing of Excess Shelter Heat. Battelle Memorial Institute Report to Office of Civil Defense.

Kaiser, E.R.; and Tolciss, J.; 1962. A Selective Bibliography on Environmental Control and Habitability of Survival Shelters, ASHRAE Symposium on Survival Shelters.

Kaiser, E.R.; 1963. A Selective Bibliography on Environmental Control and Habitability of Survival Shelters-Addendum No. 1, ASHRAE Symposium on Survival Shelters.

Peters, A.; and Gentieu, N. Soil Thermal Properties: An Annotated Bibliography. Office of Civil Defense Research Report OCD-OS-6258 AD 431-604.

Spiegel, W.F. 1968. Mechanical and Electrical System Design for Protection Shelters. Technical Manual Prepared for Office of Civil Defense.

Technical Standards for Fallout Shelters. Office of Civil Defense, Dept. of the Army, Technical Memorandum 69-1.

Webb, P. (ed.) 1964. Bioastronautics Data Book. National Aeronautics and Space Administration, Scientific and Technical Information Division, Washington, DC, NASA SP-3006.

CHAPTER 28

INDUSTRIAL AIR CONDITIONING

THIS chapter deals with air conditioning of industrial facilities, including process requirements, design considerations, and systems and equipment used. Details for specific processes are found in Chapters 13 through 23.

The industrial plant, warehouse, laboratory, nuclear power plant and facilities, or data processing room is designed for the specific processes enclosed. Environmental conditions include proper temperature, humidity, air motion, and cleanliness. Airborne contaminants generated must be collected, cleaned, and treated before discharge from the building or return to the area.

Many industrial buildings require large quantities of energy, both in manufacturing and in maintenance of building environmental conditions. Energy can be saved by proper insulation, ventilation, use of solar energy, and recovery of waste heat.

For worker efficiency, the environment should be comfortable, prevent fatigue, allow communication, and not be harmful to health. Equipment should control temperature and humidity or provide spot cooling to avoid heat stress; have low noise levels; include lighting adequate for the work performed; and control noxious and toxic fumes.

GENERAL REQUIREMENTS

Table 1 lists typical conditions of temperature and relative humidity and specific filtration requirements for the storage, manufacture, and processing of various commodities. Requirements for a specific application may vary. Improvements in processes and increased knowledge may cause further variation, so systems should be flexible for future requirements.

Inside temperature, humidity, and filtration levels and allowable variations should be established by agreement with the owner. Conditions may be limited either to heating and maximum humidity or to full air conditioning. Some conditions listed in Table 1 increase employee comfort and efficiency, since a compromise between product or process conditions and comfort conditions may optimize quality and production costs.

A work environment that allows a worker to perform assigned duties without fatigue because of high or low temperatures and exposure to harmful airborne contaminants will allow better, continued performance. Consequently, it may also improve worker morale and reduce absenteeism.

PROCESS AND PRODUCT REQUIREMENTS

The space required of a process or product may be classified to control one or more factors such as (1) regain; (2) rate of chemical reactions; (3) rate of biochemical reactions; (4) rate of crystallization; (5) product accuracy and uniformity; (6) corrosion, rust, and abrasion of highly polished surfaces; (7) static electricity; and (8) air cleanliness and product formability.

The preparation of this chapter is assigned to TC 9.2, Industrial Air Conditioning.

Regain

In the manufacture or processing of hygroscopic materials such as textiles, paper, wood, leather, tobacco, and foodstuffs, air temperature and relative humidity have a marked influence on production rate, product weight, strength, appearance, and general quality.

Moisture in vegetable or animal materials (and some minerals) reaches equilibrium content (known as *regain*) with the moisture of the surrounding air. Regain is defined as the percentage of absorbed moisture in a material compared to its bone-dry weight. If a material sample with a mass of 110 grams has a mass of 100 grams after a thorough drying under standard conditions of 220 to 230°F (104 to 110°C), the mass of absorbed moisture is 10 grams—10% of the sample's bone-dry mass. The regain, therefore, is 10%.

Table 2 lists typical values of regain for organic and inorganic materials at 75°F (24°C) in equilibrium at various relative humidities. Temperature change affects the rate of absorption or drying, which generally varies with the nature of the material, its thickness, and its density. Sudden temperature changes cause a slight regain change, even with fixed relative humidity; but the effect of temperature compared to relative humidity is comparatively unimportant.

Hygroscopic Materials

In absorbing moisture from air, hygroscopic materials deliver sensible heat to the air equal to the latent heat of the absorbed moisture. Moisture gains or losses by materials in processes are usually quite small, but in certain types, the amount of liberated heat should be included in the load estimate. Actual values of regain should be obtained for a particular application, since Table 2 is only typical. Manufacturing economy requires regain to be maintained at a level suitable for rapid and satisfactory manipulation. Uniformity allows high-speed machinery to operate with minimum loss.

Conditioning and Drying

Materials may be exposed to humidities desirable for treatment simultaneously with manufacture or processing, or they may be treated separately after conditioning and drying in special enclosures. Conditioning removes or adds hygroscopic moisture. Drying removes both hygroscopic moisture and free moisture in excess of that in equilibrium. Free moisture may be removed by evaporation, physically blowing it off, or by other means. Drying systems are discussed in Chapter 44.

Drying and conditioning may be combined to remove moisture and accurately regulate final moisture content, such as for some textile products and tobacco. Conditioning or drying is frequently a continuous process of conveying the material through a tunnel and subjecting it to various controlled atmospheric conditions. Chapter 7 of the 1983 EQUIPMENT Volume describes dehumidification and pressure drying equipment.

Table 1 Temperatures and Humidities for Industrial Air Conditioning

Process	Dry Bulb, °F (°C)	rh, %
ABRASIVE		
Manufacture	79 (26)	50
CERAMICS		
Refractory	110 to 150 (43 to 66)	50 to 90
Molding room	80 (27)	60 to 70
Clay storage	60 to 80 (16 to 27)	35 to 65
Decalcomania production	75 to 80 (24 to 27)	48
Decorating room	75 to 80 (24 to 27)	48

Use high efficiency range filtration in decorating room. To minimize the danger of silicosis in other areas, either a dust-collecting system or the proper level of mechanical filtration may be required.

Process	Dry Bulb, °F (°C)	rh, %
CEREAL		
Packaging	75 to 80 (24 to 27)	45 to 50
DISTILLING		
Storage:		
Grain	6 (16)	35 to 40
Liquid yeast	32 to 33 (0 to 1)	...
General manufacturing	60 to 75 (16 to 24)	45 to 60
Aging	65 to 72 (18 to 22)	50 to 60

Low humidity and dust control are important where grains are ground. Use high efficiency range filtration for all areas to prevent mold spore and bacteria growth. Use ultrahigh efficiency filtration where bulk flash pasteurization is performed.

Process	Dry Bulb, °F (°C)	rh, %
ELECTRICAL PRODUCTS		
Electronics and X ray:		
Coil and transformer winding	72 (22)	15
Semi conductor assembly	68 (20)	40 to 50
Electrical instruments:		
Manufacture and laboratory	70 (21)	50 to 55
Thermostat assembly and calibration	75 (24)	50 to 55
Humidistat assembly and calibration	75 (24)	50 to 55
Small mechanisms:		
Close tolerance assembly	72 (22*)	40 to 45
Meter assembly and test	75 (24)	60 to 63
Switchgear:		
Fuse and cutout assembly	73 (23)	50
Capacitor winding	73 (23)	50
Paper storage	73 (23)	50
Conductor wrapping with yarn	75 (24)	65 to 70
Lightning arrester assembly	68 (20)	20 to 40
Thermal circuit breakers assembly and test	75 (24)	30 to 60
High-Voltage transformer repair	79 (26)	5
Water wheel generators:		
Thrust runner lapping	70 (21)	30 to 50
Rectifiers:		
Processing selenium and copper oxide plates	73 (23)	30 to 40

*Temperature to be held constant.

Dust control is essential in these processes. Minimum control requires medium efficiency filters. Degree of filtration depends on the type of function in area. Smaller tolerancces and miniature components suggest high efficiency filters.

Process	Dry Bulb, °F (°C)	rh, %
FLOOR COVERING		
Linoleum:		
Mechanical oxidizing of linseed oil*	90 to 100 (32 to 38)	
Printing	80 (27)	
Stoving process	160 to 250 (70 to 120)	

*Precise temperature control required.

Air filtration is recommended for the stoving process.

Process	Dry Bulb, °F (°C)	rh, %
FOUNDRIES*		
Core making	60 to 70 (16 to 21)	
Mold making:		
Bench work	60 to 70 (16 to 21)	
Floor work	55 to 65 (13 to 18)	
Pouring	40 (5)	
Shakeout	40 to 50 (5 to 10)	
Cleaning room	55 to 65 (13 to 18)	

*Winter desing room temperatures. Spot coolers are sometimes used in larger installations.

In mold making, provide hoods at transfer points with wet-collector dust removal system. Use 600 to 800 cfm (300 to 400 L/s) per hood.

In shakeout room, provide hoods with wet-collector dust removal system. Exhaust 400 to 500 cfm (190 to 240 L/s) grate area. Room ventilators are generally not effective.

In cleaning room, provide hoods for grinders and cleaning equipment with dry cyclones or bag-type collectors. In core making, oven and adjacent cooling areas require fume exhaust hoods. Pouring rooms require two-speed powered roof ventilators. Design for minimum of 2 cfm/ft² [10 L/(s · m²)] floor area at low speed. Shielding is required to control radiation from hot surfaces. Proper introduction of air will minimize preheat requirements.

Process	Dry Bulb, °F (°C)	rh, %
FUR		
Drying	110 (43)	...
Shock treatment	18 to 20 (−8 to −7)	...
Storage	40 to 50 (4 to 10)	55 to 65

Shock treatment or eradication of any insect infestations requires the lowering of the temperature to 18 to 20°F (−7 or −8°C) for three to four days, then raising it to 60 to 70°F (16 to 21°C) for two days, then lowering it again for two days and raising it to the storage temperature.

Furs remain pliable, oxidation is reduced, and color and luster are preserved when stored at 40 to 55°F (4 to 10°C).

Mold growth is prevalent with humidities above 80% while hair splitting is common where humidity is lower than 55%.

Process	Dry Bulb, °F (°C)	rh, %
GUM		
Manufacturing	77 (25)	33
Rolling	68 (20)	63
Stripping	72 (22)	53
Breaking	73 (23)	47
Wrapping	73 (23)	58

Process	Dry Bulb, °F (°C)	rh, %
LEATHER		
Drying	68 to 125 (20 to 52)	75
Storage, winter room temp.	50 to 60 (10 to 15)	40 to 60

After leather is moistened in preparation for rolling and stretching, it is placed in an atmosphere held at room temperature with a relative humidity of 95%.

Leather is usually stored in warehouses without temperature and humidity control. However, it is necessary to keep humidity sufficiently low to prevent mildew. Air filtration is recommended for fine finish.

Process	Dry Bulb, °F (°C)	rh, %
LENSES (OPTICAL)		
Fusing	75 (24)	45
Grinding	80 (27)	80

Process	Dry Bulb, °F (°C)	rh, %
MATCHES		
Manufacture	72 to 73 (22 to 23)	50
Drying	70 to 75 (21 to 24)	60
Storage	60 to 63 (16 to 17)	50

Water evaporated is 18 to 20 lb (8 to 9 kg) per million matches, simultaneously with the setting of the glue. The match machine will turn out about 750,000 matches per hour.

Table 1   Temperatures and Humidities for Industrial Air Conditioning (*continued*)

MUSHROOMS

Sweating-out period	110 to 140 (50 to 60)	...
Spawn added	60 to 72 (16 to 22)	nearly sat.
Growing period	50 to 60 (9 to 16)	80
Storage	32 to 35 (0 to 23)	80 to 85

As spawn starts to grow, it is necessary to cool the mushroom house abruptly by 18 °F (10 °C) in a 12 hour period (approximately). Usually, this is the controlling factor in selection of refrigeration equipment, unless portable equipment is available.

Ductwork is usually of wood, because of the deterioration of ferrous metals during the sweating-out period.

In spawn rooms, high efficiency (93 to 97% atmospheric dust spot) filters are required for the control of mold spores and bacteria.

Heat of emission is 4 Btu/h·ft² (14 W/m²) of growing surface. Ventilation is 10 ft³/h per ft [0.8 L/(s·m²)] of growing surface.

PAINT APPLICATION

Lacquers: Baking	300 to 360 (150 to 180)	...
Oils paints: Paint spraying	60 to 90 (16 to 32)	80

The required air filtration efficiency depends on painting process. On fine finishes, such as car bodies, high efficiency range filters are required for the outdoor air supply. Other products may require only low or medium efficiency range filters.

Makeup air must be preheated. Spray booths must have 100 fpm (0.5 m/s) face velocity. Ovens must have air exhausted to maintain fumes below explosive concentration. Equipment must be explosion-proof.

PHARMACEUTICALS

Powder storage (prior to mfg)	*	*	
Manufactured powder storage and packing areas	75	(24)	35
Milling room	75	(24)	35
Tablet compressing	75	(24)	35
Tablet coating room	75	(24)	35
Effervescent tablets and powders	75	(24)	20
Hypodermic tablets	75	(24)	30
Colloids	75	(24)	30 to 50
Cough drops	75	(24)	40
Glandular products	75	(24)	5 to 10
Ampoule manufacturing	75	(24)	35 to 50
Gelatin capsules	75	(24)	35
Capsule storage	75	(24)	35
Microanalysis	75	(24)	50
Biological manufacturing	75	(24)	35
Liver extracts	75	(24)	35
Serums	75	(24)	50
Animal rooms	75 to 80 (24 to 27)		50
Small animal rooms	75 to 78 (24 to 26)		50

*Store in sealed plastic containers in sealed drums.

The penicillin incubation process requires holding temperature within 0.5 °F (0.25 °C), with temperatures and humidity rigidly controlled during all manufacturing phases.

If the ampoules are prepared under sterile conditions and the operators are gowned, the temperature held in the room should be 72 °F (22 °C). Liquid ampoules are prepared with humidity held in the range of 50% and sterile ampoule powders at 35% rh.

Unless a range is given, all temperatures above are maintained within 1 °F (2 °C) and relative humidity within ±5% of value as required for the item being processed. If not otherwise specified, relative humidity should not exceed 55% in summer and should be between 25 and 35% in winter.

Liver extracts require a low relative humidity after they are dried. Temperatures higher than 80 °F (27 °C) will cause the extracts to deteriorate.

Tablet coating requires temperature control of the air introduced to coating pans.

Mechanical-type high efficiency filtration is required in most production areas to prevent contamination. Biological manufacturing areas, particularly ampoule filling rooms, may require ultrahigh efficiency filters.

Process	Dry Bulb, °F (°C)	rh, %

PHOTO STUDIO

Dressing room	72 to 74 (22 to 23)	40 to 50
Studio (camera room)	72 to 74 (22 to 23)	40 to 50
Film darkroom	70 to 72 (21 to 22)	45 to 55
Print darkroom	70 to 72 (21 to 22)	45 to 55
Drying room	90 to 100 (32 to 38)	35 to 45
Finishing room	72 to 75 (22 to 24)	40 to 55
Storage room (b/w film and paper)	72 to 75 (22 to 24)	40 to 60
Storage room (color film and paper)	40 to 50 (4 to 10)	40 to 50
Motion picture studio	72 (22)	40 to 55

The above data pertain to average conditions. In some color processes, elevated temperatures as high as 105 °F (40 °C) are used, and a higher room temperature would be expected.

Conversely, ideal storage conditions for color materials necessitate refrigerated or deep-freeze temperature to ensure quality and color balance when long storage times are anticipated.

Heated liberated during printing, enlarging, and drying processes in removed through an independent exhaust system, which also serves the lamp houses and drier hoods. All areas except finished film storage require a minimum of medium efficiency range filters.

PLASTICS

Manufacturing areas:			
Thermosetting molding compounds	80	27	25 to 30
Cellophane wrapping	75 to 80 (24 to 27)		45 to 65

In manufacturing areas where plastic is exposed in the liquid state or molded, high efficiency filters may be required. Dust collection and fume control are essential.

PLYWOOD

Hot pressing (resin)	90	(32)	60
Cold pressing	90	(32)	15 to 25

RUBBER-DIPPED GOODS

Manufacture	90	(32)	...
Cementing	80	(27)	25 to 30*
Dipping surgical articles	75 to 80 (24 to 32)		25 to 30*
Storage prior to manufacture	60 to 75 (16 to 24)		40 to 50*
Laboratory (ASTM Standard)	73.4	(23)	50*

*Dew point of air must be below evaporation temperature of solvent.

Solvents used in manufacturing processes are usually explosive and toxic, requiring positive ventilation. Volume manufactures usually install a solvent-recovery system.

TEA

Packaging	65	(18)	65

Ideal moisture content is 5 to 6% for quality and weight. Low limit moisture content for quality is 4%.

TOBACCO

Cigar and cigarette making	70 to 75 (21 to 24)	55 to 65*
Softening	90 (32)	85 to 88
Stemming and stripping	75 to 85 (24 to 29)	70 to 75
Packing and shipping	73 to 75 (23 to 24)	65
Filler tobacco casing and conditioning	75 (24)	75
Filter tobacco storage and preparation	77 (26)	70
Wrapper tobacco storage and conditioning	75 (24)	75

*Rh fairly constant with range as set by cigarette machine.

Before stripping, tobacco undergoes a softening operation.

Table 2 Regain of Hygroscopic Materials
Moisture Content Expressed in Percent of Dry Weight of the Substance of Various Relative Humidities—Temperature 75°F (24°C)

| Classification | Material | Description | Relative Humidity | | | | | | | | | Authority |
			10	20	30	40	50	60	70	80	90	
Natural	Cotton	Sea Island—roving	2.5	3.7	4.6	5.5	6.6	7.9	9.5	11.5	14.1	Hartshorne
Textile	Cotton	American—cloth	2.6	3.7	4.4	5.2	5.9	6.8	8.1	10.0	14.3	Schloesing
Fibers	Cotton	Absorbent	4.8	9.0	12.5	15.7	18.5	20.8	22.8	24.3	25.8	Fuwa
	Wool	Australian Merino —skein	4.7	7.0	8.9	10.8	12.8	14.9	17.2	19.9	23.4	Hartshorne
	Silk	Raw chevennes —skein	3.2	5.5	6.9	8.0	8.9	10.2	11.9	14.3	18.3	Schloesing
	Linen	Table cloth	1.9	2.9	3.6	4.3	5.1	6.1	7.0	8.4	10.2	Atkinson
	Linen	Dry spun—yarn	3.6	5.4	6.5	7.3	8.1	8.9	9.8	11.2	13.8	Sommer
	Jute	Average of several grades	3.1	5.2	6.9	8.5	10.2	12.2	14.4	17.1	20.2	Storch
	Hemp	Manila and sisal rope	2.7	4.7	6.0	7.2	8.5	9.9	11.6	13.6	15.7	Fuwa
Rayons	Viscose nitro- cellulose	Average skein	4.0	5.7	6.8	7.9	9.2	10.8	12.4	14.2	16.0	Robertson
	Cuprammonium cellulose acetate		0.8	1.1	1.4	1.9	2.4	3.0	3.6	4.3	5.3	Robertson
Paper	M.F. newsprint	Wood pulp—24% ash	2.1	3.2	4.0	4.7	5.3	6.1	7.2	8.7	10.6	NBS
	H.M.F. writing	Wood pulp—3% ash	3.0	4.2	5.2	6.2	7.2	8.3	9.9	11.9	14.2	NBS
	White bond	Rag—1% ash	2.4	3.7	4.7	5.5	6.5	7.5	8.8	10.8	13.2	NBS
	Comm. ledger	75% rag—1% ash	3.2	4.2	5.0	5.6	6.2	6.9	8.1	10.3	13.9	NBS
	Kraft wrapping	Coniferous	3.2	4.6	5.7	6.6	7.6	8.9	10.5	12.6	14.9	NBS
Misc.	Leather	Sole oak—tanned	5.0	8.5	11.2	13.6	16.0	18.3	20.6	24.0	29.2	Phelps
Organic	Catgut	Racquet strings	4.6	7.2	8.6	10.2	12.0	14.3	17.3	19.8	21.7	Fuwa
Materials	Glue	Hide	3.4	4.8	5.8	6.6	7.6	9.0	10.7	11.8	12.5	Fuwa
	Rubber	Solid tires	0.11	0.21	0.32	0.44	0.54	0.66	0.76	0.88	0.99	Fuwa
	Wood	Timber (average)	3.0	4.4	5.9	7.6	9.3	11.3	14.0	17.5	22.0	F.P. Lab.
	Soap	White	1.9	3.8	5.7	7.6	10.0	122.9	16.1	19.8	23.8	Fuwa
	Tobacco	Cigarette	5.4	8.6	11.0	13.3	16.0	19.5	25.0	33.5	50.0	Ford
Foodstuffs	White bread		0.5	1.7	3.1	4.5	6.2	8.5	11.1	14.5	19.0	Atkinson
	Crackers		2.1	2.8	3.3	3.9	5.0	6.5	8.3	10.9	14.9	Atkinson
	Macaroni		5.1	7.4	8.8	10.2	11.7	13.7	16.2	19.0	22.1	Atkinson
	Flour		2.6	4.1	5.3	6.5	8.0	9.9	12.4	15.4	19.1	Bailey
	Starch		2.2	3.8	5.2	6.4	7.4	8.3	9.2	10.6	12.7	Atkinson
	Gelatin		0.7	1.6	2.8	3.8	4.9	6.1	7.6	9.3	11.4	Atkinson
Misc.	Asbestos fiber	Finely divided	0.16	0.24	0.26	0.32	0.41	0.51	0.62	0.73	0.84	Fuwa
Inorganic	Silica gel		5.7	9.8	12.7	15.2	17.2	18.8	20.2	21.5	22.6	Fuwa
Materials	Domestic coke		0.20	0.40	0.61	0.81	1.03	1.24	1.46	1.67	1.89	Selvig
	Activated charcoal	Steam activated	7.1	14.3	22.8	26.2	28.3	29.2	30.0	31.1	32.7	Fuwa
	Sulfuric acid	H_2SO_4	33.0	41.0	47.5	52.5	57.0	61.5	67.0	73.5	82.5	Mason

Rate of Chemical Reactions

Some processes require temperature and humidity control to regulate the chemical reactions. In rayon manufacture, pulp sheets are conditioned, cut to size, and passed through a mercerizing process, where temperature controls the rate of reaction directly while relative humidity maintains a solution of constant strength and constant rate of surface evaporation.

The oxidizing process in the drying of varnish depends on temperature. Desirable temperatures vary with the type of varnish. High relative humidity retards oxidation at the surface and allows internal gases to escape freely as the chemical oxidizers cure the varnish from within. A bubble-free surface is maintained, with a homogeneous film throughout.

Rate of Biochemical Reactions

Fermentation requires temperature and humidity control to regulate the rate of biochemical reactions. Yeast develops best at 80°F (26°C) in the dough room. A minimum 75% rh holds the dough surface open to allow carbon dioxide from fermentation to pass through. This environment produces a bread loaf of an even, fine texture, free of large voids.

Rate of Crystallization

Cooling rate determines the size of crystals formed from a saturated solution. Both temperature and relative humidity control the cooling rate significantly and change the solution density by evaporation.

In the coating pans for pills, gum, or nuts, a heavy sugar solution is added to the tumbling mass. As the water evaporates, sugar crystals cover each piece. Blowing the proper quantity of air at the correct dry- and wet-bulb temperatures forms a smooth opaque coating. If cooling and drying are too slow, the coating is rough, translucent, and unsatisfactory in appearance; if they are too fast, the coating chips through to the interior.

Product Accuracy and Uniformity

In the manufacture of precision instruments, tools, and lenses, air temperature and cleanliness affect the quality of work. Close temperature control prevents expansion and contraction of the material where tolerances of manufacture are within 0.0002 in. (5μm). A constant temperature is more important than the temperature level, so conditions are usually selected for personnel comfort and to prevent a surface moisture film.

Corrosion, Rust, and Abrasion

In the manufacture of metal articles, temperatures and relative humidities kept sufficiently low prevents sweating of hands and keeps fingerprints, tarnish, or etching from the finished article. The salt and acid in body perspiration can cause corrosion and rust within a few hours. Manufacture of polished surfaces usually requires better-than-average air filtering to prevent surface abrasion. This is also true of steel-belted radial tire manufacturing.

Static Electricity

In processing of light materials such as textile fibers and paper, and where explosive atmospheres or materials are present, humidity can reduce static electricity, which is often detrimental to processing and extremely dangerous in explosive atmospheres. Static electricity charges are kept to a minimum when the air in contact with the material processing is 55% rh or higher. The power driving the processing machines is converted into heat and raises the temperature in the machines above that of the adjacent air, where humidity is normally measured. A room with 65% rh or more may be necessary to maintain sufficiently high humidity requirements in the machines.

Air Cleanliness

Each application must be evaluated to determine the filtration needed to counter the adverse effects of (1) minute dust particles on the product or process, (2) airborne bacteria, and (3) other air contaminants such as smoke, radioactive particles, spores, and pollen. These effects include chemically altering production material, spoiling perishable goods, or clogging small openings in precision machinery. Chapter 11 of the 1985 FUNDAMENTALS Volume covers common contaminants. Chapter 10 of the 1983 EQUIPMENT Volume deals with filter types and efficiencies, and Chapters 29 through 39 in this volume describe control of a specific process.

Product Formability

Pharmaceutical tablets manufacture requires close control of humidity for optimum tablet forming.

EMPLOYEE REQUIREMENTS

The space required (health and safety) to avoid excess exposure to high temperatures and airborne contaminants is often established by the American Conference of Governmental Industrial Hygienists (ACGIH). The National Institute of Occupational Safety and Health (NIOSH) does research and recommends guidelines for workspace environmental control. The Occupational Safety and Health Administration (OSHA) sets standards from these environmental control guidelines and enforces them through compliance inspection at industrial facilities. The enforcement may be delegated to a corresponding state agency.

National standards for safe levels of contaminants in the work environment or in air exhausted from facilities do not cover all contaminants encountered. Minimum safety standards and facility design criteria are available, however, from various Department of Health, Education, and Welfare (DHEW) agencies such as the National Cancer Institute, the National Institutes of Health, and the Public Health Service (Centers for Disease Control). For radioactive substances, standards established by the Nuclear Regulatory Commission (NRC) should be followed.

Thermal Control Levels

The common thermal range in industrial plants that need no specific control for the product or process is from 68 to 100°F (20 to 37°C) and 25 to 60% rh. For a more detailed analyis, work rate, air velocity, quantity of rest, and effects of radiant heat must be considered (see Chapter 8, 1985 FUNDAMENTALS Volume). To avoid stress to workers exposed to high work rates and hot temperatures, the ACGIH established guidelines to evaluate high temperature air velocity and humidity levels in terms of heat stress (Dukes-Dobos and Henschel, 1971).

Where a comfortable environment is the concern rather than avoiding heat stress, the thermal control range becomes more specific (McNall, et al. 1967). In still air, nearly sedentary workers (120-W metabolism) prefer 72 to 75°F (22 to 24°C) dry-bulb temperature with 20 to 60% rh, and they can detect a 2°F (1°C) change per hour. Workers at a high rate of activity (300-W metabolism) prefer 63 to 66°F (17 to 19°C) db with 20 to 50% rh, but they are less sensitive to rate of change (ASHRAE Std. 55-74). An increase in air velocity over a worker increases cooling, so a high metabolic rate activity can be handled in this manner also (ASHRAE Std. 55-74).

Contaminant Control Levels

Toxic materials are present in many industrial plants and laboratories. In such plants, the air-conditioning and ventilation systems must minimize human exposure. When these materials become airborne, the body readily absorbs them and their range expands greatly, thus exposing more people. Chapter 11 of the 1985 FUNDAMENTALS Volume, current OSHA reulations, and *Threshold Limit Values of Airborne Contaminants*, published by ACGIH, give guides to evaluating the health impact of contaminants.

In addition to being a health concern, gaseous flammable substances must also be kept below explosive concentrations. Acceptable concentration limits are 20 to 25% of the lower explosive limit of the substance. Chapter 11 of the 1985 FUNDAMENTALS Volume includes information on flammable limits and means of control.

Instruments are available to measure existing concentrations of common gases and vapors. For less common gases or vapors, the air is sampled by drawing it through an impinger bottle or by inertial impaction-type air samplers, on a nutrient gel, which supports biological growth and permits subsequent enumeration after incubation. Sampling practices and techniques are discussed in Chapter 11 of the 1985 FUNDAMENTALS Volume.

Gases and vapors are found near acid baths and tanks holding process chemicals. Machine processes, plating operations, spraying, mixing, and abrasive cleaning operations generate dusts, fumes, and mists. Many routine laboratory procedures, including grinding, blending, homogenizing, sonication, weighing, dumping of animal bedding, and animal inoculation or intubation, also generate aerosols.

DESIGN CONSIDERATIONS

To apply equipment, the required environmental conditions, both for the product and personnel comfort, must be known. Consultation with the owner establishes such design criteria as temperature and humidity levels, energy availability and opportunities to recover it, cleanliness, process exhaust details, location and size of heat-producing equipment, frequency of equipment usage, load factors, frequency of truck or car loadings, and sound levels. Consideration must be given to separating dirty processes from manufacturing areas requiring relatively clean air. If not controlled by the layout, hard-to-control contaminants—such as oil mists from presses and machining, or fumes and gases from welding—can migrate to areas of final assembly, metal cleaning, or printing, and cause serious problems.

Insulation should be evaluated for initial and operating cost saving of heating and cooling, elimination of condensation (on roofs in particular), and comfort because of changing mean radiant temperature. When high levels of moisture are required within buildings, the structure and air-conditioning system must prevent condensation damage to the structure and ensure a quality product. Proper selection of insulation type and thickness, proper placing of vapor retarders, and proper selection and assembly of construction components to prevent thermal short-circuiting prevents condensation. Chapters 20 and 21 in the 1985 FUNDAMENTALS Volume have further details.

Personnel engaged with a process may be subject to a wide range of activity levels for which a broad range of indoor temperature and humidity levels are desirable. Chapter 8 of the 1985 FUNDAMENTALS Volume addresses recommended indoor conditions at various activity levels.

Table 3 Facilities Checklist

Construction:
1. Single or multistory
2. Type and location of doors, windows, crack lengths
3. Structural design live loads
4. Floor construction
5. Exposed wall materials
6. Roof materials
7. Insulation type and thicknesses
8. Location of existing exhaust equipment
9. Building orientation

Use of Building:
1. Product needs
2. Surface cleanliness required; level of acceptable airborne contamination
3. Process equipment: type, location, and exhaust requirements
4. Personnel needs, temperature levels, required activity levels, and special work place requirements
5. Floor area occupied by machines and materials
6. Clearance above floor required for material-handling equipment, piping, lights, or air-distribution systems
7. Unusual occurrences and their frequency, such as large cold or hot masses of material moved inside
8. Loading frequency and length of time of doors open for loading or unloading
9. Lighting, location, type, and capacity
10. Acoustical levels
11. Machinery loads, such as electric motors (size, diversity), large latent loads, or radiant loads from furnaces and ovens
12. Potential for temperature stratification

Design Conditions
1. Design temperatures—indoor and outdoor
2. Wind velocity
3. Makeup air required
4. Indoor temperature, allowable variance
5. Indoor relative humidity, allowable variance
6. Outdoor temperature occurrence frequencies
7. Operational periods, one, two, or three
8. Waste heat availability, energy conservation
9. Pressurization required
10. Mass loads from the energy release of productive materials

Code and Insurance Requirements:
1. State and local code requirements for ventilation rates and other conditions.
2. Governmental occupational health and safety requirements (OSHA).
3. Insuring agency requirements.

Utilities Available and Required:
1. Gas, oil, compressed air (pressure), electricity (characteristics), steam (pressure), water (pressure), wastewater, interior and site drainage
2. Rate structures for each utility
3. Potable water

If layout and construction drawings are not available, a complete survey of existing premises or a checklist (Table 3) for proposed facilities is necessary.

New industrial buildings are commonly single-story with flat roofs and with ample heights to distribute utilities and lights without interfering with process operation. For example, a common mounting height for fluorescent fixtures is up to 12 ft (3.5 m), for high output fluorescent fixtures up to 20 ft (6 m), and for high pressure sodium or mercury vapor fixtures above 20 ft (6 m).

Lighting design considers light quality, degree of diffusion and direction, room size, mounting height, and economics. Illumination levels should conform to recommended levels of the Illuminating Engineering Society (I.E.S. Lighting Handbook). Air-conditioning systems can be located in the top of the building. The designs, however, require coordination because they compete for space with sprinkler systems, piping, ventilation, ductwork, structural elements, cranes, material-handling systems, electric wiring, and lights.

Operations within the building must also be considered. Production materials may be moved through outside doors and allow large amounts of outdoor air to enter. Some operations may require close control of temperature, humidity, and contaminants. A time schedule of operation helps in estimating the heating and cooling load.

LOAD CALCULATIONS

Table 1 and specific product chapters discuss product requirements. Chapters 25 and 26 of the 1985 FUNDAMENTALS Volume cover load calculations for heating and cooling.

Solar and Transmission

The solar load on the roof is generally the largest perimeter load and is usually a significant part of the overall load. Wall loads are often insignificant, and most new plants have no windows in the manufacturing area, so a solar load through glass is not present. Large windows in old plants may be closed in.

Internal Heat Generation

The process, product, facility utilities, and employees generate an internal heat load. People, power or process loads, and lights are internal sensible loads. Of these, production machinery often creates the largest. The design should consider anticipated brake power, rather than connected motor loads. The lighting load is generally significant. Heat gain from people is usually negligible in process areas.

Heat from operating equipment is difficult to estimate accurately. Approximate values can be determined by studying the load readings of the electrical substations that serve the area in question.

In most industrial facilities, the latent heat load is minimal, with people and outdoor air being the major contributors. In these areas, the sensible heat factor approaches 1.0. Some processes release large amounts of moisture, such as in a paper-machine room. This moisture must be handled, including its condensation on cold surfaces.

Stratification Effect

The cooling load may be dramatically reduced by the work space that takes advantage of temperature stratification; that is, it establishes a warm blanket of air directly under the roof by keeping air circulation to a minimum. The roof heat gain is cancelled if the warm air blanket is warmer than the roof itself. Internal loads from lights and process equipment heat the air and, with minimal air circulation, rises to the roof. If the space has rapid air movement, the internal heat is absorbed by the moving air, and little stratification occurs.

Supply- and return-air ducts should be as low as possible to avoid mixing the warm boundary layers. For areas with supply air quantities greater than 2 cfm/ft^2 (5 L/(s·m^2)), the return air temperature is approximately that of the air entrained by the supply air stream and only slightly higher than that at the end of the throw. With lower air quantities, the return air is much warmer than the supply air at the end of the throw. The amount depends on the placement of return inlets relative to internal heat sources. The average temperature of the space is higher, thus reducing the effect of outside conditions on heat gain. Spaces with a high area-to-employee ratio adapt well to low quantities of supply air and spot cooling. For design specifics, refer to the spot cooling section of this chapter.

Makeup Air

Makeup air, which has been heated, cooled, humidified, or dehumidified, is introduced to replace exhaust air, provide ventilation, and pressurize the building. For exhaust systems to function, air must enter the building by infiltration or the air-conditioning equipment. The space air-conditioning system must be large enough to heat or cool the outside air required to replace the exhaust. A design should consider cooling or heat recovery from exhaust air to makeup air. This concept can have substantial impact on the outdoor air load.

Exhaust from air-conditioned buildings should be kept to a minimum by proper hooding or relocation of exhausted processes to areas not requiring air-conditioning. Frequently, excess makeup air is provided to pressurize the building slightly, thus reducing infiltration, flue downdrafts, or ineffective exhaust under certain wind conditions. Makeup air and exhaust systems can be interlocked so that outdoor makeup air can be reduced as needed, or makeup air units may be changed from outdoor air heating to recirculated air heating when process exhaust is off.

In some facilities, outdoor air is required for ventilation because of the function of the space. Recirculation of air is avoided to reduce harmful gas concentrations, airborne bacteria, or air-carrying radioactive substances. Ventilation rates for human occupancy should be determined by ASHRAE Standard 62 and applicable codes. Chapter 22 of the 1985 FUNDAMENTALS Volume also has further information.

Outdoor air dampers of industrial air-conditioning units can handle 100% supply air, so modulating the dampers in winter can satisfy room temperature. The outdoor air damper can often be closed in summer, with its leakage (5 to 10% of supply air) sufficient for ventilation air.

The infiltration of outdoor air often creates considerable load with many industrial buildings because of poorly sealed walls and roofs. Infiltration should be minimized to conserve energy.

Fan Heat

The heat from air-conditioning return-air fans or supply fans goes into the refrigeration load. This energy does not become part of the room sensible heat, except for supply fans downstream of the conditioning apparatus.

SYSTEM AND EQUIPMENT SELECTION

Industrial air-conditioning equipment includes heating and cooling sources, air-handling and air-conditioning apparatus, and an air-distribution system. To provide low life-cycle cost,

components should be selected and the system designed for long life and low maintenance and operating costs.

Systems may be: (1) for heating only in cool climates, where worker activity level is thermally satisfied with ventilation air; (2) air washer systems, where high humidities are desired and where the climate requires cooling; (3) heating and mechanical cooling, where temperature and/or humidity control are required by the process and where the activity level is too great to be satisfied by other means of cooling. All systems include air filtration appropriate to the contaminant control required.

A careful evaluation will determine the zones that require control, especially in large, high-bay areas where the occupied zone is a small portion of the space volume. ASHRAE Standard 55-1981 defines the occupied zone as 3 to 72 in. (80 to 1830 mm) high and more than 24 in. (600 mm) from the walls.

Air-Handling Unit

The air-handling unit heats and cools air that is distributed to the work space. The unit can supply all or any portion of outdoor air so in-plant contaminants do not become too concentrated. Units may be factory assembled or field constructed.

HEATING SYSTEMS

Panel Heating

Space heating by large surfaces at little elevation in temperature is called *panel heating*. In industrial buildings, floor heating is often desirable, particularly in large high-bay buildings, garages, and assembly areas where workers must be near the floor, or where large or fluctuating outdoor air loads make maintenance of ambient temperature difficult. As an auxiliary to the main heating system, floors may be tempered to 65 or 70°F (18 to 20°C) by embedded hydronic systems, electrical resistance cables, or warm-air ducts.

The heating elements may be buried deep, 6 to 18 in. (150 to 450 mm) in the floor to permit slab warm-up at off-peak times, thus using the floor mass for heat storage to save energy during periods of high use. Floor heating may also be the primary or sole heating means, but floor temperatures above 85°F (30°C) are uncomfortable, so such use is limited to small, well-insulated spaces.

Unit Heaters

Gas, oil, electricity, hot water, or steam unit heaters, with propeller fans or blowers, are used for spot heating areas or are arranged in multiples for heating an entire building. Temperatures can be varied by individual thermostatic control. Unit heaters are located so the discharge (or throw) will reach the floor and flow adjacent to and parallel with the outside wall. They are spaced so that the discharge of one heater is just short of the next heater, thus producing a ring of warm air moving peripherally around the building. In industrial buildings with heat-producing processes, much heat stratifies in high-bay areas. In large buildings, additional heaters should be placed in the interior so that their discharge reaches the floor to reduce stratification. Downblow unit heaters in high bays and large areas may have a revolving discharge. Chapter 27 in the 1983 EQUIPMENT Volume includes more detail.

Gas- and oil-fired unit heaters should not be used where corrosive vapors are present. Unit heaters function well with regular maintenance and periodic cleaning in dusty or dirty conditions. Propeller fans generally require less maintenance than centrifugal fans. Centrifugal fans or blowers usually are required to distribute heat to several areas. Gas- and oil-fired unit heaters require proper venting, particularly with exhaust fan use.

Ducted Heaters

Ducted heaters may include large direct- or indirect-fired heaters, door heaters, and heating and ventilating units. Ducted heaters generally have centrifugal fans.

Code changes and improved burners have led to increased use of direct-fired gas heaters (the gas burns in the air supplied to the space) for makeup air heating. With correct interlock safety precautions of supply air and exhaust, no harmful effect from direct firing occurs. The high efficiency, high turndown ratio, and simplicity of maintenance make these units suitable for makeup air heating.

Common problems and solutions with ducted heaters in industrial applications are as follows:

Steam Coil Freezeup. Steam-distributing type (sometimes called nonfreeze) coils, face-and-bypass control with steam valve wide open below 35°F (2°C) entering air; free condensate drainage; a thermostat in exit stops air flow when it falls below 40°F (5°C).

Hot Water Coil Freezeup. Adequate circulation through coil at all times; a thermostat in air and in water leaving the coil stop air flow under freezing conditions.

Temperature Override. Because of wiping action on coil with face-and-bypass control, zoning control is poor. Carefully locate face damper and use room thermostat to reset discharge air temperature controller.

Bearing Failure. Following bearing manufacturer's recommendations in application and lubrication.

Insufficient Air Quantity. Require capacity data based on testing; keep forward-curved blade fans clean or use backward-inclined blade fans; keep filters clean.

Door Heating

Unit heaters and makeup air heaters commonly temper outdoor air that enters the building at open doors. These door heaters may have directional outlets to offset the incoming draft or may resemble a vestibule where air is recirculated.

Unit heaters successfully heat air at small doors open for short periods. They temper the incoming outdoor air through mixing and quickly bring the space to the desired temperature after the door is closed. The makeup air heater should be applied as a door heater in buildings where the doors are large (those that allow railroad cars or large trucks to enter) and open for long periods. They are also needed in facilities not tightly constructed or with a sizable negative pressure. These units help pressurize the door area, mix the incoming cold air and temper it, and bring the area quickly back to the normal temperature after the door is closed.

Often, door heater nozzles direct heated air at the top or down the sides of a door. Doors that create large, cold drafts when open can best be handled by introducing air in a trench at the bottom of the door. When not tempering cold drafts through open doors, some door heaters direct heated air to nearby spots. When the door is closed, it can switch to a lower output temperature.

The door heating units that resemble a vestibule operate as shown in Figure 1. Air flows down across the opening and recirculates from the bottom, which helps reduce cold drafts across the floor. This type of unit is effective on doors routinely open and no higher than 10 ft (3 m).

Infrared

High intensity infrared heaters (gas, oil, or electric) transmit heat energy directly to warm the occupants, floor, machines, or other building contents, without appreciably warming the air. Some air heating occurs by convection from objects warmed by the infrared. These units are classed as near- or far-infrared heaters, depending on the closeness of wavelength to visible light. Near infrared heaters emit a substantial amount of visible light.

Both vented or unvented gas-fired infrared heaters are available as individual radiant panels, or as a continuous radiant pipe with burners 15 to 30 ft (5 to 10 m) apart and an exhaust vent fan at the end of the pipe. Unvented heaters require exhaust ventilation to remove flue products from the building, or moisture will condense on the roof and walls. Insulation will reduce the exhaust required. Additional information on both electric and gas infrared is given in Chapter 30 of the 1983 EQUIPMENT Volume, and Chapter 18 of the 1984 SYSTEMS Volume gives additional information on both electric and gas infrared heating.

Infrared heaters are used in the following:

1. High-bay buildings where the heaters are usually mounted 10 to 30 ft (3 to 15 m) above the floor, along outside walls, and tilted to direct maximum radiation to the floor. If the building is poorly insulated, the controlling thermostat should be shielded to avoid influence from the radiant effect of the cold walls.
2. Semi-open and outdoor areas, where people can be heated directly with some comfort and objects can be heated to avoid condensation.
3. Loading docks for snow and ice control by strategic placement of near-infrared heaters.

COOLING SYSTEMS

Common cooling systems include refrigeration equipment, evaporative coolers, and high-velocity ventilating air.

For manufacturing operations, particularly heavy industry where mechanical cooling cannot be economically justified, evaporative cooling systems often provide good working conditions: a thermal environment that nearly matches the outdoor effective temperature. If the operation requires heavy physical work, spot cooling by ventilation, evaporative cooling, or refrigerated air can be used. High outdoor air ventilation rates may be adequate in some hot process areas to minimize summer discomfort. All cases need a mechanical air supply with good distribution.

Refrigerated Cooling Systems

The refrigeration cooling source may be located at a central equipment area, or smaller packaged cooling systems may be placed near each air-handling unit. Central mechanical equip-

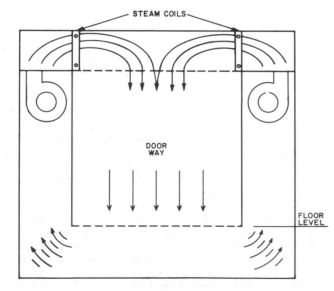

Fig. 1 Door Heating Units

ment uses positive displacement, centrifugal, or absorption refrigeration to chill water. Pumped through unit cooling coils, it absorbs heat, then returns to the cooling equipment.

Central system condenser water rejects heat through a cooling tower. The heat may be transferred to other sections of the building where heating or reheating is required, and the cooling unit becomes a heat recovery heat pump. Refrigerated heat recovery is particularly advantageous in buildings with simultaneous need for heating exterior sections and cooling interior sections.

When interior spaces are cooled with a combination of outdoor air and chilled water obtained from reciprocating or centrifugal chillers with heat recovery condensers, hot water at temperatures up to 110 °F (45 °C) is readily available. Large quantities of air at room temperature, which must be exhausted because of contaminants, can be passed through a chilled water coil first to recover heat. Heating or reheating obtained by refrigerated heat recovery occurs at a COP approaching 4, regardless of outdoor temperature, and can save considerable energy. For more information on central cooling and heat recovery equipment, refer to Chapters 12 through 22 in the 1983 EQUIPMENT Volume and Chapters 4 and 15 of this volume.

Mechanical cooling equipment should be selected in multiple units to match its reponse to load fluctuation and allow equipment maintenance during non-peak operation. Small packaged refrigeration equipment commonly uses positive displacement (reciprocating or screw) compressors with air-cooled condensers. These units usually provide up to 150 tons (500 kW) of cooling. Since equipment is often on the roof, the condensing temperature may be affected by warm ambient air, often 10 to 20 °F (5 to 10 °C) higher than the design outdoor air temperature. In this type of system, the cooling coil receives refrigerant directly.

The Safety Code for Mechanical Refrigeration limits the type and quantity of refrigerant in direct air-to-refrigerant exchangers. Fins on the air side improve heat transfer, but they increase the pressure drop through the coil, particularly as they get dirty. (See Chapter 6 in the 1983 EQUIPMENT Volume.)

Evaporative Cooling Systems

Evaporative cooling systems may be evaporative coolers or air washers. Evaporative coolers have water sprayed directly on pads through which air moves. An air washer recirculates water, and the air flows through a heavily misted area. Water atomized in the air stream evaporates and the water cools the air. Refrigerated water simultaneously cools and dehumidifies the air.

Evaporative cooling should be strongly considered, since it offers energy conservation opportunities, particularly in intermediate seasons. In many trial facilities, evaporative cooling controls both temperature and humidity. In these systems, the sprayed water is normally refrigerated, and a reheat coil is often used. Temperature and humidity of the exit air stream may be controlled by varying the temperature of the chilled water and the reheat coil and by varying the quantity of air passing through the reheat coil with a dewpoint thermostat.

Care must be taken that accumulation of dust or lint does not clog noggles or evaporating pads of the evaporative cooling systems. It may be necessary to filter before the evaporative cooler. Fan heat, air leakage through closed dampers, and the entrainment of room air into the supply air stream all affect design. Chapter 4 of the 1983 EQUIPMENT Volume covers evaporative cooling in detail.

AIR-FILTRATION SYSTEMS

Air-filtration systems remove contaminants from air supplied to or exhausted from building spaces. Supply air filtration (most frequently on the intake side of air-conditioning apparatus)

remove particulate contamination that may foul heat transfer surfaces, contaminate products, or present a health hazard to people, animals, or plants. Gaseous contaminants sometimes must be removed to prevent exposure of personnel to harm or odor nuisance. The supply air stream may consist of air recirculated from building spaces and/or outdoor air for ventilation or exhaust air makeup. Return air with a significant potential for carrying contaminants should be recirculated only when filtered enough to minimize personnel exposure.

The supply air filtration system usually includes a collection medium or filter, media-retaining device or filter frame, and a filter housing or plenum. The filter media are the most important components of the system; a mat of randomly distributed small diameter fibers is usual.

Depending on fiber material, size, density, and arrangement, fibrous filters have a wide range of performance. Low density filter media with relatively large diameter fibers remove large particles (greater than 2 μm), such as lint. These roughing filters collect a large percentage by weight of the particulates, but are ineffective in reducing the total particle concentration. The fibers are sometimes coated with an adhesive to reduce particle re-entrainment.

Small fiber, high-density filter media collects essentially all particulates effectively . Ultrahigh efficiency filters reduce total particle concentration by more than 99.9%. As filter efficiency increases, so does resistance to air flow with typical pressure drop ranging from 0.05 to 1 in. of water (12 to 250 Pa). Conversely, dust-holding capacity decreases with increasing filter efficiency, and fibrous filters should not be used for dust loading greater than 1.75×10^{-3}) g/ft^3 (4 mg/m^3) of air ("Industrial Ventilation"). For more discussion of particulate filtration systems, refer to Chapter 10 of the 1983 EQUIPMENT Volume.

Exhaust Air-Filtration Systems

Exhaust air systems are either (1) general systems that remove air from large spaces or (2) local systems that capture aerosols or gases at specific locations within a room and transport them to where they can be collected (filtered), inactivated, or safely discharged to the atmosphere. The air in a general system usually requires minimal treatment before discharging to the atmosphere. The air in local exhaust systems can sometimes be safely dispersed to the atmosphere, but, more frequently, contaminants must be removed so that the emitted air meets air quality standards.

Many types of contamination collection or inactivation systems are applied in exhaust air emission control (Industrial Ventilation, O'Connell 1976). Fabric bag filters, glass fiber-type filters, venturi scrubbers, and electrostatic precipitators all collect particulates. Packed bed or sieve towers can absorb toxic gases. Activated carbon columns or beds, often with oxidizing agents, are frequently used to absorb toxic or odorous organics and radioactive gases.

Outdoor air intakes should be carefully located to avoid recirculation of contaminated exhaust air. Because wind direction, building shape, and the location of the effluent source strongly influence concentration patterns, exact patterns are not predictable.

Air patterns resulting from wind flow over buildings are discussed in Chapter 14 of the 1985 FUNDAMENTALS Volume. The leading edge of a roof interrupts smooth air flow, resulting in reduced air pressure at the roof and on the lee side. To prevent fume damage to the roof and roof-mounted equipment and to keep fumes from the building air intakes, fumes must be discharged either through (1) vertical stacks terminating above the turbulent air boundary or (2) short stacks with a velocity high enough to project the effluent through the boundary into the undisturbed air passing over the building. A high vertical stack is the safest and simplest solution to fume dispersal.

Contaminant Control

In addition to maintaining thermal conditions, air-conditioning systems should control contaminant levels to provide (1) a safe and healthy environment, (2) good housekeeping, and (3) quality control for the processes. Contaminants may be gases, fumes, mists, and airborne particulate matter. They may be created by a process within the building or found in the outside air.

Contamination can be controlled by (1) preventing the release of aerosols or gases into the room environment and (2) diluting room air contaminants. If the process cannot be enclosed, it is best to capture aerosols or gases near their source of generation with local exhaust systems that include an enclosure or hood, ductwork, fan, motor, and exhaust stack. Chapter 43 of this volume has more detail.

Dilution controls contamination in many applications but may not provide uniform safety for personnel within a space (West 1977). High local concentrations of contaminants can exist within a room, even though the overall dilution rate is quite high. Further, if tempering of outdoor air is required, high energy costs can result from the increased air flow required for dilution.

Exhaust Systems

The exhaust system draws the contaminant near its source and removes it from the space. An exhaust hood that surrounds the point of generation contains the contaminant as much as is practical. The contaminants are transported through ductwork from the space, cleaned, as required, and exhausted to the atmosphere.

The suction air quantity in the hood is established by the velocities required to contain the contaminant.

Design values for average and minimum face velocities are a function of the characteristics of the most dangerous material that the hood is expected to handle. Minimum values are prescribed in codes for exhaust systems. Contaminants with greater mass require higher face velocities for their control. Chapters 30 and 43 of this volume include more information on exhaust hoods.

Properly sized ductwork keeps the contaminant flowing. This requires very high velocities for heavy materials. The selection of materials and the construction of exhaust ductwork and fans depend on the nature of the contaminant, the ambient temperature, the lengths and arrangement of duct runs, the method of hood fan operation, and the flame and smoke spread rating.

Exhaust systems remove chemical gases, vapors, or smokes from acids, alkalis, solvents, and oils. Care must be taken to minimize the following:

1. **Corrosion,** which denotes destruction of metal by chemical or electrochemical action; commonly used reagents in laboratories are hydrochloric, sulfuric, and nitric acid, singly or in combination, and ammonium hydroxide. Common organic chemicals include acetone, benzene, ether, petroleum, chloroform, carbon tetrachloride, and acetic acid.
2. **Dissolution,** which denotes a dissolving action. Coatings and plastics are subject to this action, particularly by solvent and oil fumes.
3. **Melting,** which can occur to certain plastics and coatings at elevated hood operating temperatures.

Low temperatures that cause condensation in ducts increase chemical destruction. Ductwork is less subject to attack when the runs are short and direct to the terminal discharge point. The longer the runs, the longer the period of exposure to fumes and the greater the degree of condensation. Horizontal runs allow moisture to remain longer than it can on vertical surfaces. Intermittent fan operation can contribute to longer periods of wetness (because of condensation) than would continuous operation.

Maintenance of Components

Any design should allow ample room to clean, service, and replace any component quickly so that design conditions are affected as little as possible. Maintenance of refrigeration and heat-rejection equipment are essential for proper performance without energy waste.

For system dependability, water treatment is important. No air washer or cooling tower should be operated without water properly treated by specialists. Chapter 56 of this volume includes more detail.

Maintenance of heating and cooling systems includes changing or cleaning system filters on a regular basis. Industrial applications are usually dirty, so frequent filter changing may be required. Dirt that lodges in ductwork and on forward-curved fan blades reduces air-handling capacity appreciably.

Fan and motor bearings require lubrication, and fan belts need periodic inspection. Infrared and panel systems usually require less maintenance than equipment with filters and fans, although gas-fired units with many burners require more attention than electric heaters.

The direct-fired makeup heater has a relatively simple burner requiring less maintenance than a comparable indirect-fired heater. The indirect oil-fired heater will require more maintenance than the comparable indirect gas-fired heater. With either type, the many safety devices and controls require periodic maintenance to ensure constant operation without nuisance cutout. Direct- and indirect-fired heaters should be completely inspected at least once a year.

Steam and hot water heaters have fewer maintenance requirements than comparable equipment having gas and oil burners. When used for makeup air in below-freezing conditions, however, the heaters must be correctly applied and controlled to prevent frozen coils.

Chapters 48 and 49 in this volume include information on owning and operating costs. Chapter 57 of this volume discusses testing and balancing.

REFERENCES

ACGIH. *Industrial Ventilation.* Lansing, MI: American Conference of Governmental Industrial Hygienists.

ASHRAE. 1981. ANSI/ASHRAE Standard 55-1981. Thermal Environmental Conditions for Human Occupancy.

ASHRAE. 1982. ANSI/ASHRAE Standard 62-1982. Ventilation for Acceptable Indoor Air Quality.

Dukes-Dubos, F. and Henschel, A. 1971. *The modification of the WBGT Index for establishing permissible heat exposure limits in occupational work.* HEW, USPHS, ROSH joint pub. TR-69.

Harstad, J. et al. 1967. Air filtration of submicron virus aerosols. *American Journal of Public Health,* 57:2186-2193.

IES. 1982. *Lighting Handbook,* 6th Edition, New York: Illuminating Engineering Society.

McNall, P.E.; Juax, J.; Rohles, F.H.; Nevins, R.G.; Springer, W. 1967. Thermal Comfort (Thermally Neutral) Conditions for Three Levels of Activity. *ASHRAE Transactions,* Vol. 73, Part I, p. I.3.1.

O'Connell, W.L. 1976. How to attack air-pollution control problems. *Chemical Engineering* (Oct.), Desktop Issue.

West, D.L. 1977. Contaminant dispersion and dilution in a ventilated space. *ASHRAE Transactions,* Vol. 83, Part I, p. 125.

Whitby, K.T. and Lundgren, D.A. 1965. Mechanics of air cleaning. *ASAE Transactions,* 8:3, p. 342. American Society of Agricultural Engineers.

CHAPTER 29

ENCLOSED VEHICULAR FACILITIES

THIS chapter deals with the ventilation requirements for cooling, pollution control, and emergency smoke and temperature control for vehicular tunnels, rapid transit tunnels and stations, enclosed parking structures, and bus terminals. Also included is the design approach and type of equipment applied to these ventilation systems.

VEHICULAR TUNNELS

CONTROL BY DILUTION

All internal combustion engines produce exhaust gases that contain toxic compounds and smoke. Therefore, vehicular tunnels require ventilation, which may be provided by natural means, traffic-induced piston effect, or mechanical equipment. Ventilation dilutes the concentrations of obnoxious or dangerous contaminants to acceptable levels. The selected ventilation system should be the most economical solution, in both construction and operating costs, which meets the specified criteria. Naturally ventilated and traffic-induced systems are considered adequate for tunnels of relatively short length and low traffic volume (or density). Long and heavily traveled tunnels should have mechanical ventilation systems.

The exhaust constituent of greatest concern is carbon monoxide (CO) because of its notorious asphyxiant nature. The ventilation system dilutes the CO content of the tunnel atmosphere to a safe and comfortable level. Tests and operating experience indicate that when CO has been properly diluted, the other dangerous and objectionable exhaust by-products are also diluted to acceptable levels. If diesel engines become more prevalent in the future, the level of oxides of nitrogen in tunnels will require careful evaluation. The section on bus terminals includes more information regarding diesel engine operation.

The ventilation discussed here will be incorporated as a permanent part of the finished tunnel and is intended primarily to serve the needs of the traveling public passing through the tunnel. Ventilation needed by workers during construction of the facility or while working in the finished tunnel is not covered. These ventilation requirements are usually specified in detail by state or local mining laws, industrial codes, or in the standards set by the U. S. Occupational Safety and Health Administration (OSHA).

ALLOWABLE CO CONCENTRATIONS

The task of establishing an allowable concentration of CO is primarily a medical determination. In 1975, the U.S. Environmental Protection Agency issued a supplement to their *Guidelines for Review of Environmental Impact Statements for Highway Projects*. In this supplement the EPA stated:

"For the users of highway tunnels at or near sea level, it has been determined that an adequate margin of safety would exist if the concentration of CO does not exceed 125 ppm (mg/kg) and the exposure time does not exceed one hour."

Since the issuance of the EPA supplement, 125 ppm (mg/kg) has been widely adopted in the United States as the design criteria for tunnels located at or below an altitude of 3,280 ft (1000 m); see also *Minimum Ventilation Rate*. Above an elevation of 3,280 ft (1000 m), the CO emission of vehicles is greatly increased, and human tolerance to CO exposure is reduced. These two effects are additive and are important factors to consider in setting an appropriate ventilation standard. For tunnels located above 3,280 ft (1000 m), the designer should seek the advice of medical authorities to assist in establishing a proper design value for CO concentrations. Unless specified otherwise, the material in this section refers to tunnels located at or below an altitude of 3,280 ft (1000 m).

CARBON MONOXIDE EMISSION FROM VEHICLES

Many studies have shown that the CO content in exhaust gases of individual vehicles varies greatly. This variation is caused by such factors as the age of the vehicle, carburetor adjustment, quality of fuel, engine horsepower, level of vehicle maintenance, and the differing driving habits of motorists. Despite these variables, several sources generally agree on average emission rates, although they apply only to vehicles without emission control devices. The bulk of the published data on CO emissions of controlled vehicles is not presently considered of sufficient accuracy for tunnel ventilation computations.

Due to the absence of suitable data, all suggested ventilation rates given in this chapter are derived using uncontrolled emission rates, but the results can be corrected, as indicated, to reflect the impact of emission control devices.

AMOUNTS OF VENTILATING AIR REQUIRED

The ventilating system must have capacity enough to protect the traveling public during the most adverse and dangerous conditons, as well as during normal conditions. In addition to the problems of many uncontrollable variables, establishing air requirements is complicated further by an extensive number of possible vehicle combinations and traffic situations that could occur during the lifetime of the facility.

Ventilating rates that meet the general criteria are computed in two parts. The first part considers a lane of tunnel traffic composed entirely of passenger cars. The following assumptions are necessary:

1. A major traffic stoppage has occurred outside of the tunnel, and traffic is blocked. This stoppage causes tunnel traffic to slow down from normal operating speeds and finally to stop

The preparation of this chapter is assigned to TC 5.9, Enclosed Vehicular Facilities with engines idling. When the stoppage has been cleared, traffic is assumed to reverse the process, *i.e.,* idle first, then proceed at 6 mph (10 km/h), then up to 25 mph (40 km/h).

2. Although CO emission rates during acceleration and deceleration of vehicles are higher than at constant speed, the effect of speed changing is neglected. (The error introduced by this assumption will be offset by a 10% safety factor included in the computations.)

3. Traffic is assumed to move as a unit with spacing between vehicles rermaining constant regardless of roadway grade.

4. Passenger cars are taken as 19 ft (5.8 m) long (the usual length of a highway design vehicle), and spaces between cars at various speeds are shown in Table 1.

From these computations, the governing ventilation rates for different roadway gradients from 6% downhill to 6% uphill are determined using the data plotted in Figure 1. In most cases, the critical traffic situation from a ventilation standpoint occurs when the lane is congested with vehicles moving at a speed of about 9.3 mph (15 km/h). On the steeper downgrades, the governing condition occurs when traffic is stopped and vehicles

Table 1   Space Between Cars at Various Speeds

Speed, mph	Spacing, ft	Speed, km/h	Spacing, m
25	72.8	40	22.0
20	54.4	35	18.6
15	36.0	25	11.6
10	17.6	15	4.6
5	9.0	10	3.0
Idle	4.0	Idle	1.2

Table 2   Emission Factors for Highway Vehicles

Calendar Year	Avg. Emission Factor (F)
1987	0.196
1988	0.179
1989	0.169
1990	0.160

are bumper-to-bumper with engines idling. This condition calls for a constant ventilation rate regardless of roadway grade.

Figure 1 shows the results of a second set of computations made for a lane of tunnel traffic composed entirely of trucks and buses. About 40% of the vehicles are assumed to be diesel-powered averaging 50 ft (15.2 m) in length, and 60% are taken as the light- to medium-duty gasoline-powered trucks averaging 30 ft (9.1 m) in length. The governing traffic conditions are similar to the passenger car lane except that on steeper upgrades, trucks traveling at a crawl speed of about 6 mph (10 km/h) become the critical traffic condition.

In both cases, the ventilating rates given in Figure 1 are based on emission rates from vehicles not equipped with control devices and on an allowable concentration of CO not to exceed 125 ppm (mg/kg). Factors for converting the ventilating rates to other criteria are given in the following paragraphs.

CONVERSION OF DIFFERENT TRAFFIC MIX

To correct the ventilation rate for emission control, the average emission factors for highway vehicles in Table 2 can be used; they are derived from nationwide EPA statistical data (EPA Suppl. 7). These emission factors are for the vehicle population mix for the calendar year shown and not for vehicles of that model year only. The values are projected emission factors based (1) on actual test results of existing sources and control systems and (2) on projected values for future years based on required emission reductions, as stipulated in the present law. The designer must be aware of any possible future revisions or corrections in the predicted factors and in emission control laws. The designer must also evaluate actual emission rates versus predicted emission rates.

Converting to any desired calendar year may be accomplished with the following equation:

$$Q = VF \tag{1}$$

where:

Q = converted ventilation rate.
V = unconverted ventilation rate.
F = emission factor for desired calendar year from Table 2.

CONVERSION OF CO CONCENTRATION

Converting ventilation rates to a CO level other than 125 ppm (mg/kg):

$$Q = V(125/C) \tag{2}$$

where:

C = desired CO concentration, ppm (mg/kg).

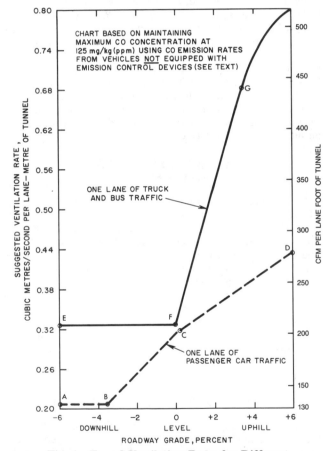

Fig. 1   Tunnel Ventilation Rates for Different Roadway Gradients

Key Values for Figure 1

Point	Grade	Vent. Rate
A	−6.0	0.206
B	−3.5	0.206
C	zero	0.313
D	+6.0	0.433
E	−6.0	0.325
F	zero	0.325
G	+3.5	0.682

Adjustment of Ventilation Rate for Ambient CO Level

Ventilation rates shown in Figure 1 assume the ventilating air contains little or no CO when it is introduced. If this is not the case, the ventilation rates may be adjusted by:

$$Q = V[125/(125 - E)] \qquad (3)$$

where:

E = ambient CO level, ppm (mg/kg).

Conversion of Truck Traffic Mix

The conversion constants given consider the size of the truck and the percentage of truck type in the traffic stream.

$$Q = V(1.22 \, P_G + 0.85 \, P_D) \qquad (4)$$

where:

P_G = ratio of gasoline-powered vehicles.
P_D = ratio of diesel-powered vehicles.

Minimum Ventilation Rate

In addition to the dilution of carbon monoxide, the ventilation system must provide sufficient ventilation for fire protection. Experience has shown that 100 cfm (47 L/s) per lane foot of tunnel is sufficient for fire protection; however, an analysis of life safety and smoke control requirements could permit a reduction in this value.

Example. Calculate the volume flow rate of a single-bore tunnel with two lanes of unidirectional traffic. The tunnel, which will open in 1989, has the grades and dimensions shown below. It has a design level of 125 ppm (mg/kg) and an ambient CO level of 5 ppm (mg/kg).

Solution from Figure 1:

4% grade   133 cfm   (63 L/s) per lane foot (m) for cars
              <u>210</u> cfm   (99 L/s) per lane foot (m) for trucks
              <u>343 cfm (162 L/s)</u>

+2% grade   228 cfm (108 L/s) per lane foot (m) for cars
              <u>342</u> cfm (161 L/s) per lane foot (m) for trucks
              <u>570 cfm (269 L/s)</u>

    343 • 2493 =   855,000
    570 • 1805 = <u>1,029,000</u>
                1,884,000 cfm   (889,200 L/s or 889 m³/s)

Adjusting for ambient CO level of 5.0 ppm (Eq. 3) and converting traffic mix for calendar year 1989 (Eq. 1):

$$Q = VF[125/(125 - 5)]$$

From Table 2, F = 0.169 (1989)

$$Q = 1,884,000 • 0.169 • 1.042$$

$$Q = 332,000 \text{ cfm } (157 \text{ m}^3/s)$$

Check for minimum ventilation rate:

    For −4% grade: (343)(0.169)(1.042) = 60 cfm
    For +2% grade: (570)(0.169)(1.042) = 100 cfm

The −4% grade requirement falls short of 100 cfm per lane foot; therefore, adequacy under fire conditions should be analyzed.

VENTILATION SYSTEM TYPES

Natural Ventilation

Naturally ventilated tunnels rely chiefly on meteorological conditions to maintain a satisfactory environment within the tun-

nel. The piston effect of traffic provides additional air flow when the traffic is moving. The chief meteorological condition affecting environment is the pressure differential between two portals of a tunnel created by differences in elevation, in ambient temperatures, or by wind. Unfortunately, none of these factors can be relied on for continued, consistent results. A sudden change in wind direction or velocity can rapidly negate all of these natural effects, including the piston effect. The sum total of all pressures must be of sufficient magnitude to overcome the tunnel resistance, which is influenced by tunnel length, coefficient of friction, hydraulic radius, and air density.

Air flow through a naturally ventilated tunnel can be portal-to-portal (Figure 2a) or portal-to-shaft (Figure 2b). Portal-to-portal flow functions best with unidirectional traffic, which produces a consistent, positive air flow. The air velocity within the roadway is uniform and the contaminant concentration increases to a maximum at the exit portal. If adverse meteorological conditions occur, the velocity is reduced and the CO concentration is increased, as shown by dashed line on Figure 2a. If bidirectional traffic is introduced into such a tunnel, further reductions in air flow result.

The naturally ventilated tunnel with an intermediate shaft (see Figure 2b) is best suited for bidirectional traffic. However, the air flow through such a shafted tunnel is also at the mercy of the elements. The added benefit of the stack effect of the shaft depends on air and rock temperatures, wind, and shaft height. The addition of more than one shaft to a naturally ventilated tunnel is more of a disadvantage than an advantage, since a pocket of contaminated air can be trapped between the shafts and cause high contaminant levels.

Most naturally ventilated urban tunnels over 500 ft (150 m) long require an emergency mechanical ventilation system to purge smoke and hot gases generated during an emergency and to remove stagnated, polluted gases during severe adverse meteorological conditions. Because of the uncertainties noted

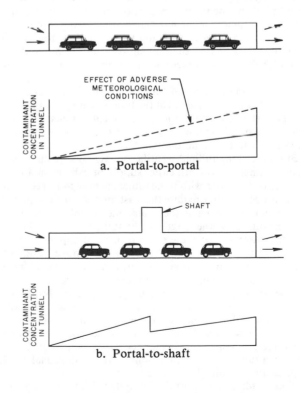
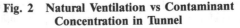

Fig. 2   Natural Ventilation vs Contaminant Concentration in Tunnel

above, reliance on natural ventilation for all tunnels over 500 ft (150 m) long should be thoroughly evaluated, specifically the effect of adverse meteorological and operating conditions. This is particularly true for a tunnel with an anticipated heavy or congested traffic flow. If the natural ventilation is inadequate, consider installing a mechanical system with fans.

Mechanical Ventilation

The most appropriate mechanical ventilation systems for tunnels are longitudinal ventilation, semitransverse ventilation, and full transverse ventilation.

Longitudinal ventilation is any system that introduces or removes air from the tunnel at a limited number of points, thus creating a longitudinal flow of air within the roadway. The injection-type longitudinal system has been frequently used in rail tunnels; however, it has also found appliction in vehicular tunnels. Air injected into the tunnel roadway at one end of the tunnel mixes with air brought in by piston effect of the incoming traffic (see Figure 3a).

This system is most effective where traffic is unidirectional. The air velocity stays uniform throughout the tunnel, and the concentration of contaminants increases from zero at the entrance to a maximum at the exit. Adverse external atmospheric conditions can reduce the effectiveness of this system. The contaminant level increases at the exit portal as the air flow decreases or the tunnel length increases.

The longitudinal system with a fan shaft (see Figure 3b) is similar to the naturally ventilated system with a shaft, except it provides a positive stack effect. Bidirectional traffic in a tunnel ventilated in this manner will cause a peak contaminant concentration at the shaft location. For unidirectional tunnels, however, the contaminant levels become unbalanced.

Another form of the longitudinal system has two shafts near the center of the tunnel: one for exhaust and one for supply (see Figure 3c). It will reduce contaminant concentration in the second half of the tunnel. A portion of the air flowing in the roadway is replaced in the interaction at the shafts. Adverse wind conditions can cause a reduction in the air flow, resulting in a subsequent rise in the contaminant concentration to rise in the second half of the tunnel and short circuit flow from fan to exhaust.

In a growing number of tunnels, longitudinal ventilation is achieved with fans mounted at the tunnel ceiling (see Figure 3d). Such a system eliminates the space needed to house ventilation fans in the building; however, it may require a tunnel of greater height or width for the booster fans.

Standard longitudinal ventilation systems (excluding the booster fan system), with either supply or exhaust at a limited number of locations within the tunnel, are the most economical systems because they require the least number of fans, place the least operating burden on these fans, and do not require distribution air ducts. As the length of the tunnel increases, however, the disadvantages of these systems become apparent, such as excessive air velocities in the roadway and smoke being drawn the entire length of the roadway during an emergency. Uniform air distribution would alleviate these problems.

Semitransverse Ventilation. This system uniformly distributes or collects air throughout the length of a tunnel. The supply air version of the system (see Figure 4a) produces a uniform level of carbon monoxide throughout the tunnel because the air and the vehicle exhaust gasses enter the roadway area at the same rate. In a tunnel with unidirectional traffic, additional air flow is generated within the roadway area.

This system, because of the fan-induced flow, is not adversely affected by atmospheric conditions. The air flows the length of the tunnel in a duct fitted with periodic supply outlets. Fresh

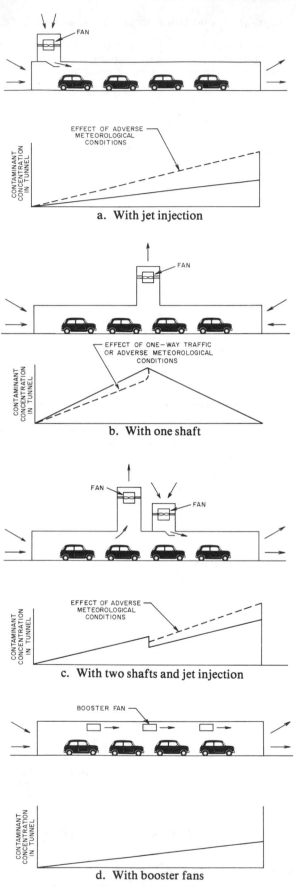

a. With jet injection

b. With one shaft

c. With two shafts and jet injection

d. With booster fans

Fig. 3 Longitudinal Ventilation

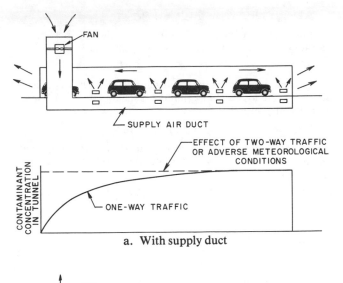

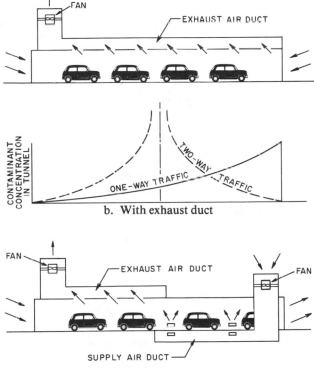

a. With supply duct

b. With exhaust duct

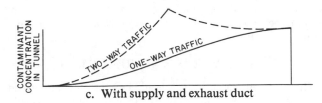

c. With supply and exhaust duct

Fig. 4   Semitransverse Ventilation

air is best introduced at exhaust pipe level of the vehicles to dilute the exhaust gases immediately. An adequate pressure differential must be generated between the duct and the roadway to counteract piston effect and atmospheric winds.

If a fire occurs within the tunnel, the air supplied will dilute the smoke. To aid in fire-fighting efforts and in emergency egress, the fresh air should enter the tunnel through the portals to create

a respirable environment for these activities. Therefore, the fans in a supply semitransverse system should be reversible, and a ceiling supply should be considered. With a ceiling supply system and reversible fans, the smoke will be drawn upward.

The exhaust semitransverse system (Figure 4b) in a unidirectional tunnel produces a maximum contaminant concentration at the exit portal. In a bidirectional tunnel, the maximum level of contaminants occurs near the center of the tunnel. A combination supply and exhaust system (see Figure 4c) applies only in a unidirectional tunnel where the air entering the traffic stream is exhausted in the first half, and air supplied in the second half exhausts through the exit portal.

The supply semitransverse system is the accepted type, which is the only one not affected by adverse meteorological conditions or opposing traffic. Semitransverse systems are used in tunnels up to about 3,000 ft (1000 m), at which point the tunnel air velocities near the portals become excessive.

Full Transverse Ventilation is used in large tunnels. A full exhaust duct added to a supply-type semitransverse system achieves uniform distribution of supply air and uniform collection of vitiated air (see Figure 5). With the arrangement, a uniform pressure will occur throughout the roadway, and no longitudinal air flow will occur except that generated by traffic piston effect, which tends to reduce contaminant levels. An adequate pressure differential between the ducts and the roadway is required to assure proper air distribution under all ventilation conditions.

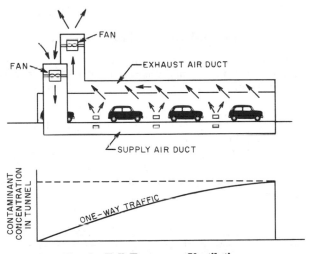

Fig. 5   Full Transverse Ventilation

U.S. Bureau of Mines full-scale tests showed for rapid dilution of exhaust gases supply air inlets should be at the level of the vehicle emission and the exhaust outlets in the ceiling. The air distribution can be one-sided or two-sided.

Other Ventilation. There are many variations and combinations of the systems described. Figure 6 shows a combined system for a unidirectional tunnel approximately 1,400 ft (425 m) long. Section 3 uses a full transverse system because of the upgrade roadway; Section 2 uses a semitransverse supply with a longitudinal exhaust, and the remainder of the tunnel (Section 1) is a semitransverse supply system. Such a system is not recommended for a long tunnel.

Emergency Conditions

An emergency condition in any vehicular tunnel, particularly one generating smoke and heat, such as during a fire, can lead to a disaster if the tunnel ventilation system is designed and

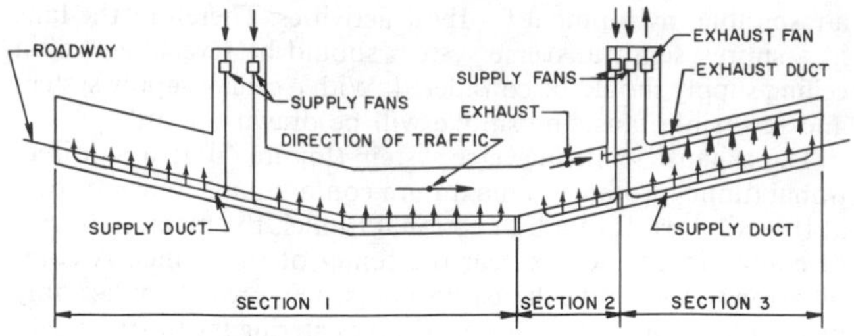

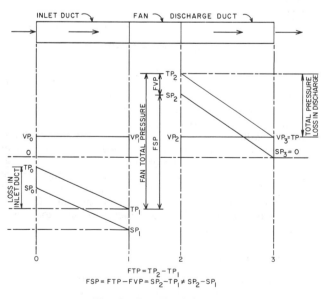

Fig. 6   Combined Ventilation System

operated improperly. The primary objective in such a situation is the rapid removal of smoke and heat from the tunnel to permit vehicles to exit safely and firefighters to reach the fire. This can be accomplished by removing the smoke and heat at a high level within the tunnel and supplying fresh air at a low level either through a designated supply system or through the tunnel portals. A full transverse ventilation system provides the ideal emergency ventilation system, *i.e.,* a high level (ceiling) exhaust and a low level positive supply (roadway). A semi-transverse ventilation system, which exhausts through the overhead system, thus causing fresh air to enter the roadway through the portals, can be an effective emergency ventilation system. Prior to the design of a tunnel, the criteria for emergency conditions must be established, including the minimum level of ventilation required to create a safe environment.

PRESSURE EVALUATIONS

Air pressure losses in the tunnel duct system must be evaluated to compute fan pressure and drive requirements. Fan selection should be based on total pressure accross the fans, not just static pressure.

Fan total pressure *(FTP)* is defined by the Air Moving and Conditioning Association (AMCA) (ASHRAE Std. 51-85) as the algebraic difference between the total pressures at the fan discharge *(TP$_2$)* and at the fan inlet *(TP$_1$)*, as shown in Figure 7. The fan velocity pressure *(FVP)* is defined by AMCA as the pressure corresponding to the air velocity and air density at the fan discharge.

$$FVP = VP_2$$

The fan static pressure *(FSP)* equals the difference between the fan total pressure and the fan velocity pressure.

$$FSP = FTP - FVP$$

The total pressure at the fan discharge *(TP$_2$)* must equal the total pressure losses *(ΔTP$_{2-3}$)* in the discharge duct and the exit velocity pressure *(VP$_3$)*.

$$TP_2 = \Delta TP_{2\text{-}3} - VP_3$$

Likewise, the total pressure at the fan inlet *(TP$_1$)* must equal the total pressure losses in the inlet duct system and the inlet pressure.

$$TP_1 = TP_0 + \Delta TP_{0\text{-}1}$$

Straight Ducts

Straight ducts in tunnel ventilation systems can be classified as: (1) those that transport air, thus having constant area and constant air velocity; and (2) those that uniformly distribute (supply) or uniformly collect (exhuast) air.

Several methods have been developed to predict pressure losses in a duct of constant cross-secitonal area that uniformly distributes or collects air. The most widely used method was developed for the Holland Tunnel (Singstad 1929). The following relationships give total pressure loss at any point in the duct.

For **supply duct:**

$$P = P_1 + \varrho V_0^2/2[aLZ^3/3H - (1 - K)Z^2/2] \qquad (5)$$

where:

P = Total pressure loss at any point in duct, in. of water (kPa).
P_1 = Pressure at last outlet, in. of water (kPa).
ϱ = Density of air, lb/ft^3 (kg/m^3).
V_0 = Velocity of air entering duct, ft/s (m/s).
a = Constant related to coefficent of friction for concrete (0.0035).
L = Total length of duct, ft (m).
Z = $(L - X)/L$.
X = Distance from duct entrance to any location ft (m).
H = Hydraulic radius, ft (m).
K = Constant that accounts for turbulence (0.615).

For **exhaust duct:**

$$P = P_1 + \varrho V_0^2/2[aLZ^3/(3 + c)H + 3Z^2/(2 + c)] \qquad (6)$$

where:

All terms are the same as for the supply duct, with the added term
C = numerical constant relating to turbulence of exhaust port (0.25).

For **transport duct:**

The pressure losses in a transport duct having constant cross-sectional area and constant velocity are due to friction alone and can be computed using the standard expressions for losses in ducts and fittings.

CO ANALYZERS AND RECORDERS

The air quality in the tunnel should be constantly monitored at several key points. Carbon monoxide is the impurity usually selected as the prime indicator of tunnel air quality. Three types of CO analyzing instruments are applied: catalytic oxidation, infrared absorption, and electrochemical oxidation.

The *catalytic oxidation* (metal oxide) instrument, the most widely used in vehicular tunnels, offers reliability and stability at a moderate initial cost. Maintenance requirements are low, and the instruments can be calibrated and serviced by maintenance personnel after only brief instruction.

The *infrared analyzer* has the advantage of sensitivity and response but the disadvantage of high initial cost. Being a very

$$FTP = TP_2 - TP_1$$
$$FSP = FTP - FVP = SP_2 - TP_1 \neq SP_2 - SP_1$$

Fig. 7   Fan Total Pressure

precise and complex instrument, it requires the services of a highly trained technician for maintenance and servicing.

The *electrochemical analyzer* has only recently been used in the United States, although similar instruments have seen service for some time in England. These instruments are precise, compact, and lightweight. The units are of moderate cost and are easily maintained.

No matter what type of CO analyzer is selected, it is important that each air sampling point be located where readings of significance can be obtained. For example, the area at or near the entrance of unidirectional tunnels usually has very low CO concentrations, and sampling points there yield little information for ventilation control. The length of piping between the sampling point and the CO analyzer should be as short as possible to maintain a reasonable air sample transport time.

In conditions where intermittent analyzers are suitable, provisions should be made to prevent the loss of more than one sampling point during periods of an air pump outage. It is advisable to provide each analyzer with a strip chart recorder to keep a permanent record of tunnel air contitions. Usually, recorders are mounted on the central control board.

Haze or smoke detectors have been used on a limited scale, but most of these instruments are optical devices and require frequent or constant cleaning with a compressed air jet. Should traffic be predominantly diesel powered, oxides of nitrogen and smoke haze require monitoring in addition to CO.

CONTROL SYSTEMS

To reduce the number of operating personnel at a tunnel, all ventilating equipment should be controlled at a central location. At many older tunnel facilities, fan operation is manual and controlled by an operator at the central control board. Many new tunnels, however, have the fan operation partially or totally controlled automatically.

CO Analyzer Control System

In this system, adjustable contacts within CO analyzers turn on additional fans or increase fan speeds as CO readings increase. The reverse occurs as CO levels decrease. The system requires a fairly complex wiring arrangement because fan opertion must normally respond to the single highest level being recorded at several analyzers. In addition to a manual override, delay devices are required to prevent the ventilation system from responding to short-lived high or low CO levels.

Time Clock Control Systems

This type of automatic fan control is best suited for those installations that experience heavy rush-hour traffic. A time clock is set to increase the ventilation level in present increments in advance of the anticipated traffic increase. The system is simple and is easily revised to suit changing traffic patterns. Because it anitcipates an increased air requirement, the ventilation system can be made to respond slowly and, thus, avoid expensive demand charges by the power company. As with the CO system, a manual override is needed to cope with unanticipated conditions.

Traffic Actuated Systems

Several automatic fan control systems based on recorded traffic flow information have been devised. Most of them require the installation of computers and other electronic equipment. These complex systems require concomitant maintenance expertise.

Local Fan Control

In addition to a central control board, each fan unit should have local control close to and within sight of the unit. It should be interlocked to permit positive isolation of the fan from remote or automatic operation during maintenance and servicing.

RAPID TRANSIT SYSTEMS

Of the approximately 100 rapid transit systems in operation today, most run at least part of their lines underground, particularly in the central business districts of urban centers.

Older subway systems have relied heavily on natural ventilation, with the primary air mover being the piston effect of the vehicles themselves. In recent years, the piston effect has been supplemented by forced mechanical ventilation. Most new systems use air-conditioned vehicles, but it is still important to provide a reasonable environment within subway tunnels and stations.

The Transit Development Corporation and the Urban Mass Transportation Administration of the U. S. Department of Transportation financed a research and development study on subway environmental controls. From the study a handbook and computer program (U. S. DOT 1976) was developed. Unproven by actual operating experience but validated by field and model tests, the handbook provides the most comprehensive and authoritative design aids developed to date.

DESIGN CONCEPTS

The factors to be considered, although interrelated, may be divided into natural ventilation, forced ventilation, and station air conditioning.

Natural Ventilation

Natural ventilation in subway systems (infiltration and exfiltration) is primarily the result of train operation in more or less tightly fitting trainways, where air generally moves in the direction of train travel. The positive pressure in front of a train expels air from the system through portals and station entrances; the negative pressure in the wake of the train induces air flow into the system through these same openings.

Considerable shortcircuiting occurs in subway structures where two trains traveling in opposite directions pass each other. It occurs especially in stations or in tunnels with perforated or no dividing walls. Such shortcircuiting tends to reduce the net ventilation rate and tends to increase and possibly cause excess air velocities on station platforms and in station entrances. During the time of peak operation and peak ambient temperatures, it can cause an undesirable amount of heat to build up.

To help counter these negative effects, ventilation shafts are customarily placed near the interface between tunnels and stations. Shafts in the approach tunnel are often called *blast shafts* through which part of the air pushed ahead of the train is expelled from the system. Shafts in the departure tunnel are sometimes called *relief shafts,* since they relieve the negative pressure created during the departure of the train and induce outside air through the shaft rather than through the station entrances. Additional ventilation shafts may be provided between stations (or between portals for underwater crossings), as dictated by tunnel length. The high cost of such ventilation structures necessitates a design for optimum effectiveness. Internal resistance because of offsets and bends should be kept to a minimum, and shaft cross-sectional areas should be approximately equal to the cross-sectional area of a single-track tunnel (U. S. DOT 1976).

Mechanical Ventilation

Mechanical ventilation in subway systems: (1) supplements the ventilation effect created by train piston action; (2) expels heated air from the system; (3) introduces cool outside air; (4) supplies makeup air for exhaust; (5) restores the cooling potential of the heat sink through extraction of heat stored during off-hours or system shutdown; (6) reduces the flow of air between the tunnel and the station; (7) provides outside air for passengers in stations or tunnels in an emergency or during other unscheduled interruption of traffic; (8) purges smoke from the system in case of fire.

The most cost-effective design for mechanical ventilation is one that serves two or more purposes. For example, a vent shaft provided for natural (piston action) ventilation may also be used for emergencies if a fan is installed in a parallel with the bypass, or vice versa (Figure 8).

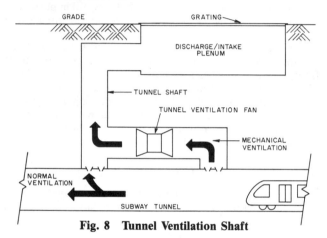

Fig. 8 Tunnel Ventilation Shaft

Several vent shafts may work together as a system, capable of meeting many, if not all, of the objectives cited above. Depending on shaft location and the given train situation, the shaft may serve as a blast or relief shaft with the bypass damper open and the fan damper closed. With the fan in operation and the bypass damper closed, this arrangement can supply or exhaust air by mechanical ventilation, depending on direction of fan rotation.

Except for emergencies, fan rotation is usually predetermined based on the overall ventilation concept. If subway stations are not air conditioned, the heated system air should be exchanged with cooler outside air at a maximum rate. If stations are air conditioned below ambient temperatures, the inflow of warmer outside air should be limited and controlled.

Figure 9 illustrates a typical tunnel ventilation system between two subway stations. In this concept, the flow of heated tunnel air into a cooler station is kept to a minimum. The dividing wall separating Track No. 1 and Track No. 2 is discontinued in the vicinity of the emergency fans. Air pushed ahead of the train on Track No. 2 then partially diverts to the emergency fan bypasses and partially into the wake of a train on Track No. 1 as a result of pressure differences (Fig. 9a). Figure 9b shows an alternative operation with the same ventilation system. When outdoor temperatures are favorable, the midtunnel fans operate as exhaust fans with makeup air introduced through the emergency fan bypasses. This concept can also provide or supplement station ventilation or both. To achieve this goal, emergency fan bypasses would be closed, and the makeup air for midtunnel exhaust fans would enter through station entrances.

A more direct ventilation concept removes station heat at its primary source, the underside of the train. Figure 10 illustrates such a trackway ventilation system. U. S. DOT (1976) tests have shown that such systems not only reduce the upwelling of heated air onto platform areas, but also remove significant portions of the heat generated by dynamic braking resistor grids and air-conditioning condensers located underneath the train. Ideally, makeup air for the exhaust should be introduced at track level to provide a positive control over the direction of air flow (Figure 10a).

Underplatform exhaust systems without makeup supply air, as illustrated in Figure 10b, are least effective and, under certain conditions, may be detrimental, since such an arrangement could cause heated tunnel air to flow into the station. Figure 10c shows a cost-effective compromise where makeup air in introduced at the ceiling of the platform. Although the heat removal effectiveness may not be as good as that of the system illustrated in Figure 10a, it negates the inflow of hot tunnel air that might occur without supply air makeup.

Emergency Ventilation

Mechanical ventilation is a major control strategy in a subway tunnel fire. An increase in air supply over stoichiometric requirements will reduce the fire progression by lowering the flame temperature. Further, ventilation can control the direction of smoke emissions to permit safe evacuation of passengers and facilitate access by fire fighters.

Emergency ventilation must allow for the unpredictable location of a disabled train or the source of fire and smoke. Therefore, emergency ventilation fans should have nearly full reverse flow capability so that fans on either side of a stalled train operate together to control the direction of air flow and to counteract the migration of smoke. When a train is stalled between two stations and smoke is present, outside air is supplied from the nearest station and contaminated air is exhausted at the opposite end of the train (unless location of the fire dictates otherwise). Then the passengers can be evacuated along walkways in the tunnel via the shortest route (Figure 11).

It is essential that providions be made to (1) quickly assess any emergency situation, (2) communicate the situation to central control, (3) establish the location of the train, and (4) start, stop, and reverse emergency ventilation fans from the central console as quickly as possible to establish smoke control.

Midtunnel and station trackway ventilation fans may be used to enhance the emergency ventilation system; however, these fans must withstand elevated temperatures for a prolonged period and have reverse flow capacity.

Station Air Conditioning

Higher approach speeds and closer headways, made possible by computerized automatic train control systems, have increased the amount of heat gains. The net internal sensible heat gain in a typical double-track subway station, with 40 trains/hour per track, traveling at top speeds of 50 mph (80 km/h) may reach 5×10^6 Btu/h (1.5 MW) even after credit is taken for heat removal by the heat sink, by station underplatform exhaust systems, and by tunnel ventilation. To remove such a quantity of heat by station ventilation with outside air at a 3 °F (1.6 °C) temperature rise, for example, requires roughly 1.4×10^6 cfm (660 m³/s).

Not only would such a system be costly, but the resulting air velocities on station platforms would be objectionable to passengers. The same amount of sensible heat gain, plus latent heat, plus outside air load with a 7 °F (4 °C) lower-than-ambient station design temperature could be handled by about 630 tons (2.2 MW) of refrigeration. Even if station air conditioning should be more costly initially, the long-term benefits will result in: (1) reduced design air flow rates; (2) improved environment for

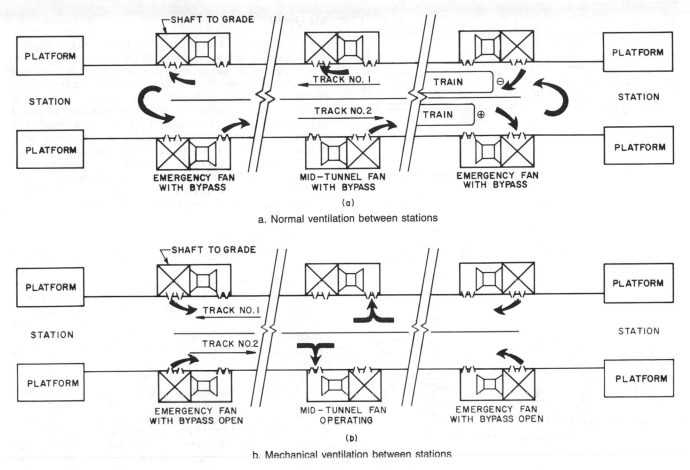

a. Normal ventilation between stations

b. Mechanical ventilation between stations

Fig. 9 Tunnel Ventilation Concept

passengers; (3) increased equipment life; (4) reduced maintenance of equipment and structures; and (5) increased acceptance by subway passengers as a viable means of public transportation.

In addition to the station platform, other ancillary station areas such as concourses, concession areas, and transfer levels should be evaluated for air conditioning. However, unless these ancillary areas are designed to attract patronage to concessions, the air-conditioning cost for walk-through areas is not usually warranted.

The physical configuration of the platform level usually determines the cooling distribution pattern. High ceiling heights in domed stations, local hot spots as a result of train location, high density passenger accumulation, or high level lighting may need spot cooling. Conversely, where train length equals platform length and ceiling height above the platform is limited to 10 to 11.5 ft (3 to 3.5 m), isolation of heat sources and application of spot cooling is normally not feasible.

Use of available space in the station structure for air distribution systems should be of prime concern because of the high cost of underground construction. Overhead distribution ductwork, which adds to building height in commercial construction, could add to the depth of excavation in subway construction. The space beneath a subway platform normally offers an excellent area for low-cost distribution of supply, return, and/or exhaust air.

DESIGN APPROACH

A subway system may require two separate environmental criteria: (1) for normal operations and (2) for emergencies. Criteria for normal operations generally include limits on temperature and humidity for various times of the year, a minimum ventilation rate to dilute contaminants generated within the subway, and limits on air velocity and the rate of air pressure change to which commuters may be exposed. Some of these criteria are subjective and may vary on a demographic basis. Criteria for emergencies generally include a minimum purge time for sections of the subway in which smoke or fire may occur, and minimum and maximum fan-induced tunnel air velocities.

Given a set of criteria and a set of outdoor design conditions, coupled with appropriate tools for estimating interior heat loads, earth heat sink, ventilation, air velocity, and air pressure changes, the design engineer then selects the elements of the environmental control system. Selection considers air temperature control, air velocity control, air quality control, and air pressure control. The system selected will generally include a combination of unpowered ventilation shafts, powered ventilation shafts, underplatform exhaust, and air-conditioning systems.

Decisions on train propulsion/braking systems, the configurations of tunnels and stations, and the like greatly affect the subway environment. Since these decisions are often made during the early stages of design, they must consider an environmental point of view. The factors affecting a subway environmental control system are further discussed below. *The Subway Environmental Design Handbook* (U. S. DOT 1976) and NFPA Standard 130-83, "Fixed Guideway Transit Systems," has more information.

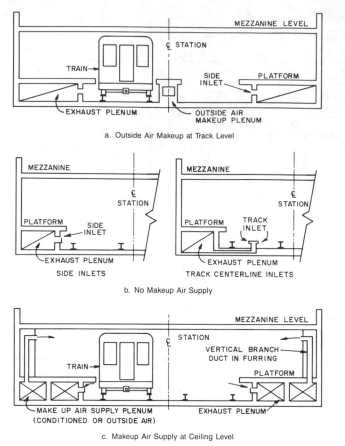

a. Outside Air Makeup at Track Level

b. No Makeup Air Supply

c. Makeup Air Supply at Ceiling Level

Fig. 10 Trackway Ventilation Concepts (Cross Sections)

Comfort Criteria

Because of the transient nature of the environment experienced by a person during entry, passage through, and exit from a subway station, special considerations (as opposed to selecting comfort levels for spaces having continuous occupancy) are permissible.

As a general principle, the environment within a subway station should provide a smooth transition between conditions outside and those within the transit vehicles. People entering a subway station from the outside should not experience a substantial degradation of environmental conditions. Based on nuisance considerations, it is recommended that peak air velocities in public areas be limited to 1,000 fpm (5 m/s).

Air Quality

Air quality within a subway system is influenced by many factors, some of which are not directly under the control of the HVAC engineer. Some particulates, gaseous contaminants, and odorants existing on the outside can be prevented from entering the subway by the judicious location of ventilation shafts. Particulate matter, including iron and graphite dust generated by train operations, is best controlled by a regular cleaning of the subway system. However, the only viable way to control gaseous contaminants such as ozone from electrical equipment and CO generated by human respiration is through adequate ventilation from outside. A minimum of 7.5 cfm (3.5 L/s) of filtered outside air per person should be introduced into tunnels and stations to dilute gaseous contaminants.

Pressure Transients

The passage of trains through aerodynamic discontinuities in the subway system can cause time-varying changes in static pressure. These pressure transients can irritate passengers' ears and sinuses. Pressure transients may also cause additional load on various structures (*e.g.,* acoustical panels) and equipment (*e.g.,* fans). In consideration of potential nuisance to humans, it is recommended that if the total change in pressure is greater than 2.8 in. of water (700 Pa), the rate of static pressure change should be kept below 1.7 in. of water/s (400 Pa/s).

During emergencies, it is essential to provide ventilation to control smoke and reduce air temperatures to permit passenger evacuation and fire-fighting operations. The minimum air velocity within the tunnel section experiencing the fire emergency should be sufficient to prevent back layering of the smoke, *i.e.,* a flow of smoke in the upper cross section of the tunnel opposite in direction to the forced outside ventilation air. The method to ascertain this minimum velocity is provided in the SES Handbook and Computer Program (U. S. DOT 1976). Further, the maximum air velocity experienced by evacuating passengers should be 2,200 fpm (11 m/s).

Interior Heat Loads

Heat within a subway system is generated mostly by: (1) braking of trains; (2) acceleration of trains; (3) car air conditioning and miscellaneous accessories; (4) station lights, people and equipment; and (5) ventilation (outside) air.

Deceleration. The majority of heat generated within a subway system (40 to 60%) ordinarily arises from the braking of trains. Many rapid-transit vehicles use non-regenerative braking systems. For these systems, the kinetic energy of a train at the initiation of braking is dissipated as waste heat from dynamic and/or friction brakes, rolling resistance, and aerodynamic drag.

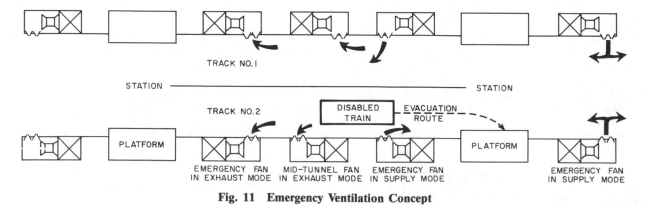

Fig. 11 Emergency Ventilation Concept

Acceleration. Heat is also generated as a result of train acceleration. Many operational trains use a cam-controlled variable resistance to regulate voltage across DC traction motors during acceleration. Electrical power dissipated by these resistors and by the third rail appears as heat within a subway system. Heat released during acceleration also includes that due to traction motor losses, rolling resistance, and aerodynamic drag. Heat released by train acceleration is generally from 10 to 20% of total heat released within a subway system.

For closely spaced stations, trains frequently undergo only acceleration or braking with little operation at constant speed. In these cases, maximum train speed between station stops is controlled by the distance between stops.

Car Air-Conditioning Systems

Most new cars are fully climate-controlled. Air-conditioning equipment removes patron and lighting heat from the cars and, along with the condenser fan heat and compressor heat, deposits it into the subway system. Air-conditioning capacities generally range between 10 tons (35 kW) per car for the shorter cars (about 50 ft or 15 m) up to about 20 tons (70 kW) for the longer cars (about 70 ft or 22 m). Heat from car air conditioners and other accessories may range from 25 to 30% of total heat generated within a subway.

Other Sources

Heat released within a subway system from non-train sources includes that from people, lighting, induced outside air, and miscellaneous equipment (fare vending machines, escalators, and the like). These sources range from 10 to 30% of total heat generated within a subway system. For analysis of heat balance within a subway, it is convenient to define a control volume about each station, including the station and its approach and departure tunnels.

Heat Sink

The amount of heat flow from subway walls to subway air varies on a seasonal basis, as well as for morning and evening rush-hour operations. For portions of a subway not heated or air conditioned, short periods of abnormally high or low outside air temperature may temporarily cause a departure from the heat sink effect. Such outside air temperature phenomena (lasting up to several days) will, in turn, cause a related air temperature change within a subway. However, the departure of subway air temperature from normal is diminished by the thermal inertia of the subway structure. Thus, during abnormally hot periods, heat flow to the subway structure increases. Similarly, during abnormally cold periods, heat flow from the subway structure to the air increases. Further research in this area is needed to fully quantify this phenomenon.

For subways where daily station air temperatures are held constant by heating and cooling, heat flux from station walls is negligible. Depending on the infiltration of station air into the adjoining tunnels, heat flux from tunnel sections may also be reduced in magnitude. Other factors affecting the heat sink component are type of soil (dense rock or light dry soil), migrating ground water, and the surface configuration of the tunnel walls (ribbed or flat).

Measures to Limit Heat Loads

Various mesures have been proposed to limit the interior heat load within subway systems. Among these are: regenerative braking, thyristor (chopper) motor controls, track profile optimization, and underplatform exhaust systems.

Electrical regenerative braking, which would otherwise appear as waste heat, is converted to electrical energy for use by other trains. Flywheel energy storage, an alternative form of regenerative braking, would store part of the braking energy of a train in high speed flywheels for subsequent use in vehicle acceleration. Using these methods, the reduction in heat generated by braking is limited by present technology to approximately 25%.

Conventional cam-controlled propulsion systems apply a set of resistance elements to regulate traction motor current during acceleration. Electrical energy dissipated by these resistors appears as waste heat within a subway system. Thyristor motor controls replace the acceleration resistors by solid-state controls. Such solid-state motor controls would reduce acceleration heat loss by from about 10% on high speed subways to about 25% on low speed subway systems.

Track profile optimization refers to a depressed trackway between stations that reduces vehicle heat emissions. In this way, less power is used for acceleration, since some of the train's potential energy, while in the station, is converted to kinetic energy as it accelerates toward the tunnel low point. Conversely, some of the kinetic energy of the train at maximum speed is converted to potential energy as it approaches the next station. The maximum reduction in total vehicle heat loss from acceleration and braking, using this method, is approximately 10%.

An underplatform exhaust system is essentially a *hooding* technique designed to prevent some of the heat generated by vehicle underfloor equipment (such as resistors and air-conditioning condensers) from entering the station environment. Exhaust ports beneath the station platform edge withdraw heated under car air.

For preliminary calculations, it may be assumed that train heat release within the station box is about two-thirds of control volume heat load due to braking and the train air conditioning, and the underplatform exhaust system is about 50% effective.

A quantity of air equal to that withdrawn by the underplatform exhaust system enters the control volume from the outside. Thus, when station design temperature is below outside ambient, an underplatform exhaust system reduces the subway heat load by drawing off undercar heat but increases the heat load by drawing in outside air. To reduce the uncontrolled infiltration of outside air, a proposed technique is to provide a complementary supply of outside air on the opposite side of the trackway underplatform exhaust ports. While in principle the underplatform exhaust system, with complementary supply, tends to reduce the mixing of outside air with air in public areas of the subway, no test results on such systems are available.

PARKING GARAGES

Automobile parking garages are either fully enclosed or partially open. The fully enclosed parking areas are usually underground and require mechanical ventilation. The partially open parking levels are generally above-grade structural decks having open sides (except for barricades), with a complete deck above. Natural or mechanical ventilation, or a combination of both methods, can be used for partially open garages.

The operation of automobiles presents two concerns. The most serious is the emission of carbon monoxide, with its known risks. The second concern is the presence of oil and gasoline fumes, which may cause nausea and headaches, as well as present a fire hazard. Additional concerns regarding oxides of nitrogen and smoke haze from diesel engines may require future consideration. For the present, however, the ventilation required to dilute carbon monoxide to acceptable levels will also control the other contaminants satisfactorily.

Two factors are required to determine the ventilation quantity: the number of cars in operation and the emission quantities. Most codes simplify this determination by requiring four to six air changes per hour, or 0.75 to 1 cfm per ft^2 (4 L/s per m^2), for fully enclosed parking garages. For partially open parking garages, 2.5 to 5% of the floor area is required as a free opening to permit natural ventilation. Applicable codes and National Fire Protection Association (NFPA) standards should be consulted for the specific requirements.

NUMBER OF CARS IN OPERATION

The number of cars in operation depends on the type of facility served by the parking garage. The variation is generally from 3% of the total vehicle capacity to 5% for a distributed, continuous use such as an apartment house or shopping area. It could reach 15 to 20% for peak use such as a sports stadium or short-haul airport.

The length of time that a car remains in operation within a parking garage is a function of the size and layout, as well as the number of cars attempting to enter or exit at a given time. This time could vary from 60 to 600 s, but on the average it ranges from 60 to 180 s.

It is desirable to conduct a survey of existing parking garages serving a facility having similar use and physical characteristics as the proposed design. Data can then be recorded on car entry and exiting rate by hour, as well as time in operation within the parking garage.

CONTAMINANT LEVEL CRITERIA

It is recommended that the ventilation rate be designed to maintain a CO level of 50 ppm (mg/kg) with peak levels not to exceed 125 ppm (mg/kg). The American Conference of Governmental Industrial Hygienists recommends a threshold limit of 50 ppm (mg/kg) for an eight-hour exposure, and EPA has determined that, at or near sea level, a CO concentration of 125 ppm (mg/kg) for exposure up to one hour would be safe. For installations above 3,500 ft (1000 m), far more stringent limits would be required.

Design Approach

The operation of a car engine within a parking garage differs considerably from normal vehicle operation, including the normal operation within a vehicular tunnel. On entry, the car travels slowly. On exiting, the engine is cold, and thus, at full choke. As it proceeds from the garage, the engine operates with a rich mixture and in low gear. Emissions for the cold start are considerably higher, and the distinction between hot and cold emission will play a critical role in determining the ventilation rate. Motor vehicle emission factors for hot and cold start operation are presented in Table 3. An accurate analysis requires correlation of CO readings with the survey data on car movements

(Hama, et. al. 1974). Table 4 lists approximate data for vehicle movements. This data should be adjusted to suit the specific physical configuration of the facility.

While emission controls were instituted in 1968 with progressively more stringent controls programmed through 1990, the precise reduction for the modes of engine operation within parking garages has not been evaluated. Access tunnels or fully enclosed ramps should be designed in accordance with the recommendations herein noted for vehicular tunnels. When natural ventilation is used, the wall opening free area should be as large as possible. A portion of the free area should be placed at floor level. In parking levels with large interior floor areas, a central emergency smoke exhaust system should be considered. This measure would improve safety in the event that fume removal during calm weather or smoke removal is necessary.

The ventilation system, whether mechanical, natural, or both, should be designed to meet the applicable codes and maintain an acceptable contaminant level. To conserve energy, fan systems should be controlled by carbon monoxide meters with multiple fan or variable-speed stages for larger systems, if permitted by local codes. In multilevel parking garages or single-level structures of extensive area, independent fan systems, each under individual control, are recommended.

Systems can be classified as supply-only, exhaust-only, or combined systems. Whichever system is chosen should consider: (1) avoiding short circuiting of supply air, (2) avoiding long flow fields that permit the contaminant levels to build up above an acceptable level at the end of the flow field, (3) providing short flow fields in areas of high pollutant emission, thereby limiting time to mix throughout the facility, and, (4) providing an efficient, adequate flow throughout the volume of the parking structure.

Noise

The ventilation system in parking garages, in general, moves large quantities of air through large openings without extensive ductwork. These conditions, in addition to the highly reverberant nature of the space, contribute to high noise levels. For this reason, sound attenuation should be considered. This is a safety concern as well, since high noise levels may mask the sound of an approaching car.

Ambient Standards and Pollution Control

Some state and municipal authorities have developed ambient air quality standards. The exhaust system discharge should meet these requirements.

BUS TERMINALS

Bus terminals vary considerably in physical configuration. Most terminals consist of a fully enclosed space containing passenger waiting area, ticket counters, and some vending food service. Buses load and unload outside the building, generally

Table 3   Predicted CO Emissions within Parking Garages (5 mph or 8 km/h Assumed Vehicle Speed)

Location	Hot Emissions (Stabilized) gm/min		Cold Emissions gm/min	
	1987	1992	1987	1992
Sea Level				
Summer	9.7	4.3	8.7	5.5
Winter	6.3	4.3	27.4	21.0
High Altitude				
Summer	15.3	8.8	14.5	12.2
Winter	11.3	10.0	43.2	35.9

*Results from EPA Mobil 3 Emission Factor Model.

Table 4   Approximate Entrance, Exit, and Pass-Through* Times For Vehicles (ASHRAE TRP-223)

Level	Avg. Entr. Time, s	Avg. Exit Time, s
1	35	45
3	40	50
5	70	100

*Average Pass-Through Time-30 s.

under a canopy to provide some weather protection. In larger cities, where space is at a premium and an extensive bus service exists, multiple levels may be required with the attendant busway tunnels and/or ramps, as well as extensive customer services.

Waiting rooms and consumer spaces should have a controlled environment in accordance with normal practice for public terminal occupancy. The space should be pressurized against intrusion of the busway environment. Waiting rooms and passenger concourse areas are subject to a highly variable people load. The occupant density may reach 10 ft² (1 m²) per person and, at extreme congestion periods, 3 to 5 ft² (0.3 to 0.5 m²) per person.

Basically, two types of bus service exist—urban-suburban and long distance. Urban-suburban service is characterized by frequent bus movements with rapid loading and unloading requirements. Therefore, the ideal passenger platforms are long, narrow, and the drive-through type, not requiring bus backup movements on departure. Long-distance operations, basically those with greater headways, generally use sawtooth gate configurations.

Ventilation systems to serve bus operating levels can be either natural or forced ventilation. When natural ventilation is selected, the bus levels should be open on all sides, and the slab-to-ceiling dimension should be sufficiently high, or contoured, to permit free air circulation. The installation of jet fans improves the natural air flow at a relatively low energy requirement. Mechanical systems that ventilate open platforms or gate positions should be configured to serve the bus operating areas, as shown in Figures 12 and 13.

PLATFORMS

Where naturally ventilated and drive-through platforms may expose passengers to inclement weather and strong winds, enclosed platforms, except for an open front, should be considered and the appropriate mechanical systems provided. Even partially enclosed platforms, however, may trap contaminants and require mechanical ventilation.

Multilevel bus terminals have limited headroom, thus restricting natural ventilation. In this case, mechanical ventilation should be selected, and all platforms should be partially or fully enclosed. Ventilation supplied to partially enclosed platforms should be designed to minimize the induction of contaminated air from the busway. Figure 12 indicates a partially enclosed

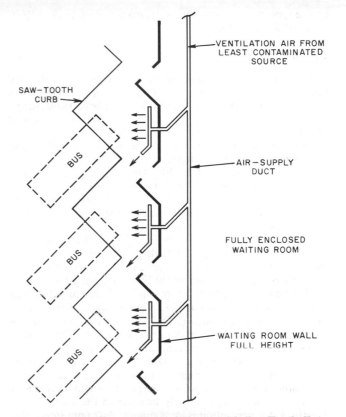

Fig. 13 Fully Enclosed Waiting Room with Saw-Tooth Gates

drive-through platform and an air distribution system. Supply air velocity should be limited to 250 fpm (1.3 m/s) to avoid drafty conditions on the platform. Partially enclosed platforms require large amounts of outside air to provide an effective barrier against fume penetration. Present experience indicates that a minimum of 17 cfm/ft² (86.4 L/s · m²) of platform area is required during the rush hours and approximately half of this quantity during the remaining time.

Platform air quality remains essentially the same as the ventilation air introduced. Because of the piston effect of buses, however, some momentary higher concentrations of pollutants will occur on the platform. Separate ventilation systems for each platform with two-speed fans permit operational flexibility. Fans should be controlled automatically to conform to bus operating schedules. In northern areas, mechanical ventilation could possibly be reduced during extreme winter weather.

Fully enclosed platforms are strongly recommended for large terminals with heavy bus traffic. They can be pressurized adequately and ventilated with approximately the normal heating and cooling air quantities, depending on the tightness of construction, number of boarding doors, and other openings. Air distribution can be of the conventional type used for air-conditioning systems. Air should not be recirculated. Openings around doors and in the enclosure walls are usually adequate to relieve air, without additional relief openings, unless platform construction is extraordinarily tight.

BUS OPERATION AREAS

Most buses are powered by diesel engines. Certain models have small auxiliary gasoline engines to drive the air-conditioning system. Tests performed on the volume and composition of exhaust gases emitted from diesel engines in various traffic conditions indicate large variations. These variations depend on

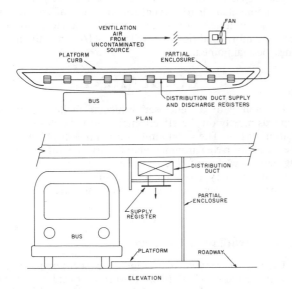

Fig. 12 Partially Enclosed Platform, Drive-Through Type

engine type, temperature, humidity, manufacturer, size, adjustment, and fuel burned.

Contaminants

The components of diesel exhaust gases that affect the ventilation system design are oxides of nitrogen, hydrocarbons, formaldehyde, odor constituents, aldehydes, smoke particulates, and a relatively small amount of carbon monoxide. Operation of diesel engines in enclosed spaces, therefore, causes visibility obstruction and odors, as well as contaminants. Table 5 provides approximate diesel engine exhaust gas data for the major contaminants that affect health. The nature of bus engines should be determined for each project, however.

The Federal Occupational Health and Environmental Control Regulation, Subpart G, sets the contaminant levels for an 8-hour exposure as: carbon monoxide, 50 ppm (mg/kg); and nitric oxide, 25 ppm (mg/kg). Subpart G sets the ceiling (maximum) limit for nitrogen dioxide at 5 ppm (mg/kg). The American Conference of Governmental Industrial Hygienists also recommends these threshold limits and, in addition, lists a ceiling (maximum) limit for formaldehyde at 3 ppm (mg/kg).

Oxides of nitrogen occur in two basic forms: nitrogen dioxide (NO_2) and nitric oxide (NO). Nitrogen dioxide is the major contaminant to be considered in the design of the ventilation system. Exposure to concentrations of 10 ppm (mg/kg) and higher will cause adverse health conditions. Furthermore, nitrogen dioxide affects light transmission, causing visibility reduction. It is intensely colored and absorbs light over the entire visible spectrum, primarily however in the shorter wavelengths. Odor perception is immediate at 0.42 ppm (mg/kg) of NO_2 and can be perceived by some at levels as low as 0.12 ppm (mg/kg).

Terminal operation will also affect the quality of surrounding ambient air. The dilution rate and the location and design of the intakes and discharges control the impact on ambient air quality. Also, the installation is subject to state and local regulations, which will require consideration of local atmospheric conditions and ambient contaminant levels.

Calculation of Ventilation Rate

To calculate the ventilation rate, the total amount of engine exhaust gases should be determined. The bus operating schedule, the duration of time that buses are in different modes of operation—that is, cruising, decelerating, idling, and accelerating—and the use of Table 5 will permit computing the contaminant level. The design engineer must ascertain, from the configuration of the terminal, the grade (if any) within the terminal and whether the platforms are the drive-through type, drive-through with bypass lanes, or sawtooth type. The engineer must also evaluate bus headways and bus operating speeds and modes.

For instance, with sawtooth platforms, the bus upon departure will have to accelerate backwards, brake, and then accelerate

Table 5   Approximate Diesel Bus Engine Emissions in ppm (mg/kg)

Total Exhaust Gases	Idling 117 scfm (55.2 L/s)	Accelerating 476 scfm (224.7 L/s)	Cruising 345 scfm (162.8 L/s)	Decelerating 302 scfm (142.5 L/s)
Carbon Monoxide	215	500	230	130
Hydrocarbons	390	210	90	330
Oxides of Nitrogen (NO_x)	60	850	235	30
Formaldehydes (HCHO)	9	17	11	30

forward. The drive-through platform requires a different mode of operation. Certain codes prescribe a maximum idling time for engines, usually 180 to 300 s. However, aside from considering the degree of enforcement of such ordinances, it should be recognized that 60 to 120 s of engine operation are required to build up brake air pressure.

The discharged contaminant quantities should be diluted by natural and/or forced ventilation to acceptable, legally prescribed levels. To maintain visibility and odor control, the exhaust gas contaminants should be diluted in the proportion of 75 to 1 with outside air. Where urban-suburban operations are involved, the ventilation rate will vary considerably throughout the day and on weekdays compared to weekends. Fan speed or blade control should be used to conserve energy.

Source of Ventilation Air

Since dilution is the primary means of contaminant level control, the source of ventilation air is extremely important. The cleanest available ambient air, which is generally above the roof in an urban area, should be used. Surveys of ambient air contaminant levels should be conducted and the most favorable source located. Possible shortcircuiting of exhaust air due to prevailing winds and building air flow patterns should be evaluated.

Control By Contaminant Level Monitoring

Time clocks or tapes coordinated with bus movement schedules and smoke monitors (obscurity meters) provide the most practical means of controlling the ventilation system.

Instrumentation is available for monitoring the various contaminants. Also, control by instrumentation can be simplified by monitoring carbon dioxide (CO_2). Studies have shown a relationship between the levels of various diesel engine pollutants and carbon dioxide, thus permitting the use of CO_2 detection and control equipment. However, the mix and quantity of pollutants varies with the rate of operation and the maintained condition of the bus engines. Therefore, if CO_2 monitoring is employed, actual conditions should be obtained under specific bus traffic conditions (schedule) to verify the selected CO_2 settings.

Dispatcher's Booth

The dispatcher's booth should be kept under pressure with uncontaminated air to prevent the intrusion of engine fumes. It will be occupied for sustained periods; therefore, normal interior comfort conditions, as well as OSHA contaminant levels, must be maintained.

EQUIPMENT

The ability of an enclosed vehicular facility to function depends mostly on the effectiveness and reliability of its ventilation system. The system must be completely effective under the most adverse environmental and traffic conditions and during periods when not all equipment is operational. For a tunnel, it is necessary to provide more than one dependable source of power to prevent an interruption of service.

FANS

Reserve Ventilation Capacity

The total theoretical ventilating air capacity required and a reasonable factor of safety are the prime considerations in selecting the type and number of fans. In addition, this selection will be influenced by the manner in which reserve capacity is provided during those times when a fan is inoperative, during repair of equipment or of the power supply.

Selection of fans (number and size) to meet normal and reserve capacity requirements is based on the principles of parallel fan operation. Chapter 3 of the 1983 EQUIPMENT Volume indicates that capacity and pressure associated with parallel fan operation depend on characteristics of the fan and the system. Actual capacities can be determined by fan performance and system curves plotted on the same pressure-volume diagram.

It is important that fans selected for parallel operation operate in that region of their performance curves where transferral of capacity back and forth between fans will not occur. This is accomplished by selecting a fan size and speed where the duty point, no matter how many fans are operating, falls well below the unstable range of fan performance. Fans operating in parallel on the same system should be of equal size and, if multiple speed, should always be operated at the same speed i.e., if one fan is operating at low speed, all other fans must be at low speed.

Number and Size of Fans

At locations where no space limitations or other restrictions are placed on the structures that house the ventilation equipment, the number and size of fans should be selected by comparing several alternative fan arrangements. These comparisons should be based on the practicality and overall economy of the layouts, including an estimate of: (1) annual power costs to operate equipment; (2) annual capital cost of the ventilation equipment (usually capitalized over an assumed equipment life of 30 years); and (3) annual capital cost of structure required to house equipment (usually capitalized over an arbitrary structure life of 50 years).

Two opposing views prevail on the proper number and size of fans. The first advocates a few large-capacity fans; the second prefers numerous small units. In most cases, a compromise arrangement produces a system with the greatest operating efficiency. Regardless of the design philosophy followed, the number and size of fans should be selected to build sufficient flexibility into the system to meet the varying air demands created by daily and seasonal traffic fluctuations.

Type of Fan

Normally, the ventilation system of a vehicular facility requires large air volumes working against relatively low pressures. Under these conditions, some fan designs have low efficiencies, thus, the choice of suitable fan type is often limited to either centrifugal or vaneaxial. Chapter 3 of the 1983 EQUIPMENT Volume contains details of operating characteristics and performance of these fan types.

Special Considerations. For rapid-transit systems, any fan installed in a duct leading from the train tube needs special consideration, since fans operate in the presence of the flow and pressure transients caused by train passage. If the transient tends to increase flow to the fan—i.e., the positive flow in front of a train to an exhaust fan or negative flow behind the train to a supply fan—it is important that blade loading does not become so high as to produce long-term fatigue failures.

If the disturbance tends to decrease flow to the fan—i.e., the negative flow behind the train to an exhaust fan or the positive flow in front of the train to a supply fan—the fan performance characteristic must have adequate margin to prevent aerodynamic stall of the fan.

In most cases, ability to reverse the rotation of tunnel supply, exhaust, and emergency fans rapidly is important in an emergency. The effects of this requirement must be considered in the selection and design of the fan and drive system.

DAMPERS

Shutoff dampers can be installed: (1) to isolate any parallel nonoperating fan from those operating to prevent shortcircuiting, with consequent pressure and flow loss through the inoperative fan; (2) to prevent serious windmilling of an inoperative fan, and (3) to provide a safe environment for maintenance and repair work on each fan.

Single-fan installations could have an isolating damper to prevent serious windmilling because of natural or piston effect drafts and to facilitate fan maintenance.

Two types of dampers have generally been used in ventilation systems: (1) the trapdoor type installed in a vertical duct so that the door lies flat when closed and (2) the multiple-blade louver type, with parallel operating blades. Both types are usually driven by a gear motor, which is operated by the fan controller who closes the damper when the fan is off and reopens it when the fan is on.

The trapdoor damper is simple and works satisfactorily where a vertical duct enters a plenum-type fan room through an opening in the floor. The damper, usually constructed of steel plate with welded angle reinforcing hinged on one side, closes by gravity against an embedded angle frame of the opening. The opening mechanism is usually a shaft sprocket-and-chain device. The drive motor and gear drive must develop sufficient force to open the damper door against the maximum static pressure difference the fan can develop. This pressure can be obtained from fan performance curves. Limit switches start and stop the gear-motor drive at the proper position.

Dampers placed in ducts other than vertical should be the multiple-blade louver type. These dampers usually consist of a rugged channel frame whose flanges are bolted to the flanges of the fan, duct, or duct opening. Louver blades are mounted on shafts that turn in bearings mounted on the outside of the channel frame. This arrangement requires accessible space on the outside of the duct for bearing and shaft lubrication and maintenance, and space for operating linkages. Louver dampers should have edge and end seals to make them airtight.

The trapdoor-type damper, if properly fabricated, is inherently airtight due to its weight and overlap at its edges. However, louver dampers must be carefully constructed to ensure tightness upon closing. A damper that leaks under pressure will cause the fan to rotate counter to its power rotation, thus making restarting dangerous and possibly damaging the drive motor.

SUPPLY AIR INTAKE

Supply air intakes require careful design to ensure that the quality of air drawn into the system is the best available. Such factors as recirculation of exhaust air or intake of contaminants from nearby sources should be considered.

Louvers or grillwork are usually installed over air intakes for aesthetic, security, or safety reasons. Bird screens are also important if openings between louver blades or grillwork are large enough to allow birds to enter.

Louvers with sufficiently low face velocities to be weatherproof may not be possible in certain ventilation systems, due to the large quantities of intake air required. Therefore, intake plenums, shafts, fan rooms, and fan housings need water drains. Blowing snow can also fill the fan room or plenum with drifts of snow, but this usually will not stop the ventilation system from operating satisfactorily.

Situations may require installing noise elimination devices in fresh air intakes to keep fan and air noise from disturbing the outside environment. If sound reduction is required, it should be investigated as a total system—the fan, the fan plenum, the building, fan housing, and the air intake (location and size). In designing the sound reduction system, fan selection should also be based on a total system, including the pressure drop that results from sound attenuation devices.

EXHAUST OUTLETS

The discharge of exhaust air should be remote from the street level or from areas with human occupancy. Contaminant concentrations in this exhaust air are not of concern if the system is working effectively. However, odors and entrained particulate matter make this air undesirable in occupied areas. Exhaust stack discharge velocity should be high enough to facilitate dispersion of contaminants into the atmosphere. A minimum of 2,000 fpm (10 m/s) is usually necessary.

In the past, evase outlets were used to regain some static pressure and, thereby, reduce the energy consumption by the exhaust fan. Unless the fan discharge velocity is in excess of 2,000 fpm (10 m/s), however, the energy savings compared to the cost of the evase is questionable.

In a vertical or near-vertical exhaust fan discharge connection to an exhaust duct or shaft, rain water will run down the inside of the stack into the fan. Experience has shown that this water will dissolve material deposited from vehicle exhausts on the inner surface of the stack and become extremely corrosive. The fan housing should be fabricated of a corrosion resistant material or be specially coated to protect the metal of the housing from corrosion.

REFERENCES

American Conference of Governmental Industrial Hygienists. *Industrial Ventilation, A Manual of Recommended Practice*, 11th Edition.

ASHRAE. 1975. Laboratory Methods of Testing Fans for Rating. *ASHRAE Standard 51-75.*

Ball, D. and Campbell, J. 1973. Lighting, heating and ventilation in multistory and underground car park. (Paper presented at the Institution for Structural Engineers and The Institution of Highway Engineers' Joint Conference on Multi-story and Underground Car Parks, May 16-17.)

EPA. Average emission factors for highway vehicles for selected calendar years. *Supplement No. 7 for Compilation of Air Pollutant Emission Factors*, 3rd Edition, Table I-3.

Federal Register. 1974. Vol. 39, No. 125 (June).

Hama, G.M.; Frederick, W.G.; and Monteith, H.G. 1974. How to design ventilation systems for underground garages. *Air Engineering* (a study by the Detroit Bureau of Industrial Hygiene), Detroit. April.

Ricker, E.R. The Traffic Design of Parking Garages. *ENO Foundation for Highway Traffic Control.*

Round, F.G. and Pearall, H.W. Diesel Exhaust Odor: Its Evaluation and Relation to Exhaust Gas Composition. Research Laboratories, General Motors Corporation, *Society of Automotive Engineers Technical Progress Series*, Vol. 6.

Singstad, O. 1929. Ventilation of Vehicular Tunnels. Tokyo, Japan: World Engineering Congress.

The Research Corporation of New England. 1979. Contaminant Level Control in Parking Garages. *ASHRAE Research Project*, Corporation of America, April 25.

Turk, A. 1963. Measurement of odorous vapors in test chambers: theoretical. *ASHRAE Journal*. Oct.

U.S. Department of Transportation. 1976. *Subway Environmental Design Handbook*, Urban Mass Transportation Administration, U.S. Government Printing Office.

Wendell, R.E.; Norco, J.E.; and Croke, K.G. 1973. Emission prediction and control strategy: evaluation and pollution from transportation systems. *Air Pollution Control Association Journal*. Feb.

CHAPTER 30

LABORATORIES

THE research laboratory requires regulation of temperature, humidity, air pressure, air motion, air cleanliness, light, sound, and vibration. Information needed for design include room conditions, research equipment heat loads, air flow patterns, contaminant control, sound levels, vibration limits, and any special user requirements. Local requirements about "energy use limits" is an important topic in the predesign effort because laboratories require more energy for HVAC than offices, stores, etc. The development of these parameters requires frequent communication between the designer, the researcher, and the researcher's safety office. The designer must obtain all HVAC performance information and explain the operational capabilities and limitations of the proposed design to the laboratory user before design can begin. The initial approval of the user's Safety Officer and Laboratory Director is essential.

Because all research programs change, the occupancy and arrangement of laboratory space is altered frequently. A successful laboratory can accommodate these changes (within the limits of the design) without major alteration and interference to adjacent areas. The HVAC system should have flexibility so changes can be made with minimal alteration to HVAC equipment. The HVAC system does not need an initial capacity of 100% of the ultimate needs.

Early mutual agreement can prevent redesign and improve the final result a facility that meets the needs of the current and potential future research programs. The HVAC engineer should develop a 10-year concept of the laboratory use and then design a facility to meet this long-range plan.

Most aging laboratory facilities (over 15 years old) need extensive HVAC renovation. A survey (Kiil 1984) indicated that 43% of the nation's research facilities are more than 20 years old and that they lack mechanical services to support current research needs. Due to rapidly changing research procedures and environmental requirements, many newer facilities may also need renovation.

RISK ASSESSMENT

Laboratory research always involves some risk. Relative risks for work with infectious agents, radioactive materials, and toxic substances have been documented. Recently, research has been directed toward oncogenic viruses, chemical carcinogens, and modification of genetic information in microorganisms (recombinant DNA). Pike (1976) summarizes laboratory-associated infections that occurred in the United States and in foreign countries through 1974. The data show that a high fatality rate from laboratory-acquired infections can occur and points to the fact that risk assessment (involving the HVAC design engineer) and safe laboratory operation can be a life and death matter. Currently, laboratory associated infections have decreased from the peak decade of 1945 through 1954. This trend may be due to increased awareness of the hazards of working with infectious agents, as well as the increased use of safety devices (fume hoods and biological safety cabinets) and other safety features included in recent laboratory designs.

After the design purpose and scope have been determined, risk assessment is the next task that must be completed before a laboratory can be designed. Table 1 shows guidelines to assess risk. A typical laboratory room may require several laboratory safety guidelines.

The design engineer must consult the scientific staff and the health and safety personnel to obtain a risk assessment (from them) of the risk of the materials and procedures to be used over the life of the proposed laboratories. The design team (the architect, engineer, and manager) translates this risk assessment into the proper design approach. The design team should then visit similar laboratories to guide them in their design. But each research laboratory is unique, and its design must be evaluated using current standards and practices, rather than duplicating the designs of outmoded existing facilities.

Table 1 Compilation of Laboratory Safety Guidelines

Laboratory Safety	Fundamentals of Industrial Hygiene (National Safety Council 1979)
Microbiological and Biomedical Safety	Biosafety in Microbiological and Biomedical Laboratories (DHHS 1984)
Recombinant DNA	Guidelines for Research Involving Recombinant DNA Molecules (DHHS 1986)
Oncogenic (cancer causing) viral agents	Safety Standards for Research Involving Oncogenic Virus (DHHS 1974)
	Design Criteria for Viral Oncology Research Facilities (DHHS 1975)
Chemical Carcinogens	OSHA Safety and Health Standards (See current standards)
	Prudent Practices for Handling Hazardous Chemicals in Laboratories (National Research Council 1981)
	Handling Chemical Carcinogens in the Laboratory - Problems of Safety (International Agency for Research on Cancer 1979)
	NIH Guidelines for the Laboratory Use of Chemical Carcinogens (DHHS 1981)
Fire Safety	Fire Protection for Laboratories Using Chemicals (National Fire Protection Association 1982)
	Laboratories in Health-Related Institutions (National Fire Protection Association 1980)

The preparation of this chapter is assigned to TC 9.2, Industrial Air Conditioning.

The nature of the contaminant, the quantities present, the types of operations, and the degree of hazard dictate the type of containment and local exhaust devices. For personnel convenience, those operations posing lower degrees of hazard are conducted in devices that use air currents for personnel protection, e.g., laboratory fume hoods and biological safety cabinets; however, these devices do not provide absolute containment. Operations that have a significant hazard potential are conducted in devices that provide greater protection but are more restrictive, e.g., sealed glove boxes. Glove boxes require far less exhaust air than laboratory fume hoods and biological safety cabinets. Laboratories for low and moderate hazard work may, therefore, have greater exhaust air requirements than laboratories for high hazard work. Laboratory exhaust air requirements are determined by the type, number, size, and operating frequency of the containment devices. These requirements are critical in system design and in establishing supply air rates and flow patterns. The research laboratory design should include the following criteria:

1. Design is economical to construct and operate.
2. Design meets the requirements for safe management of the various hazards encountered.
3. Design facilitates research productivity.
4. Design is sufficiently flexible to accommodate changes in research programs.
5. Safety features designed into the laboratory closely match the assessed degree of risk of the research (West 1978).

DESIGN CONDITIONS AND THERMAL LOSS

Dry-bulb temperature and wet-bulb temperature (or relative humidity), with specified tolerances for each value, define indoor conditions. These temperatures should be based upon agreements with the research staff (user) and upon a ten-year plan for the facility use. Table 2 presents recommended design conditions for typical laboratories and offices. Indoor design conditions for laboratory animal rooms are presented later in this chapter. The designer should determine whether a stated set of conditions represents the limiting values or the levels to be maintained. For variable temperature rooms, it is necessary to establish the humidity requirements for the specified dry-bulb range or at selected dry-bulb temperatures.

Heat and vapor from the laboratory equipment substantially adds to the room sensible and latent loads. Table 3 presents information about this major heat gain. Alereza and Breen (1984) provide additional information about other equipment. The designer needs to evaluate equipment nameplate ratings, applicable load and use factors, and the overall diversity factor. Heat released by equipment located in chemical fume hoods can be discounted. Equipment that is directly vented or water-cooled should have appropriate reductions made in the heat released to the room. Any unconditioned auxiliary air that is not captured by the fume hood must be included in the room's load calculation.

Table 2   Thermally Acceptable Conditions For Laboratories and Offices

Season	Temperature	Dewpoint Min.	Dewpoint Max.
Winter	71 °F (21.7 °C)	35 °F (1.7 °C)	62 °F (16.7 °C)
Summer	76 °F (24.4 °C)	35 °F (1.7 °C)	62 °F (16.7 °C)

Source: ASHRAE Standard 55-1981, Thermal Environmental Conditions for Human Occupancy.

Laboratory (room) cooling and heating loads are always highly variable due to the operation of laboratory equipment. For this reason, individual laboratory rooms should always have separate thermostats.

Laboratories that contain harmful substances should be designed and field balanced so that air flows into the laboratory from adjacent (clean) spaces and corridors.

Exhaust of contaminants from the laboratory to the atmosphere requires conditioning of large quantities of outdoor air. Laboratories requiring 100% outdoor air require large HVAC equipment and consume large amounts of energy. Thus, the selection of outdoor conditions affect the size and cost of refrigeration and heating facilities.

SUPPLY SYSTEMS

The minimum unit served by the air supply is the laboratory module, such as a 10 by 20 ft (3 by 6 m) room. The room size, physical arrangement, occupancy, type of exhaust system, and economics contribute to determining the type of supply air system.

Air may be supplied at high-, medium-, or low-pressure and through single-duct, dual-duct, and terminal reheat systems. Air may be introduced into the laboratory through ceiling diffusers, sidewall grilles, perforated ceiling panels, or outlets under windows. The important factor is whether the air supply satisfies safe operating conditions.

Refer to Chapter 14 of the 1985 FUNDAMENTALS Volume for information on the locations for supply air system intakes and the flow of air around buildings. It is very important to consider air flow around laboratory buildings because exhaust air, which is often untreated, may reenter and contaminate the laboratory rooms.

Caution must be used when a Variable Air Volume (VAV) system for makeup air is used to ensure that the room pressure changes do not affect the performance of the exhaust hoods within the room. The design must ensure that any recirculated, filtered air is not contaminating the lab or its occupants. Constant monitoring of the recirculated air and an alarm to the laboratory will ensure that occupants can evacuate, if necessary.

Filtration

The filtration necessary for supply air depends on the activity in the laboratory. Conventional chemistry and physics laboratories commonly have 85% efficient filters (ASHRAE Standard 52-76 Test Method). Biomedical laboratories usually require 85 to 95% efficient filters. High Efficiency Particulate Air (HEPA) filters should be provided for special spaces where research materials or animals are particularly susceptible to contamination from external sources. HEPA filtration of the supply air is considered necessary in only the most critical applications such as environmental studies, specific pathogenfree ("SPF") research animals, "nude mice," dust-sensitive work, and electronic assemblies. In many instances, biological safety cabinets (which are HEPA filtered), rather than HEPA filtration for the entire room, are satisfactory.

Air Distribution

Air supplied to a laboratory space must keep temperature gradients and air turbulence to a minimum, especially near the face of the laboratory fume hoods and biological safety cabinets. It is very important that air outlets not discharge into the face of fume hoods. The large quantities of supply air can best be introduced through perforated plate air outlets or diffusers designed for large air volumes. The air supply should not discharge on a fire detector, since this will slow its response.

**Table 3 (IP) Recommended Rate of Heat Gain From Hospital Equipment
Located in the Air-Conditioned Area (Inch-Pound Units)**

Appliance Type	Size	Maximum Input Rating, Btu/h	Recommended Rate of Heat Gain, Btu/h[a]
Autoclave (bench)	0.7 ft^3	4270	480
Bath, hot or cold circ., small	1.0 to 9.7 gallons, -22 to 212°F	2560 to 6140	440 to 1060[s]
			850 to 2010[l]
Blood analyser	120 samples/hour	2510	2510
Blood analyser with CRT screen	115 samples/hour	5120	5120
Centrifuge (large)	8 to 24 places	3750	3580
Centrifuge (small)	4 to 12 places	510	480
Chromatograph	---	6820	6820
Cytometer (Cell sorter/analyser)	1000 cells/second	73230	73230
Electrophoresis power supply	---	1360	850
Freezer, blood plasma, medium	13 ft^3, down to -40°F	340[b]	136[b]
Hot plate, concentric ring	4 holes, 212°F	3750	2970
Incubator, CO_2	5 to 10 ft^3, up to 130°F	9660	4810
Incubator, forced draft	10 ft^3, 80 to 140°F	2460	1230
Incubator, general application	1.4 to 11 ft^3, up to 160°F	160 to 220[b]	80 to 110[b]
Magnetic stirrer	---	2050	2050
Microcomputer	16 to 256 kbytes[c]	341 to 2047	300 to 1800
Minicomputer	---	7500 to 15000	7500 to 15000
Oven, general purpose, small	1.4 to 2.8 ft^3, 460°F	2120[b]	290[b]
Refrigerator, laboratory	22 to 106 ft^3, 39°F	80[d]	34[d]
Refrigerator, blood, small	7 to 20 ft^3, 39°F	260[b]	102[b]
Spectrophotometer	---	1710	1710
Sterilizer, freestanding	3.9 ft^3, 212 to 270°F	71400	8100
Ultrasonic cleaner, small	1.4 ft^3	410	410
Washer, glassware	7.8 ft^3 load area	15220	10000
Water still	5 to 15 gallons	14500[e]	320[c]

[a]For hospital equipment installed under a hood, the heat gain is assumed to be zero.
[b]Heat gain per cubic foot of interior space
[c]Input is not proportional to memory size
[d]Heat gain per 10 ft^3 of interior space
[e]Heat gain per gallon of capacity
[s]Sensible heat
[l]Latent heat

Source: T. Alereza and J. Breen III: Estimates of recommended heat gains due to commercial appliances and equipment. 1984. ASHRAE Transactions, Vol. 90, Pt. 2, No. 2828.

Sidewall grilles are acceptable if their terminal velocity, location, and air distribution patterns are analyzed and are consistent with the ceiling system's space requirements. Cost savings are sometimes realized by not extending the supply air ductwork into the room, but careful evaluation of air distribution in needed. Sidewall outlets may best serve the interior portion of a deep laboratory (over 10 to 15 ft. or 3 to 5 m), whereas the exterior is best served from other outlets.

Air outlets discharging through the window sill may be either at the terminal of a supply duct or at the discharge of a terminal reheat induction unit. In either case, the air should discharge up along the window. Supply grilles in the floor should be avoided because discharge from these grilles entrain dirt from the floor and distribute it into the room. In some special applications, they may be used if the air must enter near equipment in the center of an open space. Provisions for cleanout and modifications to elevate the grille face above the floor are necessary.

Some general air distribution guidelines are (Caplin and Knutson 1978):

1. Terminal velocity of supply air jets (near hoods) is at least as important as hood face velocity in the range of 50 to 150 fpm (0.25 to 0.75 m/s) face velocity.
2. The terminal throw velocity of supply air jets (near hoods) should be less than the hood face velocity, preferably no more than one-half to two-thirds the face velocity. Such terminal throw velocities are far less than those for conventional room air supply.
3. Perforated ceiling panels provide a better supply system than grilles or ceiling diffusers because the system design criteria

are simpler and easier to apply, and precise adjustment of fixtures is not required. Ceiling panels also permit a greater concentration of hoods than do wall grilles or ceiling diffusers.

4. Wall grilles or registers should have double deflection louvers set for maximum deflection. The terminal velocity (near hoods) should be less than half of the face of the velocity of the hood.
5. If the wall grilles are located on the wall adjacent to the hood, the supply air jet should be above the top of the hood face opening. If possible, grilles on the adjacent wall cause less spillage than grilles located on the opposite wall, for equal terminal throw velocities.
6. The terminal throw velocity from ceiling diffusers at the hood face should be less than the hood face velocity.
7. Diffusers should be kept away from the front of the hood face. A larger number of smaller diffusers would be an advantage, if the necessary low terminal velocity can be maintained.
8. Blocking the quadrant of the ceiling diffuser blowing at the hood face results in less spillage.
9. Perforated ceiling panels should be sized so the panel face velocity is less than the hood face velocity, preferable no more than two-thirds of the hood face velocity.
10. Perforated ceiling panels should be placed so that approximately one-third or more of the panel area is remote (more than 4 ft. or 1.2 m) from the hood.
11. Additional tests are needed to determine laboratory fume hood performance; Peterson et. al. (1983) indicate that the only way to determine hood effectiveness is to test the specific hood under actual room conditions.

Table 3 (SI) Recommended Rate of Heat Gain From Hospital Equipment Located in the Air Conditioned Area (SI Units)

Appliance Type	Size	Maximum Input Rating, Watts	Recommended Rate of Heat Gain, Watts[a]
Autoclave (bench)	0.02 m^3	1250	140
Bath, hot or cold circ., small	3.7 to 36.7 litres, -30 to 100 °C	750 to 1800	130 to 310[s] 250 to 590[l]
Blood analyser	120 samples/hour	735	735
Blood analyser with CRT screen	115 samples/hour	1500	1500
Centrifuge (large)	8 to 24 places	1100	1050
Centrifuge (small)	4 to 12 places	150	140
Chromatograph	---	2000	2000
Cytometer (Cell sorter/analyser)	1000 cells/second	21 460	21 460
Electrophoresis power supply	---	400	250
Freezer, blood plasma, medium	0.37 m^3, down to -40 °C	3530[b]	1410[b]
Hot plate, concentric ring	4 holes, 100 °C	1100	870
Incubator, CO_2	0.14 to 0.28 m^3, up to 55 °C	2830	1410
Incubator, forced draft	0.28 m^3, 27 to 60 °C	720	360
Incubator, general application	0.04 to 0.31 m^3, up to 70 °C	1660 to 2260[b]	850 to 1130[b]
Magnetic stirrer	---	600	600
Microcomputer	16 to 256 kbytes[c]	100 to 600	88 to 528
Minicomputer	---	2200 to 6000	2200 to 6600
Oven, general purpose, small	0.04 to 0.08 m^3, 240 °C	21 900[b]	2970[b]
Refrigerator, laboratory	0.63 to 3.0 m^3, 4 °C	880[d]	350[d]
Refrigerator, blood, small	0.20 to 0.56 m^3, 4 °C	2680[b]	1060[b]
Spectrophotometer	---	500	500
Sterilizer, freestanding	0.11 m^3, 100 to 132 °C	20 900	2370
Ultrasonic cleaner, small	0.04 m^3	120	120
Washer, glassware	0.22 m^3 load area	4460	2930
Water still	19 to 57 litres	1120[e]	25[e]

[a]For hospital equipment installed under a hood, the heat gain is assumed to be zero.
[b]Heat gain per cubic metre of interior space
[c]Input is not proportional to memory size
[d]Heat gain per 10 m^3 of interior space
[e]Heat gain per litre of capacity
[s]Sensible heat
[l]Latent heat

Source: T. Alereza and J. Breen III: Estimates of recommended heat gains due to commercial appliances and equipment. 1984. ASHRAE Transactions, Vol. 90, Pt. 2, No. 2828.

Unitary Systems

The most adaptable form of air supply consists of a separate air handling unit for each laboratory space. Each unit is made up of a fan and air treatment apparatus with a capacity equal to that required to maintain space temperature and to balance the exhaust air requirements. The unit typically contains a cooling coil, heating coil, humidifier, and filter. It is serviced with electricity, chilled water, and steam or hot water.

The unitary system shuts down when its operation is not required. It can be designed to match exhaust fan capacity and can be regulated to balance exhaust quantities, if they are variable. Each unit is capable of delivering sufficient heating and/or cooling to satisfy the peak requirements of the space it serves. Each unit is also capable of separately reducing the heating and cooling capacity as the load in the laboratory space varies. Also, laboratories not requiring continuous service can be shut down without disrupting other laboratories.

The unitary system, when constructed to high quality standards, is initially expensive, takes considerable space, and is often costly to maintain. Its chief application is for isolated laboratory spaces and for buildings where hours of operation are irregular. Unitary equipment with limited air treatment capabilities is used to supplement central apparatus in areas where the central system would be overloaded.

In biomedical laboratories, the installation of unitary systems is discouraged where the cooling coil with condensate drip pan and roughing filter would be located within the laboratory. The moisture associated with the coil and drip pan and the dust-collecting areas of the unit contribute to growth and dissemination of molds and other organisms commonly found in the environment. These organisms may be undesirable contaminants to experimental cultures, specimens, and biological products.

Central Systems

The simplest form of a central system that can be sucessfully applied to a laboratory subjected to variations in internal heat gain is a constant volume terminal reheat system in which the supply air is conditioned to (1) a dry-bulb temperature that will satisfy the maximum sensible heat release in any space and (2) a dewpoint satisfactory for maintenance of room humidity within an acceptable range. Variations in heat gain in individual laboratory modules can be thermostatically controlled by reheat coils in the branch duct serving each space.

This system is economical if (1) close humidity control is not critical; (2) internal heat gains are moderate and fairly constant within a space and do not vary greatly between spaces; and (3) the exhaust air quantities are constant and in balance with the supply air necessary to maintain space conditions.

Hours of occupancy or operation for each laboratory space should be approximately the same, since the entire central system must be in operation if any one space is being used. Many laboratories operate 24 hours a day or on a similar work schedule, so this requirement does not always impose a hardship.

Central systems with supplementary conditioning or central systems with auxiliary air supply should be considered when (1) heat gains are high and subject to variation and (2) the exhaust air quantities are greater than supply air requirements for cooling.

EXHAUST SYSTEMS

The total volume of air required for a research laboratory is often dictated by the number and size of the fume hoods and biological safety cabinets. One fume hood may exhaust over 1,000 cfm (500 L/s) and thus determine the amount of supply air to a room. The designer should discuss the impact of fume hood requirements with the research staff. Often, a smaller 4-ft. (1.2-m) or a larger 6-ft. (1.8-m) fume hood with a smaller opening should be considered. In some situations, the research staff may not need all of the hoods initially installed; relocation of hoods could be planned to meet future requirements. An alternative is to have common support laboratories with laboratory fume hoods and biological safety cabinets available for several research groups. This alternative is frequently acceptable to the researchers because it enables them to obtain additional research space in their own laboratory space.

A laboratory module may not initially require a laboratory fume hood or biological safety cabinet, but the laboratory should be capable of accommodating these units at a later date. Sometimes, a small local exhaust for special equipment will suffice rather than an expensive laboratory fume hood.

Another alternative is the horizontal sliding sash fume hood. These hoods require considerably less exhaust air for the same face velocity, thus lowering energy costs substantially. Additional information is provided later in this chapter.

Laboratory exhaust systems can be classified as: (1) constant volume or (2) variable volume based on the laboratory fume hood and biological safety cabinet characteristics and the method of system operation and control. These classifications can be further divided into (1) individual, (2) central, or (3) combination systems, based on the arrangement of the major system components such as the fans, plenums, or duct mains and branches.

Heider (1972) presents a thorough overview of the design parameters of exhaust systems for research laboratories.

Degenhardt and Pfost (1983) describe a recent design of hospital laboratory fume hood exhaust system. Sessler and Hoover (1983) describe ways to avoid high noise levels sometimes generated by the laboratory fume hood exhaust system.

All laboratory fume hoods and safety cabinets should be equipped with visual and audible alarms to warn the laboratory workers of unsafe air flows.

Variable Volume Exhaust Systems

The decision to select a variable volume exhaust system should not be made without the understanding and approval of the research staff and local safety officials. The level of sophistication and ability of the maintenance staff to maintain such a complex system is also a very important consideration.

In many laboratories, all hoods and safety cabinets are seldom needed at the same time. Thus, a laboratory that permits a usage diversity factor allows the exhaust system to have less capacity than that required for the full operation of all units. Even if the exhaust system is sized for full operation of all units, reducing the air flow during periods when some of the hoods and safety cabinets are not in use reduces operational (energy) costs.

Exhaust air volume may be reduced by a velocity-controlled hood. In addition, the hood velocity remains constant when the hood face opening is partially closed. A sensing element responds to changes in hood face velocity and operates a volume control device (inlet vanes, discharge damper, or variable speed drive) to maintain the face velocity within the desired range. In large central systems, a volume control device gives a satisfactory control for branch ducts, but system volume regulation must be supplemented by static pressure regulators (in the exhaust plenums) to control fan air volume. A hood served by an individual fan

may obtain constant face velocity with either a duct control device or fan control device. Complete exhaust air system shutdown may cause cold air and contaminants to enter the laboratory through the exhaust system. Variable volume exhaust systems allow more freedom in the installation of the hoods and safety cabinets because the number of units that may be connected are not entirely dependent on the capacity of the exhaust system.

Variable volume systems are difficult to balance and control, and they are less stable in operation than constant volume systems. These systems require extensive instrumentation and controls that, in turn, cause high installation and maintenance costs. Balancing dampers in exhaust ducts are prohibited by codes for some applications. In a corrosive atmosphere, reliability of variable volume control equipment is highly questionable.

A potential hazard of diversified variable volume system occurs when the collective area of operating hood and safety cabinet openings exceeds design opening diversity values. If this condition occurs, the proper face velocity requirements will not be achieved and laboratory personnel could be endangered. If, on the other hand, total usage is less than design values, bypass devices may be required on hoods to maintain supply air rates, provide adequate thermal capacity, and ensure air balance and flow patterns.

Individual Exhaust Systems

Individual exhaust systems include a separate exhaust connection, exhaust fan, and discharge duct for each laboratory fume hood or biological safety cabinet. This arrangement is extremely flexible because the exhaust for the fume hood or biological safety cabinet does not directly affect the operation of any other area. The system permits selective operation of individual hoods and safety cabinets merely by the starting or stopping of the fan motor. Shutdowns for repair or maintenance are localized. The unitary arrangement permits selective application of (1) special exhaust air filtration; (2) special duct and fan construction for corrosive effluents; (3) emergency power connections to selective fan motor; and (4) off-hour operation.

Individual exhaust fans are simple to balance and, when installed with a constant volume supply air system, provide a stable and easily controlled system. The recommended operation is to keep exhaust fans on at all times and to interlock them electrically with the supply fans so that if any critical exhaust fan is shut down, the supply fans will shut down automatically. The individual exhaust system requires more fans than central systems and there are usually more overall duct shaft space requirements because of the many small ducts. The use of more fans also increases capital and maintenance costs.

Most research laboratories require directional air flow from the corridor into the laboratory to contain airborne contamination. The shutdown of individual exhaust systems will upset the proper directional air flow and cause hazardous contaminants and odors to flow out of the laboratory and into the corridor and adjacent rooms. If such a system is considered, appropriate precautions (such as air locks) should be installed to prevent reverse air flow.

Central Exhaust Systems

Central exhaust systems consist of one fan, a common suction plenum, and branch connections to multiple exhaust terminals. Central exhaust systems are generally less costly in capital and maintenance than individual exhaust systems. Central exhaust systems frequently have standby fans. Central systems are more difficult to balance initially and require periodic rebalancing to ensure proper air flow. The effects of mixing of effluents from different research operations must also be considered with central systems.

The central exhaust system is best for exhausting similar types of units such as laboratory fume hoods. The exhausting of laboratory fume hoods, biological safety cabinets, and special filtered units with one central system is almost impossible because there are different pressure losses in the different types of laboratory hoods and biological safety cabinets. Another major problem is the varying, uneven filter loading.

Exhaust Fans and Ductwork

Exhaust fans that handle contaminants should always be located outside of occupied building areas and be very close to the point of discharge. The ductwork on the discharge side of the fan should be sealed airtight. It is easy for air leakage from and unsealed, pressurized exhaust duct to contaminate a mechanical equipment room or an entire building. The fan discharge should be connected directly to the vertical discharge stack without connections to other exhaust systems.

Table 4 presents ranges of exhaust dust velocities. An exhaust fan should discharge into a vertical stack usually extending 7 ft (2.1 m) above any obstructions on the roof. The stack should have a terminal velocity of about 2,500 fpm (12.7 m/s) and discharge the exhaust air above the building envelope. Refer to "Air Flow Around Buildings," Chapter 14 in the 1985 FUNDAMENTALS Volume, for information about recirculation of building exhaust air back into fresh air intakes. Discharges (rain caps, mushroom-type roof exhausters, etc.) that direct the exhaust air down toward the roof should be avoided because they concentrate the exhaust air and may contaminate the building's fresh air intakes (Heider 1972). Care must also be taken to discharge the exhaust away from any present or future air intakes. Exhaust fans should have adjustable V-belt drives to allow field balancing of the system.

Materials and Construction

The selection of materials and the construction of exhaust ductwork and fans depend on the following:

- Nature of the effluents
- Ambient temperature
- Lengths and arrangement of duct runs
- Method of hood fan operation
- Flame and smoke spread rating
- Duct velocities and pressures
- Effluent temperature

Effluents may be classified generically as organic or inorganic chemical gases, vapors, fumes, or smokes; and qualitatively as acids, alkalis, solvents, or oils. Exhaust system ducts, fans, and coatings are subject to corrosion, which destroys metal by chemical or electrochemical action; dissolution, which dissolves materials (coatings and plastics are subject to this action, particularly by solvent and oil effluents); and melting, which can occur in certain plastics and coatings at elevated hood operating temperatures.

Commonly used reagents in laboratories include hydrochloric, sulfuric, and nitric acid (singularly or in combination) and ammonium hydroxide. Common organic chemicals include acetone, benzene, ether, petroleum ether, chloroform, carbon tetrachloride, and acetic acid.

Ambient temperature of the space in which ductwork and fans are located affects the condensation of vapors in the exhaust system. Condensation contributes to the corrosion of metals with or without the presence of chemicals.

Ductwork is less subject to attack when the runs are short and direct and when flow is maintained at reasonable (higher) velocities. The longer the duct, the longer the exposure to effluents and the greater the degree of condensation. Horizontal runs provide surfaces where moisture can remain longer than it may on vertical surfaces. If condensation is probable, provide sloped ductwork and condensate drains. (The condensate drains may accumulate hazardous materials.)

Fan operation may be continuous or intermittent. Intermittent fan operation may allow longer periods of wetness due to condensation than would continuous fan operation.

Flame and smoke spread rating requirements established by codes and insurance underwriters must also be considered in selecting ductwork materials.

The procedures and recommendations for the selection of materials and construction are as follows:

1. Determine the types of effluents (and possible combinations of effluents) that will be generated in the hood and handled by the exhaust system. Consider both present and future operations.
2. Classify the effluents as organic or inorganic and whether they occur in gaseous, vapor, or particulate form. Also, classify decontamination materials, if used.
3. Determine the concentration of the reagents that will be used and the temperature of the effluents at the hood exhaust port. In research laboratories, this determination is almost impossible.
4. Estimate the highest probable dew point of the effluents.
5. Determine the ambient temperature of the spaces where the ductwork will be routed and in which the exhaust fans are located.
6. Consider the length and arrangement of duct runs and how they may affect the periods of exposure to fumes and the degree of condensation that may occur.
7. Consider the effects of intermittent versus continuous fan operation. If intermittent operation is desired, provide a time delay (about one hour) to dry wet surfaces before fan shutdown. Intermittent operation can easily unbalance air flows in the laboratory and cause unsafe conditions; continuous operation during working hours is better.

Table 4 Range of Design Duct Velocities for Exhaust System

Nature of Contaminant	Examples of Exhaust Materials	Desired Velocity Range fpm, (m/s)
Vapors, gases, smoke	All vapors, gases, and smokes	1,000 - 1,200 (5.1 - 6.1)
Fumes	Zinc and aluminum oxide fumes	1,400 - 2,000 (7.1 - 10.2)
Very fine, light dust	Cotton lint, wood flour, litho powder	2,000 - 2,500 (10.2 - 12.7)
Dry dust and powders	Cotton dust, light shavings	2,500 - 3,500 (12.7 - 17.8)

Source: American Conference of Government Industrial Hygienists. 1984. *Industrial Ventilation: A Manual of Recommended Practice.* Edward Brothers, Ann Arbor, Michigan, pp. 4-7.

8. Determine whether insulation, watertight construction, slope, and drains will be required.
9. Select materials and construction most suitable for the application by considering the following:
   a. resistance to chemical attack
   b. weight
   c. flame and smoke spread rating
   d. installation and maintenance costs

Standard references and manufacturers have information on material properties. Materials for chemical fume exhaust duct systems and their characteristics include the following:

Glazed Tile: resistant to practically all corrosive agents except hydrofluoric acid; heavy in weight, limited to round sections, joint sealants subject to attack, considerable space required for directional changes; material costs low, installation costs high.

Cementatious Material: highly resistant, porous surface requires an internal impervious coating to prevent retention of potentially flammable materials; limited to round sections because of the difficulty in sealing joints, constructing directional changes and transitions, and bracing and supporting rectangular sections; joint sealants subject to attack; cost moderately high.

Galvanized Iron: subject to acid and alkali attack, particularly at cut edges and under wet conditions; easily formed; low in cost.

Stainless Steel: subject to acid and chloride compound attack varying with the chromium and nickel content of the alloy; relatively high in cost. (The higher the alloy content, the higher the resistance. Stainless steels range from the commercial 200 to the 400 alloy series, with ascending chromium and nickel content to proprietary alloys with custom chromium and nickel composition. (Costs increase with chromium and nickel content.)

Asphaltum Coated Steel: resistant to acids; subject to solvent and oil attack; high flame and smoke spread rating; base metal vulnerable when exposed by coating imperfections and cut edges; moderate cost.

Epoxy Coated Steel: epoxy phenolic resin coatings on mild black steel can be selected for particular characteristics and applications; these have been successfully applied for both specific and general use, but no one compound is inert or resistive to all effluents; requires sand blast surface preparation for shop applied coating and field touchup of coating imperfections; cost is moderate.

Fiberglass: particularly good for acid applications including hydrofluoric, when additional glaze coats are provided.

Plastic Materials: have particular resistance properties to particular corrosive effluents; their limitations are in physical strength, flame spread rating, heat distortion, and high cost of fabrication.

10. Select fans constructed of the same materials as the ductwork or of mild steel with a suitable coating.
11. Provide outboard bearings, shaft seals, access doors, and multiple 200% rated belts for hood exhaust fans. Bearings should have a minimum L-10 life of 100,000 hours.
12. Design the ductwork and select the fan with consideration of potential fire and explosive hazard. Ductwork must meet flame spread and other requirements, as described in NFPA Standards.
13. For some systems, such as perchloric acid hoods, provide wash-down capability.
14. Develop layouts so that ducts may be easily inspected, decontaminated, and replaced, if necessary.

Exhaust Air Filtration

Depending on the hazard level assoicated with the laboratory operation and the degree of physical containment desired, filtration facilities for exhaust systems may be required. The hazardous or obnoxious pollutants to be removed from the exhaust air may be particulate and/or gaseous in nature.

Dry media filters, e.g., 95% efficient by ASHRAE Standard 52-68 Test Method, or HEPA filters (99.97% efficient by DOP Test Method) may be required to meet specified design criteria. The filter assembly may include a pre-filter for coarse particle separation and a filter enclosure arranged for ready access and easy transfer of the contaminated filter to a disposal enclosure. Manufactured filter enclosures that feature bag-in/bag-out filter changing should be considered for hazardous exhaust situations. A procedure for testing of the filter system integrity and suitable test openings is also necessary. A damper is often added to balance airflow by compensating for the change in the resistance of the HEPA filter.

For convenient handling, replacement, and disposal, with minimum hazard to personnel, the filter should be: (1) located immediately outside the laboratory area, unless it is an integral part of a safety cabinet or hood; (2) located on the suction side of the exhaust fan; (3) installed in adequate space that provides free, unobstructed access; and (4) positioned at a convenient working height. Some installations will require shutoff dampers and hardware for filter decontamination in the ductwork. The filter should be located on the suction side of the exhaust fan and as close as practical to the source of contamination (laboratory) to minimize the length of contaminated ductwork. Parallel redundant filters and bypass arrangements should be considered for continuous operation of exhaust systems during filter change. Static pressure monitors should be placed across filter and pre-filter banks to help determine time for filter change and damper adjustment.

Wet collectors or adsorption systems, such as activated charcoal, are often satisfactory for the removal of gas-phase toxic or odorous pollutants from exhaust air. In designing the installation of these devices, the safety of maintenance and service personnel, the potential of concentrations of exhaust materials, and the frequency of filter replacement must be considered. When using charcoal filters, it is important to provide a gas monitoring system to determine time for changeout; otherwise, filters will outgas when saturated.

Fire Safety for the Exhaust System

Most local authorities have laws that incorporate based upon National Fire Protection Association (NFPA) *Standard No. 45, "Fire Protection for Laboratories Using Chemicals 1982."* Laboratories located in patient care building require fire standards based upon NFPA *Standard No. 56C, "Laboratories in Health-Related Institutions 1980"* in lieu of NFPA Standard No. 45.

Selected NFPA design criteria from NFPA Standard No. 45 include the following (references to specific items are noted):

Air Balance. "Laboratory...shall be maintained at an air pressure that is negative relative to the corridors or adjacent nonlaboratory areas." para. 6-4.2

Controls. "Controls and dampers...shall be of a type that, in the event of failure, will fall open to assure continuous draft." para. 6-6.7

Diffuser Locations. "Care shall be exercised in the selection and placement of air supply diffusion devices to avoid air currents that would adversely affect the performance of laboratory hoods..." para. 6-4.3

Exhaust Stacks. "Exhaust stacks should extend at least 7ft. above the roof..." para. A-6-8.7

Fire Dampers. "Automatic fire dampers shall not be used in laboratory hood exhaust systems. Fire detection and alarm systems shall not be interlocked to automatically shut down laboratory hood exhaust fans..." para. 6-11.3

Hood Alarms. "Airflow indicators shall be installed on new laboratory hoods or on existing laboratory hoods, when modified." para. 6-9.7

Hood Placement. "A second means of access to an exit shall be provided from a laboratory work area if ...a hood...is located adjacent to the primary means of exit access." para. 3-3.2 (d) "For new installations, laboratory hoods shall not be located adjacent to a single means of access to an exit or high traffic areas." para. 6-10.2

Recirculation. "Air exhausted from laboratory hoods or other special local exhaust systems shall not be recirculated." para. 6-5.1. "Air exhausted from laboratory work areas shall not pass unducted through other areas." para. 6-5.3

The designer engineer should review the entire NFPA standard, determine if it is incorporated into the local code, and advise the other members of the design team of their responsibilities (such as fume hood placement).

The incorrect placement of fume hoods and biological safety cabinets is a frequent design error and a common cause of costly redesign work. The placement of the fume hood involves an analysis of the laboratories work pattern and the location of casework, sinks, utilities, etc.

AUXILIARY AIR SUPPLY

Exhaust air requirements for laboratory fume hoods and biological safety cabinets often exceed the supply air needed for air-conditioning. The exhaust air requirements often dictate the supply air quantity for a laboratory. The supply air required to maintain building air pressure requirements can be obtained from primary and auxiliary systems. Primary supply air systems meet the air-conditioning needs of the laboratory. Auxiliary air supply systems augment the primary system to meet the air quantity requirements of hoods, etc. Auxiliary air can be ducted directly to auxiliary air fume hoods or supplied directly to the room. Auxiliary air should be conditioned to meet the temperature and humidity needs of the laboratory. Operational costs may be reduced by keeping the heating, cooling, and humidifying energy requirements of the auxiliary air system to a minimum.

In some laboratory buildings, office and research areas are separated by a corridor. The offices are kept under pressure, so air exits from the offices into the corridor, and then into the laboratories. Transfer is simple, and air flows from less hazardous to more hazardous areas. Corridors may convey and distribute air as plenums within the limits established by NFPA 90A. Using this air from offices may eliminate or reduce the size of auxiliary air systems.

Constant Volume Auxiliary Air Supply

The air flow in a constant volume auxiliary air flow system remains unchanged during normal day-to-day operation. This system can be installed with excess capacity so, as laboratory fume hoods or biological safety cabinets are added or relocated, appropriate changes in fan speed, inlet vane setting, or distribution system can be made to maintain an air balance.

Constant air flow systems adapt to supplement cooling, particularly when high exhaust requirements and high internal heat gains occur simultaneously.

Variable Volume Auxiliary Air Supply

When exhaust air varies, the auxiliary supply air must vary to maintain an air balance. Central systems having many variable exhaust openings and a few central supply fans can be controlled by static pressure regulators cycling the fans, modulating the fan capacity, or by controlling dampers in a bypass duct section connecting the fan discharge and inlet. Such systems are complex and difficult to balance, however.

Variable supplementary supply systems are not suitable for cooling unless the exhaust and supplementary supply air are directly proportional to the internal heat gain. This condition may exist in areas of extremely high and variable heat release, such as engine test cells, where the exhaust is primarily for heat removal.

The distribution of variable quantities of auxiliary air is complicated because it not only adds to the base system, but it is constantly changing. This problem can be solved if air can be safely supplied to an adjacent corridor and transferred into the laboratory through louvers.

Unconditioned Auxiliary Air Supply

Some air-conditioned laboratories have unconditioned (outdoor) auxiliary supply air introduced within or directly adjacent to the exhaust hoods. This air must be used with great care. Air introduced within the fume hood can adversely affect safety and health by forcing fumes, etc., into the face of the researcher. Auxiliary air introduced outside the hood, via a well-engineered terminal, avoids this potential danger if adequate capture velocity is maintained at the face of the hood. Careful initial evaluation of the installed hood and subsequent monitoring will ensure proper hood performance in the laboratory.

The unconditioned auxiliary air system must be arranged properly and the air introduced to the hood so that temperature and moisture levels in the room are not changed. The added cost of this type of system may be greater than the value of the cooling capacity saved, since the air must be heated to a reasonable temperature in winter and, in some cases, cooled in summer.

RECIRCULATION

Air exhausted from chemical or biological laboratories should not be recirculated because it may expose both personnel and research materials to airborne contaminants. However, it is acceptable to recondition (e.g., fan coil) non-contaminated air within individual laboratories.

In large facilities, the ventilation system serving chemistry and biological laboratories should discharge all exhaust air to the outdoors. Other laboratories in the same facility (e.g., electronics) may be served by a recirculating system, providing air quality is acceptable. Recirculation of a large percentage of air can cause odors or entrain contaminants.

Office areas in a chemical or biological research facility should be segregated from the laboratories and served by a conventional office recirculating ventilation system. These areas are not suitable for future use as laboratories without major upgrading of their HVAC systems.

AIR BALANCE AND
FLOW PATTERNS

Control of the direction of air flow in research laboratories controls the spread of airborne contaminants, protects personnel from toxic and hazardous substances, and protects the integrity of experiments. In these facilities, the once-through principle of air flow is applied based on: (1) exhausting 100% of the supplied air; (2) maintaining constant volume air flow with all exhaust units operating at capacity; and (3) providing directional flow of air from areas of least contamination to those of greatest contamination. (In support facilities such as office suites where contamination is not likely, standard HVAC systems can be provided.) Determinants for air pattern control are: (1) type of research materials handled or generated in each space; (2) type, size, and number of laboratory fume hoods, biological safety cabinets, and auxiliary exhaust equipment in each space; and (3) permissibility of air transfer into or out of spaces.

Supply and exhaust air flow patterns may impact on fire detector or suppression system operation. For example, a sidewall supply grille with a relatively high discharge velocity may retard the activation of a nearby detector or automatic sprinkler head. Coordination within the design team will reduce this potential.

For critical air balance conditions, a personnel entry or exit air lock provides a positive means of air control. An air lock is an anteroom with airtight doors between a controlled and uncontrolled space. The air pattern in the air lock suits the foregoing laboratory space air balance requirements.

Supply air quantities are not fully established by the room cooling requirements and load characteristics. Additional supply air required to make up the differences between room exhaust requirements and primary supply may be designated: (1) infiltrated supply, if induced indirectly from the corridors and other spaces or (2) secondary supply, if conducted directly to the room.

Exhaust air quantities are established by requirements for the removal of heat, odor, and airborne contaminants. A variety of containment and local exhaust devices are available to control the spread of airborne contaminants in laboratories, and most require relatively large volumes of make-up air. The most common general-purpose enclosures are laboratory fume hoods and biological safety cabinets. Other special enclosures for the containment of biohazardous materials or of highly toxic contaminants are also available.

LABORATORY FUME HOODS

The Scientific Apparatus Makers Association (SAMA) defines a laboratory fume hood as "a ventilated enclosed work space intended to capture, contain, and exhaust fumes, vapors, and particulate matter generated inside the enclosure. It consists basically of side, back, and top enclosure panels, a work surface or counter top, and access opening called the face, a sash, and an exhaust plenum equipped with a baffle system for the regulation of air flow distribution" (SAMA 1975). The work opening has operable glass sash(es) for observation and shielding. A sash may be: (1) vertically operable, (2) horizontally operable, or (3) vertically and horizontally operable. The latter provides maximum access for setting up apparatus, conserves energy due to the smaller face opening, and provides movable protective shielding. The horizontally operable sash-type fume hood has similar energy saving value. Laboratory fume hoods may be equipped with a variety of accessories, such as internal lights, service outlets, sinks, air bypass openings, airfoil entry devices, flow alarms, special linings, ventilated base unit (for storage of chemicals), and exhaust filters.

Figure 1 illustrates the basic elements of a general-purpose bench-type fume hood. Figures 2 and 3 show the basic features of a bypass-type fume hood and the auxiliary air fume hood, respectively.

Chemical fume hoods are manufactured to meet different research needs. Table 5 lists the different types and their typical application in laboratory facilities.

Operating Principles

Containment of contaminants is based on the principle that a flow of air entering at the face, passing through the enclosure, and exiting at the exhaust port will prevent the escape of airborne contaminants from the hood into the room. The degree to which this is accomplished depends on the design of the hood,

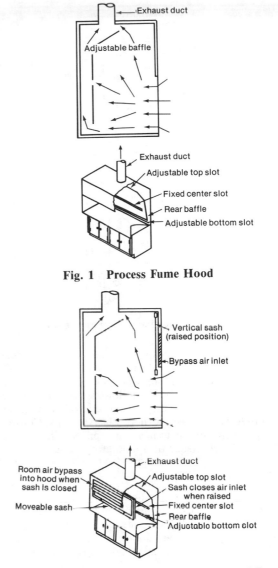

Fig. 1   Process Fume Hood

Fig. 2   Bypass Fume Hood with Vertical Sash and Bypass Air Inlet

its installation, and its operation. The critical design parameters of a hood are as follows:

Containment of contaminants:

    Face velocity
    Size of the face opening
    Shape of the opening surfaces
    Inside dimensions and location of work area relative to
      face edge
    Size and number of exhaust ports
    Back baffle and exhaust plenum arrangement
    Proportional bypass

Critical installation parameters:

    Distance from supply air outlets
    Type of air outlets
    Air velocity near hood
    Distance from doors
    Pedestrian traffic next to the hood face velocity
    Movements of researcher in hood face
    Location and type of research apparatus placed inside the
      hood

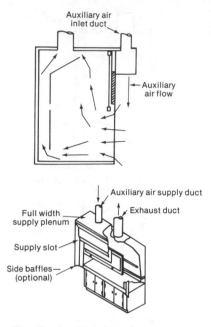

Fig. 3 Auxiliary Air Fume Hood

ASHRAE conducted tests to determine the interactions between room air motion and hood face velocity upon the spillage of contaminants into the room (Caplan and Knutson 1977, 1978). Test conclusions included the following observation: the effect of room air challenge is significant and of the same order of magnitude as the effect of (hood) face velocity. Consequently, improper design of replacement air supply can have a disastrous effect on the efficiency of a laboratory hood.

Hood Performance

Air currents external to a hood easily disturb the hood's air pattern and cause flow of contaminants into the breathing zone of the researcher. Cross currents are generated by movements of the researcher, people walking past the hood, thermal convection, supply air movement, and rapid operation of room

Table 5 Applications of Chemical Fume Hoods

Type of Hood	Research Applications
Process	Process laboratories—intermittent use. Low hazard process; known procedures. No sash provided; use of specific operation.
Bypass	Research laboratories—continuous use. Moderate and high hazard processes; varying procedures. Has sliding sash.
Auxiliary air	Same application as *bypass hoods*.
Radioisotope	Process and research laboratories using radioactive isotopes. Special shielding and filters involved.
Perchloric acid	Process and research laboratories using perchloric acid. Mandatory use because of explosion hazard. Special washdown of hood and ductwork required.
California	For enclosing large and complex research apparatus. Size may be 6 ft (1.8 m) wide by 8 ft (2.4 m) high by 3 ft (0.9 m) deep.
Walk-in	Similar application to California fume hood.
Canopy	Not a fume hood. Useful for heat removal over some work areas. Not to be substituted for chemical fume hood.

doors and windows. Terminal supply air velocity in the vicinity of the hood should be limited to 35 fpm (0.18 m/s). It is very important to locate hoods away from doors and active aisles. This problem needs coordination between the designer and the research staff.

Performance Criteria

Performance criteria for fume hoods are: (1) flow control, (2) spillage, and (3) face velocity control. Flow is adjusted (regulation of flow over the face opening of a hood) by horizontal slots in the back baffle. One at the bottom of the back baffle draws air across the working surface; another at the top exhausts the canopy; and a third is frequently midway on the baffle. These adjustable openings regulate exhaust distribution for specific operations; the openings should be set and locked by the engineer. All fume hoods should be tested annually by the engineer and certified. Often, the vertical sash needs to be placed in a certain position for proper face velocity; the annual inspeciton should clearly mark this sash position.

Spillage (leakage outward through the face opening) of contaminates from hoods into the laboratory can be caused by: (1) drafts in the room; (2) eddy currents generated at hood opening edges, surface projections, or depressions; (3) thermal heads; and (4) high turbulence operations (blenders, mixers) within the hood. Corner and intermediate posts, deep deck lip depressions, sinks, and projecting service fittings near the face produce air turbulence and potential spillage conditions. Plain entrance edges produce a *vena contracta* within 1 in. (25 mm) of the surface and to a depth of 6 in (150 mm). Fumes generated in this area will be disturbed and possibly escape the hood enclosure. Air foil shapes at the entry edges correct this condition. Correcting this one feature on existing hoods has been the key to making satisfactory hoods from previously unacceptable units. Sinks and service fittings should be located at least 6 in. (150 mm) inside the hood face, and deck lips should have minimal projections.

Face velocity is affected by variations in the resistance of a hood exhaust system. Two common causes are: (1) variations in the face opening and (2) buildup of exhaust filter resistance. Increases in fume hood exhaust system pressures due to filter loading can range from 50 to 100% of the clean filter condition when high-efficiency filters are used. Pressure may be regulated by an automatic pressure controlled damper in the duct system, by a manually adjusted damper, or by exhaust fan vortex control. Most laboratory fume hoods do not require exhaust filters.

It is good practice to equip laboratory fume hoods with alarm devices to detect failure of exhaust air flow. Devices monitoring the rotation of the fan shaft are also recommended. An alarm, visual and/or audible, should be extended to all hoods served by the respective exhaust fan.

Performance Tests

Tests should be performed with the hood sash opened to three positions (1) *normal* operating position, (2) 25% opening, and (3) 50% opening. Place the usual amount of research equipment in the hood and test in the following manner:

Face Velocity. Form an imaginary grid pattern by dividing the vertical and horizontal dimensions to obtain one measurement per square foot (0.1 m²). Take velocity readings with a calibrated heated wire anemometer, 4 in. (100 mm) behind the front face of the hood, at the intersections of the grid lines.

If the face velocity (design and operation) must be maintained at 100 fpm (0.5 m/s) ±10%, this average may be allowed to deteriorate to 85 fpm (0.47 m/s) before correction and then the face velocity must be returned to 100 fpm (0.5 m/s). Individual readings may not vary more than ±15% with the hood empty or ±25% with research equipment in the hood.

Reverse Air Flows and Dead Air Spaces. Swab a strip of titanium tetrachloride along both walls and the hood floor in a line parallel to the hood face and 6 in. (150 mm) back into the hood. (Titanium tetrachloride is corrosive to the skin and extremely irritating to the eyes and respiratory system.) Swab a large *A* on the back of the hood and on each side. Define air movement toward the face of the hood as reverse air flow and define lack of movement as dead air space. Swab the work top of the hood, being sure to swab lines around all equipment in the hoods. All smoke should be carried to the back of the hood and out. Test the operation of the bottom air bypass air foil by running the cotton swab under the air foil. Before going to the next test, move the cotton swab around the face of the hood; if there is any outfall, the exhaust capacity test should not be made.

Exhaust Capacity. Ignite and place a 30-second smoke bomb near the center of the work surface, making sure the hole on the side of the smoke bomb faces into the hood. After the smoke bomb begins to work, pick it up with tongs and move it around in the hood; there should be no visual or odor indications of smoke outside the hood. The fire department should be notified before conducting this test to prevent false alarms.

Air Flow Indicator. Check the air flow indicator alarm to see if it is operating properly.

Exhaust Fan. Check for proper performance.

Building Conditions. During the tests, the building air conditioning or ventilating system should be operating in a normal fashion. During the smoke test, the room doors shuld be opened and closed to ensure that no leakage from the hood occurs.

Auxiliary Air Hoods

Auxiliary air hoods connect directly to an auxiliary air supply system. These hoods reduce the volume of conditioned room air exhausted and, thereby, reduce the overall cooling load. Auxiliary air should not be introduced within the hood because less air is drawn through the hood face and the face velocity is lowered correspondingly. When auxiliary air is introduced across or in front of the opening, the flow pattern of the auxiliary air stream is critical to hood performance. When auxiliary air is dispersed into the laboratory, it often causes undesirable changes to room temperature and humidity; additionally, condensation on cold surfaces may result. Air turbulence can occur if the air stream strikes personnel working at the hood or any hood surfaces. Make-up air to the auxiliary air hoods should be heated during the heating season so that cold, moist, dense outside air does not fall below face opening. Cold air also makes the operator uncomfortable.

The application of auxiliary air hoods should be based on the performance characteristics of the specific model, as determined by tests, and full consideration of the extreme level of toxicity that may occur within the hood. For proper hood performance, air balance must be carefully maintained. If the exhaust flow decreases while the auxiliary air flow remains constant, control may be lost. Also, laboratory air flow may reverse and flow from the laboratory into the corridor.

Special Laboratory Hoods and Exhausts

Perchloric acid fume hoods are required for research in which perchloric acid is volatized. These hoods have exhaust ducts of smooth, impervious, and cleanable materials resistant to acid attack. Stainless steels with high chromium and nickel content (not less than No. 316) or nonmetallic materials are recommended. Duct work should be short, direct, and vertical to the terminal discharge point. Internal water spray systems for periodic washing of the duct surfaces are mandatory. The wash-down prevents the accumulation of perchloric acid deposits, which are

a major explosion hazard. Since perchloric acid is an extremely active oxidizing agent, organic materials should not be used in the exhaust system in such places as joint gaskets. Joints should be welded and ground smooth. A perchloric acid hood should only be used for work involving the use of perchloric acid.

Radioactive hood exhaust ducts have flanged, neoprene-gasketed joints with quick disconnect fasteners that can be dismantled quickly for decontamination.

BIOLOGICAL SAFETY CABINETS

Biological safety cabinets are called safety cabinets, ventilated safety cabinets, laminar flow cabinets, and glove boxes. They are categorized as Class I, Class II, or Class III cabinets. Class II includes Type A and Type B. Type B includes three sub-types. In Class I and II, 4 and 6-ft. (1.2 and 1.8 m) lengths are usually available; the 6-ft. (1.8 m) size is the common selection. Figure 4 shows the internal air flows and integral HEPA filters. Information for other Type B cabinets is available from manufacturers.

The National Sanitation Foundation Standard 49, *Class II (Laminar Flow) Biohazard Cabinetry* is available to assist in procurement and testing of Class II cabinets. A listing of NSF-approved models may be obtained from the National Sanitation Foundation, P. O. Box 1468, Ann Arbor, Michigan 48106.

Class I Cabinets

The Class I cabinet is a partial containment cabinet designed for general research operations with low- and moderate-risk etiologic agents. It is useful for the containment of mixers, blenders, and other equipment. Room air flows through a fixed opening and prevents aerosols, which may be released within the cabinet enclosure, from escaping into the room. Entrained particles are removed by the exhaust air, which may be HEPA-filtered before being discharged from the cabinet to the exhaust system. The HEPA exhaust filter is optional and depends on the cabinet usage. For adequate personnel protection, the front opening of the cabinet, through which the worker operates, should be approximately 8 in. (200 mm) high. Air velocity through that opening must be a minimum of 75 fpm (0.4 m/s). This type of cabinet will not prevent contact exposure.

The Class I cabinet can be modified to contain chemical carcinogens by adding an appropriate exhaust air treatment system and by increasing the velocity through the front opening to 100 fpm (0.5 m/s). Specific OSHA criteria should be consulted. Large pieces of research equipment such as centrifuges, blenders, and sonicators should be placed inside the cabinet and specially shielded. The cabinet, however, is not appropriate for containing experimental systems that are vulnerable to airborne contamination, since the inward flow of air can carry microbial contaminants into the cabinet. The Class I cabinet is also not recommended for use with highly infectious agents, since an interruption in the inward air flow, caused by drafts or fan failure, may allow aerosolized particles to escape.

Class II Cabinets

Class II cabinets provide protection to personnel, product, and environment. The cabinet features an open front with inward airflow and HEPA-filtered recirculated and exhaust air.

The Class II, Type A cabinet (formerly designated Type 1) has a fixed work opening with a minimum inflow velocity of 75 fpm (0.4 m/s). The average minimum downward air velocity is 75 fpm (0.4 m/s). Because this design recirculates approximately 70% of the total cabinet air, it should not be used with flammable solvents, toxic agents, or radioactive materials. Although

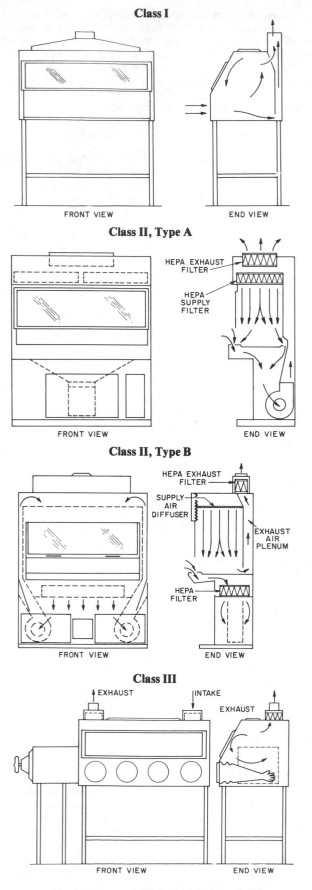

Class I

FRONT VIEW   END VIEW

Class II, Type A

HEPA EXHAUST FILTER

HEPA SUPPLY FILTER

FRONT VIEW   END VIEW

Class II, Type B

HEPA EXHAUST FILTER

SUPPLY AIR DIFFUSER

EXHAUST AIR PLENUM

HEPA FILTER

FRONT VIEW   END VIEW

Class III

EXHAUST   INTAKE

EXHAUST

FRONT VIEW   END VIEW

Fig. 4 Types of Biological Safety Cabinets

the Class II, Type A cabinet can be installed to discharge exhaust air to the room, it is preferable to have the cabinet discharge the exhaust air to the laboratory exhaust system via a special canopy hood or "thimble unit" available from the manufacturer of the cabinet (National Sanitation Foundation 1983). The Type A cabinet is suitable for work with agents meeting Biosafety Level 2 criteria in the absence of volatile or toxic chemicals and volatile radionuclides (National Safety Council 1979).

The Class II, Type B1 (formerly designated Type 2) cabinet has a vertical sliding sash and maintains an inward air flow of 100 fpm (0.5 m/s) at a sash opening of 8 in. (200 mm). The average downward vertical air velocity is 50 fpm (0.25 m/s). The cabinet exhausts approximately 70% of the air flowing through the work area to the outdoors after passage through a HEPA filter. Type B1 cabinets are suitable for work with agents meeting Biosafety Level 3 criteria (DHHS 1984). The unit may also be used with biological agents treated with limited quantities of toxic chemicals and trace quantities of radionuclides, provided the work is performed in the direct exhausted area of the cabinet.

The Class II, Type B2 (referred to as Total Exhaust) cabinet is designed to maintain an inward air flow of 100 fpm (0.5 m/s) through the work access opening. The downflow air is drawn from the laboratory or the outside and passes through a HEPA filter before entering the work space. There is no recirculation of air in these units, and the HEPA-filtered exhaust is discharged to the outdoors. The Type B2 cabinet may be used for the same level of work as the Type B1 with the added feature that the design permits use of toxic chemicals and radionuclides as adjuncts to microbiological studies.

The Class II, Type B3 cabinets are called Convertible Cabinets. These are designed to maintain an inward air flow of 100 fpm (0.5 m/s) and are essentially the same as the Type B1 in performance and use.

Class III Cabinets

The Class III biological safety cabinet is a gas-tight, negative-pressure containment system that physically separates the agent from the worker. These cabinets provide the highest degree of personnel protection. Work is performed through arm-length rubber gloves attached to a sealed front panel. Room air is drawn into the cabinet through HEPA filters. Particulate materials entrained in the exhaust air are removed by HEPA filtration or incineration before discharge to the atmosphere. A Class III system may be constructed to enclose and isolate incubators, refrigerators, freezers, centrifuges, and other research equipment. Double-door autoclaves, liquid disinfectant dunk tanks, and pass boxes are used to transfer materials into and out of the cabinet. Class III systems contain highly infectious materials and radioactive contaminants. Although there are operational inconveniences with these cabinets, they are the equipment of choice when a high degree of personnel protection is required. The use of Class III cabinets for research involving volatile substances has resulted in explosions.

LAMINAR FLOW HOODS (CLEAN BENCHES)

Horizontal (i.e., cross-flow) and vertical (i.e., down-flow) laminar flow clean benches, which discharge air out of the front opening and into the room, should not be used in a biomedical laboratory without critical assessment of risk. They provide product protection but expose the worker to potentially hazardous or allergenic substances because they discharge air across the research material directly into the face of the worker. Clean benches are not recommended for work involving any biological, chemical, or radionuclide.

LABORATORY ANIMAL ROOMS

Laboratory animals must be housed in comfortable, clean, and air-conditioned animal rooms, with animal welfare considered in the design.

It is also important that the air-conditioning system provide the desired "microenvironment" (animal cage environment) as specified by the facility's veterinarian (Allander and Abel 1973, Woods 1980, Besch 1975, ILAR 1985). Early detailed discussions with the *laboratory animal veterinarian* concerning air flow patterns, cage layout, and risk assessment will help to ensure a successful animal room air-conditioning design. The elimination of research variables (fluctuating temperatures and humidities, drafts, and spreading of airborne diseases) is another reason for a high quality air-conditioning system (Enold 1980).

Table 6 gives minimum ventilation rates recommended by the Institute of Laboratory Animal Resource (ILAR). The ability to control odor in animal facilities depends primarily on the number and species of animals housed, the amount of cleanable surfaces (including exposed ducts, pipes, etc.), the sanitation practices, and the proper design and operation of the air-conditioning system. The designer should not confuse these ventilation rates with the air-conditioning rate.

The air-conditioning flow rate for an animal room should be determined by the following factors: desired animal microenvironment (Besch 1975, 1980; ILAR 1985); species of animal(s); animal room population; recommended minimum ventilation rate (Table 6); recommended ambient temperature and humidity (Table 7); and heat produced by the animals (Table 8). Additional design factors include: method of animal cage ventilation; operational use of a fume hood or a biological safety cabinet during procedures such as animal cage cleaning, animal examination, etc; airborne contaminants (generated by animals, bedding, cage cleaning, and room cleaning); and institutional animal care standards (Besch 1980, White 1982, ILAR 1985).

Table 6 Recommended Ventilation For Laboratory Animal Rooms

Species	Minimum Room Air Changes per Hour (Using 100% Outside Air)	Reference
Mouse	15	ILAR (1977)
Hamster	15	ILAR (1977)
Rat	15	ILAR (1977)
Guinea Pig	15	ILAR (1977)
Rabbit	10	ILAR (1967)
Cat	10	ILAR (1978)
Dog	10	ILAR (1973)
Nonhuman Primate	10-15	ILAR (1980)

Table 7 Recommended Ambient Temperatures and Humidity Ranges for Animal Rooms

Species	Temperature °F	°C	Relative Humidity %	Reference
Mouse	64-79	18-26	40-70	ILAR(1977)
Hamster	64-79	18-26	40-70	ILAR(1977)
Rat	64-79	18-26	40-70	ILAR(1977)
Guinea Pig	64-79	18-26	40-70	ILAR(1977)
Rabbit	61-70	16-21	40-60	ILAR(1967)
Cat	64-84	18-29	30-70	ILAR(1978)
Dog	64-84	18-29	30-70	ILAR(1973)
Nonhuman Primate	64-84	18-29	30-70	ILAR(1980)

Note: The above ranges permit the scientific personnel who will use the facility to select optimum conditions (set points). The ranges do not represent acceptable fluctuation ranges.

Table 8 (I-P) Heat Generated by Laboratory Animals

Species	Weight, lb	Heat Generation, Normally Active Btu/hr per animal		
		Sensible	Latent	Total
Mouse	0.046	1.11	0.54	1.65
Hamster	0.260	4.02	1.98	6.00
Rat	0.62	7.77	3.83	11.6
Guinea Pig	0.90	10.2	5.03	15.2
Rabbit	5.41	39.2	19.3	58.5
Cat	6.61	45.6	22.5	68.1
Nonhuman Primate	12.0	71.3	35.1	106.
Dog	22.7	105.	56.4	161.
Dog	50.0	231.	124.	355.

Sources:
ASHRAE: 1985 FUNDAMENTALS Volume, p. 9.10
R. Gorton, J. Woods, E.L. Besch. 1976. System Load Characteristics and Estimation of Annual Heat Loads for Animal Facilities. ASHRAE Transactions, Vol. 82, Part I, pp. 107-112.

Table 8 (SI) Heat Generated by Laboratory Animals

Species	Mass, kg	Heat Generation, Normally Active W/animal		
		Sensible	Latent	Total
Mouse	0.021	0.33	0.16	0.49
Hamster	0.118	1.18	0.58	1.76
Rat	0.281	2.28	1.12	3.40
Guinea Pig	0.41	2.99	1.47	4.46
Rabbit	2.46	11.49	5.66	17.15
Cat	3.00	13.35	6.58	19.93
Nonhuman Primate	5.45	20.9	10.3	31.2
Dog	10.31	30.7	16.5	47.2
Dog	22.70	67.6	36.4	104.0

Sources:
ASHRAE: 1985 FUNDAMENTALS Volume, p. 9.10
R. Gorton, J. Woods, E.L. Besch. 1976. System Load Characteristics and Estimation of Annual Heat Loads for Animal Facilities. ASHRAE Transactions, Vol. 82, Part I, pp. 107-112.

Air conditioning design temperature and humidity set points are usually required by the nature of the research programs. Research animal facilities require more precise control of the environment than farm animal or production facilities because variations affect the experimental results. An ideal system will permit control of the temperature of individual rooms to within ±2°F (±1°C) for any temperature set point in a range of 64 to 85°F (18 to 29°C). Table 7 recommends ranges of room temperatures and relative humidities from which set points are selected. The relative humidity should be maintained between 30 to 70% throughout the year, according to the needs of the species.

If the entire animal facility or extensive portions of the facility are permanently planned for species with similar requirements, the range of individual adjustments should be reduced. Each animal room or group of rooms serving a common purpose should have controls for the regulation of temperature and humidity.

Control of air pressure in animal housing and service areas is important to ensure directional air flow. For example, quarantine, isolation, soiled-equipment, and biohazard areas should be kept under negative pressure, whereas clean-equipment and pathogen-free animal housing areas should be kept under positive pressure (ILAR 1985).

The animal facility and human occupancy areas should be conditioned separately. The human areas may use a return air HVAC System and may be shut down on weekends for energy conservation. Separation also prevents exposure of personnel to biological agents and odors present in animal rooms.

Supply air outlets should not cause drafts on research animals. A study by Neil and Larsen (1982) showed that the pre-design evaluation of a full-size mockup of the animal room and its HVAC System was a cost-effective way to select a system that distributes air to *all* areas of the animal holding room effectively. Wier (1983) describes many typical design problems and their resolutions.

Air-conditioning systems must remove the sensible and latent heat produced by laboratory animals. The literature concerning the metabolic heat production appears to be divergent, but new data is consistent. Table 8 presents current recommended values. These values are based upon experimental results and the following formula:

$$ATHG = 2.5 \, M,$$

where

$ATHG$ = Average Total Heat Gain, Btu/h per animal
M = Metabolic rate of animal, Btu/h per animal = $6.6 \, W^{0.75}$
W = Weight, of animal, lb

In SI units, $M = 3.5 W^{0.75}$, where $ATHG$ and M are in watts per animal and W is in kilograms. (This formula was incorrectly presented in the 1985 ASHRAE FUNDAMENTALS Volume, p. 9.10.)

Conditions in animal rooms must be maintained at constant values. This requires year-round availability of refrigeration and, in some cases, dual/standby chillers and emergency electrical power for motors and control instrumentation. The storage of critical spare parts is one alternative to installing standby refrigeration systems.

It is important that the HVAC ductwork and utility penetrations present few cracks in animal rooms so that all wall and ceiling surfaces can be easily cleaned. Exposed ductwork is not recommended. Joints around diffusers, grilles, etc., should be sealed. Return air grilles having 1-in. (25-mm) disposable filters are normally used.

A widely recognized reference for the design, construction, and operation of laboratory animal facilities is *Guide for the Care and Use of Laboratory Animals* (ILAR 1985). It is updated periodically.

ENERGY RECOVERY INTERFACE

Energy recovery is often justified in laboratory buildings with large quantities of exhaust air. Chapter 35 of the 1983 EQUIPMENT Volume describes the selection, etc. For many research laboratory projects, either the coil energy-recovery loop or the twin-tower enthalpy recovery loop is selected because the fresh air intakes are located near ground level, and the exhaust discharges are located on the roof.

In the energy conservation analysis, most savings are obtained when a team (architect-engineer-owner) reevaluates the standard design parameters and makes reasonable changes. The following have major impacts on energy consumption in laboratory facilities:

a. Fume hood selection and operation. Consider fume hood diversity (Moyer 1983).
b. Fume hood sizing and air flow requirements. Consider horizontal sliding sash.
c. Use of biological safety cabinets for some research procedures.
d. Thermal storage (Edison Elec. Inst. 1983).
e. User experience with energy exchange units (Carnes 1984, Bridges 1980, Moyer 1978, Carroll 1979)
f. User experience with modification of existing terminal reheat systems. (Cook 1980, Haines 1984).

g. Owner requirements for number of air changes per hour.
h. Monitoring of energy usage and increased maintenance (Fed. Programs Adv. Svc. 1983, ASHRAE Editor 1985).
i. Analysis of energy consumption (Wulfinghoff 1984; Cowan and Jarvis 1984).

SUPPLEMENTARY CONDITIONING

Supplementary conditioning equipment (fan coil units) handle cooling load when it: (1) varies sufficiently in intensity, frequency, or duration, or (2) occurs in a small percentage of the research spaces. High heat gains in limited areas may be handled more efficiently by adding cooling capacity in those specific areas than by cooling the air in a central system and then reheating it for all other spaces.

Supplementary conditioning equipment (fan coils) can be justified easily for spaces where the cooling requirements differ from those of the majority of spaces served by the central system.

SPECIAL REQUIREMENTS

Isolated rooms (cold rooms, warm rooms, etc.) requiring the maintenance of special temperature, humidity, or other conditions for research are usually beyond the capability of the central systems; they should have separate HVAC systems. These rooms should not upset the building air balance. If these rooms are personnel working areas, they need to be ventilated.

CONTAINMENT LABORATORIES

With the initiation of biomedical research involving recombinant DNA technology, Federal guidelines (DHHS 1984, 1986, 1981) about laboratory safety were published for the design team, researchers, and others.

The term "containment" describes safe methods for managing hazardous chemicals and infectious agents in laboratories. The three elements of containment are laborabory operational practices and procedures, the safety equipment (biological safety cabinets, chemical fume hoods, etc.), and the facility design (including HVAC systems). Thus, the HVAC design engineer helps decide two of the three containment elements during the design phase.

Biomedical research laboratory facilities usually meet one of the following three containment levels:

Biosafety Level One is suitable for work involving agents of no known or of minimal potential hazard to laboratory personnel and the environment. The laboratory is not required to be separated from the general traffic patterns in the building. Work may be conducted either on an open bench top or in a chemical fume hood. Special containment equipment is not required nor generally used. The laboratory can be cleaned easily and contains a sink for washing hands. The Federal guidelines for these laboratories contain no specific HVAC requirements, and typical college laboratories are usually acceptable. Many colleges and research institutions require directional air flow from the corridor into the laboratory, chemical fume hoods, and approximately three to four air changes per hour of outside air. These requirements protect the research materials from contamination, thereby, improving research efficiency. Directional air flow from the corridor into the laboratory helps to control odors.

Biosafety Level Two is similar to Level One. It is suitable for work involving agents of moderate potential hazard to personnel and the environment. Guidelines (DHHS 1984, DHHS 1986, and DHHS 1981) contain lists that explain the levels of containment needed for various hazardous agents. Laboratory access is limited when certain work is in progress. The laboratory can be cleaned easily and contains a sink for washing hands.

Biological safety cabinets (Class I or II) are used whenever:

1. Procedures with a high potential for creating infectious aerosols are conducted. The procedures include centrifuging, grinding, blending, vigorous shaking or mixing, sonic disruption, opening some containers of infectious materials, inoculating animals intranasally, and harvesting infected tissues from animals of eggs.
2. High concentrations or large volumes of infectious agents are used. Federal guidelines for these laboratories contain minimum facility standards, as described above.

At this level of biohazard, most research institutions have a full-time safety officer (or safety committee) who establishes facility standards. The usual HVAC design criteria includes the following requirements:

a. 100% outside air systems
b. 6 to 15 air changes per hour
c. directional air flow into the laboratory rooms
d. 100 fpm (0.5 m/s) face velocity at fume hoods
e. research equipment heat load in a room of ±15 Watts per assignable (net) square foot of laboratory space (160 W/m²).

Biosafety Level Three applies to facilities in which work is done with indigenous or exotic agents that may cause serious or potentially lethal disease as a result of exposure by inhalation. All procedures involving the manipulation of infectious materials are conducted within biological safety cabinets. The laboratory has special engineering (HVAC) features such as airlocks, a separate ventilation system, etc.

Most biomedical research laboratories are currently designed for Biosafety Level Two. However, the laboratory director must evaluate the risks and determine the correct containment level before design begins. Process laboratories may have hazardous materials and, therefore, the laboratories are designed to meet the criteria contained in Public Health Service Guidelines (1984).

REFERENCES

Alereza, T. and Breen, J. III. 1984. Estimates of recommended heat gains due to commercial appliances and equipment. *ASHRAE Transactions*, Vol. 90, Part 2, No. 2828 [RP-391].

Allander, C. and Abel, E. 1973. Some aspects of the differences of air conditions inside a cage for small laboratory animals and its surroundings." *Z. Versuchstierk*, Bd. 15, pp. 20-33.

ASHRAE Editor. 1985. A biological evolution. *ASHRAE Journal* March, Vol. 27, No. 3, pp. 62-64.

Besch, E. 1975. Animal cage room dry-bulb and dew-point temperature differentials. *ASHRAE Transactions*, Vol. 81, Part II, pp. 549-558.

Besch, E. 1980. Environmental quality within animal facilities. *Laboratory Animal Science*, Vol. 30, No. 2, Part II, pp. 385-406.

Bridges, F. 1980. Efficiency study: preheating outdoor air for industrial and institutional applications. *ASHRAE Journal*, Vol. 22, No. 2 (Feb.), pp. 29-31.

Caplan, K.J. and Knutson, G.W. 1977. The Effect of Room Air Challenge on the Efficiency of Laboratory Fume Hoods. *ASHRAE Transactions*, Vol. 83, Part 1, No. 2438 RP 70, pp. 141-156.

Caplan, K.J. and Knutson, G.W. 1978. Laboratory Fume Hoods: Influence of Room Air Supply. *ASHRAE Transactions*, Vol. 83, Part 1, No. AT-78-3, RP 70, pp. 511-537.

Carnes, L. 1984. Air-to-air heat recovery systems for research laboratories. *ASHRAE Transactions*, Vol. 90, Part 2, No. 2847.

Carroll, F. 1979. Energy savings HVAC for research labs. *Heating, Piping and Air Conditioning* (Feb.), pp. 67-70.

Cook, E. 1980. An energy primer for terminal reheat. *Heating, Piping and Air Conditioning* July, pp. 83-85.

Cowan, J. and Jarvis, I. 1984. Component analysis of utility bills: a tool for the energy auditor. *ASHRAE Transactions*, Vol. 90, Part 1, AT-84-08, No. 2.

Degenhardt, R. and Pfost, J. 1983. Fume hood system design and application for medical facilities. *ASHRAE Transactions*, Vol. 89, Part 2A & B, No. DC-83-10, No. 4.

DHHS, Department of Health and Human Services. 1984. Biosafety in Microbiological and Biomedical Laboratories. Washington, D.C.: Public Health Service Centers for Disease Control and National Institutes of Health, Pub. No. (CDC) 84-8395.

DHHS, National Cancer Institute. 1974. Safety standards for research involving oncogenic viruses. Bethesda, MD: Office of Research Safety, National Cancer Institute, NIH Pub. No. 78-790.

DHHS, National Cancer Institute. 1975. Design criteria for viral oncology research facilities. Bethesda, MD: Office of Research Safety, National Cancer Institute, NIH Pub. No. 78-891.

DHHS, National Institutes of Health. 1981. NIH guidelines for the laboratory use of chemical carcinogens. Bethesda, MD: National Institutes of Health, NIH Pub. No. 81-2385.

DHHS, National Institutes of Health. 1986. Guidelines for research involving recombinant DNA molecules." *Federal Register*, Vol. 51, No. 88, May, p. 16958-16985.

DHHS, Public Health Service. 1984. Guidelines for Construction and Equipment for Hospital and Medical Facilities. U. S. Department of Health and Human Services Pub. No. (HRS-M-HF) 84-1.

Edison Electric Institute. 1983. A million pounds of ice melt energy costs at Union Oil research facility. *ASHRAE Journal*, Vol. 89, Sept., pp. 41-44.

Enold, G. 1980. Monitoring and Controlling the animal room atmosphere. *Laboratory Animal Science*. Jan.-Feb., pp. 50-53.

Federal Programs Advisory Service. 1983. NASA research center controls energy use by extensive metering. *Facilities Management Newsletter*, Vol. 4 (Apr.), No. 7, pp. 4-6.

Haines, R. 1984. Retrofitting reheat-type systems. *ASHRAE Journal*, Vol. 26, September, pp. 35-38.

Helder, S. 1972. How to design fume hoods, exhaust systems for research labs. *Heating, Piping and Air Conditioning*, March, pp. 103-112.

ILAR. Institute of Laboratory Animal Resources. 1967. Standard for the breeding, care, and management of laboratory rabbits. National Research Council. Washington, D.C.: *ILAR News*, March.

ILAR. Institute of Laboratory Animal Resources. 1973. Standards and guidelines for the breeding, care, and management of laboratory animals—dogs. National Research Council. Washington, D.C.: National Academy of Sciences.

ILAR. Institute of Laboratory Animal Resources. 1977. Laboratory animal management—rodents. National Research Council. *ILAR News*, Vol. XX, No. 3.

ILAR. Institute of Laboratory Animal Resources. 1978. Laboratory animal management—cats. National Research Council. *ILAR News* (Summer), Vol. XXI, No. 3.

ILAR. Institute of Laboratory Animal Resources. 1980. Laboratory animal management—nonhuman primates. National Research Council. *ILAR News*, Vol. XXIII, No. 2-3.

Institute of Laboratory Animal Resources. 1985. Guide for the care and use of laboratory animals. Bethesda, MD: National Institutes of Health, NIH Pub. No. 85-23.

International Agency for Research on Cancer, World Health Organization. 1979. Handling chemical carcinogens in the laboratory—problems of safety. Lyon, France: International Agency for Research on Cancer, IARC Scientific Pub. No. 33.

Kiil, L. 1984. Aging labs need extensive renovation. *Building Design and Construction*, Nov., pp. 75-78.

Moyer, R. 1978. Energy recovery performance in the research laboratory. *ASHRAE Journal*, Vol. 20, No. 5 (May), pp. 32-35.

Moyer, R. 1983. Fume hood diversity for reduced energy conservation. *ASHRAE Journal*, Vol. 89, Sept., pp. 50-52.

NFPA. 1980. Laboratories in health-related institutions. Boston: National Fire Protection Association, NFPA No. 56C.

NFPA. 1982. Fire protection for laboratories using chemicals. Boston: National Fire Protection Association, NFPA No. 45.

National Research Council. 1981. Prudent practices for handling hazardous chemicals in laboratories. Washington, D.C.: National Academy Press.

National Safety Council. 1979. Fundamentals of industrial hygiene. Chicago: National Safety Council.

National Sanitation Foundation. 1983. Standard 49, Class II (laminar flow) biohazard cabinetry. Ann Arbor, MI: National Sanitation Foundation. May.

Neil, D. and Larsen, R. 1982. How to develop cost-effective animal room ventilation: build a mock-up. *Laboratory Animal Science*. Jan.-Feb., pp. 32-37.

Peterson, R.; Schofer, E.; and Martin, D. 1983. Laboratory air systems—further testing. *ASHRAE Transactions*, Vol. 89, Part 2A & B, DC-83-10, No. 5.

Pike, R. 1976. Laboratory-associated infections: summary and analysis of 3,921 cases. *Health Laboratory Science*, Vol. 13, No. 2 (April), pp. 105-114.

SAMA. 1975. SAMA standard for laboratory fume hoods. Washington, D.C.: Scientific Apparatus Makers Association, LF 7, p. 1.

Sessler, S. and Hoover, R. 1983. Laboratory fume hood noise. *Heating, Piping and Air Conditioning*. Sept., pp. 124-137.

West, D.L. 1978. Assessment of risk in the research laboratory: a basis for facility design. *ASHRAE Transactions*, Vol. 84, Part 1, AT-78-3, No. 3.

White, W. 1982. Energy savings in the animal facility: opportunities and limitations. *Lab Animal*, Vol. II (2), March, pp. 28-35.

Wier, R. 1983. Toxicology and animal facilities for research and development. *ASHRAE Transactions*, Vol. 89, Part 2A & B, DC-83-10, No. 1.

Woods, J. 1980. The animal enclosure—a microenvironment. *Laboratory Animal Science*, Vol. 30, No. 2, Part II, pp. 407-413.

Wulfinghoff, D. 1984. Common sense about building energy consumption analysis. *ASHRAE Transactions*, Vol. 90, Part 1, AT-84-08, No. 4.

CHAPTER 31

ENGINE TEST FACILITIES

INDUSTRIAL testing of internal combustion engines is done in test cells to test the engine itself and in chassis dynamometer rooms to test the engine in a complete vehicle. In both cases, the spaces are enclosed to control noise, heat, and fumes and to isolate the test for safety or security. When temperature, noise, and safety conditions can be resolved adequately, chassis dynamometers may be installed outdoors only with the control rooms enclosed. Large open areas in the plant are sometimes used for production testing and emissions measurements, but the principles of ventilation and safety for test cells generally apply.

Enclosed test cells are normally found in design facilities. Test cells may need instruments to measure cooling water flow and temperature, exhaust gas flow and temperature, fuel flow, power output, and combustion air volume and temperature.

VENTILATION SYSTEMS

Ventilation and air conditioning of test cells must: (1) supply and exhaust proper quantities of air to remove heat and control temperature; (2) exhaust sufficient air at proper locations to prevent buildup of combustible vapors; (3) modulate large air quantities to meet changing conditions; (4) remove engine exhaust fumes; (5) supply combustion air; (6) prevent noise transmission through the system; and (7) provide for human comfort and safety during set-up, testing, and tear-down procedures. Supply and exhaust systems for test cells are unitary, central, or a combination of both. Mechanical exhaust must be supplied in all cases, and ventilation is generally controlled on the exhaust side (Figure 1).

Constant-volume systems with variable supply temperatures can be used; however, variable-volume, variable-temperature systems are usually selected. Unitary variable-volume systems (Figure 1A) use an individual exhaust fan and makeup air supply for each cell. Supply and exhaust fans are interlocked and operation is coordinated with the engine, usually by sensing room temperature. Some systems have only exhaust supply induced directly from the outside (Figure 1B). Volume variation can be accomplished by changing fan speed or by various dampers.

Ventilation systems with central supply or exhaust fans, or both (Figure 1C) regulate air quantities by test cell temperature

control of individual dampers or by two-position switches actuated by dynamometer operations; they also maintain air balance by static pressure regulation within the cell. Constant pressure in the supply duct is obtained by controlling inlet vanes, modulating dampers, or varying fan speed.

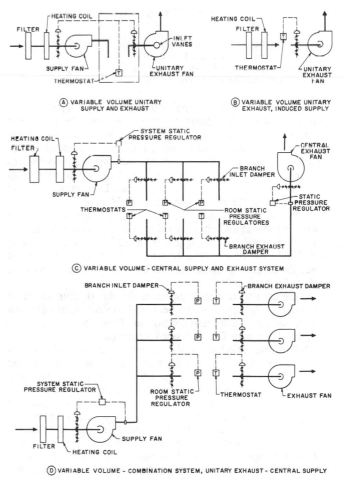

Fig. 1 Heat Removal Ventilation Systems

The preparation of this chapter is assigned to TC 9.2, Industrial Air Conditioning.

31.1

For individual exhaust fans combined with central supply, the exhaust system is regulated by cell temperature or a two-position switch actuated by dynamometer operation, while the central supply system is controlled by a static pressure device located within the cell to maintain room pressure (Figure 1D). Variable volume exhaust air flow should not drop below minimum requirements. The exhaust requirements should override cell temperature requirements, so reheat may be needed.

Ventilation should be interlocked with the fire protection system to shutdown supply and exhaust to the cell in case of fire. Exhaust fans should be non-sparking, and heating of makeup air should be by steam or hot water coils.

TEST CELL EXHAUST

Ventilation for test cells is based on exhaust requirements designed to satisfy: (1) removal of heat generated by the engine when operating; (2) emergency purging (removal of fumes after fuel spills); and (3) a rate of continuous exhaust during nonoperating periods, called cell scavenging.

During engine operation, heat convects to the air in the cell and also radiates to surrounding surfaces. The flow of air through the cell to remove convected heat is determined by:

I-P units:

$$Q = 0.9H/(t_e - t_s) \qquad (1)$$

SI units:

$$Q = 830H/(t_e - t_s)$$

where

Q = air flow, cfm (L/s)
H = engine heat release, Btu/h (W)
t_e = temperature of exhaust air, °F (°C)
t_s = temperature of supply air, °F (°C)

Heat radiated from the engine and exhaust piping must first warm the surrounding surfaces, which, in turn, release the heat to the air in the space by convection. The rate of release is governed by the temperature differences, film coefficients, and other factors discussed in Chapter 5 of the 1985 FUNDAMENTALS Volume. The value for $(t_e - t_s)$ in Eq. 1 cannot be arbitrarily set when a portion of H is radiated heat. Determination of H is discussed in the section on "Engine Heat Release."

Vapor removal exhaust should be at the maximum rate to remove vapors as quickly as possible. The air required for engine heat removal is generally the quantity used for emergency purging but should not be less than 10 cfm/ft² [50 L/(s · m²)] of floor area. Emergency purging should be by a manual overriding switch for each cell.

In the case of fire, the operation should: (1) shut down all equipment, (2) close fire dampers at all openings, and (3) shut off the solenoid valves that control fuel flow. Chapter 58 of this volume deals with fire and smoke control.

Cell scavenging exhaust is the minimum required to keep combustible vapors of fuel leaks from accumulating, or the amount required for heating and cooling, whichever is greater. Generally 2 cfm (10 L/s) per ft² (m²) of floor area is sufficient.

Exhaust grilles should be low, even when ceiling exhaust is used, since gasoline vapors are heavier than air. If exhaust is removed close to the engine, the convective heat that actually escapes into the cell is minimized. Some installations exhaust all air through a floor grating immediately surrounding the engine bedplate into a cubicle or duct below. In this case, supply slots in the ceiling over the bedplate are located to cover the

engine with a curtain of air to remove the heat. This scheme, illustrated in Figure 2, has worked quite successfully in a number of installations and is particularly applicable for central exhaust systems. Water sprays in the cubicle or exhaust duct lessen the danger of fire or explosion in case of fuel spills.

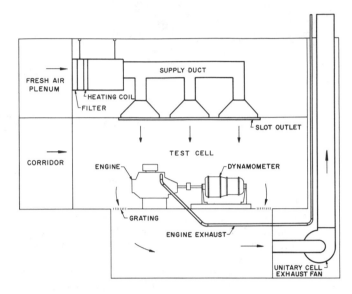

Fig. 2　Engine Test Cell Showing Direct Engine Exhaust—Unitary Ventilation System

Trenches or pits in test cells should be avoided. If they exist, they should be mechanically exhausted at all times, with a minimum rate of 10 cfm (50 L/s) per ft² (m²) of horizontal area. Excessively long trenches require multiple takeoff exhaust points. The exhaust should sweep the entire area and leave no dead spaces. Test cells should have no suspended ceilings or basements located directly below where fuel spills and vapor accumulation can occur. If such spaces exist, they should be ventilated continuously, and fuel lines should never run through them.

Although the exhaust quantities should be determined individually for each test cell on the basis of heat to be removed, evaporation of possible fuel spills, and minimum down time ventilation, a general idea of current practice can be obtained from Table 1.

Table 1　Exhaust Quantities for Test Cells

	Minimum Range of Exhaust Rates per Unit Floor Area		
	cfm per ft²	L/s per m²	Air changes per hour**
Engine testing— cell operating	10 to 20	50 to 100	60 to 120*
Cell idle	2 to 3	10 to 15	12 to 18
Trenches and pits	10	50	—
Accessory testing	4	20	24
Control rooms and corridors	1	5	6 to 10

*For chasis dynamometer rooms, this quantity is usually determined by test requirements.
**Based on a cell height of 10 ft (3m).

TEST CELL SUPPLY

Air supplied to a test cell should be slightly less than that exhausted. Recirculation of test cell air during engine testing is not recommended. Return air from other non-test areas can be used when available, provided good ventilation practice is followed.

Air distribution methods for introducing large quantities of ventilation air are important, especially if the cell is occupied. It is desirable to project air to separate occupants from heat released from the engine. Slot-type outlets with automatic dampers to maintain constant discharge velocity have been used with variable-volume systems.

A variation of Systems C and D, Figure 1, includes a separate supply to the cell sized for the minimum downtime ventilation rate, with heated and chilled water coils regulated by a room thermostat to control the temperature within the cell. This is useful in installations where much time is devoted to setup and preparation of tests or where constant temperature is required for complicated or sensitive instrumentation. Except for production and endurance testing, the actual engine operating time in test cells may be suprisingly low. Industry-wide test cells are used about 15 to 20%.

Filtration of all air to the cell is ordinarily required to remove atmospheric particulates and insects. The degree of filtration is a matter of choice or a requirement of the test. Facilities located in clean areas may sometimes use outdoor air without filtration.

Tempering supply air by heating coils is usually necessary for personnel if there is danger of freezing equipment or if low temperatures adversely affect the test performance.

ENGINE HEAT RELEASE

Engine heat released to the space is the total energy input to the engine less the energy transmitted to the dynamometer as work, heat removed by the jacket cooling water, and heat discharged in the exhaust gas. The relative quantities vary with the engine, operating speed and load, fuel used, type of dynamometer, and piping configurations external to the engine. The heat balance of an internal combustion engine at full load is approximately one-third useful work to the shaft, one-third to jacket cooling water, and one-third to exhaust; and for a gas turbine at full load, it is roughly one-third to shaft and two-thirds to exhaust. In both cases, there are losses by convection and radiation from the engine itself and from the exhaust piping. Table 2 shows a representative breakdown of heat release by engine type and size.

The energy absorbed by the dynamometer as work is removed from the test cell, except for that portion transmitted to the space from the dynamometer. Absorbed energy is returned to the electrical system, dissipated in remote resistance grids, or removed by the cooling water when induction dynamometers are used.

Engine coolant system heat is normally removed by city or recirculated tower water through heat exchangers. Heat exchangers for engine oil are also required under many test conditions. Radiators within the cell that dissipate this heat require the exhaust air quantity to be increased accordingly.

For an L-head engine, heat rejected to the jacket water in Btu/h is 3.5 times RPM per cubic inch (RPM/1110 = kW/L) displacement, which is about 2520 Btu/h per brake horsepower output (1 kW per kW output). For an overhead valve engine, 3.2 RPM = Btu/h per cubic inch (RPM/1210 = kW/L) displacement, which is 2280 Btu/h (0.9 kW) per brake horsepower (kW) output.

Table 2   Heat Balance for Internal Combustion Engine at Wide-Open Throttle

Engine Type and Size	Engine Heat Balance, %			
	Work Output	To Exhaust	To Coolant	Engine Convection, Radiation and Oil
Air-cooled I.C.				
To 15 hp (11 kW)	15	45	—	40
15 to 150 hp (11 to 110 kW)	20	43	—	37
Water-cooled I.C.				
150 to 500 hp (110 to 370 kW)	23.5	36	26	14.5
Diesel	32	36	22	10
G.T. regenerator To 400 hp (300 kW)	23	66	—	10

Heat lost by convection from engine block, head, and oil pan depends largely on engine coolant temperature, air temperature, and quantity passing over the engine. Surface temperature of 180 to 300°F (80 to 150°C) may be expected for internal combustion engines, and 400 to 500°F (200 to 260°C) for automotive gas turbines.

Engine exhaust pipes release considerable heat through radiation and convection, exhaust gas temperatures being from 1200 to 1800°F (650 to 1000°C). Only a minimum amount of piping should be within the cell. Commonly, engine exhaust pipes are placed in a vault below the cell. Catalytic converters and other emission devices are usually installed within the cell, adding to the heat load. Cooling of the engine exhaust system by jacketing or injecting water directly into the pipe is common.

Methods for calculating convection and radiation losses from exhaust pipe surfaces are found in Chapter 3 of the 1985 FUNDAMENTALS Volume. Because exhaust piping, mufflers, and add-on devices are so subject to change with the tests, it is usual to estimate this heat loss. A good estimate is to consider that the maximum heat loss will occur at wide open throttle with the largest engine the installed dynamometer can handle. On this basis, the power going into the test cell ambient from the exhaust is considered to be 1% of the rating of the dynamometer per foot (3%/m) of exposed exhaust pipe (the exhaust manifold should be included in that calculation) for a diesel engine and 1.5% per foot (4.5%/m) of pipe for a gasoline-powered engine. The actual diameter of the pipe has only a second-order effect due to several compensating factors.

In summary, the total Engine Heat Release is:

$$BHP\ (L_d + L_e + L_c + C)$$

where

BHP = engine brake horsepower (kW)
L_d = dynamometer loss per bhp (kW)
L_e = exhaust pipe losses per bhp (kW)
L_c = engine connection losses per bhp (kW)
C = cooling system losses per bhp (kW)

GAS TURBINE TEST CELLS

Aircraft gas turbine test cells must handle large quantites of air required by the turbine itself, attenuate the noise generated, and operate safely with the large flow of fuel required. Such cells are unitary in nature and use the gas turbine to draw in the untreated air and exhaust it through mufflers.

Small gas turbines for automotive and truck application can generally be tested in a conventional engine test cell with relatively minor modificatons. Test cell ventilation supply and exhaust are sized for the heat generated by the turbine in the same manner as for conventional engines. Combustion air supply for the turbine is considerably more, but it may be drawn from the cell, from outdoors, or through separate conditioning units that handle air only for combustion.

Exhaust quantities are higher than from internal combustion engines and are usually ducted directly outdoors through suitable muffling devices that provide little restriction to flow. Water cooling of exhaust air may be used, as temperature may range from 300 to 700 °F (150 to 370 °C), or for regenerative gas turbines, 500 to 600 °F (260 to 315 °C).

CHASSIS DYNAMOMETER ROOMS

A chassis dynamometer (as shown in Figure 3) simulates road driving and acceleration conditions. The vehicles drive wheels rest on a large roll, which drives a dynamometer. To approximate the effect of operation at varying road speeds on the body of the vehicle (and for radiator cooling), air quantities calibrated to coincide with air velocities at that particular speed are blown across the front of the vehicle. Additional refinements may vary temperature and moisture conditions of the air within prescribed limits from ambient to 130 °F (55 °C). Usually, air is introduced through an area approximating the frontal area of the vehicle. A return grille in a duct may be lowered to a position at the rear of the vehicle, causing the air to remain near the floor rather than short-cycle through a ceiling grille. The air is recirculated above the ceiling to the air-handling equipment.

Chassis dynamometers are also installed in cold rooms, where temperatures may be as low as −100 °F (−70 °C), and in full-sized wind tunnels with throat areas many times the cross-sectional area of the vehicle. Combustion air is drawn directly from the room, but a mechanical engine exhaust through the engine must be introduced into the facility in a way that will maintain the low temperatures and humidities.

ENGINE EXHAUST

Engine exhaust systems remove products of combustion, unburned fuel vapors, and water vapor resulting from injection of water for gas cooling. Design criteria are flow loads and system operating pressure.

Flow loads are based on the number of engines, engine size, and load and use factors.

System operating pressure is governed by engine discharge pressures and the range of allowable suction or back pressure at the point of connection to the exhaust system. Systems may operate at positive pressure, using available engine tail pipe pressure to force flow of gas, or they may operate at negative pressure, with mechanically induced flow.

The simplest method for inducing engine exhaust from a test cell is to size the exhaust pipe to minimize pressure variations on the engine and to connect it directly to the atmosphere (Figure 4A).

Such direct systems are limited in length of run by the cost of adequate pipe size needed to keep back pressure to a minimum. Direct exhaust to outdoors is subject to wind currents and air pressures, may be hazardous because of positive pressures within the system, and cannot be as closely regulated as mechanically ventilated systems.

Mechanical engine exhaust systems are unitary or central. *Unitary systems* use a fan and conductors to serve an individual test cell and can be closely regulated to match operation to the engine's requirements (see Figure 4B). *Central systems* use single or multiple fans, main ducts, and branch connections to individual cells (Figure 4D).

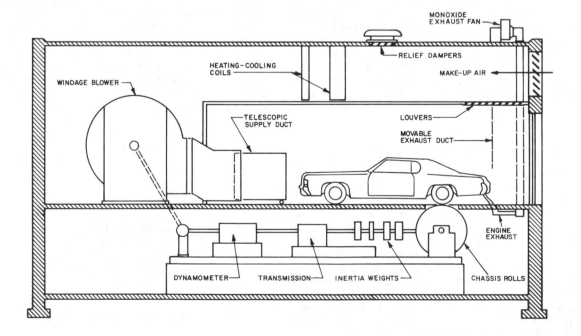

Fig. 3   Chassis Dynamometer Room

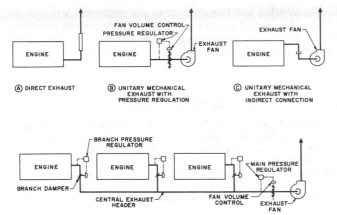

Fig. 4 Engine Exhaust Systems

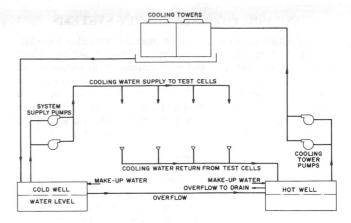

Fig. 5 Cooling Water System Using Cooling Towers

Pressures in all engine exhaust systems fluctuate with capacity of engine operation in relation to system design. The exhaust system should be designed such that load variations in individual cells exert a minimum effect on the system. Dampers and pressure regulators, if needed, keep the pressures within test tolerances. Engine characteristics and diversity of operation determine the maximum exhaust to be handled by the system, and allowable back pressure and tolerance for its variation are the basis for system size and regulation.

An indirect connection between the engine exhaust pipe and a mechanical removal system simplifies back pressure regulation (Figure 4C). The exhaust pipe terminates within an inlet to the collecting system with a clearance of 2 to 3 in. (50 to 75 mm). It then removes a mixture of exhaust fumes and room air from the test cell.

An indirect connection does require noise control if it is not within the test cell or in the open. Also, this connection can self-ignite when the engine is motored by the dynamometer, and a fuel rich mixture exhausts from the pipe at temperatures above 700°F (350°C).

Since the exhaust piping is open to the room, the system is essentially self-regulating. Room air mixes with the exhaust and cools the mixture. Materials for the indirect-connected system are not required to withstand the higher temperature conditions of a direct-connected system, although corrosion may be more severe.

To reduce exhaust gas temperatures, usually about 1500°F (800°C) but sometimes as high as 1800°F (1000°C), water may be injected directly into the exhaust pipe, the pipe may be water-jacketed, or a heat shield or shroud may be placed around the exhaust pipe with air mechanically exhausted through the shrouded enclosure. Exhaust piping and fans must often use high strength, high temperature alloys to withstand corrosion, thermal stresses, and pressure pulsations resulting from rapid flow fluctuations. The equipment must be adequately supported and anchored to relieve thermal expansion stresses.

Exhaust systems for chassis dynamometer installations must capture the high velocity exhaust from the tail pipe to prevent buildup of fumes in the test area.

Engine exhaust should discharge through a stack extending above the roof at an elevation and velocity sufficient to allow the fumes to clear the building windstream wake. If high stacks are not practical, a combination of shorter stack and increased ejection velocity may propel the exhaust gases above the building wake. Chapter 14 of the FUNDAMENTALS Volume has more

details. Ejection systems must keep the discharge velocity relatively constant, as the gas volume varies with load changes. Local or federal laws may require that exhaust gases be cleaned before they enter the atmosphere.

COOLING WATER SYSTEMS

Dynamometers absorb and measure the useful output of an engine or components. Two basic classes of dynamometers are the *water-cooled induction* type and the *electrical* type. In the water-cooled dynamometer, engine work is converted to heat that is absorbed by a circulating water system. Electrical dynamometers convert engine work to electrical energy that can be used or dissipated as heat in resistance grids. Grids should be outdoors or adequately ventilated.

Heat loss from electric dynamometers is approximately 8% of the output measured, plus a constant load of about 5 kW for auxiliaries within the cell. Cooling water systems for absorbing heat from the engine jacket, oil coolers, and water-cooled dynamometers are usually designed for recirculation through a system of circulating pumps, cooling towers, or atmospheric coolers and hot and cold well-collecting tanks (Figure 5).

Table 3 Typical Noise Levels in Test Cells

	Decibel Reading 3 ft (0.9 m) from Engine			
Type and Size of Engine	Dba	124 Hz	500 Hz	2000 Hz
Diesel				
Full load	105	107	98	99
Part load	70	84	56	49
Gasoline engine 440 in³ (7.2 L) @5000 rpm				
Full load	107	108	104	104
Part load	75	—	—	—
Rotary engine 100 hp (75 kW)				
Full load	90	90	83.5	86
Part load	79	78	75	72

COMBUSTION AIR SUPPLY SYSTEMS

Combustion air is usually drawn from the test cell or introduced directly from outdoors. Where combustion air conditions must be closely regulated and conditioning of the entire test cell is not practical, separate units that condition only the air for combustion can be used. These units filter, heat, cool, and regulate supply air humidity and barometric pressure, and usually provide air directly to the carburetor. Combustion air systems may be central or portable package types of units.

NOISE

Characteristics of noise generated by internal combustion engines and gas turbines must be recognized in design of the air-handling system. Part of the engine noise is discharged through the tail pipe. If possible, internal mufflers should be installed at the engine to attenuate this noise at its source. Ventilation ducts or pipe trenches that penetrate the cells must be protected against sound transmission from the cells through the ducts to other building areas or to the outdoors. Attenuation should be applied to the duct penetrations equivalent to what is provided by the structure of the cell. Table 3 lists typical noise levels within test cells during engine operation.

BIBLIOGRAPHY

Associated Factory Mutual Fire Insurance Company. *Testing Internal Combustion Engines and Accessories.* Loss Prevention Bulletin 13.50.
Computer controls engine test cells. *Control Engineering,* Vol. 16, No. 75, p. 69.
Factory Insurance Associates. 1952. *Recommended Good Practice for Safeguarding Combustion or Jet Engine Test Cells,* January 15, 1952.
Hazardous gases need ventilation for safety. *Power,* Vol. 112, May, 1968, p. 92.
Heldt, P.M.. 1956 *High Speed Combustion Engines.* Chilton Co., Philadelphia, Pa.
Ricardo and Hempson. 1968. *The High Speed Internal Combustion Engine.* Blacke and Son Limited, London, England.

CHAPTER 32

CLEAN SPACES

OUR environment contains large amounts of gaseous, liquid, and particulate comtamination. However, the application of clean spaces or clean rooms pertains primarily to the problem of particulate contamination.

Increased contamination not only poses a threat to health but finds its way into our sophisticated manufacturing and assembly plants, laboratories, hospitals, and other critical areas that require cleaner atmospheres. This applies to the fabrication of microscopically small subassemblies, electronic devices and instruments, and to the increasing demand for more sterility and purity in drugs and more germ-free atmospheres for medical and biological applications.

Such operations are performed in clean spaces, wherein: (1) airborne particulates are limited, (2) air flow patterns are selected, (3) temperature and humidity are controlled, (4) air pressure is predetermined and regulated, (5) special materials and construction are used, and (6) operating and maintenance procedures are regulated. These spaces may be rooms or work stations within a room.

TERMINOLOGY

Class 10: particle count not to exceed 10 particles per ft^3 (350 particles/m^3) of a size 0.5 μm and larger, with no particle exceeding 5.0 μm.

Class 100: particle count not to exceed 100 particles per ft^3 (3,500 particles/m^3) of a size 0.5 μm and larger.

Class 10,000: particle count not to exceed 10,000 particles per ft^3 (353,000 particles/m^3) of a size 0.5 μm and larger or 65 particles per ft^3 (2300 particles/m^3) of a size 5.0 μm and larger.

Class 100,000: particle count not to exceed 100,000 particles per ft^3 (3,530,000 particles/m^3) of a size 0.5 μm and larger or 700 particles per ft^3 (24,700 particles/m^3) of a size 5.0 μm and larger.

Clean Room: a specially constructed enclosed area environmentally controlled with respect to airborne particulates, temperature, humidity, air pressure, air pressure flow patterns, air motion, vibration, noise, viable organisms, and lighting.

Conventional Flow (Nonlaminar Flow) Clean Room: a clean room with non-uniform or mixed air flow patterns and velocities.

Critical Surface: the surface of the work part to be protected from particulate contamination.

Design Conditions: the environmental conditions for which the clean space is designed.

First Air: the air that issues directly from the HEPA filter before it passes over any work location.

First Work Location: the location in the path of the first air stream.

High Efficiency Particulate Air (HEPA) Filter: a filter with an efficiency in excess of 99.97% of 0.3 micrometer particles, as determined by Dioctyl Phthalate (DOP) Test, according to *Military Specification* MIL-STD-282.

Laminar Air Flow: air flow in parallel flow lines with uniform velocity and minimum eddies.

Laminar Air Flow Work Station: a work station with laminar air flow through the work area.

Laminar Flow Clean Room: a clean room with laminar air flow.

Makeup Air: air introduced to the secondary air system for ventilation, pressurization, and replacement or exhaust air.

Nonlaminar Flow Work Station: a work station without uniform air flow patterns and velocities.

Operational Conditions: the environment that exists within a clean space.

Particle Size: the maximum linear dimension of a particle.

Primary Air: air that recirculates through the work space.

Secondary Air: that portion of the primary air circulated through the air-conditioning equipment.

Work Station: an open or enclosed work surface with direct air supply.

AIRBORNE PARTICLES

Airborne particulate matter can be organic or inorganic, viable or nonviable. Most contamination control problems concern the total (gross) contamination within the air, but applications exist for specific contamination control of bacteria, spores, and viruses that are contained in the air. Airborne particles range in size from 0.001 to several hundred micrometres (Figure 1).

Aerosolized particles tend to settle at a rate that depend on the size and density of the particle. For example, according to Stokes Law, in an 8 ft (2.4-m) high room, a particle in the 50 μm range would take less than 60 s to settle, while a particle in the 1 μm range would take 15 or 20 h to settle.

Conditions for a clean space vary widely with industrial and research requirements. Two references on the control of airborne particulates are Federal Standard No. 2096, *Clean Room and Work Station Requirements, Controlled Environment*, and the U.S. Air Force Technical Order T.O. 00-25-2-3, *Standards and Guidelines for the Design and Operation of Clean Rooms and Clean Work Stations*. For information on control of nonparticulate contaminants, refer to Chapters 11 and 12 of the 1985 FUNDAMENTALS Volume and Chapters 10 and 11 of the 1983 EQUIPMENT Volume.

PARTICULATE CONTROL

Before any methods of contamination control of airborne particles can be applied successfully, a decision must be made as to how critical this particulate matter is to the process or operation. The allowable size of an airborne particle at a point within an area depends on the most critical dimensions and tolerances of the process to be performed at that particular point.

At the same time, the quantity of the particles of a given size that might be present at a particular point within the area must be considered. Since a definite relationship exists between the

---

The preparation of this chapter is assigned to TC 9.2, Industrial Air Conditioning.

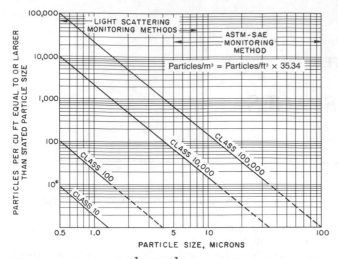

**Particle counts below 10/ft³ (0.28/m³) are unreliable except when a large number of samplings is taken.

Fig. 1　Particle Size Distribution Curves

size of a particle and the time in which it may be airborne, as defined by Stokes, it is most meaningful to discuss airborne particles by quantity of a given size. Both Federal Standard 209b and the Air Force Technical Order 00-25-203 show typical relationships.

To further analyze the level of contamination control required, the source of the contamination should be considered. Basically, this is divided into external sources and internal sources.

External Sources

For any given space, there exists the external influence of gross atmospheric contamination or air pollution, which tends to find its way into all areas of the working environment. External contamination is brought in primarily through the air-conditioning system, which supplies the working space with outdoor ventilation makeup air. In addition to the air-conditioning system, external contamination can infiltrate through doors, windows, and cracks within the structure. The external contamination in contact with the process is controlled primarily by the type of filtration used, along with space pressurization.

Internal Sources

Internal contamination is generally generated through the activity of service equipment and personnel within the area. Such products as pharmaceuticals and such solids as beryllium, carbon, and other dusts generate contamination. Service equipment such as soldering irons, solder, flux, instrumentation equipment, cleaning agents, etc., must also be considered as possible sources of contamination.

However, people are one of the greatest sources of internal contamination. People continually shed particles (viable and nonviable); the amount can vary from as few as several hundred particles per hour to several thousand particles per hour, depending on the individual. Skin is constantly *flaking-off* and generating particles in the 1 μm range, and exhaled breath contains large quantities of particles ranging in size from submicrometer to several hundred micrometers.

In addition to people, every activity involving contact between surfaces creates some type of contamination. For example, writing with a pencil on a piece of paper generates an aerosol cloud of many thousands of very fine carbon particles and paper fibers. Even the movement of two pieces of metal together generates particulate matter, which forms a very fine metallic dust as an airborne contaminant.

Within any working environment, air movement results from people working, machines in operation, fans blowing, motors rotating, and the like. All of these motions impart kinetic energy to the air and cause it to move at random velocities within the space. Fine particles caught in the random current within a space easily move from one area to another. This transfer of contamination via random air currents from one part of the space to another or to adjacent areas is known as *cross contamination* and is a significant contributor to the contamination level at the work site.

A resulting contamination buildup occurs within the space and reaches a plateau of steady state condition. A plateau count of 0.5 μm particles and larger would range anywhere from several thousand to several million particles in a typical manufacturing environment. During off-hours or lunch breaks, a noticeable reduction in the contamination level will occur. Figure 1 gives the size distribution relationship between the cleanliness levels as noted in Federal Standard 209b.

Application of Contamination Control Equipment

Once the required cleanliness level is established for a specific facility, the location of each process to be performed within this facility should be decided. The location of each process should include the position of each operator. The area required by each process, each operator, and the necessary service equipment also needs to be considered. The position of the operator relative to the process, and the location of each process relative to another will indicate the need for laminar flow. The area required for each process, the total area of the facility, and the cleanliness levels required also will indicate whether unitary equipment should be used or if the entire facility should be controlled.

The selection of the contamination control equipment is influenced by the size and quantity of airborne particles. The following are some typical concerns:

1. Is the product affected by viable particles?
2. Will toxic, explosive, or other harmful fumes be present in this process?
3. Will odors be generated?
4. What type of airborne contamination will affect the process?

The answers to these questions will determine: (1) if airstreams may be recirculated, (2) if they must be exhausted, and (3) if and how the supply of exhaust air (or both) must be treated or conditioned.

AIR PATTERN CONTROL

Air should be directed to obtain the cleanest air at the most critical work areas. As contaminants are entrained, they are conveyed to less critical portions of the room for removal.

These criteria generally result in (1) the introduction of large quantities of air at low velocities in the area of the most critical work surfaces and (2) unidirectional movement, usually downward across the room, prior to removal from the space. The choice of a specific air flow arrangement should be based on the criticality of the conditions to be maintained in the space, the size of the room, and the ratio of space occupied by critical operations to the overall room size.

Non-Laminar Flow

A satisfactory arrangement for conventional or non-laminar flow air distribution is shown in Figure 2. Air is supplied through large ceiling outlets, flows generally downward, and is removed near the floor level.

Non-laminar air systems function satisfactorily for many applications. When they are supplemented by local laminar flow

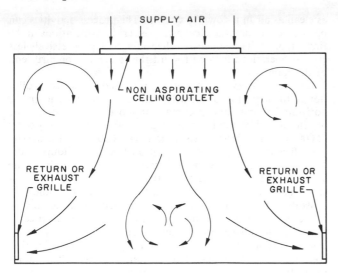

Fig. 2 Non-Laminar Flow Room

work stations, they can provide a high degree of contaminant control for critical operations.

Using non-laminar air flow to satisfy stringent contamination control criteria requires close regulation of personnel clothing and operations within the room. The entry must be protected and strict housekeeping procedures must be followed. It is possible to develop an environment in which the contamination level is reduced from as high as 5,000,000 particles per ft³ (180 particles/L), to as low as 100,000 particles per ft³ (3.5 particles/L) by adding dry-type extended surface high efficiency filters in the air-conditioning system. Although this is a substantial reduction in contamination level, airborne particles several hundred micrometres in diameter can still be present within the enclosure. This method also does not protect from cross contamination between areas within the space.

Laminar Flow

In a laminar flow system, air is introduced evenly from one entire surface of the room, such as the ceiling or a wall, flows at constant velocity across the room, and is removed through the entire area of an opposite surface. Laminar flow provides a direct, predictable path that a submicrometer size particle will follow through the clean room, with the minimum opportunity for contaminating room components. It also captures the particles constantly generated within the room and introduced into the air stream, thereby reducing the potential for cross-contamination.

Ideally, the flow streamlines would be uninterrupted and, although personnel and equipment in the air stream do distort the streamlines, a state of constant velocity is approximated. Most particles that encounter an obstruction in a laminar air flow strike the obstruction and continue around it as the laminar air stream reestablishes itself downstream of the obstruction.

Two of the many possible conditions for particulate deposition that exist in laminar flow rooms are: (1) the eddies immediately downstream of non-airfoil shaped obstructions and (2) the area of virtually zero velocity at surfaces parallel to the air stream caused by friction drag. Particles can drop out in these areas and later be reentrained in the air stream. Electrostatic charges due to the motion of the air can magnify the deposition.

To provide good dilution and sufficient air motion to prevent settling of particles, air flow velocities of approximately 90 fpm ± 20 fpm (0.46 m/s ± 0.1 m/s) are recommended as standard design for laminar flow clean rooms. These average air velocities can be used in laminar flow rooms because areas of local high velocity are minimized. It has been found by experimentation that at air velocities below 70 fpm (0.36 m/s), contamination will generally diffuse. Normal motions have minimal effect above 70 fpm (0.36 m/s), while air velocities above 110 to 120 fpm (0.56 to 0.66 m/s) contribute little contamination control advantage and may generate turbulence at obstructions.

A pressurized ceiling plenum or individual ducted filter boots are used to direct HEPA filtered air to the clean space. Care must be taken with the pressurized ceiling plenum to diffuse the air to keep the velocity through each filter uniform. The filter should be factory-tested and the pressure drop recorded. Filters within the same plenum should have equal pressure drops. Balancing can be accomplished by dampers built into the perforated raised floor or in the sidewall returns. Individual ducted filter boots should have dampers for each filter to accomplish balancing.

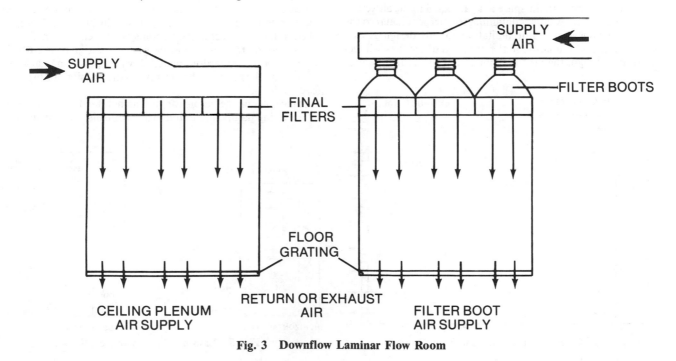

Fig. 3 Downflow Laminar Flow Room

It should be noted that when using ducted filters, the area above the ceiling is not normally a clean area. Though the clean room will normally be at a higher pressure than this space, contamination can infiltrate if the seals of the ceiling are not completely effective.

Laminar flow rooms can usually be operated without air locks, air showers, and encumbering occupant restrictions. The rooms fall into two general categories: downflow and horizontal flow rooms.

Downflow clean room. This room (see Figure 3) has a ceiling consisting of HEPA filters. As the class of the clean room gets lower, a greater percentage of the ceiling will require HEPA filters. For a Class 100 room, the entire ceiling will require HEPA filtration. Ideally, a grated or perforated floor serves as the air exhaust. Air in the downflow room moves uniformly from the ceiling to the floor. As it moves through the ceiling, it is filtered essentially free of all particles 0.3 microns and larger.

This type of air flow produces a uniform shower of air that bathes the entire room in a downward flow of ultraclean air. Contamination generated in the space will not move laterally against the downward flow of air (it is swept down and out through the floor) and will not contribute to a contamination level buildup in the room. Care must be taken in the design, selection, and installation of the system to seal the HEPA ceiling. Assuming that the HEPA filters installed in the ceiling have been properly sealed, this design can provide the cleanest working environment presently available.

A second approach for returning air is to use low side wall returns. In this approach the same conditions, as noted above, can be obtained within the general work area (nominally from 3 to 6 ft (0.9 to 1.8 m) above the finished floor). This method can only be used in rooms that are long and narrow. The width of the room should not exceed 12 ft (3.7 m).

The **horizontal flow clean room.** This room (see Figure 4) uses the same filtration air flow technique as the downflow system, except that the air flows from one wall of the room to the opposite wall. The supply wall consists entirely of HEPA filters supplying air at approximately 90 fpm (0.46 m/s) across the entire section of the room. The air then exits through the return wall at the opposite end of the room and recirculates within the system. As with the downflow room, this design removes contamination generated in the space at a rate equal to the air velocity and does not allow cross contamination perpendicular to the air flow. However, a major limitation to this design is that downstream contamination in the direction of air flow will occur. In this design, the air first coming out of the filter wall is

as clean as air in a downflow room. The process activities can be oriented to have the cleanest, most critical operations in the first air, or at the clean end of the room, with progressively less critical operations located toward the return air, or dirty end of the room.

A plateau, or leveling-off effect, is caused primarily by dilution of the high flow or ultraclean air. By actual measurement, horizontal rooms vary in contamination levels at the dirty or return air end of the room as high as 60,000 particles per ft³ (2,000,000 particles/m³) to as low as 5,000 particles per ft³ (35,000 particles/m³). Contamination level or buildup at the dirty end of the room varies because it depends entirely on the activities within the clean room, the length of room, the orientation and flow of the work, and the number of people.

Work Stations. Both laminar flow arrangements are applicable to individual work stations,, as well as entire rooms. In combination with conventional flow systems, these work stations can provide small areas with a high degree of contamination control. Where extremes of control are required, the laminar work station is often the most practical means of meeting the operational criteria (see Figure 5).

Flow Pattern Selection

Laminar and non-laminar flow clean space systems use different principles of airborne particle control and require a different philosophy of operation. The test of clean space performance is that components processed within the facilities economically meet the manufacturing standards imposed upon them.

Government agencies formulating clean space standards have proposed guidelines for system selection. Table 1 lists methods for achieving clean room performance.

PRESSURIZATION

A clean room facility may consist of multiple rooms with different requirements for contamination control. Rooms in a clean facility should be maintained at static pressures sufficiently higher than atmospheric to prevent infiltration by wind or other effects. Differential pressures should be maintained between the rooms sufficient to ensure air flow outward progressively from the cleanest spaces to the least clean during normal operation and during periods of temporary upsets in the air balance, as when a door connecting two rooms is suddenly opened. The only exception to using a positive pressure design is when dealing with specific hazardous materials where governmental agencies require the rooms to be negative to the exterior atmosphere. (See Table 2).

Static pressure regulators can maintain desired room pressures by operating dampers, fan inlet vane controls, vane axial fans,

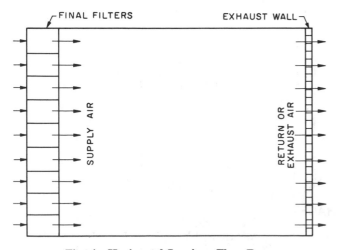

Fig. 4 Horizontal Laminar Flow Room

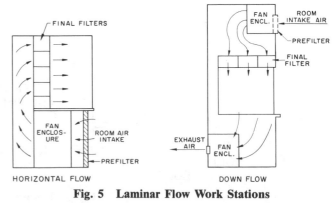

Fig. 5 Laminar Flow Work Stations

Table 1 Contamination Control Application Summary Sheet[a]

		Air Flow		Equipment	
		Laminar (LF)			
	Conventional	Horizontal (HF)	Downflow (DF)	Unitary	System
1. Air cleanliness level					
a) Class 100,000	General application	General application	LF unitary equipment	LF unitary equipment may clean entire room	Rate of air change required approximately 20-30 changes per hour
b) Class 10,000	Generally not applicable	General application	General application	General application	General application
c) Class 100	Not applicable	First work stations from Filter bank	General application	General application	Specific application for HF Rooms—General applications for DF Rooms
2. Sources of contamination					
a) External	Specific applications to 0.3 μm	General applications to 0.3μm	General applications to 0.3μm	General applications to 0.3μm	General applications to 0.3μm
b) Internal	Limited applications for protection of product, equipment, or personnel	General applications with prevention of cross contamination in planes parallel to filter wall	General applications with prevention of cross contamination in planes parallel to filter ceiling	DF unitary equipment provides greatest protection of product, equipment, and personnel, HF unitary equipment for protection of product and equipment, or both	DF system provides greatest protection, HF next; conventional system provides little protection from internal sources of contamination
3. Properties of particulate contaminants					
a) Viable	Very little protection to product or operator	Protection dependent on location of product and operator	High degree of protection to product and operator	General application for DF unitary equipment; specific application for HF unitary equipment	Specific applications for both DF and HF systems
b) Toxic	Least degree of protection	Moderate degree of protection	High degree of protection	Fumes easiest to isolate in DF unitary equipment	Toxic fumes generally require separate exhaust system
c) Explosive	Entire system must be protected, as per NEC[b] Turbulent system, provides least amount of dilution	Generally provides more dilution than turbulent system, requires protection of area as per NEC[b]	Generally provides greatest amount of dilution protection required as per NEC[b]	DF unitary equipment provides greatest isolation and protection	NEC[b] regulations for explosive atmospheres should be complied with
d) Odorous	Odors more noticeable due to lower rate of air changes and turbulent pockets	Better odor removing capabilities than conventional flow due to higher air change rate and no turbulent pockets	Best odor removing capabilities due to highest air change rate and amount of isolation afforded	DF equipment provides best isolation	DF equipment provides best isolation
4. Methods of isolation					
a) Direct	Limited application for noncritical classes, 10,000 or more	General applications where downstream processes are less critical than first air condition	General applications where cleanliness is equally critical throughout area	General applications dependent upon size of product and other parameters	General applications
b) Reverse	Generally not applicable	For applications where personnel can be located with respect to process	General applications	DF unitary equipment especially suited for this application	DF systems best suited for this application
c) Mutual	Generally not applicable	For applications where a minimum of 30 in. (760 mm) *free area* will exist in plane parallel to filter wall between adjacent processes	General applications where a minimum of 30 in. (760 mm) *free area* will exist between adjacent processes	HF units provide isolation between processes —DF units provide isolation between adjacent processes and between process and personnel	HF system provides isolation between adjacent processes in same plane—DF system provides isolation between adjacent processes and between processes and personnel

[a]Based on Federal Standard 209b. These guidelines are not mandatory.
[b]National Electrical Code.

controllable-pitch-in-motion controls, or a combination of these to control the pressure differential between supply and return or exhaust air. To control room pressures, air flow variations should be minimized. Exhaust air flow from rooms through hoods should be maintained constant by continuous hood operation or appropriate bypasses. In many systems, door openings

**Table 2 Air Pressure Relationships
(US Govt. 1973, USAF 1965)**

Application	Pressure Differential
General	0.05 in. of water (12 Pa) higher than surroundings
Between clean room and un-contaminated section	0.05 in. of water (12 Pa), miminum
Between uncontaminated and semicontaminated section	0.05 in. of water (12 Pa)
Between semicontaminated section and locker area	0.01 in. of water (2.5 Pa)

to the clean areas are protected by air locks, and provision are made to offset the pressure loss variations across filters as the dust-loading increases.

LIGHTING

In clean rooms, lighting may be supplied as part of the HEPA filter ceiling system, or may be separate fixtures with a stream-lined teardrop shape to minimize air turbulence. A typical lighting level may be established at approximately 70 footcandles (750 lx) at table-top height and 30 in. (760 mm), above the floor.

TEMPERATURE CONTROL

Temperature control is required to provide stable conditions for materials, instruments, and personnel comfort. Heat loads from lighting and fan motors are stable (see Table 3); personnel loads vary; the heat generated by process operations including soldering, welding, heat-treating, and heated pressure vessels is usually high and variable.

The large air quantities required for contamination control offfset internal heat gains, which causes low air temperature differentials. However, areas of concentration of heat-producing equipment and supply air patterns should be analyzed to determine resulting temperature gradients (Table 4).

For critical applications, proportional with integral and derivative controls should be considered to achieve the tolerances listed in Table 4. Some very critical spaces now require control to ±0.30°F (0.17°C) or lower.

HUMIDITY CONTROL

Humidity control is necessary to: (1) prevent corrosion, (2) prevent condensation on work surfaces, (3) reduce static elec-

Table 3 Clean Room Lighting Levels

Standard	Footcandles (Lux) at Work Surface
Operational	70 (750)

**Table 4 Clean Room Temperature and Humidity
(USAF 1965, US Govt. 1973)**

	Temperature	Humidity
Capacity range	67 to 77 (19 to 25)	40 to 55%
Control point	(72) 22	45%
Control tolerance		
General applications	±2°F (±1.1°C)	±5%
Critical applications	±0.5°F (±0.3°C)	±2%
Capacity and control response rate	2.5 to 4°F (1.4 to 2.2°C) change per h	...

tricity, (4) prevent product contamination, (5) provide personnel comfort, (6) compensate for hygroscopic materials, and (7) control microbial growth. Recommended conditions are given in Table 4.

Corrosion of precisely manufactured surfaces such as bearings, electrical contact surfaces, etc., occurs with 50% rh. At relative humidities much below 40%, static charges may form, attracting dust particles that later may become airborne in objectionable concentrations.

In clean rooms, humidity control is affected more by external influences (such as weather changes) than by variations in moisture generated within the space. If processes involving evaporation must take place within the clean room, they should be confined within ventilated enclosures. Some precision manufacturing processes require humidities lower than 35%. Precautions often must be taken to control static electricity by such equipment as ionization grids and grounding straps.

MAKEUP AND EXHAUST AIR

Ventilation and makeup air must also be considered for both room and unitary equipment application. When suction exhaust benches are used and where the exhaust air is discharged from the area through ductwork, the makeup air may be supplied from the room or may be ducted in. If this supply air is ducted from an external source, it should be pre-filtered and conditioned. If the air is supplied from within the area, the space air conditions must not be adversely affected.

Exhaust systems, in which contamination control is necessary, may be contained within unitary equipment or may be remote with central ducts. If the air being exhausted is acidic, toxic, or pyrophoric, the exhaust duct may be epoxy-coated or constructed of stainless steel, polypropylene, Teflon, or other corrosion-resistant materials. In addition, special pollution control systems may also be necessary before the air can be discharged to the atmosphere. As a safety precaution, exhausts ducts for highly toxic materials should be kept at a negative pressure within the entire confines of the building.

NOISE AND VIBRATION

Noise is one of the most difficult variables to control. Due to the high volumes of air necessary to provide the cleanliness levels required, particular attention must be given to the noise generated with the contamination control equipment. For normal applications of laminar flow equipment, the noise level is designed to be below 65 decibels, as measured on the A Scale of a calibrated noise-level meter. In applications where quiet is of utmost importance, the noise levels of this equipment may have to be reduced to about 50 decibels (A Scale). Prior to the start of the design, the noise and vibration criteria should be established.

In normal applications of contamination control equipment, vibration displacement levels need not be dampened below 0.5 μm (20 microinches) in the 1 to 50 Hz range. However, when electronic microscopes and other ultrasensitive instrumentation are used, smaller deflections in different frequency ranges might become critical.

For highly critical areas, the use of vane axial fans should be considered. These fans are easier to silence in the lower frequencies, which are crucial in certain microelectronic operations.

ROOM CONSTRUCTION AND OPERATION

Controlling particulate contamination from other than supply air will depend upon the classification of the space and the type of system and operation involved. Typical items, which may vary with the room class, include the following:

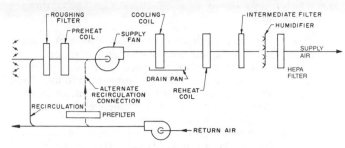

**Fig. 6   Typical Non-Laminar Flow Clean Room
Air-Conditioning Components
Class 100,000**

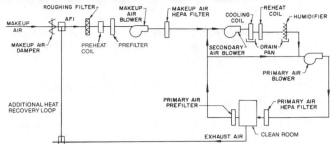

**Fig. 7   Typical Components of a Clean Room
Air-Conditioning System Class 100**

Construction Finishes

1. *General.* Smooth, monolithic, cleanable, and chip resistant, with minimum seams, joints, and no crevices or mouldings.
2. *Floors.* Sheet vinyl, epoxy, or polyester coating with carried-up wall base, or raised floor with and without perforations using the above materials.
3. *Walls.* Plastic, epoxy-coated dry wall, baked enamel, polyester, or porcelain with minimum projections.
4. *Ceilings.* Plaster covered with plastic, epoxy, or polyester coating or with plastic-finished acoustical tiles when entire ceiling is not fully HEPA filtered.
5. *Lights.* Teardrop shaped single lamp fixtures mounted between filters or flush mounted and sealed.
6. *Service Penetrations.* All penetrations for pipes, ducts, conduit runs, etc., should be fully sealed or gasketed.
7. *Appurtenances.* All doors, vision panels, switches, clocks, etc., should have either flush mounted or sloped tops.

Personnel and Garments

1. Hands and face are cleaned before entering area.
2. Lotions and soap containing lanolin are used to lessen skin particles from being emitted.
3. Wearing cosmetics and skin medications are not permitted.
4. Smoking and eating are not permitted.
5. Lint-free smocks, coveralls, gloves, and head and shoe covers are worn.

Materials and Equipment

1. Equipment and materials are cleaned before entry.
2. Nonshedding paper and ballpoint pens are used. Pencils and erasers are not permitted.
3. Work parts are handled with gloved hands, finger cots, tweezers, and other methods to avoid transfer of skin oils and particles.

Particulate Producing Operations

1. Grinding, welding, and soldering operations are shielded and exhausted.
2. Containers are used for transfer and storage of materials.

Entries

1. Air locks and pass-throughs are used to maintain pressure differentials and reduce contamination.

CENTRAL EQUIPMENT

Central air-handling and treatment equipment may include any of the elements indicated in Figures 6 and 7, depending on the conditions required in the space. The sequence of heat transfer and humidification elements may vary, but it is desirable to locate the maximum air treatment equipment downstream of the fan so that leakage is outward from the system.

Filters

Three basic principles or mechanisms of particle collection that apply to clean room filter systems are: (1) impingement, impaction, and interception; (2) straining; or (3) diffusional effects. For more information, refer to Chapter 10 of the 1983 ASHRAE EQUIPMENT Handbook.

The HEPA filter accomplishes filtration by a combination of impingement and interception. The efficiency of this combined method is the sum of these functions. Efficiency increases as: (1) the size of the particle being filtered for an impingement filter increases and (2) the size of the filtered particle for an interception filter decreases. Table 5 may be used as a guide in selecting the type of filters most commonly used in clean room design.

Secondary Air System

If a secondary air system is used, secondary air is drawn from the primary air system return, is conditioned, and reenters the primary system on the suction side of the primary air blowers. Introducing conditioned air in this manner means that the air inlets and outlets operate at substantially the same static pressure level and that the conditioned air fan need only overcome the static pressure losses of the heating, cooling, and humidifying equipment.

Table 5   Ratings of Clean Room Filters

Filter Use	Weight Efficiency AFI Synthetic Dust	Atmospheric Dust Spot Efficiency, NBS and AFI Methods	DOP Method	Dust Loading Capacity
ULPA	a	a	99.9995%	Not Applicable
HEPA—primary air supply bank	a	a	99.97+%	Not Applicable
Prefilter—makeup air or primary	92 to 98%	36 to 65%	20 to 40%	200 to 400 grams 1,000 cfm (470 L/s)
Roughing—makeup filter air	50 to 75%	15 to 51%	1 to 8%	300 to 400 grams 1,000 cfm (470 L/s)

[a]Nondiscriminating results.

Clean Spaces

Figure 8a shows conditioned air flow in a primary air recirculating plenum and ceiling system for a horizontal flow room. Figure 8b shows conditioned air flow with a ceiling air supply plenum. Ductwork with individual filter boots is an alternative to supply plenums. A discussion of the design considerations for each approach are discussed above in the section on air pattern control.

When a plenum is used, air diffusion is critical. Secondary air supply ducts should enter the plenum at a minimum of 10 ft (3 m) upstream of the primary blowers to ensure efficient blower operation. A manually adjustable, opposed blade damper should be installed at each discharge outlet. This method of discharging secondary air allows each primary blower to handle an equal volume of secondary and primary air, this ensuring a more uniform room temperature and humidity gradient. The supply duct may be installed within the plenum, or if insufficient plenum height is available, the duct may be routed above the plenum with each discharge outlet entering the plenum for best air distribution.

Exhaust Air

An activity in the clean room often requires the use of exhaust air equipment. Work stations emitting toxic fumes, ovens emitting heated fumes, small machinery operations, and the like, all must have exhaust air capability. Work stations use the clean room air as their source of makeup air: therefore, the clean room makeup air volume must be increased by the volume of exhaust air. The exhaust air ducts for the equipment should be carefully routed to maintain laminar air flow within the clean room.

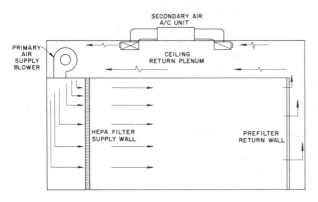

Fig. 8a Typical Secondary Air Location: Horizontal Flow Room

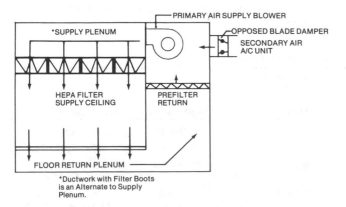

*Ductwork with Filter Boots is an Alternate to Supply Plenum.

Fig. 8b Typical Secondary Air Location: Downflow Laminar Flow Room

Dilution Air

Many clean room activities require the use of solvents, vapors, gases, and the like, which are normally harmless to the operating personnel if concentrations are maintained below certain levels. For example, solvents and solder flux, often used in manufacturing electronic components, are not toxic in dilute concentrations; therefore, it is not necessary to completely isolate these substances from the room atmosphere.

For many airborne substances, the American Conference of Governmental Industrial Hygienists (ACGIH) has established requirements to avoid excessive worker exposure. Specific standards for the allowable concentration of airborne substances are set by the U.S. Occupational Safety and Health Administration (OSHA). These limits are based on working experience, laboratory research, and medical data, and are subject to constant revision. Reference to the latest standards available should be made when evaluating a clean room exposure. The ACGIH publishes a handbook, *Industrial Ventilation,* which may be referred to when limits are to be determined.

TESTS

Three basic test modes for clean room systems are used to evaluate a facility properly: (1) as built, (2) at rest, and (3) operational. A clean room facility cannot be fully evaluated until it has performed under full occupancy and the process to be performed within it is operational. Thus, the techniques for conducting initial performance tests and operational monitoring must be similar and are so treated in this chapter.

Sources of contamination, as previously described, are both external and internal. For both laminar and non-laminar flow clean rooms, the primary air loop is the major source for external contamination. Equipment that applies laser or light scattering principles may be used to detect particles of very small sizes. Some laser particle counters can detect particles as small as 0.1 microns. For particles sizes 5.0 μm and larger, microscopic counting can be used, with the particles collected on a membrane filter through which a sample of air has been drawn.

HEPA filters should be tested for pinhole leaks at the following places: the filter media, the sealant between the media and the filter frame, the filter frame gasket, and the filter bank supporting frames. The area between the wall or ceiling and the frame should also be tested. A pinhole leak at the filter bank can be extremely critical, since the concentration of the leak varies inversely as the square of the pressure drops across the hole.

There are 14 tests for clean rooms described in the Clean Room Testing procedure of the Institute of Environmental Sciences (1984). A determination should be made as to which tests are applicable to a specific clean room project.

REFERENCES

ACGIH. 1984. *Industrial Ventilation, A Manual of Recommended Practice,* American Conference of Governmental Industrial Hygienists, 18th Ed.

Institute of Environmental Sciences. 1984. *Testing Clean Rooms,* IES-RP-CC-006-84-T, November.

Thomas, J.W. 1966. *Aerosol Properties and Aerosol Filtration.* Fifth Annual Technical Meeting and Exhibit, American Association of Contamination Control, March 29-April 1.

USAF. 1965. *Standards and Guidelines for the Design and Operation of Clean Rooms and Clean Work Stations.* U.S. Air Force *Technical Order,* T.O. 00-25-203, August 31.

U.S. Government. 1973. *Clean Room and Work Station Requirements, Controlled Environment Federal Standard* No., 209b, April 24.

CHAPTER 33

DATA PROCESSING SYSTEM AREAS

DATA processing system areas contain computer equipment, as well as the necessary ancillary equipment to meet a particular data processing function. Computers generate heat and contain components sensitive to extremes of temperature, humidity, and the presence of dust. Exposure to conditions outside prescribed limits can cause improper operation or complete shutdown of the equipment.

Ancillary spaces for activities directly related to the computer or for the storage of computer components and materials (including magnetic tape, disk packs and cartridges, data cells, paper, and punch cards) should have environmental conditions comparable to the areas housing the computers, although tolerances generally are wider and the degree of criticality is usually much less. If components and supplies are exposed to temperature and humidity levels outside the limits established by the manufacturer, they must be conditioned to the operating environment in accordance with the manufacturer's recommendations.

Other areas in the data processing complex may house such auxiliary equipment as engine-generators, motor-generators, uninterruptible power supplies (UPS), and transformers. The air-conditioning and ventilating quality requirements are less severe than those for computers, but the continuing satisfactory operation is vital to the proper functioning of the computer system.

DESIGN CRITERIA

The data processing system spaces that house the computers, computer personnel, and associated equipment require air conditioning to maintain proper environmental conditions for both the equipment and the comfort of personnel.

Computer room air conditioning does not require quick response to changes in set points for the environmental conditions, but *maintaining* conditions within established limits is essential to the operation. System reliability is so vital that the

potential cost of system failure often justifies redundant capacity and/or components.

The environmental conditions required by computer equipment vary widely, depending on the manufacturer. Table 1 lists general recommendations on conditions for the computer room. Most manufacturers recommend that the computer equipment draw conditioned air from the room; some, however, permit or recommend direct cooling by supply air. Criteria for air introduced directly to computers differ from usual room air supply conditions; this air supply must remove computer equipment heat adequately and preclude the possibility of condensation within the equipment (see Table 2).

Table 1 Typical Computer Room Design Conditions[a]

Temperature set point and offset	72 ± 2°F (22 ± 1°C)
Relative humidity set point and offset	50 ± 5%
Filtration quality (ASHRAE Std. 52-76 dust spot efficiency test)	45%, minimum 20%

[a]These conditions are typical and fall within the conditions recommended by most computer equipment manufacturers.

Table 2 Design Conditions for Air Supply Directly to Computer Equipment[a]

Conditions	Recommended Levels
Temperature	As required for heat removal but no lower than 60°F (16°C)
Relative humidity	Maximum 65% (some manufacturers permit up to 80%)
Filtration Quality (ASHRAE Std. 52-76, dust spot efficiency test)	45%

[a]These conditions are typical and fall within the conditions recommended by most computer equipment manufacturers, but under no circumstances should conditioned air be supplied directly to a computer unless it is designed and controlled within the manufacturer's limits for the particular piece of equipment.

The preparation of this chapter is assigned to TC 9.2, Industrial Air Conditioning.

Because of the high energy needed to maintain proper environment in data processing areas, the design should hold *net* energy use as low as possible. For instance, heat energy recovery is quite feasible in many installations.

Computer Room Environment

Computer rooms should be kept at the lower end of the temperature tolerance of 72 $\pm$ 2°F (22 $\pm$ 1°C) for two reasons. First, the equipment distributes heat nonuniformly, which may not match the air distribution and/or response of the controls. Setting the controls no higher than 72°F (22°C) generally assures that all equipment will be within the established range for satisfactory operation. Secondly, the lower control temperature provides a cushion for short-term peak load temperature rise without adversely affecting computer operation.

High relative humidity levels may cause improper feeding of cards and paper and, in extreme cases, condensation on machine surfaces. Low relative humidity in combination with other factors may result in static discharge, which can adversely affect the operation of data processing and other electronic equipment.

To maintain proper relative humidity in a computer room, vapor transmission retarders should be installed around the entire envelope sufficient to restrain moisture migration during the maximum expected vapor pressure differences between computer room and surrounding areas. Cable and pipe entrances should be sealed and caulked with a vaporproof material. Door jambs should fit tightly. Windows in colder climates should be double- or triple-glazed.

In localities where the outdoor air contains unusually high quantities of dust, dirt, salt, or corrosive gases, it may be necessary to pass it through higher-efficiency filters or adsorption chemicals before it is introduced into the computer room.

The presence of dust can affect the operation of data processing equipment, so good quality filtration is important. Proper maintenance of filters is very important in the computer room. Dirty filters can reduce air flow, and thereby decrease the sensible heat ratio of computer room air-conditioning equipment. This, in turn, will load the computer room with energy intensive humidification, thereby needlessly increasing the operating cost.

Computer room systems should provide only enough outdoor air for personnel requirements and to maintain the room under a positive pressure relative to surrounding spaces. Since most computer rooms have few occupants and the quantity of conditioned air circulated is high compared with comfort applications, the need to maintain positive pressure is usually the controlling design criterion. In most computer rooms, an outdoor air quantity less than 5% of total supply air will satisfy ventilation requirements and assure against inward leakage. Outdoor air beyond the required minimum increases the cooling and heating loads, and makes control of atmospheric contaminants and winter humidity more difficult.

The air-conditioning system should operate within the noise levels of the computer equipment. This is ordinarily not a difficult criterion to satisfy. Vibration should be isolated to prevent structural transmission of the computer equipment. The computer manufacturer should be consulted regarding computer equipment sound levels and specific special requirements for vibration isolation.

Personnel comfort is also important. Temperature, humidity, and filtration requirements for the equipment are within the comfort range for the room occupants, but drafts and cold surfaces must be kept to a minimum in occupied areas.

Some manufacturers have established criteria for allowable rates of environmental change to prevent shock to the computer equipment. These can usually be satisfied by high quality commercially available controls responding to $\pm 1°$ and $\pm 5\%$ rh. The manufacturer's requirements should be reviewed to be sure that the system will function properly during normal operation and during periods of start-up and shutdown.

Computer equipment will tolerate a somewhat wider range of environmental conditions when not in operation; but to keep the room within those limits and to minimize thermal shock, it may be desirable to operate the air conditioning.

Computer technology is continually changing; during the life of a system, the computer equipment will almost certainly be changed and/or rearranged. The air-conditioning system must be sufficiently flexible to facilitate this rearrangement of components and permit expansion without requiring the system to be rebuilt. In the usual applications, it should be possible to make modifications without extensive air-conditioning shutdowns, and, in highly critical applications, with no shutdown at all.

Ancillary Spaces Environment

Spaces storing products such as paper, cards, and tape generally require the same environmental limits as the computer room itself.

Electrical power supply and conditioning equipment has more tolerance to variation in temperature and humidity than does computer equipment; generally it needs to be treated environmentally in some fashion. Normally, ventilation to remove heat from the equipment is sufficient. Equipment in this category includes motor generators, uninterruptible power supplies (UPS), batteries, voltage regulators, and transformers. Manufacturers' data should be followed to determine the amount of heat release and design conditions for satisfactory operation.

Battery rooms require ventilation to remove hydrogen and control space temperature (optimum 77°F or 25°C). Hydrogen accumulation must be no greater than 3% by volume, with the ventilation system designed to prevent pockets of concentration, particularly at ceilings (EXIDE 1972).

Many computer installations include an engine generator for emergency power, which requires a large amount of ventilation when running. Starting is easier if low ambient temperatures are avoided.

COOLING LOADS

The equipment in a computer room is the major heat source, and it is highly concentrated and distributed nonuniformly. Heat gain from lights should be no greater than that for good quality office space; occupancy loads and outdoor air requirements will be low to moderate. Heat gains through the structure depend on the location and construction of the room. Transmission heat gain to supply spaces should be carefully evaluated and provided for in the design.

Information on computer equipment heat release should be obtained from the computer manufacturer. In general, the data is used without reduction for diversity, unless experience with a similar installation or the computer manufacturer recommends a reduction.

Because of the relatively low occupancy and the low proportion of outdoor air, computer room heat gains are almost entirely sensible. Because of this and the low room design temperatures, air supply quantity per unit of cooling load will be greater than for most comfort applications. Figure 1 shows

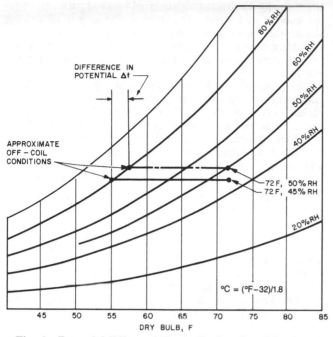

**Fig. 1   Potential Effect of Room Design Conditions on
Design Supply Air Quantity**

how the choice of room design at 72°F (22°C), 45% rh can
reduce air supply quantity by approximately 10% as compared
to a slightly more humid room design of 72°F (22°C), 50% rh.

A sensible heat ratio, approximately 0.9 to 1.0, is common
for computer room applications. This relatively small amount
of latent cooling is adequate to handle the minimum moisture
loads incurred and will not cause needless dehumidification.

AIR-CONDITIONING SYSTEMS

The air-handling apparatus for the computer air-conditioning
system should be independent of other systems in the building,
although it may be desired that systems be cross-connected,
within or without the data processing area, to provide backup.
Redundant air-handling equipment is frequently used; normally automatic operation of such equipment is desired. The air-
handling facilities should provide filtration, cooling and
dehumidification, humidification, and heating of air.

The refrigeration systems should be independent of other
systems and should be capable of year-round operation. It may
be desirable to cross-connect refrigeration equipment, for
backup, as suggested for air-handling equipment. Redundant
refrigeration may be required; the extent of the redundancy will
depend on the importance of the computer installation.

In many cases, standby power is justified for the computer
room air-conditioning system. The system components to receive
standby power require careful analysis to ensure that they provide 24 hour a day, year-round operation.

Computer rooms are being successfully conditioned with a
wide variety of systems including: (1) complete self-contained
packaged units, with air handling and refrigeration apparatus
close-coupled within a common housing and installed within
the computer room; (2) chilled water packaged units located
within the computer room and served by remotely located
refrigeration equipment; and (3) central station air-handling units
with both air-handling and refrigeration equipment located outside the computer room.

Self-Contained Packaged Units

Self-contained units should be specifically designed for computer room applications. These units are built to higher overall
standards of performance and reliability than conventional
packaged air conditioners intended for comfort, although some
major components are identical to those in standard unitary
equipment.

Packaged units are available with (1) multiple reciprocating
compressors and separate multiple refrigeration circuits through
the cooling coil and condensers; (2) air filters to meet computer
room criteria; (3) humidifiers; (4) a reheat coil; (5) corrosion-
resistant construction for coils, humidifiers, and other components; (6) controls; (7) instrumentation such as indicator lights
to show which equipment components are in operation, and
alarms to signal dirty filters and component failure; and (8) filter
gauges to indicate the status of filter loading. Status and/or
alarm devices may be connected to remote monitoring panels.

Although the placement of components varies with the
manufacturer, a typical unit arrangement is shown in Figure 2.
The units can supply air either downward to the computer room
floor cavity or upward to overhead ducts and/or a ceiling
plenum.

The refrigeration cycles for computer room units require a
means for condensing, and this is provided by water-cooled condensers connected with a remote cooling tower, water- or glycol-
cooled condensers connected with a remote radiator, or connections with remotely located air-cooled or evaporative condensers.

Self-contained air conditioners are usually located within the
computer room, but may also be remotely located and ducted
to the conditioned space. If they are remotely located,
temperature and humidity controls should be located in the conditioned space. A major benefit of locating the air conditioner
close to the load is the flexibility of such an arrangement, which
accommodates the ever-changing load pattern within many computer rooms. The space occupied by these packaged units in the
computer room may be expensive, but security considerations

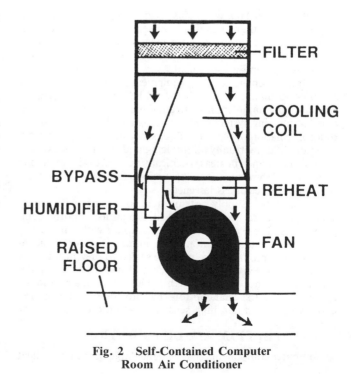

**Fig. 2   Self-Contained Computer
Room Air Conditioner**

alone make it practical to place them there, since normally a central system serving a computer room has no security protection beyond normal building maintenance.

In systems with multiple unitary conditioners, it may be advantageous to introduce outdoor air through one conditioner that serves all of the spaces in the data processing area. Self-contained systems achieve redundancy by providing multiple units, so that the loss of one or more units will have a minimum effect on system performance. Additionally, expansion of the data processing facility is generally much easier to handle with self-contained units.

Chilled Water Packaged Units

These units are similar to complete, self-contained packaged units, except that they are served by remotely located refrigeration units, usually though chilled water connections, so they contain no refrigeration equipment. Since computer components in some systems require a source of chilled water for cooling, the use of chilled water packaged units may be more advantageous in this application. Chilled water supply temperatures suitable for water-cooled computer equipment can range from a low of 42°F (5.5°C), to a high of 60°F (15°C). These chilled water temperatures will normally be compatible with those required for computer room air-conditioning units.

When using chilled water packaged units, reliability of the remote refrigeration system must be considered. This system generally must be capable of operating 24 hours a day, year-round. Low ambient operation must be provided in severe winter locations. Packaged units with chilled water coils, as well as direct expansion coils, are available and afford an alternate refrigeration source when the chilled water plant shuts down.

Chilled water packaged units occupy an area within the computer room, but since they do not contain refrigeration equipment, they require less servicing within the computer room than self-contained equipment.

Central Station Air-Handling Units

Central station supply systems permit using components with larger capacity than is available in self-contained equipment; also, since the equipment is not located within the computer room, it permits a greater variety of choices in air-conditioning system design and arrangement.

Central station air-handling equipment must satisfy computer room performance criteria; it should be arranged to facilitate servicing and maintenance. Redundancy can be achieved by cross-connecting systems, by providing standby equipment, or by a combination of these. No floor space in the computer room is required, and virtually all servicing and maintenance operations are performed in areas specifically devoted to air-conditiong equipment. However, as cooling equipment is outside the computer room, security is lessened.

Central station supply systems must be designed with expansion capability to accommodate additional loads in the computer areas. These systems must be complete with humidification, reheat, dehumidification, and controls. Ductwork penetration of the computer space must be sealed to prevent moisture migration to the computer areas. Central systems for computer rooms should not be tied together with building air-handling systems without special controls that provide for a year-round cooling operation and high sensible heat ratio design factors.

SUPPLY AIR DISTRIBUTION

Computer components that generate large quantities of heat are normally constructed with internal fans and passages to convey cooling air through the machine. The inlet usually draws the air from the computer room, but some manufacturers recommend that certain components of their systems take cooling air directly from the conditioned air supply before it reaches room conditions.

Computer room heat gains are often highly concentrated. For minimum room temperature gradients, supply air distribution should closely match load distribution, and the control thermostat must be located where it will sense average conditons in the area it serves. Return-air thermostats have generally best met computer requirements because of the constantly changing computer equipment arrangement. The distribution system should be sufficiently flexible to accommodate changes in the location and magnitude of the heat gains with a minimum amount of change in the basic distribution system.

Supply air systems usually require approximately 550 cfm per ton (74 L/s per kW) of cooling to satisfy computer room conditions. This airflow rate reduces the hot spots and maintains an even temperature distribution.

The construction materials and methods chosen for air distribution should recognize the need for a clean air supply. Duct or plenum material that may erode must be avoided. Access for cleaning is desirable.

Zoning

Computer rooms should be adequately zoned to maintain temperatures within the design criteria. The extent of zoning is reduced because of the relative small number of rooms and the generally open character of the spaces involved. Except in the smallest computer rooms, some zoning is usually required to minimize temperature variations because of fluctuations in load. As a minimum, individual control for each major space is desirable and, in larger areas, potential for temperature variations may occur within a single room.

Packaged air-conditioning systems using the under floor air supply plenum (Figure 3) adequately self-zone the large computer room area. These systems have return-air temperature and humidity contol, which automatically controls the air being circulated in its zone. The area of the zoning is controlled by the various floor registers and perforated floor panels. These systems give adequate flexibility for relocation of computer equipment and additional future heat loads.

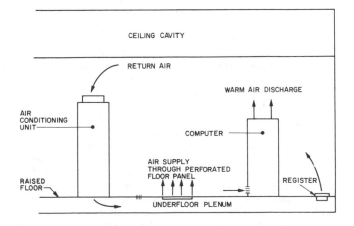

Fig. 3 Typical Underfloor Distribution

Underfloor Plenum Supply

To facilitate interconnection of equipment components by electric cables, data processing equipment is usually set above a false floor, which affords a flat walking surface over the space where the connecting cables are installed. This space can be an air-distribution channel for systems that use it either as a plenum or, less often, to accommodate ducts. Underfloor air is distributed to the room through perforated panels or registers set or built into the floor panels located around the room and in the vicinity of computer equipment with especially high heat release.

Some computer room floor manufacturers produce perforated floor panels similar in appearance to, and interchangeable with, conventional computer room floor panels. These panels allow the supply air to be easily changed to accommodate shifting equipment loads. The free area of various manufacturers' panels vary significantly. One configuration has slide-type dampers so airflow may be balanced in a manner comparable to a floor-mounted register (Figures 3 and 4).

Floor-mounted registers allow volume adjustment and are capable of longer throws and better directional control than perforated floor outlets. However, they are usually located outside traffic areas because some types are not completely flush-mounted and almost all tend to be drafty for nearby personnel. Perforated floor panels are especially suitable for installation in normal traffic aisles because they are completely level with the floors. In addition, when operated with moderate air flow, they produce a high degree of mixing near the point of discharge. For this reason, they may be located fairly close to equipment air inlets, with less danger of direct injection of unmixed conditioned air to the computer than with registers that have lower induction ratios.

Air flow is through all openings in the floor cavity; if direct flow to a computer unit is not desired, all openings between the unit and the floor cavity should be sealed. Most openings between the underfloor space and the equipment accommodate cables; collars are available to fit the cable and seal the opening.

It is important that there be sufficient clearance area within the raised floor cavity to permit air flow. At least 12 in. (300 mm) clearance is desirable and 10 in. (250 mm) is the normal minimum; in applications where cabling is extensive and/or air quantities are especially high, additional clearance may be required.

The supply connection from unitary equipment to an underfloor cavity should allow minimum turbulence; turning vanes at the unit discharge sometimes helps accomplish this. The supply to the cavity should be central to the area served, where possible, and abrupt changes in direction should be avoided. Piping and conduit to unitary equipment should not interfere with airflow from the unit.

Where multiple zones are served from the underfloor plenum, dividing baffles may generally be avoided, as supply and return-air flow can be preducted, *i.e.*, to flow through the course of least resistance. If zone configurations require dividing baffles, or if codes require them to protect against spread of fire, they may inhibit the flexibility of the computer system as a whole, because computer units in different zones often require cabling interconnection, which requires penetration of the zone baffles whenever cabling changes are made.

Surfaces of underfloor plenums may require insulation or vapor barriers if (1) supply air temperatures drop low enough to cause condensation on either side of plenum surfaces or (2) temperatures on the floor above a ceiling plenum become so low as to cause discomfort to occupants. Insulation may also be required to reduce heat transmission through plenum surfaces. Plenums should be constructed airtight and be thoroughly cleaned and smoothly finished to prevent entrainment of foreign materials in the air stream. The use and method of construction of plenums may be limited by local codes or fire underwriter regulations.

The potential adverse effects of direct air supply on the computer equipment (condensation within the machine) are serious enough to discourage its use unless the manufacturer insists on it. If this occurs, sufficient controls and safety devices must be installed to ensure operation within specified limits.

Ceiling Plenum Supply

Overhead supply through perforated ceiling panels as diffusers are occasionally suited to computer rooms; this arrangement may be used with either central station or packaged-unit unitary equipment. Such systems can satisfy equipment requirements, as well as personal comfort; however, they are generally not as flexible as underfloor plenum supply systems.

Distribution of air can be regulated either by selective placement of acoustical pads on the perforated panels of a metal panel ceiling or the location of *active* perforated sections of a lay-in acoustical tile ceiling. Where precise distribution is essential, active ceiling panels or air supply zones may be equipped with

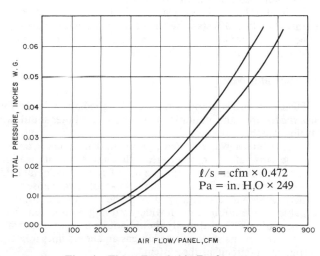

$$\ell/s = cfm \times 0.472$$
$$Pa = in. \ H_2O \times 249$$

Fig. 4   Floor Panel Air Performance

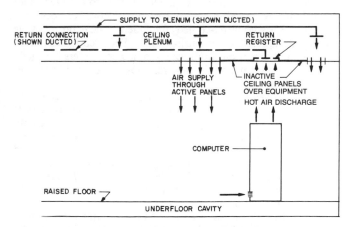

Fig. 5   Typical Ceiling Plenum Distribution

air valves. When required for zoning or to meet codes, overhead plenums may be divided by baffles without interference with underfloor computer system cabling. Ceiling plenums, if properly constructed and cleaned, are more likely to remain clean than are underfloor plenums.

Plenums must be sufficiently deep to permit airflow without turbulence; the depth will depend on air quantities. Best conditions may be achieved by the use of distribution ductwork, with the air discharged into the plenum through adjustable outlets above the ceiling (Figure 5). Sealing, surfaces, and insulation of ceiling plenums must be constructed as shown previously in the "Underfloor Plenum Supply" section.

Overhead Ducted Supply

Overhead ducted supply systems should be limited to applications where air supply concentrations are not high or the need for flexibility is not great. These factors impose a severe limitation on the use of overhead ducted supply systems. Where loads are high, overhead diffusers may cause drafts, especially where ceilings are low. Relocation of outlets can be diffiult to accomplish in a facility that must remain in operation.

RETURN AIR

The more common return-air method has a minimum number of return openings. With packaged units, the use of a free return from supply outlets back to the return on the unit is typical (Figure 3). Inlets should be located near high-heat loads, and the effect of future modifications of the computer installation should be considered.

Ceiling plenum returns have successfully captured a portion of the computer heat, as well as a portion of the heat from the lights, directly in the return-air stream. This allows a reduction in the supply air circulation rate. A duct collar is usually provided to the top of the self-contained unit; the unit will draw the air from the return-plenum area, treat it, and discharge it into the underfloor supply plenum.

WATER-COOLED COMPUTER EQUIPMENT

Some computer equipment requires water cooling to maintain equipment environment within levels established by the manufacturer. Generally, a closed system circulates distilled water through passages in the computer to cool it. The manufacturer supplies this cooling system as part of the computer equipment, and a water-to-water heat exchanger attached to a chilled water connection to the air-conditioning system does the cooling.

In systems with water-cooled components, the majority of the total cooling is still accomplished by air. The overall heat release to the computer room from water-cooled computers is usually equal to (or greater than) that for most air-cooled computer systems.

Water-cooled equipment requires chilled water in the computer room. This can be provided either by a small separate chiller matched in capacity to the water-cooled computer equipment or by a branch of the chilled water serving central or decentralized air-handling units. Construction and insulation of chilled water piping and selection of the operating temperatures should be such that they minimize the possibility of leaks and condensation—especially within the computer room, while satisfying the requirements of the systems served.

Chilled water systems for water-cooled computer equipment must be designed for water temperature within the computer

manufacturers' tolerances and for continuous availability. Refrigeration systems for chilled water must be capable of operating year-round, 24 hours a day.

AIR-CONDITIONING COMPONENTS

Controls

A well-planned control system must coordinate the performance of the temperature and humidity equipment.

Controls of self-contained, packaged computer air-conditioning systems have been tested, coordinated, and most likely improved upon over several installations. Controls for systems not air-conditioned by packaged equipment may be included in a project-specific contol system, which may be computer based.

Space thermostats and humidistats should be carefully located to sample room conditions most accurately.

Where backup power is provided for the computer installation and some portion of the HVAC equipment, it is imperative that the necessary control equipment also have power backup. Liquid detectors, for underfloor plenum systems, are useful in warning of accidental water spillage, which otherwise could go undetected for some time.

Refrigeration

Separate refrigeration facilities for the data processing area are desirable because performance requirements often differ drastically from those for comfort systems. Refrigeration systems should generally satisfy the following criteria: (1) match the cooling load, be capable of expansion, and have a degree of flexibility comparable to other components; (2) be capable of year-round and continous operation; (3) provide the degree of reliability and redundancy required by the particular operation; (4) be capable of being operated, serviced, and maintained without interfering with normal operation; and (5) be operable with emergency power if this is a system requirement. Fulfillment of these requirements results in the use of multiple units or cross-connections with other reliable systems.

Self-contained systems invariably use reciprocating compressors and direct-expansion cooling. Central systems and systems using decentralized air handling have a wider range of choice, because reciprocating, centrifugal, or absorption refrigeration equipment can be selected.

If the installation is especially critical, it may be necessary to install up to 100% standby refrigeration capacity or capacity adequate to provide the minimum requirements that can be tolerated until repair or replacement.

Condensing Methods

Heat rejection equipment must be designed and selected for *worst case* operating conditions to prevent computer shutdown during weather extremes.

In some areas, water-cooled equipment using cooling towers may be satisfactory; in other areas, the need for winterization and water treatment may preclude use of systems vulnerable to freezing or open to the atmosphere. Air-cooled condensers are widely used and are equipped with head pressure controls capable of operation through widely varying outdoor ambient temperatures. They ordinarily should not be used with separate condenser curcuits and separate hot gas and liquid lines for each refrigeration circuit in the system.

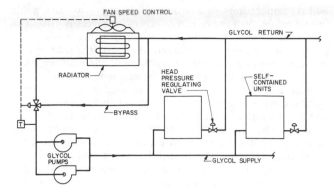

Fig. 6   Glycol System for Condensing

Glycol-cooled radiators, or water-cooled radiators in climates not subject to freezing, permit using a closed system on the condensing side and facilitate head pressure control by permitting control of the condensing medium. In systems where multiple refrigeration systems or units are remote from the point of heat rejection to the atmosphere, radiator-cooled systems may significantly simplify piping and capacity control (Figure 6).

Glycol-cooled or water-cooled systems require water piping in the computer areas, and precautions must be taken to prevent and detect possible leaks.

Humidification

Many types of humidifiers are used to serve data processing system areas. Types of humidifiers include: steam with outside source of steam, steam-generating, pan with immersion element, pan with infrared (quartz lamp), and wetted-pad. Where a continuously available clean source is available, steam humidification should be considered. The humidification method chosen must be responsive to control, low in maintenance, and free of moisture carryover.

Chilled Water

Chilled water distribution systems should be designed to the same standards of quality, reliability, and flexibility as the rest of the system. Multiple units should be provided for those components that must be shut down for servicing or routine maintenance. The chilled water system should be designed for

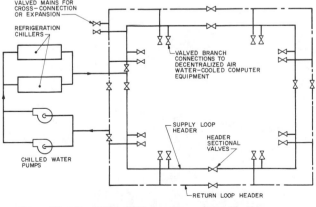

Fig. 7   Chilled Water Loop Distribution

expansion or the addition of new conditioners without extensive shutdown where any likelihood of growth exists.

Figure 7 illustrates a looped chilled water system with sectional valves and multiple valved branch connections. The branches could serve air handlers or water-cooled computer equipment. The valves permit modifications or repairs without requiring complete shutdown.

Chilled water temperature should match the load and minimize the possibility of condensation, especially if portions of the system are installed within the computer room. Since computer room loads are primarily sensible, relatively high chilled water temperatures should be circulated. Although this may result in some reduction in unit capacity or require a deeper cooling coil, the net effect on system operation and efficiency will be positive.

Water temperatures as high as 48 °F (9 °C) are still slightly below the dew point of a 72 °F (22 °C), 45% rh room and several degrees below that of a 72 °F (22 °C), 50% rh room. Because of this and because the operation of system controls may not regulate chilled water temperature precisely, the chilled water piping must be fully insulated.

The piping system should be pressure tested. The test pressure should be applied in increments in occupied areas if a leak could interfere with the operation of the computer system. Drip pans should be placed below any valves or other components that cannot be satisfactorily insulated within the computer room. A good quality strainer should be used to prevent clogging heat exchanger passages.

If cross-connections with other systems are made, the possible effects of the introduction of dirt, scale, or other impurities on the computer room system must be evaluated and handled.

INSTRUMENTATION

Because computer equipment malfunctions may be caused by, or attributed to, improper regulation of the computer room thermal environment, it may be desirable to keep permanent records of the space temperature and humidity. If direct air supply to the machines is used, these records can then be correlated with machine function. Alarms should be incorporated with the recorder to signal if temperature or humidity limitations are not satisfied. Where chilled water is supplied directly to computer units, records should be made of the chilled water temperature and pressure: entering and leaving.

A sufficient number of indicating thermometers and pressure gauges should be placed throughout the system so that operating personnel can tell, at a glance, when unusual conditions prevail. Properly maintained and accurate filter guages are simple devices that, when properly used, can help prevent loss of system capacity and maintain correct computer room conditions.

Sensing devices to indicate leaks or the presence of water in the computer room underfloor cavity are desirable, especially if glycol or chilled water distribution lines are installed under pressure within the computer room. Low points in drip pans installed below piping should also be monitored.

All monitoring and alarm devices should give local indication; if the system is in a building with a remote monitoring point, indications of system malfunctions should be transmitted to activate alarms in the remote location.

FIRE PROTECTION

Fire protection for the air-conditioning system should be fully integrated with fire protection for the computer room and the building as a whole. Applicable codes must be complied with, and the owner's insurers consulted. Automatic extinguishing systems afford the highest degree of protection. Fire underwriters often recommend an automatic sprinkler system (Jacobson 1967). Most computer system owners are reluctant to install such a system because of the use of water, so most computer rooms are not so protected.

Use of Halon® fire-extinguishing systems in computer facilities have become more frequent (NFPA 1981). In facilities using Halon® equipment, a prompt means of ventilation should be considered. Also, any openings, such as ventilation ducts, leading outside the Halon-protected space must have dampers that close immediately upon discharge of the Halon.

At a minimum, sensing devices should be placed in both the room and the air-conditioned air stream to warn of fire. Sensing devices should be located in supply and return-air passages and in the underfloor cavity when electric cables are installed, whether or not this space is used for air supply. These devices should provide early warning to products of combustion, even if smoke is not visible and temperatures are at or near normal levels.

Any fire protection system should include a shutdown of computer power, either manual or automatic, depending on the criticality of the system and on the potential effect of shutdown because of false alarms (NFPA 1984).

HEAT RECOVERY AND ENERGY CONSERVATION

Computer room systems are attractive candidates for heat-recovery systems because of their large, relatively steady year-round loads. If the heat removed by the conditioning system can be efficiently transferred and applied elsewhere in the building, some cost saving may be realized. However, reliability is a prime requirement in most computer installations, and any added complication to the basic conditioning system that might impair reliability of the system or otherwise adversely affect performance should be carefully considered before being incorporated into the design. Potential monetary loss from system malfunction or unscheduled shutdown will often outweigh savings because of increased operating efficiency.

Heat rejected for condensing can be used for space heating, domestic water heating, or other process heat. Packaged, self-contained units are available with such heat-recovery components. When an airside economizer is used in cooling computer areas, outdoor air humidification requirements should be considered. Use of a liquid heat exchange between cool outdoor air and the interior air is economically feasible in some climates. Packaged, self-contained units are available with an additional cooling coil for chilled glycol solution.

Energy conservation can be achieved by effecting optimum operating conditions. For instance, coil surface temperatures should be maintained as high as possible to cool the space adequately, yet dehumidify no more than necessary. Coil temperatures lower than necessary waste energy, both through higher refrigeration energy consumption and over-dehumidifying. Annual energy-use calculations or simulations to evaluate the economics of various designs are often desirable.

REFERENCES

Jacobson, D.W. 1967. Automatic sprinkler protection for essential electric and electronic equipment. *NFPA Fire Journal,* January, p. 48.
NFPA. 1981. *Protection of Electronic Computer/Data Processing Equipment.* National Fire Code 75-81. National Fire Protection Assn., Quincy, MA.
NFPA. 1984. *National Electrical Code.* National Fire Protection Assn., Quincy, MA.
NFPA. 1980. Halon 1301 Fire Extinguishing Systems. National Fire Code 12A-80. National Fire Protection Assn., Quincy, MA.

CHAPTER 34

PRINTING PLANTS

THIS chapter outlines air-conditioning requirements for key printing operations. Air conditioning of printing plants can provide controlled, uniform air moisture content and temperature in working spaces. Paper, the principal material used in printing, is hygroscopic and very sensitive to variations in the humidity of the surrounding air. Problems caused by expansion and contraction of paper in the printing process are solved by controlling moisture content and exposure of paper from the mill until printing is complete.

GENERAL DESIGN CRITERIA

The three basic methods of printing are as follows:

1. Letterpress (relief printing): ink is applied to a raised surface that does the printing.
2. Lithography (Planographic printing): the inked surface that does the printing is neither in relief nor recessed.
3. Gravure (intaglio printing): the linked areas are recessed below the surface.

Figure 1 describes the general work flow through a printing plant. The operation begins at the publisher and ends with two products: (1) finished printing and (2) paper waste. Paper waste may be as high as 20% of the total paper used. The profitability of a printing operation requires efficient paper use. Without proper air conditioning, quality control is extremely difficult to achieve.

Sheetfed printing feeds individual sheets through the press from a stack or load of sheets, then collects the printed sheets. Webfed rotary printing uses a continuous web of paper, which is fed through the press from a roll. The printed material is cut and folded and delivered from the press as signatures.

Sheetfed printing is a slow process in which the ink is essentially dry as the sheets are delivered from the press. *Offsetting*, the transference of an image from one sheet to another, is prevented by applying a powder or starch to each sheet as it is delivered from the press. The starch separates the sheets enough for sufficient drying to prevent offsetting. Starches present a housekeeping problem. The starch particles (30 to 40 μm in size) tend to fly and eventually settle on any horizontal surface.

The preparation of this chapter is assigned to TC 9.2, Industrial Air Conditioning.

Temperature and relative humidity have little to do with web breaks or runability of paper in a webfed press, if both are controlled within normal human comfort limits (Darnall 1970). At extremely low humidity, static electricity causes the paper to cling to the rollers, creating undue stress on the web, particularly with high-speed presses, and can be a hazard when flammable solvent inks are used.

Various areas in the printing plant require special attention to processing and heat loads. For example, an engraving department must have very clean air—not as clean as an industrial clean room, but cleaner than that required for an office.

Engraving and photographic areas require special ventilation standards because of the chemicals used. The nitric acid fumes used in powderless etching require stainless steel or aluminum ducts. Stereotype departments have very high heat loads. Composing room operations, which may include computer equipment, should be given the same attention as similar office areas. The high loads created by lead pots on typecasting machines are no longer common with new processes. Excessive dust carried into the mailroom from the cutting operation in the press folders must be handled properly.

The pressroom exhaust air must be treated to eliminate pollutants (pigments, oils, resins, solvents, and dust) exhausted into the atmosphere. Ink mist suppression systems, applied as part of the presses, have reduced the ink mist carried into the exhaust filtration system.

Air-conditioning and air-handling equipment used in printing plants is conventional. Ventilation of storage areas should be about one-half air change per hour, and bindery ventilation should be about one air change per hour. High-piled storage may need roof-mounted smoke and heat-venting devices. Air distribution in pressrooms is a compromise. The air supplied must not be close enough to the press equipment to cause flutter of the web and not too high to force contaminants or heat (which normally would be removed by roof vents) down to the occupied level.

In the bindery, loads of loose signatures are stacked near the equipment. Thus, it is difficult to supply air to occupants without scattering signatures. One approach is to run the main ducts at the ceiling with many supply branches dropped to within 8 to 10 ft (2.5 to 3 m) of the floor. Conventional adjustable-blow diffusers, often linear type, are used.

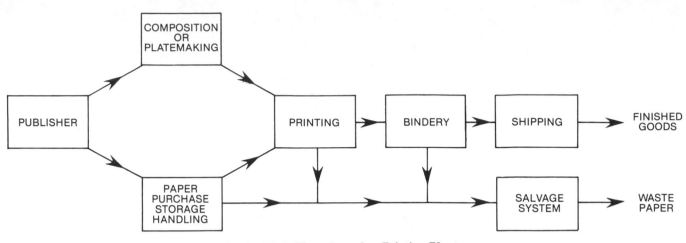

Fig. 1 **Work Flow through a Printing Plant**

CONTROL OF PAPER

Control of paper's moisture content and temperature is important in all printing, particularly in multicolor lithography. Paper should be received at the printing plant in moistureproof wrappers, which are not removed or broken until the paper is brought to pressroom temperature. Exposed paper at temperatures substantially below the room temperature rapidly absorbs moisture from the air, with resulting distortion. Figure 2 shows the time required to temperature-condition wrapped paper. Paper is usually ordered by the printer at a moisture content approximately in equilibrium with the relative humidity maintained in the pressroom. Paper makers find it difficult to supply paper in equilibrium with higher than 50% rh.

The sword hygrometer (or paper hygroscope) can check the hygroscopic condition of paper relative to the surrounding air. The blade contains a moisture-sensitive element, and its expansion or contraction actuates the pointer in a dial on the handle. The instrument is waved in the air until the pointer comes to rest, and the dial is set at zero. The sword is then inserted into the paper, and the pointer movement from zero indicates the paper's moisture relative to the surrounding air.

Figure 3 illustrates sword readings taken on three piles of paper in a pressroom. The first indicates that the paper is too dry to be exposed to room air without forming wavy edges. The second indicates that the paper is in equilibrium with the air, correct for all sheetfed printing, except multi-color lithography. The third was taken on paper wetter than the air in the pressroom. This paper was conditioned to balance with the air in the paper stock room, where the relative humidity was 7% above that in the pressroom, optimal for multicolor lithographic printing.

Mill wrappings and roll tightness normally prevent detrimental effects on a paper roll for about six months. If the wrapper is damaged, moisture penetration of not more than 0.125 in. (3 mm) may be expected.

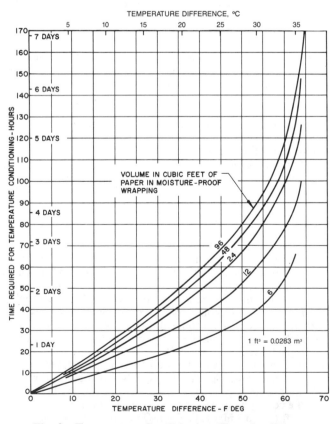

Fig. 2 **Temperature Conditioning Chart for Paper**

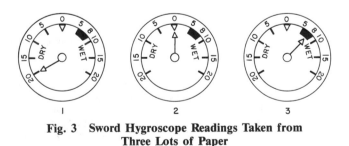

Fig. 3 **Sword Hygroscope Readings Taken from Three Lots of Paper**

PLATEMAKING

Humidity and temperature control are important in making lithographic and collotype plates, photoengravings, and gravure plates and cylinders. The moisture content and temperature of the plates affect the sensitivity of the coating. The coatings increase in light senstivity with increasing relative humidity and temperature, requiring adjustments in light intensity or length of exposure to give uniformity.

Maintaining constant dry-bulb temperature and relative humidity in platemaking rooms provides a plate at a known control point. A bichromated colloid coating starts to age and harden as soon as it is dry. The rate will vary with the atmosphere, so exposures made a few hours apart may be quite different. This rate of reaction can be estimated more closely when the space is air conditioned. Exposure can then be reduced progressively to maintain uniformity. An optimum relative humidity of 45% or less substantially increases the useful life of bichromated colloid coatings; the rh control should be within 2%. A dry-bulb temperature of 75 to 80 °F (24 to 27 °C) maintained within 2 °F (1 °C) is good practice. The ventilation air requirements of the plate room should be investigated. A plant with a large production of deep-etch plates should consider locating this operation outside the conditioned area.

Exhausts for platemaking operations consist primarily of lateral or downdraft systems at each operation. Because of their bulkiness or weight, plates or cylinders are generally conveyed by an overhead rail system to the work station, where they are lowered into the tank for plating, etching, or grinding. Exhaust ducts must be below or to one side of the working area, so lateral exhausts are generally used for open surface tanks.

Exhaust quantities vary, depending on the nature of the solution, but they should provide 100 cfm/ft² (500 L/s per m²) at standard conditions of surface of solution and/or a control velocity of 50 fpm (0.25 m/s) at the side of the tank opposite the exhaust intake. To minimize air quantities and increase efficiency, tanks should be covered. Excessive supply air ventilation across open tanks should be avoided. Because of the nature of the exhaust, the duct construction in many systems must be acid-proof and liquid-tight to prevent moisture condensation.

Webfed offset operation and related departments are similar to webfed letterpress operation, without the heat loads created in the composing room and stereotype departments. Special attention should be given to air cleanliness and ventilation in platemaking to eliminate chemical fumes and dust errors in the plates.

A rotogravure plant can be hazardous because highly volatile solvents are used. Equipment must be explosion-proof, and air-handling equipment must be sparkproof. Clean air must be supplied at controlled temperature and relative humidity, and the exhaust requires reclamation or destruction systems to keep photosensitive hydrocarbons from the atmosphere.

Currently available systems use activated carbon for continuous processing or eliminate the pollutants by rapid oxidation. The amount of solvents reclaimed may exceed that added to the ink.

LETTERPRESS

Letterpress printing relies on a raised surface to transfer ink by pressure directly to paper. Ink rollers apply ink only to the raised surface of the printing plate. Only the raised surface touches the paper to transfer the desired image.

Air conditioning in newspaper pressrooms and other web letterpress printing processes minimize problems caused by static electricity, ink mist, and expansion or contraction of the paper during printing. A wide range of operating conditions is satisfactory. The temperature should be selected for operator comfort.

At web speeds of 1000 to 2000 fpm (5 to 10 m/s), control of relative humidity is not essential because of the application of heat to dry inks. Moisture is applied to the web in some types of printing and passing the web over chill rolls further sets the ink.

The webfed letterpress ink is a heat-set ink, made with high boiling, slow evaporating synthetic resins and petroleum oils dissolved or dispersed in hydrocarbon solvents. The solvent has a narrow boiling range with a low volatility at room temperatures and a fast evaporating rate at elevated temperatures. The solvents are vaporized in the driers (part of the press) at temperatures of 400 to 500 °F (200 to 260 °C), leaving the resins and oils on the paper. Webfed letterpress ink is dried after all colors of ink are applied to the web.

The paper, at speeds of 1000 to 2000 fpm (5 to 10 m/s), passes through driers of several types: open-flame gas cup, flame impingement, high velocity hot air, or steam drum type.

Exhaust quantities through a press-drier system vary with the type of driers used and the speed of the press from about 7000 to 15,000 cfm (3000 to 7000 L/s) at standard conditions. Exhaust temperatures range between 250 and 400 °F (120 and 200 °C).

The solvent-containing exhaust is heated to temperatures of 1300 °F (700 °C) in an air pollution control device to incinerate the effluent. A catalyst can be used to reduce the temperature required for combustion from 1000 °F (540 °C) but requires periodic inspection and rejuvenation. Heat recovery is used to reduce the fuel required for incineration and to heat pressroom makeup air.

LITHOGRAPHY

Lithography prints with a grease-treated printing image receptive to ink, on a surface that is neither raised nor depressed. Both grease and ink repel water. This method applies water to all areas of the plate, except the printing image. Ink is then applied only to the printing image and transferred to the paper.

Offset printing transfers the image first to a rubber blanket and then to the paper. Sheetfed and web offset printing are similar to letterpress printing. The inks are similar but contain water-resistant vehicles and pigment. In web offset and gravure printing, relative humidity in the pressroom should be controlled at a low level, and the temperature should be selected for comfort or, at worst, to avoid heat stress. It is important to maintain steady conditions.

The pressroom for sheet multicolor offset printing has more exacting humidity requirements than other printing processes. The paper must remain flat with constant dimensions during multicolor printing in which the paper may make up to six or more passes through the press over a period of a week or more. If the paper does not have the right moisture content at the start, or if there are significant changes in atmospheric humidity during the process, the paper will not retain its dimensions and flatness, and misregister will result. In many cases of color printing, a register accuracy of 0.005 in. (0.13 mm) is required. Figure 4 shows the necessity of close control of the air relative humidi-

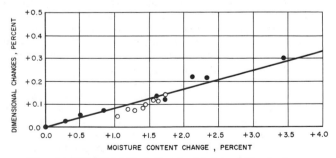

Fig. 4   Effects of Variation in Moisture Content on Dimensions of Printing Papers (Weber and Snyder 1934)

ty to achieve this result. The data shown in this figure are for composite lithographic paper.

Maintaining constant moisture content of the paper is complicated because paper picks up moisture from the moist offset blanket during printing—0.1 to 0.3% for each impression (Latham 1962). When two or more printings are made in close register work, the paper at the start of the printing process should have a moisture content in equilibrium with air at 5 to 8% rh above the pressroom air. At this condition, the moisture evaporated from the paper into the air nearly balances the moisture added by the press. In obtaining register, it is important to keep the sheet flat and free from wavy or tight edges. To do this, the relative humidity balance of the paper should be slightly above that of the pressroom atmosphere. This balance is not as critical in four-color presses because the press moisture does not penetrate the paper fast enough between colors to affect sheet dimensions or sheet distortion.

Recommended Environment

The Graphic Arts Technical Foundation recommends 76 to 80°F (25 to 27°C) dry-bulb temperature and 43 to 47% rh as ideal conditions in a lithographic pressroom, with control ±2% rh and ±2°F (±1°C) dry-bulb temperature. The result of relative humidity variations on register may be estimated for offset paper from Figure 4. Closer relative humidity control of the pressroom air is required for multicolor printing of 76 in. (2 m) sheets as compared with 22 in. (0.6 m) sheets for the same register accuracy. Closer control is required for multicolor printing, where the sheet makes two or more trips through the press, than for one-color printing. Comfort and economy of operation influence the choice of temperature.

Drying of ink is affected by temperature and humidity, so uniform results and standardized procedures are difficult to obtain without control of the atmospheric conditions. Printing inks must dry rapidly to prevent offsetting and smearing. High relative humidity and high moisture content of paper tend to prevent ink penetration, and more ink remains on the surface than can be quickly oxidized. This affects drying time, intensity of color, and uniformity of ink on the surface. Relative humidity below 60% is favorable for drying at a comfortable temperature.

The air-conditioning system for the pressroom of a lithographic plant should control air temperature and relative humidity, filter the air, supply ventilation air, and distribute the air without pronounced drafts around the presses. Use of anti-offset sprays to set the ink creates an additional air-filtering load from the pressroom air. Drafts and high air flow over the press lead to excessive drying of the ink and water, which may cause operation troubles due to scumming.

The operating procedures of the pressroom should be analyzed to determine the heat removal load. The lighting load is high and constant throughout the day. The temperature of the paper brought into the pressroom and the length of time it is in the room should be considered to determine the sensible load from the paper. Figure 2 shows the hours required for wrapped paper to reach room temperature. The press motors usually constitute a large portion of the internal sensible heat gain.

Readings should be taken to obtain the running power load of the larger multicolor presses. The moisture content of the paper fed to the press and the relative humidity of the air must be considered in computing the internal latent heat gain. The printer usually specifies paper that is in equilibrium with air at a relative humidity somewhat higher than the pressroom condition. This means the paper will give up moisture to the space

as it absorbs moisture from the press. If the moisture transfer is in balance, the water used in the printing process would be included in the internal moisture load. It is preferable to determine the water evaporation from the presses by test.

Air-Conditioning Systems

Precise multicolor offset lithography printing requires refrigeration with provision for separate humidity control, or sorption dehumidifying equipment for independent humidity control and provision for cooling. The need for humidity control in the pressroom may be determined by calculating the dimensional change of the paper for each percent change in relative humidity and checking this with the required register for the printing process.

The photographic department air conditioning is usually considered next in importance to the pressroom. Most of the work in offset lithography is done on film. Air conditioning controls cleanliness and comfort and holds the size of the film on register work. The quality of work and accuracy in this department carries over to other departments.

Air conditioning is important in the stripping department, both for comfort and for maintaining size and register. Curling of the film and flats, and shrinkage or stretch of materials can be minimized by maintaining constant relative humidity. This is particularly important on close register color work. The photographic area, stripping room, and platemaking area are usually maintained at the same conditions as the pressroom. Driers used for web offset printing are the same type as for web-fed letterpress. Drying is less of a problem, partly because of the lesser amounts of ink applied and because of lower press speeds—800 to 1800 fpm (4 to 9 m/s).

ROTOGRAVURE

Rotogravure printing uses a cylinder with minute ink wells etched in the surface to form the printing image. Ink is applied to the cylinder, filling the wells. All excess ink is then removed from the cylinder surface by doctor blades, leaving only the ink in the wells, which make up the printing image. The image is then transferred to the paper as it passes between the printing cylinder and an impression cylinder.

Expansion, contraction, and distortion in sheetfed gravure printing, as in offset printing, should be prevented because of the importance of correct register. The paper need not be in equilibrium with air at a relative humidity higher than that of the pressroom, because no moisture is added to the paper in the printing process. The humidity and temperature control is exacting, as in offset printing. The relative humidity should be 45 to 50%, controlled within ±2%, and a comfort temperature within ±2°F (±1°C).

Gravure printing ink dries principally by evaporating the solvent in the ink, leaving a solid film of pigment and resin. The solvent is low-boiling hydrocarbon, and evaporation takes place rapidly, even without the use of heat. The solvents have closed-cup flash points from 22 to 80°F (−5 to 27°C) and are classified as Group I or special hazard liquids by local code and insurance company standards.

As a result, in areas adjacent to gravure press equipment and solvent and ink storage areas, electrical equipment must be Class I, Division 1 or 2, as described by the National Electrical Code, and ventilation requirements (both supply and exhaust) are stringent. Ventilating systems should be designed for high reliability, with sensors to detect unsafe pollutant concentrations and initiate alarm or safety shutdown.

Rotogravure printing units operate in tandem, each superimposing printing over that printed from a preceding unit. Press speeds range from 1200 to 2400 fpm (6 to 12 m/s). Each unit is equipped with its own drier to prevent subsequent smearing or smudging.

A typical drying system consists of four driers (or perhaps a total of 12 driers for 12 printing units) connected to an exhaust fan. Each dryer is equipped with recirculating fans and heating coils. An air quantity of 5000 to 8000 cfm (2500 to 4000 L/s) at standard conditions is recirculated by a blower through a steam or hot water coil and then through jet nozzles at 130°F (55°C). The hot air impinges on the web and drives off the solvent-laden vapors from the ink. It is normal to exhaust half of this air. The system should be designed and adjusted to prevent solvent vapor concentration from exceeding 25% of its lower flammable limit (Marsailes 1970). Where this is not possible, constant lower-flammable-limit (LFL) monitoring, concentration control, and safety shutdown capability should be included.

In exhaust-system design for a particular process, solvent vapor should be captured from the printing unit where paper enters and leaves the drier, from the fountain and sump area, and from the printed paper, which continues to release solvent vapor as it passes from printing unit to unit. Details of the process, such as ink and paper characteristics and rate of use, are required to determine exhaust quantities (Ruby).

When dilution-type ventilation is used, exhaust of 1000 to 1500 scfm (500 to 750 L/s) at standard conditions at the floor is often provided between each unit. The makeup air units are adjusted to supply slightly less air to the pressroom than that exhausted to move air from surroundings into the pressroom.

OTHER PLANT FUNCTIONS

Flexography

Flexography is a type of printing that requires rubber raised printing plates and functions much like letterpress. Flexography is used principally in the packaging industry to print labels. Flexographic printing is also used to print on smooth surfaces, such as plastics and glass.

Collotype Printing

Collotype or photogelatin printing is a sheetfed printing process related to lithography. The printing surface is bichromated gelatin with varying affinity for ink and moisture, depending on the degree of light exposure received. There is no mechanical dampening as in lithography, and the necessary moisture in the gelatin printing surface is maintained by operating the press in an atmosphere of high relative humidity, usually about 85%. Since the tone values printed are very sensitive to changes in moisture content of the gelatin, relative humidity should be maintained within ±2%.

Temperature must also be closely maintained, since tone values are very sensitive to changes in ink viscosity; 80 ± 3°F (27 ±2°C) is recommended. Collotype presses are usually partitioned off from the main plant, which is kept at a lower relative humidity, and the paper is exposed to the high relative humidity only while it is being printed.

Salvage Systems

Salvage systems remove paper trim and shredded paper waste from production areas and carry airborne shavings to a cyclone collector, where they are baled for removal. Air quantities per pound of paper trim are 40 to 45 ft³/lb (2.5 to 2.8 m³/kg) and

transport velocity in ductwork is 4500 to 5000 fpm (22 to 25 m/s)(Marsailes 1970). Humidification may be provided to prevent the buildup of a static charge and consequent system blockage.

Air Filtration

Filters commonly used in ventilation and air-conditioning systems for printing plants are electronic automatic moving curtain filters with renewable media, having a weight arrestance of 80 to 90% (ASHRAE *Standard* 52-76).

In sheetfed pressrooms, a high performance bag-type afterfilter is used to filter the starch particles, which require about 85% ASHRAE dust spot efficiency. In film processing areas where relatively dust-free conditions are needed, high efficiency air filters are installed, with 90 to 95% ASHRAE dust spot efficiency.

A different type of filtration problem in printing is ink mist or ink fly, common in newspaper pressrooms and not unusual in heatset letterpress or offset pressrooms. Minute droplets of ink are dispersed by ink rollers rotating in opposite directions. The cloud of ink droplets is electrostatically charged and of 5 to 10 μm size. Generally used are the ink mist suppressors, charged to repel the ink back to the ink roller. Additional control is provided by automatic moving curtain filters.

Binding and Shipping

After printing, some work must be bound. Two main methods of binding are perfect binding and stitching. In perfect binding, sections of a book (signatures) are gathered, ruffed, glued, and trimmed. The product has a flat edge where the book was glued. Large books are more easily bound by this type of binding. A low-pressure compressed air system and a vacuum system are usually required to operate a perfect binder, and paper shavings must be removed by the trimmer. Using heated glue requires an exhaust system, since the glue fumes may be toxic.

In stitching, sections of a book are collected and stitched (stapled) together. Stitching requires that each signature be opened individually and laid over a moving chain. Careful handling of the paper is important. This system has the same basic air requirements as perfect binding.

Mailing areas of a printing plant wrap, label, and/or ship the manufactured goods. The wrapper machine can be affected by low humidity. In winter, humidification of the bindery and mailing area to about 40 to 50% rh may be necessary to prevent static buildup.

REFERENCES

ASHRAE. 1976. *Methods of Testing Air Cleaning Devices Used in General Ventilation for Removing Particulate Matter.* ASHRAE *Standard* 52-1976.
Darnall, J.C. 1970. *Problems Involved in Modern Printing Plant Air Conditioning.* ASHRAE Symposium on Environmental Control of Printing Plants, San Francisco, CA, January.
Marsailes, T.P. 1970. Ventilation, filtration and exhaust techniques applied to printing plant operation. ASHRAE *Journal*. December, p. 27.
Ruby, G.M. Private Communication.
Weber, C.G.; Snyder, L.W. 1934. Reactions of lithographic papers to variations in humidity and temperature. *Journal of Research,* National Bureau of Standards, Vol. 12, January.

BIBLIOGRAPHY

American Newspaper Publishers Association. 1965. *The Effect of Newsprint Moisture Content and Relative Humidity Upon Pressroom Web Breaks.* R.I. Bulletin 857, Easton, Pa., June, 18.

Brown, S.W. 1971. MTW, close control highlight printing plant air conditioning. *Heating, Piping & Air Conditioning,* February.

Donegani, B.L. 1962. Heating and air conditioning problems in colour printing industry. *Institution of Heating and Ventilating Engineers Journal,* Vol. 30, July 1962.

Latham, C.W. 1962. Why your offset plant needs humidity control. *Inland Printer/American Lithographer,* Vol. 148, No. 6, March.

Reed, R.F. 1970. *What the Printer Should Know About Paper.* Graphic Arts Technical Foundation, Pittsburgh, Pa.

Shaw, V.J. 1965. Lack of humidity control can cause trouble in offset pressroom. *Inland Printer/American Lithographer,* Vol. 155, No. 5, August.

Spethman, D.H. 1970. *Printing Plant Temperature and Relative Humidity Control System Considerations.* ASHRAE Symposium on Environmental Control of Printing Plants, San Francisco, CA, January.

Stevenson, F.F. 1966. Air conditioning design for graphic arts building. *Heating, Piping & Air Conditioning,* February.

Subt, S.S.Y.; Praskievicz, R.W.; and Materazzi, A.R. 1978. *Flammability of Alcohol Containing Fountain Solutions.* TAPPI, Printing and Reprography Conference Proceedings, November.

CHAPTER 35

TEXTILE PROCESSING

THIS chapter covers (1) the basic processes of making fiber, yarn, and fabric; (2) various types of air-conditioning systems used in textile manufacturing plants; (3) relevant health and safety considerations; and (4) energy conservation procedures.

Most textile manufacturing processes may be put into one of three general classifications: (1) synthetic fiber manufacturing, (2) yarn making, and (3) fabric making. Synthetic fiber manufacturing is divided into staple processing, tow-to-top conversion, and continuous fiber processing; yarn making is divided into spinning and twisting; fabric making is divided into weaving and knitting. Although these processes vary, their descriptions reveal the principles upon which the design of air conditioning is based.

FIBER MAKING

Processes preceding fiber extrusion have diverse ventilating and air conditioning requirements. However, principles that apply to air conditioning or ventilation of chemical plants apply to pre-extrusion areas as well.

Synthetic fibers are extruded from metallic spinnerets and solidified as continuous parallel filaments. This process, called *continuous spinning,* differs from mechanical spinning of fibers or tow into yarn, which is generally referred to as *spinning* and is described later.

Synthetic fibers may be formed by melt-spinning, dry-spinning, or wet-spinning. Melt-spun fibers are solidified by cooling the molten polymer; dry-spun fibers by evaporating a solvent, leaving the polymer in fiber form; and wet-spun fibers by hardening the extruded filaments in a liquid bath. Economic and chemical considerations determine which type of spinning is required. Generally, nylons, polyesters, and glass fibers are melt-spun, acetates dry-spun, rayons wet-spun, and acrylics dry- or wet-spun.

For melt-spun and dry-spun fibers, the filaments of each spinneret are usually drawn through a long vertical tube called a *chimney* or *quench stack,* within which the solidification takes place. For wet-spun fibers, the spinneret is suspended in a chemical bath where the coagulation of the fibers takes place. Wet-spinning is followed by a succession of washings, the application of a suitable finish, and drying.

Synthetic continuous fibers are extruded as a heavy denier tow if intended to be cut into short lengths called staple, or somewhat longer lengths for tow-to-top conversion; or they are extruded as light denier filaments if intended to be processed as continuous fibers. An oil is then applied to lubricate, give anti-static properties, and control fiber cohesion. The extruded filaments are usually drawn (stretched) both to align the molecules along the axis of the fiber, and to improve the crystalline structure of the molecules, which increases the fiber's strength and resistance to stretching.

The preparation of this chapter is assigned to TC 9.2, Industrial Air Conditioning.

Heat applied to the fiber when drawing heavy denier or high-strength synthetics liberates a troublesome oil mist. In addition, the mechanical work of drawing generates a high localized heat load. If the draw is accompanied by twist, it is called *draw-twist.* If not, it is called *draw-wind.* After draw-twisting, continuous fibers may be given additional twist or may be sent directly to warping.

When tow is cut to make staple, the short fibers are allowed to assume a random orientation. The staple, alone or in a blend, is then usually processed, as described for the cotton system. However, tow-to-top conversion, a more efficient process, has been gaining ground over the processing of staple. The longer tow is broken or cut in a way that maintains parallel orientation. Most of the steps of the cotton system are by-passed; the parallel fibers are ready for blending and mechanical spinning into yarn.

Glass fiber yarn is formed by attenuating molten glass through platinum bushings at very high temperatures and speeds, as light denier multifilaments. These are drawn together while being cooled with a water spray. A chemical size is then applied to protect the fiber during further processing. This is all accomplished in a single process prior to winding the fiber in preparation for further processing.

YARN MAKING

The fiber length determines which of the two general classifications (spinning or twisting) must be used. Spun yarns are produced by loosely gathering synthetic staple, natural fibers, or blends into rope-like form; drawing them out to increase fiber parallelism, if required; and then applying twist. Twisted (continuous filament) yarns are made from mile-long monofilaments or multifilaments by twisting alone. Ply yarns are made in a similar manner from spun or twisted yarns.

The principles of mechanical spinning are applied in three different systems: cotton, woolen, and worsted. The cotton system is used for all cotton, most synthetic staple, and many blends. Woolen and worsted systems are used to spin most wool yarns, some wool blends, and some synthetic fibers such as acrylics.

Except in novelty yarns featuring irregularities, two criteria of top quality are uniformity of twist and uniformity of cross section. Twist, in turns per unit length, may be hard or soft, right (S), or left (Z), according to the desired characteristics of the yarn. The uniformity with which individual fibers are distributed in a spun yarn largely determines its uniformity of strength.

Cotton System

The cotton system was originally developed for spinning cotton yarn, but now its basic machinery is also used to spin all varieties of staple including wool, polyester, and blends. Most of the steps from raw materials to fabrics, along with the ranges of frequently used humidities, are outlined in Figure 1.

Opening, Blending, and Picking. The compressed tufts are partly opened, most foreign matter and some short fibers are removed, and the mass is put in an organized form. Blending is either necessary or desirable to average the irregularities between bales or to mix different kinds of fiber. Synthetic staple, being cleaner and more uniform, usually requires less preparation. The product of the picker is pneumatically conveyed to the feed rolls of the card.

Carding. This process lengthens the lap into a thin web, which is gathered into a rope-like form called a *sliver*. Further opening and fiber separation is accomplished, as well as the partial removal of short fiber and trash. The sliver is laid in an ascending spiral in cans of various diameters.

For heavy, low-count (length per unit of weight) yarns of average or lower quality, the card sliver will go directly to drawing. For lighter, high-count yarns requiring fineness, smoothness, and strength, the card sliver must first be combed.

Lapping. In lapping, several slivers are placed side by side and drafted. In ribbon lapping, the resulting ribbons are laid one upon another and drafted again. The doubling and redoubling averages out sliver irregularities, while drafting improves fiber parallelism. Some recent processes lap only once before combing.

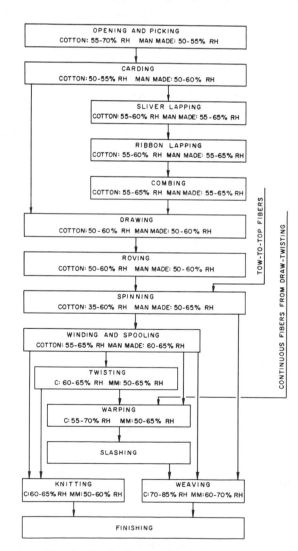

Fig. 1　Textile Process Flow Chart and Ranges of Humidity

Combing. After lapping, the fibers are combed with fine metal teeth. Combing substantially removes all fibers below a predetermined length, removes any remaining foreign matter, and improves fiber arrangement. The combed lap is then attenuated by drawing rolls and again condensed into a single sliver.

Drawing. Drawing, as applied to yarn making, follows either carding or combing, and further improves uniformity and fiber parallelism by doubling and drafting several individual slivers into a single composite strand. Doubling averages the thick and thin portions, while the drafting action further attenuates the mass and improves parallelism.

Roving. Roving continues the processes of drafting and paralleling until the strand is at a size suitable for spinning. A slight twist is inserted and the strand is wound on large bobbins suitable for the next roving step or for spinning.

Spinning. Mechanical spinning simultaneously applies draft and twist. The packages (any form into or on which one or more ends can be wound) of roving are creeled at the top of the frame. The unwinding strand passes progressively through gear-driven drafting rolls, a yarn guide, the C-shaped traveler, and then to the bobbin. The vertical traverse of the ring causes the yarn to be placed in predetermined layers.

The difference in peripheral speed between the back and front rolls determines the draft. The rate of front roll feed, the spindle speed, and the drag, which is related to the weight of the traveler, all determine the twist.

The space between the nip or bite of the rolls is adjustable and must be slightly greater than the longest fiber. The speeds of front and back rolls are independently adjustable. Cotton spindles normally run at 8000 to 9000 rpm but may exceed 14,000 rpm. In ring twisting, the drawing rolls are omitted, and a few spindles are run as high as 18,000 rpm.

Open-end, or turbine spinning, combines drawing, roving, lapping, and spinning in one operation. Staple fibers are fragmented as drawn from a sliver and fed into a very fast spinning, small centrifugal device. Within this device, the fibers are oriented and discharged as yarn, twist being imparted by the rotation of the turbine. This system is much faster, quieter, and less dusty than ring spinning.

Spinning is the final step in the cotton system, and the one feature that distinguishes it from twisting is the application of draft. The amount and point of application of draft also account for many of the subtle differences that require different humidities for apparently identical processes.

Atmospheric Conditions. From carding to roving, the loosely bound fibers are especially vulnerable to static electricity. In most instances, static can be adequately suppressed with humidity, which, however, should not be so high as to cause other troubles. In other instances, it is necessary to suppress electrostatic properties with antistatic agents. Wherever draft is applied, constant humidity is needed to maintain the optimum of frictional uniformity between adjacent fibers and, hence, uniformity of cross section.

Woolen and Worsted Systems

The woolen system generally makes coarser yarns, while the worsted system makes finer ones of a somewhat harder twist. Both may be used for lighter blends of wool, as well as for synthetic fibers with the characteristics of wool. The machinery used in both systems applies the same principles of draft and twist, but differs greatly in detail and is more complex than that used for cotton.

Wool fibers are dirtier, greasier, and more irregular. They must be scoured to remove grease and then usually re-impregnated with controlled amounts of oil to make them less hydrophilic and provide better interfiber behavior. Being scaly and curly,

**Table 1   Recommended Humidities for Wool
Processing at 75—80°F (24 to 27°C)**

Departments	Humidity,%
Raw wool storage	50-55
Mixing and blending	65-70
Carding—worsted	60-70
—woolen	60-75
Combing, worsted	65-75
Drawing, worsted—Bradford system	50-60
—French system	65-70
Spinning—Bradford worsted	50-55
—French (mule)	75-85
—woolen (mule)	65-75
Winding and spooling	55-60
Warping, worsted	50-55
Weaving, woolen and worsted	50-60
Perching or clothroom	55-60

Reprinted by permission of copyright owner, Interscience Division of John Wiley
and Sons, Inc., New York, N.Y.

they are more cohesive and require different treatment. Wool
differs from cotton and synthetic fibers in that it requires higher
humidities in the processes up to and including spinning than
it does in the processes that follow. Approximate humidities are
given in Table 1.

Twisting Filaments and Yarns

Twisting was originally applied to silk filaments and was
known as throwing: several filaments were doubled and then
twisted to improve strength, uniformity, and elasticity. Essentially, the same process is used today, but it is now extended to
spun yarns, as well as to single or multiple filaments of synthetic fibers. Twisting is widely used in the manufacture of sewing thread, twine, tire cord, tufting yarn, rug yarn, ply yarn, some
knitting yarns, and others.

Twisting and doubling is done on a *down-* or *ring-twister,*
which draws in two or more ends from packages on an elevated
creel, twists them together, and winds them into a package. Except for the omission of drafting, down-twisters are similar to
conventional ring-spinning frames.

Where yarns are to be twisted without doubling, an *up-twister*
(so named because the yarn passes from the bottom to the top
of each deck of double and triple deck arrangements) is used.
Up-twisters are used primarily for throwing synthetic
monofilaments and multifilaments to add to or vary elasticity,
light reflection, and abrasion resistance. As with spinning, yarn
characteristics are controlled by making the twist hard or soft,
right or left. Quality is determined largely by the uniformity of
twist, which, in turn, depends primarily on tension and the
stability of atmospheric conditions (Figure 1 and Table 1). Since
the frame may be double or triple decked, twisting requires concentrations of power. The frames are otherwise similar to those
used in spinning and present the same problems in air distribution. In twisting, lint is not a serious problem.

FABRIC MAKING

Preparatory Processes

When spinning or twisting has been completed, both types
of yarn may be prepared for weaving or knitting. The principal
processes may include winding, spooling, creeling, beaming,
slashing, sizing, dyeing, etc. The broad purpose is two-fold: (1)
to transfer the yarn from the type of package dictated by the
preceding process to a type suitable for the next and (2) to im-

pregnate some of it with sizes, gums, or other chemicals that
may not be left in the final product.

Filling Yarn. Filling yarn is wound on quills suitable for use
in the loom shuttle. It is sometimes pre-dyed and must be put
into a form suitable for package or skein dyeing before it is quill-
ed. If the filling is of relatively hard twist, it may be put through
a twist-setting or conditioning operation in which internal
stresses are relieved by the application of heat, moisture, or both.

Warp Yarn. Warp yarn is impregnated with a transient coating
of size or starch, which adds strength and resistance to the chaf-
ing to which the yarn will be subjected in the loom. The yarn
is first rewound onto a cone or other large package from which
it will unwind speedily and smoothly. The second step is warping, which rewinds a multiplicity of ends in parallel arrangement on large spools, called warp or section beams. In the third
step, slashing, the threads pass progressively through the sizing
solution, squeeze rolls, and around cans or steam-heated drying cylinders—or, as an alternative, through an air-drying
chamber. As much as several thousand pounds may be wound
on a single loom beam.

Knitting Yarn. If hard spun, knitting yarn must be twist-set
to minimize kinking. Filament yarns must be sized to reduce
strip-backs and improve other running qualities. Both must be
put in the form of cones or other suitable packages.

Uniform tension is of great importance in maintaining
uniform package density. Yarns tend to hang up when unwound
from a hard package or slough off from a soft one, and both
tendencies are aggravated by spottiness. The processes that require air conditioning, along with recommended relative
humidities, are shown in Figure 1 and Table 1.

Weaving

In the simplest form of weaving, harnesses raise or depress
alternate warp threads to form an opening called a *shed.* A shuttle containing a quill is kicked through the opening, trailing a
thread of filling behind it. The lay and the reed then beat the
thread firmly into one apex of the shed and up to the fell of
the previously woven cloth. Each shuttle passage forms a pick,
and these actions are repeated up to frequencies of five per
second.

Each warp thread usually passes through a drop-wire, which
is released by a thread break and automatically stops the loom.
Another automatic mechanism will insert a new quill in the shuttle as the previous one is emptied, without stopping the loom.
Other mechanisms are actuated by filling breaks, improper shuttle boxing, and the like, which stop the loom until restarted
manually. Each cycle may leave a stopmark sufficient to cause
an imperfection that may not become apparent until the fabric
is dyed.

Beyond this basic machine and pattern are many complex
variations in harness and shuttle control, which give intricate
and novel weaving effects. The most complex is the jacquard,
with which individual warp threads may be separately controlled.
Other variations appear in looms for such products as narrow
fabrics, carpets, and pile fabrics. In the Sulzer weaving machine,
a special filling carrier replaces the conventional shuttle. In the
rapier, a flat, spring-like tape uncoils from each side and meets
in the middle to transfer the grasp on the filling. In the water
set loom, a very tiny jet of high pressure water carries the filling through the shed of the warp. Other looms transport the filling with compressed air.

High humidity increases the abrasion resistance of the warp,
and many weave rooms require 80 to 85% and even higher
humidities for cotton and up to 70% for synthetic fibers. Improved sizes have made it possible to reduce the higher values.
Many looms can run faster when room humidity and
temperature are precisely controlled.

In the weave room, the distribution of power is quite uniform, with an average concentration somewhat lower than in spinning. The rough treatment of fibers causes the liberation of many minute particles of both fiber and size, thereby creating considerable amounts of airborne dust. Air changes average from four to eight per hour due to high humidity. It is necessary to make special provisions for maintaining conditions during production shutdown periods, usually at a lower relative humidity.

Knitting

Typical of knitted products are seamless articles such as undershirts, socks, and hosiery made on circular machines, and those knitted flat, such as full-fashioned hosiery, tricot, milanese, and warp fabrics.

The basic process is one of generating fabric by forming millions of interlocking loops. In its simplest form, a single end is fed to needles, which are actuated in sequence. In more complex constructions, hundreds of ends may be fed to groups of elements that function more or less in parallel.

Knitting yarns may be either single or ply and must be of uniform high quaity and free from neps or knots. These yarns, particularly the multifilament, are usually treated with special sizes to keep broken filaments from stripping back and to provide lubrication.

Precise control of yarn tension, through controlled temperature and relative humidity, increases in necessity with the fineness of the product. For example, in finer gages of full-fashioned hosiery, a 2°F (1°C) change in temperature is the limit, and a 10% change in humidity may add or subtract 3 in. (75 mm) in the length of a stocking. For knitting, desirable room conditions are approximately 76°F (24°C) dry-bulb and 45 to 65% relative humidity.

Dyeing and Finishing

Finishing is the final readying of a mill product for its particular market. Its scope is broad and varied, ranging from cleaning to imparting special characteristics. The individual operations and the number involved vary considerably, depending on the type of fiber, yarn, or fabric, and the end product usage; operations are usually done in separate plants.

Inspection is the only finishing operation to which air conditioning is regularly applied, although most of the others require ventilation. Those that employ wet processes usually keep their solutions at high temperature and require special ventilation to prevent destructive condensation and fog. Where the release of sensible, latent, or radiant heat is great, spot cooling is necessary.

AIR-CONDITIONING DESIGN

Although any of the equipment described in Chapter 28 may be found in textile manufacturing plants, air washers are especially important. These may be either conventional low velocity or high velocity units in built-up systems. Unitary high velocity equipment using rotating eliminators, although no longer in favor, may still be found in some plants. For air washer details, see Chapter 4 of the 1983 EQUIPMENT Volume.

Integrated Systems

Many mills use a refinement of the air washer system by blending the air-conditioning system and the collector system (see later section) into an integrated unit. The air handled by the collector system fans is delivered back to the air-conditioning apparatus through a central duct, together with any air required to make up total return air. The design engineer and the collector system manufacturer work together to accomplish this refine-

ment. The air quantity returned by the individual yarn processing machine cleaning systems must not exceed the air-conditioning supply air quantity. The air discharged by these individual suction systems is carried by return air ducts directly to the air-conditioning system. Before entering the duct, some of the cleaning system air usually passes over the yarn processing machine drive motor and through a special enclosure to capture the heat losses from the motor.

Integrated systems may occasionally exceed the supply air requirements of the area served. In such cases, the surplus air must be reintroduced after filtering.

Individual suction cleaning systems that can integrate with air conditioning are available for cards, drawing frames, lap winders, combers, roving frames, spinning frames, spoolers, and warpers. The following advantages result from this arrangement:

1. With a constant supply of air, the best possible uniformity of air distribution can be maintained year-round.
2. Downward flow of air can be controlled; cross-currents in the room are minimized or eliminated; drift or fly from one process to another is minimized or eliminated. Room partitioning between systems serving different types of manufacturing processes will further enhance the value of this arrangement in controlling room air pattern year-round.
3. The heat losses of the yarn processing frame motor and any portion of the processing frame heat captured in the duct, as well as the heat of the collector system equipment, cannot influence room conditions; hot spots in motor alleys are eliminated, and although this heat goes into the refrigeration load, it does not enter the room, and, as a result, the supply air quantity is reduced.
4. Uniform conditions in the room improve production; conditioned air is drawn directly to the work areas on the machines, minimizing or eliminating wet or dry spots.
5. Maximum cleaning use is made of the air being moved.

A guide for cleaning air requirements is:

Pickers, per picker	2500 to 4000 cfm	(1200 to 1900 L/s)
Cards, per card	700 to 1500 cfm	(300 to 700 L/s)
Spinning, per spindle	4 to 8 cfm	(2 to 4 L/s)
Spooling, per spool	40 cfm	(19 L/s)

Collector Systems

To understand the above advantages of integrating the air-conditioning and the collector system, it is necessary to know something about the collector system.

A collector system is a waste-capturing device, which uses many orifices operating at high suction pressures. Each production machine is equipped with suction orifices at all points of major lint generation. The captured waste is generally collected in a fan and filter unit on each machine. (This arrangement is most popular on drawing, combing, roving, and mechanical spinning units). The waste from a group of machines may be collected by a central fan-filter unit. This collector may be in the production area (often in carding) or in a service area (in new mills—usually in carding).

A collector in the production area may discharge air from which the waste has been filtered either back into the production area or into a return duct to the air-conditioning system. It then either enters the air washer or is relieved through dampers to the outdoors. The collector air duct connecting individual production machines to the collector chamber may be mounted under the production room floor (usually in new mills) or be suspended from the ceiling. When air from the collector unit is returned to the air-conditioning system, the collector fans

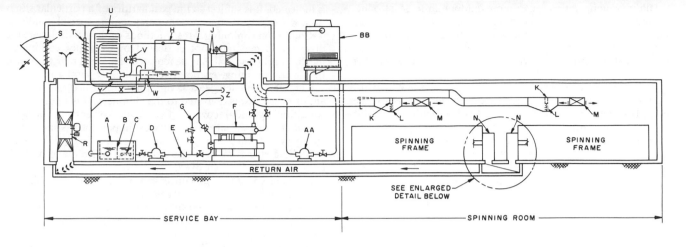

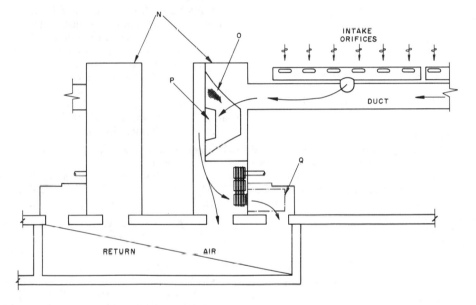

Fig. 2 Combined Air-Conditioning and Collector System

deliver it to the return air duct openings. This return system allows the air-conditioning system return duct and fans to operate in low pressure ranges, reducing construction and equipment costs.

In a spinning room that uses the collector system for the entire return air, as little as 5% outdoor air is used for ventilation in summer; but in other seasons, the system may use up to 100% outdoor air.

Figure 2 shows a mechanical spinning room with air-conditioning and collector systems combined into an integrated unit. The collector system returns all of its air to the air-conditioning system. If supply air from the air-conditioning system exceeds the maximum that can be handled by the collector system, additional air may be returned through slots in the floor beneath the spinning frame, or by other means.

Figure 2 shows return air entering the air-conditioning system through damper T, passing through air washer H, and being delivered by fan J to the supply duct, which distributes it to maintain conditions within the spinning room. At the other end of each spinning frame are unitary-type filter-collectors consisting of enclosure N, collector unit screen O, and collector unit fan P.

Collector fan P draws air through the intake orifices spaced along the spinning frame. This air passes through the duct running lengthwise to the spinning frame, through the screen O, and then discharged into the enclosure base (beneath the fan and screen). The air quantity is not constant, but drops slightly as material builds up on the filter screen.

Since the return air quantity must remain constant and the air quantity discharged by fan P is slightly reduced at times, it is necessary to provide relief openings. Relief openings also may be required when the return air volume is greater than the amount of air that can be handled by the collector suction system.

The discharge of fan P is split, so part of the air cools the spinning frame drive motor before rejoining the rest of the air in the return air tunnel. Regardless of whether the total return air quantity enters the return air tunnel through collector units, or through a combination of collector units and floor openings beneath spinning frames, return air fan R delivers it into the apparatus, ahead of the return air damper T. Consideration should be given to filtering the return air prior to its delivery into the air-conditioning apparatus.

Mild-season operation causes more outdoor air to be introduced through damper U. This amount of air is relieved through motorized damper S, which opens gradually as outdoor damper U opens, while return damper T closes in proportion. All other components perform as typical central station air-washer systems.

A system of the general configuration of Figure 2 may also be used for carding; the collector system portion of this arrangement is shown in Figure 3. A central collector filters the lint-laden air taken from multiple points on each card. This air is discharged to return air duct A and then is either returned to the air-conditioning system, exhausted outside, or returned directly to the room. A central collector filter may also be used with the spinning room system of Figure 2.

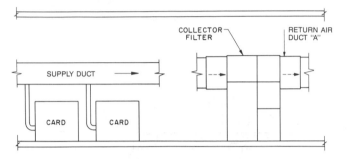

Fig. 3　Central Collector for Carding Machines

While many mills use the kind of system shown in Figure 2 for spinning rooms, much existing equipment cannot be used with that type of system. In these instances, the collector is a unitary type that does not permit a direct return of all air through floor openings and over the spinning frame drive motor. The collector unit housing is smaller, enclosing only the fan and screen, and has a top, bottom, or all-four-sides air discharge.

Spinning frames are frequently arranged as shown in Figure 2, with the drive ends and collector ends adjacent to each other. The concentrated heat losses of the spinning frame drive motor and the collector unit fan are concentrated in this motor alley, which becomes considerably warmer than the adjacent areas. When the discharge from the unitary collector of this type is down, the strong blast of air sweeps over the frame motor, strikes the floor, and fans out, sweeping under the spinning frame.

The discharge of air leads to high temperature and low relative humidity at the double motor alley, with temperature decreasing and relative humidity increasing as distance from the motor alley along the spinning frame increases. When air discharges up from the unitary collector, the motor alley tends to be somewhat warmer than with bottom discharge because the motor is not swept by a constant stream of air, and the heat remains more localized. The air-conditioning design engineer should supply additional air to the hot spots. With collectors of this type, the collector fan heat can be removed from the room by using a top discharge collector with ductwork and an intake grill for each collector.

Many mills divide the discharge between top and bottom. When this is done, the gentle upward force of the air from the top discharge offers little or no interference with the air delivery from sidewall supply air outlets, and air from the bottom discharge sweeps the frame motor and does not greatly affect the drafting area.

Air Distribution

Some general statements pertaining to distribution of air for process areas follow. Whenever *generally uniform distribution*

is indicated, it is subject to the peculiarities of a particular situation, wherein load concentration may require special handling.

Continuous Spinning Area. Methods of distribution here are diverse and generally not critical. However, spot cooling or localized heat removal may be required. This area may be cooled by air conditioning, evaporative cooling, or ventilation.

Chimney (Quench Stack). Carefully controlled and filtered air, or other gas, is delivered to the chimneys; it is returned for conditioning and recovery of valuable solvents, if present. Distribution of the air is of the utmost importance. Nonuniform air flow will disturb the yarn, causing variations in fiber diameter, crystalline structure, and orientation. A fabric made of such fibers will streak when dyed.

For melt spinning, the concentration of solvent in chimney air must be maintained below the explosive limit of the solvent in the air. Even below the explosive limit, care must be exercised that the vapors are not ignited by a spark or flame. The air-conditioning system must be very reliable, because an interruption of the spinning will cause the solution to solidify in the spinnerets.

Wind-up or Take-up Areas of Continuous Spinning. These areas develop a heavy air-conditioning load. Air is often delivered through branch ducts alongside each spinning machine, with returns under the floor. Provisions may be made to close the dampers of the branches of those machines not spinning. Diffusers are of the low velocity, low aspiration type, sized so as not to agitate the delicate fibers.

In some plants, the distribution pattern has been reversed; air is delivered through underfloor ducts and returned overhead. Advantages claimed for this system are as follows:

1. Heat stratification allows a reduction in air volume requirements.
2. Lint and dust removal is assisted by rising heat currents.
3. The risk of roof condensation is reduced in cold climates as the cool moist air is supplied at the floor.

Draw-Twist or Draw-Wind Areas of Fiber Manufacture. These areas also have a heavy air-conditioning load. Distribution, diffusion, and return systems are similar to those for the continuous spinning take-up area.

Opening and Picking. Generally requires only a uniform distribution system. The area is subject to shutdown of machinery during portions of the day. Generally, an all-air system with independent zoning is installed.

Carding. Generally, a uniform distribution system is installed. Low air motion is required around the web. Older installations frequently used an overhead belt drive, sometimes making distribution difficult. Central lint, collecting systems are available for this process, but this must be considered in the system design. Generally, an all-air system is selected for cotton carding.

In wool carding, air motion is frequently much more important than in cotton carding, not only around the web but also to reduce cross-contamination between adjacent cards, since different colors of pre-dyed wool may be run side by side on adjacent cards. A split system may be considered for wool carding to reduce air motion. The method of returning air is also critical for achieving uniform conditions.

Drawing and Roving. Generally, a uniform distribution all-air system works well.

Mechanical Spinning Areas. These areas generate a heavy air-conditioning load, consisting of spinning frame power uniformly distributed along the frame length, frame driver motor losses concentrated in the motor alley at one end of the frame, and lint-collector system fans concentrated in the motor alley at one end of the frame. The lint-collector systems may either be unitary, with a fan at the end of each frame discharging up or down into the room, or they may have a central fan drawing all collection system air from all spinning frames to a single point through ductwork, and discharging it outside the spinning room. (See the previous section on Collector Systems).

Supply air ducts should run across the frames at right angles. Sidewall outlets between each of the two adjacent frames then direct the supply air down between the frames, where conditions must be maintained. Where concentrated heat loads occur, as in double motor alleys, placing a supply air duct directly over the double motor alley should be considered. Sidewall outlets with industrial-type rectangular plaque diffusers spaced along the bottom of the duct diffuse air into the motor alley. This diffuser consists of a set of turning or straightening vanes inside an opening in the bottom of the duct, with a horizontal perforated metal plate 12 in. (300 mm) larger than the opening size, suspended 4 to 6 in. (100 to 150 mm) below the opening by four adjustable straps.

A central collecting system with a central fan discharges air outside the spinning room (into the return air), so the collecting system fan heat does not become a room sensible load, but rather a refrigeration load only.

The collecting system, whether unitary or central, with intake points distributed along the frame length at the working level, assists in pulling supply air down to the frame, where maintenance of conditions is most important. A small percentage of the air handled by a central collecting system may be used to convey the collected lint and yarn to a central collecting point and is lost from the spinning room.

Winding and Spooling. Generally, a uniform distribution, all-air system is used in this area.

Twisting. This area has a heavy air-conditioning load. Distribution considerations are similar to those in spinning. Either all-air or split systems are installed.

Warping. Very light load. Long lengths of yarn may be exposed unsupported in this area; duct location and distribution should consider this. Generally an all-air system with uniform distribution. Diffusers may be low aspiration type. Return air is often low near the floor.

Weaving. Generally, a uniform distribution system is necessary. Now that synthetic fibers are more commonly woven than natural fibers, lower humidity requirements allow the use of all-air systems rather than the previously common split system. When the lower humidity is coupled with the water jet loom, a high latent load will result. In the older weaving rooms, split systems are generally found. (See Chapter 28 of this volume.)

Health and Safety Considerations

Control of Oil Mist. Whenever textiles that have been coated with lubricating oils are heated above 200°F (93°C) in drawing operations in ovens, tenterframes, or dryers, an oil mist is liberated, which, if not collected at the source of emission and disposed of, produces a slightly odorous haze. If this oil is collected at the source but not removed from the exhaust air, it will damage roofing and, if residences are nearby, cause complaints.

Various devices have been proposed to separate the oil mist from the exhaust air, such as process changes, fume incinerators, electrostatic precipitators, high energy scrubbers, absorption devices, high velocity filters, and condensers. For more information on these methods of separation, see Chapters 10 and 11 of the 1983 EQUIPMENT Volume.

Control of Cotton Dust. Byssinosis, known as brown or white lung disease, is believed by some medical researchers to be caused by a histamine-releasing substance in cotton, flax, and hemp dust. When a cotton worker returns to work after a weekend, he experiences difficulty in breathing, which is not relieved until later in the week. After 10 to 20 years, the breathing difficul-

ty becomes continuous, and even leaving the mill does not provide relief.

The U.S. Labor Department is presently enforcing an OSHA standard of 0.2 mg/m³ of lint-free dust. The most promising means of control for this stringent requirement is improved exhaust procedures and filtration of recirculated air. Since the particles of concern are 1 to 15 micrometres in diameter, filtration equipment must be efficient in this size range. See Chapters 10 and 11 of the 1983 EQUIPMENT Volume for information on air cleaning. To comply with this value, greatly improved filtration of return air is required. Improvements in carding and picking so that less trash is left in the raw cotton can also help control this dust.

Noise Control. OSHA requires that employers monitor noise exposure levels to identify employees who are exposed at or above 85 dBA. If any employee is exposed to 85 dBA for an 8-hour day on a time weighted average (TWA), the employer must institute a hearing conservation program. This program includes administering annual hearing tests and providing the employees with hearing protection for those who want it. If the test should indicate a hearing loss for an employee, the employee must wear hearing protection.

If the noise exposure exceeds 90 dBA, the same program is put into effect, but the affected employees are required to wear hearing protection. In addition, feasible engineering or administrative controls are required.

Noise levels in the opening, picking, carding, and combing areas range from about 87 to 93 dBA. Much of this noise is often caused by ventilating equipment. An analysis of all the noise sources in the area will determine the corrections required.

The noise levels in the mechanical spinning, draw-twist, texturizing, and particularly the weaving areas are much higher than for the previous group, but are all caused by process equipment. When this equipment is modified to meet OSHA criteria, the noise generated by HVAC equipment will become significant, and its effects will have to be combined with that of the process equipment to establish further correction. For procedures to analyze and correct the noise due to ventilating equipment, see Chapter 52 of this volume.

Control of Heat Stress. If legal limits are imposed on allowable heat stress, many changes in fiber plant design will be required. Air conditioning, already quite common, will be applied to more areas. Heat shields separating textile workers from heat-radiating surfaces will become more common.

Safety. While safety has long been a concern of the textile plant engineer, OSHA has recently stipulated extensive rules for the protection of workers from equipment, valves, caustic materials, etc. The HVAC engineer is more specifically concerned with OSHA ventilation requirements specified in Subpart C of U. S. Department of Labor OSHA Standards 29 CFR 1910.

ENERGY CONSERVATION

The textile industry ranks tenth in energy consumption among manufacturing industries in the United States. Many mills have taken significant steps in reducing energy usage and converting to coal-based energy. Some of the steps taken are as follows:

1. Heat recovery applied to water and air.
2. Automation of high-pressure driers to save heat and compressed air.
3. Improving insulation on walls and roofs.
4. Increasing condensate return.
5. Lowering hot water and raising chilled water temperatures for rinsing and washing in the dying operations.
6. Updating boiler controls.
7. Replacing incandescent with fluorescent light fixtures.
8. Reducing light levels, where appropriate.

9. Increasing summer and decreasing winter room temperatures, whenever possible.
10. Enclosing drive-in loading docks.
11. Replacing running washes with recirculating washes, where possible.
12. Revising double bleaching procedures to single bleaching, where possible.
13. Eliminating rinses and final wash in dye operations, where possible.
14. Drying by means of the "bump and run" process.
15. Applying computerized watt-shaving techniques to monitor peak demands.
16. Modifying the drying or curing oven air circulation systems to provide counterflow.
17. Using modern, energy efficient textile machinery.

Among many other possibilities, future achievements in energy reduction may be accomplished by the following:

1. Solar preheating of process water.
2. Infrared or dielectric drying of yarns and fabrics.
3. Cogenerating of steam and electricity.

REFERENCE

Federal Register. 1981. Occupational Safety and Health Administration, Department of Labor, Standards (29 CFR 1910, June).

BIBLIOGRAPHY

Ashmore, W.G. 1962. Air conditioning textile mills today. *Textile World,* December, p. 42.

Ballew, J.T. 1965. Textile area requirements for air conditioning. *Air Conditioning, Heating, & Ventilating,* April, p. 58.

Beltran, M.R. 1972. Smoke abatement for textile finishers. *American Dyestuff Reporter,* August, p. 42.

Carrol-Porezynski. *Inorganic Fibers.* Academic Press, New York, NY.

Hearle and Peters. *Moisture in Textiles.* Textile Book Publishers, Inc., New York, NY.

Kirk and Othmer, eds. *Vol. 9, Encyclopedia of Chemical Technology,* 2nd ed. Interscience Publishers., New York, NY.

Labarthe, J. *Textiles: Origins to Usage.* Macmillan Co., New York, NY.

Mark, J.F; Atlas, S.M.; and Cernin, E., eds. *Man-Made Fibers: Science & Technology,* Vol. 1. Interscience Publishers, New York, NY.

Nissan. *Textile Engineering Processes.* Textile Book Publishers, Inc., New York, NY.

Press, J.J., ed. *Man Made Textile Encyclopedia.* Textile Book Publishers, Inc., New York, NY.

Quarles, William. 1965. Flow of materials in the textile industry. *Air Conditioning, Heating & Ventilating,* April, p. 62.

Reynolds, J.R., Jr. 1967. Energy for industrial air conditioning. *Air Conditioning, Heating & Ventilation,* September, p. 55.

Ridgeway, R.F. 1965. Air conditioning systems for textile mills. *Air Conditioning, Heating & Ventilating,* April, p. 62.

Sherwood, P.W. 1963. Static electricity. *Modern Textiles Magazine,* August, p. 44.

Static and Textiles—Review of Literature. North Carolina State University, Durham, NC.

Survey of Carbon Disulphide and Hydrogen Sulphide Hazards in the Viscose Rayon Industry. Commonwealth of Pennsylvania, Department of Labor and Industry, Occupational Disease Prevention Division. *Bulletin,* No. 46.

U.S. Dept. of Energy. 1978. *Annual Report;* Support Document, Vol. II, June, Industrial Energy Efficiency Improvement Program.

U.S. Dept of Energy. *In-Plant Demonstration of Energy Optimization in Beck Dying of Carpet.* Georgia Institute of Technology.

CHAPTER 36

PHOTOGRAPHIC MATERIALS

THE manufacture, processing, and storage of sensitized photographic products requires that the temperature, humidity, and quality of air be controlled. This chapter explains these conditions.

MANUFACTURE

Light-sensitive photographic products generally consist of a flexible support, called the *base,* coated with a gelatin emulsion containing salts of silver. For photographic film, a transparent base is cast from cellulose esters dissolved in solvents or made from synthetic polymers cast from a melt. Forming such a film base of required uniformity at safe and environmentally acceptable solvent concentration levels requires careful control of temperature and solvent vapor concentration in the coating machine.

It also requires accurate temperature control of the coating wheel and systems to heat and stretch the base to required thickness. Air in the heat-setting sections of the coating machine must be at the correct temperature for polymer crystallization and desired base characteristics.

Methods of solvent removal from the air systems during curing include condensation, activated carbon, molecular sieve adsorption, scrubbers, and incineration. Treatment selection depends on such factors as solvent recovery, safety, and environmental conservation.

Condensation systems can involve temperatures as low as $-85\,°F$ ($-65\,°C$) using a circulating medium such as methylene chloride. At such low temperatures, alloy steels with a percentage of nickel are being sucessfully used. Required insulation

thickness at $-85\,°F$ ($-65\,°C$) is 6 in. (150 mm) cork or equivalent.

Other solvent treatment systems require materials resistant to the corrosive solvents and high temperatures. Safety considerations for handling flammable solvents must be observed. System performance under all possible operating conditions and potential problems due to malfunctions, new solvents, and changed quantities must be evaluated. This often requires *fail safe* design, system or component redundancy, precise control sequence in the process, and fire detection and control systems.

Photographic paper support is produced in a paper mill that controls stock consistency to about 1.1% and temperature at $130\,°F$ ($55\,°C$), although the specific value is a function of the paper grade and speed of production. Dissolved and entrained air must be removed. Paper formation and subsequent operations of wet pressing, drying, calendaring, reeling, and winding all require precise control to produce paper free from photographic contamination, with high brightness, good permanence, high wet strength, stability under repeated wetting and drying, and high internal strength. Various aqueous or resin-extrusion coatings are applied to the paper to achieve desired surface characteristics before the light-sensitive emulsion is applied. These layers are applied by a series of application devices, then the paper is dried, and sometimes further calendared. Many of these operations require accurately controlled air and water systems for temperature and moisture control.

The produced film or paper must be stored in conditioned areas to preserve the characteristics of the material and keep it satisfactory for subsequent operations (see "Storage of Unprocessed Film and Paper").

In preparation of light-sensitive photographic emulsions for film and paper, gelatin and one or more salts of the alkali halides are dissolved in water, and silver nitrate and other chemicals are added at a specific temperature. Some desired characteristics of

---

The preparation of this chapter is assigned to TC 9.2, Industrial Air Conditioning.

finished photographic emulsions are obtained by the temperature and length of time the emulsion is allowed to ripen subsequent to precipitation.

Because of the nearly limitless variations of emulsion manufacturing processes, none is typical. The processes require close control of temperature, ingredient flow rate, agitation, precise addition of chemicals, and timing of sequences to fix the properties of the emulsion.

The emulsion, held at the exact temperature in a liquid state, is coated onto the film or paper base and passed directly into a chilling chamber, where it is gelled as quickly as possible at 50°F (10°C) or lower. After chilling, the emulsion-coated film or paper enters the drying section. Temperature, moisture content, air purity, and drying time are carefully controlled to provide a high quality product. When the film or paper has reached the correct moisture content (usually 1.5 to 3% for films and 5 to 8% for papers), it is wound in rolls and subsequently slit and cut into various sizes for packing.

A calcium or sodium chloride brine system is satisfactory where colder storage facilities are required or where process room conditions must be maintained below 30°F (−1°C) and dew points below 40°F (4°C). Brine systems using aqueous solutions of calcium chloride, sodium chloride, or ethylene glycol can be −25 to −35°F (−32 to 37°C); chromates and caustic soda should be used in brine systems other than ethylene glycol to control pH and corrosion. Systems needing low dew point air for either storage or process may use refrigeration, sorption, or both. (See Chapter 7 of the 1983 EQUIPMENT Volume and Chapter 19 of the 1985 FUNDAMENTALS Volume.)

All processes must be reviewed for energy conservation opportunities such as heat reclamation, enthalpy exchange, reduction in energy use, and reduction in peak energy demand.

Inert particles many times smaller than those visible to the human eye may become visible when photographic images are enlarged or projected. Photographically active contaminants (those that react chemically with light-sensitive products) may destroy an area of film or paper many times greater than the particle size. Active submicron particles can be more destructive than large inert particles. When minute particles agglomerate and impinge on sensitized products, they can cause the same imperfections as large particles. Radioactive dust is the largest source of active contaminants in the atmosphere. Most radioactive dust is less than one micron (micrometre) in size.

Where process air contacts photographic products, a high degree of cleaning is required to protect product quality. While intermediate efficiency filters may remove most harmful inert contaminants, the highest efficiency filters are required to reduce contamination effectively from radioactive dust.

Table 1 shows recommended filter efficiency requirements for general ventilation and process air systems. The filter requirements are classified as high, intermediate, and low efficiency. For general ventilation, the efficiency requirement is based on the use of the area, but for process air systems, the required efficiency depends on the particular process and product. In some operations, laminar flow systems, with highest efficiency filters, are needed to control contamination in the manufacturing process.

Dirt problems cannot be eliminated simply by efficient filtration for supply air systems. Atmospheric contaminants entering through supply air systems are often only a small portion of the overall particulate contamination in an area. More efficient filters on the supply air would not then significantly reduce the area dirt level. Dirt smudges on walls, ceilings, and around diffusers usually result from room air aspirating into low pressure areas created by the velocity of the air supply. If dirt in the room is largely room-generated or carried in by occupants, efficient filtration of supply air will not significantly reduce these smudges, nor will it lower the possibility of indirect product damage by contaminants settling from the room air. If a large portion of room air is recirculated, efficient filters will reduce the builtup dirt levels in the area. In manufacturing areas, good control should be maintained over all sources of internal contaminant generation.

STORAGE OF UNPROCESSED PHOTOGRAPHIC MATERIALS

While virtually all photosensitive materials deteriorate with age, the rate is largely dependent on the storage conditions. Deterioration increases by both high temperature and high

Table 1   Filter Requirements in Manufacture of Sensitized Photographic Materials

Efficiency Requirement	Low	Intermediate	High
General Application	Comfort, Cleanliness, Prefilters	Non-Critical, But Cleanliness Required	Best Available Protection From All Contamination
TYPES OF AREAS	Maintenance Areas / Office Areas / Storage of Packaged Products / New-Product Laboratories	Processing and Printing / Storage of Unpackaged Products / Finished Product Testing / Process Air	Manufacturing Areas
Relative Efficiency (NBS Discoloration Test)	0 10 20 30 40	50 60 70 80	90 95 100
TYPES OF FILTERS	Panel Throwaway / Manual Roll / Automatic Roll / Pleated Type With Disposable Cartridge	Deep Bed With Disposable Media / Electrostatic	AEC High Efficiency (Complete Unit Disposable)

relative humidity and usually decreases by lower temperature and humidity.

High relative humidity alone is usually more harmful than high temperature alone. High humidity can accelerate loss of sensitivity and contrast, increase shrinkage, produce mottle, cause softening of the emulsion, and promote fungus growth. Low relative humidity can increase the susceptibility of the film or paper to static markings, abrasions, brittleness, and curl. Modern three-layer substractive-type color films and papers are more seriously affected than black-and-white products because heat and moisture usually affect the three emulsion layers to different degrees, causing a change in color balance and overall film and paper speed and contrast.

Film or paper for domestic consumption may be packaged in a container sufficiently moisture-resistant for protection in temperate zones only. Photographic film or paper intended for the tropics or other places of high humidity are provided extra protection against moisture and harmful gases. Modern packaging, often employing heat-sealed foil pouches, snap-cover plastic cans, and taped metal or plastic cans, is usually adequate to protect film or paper in tropical or high-humidity areas, as long as the original packaging remains intact. The packaging used for a particular product should be determined from the manufacturer and the appropriate recommended storage conditions then maintained. At least one manufacturer currently packages film products for both domestic and tropical consumption in vaportight containers suitable for refrigerated storage without need of further humidity control. The film is packaged in equilibrium with air at a relative humidity between 40 to 60% ±2% at 75°F (24°C).

Products packed in vaportight containers maintain their moisture content and do not require storage in an area with controlled humidity as long as the seal is unbroken. Products that are not in vaportight packages or that are in opened packages should not be stored in damp basements, ice boxes, refrigerators, or other high relative humidity locations. The relative humidity for storage should be between 40 and 60%, preferably near 40% and at 60°F (16°C). A moderate temperature with low relative humidity, such as 60°F (16°C) and 40% rh, is better than a lower temperature with a high relative humidity such as 40°F (4°C) with 80% rh.

When humid storage conditions cannot be avoided or when use of a refrigerator is necessary for cooling, products in opened or non-vaportight packages should be placed in a container that can be tightly sealed, or the original packaging material should be tightly resealed.

In tropical zones or in the summer in temperature zones, refrigerated storage is recommended to keep products cool if they are in vaportight packages or sealed in cans or jars. Black-and-white film can be stored below 70°F (21°C) for up to two months, below 60°F (16°C) for up to six months, and below 50°F (10°C) for up to 12 months. Black-and-white papers should be stored at 70°F (21°C) or below, regardless of the storage time. Color films or papers kept for several months should be stored at 45 to 50°F (7 to 13°C). Storage at temperatures above 70°F (21°C) for more than four weeks may change speed and color balance. To minimize a change in the latent image, process control strip films should be stored at 0°F (−18°C). Some special application products require stringent storage conditions, as recommended by labels or instruction sheets.

Films that must be stored for more than a year should be kept at 0 to −10°F (−18 to −23°C). This low temperature arrests changes in photographic characteristics almost completely, if the product is adequately protected from background and stray radiaiton. The effects of adverse storage conditions between removal from refrigeration and exposure, or between exposure and processing, may cause unsatisfactory results in spite of previous low-temperature storage.

Except for motion picture films, temperatures below 32°F (0°C) are not harmful to photographic products. The water content of either film or paper is relatively small and ice crystals do not form inside at normal moisture levels, regardless of how low the temperature or how rapid the cooling. Motion picture film should be stored at 50°F (10°C), because when it is stored at lower temperatures, it contracts and a loosely wound roll results (Carver, Talbot, and Loomis 1943).

Film or paper stored in a refrigerator or freezer should be removed sometime before it is used, to allow it to warm to the outside temperature. Otherwise, moisture may condense on the cold film or paper when the sealed package is opened.

Table 2 shows the time needed to reach equilibrium for individual packages separated from each other. Cold packages stacked on top of each other would require much longer to warm up (proportional to total thickness).

Products not packaged in sealed foil envelopes or vaportight containers are vulnerable to contaminants. They must be kept away from formaldehyde vapor (emitted by particle board, some insulation, some plastics, and some glues), industrial gases, motor exhausts, and vapors of solvents and cleansers. In hospitals, industrial plants, and laboratories, all photosensitive products, regardless of the type of packaging, must be protected from x-rays, radium, and other radioactive materials.

For example, films stored 25 ft (8 m) away from 100 mg of radium require the protection of 3.5 in. (90 mm) of lead around the radium.

Under extremely humid conditions, film or paper should be both exposed and processed as soon as possible after the package is opened. If exposed products cannot be processed the same day as they are exposed, they should be kept in a dehumidified cabinet or storeroom or desiccated and resealed in a moisture-proof container. Color films or papers should also be stored at 50°F (10°C) or lower. Air conditioning with relative humidity control would provide the most desirable storage conditions for unprocessed products. An electric refrigerating dehumidifier con-

Table 2 Suggested Warmup Time for Film and Paper

Type of Film Package	Warmup Time (Hours)	
	20°F (11°C)	75°F (42°C) Rise
Roll Film, including 828	0.5	1
135 magazines, 110 and 126 cartridges	1	1.5
10 sheet box	1	1.5
50 sheet box	2	3
35 mm, any length	3	5
16 mm, any length	1	1.5

Paper Size	Warmup Time (Hours)		
	0 to 70°F (−18 to 21°C)	35 to 70°F (2 to 21°C)	50 to 70°F (10 to 21°C)
16 × 20 in. (50 sheet box)	3	2	2
30 × 40 in. (50 sheet box)	3	2	2
16 in. × 250 ft roll	10	7	4
40 in × 50 ft roll	12	8	5

trolled by a humidistat can be used for a storage cabinet or small storeroom. Also suitable is an electrically operated desiccating dehumidifier, which uses a desiccating agent such as silica gel or activated alumina with an automatic reactivation cycle.

PROCESSING AND PRINTING PHOTOGRAPHIC MATERIALS

Air Conditioning in Preparatory Operations

During receiving operations, exposed film is removed from protective packaging from pre-splicing and processing. Photographic emulsions become soft and can be mechanically damaged at high relative humidity. At excessively low relative humidity, the film base is prone to static, sparking, and curl deformation. Pre-splicing combines many individual rolls of film into a long roll to be processed. The pre-splice work area should be maintained between 50 to 55% rh and 70 to 75 °F (21 to 24 °C) dry-bulb temperature.

Air Conditioning and Processing Operation

Processing of exposed films or paper involves a series of tempered chemical and wash tanks that emit heat, humidity, and fumes. A room exhaust system must be provided, together with local exhaust at noxious tanks. Air from the pressurized pre-splice rooms can be used as makeup for processing room exhaust to conserve energy. Further supply air should maintain the processing space at a maximum of 80 °F (27 °C) dry-bulb temperature, 50% rh.

The processed film or paper proceeds from the final wash to the drier to control the moisture remaining in the product. Too little drying will cause the film to stick when wound, while too much drying will cause undesirable curl. Drying can be regulated by control of contact time, humidity, or, most often, temperature.

Air distribution to the drying area must provide a tolerable environment for operating personnel. The exposed sides of the drier should be insulated as much as is practical to reduce the large radiant and convected heat losses to the space. Return or exhaust grilles above the drier can directly remove much of its rejected heat and moisture. The supply air should be directed to offset the remaining radiant losses.

A solvent and wax mixture to provide lubrication is normally applied to motion picture film as it leaves the drier, with an exhaust to draw off the solvent vapor.

Air Conditioning for the Printing/Finishing Operation

In printing, where another sensitized product is exposed through the processed original, the amount of environmental control depends on the size and type of operation. For small-scale printing, close control of the environment is not necessary, except to minimize dust. In a modern photo-finishing plant, printers for colored products emit substantial heat. The effect on the room can be reduced by removing the lamphouse heat directly. Computer-controlled electronic printers transport original film and raw film or paper at high speed. The proper temperature and humidity are especially important because, in some cases, two or three images from many separate films may be superimposed in register onto one film. For best results, the printing room should be maintained at between 70 and 75 °F (21 and 24 °C) and 50 to 60% rh to prevent curl, deformation, and static. Curl and film deformation affect the register and sharpness of the images produced. The elimination of the static charge prevents static marks and also helps to keep the final product clean.

Mounting of reversal film into slides is a critical operation of the finishing department, requiring a 70 to 75 °F (21 to 24 °C) dry-bulb temperature and 50 to 55% rh room.

Particulate in Air

The air-conditioning systems for most photographic operations require 85% disposable bag-type filters, as indicated in Table 1, with lower efficiency prefilters to extend filter life. In critical applications of photography such as high altitude serial films, and microminiature images, freedom from foreign matter is extremely important. These products are handled in a laminar air flow room or workbench with HEPA filters plus prefilters.

Processing Temperature Control

The density of a developed image on photographic material depends on the emulsion characteristics, the exposure it has received, and the degree of development. With a particular emulsion, the degree of development depends on the time, temperature, degree of agitation, and developer activity.

With low developer temperature, the reaction is slow, and the development time recommended for the normal temperature would produce underdevelopment; at high temperature, the reaction is fast, and the same treatment time produces overdevelopment. Within limits, these changes in the rate of development can be compensated by increasing or decreasing the development time. Once a temperature for development is determined, it should be maintained within 1 °F (0.5 °C) for black-and-white products and within at least 0.5 °F (0.3 °C) for color materials. Other solutions in the processor can be maintained at wider temperature tolerances.

Changes in the temperature of color film or paper developer cannot readily be compensated by changes in development time. Temperature change affects development characteristics of emulsion layers in different manners, upsetting the color balancce. Contrast and speed are affected, and fog can occur.

Figure 1 shows a suggested method to control temperature of a critical tank solution. A pump recirculates solution from the top of the tank to the bottom through a hot water heat exchanger. The heat input into the heat exchangers is regulated in response to the loop temperature. The recirculation eliminates temperature stratification, agitates the solution, allows continuous filtration, and brings the solution quickly to temperature at startup.

Many processing machines have tanks with water jackets through which a continuous flow of controlled temperature water is circulated. To conserve water and energy, the heater water should be recirculated through an external heat exchanger or electric heater.

Wash tanks remove unwanted chemicals from the photographic image to prevent its degradation. Streams of continuously flowing water at a controlled temperature are supplied to the bottom of the final wash tank. The overflow of the final wash is connected to the bottom of the preceding wash tank, which saves water by countercurrent flow. A series of wash tanks can then be arranged.

The source of temperature-controlled wash water may be a central system for an entire laboratory or an individual self-contained thermostatic mixer for one processor. Thermostatic mixing-valve performance depends on proper valve sizing and pressure equalization of the hot and cold supplies.

The mixing valve and recirculating systems may be combined for accuracy and economy. In one packaged unit, a thermostatic mixing valve supplies tempered water to all tanks ex-

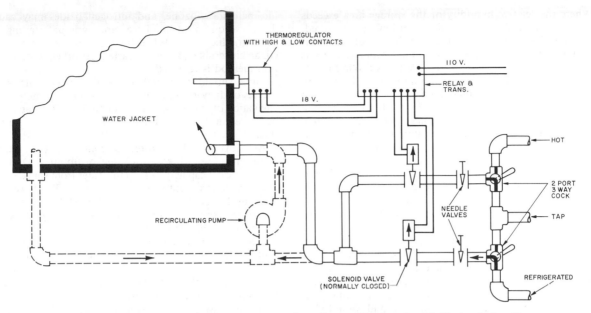

Fig. 1   Automatic Water Temperature Control in a System Equipped with Recirculating Pump

cept the developer tank. After leaving the mixing valve, the water flows into the solution-tank jackets and then to the wash tanks as rinse water, from which it drains to waste. The water in the developer tank jacket is in a completely closed system and recirculates through a temperature control unit comprising an air-cooled refrigeration unit, cooling coils, two immersion heaters, a pump, and a thermostat, which maintains a temperature differential of ±0.2°F (±0.1°C).

STORAGE OF PROCESSED FILM AND PAPER

Storage of developed film and paper differs from storage of the raw stock. The materials are no longer photosensitive, seldom sealed against moisture, and are generally stored for much longer periods. Required storage conditions depend on (1) the value of the records, (2) the length of storage time, (3) whether the films are on nitrate or safety base, (4) whether the paper base is resin coated, and (5) the type of photographic image.

Photographic materials must be protected against fire, water, mold, chemical or physical damage, extreme relative humidity, and high temperature. Relative humidity is much more important than temperature. High humidity damages gelatin, encourages the growth of mold, increases dimensional changes, accelerates decomposition of nitrate support, and accelerates deterioration of both black-and-white and color images. Low relative humidity causes a temporary increase in curl and a decrease in flexibility, but this is usually reversed when the humidity rises again. An exception to this reversal occurs when motion picture film is stored for a long time in loosely wound rolls at very low humidities. The curl causes the film roll to take the shape of a polygon rather than a circle when viewed from the side. This *spokiness* occurs because a highly curled roll of film resists being bent in the length direction when it is already bent in the width direction. When a spoky roll is stored for a long time, the film permanently flows into the spoky condition, with resulting film distortion. Very low relative humidity in storage may also cause the film or paper to crack or break if handled carelessly.

Low temperature is desirable for film and paper storage provided that (1) the relative humidity of the cold air is controlled

and (2) the material is warmed sufficiently before opening to avoid moisture condensation. High temperature can be harmful, accelerating the fading of dye images and accelerating film shrinkage, which may produce physical distortions. High temperature is also detrimental to the stability of nitrate film, which may still be in storage.

The storage life of processed photographic products is controlled by the composition, photographic processing, and storage conditions. Proper preservation of photographic materials is complicated, since each of these factors is controlled by different organizations. The composition of the film or paper is controlled by the manufacturer, the processing by the processing laboratory, and the storage conditions by the customer. The importance of all three must be recognized.

PHOTOGRAPHIC FILMS

ANSI has specified three levels of photographic film (medium-term, long-term, and archival) and two levels of storage conditions (medium-term and archival). *Medium-term Film* is suitable for preservation for a minimum of 10 years when stored under medium-term conditions. *Long-term Film* is suitable for the preservation of records for a minimum of 100 years when stored under archival conditions. *Archival Film,* when stored under archival storage conditions, is suitable for the preservation of records having permanent value (Rhodes and Adelstein 1976).

Only films on safety base can qualify for these film types. Nitrate base films are no longer manufactured and not a suitable storage medium. Presently, only silver-gelatin films can be classified as archival films. Diazo films can be specified as either medium- or long-term films.

Medium-term Storage

Medium-term storage rooms of safety-base film should be protected from accidental water damage by rain, flood, or pipe leaks. Air conditioning with controlled relative humidity is desirable but not always essential in moderate climates. Extremes of relative humidity are detrimental to film.

The most satisfactory storage relative humidity for processed film is about 50%, although the range 30 to 60% is satisfactory. Where the relative humidity of the storage area exceeds 60% for any appreciable period, air conditioning is required. If air conditioning cannot be installed, an electric refrigeration-type dehumidifier may be used for a small room. The walls should be coated with a vapor retarder such as asphalt paint, aluminum paint, or paper-laminated aluminum foil (see 1985 FUNDAMENTALS Volume Chapters 20 and 21). The controlling humidistat should be set at about 40% rh. If the prevailing relative humidity is under 25% for long periods, and trouble is encountered from curl or brittleness, humidity should be controlled with a mechanical humidifier set with a controlling humidistat at 40%.

For medium-term storage, room temperature between 68 and 77 °F (20 and 25 °C) is recommended. Higher temperatures may cause dye fading, shrinkage, and distortion. Occasional peak temperature of 95 °F (32 °C) should not be serious. Color films should be stored below 50 °F (10 °C) to reduce dye fading. Films stored below the ambient dew point should be allowed to warm up before opening to prevent moisture condensation (see Table 2).

An oxidizing or reducing atmosphere may deteriorate the film base and gradual fade the photographic image. Oxidizing agents may also cause microscopically small colored spots on fine grain film such as microfilm (Adelstein, Graham, and West 1970). Typical gaseous contaminants include hydrogen sulfide, sulfur dioxide, peroxides, ozone, nitrogen oxides, and paint fumes. When such fumes are present in the intended storage space, they must be eliminated or the film must be protected from contact with the atmosphere (Chapter 44 in this volume has further details).

Archival Storage

For long-term films or for archival records that are to be preserved indefinitely, archival storage conditions should be used. Such film should be stored in an air-conditioned environment. The recommended space relative humidity varies between 15 and 50% rh, depending on the film type. When several film types are stored within the same area, 30% rh is a good compromise. The recommended storage temperature is below 70 °F (21 °C). Low temperature aids preservation, but if storage temperature is below the dew point of the outdoor air, the records must be allowed to warm up in a closed container before they are used, to prevent condensation of moisture. Temperature and humidity conditions must be maintained year-round and should be continuously monitored.

Requirements of a particular storage application can be met by any one of several air-conditioning equipment/system combinations. Chapter 1 of this volume includes more information. Standby equipment should be considered. Sufficient outdoor air should be provided to keep the room under a slight positive pressure for ventilation and to retard the entrance of untreated air. The air-conditioning unit should be located outside the vault for ease of maintenance, with precautions taken to prevent water leakage into the vault. The conditioner casing and all ductwork must be well insulated. Room conditions should be controlled by a dry-bulb thermostat and either a wet-bulb thermostat, a hydrostat, or a dew point controller (See Chapter 51).

Air-conditioning installations and fire dampers in ducts carrying air to or from the storage vault should be constructed and maintained to National Fire Protection Association (NFPA) recommendations (NFPA 1985) for air conditioning and for fire-resistant file rooms (NFPA 1980).

All supply air should be filtered with noncombustible HEPA filters to remove dust that may abrade the film or react with the photographic image. As with medium-term storage, gaseous contaminants such as paint fumes, hydrogen sulfide, sulfur diox-

ide, peroxides, ozone, and nitrogen oxides may cause slow deterioration of film base and gradual fading of the photographic image. When these substances cannot be avoided, an air scrubber, activated carbon adsorber, or other purification method is required.

Films should be stored in metal cabinets with adjustable shelves or drawers, and louvers or openings located to facilitate circulation of conditioned air through them. The cabinets should be spaced in the room to permit free circulation of air around them.

All films should be protected from water damage, whether from leaks, fire sprinkler discharge, or flooding. Drains should have sufficient capacity to keep the water from spinkler discharge from reaching a depth of 3 in. (75 mm). The lowest cabinet, shelf, or drawer should be at least 6 in. (150 mm) off the floor, constructed so that water cannot splash through the ventilating louvers onto the records.

When fire-protected storage is required, the film should be kept in either fire-resistant vaults or insulated record containers (Class 150). Fire-resistant vaults should be constructed in accordance with NFPA Standards (NFPA 1980). Although the NFPA advises against air conditioning in valuable-paper record rooms because of the possible fire hazard from outside, properly controlled air conditioning is essential for long-term preservation of archival films. The fire hazard introduced by the openings in the room for air-conditioning ducts may be reduced by fire and smoke dampers activated by ionization detectors in the supply and return ducts.

When the quantity of film is relatively small, insulated record containers (Class 150) may be used, as defined by Underwriters Laboratories. Class 150 containers will not exceed an interior temperature of 140 °F (66 °C) and an interior relative humidity of 85% under a fire-exposure test lasting from 1 to 4 hours, depending on the classification. Insulated record containers should be on a ground-supported floor if the building is not fire resistant. For best fire protection, duplicate copies of film records should be placed in another storage area.

Storage of Nitrate Base Film

Photographic film has not been manufactured on cellulose nitrate film base for several decades. Many archives, libraries, and museums still have valuable records on this material. The preservation of the nitrate film is of considerable importance until printing on safety base has been accomplished.

Cellulose nitrate film base is chemically unstable and highly flammable. It decomposes slowly but continuously even under normal room conditions. The decomposition produces small amounts of nitric oxide, nitrogen dioxide, and other gases. Unless the nitrogen dioxide can escape readily, it reacts with the film base, accelerating the decomposition (Carro and Calhoun 1955). The rate of decomposition is further accelerated by moisture in the film and is approximately doubled with every 10 °F (5.5 °C) increase in temperature. This process ends only with complete decomposition of the film or, under certain conditions, spontaneous combustion.

Nitrogen dioxide gas also attacks the photographic image. The silver image in black-and-white film fades and bleaches until it disappears, and the dye images in color film discolor and bleach. This fading of the image is often the first sign of nitrate film decomposition. Nitrogen dioxide also chemically breaks down the gelatin in the emulsion layer until it becomes either very brittle or sticky and readily soluble in water.

All nitrate film must be stored in an approved vented cabinet or vault. Nitrate films should never be stored in the same vault with safety base films, because any decomposition of the nitrate film will cause decomposition of the safety film. Cans in which nitrate film is stored should never be sealed, since this traps the nitrogen oxide gas. Standards for the storage of nitrate film have been established (NFPA 1982). The National Archives and the National Bureau of Standards have also investigated the effect of a number of factors on fires in nitrate film vaults (Ryan, Cummings, and Hutton 1956).

The storage temperature should be kept as low as economical and practical factors permit. This is particularly important for a material whose decomposition rate is so temperature-dependent. The film should also be kept at humidities below 50% rh. The temperature and humidity recommendations made in the following section for the cold storage of color film also apply to nitrate film.

Storage of Color Film and Prints

All dyes fade in time. ANSI specifically excludes color film as an archival medium (1976) and ANSI documents on photographic paper only include black-and-white images (1974 and 1979). However, many valuable color films and prints exist, and it is important to preserve them as long as possible.

Light, heat, moisture, and atmospheric pollution contribute to fading of color photographic images (Eastman Kodak 1979). Storage temperature for the preservation of dyes should be as low as possible. For maximum permanence, the materials should be stored in light-tight sealed containers or moisture-proof wrapping materials at a temperature below freezing and at a relative humidity of 15 to 30%. The containers should be warmed to room temperature prior to opening to avoid moisture condensation on the surface. Photographic films can be conditioned to the recommended humidity by passing them through a conditioning cabinet with air circulating at about 15% rh for about 15 minutes.

An alternate procedure is the use of a storage room or cabinet controlled at a steady (non-cycled) low temperature and maintained at the recommended relative humidity. This procedure eliminates the requirement for sealed containers but involves an expensive installation. The dye-fading rate decreases rapidly with decreasing storage temperature, as shown in Table 3.

PHOTOGRAPHIC PAPER PRINTS

Two main compositions of support are used for photographic papers. The *fiber base* generally has a baryta coating under the silver layer for improved smoothness. More recently, *resin-coated* paper is used, allowing shorter fixing, washing, and drying times. Resin-coated papers are relatively new, so reliable long-term keeping data are not yet available, and prints that require long-term keeping under adverse storage or display conditions should be made using conventional fiber support.

Table 3 Effect of Temperature on Dye-Fading Rate
(40% Relative Humidity)

Storage Temperature	Approximate Relative Fading Rate	Approximate Relative Storage Time
86°F (30°C)	2	0.5
75°F (24°C)	1	1
66°F (19°C)	0.5	2
54°F (12°C)	0.2	5
45°F (7°C)	0.1	10
14°F (−10°C)	0.01	100
−15°F (−26°C)	0.001	1000

The recommended storage conditions for processed paper prints are given by an ANSI standard practice (1974). The optimum limits for relative humidity of the ambient air are 30% to 50%, but daily cycling between these limits should be avoided.

A variation in temperature can drive relative humidity beyond its acceptable range. A temperature between 59 and 77°F (15 and 25°C) is acceptable, but daily variations of more than 7°F (4°C) should be avoided. Prolonged temperature above 86°F (30°C) should also be avoided. The degradative processes in black-and-white prints can be slowed considerably by low storage temperature.

As with color prints, moisture-proof wrapping materials should be used. These packages must exceed the dew point temperature before they are opened, to avoid moisture condensation.

Exposure to direct sunlight may lead to deterioration, especially in poorly processed prints. Light sources containing high levels of ultraviolet radiation should be avoided. Tungsten lights and ultraviolet-free fluorescent lamps are recommended for viewing or exhibiting.

Exposure to airborne particles and oxidizing or reducing atmospheres should also be avoided, as mentioned, for films. Protection from these atmospheres can be obtained by modifying the images or by converting them to a less reactive form. Treatment with toners that convert all or substantially all of the image to silver sulfide or silver selenide, or that modify the image by the deposition of gold, produce very stable images. Several commercially available toners can be used.

Display prints should be protected from accidental damage because of fire and water. Storage of collections should be undertaken with the same precautions as for archival storage of films.

REFERENCES

Adelstein, P.Z.; Graham, C.L.; and West, L.E. 1970. Preservation of motion picture color films having permanent value. *Journal of the Society of Motion Picture and Television Engineers*, Vol. 79, November, p. 1011.

ANSI. 1974. *Practice for Storage of Black-and-White Photographic Prints.* American National Standard PH1,48.

ANSI. 1976a. *Specifications for Photographic Film for Archival Records, Silver-Gelatin Type, on Cellulose Ester Base.* American National Standard PH1,28.

ANSI. 1976b. *Specifications for Safety Photographic Film.* American National Standard PH1,25.

ANSI. 1978. *Requirements for Photographic Filing Enclosures for Storing Processed Photographic Films, Plates, and Papers.* American National Standard PH1, 53.

ANSI. 1979a. *Method for Evaluating the Processing of Black-and-White Photographic Papers with Respect to the Stability of the Resultant Image.* American National Standard PH4, 32.

ANSI. 1979b. *Practice for Storage of Processed Safety Photographic Film.* American National Standard PH1,43.

ANSI. 1979c. *Processed Diazo Photographic Film.* American National Standard PH1, 60.

Carrol, J.F.; and Calhoun, J.M. 1955. Effect of nitrogen oxide gases on processed acetate film. *Journal of the Society of Motion Picture and Television Engineers,* Vol. 64, September, p. 601.

Carver, E.K.; Talbot, R.H.; and Loomis, H.A. 1943. Film distortions and their effect upon protection quality. *Journal Society of Motion Picture and Television Engineers,* Vol. 41, July, p. 88.

Eastman Kodak. 1977. *Storage and Care of Kodak Films.* Eastman Kodak Company, No. E-30.

Eastman Kodak. 1979. *Preservation of Photographs.* Eastman Kodak Company, No. E-30.

Eastman Kodak. 1980. *Construction Materials for Photographic Processing Equipment.* Eastman Kodak Company, No. K-12.

Henn, R.W.; and Wiest, D.G. 1963. Microscopic spots in processed microfilm: their nature and prevention. *Photographic Science and Engineering,* Vol. 7, September-October, p. 253.

IES. *Standard for HEPA Filters,* CS-1. Institute of Environment Sciences, Mt. Prospect, IL.

NFPA. 1980. *Protection of Records.* National Fire Protection Association Standard 232-80.

NFPA. 1982. *Storage and Handling of Cellulose Nitrate Motion Picture Film.* National Fire Protection Association, Standard 40-82.

NFPA. 1985. *Installation of Air Conditioning and Ventilating Systems.* National Fire Protection Association Standard 90A-85.

Rhoads, J.B.; and Adelstein, P.Z. Letters on archival permanence. 1976. *The Journal of Micrographics,* Vol. 9, March, p. 193.

Ryan, J.V.; Cummings, J.W.; and Hutton, A.C. 1956. *Fire Effects and Fire Control in Nitro-Cellulose Photographic-Film Storage* (Building Materials and Structures Report, No. 145, U. S. Department of Commerce, April.

Underwriter's Laboratory. 1983. *Test for Fire Resistance of Record Protection Equipment.* Underwriters Laboratory Standard 72-83.

CHAPTER 37

ENVIRONMENT FOR ANIMALS AND PLANTS

THE design of plant and animal housing is complicated by the many environmental factors affecting growth and production of living organisms and the financial constraint that equipment must repay costs through improved economic productivity. The engineer must balance the economic costs of modifying the environment against the economic losses of a plant or animal in a less-than-ideal environment. Economics are no longer the only concern relating to animals. Concerns for both workers and the care and welfare of animals influence design, as well.

DESIGN FOR ANIMAL ENVIRONMENTS

Typical animal production systems modify environment, to some degree, by housing or sheltering animals for all or parts of a year. The amount of modification is generally based upon the expected increase in production. Animal sensible heat and moisture production data, combined with information on the effects of environment on growth, productivity, and reproduction, help designers select optimum equipment (see Chapter 10 of the 1985 FUNDAMENTALS Volume). The Midwest Plan Service, *Structures and Environment Handbook* (1983), and ASAE Monograph-6, *Ventilation of Agricultural Structures* (1984), give more detailed information.

Ventilation design methods generally use both a steady-state analysis and the principle of conservation of energy or matter to calculate the required airflow rate to control moisture, temperature, or other contaminants within the building. The following relationship and Figure 1 summarize these two principles:

$$\dot{m}X_e + q = \dot{m}X_i + (X_i - X_o)/Y \qquad (1)$$

where

$\dot{m}$ = the mass flow rate of dry air.

X = the concentration of the quantity considered (heat, moisture, or contaminants).

q = the generation rate of the quantity considered within the system.

Y = the resistance to transfer through the enclosure surfaces.

The subscripts refer to the conditions in the air (1) entering the system (*e*); (2) within the system when well mixed (*i*); and (3) surrounding the shelter on the outside (*o*).

The value of $\dot{m}$ in Equation (1) is usually large in comparison with $1/Y$. Thus, the transfer of any quantity, except heat through the structure, is usually neglected in balance calculations. However, moisture transfer through walls may lead to concealed condensation and subsequent structural damage (see Chapter 21 in the 1985 FUNDAMENTALS Volume).

The preparation of this chapter is assigned to TC 2.2, Plant and Animal Environment.

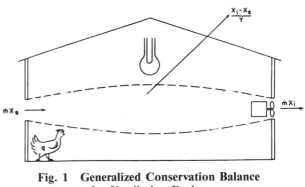

Fig. 1 Generalized Conservation Balance for Ventilation Design

Temperature Control

The temperature within an animal structure is computed from the sensible heat balance of the system, usually disregarding transient effects. Nonstandard systems with low airflow rates and/or large thermal mass may require transient analysis. Steady-state heat transfer through walls, ceiling or roof, and ground are calculated as presented in Chapter 23 of the 1985 FUNDAMENTALS Volume.

Densely housed, mature animals typically produce most of the total heat load within a building. Chapter 9 of the 1985 FUNDAMENTALS Volume gives estimates of animal heat load. Lighting and equipment loads are estimated from power ratings and operating times. Typically, the designer selects indoor and outdoor design temperatures and calculates the ventilation rate to maintain the temperature difference. Outdoor design temperatures are given in Chapter 24 of the 1985 FUNDAMENTALS Volume. The section on "Current Recommended Practices" in this chapter discuss indoor design values of temperature for various livestock.

Moisture Control

Moisture loads produced within an animal building may be calculated from data in the 1985 FUNDAMENTALS Volume. The weight of water vapor produced is then estimated by dividing the animal latent heat production by the latent heat of vaporization of water at the expected inside air temperature. Water spilled and evaporation of fecal water must be included in the estimates of animal latent heat production. Water vapor removed by ventilation from a totally slatted (manure storage beneath floor) swine facility may be up to 40% less than the amount removed from a conventional concrete floor (solid). If the floor is partially slatted, the 40% maximum reduction is reduced proportionally to the percentage of the floor that is slatted.

The ventilation system should remove enough moisture to prevent condensation but should not reduce the relative humidity so low (less than 50%) as to create dusty conditions. Design indoor relative humidities for winter ventilation are usually between 75 to 80%. The walls should have sufficient insulation to prevent surface condensation at 80% rh inside. Chapter (21) of the 1985 FUNDAMENTALS Volume outlines design procedures for condensation control within walls.

During cold weather, the ventilation needed for moisture control usually exceeds that needed to control temperature. Minimum ventilation must always be provided to remove animal moisture. Up to a full day of high humidity may be tolerated during extreme cold periods when normal ventilation rates could cause an excessive heating demand. Conversely, summer ventilation primarily controls temperature, as humidity level is not a concern.

Modification of Air Contaminants

The amount of dust varies with animal density; size; and degree of activity, type of litter or bedding, type of feed, and relative humidity of the air. A high moisture content of 25 to 30%, wet basis, in the litter or bedding keeps dust to a minimum.

Gaseous contaminants within a building are usually controlled as a result of ventilation for moisture or temperature control. Ammonia generated in litter is diluted by the ventilating air. Dry litter and clean floors retard manure decomposition and production of ammonia. When sufficient air is provided for moisture control, air purity is usually satisfactory. Best air conditions are enhanced by removing manure as quickly as possible.

Buildings with manure storage should be mechanically ventilated directly to the outside to reduce noxious and toxic gases and odors inside the building. Hydrogen sulfide levels have sometimes exceeded 800 ppm during manure storage agitation. Since adverse effects on production will begin to occur at 20 ppm, ventilation systems should be designed to maintain hydrogen sulfide levels below 20 ppm during agitation. When manure is agitated and removed from the storage, the building should be well ventilated and all animals and occupants removed from the building because of potential deadly concentrations of gases.

CURRENT PRACTICES OF
ENVIRONMENTAL MODIFICATION

Shelters and Shades

Livestock need some protection from adverse climate in most of the world during some seasons. Mature cattle and sheep on range need protection during severe winter conditions. Dairy cattle and swine may be protected from precipitation, wind, and drafts in winter with a three-sided, roofed shelter open on the leeward side. The windward side should also have approximately 10% of the wall surface area open to prevent a negative pressure inside the shelter, which can cause rain and snow to be drawn into the building on the leeward side. Such shelters do not protect against extreme temperatures or high humidity. Young animals are more sensitive to environment and thus require some environmental modification to ensure early growth.

Shades often provide adequate shelter, especially for large, mature animals such as dairy cows located in warmer climates. Shades are in common use in Arizona, and research in Florida has shown an approximate 10% increase in milk production and a 75% increase in conception efficiency for shaded cows versus unshaded cows. The benefit of shades has not been documented for areas with less severe summer temperatures.

Although shades for beef are also common practice in the southwest, beef cattle are somewhat less susceptible to heat stress, and extensive comparisons of various shade types in Florida have detected little or no differences in daily weight gain or feed conversion.

Figure 2 illustrates the energy exchange between an animal and various areas of the environment. A well-designed shade makes maximum use of radiant heat sinks such as the cold sky and gives maximum protection from direct solar radiation and high surface temperatures under the shade. Ground design considers geometric orientation and material selection, including roof surface treatment and insulation materials on the lower surface.

An ideal shade has a top surface highly reflective to solar energy and a lower surface highly absorptive to solar radiation reflected from the ground. A white-painted upper surface reflects solar radiation, yet emits infrared energy better than aluminum. The undersurface should be painted a dark color to prevent multiple reflection of shortwave energy onto animals under the shade.

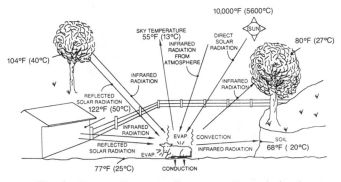

**Fig. 2   Energy Exchange Between a Farm Animal
and Its Surroundings in a Hot Environment**

Air Movement

Increased air movement during hot weather (as long as air temperatures are below animal body temperature) increases growth and feed conversion efficiency, decreases water consumption, and improves heat tolerance. Overhead paddle fans or propeller fans move extra air around animals.

Evaporative Cooling

Supplemental cooling of animals in intensive housing conditions may be necessary during heat waves to prevent heat prostration, mortality, or serious losses in production and reproduction. Evaporative cooling systems, which may reduce ventilation air to 80°F (27°C) or lower in most of the United States, are very popular for poultry houses, both breeders and layers, and sometimes for swine houses. Potential benefits to production and reproduction of dairy cows also exist.

Evaporative cooling is well-suited to animal housing because the high air exchange rates also effectively remove odors and ammonia and increase air movement for convective heat relief. Initial cost, operating expense, and maintenance problems are all relatively low compared with other heating and ventilating equipment costs normally associated with controlled environment housing. Evaporative cooling works best in areas of low relative humidity, but significant benefits can be obtained even in the humid Southeastern United States.

Pad area should be sized to maintain air velocities between 200 and 275 fpm (1.0 and 1.4 m/s) through the pads. For most pad systems, these velocities produce evaporative efficiencies between 75 to 85%, but also increase the pressures against the ventilating fans from 0.04 to 0.12 in. of water (10 to 30 Pa). Therefore, fans should be selected accordingly.

Clogging by dust and other airborne particles has caused the most serious problem of evaporative pad systems for agricultural applications. When possible, fans should exhaust away from pads on adjacent buildings. In addition, regular preventive maintenance must be practiced. Water bleed-off and addition of algaecides to the water are recommended. When pads are not used in cool weather, they should be sealed to prevent dusty inside air from exhausting through them.

High pressure fogging systems with water pressures of 500 psi (3.5 MPa), are preferred to pad coolers for cooling the air in broiler houses with built-up litter. The high pressure creates a fine aerosol, causing minimal litter wetting. Timers and/or thermostats control the system. Evaporative efficiencies and installation costs are about half those of a well-designed evaporative pad system. Foggers can also be used with naturally ventilated, open-sided housing. Low pressure systems are not recommended for poultry but may be considered during emergencies.

Nozzles that produce water mist or spray droplets to wet animals directly are used extensively during hot weather in swine confinement facilities with solid concrete or slatted floors. Currently, misting or sprinkling systems that directly wet the skin surface of the animals (not merely the outer portion of the hair coat) are preferred. Timers that operate a system periodically, e.g., 30 seconds on a 5-minute cycle, help conserve water. Some applications may benefit by running the inlet air through drainage tubing buried 6 to 13 ft (2 to 4 m) below grade.

Mechanical Refrigeration

Mechanical refrigeration systems can be designed for effective animal cooling, but they are considered uneconomical for most production animals. Air conditioning loads for dairy housing may require 2.5 kW or more per cow. Recirculation of refrigeration air is usually not feasible due to high contaminant loads in the air within the animal housing.

Sometimes zone cooling of individual animals is used instead of whole-room cooling, particularly in swine farrowing houses where a lower air temperature is needed for the sow than for the unweaned piglets. Refrigerated air, 18 to 36°F (10 to 20°C) below ambient, is supplied through insulated ducts directly to the head and face of the animal. Air delivery rates are typically 10 to 30 cfm (5 to 15 L/s) per sow for snout cooling and 60 to 80 cfm (30 to 40 L/s) per sow for zone cooling.

VENTILATION DESIGN

A well-designed ventilation system produces uniform air movement at animal height and maintains the following conditions:

1. Dry floors and dry litter
2. Uniform temperature at all animal locations
3. Noxious gas concentrations at or below acceptable levels
4. A minimum of rapid changes and wide fluctuations in the environmental temperature
5. No air drafts (moving air, which is colder than the existing environment) over the animal during winter

To prevent drafts, cold, fresh ventilating air should mix with air inside the building before it reaches the animals. Uniform air distribution keeps all the animals at uniform temperatures.

Ventilation rate may be determined by four control regimes, as shown in Figure 3 (all four do not necessarily apply to a specific application in a specific climate). These regimes include the following:

Maximum Rate: Maximum practical ventilation rate for maintaining comfort.

Temperature Control: Minimum ventilation rate to maintain an optimum temperature.

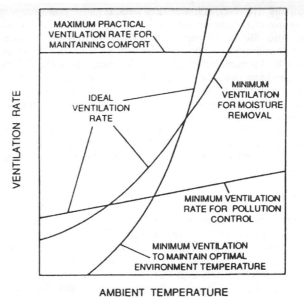

Fig. 3 Temperature Influences on Ventilation Requirements for an Unheated Livestock Building (Hellickson and Walker 1983)

Humidity Control: Minimum ventilation rate for moisture removal.

Pollution Control: Minimum ventilation rate for pollution control.

Mechanical Ventilation

Mechanical ventilation depends on fans to create a static pressure difference between the inside and outside of a building. Either positive pressure, where fans force air into a building, or negative pressure, with exhaust fans, is used in farm buildings. Some ventilation systems use a combination of positive pressure to introduce air into a building, with separate fans to remove air. These zero-pressure systems are particularly appropriate for heat exchangers. Positive and negative pressure systems have the following characteristics:

Positive pressure systems. Fans force humid air out through planned outlets, if any, and through leaks in walls and ceilings. Thus, moisture condensation during cold weather will occur within the walls and ceiling if vapor barriers are not complete. Condensation causes deterioration of building materials and reduces insulation effectiveness. The energy used by fan motors that is rejected as heat is added to the building, an advantage in winter but a disadvantage in summer.

Positive pressure systems can allow greater control to minimize house-to-house or room-to-room transmission of airborne diseases, if the incoming air is filtered. If a filter is necessary, recommendations include the following:

1. Use air filters having at least 95% efficiency based on ASHRAE *Standard* 52-76, Method of Testing Air-Cleaning Devices Used in General Ventilation for Removing Particulate Matter.
2. Maintain a positive pressure of 0.25 to 0.28 in. of water (60 to 70 Pa) inside the house or room (relative to outside static pressure) for locations where the outside wind speed seldom exceeds 22 mph (10 m/s) (higher pressures are required for higher winds).

Negative pressure systems. Air distribution in a negative pressure system is often less complex and costly. Simple openings and baffled slots in walls control and distribute air in the building. However, at low airflow rates, negative pressure systems may not distribute air uniformly because of air leaks and wind pressure effects. Supplemental air mixing may be necessary.

Allowances should be made for reduced fan efficiency because some dust accumulation on fan blades cannot be avoided. Totally enclosed fan motors are protected from exhaust air contaminants and humidity. Periodic cleaning helps prevent overheating. Negative pressure systems are more commonly used than positive pressure systems.

The ventilation system should always be designed so that manure gases are not drawn into the building from manure storages connected to the building by underground pipes or channels.

Air Distribution

Pressure differences across walls and inlet or fan openings are usually maintained between 0.04 to 0.12 in. of water (10 to 30 Pa). This pressure difference creates 600 to 1000 fpm (3 to 5 m/s) inlet velocities, sufficient for effective air mixing, but is low enough to cause only a small reduction in air delivery. A properly planned inlet system distributes fresh air equally throughout the building. Negative pressure systems that rely on cracks around doors and windows do not distribute fresh air effectively. Inlets require adjustment, since winter flow rates are typically less than 10% of summer airflow rates. Automatic controllers that regulate inlet area (slot openings) by sensing inside air pressure are recommended. Positive pressure systems, with fans connected directly to perforated, polyethylene air distribution tubes, combine heating, circulation, and ventilation in one system. Air distribution tubes or ducts connected to circulating fans are sometimes used in negative pressure systems to promote air mixing.

Inlet Design for Negative Pressure System

Inlet location and size most critically affect air distribution within a building. Continuous or intermittent inlets can be placed along the entire length of one or both outside walls. Building widths less than 23 ft (7 m) may need only a single inlet along one wall. The total inlet area may be calculated by the system characteristic technique (described below). The distribution of the inlet area is based upon the geometry and size of the building, which makes specific recommendations difficult.

System characteristic technique: This technique determines the operating points for ventilation rate and pressure difference across inlets. Fan airflow rate as a function of pressure difference across the fan should be available from the manufacturer. Allowances should be made for additional pressure losses from fan shutters or other devices such as light restriction systems or cooling pads.

Inlet flow characteristics are available for hinged baffle and center-ceiling flat baffle slotted inlets (diagrammed in Figure 4). Airflow rates can be calculated for the baffles in Figure 4 by the following:

For Case A

$$Q = C_1 W \Delta p^{0.5} \qquad (2)$$

For Case B

$$Q = C_2 W \Delta p^{0.5} \qquad (3)$$

For Case C

$$Q = C_3 W \Delta p^{0.49} (D/T)^{0.08} e^{(-0.867 W/T)} \qquad (4)$$

where

Q = airflow rate, cfm per foot length of slot opening (L/s per m)
W = slot width, in. (mm)
Δp = pressure difference across the inlet, in. of water gauge (Pa)

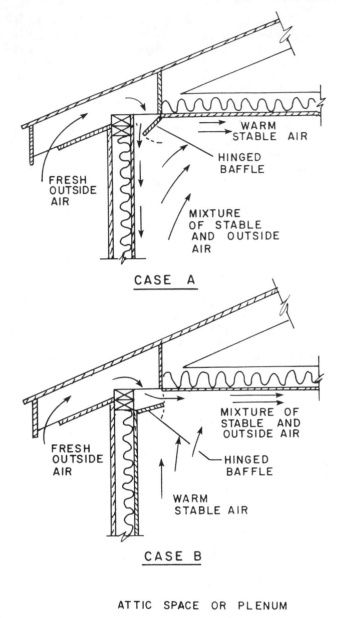

CASE A

CASE B

CASE C

Fig. 4 Typical Livestock Building Inlet Configurations

D = baffle width, in. (mm) (see Figure 4)
T = width of slot in ceiling, in. (mm) (see Figure 4)
C_1 = 285 (1.1)
C_2 = 183 (0.71)
C_3 = 320 (1.3)

In addition to airflow through the inlet, infiltration airflow should be included. Figure 5 illustrates infiltration rates for two types of dairy barn construction (appropriate for other animal buildings, also). The infiltration rates can be described as:

Average construction:
$$I = C_4 \Delta p^{0.67} \tag{5}$$
Tight construction:
$$I = C_5 \Delta p^{0.67} \tag{6}$$

where

I = infiltration rate, cfm per ft^2 of floor area [L/(s · m^2)].
C_4 = 26.7 (3.4)
C_5 = 9.42 (1.2)

Example. A dairy barn with a total floor area of 600 m^2 is to be ventilated with hinged baffle, wall flow, and slotted inlets. A total inlet length of 140 m is available. The barn is considered to have tight construction. The total fresh air ventilation rate, Q_{tot}, is thus described by the following:

$$Q_{tot} = Q + I = (0.0011 \; W\Delta p^{0.5})(140) + (600)(0.0012 \; \Delta p^{0.67})$$
$$Q_{tot} = 0.154 \; W\Delta p^{0.5} + 0.72 \; \Delta p^{0.67}$$

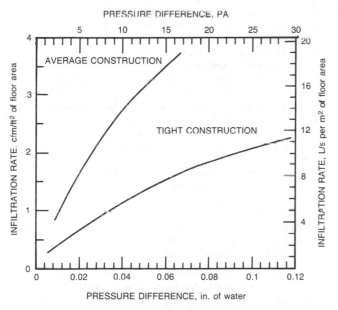

Fig. 5   Infiltration due to Cracks for Average and Tight Animal Building Construction (Adapted from ASAE Data: D270.4)

The above equation can be graphed as a system ventilation rate curve for various slot widths. Then, in conjunction with fan data, a ventilation schedule for expected weather and seasonal conditions can be developed.

Room Air Velocity

The average air velocity inside a slot ventilated structure relates to the slot velocity, inlet slot width (or equivalent continuous length for boxed inlets), building width, and ceiling height. Estimates of air velocity within a barn, based upon air exchange rates, may be very low due to effects of jet velocity and recirculation. An estimate of expected room air velocity under fully turbulent flow conditions where substantial air flow barriers are not present may be calculated as the following:

$$V/V_{inlet} = 0.477 - 0.0058 \sqrt{HB/W} \tag{7}$$

where

V = average air velocity within ventilated air space, fpm (m/s)
V_{inlet} = average inlet velocity, fpm (m/s)
W = slot width, in. (mm) (if two continuous slots, use 2 W)
H = ceiling height, ft (m)
B = room width, ft (m)

Fans and Thermostats

Fans should not exhaust against prevailing winds. If structural or other factors require installing fans on the windward side, select fans rated to deliver the required capacity against at least 0.12 in. of water (30 Pa) static pressure and with a relatively flat power curve. The fan motor should withstand a wind velocity of 30 mph (50 km/h), equivalent to a static pressure of 0.4 in. of water (100 Pa), without overloading beyond its service factor. Wind hoods on the fans or wind break fences reduce wind effects.

Control thermostats should be placed to respond to a representative temperature as sensed by the animals. The thermostat needs protection or should be placed to prevent potential physical damage. They should not be placed near animals, ventilation inlets, water pipes, lights, heater exhausts, outside walls or any other objects that will unduly affect performance. They are commonly placed near a fan exhaust. They also require periodic adjustment based on accurate thermometer readings taken in the immediate animal area.

Flow Control

Since numbers and sizes of livestock and climatic conditions may vary, means to modulate ventilation rates are often required beyond the conventional off/on thermostat switch. The minimum ventilation rate to remove moisture, reduce noxious gases, and keep water from freezing should always be provided. Methods include: (1) intermittent fan operation—fans run on a percentage of time controlled by a percentage timer with a 10-minute cycle; (2) staging of fans using multiple units or fans with high/low exhaust capability; (3) multi-speed fans—larger fans (1/2 hp and up) with two flow rates, the lower being about 60% of the maximum rate; and (4) variable speed fans—split capacitor motors designed to modulate fan speed smoothly from maximum down to 10 to 20% of maximum rate (the controller is usually thermostatically adjusted).

Fans generally are spaced uniformly along the lee side of a building. Maximum distance between fans is between 115 to 165 ft (35 to 40 m). Fans may be grouped in a bank if this range is not exceeded. In housing with side curtains, exhaust fans that can be reversed or removed and placed inside the building in the summer sometimes are installed to increase air movement in combination with doors, walls, or windows being opened for natural ventilation.

Emergency Warning System

Animals housed in a high density, mechanically controlled environment are subject to considerable risk of heat prostration if a power or ventilation equipment failure occurs. To reduce this danger, an alarm system and an automatic standby electric generator are highly recommended. Many alarm systems will detect failure of the ventilation system. These range from inexpensive "power off" alarms to systems that sense temperature extremes, and certain gases. Automatic telephone dialing systems have demonstrated effectiveness as alarms and are relatively inexpensive for the protection provided. Building designs that allow some side wall panels, e.g., 25% of wall area, to be removed for emergency situations are recommended.

Natural Ventilation

Either natural or mechanical ventilation systems will modify environments within livestock shelters. Natural ventilation is most common for mature animal housing, such as free stall dairy and swine finishing houses. Natural ventilation depends upon pressure differences caused by wind and temperature difference. A well-designed natural ventilation system keeps temperature reasonably stable, if automatic controls regulate ventilation openings. Usually, a design includes an open ridge (with or without a rain cover) and openable sidewalls. Sidewall openings should cover at least 50% of the wall for summer operation; ridge openings are about 2 in. (50 mm) wide for each 10 ft (3 m) of house width with a minimum ridge width 6 in. (150 mm).

Openings can be adjusted automatically with control based upon air temperature. Some designs, referred to as flex housing, include a combination of mechanical ventilation and natural ventilation usually dictated by outside air temperature and/or the amount of ventilation required.

Insulation and Supplemental Heating

For poultry weighing 3.3 lb. (1.5 kgs) or more, for pigs heavier than 50 lb. (23 kg), and for other large animals such as dairy cows, the body heat of the animals at recommended space allocations is usually sufficient to maintain moderate temperatures, e.g., above 50°F (10°C), in a well-insulated structure. Combustion-type heaters supplement heat for baby chicks and pigs. Supplemental heating also increases the moisture-holding capacity of the air, which reduces the quantity of air required for removal of moisture. Various types of heating equipment may be included in ventilation systems, but it needs to perform well in a dusty and corrosive atmosphere.

The amount of building insulation required depends on climate, animal space allocations, and animal heat and moisture production. Usually, structures with an overall heat transmission coefficient of 0.08 to 0.12 Btu/h ft^2 °F [0.45 to 0.68 W/(m^2 K)] are adequate for northern climates. In moderate climates, values ranging from 0.15 to 0.25 Btu/h ft^2 °F [0.85 to 1.4 W/(m^2 K)] are adequate for adult animals, but may be decreased in cold areas to conserve fuel when heating for young animals. In warm weather, ventilation between the roof and insulation helps reduce the radiant heat load from the ceiling. Insulation in warm climates can be more important for reducing radiant heat loads in summer than reducing building heat loss in winter.

Heat Exchangers

Ventilation accounts for 70 to 90% of the heat losses in typical livestock facilities during winter. Heat exchangers can reclaim some of the heat lost with the exhaust ventilating air. However, predicting fuel savings based upon savings obtained during the coldest periods will overestimate yearly savings from a heat exchanger. Estimates of energy savings based upon air enthalpy can improve predictive accuracy.

Heat exchanger design must address the problems with condensate freezing and/or dust accumulation on the heat exchanging surfaces. This problem causes either reduced efficiency and/or the inconvenience of frequent cleaning. Finned heat exchangers should have a fin spacing of at least 4 per inch (6 mm). Fouling problems are reduced, but not eliminated, in units without fins. Three basic heat exchange designs have evolved for general use in animal confinement buildings: cross, diagonal, and counterflow heat exchangers.

Pipe buried to condition inlet air is used in some areas. Pipes should be buried 6 to 13 ft (2 m to 4 m) below grade. A typical design uses 150 ft (50 m) of 8-in. (0.20-m) diameter pipe to provide 100 cfm (50 L/s) of tempered inlet air. Soil type and moisture, pipe depth, airflow, and climate are other factors that affect the efficiency of a buried pipe system.

CURRENT RECOMMENDED PRACTICES

Mature animals readily adapt to temperatures within a broad range, but efficiency of production will vary. Younger animals are more temperature sensitive. Figure 6 illustrates animal production response to temperature and ranges of lower and upper critical temperatures.

Relative humidity has not been shown to influence animal performance, except when accompanied by thermal stress. Relative humidity consistently below 50% may contribute to excessive dustiness, and above 80% may increase building and equipment deterioration. Disease pathogens also appear to be more viable at either low or high humidities.

Dairy cattle

Dairy cattle shelters include confinement stall barns, free stalls, and loose housing. In the stall barn, cattle are usually confined to stalls approximately 4 ft (1.2 m) wide and all chores, including milking and feeding, are conducted there. Such a structure requires environmental modification, primarily through ventilation. Total space requirements are 50 to 75 ft^2 (5 to 7 m^2) per cow. In free-stall housing, cattle are not confined to stalls but are free to move about. Space requirements per cow are 75 to 100 ft^2 (7 to 9 m^2). In loose housing, cattle are free to move within a fenced lot containing resting, feeding, and milking areas. Space required in sheltered loose housing is similar to free-stall housing. The shelters for resting and feeding areas are generally open-sided and require no air conditioning or mechanical ventilation, but supplemental air mixing often is beneficial during warm weather. The milking area is in a separate area or facility and may be fully or partially enclosed and thus may require some ventilation.

For dairy cattle, climate requirements for minimal economic loss are broad and range from 35 to 75°F (2 to 24°C), from 40 to 80% relative humidity. Below 35°F (2°C), production efficiency declines and management problems increase. However, the effect of low temperature on milk production is not as extreme as are high temperatures, where evaporative coolers or other cooling methods may be warranted.

Ventilation Rates for Each 1100 lb (500 kg) Cow		
Winter	Spring/Fall	Summer
36 to 47 cfm	142 to 190 cfm	230 to 470 cfm
(17-22 L/s)	(67-90 L/s)	(110-220 L/s)

Required ventilation rates depend on specific thermal characteristics of individual buildings and internal heating load. The relative humidity should be maintained between 50 and 80%.

Both loose housing and stall barns require an additional milkroom to cool and hold the milk. Sanitation codes for milk contain minimum ventilation requirements. The market being supplied should be consulted for all codes. Some state codes require positive pressure ventilation of milk rooms. Milk rooms are usually ventilated with fans at rates of 4 to 10 air changes per hour to satisfy requirements of local milk codes and to remove heat from milk coolers. Most milk codes require ventilation in the passageway between the milking area and milk room, if there is one.

Beef cattle

Beef cattle ventilation requirements are similar to those of

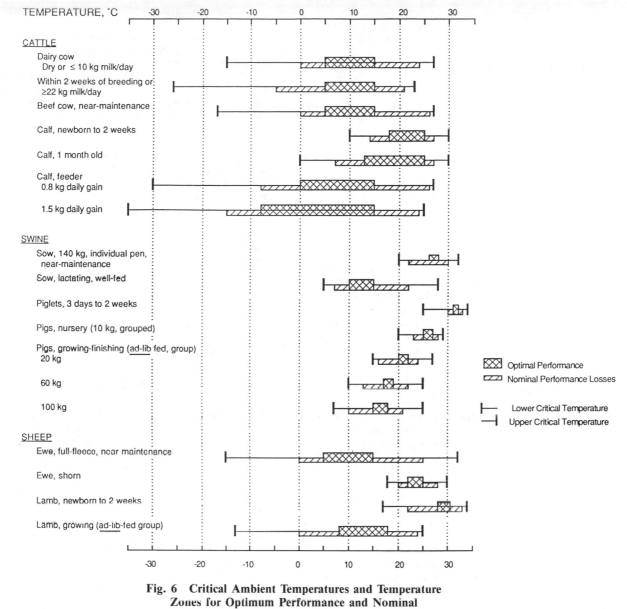

**Fig. 6   Critical Ambient Temperatures and Temperature
Zones for Optimum Performance and Nominal
Performance Losses in Farm Animals (Hahn 1985)**

dairy on a unit weight basis. Beef production facilities often provide only shade and wind breaks.

Swine

Swine housing can be grouped into four general classifications:

1. **Farrowing** pigs from birth to 15 lbs (7 kg).
2. **Nursery** pigs from 15 to 50 lbs (7 to 23 kg).
3. **Growing** pigs from 50 lbs (23 kg to market weight).
4. **Breeding and gestation.**

In farrowing barns, two environments must be provided: one for sows and one for piglets. Because each requires a different temperature, zone heating and/or cooling is used. The environment within the nursery is similar to those within the farrowing barn for piglets. Also, requirements for breeding stock housing will approach, but are less stringent than, those for growing barns.

Currently recommended practices for **Farrowing Houses** are:
Temperature: 50 to 68 °F (10 to 20 °C) with small areas warmed

for pigs to 82 to 90 °F (28 to 32 °C) by means of brooders, heat lamps, or floor heat. Avoid cold drafts and extreme temperatures. Hovers are sometimes used. Provide supplemental cooling in extreme heat (usually sprinklers or evaporative cooling systems).
Relative Humidity: up to 75% maximum.
Ventilation Rate: 40 to 530 cfm (18 to 250 L/s) per sow and litter (about 400 lbs. (180 kg) total weight). The low rate is for winter; the high rate is for summer temperature control.
Space: 34 ft² (3.2 m²) per sow and litter (stall) 65 ft² (6.0 m²) per sow and litter (pens).

Recommendations for **Nursery Barns** are:
Temperature: 79 °F (26 °C) for first week after weaning. Lower room temperature 3 °F (1.5 °C) per week to 72 °F (21 °C). Provide warm, draft-free floors. Provide supplemental cooling for extreme heat [temperatures 80 °F (28 °C) and above].
Ventilation Rates: 3 to 38 cfm (1.5 to 18 L/s) per pig 13 to 79 lb (6 to 36 kg each).
Space: 1.7 to 3.9 ft² (0.16 to 0.36²) per pig 13 to 31 lb (6 to 14 kg each).

Recommendations for **Growing/Gestation** barns are:

Temperature: 55 to 72°F (13 to 22°C) preferred. Provide supplemental cooling (sprinklers or evaporative coolers) for extreme heat.

Relative Humidity: 75% maximum in winter, no established limit in summer.

Ventilation Rate:

Growing pig [75 to 150 lb (34 to 68 kg)] – 6 to 85 cfm (3 to 40 L/s).

Finishing pig [150 to 220 lb (68 to 100 kg)] – 11 to 127 cfm (5 to 60 L/s).

Gestating sow [240 to 500 lb (110 to 230 kg)] – 0.5 cfm/16 [0.5 L/(s · kg)].

Space: 5.8 ft² (0.54 m²) per pig 75 to 150 lbs (34 to 68 kg) each. 7.8 ft² (0.72 m²) per pig 150 to 220 lbs (68 to 100 kg) each. 14 to 23.7 ft² (1.3 to 2.2 m²) per sow 240 to 500 lbs (110 to 130 kg) each.

Poultry

In broiler and brooder houses, growing chicks require changing environmental conditions, and heat and moisture dissipation rates increase as the chicks grow older. Supplemental heat, usually from brooders, is used until sensible heat produced by the birds is adequate to maintain an acceptable air temperature. At early stages of growth, moisture dissipation per bird is low. Consequently, low ventilation rates are recommended to prevent excessive heat loss. Litter is allowed to accumulate over 3 to 5 flock placements. Lack of low cost litter material may justify use of concrete floors. After each flock, caked litter is removed and fresh litter is added for the next flock.

Housing for poultry may either be open, curtain sided (dominant style in the south), or totally enclosed (dominant style in northern climates). Mechanical ventilation depends on the type of housing used. For open sided housing, ventilation is generally natural air flow in warm weather, supplemented with stirring fans, and by fans with closed curtains in cold weather or during the brooding period. Totally enclosed housing depends on mechanical ventilation. Newer houses have smaller curtains and well-insulated construction to accommodate both natural and mechanical ventilation operation.

Recommendations for **Broiler Houses:**

Room temperature: 60 to 80°F (15 to 27°C).

Temperature Under Brooder Hover: 86 to 91°F (30 to 33°C), reducing 5°F (3°C) per week until room temperature is reached.

Relative Humidity: 50 to 80%.

Ventilation Rate: sufficient to maintain house within 2 to 4°F (1 to 2°C) of outside air conditions during summer. Generally, rates are about 0.1 cfm per lb live weight (0.1 L/s per kg) during winter and 1 to 2 cfm per lb (1 to 2 L/s per kg) for summer conditions.

Space: 0.6 to 1.0 ft² (0.06 to 0.09 m²) per bird (for the first 21 days of brooding, only 50% of floor space is used).

Light: minimum of 10 lux to 28 days of age, 1 to 20 lux for growout (in enclosed housing).

Recommendations for **Breeder Houses** with birds on litter and slatted floors:

Temperature: 50 to 86°F (10 to 30°C) maximum (consider evaporative cooling if higher temperatures are expected).

Relative Humidity: 50 to 75%.

Ventilation Rate: same as for broilers on live weight basis.

Space: 2 to 3 ft² (0.2 to 0.3 m²) per bird.

Recommendations for **Laying Houses** with birds in cages:

Temperature, Relative Humidity and Ventilation Rate: same as for breeders.

Space: 50 to 65 in.² (0.032 to 0.042 m²) per hen minimum.

Light: Controlled day length using light-controlled housing is generally practiced (January through June).

Laboratory Animals

Proper management of laboratory animals includes any system of housing and care that permits animals to grow, mature, reproduce, behave normally, and be maintained in physical comfort and good health. Most recommendations for temperature and relative humidity are based upon room temperature and humidity measurements, which may not be indicative of the microenvironment of the animal cage. Ventilation of the animal room (or cage) is necessary to regulate temperature and promote the comfort of animals.

Ideally, a system should permit individual compartment adjustments within ±2°F (±1°C) for any temperature within a range of 64 to 86°F (18 to 30°C). The relative humidity should be maintained throughout the year within a range of 30 to 75%, according to the needs of the species and local climatic conditions. Room air changes at a rate of 10 to 15 per hour are recommended for odor control. Additional information regarding laboratory animals is contained in Chapter 30 of this volume and in the 1985 FUNDAMENTALS Volume. The National Research Council has published a thorough document on this subject (see current references under "Laboratory Animals").

PLANTS: GREENHOUSES AND OTHER FACILITIES

GENERAL

Greenhouses, plant growth chambers, and other facilities for indoor crop production overcome adverse outdoor environments and provide conditions conducive to economic crop production. The basic requirements of indoor crop production are (1) adequate light; (2) favorable temperatures; (3) favorable air or gas content; (4) protection from insects and disease; and (5) suitable growing media, substrate, and moisture. Greenhouses, because of their lower cost per unit of usable space, are preferred over plant growth chambers for protected crop production. This section concerns greenhouses and plant growth facilities, including commercial greenhouses, marketing facilities, plant warehouses, conservatories for display of plants, home greenhouses, and completely environmentally controlled indoor facilities. Chapter 9 of the 1985 FUNDAMENTALS Volume describes the environmental requirements in these facilities. Figure 7 shows the structural shapes of typical commercial greenhouses. Other greenhouses

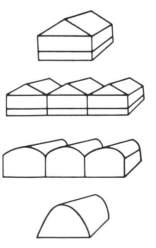

Fig. 7 Structural Shapes of Commercial Greenhouses

may have Gothic arches, curved glazing, or simple lean-to shapes. Glazing, in addition to traditional glass, now includes both film and rigid plastics. High light transmission by the glazing is usually important. Good location and orientation of the house are important in providing desired light conditions. Since location also affects heating and labor costs, exposure to plant disease and air pollution, and material handling requirements, economic success partly depends on the proper site selection. As a general rule in the northern hemisphere, a greenhouse should be placed at a distance of at least 2.5 times the height of the object closest to it in the eastern, western, and southern directions.

GREENHOUSES

Site Selection

Sunlight. Sunlight provides energy for plant growth and is often the limiting growth factor in greenhouses of central and northern areas of North America during the winter. When planning the construction of greenhouses to be operated all year, the designer should design for the greatest sunlight exposure during the short days of midwinter. The building site should have an open southern exposure, and if the land slopes, it should slope to the south.

Soil and Drainage. When plants are to be grown in the soil covered by the greenhouse, the growing site chosen should have a deep, well-drained, fertile soil, preferably sandy loam or silt loam. Even though organic soil amendments can be added to poor soil and fewer problems occur with good natural soil. When a good soil is not available, growing in artificial media should be considered. The greenhouse should be level, but site can and often should be sloped and well-drained to reduce salt buildup and insufficient soil aeration. A high water table, or a hardpan, may produce water-saturated soil, increase greenhouse humidity, promote diseases, and prevent effective use of the greenhouse. These problems can, if necessary, be alleviated by tile drain systems under and around the greenhouse. Ground beds should be level to avoid concentrating water in low areas. Slopes within greenhouses also increase temperature and humidity stratification and create added environmental problems.

Sheltered Areas. Surrounding trees, provided they do not shade the greenhouse, act as wind barriers and help prevent winter heat loss. Deciduous trees are less effective than coniferous ones in midwinter when the heat loss potential is greatest. In areas where snowdrifts occur, windbreaks and snowbreaks should be 100 ft (30 m) or more away from the greenhouse to prevent damage from major drifts.

Orientation

Optimum greenhouse orientation has been debated for many years. Generally, in the northern hemisphere, for single-span greenhouses located north of 35 latitude, maximum transmission during winter is attained by an east-west orientation. South of 35 latitude, some data suggest that orientation is not an important factor, provided headhouse structures do not shade the greenhouse. Other data show that north-south orientation provides more light.

Gutter-connected or ridge and furrow greenhouses should be oriented with the ridge line north-south regardless of latitude. This orientation permits the shadow pattern caused by the gutter superstructure to move from the west to the east side of the gutter during the day. With an east-west orientation, the shadow pattern would remain north of the gutter, and the shadow would be widest and create the most shade during winter when light levels are already low. Also, the north-south orientation allows rows of tall crops, such as roses and staked tomatoes, to align with the long dimension of the house—an alignment that is

generally more suitable to long rows and the plant support methods preferred by many growers.

The slope of the greenhouse roof is a critical part of greenhouse design. If the slope is too flat, a greater percentage of the sunlight will reflect from the roof surface (Figure 8). A slope with a 1:2 rise to run ratio is the usual inclination for a gable roof.

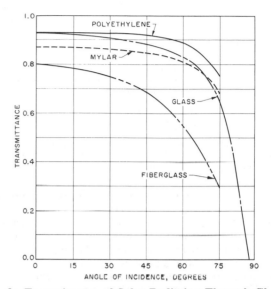

Fig. 8 Transmittance of Solar Radiation Through Glazing Materials for Various Angles of Incidence

Energy Balance

Structural Heat Loss. Estimates for heating and cooling a greenhouse consider conduction, infiltration, and ventilation energy exchange. In addition, the calculations must consider a solar energy load and electrical input, such as light sources, that are usually much greater than for conventional buildings. Generally, conduction (Q_c) plus infiltration (Q_i) are used to determine the peak requirements (Q_t) for heating.

$$Q_t = Q_c + Q_i$$
$$Q_c = UA \, (t_i - t_o)$$
$$Q_i = 0.5 \, VN \, (t_i - t_o)$$

where:

U = overall heat loss coefficient, Btu/h ft$^2 \cdot$ °F (W/m$^2 \cdot$ K) (Table 1)
A = exposed surface area, ft^2 (m^2)
t_i = inside temperature, °F (°C)
t_o = outside temperature, °F (°C)
V = greenhouse internal volume, ft^3 (m^3)
N = number of air exchanges per hour (Table 1)

Radiation Energy Exchange. Solar gain can be estimated using the procedures in Chapter 27 of the 1985 FUNDAMENTALS Volume. As a guide, when a greenhouse is filled with a mature crop of plants, one-half the incoming solar energy is converted to latent heat, and a quarter to a third to sensible heat. The rest is either reflected out of the greenhouse or absorbed by the plants and used in photosynthesis.

Radiation from a greenhouse to a cold sky is more complex. Glass admits a large portion of solar radiation but does not transmit long wavelength thermal radiation in excess of approximately 5000 nm. Plastic films transmit more of the thermal radiation, but, in general, the total heat gains and losses are similar to those of glass. Newer plastic films containing IR (infrared) inhibitors reduce the thermal radiation loss. Plastic films

Table 1   Approximate Heat Loss Coefficients (U) and Suggested Design Air

Greenhouse Covering	Value of U Btu/h·ft²·°F	W/(m·K)	Air Exchanges per hour[f]
Single glass	1.1	6.3	1.5
Single plastic[a]	1.2	6.8	0.8
Single fiber glass (FRP)	1.2	6.8	1.0
Double plastic[b]	0.8	4.5	0.7
Rigid double-wall plastic[c]	0.7	3.0	0.8
Double glass	0.5	3.0	0.8
Single or Double plastic over glass[d]	0.5	3.0	0.6
Single glass and thermal blanket[e]	0.5	3.0	0.5
Double plastic and thermal blanket	0.4	2.5	0.3

[a]Indicates plastic films, polyethylene, vinyl, etc.
[b]Inflated plastic films, enclosing in airspace.
[c]Twin-wall rigid panels of acrylic, polycarbonate, or polypropylene.
[d]On the outside, with one airspace enclosed.
[e]Solid blanket.
[f]Low wind or protection from wind reduces the air exchange rate. In glass houses, values should be 0.5 or less for subfreezing outside temperatures, since freezing condensate usually seals small cracks.

and glass with improved radiation reflection are becoming available at somewhat increased cost.

Heating. Greenhouses have a variety of heating systems. The most common is a convection system that circulates hot water or steam through plain or finned pipe. The pipe is most commonly placed along walls and occasionally beneath plant benches to create desirable convection currents. A typical temperature-distribution pattern created by perimeter heating is shown in Figure 9. More uniform temperatures can be achieved when about one-third the total heat comes from pipes spaced uniformly across the house. These pipes can be placed above or below the crop, but temperature stratification and shading are avoided when they are placed below. Outdoor weather conditions affect temperature distribution, especially on windy days in loosely constructed greenhouses. Manual or automatic overhead pipes are also used for supplemental heating to prevent snow buildup on the roof. In a gutter-connected greenhouse located in a cold climate, a heat pipe should be placed under each gutter to prevent snow accumulation.

Overhead tube systems consist of a unit heater that discharges into 12- to 30-in. (300- to 750-mm) diameter plastic film tubing perforated to provide uniform air distribution. The tube is suspended at 6 to 10 ft (2 to 3 m) intervals and extends the length of the greenhouse. Variations include a tube and fan receiving the discharge of several unit heaters. The fan and tube system is used without heat to recirculate the air and, during cold weather, to introduce ventilation air. However, tubes sized for heat distribution may not be large enough for effective ventilation during warm weather. A fan and tube system can also distribute fumigants and insecticides.

Perforated tubing, 6- to 10-in. (150- to 250-mm) diameter, placed at ground level (underbench) also can improve heat distribution compared to perimeter heating. Ideally, the ground level tubing should draw air from the top of the greenhouse for recirculation or heating. Tubes on or near the floor have the disadvantages of obstacles to workers and reduce usable floor space.

Under-floor heating can supply up to 25 to 30% of the peak heating requirements of northern greenhouses. A typical under-floor system uses 0.75 in. (20 mm) plastic pipe with nylon fittings in the floor 4 in. (100 mm) below the surface, spaced 12 to 16 in. (300 to 400 mm) on centers, and covered with loose gravel or porous concrete. Hot water, not exceeding 104°F (40°C), circulates at a rate of 8 to 16 gpm (0.5 to 1.0 L/s). The pipe loops generally should not exceed 400 ft (130 m) in length. This system can provide 16 to 20 Btu/h·ft² (50 to 65 W/m²) from a bare floor, and about 75% as much when potted plants or seedling flats cover most of the floor.

Similar systems can heat soil directly, but root temperature must not exceed 77°F (25°C). When used with water from solar collectors or other heat sources, the under-floor area can store heat. The storage consists of a vinyl swimming pool liner placed on top of insulation and a moisture barrier at a depth below grade of 8 to 12 in. (200 to 300 mm), and filled with 50% void gravel. Hot water from solar collectors or other clean sources enters and is pumped out on demand. Some heat sources, such as cooling water from power plants, cannot be used directly but require a closed loop heat transfer system to avoid fouling the storage system and the power plant cooling water.

Greenhouses can also be bottom heated with 0.25-in. (6-mm) diameter EPDM tubing, or variations of that method, in a closed loop system. The tubes can be placed directly in the growing medium of ground beds or under plant containers on raised benches. Best temperature uniformity is obtained by flow in alternate tubes in opposite directions. This method can supply all the greenhouse heat needed in mild climates.

Bottom heat, under-floor heating, and under-bench heating are, because of the location of the heat source, more effective than overhead or peripheral heating and can reduce energy loss 20 to 30%.

Low-temperature, infrared heating from overhead sources has been used. High temperature, electric infrared systems also emit short wavelength radiation so they cannot be used for plants intolerant of continuous light. Gas-fired units include a reflector that distributes the radiation from a 4-in. (100-mm) diameter pipe heated to 600 to 750°F (300 to 400°C) by inline burners. Exhaust gases from the burner are cooled to about 120°F (50°C) by additional distribution piping prior to exhaust outside the greenhouse.

These infrared systems are reported to reduce energy consumption up to 30% compared to conventional systems. However, soil and plant temperatures may be higher, and air temperatures lower than those of conventional heating systems, and problems in obtaining temperature uniformity have been reported. Moreover, since there is little or no modulation of control, temperature variation about the set point may be greater than with conventional systems. Also, infrared radiation can cause stem elongation in some species, partly through increases in plant and soil temperatures, but also due to direct photomorphological effects. This problem can be greatly exaggerated in a tall crop such as roses or staked tomatoes. Lower-than-normal thermostat settings may alleviate problems.

Air-to-air and water-to-air heat pumps have been tried experimentally on small-scale installations. Their usefulness is especially sensitive to the availability of a low-cost heat source.

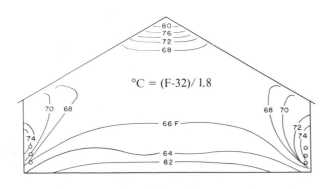

°C = (F-32)/1.8

Fig. 9   Temperature Profiles in a Greenhouse Heated with Radiation Piping Along the Sidewalls

Overhead steam, hot-water, or hot-air unit heaters do not give uniform temperature at plant level. Unit heaters must be carefully aimed to obtain uniform temperature within the greenhouse. Horizontal airflow fans or overhead circulators reduce the vertical temperature gradient while reducing temperatures in the peak of the greenhouse. Hot air, combustion unit heaters have been used successfully in small greenhouses as an alternative to a central boiler, but since the combustion device is located in the greenhouse, additional precautions are necessary. Combustion gases must be vented from the house and fresh air brought in. About 3 ft² of opening for make-up air be added per therm of installed heating capacity (1000 mm²/kW).

Conventional, unvented gas and oil heaters should not be used for heating greenhouses because of adverse effects on the crops of oxygen depletion and combustion fume toxicity. Specially designed, direct-combustion units are available, principally for carbon dioxide enrichment, that do not produce toxic gases. Make-up air, however, must still be provided for these units.

Ventilation. Greenhouse ventilation primarily prevents excessive temperature rise because of solar insolation. A secondary purpose is to prevent carbon dioxide depletion and keep relative humidity at a reasonable level. Ventilation (and cooling systems) should be designed to achieve uniform temperature distribution in the plant growing zone. During cold weather, fresh air should normally be introduced or directed at the top of the greenhouse to retard the tendency of cool air to settle directly to the floor and produce large, vertical temperature gradients. As noted earlier, perforated polyethylene tubing can effectively distribute ventilation air in the winter. Perforations in the tubing at the 10:00 and 14:00 hour positions produce an upward airflow and prevent cold air from being directed onto the plants. Tubing of this kind can be used in either positive or negative pressure ventilation systems.

In summer, the cooler air should be directed across the greenhouse at or near plant level. Typical maximum ventilation rates provide for up to 1 air change per minute, and distances between fans and inlets should be limited to 80 ft (25 m) to prevent excessive temperature rise. Such a system requires proper installation to ensure reasonably uniform airflow across all plants and to keep the air speed over the plants nearest the inlets from being much higher than over plants at the center.

Most older greenhouses, and some newer ones, are ventilated by natural air exchange through ridge and side ventilators (Figure 10A). Automatic vent controls are used in some cases. With natural ventilation systems, the degree of temperature control depends on the house configuration, external wind speed, and outside air temperature. If natural ventilation is to occur, wind or thermal buoyancy must create a pressure difference. Vent openings on both sides of the greenhouse and the ridge take the best advantage of pressure differences created by the wind. Large vent openings supply sufficient ventilation when the wind is light or thermal buoyancy forces are small. The total vent area should be from 15 to 25% of the floor area. For a single greenhouse, the combined sidewall vent area should equal the combined roof vent area for best ventilation by thermal buoyancy. Both sidewall and ridge vent openings should be continuous along the greenhouse. Sensors should be included in automatic control (or alarm) systems for times of rain and high wind, which could damage the crops.

Fans give a more positive control over ventilation than naturally vented systems (Figure 10). Generally, exhaust fans located in the side walls or ends of the greenhouse draw air through partially opened ridge vents, or end or side vents that may be equipped with evaporative pads. Inlet design is important, and inlets should be sized to maintain an air speed between 700 and 1000 fpm (3.5 and 5 m/s) at any ventilation stage, and they should automatically adjust to maintain this speed as ventilation capacity changes. A common inlet is a top-hinged window vent located opposite the fans. Controls can be installed to vary the inlet opening automatically. Typically, the fans and inlets are controlled by (aspirated) thermostats located in the middle of the greenhouse at plant height.

The control over temperature rise achieved with fans directly relates to the air exchange rate. As shown in Figure 11, air exchange rates between 0.75 and 1 change per minute are effective. At lower air flows, the temperature differential increases rapidly. At higher air flow, the reduction of temperature rise is relatively small, fan power requirements increase, and plant damage can occur from increased air speed.

Shading. Shading compounds are commonly applied to

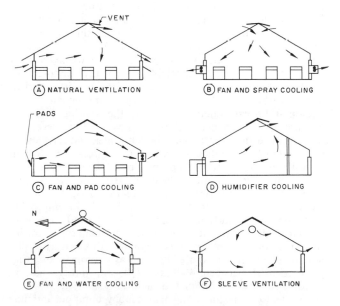

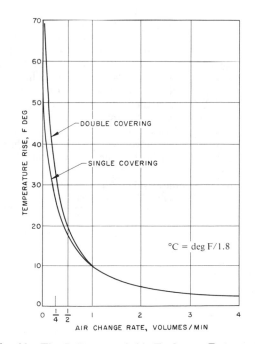

Fig. 11 **The Influence of Air-Exchange Rate on the Temperature Rise in Single- and Double-Covered Greenhouses**

Fig. 10 **Methods of Ventilating and Cooling Greenhouses**

greenhouse glazings to reduce temperature during summer. Up to 50% shading can be achieved. Many shading compounds are forms of lime having varying durability. However, lime corrodes aluminum and damages some caulking. White latex paint diluted with water and sprayed rather than painted on the glass is more widely used with aluminum structures. For plastic glazings, the manufacturer can advise on the correct shading compound; some cannot be removed from plastic. Ideally, the shading will wear away naturally during the summer air and leave the glazing clean by fall when the natural light level declines to critical levels. In practice, some physical cleaning is usually needed.

Mechanically operated shade cloth and aluminum or wooden laths give the operator great control over the summer weather conditions. The shade can be retracted on cloudy days in the summer and can insulate for energy conservation in winter.

Evaporative Cooling. Some form of cooling must be used during the day to maintain greenhouse temperatures equal to or less than those outside. Mechanical refrigeration is expensive and seldom used in commercial greenhouses because of the high solar heat loads. Evaporative cooling, either wet pads, unit coolers, or fog spray systems, can accomplish economical greenhouse cooling. But evaporative cooling adds moisture to the air that, while reducing the potential for plant moisture stress, also may increase disease problems.

Wetted pads of aspen wood fibers, or paper in honeycomb format, are typically placed in an end wall or side wall, and exhaust fans are placed in the opposite wall. Fans and pads should be no more than 160 ft (50 m) apart. Table 2 shows data recommended for sizing the pad area. The water flow rate through the pad should be approximately 1.0 to 2.5 gpm (0.06 to 0.16 L/s) per linear foot (metre) of pad (Table 3). The pads should be continuous the length of the wall and high enough to obtain the required pad area. The pad material should operate at an evaporative efficiency of 85%. In practice, the outside air is cooled to within about 4°F (2°C) of the wet-bulb temperature in a properly designed and well-managed system.

The fog-evaporative system consists of fogging nozzles located in the upper portion of the house. A typical fogging arrangement locates fog nozzles on 3-ft (1-m) centers, and about 18 in. (0.5 m) above the plants. Although the fog can be operated continuously, it is more common to operate on a timer of 5 to 10 seconds every 5 minutes. Air should flow from the fog nozzles to the plants. Water or air pressure of 200 to 500 psi (1.4 to 3.5 MPa) develops a fine mist and keeps coarse droplets from falling on the plant. Because some water, even with high pressure nozzles, is likely to fall or condense on plant surfaces, all piping should be PVC rather than copper, which is toxic to some plants. The amount of water required to saturate the air is highly variable. A high-pressure system does not have wide variations in water output. A system adequate for extreme conditions will generate an excess fog at cooler times and will wet the crop. A

Table 2   Recommended Air Velocity Through Various Pad Materials

Type	Air Face Velocity Through Pad*	
	fpm	m/s
Aspen fiber mounted vertically 2 to 4 in. (50 to 100 mm) thick	150	0.75
Aspen fiber mounted horizontally 2 to 4 in. (50 to 100 mm) thick	200	1.0
Corrugated cellulose, 4 in. (100 mm) thick	250	1.25
Corrugated cellulose, 6 in. (150 mm) thick	350	1.75

*Speed may be increased by 25% where construction is limiting.

Table 3   Recommended Water Flow and Sump Capacity for Vertically Mounted Cooling Pad Materials

Pad Type and Thickness	Minimum Water Rate per Lineal Length of Pad		Minimum Sump Capacity per Unit Pad Area	
	gpm/ft	L/(s·m)	gal/ft^2	L/m^2
Aspen fiber 2 to 4 in. (50 to 100 mm)	0.3	.06	0.5	20
Aspen fiber, desert conditions 2 to 4 in. (50 to 100 mm)	0.4	.08	0.5	20
Corrugated cullulose, 4 in. (100 mm)	0.5	.10	0.8	30
Corrugated cellulose, 6 in. (150 mm)	0.8	.16	1.0	40

fog system with nozzles in staged groups can be modulated to meet demand.

Other Environmental Factors

Humidity Control. Maintaining sufficient relative humidity during the day, and dissipating it at night, is a problem in greenhouse crop production. Relative humidity should be kept high during the day to reduce water loss by transpiration, but high relative humidity of 85 to 90% at night enhances growth of many disease organisms. Thus, a high relative humidity during the day condenses on plant leaf surfaces at night when the temperature drops. Opening ventilators or heating the greenhouse a few degrees at night are helpful but usually inadequate. Fan ventilation, especially when coupled to perforated polyethylene tubing, plus some greenhouse heating (even in mild weather) are reasonably effective means of lowering the relative humidity.

Carbon Dioxide Enrichment. Carbon dioxide enrichment is practiced in some greenhouse operations to increase growth and enhance yields. CO_2 enrichment, however, is practical only when little or no ventilation is required for temperature control. Carbon dioxide can be generated from burning fossil fuels, solid CO_2 (dry ice), bottled CO_2, and misting carbonated water. Care must be taken when generating CO_2 from fossil fuels to ensure that complete combustion has taken place and to provide make-up air so oxygen is not depleted as combustion proceeds. Bulk or bottled CO_2 gas is usually distributed through perforated tubing placed near the plant canopy. Carbon dioxide from dry ice is distributed by passing greenhouse air through an enclosure containing dry ice. Air movement around the plant leaf increases the efficiency with which the plant absorbs whatever CO_2 is available. One study found an air speed of 100 fpm (0.5 m/s) to be equivalent to a 50% enrichment in carbon dioxide without forced air movement.

Radiant Energy. Light is normally the limiting factor in greenhouse crop production during the winter. Light levels are especially inadequate or marginal in fall, winter, and early spring north of the 35th parallel. Artificial light sources, usually high intensity discharge (HID) lamps, may be added to greenhouses to supplement low natural light levels. High pressure sodium (HPS), metal halide (MH), low pressure sodium (LPS), and occasionally mercury lamps coated with a color-improving phosphor are currently used. Since differing irradiance or illuminance ratios are emitted by the various lamp types, the incident radiation is best described as radiant flux density (W/ft^2 or W/m^2) between 400 and 850 nm, or as photon flux density [μmol/(s·m^2)] between 400 and 700 nm, rather than in photometric terms of lux or footcandles. Data in Table 4 suggest irradiance at the top of the plant canopy, duration, and time of day for supplementing natural light levels for specific plants.

Table 4 Suggested Radiant Energy, Duration, and Time for Using Supplemental Lighting in Greenhouses

Plant and Stage of Growth	W/ft²	W/m²	Duration (hrs)	Time
African Violets early-flowering	1 to 2	12 to 24	12 to16	06:00-18:00 06:00-22:00
Ageratum early-flowering	1 to 4.5	12 to 48	24	
Begonias—fibrous rooted branching and early-flowering	1 to 2	12 to 24	24	
Carnation branching and early-flowering	1 to 2	12 to 24	16	08:00-24:00
Chrysanthemums	1 to 2	12 to 24	16	08:00-24:00
vegetable growth branching and multiflowering	1 to 2	12 to 24	8	08:00-16:00
Cineraria seedling growth (four weeks)	0.6 to 1	6 to 12	24	
Cucumber rapid growth and early-flowering	1 to 2	12 to 24	24	
Eggplant early-fruiting	2 to 4.5	12 to 48	24	
Foliage plants (Philodendron, Schefflera) rapid growth	0.6 to 1	6 to 12	24	
Geranium branching and early-flowering	1 to 4.5	12 to 48	24	
Gloxinia	1 to 4.5	12 to 48	16	08:00-24:00
early-flowering	0.6 to 1	6 to 12	24	
Lettuce rapid growth	1 to 4.5	12 to 48	24	
Marigold early-flowering	1 to 4.5	12 to 48	24	
Impatiens—New Guinea branching and early-flowering	1	12	16	08:00-24:00
Impatiens—Sultana branching and early-flowering	1 to 2	12 to 24	24	
Juniper vegetative growth	1 to 4.5	12 to 48	24	
Pepper early-fruiting, compact growth	1 to 2	12 to 24	24	
Petunia branching and early-flowering	1 to 4.5	12 to 48	24	
Poinsettia—vegetative growth	1	12	24	
branching and multiflowering	1 to 2	12 to 24	8	08:00-16:00
Rhodendron vegetative growth (shearing tips)	1	12	16	08:00-24:00
Roses (hybrid teas, miniatures) early-flowering and rapid regrowth	1 to 4.5	12 to 48	24	
Salvia early-flowering	1 to 4.5	12 to 48	24	
Snapdragon early-flowering	1 to 4.5	12 to 48	24	
Streptocarpus early-flowering	1	12	16	08:00-24:00
Tomato rapid growth and early-flowering	1 to 2	12 to 24	16	08:00-24:00
Trees (deciduous) vegetative growth	0.6	6	16	16:00-08:00
Zinnia early-flowering	1 to 4.5	12 to 48	24	

Table 5 shows conversions of HPS, MH, and LPS irradiance (W/ft² or W/m²) to illuminance (lux) and photon flux density to assist in relating irradiance to more familiar illuminance values. A footcandle is approximately 10 lux.

Table 5 Constants to Convert to W/m²

Light Source	klx	μmol/s²·m
400-700 nm		
INC	3.99	0.20
FCW	2.93	0.22
FWW	2.81	0.21
HG	2.62	0.22
MH	3.05	0.22
HPS	2.45	0.20
LPS	1.92	0.20
Daylight	4.02	0.22
400-850 nm		
INC	9.00	0.45
FCW	2.99	0.22
FWW	2.86	0.22
HG	2.81	0.24
MH	3.42	0.24
HPS	3.38	0.28
LPS	2.18	0.23
Daylight	5.45	0.30

1 μmol/(s·m²) − 1 einstein/(s·m²)

Luminaires have been developed specifically for greenhouse use of HID lamps. The lamps in these special greenhouse luminaires often are placed in a horizontal position, which may decrease both light output and life of the lamp. These drawbacks may be balanced by improved horizontal and vertical uniformity as compared to industrial parabolic reflectors.

Photoperiod Control. Artificial light sources are also used to lengthen the photoperiod during the short days of winter. Photoperiod control requires much lower light levels than those needed for photosynthesis and growth. Thus, photoperiod illuminance only needs to be 0.6 to 1.1 W/ft² [6 to 12 W/m² or 20 to 40 μmol/ (s·m²)]. The incandescent lamp has proved to be the most effective light source for this purpose due to its higher far red component. Lamps such as 150 W (PS-30) silverneck lamps spaced 10 to 13 ft (3 to 4 m) on centers and 13 ft (4 m) above the plants provides a cost-effective system. Where a 13 ft (4 m) height is not practical, 60 W extended service lamps on 6.5 ft (2 m) centers are satisfactory. The usual method of photoperiod control is to interrupt the dark period by turning the lamps on at 22:00 hours and off at 02:00. The four-hour interruption, initially based on chrysanthemum response, induces a satisfactory long-day response in all photoperiodically sensitive species. Many species, however, will respond to interruptions of 1 hour or less. Demand charges can be reduced in large installations by operating some sections from 20:00 to 24:00 and others from 24:00 to 04:00. The biological response to these schedules, however, is much weaker than with the 22:00 to 02:00 schedule, so some varieties may flower prematurely. If the 4 hour interruption period is used, it is not necessary to keep the light on throughout the interruption period. Photoperiod control of most plants can be accomplished by operating the lamps on light and dark cycles with 20% 'on' times; for example, 12 seconds per minute. The length of the dark period in the cycle is critical, and the system may fail if the dark period exceeds about 30 minutes. Demand charges can be reduced by alternate scheduling of the 'on' times between houses or benches without reducing the biological effectiveness of the interruption.

Plant displays in showrooms, shopping malls, etc., require enough light for plant maintenance and a spectral distribution that will show the plants to best advantage. Metal halide lamps, with or without incandescent highlighting, are often used in plant display. Fluorescent lamps, frequently of the special phosphor, plant growth type, enhance color rendition, but are more difficult to install in aesthetically pleasing designs.

Alternate Energy Sources and Energy Conservation

Limited progress has been achieved heating commercial greenhouses with solar energy. Collecting and storing the heat requires a volume at least half the volume of the greenhouse. Passive solar units will work at certain times of the year, and in a few localities, year-round.

Reject heat, if available, is a possible source of winter heat. Winter energy and solar (photovoltaic) sources are possible future energy sources for greenhouses, but the development of such systems is still in the research stage.

Energy Conservation. A number of energy-saving measures (e.g., thermal curtains, double glazing, and perimeter insulation) have been retrofitted to existing greenhouses and incorporated into new construction. Sound maintenance is necessary to keep heating system efficiency at a maximum level.

Automatic controls, such as thermostats, should be calibrated and cleaned at regular intervals, and heating-ventilation controls should interlock to avoid simultaneous operation. Boilers that can burn more than one type of fuel permit using the lowest cost fuel available.

Modifications to Reduce Heat Loss

Film Covers for heat loss reduction have received widespread use in commercial greenhouses, particularly for growing foliage plants and other species that can grow under low light levels. Irradiance (intensity) is reduced 10 to 15% per layer of plastic film.

One or two layers of transparent 4- or 6-mil continuous-sheet plastic is stretched over the entire greenhouse, leaving some vents uncovered, or from the ridge to the sidewall ventilation opening. When two layers are used, (outdoor) air at a pressure of 0.2 to 0.25 in. of water (50 to 60 Pa) is introduced continuously between the layers of film to maintain the air space between them. When a single layer is used, an airspace can be established by stretching the plastic over the glazing bars and fastening it around the edges, or a length of polyethylene tubing can be placed between the glass and the plastic and inflated (using outside air) to stretch the plastic sheet.

Double-Glazing Rigid Plastic. Double wall panels are manufactured from acrylic, polycarbonate, and polypropylene plastics, with walls separated by about 0.4 in. (10 mm). Panels are usually 48-in. (1.2-m) wide and 96-in. (2.4-m) or more long. Nearly all types of plastic panels have a high thermal expansion coefficient and require about 1% expansion space (0.12 in/ft or 10 mm/m). Light reduction when a panel is new is roughly 10 to 20% compared to single pane glass. Moisture accumulation between the walls of the panels must be avoided.

Double-Glazing Glass. The framing of most older greenhouses must be modified or replaced to accept double glazing with glass. Light reduction is 10% more than with single glazing. Moisture and dust accumulation between glazings increases light loss. As with all types of double glazing, snow on the roof melts slowly and increases light loss. Snow may even accumulate sufficiently to cause structural damage, especially in gutter-connected greenhouses.

Silicone Sealants. Transparent silicone sealant in the glass overlaps of conventional greenhouses reduces infiltration and may produce heat savings of 5 to 10% in older structures. There is little change in light transmission, and sealants may, in fact, cause slightly higher light levels in a glass house by preventing dirt accumulation between the glass overlaps.

Precautions. The various methods described above reduce heat loss by reducing conduction and infiltration. They may also cause more condensation, higher relative humidity, lower carbon dioxide concentrations, and an increase in ethylene and other pollutants. Combined with the reduced light levels, these factors may cause delayed crop production, elongated plants, soft plants, and various deformities and diseases, all of which reduce the marketable crop. Consultation with an expert familiar with local conditions is important in avoiding problems.

Thermal Blankets are any flexible material that is pulled from gutter to gutter and end to end in a greenhouse, or around and over each bench, at night. Materials ranging from plastic film to heavy cloth, or laminated combinations, have successfully reduced heat losses by 25 to 35% overall. Tightness of fit around edges and other obstructions is more important than the kind of material used. Some of these films are vapor tight and retain moisture and gases. Others are porous and permit some gas exchange between the plants and air outside the blanket. Opaque materials can control crop day length when short days are part of the crop requirement. Condensation may drip onto and collect on the upper sides of some blanket materials to such an extent that they collapse.

Multiple-layer blankets with two or more layers separated by air spaces have been developed. One such system combines a porous-material blanket and a transparent film blanket; the latter is used for summer shading. Another system has four layers of porous, aluminum foil-covered cloths, with the layers separated by air.

Thermal blankets may be opened and closed manually, as well as automatically. The opening and closing decision should be based on the irradiance level rather than time of day. Two difficulties with thermal blankets are the physical problems of installation and use in greenhouses with interior supporting columns, and the loss of space due to shading by the blanket when it is not in use during the day.

Other Recommendations to Reduce Heat Loss. The foundation can be insulated, but the insulating materials must be protected from moisture, and the foundation wall should be protected from freezing. All or most of the north wall can be insulated with opaque or reflective-surface materials. The insulation will reduce the amount of diffuse light entering the greenhouse, and, in cloudy climates, cause reduced crop growth near the north wall.

Ventilation fan cabinets should be insulated, and fans not needed during the winter should be sealed against air leaks. Efficient management and operation of existing facilities are, of course, the most cost-effective methods to reduce energy use. This includes continued contact with local Cooperative Extension personnel to obtain area-specific, current information on greenhouse operation techniques.

PLANT GROWTH ENVIRONMENTAL FACILITIES

Controlled-environment rooms (CER), also called plant growth chambers, include all controlled or partially controlled environmental facilities for growing plants, except greenhouses. CERs are indoor facilities. Units with floor areas less than 50 ft^2 (5 m^2) may be moveable with self-contained or attached refrigeration units. CERs usually have artificial light sources, provide control of temperature and, in some cases, relative humidity and carbon dioxide level.

CERs were originally designed to study plant responses to various environmental factors, but today many stabilize the environment for plants grown to study all aspects of plant science. Some growers are using growing rooms to increase seedling growth rate, produce more uniform seedlings, and grow specialized, high-value crops. The main components of the CER are (1) an insulated room, or an insulated box with an access door; (2) a heating and cooling mechanism with associated air-moving devices and controls; and (3) a lamp module at the top of the insulated box or room. CERs are similar to walk-in cold storage rooms, except for the lighting and larger refrigeration system needed to handle heat produced by the lighting.

Location

The location for a CER must have space for the outside dimensions of the chamber, the refrigeration equipment, ballast rack, and control panels. Additional area around the unit is necessary for servicing the various components of the system, and, in some cases, for substrate, pots, nutrient solutions, and other paraphernalia associated with plant research. The location also requires an electrical supply, on the order of 28 W/ft^2 (300W/m^2) of controlled environment space, a water supply, and usually with a supply of compressed air.

Construction and Materials

Wall insulation should have a unit thermal conductance value of less than 0.026 Btu/h $\cdot$ ft^2 $\cdot$ °F [0.15 W/(m^2 $\cdot$ K)]. Materials should resist corrosion and moisture. The interior wall covering should be metal with a high-reflectance white paint or specular aluminum with a reflectivity of not less than 80%. Reflective films or similar materials can be used but will require periodic replacement.

Floors and Drains

Floors that are part of the CER should be corrosion resistant. Tar or asphalt waterproofing materials and volatile caulking compounds should not be used because they will likely release phytotoxic gases into the chamber atmosphere. The floor must have a drain to remove spilled water and nutrient solutions. The drains should be trapped and equipped with screens to catch plant and substrate debris.

Plant Benches

Three bench styles for supporting the pots and other types of plant containers are normally encountered in plant growth chambers: (1) stationary benches; (2) benches or shelves built in sections that are adjustable in height; and (3) plant trucks, carts, or dollies on casters, which are used to move plants between chambers, greenhouses, and darkrooms. The bench supports containers filled with moist sand, soil, or other substrate and is usually designed for a minimum loading of 50 lb/ft^2 (240 kg/m^2). The bench or truck top should be constructed from non-ferrous perforated metal or metal mesh to allow free passage of air around the plants and to let excess water drain from the containers to the floor and subsequently to the floor drain.

Normally, benches, shelves or truck tops are adjustable in height so small plants can be placed close to the lamps and receive a greater amount of light. As the plants grow, the shelf or bench is lowered so the tops of the plants continue to receive the original radiant flux density.

Controls

Environmental chambers require complex controls to provide the following:

1. Automatic transfer from heating to cooling with 2°F (1°C) or less dead zone and adjustable time delay.
2. Automatic daily switching of the temperature set point for different day and night temperatures [setback may be as much as 10°F (5°C)].
3. Protection of sensors from radiation. Ideally the sensors are located in a shielded, aspirated housing, but satisfactory per-

formance can be attained by locating them in the return air duct.
4. Control of the daily duration of the light and dark periods. Ideally, this control should be programmable to change the light period each day to simulate the natural progression of day length. Photoperiod control, however, is normally accomplished with mechanical time clocks, which must have a control interval of 5 minutes or less for satisfactory timing.
5. Protective controls to prevent the chamber temperature from going more than a few degrees above or below the set point. Controls should also prevent short cycling of the refrigeration system, especially when the condensers are remotely located.
6. Audible and visual alarms should be provided to alert personnel of malfunctions.
7. Maintenance of relative humidity to prescribed limits.

Data loggers, recorders, or recording controllers are recommended to aid in monitoring daily operation of the system. Solid-state, microprocessor-based control is not yet widely used. However, programming flexibility and control performance are expected to improve as microprocessor control is developed for CER use.

Heating, Air Conditioning, and Airflow

When the lights are on, cooling will normally be required, and the heating system will be rarely called upon to operate. When the lights are off, however, both heating and cooling may be needed. Conventional refrigeration systems are generally used, although with some modification. Direct expansion units usually operate with a hot-gas bypass to prevent numerous on-off cycles, and secondary coolant systems may use aqueous ethylene glycol rather than chilled water. Heat is usually provided by electric heaters, but other energy sources can be used, including hot gas from the refrigeration system.

The plant compartment is the heart of the growth chamber. The primary design objective, therefore, is to provide the most uniform, consistent, and regulated environmental conditions possible. Thus, airflow must be adequate to meet the specified psychrometric conditions, but is limited by the effects of high air speeds on plant growth. As a rule, the average air speed in CERs is restricted to about 100 fpm (0.5 m/s).

To meet the uniform conditions required by a CER, conditioned air is normally moved through the space from bottom to top, although an increasing number use top-to-bottom airflow. There is no apparent difference in plant growth between horizontal, upward, or downward airflow when the speed is less than 175 fpm (0.9 m/s). Regardless of the method, a temperature gradient is certain to exist, and the design should keep the gradient as small as possible. Uniform airflow is more important than the direction of flow, so selection of properly designed diffusers or plenums with perforations is essential for achieving it.

The ducts or false side walls that direct air from the evaporator to the growing area should be small, but not so small that the noise level increases appreciably more than acceptable building air duct noise. CER design should include some provision for cleaning the interior of the air ducts.

Air-conditioning equipment for relatively standard chambers provide temperatures over 45 to 90°F (7 to 35°C). Specialized CERs that require temperatures as low as −5°F (−20°C) need low temperature refrigeration equipment and devices to defrost the evaporator without increasing the growing area temperature. Other chambers that require temperatures as high as 115°F (45°C) need high temperature components. The air temperature in the growing area must be controlled with the least possible variation about the set point. Temperature variation about the set point can be held to 0.5°F (0.25°C) using solid-state controls, but in most existing facilities, the variation is 1 to 2°F (0.5 to 1.0°C).

The relative humidity in many CERs is simply an indicator of the existing psychrometric conditions and usually is between 50 and 80%, depending on temperature. The relative humidity in the chamber can be increased by steam injection, misting, hot water evaporators, and other conventional humidification methods. Steam injection causes the least temperature disturbance, and sprays or misting causes the greatest disturbance. Complete control of relative humidity, of course, requires dehumidification, as well as humidification.

A typical humidity control system includes a cold evaporator or steam injection to adjust the chamber air dew point. The air is then conditioned to the desired dry-bulb temperature by electric heaters, hot gas bypass evaporator, or a temperature-controlled evaporator. A dew point lower than about 5°C cannot be obtained with a cold plate dehumidifier because of icing. Dew points lower than 5°C will require, usually in addition to the cold evaporator, a chemical dehumidifier.

Lighting the Environmental Chambers

The type of light source and the number of lamps used in CERs are determined by the desired plant response. Traditionally, cool white fluorescent, plus incandescent lamps that produce 10% of the fluorescent illuminance, are used. Nearly all illumination data have been based on either cool white or warm white fluorescent, plus incandescent. A number of fluorescent lamps have special phosphors hypothesized to be the spectral requirements of the plant. Some of these lamps are used in CERs, but there is little data to suggest that they are superior to the cool white and warm white lamps. In recent years, high intensity discharge lamps have been installed in CERs, either to obtain very high radiant flux densities, or to reduce the electrical load while maintaining a light level equal to that produced by the less efficient fluorescent-incandescent systems.

One approach to design from the biological point of view is to base light source output recommendations on photon flux density ($\mu mol/(s \cdot m^2)$) between 400-700 nm, or less frequently as radiant flux density between 400-700 nm, or 400-850 nm. This enables comparisons between light sources as a function of plant photosynthetic potential rather than basing illuminance measurements on human vision. Table 5 shows the conversion of various measurement units to W/m^2. However, instruments that measure the 400-850 nm spectral range are not generally available, and some controversy exists about the effectiveness of 400-850 nm as compared to the 400-700 nm range in photosynthesis. Excellent instruments are available for the 400-700 nm range. Table 5 shows conversion to both 400-700 and 400-850 nm to include the irradiance measurement recommendations from the 1985 FUNDAMENTALS Volume, and the measurements more common among biologists. (See 1985 FUNDAMENTALS Chapter 9 for conversion of illuminance measurements to W/m^2.)

A considerable difference exists between the design requirements for plant growth lighting and vision lighting. Plant growth

lighting requires a greater degree of horizontal uniformity and, usually, higher light levels than vision lighting. In addition, plant growth lighting should have as much vertical uniformity as possible—a factor rarely important in vision lighting. Horizontal and vertical uniformity are, of course, much easier to attain with linear or broad sources like fluorescent lamps than with point sources such as HID lamps. Tables 6 and 7 show the type and number of lamps, mounting height, and spacing required to obtain several levels of incident energy. Since the data were taken directly under lamps with no reflecting wall surfaces nearby, the incident energy is perhaps half what would be received by the plants if the lamps had been placed in a small chamber with highly reflective walls.

Extended life incandescents or traffic signal lamps, with much longer life, will lower lamp replacement requirements. These lamps have lower lumen output, but they are nearly equivalent in the red portion of the spectrum. Short life of incandescent lamps has been attributed to vibration in chambers. Porcelain lamp holders and heat resistant lamp wiring should be used.

Lamps used for CER lighting have included fluorescent lamps (usually 1500 ma), 250, 400, and occasionally 1000 W HPS and MH lamps, 180 W LPS and various sizes of incandescent lamps. Extended life lamps may be used, but these sacrifice light output for longer life. In many installations, the abnormally short

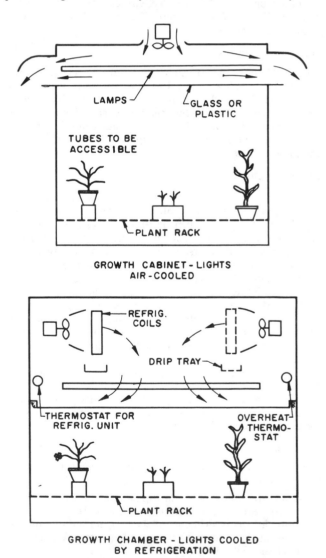

GROWTH CABINET - LIGHTS AIR-COOLED

GROWTH CHAMBER - LIGHTS COOLED BY REFRIGERATION

Fig. 12 Cooling Lamps in Growth Chambers

Table 6 Approximate Mounting Height and Spacing of Luminaires in Greenhouses

Lamp and Wattage	Irradiation, W per 10 ft² or W/m²			
	6	12	24	48
	Height and Spacing , in. (m)			
HPS (400 W)	118 (3.0)	90 (2.3)	63 (1.6)	39 (1.0)
LPS (180 W)	94 (2.4)	67 (1.7)	47 (1.2)	31 (0.8)
MH (400 W)	106 (2.7)	79 (2.0)	55 (1.4)	35 (0.9)

Table 7 Height and Spacing of Luminaires

Light Sources	Radiant Flux Density, W/m²						
	0.3	0.9	3	9	18	24	50
Fluorescent—Cool White							
40 W single 4 ft lamp, 3.2 klm							
Radiant power, W/m², 400-700 nm	0.3	0.9	2.9	8.8			
Illumination, klx	0.10	0.30	1.0	3.0			
Lamps per 9 ft² or m²	0.12	0.36	1.2	3.6	NA	NA	NA
Distance from plants, in. (m)	114 (2.9)	67 (1.7)	36 (0.92)	21 (0.53)			
40 W 2-lamp fixtures (4 ft) 6.4 klm							
Radiant power, W/m², 400-700 nm	0.3	0.9	2.9	8.8			
Illumination, klx	0.10	0.30	1.0	3.0			
Fixtures per 9 ft² or m²	0.06	0.18	0.60	1.8	NA	NA	NA
Distance from plants, in. (m)	161 (4.1)	94 (2.4)	51 (1.3)	30 (0.75)			
215 Watt 2-8 ft lamps 31.4 klm							
Radiant power, W/m², 400-700 nm	0.3	0.9	2.9	8.8	17.6	23.5	49.0
Illumination, klx	0.10	0.30	1.0	3.0	6.0	8.0	16.7
Fixtures per 9 ft² or m²	0.01+	0.04	0.13	0.39	0.77	1.0	2.2
Distance from plants, in. (m)	346 (8.8)	201 (5.1)	110 (2.8)	63 (1.6)	43 (1.1)	39 (1.0)	28 (0.7)
High Intensity Discharge							
Mercury-1 400 W parabolic reflector							
Radiant power, W/m², 400-700 nm	0.28	0.84	2.80	8.39	16.8	22.4	46.6
Illumination, klx	0.1	0.32	1.1	3.2	6.4	8.6	18.0
Lamps per 9 ft² or m²	0.02	0.05	0.17	0.52	1.0	1.4	2.9
Distance from plants, in. (m)	299 (7.6)	173 (4.4)	94 (2.4)	55 (1.4)	39 (1.0)	31 (0.8)	24 (0.6)
Metal halide-1 400 W							
Radiant power, W/m², 400-700 nm	0.77	0.80	2.68	8.03	16.1	21.4	44.6
Illumination, klx	0.09	0.26	0.88	2.6	5.3	7.0	15.0
Lamps per 9 ft² or m²	0.01	0.02	0.08	0.24	0.47	0.63	1.3
Distance from plants, in. (m)	445 (11.3)	256 (6.5)	142 (3.6)	83 (2.1)	59 (1.5)	51 (1.3)	34 (0.87)
High-pressure sodium 400 W							
Radiant power, W/m², 400-700 nm	0.22	0.65	2.18	6.52	13.0	17.4	36.2
Illumination, klx	0.09	0.27	0.89	2.7	5.3	7.1	15.0
Lamps per 9 ft² or m²	0.005	0.015	0.05	0.15	0.3	0.39	0.82
Distance from plants, in. (m)	559 (14.2)	323 (8.2)	177 (4.5)	102 (2.6)	71 (1.8)	63 (1.6)	43 (1.1)
Low-pressure sodium 180 W							
Radiant power, W/m², 400-700 nm	0.26	0.79	2.64	7.93	15.9	21.1	44.0
Illumination, klx	0.14	0.41	1.4	4.1	8.3	11.0	23.0
Lamps per 9 ft² or m²	0.009	0.026	0.088	0.26	0.53	0.70	1.46
Distance from plants, in. (m)	421 (10.7)	244 (6.2)	134 (3.4)	9 (2.0)	55 (1.4)	47 (1.2)	33 (0.83)
Incandescent							
Incandescent 100 W							
Radiant power, W/m², 400-700 nm	0.14	0.41	1.38	4.14	8.28	11.0	23.0
Illumination, klx	0.033	0.10	0.33	1.0	2.0	2.7	5.6
Lamps per 9 ft² or m²	0.056	0.17	0.56	1.7	3.4	4.5	9.4
Distance from plants, in. (m)	165 (4.2)	94 (4.2)	51 (1.3)	30 (0.77)	21 (0.54)	18 (0.47)	13 (0.33)
Incandescent 150 W flood							
Radiant power, W/m², 400-700 nm	0.14	0.41	1.38	4.14	8.28	11.0	23.0
Illumination, klx	0.033	0.098	0.33	1.0	2.0	2.6	5.5
Lamps per 9 ft² or m²	0.035	0.10	0.35	1.0	2.1	2.8	5.8
Distance from plants, in. (m)	212 (5.4)	122 (3.1)	67 (1.7)	39 (1.0)	28 (0.7)	24 (0.6)	16 (0.4)
Incandescent-Hg 160 W							
Radiant power, W/m², 400-700 nm	0.14	0.41	1.38	4.14	8.28	11.0	23.0
Illumination, klx	0.050	0.15	0.50	1.5	3.0	4.0	8.3
Lamps per 9 ft² or m²	0.07	0.22	0.74	2.2	4.5	6.0	12.0
Distance from plants, in. (m)	146 (3.7)	83 (2.1)	47 (1.2)	26 (0.67)	18 (0.47)	16 (0.41)	11 (0.28)
Sunlight							
Radiant power, W per 9 ft² or m²	0.22	0.66	2.21	6.64	13.3	17.7	76.9
Illumination, klx	0.054	0.16	0.54	1.6	3.2	4.3	8.9

life of the incandescent lamp is due to vibration from the lamp loft ventilation or cooling fans. Increased incandescent lamp life under these conditions can be attained by using lamps constructed with a C9 filament. All lamps used in CERs should be installed in porcelain lamp holders, and wiring should have heat resistant insulation.

Energy-saving lamps have approximately equal or slightly lower irradiance per input watt. Since the irradiance per lamp is lower, there is no advantage to these lamps, except in tasks that can be accomplished with low light levels. Light output of all lamps declines with use, except perhaps for the low-pressure sodium lamps that appear to maintain approximately constant output but with an increase in input watts during use. Fluorescent and metal halide designs should be based on 80% of the initial lumens. Most CER lighting systems have difficulty maintaining a relatively constant light level over considerable periods of time. Combinations of MH and HPS lamps compound the problem because the lumen depreciation of the two light sources

Table 8 Input Power Conversion of Light Sources*

Lamp Identification		Total Input Power, Watts	Radiation (400-700 nm), %	Radiation (400-850 nm), %	Other Radiation, %	Conduction and Convection, %	Ballasts Loss, %
Incandescent							
(INC)	100A	100	7	15	75	10	0
Fluorescent							
Cool white	FCW	46	21	21	32	34	13
Cool white	FCW	225	19	19	34	35	12
Warm white	FWW	46	20	20	32	35	13
Plant growth A	PGA	46	13	13	35	39	13
Plant growth B	PGB	46	15	16	34	37	13
Infrared	FIR	46	2	9	39	39	13
Discharge							
Clear mercury	HG	440	12	13	61	17	9
Mercury deluxe	HG/DX	440	13	14	59	18	9
Metal halide	MH	460	27	30	42	15	13
High-pressure sodium	HPS	470	26	36	36	13	15
Low-pressure sodium	LPS	230	27	31	25	22	22

*Conversion efficiency is for lamps without luminaire. Values compiled from manufacturers' data, published information, and unpublished test data by R.W. Thimijan.

is significantly different. Thus, over time, the spectral energy distribution at plant level will shift toward the HPS. Lumen output can be maintained in two ways: (1) Individual lamps, or a combination of lamps, can be switched off initially and activated as the lumen output decreases and (2) by periodically replacing the oldest 25 to 33% of the lamps. Solid-state dimmer systems currently are commercially available only for low-wattage fluorescent lamps and for mercury lamps; but in the future, it may be possible to apply the technology to metal halide lamps.

Large rooms, especially those constructed as an integral part of the building and retrofitted as CERs, rarely separate the lamps from the growing area with a transparent barrier. Rooms designed as CERs at the time a building is constructed, and freestanding rooms or chambers usually separate the lamp from the growing area with a barrier of glass or rigid plastic. Light output from fluorescent lamps is a function of the temperature of the lamp. Thus, the barrier serves a two-fold purpose: (1) to maintain optimum lamp temperature when the growing area temperature is higher or lower than that optimum and (2) to reduce the thermal radiation entering the growing area. Fluorescent lamps should operate in an ambient temperature and airflow environment that will maintain the tube wall temperature at 104°F (40°C). The light output of HID lamps is, under most conditions, not affected by ambient temperature. The heat must be removed, however, to prevent high thermal radiation from causing adverse biological effects. (See Figure 12).

Transparent glass barriers remove nearly all radiation from about 350 to 2500 nm. Rigid plastic is less effective than glass; however, the lighter weight and lower risk due to breakage makes it a popular barrier material. Ultraviolet is also screened by both glass and plastic (but more by plastic). Special UV transmitting plastic can be obtained (but degrades rapidly) if the biological process requires UV light. When irradiance is very high, especially from HID lamps or large numbers of incandescent lamps or both, rigid plastic can soften from the heat and fall from the supports. Further, very high irradiance and resulting high temperature can cause the plastic to darken, which increases absorptivity and the temperature enough to destroy it. Under these conditions, heat resistant glass may be necessary. The lamp compartment and barrier absolutely require positive ventilation regardless of the light source, and the lamp loft should have limit switches that will shut down the lamps if the temperature rises to a critical level.

OTHER PLANT ENVIRONMENTAL FACILITIES

Plants may be held or processed in warehouse-type structures

prior to sale or use in interior landscaping. Required temperatures range from slightly above freezing for cold storage of root stock and cut flowers, to 68 to 77°F (20 to 25°C) for maintaining growing plants, usually in pots or containers. Provision must be made for venting fresh air to avoid carbon dioxide depletion.

Light duration must be controlled by a time clock. When they are in use, lamps and ballasts produce almost all heat required in an insulated building. Ventilation and cooling may be required. Illumination levels depend on the plant requirements. Table 9 shows approximate mountng heights for two levels of illumination. Luminaires mounted on chains permit lamp height to be adjusted to compensate for varying plant hights.

The main concerns for interior landscape lighting are how it renders the color of plants, people, and furnishings and the minimum irradiation requirements of plants. The temperature required for human occupancy is normally acceptable for plants. Light level and duration determine the types of plants that can be grown or maintained. Plants may be grouped into three levels based on level of irradiance. Plants grow when exposed to higher levels, but do not survive below the mininum levels suggested. Irradiance levels are as follows:

Low (Survival): A mimimum light level of 0.07 W/ft^2 (0.75 W/m^2) and a preferred level of 0.3 W/ft^2 (3 W/m^2) irradiance for 8 to 12 h daily.

Medium (Maintenance): a mimimum of 0.3 W/ft^2 (3 W/m^2) and a preferred level of 0.8 W/ft^2 (9 W/m^2) irradiance for 8 to 12 h daily.

Table 9 Mounting Height for Luminaires in Storage Areas

	Survival = 3 W/m² Distance		Maintenance = 9 W/m² Distance	
	ft (m)	lux	ft (m)	lux
Fluorescent (F)				
CWF 2-40 watts	3.0 (0.9)	1000	2.5 (0.75)	3000
WWF	3.0 (0.9)	1000	2.5 (0.75)	3000
CWF 2-215 watts	9.2 (2.8)	1000	5.2 (1.6)	3000
Discharge (HID)				
MH 400 watt	10.8 (3.3)	800	6.6 (2.0)	2400
HPS 400 watt	14.8 (4.5)	800	8.2 (2.5)	2400
LPS 180 watt	11.2 (3.4)	1300	3.9 (1.2)	4000
Incandescent (INC)				
INC 160 watt	4.3 (1.3)	350	1.0 (0.3)	1000
INC-HG 160 watt	3.9 (1.2)	500	5.2 (1.6)	1500
DL	— —	500	— —	1500

High (Propagation): A mimimum of 0.8 W/ft² (9 W/m²) and a preferred level of 2.2 W/ft² (24 W/m²) irradiance for 8 to 12 h daily.

Fluorescent (warm-white), metal halide, or incandescent lighting is usually chosen for public places. Table 7 lists irradiance levels with various light sources.

BIBLIOGRAPHY
ANIMALS

Handbooks & Proceedings

ASAE. 1981. Agricultural Energy. Solar Energy Livestock Production, Vol. 1, ASAE National Energy Symposium, Kansas City, MO. ASAE Publ. 3, 81, 271 pp.

ASAE. 1982. Dairy housing II. 2nd National Dairy Housing Conference Proceedings, Madison, Wisconsin. ASAE Publ. 4:83.

ASAE. 1982. Livestock Environment II. 2nd International Livestock Environment Symposium, Ames, Iowa. ASAE Publ. 3:82.

ASAE. 1983. Design of ventilation systems for livestock and poultry shelters. American Society of Agricultural Engineers Standard ASAE D272.4.

Hahn, G.L. 1985. Management and housing of farm animals in hot environments. Chapter 11, pp. 151-174 from *Stress Physiology in Livestock, Vol. II* (ed. by M.K. Yousef). CRC Press, Boca Raton, FL.

Hellickson, M.A.; and Walker, J.N. (Eds). 1983. *Ventilation of Agricultural Structures.* ASAE Monograph No. 6, ASAE, St. Joseph, MI.

HEW. 1978. Guide for the care and use of laboratory animals. U.S. Department of Health, Education and Welfare. Publ. No. (NIH)78-23.

MWPS. 1983. Structures and Environment Handbook. Midwest Plan Service, MWPS-1, 11th Edition, Ames, IA.

Rechcigl, M., Jr. (ed). 1982. *Handbook of Agricultural Productivity, Vol. II, Animal Productivity.* CRC Press, Boca Raton, FL.

Air Cooling

Canton, G.H.; Buffington, D.E.; and Collier, R.J. 1982. Inspired-air cooling for dairy cows. Trans. ASAE 25(3):730-734.

Hahn, G.L.; and Osburn, D.D. 1970. Feasibility of evaporative cooling for dairy cattle based on expected production losses. Trans. ASAE 12(3):289-291.

Hahn, G.L.; and Osburn, D.D. 1969. Feasibility of summer environmental control for dairy cattle based on expected production losses. Trans. ASAE 12(4):448-451.

Kimball, B.A.; Benham, D.S.; and Wiersma, F. 1977. Heat and mass transfer coefficients for water and air in aspen excelsior pads. Trans. ASAE 20(3):509.

Morrison, S.R.; Heitman, H., Jr.; and Givens, R.L. 1979. Effect of air movement and type of slotted floor on sprinkled pigs. Tropical Agriculture 56(3):257.

Morrison, S.R.; Prokop, M.; and Lofgreen, G.P. 1981. Sprinkling cattle for heat stress relief: activation, temperature, duration of sprinkling, and pen area sprinkled. Trans. ASAE 24(5):1299-1300.

Stewart, R.E., et al. 1966. Field tests of summer air conditioning for dairy cattle in Ohio. ASHRAE Trans. 72(1):271.

Timmons, M.B.; and Baughman, G.R. 1983. Experimental evaluation of poultry mist-fog systems. Trans. ASAE 26(1):207-210.

Timmons, M.B.; and G.R. Baughman. 1984. A plenum concept applied to evaporative pad cooling for broiler housing. Trans. ASAE 27:(6):1877-1881.

Wilson, J.L.; Hughes, H.A.; and Weaver, W.D., Jr. 1983. Evaporative cooling with fogging nozzles in broiler houses. Trans. ASAE 26(2):557-561.

Air Pollution in Buildings

Avery, G.L.; Merva, G.E.; and Gerrish, J.B. 1975. Hydrogen sulphide production in swine confinement units. Trans. ASAE 18(1):149.

Bundy, D.S.; and Hazen, T.E. 1975. Dust levels in swine confinement systems associated with different feeding methods. Trans. ASAE 18(1):137.

Grub, W.; Rollo, C.A.; and Howes, J.R. 1965. Dust problems in poultry environment. Trans. ASAE 8(3):338.

Logsdon, R.F. 1965. Methods of air filtration and protection of air-tempering equipment. Trans. ASAE 8(3):345.

Van Wicklen, G.; and Albright, L.D. 1982. An empirical model of respirable aerosol concentration in an enclosed calf barn. Proc., 2nd Int. Livestock Envir. Symp. ASAE, St. Joseph, MI. pp. 534-539.

Effects of Environment on Production and Growth of Animals

Cattle

Anderson, J.F.; Bates, D.W.; and Jordan, K.A. 1978. Medical and engineering factors relating to calf health as influenced by the environment. Trans. ASAE 21(6):1169.

Berry, I.L.; Shanklin, M.C.; and Johnson, H.D. 1964. Dairy shelter design based on milk production decline as affected by temperature and humidity. Trans. ASAE 7:329-333.

Garrett, W.N. 1980. Factors influencing energetic efficiency of beef production. Journal of Animal Science 51(6):1434.

Gebremedhin, K.G.; Cramer, C.O.; and Porter, W.P. 1981. Predictions and measurements of heat production and food and water requirements of Holstein calves in different environments. Trans. ASAE 24(3):715.

Gebremedhin, K.G.; Porter, W.P.; and Cramer, C.O. 1983. Quantitative analysis of heat exchange through the fur layer of Holstein calves. Trans. ASAE 28(1):188-193.

Holmes, C.W.; and McLean, N.A. 1975. Effects of air temperature and air movement on the heat produced by young Friesian and Jersey calves, with some measurements of the effects of artificial rain. New Zealand Journal of Agr. Res. 18(3):277.

Morrison, S.R.; Lofgreen, G.P.; and Givens, R.L. 1976. Effect of ventilation rate on beef cattle performance. Trans. ASAE 19(3):530.

Morrison, S.R.; Prokop, M. 1983. Beef cattle performance on slotted floors: effect of animal weight on space allotment. Trans. ASAE 26(2):525-528.

Webster, A.J.F.; Gordon, J.G.; and Smith, J.S. 1976. Energy exchanges of veal calves in relation to body weight, food intake and air temperature. Animal Production. 23(1):35.

Phillips, P.A.; and F.V. MacHardy. 1983. Predicting heat production in young calves housed at low temperature. Trans. ASAE 26(1):175-178.

General

Hahn, G.L. 1982. Compensatory performance in livestock: influences on environmental criteria. Proceedings, 2nd Int'l. Livestock Environ. Sympos., ASAE, St. Joseph, MI, pp. 285-294.

Hahn, G.L. 1981. Housing and management to reduce climatic impacts on livestock. J. Anim. Sci. 52(1):175-186.

Pigs

Boon, C.R. 1982. The effect of air speed changes on the group postural behaviour of pigs. J. Agric. Engineering Res. 27(1):71-79.

Bruce, J.M.; and Clark, J.J. 1971. Models of heat production and critical temperature for growing pigs. Animal Production 13(2):285.

Close, W.H.; Mount, L.E.; and Start, I.B. 1971. The influence of environmental temperature and plane of nutrition on heat losses from groups of growing pigs. Animal Production 13(2):285.

Driggers, L.B.; Stanislaw, C.M.; and Weathers, C.R. 1976. Breeding facility design to eliminate effects of high environmental temperatures. Trans. ASAE 19(5):903.

Holmes, C.W.; and McLean, N.A. 1977. The heat production of groups of young pigs exposed to reflective and non-reflective surfaces on walls and ceilings. Trans. ASAE 20(3):527.

McCracken, K.J.; Caldwell, B.J.; and Walker, N. 1979. A note on the performance of early-weaned pigs. Animal Production 29(3):423.

McCracken, K.J.; and Gray, R. 1984. Further studies on the heat production and affective lower critical temperature of early-weaned pigs under commercial conditions of feeding and management. Anim. Prod. 39:283-290.

Morrison, S.R.; Heitman, H., Jr.; and Givens, R.L. 1979. Effect of air movement and type of slotted floor on sprinkled pigs. Tropical Agriculture 56(3):257.

Mount, L.E.; and Start, I.B. 1980. A note on the effects of forced air movement and environmental temperature on weight gain in the pig after weaning. Animal Production 30(2):295.

Phillips, P.A.; Young, B.A.; and McQuitty, J.B. 1982. Liveweight, protein deposition and digestibility responses in growing pigs exposed to low temperature. Canadian Jour. Anim. Sci. 62:95-108.

Phillips, P.A.; and MacHardy, F.V. 1982. Modelling protein and lipid gains in growing pigs exposed to low temperature. Canadian Jour. Anim. Sci. 62:109-121.

Poultry

Buffington, D.E.; Jordan, K.A.; Junnila, W.A.; and Boyd, L.L. 1974. Heat production of active, growing turkeys. Trans. ASAE 17(3):542.

Carr, L.E.; Carter, T.A.; and Felton, K.E. 1976. Low temperature brooding of broilers. Trans. ASAE 19(3):553.

Riskowski, G.L.; DeShazer, J.A.; and Mather, F.B. 1977. Heat losses of white leghorn laying hens as affected by intermittent lighting schedules. Trans. ASAE 20(4):727-731.

Siopes, T.D.; Timmons, M.B., Baughman, G.R.; and Parkhurst, C.R. 1983. The effect of light intensity on the growth performance of male turkeys. Poultry Science 62:2336-2342.

Sheep

Schanbacher, B.D.; Hahn, G.L.; and Nienaber, J.A. 1982. Photoperiodic influences on performance of market lambs. Proceedings, 2nd Int'l. Livestock Environ. Sympos., ASAE, St. Joseph, MI, 1982, pp. 400-405.

Vesely, J.A. 1978. Application of light control to shorten the production cycle in two breeds of sheep. Animal Production 26(2):169.

Modeling and Analysis

Albright, L.D.; and Scott, N.R. 1974. An analysis of steady periodic building temperature variations in warm weather—Part I: A mathematical model. Trans. ASAE 17(1):88-92, 98.

Albright, L.D.; and Scott, N.R. 1974. An analysis of steady periodic building temperature variations in warm weather—Part II: Experimental verification and simulation. Trans. ASAE 17(1):93-98.

Albright, L.D.; and Scott, N.R. 1977. Diurnal temperature fluctuations in multi-air spaced buildings. Trans. ASAE 20(2):319-326.

Bruce, J.M.; and Clark, J.J. 1979. Models of heat production and critical temperature for growing pigs. Animal Production 28:353-369.

Buffington, D.E. 1978. Simulation models of time-varying energy requirements for heating and cooling buildings. Trans. ASAE 21(4):786.

Christianson, L.L.; and Hellickson, H.A. 1977. Simulation and optimization of energy requirements for livestock housing. Trans. ASAE 20(2):327-335.

Hellickson, M.L.; Jordan, K.A.; and Goodrich, R.D. 1978. Predicting beef animal performance with a mathematical model. Trans. ASAE 21(5):938-943.

Teter, N.C.; DeShazer, J.A.; and Thompson, T.L. 1973. Operational characteristics of meat animals—Part I: Swine; Part II: Beef; Part III: Broilers. Trans. ASAE 16:157-159; 740-742; 1165-1167.

Timmons, M.B. 1984. Use of physical models to predict the fluid motion in slot-ventilated livestock structures. Trans. ASAE 27(2):502-507.

Timmons, M.B.; Albright, L.D.; and Furry, R.B. 1978. Similitude aspects of predicting building thermal behavior. Trans. ASAE, 21(5):957.

Timmons, M.B.; Albright, L.D.; Furry, R.B.; and Torrance, K.E. 1980. Experimental and numerical study of air movement in slot-ventilated enclosures. ASHRAE Transactions 86(1):No.2569.

Shades for Livestock

Bedwell, R.L.; and Shanklin, M.D. 1962. Influence of radiant heat sink on thermally-induced stress in dairy cattle. Missouri Agricultural Experiment Station Research Bulletin No. 808.

Bond, T.E.; Neubauer, L.W.; and Givens, R.L. 1976. The influence of slope and orientation of effectiveness of livestock shades. Trans. ASAE 19(1):134-137.

Roman-Ponce, H.; Thatcher, W.W.; Buffington, D.E.; Wilcox, C.J.; and VanHorn, H.H. 1977. Physiological and production responses of dairy cattle to a shade structure in a subtropical environment. Jour. Dairy Science 60(3):424.

Transport of Animals

Ashby, B.H.; Stevens, D.G.; Bailey, W.A.; Hoke, K.E.; and Kindya, W.G. 1979. Environmental conditions on air shipment of livestock. USDA, SEA, Advances in Agricultural Technology, Northeastern Series No. 5.

Ashby, B.H.; Sharp, A.J.; Friend, T.H.; Bailey, W.A.; and Irwin, M.R. 1981. Experimental railcar for cattle transport. Trans. ASAE 24(2):452.

Ashby, B.H.; Ota, H.; Bailey, W.A.; Whitehead, J.A.; and Kindya, W.G. 1980. Heat and weight loss of rabbits during simulated air transport. Trans. ASAE 23(1):162.

Jackson, W.T. 1974. Air transport of Hereford cattle to the People's Republic of China. Veterinary Records 9(1):209.

Scher, S. 1980. Lab animal transportation receiving and quarantine. Lab Animal 9(3):53.

Stermer, R.A.; Camp, T.H.; and Stevens, D.G. 1982. Feeder cattle stress during handlin and transportation. Trans. ASAE 25(1):246248.

Stevens, D.G.; Hahn, G.L.; Bond, T.E.; and Langridge, J.H. 1974. Environmental considerations for shipment of livestock by air freight. USDA, APHIS, May, 19-21.

Stevens, D.G.; and Hahn, G.L. 1981. Minimum ventilation requirement for the air transportation of sheep. Trans. ASAE, 24(1):180.

Laboratory Animals

NIH. 1978. Laboratory Animal Housing. Proceedings of a Symposium held at Hunt Valley, MD, September 1976, National Academy of Sciences, Washington, DC, pp. 220.

McSheehy, T. 1976. *Laboratory Animal Handbook 7—Control of the Animal House Environment.* Laboratory Animals, Ltd.

Soave, O.; Hoag, W.; et al. 1980. The laboratory animal data bank. Lab Animal 9(5):46.

Ventilation Systems

Albright, L.D. 1976. Air flows through hinged-baffle, slotted inlets. Trans. ASAE 19(4):728, 732, 735.

Albright, L.D. 1978. Air flow through baffled, center-ceiling, slotted inlets. Trans. ASAE 21(5):944-947, 952.

Albright, L.D. 1979. Designing slotted inlet ventilation by the systems characteristic technique. Trans. ASAE 22(1):158.

Goetsch, W.D.; Stombaugh, D.P.; and Muehling, A.T. 1984. Earth-tube heat exchange systems. AED-25, Midwest Plan Service, Ames, IA.

McGinnis, D.S.; Ogilvie, J.R.; Pattie, D.R.; Blenkhorn, K.W.; and Turnbull, J.E. 1983. Shell-and-tube heat exchanger for swine buildings. Canadian Agric. Engr. 25(1):69-74.

Person, H.L.; Jacobson, L.D., and Jordan, K.A. 1979. Effect of dirt, louvers and other attachments on fan performance. Trans. ASAE 22(3):612-616.

Pohl, S.H.; and Hellickson, M.A. 1978. Model study of five types of manure pit ventilation systems. Trans. ASAE 21(3):542.

Randall, J.M. 1975. The prediction of air flow patterns in livestock buildings. Jour. Agric. Engng. Research 20(2):199-215.

Randall, J.M. and Battams, V.A. 1979. Stability criteria for air flow patterns in livestock buildings. Jour. Agric. Engng. Research 24(4):361-374.

Randall, J.M. 1980. Selection of piggery ventilation systems and penning layouts based on the cooling effects of air speed and temperature. Jour. Agric. Engng. Research 25(2):169-187.

Sokhansanj, S.; Jordan, K.A.; Jacobson, L.A.; and Messers, G.L. 1980. Economic feasibility of using heat exchangers in ventilation of animal buildings. Trans. ASAE 23(6):1525-1528.

Spengler, R.W.; and Stombaugh, D.P. 1983. Optimization of earth-tube exchangers for winter ventilation of swine housing. Trans. ASAE 26(4):1186-1193.

Timmons, M.B. 1984. Internal air velocities as affected by the size and location of continuous inlet slots. Trans. ASAE. 27(5):1514-1517.

Timmons, M.B.; and Baughman, G.R. 1983. The FLEX House: A new concept in poultry housing. Trans. of ASAE 26(2):529-532.

Witz, R.L.; Pratt, G.L.; and Buchanan, M.L. 1976. Livestock ventilation with heat exchanger. Trans. ASAE 19(6):1187.

Alarm Systems

Clark, W.D.; and Hahn, G.L. 1971. Automatic telephone warning systems for animal and plant laboratories or production systems. Jour. Dairy Science 54(k6):932-935.

Natural Ventilation

Bruce, J.M. 1982. Ventilation of a model livestock building by thermal buoyancy. Trans. ASAE 25(6):1724-1726.

Jedele, D.G. 1979. Cold weather natural ventilation of buildings for swine finishing and gestation. Trans. ASAE 22(3):598-601.

Timmons, M.B.; and Baughman, G.R. 1981. Similitude analysis of ventilation by the stack effect from an open ridge livestock structure. Trans. ASAE 24(4):1030-1034.

Timmons, M.B.; Bottcher, R.W.; and Baughman, G.R. 1984. Nomographs for predicting ventilation by thermal buoyancy. Trans. ASAE 27(6):1891-1893.

PLANTS

Greenhouse and Plant Environment

Aldrich, R.A.; and Bartok, J.W. 1984. Greenhouse Engineering Department of Agricultural Engineering, University of Connecticut, Storrs CT.

ASAE. 1986. Engineering Practice EP411: Guidelines for Measuring and Reporting Environmental Parameters for Plant Experiments in Growth Chambers. ASAE Standards 1986, Amer. Soc. of Agricultural Engineers, St. Joseph MI.

Clegg, P.; and Watkins, D. 1978. The Complete Greenhouse Book. Garden Way Publishing, Charlotte, VT.

Downs, R.J. 1975. Controlled Environments for Plant Research. Columbia University Press, New York, NY.

Hellmers, H.; and Downs, R.J. 1967. Controlled Environments for Plant-Life Research. ASHRAE Journal, February, p. 37.

Hellickson, M.; and Walker, J. 1983. Ventilation of Agricultural Structures, Monograph 6, Amer. Soc. of Agricultural Engineers, St. Joseph MI.

Langhans, R.W. A Growth Chamber Manual. Cornell University Press, Ithaca NY.

Langhans, R.W. 1985. Greenhouse Management. Halcyon Press, Ithaca, NY.

Mastalerz, J.W. 1977. The Greenhouse Environment. John Wiley & Sons, New York, NY.

Nelson, P.V. 1978. Greenhouse Operation and Management. Reston Publishing Co., Reston VA.

Pierce, J.H. 1977. Greenhouse Grow How. Plants Alive Books, Seattle, WA.

Riekels, J.W. 1977. Hydroponics. Ontario Ministry of Agriculture and Food, Fact Sheet No. 200-24, Toronto, Ontario, Canada.

Riekels, J.W. 1975. Nutrient Solutions for Hydroponics. Ontario Ministry of Agriculture and Food, Fact Sheet No. 200-532, Toronto, Ontario, Canada.

Sheldrake, Jr. R.; and Boodley, J.W. Commercial Production of Vegetable and Flower Plants. Research Park, 1B-82, Cornell University, Ithaca, NY.

Tibbitts, T.W.; and Kozlowski, T.T., eds. 1979. Controlled Environment Guidelines for Plant Research. Academic Press, New York, NY.

Light and Radiation

Armitage, A.M.; and Tsugita, M.J. 1974. The Effect of Supplemental Lights source, Illumination, and Quantum Flux Density on the Flowering of Seed Propagated Geraniums. Journal of the American Society for Horticultural Science, Vol. 54, p. 195.

Bickford, E.D.; and Dunn, S. 1972. Lighting for Plant Growth. Kent State University Press, Kent, OH.

Boodley, J.W. 1970. Artificial Light Sources for Gloxinia, African Violet, and Tuberous Begonia. Plants & Gardens, Vol. 26, p. 38.

Carpenter, G.C.; and Mousley, L.J. 1960. The Artificial Illumination of Environmental Control Chambers for Plant Growth. Journal of Agricultural Engineering Research [England], Vol. 5, p. 283.

Carpenter, G.A.; Mousley, L.J.; and Cottrell, P.A. 1964. Maintenance of Constant Light Intensity in Plant Growth Chambers by Group Replacement of Lamps. Journal of Agricultural Engineering Research, Vol. 9.

Campbell, L.E.; Thimijan, R.W.; and Cathey, H.M. 1975. Special Radiant Power of Lamps Used in Horticulture. Transactions of ASAE, Vol. 18, Part 5, p. 952.

Cathey, H.M.; and Campbell, L.E. 1974. Lamps and Lighting: A Horticultural View Lighting Design & Application, Vol. 4, p. 41.

Cathey, H.M.; and Campbell, L.E. 1975. Effectiveness of Five Vision Lighting Sources on Photo-Regulation of 22 Species of Ornamental Plants. Journal of the American Society for Horticultural Science, Vol. 100, Part 1, p. 65.

Cathey, H.M.; and Campbell, L.E. 1977. Plant Productivity: New approaches to Efficient Sources and Evironmental Control. Transactions of ASAE, Vol, Part 2, p. 360.

Cathey, H.M.; Campbell, L.E.; and Thimijan, R.W. 1978. Comparative Development of 11 Plants Grown Under Various Fluorescent Lamps and Different Duration of Irradiation With and Without Additional Incandescent Lighting. Journal of the American Society for Horticultural Science, Vol. 103, p. 781.

Cathey, H.M.; and Campbell, L.E. 1979. Relative Efficiency of High- and Low-Pressure Sodium and Incandescent Filament Lamps used to Supplement Natural Winter Light in Greenhouses Journal of the American society for Horticultural Science, Vol. 104, No. 6, p. 812.

Cathey, H.M.; and Campbell, L.E. 1980. Light and Lighting Systems for Horticultural Plants. Horticultural Reviews, AVI Publishing Co., Westport, CT, Vol. 11, Chapter 10, p. 491.

Fonteno, W.C.; and McWilliams, E.L. 1978. Light compensation Points and Acclimatization of Four Tropical Foliage Plants Journal of the American Society for Horticultural Science, Vol. 103, p. 52.

Hughes, J.; Tsujita, M.J.; and Ormrod, D.P. 1979. Commercial Applications of Supplementary Lighting in Greenhouses. Ontario Ministry of Agriculture and Food, Fact Sheet No. 290-717, Toronto, Ontario, Canada.

Kaufman, J.E.; ed. 1981. IES Lighting Handbook, Application Volume. IES, 345 East 47th Street, New York, NY.

Kaufman, J.E.; ed. 1981. IES Lighting Handbook, Reference Volume. IES, 345 East 47th Street, New York, NY.

Poole, R.T.; and Conover, C.A. Influence of Shade and Nutrition During Production and Dark Storage Stimulating Shipment on Subsequent Quality and Chlorophyll Content of Foliage Plants. HortScience, Vol. 14, p. 617.

Robbins, F.V.; and Spillman, C.K. 1980. Solar Energy Transmission Through Two Transparent covers. Transactions of ASAE, vol. 23, No. 5.

Sager, J.C.; Edwards, J.L.; and Klein, W.H. 1982. Light Energy Utilization Efficiency for Photosynthesis.. Transactions of the ASAE, Vol. 25, No. 6, pp. 1737-1746.

Photoperiod

Cathey, H.M.; and Borthwick, H.A. 1961. Cyclic Lighting for Controlling Flowering of Chrysanthemums. Proceedings of the ASAE, Vol. 78, p. 545.

Heins, R.D.; Healy, W.H.; and Wilkens, H.F. 1980. Influence of Night Lighting with Red, Far Red, and Incandescent Light on Rooting of Chrysanthemum Cuttings. HortScience, Vol. 15, p. 84.

Piringer, A.A.; and Cathey, H.M. 1960. Effect of Photoperiod, Kind of Supplemental Light, and Temperature on the Growth and Flowering of Petunia Plants. Proceedings of the American Society for Horticultural Science, Vol. 76, p. 649.

Carbon Dioxide

Bailey, W.A. et al., 1970. CO_2 Systems for Growing Plants. Transactions of ASAE, Vol. 13, No. 2, p. 263.

Gates, D.M. 1968. Transpiration and Leaf Temperature. Annual Review of Plant Physiology, Vol. 19, p. 211.

Holley, W.D. 1970. CO_2 Enrichment for Flower Production. Transactions of ASAE, Vol. 13, No. 3, p. 257.

Kretchman, J.; and Howlett, F.S. 1970. Enrichment for Vegetable Production. Transactions of ASAE, Vol. 13, No. 2, p. 252.

Pettibone, C.A.; et al. 1970. The Control and Effects of Supplemental Carbon Dioxide in Air-Supported Plastic Greenhouses. Transactions of ASAE, Vol. 13, No. 2, p. 259.

Tibbitts, T.W.; McFarlane, J.C.; Krizek, D.T.; Berry, W.L.; Hammer, P.A.; Hodgsen, R.H.; and Langhans, R.W. 1977. Contaminants in Plant Growth Chambers. Horticulture Science, Vol. 12, p. 310.

Watt, A.D. 1971. Placing Atmospheric CO_2 in perspective. IEEE Spectrum, Vol. 8, No. 11, p. 59.

Wittwer, S.H. 1970. Aspects of CO_2 Enrichment for Crop Production. Transactions of ASAE, Vol. 13, No. 2, p. 249.

Heating, Cooling, and Ventilation

ASAE. 1986. Engineering Practice: EP406: Heating, Ventilating and Cooling Greenhouses. ASAE Standards, American Society of Agricultural Engineers, St. Joseph, MI.

Albright, L.D.; Seginer, I.; Marsh, L.S.; and Oko, A. 1985. InSitu Thermal Calibration of Unventilated Greenhouses. Journal of Agricultural Engineering Research, 31(3):265-281.

Buffington, D.E.; and Skinner, T.C. 1979. Maintenance Guide for Greenhouse Ventilation, Evaporative Cooling, and Heating Systems. Department of Agricultural Engineering, Publication No. AE-17, University of Florida, Gainesville, FL.

Duncan, G.A.; and Walker, J.N. 1979. Poly-Tube HeatingVentilation Systems and Equipment. Agricultural Engineering Department, Publication No. AEN-7, University of Kentucky, Lexington, KY.

Elwell, D.L.; Hamdy, M.Y.; Roller, W.L.; Ahmed, A.E.; Shapiro, H.N.; Parker, J.J.; and S.E. Johnson. 1985. Soil Heating Using Subsurface Pipes. Department of Agricultural Engineering, Ohio State University; Columbus OH.

Hanan, J.J.; Ozone and Ethylene Effects on Some Ornamental Plant Species, General Series Bulletin No. 974, Colorado State University, Fort Collins, CO.

Heins, R.; and Rotz, Alan. 1980. Plant Growth and Energy Savings with Infrared Heating. Florists' Review, October p. 20.

Kimball, B.A. 1983. A Modular Energy Balance Program Including Subroutines for Greenhouses and Other Latent Heat Devices. Agricultural Research Service, 4331 East Broadway, Phoenix AZ 85040.

NGMA. Standards for Ventilating and Cooling Greenhouses. National Greenhouse Manufacturers' Association, St. Paul, MN.

Roberts, W.J.; and Mears, D. 1984. Floor Heating and Bench Heating Extension Bulletin for Greenhouses. Department of Agricultural and Biological Engineering, Cook College, Rutgers University, New Brunswick NJ.

Roberts, W.J.; and Mears, D. 1984. Heating and Ventilating Greenhouses. Department of Agricultural and Biological Engineering, Cook College, Rutgers University, New Brunswick NJ.

Roberts, W.J.; and Mears, D.R. 1979. Floor Heating of Greenhouses. Miscellaneous Publication, Rutgers University, New Brunswick, NJ.

Rogers, B.T. 1979. Wood and The Curious Case of the Rock Salt Greenhouse. ASHRAE Journal, November, p. 74. (See also Silverstein.)

Rotz, C.A.; and Heins, R.D. 1980. An Economic Comparison of Greenhouse Heating Systems. Florists' Review, October p. 24.

Silverstein, S.D. 1976. Effect of Infrared Transparency on Heat Transfer Through Windows: A Clarification of the Greenhouse Effect. Science, Vol. 193, p. 229. (See also Rogers.)

Skinner, T.C.; and Buffington, D.E. 1977. Evaporative Cooling of Greenhouses in Florida. Department of Agricultural Engineering, Publication No. AE-14, University of Florida, Gainesville, FL.

Walker, J.N. 1965. Predicting Temperatures in Ventilated Greenhouses. Transaction of ASAE, Vol. 8, No. 3, p. 445.

Walker, J.N.; and Duncan, G.A. 1975. Greenhouse Heating Systems. Agricultural Engineering Department, Publication No. AEN-31, University of Kentucky, Lexington, KY.

Walker, J.N.; and Duncan, G.A. 1979. Greenhouse Ventilation Systems. Agricultural Engineering Department, Publication No. AEN-30, University of Kentucky, Lexington, KY.

Walker, P.N. Waste Energy Heats Greenhouse. Illinois Research, Vol. 20, No. 2, p. 6.

Walker, P.N. 1979. Greenhouse Surface Heating with Power Plant Cooling Water: Heat Transfer Characteristics. Transactions of ASAE, Vol. 22, No. 6, p. 1370, p. 1380.

Energy Conservation

Badger, P.C.; and Poole, H.A. 1979. Conserving Energy in Ohio Greenhouses. OARDC Special Circular No. 102, Ohio Agricultural Research and Development Center, Ohio State University, Wooster, OH.

Blom, T.; Hughes, J.; and Ingratta, F. 1978. Energy Conservation in Ontario Greenhouses. Ontario Ministry of Agriculture and Food, Publication No. 65, Toronto, Ontario, Canada.

Roberts, W.J.; Bartok, J.W., Jr.; Fabian, E.E.; and Simpkins, J. 1985. Energy Conservation for Commercial Greenhouses. NRAES-3. Department of Agricultural Engineering, Cornell University, Ithaca NY.

Solar Energy Use

Albright, L.D.; Langhans, R.W.; White, G.B.; and Donohoe, A.J. 1980. Enhancing Passive Solar Heating of Commercial Greenhouses. Proceedings of the ASAE National Energy Symposium, St. Joseph, MI.

Albright, L.D. et al. 1980. Passive Solar Heating Applied to Commercial Greenhouses. Acta Horticultura, Publication No. 115, Energy in Protected Civilization.

Cathey, H.M. 1980. Energy-Efficient Crop Production in Greenhouses ASHRAE Transactions, Vol. 86, Part 2, p. 455.

Duncan, G.A.; Walker, J.N.; and Turner, L.W. 1979. Energy for Greenhouses, Part I. Energy Conservation. College of Agriculture, Publication No. AEES-16, University of Kentucky, Lexington, KY.

Duncan, G.A.; Walker, J.N.; and Turner, L.W. 1980. Energy for Greenhouses, Part II. Alternative Sources of Energy. College of Agriculture, University of Kentucky, Lexington, KY.

Gray, H.E. 1980. Energy Management and Conservation in Greenhouses: A Manufacturer's View. ASHRAE Transactions, Vol. 86, Part 2, p. 443.

Roberts, W.J.; Mears, D.R. 1980. Research Conservation and Solar Energy Utilization in Greenhouses. ASHRAE Transactions, Vol. 86, Part 2, p. 433.

Short, T.H.; Brugger, M.F.; and Bauerle, W.L. 1980. Energy Conservation Ideas for New and Existing Commercial Greenhouses. ASHRAE Transactions, Vol. 86, Part 2, p. 448.

Interior Plantscaping

Gaines, R.L. 1980. Interior Plantscaping. Architectural Record, McGraw-Hill, New York, NY.

Cathey, H.M.; and Campbell, L.E. 1978. Indoor Gardening Artificial Lighting, Terrariums, Hanging Baskets and Plant Selection. USDA Home and Garden Bulletin No. 220.

CHAPTER 38

DRYING AND STORING FARM CROPS

Preservation of the quality of cereal grain and other farm crops is critical from crop harvesting to its use by the consumer. A requirement for preserving quality is control of the moisture content and temperature during storage. Figure 1 shows how moisture and temperature affect mold growth, which is reduced to a minimum if the crop is kept cooler than 50°F (10°C) and the relative humidity of the air in equilibrium with the stored crop is less than 60%.

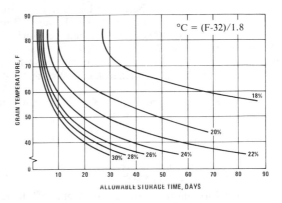
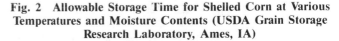

Fig. 2   Allowable Storage Time for Shelled Corn at Various Temperatures and Moisture Contents (USDA Grain Storage Research Laboratory, Ames, IA)

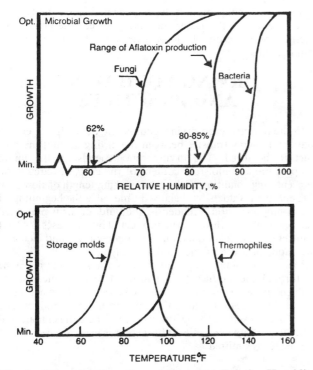

Fig. 1   Microbial Growth as Affected by Relative Humidity and Temperature

Mold growth and spoilage are a function of elapsed storage time, temperature, and moisture content above the critical value. Thus, early reduction of moisture content and temperature helps maintain the as-harvested quality of the crop. Figure 2 shows the allowable storage time for shelled corn. Corn at 60°F (16°C) and 20% moisture has a storage life of about 26 days. If the corn is dried to 18% after 13 days, one-half of its storage life has elapsed. So the remaining storage life at 60°F (16°C) and 18% moisture content is 33 days, not 66 days.

Insects also thrive in stored grain if the moisture content and temperature are sufficiently high. At low moisture contents and temperatures less than 50°F (10°C), the insects will remain dormant or die.

Most farm crops must be dried to, and maintained at, a moisture content of 12 to 13%, wet basis, depending on the specific crop, storage temperature, and length of storage. Oil

seeds such as peanuts, sunflowers, and flaxseed must be dried to a moisture content of 8 to 9%. Grain stored more than a year or seed stock should be dried to a lower moisture level. Moisture levels above these critical values can lead to growth and proliferation of fungi, which may produce compounds toxic to humans or animals.

The maximum yield of dry matter can be obtained by starting harvest when corn has dried in the field to an average moisture content of 26%. Wheat can be harvested when it has dried to 20%. However, harvesting at these moisture contents requires expensive mechanical drying. Although field drying requires less expense for operating drying equipment, it may be more costly because field losses generally increase as the moisture content decreases.

Grain to be sold through commercial market channels is price based on a specified moisture content, with discounts for moisture levels above that. These discounts compensate for the weight of excess water, cover the cost of water removal, and control the supply of wet grain delivered to market. Grain dried below the market standard moisture content (15.5% for corn, 13.0% for soybeans, and 13.5% for wheat) generally does not receive a premium, and so the seller loses the opportunity to sell water for the price of the grain.

Grain Quantity

The bushel has been the common measure used for marketing grain in the United States. Accordingly, most dryers are rated in bushels per hour for a specified moisture content reduction. Considerable confusion arises from the use of a bushel as a measure of grain. Bushel is a volume measure equal to 1.244 ft³ (0.03524 m³). However, the bushel is used as a volume measure only to estimate holding capacity of bins, dryers, and other containers.

For buying and selling grain, reporting production and consumption data, and for most other uses, the bushel weight is used. The legal weight of a bushel is set, for example, at 56 lb (25.42 kg) for corn and 60 lb (27.24 kg) for wheat. When grain

The preparation of this chapter is assigned to TC 2.2, Plant and Animal Environment.

is marketed, bushels are computed as the load weight divided by the bushel weight. For example, 56,000 pounds of corn (regardless of moisture content) is 1000 bushels. Rice, grain sorghum, and sunflower are more commonly traded on the basis of hundredweight (100 lb or 45.4 kg), thus separating these measures from the volume connotation. Table 1 lists the density of some crops.

The terms wet bushels and dry bushels are sometimes used to refer to the volume of grain before and after drying. For example, 56,000 lb of 25% moisture corn may be referred to as 1000 wet bushels or simply 1000 bushels. When the corn is dried to 15.5% moisture, only 49,700 lb or 49,700/56 = 888 bushels remain. Thus, a dryer rated on the basis of wet bushels (25% m.c.) will show a capacity 12.6% higher than if rated on the basis of dry bushels (15.5% m.c.).

The percent of initial weight lost due to water removed may be calculated by the following equation

$$\text{Moisture Shrink, } \% = \frac{M_o - M_f}{100 - M_f} \cdot 100$$

where:

M_o = Original or initial moisture content, wet basis
M_f = Final moisture content, wet basis

Applying the formula to drying a crop from 25% to 15%:

$$\text{Moisture Shrink} = \frac{25 - 15}{100 - 15} \cdot 100 = 11.76\%$$

In this case the moisture shrink is 11.76%, or an average 1.176% weight reduction for each percentage point of moisture reduction. The moisture shrink varies, depending on the final moisture content. For example, the average shrink per point of moisture drying from 20% to 10% is 1.111.

Economics

Producers generally have the choice of drying their grain on the farm before delivering it to market or delivering wet grain at a price discount for excess moisture. Costs of drying on the farm consist of fixed costs and variable costs. Once a given size

Table 1   Calculated Densities of Grain and Seeds Based on Weights and Measures Used by the U.S. Department of Agriculture

	Bulk Density	
	lb/ft³	kg/m³
Alfalfa	48.0	768
Barley	38.4	614
Beans, dry	48.0	768
Bluegrass	11.2 to 24.0	180 to 384
Clover	48.0	768
Corn[a]		
Ear, husked	28.0	448
Shelled	44.8	717
Cotton seed	25.6	410
Oats	25.6	410
Peanuts, unshelled		
Virginia type	13.6	218
Runner, Southeastern	16.8	269
Spanish	19.8	317
Rice, rough	36.0	576
Rye	44.8	717
Sorghum	40.0	640
Soybeans	48.0	768
Sudan Grass	32.0	512
Sunflower		
Confectionery	19.2	307
Oil Seed	25.6	410
Wheat	48.0	768

[a]70 lb of husked earcorn yields 1 bushel, or 56 lb of shelled corn. 70 lb of earcorn occupies 2 bushels (2.5 ft³).

Table 2   Estimated Drying Energy Requirement

Dryer Type	Btu/lb. of Water Removed	kJ/kg of Water Removed
Natural Air	1000-1200	2300-2800
Low Temperature	1200-1500	2800-3500
Batch-In-Bin	1500-2000	3500-4700
High Temperature		
Air Recirculating	1800-2200	4200-5100
W/O Air Recirculating	2000-3000	4700-7000

*Includes all energy requirements for fans and heat.

of dryer is purchased, depreciation, interest, taxes, and repairs are fixed and not affected by volume. Costs of labor, fuel, and electricity are variable costs that vary directly with the volume dried. Total costs of drying vary widely, depending on the volume dried, the drying equipment, and the prices for fuel and equipment.

The energy consumption depends primarily on the type of dryer. Generally, the faster the drying speed, the greater the energy consumption. Table 2 gives an estimate of energy requirements.

DRYING EQUIPMENT AND PRACTICES

Contemporary crop-drying equipment depends largely on mass and energy transfer between the drying air and the product to be dried. The drying rate depends on the initial temperature and moisture content of the crop, air circulation rate, entering condition of the circulated air, length of flow path through the products, and elapsed time since the beginning of the drying operation. Frequently, the outdoor air is preheated before circulation through the product. This increases the heat transfer rate to the product, raises its temperature, and increases the vapor pressure of the product moisture.

Most crop-drying equipment consists of (1) a fan to move the air through the product, (2) a controlled heater to increase the ambient air temperature to the desired level, and (3) a container to distribute the drying air uniformly through the product. The exhaust air is vented to the atmosphere. Where the climate and other factors are favorable, unheated air is used for drying, and the heater is omitted.

Fans

The fan selected for a given drying application should meet the same factors important in any air-moving application. The fan must deliver the desired amount of air against the static resistance of the product in the bin or column. This factor determines the type of fan to be used, although most fan types are found in drying applications. Figure 5 in Chapter 10 of the 1985 FUNDAMENTALS Volume shows the resistance of some clean grains and seeds to airflow.

Foreign material in the grain can change the required air pressure significantly in the following ways:

1. Foreign particles larger than the grain (straw, weed parts, larger seeds, etc.) reduce the resistance to airflow.
2. Foreign particles smaller than the grain (broken grain, dust, small seeds, etc.) increase the resistance to airflow.
3. The effect in either case may be dramatic, even when very little foreign material is present. The airflow rate may be affected as much as 60% or more where large particles are present and 100% or more where small particles are present.
4. The filling method used or agitation of the grain after it is placed in the dryer can increase the pressure requirements up

to 100%. High moisture in grain causes less pressure drop than in dry grain.

Backward-curved centrifugal fans are commonly recommended when static pressures are higher than 4 in. water gauge (1.0 kPa) and for lower noise levels. Vane-axial fans are normally recommended when static pressures are less than 3 in. water gauge (0.75 kPa). Either fan can be used between 3 and 4 in. of static pressure.

Initial cost is the next most important factor, after functional considerations, in the selection of dryer fans. Drying equipment has a rather low percentage of annual use in many applications, so the cost of dryer ownership per unit of material dried is sometimes greater than the energy cost of operation. Therefore, fan efficiency may become less important than cost. The same considerations apply to other components of the dryer.

Heaters

Crop dryer heaters are fueled by natural gas, liquified petroleum gas, or fuel oil, although some electric heaters are used. Dryers using coal; biomass such as corn cobs, stubble or wood; and solar energy have also been built. Combustion of the fuel in crop dryers is similar to combustion in domestic and industrial furnaces. Heat is transferred to the drying air either indirectly by means of a heat exchanger or directly by combining the combustion gases with the drying air. Most grain dryers use direct combustion. Indirect heating is used in drying some products such as hay and sunflower, because of their greater fire hazard.

Controls

In addition to the usual temperature control for drying air, all heated air units must have safety controls similar to those found on space-heating equipment. These safety controls shut off the fuel in case of flame failure and stop the burner in case of overheating or excessive drying air temperatures. All controls should be arranged to operate safely in case of power failure.

COLUMN DRYERS

Batch Dryers

The batch dryer simply cycles through load, dry, cool, and unload of the grain. Fans force hot air through grain columns, which are generally about 12-in. (300-mm) thick. Drying time depends on the type of grain and the amount of moisture removed. A general rule is 10 minutes per point (percent) of moisture removed. Many dryers circulate and mix the grain to prevent significant moisture content gradients from forming across the column. A circulation rate that is too fast or a poor selection of handling equipment may cause undue damage and loss of market quality. This type of dryer is suitable for farm operations and is often portable.

Continuous Flow Dryers

This type of self-contained dryer passes a continuous stream of grain through the drying chamber. A second chamber cools the hot, dry grain prior to storage. Handling and storage equipment must be available at all times to move grain to and from the dryers. The design of these dryers can be classified as crossflow, concurrent flow, and counterflow.

Crossflow Dryers move air perpendicular to the grain movement. This type of column dryer consists most commonly of two or more vertical columns surrounding the drying and cooling air plenums. The columns range in thickness from 8 to 16 in. (200 to 400 mm).

The airflow rates fall in the range of 40 to 160 cfm per ft^3 of grain (0.67 to 2.67 m^3/s per m^3). Thermal efficiency of the drying process increases with column depth and decreases as airflow increases. However, moisture uniformity and drying capacity increase with an increase in airflow and a decrease in column depth. Dryer design obtains a desirable balance of the factors of airflow and column depth for the expected moisture levels and drying air temperatures. Performance is evaluated in terms of drying capacity, thermal efficiency, and product uniformity.

As with the batch dryer, a moisture gradient forms across the column because the grain nearest the inside of the column is exposed to the driest air during the complete cycle. Several methods currently minimize this problem. One method includes turnflow devices into the columns, which split the grain stream and move the inside half of the column to the outside and the outside half to the inside. Although effective, turnflow devices tend to plug if the grain is trashy. Under these conditions, a scalper/cleaner should be used ahead of a dryer to clean the grain. Another method separates the drying chamber into sections and ducts the hot air so that its direction through the grain is reversed in alternate sections. The effect is about the same as the turnflow devices. A third method separates the drying chamber into sections and reduces the drying air temperature in each consecutive section. This method is the least effective of the three.

Rack-Type Dryer. In this type of crossflow dryer shown in Figure 3, grain flows over alternating rows of heated air supply ducts and air exhaust ducts. This action mixes the grain and alternates exposure to relatively hot drying air and air cooled by previous contact with the grain. It promotes moisture uniformity and equal exposure of the product to the drying air.

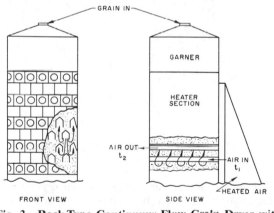

Fig. 3   Rack-Type Continuous-Flow Grain Dryer with Alternate Rows of Air Inlet and Outlet Ducts

Concurrent-Flow Dryer. In the concurrent-flow dryer, grain and drying air move in the same direction in the drying chamber. The drying chamber is then coupled to a counterflow cooling section. Thus, the hottest air is in contact with the wettest grain, allowing higher drying air temperatures (up to 450°F or 230°C) to be used. Rapid evaporative cooling in the wettest grain prevents the grain temperature from reaching excessive levels. Because higher drying air temperatures are used, the energy efficiency is better than that obtained with a conventional crossflow dryer. In the cooling section, the coolest air initially contacts the coolest grain. The combination of drying and cooling chambers results in lower thermal stresses in the grain kernels during drying and cooling. The result is a higher quality product.

Counterflow Dryer. The grain and drying air move in opposite directions in the drying chamber of this dryer. Counterflow is common for in-bin dryers. Drying air flows from the bottom of the bin and out the top. The wet grain is loaded from overhead, and floor sweep augers can be used to bring the hot dry grain to a center sump where it is removed by another auger. The travel of the sweep is normally controlled by temperature-sensing elements.

A drying zone exists only in the lower layers of the grain mass and is truncated at its lower edge so that the grain being removed is not overdried. As part of the counterflow process, the warm, saturated, or near-saturated air leaving the drying zone passes through the cool incoming grain. Some energy heats the cool grain, but some moisture may condense on the cool grain if the bed is deep and the initial grain temperature is low enough.

Reducing Energy Costs

Recirculation. Cost of fuel has had an impact on the design and operation of dryers. Nearly all commercially available driers have optional ducting systems to recycle some of the exhaust air from the drying and cooling chambers back to the inlet of the drying chamber as in Figure 4. Variations in systems exist, but most make it possible to recirculate all of the air from the cooling chamber and the air from the lower two-thirds of the drying chamber. Relative humidity of this air for most crossflow dryers is less than 50%. Energy savings of up to 30% can be obtained in a well-designed system.

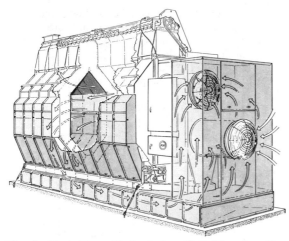

Fig. 4   Crop Dryer Recirculation Unit (Courtesy Farm Fans, Inc.)

Dryeration is another means of reducing energy consumption and improving grain quality. In this process, hot grain is removed from the dryer with a moisture content 1 or 2 percentage points above that desired for storage (Figure 5). The hot grain is placed in a dryeration bin, where it tempers without airflow for at least 4 to 6 hours. After the first grain delivered to the bin has tempered, the cooling fan is turned on as additional hot grain is delivered to the bin. The air cools the grain and removes 1 to 2% moisture before it is moved to final storage. Cooling is normally completed about 6 hours after the last hot grain is added, if the cooling rate equals the filling rate.

The crop cooling rate should equal the filling rate of the dryeration bin. A faster cooling rate will cool the grain before it has tempered. A slower rate may result in spoilage, since the allowable storage time of hot damp grain may be only a few days. The required airflow rate is based on dryer capacity and crop density. A minimum airflow rate of 12 cfm for each bushel per hour (bu/hr) of dryer capacity provides cooling capacity to keep up with the dryer when drying corn that weighs 56 lb/bu (airflow of 800 L/kg). Recommended airflow rates for some crops are listed in Table 3.

Table 3   Recommended Airflow Rates for Dryeration[a]

Crop	Weight, lb/bu.	Recommended Dryeration Airflow Rate, cfm per bu/hr.
Barley	48	10
Corn	56	12
Durum	60	13
Edible Beans	60	13
Flaxseed	56	12
Millet	50	11
Oats	32	7
Rye	56	12
Sorghum	56	12
Soybean	60	13
Confectionary Sunflower	24	5
Oil Sunflower	32	7
HRS Wheat	60	13

[a]Basic airflow is 12.86 ft^3/lb (800 L/kg).

The concept of **combination drying** was developed to improve the thermal efficiency and grain quality drying corn. A continuous-flow dryer dries the corn to 18 to 20% moisture, at which time it is transferred to a bin. The in-bin drying system then brings the moisture down to a safe storage level.

For energy savings, operating temperatures of batch and continuous-flow dryers are usually set at the highest level that will not damage the product for its particular end use. Figure 6 shows the energy requirements of a conventional crossflow dryer as a function of drying air temperature and airflow rate.

DEEP BED DRYING

The deep bed drying system can be installed in any structure that will hold grain. Most grain storage structures can be designed or adapted for drying by providing a means of distributing the drying air uniformly through the grain. This is most commonly done by either a perforated false floor (Figure 7) or duct systems placed on the floor of the bin (Figure 8).

Perforations in the false floor should have a total area of at least 10% of the floor area; 15% is better. The perforated floor distributes the air more uniformly and offers less resistance to airflow than ducts, but the duct system is less expensive for larger surface area systems. The ducts can be removed after removal of the grain, and the structure can be cleaned and used for other purposes. Ducts must not be spaced further apart than one-half times the depth of the grain. The amount of perforated area and duct length will affect airflow distribution uniformity.

Air ducts and tunnels that disperse air into the grain should be large enough to prevent the air velocity from exceeding 2000 fpm (10 m/s), and slower speeds are desirable. Sharp turns or obstructions in ducts should be eliminated, since they cause loss of pressure. Several operating methods for drying grain in storage bins are in use. They may be classified as full-bin drying, layer drying, and batch drying.

Full-Bin Drying

Full-bin drying is generally done with unheated air or air heated 10 to 20°F (6 to 11°C) above ambient. A humidistat is frequently used to sense the humidity of the drying air and turn off the heater if the weather conditions are such that heated air would cause overdrying. A humidistat setting of 55% limits drying to approximately the 12% moisture level for most farm

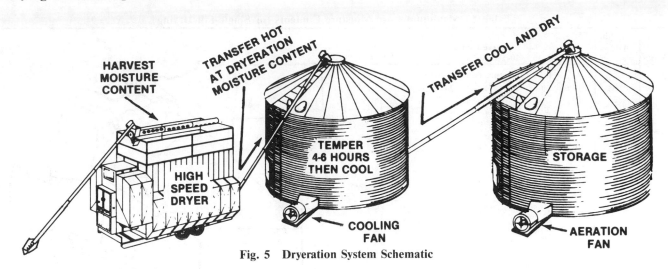

Fig. 5 Dryeration System Schematic

grains, assuming that the ambient humidity does not go below this point.

Airflow requirements for full-bin drying are generally made on the basis of cfm of air required per ft³ of grain (L/s of air per m³ of grain). The airflow recommendations depend on the type of grain, the moisture content, and the weather conditions. Some recommendations for drying with unheated air are shown in Tables 4 and 5. These apply to the principal production areas of the continental United States and are based on experience under average conditions; they may not be applicable under unusual weather conditions or even usual weather conditions in the case of late maturing crops. Much of the weather hazard can be removed by supplemental heat. Full-bin drying may not be applicable in some geographical areas.

The depth of grain (distance of air travel) is limited only by the cost of the fan, motor, air distribution system, and power required. The maximum practical depth appears to be 20 ft (6 m) for corn and beans, and 13 ft (4 m) for wheat.

Airflow rate is very important for successful drying. Because faster drying results from higher air rates, the highest economical air rate should be used. The cost of drying should be calculated,

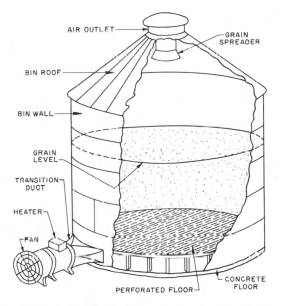

Fig. 7 Perforated False-Floor System for Bin Drying of Grain

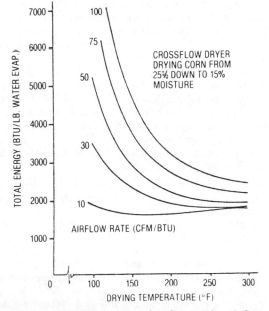

Fig. 6 Energy Requirements of a Conventional Crossflow Dryer as a Function of Drying Air Temperature and Air Flow Rate (Univ. of Nebraska)

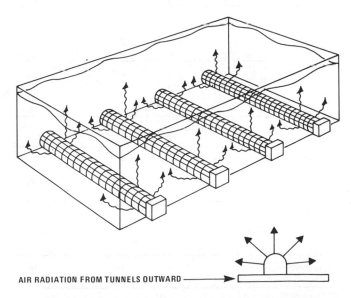

AIR RADIATION FROM TUNNELS OUTWARD

Fig. 8 Tunnel or Duct Air Distribution System

Table 4　Maximum Corn Moisture Contents for Single-Fill Drying

Zone	Full-bin airflow, cfm/bu	9-1	9-15	10-1	10-15	11-1	11-15	12-1
		Initial moisture content, percent						
A	1.0	18	19.5	21	22	24	20	18
	1.25	20	20.5	21.5	23	24.5	20.5	18
	1.5	20	20.5	22.5	23	25	21	18
	2.0	20.5	21	23	24	25.5	21.5	18
	3.0	22	22.5	24	25.5	27	22	18
B	1.0	19	20	20	21	23	20	18
	1.25	19	20	20.5	21.5	24	20.5	18
	1.5	19.5	20.5	21	22.5	24	21	18
	2.0	20	21	22.5	23.5	25	21.5	18
	3.0	21	22.5	23.5	24.5	26	22	18
C	1.0	19	19.5	20	21	22	20	18
	1.25	19	20	20.5	21.5	22.5	20.5	18
	1.5	19.5	20	21	22	23.5	21.5	18
	2.0	20	21	22	23	24.5	21.5	18
	3.0	21	22	23.5	24.5	25.5	22	18
D	1.0	19	19.5	20	21	22	20	18
	1.25	19	19.5	20.5	21	22.5	20.5	18
	1.5	19	19.5	21	22	23	21	18
	2.0	19.5	21	21.5	23	24	21.5	18
	3.0	20.5	21.5	23	24	25	22	18

Developed by T.L. Thompson, Univ. of Nebraska.

since at high airflow rates the cost may exceed the cost of using column dryers.

Heated air may be used during periods of prolonged fog or rain to ensure satisfactory drying. Burners should be sized to raise the temperature of the drying air only 10 to 20°F (6 to 11°C). In any case, the temperature should not exceed 82 to 84°F (28 to 29°C) after heating. Overheating the drying air will cause the grain to overdry and dry nonuniformly; heat is not recommended, except to counteract adverse weather conditions.

Drying takes place in a drying zone, which advances upward through the grain (Figure 9). Grain above this drying zone remains at the initial moisture content or slightly above, while grain below the drying zone is at a moisture content in equilibrium with the drying air. The equilibrium moisture content of a material is the moisture content that it approaches when exposed to air at a specified relative humidity. Figure 2 on Page 10.4 of the 1985 FUNDAMENTALS Volume shows equilibrium moisture content of selected crops.

The direction of air movement does not affect the rate of drying; other factors must then be considered in choosing the direction of air movement. A pressure system moves the moisture-laden air up through the grain, where it is discharged under the roof. Moisture may condense on the underside of metal roofs if there is insufficient ventilation at that spot. The wettest grain during pressure system ventilation is near the top surface and is easy to sample. Fan and motor waste heat are put into the air stream and contribute drying.

A suction system moves the air down through the grain. The moisture-laden air is discharged from the fan into the outside atmosphere, so roof condensation is no problem. However, the wettest grain is near the bottom of the mass and is difficult to sample. Of the two systems, the pressure system is recommended because management is easier.

The following management practices must be observed to ensure the best performance of the dryer:

1. Minimize foreign material. A scalper cleaner is recommended for cleaning the grain to reduce wet pockets and air pressure requirements.
2. Distribute the remaining foreign material uniformly by installing a grain distributor on the end of the storage filling chute.
3. Place the grain in layers and keep it level.
4. Start the fan as soon as the floor or tunnels are covered with grain.
5. Operate the fan continuously unless it is raining heavily or there is a dense ground fog. Once all the grain is within 1% of storage moisture content, run the fans only when the relative humidity is below 70%.

Table 5　Recommended Air Flow Rates for Different Grains and Moisture Contents Using Unheated Air

Type of Grain	Grain Moisture Content, %	Recommended Airflow Rate cfm/ft³	L/(s · m³)
Wheat	25	4.8	80.0
	22	4.0	66.7
	20	2.4	40.0
	18	1.6	26.7
	16	0.8	13.3
Oats	25	2.4	40.0
	20	1.6	26.7
	18	1.2	20.0
	16	0.8	13.3
Shelled Corn	25	4.0	66.7
	20	2.4	40.0
	18	1.6	26.7
	16	0.8	13.3
Ear Corn	25	6.4	106.7
	18	3.2	53.3
Grain Sorghum	25	4.8	80.0
	22	4.0	66.7
	18	2.4	40.0
	15	1.6	26.7
Soybeans	25	4.8	80.0
	22	4.0	66.7
	18	2.4	40.0
	15	1.6	26.7
Sunflower	17	1.0	16.7
	15	0.5	8.3

Compiled from USDA Leaflet 332, 1952, and University of Georgia Bulletin NS 33, 1958.

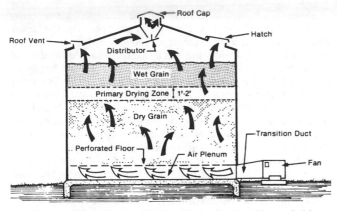

Fig. 9   Three Zones Within Grain During Natural Air Drying in a Typical Bin

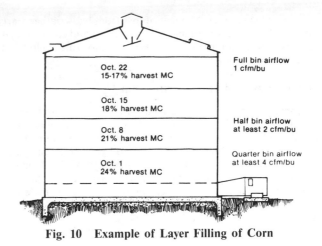

Fig. 10   Example of Layer Filling of Corn

Layer Drying

Layer drying is done by placing successive layers of wet grain on top of grain that has been previously dried. When the top 6 in. (150 mm) has dried to within 1% of the desired moisture content, another layer is added (Figure 10). This reduces the time that the top layers of grain are left undried in comparison to full-bin drying. Either unheated or air heated 10 to 20°F (6 to 11°C) above the ambient is used, but the use of heated air controlled with a humidistat to prevent overdrying is most common. The first layer may be about 7 ft (2 m) in depth, with successive layers of about 3 ft (1 m).

Batch-in-Bin. A storage bin adapted for drying may be used to dry several batches of grain during a harvest season, if the grain is placed in shallow depths so that higher airflow rates and temperatures can be used. The bin is emptied, usually by a system of augers, and the cycle is repeated. The drying capacity of the batch system is greater than other in-storage drying systems. Typical operating conditions are those where corn in 3 ft (1-m) depths is dried from an initial moisture content of 25% with 130°F (55°C) air at the rate of about 20 cfm/ft³ (330 L/s per m³). Considerable nonuniformity of moisture content may be present in the batch when drying is stopped; therefore, the grain should be well mixed as it is placed into storage. Grain that is too wet tends to equalize in moisture with grain that is too dry before spoilage occurs if it is mixed well.

The grain may be cooled in the dryer to ambient temperature before it is placed in storage. This is done by operating the fan without the heater for about an hour. Some additional drying occurs during the cooling process—particularly in the wetter portions of the batch.

Grain stirring devices are used with both full-bin systems and batch-in-bin drying systems. These devices typically consist of one or more open, 2-in. (50-mm) diameter, standard pitch augers suspended from the bin roof and side wall and extending to near the bin floor. The augers rotate and simultaneously travel horizontally. The device mixes the grain being dried to reduce moisture gradients and prevent overdrying the bottom. In addition, the grain is also loosened, allowing a higher airflow rate for a given fan. Stirring equipment does reduce bin capacity by about 10% and may cost as much as and do no more than a larger dryer fan. Futhermore, commercial stirring devices are available for round storage enclosures only. Increased grain breakage can result from improper use of stirring devices.

Recirculating/Continuous Flow Bin Dryer

This dryer incorporates a tapered sweep auger that removes grain as it dries from the bottom of the bin (Figure 11). This

dry grain is then redistributed on top of the bin or moved to a second bin for cooling. The sweep auger may be controlled by temperature or moisture sensors. When the desired condition is reached, the sensor starts the sweep auger, which removes a layer of grain. After a complete circuit of the bin, the sweep auger stops until the sensor again determines that another layer is dry. Some drying will take place in the cooling bin. Up to two points of moisture may be removed depending upon the management of the cooling bin.

DRYING SPECIFIC CROPS

SOYBEAN DRYING

Soybeans usually only need drying when inclement weather occurs during the harvest season. Mature soybeans left exposed to rain or damp weather develop a dark brown color and a mealy or chalky texture. Seed quality deteriorates rapidly. Oil from weather-damaged beans is more costly to refine and is often not of edible grade. Artificial drying of soybeans offers advantages in addition to preventing deterioration. It permits earlier

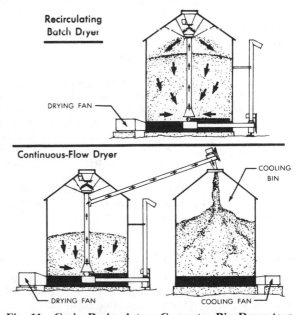

Fig. 11   Grain Recirculators Convert a Bin Dryer to a High-Speed Continuous Flow Dryer

harvest, which reduces chances of loss from bad weather. Early harvest also reduces both natural shatter loss and combine shatter loss. Soybeans harvested above 13.5% moisture exhibit considerably less damage.

Drying Soybeans for Commercial Use

Conventional drying equipment for corn can be used for soybeans, with some limitations on heat input. Soybeans can be dried at 130 to 140°F (54 to 60°C) for commercial use. Drying temperatures of 190°F (88°C) reduce oil yield. Excessive seed-coat cracking occurs if the relative humidity of the drying air is below 40%. Cracks from drying will cause many split beans in subsequent handling. Physically damaged beans can develop fungal growth and cause storage problems for processors, as well as a slight reduction in both oil yield and quality. Flow-retarding devices should be used, and beans should not be dropped more than 20 ft (6 m) onto concrete floors.

Drying Soybeans for Seed and Food

The relative humidity of drying air should be kept above 40%, regardless of the amount of heat used. Maximum drying temperatures to avoid germination loss is 110°F (43°C). Natural air drying at a flow rate of 1.6 cfm/ft³ [26.7 L/(s·m³)] is adequate for drying seed with starting moisture contents up to 16%.

Low temperature drying in bins is another method used in the midwest United States. Adding only a little heat to raise the ambient temperature up to 5°F (3°C) is a slow process, but it results in excellent quality and avoids overdrying. However, drying must be completed before spoilage occurs. At an airflow of 1.6 cfm/ft³ [26.7 L/(s·m³)], soybeans usually take about five days to dry from 16% down to 13%. At higher moisture contents, good results have been obtained using 3.2 cfm/ft³ [53.4 L/(s·m³)] with humidity control. Data on allowable drying time for soybeans are not available as they are for corn, as seen in Figure 2. In the absence of better information, the percentage moisture content values on the curves for corn may be reduced 2% for use with soybeans, but only as a guide to allowable drying time. Soybeans will probably not be dried from as high an initial moisture content as corn.

Soybean seed technologists suggest drying high-moisture soybeans in a bin with air controlled by heat to maintain the relative humidity at 40% or higher. Airflow rates of 8.0 cfm/ft³ [133 L/(s·m³)] are recommended, with the depth of beans not to exceed 4 ft (1.2 m).

HAY DRYING

Hay normally contains 65 to 80% moisture at cutting. Field drying to 20% may result in a serious loss of leaves. In alfalfa hay, the leaves average about 50% of the crop by weight, but they contain 70% of the protein and 90% of the carotene. The quality of hay can be increased and the risk of loss from weather reduced if the hay is put under shelter when partially sun dried (35% moisture) and then artificially dried to a safe storage moisture content (about 20% moisture). With good drying weather, the hay can be dried sufficiently in one day and placed on the dryer, if the hay is conditioned with a crusher. Hay may be long, chopped, or baled for this operation; and either unheated or heated air can be used.

In-Storage Drying

Unheated air is normally used for in-storage or mow drying. The hay is dried in the field to 30 to 40% moisture before being placed on the dryer. The fan should be capable of delivering 0.25 cfm/lb [260 L/(s·Mg)] of hay against a static pressures of 1 to 2 in. of water (250 to 500 Pa).

Slotted floors, with at least 50% of the area open, are generally used for drying baled hay. For long or chopped hay, the center duct system is the most popular for mows less than 36-ft (11-m) wide. If the mow is wider than 28 ft (8.5 m), a slotted floor equal to one-half the width in excess of 28 ft (8.5 m) should be placed on each side of the duct as in Figure 12. If the width is greater than 36 ft (11 m), the mow should be divided crosswise into units of 28 ft (8.5 m) or less. These should then be treated as individual dryers. If storage depth exceeds about 13 ft (4 m), either vertical flues or additional levels of ducts may be used. If tiered ducts are used, a vertical air chamber, about 75% of the probable hay depth, should be used. The supply ducts then are connected at the 7 to 10 ft (2 to 3 m) vertical intervals as the mow is filled. With either of these methods, total hay depths up to 30 ft (9 m) can be dried, considering the total depth of wet hay to be dried and that dried in previous loadings. The duct size should be such that the air velocity is less than 1000 fpm (5 m/s). The maximum depth of wet hay, which should be placed on a hay drying system at any time, depends on moisture content, weather conditions, the hay's physical form, and airflow rate. The maximum safe depths are about 16 ft (5 m) for long hay, 13 ft (4 m) for chopped hay, and seven bales deep for baled hay. Baled hay should have a density of about 8 lb/ft³ (128 kg/m³).

For mow drying, the fan should run continuously during the first few days. Afterwards, it should be operated only during good drying weather. During prolonged wet periods, the fan should be operated only often enough to keep the hay cool.

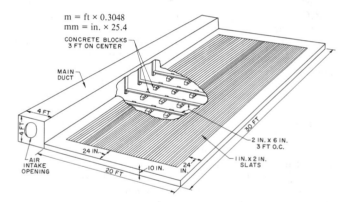

Fig. 12   Central Duct Hay-Drying System with a Lateral Slotted Floor for Wide Mows

Batch Wagon Drying

A heated air batch drier should be used when a total of 100 tons (90 Mg) or more of hay is to be dried per season. Batch drying can be done on a slotted floor platform; however, because this method has high labor requirements, wagon dryers are more commonly used. With the wagon dryer system, the hay is baled at about 45% moisture content to a density of about 11 lb/ft³ (176 kg/m³). The hay is then stacked onto a wagon with tight, high sides and either slotted or expanded metal floors. Drying is most efficiently accomplished by forcing the heated air (up to 158°F or 70°C) down a canvas duct of a plenum chamber secured to the top of the wagon. After four or five hours of drying, the exhaust air is no longer saturated with moisture, and about 75% of it may be recirculated or passed through a second wagon of wet hay for greater drying efficiency.

With this method, the amount of hay harvested each day is limited by the capacity of the drying wagons. Since it is a 24-h process, the hay cut one day is stored the following day; only enough hay should be harvested each day to load the drying wagons.

The airflow rate is normally much higher with this method than when unheated air is used. About 40 cfm per ft^2 of wagon floor space [200 L/(s·m^2)] is required. As with mow drying, the duct size should be such that the air velocity is less than 1000 fpm (5 m/s).

COTTON DRYING

Producers normally allow cotton to dry naturally in the field to a level of 12% or less before harvest. Cotton harvested under these conditions can be stored in trailers, baskets, or compacted stacks for extended periods with little loss in fiber or seed quality. Thus, cotton is not normally aerated or artificially dried prior to ginning. Cotton harvested during inclement weather, or stored cotton exposed to rain or snow, must be dried at the cotton gin within a few days to prevent self-heating and deterioration of the fiber and seed.

Even though cotton may be safely stored at moisture contents as high as 12%, moisture levels near the upper limit are too high for efficient ginning and for obtaining optimum fiber grade. Consequently, cotton gins have equipment to dry cotton to a fiber moisture content within the 6.5 to 8% range for proper cleaning and efficient fiber seed separation. Cotton should not be gin dried, however, when the moisture content is below this level. Instead, moisture should be added before cotton reaches the fiber seed separation process to improve the ginning quality of the cotton.

Although several types of dryers are commercially available, the tower dryer is the one most commonly used at cotton gins. This device operates on a parallel flow principle where 14 to 24 cfm of drying air per lb of cotton [15 to 25 L/(s·kg)]) also serves as the conveying medium. Cotton impacts upon the dryer walls as it moves through the dryer's serpentine passages. This action agitates the cotton for improved drying and lengthens the exposure time. The drying time depends on many variables, but total exposure seldom exceeds 12 seconds. For extremely wet cotton, two stages of drying are necessary for adequate moisture control.

Wide variations in initial moisture content dictate different amounts of drying for each load of cotton. Rapid changes in drying requirements are accomplished by automatically controlling drying air temperature in response to moisture measurements taken before or after drying. These control systems prevent serious overdrying problems and reduce energy requirements. For safety and to preserve fiber quality, drying air temperature should not exceed 175°F (79°C) in any portion of the drying system.

The germination of cottonseed is unimpaired by drying, if the internal cottonseed temperature does not exceed 140°F (60°C). This temperature is not exceeded in a tower dryer; however, the moisture content of the seed after drying may be above the 12% level recommended for safe long-term storage. Wet cottonseed is normally stored processed immediately at a cottonseed oil mill. Cottonseed under 12% moisture is frequently stored for several months prior to milling, or prior to delinting and treatment at a planting seed processing plant. Aeration for cooling deep beds of stored cottonseed effectively maintains viability and prevents an increase in free fatty acid content. For aeration, ambient air is normally drawn downward through the bed at a minimum rate of 0.025 cfm per ft^3 of oil mill seed [0.4 L/(s·m^3)] and 0.125 cfm/ft^3 [2.1 L/(s·m^3)] of planting seed.

PEANUT DRYING

Peanuts normally have a moisture content of about 50% at the time of digging. Allowing the peanuts to dry on the vines in the wind row for a few days removes much of this water. However, peanuts normally contain 20 to 30% moisture when removed from the vines, and some artificial drying is necessary.

Drying should begin within 6 hours after harvesting to keep the peanuts from self-heating. Both the maximum temperature and the rate of drying must be carefully controlled to maintain quality.

High temperatures result in off flavor or bitterness. Drying too rapidly without high temperatures results in blandness or nuts that do not develop flavor on roasting. High temperatures, rapid drying, or excessive drying will also cause the skin to slip easily and the kernels to become brittle. These conditions result in high damage rates in the shelling operation, but they can be avoided if the moisture removal rate does not exceed 0.5% per hour. Because of these limitations, continuous flow drying is not usually recommended for peanuts.

Peanuts can be dried in bulk bins using unheated air or air with supplemental heat. During poor drying conditions, unheated air may cause spoilage, so supplemental heat is preferred. Air should be heated no more than 13 to 14°F (7 to 8°C) with a maximum temperature of 95°F (35°C). An airflow rate of 10 to 25 cfm/ft^3 of peanuts [50 to 130 L/(s·m^3)] should be used, depending on the initial moisture content.

The most common method of drying peanuts is bulk wagon drying. Peanuts are dried in depths of 5 to 6 ft (1.5 to 1.8 m), using air flow rates of 10 to 15 cfm/ft^3 of peanuts [50 to 75 L/(s·m^3)] and air heated 11 to 14°F (6 to 8°C) above ambient. This method retains quality and usually dries the peanuts in three to four days. Wagon drying reduces handling labor but may require additional investment in equipment.

RICE DRYING

Of all grains, rice is probably the most difficult to process without quality loss. Rice containing more than 13.5% moisture cannot be safely stored for long periods, yet the recommended harvest moisture content for best milling and germination ranges from 20 to 26%. When harvested at this moisture content, drying must be started promptly to prevent the rice from souring. Heated air is normally used in continuous flow dryers where large volumes of air are forced through 4 to 10 in. (100 to 250 mm) layers of rice. Temperatures as high as 130°F (55°C) may be used, if the temperature drop across the rice does not exceed 20 to 30°F (11 to 17°C), the moisture reduction does not exceed two percentage points in a 0.5 hour exposure, and the rice temperature does not exceed 100°F (38°C). Following drying, the rice should be aerated to ambient temperature before the next drying exposure. Aeration during the tempering period following each pass through the dryer removes additional moisture from rice and eliminates one to two dryer passes that would be needed if the rice were tempered without cooling. It is estimated that full use of aeration following dryer passes could increase maximum daily drying capacity by about 14%.

Unheated air or air with a small amount of added heat (13°F or 7°C above ambient, but not exceeding 95°F or 35°C) should be used for deep-bed drying of rice. Too much heat will overdry the bottom, resulting in checking and reduced milling qualities, and possible spoilage in the top. Because unheated air drying requires less investment and attention than supplemental heat drying, it is preferred when conditions permit. In the more humid rice-growing areas, supplemental heat is desirable to ensure that the rice can be dried. The time required for drying will vary with weather conditions, moisture content, and airflow rate. The recommended airflow rate is 0.2 to 2.4 cfm/ft^3 [1 to 12 L/(s·m^3)] in California. Because of less favorable drying conditions in Arkansas, Louisiana, and Texas, greater airflow rates are recommended: e.g., a minimum of 2.0 cfm/ft^3 [10 L/(s·m^3)] is recommended in Texas. Whether unheated air or supplemental heat is used, the fan should be turned on as soon as rice covers the air distribution system uniformly. Then it should run continuously until the moisture content in the top foot (300 mm) of rice is reduced to about 15%. When the moisture content has been reduced to this level, the supplemental heat should be turned off. Then the rice can be dried to a safe storage level by operating the fan only when the relative humidity is below 75%.

STORAGE PROBLEMS AND PRACTICES

MOISTURE MIGRATION

Redistribution of moisture generally occurs in stored grain, causing localized spoilage, even though the grain was stored at a safe moisture level. Caused by temperature variations within the grain mass, one of the most common situations is that shown in Figure 13. Grain placed in storage in the fall at relatively high temperatures cools nonuniformly by conduction from the outer surfaces of the storage bin as winter approaches. Thus, the grain near the outside walls and top surface may be at temperatures of about 9°F (5°C), while the grain nearer the center is still at the same temperature it was at harvest, typically 77°F (25°C). The temperature differentials induce air convection currents that flow downward along the outside boundaries of the porous grain mass and upward through the center. When the cool air from the outer regions contacts the warm grain in the interior, the air is heated and its relative humidity is lowered. This increases the capacity of the air to absorb moisture from the grain as it moves up. Then, when the warm, humid air reaches the cool grain near the top the storage, it again cools and transfers vapor to the grain. Under extreme conditions, water will condense on the grain. The concentration of moisture near the center of the grain surface results in significant spoilage if moisture migration is uncontrolled. During spring and summer, the temperature gradients are reversed. Daily variations in temperature do not cause significant moisture migration. Aside from seasonal temperature variations, the size of the grain mass is the most important factor in moisture migration. Storages containing less than 1200 ft³ (35 m³) do not experience as much trouble with moisture migration. The problem becomes critical in large storages and is aggravated by incomplete cooling of artificially dried grain. Artificially dried grain should be cooled to ambient temperature when dried.

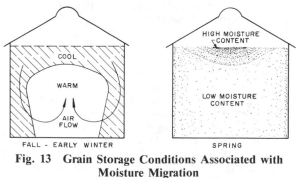

Fig. 13 Grain Storage Conditions Associated with Moisture Migration

GRAIN AERATION

Aeration by mechanically circulating ambient air through the grain mass is the best way to control moisture migration through it. Aeration systems are also used to cool grain after harvest, particularly in the warmer climates where grain may be placed in storage at temperatures approaching 95 to 104°F (35 to 40°C). After harvest heat is removed, aeration may be continued in cooler weather to bring the grain to a more desirable storage temperature of 32 to 50°F (0 to 10°C).

Aeration systems are not a means of drying because airflow rates are too low. However, in areas where the climate is favorable, carefully controlled aeration may be used to remove small amounts of moisture.

Commercial storages may have pockets of higher moisture grain because of delivery of batches of higher moisture wheat harvested, for example, after a rain shower or early in the morning. Aeration can control grain damage from heating in those higher moisture pockets.

Aeration Systems Designs

Aeration systems generally include fans capable of delivering the required amount of air at the required static pressure, suitable ducts to distribute the air into the grain, and controls to regulate the operation of the fan.

The airflow rate determines how many hours are required to cool the crop (Table 6). Most aeration systems are designed with airflow rates between 0.05 and 0.2 cfm/bu [0.7 to 2.7 L/(s·m³].

Air is usually drawn down through the grain (particularly in cool areas) to prevent possible condensation of moisture in the exhaust air at either the cool grain surface or underneath the roof of the storage. In warmer areas, upward airflow may avoid preheating the cooler air as it passes under the roof in a downdraft system. Upward airflow results in more uniform air distribution than downdraft systems in large flat storages with long ducts.

During aeration, a warming or cooling front moves through the crop (Figure 14). It is important to run the fan long enough to move the front completely through the crop.

In tall tower storages, airflow rates should be limited or excessive power will be required because of the long flow path through the grain. Crossflow aeration reduces the length of flow path, resulting in reduced system static pressure for a given aeration rate (Figure 15). Crossflow systems, however, are less easily adapted to aeration of partially filled bins than upflow or downflow systems, and installation costs are likely to be higher.

Static pressure can be determined for an aeration system, using the airflow data in Figure 5 on Page 10.4 of the 1985 FUNDAMENTALS Volume. All common types of fans are used in aeration systems. Attention should be given to noise levels with fans that will be operated near residential areas or where people work for extended periods.

The supply ducts connecting the fan to the distribution ducts in the grain should be designed and constructed according to the standards of good practice for any air-moving application. A maximum air velocity of 2500 fpm (13 m/s) may be used, but 1600 to 2000 fpm (8 to 10 m/s) is preferred. In large systems, one large fan may be attached to a manifold duct that leads to several distribution ducts in one or more storages, or smaller individual fans may serve individual distribution ducts. Where a manifold is used, valves or dampers should be installed at each takeoff to allow adjustment or closure of airflow when part of the system is not needed.

Table 6 Air Flow Rates Corresponding To Approximate Grain Cooling Time

| Air flow rate, | | Cooling |
cfm/Bu	L/s·m³	Time, h
0.05	0.7	240
0.1	1.3	120
0.2	2.7	60
0.3	4.0	40
0.4	5.4	30
0.5	6.7	24
0.6	8.0	20
0.8	10.7	15
1.0	13.4	12

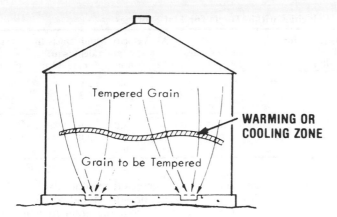

Negative pressure—cooling or warming zone
moves down through the grain.

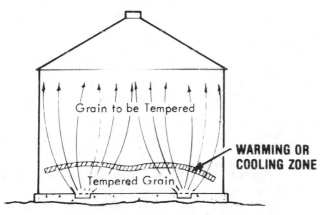

Fig. 14   Aerating to Change Grain Temperature

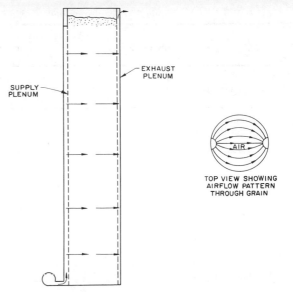

**Fig. 15   Crossflow Aeration System in a Deep Cylindrical
Bin**

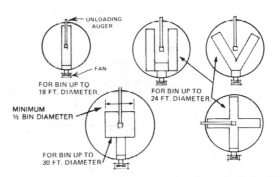

Fig. 16   Common Duct Patterns for Round Grain Bins

Distribution ducts are usually perforated sheet metal with a circular or inverted U-shaped cross section, although many functional arrangements are possible. The area of the perforations should be at least 10% of the total duct surface area. The holes should be uniformly spaced and small enough to prevent the passage of the grain into the duct. For example, 0.1-in. (2.5-mm) holes or 0.08-in.-wide (2-mm) slots will not pass wheat.

Since most problems develop in the center of the storage, and the crop will cool naturally near the wall, the aeration system must provide good airflow in the center. If ducts placed directly on the floor are to be held in place by the crop, the crop flow should be directly on top of the ducts to prevent movement and damage to them. Flush floor systems work well in storages with sweep augers and unloading equipment. Ducts should be easily removable for cleaning. Duct spacing should not exceed the depth of the crop and the distance between the duct and storage structure wall should not exceed one-half the depth of the crop for bins and flat storages. Figure 16 shows common duct patterns for round bins. Figure 17 shows duct spacing for flat storages.

In designing the distribution duct system for any type of storage, the following should be considered: (1) the cross sectional area and length of the duct, which influences the air velocity within the duct and the uniformity of air distribution; (2) the duct surface area, which affects the static pressure losses in the grain surrounding the duct; and (3) the distance between ducts, which influences the uniformity of airflow.

For upright storages where the distribution ducts are relatively short, distribution duct velocities up to 2000 fpm (10 m/s) are permissible. Maximum recommended air velocities in ducts for flat storages are shown in Table 7.

The duct surface area that is perforated or otherwise open for air distribution must be great enough that the air velocity through the grain surrounding the duct is not high enough to cause excessive pressure loss. When a semicircular perforated duct is used, the entire surface area is effective, while only 80% of the area of a circular duct resting on the floor is effective. For upright storages, the air velocity through the grain near the duct (duct face velocity) should be limited to 30 fpm (0.15 m/s) or less; in flat storages to 20 fpm (0.10 m/s) or less.

Duct strength and anchoring are an important concern. Distribution ducts buried in the grain must be strong enough to withstand the pressure of the grain over them. In tall upright storages, the static grain pressures may reach 10 psi (70 kPa). When ducts are located in the path of grain flow, as in a hopper, they may be subjected to many times this pressure during grain unloading.

Operating Aeration Systems

The operation of aeration systems depends largely on the objectives to be attained and the locality. In general, cooling should be carried out at any time the outdoor air temperature is 10°F (6°C) cooler than the grain. Stored grain should not be aerated when the air humidity is much above the equilibrium humidity of the grain because moisture will be added to it. Running the fan just long enough to cool the crop will limit the amount of grain rewetted. The fan should be operated long enough to cool the crop completely, but it should then be shut off.

Table 7   Recommended Maximum Air Velocities within Ducts for Flat Storages

Grain	Airflow rate, cfm/bu	Air Velocity within Ducts (fpm) for grain depths of:					Airflow rate, L/s per m³	Air Velocity within Ducts (m/s) for grain depths of:				
		10 ft	20 ft	30 ft	40 ft	50 ft		3 m	6 m	9 m	12 m	15 m
Corn, Soybeans, and	0.05	—	750	1000	1250	1250	0.67	—	3.8	5.0	6.3	6.3
Other Large Grains	0.1	750	1000	1250	1500	1750	1.34	3.8	5.0	6.3	7.6	8.8
	0.2	1000	1250	—	—	—	2.68	5.0	6.3	—	—	—
Wheat, Grain Sorghum,	0.05	—	1000	1500	1750	2000	0.67	—	5.0	7.6	8.8	10.0
and Other Small Grains	0.1	750	1500	2000	—	—	1.34	3.8	7.6	10.0	—	—
	0.2	1000	2000	—	—	—	2.68	5.0	10.0	—	—	—

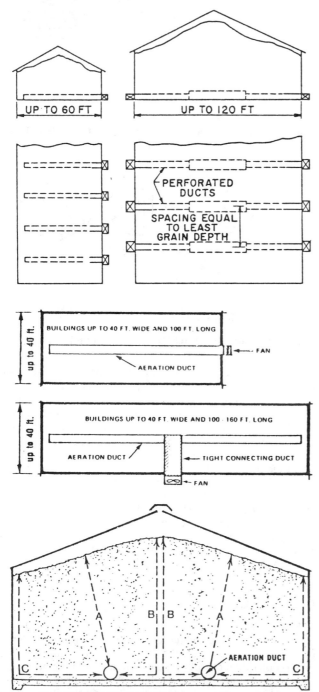

(A) IS THE SHORTEST AIR PATH.
(B) AND (C) ARE LONGER AIR PATHS THAN (A).
(B) OR (C) SHOULD BE NO LONGER THAN 1½ TIMES (A).

Fig. 17   Duct Arrangements for Large Flat Storages

Crops at harvest often are at temperatures conducive to mold growth and insect activity. Aeration fans should be started as soon as the storage is filled to cool the grain to ambient temperature. Aeration to prevent moisture migration by equalizing grain temperatures should be started at any time the air temperature is 10 to 15°F (6 to 8°C) below the highest grain temperature. It is usually continued as weather permits until the grain is uniformly cooled to within 20°F (11°C) of the average temperature of the coldest month.

Grain temperatures of about 32 to 50°F (0 to 10°C) are considered desirable. Lower temperatures may cause condensation of moisture on the grain if it is moved during warm weather or during rewarming of the grain. In the northern corn belt, aeration may be resumed in the spring months to equalize and raise the grain temperatures to within 18°F (10°C) of the average summer air temperature. This reduces risks of localized heating from moisture migration. Grain should be kept below 60°F (15°C) to limit insect activity and mold growth.

In storages where the fans are usually operated daily in the fall and winter months, automatic controls work well when the air is not too warm or humid. One thermostat usually prevents fan operation when the air temperature is too high and another prevents operation when the air is too cold. A humidistat allows operation when the air is not too humid. Fan controllers that determine the equilibrium moisture content of the crop based on existing air conditions and regulate the fan based on entered information are available.

SEED STORAGE

Seed must be stored in a cool, dry environment to maintain viability. Most seed storages have refrigeration equipment to maintain a storage environment of 45 to 55°F (7 to 12°C). Seed conditions for storage must be achieved before mold and insect damage can occur. Desired conditions can be met in 220 hours at an airflow rate of 0.04 cfm/ft³ [0.7 L/(s·m³)] and 140 h at 0.08 cfm/ft³ [1.3 L/(s·m³)].

REFERENCES

ASAE. 1986a. Density, Specific Gravity, And Weight-Moisture Relationships of Grain for Storage. ASAE D241.2. American Society of Agricultural Engineers. St. Joseph, MI.

ASAE. 1986b. Moisture Relationships of Grain. ASAE D245.4. American Society of Agricultural Engineers. St. Joseph, MI.

ASAE. 1986c. Resistance of Airflow Through Grains, Seeds, and Perforated Metal Sheets. ASAE D272.1. American Society of Agricultural Engineers. St. Joseph, MI.

Brooker, D.B.; Bakker-Arkema, F.; and Hall, C.A. 1974. *Drying Cereal Grains.* AVI Publishing, Westport, CT 06880.

Foster, G.H. 1982. *Storage of Cereal Grains and Their Products*, 3rd ed. American Association of Cereal Chemists, St. Paul, MN.

Hall, C.A. 1980. *Drying and Storage of Agricultural Crops.* AVI Publishing, Westport, CT 06880.

Henderson, S.M.; and Perry, R.L. *Agricultural Process Engineering.* AVI Publishing, Westport, CT 06880.

CHAPTER 39

AIR CONDITIONING OF WOOD AND PAPER PRODUCTS FACILITIES

THIS chapter covers some of the standard requirements for facilities involved in the manufacture of finished wood products, including pulp and paper manufacture.

GENERAL WOOD PRODUCT OPERATIONS

If the finished lumber product is to be used in a heated building, the stock storage areas should be heated 10 to 20°F (6 to 11°C) above ambient. This provides sufficient protection for furniture stock, interior trim, cabinet material, and stock for the manufacture of such items as ax handles and glue-laminated beams. Air should be circulated within the storage areas. Lumber kiln-dried to a moisture content of 12% or less can be controlled within a given moisture content range through storage in a heated shed. The moisture content can be regulated either manually or automatically by altering the dry-bulb temperature (Figure 1).

The preparation of this chapter is assigned to TC 9.2, Industrial Air Conditioning.

Some special materials require close control of moisture content. Musical instrument stock must be dried to a given moisture level and maintained there because the moisture content of the wood affects the harmonics of most stringed wooden instruments. This degree of control requires an air-conditioning system with reheat and a heating system with humidification.

Process Area Air Conditioning

Temperature and humidity requirements within wood product process areas vary according to product, manufacturer, and governing code. Here, only important design items are mentioned. For example, in match manufacturing, close temperature and humidity controls are required to dry or cure the match heat after dipping—primarily to avoid being close to the ignition point. Any process involving applicaion of flammable substances should follow the ventilation recommendations of the NFPA,

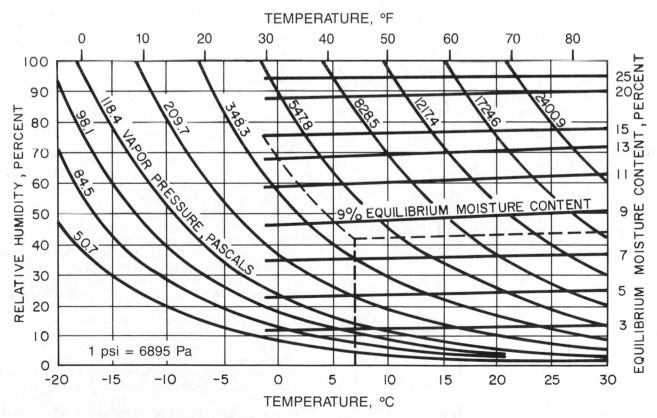

Fig. 1   Relationship between Temperature, Relative Humidity, and Vapor Pressure of Air and the Equilibrium Moisture Content of Wood

the National Fire Code, and the U.S. Occupational Safety and Health Act.

Finished Product Storage

Finished lumber products manufactured from pre-dried stock (moisture content of 10% or less) regain moisture if exposed to high relative humidities for an extended period. All storage areas housing finished products, including furniture and musical instruments, should be conditioned, as close as is practical, to the environment in which the item is to be used.

The designer should be familiar with the client's entire operation. The designer should also remain aware of the potential problem of moisture regain.

PULP AND PAPER OPERATIONS

The paper-making process consists of two basic steps: (1) wood is reduced to pulp, a water mass of wood fibers, and (2) the pulp is converted to paper. Wood may be reduced to pulp either by grinding (as in the groundwood-type pulp mill) or by chemical action.

Many different types of paper may be produced from the prepared pulp, ranging from the finest glossy finish to newsprint to bleached pulp board. For example, to make newsprint, a mixture of the two pulps is fed into the paper machine. To make kraft paper (grocery bags, corrugated containers, etc.), however, only unbleached chemical pulp is used. Disposable diaper material and photographic film and paper require bleached chemical pulp with very low moisture content.

Paper Machine Area

In the papermaking process, extensive air systems are required to support and enhance the process and provide reasonable comfort for machine personnel. Radiant heat from steam and hot water sources and mechanical energy dissipated as heat can result in summer temperature in the machine room ranging as high as 104 to 120°F (40 to 49°C). In addition, high paper machine operating speeds from 2000 to 4500 ft/min (600 to 1200 m/min) and stock temperatures in the range of 122°F (50°C) produce warm vapor in the machine room. A designed ventilation system prevents condensation and maintains a safe, efficient environment for personnel.

Outside air make-up units absorb and remove water vapor released from the paper as it is dried (Figures 2 and 3). The make-up air is distributed to the working areas above and below the operating floor. Part of the air delivered to the basement will

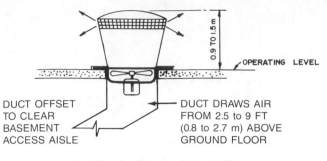

Fig. 3   Personnel Cooler

migrate to the operating floor through hatches and stairwells. Motor cooling systems should distribute cooler basement air to the paper machine DC drive motors. The intake to the personnel coolers should be taken in the basement below the warm stratified air that accumulates under the operating floor. A basement exhaust system for the wet end of the process should vent this stratum during the warmer months.

The most severe ventilation demand occurs in the area between the wet-end forming section and water removal press section and the machine dryer section. When the pulp fiber is introduced to the forming section, more than 99% water is deposited on a traveling screen. Water is removed sequentially by gravity, rolls, foils, vacuum boxes, and mechanically by three or more press roll nips. Evaporation of moisture at elevated temperatures and mechanical generation of vapor from turning rolls and cleaning showers create a very humid atmosphere at the wet end. Baffles and custom-designed exhaust systems in the forming section help control the vapor. A drive side exhaust system in the wet end area keeps heat from the DC drive motor vent air and vapor generated in the wet end to a minimum. To prevent condensation or accumulated fiber from falling on the traveling web, a false ceiling with duct connections to roof exhausters removes humid air, which has not been captured at a lower elevation. The wet-end area usually has a heated inside air circulation system that scrubs the underside of the roof to prevent condensation in cold weather. Additional roof exhaust may also remove accumulated heat from the dryer section and the dry-end area during warmer periods. Roof exhaust should be dominant in the wet end of the machine room.

In the dryer section of a paper machine, steam-heated rotating drums dry the paper web traveling in a serpentine path in contact with the dryer surface. Exhaust hoods control the heat from the dryers and the moisture evaporated from the paper web. Most modern machines have enclosed hoods, which reduce the mass flow of air required to less than 50% of an open hood exhaust. Temperatures inside an enclosed hood will range from 130 to 140°F (54 to 60°C) at the operating floor level to 180 to 200°F (82 to 93°C) in the hood exhaust plenum.

Pocket ventilation air and hood supply air are drawn from the upper level of the machine room, where possible, to benefit from the preheating of the make-up air from process heat as it rises. The basement of the dryer section is also enclosed to control infiltration of machine room air to the enclosed hood. The hood supply and pocket ventilation air typically operates at 200°F (93°C), while some systems run at temperatures as high as 250°F (121°C). Enclosed hood exhaust is typically in the range of 300 cfm per ton [(0.16 L/(s·kg)] of machine capacity. The pocket ventilation and hood supply is designed for 75 to 80% of the exhaust, with the balance infiltrated from the basement and machine room.

Heat recovery potential from the hood exhaust air should be evaluated. Most of the energy in the steam supplied to the paper dryers is converted to latent heat in the hood exhaust as water

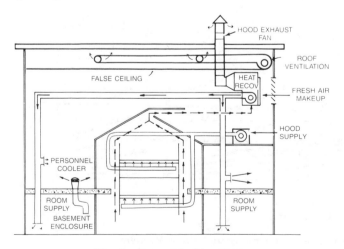

Fig. 2   Paper Machine Area

is evaporated from the paper web. Air-to-air heat exchangers are used where the air supply is located close to the exhaust. Air-to-liquid heat exchangers that recirculate water-glycol to heat remote make-up air units may also be used. Air-to-liquid systems provide more latent heat recovery, resulting in 3 to 4 times more total heat recovery than air-to-air units. Some machines use heat recovered from the exhaust air to heat process water. Ventilation rates in paper machine buildings range from 6 to 15 air changes per hour in northern mills to 18 to 30 in southern mills. Some plants use computer control of air systems that account for variable production rates and changes in the outside air temperature to optimize the operation of the total system and conserve energy.

Finishing Area

To produce a precisely cut paper that will stabilize at a desirable equilibrium moisture content, the finishing areas require temperature and humidity controls. Further converting operations of printing and die-cutting of the paper require optimum sheet moistures for efficient processing. Finishing room conditions will range from 70 to 75 °F (21 to 24 °C) db and from 40 to 45% rh. The system should maintain the selected conditions within reasonably close limits. Without precise environmental control, the paper equilibrium moisture content will vary, influencing dimensional stability, tendency to curl, and further processing.

CONTROL AND MOTOR CONTROL CENTER ROOMS

In most pulp and paper applications, process control, motor control, and switchgear rooms are located in separate rooms isolated from the process environment. Air conditioning removes the heat generated by equipment, lights, etc., and reduces the air-cleaning requirements. If the control room includes a computer, a computer terminal, or data processing equipment, see Chapter 33, "Data Processing System Areas," and its references. Ceiling grilles or diffusers should be located above access aisles to avoid the risk of condensation on control consoles or electrical equipment on start-up and on recovery after an air-conditioning shutdown. Electrical rooms are usually maintained in the range of 75 to 80 °F (24° to 27 °C), with control rooms at 73 °F (23 °C). Humidities are maintained in the 45 to 55% rh range in process control rooms and are not normally controlled in electrical equipment rooms.

Today, more electronic equipment is used in electrical control rooms for both distributed control and for control rooms with centralized computer process control. This equipment is susceptible to corrosion. The typical pulp and paper mill environment contains both particulate and vapor phase contaminants with sulfur- and chloride-based compounds. Carefully designed multi-stage particulate and adsorbent filter systems with treated activated charcoal and potassium permanganate impregnated alumina sections for vapor phase contaminants and fiberglas and cloth media for particulate should be used to protect the equipment. A minimum amount of outside air should be used. Air conditioning and filtration of the outside air and a portion of the recirculated air will control the problem if filters are carefully maintained.

Switchgear and motor control centers are not as heat sensitive as control rooms, but the moisture-laden air carries chemical residue onto the contact surfaces. Arcing and general deterioration usually result. In general, a minimum of outside air is used, and air conditioning is provided to protect these areas.

Paper Test Laboratories

Design conditions within paper mill laboratories are critical and must be followed rigidly. The most recognized standard for testing environments for paper and paper products, including paperboard, fiberboard, and containers made from them, is TAPPI T402 (published by *Technical Association of Pulp and Paper Industry*). Other standards include ASTM E171, *Standard Atmospheres for Conditioning and Testing Materials,* and ISO/TC 125 on *Enclosures and Conditions for Testing*. However, only the TAPPI T402 standard is discussed in this chapter.

Standard pulp and paper testing laboratories have three environments: a preconditioning atmosphere, a conditioning atmosphere, and a testing atmosphere. A sample tests differently physically if it is brought to a testing humidity from a high humidity than if it were brought to the same conditions from a lower humidity. Preconditioning at lower relative humidity tends to eliminate hysteresis. For a preconditioning atmosphere, TAPPI T402 recommends 10 to 35% rh and 72 to 104 °F (22 to 40 °C) db. This is usually accomplished in a controlled, conditioned cabinet.

Conditioning and testing atmospheres carry the same TAPPI T402 standard of 50 ± 2.0% rh and 73 ± 2 °F (23 ± 1 °C) db. The designer should realize, however, that a change of 2 °F (1 °C db) at 73 °F (23 °C) makes the relative humidity fluctuate as much as 3%. A dry-bulb temperature tolerance of ±1 °F (±0.5 °C) must be held to maintain a ± 2.0% rh. These low humidity variations suggest reheat or chemical driers of some type. Humidistatic and temperature instrumentation should be provided for the laboratories, as well as graphical wet- and dry-bulb recorders.

Miscellaneous Areas

The pulp digester area contains many items contributing to high heat release and possibly dusty conditions. With batch digester use, the chip feeders are a source of dust requiring hooded exhaust and makeup air. The wash and screen areas have many items with hood exhausts that require considerable makeup air. Good ventilation is required to control fumes and limit humidity. The lime kiln feed-end is a room with extremely large heat releases requiring high ventilation rates or air conditioning.

Recovery-boiler and bark-boiler buildings have conditions similar to many power plants, and the ventilation rates are similar. The control rooms are generally air conditioned. In making ground wood products, the grinding motor room contains many very large motors requiring ventilation. Grinding room ventilation is required to keep humidity low.

SYSTEM SELECTION

System and equipment selection for a pulp and paper project depends on variables unique to the particular application; *i.e.,* plant mediums available, plant layout, plant atmosphere, geographic location, and degree of control desired.

Chilled water systems are economical and practical for most pulp and paper operations, because they require both large cooling capacity and precision of control to maintain the temperature and humidity requirements of the laboratories and the finishing areas. In the bleach plant, the manufacture of chlorine dioxide is enhanced by the use of 45 °F (7 °C) or lower temperature water. This water is often supplied by the mill air-conditioning, chilled-water system. If clean plant or process water is available, water-cooled chillers, supplemented by water-cooled direct expansion package units for remote, small areas, are satisfactory. However, if plant water is not clean enough for this application, a separate cooling tower and condenser water system must be installed for the air-conditioning systems.

Most manufacturers prefer water-cooled over air-cooled systems because of gases and particulates present in most paper plant atmospheres. The most prevalent contaminants are chlorine gas, caustic soda, and sulfur compounds. With more efficient air-cleaning, the air quality in and about most mills is becoming adequate for properly placed air-cooled chillers or condensing units, which have well-analyzed and properly applied coil and housing coatings. Phosphor-free brazed coil joints are recommended in areas where sulfur compounds are present.

Heat is readily available from the processing operations and should be used whenever possible. Most plants have quality hot water and steam, which can be geared to unit heater, central station, or reheat use quite easily. Evaporative cooling should not be ignored. Newer plant air-conditioning methods, using energy conservation techniques such as temperature stratification, apply themselves well to this type of large structure. As in most industrial applications, absorption systems can be considered for pulp and paper plants, since they afford some degree of energy recovery from high temperature steam processes.

BIBLIOGRAPHY

American Conference of Industrial Hygienists. *Industrial Ventilation. Manual of Recommended Practice,* 14th ed.

Britt, K.W. 1970. *Handbook of Pulp and Paper Technology.* 2nd ed., Van Nostrand Reinhold.

Casey, J.T. 1960. *Pulp and Paper Chemistry and Chemical Technology.* Vol. 3, Interscience Publishers, Inc.

Houston Mill Guide. Southland Paper Company, Houston, TX.
Rasmussen, E.F. 1961. *Dry Kiln Operator's Manual.* Agriculture Handbook, No. 188, USDA.

Stephenson, J.N. 1950. *Preparation and Treatment of Wood Pulp.* Vol. 1, McGraw-Hill Publishing Co., New York, NY.

TAPPI. 1983. *Standard Conditioning and Testing Atmospheres for Paper, Board, Pulp Handsheets, and Related Products.* Test Method T402 OM-83. Technical Association of the Pulp and Paper Industry. Atlanta, GA.

CHAPTER 40

HEATING, VENTILATING, AND AIR CONDITIONING FOR NUCLEAR FACILITIES

THIS chapter describes heating, ventilating, and air-conditioning (HVAC) design for nuclear facilities beyond those normally required for commercial or industrial facilities. Nuclear facilities contain operations involving radioactive materials. They include nuclear power plants, fuel fabrication or processing plants, plutonium processing plants, radiochemical laboratories, and other facilities housing nuclear operations or materials.

The design of HVAC systems for nuclear facilities is subject to federal law, and Nuclear Regulatory Commission (NRC) and/or Department of Energy (DOE) regulations and guides, in addition to normal industrial standards. Sections of the Code of Federal Regulations (CFR), as listed in the references, contain federal statutes binding on the owners of the facilities for which a permit to operate is secured or in which radioactive materials are used or stored.

NUCLEAR DESIGN CRITERIA

HVAC requirements for nuclear facilities depend on the type of facility and the specific service required. The following two major factors need consideration:

1. Potential airborne radioactivity that could be encountered, either particulate or gaseous
2. Whether the HVAC system for the facility can be controlled effectively and portions shut down as applicable in case of any event, accident, or natural catastrophe

DESIGN BASIS

The design basis is especially important for nuclear facilities, such as power plants, where control is a major consideration. This means that active control of all the systems and their components during and after any event—accident or natural catastrophe—is required. Thus, two design bases are identified—normal or power design basis and safety design basis.

Normal or Power Design Basis

The normal design basis—called power design basis for nuclear power plants—covers the normal plant operation, including normal operations mode and normal shut-down mode. This design basis does not impose requirements on the various systems or components above and beyond those imposed by the standard normal criteria specified for Indoor Conditions.

Safety Design Basis

A safety design basis must be defined if the facility cannot readily be shut down and isolated to an inactive state anytime during and after an accident or natural catastrophic event. The safety design basis covers plant emergency operation. It establishes the special requirements imposed on the systems and the components by establishing a safe working environment and by ensuring that the public is protected from exposure to radioactivity.

Any system designated as "essential" or "safety related" is required to prevent an event or accident, or to mitigate the effect of an event, accident, or natural catastrophe that may cause the release of radioactivity to the surroundings or to the plant atmosphere where there are operating personnel. Such a system must be available at any time. It must function during and after a design basis accident (DBA) or appropriate simultaneous events, such as Safe Shutdown Earthquake (SSE), tornado, Loss of Cooling Accident (LOCA), and loss of offsite power. All non-safety-related equipment must prevent adverse effects on safety-related equipment. Therefore, the following additional requirements are imposed on any safety-related systems and components.

System Redundancy. Systems must be redundant, so the function can be performed, even if a component in one system fails, and such failure cannot cause a failure to the other subsystem. For additional redundancy requirements, i.e., for turbine-driven feedwater pumps in nuclear power plants, refer to the "Nuclear Power Plant" section.

Seismic Qualification. All safety-related components must be seismically qualified by testing or calculation to document that they can withstand and perform under the shock and vibration caused by a Safe Shutdown Earthquake—the largest earthquake postulated for the region where the plant is located. This qualification includes any amplification by the building structure. In addition, any component whose failure could jeopardize the essential function of a safety-related function must be seismically qualified to prevent such failure.

Environmental Qualification. Often components must be environmentally qualified; that is, the useful life of the component in the environment in which it is operating must be determined through a program of accelerated aging. The various factors of the environment must be considered, including temperature, humidity, pressure, and accumulated radioactivity.

Q-Class Equipment. All components of essential systems in power plants must be "Q-Class" equipment; that is, the manufacturer must comply with the requirements of a special Quality Assurance (QA) Program for inspection, documentation, and traceability of material. Refer to 10 CFR 50, Appendix B, for QA Program requirements.

Emergency Power. All essential systems must be powered by onsite engine generators and provided with chilled water or cooling water from essential or safety-related systems, if required.

This chapter was prepared by TC 9.2, Industrial Air Conditioning.

ZONING

Zones are basic for control of radioactive contamination in nuclear facilities. The zones are defined in ERDA 21-76 and in DOE 6430.1, Chapter XXI, as follows:

Zone I

Zone I includes the interior of a hot cell, glovebox, or other containment for handling highly radioactive material. Containment features must prevent the spread of radioactive material within and release from the building under both normal and upset conditions up to and including a design basis accident for the facility.

Complete isolation (physical separation) from neighboring facilities is necessary. High-efficiency particulate air (HEPA) filtration of the exhaust is required. Reentry of a Zone I area of a facility is forbidden either until the area is cleaned up to Zone II classification conditions, or with full-body protective clothing and respirators or full-face gas masks, as specified by health physicists.

Zone II

Zone II includes glovebox operation areas, hot-cell service and maintenance areas, and other building space where high levels of radiation are likely to be present at some time or where particularly hazardous operations are conducted in chemical fume hoods.

These areas require continued monitoring for airborne radioactive material. Restricted access areas are generally considered Zone II hazard classification.

Zone III

Zone III includes hot-cell operating areas, general chemical laboratories, maintenance, and other general working areas that are usually "cold" but subject to low levels of airborne radiation. Chemical fume hoods are required for operations that could produce radioactive material, or toxic or noxious material. Health/physics personnel must approve the use of chemical fume hoods for operations that produce radioactive material. Routine airborne radiation monitoring is required.

Air locks or personnel clothing-change facilities are required for entry to Zone II.

Zone IV

Zone IV includes office and "cold" shop areas. Radiation monitoring may be required at exit points.

Zone Pressure Control

Negative static pressure increases as zone classifications move from Zone IV to Zone I. These static pressure levels cause all air leakage to flow from lower to higher zones of potential classification. All zones are to be maintained at negative pressure with respect to the ambient atmospheric pressure.

The terms "recirculating" and "cascading" refer to the reuse of air in a particular zone or area. Room air recirculated from a space or zone can be returned to the primary air-handling unit for reconditioning and then returned to the same space (zone), on approval of health/physics personnel.

Air cascaded from a space or zone flows to a secondary air-handling unit in that zone for reconditioning and then returned to an area or zone of lower classification.

LABORATORIES

Laboratory containment equipment for nuclear processing facilities, consisting of gloveboxes, radiobenches, and hoods, are treated as Zone II or III, depending on the level of radioactivity anticipated for the area, and considering the materials to be handled.

Gloveboxes

Gloveboxes are windowed enclosures equipped with one or more flexible gloves for manual handling of material inside the enclosure from the outside. Gloveboxes permit the use of hands in the manipulation of hazardous materials through a membrane (the glove) while preventing the release of the material to the environment.

Since the glovebox is a Zone I area, the exhaust is HEPA-filtered locally before leaving the box and prior to entering the main exhaust duct. Detailed information is given in Chapter 7 of the ERDA 21-76 and in ERDA 76-21.

Radiobenches

Radiobenches have the same geometric shape as a glovebox; in lieu of the panel for the gloves, the glove area is open. Air velocity across this opening is the same as for laboratory hoods. The level of contamination handled in a radiobench is much lower than the level handled in a glovebox. Hence, the radiobench is not a Zone I area and, therefore, does not have its own HEPA filters.

Hoods

Laboratory hoods are similar to those used in non-nuclear laboratory applications. Air velocity across the hood opening should be evaluated based on plant requirements. For energy conservation, the hood-operating opening should be limited to 40% of the maximum sash opening for vertical sash hoods. Horizontal sash hoods are preferred.

WAREHOUSE AND STORAGE (Q-CLASS EQUIPMENT)

ANSI N45.2 specifies various levels of storage applicable for Q-Class equipment (see the "Design Criteria" section), depending on the type of equipment and the way it is packed for shipment and storage.

Level A is outdoor storage protected by tarpaulins.

Level B is indoor storage without heating or air conditioning.

Level C is indoor storage in air-conditioned space where the relative humidity also is controlled. Furthermore, records of the storage conditions must be maintained (from recording thermographs and humidigraphs).

OUTDOOR CONDITIONS

The FUNDAMENTALS Volume, National Weather Service, or site meteorology give information on outdoor conditions, temperature, humidity, solar load, altitude, and wind. DOE 6430.1 may also specify requirements.

Nuclear facilities generally consist of heavy structures with high thermal inertia. For solar loads, the time lag should be considered. In many cases, even 24-hour averages suffice. The 2-1/2% conditions normally are satisfactory for summer and the 97-1/2% conditions for winter. The 1% and the 99% conditions, for process facilities, may be necessary for essential or safety-related systems with very high flow rates and/or low thermal inertia in relation to the heat loads. This criteria applies to the Diesel Generator Building, where a complete air change occurs in less than a minute, or to the safety-related pump house for nuclear power plants.

INDOOR CONDITIONS

Indoor temperatures are dictated by occupancy, equipment requirements, and the activities of personnel. For safety-related systems, temperatures are dictated by the environmental qualification of the safety-related equipment located in the air-conditioned space and by ambient conditions during the various operating modes of the safety-related equipment.

Holding pools for irradiated fuel elements require cooling and special humidity control to prevent condensation on pipes in the facility.

Indoor Pressure

A specific pressure, in relation to the outside atmosphere or the adjacent areas, must be specified where control of the airflow pattern is required. For process facilities where zones are identified, the pressures are specified in the "Zoning" section.

In other facilities where zoning is different from that of processing facilities, and in cases where rooms are within the same zone but where potential airborne radioactivity must not spread, any airborne radioactivity must be controlled by the air flow.

Certain areas, such as the control room in a nuclear power plant, must be kept at positive pressure to prevent infiltration of untreated air that may contain poisonous or incapacitating gases, or airborne radioactivity.

The Fuel Building is kept under negative pressure in case a fuel-handling accident releases radioactive iodine to the atmosphere.

To control and contain potential airborne radioactivity within the same zone, air is never exhausted from hallways, corridors, or common areas—only supplied from them. All exhaust is taken from the various rooms so air flows away from the common areas and there is less risk of cross-contamination.

Airborne Radioactivity

The level of airborne radioactivity within the facility, and the amount released to the surroundings, is controlled to meet the requirements of 10 CFR 20, 10 CFR 50, and 10 CFR 100.

Tornado Protection

Tornado and tornado-generated missile protection is normally required to prevent the loss of containment. When a tornado passes over the facility, there will be a sharp drop in pressure at a fast rate. This transient pressure could cause a collapse of the ducts and filter housings if they were exposed to it, since the pressure in the structure would be equal to that of the environment prior to the reduction caused by the tornado. The protection normally consists of tornado dampers and missile barriers in all appropriate openings in the outside walls of the structure. Tornado dampers are heavy-duty low-leakage dampers designed for pressure differences in excess of 3 psi (20 kPa). They are normally Q-Class, environmentally and seismically qualified, and connected to emergency power.

GENERAL HVAC SYSTEM DESIGN CRITERIA

Specific Area Requirements

The following are general HVAC requirements for areas common to all nuclear facilities. Zones are defined in the "Nuclear Design Criteria" section.

Office Areas

These are Zone IV areas normal, commercial design practices usually apply, except that air pressure differences must be maintained between adjacent zones.

Change Rooms and Toilet Facilities

These areas are air conditioned for human comfort. The design must consider the various stages of undress of personnel. These areas can be classified as Zone IV or Zone III (regulated). Zone IV change rooms follow normal, commercial design practices.

In change areas treated as Zone III areas (see the "Nuclear Design Criteria" section), the exhaust may need to be monitored and HEPA-filtered, depending on the materials handled in the facility.

Mechanical and Electrical Equipment Rooms

Mechanical and electrical equipment rooms are only occasionally occupied by personnel, so temperature requirements are dictated by equipment. For non-safety-related equipment, the maximum temperature is dictated by the rating of the electrical equipment, normally 104°F (40°C), 122°F (50°C), or 140°F (60°C). For safety-related equipment, refer to the section on "Safety Design Basis," under "Nuclear Design Criteria."

Battery Rooms

Batteries normally perform best within the specified temperature range. Capacity will be reduced if the battery temperature falls below the specified minimum, and the useful life of the battery will be significantly reduced if the temperature exceeds the specified maximum. Ventilation is required to keep the hydrogen concentration below 2% by volume. Hydrogen generation is 0.016 ft^3/h (0.13 mL/s) per ampere per cell. In this case, the ampere is the floating charge, not the rated ampere/hour capacity. Performance and qualified useful life for safety-related batteries must be documented. For safety-related battery rooms, refer to the section on "Safety Design Basis."

Airlocks

An airlock is a vestibule with doors that interlock so that both doors cannot open simultaneously. Airlocks, in conjunction with the ventilation system, ensure that all air flow is in the direction of the most contaminated zone.

Alarm Stations

Both a Central Alarm Station and Secondary Alarm Station are required for physical security. The HVAC System for alarm stations should switch over to an isolated closed loop, recirculating system during security alerts or attacks to protect against incapacitation from poisonous gases or aerosols from the outside.

Control Room Habitability Zone

The Control Room habitability zone includes of the main control room and supporting area such as toilet, kitchen, and office facilities. It is from this area that personnel monitor and control the operation of the plant.

The Control Room HVAC System is a safety-related system that must fulfill the following requirements during all normal and postulated accident conditions to ensure that continuous occupancy can be maintained.

1. Maintain conditions confortable to personnel and ensure the continuous functioning of the control room equipment, including any computers installed in room.

2. Protect personnel from exposure to potential airborne radioactivity present in the outside atmosphere or surrounding plant areas.
3. Protect personnel from exposure to potential toxic chemicals that are postulated to be released from the site or surrounding areas.
4. Protect personnel from the effects of high-energy line breaks in the surrounding plant areas.
5. Protect personnel from combustion products that are postulated from fires on site.

To perform these functions, the control room habitability zone envelope is designed to low leakage requirements—typically one air change per hour or less. The low leakage requirements apply not only to the wall, ceiling, and floor structures, but also to any control room HVAC components located outside the inhabited zone that could be a pathway for contaminants. Airlocks should be placed at all access points to the control room habitability zone.

The control room HVAC System typically consists of redundant, recirculating-type air-conditioning systems composed of cooling coils, humidifiers, heating coils, and filtration to maintain the environmental conditions within the ASHRAE comfort zone for all normal accident conditions. During normal plant operating conditions, sufficient outdoor air is introduced to maintain the habitability zone at a slight positive pressure in relation to surrounding areas.

The outdoor air intakes to the control room HVAC System have appropriate monitoring devices to detect radiation, chlorine, toxic chemicals, or smoke that may be present. Upon detection of these contaminants, the control room HVAC System changes either automatically or manually to the control room isolation mode. Various designs for the control room isolation are used, depending on potential hazards present, leak tightness of the zone, and meteorological conditions. Typical designs isolate normal outdoor air sources with fast-closing, gas-tight isolation dampers. Filtration systems consisting of HEPA and charcoal filters then filter the outdoor air supply and/or recirculate and clean a portion of the control room air. Regulatory Guides 1.95 and 1.78, SRP 6.4 and SRP 9.4 give further information.

Technical Support Center (for Power Plants)

The Technical Support Center (TSC) is an outside facility located close to the control room and is used by plant management and technical support personnel to provide assistance to control room operators during accident conditions.

The TSC HVAC must maintain comfort conditions, as well as provide the same radiological habitability conditions as the control room under accident conditions. The system is generally designed to commercial HVAC standards. An outside air filtration system (HEPA-Charcoal-HEPA) pressurizes the facility with filtered outside air during emergency conditions. The TSC HVAC System does not have to be designed to safety-related standards. (Ref: NUREG-0696, "Functional Criteria for Emergency Response Facilities").

HEAT GAIN CALCULATIONS

The information needed for design of the HVAC systems is often limited at the start of calculations. First, the preliminary heat loads are to be calculated, and later verified or corrected. Design changes are likely because any changes that are made to systems or equipment anywhere in the facility or power plant are likely to have an impact on the HVAC System.

The design of a nuclear power plant generally takes many years, and the normal contingency is not adequate. Preliminary sizes of all major components, chillers, major air-handling units, and filtration trains should be designed with contingencies.

However, excess dehumidification due to oversized air-handling units must be considered.

The overall heat loads include the following:

Heat Transfer from the Outside. For most structures in a nuclear facility, whose thickness exceed 1 foot (300 mm) heat transfer should be based on infiltration and average outside conditions, since daily variations will be small on the inside of the walls.

Miscellaneous Heat Loads. The miscellaneous heat loads from equipment and hot surfaces, piping, lighting, personnel, and infiltration are treated as in conventional facilities.

Outside Air. Outside air, supplied through the air-handling equipment and infiltration must be considered, since a "once through" system is common as a means of controlling potential airborne radioactivity. If heat recovery is considered, the type of equipment selected must not cross-contaminate incoming air with outgoing air. Occasionally, the concern for control of airborne radioactivity is so dominant that the heat recovery may be waived.

Once the criteria is established and the preliminary heating and cooling loads are determined, the appropriate system can be selected. The same considerations for system selection apply for nuclear facilities as for industrial facilities in terms of ventilation—natural or forced heating and adiabatic cooling or refrigeration cooling—as long as the criteria for the individual facilities are met in terms of temperature, humidity, pressure, and control of airflow.

FILTRATION TRAINS

In nuclear generating stations, HVAC filter systems are generally provided to remove radioactive particulate and radioactive iodine gases. They filter all potentially contaminated exhaust prior to discharge to the environment or to protect personnel in plant areas such as the control room.

The filter train typically consists of the following components in series, as required: demister, heater, prefilter, and HEPA filter. Safety-related filtration systems must meet the requirements of Regulatory Guide 1.52. Non-safety-related filtration systems must meet the requirements of Regulatory Guide 1.140.

For nuclear processing facilities, Zone I areas are normally exhausted through multiple HEPA filters, a sand filter (see the following section on "Filters"), or a combination of both, while Zones II and III areas are exhausted through HEPA filters. However, the number of stages may be different, depending on specific conditions. Nuclear power plants and reactor facilities normally are exhausted through a combination of prefilters, HEPA filters, and charcoal filters. Prefilters extend the life of the HEPA filters. Filtration trains may be used on a recirculation basis where they frequently are called "kidney filters."

In the design of the filtration train, special attention must be paid to instrumentation required to evaluate system performance and to periodic filter testing that must be performed. Refer to Regulatory Guides 1.51 and 1.140, SRP 6.5.1., and ANSI N-510.

An example of this application is in the essential air-conditioning system for a control room environment. The filter system must keep the areas free from contamination so operating personnel can inhabit it during a design basis accident, security alert, or attack. Charcoal filters may be required to adsorb gases present.

Filters

Filters must be selected for the contaminant to be controlled. The available quality assurance services identified in Chapter V of DOE 6430.1 should be used for independent inspection and testing of HEPA filters used in nuclear facilities.

The systems must allow reliable in-place testing of the high-efficiency filters and ease of filter replacement per ANSI N520-1975. Materials and construction of filter housings must be in accordance with ANSI/ASME-N509 and ANSI/ASME-N510. The following types of filters are described in ERDA 21-76 and in ERDA 76-21:

Sand Filters. A sand filter consists of multiple beds of sand and gravel through which air is drawn. The air enters an inlet tunnel that runs the entire length of the sand filter. Smaller cross-sectional laterals running perpendicular to the inlet distribute the air across the base of the sand. The air then rises through several layers of various sizes of sand and gravel at the rate of about 5 fpm (25 mm/s) and gathers in the outlet tunnel for discharge to the atmosphere. Chapter 9 in ERDA 21-76 has further details for sand filters.

Dust Filters. Dust filters are selected for the efficiency deemed necessary for the particular ventilation required. High-efficiency dust filters are frequently used as prefilters for the special filters mentioned below to prevent them from being loaded with atmospheric dust and to minimize replacement cost.

HEPA Filters. High Efficiency Particulate filters are generally used where there is a risk of particulate airborne radioactivity. These filters have a 99.97% efficiency for removing 0.3 micron (μm) particles. They are tested by a special standard procedure using a cold generated "smoke" of dioctylphthalate (DOP) per ANSI/ASME N510

Charcoal Filters. Charcoal filters, or more correctly charcoal adsorbers, use activated charcoal to remove radioactive iodine, which is a vapor or gas. The charcoal bed depths are 2 in. (50 mm) These filters have an efficiency of 99.9% for elemental iodine and 95 to 99% for organic iodine. These filters lose efficiency rapidly as the relative humidity increases. They are generally preceeded by a heating element to keep relative humidity below 70%, for entering air conditions up to saturation.

Argon is adsorbed on charcoal at extremely low, cryogenic temperature to control the argon content in the primary coolant, helium, in a High Temperature Gas Cooled Reactor (HTGR), or in the off-gas system for a Boiling Water Reactor (BWR).

Demisters (Mist Eliminators). Demisters are required to protect HEPA and Charcoal filters if entrained moisture droplets are expected in the air stream.

HVAC DESIGN FOR PLUTONIUM PROCESSING FACILITIES

The HVAC System must be designed in accordance with DOE 6430.1, Chapter XXI. Critical items and systems of Plutonium Processing Facilities are designed to confine radioactive materials under normal operations and DBA conditions (tornadoes, earthquakes, loss of emergency power, fire, etc.), as required by 10 CFR 100. The degree of confinement must be sufficient to limit releases of radioactive materials to the environment to the lower, reasonably achievable level. In no case can the applicable exposure regulations be exceeded, either with respect to the operating personnel, or to the public at the boundary or nearest point of public access.

The probability and effects of DBAs must be considered. Protection of employees within the facility is the primary concern in all aspects of the design. The nature of the material to be handled, including the isotopes of plutonium and/or other radioactive elements present, is taken into account in making these assessments.

The processing areas or canyons, which are totally enclosed, are treated as Zone I areas. Pressure control and control of air flow shall be as required for the zone applicable to the radioactivity level anticipated.

VENTILATION

Ventilation systems are designed to confine radioactive materials under normal and DBA conditions and to limit radioactive discharges to the required minimum. Where the processes or other considerations dictate, inert atmospheres are used in enclosures. In such cases, recycle ventilation should be considered, taking into account both safety and economic factors.

Suitable means of bypassing the recirculating system should be considered if it is desirable to discharge the ventilation flow directly to the exhaust system. In general, recirculating air systems should be considered only in nonradioactive or non-toxic environments. Exceptions may be considered only after a careful evaluation of comparative safety risks. Ventilation systems ensure that air flows are, under all normal conditions, toward areas (zones) of progressively higher radioactive contamination. Air-handling equipment should be sized conservatively so that minor upsets in air-flow balance (e.g., improper use of an air lock or occurrence of a credible breach in a confinement barrier) do not cause air to reverse from higher to lower zone classifications.

HEPA filters at ventilation inlets in confinement zone barriers prevent movement of contamination from high to low level zones, if air flow should reverse. Ventilation system balancing ensures that the building air pressure is always negative with respect to the outside atmosphere.

A safety analysis is necessary to establish the minimum acceptable response requirements for the ventilation system, its components, instruments, and controls under normal, abnormal, and accident conditions. Minimum acceptable system response requirements may range from none, remaining intact but not necessarily operable, being operable in a derated fashion, to operating at full capacity before, during, and after a DBA. These requirements determine system and component design characteristics such as installation of standby spare units, provisions of emergency power for fans, installation of tornado dampers, seismic qualification of filter units, heat protection, fail-safe valve positioners, and so forth.

The number of required exhaust filtration stages from any area of the facility is determined by analysis to limit quantities and concentrations of airborne radioactive or toxic material released to the environment during normal and accident conditions, in conformance with applicable standards, policies, and guidelines. See Chapter V of DOE 6430.1 for air-cleaning system criteria.

The principle of compartmentalization is used to limit the extent of contamination and to minimize loss of productivity and property in the event of a DBA.

Downdraft ventilation within enclosures must be considered as a means of reducing fire and contamination spread potential.

Ventilation Requirements

A partial recirculating ventilation system should be considered for economic reasons. However, such systems must be designed to prevent the entry of contaminated exhaust into room air-recirculating systems.

Critical items of the ventilation system, usually the exhaust and the related fire suppression and detection system, are supplied with emergency power. Controls for these systems are supplied with an uninterruptible emergency power supply.

Sufficient redundancy and/or spare capacity ensures adequate ventilation during normal operations and DBA conditions. Failure of any single component or control function must not compromise minimum adequate ventilation.

The exhaust system is designed to clean radioactivity, toxic, and noxious chemicals from the discharge air, to safely handle products of combustion, and to maintain the building under negative pressure relative to the outside.

Provisions may be made for independent shutdown of ventilation systems, where it could be an advantage to operations, filter change, maintenance, or emergency procedures such as firefighting. All possible effects of the shutdown on air flows in other, interfacing ventilation systems should be considered. Positive means must be provided to control backflow of air that might transport contamination. A HEPA filter installed at the interface between the enclosure and the ventilation system minimizes the contamination of ductwork. A prefilter reduces HEPA filter loading. Such filters are not to be considered the first stage of the airborne contamination cleaning system, however.

VENTILATION SYSTEMS

Airborne contamination cleaning systems may include any or all of the following elements in the design of the overall filtration/treating system.

Prefilters
Scrubbers
Process vessel vent systems
HEPA filters
Sand filters
Glass fiber filters
Demisters
Condensers
Distribution baffles
Fire-suppression systems
Heat-removal systems
Pressure and flow measurement devices
Acid and radiation measurement devices
Drain system, including tanks to prevent the formation of an unsafe geometry when water is used in fire-suppression activities.
Tornado dampers
Redundancy

Supply air is filtered with high-efficiency filters. If room air is recirculated, at least one stage of HEPA filtration is needed in the recirculation circuit.

The ventilation system and associated fire-suppression system are designed for fail-safe operations. The ventilation system is appropriately instrumented and alarmed to report and record its behavior, with readouts in control areas and in the utilities services area.

Both automatic and manual controls to alter system operation during unusual conditions should be considered. Provisions for convenient maintenance, decontamination, and/or replacement of components in the supply, exhaust, and filtration systems are necessary

Damper valves are located so that a bank of filters can be completely isolated from the ventilation systems during filter-element replacement operations. This operation also requires redundancy.

AIRLOCKS

Airlocks allow movement between plutonium-handling areas and other areas. Airlocks, in conjunction with the ventilation system, ensure that all air flows toward the most contaminated area.

AIR AND GASEOUS EFFLUENTS CONTAINING RADIOACTIVITY

All air and other gaseous effluents are exhausted through a ventilation system designed to remove radioactive particulates. All exhaust ducts (or stacks) that may contain plutonium contaminants have two monitoring systems. One should be of the continuous type (Continuous Air Monitoring System (CAMS) and the other, a fixed sampler. These systems may be a combination unit. The probes are designed for isokinetic sampling and are located according to good industrial hygiene practices. Each monitoring system is connected to an emergency power supply.

HVAC DESIGN FOR NUCLEAR FUEL-PROCESSING FACILITIES

Processing areas and cells or canyons, which are totally enclosed, are treated as Zone I areas, as described in the "Nuclear Design Criteria" section. Requirements for temperature and humidity are dictated by the process taking place in the area. Personnel comfort is not a concern. Air flow control is required for the radioactivity level anticipated.

Nuclear reaction buildings in a nuclear processing facility are totally enclosed, and are treated as a Zone I area, as described in the "Nuclear Design Criteria" section.

HVAC DESIGN FOR NUCLEAR POWER PLANTS

Two basic commercial light water reactors are used in the United States today: the Boiling Water Reactor (BWR) and the Pressurized Water Reactor (PWR). For both types, the main objective of the HVAC systems (besides space conditioning for personnel comfort and reliable equipment operation) is to protect operating personnel and the general public from radioactive airborne contamination during all normal and emergency operating conditions. The ALARA (as-low-as-is-reasonably-achievable) concept is used to accomplish these goals, and in no case is the radiological dose allowed to exceed the limits as defined in 10 CFR 20, 10 CFR 50, and 10 CFR 100 in the Code of Federal Regulations.

The nuclear power plant HVAC systems must meet the appropriate design criteria in 10 CFR 50. The U. S. Nuclear Regulatory Commission (NRC) has developed Regulatory Guides that are considered acceptable design methods for meeting the design criteria—several of which relate to HVAC System design. Deviations from the Regulatory Guide criteria must be justified by the owner and approved by the NRC.

The design of the nuclear generating station HVAC systems must ultimately be approved by the NRC staff in accordance with 10 CFR 50, Appendix O. The NRC has developed Standard Review Plans (SRP) to provide an orderly and thorough review. Technical Specifications for the nuclear power plant systems are developed by the owner and approved by the NRC, as defined in 10 CFR 50.36. The Technical Specifications define safety limits, limiting conditions for operation, and surveillance requirements for all systems important to safety that must be met for the operating life of the plant.

It is imperative that the HVAC designer be familiar with all the appropriate Federal Regulations, Regulatory Guides, Standard Review Plans, and Technical Specification requirements that are related to the HVAC system design. Failure to consider all aspects of these documents in the original design result in costly and time-consuming changes.

PRESSURIZED WATER REACTOR HVAC SYSTEMS

Reactor Containment Building

The containment building houses the reactor in a nuclear power plant. The conditions for temperature and humidity are dictated by the Nuclear Steam Supply System (NSSS). Generally, these are the criteria specified for three sets of operating conditions: Normal Operation (including Forced Shutdown at loss of offsite power), Refueling Operation, and Post-LOCA Condition.

Normal Operating Conditions

Temperatures and humidities are as specified below by the NSSS supplier.

Cooling air is required for the reactor cavity and the reactor supports. The concrete temperature must stay below 150°F (65°C) at the inside of the cavity wall and below 200°F (93°C) at the support interfaces, legs, and spiders.

Induction ventilation is required for the Control Rod Drive Mechanism (CRDM) or the Control Element Drive Mechanism (CEDM). The temperature of the air leaving the CRDM or CEDM at the interface is normally high—about 165°F (75°C)—so it is advantageous to cool the air before it is released to the containment atmosphere.

Some power plants require recirculation filtration trains in the containment building to control the level of airborne radioactivity. This requirement is a function of the calculated level of airborne radioactivity at the site boundary. These filters should only be used as a last resort: their maintenance is difficult and costly, especially since the life of the charcoal is short.

Ventilation with outside air is required during normal operation, at least for a time before personnel access, to control the level of airborne radioactivity inside the containment building. Exhausted air must be filtered to meet the requirements for site-boundary dosage.

Ventilation is also restricted by the maximum size of opening (containment penetration) permissible during operation with the reactor in hot condition, normal operation, or hot standby. The opening, which is provided with two fast-closing butterfly valves in series, can be 8in. (200 mm) maximum.

Refueling Condition

The maximum termperature during refueling is dictated by the refueling personnel, working in protective clothing, whose activities would be slowed by discomfort and prolong the refueling outage. The required cooling can be accomplished by normal cooling units, as the cooling load is low when the reactor is shut-down and cooled-off.

Ventilation with outside air is normally required to control the level of airborne radioactivity. There is, however, no need for filtration at the exhaust, since the airborne radioactivity is low and consists essentially of gases, argon, and tritium, which readily disperse in the atmosphere and cannot be filtered out. The ventilation rate is high, approximately 20,000 to 30,000 cfm (9 to 14 m³/s).

LOCA Condition

A LOCA condition occurs if the primary coolant loop breaks. When this condition occurs, circulating water under high pressure and temperature flashes and fills the containment building with radioactive steam. The pressure within the containment building instantaneously rises to as much as 60 to 65 psi (400 to 450 kPa), the temperature rises to 350 to 450°F (180 to 230°C), and the relative humidity remains very high. Main steam line breaks can produce higher temperatures.

Radioactivity is caused by radioactive iodine dissolved in the water. Iodine is one of the fission products, and it migrates from the fuel elements to the water through minute cracks in the fuel element cladding.

Should such an accident occur, the primary actions taken are directed toward reducing the pressure in the containment building and lowering the amount of radioactive products in the containment atmosphere. This action reduces the amount of radiation that could leak out of the building to the surroundings.

Pressure is reduced by air-handling units used in combination with the containment spray to cool the atmosphere and condense the steam, thus lowering containment pressure.

System Redundancy

Nuclear power plants must have two independent "trains" of essential or safety-related equipment, which control the reactor and bring it to a cold shutdown in any emergency. Therefore, two 100% capacity, independent trains of emergency or safety-related equipment consist of controls, pumps, heat exchangers and HVAC equipment, air-handling units, filters, and chillers with circulating pumps. These two trains are designated as "Train A" and "Train B". Each train is powered from an independent emergency power supply, called a "Class 1E" buss. For additional redundancy requirements for turbine-driven auxiliary feedwater pumps in nuclear power plants, refer to the "Nuclear Power Plant" section.

Emergency Power

Emergency power must be provided from two Class IE busses, which must be energized at all times or be restored to full voltage level within 10 seconds and be capable of accepting full load within 60 seconds after loss of offsite power. Therefore, each Class IE buss must be powered from a Class IE generator driven by a diesel engine, which is started automatically in case the voltage on the Class IE is lost. These diesel generators are normally in the 5 to 7 MW range.

Containment Cooling

Normally, the following systems are provided for containment cooling:

Normal Air-Handling Units with Cooling Coils. These units remove the major part of the heat load. Distribution of the air supply depends on the containment layout and the location of the major heat sources. Cooled air is supplied to spaces with high heat load, such as the steam generator cavities, and is returned to the air-handling units from the upper part of the containment.

Normal Reactor Cavity Air-Handling Units or Fans. These units generally transfer fans without coils and cool air to the reactor cavity.

Normal Control Rod or Element Drive Mechanism (CRDM or CEDM) Air-Handling Units. The CRDM and CEDM are generally cooled by an induced-draft system using exhaust fans. The flow rates, pressure drops, and heat loads are generally high, so it is desirable to cool the air before it returns to the containment atmosphere.

Essential Containment Air-Handling Units. Normally, the containment air cooling system, or part of the containment air cooling system, cools after a postulated accident. Therefore, the equipment performs at high temperature, high pressure, high humidity, and a high level of radioactivity.

Radioactivity Control

Airborne radioactivity is controlled by the following means:
Essential Containment Air Filtration Units. For some older power plants, two of this type of filter, powered from the two Class IE busses, is relied on to reduce the amount of post-LOCA airborne radioactivity, demister, a heater, a HEPA filter, and a

charcoal filter followed by a HEPA filter. The electric heater is sized to reduce the relative humidity from 100% to below 70%. All of the components must be designed and manufactured to meet the requirements of an LOCA environment, as described in the "Design Criteria" section.

In case of LOCA and subsequent operation of the filtration train, the charcoal is loaded with radioactive iodine so that the decay heat could cause self-ignition of the charcoal, if the air flow stops. Therefore, a secondary fan maintains a minimum air flow through the charcoal bed to remove the heat generated by the radioactivity, in case the primary fan should stop. The decay heat fan is powered from the other Class IE power supply. These filtration units are located inside the containment.

Containment Power Access Purge or Mini Purge. It is necessary to ventilate during normal operation when the reactor is under pressure to control the level of airborne radioactivity within the containment. The maximum allowed openings in the containment boundary during normal operation of the reactor is 8 to 12 in. (200 to 300 mm), so the maximum possible ventilation rate is low—normally about 2000 cfm (950 L/s).

The system consists of a supply fan, double butterfly valves in each of the penetrations (supply and exhaust), and an exhaust filtration unit with a fan. The filtration unit has a prefilter, HEPA filter, and a charcoal filter followed by a HEPA filter, as described in the "Systems" section.

This system should not be connected to any duct system inside the containment. It should only have a grille over the inlet and outlet inside the containment so that the valves can close, even when blocked by debris or collapsed ducts.

Containment Refueling Purge. Ventilation is required to control the level of airborne radioactivity during refueling. Since the reactor is not under pressure during refueling, there are no restrictions on the allowed size of penetrations through the containment boundary. Large openings, 42 to 48 in. (1.1 to 1.2 m), each protected by double butterfly valves, may be provided. The required high level of ventilation is normally about of 30,000 cfm (14 m³/s).

The system consists of a supply air-handling unit, double butterfly valves at each supply and exhaust penetration, and an exhaust fan. No filters are required, since the exhaust air has only a low level of radioactive gases consisting essentially of argon and tritium, which cannot be filtered out.

Containment Combustible Gas Control. In case of an LOCA, when water with a strong solution of sodium hydroxide or boric acid is sprayed into the containment, various metals (zinc and aluminum) react to generate free hydrogen. Also, the fuel-rod cladding could react with steam at elevated temperatures, if some of the fuel rods were not covered by water. This reaction could also release hydrogen to the containment atmosphere. Therefore, two hydrogen recombiners are needed to remove the air from the containment atmosphere, recombine the hydrogen with the oxygen, and then return the air to the containment. The flow rate for these recombiners is about 100 cfm (50 L/s). The recombiners are backed up by special exhaust filtration trains.

BOILING WATER REACTOR HVAC SYSTEMS

Primary Containment

The BWR Primary Containment is a low leakage, pressure-retaining structure that surrounds the reactor pressure vessel and associated piping. It is designed to withstand, with minimum leakage, the postulated effects of a major reactor coolant line break, which would cause high temperature and pressure conditions.

The primary containment HVAC System typically consists of recirculating fan/cooler systems. It normally recirculates and cools the primary containment atmosphere to maintain the en-

vironmental conditions specified by the NSSS supplier. In an accident, the system has a safety-related function of recirculating the air to prevent stratification of oxygen that may be generated. The cooling function may or may not be safety-related, depending on plant-specific design.

System design must accommodate both normal and accident conditions. The ductwork must be analyzed to ensure that it will not collapse due to the rapid pressure build-up associated with accident conditions. Fan motors must be sized to handle the high density of air during accident conditions.

Primary containment temperature problems have been experienced at many BWR's due to temperature stratification effects and underestimation of heat loads. The ductwork should adequately mix the air to prevent stratification. Heat load calculations should include a sufficient safety factor to account for deficiencies in insulation installation. In addition, a temperature-monitoring system must be installed in the primary containment to ensure that specified average daily temperatures are being maintained (SRP 6.2.5).

Reactor Building

The Reactor Building completely encloses the primary containment, auxiliary support equipment, and the refueling area. During normal, non-safety-related conditions, the reactor building HVAC maintains the design space conditions and minimizes the release of radioactivity to the environment. The HVAC System consists of a 100% outside air ventilation system. Outside air is filtered and heated, as required, prior to being distributed to the various building areas. The exhaust air flows from areas with the potential of least contaminated to most contaminated. Prior to exhausting to the environment, potentially contaminated air is filtered with HEPA and charcoal filters, as required, and all exhaust air is monitored for radioactivity. To ensure that no unmonitored exfiltration occurs during normal operations, the ventilation systems maintain the reactor building at a negative pressure of 0.25 in. of water (60 Pa) relative to atmosphere.

Upon detecting abnormal plant conditions, (such as LOCA, high radiation in the ventilation exhaust, or loss of negative pressure), the HVAC System's safety-related function is to isolate the reactor to limit releases to the environment. Once isolated, via fast closing, gas-tight isolation valves, the reactor building functions as a secondary containment boundary.

The secondary containment boundary is designed to low leakage criteria (typically 100% volume leakage per day at 0.25 in. of water or 60 Pa) and contains any leakage from the primary containment or refueling area following an accident.

Upon isolation, the secondary containment pressure rises due to the loss of the normal ventilation system and the thermal expansion of the confined air. A safety-related filter exhaust system, called the Standby Gas Treatment System (SGTS), is started to reduce and maintain the pressure at a negative 0.25 inch of water (60 Pa).

The SGTS exhausts air from the secondary containment and filters it prior to release to the environment through HEPA and charcoal filters. The capacity of the SGTS is determined from an analysis of how much exhaust air is required to reduce and maintain the secondary containment at the design negative pressure. Typically, SGTS capacity is about 3,000 to 10,000 cfm (1400 to 4700 L/s), depending on secondary containment leak rates and required drawdown times.

In addition to the SGTS, some designs include safety-related recirculating air systems within the secondary containment to mix, cool, and/or HEPA and charcoal filter the air during accident conditions. These recirculating systems use portions of the normal ventilation system ductwork; therefore, the ductwork must be classified as safety-related.

If the isolated secondary containment area is not cooled during accident conditions, it is necessary to determine the maximum temperatures attained during the accident. All safety-related components in the secondary containment must be environmentally qualified to operate at these temperatures. In most plant designs, safety-related unit coolers handle the high heat released with the operation of the Emergency Core Cooling System (ECCS) pumps. References SRP 6.5.3., SRP 6.2.3, SRP 9.4.2, and SRP 9.4.5 have more details.

Emergency Electrical Switchgear Rooms

These rooms house the electrical switchgear that controls essential or safety-related equipment. Switchgear located in these rooms must be protected from excessive temperatures to prevent loss of power circuits required for proper operation of the plant, especially its safety-related equipment, and to retain a reasonable equipment life in accordance with the environmental qualification of the equipment. The HVAC systems for these rooms are baked by air conditioning from essential or safety-related sources.

Cable Spreading Rooms

These rooms, which contain many cables, are directly above and below the control room. They usually are served by the same air-handling units that serve the electrical switchgear rooms; but since the heat load is low, they generally do not require essential air conditioning.

Turbine Building

Only the boiling water reactor supplies radioactive steam directly to the turbine, which may cause a direct release of airborne radioactivity to the surroundings. Therefore, a part of the turbine building for a BWR should be enclosed—at least in the areas where release of airborne radioactivity is a possibility. These areas must be ventilated and the exhaust filtered to ensure that no radioactivity releases to the surrounding atmosphere. The filters consist of trains of prefilter, HEPA filter, and a charcoal filter followed by another HEPA filter. The extent of filtration required to meet the requirements of SRP 9.4.4, 10 CFR 20, 10 CFR 50, and 10 CFR 100 is based on the plant and site configuration, as determined by the Nuclear Licensing Group.

Some plants are required to have this kind of filtration train on the condenser exhaust, no matter whether they are PWR or BWR power plants.

Personnel Facilities

For nuclear power plants, this area usually includes decontamination facilities, laboratories, and medical treatment rooms. The exhaust may have to be filtered by trains of filters to prevent possible release of airborne radioactivity to the surrounding atmosphere.

Auxiliary Building

The auxiliary building contains a large amount of support equipment (pumps, heat exchangers, and piping), much of which handles potentially radioactive material. The building is air conditioned for equipment protection, and the exhaust is filtered to prevent release of potential airborne radioactivity.

The filtration trains consist of prefilters, HEPA filters, and charcoal filters followed by HEPA filters.

The exhaust exceeds the supply by approximately 10% so that there will be no exfiltration. The HVAC System is a once-through system, as needed for general cooling. Ventilation is augmented by local recirculation air-handling units located in the individual equipment rooms, where additional cooling is required due to the localized heat loads from the equipment.

If the equipment in these rooms operates during normal operation, it is cooled by normal air-handling units. If the equipment is safety-related, the area is also cooled by safety-related or essential air-handling units powered from the Class IE busses of the same train as the equipment in the room.

The normal and the essential unit may be combined into one unit with both a normal and an essential cooling coil and a safety-related fan served from a Class IE buss. The normal coil is served with chilled water from the normal chilled-water system, while the essential coil operates with chilled water from a safety-related chilled-water system, which is generally only operated under emergency conditions.

A Q-Class air-handling unit must be designed and manufactured to conform to both the environmental and seismic qualification, as specified in the "Design Basis" section.

A non-Q-Class air-handling unit located in a room with safety-related equipment does not need environmental qualification. However, it must be seismically qualified to the extent that it may not need to operate during or after a seismic event, but it must retain its structure/pressure boundary integrity so that it does not become a source of debris or missiles. Furthermore, the supports of the unit must be seismically qualified.

Fuel-Handling Building

New and spent fuel is stored in the fuel-handling building. The building is air conditioned for equipment protection and is ventilated with a once-through system to control potential airborne radioactivity.

Normally, the level of airborne radioactivity is so low that the exhaust does not need to be filtered. It is monitored, however, and if significant airborne radioactivity is detected, the building is sealed off and kept under negative pressure by exhaust through filtration trains powered from Class IE busses.

Radwaste Building

Except for spent fuel, radioactive waste is stored, shredded, baled, or packaged in this building for disposal. The building is air conditioned for equipment protection, and ventilated to control potential airborne radioactivity. The ventilation may require filtration through HEPA and/or charcoal filters prior to release to the atmosphere.

Diesel Generator Building

Nuclear power plants have auxiliary power plants to generate electric power for all essential or safety-related equipment in case of a loss of offsite power. This auxiliary power plant consists of at least two independent diesel generators, each sized to meet the emergency power load. The heat load from a diesel generator is high for the room size. The diesel generator room is normally ventilated with outside air to remove the heat generated by the unit.

In a desert environment, the diesel generator must operate in a high temperature environment, possibly up to 150 °F (60 °C). Even then, an evaporative cooling system (such as water-spray injected into the supply air stream) or a mechanical cooling system should be considered to lower the temperature when the room is occupied during the periodic testing of the diesel generator. In such cases, there should also be a separate room for the electrical switchgear and control equipment. A separate room has the advantage of controlling temperature with a separate ventilation or air-conditioning system and dust with filters in the air supply.

The spray system and possible ventilation for normal standby operation may be normal equipment, but equipment required for emergency operation must be safety-related and must meet the requirements described in the "Design Criteria" section.

For the high flow rates described above, the system is extremely sensitive to outside temperature. Therefore, the flow rate must be based on the highest temperature of record for the site; the 1% condition may not be adequate.

Pump Houses

Cooling-water pumps are protected by houses that are often ventilated by fans to remove heat from the pump motors. The motor sizes are large, about 1000 hp (750 kW).

If the pumps are essential or safety-related, the ventilation equipment must also be safety-related. The design and manufacturing must meet the requirement described in the "Design Criteria" section, and the equipment must be powered from Class IE busses, of the same train as the pump it serves.

Chilled Water Systems

The refrigeration for air conditioning may be accomplished by direct expansion equipment. However, for most power plants, chilled water systems are used and must meet ASME Section III, Class 3 requirements.

For essential systems, the chillers and circulation pumps are manufactured and designed to meet the requirements described in the "Design Criteria" section. The system is provided power from Class IE busses and provided cooling water from the essential-component cooling-water system.

Nuclear Non-power Medical and Research Reactors

There are no general requirements for HVAC and filtration systems for nuclear non-power medical and research reactors. The criteria for the HVAC and filtration systems depend on the type of reactor (which may range from a non-pressurized "swim-ming pool" type, to a 10 megawatt or more pressurized reactor), the type of fuel, the degree of enrichment, and the type of facility and environment.

CODES AND STANDARDS

10 CFR 20	*Standards for Protection Against Radiation.* Code of Federal Register.
10 CFR 50	*Appendix A and B, General Design Criteria.* Code of Federal Register.
10 CFR 100	*Reactor Site Criteria.* Code of Federal Register.
NRA	Regulatory Guides.
DOE 6430.1	*Department of Energy General Design Criteria Manual.*
ANSI/ASME N45.2	*Nuclear Power Plants.*
ANSI/ASME N509	*Nuclear Power Plant Air-Cleaning Units and Components.*
ANSI/ASME N510	*Testing of Nuclear Air-Cleaning Systems.* [NOTE: ANSI N509 and ANSI N510 are obsolete and are not listed in current ANSI Standards catalogs.]
ERDA 21-76	*Nuclear Power Plant Air-Cleaning Units and Components.*
ERDA 76-21	*Nuclear Air Cleaning Handbook.*
SRP 6.2.3	Secondary Containment Functional Design.
SRP 6.2.5	Combustible Gas Control in Containment.
SRP 6.4	Control Room Habitability Systems.
SRP 6.5.1	ESF Atmosphere Cleanup Systems.
SRP 6.5.3	Fission Product Control Systems and Structures.
SRP 9.4.1	Control Room Area Ventilation System.
SRP 9.4.2	Spent Fuel Pool Area Ventilation System.
SRP 9.4.4	Turbine Area Ventilation System.
SRP 9.4.5	Engineered Safety Feature Ventilation System.

CHAPTER 41

VENTILATION OF THE INDUSTRIAL ENVIRONMENT

CONTROL of the industrial environment deals with the design and application of equipment that provides the necessary conditions for maintaining the efficiency, health, and safety of workers. This chapter addresses general ventilation for heat control, spot cooling for heat relief, and dilution ventilation for contaminant control. Chapter 20 covers local exhaust ventilation for contaminant control.

Chapter 22 of the 1985 FUNDAMENTALS Volume ("Ventilation and Infiltration"), Chapters 1 through 6, 10, and 11 of the 1983 EQUIPMENT Volume (air-handling equipment), and Chapter 50 of this volume have additional information on ventilation methods. Chapters 23 through 27 of the 1985 FUNDAMENTALS Volume cover heating and cooling loads. Chapters 28 through 39 of this volume provide information for specific process requirements.

Evaluating work place exposures to hazardous materials is part of the industrial hygiene field. Acceptable exposure levels for many contaminants have been established by the Occupational Safety and Health Administration (Permissible Exposure Limits or PEL's, which are legally binding standards), the American Conference of Governmental Industrial Hygienists (Threshold Limit Values or TLV's, which are guidelines for professional interpretation), and other agencies or organizations. Often a workroom contaminant has not been assigned a PEL or TLV, and an *in-house* TLV must be established based on toxicological information.

Good practice requires cooperation between an experienced industrial hygienist, who can evaluate the degree of work place hazard, and an engineer, who is skilled in design of appropriate corrective measures.

HEAT CONTROL IN INDUSTRIAL WORK AREAS

In certain industrial work situations, considerable heat is released from process equipment to the environment. It is not economically feasible to stop the escape of all of this process heat or to offset it completely by the usual methods of comfort ventilation and air conditioning. In the design and operation of control measures, some heat exposure above simple comfort requirements must often be accepted. See Chapter 8 of the 1985 FUNDAMENTALS Volume for the physiological principles of comfort control.

The engineer must distinguish between the control needs for *hot-dry* industrial areas and *warm-moist* conditions. In the first case, the process gives off only sensible and radiant heat without adding moisture to the air. The heat load on exposed workers is thereby increased, but the rate of cooling by evaporation of sweat is not reduced. Heat balance may be maintained, although this may be at the expense of excessive sweating. In the warm-moist situation, the wet process gives off mainly latent heat. The rise in the heat load on the worker may not be significant, but the increase in moisture content of the air seriously reduces heat loss by evaporation of sweat. The warm-moist condition is potentially more hazardous than the hot-dry condition.

The preparation of this chapter is assigned to TC 5.8, Industrial Ventilation.

Hot-dry work situations occur around hot furnaces, forges, metal-extruding and rolling mills, glass-forming machines, and so forth. Typical warm-moist operations are found in many textile mills, laundries, dye houses, and deep mines where water is used extensively for dust control.

The industrial heat problem varies with local climatic conditions. Solar heat gain and an elevated outdoor temperature will increase the heat load at the work place, but these contributions may be insignificant when compared with the locally generated process heat. The moisture content of the outdoor air is an important climatic factor affecting hot-dry work situations, and, on a moist summer day, it will seriously restrict an individual's cooling by evaporation. For the warm-moist job, solar heat gain and elevated outdoor temperature are more important because, compared with the moisture release on the job, the release contributed by the outdoor air will be of little significance.

Thermal Standards

Heat stress is the thermal condition of the environment which, in combination with the metabolic heat generation of the body, causes the deep body temperature to exceed 100°F (38°C). The recommended method for evaluating an environment's heat stress potential is the Wet-Bulb Globe Temperature (WBGT), defined as follows:

Outdoors with solar load:

$$WBGT = 0.7\ WB + 0.2\ GT + 0.1\ DB \qquad (1)$$

Indoors or outdoors with no solar load:

$$WBGT = 0.7\ WB + 0.3\ GT \qquad (2)$$

where

WB = natural wet-bulb temperature (no defined range of air velocity; not the same as adiabatic saturation temperature or psychrometric wet bulb).
DB = dry-bulb temperature (shielded thermometer).
GT = globe temperature (Vernon bulb thermometer 6 in. or 150 mm diameter).

The Threshold Limit Value (TLV) for heat stress is set for different levels of physical stress, as shown in Figure 1 (ACGIH 1985). This chart depicts the allowable work regime, in terms of rest periods and work periods each hour, for different levels of work, over a range of WBGT. For applying Figure 1, it is assumed that the rest area has the same WBGT as the work area. If the rest area is at or below 75°F (24°C) WBGT, the resting time is reduced by 25%. The curves are valid for people acclimatized to heat.

The WBGT index is an International Standard (ISO 7243) for evaluation of hot environments. It is recommended that the WBGT index and activity values be evaluated on 1-hour mean values, i.e., WBGT and activity are measured and estimated as time weighted averages on a 1-hour basis. Although recommended by NIOSH (National Institute of Occupational Safety and Health), the WBGT has not been accepted as a legal standard by OSHA. It is generally used in conjunction with other methods to determine heat stress.

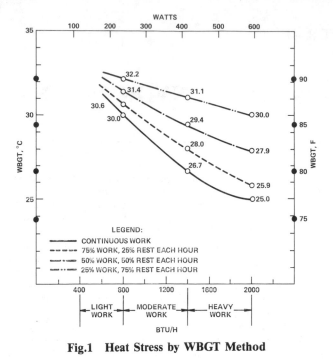

Fig.1   Heat Stress by WBGT Method

Caplan (1980) presents a graphical method of evaluating several heat stress factors and a prediction on the beneficial results of various possible corrective actions.

Biophysical Basis for Thermal Standards

Under conditions of thermal comfort, the rate of internal heat production (metabolism) is balanced by the rate of heat loss to the environment. This comfortable balance is maintained without active sweating, with optimum skin and deep-body temperatures, and without unusual load on the heart. At the upper limits of physiological tolerance to sustained heat exposure, thermal balance may also be established, but this is possible only with active sweating, elevated skin and body temperatures, and accelerated heart rate. The limit is fixed by the maximum permissible degree to which these indexes of physiological strain—sweating, body temperature, and heart rate—can be safely elevated. For practical work situations in the industry, the permissible limits of these indexes must be set below the absolute physiological maximums.

The thermal relationship between man and the surrounding environment depends on four independently variable characteristics: air temperature, radiant temperature, moisture content of the air, and air velocity. These may combine in various ways, together with the rate of internal heat production, to create widely different degrees of heat stress.

A sense of comfort depends on many factors; some can be qualified, such as temperature, humidity, air velocity, light level, and noise. Others are difficult to evaluate, such as health of workers, physical appearance of work space, and various psychological factors (Yamazaki 1981).

HEAT EXPOSURE CONTROL

Control at Source

The magnitude of heat exposure can be reduced by insulating hot equipment, locating such equipment in zones with good general ventilation within buildings or outdoors, covering steaming water tanks, providing covered drains for direct removal of hot water, and maintaining tight joints and valves where steam may escape.

Local Exhaust Ventilation

Where appropriate, local exhaust ventilation can remove the natural convection column of heated air rising from a hot process with a minimum of air from the surrounding space. Chapter 43 covers design of exhaust hoods and duct systems for local exhaust.

Radiation Shielding

In some industries, the major environmental heat load is radiant heat. Sources are hot objects and surfaces, e.g., furnaces, ovens, furnace flues and stacks, boilers, molten metal, hot ingots, castings or forgings, and other hot surfaces. Because air temperature has no significant influence on radiant heat flow, ventilation is of little help in controlling such exposure. The only effective control is reducing the amount of radiant heat impinging on the workers. Radiant heat exposures can be reduced by insulating or placing radiation shields around the emitting source. (Chapter 3, 1985 FUNDAMENTALS).

Radiation shields are effective in the following forms (AIHA 1975):

Reflective Shielding. Sheets of reflective material or insulating board, semipermanently attached to the hot equipment or arranged in a semi-portable floor stand.

Absorptive Shielding (Water-Cooled). The shields absorb and remove the heat from the hot equipment.

Transparent Shields. Heat reflective tempered plate glass, reflective metal chain curtains, and close mesh wire screens moderate radiation without obstructing visual contact with the hot equipment.

Flexible Shielding. Aluminum treated fabrics give a high degree of radiation shielding.

Protective Clothing. Reflective garments such as aprons, gauntlet gloves, and face shields provide moderate radiation shielding. For extreme radiation exposures, complete suits with Vortex tube cooling may be required.

If the shield is a good reflector, it will remain relatively cool in severe radiant heat. Bright or highly polished tinplate, stainless steel, and ordinary flat or corrugated aluminum sheets are efficient and durable. See Chapter 2 of the 1985 FUNDAMENTALS Volume. Foil-faced plaster board, though less durable, gives good reflectivity on one side. To be efficient, however, the reflective shield must remain bright.

The best radiation shields are infrared reflectors, which must be installed properly to avoid transferring a radiant heat load to the wrong place. The shield should reflect the radiant heat back to the primary source, where it is removed by local exhaust. However, unless the shield completely surrounds the primary source, some of the infrared energy will be reflected into the cooler surroundings and possibly into an occupied area. Therefore, the direction of the reflected heat should be studied before shielding is installed.

GENERAL VENTILATION

General ventilation is the supply and/or exhaust of air to control comfort or to replace exhaust air. General ventilation systems can make up air for an exhaust system and, in some cases, can recover heat and conserve energy.

Dilution ventilation reduces contaminants to an acceptable level.

Compensating air is conditioned outside air that is introduced into occupied spaces to replace exhausted process air.

Makeup air is outside air introduced to replace air that is exhausted or leaks from a building. It is considered part of the building's HVAC system. Design engineers generally refer to both compensating air and makeup air as makeup air. Further, it is sometimes not clear when a particular unit provides makeup air, compensating air, or both. For these reasons, this chapter calls both terms makeup air.

General ventilation may be provided with either natural or mechanical supply and/or exhaust systems. Some factors to consider in selection and design are as follows:

1. Local exhaust systems provide general ventilation for the work area.
2. A balance of the supply and exhaust systems is required for either system to function as designed.
3. Natural ventilation systems are not satisfactory for most work areas unless the climate is cool and the internal heat loads, work loads, and worker population are low. The amount of natural ventilation for any building configuration depends on the size and shape of the building, temperature differences between inside and outside, and wind patterns. Chapter 22 of the FUNDAMENTALS Volume has more details.
4. To provide effective general ventilation for heat relief by either natural or mechanical supply, the air must be delivered in the work zones [below 10 ft (3 m)] with an appreciable air velocity. A sufficient exhaust volume is necessary to remove the heat liberated in the space. Local relief systems may require supplementary supply air for heat removal.
5. Supply and exhaust air cannot be used interchangeably. Supply air can be delivered where it is wanted at controlled velocities, temperature, and humidity. Exhaust systems must be used to capture heat and fumes at the source.
6. General building exhaust may be required in addition to local exhaust systems.
7. The exhaust discharge, whether local or general, should be located to reduce the effect of re-entry. See Chapter 14 of the 1985 FUNDAMENTALS Volume.

Need for Makeup Air

For safe, effective operation, most industrial plants require makeup air to replace the large volumes of air exhausted to provide conditions for personnel comfort, safety, and process operations. If makeup air is provided consistently with good air distribution, more effective cooling can be provided in the summer, and more efficient and effective heating will result in the winter. Using windows or other inlets that cannot be used in stormy weather should be discouraged. The most important needs for compensating air can be summarized as follows:

1. To replace air being exhausted through combustion processes and local and general exhaust systems (see Chapter 20).
2. To secure the required exhaust for hoods, combustion, process, and building heat removal.
3. To eliminate cross drafts by proper arrangement of supply air and prevent infiltration (through doors, windows, and similar openings) that may make hoods unsafe or ineffective, defeat environmental control, bring in or stir up dust, or adversely affect processes by cooling or disturbance.
4. To obtain air from the cleanest source. Supply air can be filtered; infiltration air cannot.
5. To control building pressure and air flow from space to space. Such control is necessary for three reasons:
    a. To avoid positive or negative pressures that will make it difficult or unsafe to open doors and to avoid the conditions mentioned in Items 1, 2, and 3.
    b. To confine contaminants and reduce their concentration and to control temperature, humidity, and air movement positively.
    c. To recover heat and conserve energy.

Wherever possible, building pressure should be controlled by flow from one space to another rather than by appreciable pressure differential. Otherwise, very large volumes of makeup air will be required. Chapter 43 of this volume has more information.

Heat Conservation and Recovery

Because of the large volumes of ventilation required for industrial plants, heat conservation and recovery should be used. The savings can be substantial. For example, assume a plant required 106,000 cfm (50 000 L/s) makeup air in a heating season of 4300 h. If No. 2 fuel oil is used, with a heat content of 131,500 Btu/gal (36.7 MJ/L) and a conversion efficiency of 75%, then 1100 barrels of oil can be saved for each 9°F (5°C) reduction in heating temperature. The savings each hour are:

$$H = (1.08)(9)(106,000) = 1,030,000 \text{ Btu/h}$$
$$[H = (1.2)(5)(50\ 000) = 300\ 000 \text{ W}]$$

The fuel savings, with 4300 h of operation are:

Fuel Savings =

$$\frac{(1,030,000 \text{ Btu/h})(4300 \text{ h})}{131,500 \text{ Btu/gal})(42 \text{ gal/bbl})0.75} = 1100 \text{ bbl}$$

$$\left[\text{Fuel Savings} = \frac{(300\ 000 \text{ W})(4300 \text{ h})(3600 \text{ s/h})}{(36.7 \text{ MJ/L})(159 \text{ L/bbl})0.75} = 1100 \text{ bbl} \right]$$

In some cases, it is possible to provide unheated or partially heated makeup air to the building. Rotary, regenerative heat exchangers recover up to 80% of the heat represented by the difference between the exhaust and the outdoor air temperatures. Reductions of 9 to 18°F (5 to 10°C) in the heating requirement for most industrial systems should be routine. While most of the heat conservation and recovery methods outlined in this section apply to heating, the saving possibility of air conditioning systems is equally impressive. Heat conservation and recovery should be incorporated in preliminary planning for an industrial plant. Some methods follow:

1. In the original design of the building, process, and equipment, provide insulation and heat shields to minimize heat loads. Vapor proofing and reduction of glass area may be required. Changes in process design may be required to keep the building heat loads within reasonable bounds. Review the exhaust needs for hoods and process and keep those to a practical, safe minimum.
2. Design the supply air systems for efficient distribution by delivering the air directly to the work zones; by mixing the supply with hot building air in the winter; by using recirculated air within the requirements of winter makeup; and by bringing unheated or partially heated air to hoods or process whenever possible.
3. Design the system to achieve highest efficiency and lowest residence time for contaminants. In the design, consider that it is psychologically sound and good practice to permit workers to adjust and modify the air patterns to which they are exposed; people desire direct personal control over their working environment.
4. Conserve exhaust air by using it; e.g., office exhaust can be directed first to work areas, then to locker rooms or process, and finally, outside. Clean, heated air can be used from motor or generator rooms after it has been used for cooling the equipment. Similarly, the cooling systems for many large motors and generators have been arranged to discharge into the building in the winter to provide heat and to the outside in summer to avoid heat loads.
5. Supply air can be passed through air-to-air, liquid-to-air, or hot-gas-to-air heat exchangers to recover building or process heat. Rotary, regenerative, air-to-air heat exchangers are

discussed in Chapter 35 of the 1983 EQUIPMENT Volume.

6. Operate the system for economy. Shut the systems down at night or weekends whenever possible, and operate the makeup air in balance with the needs of operating process equipment and hoods. Keep supply air temperatures at the minimum for heating and the maximum for cooling, consistent with the needs of process and employee comfort. Keep the building in balance so that uncomfortable drafts do not require excessive heating.

Air Requirements for Adequate Ventilation

The rules of thumb for ventilation (e.g., air changes per hour, temperature rise between supply, and exhaust air and volume per floor area) can help predict effective general ventilation, if the specific rate is established by successful existing systems similar to the proposed installation. These criteria, when properly interpreted, serve as guides to check ventilation design.

Air change rates in the upper level of the building do not necessarily provide relief at the lower work zones. Temperature rise can be estimated by the following equation:

$$H = 1.08 \, \Delta Tq \quad (H = 1.2 \cdot \Delta Tq) \tag{3}$$

where

ΔT = temperature rise of the air, °F (°C).
H = heat to be removed, Btu/h (W).
q = air supply, cfm (L/s).

The quantity H must include all internal heat from equipment, process, lights, occupancy, and solar and roof transmission gains.

Ventilation is often expressed as volume per unit of floor area. This is a more rational approach than air changes per hour, since appropriately designed supply ventilation will provide the desired heat relief independent of the ceiling height of the space. A ventilation rate of 2 cfm/ft² [10 L/(s · m²)] gives reasonably good results for many plants having an internal load of 100 to 125 Btu/h · ft² (300 to 400 W/m²).

When local exhaust ventilation is required for contaminant control, the exhaust rates are frequently greater than the required general ventilation for comfort control. Under these conditions, the exhaust rate determines makeup air rates. A supply system with air distribution arranged so that the makeup air is provided without disturbance at the hoods and process is mandatory.

Caplan and Knutson (1978) and Peterson, et. al. (1983) established that the manner of air supply to a room with a hood has a major impact on the hood performance factor. The hood performance factor is defined as the logarithm of the ratio of contamination concentration within the hood to the contamination concentration just outside the hood. Adequate hood performance factors range from 4 to 6, with the higher number indicating a more effective hood installation.

Locker Room, Toilet, and Shower Space Ventilation

The ventilation of locker rooms, toilets, and shower spaces is important in modern industrial facilities to remove odor and reduce humidity. In some industries, adequate control of workroom contamination requires prevention of ingestion, as well as inhalation, so adequate hygienic facilities, including appropriate ventilation, may be required in locker rooms, change rooms, showers, lunchrooms, and break rooms. State and local regulations should be consulted at early stages of design.

Supply air may be introduced through door or wall grilles. In some cases, plant air may be so contaminated that filtration or, preferably, mechanical ventilation, may be required. When control of workroom contaminants is inadequate or not feasible, the total exposure to employees can be reduced by ensuring that the level of contamination in the locker rooms, lunchrooms,

Table 1 Ventilation for Locker Rooms, Toilets, and Shower Spaces

Description	Inch-Pound Units	SI Units
Locker Rooms		
Coat hanging or clean change room for non-laboring shift employees with clean work clothes	1 cfm/ft²	5 L/(s·m²)
Change room for laboring employees with wet or sweaty clothes	2 cfm/ft²; 7 cfm exhausted from each locker	10 L/(s·m²); 3 L/s exhausted from each locker
Change room for heavy laborers or workers assigned to working and cleaning where clothes will be wet or pick up odors	3 cfm/ft²; 10 cfm exhausted from each locker	20 L/(s·m²); 5 L/s exhausted from each locker
Toilet Spaces	2 cfm/ft²; at least 25 cfm per toilet facility; 200 cfm min.	10 L/(s·m²); at least 10 L/s per toilet facility; 90 L/s mimimum
Shower Spaces	2 cfm/ft²; at least 50 cfm per shower head; 200 cfm min.	10 L/(s·m²); at least 20 L/s per shower head; 90 L/s minimum

and break rooms is minimized by pressurizing these areas with excess supply air.

When mechanical ventilation is used, the supply system should have supply fixtures such as wall grilles, ceiling diffusers, or supply plenums to distribute the air adequately throughout the area. In the locker rooms, the exhaust should be taken primarily from the toilet and shower spaces, as needed, and the remainder from the lockers and the room ceiling. In the absence of specific codes, Table 1 provides a guide for ventilation of these spaces.

Roof Ventilators

Roof ventilators are basically heat escape ports located high in a building and properly enclosed for weathertightness. Stack effect plus some wind induction are the motive forces for gravity operation of continuous and round ventilators. The latter can be equipped with fan barrel and motor, thus permitting gravity operation or motorized operation.

Many ventilator designs are available; two designs are the low ventilator that consists of a stack fan with a rainhood, and the ventilator with a split butterfly closure that floats open to discharge air and self-closes. Both use minimum enclosures and have little or no gravity capacity. Split butterfly dampers tend to make the fans noisy and are subject to damage because of slamming during strong wind conditions. Because noise is frequently a problem in many powered roof ventilators, the manufacturer's sound rating should be reviewed.

Roof ventilators can be listed in diminishing order of heat removal capacity. The continuous ventilation monitor most effectively removes substantial concentrated heat loads. An efficient type is the streamlined continuous ventilator. It is designed to prevent backdraft, is weathertight, and usually has dampers that may be closed readily in the winter to conserve building heat. Its capacity is limited only by the available roof area and the proper location and sizing of low level air inlets.

Next in capacity are: (1) round gravity or windband ventilator, (2) round gravity with fan and motor added, (3) low hood powered ventilator, and (4) vertical upblast powered ventilator. The shroud for the vertical upblast design has a peripheral baffle to deflect the air up instead of down. Vertical discharge is highly desirable to reduce roof damage caused by the hot air, if it contains condensable oil or solvent vapor. Ventilators with direct-connected motors are desirable, because of the locations of the units and the belt maintenance required for units having short shaft centerline distances. Round gravity ventilators have low capacity and are applicable to warehouses with light heat loads and to manufacturing areas having high roofs and light loads.

Streamlined continuous ventilators must operate effectively without mechanical power. Efficient ventilator operation is generally obtained when the difference in elevation between the average air inlet level and the roof ventilation is at least 30 ft (10 m) and the exit temperature is 25 °F (14 °C) above the prevailing outdoor temperature. Chapter 22, 1985 FUNDAMENTALS, has further details. Under these conditions and with the wind velocity of 5 mph (2.2 m/s) the ventilator throat velocity will be about 375 fpm (1.9 m/s) and it will remove 1.08 • 25 °F • 375 = 10,000 Btu/h • ft^2 (1.2 • 14 °C • 1.9 m/s = 32 kW/m^2).

To ensure this level of performance, sufficient low-level openings must be provided for the incoming air. Manufacturers recommend 250 to 450 fpm (1.3 to 2.5 m/s) inlet velocity. Insufficient inlet area and significant air currents are the most common reasons gravity roof ventilators malfunction. A positive supply of air around the hot equipment may be necessary within large buildings where the external wall inlets are remote from the equipment.

The cost of electrical power for mechanical ventilation is offset by the advantage of constant air flow. Mechanical ventilation also can create the pressure differential necessary for good air flow, even with small inlets. But inlets should be sized correctly to avoid infiltration and other problems caused by high negative pressure in the building. Often a mechanical system is justified to supply enough makeup air to maintain the work area under positive pressure.

Careful study of air flow around buildings is necessary to avoid reintroducing contaminants from the exhaust into the ventilation system. Even discharging the exhaust from an area opposite the outside intake may still allow it to reenter the building. Chapter 14, FUNDAMENTALS, describes, in detail, the nature of airflow around buildings.

Fusible link dampers, which release heat in case of fire, should also be considered.

LOCAL COMFORT VENTILATION

Effective local comfort ventilation is based on the principle that air must be delivered directly to the work zone with sufficient air motion and at a low enough temperature to cool the worker by convection and evaporation. In most cases, the objective is to provide tolerable working conditions rather than complete comfort. In each case, the methods described for local comfort ventilation are based on the assumption that exhaust ventilation, radiation shielding, equipment insulation and possible changes in process design have been fully used to minimize the heat loads. In addition, supply air must not blow on or at hot equipment or hoods nor through the layers of hot ceiling air before reaching the work zone. In the former case, the ventilation disturbs the capture velocity of the hood or thermal rise from the hot equipment and distributes hot and/or contaminated air into the work room. In the latter case, huge volumes of hot and possibly contaminated air are entrained and brought down to the work zone.

Ventilation Methods

The following two types of local relief ventilation are used:
General Ventilation: This might be termed **low-level** or **displacement ventilation** because the supply air is delivered at

the 8 to 12 ft (2.4 to 3.6 m) level and displaces the warm air rising from equipment, lights, and occupants. The internal heat is picked up as the supply air leaves the work zone, and the work zone may be maintained within a few degrees of the supply air temperature with relatively low supply air volumes. Such low-level systems should be applied to large work areas having high, uniform worker population. These systems are local in the sense that no attempt is made to maintain conditions in the upper levels of the building (see Figures 2 and 3).

Local-Area or Spot-Cooling Ventilation. In buildings having only a few work areas, it would be impractical and wasteful to attempt to treat the entire building. In such cases, relief may be provided by the following methods:

1. Provide a complete enclosure around the worker with separate ventilation to maintain cooler working conditions; e.g., a control room, small shelter booth, or ventilated crane cab. In effect, this is *localized* general ventilation, differing only in the conditions of air temperature, humidity, and motion required.
2. Surround the worker with a relatively cool atmosphere by a direct supply of air introduced at a low level over a small area of the plant. In such cases, the temperature at higher levels in the space is of little or no concern (see Figures 3 and 4).
3. Direct a high-velocity airstream at the worker to increase the convective and evaporative cooling effect. This method, called **spot cooling**, will incorporate varying degrees of Method 2, depending on the number of employees and the distribution of the work stations.

A work-station enclosure of Method 1 is the most desirable because it completely controls the environment. Method 2 is effective in large areas with many work stations, such as machine shops and assembly lines. Method 3 cools large spaces with scattered work stations and localized heat sources.

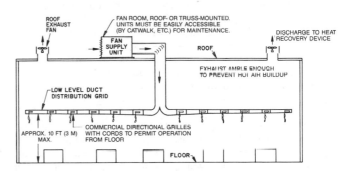

Fig. 2 Low-Level Air Distribution System for Plant Heating, Relief Ventilation, and Heat Recovery

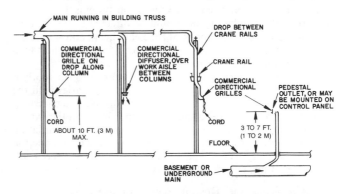

Fig. 3 Additional Means for Providing Low-Level Heating and Summer Relief Ventilation

Physiological Aspects

Two different heat load situations that affect design are when (1) radiant heat sources are not important and (2) radiant heat sources are important.

Radiant Heat Is Not Important. Where no important sources of radiant heat are located within or close to the work area, the relief air need only be introduced into the work space to displace the hot air, thus surrounding the worker with acceptable temperature and air motion.

Radiant Heat Is Important. Where important sources of radiant heat are present and cannot be entirely controlled by radiation shielding, the relief air must greatly increase heat removal by convection and evaporation from the worker to offset the radiation load. Where the radiant load cannot be offset, intermittent work periods may also be necessary, which further emphasizes the importance of shielding to reduce the load. Radiant heat shields or other barriers are the only reasonable protection from radiant heat. In other cases, the supply air temperature may be reduced by refrigeration or evaporative cooling to a level at which the worker can maintain body heat balance without strain.

Regardless of the heat source or load, if the temperature of the relief air exceeds skin temperature, a convective load is then added to any existing radiative load, and these, together with metabolic heat, must be removed by evaporation. It is important to direct the air flow to the parts of the body exposed to the radiation. Additional velocity over the worker simply increases the convective load, making the working condition less tolerable.

While increased velocity will also increase evaporation, a critical point is reached when the convective addition exceeds heat removal by evaporation. At low velocities, below the critical point, maximum cooling may not occur because of incomplete evaporation. Again, cool air is very important for high heat level conditions and the reason that evaporatively-cooled supply air systems are used so frequently in hot industrial areas.

The level of air motion at the worker is important. At fixed work positions with light activity, particularly when the individual is seated at a desk or bench, the impingement velocity should not exceed 200 fpm (1 m/s) for continuous exposure. With high work levels and intermittent exposures (relief stations), velocities of 400 to 800 fpm (2 to 4 m/s) may be used. In hot industries such as foundries and steel mills, velocities as high as 1000 to 2000 fpm (5 to 10 m/s) are common. When high velocity air is used, it is important to avoid the undesirable effects or hot air convection, dust entrainment with its eye hazard potential, and the disturbance of local exhaust ventilation systems.

The temperature at the work place and not at the outlet should be in the range of 68 to 86 °F (20 to 30 °C), depending on the heat load. Evaporative cooling ventilation systems usually provide this. Preferably, the air should be directed to the front of the torso and not on the back of the head, neck, and shoulders. The air may need warming in winter, except in areas of heat load where air may need to be cooled.

People vary considerably in their tolerance to air motion, temperature, and humidity, and this tolerance varies with the season. An air motion level that feels comfortable and refreshing in hot weather may feel disagreeable and drafty in the winter. Therefore, the air supply outlets for most local ventilation systems should be adjustable in direction and permit reduction in outlet velocity. This will increase the acceptance of spot cooling (Olesen and Nielsen 1980, 1983).

System Types and Design Recommendations

Supply air can be provided by outdoor air introduced direct-ly or after dehumidification or cooling (evaporative or mechanical). It can also be provided by combinations of outdoor and recirculated air.

Local cooling fans should be used with caution other than in light heat-load areas where ambient temperature is below skin temperature. Where an elevated ambient temperature exists, the high velocity may add considerably to the convective heat load and, thus, seriously increase the demand for evaporative cooling, with little or no relief for the worker.

A supply system using outdoor air will provide excellent relief in most industrial areas. However, where the outdoor air temperature exceeds the skin temperature, the direct supply of outdoor air is obviously reduced in effectiveness. Such a system is best used in climates where hot weather periods are brief.

Evaporative cooling systems offer greater relief for workers in that the discharge temperature can be lowered within 5 °F (3 °C) of the wet-bulb temperature to obtain adequate convective body cooling. Because of the increase in wet-bulb temperature of evaporative cooling, it is usually unwise to recirculate evaporatively cooled air.

For economic reasons, evaporative cooling systems generally are used to provide heat relief. Separate supply systems or roof ventilators provide additional makeup air and heat removal. However, evaporatively cooled systems supplying 100% of the ventilation air have been used with excellent results in laundries and similar applications. Chapter 4 of the 1983 EQUIPMENT Volume, Chapter 57 of this volume, and Phillips et. al. (1955) have further information.

An air supply with mechanical refrigeration offers the greatest relief. Such systems have high initial cost, but they are used increasingly in precision work and testing areas, in areas requiring constant ambient conditions for product uniformity or control, and where increased worker efficiency is reflected in a reasonable return on the investment.

Outdoor air should be brought as directly as feasible to the proximity of the work station. It should not impinge on hot equipment or mix with hot ambient air. Supply ducts passing through hot areas should be insulated. Aluminum ducts keep heat gain from radiant sources to a minimum. For large work areas with a high rate of ventilation, local relief can best be obtained by locating the outlets as close to the floor as possible (Azer 1982a, 1982b, 1984; Tillman et. al. 1984).

The outside air intake should be located with great care to avoid cross contamination from external sources. Frequently, this is a problem in the industrial environment (Yamazaki 1982). Figures 2 and 3 include details.

Outlet Design

When designing outlets for local relief, consider the following:

Location. For general low-level ventilation, the outlets should be at about the 10 ft (3 m) level, although 8 to 12 ft (2.5 to 3.5 m) is acceptable. For spot cooling, the outlets should be kept close to the worker to minimize mixing with the warmer air in the space. In most spot cooling installations, the outlets should be brought down to the 7 ft (2 m) level.

Discharge Velocity. Discharge velocity may be as high as necessary (consistent with good practice) to obtain the desired velocity at the work station. For the throw of the outlets, consult the manufacturer's data for the particular outlet. Velocities of 1000 to 2000 fpm (5 to 10 m/s) are most frequently used for outlets at the 10 ft (3 m) level. When the supply air is cooled, the velocity through an outlet directly at or over a worker should be kept low—about 50 fpm (0.25 m/s). These recommended velocities are for conditions of maximum heat load. For more moderate weather and ambient conditions, the worker will want to reduce the velocities. Outlet dampers for velocity control should always be provided.

Discharge Volume. The outlet volume required will vary widely, depending on whether the system is designed to provide spot cooling or general ventilation. Generally, 1500 to 2000 cfm (700 to 1000 L/s) per station will be adequate for moderate loads, and 3000 to 5000 cfm (1500 to 2500 L/s) for areas having high heat loads. With remote outlets, large air volumes air required to ensure adequate relief because of the mixing of the supply air with the warmer surrounding air through which it is projected.

The airstream from a large outlet will maintain an appreciable core of air at the original supply air temperature for a considerable distance from the outlet. Small outlets and slot outlets have small cores that rapidly dissipate through induction. In small enclosures or semi-enclosures, the low induction characteristics of perforated panel supply outlets make them very effective for mechanically cooled installations.

Direction Control. Directional outlets can be directed down in the summer when cooling is needed and up in winter for ventilation, heating, and makeup air. From the production standpoint, control may be necessary to direct the relief ventilation so as not to disturb the product or upset the performance of local exhaust hoods.

Types of Outlets

Chapter 32 and 33 of the 1985 FUNDAMENTALS Volume and Chapter 2 of the 1983 EQUIPMENT Volume should be reviewed before selecting outlets for a specific application.

Commercial grilles and diffusers are used for many industrial applications, for fully air-conditioned spaces where directional adjustment and vigorous air motion are not needed or desired. Directional grilles, diffusers, and nozzles designed specifically for industrial relief systems are also available. To permit control of the discharge direction and the air motion at the worker, these outlets should be readily adjustable from the floor. Frequent directional adjustment is *required* for most systems to provide desirable working conditions.

Directional grilles are used for long horizontal throws in large open areas. Circular diffusers may be used for similar applications and also will provide good spot cooling. Nozzle outlets such as the ordinary ball and socket, the *punkah louver* (a small ball and socket outlet frequently seen in aircraft), and drum outlets are often used for spot cooling. The drum outlet also provides good general ventilation and is frequently used for this purpose. This outlet is similar to the punkah louver but is rectangular, has only horizontal adjustment, and is fitted with louvers for manual vertical adjustment.

The variety of custom outlets is limited only by the designer's imagination and ingenuity. The important thing is that such outlets should do the required job. Good velocity distribution through the outlet face area is necessary, or predicted performance must be modified to suit the nonuniform flow. Outlets in the sides and bottoms of ducts should have turning vanes. Diffuser outlets should have turning vanes at the drop connections.

Figure 4 shows some of the directional outlets that have been used for low-level general ventilation and spot cooling. Outlet *A* (the Navy Type E) in various forms has been used for many years in ship machinery spaces. Outlets *B* and *C* are excellent for local area or spot cooling. The adjustable louvers of *D* applied to directional outlets such as *E* or *F* provide excellent control. The commercial directional grilles serve the same purpose. The two-way damper arrangement *E* is used in local area or aisleway ventilation, to direct the supply air to the ceiling in winter to mix the discharge air with warm or hot air rising from internal sources.

Outlet *G* indicates the use of a commercial directional diffuser that can be adjusted to provide a variable downward air

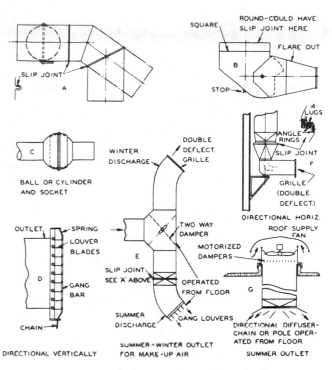

Fig. 4 Directional Outlets for Spot Cooling

flow pattern from flat to vertical. The outlet is shown on a roof supply fan, which is a common application, but the outlet drop must extend through the layer of hot ceiling air to provide effective relief ventilation.

Where overhead installations are not possible because of interferences, outlets near the floor may be used. These may be grilles located in pilasters, control panels, tables, equipment, or in the floor itself. Such outlets have been successful in welding and foundry areas and at work locations in kitchens.

DILUTION VENTILATION

Dilution ventilation is general ventilation used to dilute contaminated air with uncontaminated air within the building or workroom. In many cases, dilution ventilation is less satisfactory than local exhaust ventilation (see Chapter 36), from either a health hazard control or energy conservation point of view. Dilution ventilation may be preferred when (1) moving sources are involved, (2) many small sources are scattered throughout the workroom and effectively prohibit local exhaust ventilation, and (3) when general ventilation is required for comfort control.

Dilution ventilation may be inappropriate if (1) large volumes of contaminant are released or the contaminant has a high degree of toxicity, (2) the employee must work close to the source so that insufficient dilution occurs before the contaminated air passes through his breathing zone, and (3) operator exposure is highly variable and not predictable.

Dilution ventilation required by ventilation systems that address the problem of fire, smoke, and explosion need careful study. Numerous recent publications cover this issue.

Design of Dilution Systems

The first step in the design of a dilution ventilation system is to determine an acceptable level of exposure. These levels could be Permissible Exposure Limits (PELs), Threshold Limit Values (TVLs), or in-house TLVs. It may be desirable to set design objectives below statutory PELs and TLVs because of the variability of individual sensitivity to contaminants and the knowledge that acceptable limits do change—usually in the direction of lower values.

The second step is to determine the generation rate of the contaminant. Production records, material balance, existing ventilation rate, contaminant exposure, similar operations, and experienced engineering judgment can assist in determining the generation rate. However obtained, the acceptable exposure level and the contaminant generation rate are necessary to design a dilution ventilation system properly. Design based on the number of air changes per hour, or other estimates, are inadequate and could lead to unacceptably high exposure levels or to unnecessarily high installation costs and/or energy consumption.

The third step in calculating the dilution rate is to determine the mixing factor, K. Typically, K ranges between 3 and 10 and is required to ensure that employee exposure is maintained below the acceptable level, not just that the average concentration in the room or the exhaust duct is sufficiently low. K will depend on several factors: (1) toxicity of the contaminant, (2) physiological effects of overexposure, (3) uniformity of contaminant generation, (4) effectiveness of the ventilation system, (5) geometry of the work area, and (6) contaminant concentration in the uncontaminated replacement air.

Dilution ventilation is applied most often to the dilution of solvent vapors. In this case, the required dilution rate, at normal temperature and pressure, is given by:

$$\text{ft}^3/\text{pt evaporated} = 403 \cdot SpGv \cdot 10^6 \cdot K/(MW \cdot TLV) \quad (4)$$

$$[\text{m}^3/\text{L evaporated} = 24.45 \cdot SpGv \cdot 10^6 \cdot K/(MW \cdot TLV)]$$

$$\text{ft}^3/\text{lb evaporated} = 387 \cdot 10^6 \cdot K/(MW \cdot TLV) \quad (5)$$

$$[\text{m}^3/\text{kg evaporated} = 24.45 \cdot 10^6 \cdot K/(MW \cdot TLV)]$$

where

$SpGv$ = specific gravity of the liquid.
MW = molecular weight of solvent.
TLV = threshold limit value, ppm (mg/kg).
K = mixing factor.

Dilution for gases can be given by:

$$Qd = Qg \cdot 10^6 \cdot K/TLV$$

where

Qd = dilution rate required, cfm (L/s).
Qg = generation of contaminant, cfm (L/s).
K = mixing factor.

Dilution ventilation for dust and fumes is frequently unsuccessful because (1) the lower TLV (higher toxicity of the material) requires excessive exhaust rate, (2) the rate of evolution and violence of dispersion frequently makes dilution ventilation ineffective, and (3) quantity or release rate of contaminant is extremely difficult to obtain.

Mixtures

When more than one hazardous material is present in the work place, the combined effect of the contaminants must be considered. In the absence of contrary data, their effect should be considered as additive. When designing a dilution ventilation system, this requires calculating the dilution rate of each component and using the sum of the rates as the dilution rate for the mixtures.

REFERENCES

ACGIH. 1985. Threshold Limit Values for Chemical Substances and Physical Agents in the Work Environment and Biological Exposure Indices with Intended Changes for 1985-86. American Conference of Governmental Industrial Hygienists, Cincinnati, OH.

Azer, N.Z. 1982. Design Guidelines for Spot Cooling Systems: Part 1—Assessing the Acceptability of the Environment. *ASHRAE Transactions*, Vol. 88, Part 1.

Azer, N.Z. 1982. Design Guidelines for Spot Cooling Systems: Part 2—Cooling Jet Model and Design Procedure. *ASHRAE Transactions*, Vol. 88, Part 2.

Azer, N.Z. 1984. Design of Spot Cooling Systems for Hot Industrial Environments. *ASHRAE Transactions*, Vol. 90, Part 1.

Caplan, K.J. 1980. Heat Stress Measurements. *Heating, Piping and Air-Conditioning*, Feb., pp. 55-62.

Caplan, K.J., and Knutson, G.W. 1978. Laboratory Fume Hoods: Part 2—Influence of Room Air Supply. *ASHRAE Transactions*, Vol. 84, Part 2, p. 522.

Heating and Cooling for Men in Industry. 1975. American Industrial Hygienists Association, 2nd Edition, Akron, OH.

Industrial Ventilation, A Manual of Recommended Practice. 1984. American Conference of Governmental Industrial Hygienists, 18th Edition, Cincinnati, OH.

ISO. 1982. Hot Environments—Estimation of the Heat Stress on a Working Man, Based on the WBGT—Index (Wet Bulb Globe Temperature). Geneva: International Standard Organization.

Olesen, B.W., and Nielsen, R. 1980. Spot Cooling of Workplaces in Hot Industries. *Final Report to the European Coal-and Steel Union. Research Programme "Ergonomics—Rehabilitation III*, No. 7245-35-004, (Oct.), p. 88.

Olesen, B.W., and Nielson, R. 1981. Radiant Spot Cooling of Hot Places of Work. *ASHRAE Transactions,* Vol. 87, Part1.

Olesen, B.W., and Nielson, R. 1983. Convective Spot-Cooling of Hot Working Environments. *Proceedings of the XVIth International Congress of Refrigeration,* Sept. Paris.

Peterson, R.L.; Schofer, E.L.; and Martin, D.W. 1983. Laboratory Air Systems - Further Testing. *ASHRAE Transactions*, Vol. 89, Part 2B, p. 571.

Phillips, R.E., Jr. et al. 1955. Evaporative Cooling—a Symposium. *Heating, Piping and Air Conditioning*, ASHRAE Journal Section (Aug.), p. 141.

Sanberg, M. Ventilation Efficiency. *ASHRAE Transactions*, Vol. 89, Part 2B, p. 455.

Skaret, E. Ventilation Efficiency. *ASHRAE Transactions*, Vol. 89, Part 2B, p. 480.

Tillman, F.A.; Hwang, C.L.; and Lin, M.J. 1984. Optimal Design of an Air Jet for Spot Cooling. *ASHRAE Transactions*, Vol. 90, Part 1B, p. 476.

Wilson, D.J. A Design Procedure for Estimating Air Intake Contamination from Nearby Exhaust Vents. *ASHRAE Transactions*, Vol. 89, Part 2A, p. 136.

Yamazaki, K. 1982. Factorial Analysis on Conditions Affecting the Sense of Comfort of Workers in the Air-Conditioned Working Environment. *ASHRAE Transactions*, Vol. 88, Part 1, p. 241.

CHAPTER 42

UNDERGROUND MINE AIR CONDITIONING AND VENTILATION

EXCESS humidity, high temperature, and the need for adequate oxygen have always been points of concern in underground mines. A combination of heat and humidity lowers efficiency and productivity, and can cause illness and death. Air cooling and ventilation are needed in deep underground mines to minimize heat stress. As mines have become deeper, heat removal and ventilation problems have become more difficult to solve. This chapter discusses the following:

(1) Worker heat stress
(2) Sources of heat in mine air design
(3) Mine air cooling with dehumidification
(4) Cooling surface air
(5) Mechanical refrigeration plants
(6) Underground heat exchangers
(7) Evaporative cooling system
(8) Energy recovery systems

WORKER HEAT STRESS

Mine cooling must maintain both air temperatures and humidities at levels that maintain the health and comfort of the miners so they may work safely and efficiently. Chapter 8 of the 1985 FUNDAMENTALS Handbook addresses human response to heat and humidity. The upper temperature limit for humans at rest in still, saturated air is about 90 °F (32 °C). If air is moving at 200 fpm (1 m/s), the upper limit shifts to 90 °F (77 °C). A relative humidity of less than 80% in a hot, humid mine environment is desirable.

Hot, humid environments are improved to a limited extent by providing air movement of 150 to 500 fpm (0.8 to 2.5 m/s). A greater air volume may lower the mine temperature, but air velocity has limited value in increasing the individual's comfort.

Usual indices for defining acceptable temperature limits are:

The effective temperature scale. An 80 °F (26.7 °C) effective temperature is the upper limit for worker comfort and high efficiency.

The Wet-Bulb Globe Temperature (WBGT) Index. An 80 °F (26.7 °C) WBGT is the permissible temperature exposure limit during moderate continuous work, and 77 °F (25.0 °C) WBGT for heavy continuous work.

Figure 1 shows acceptable heat exposure limits for different levels of work efforts.

DESIGN CONSIDERATIONS: SOURCES OF HEAT ENTERING MINE AIR

Adiabatic Compression

Air descending a shaft increases in pressure (due to the weight above it) and temperature. As air flows down a shaft, with no heat interchange between the shaft and air and no evaporation of moisture, it is heated as if compressed in a compressor.

The presentation of this chapter is assigned to TC 9.2, Industrial Air Conditioning.

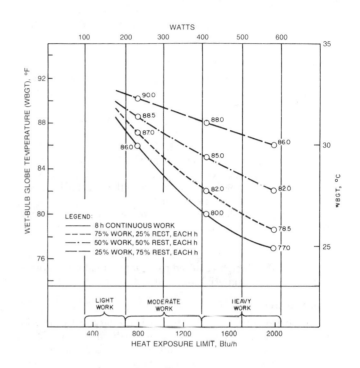

Fig. 1 Permissible Heat Exposure Threshold Limit Value

One Btu is added to each pound of air for every 778 feet (9.8 J/kg·m) elevation or is subtracted for the same elevation increase. For dry air, the dry-bulb temperature change is $1/(0.24 \times 778) = 778 = 0.00535 °F/ft$ $(0.00975 °C)/m)$ or $1 °F/187$ ft $(1 °C/102$ m) elevation. For constant air-vapor mixtures, the change in dry-bulb temperatures equals $(1 + W)/(0.24 = .45W)$ per 778 feet of elevation, depending upon the vapor content W (pounds of water per pound of air).

Theoretically, when 100,000 cfm (47 m³/s) of standard air is delivered underground via an inlet airway, the heat of auto-compression for every 1,000 feet of depth is:

$$100{,}000 \times 0.075 \times \frac{1}{\text{lb./778}} \times 1{,}000 \text{ ft} = 9640 \text{ Btu/min}$$

$$= 48.2 \text{ tons refrigeration (560 W/m)}$$

Auto-compression of air may be masked by the presence of other heating or cooling sources, such as shaft wall rock, ground water, air and water lines, or electrical facilities. The actual temperature of air descending a shaft does not usually match the theoretical adiabatic temperature increases, due to the following:

1. the night cool air temperature effect on the rock or lining of the shaft
2. temperature gradient of ground rock related to depth
3. evaporation of moisture within the shaft, which decreases the temperature while increasing the moisture content of the air

The seasonal variation in surface air temperature has a major effect. If surface air temperature is high, much heat is liberated to the shaft walls so the temperature rise may not reach the adiabatic rate. When the surface temperature is low, heat is taken from the shaft walls and temperature increases more than the adiabatic rate. Similar diurnal variations may occur. As air flows down a shaft and increases in temperature and density, its volume and cooling ability decreases. Additionally, the mine ventilation requirements increase with depth. Underground fan pressures up to 10 in. water gage (2.5 kPa) static pressure are commonplace in mine ventilation and also raise the air's temperature about 0.45 °F per inch of water (1 °C/kPa) fan static pressure.

Electromechanical Equipment

Underground power-operated equipment transfers the heat to air. Common underground mine power systems are electricity, diesel, and compressed air.

Heat produced by underground diesel equipment equals about 90% of the heat value of the fuel consumed. Therefore, a value of 125,000 Btu/gallon (34.9 MJ/L) for fuel consumed by diesel equipment is dissipated as heat to the ventilating airstream. If the exhaust gas is bubbled through a wet scrubber, thus cooling the gases by adiabatic saturation, both the sensible heat and moisture content of the air are increased.

Vehicles with electric drive or an electric-hydraulic system may release from one-third to one-half the heat of diesel-driven equipment.

All energy used in a horizontal plane appears as heat added to the mine air. Energy required to elevate a load gives potential energy to the material and will not appear as heat.

Groundwater

Transport of heat by groundwater is the largest variable in mine ventilation. Groundwater is ordinarily the same temperature as the virgin rock temperature. If a ditch containing hot water is not covered, there may be more heat picked up by the ventilation cooling air from the ditch water than from the heat conducted through the hot wall rock. It is very important to contain warm drainage water in pipelines or in a covered ditch.

Significance of heat from open ditches increases as airways get older and the flow of heat from the surrounding rock decreases. In one Montana mine, water in open ditches was 40 °F (22.4 °C) cooler than when it issued from the wall rock; the heat was transferred to the air. Evaporation of water from wall rock surfaces lowers the surface temperature of the rock, which increases the temperature gradient of the rock, depresses the dry-bulb temperature of the air, and allows more heat to flow from the rock. Most of this extra heat is usually expended in evaporation.

WALL ROCK HEAT FLOW

Heat flow from the wall rock into an airway is complex. The heat flow from wall rock with constant thermal conductivity is considerably higher after a mine opening is first excavated (transient heat flow) than several years later when steady state conditions have developed. An empirical equation can be used for the calculations:

$$Q = UA \, \Delta t$$

where:

Q = Heat Flow in Btu/h (kw)
U = Overall coefficient of heat transfer, Btu/h · ft^2 · °F (W/m^2·K) (from Figure 2 or 3)
A = Area
Δt = Temperature difference between the virgin rock and the dry-bulb air temperature

The above equation in conjunction with mine ventilation rates, virgin rock temperature, and the age of airways will permit wall rock heat flow calculations to be made throughout a mine.

In young mining areas, heat inflow must be computed by transient heat flow techniques. A heat flow graph from wall rock to air versus time can be plotted. Figures 2 and 3 show examples of heat flow with time from two types of mines. The temperature difference is not constant along the entire length of the airway, so it is advisable to treat the long airway as a series of consecutive lengths. Figures 2 and 3 are based on the following:

1. Figures 2 and 3 are based on calculations of mine openings with cross-sectional areas range from 225 to 450 ft^2 (20 to 42 m^2).
2. The heat transfer coefficient decreases from the time the heading is excavated and ventilated.
3. Steady-state heat transfer coefficients are approximately 0.10 to 0.15 Btu/hr · ft^2 · °F (5.7 to 8.5 W/m^2·K) for salt or granite envelopes.

The Starfield and Goch-Patterson methods of calculating heat rate from underground exposed rock surfaces are often used and cited in the literature. The Starfield method is often difficult to apply because of its dependence on air velocity criteria. The errors in obtaining or projecting velocity, length, and cross-sectional dimensions are often worse than this theoretically, more accurate method.

The Goch-Patterson method of calculating is widely used. It assumes that the rock face temperature is the same as that of the air. Heat load calculated for airways is overestimated by 10 to 20%, so a contingency is normally not added to the heat load. When using the Goch-Patterson tables, care should be taken that the correct value of instantaneous versus average heat load data is used for shafts and older connecting airways. Time average heat load data should be used for excavations that are continuous and active.

Since heat from the wall rock is one of the major sources of heat into a mine, its rate may be accurately estimated horizontally and vertically. It is desirable that virgin rock temperatures (VRT) be taken of the wall rock at various elevations throughout the mine.

Before the actual gradient can be constructed to estimate the temperatures at various elevations, a base point for measurement must be determined. It is generally agreed that a virgin rock temperature taken 50 ft (15.2 m) below the earth's surface represents a good datum point. This value is normally equal to the mean surface air temperature (dry-bulb) taken over a number of years.

Figure 4 graphically shows approximate geothermal gradient of various mining districts of the world. Table 1 lists maximum virgin rock temperatures at the bottom of various mines.

Heat from Blasting

Short-term heat produced by blasting can be appreciable. Virtually all the explosive energy is converted to heat during detonation. The typical heat potential in various types of explosives is similar to that of 60% dynamite, about 1800 Btu/lb (4.2 MJ/kg).

MINE AIR COOLING AND DEHUMIDIFICATION

Sources of underground mine heat are hot wall rock, hot water issuing from underground sources, adiabatic compression of the inlet air down deep shafts, operation of electromechanical equipment, heat exchange between hot-compressed air lines or hot mine-water draining lines and the cool ventilation air in the entrance airway or shaft, oxidation

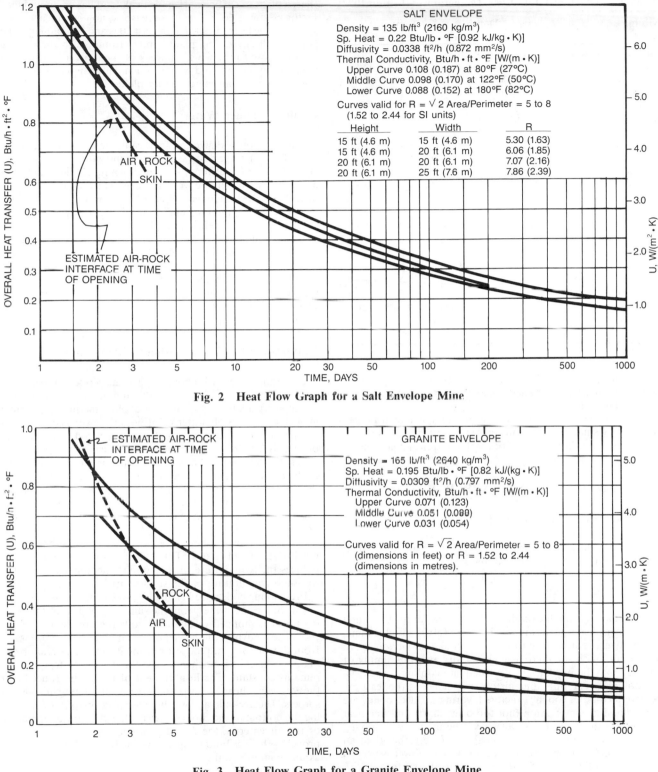

Fig. 2   Heat Flow Graph for a Salt Envelope Mine

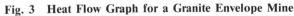

Fig. 3   Heat Flow Graph for a Granite Envelope Mine

of timber and sulfide minerals, heat liberated by blasting, friction and shock losses of moving air, body metabolism, friction heat from rock movement, and heat generated by internal combustion engines (Fenton 1972).

Geothermic gradients of the world's major mining districts vary from approximately 0.5 °F to over 4 °F per 100 ft of elevation decrease (0.9 to 7.3 °C per 100 m).

When air is cooled underground, the heat taken from this air must be moved in some manner. If enough cool, uncontaminated air is available, the warmed air can be mixed with it and the resulting mixture can then be removed from the mine. In a water heat exchanger, the water is warmed while the air is cooled. The warm water is either returned to the cooling plant (cooling tower, underground mechanical refrigeration units, or

Table 1 Maximum Virgin Rock Temperatures (Fenton 1972)

Mining District	Depth feet	metres	Temperature °F	°C
Kolar Gold Field, India	11,000	3,353	152	67
South Africa	10,000	3,048	125-130	52-54
Morro Velho, Brazil	8,000	2,438	130	54
N. Broken Hill, Australia	3,530	1,076	112	44
Great Britain	4,000	1,219	114	46
Braloroe BC Canada	4,100	1,250	112.5	50
Kirkland Lake, Ont.	4,000-6,000	1,219-1,829	66-81	19-27
Falconbridge Mine, Ont.	4,000-6,000	1,219-1,819	70-84	21-29
Lockerby Mine, Ont.	3,000-4,000	914-1,219	67-96	19-36
Levac Borehold (Inco) Ont.	7,000-10,000	2,134-3,048	99-128	37-53
Garson Mine, Ont.	2,000-5,000	610-1,524	54-78	12-26
Lake Shore Mine, Ont.	6,000	1,829	73	23
Hollinger Mine, Ont.	4,000	1,219	58	14
Creighton Mine, Ont.	2,000-10,000	610-3,049	60-138	16-59
Superior, AZ	4,000	1,219	140	60
San Manuel, AZ	4,500	1,372	118	48
Butte, Montana	5,200	1,585	145-150	63-66
Ambrosia Lake, NM	4,000	1,219	140	60
Brunswick, No. 12 New Brunswick, CA	3,700	1,128	73	23
Belle Island Salt Mine, LA	1,400	427	88	31

heat exchangers) in a closed circuit where it is again cooled, discharged to the mine drainage system, or sprayed into the mine exhaust air system.

Water, if available, is the best heat transfer medium in a mine. A relatively small pipeline can remove as much heat as would be removed by a large volume of air that requires a large shaft and inlet airways.

EQUIPMENT AND APPLICATIONS

Air Conditioning Components and Practices

Figures 4 through 7 show components normally used in underground air-conditioning systems.

Cooling Surface Air

If cold air is available on the surface, as in far northern and far southern hemisphere winters, it can be forced into the mine. It may even be necessary to heat the intake air in winter. In deep mines with small cross-sectional airways, this supply of cold air may be insufficient for adequate cooling.

Cooling of entering mine air on the surface is the least expensive method of cooling. Factors favoring surface cooling are low adiabatic compression (not too deep shaft) and low heat gain in the shaft and intake airways. The main energy-saving advantage of cooling inlet air on the surface rather than an underground cooling plant is that no electric power is needed to return cooling water from the plant to the surface.

In a surface plant installation, air is chilled by cold water or brine produced from mechanical refrigeration units. It then is delivered to the intake shaft to be taken underground. Condenser water is usually cooled in towers or spray ponds. Such installations have been used in Morro Velho, Brazil; Robinson Deep Mine, Rand, South Africa; Kolar, India; and Rieu du Coeur, Belgium.

When air reaches the working headings, it has warmed considerably by auto-compression and heat from the wall rock. Fur-

ther, a plant of sufficient size for peak load has an annual load factor as low as 60%. For these reasons, no new surface plant systems have been installed in the last 20 years. The present trend is to install air-cooling plants underground, with the cooling coils as close to the working areas of the mine as possible. If a large supply of cold water is available, it can be piped underground to air-conditioning plants.

Cooling Surface Water

The concept of delivering surface-made ice or an ice slurry in 32 °F (0 °C) water down a pipeline is intriguing. Chilled water could be used for drilling, wetting down muckpiles, and other activities where men are working. Chilled water at 32 °F (0 °C) available underground reduces circulated flow rate to 50 to 70%, which reduces pumping capital and power costs of the usual chilled water air-conditioning plants.

Ice-making machines, however, have a lower coefficient of performance and higher capital costs compared to normal mechanical refrigeration units used to chill mine water.

In one Canadian mine, large, cold, mined-out areas are sprayed with water during the winter months, allowing ice to form in the openings. In summer, intake air is cooled by drawing it over this ice.

Evaporative Cooling of Mine Chilled Water

Geographic areas with both low average winter temperatures and low relative humidity during the summer have natural cooling capacity adaptable to mine air cooling methods. A system in such an area cools water or brine on the surface, carries it through closed-circuit piping to an underground air-cooling plant close to the working zone, and returns it to the cooling tower through a second pipeline. At the mine underground air-cooling plant, heat is adsorbed by the water circulating through the system and is dissipated to the surface atmosphere in the surface cooling tower. The closed-circuit piping balances the hydrostatic head, so pumping power must only overcome frictional resistance.

An evaporative cooling tower was installed at a mine in the northwest United States. This "dew point" cooling system reduces the temperature of the cooling medium to below the wet-bulb temperature of the surface atmosphere (Figure 4).

Pre-cooling coils were installed between the fan and cooling tower. Some cool water from the sump at the base of the cooling tower is pumped through the coils then to the top of the cooling tower where this heated flow joins the warm return water from the airflow, and moisture content in the airstream passing over the coils is unchanged, so the dew-point temperature remains constant. The heat content of the air is reduced and the equivalent heat is added to the water circulating in coils adsorbers. The dry-bulb and wet-bulb temperature of the air entering the bottom of the cooling tower is less than the temperature of the air entering the fan. The water leaving the tower approaches the wet-bulb temperature of the surface atmosphere as an economic limit.

Evaporative Cooling Plus Mechanical Refrigeration

On humid summer days, the wet-bulb temperature may increase over extended periods, severely hampering the effectiveness of evaporative cooling. This factor, plus the warming of the air entering the mine, may necessitate the series installation of a mechanical refrigeration unit to chill the water delivered underground.

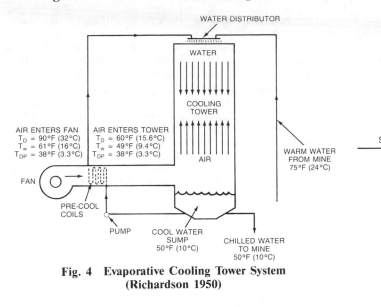

**Fig. 4 Evaporative Cooling Tower System
(Richardson 1950)**

Performance characteristics at one northern United States mine on a spring day were as follows:

Evaporative Cooling Tower	1224 tons (4305 kw)
Mechanical Refrigeration Unit (in series)	816 tons (2870 kw)
Water Volume Circulated	1750 gpm
Water Temperature Entering Mine	40°F (4.4°C)
Water Temperature Leaving Mine	68°F (20°C)

Combination Systems

Components may be arranged in various ways for the greatest efficiency. For example, air-cooling towers may be used to cool water during the cool months of the year and supplemented with a mechanical refrigerator during the warm months of the year.

Surface-installed mechanical refrigeration units provide the bulk of cooling in summer. In winter, much of the cooling comes from the pre-cooling tower when the ambient wet-bulb temperature is usually lower than the temperature of water entering the tower. The pre-cooling tower is normally located above the return water storage reservoir. An evaporative cooling tower is more cost effective (capital and operating costs) than mechanical refrigeration with comparable capacity.

Reducing High Pressure Liquids

Use of underground refrigerated water chillers is increasing, due to system efficiency, because of their location close to the work. Transfer of heat from condensers is the major problem with these systems. If hot mine water is used to cool condenser, efficiency is lost due to high condensing temperature, plus probable corrosion and fouling. If surface water is used, it must be piped both in and out of the mine after use. If water is non-corrosive and non-fouling, fairly good chiller efficiencies can be obtained up to 125°F (52°C) entering condenser water.

Surface water is usually allowed to flow into tanks at intervals down the shaft to break the high water head that develops in a vertical pipe. Energy is wasted and the temperature will rise about 1°F for every 1000 ft (1.8°C/km) of drop. The water must be pumped out of the mine, which adds cost. The water pressure can be reduced for use at the mine level and then discharged to the mine drainage system. But the costs for pumping the water to the surface are high, thus offsetting the convenience of low-pressure mine cooling.

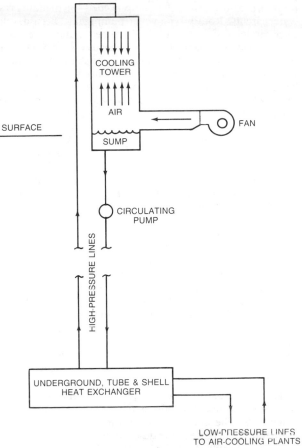

**Fig. 5 Underground Heat Exchanger, Pressure
Reduction System**

In a pipe 4000 ft (200 m) high filled with water (density = 62.4 lb/ft³), the pressure would be 62.4·4000/144 = 1730 psi (11.8 MPa). In an open piping system, the pressure at the bottom is further increased by the head necessary to raise the water up the pipe and out of the mine. Water pipes and coils in deep mines must resist this high pressure. Fittings and pipe specialties are costly, and safety precautions and care must be taken with such high-pressure equipment. Closed-circuit piping has the same static pressures, but pumps must only overcome pipe friction.

High construction cost constrains frequent movement of surface cooling towers, a desired feature for shifting mining operations. Closed-circuit systems have been used in various mines in the United States to overcome the cost of pumping brine or cooling water out of the mine.

To achieve the advantage of both low pressure and closed-circuit, the Magma mine in Arizona has installed heat exchangers underground at the mining horizon. The shell and tube heat exchanger converts surface chilled water in a high pressure closed-circuit to a low-pressure chilled-water system on mine production levels. Air-cooling plants and chilled water lines can be constructed of standard materials, permitting frequent relocation (see Figure 5). Although desirable, this system has not been widely used.

Energy-Recovery Systems

Pumping costs can be reduced by combining a water turbine with the pump. The energy of high-pressure water flowing to a lower pressure drives the pump needed for the low pressure water circuit. Rotary-type water pumps have been developed to pump against a 5000-ft (1550 m) head, and water turbines are also available to operate under head. Figure 6 shows a turbine pump-motor combination. Only the shaft and the pipe and fittings to the unit on the working level need high-strength pipes. The system connects to underground refrigeration water-chilling units, whose return chilled water is used for condensing before being pumped out.

Two types of turbines are suitable for mine use—the Pelton Wheel and a pump in reverse. The Pelton Wheel has a high-duty efficiency of about 80%, is simply constructed, and is readily controlled. A pump in reverse is only 10 to 15% efficient, but mine maintenance and operating personnel are very familiar with this equipment. Turbine energy recovery may have a problem when operating on chilled mine service water. Mine demands fluctuate widely, often outside the operating range of the turbine. Operating experience shows that coupling a Pelton Wheel to an electric generator is the best approach.

South African mines have mechanical refrigeration units, surface heat-recovery systems, and turbine pumps incorporated into their air-cooling plants in a closed circuit.

A surface-sited plant has two disadvantages. Chilled water delivered underground at low operating pressure heats up at a rate of 1 °F per 1000 ft (1.8 °C/km) of shaft depth. The pumping of this water back to the surface is expensive. The installation of energy-recovery turbines underground and a heat-recovery system on the surface helps economically justify the installation.

The descending chilled water is fed through a turbine mechanically linked to pumps operating in the return chilled water line. The energy-recovery turbine reduces the rate of temperature increase in the descending chilled water column to about 0.3 °F/1000 ft (0.5 °C/km) of shaft depth.

Pre-cooling towers on the surface reduce the water temperature a few degrees before it enters the refrigeration plant. Operating cost of a surface refrigeration plant is about one-half that of a comparable underground plant because of the unlimited supply of relatively cool ambient air for heat rejection.

In a uranium mine in South Africa, waste heat comes from surface refrigeration units and a high condensing heat pump. Condensing water from the refrigeration units is the source for the heat pump, which will discharge 130 °F (55 °C) water. This water can be used as service hot water or as preheated feed water for steam generation in the uranium plant. The total additional costs of a heat pump over a conventional refrigeration plant have a simple pay back of about 1½ years.

Pelton turbines are used by the South African gold mining industry to recover energy from chilled water flowing down the shafts. About 1000 kW might be recovered at a typical installation, thus partially offsetting the power requirements for pumping return water to surface.

One U. S. mining company has installed an energy-recovery system of two separate units at the 2500 ft (750 m) level and the 5000 ft (1500 m) level. Each installation consists of turbines directly connected to 200 HP (150 kW), 3600 rpm induction motors operating as generators. Rated output is 144 kW at 550 gpm (34.7 L/s) water flow at approximately 2500 ft (750 m) head.

A surface level installation chills the service water used throughout the mining operation. A 6-in. (250-mm) chilled water line feeds chilled water to the turbine through a pneumatically controlled valve. The water level in an adjacent discharge reservoir is sensed to modulate the position of this valve proportional to the water demand in the reservoir. When the system is shut down, the inlet valve to the turbine slowly closes by spring pressure. Simultaneously, the bypass valve opens slowly and

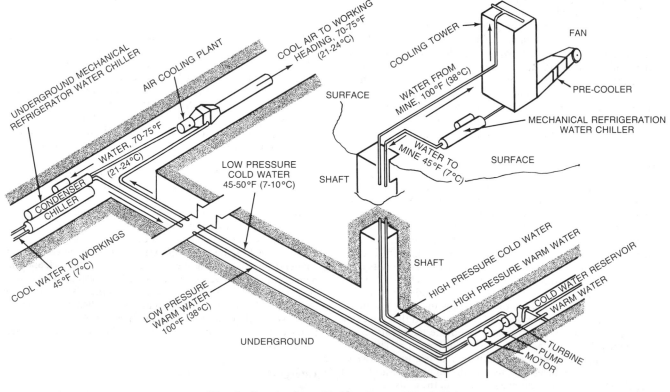

**Fig. 6　Layout for a Turbine-Pump-Motor Unit
with Air-Cooling Plants and Mechanical Refrigeration**

water discharges through an orifice into the sump. Typical operating data are as follows:

Bypass Discharge Temp.	43.7 °F (6.5 °C)
Turbine Inlet Temp.	40.2 °F (4.6 °C)
Turbine Discharge Temp.	40.8 °F (4.9 °C)
Turbine Output	144 kW
Volume Through Turbine	550 gpm (34.7 L/s)

Installed cost for the energy-recovery system on one level was approximately $70,000 in 1978, and it saved $13,000 per year in power costs.

MECHANICAL REFRIGERATION PLANTS

In most underground applications, mechanical refrigeration plants (Figure 6) provide chilled water for delivery underground where some or all may be supplied condensed to direct-expansion air-to-air cooling systems. Air that is passed over the direct-expansion evaporator coils is cooled and delivered to working headings.

Underground mechanical refrigeration plants avoid heat added by auto-compression of air coming down the shafts. The main disadvantage of these units is disposal of heat from the condensers. The condenser discharge water can either be run into the mine drainage system, returned to surface for cooling, or sprayed into the mine discharge air system.

Hot water discharged from condensers of underground refrigeration units may be ejected into the sumps of the mine water-pumping system. This procedure requires a constant resupply of condenser water from fresh water lines or mine drainage sources and increases mine pumping costs. Underground cooling towers are seldom used, since they suffer from air shortage, which results in higher condensing temperatures underground than on the surface. It is difficult to predict the performance of underground cooling towers and condensing temperatures of equipment over the life of a mine. High condenser temperatures cause excessive power consumption. In addition, the water is often contaminated with dust and fumes, which cause fouling, scaling, and corrosion of the piping system and condenser tubes. These problems tend to favor placing mechanical refrigeration units on the surface.

Spot Cooling

Spot cooling permits the driving of long headings for exploration or extended development prior to establishment of primary ventilation equipment. Using mechanical refrigeration systems with direct-expansion air coolers, they service a single heading or localized mining area. Spot coolers allow the mine to advance development headings more rapidly and under more desirable conditions. Spot cooling of selected development headings may also be required in many mines where rock temperatures exceed 100 °F (38 °C).

UNDERGROUND HEAT EXCHANGER TYPES

Two types of heat exchangers are used underground—air-to-water and water-to-water. Air-to-water exchanges include those with water sprays in the airstream and finned tubes.

Air Cooling Versus Working Place Cooling

Figure 7 shows a typical underground central plant to serve a large area of the mine with air cooled by chilled water. Air flows through ventilation ducts or headings from the chiller to the working headings. When working headings are distant, the air warms and, in some cases, picks up moisture in transit. This

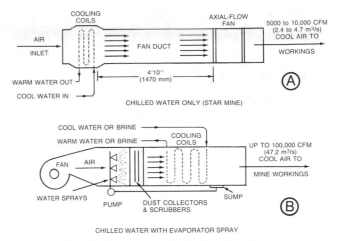

Fig. 7 Underground Air-Cooling Plants

limits available cooled air in the production area. The performance characteristics of one plant is as follows:

Air Volume Cooled	100,000 cfm (47 m³/s)
Entering Air Temp.	
Dry Bulb	80.5 °F (26.8 °C)
Wet Bulb	74.3 °F (23.5 °C)
Discharge Air Temp.	56.4 °F (5.6 °C)
Entering Water Temp.	42 °F (5.6 °C)
Discharge Water Temp.	67 °F (19.4 °C)
Heat Extracted from Air	508 tons (2788 kW)

If one of the air-conditioning plants from the workings becomes a problem, it is preferable to pump chilled water in closed circuit to cooling plants close to or serving individual productive headings.

Another underground cooling plant arrangement (Figure 7A) at a mine in Wallace, Idaho, is a light, portable unit that attaches to the normal auxiliary ventilation system and requires no extra excavation. This system uses no separate spray and dust-collection system, and the condensed water drips from the duct. The fan gives good service downstream from the cooler. A mechanical refrigeration unit located on the same or a nearby level chills water to cool the air, using potable water in the condenser and discharging the same to the mine discharge water sumping system.

This system avoids the central plant problem in which air is cooled and then exposed to wall rock as it is delivered many hundreds or several thousand feet or metres down an airway for pick-up by auxiliary ventilation equipment. The cooling coils are normally located within 300 ft (90 m) of the working place and reduce overall air-cooling plant requirements. Table 2 shows typical performance characteristics of the units.

Table 2 Typical Performance of Portable, Underground Cooling Units

Size Rating	30 by 48 in. (760 by 1220) 40 ton (141 kW)		24 to 36 in. (610 by 910 mm) 20 ton (70 kW)	
Location	Drift	Shaft	Stope	Stope
Entering Air Temp.	80 °F sat. (26.7 °C)	80 ° sat. (26.7 °C)	80 °F sat. (26.7 °C)	80 ° sat. (26.7 °C)
Discharge Air Temp.	70 °F sat. (21.1 °C)	64 °F sat. (17.8 °C)	68 °F sat. (20.0 °C)	80 °F sat. (17.2 °C)
Volume, cfm (m³/s)	12,000 (5.7)	12,000 (5.7)	6,000 (2.8)	6,000 (2.8)
Calculated tons (kW)	45(158)	60 (211)	22.5 (79)	26 (98)

Cooling Coils and Fan Position

The fan may be upstream or downstream of the cooling coils in underground cooling plants. An upstream fan provides a few degrees lower discharge temperature, but downstream fan distributes air more efficiently over the coils.

WATER SPRAYS AND EVAPORATIVE COOLING SYSTEMS

Finned tube heat exchangers need periodic cleaning—especially when they are upstream from the fan. The downstream position has spray water, which helps to wash some of the dirt away.

Another type of bulk-spraying cooling plant in South Africa consists of a spray chamber serving a section of isolated drift up to several hundred feet long. Chilled water is introduced through a manifold of spray nozzles. Warm mild air flows countercurrent to the various stages of water sprays. Air cooled by this direct air-to-water cooling system is delivered to the active mine workings by the primary and secondary ventilation system. These bulk-spray coolers have proven to be efficient and economical.

A uranium mine developed a portable bulk-spray cooling plant that could be advanced with the working faces, to overcome the high heat load between a stationary spray chamber and the production heading.

The 300-ton (1060 kW) capacity plant has a 81-in. long, 87-in. wide, and 102-in. high (2060 by 2210 by 2590 mm) stainless steel chamber containing two stages of spray nozzles and a demister baffle. The skid-mounted unit weighs about 2200 pounds (1000 kg) and is divided into four components (spray chamber, demister assembly, and two sump halves).

Portable bulk-spray coolers have a wide range of cooling capacity and are cost effective. A new, smaller portable spray cooling plant has been developed to cool mine air adjacent to the work place. It air cools and cleans through direct air-to-water contact. The cooler is tubular-shaped and is normally mounted in a remote location. The mine inlet and discharge air ventilation ducts are connected to duct transitions from the unit. Chilled water is piped to an exposed manifold, and warm water is discharged from the unit into a sump drain.

Hot, humid air enters the cooler at the bottom; it then slows down and flows through egg crate flow straighteners. Initial heat exchange occurs as the air passes through plastic mesh and contacts suspended water droplets.

Vertically sprayed water in a spray chamber then directly contacts the ascending warm air. The air passes through the mist eliminator, which removes suspended water droplets. Cool, dehumidified air exits from the cooler through the top outlet transition. The warmed spray water drops to the sump and discharges through a drain pipe.

REFERENCES

Anonymous. 1980. Surface Refrigeration Proves Energy Efficient at Anglo Mine. *Mine Engineering* (May).

Bossard, F.C. 1983. *A Manual of Mine Ventilation Design Practices.*

Bell, A. R. 1970. Ventilation and Refrigeration as Practiced at Rhokana Corporation Ltd., Zambia. *Journal of the Mine Ventilation Society of South Africa*, Vol. 23, No. 3, pp. 29-35.

Beskine, J. M. 1949. Priorities in Deep Mine Cooling. *Mine and Quarry Engineering* (Dec.), pp. 379-384.

Bossard, F. C. and Stout, K. S. Underground Mine Air-Cooling Practices. USBM Sponsored Research Contract G0122137.

Bromilow, J.G. 1955. Ventilation of Deep Coal Mines. *Iron and Coal Trades Review*. Part I, Feb. 11, pp. 303-308; Part II, Feb. 18, p. 376; Part III, Feb. 25, pp. 427-434.

Brown, U. E. 1945. Spot Coolers Increase Comfort of Mine Workers. *Engineering and Mining Journal*, Vol. 146, No. 1, pp. 49-58.

Caw, J. M. 1953. Some problems Raised by Underground Air Cooling on the Kolar Gold Field. *Journal of the Mine Ventilation Society of South Africa*, Vol. 2, No. 2, pp. 83-137.

Caw, J. M. 1957. Air Refrigeration. *Mine and Quarry Engineering*, pp. 111-117, March; pp. 148-156, April.

Caw, J. M. 1958. Current Ventilation Practice in Hot Deep Mines in India. *Journal of the Mine Ventilation Society of South Africa* (Aug.), Vol. 11, No. 8, pp. 145-161.

Caw, J. M. 1959. Observations at an Underground Air Conditioning Plant. *Journal of the Mine Ventilation Society of South Africa* (Nov.), Vol. 12, No. 11, pp. 270-274.

Cleland, R. 1933. Rock Temperatures and Some Ventilation Conditions in Mines of Northern Ontario. C.I.M.M. Bulletin Transactions Section, Aug., pp. 370-407.

Fenton, James L. 1972. *Survey of Underground Mine Heat Sources.* Masters Thesis, Montana College of Mineral Science and Technology.

Field, W. E. 1963. Combatting Excessive Heat Underground at Bralorne. *Mining Engineering* (Dec.), pp. 76-77.

Goch, D. C. and Patterson, H. S. 1940. The Heat Flow into Tunnels. *Journal of the Chemical Metallurgical and Mining Society of South Africa*, Vol. 41, No. 3, pp. 117-128.

Hartman, H. L. 1961. *Mine Ventilation and Air Conditioning.* New York: The Ronald Press Company.

Hill, M. 1961. Refrigeration Applied to Longwall Stopes and Longwall Stope Ventilation. *Journal of the Mine Ventilation Society of South Africa*, Vol. 14, No. 5, pp. 65-73.

Kock, H. 1967. Refrigeration in Industry. *The South African Mechanical Engineer* (Nov.), pp. 188-196.

LeRoux, W. L. 1959. Heat Exchange Between Water and Air at Underground Cooling Plants. *Journal of the Mine Ventilation Society of South Africa*, Vol. 12, No. 5, pp. 106-119.

Marks, John. 1969. *Design of Air Cooler—Star Mine.* Hecla Mining Company, Wallace, Idaho.

Minich, G. S. 1962. The Pressure Recuperator and Its Application to Mine Cooling. *The South African Mechanical Engineer* (Oct.), pp. 57-78.

Muller, F. T. and Hill, M. 1966. Ventilation and Cooling as Practiced on E.R.P.M. Ltd., South Africa. *Journal of the South African Institute of Mining and Metallurgy.*

Richardson, A. S. 1950. A Review of Progress in the Ventilation of the Mines of the Butte, Montana District. *Quarterly of the Colorado School of Mines* (Apr.), Golden, Colorado.

Sandys, M. P. J. 1961. The Use of Underground Refrigeration in Stope Ventilation. *Journal of the Mine Ventilation Society of South Africa*, Vol. 14, No. 6, pp. 93-95.

Schlosser, R. B. 1967. The Crescent Mine Cooling System. Northwest Mining Association Convention, December 2.

Short, B. 1957. Ventilation and Air Conditioning at the Magma Mine. *Mining Engineering* (Mar.), pp. 344-348.

Starfield, A. M. 1966. Tables for the Flow of Heat into a Rock Tunnel with Different Surface Heat Transfer Coefficients. *Journal of the South African Institute of Mining and Metallurgy*, Vol. 66, No. 12, pp. 692-694.

Thimons, E.; Vinson, R.; and Kissel, F. 1980. Water Spray Vent Tube Cooler for Hot Stopes. USBM TPR 107.

Thompson, J. J. 1967. Recent Developments at the Bralorne Mine. *Canadian Mining and Metallurgy Bulletin* (Nov.), pp. 1301-1305.

Torrance, B. and Minish, G. S. 1962. Heat Exchanger Data. *Journal of the Mine Ventilation Society of South Africa*, Vol. 15, No. 7, pp. 129-138.

Van Der Walt, J.; DeKock, E.; and Smith, L. *Analyzing Ventilation and Cooling Requirements for Mines.* Engineering Management Services, Ltd., P. O. Box 585, Johannesburg, 2000, R. S. A.

Warren, J. W. 1958. The Science of Mine Ventilation. Presented at the American Mining Congress, San Francisco, CA, Sept.

Warren, J.W. 1965. Supplemental Cooling for Deep-Level Ventilation. *Mining Congress Journal* (Apr.) pp. 34-37.

Whillier, A. 1972. Heat—A Challenge in Deep-Level Mining. *Journal of the Mine Ventilation Society of South Africa*, Vol. 25, No. 11, pp. 205-213.

CHAPTER 43

INDUSTRIAL EXHAUST SYSTEMS

INDUSTRIAL exhaust ventilation systems collect and remove dusts, fumes, gases, mists, and vapors that can create an unsafe, unhealthy, or undesirable atmosphere. They also salvage usable material and improve plant housekeeping. Chapter 11 of the 1985 FUNDAMENTALS Volume covers definitions, particle sizes, allowable concentrations, and upper and lower explosive limits of various air contaminants.

There are two types of exhaust systems: (1) *General exhaust* (dilution ventilation), in which an entire work space is exhausted without considering specific operations and (2) *Local exhaust*, in which the contaminant is captured at its source. Local exhaust is preferable because it offers better contaminant control with minium air volumes, thereby lowering the cost of air cleaning and makeup air equipment. Chapter 41 of this volume and Section 2 of the *Industrial Ventilation Manual* detail steps to determine the air volumes necessary to dilute the contaminant concentration for general exhaust.

Compensating air, which is usually conditioned, provides air to the work space to replace exhausted air. Therefore, the systems are not isolated from each other. (Refer to Chapter 41, "General Ventilation" section, for more information on compensating air and makeup air.) A complete industrial ventilation program includes makeup air systems that provide a total volumetric flow rate equal to the total exhaust rate. If not enough makeup air is provided, the building's pressure will be negative relative to local atmospheric pressure. Negative pressure allows air to infiltrate through open doors, window cracks, and combustion equipment vents. As little as 0.05 in. of water (12 Pa) negative pressure can cause workers to complain about drafts and might cause downdrafting of combustion vents, creating a potential health hazard. Negative plant pressures can also cause excessive energy use. If workers near the plant perimeter complain about cold drafts, unit heaters are often installed. Heat from these units is usually drawn into the plant interior because of the velocity of the infiltration air. This leads to overheating and further complaints. Too often, the "solution" is to exhaust more air from the interior, causing increased negative pressure and more infiltration.

Negative plant pressures reduce the exhaust volumetric flow rate because of increased system resistance. Balanced plants that have equal exhaust and makeup air rates use less energy. Wind effects on building balance are discussed in Chapter 14 of the 1985 FUNDAMENTALS Volume.

FLUID MECHANICS

Chapters 2 and 33 of the 1985 FUNDAMENTALS Volume describe basic fluid mechanics and its applications to duct systems. A thorough understanding of that material is essential to an economical local exhaust system design. Some of the content of those chapters is repeated here for convenience.

The equation for *volumetric flow rate* (volume) is

$$Q = VAcf \text{ or } V = Q/(Acf) \text{ or } A = Q/(Vcf) \qquad (1)$$

where

Q = volumetric flow rate, cfm (L/s)
V = average flow velocity, fpm (m/s)
A = flow cross-sectional area, ft^2 (m^2)
cf = conversion factor, 1 (1000)

Another equation relates velocity to velocity pressure:

$$V = cf \sqrt{P_v/\varrho} \text{ or } P_v = \varrho(V/cf)^2 \qquad (2)$$

where

P_v = velocity pressure, in. of water (Pa)
ϱ = density, lb/ft^3 (kg/m^3)
cf = conversion factor, 1097 ($\sqrt{2}$)

If the air temperature is 68°F ± 30°F (20°C ± 15°C), the ambient pressure is standard [14.7 psia (101.325 kPa)], the duct pressure is no more than 20 in. of water (5 kPa) different from the ambient pressure, the dust loading is low [0.1 to 1.0 grains/ft^3 (0.23 to 2.3 g/m^3)], and moisture is not a consideration, then the density in Eq. (2) is standard without significant error. For a standard air density of 0.075 lb/ft^3 (1.204 kg/m^3), Eq. (2) simplifies to:

$$V = cf \sqrt{P_v} \text{ or } P_v = (V/cf)^2 \qquad (3)$$

where

cf = conversion factor, 4005 (1.29)

LOCAL EXHAUST SYSTEM COMPONENTS

Local exhaust systems have four basic components: (1) the *hood*, or entry point of the system, (2) the *duct system*, which transports air, (3) the *air cleaning device*, which removes contaminants from the air stream, and (4) the *air-moving device*, which provides motive power for overcoming system resistance.

Hoods

The most effective hood uses the minimum exhaust volumetric flow rate to provide maximum contaminant control. Knowledge of the process or operation is essential before a hood can be designed.

Hoods are either *enclosing* or *non-enclosing* (see Figure 1). Enclosing hoods provide better and more economical contaminant control because the exhaust rate and the effects of room air currents are minimal compared to those with a non-enclosing hood. There should be access for inspection and maintenance where required. Hood access openings should be as small as possible and placed out of the natural path of the contaminant. Hood performance (i.e., how well it controls the contaminant) should be checked by an industrial hygienist.

Where access requirements make it necessary to leave all or part of the process open, a non-enclosing hood is used. Careful

---

The preparation of this chapter is assigned to TC 5.8, Industrial Ventilation.

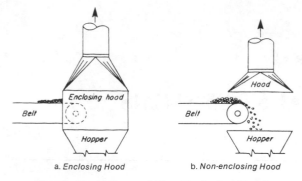

Fig. 1   Enclosing and Non-Enclosing Hoods

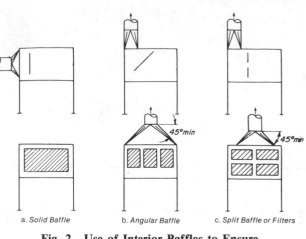

**Fig. 2   Use of Interior Baffles to Ensure
Good Air Distribution**

attention to air flow patterns around the process and hood and to the characteristics of the process are required to make non-enclosing hoods functional.

Capture Velocities

To select an adequate rate *(Q)* to withdraw air through a hood, designers use the concept of "capture velocities." Capture velocities are air velocities at points upstream of a hood; they are believed to cause contaminants to enter the hood. Table 1 shows ranges of capture velocities for several industrial operations. These capture velocities are based on successful experience under ideal conditions. If velocities anywhere upstream of a hood are known [$v = f(Q,x,y,z)$], such as for flanged circular openings (2), the capture velocity is set equal to v at points *(x,y,z)* where contaminants are to be captured and Q is found. To ensure that contaminants enter an inlet, the transport equations have to be solved between the source and hood.

Hood Volumetric Flow Rate

After the hood configuration and capture velocity are determined, the exhaust volumetric flow rate can be calculated.

For *enclosing hoods*, the exhaust volumetric flow rate is the product of the hood face area and the velocity required to prevent outflow of the contaminant [see Eq. (1)]. The inflow velocity is typically 100 fpm (0.5 m/s). However, research (Caplan and Knutson 1977) with laboratory hoods indicates that lower velocities can reduce the vortex downstream of the human body and, therefore, lessen the re-entrainment of contaminant into the operator's breathing zone. These lower face velocities require

the makeup air system to be distributed to minimize the effects of room air currents. This is one reason why makeup systems must be designed with exhaust systems in mind. Because air must enter the hood uniformly, interior baffles are sometimes necessary (see Figure 2).

For *non-enclosing hoods*, the air velocity at the point of contaminant release must equal the capture velocity and be directed so that the contaminant enters the hood. The simplest form of non-enclosing hood is the *plain opening* (Figure 3), Alden and Kane 1982). For unflanged round and rectangular openings, the required flow rate can be approximated by:

$$Q = V(10X^2 + A)cf \qquad (4)$$

where

V = capture velocity, fpm (m/s)
X = centerline distance from the hood face to the point of contaminant generation, ft (m)
A = hood face area, ft^2 (m^2)
cf = conversion factor, 1 (1000)

Figure 3 shows lines of equal velocities (velocity contours) for a plain round opening. The velocities are expressed as percentages of the hood face velocity. Studies (DallaValle 1952) have established the *principle of similarity of contours*, which states that the positions of the velocity contours, when expressed as a percentage of the hood face velocity, are functions only of the hood shape.

Table 1   Range of Capture Velocities

Condition of Contaminant Dispersion	Examples	Capture (Control) Velocity	
		fpm	m/s
Released with essentially no velocity into still air	Evaporation from tanks, degreasing, plating	50 to 100	0.25 to 0.5
Released at low velocity into moderately still air	Container filling, low speed conveyor transfers, welding	100 to 200	0.5 to 1.0
Active generation into zone of rapid air motion	Barrel filling, chute loading of conveyors, crushing, cool shakeout	200 to 500	1.0 to 2.5
Released at high velocity into zone of very rapid air motion	Grinding, abrasive blasting, tumbling, hot shakeout	500 to 2000	2.5 to 10

In each category above, a range of capture velocities is shown. The proper choice of values depends on several factors (Alden and Kane 1982):

Lower End of Range	**Upper End of Range**
1. Room air currents are favorable to capture.	1. Distributing room air currents.
2. Contaminants of low toxicity or of nuisance value only.	2. Contaminants of high toxicity.
3. Intermittent, low production.	3. High production, heavy use.
4. Large hood-large air mass in motion.	4. Small hood-local control only.

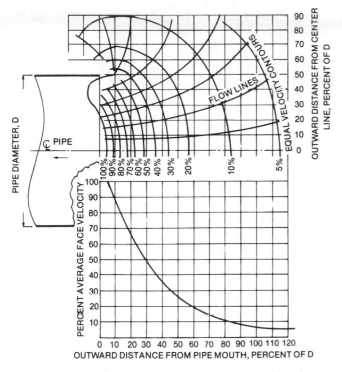

Fig. 3   Velocity Contours for a Plain Round Opening

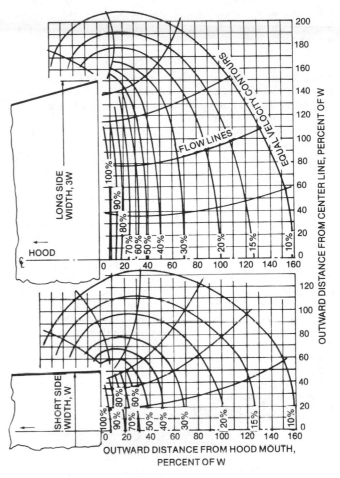

Fig. 4   Velocity Contours for a Plain Rectangular Opening with Sides in a 1:3 Ratio

Figure 4 (Alden and Kane 1972) shows velocity contours for a rectangular hood with an aspect ratio of 0.333 (sides in the ratio of 1 to 3). The profiles are similar to those for the round hood but are more elongated.

If the aspect ratio is lower than about 0.2 (0.15 if flanged), then the shape of the flow pattern in front of the hood changes from approximately spherical to approximately cylindrical, and Eq. (4) is no longer valid. For this type of non-enclosing hood, commonly called a *slot hood*, the required flow rate is predicted by an equation developed by Silverman (1942) for openings of 0.5 to 2 in. (13 to 50 mm) in width:

$$Q = 3.7 \, LVX \cdot cf \qquad (5)$$

where

L = long dimension of the slot, ft (m)
cf = conversion factor, 1 (1000)

The boundary between the plain opening and the slot hood is not precisely defined.

In Figures 3 and 4, air migrates from behind the hood. If a *flange* (defined as a solid barrier to reduce flow from behind the hood face) is installed, the required flow rate for plain openings is about 75% of that for the corresponding unflanged plain opening (Hemeon). Therefore, a flange can reduce the required exhaust volumetric flow rate for a given capture velocity. Alden and Kane (1982) state that the flange size should be approximately equal to the hydraulic diameter (four times the area divided by the perimeter) of the hood face. Brandt (1947) states that the flange should equal the capture distance.

For flanged slots with aspect ratios less than 0.15 and flanges greater than 3 times the slot width, Silverman (1942) reported that:

$$Q = 2.6 LVX \cdot cf \qquad (6)$$

where

cf = 1 (1000)

Multiple slots are often used on a hood face. The slot hood equations [(5) or (6)] are *incorrect* in this situation. The volumetric flow rate should be determined by Eq. (4), where A is the overall face area, because the slots on such a hood are for air distribution over the hood face only.

Another device that helps increase the effectiveness of a non-enclosing hood is a *baffle*, a solid barrier that prevents air flow from unwanted areas in front of the hood. For example, if a rectangular hood is placed on a bench surface, flow cannot come from below the hood and the hood is more effective. Equation

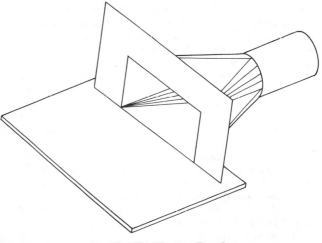

Fig. 5   Hood on a Bench

(4) can be modified for this situation by assuming that a mirror image of the flow exists on the underside of the bench. This will yield:

$$Q = V(5X^2 + A)cf \qquad (7)$$

This is known as the *DallaValle "half-hood"* equation (DallaValle 1952). For better collection, the hood should be flanged. Flanging and baffling a non-enclosing hood create a situation more similar to an enclosure.

Non-enclosing hoods should be placed as near as possible to the source of contamination to prevent excessive exhaust rates. Figures 3 and 4 show that the velocity decreases very quickly as the distance in front of the hood increases, reaching 10% of the face velocity at approximately one hydraulic diameter in front of the hood. Because the volumetric flow rate is a direct function of distance squared (except for single slots), the required flow rate increases rapidly with capture distance. Typically, non-enclosing hoods are ineffective if the capture distance is greater than about 3 ft (1 m). Large capture distances can decrease contaminant control. Room air currents caused by thermal currents, supply air grilles, mechanical action of the process, or personnel-cooling fans can disturb the flow toward the hood enough to deflect the contaminant-laden air stream away from the hood. If capture distances greater than 3 ft (1 m) are required, the designer should consider a push-pull ventilation system, as discussed below.

Example 1: A non-enclosing hood is to be designed to capture a contaminant that is liberated with a very low velocity 2 ft (0.6 m) in front of the face of the hood. The nature of the operation requires hood face dimensions of 1.5 ft (0.45 m) by 4 ft (1.2 m). The hood rests on a bench, and a flange is placed on the sides and top of the face (see Figure 5). Determine the volumetric flow rate required to capture the contaminant. Assume (1) the room air currents are variable in direction but less than 50 fpm (0.25 m/s), (2) the contaminant has low toxicity, and (3) the hood is used continuously.

Solution: From Table 1, a capture velocity of 50 to 100 fpm (0.25 to 0.5 m/s) is required. The selected capture velocity must be higher than the room air currents; assume that 80 fpm (0.4 m/s) is sufficient. The flow rate required can be predicted by modifying Eq. (7) to account for the flanges. Thus,

$$Q = 0.75 \ V(5x^2 + A)cf$$

adequately predicts the flow pattern in front of the hood. For this example, the required flow rate is:

$$Q = (0.75)(80)[(5)(2)^2 + (1.5)(4)](1) = 1560 \text{ cfm}$$

In SI units,

$$Q = (0.75)(0.4)[(5)(0.6)^2 + (0.45)(1.2)](1000) = 702 \text{ L/s}$$

Hot Process Hoods. The exhaust from hot processes requires special consideration because of the buoyant effect of heated air near the hot process. The minimum exhaust rate is obtained by completely enclosing the process and placing the exhaust connection at the top of the enclosure. Determining the exhaust rate for hot processes requires knowing the convectional heat transfer rate (see Chapter 3 of the 1985 FUNDAMENTALS Volume) and the physical size of the process.

If the process cannot be completely enclosed, place the canopy hood above the process so that the contaminant's natural path is directed toward the hood. Canopy hoods should be designed with caution; contaminants may be drawn across the operator's breathing zone. The height of the hood above the process should be kept to a minimum to reduce the total exhaust air rate.

The **low canopy hood**, which is within 3 ft (1 m) of the process, is the non-enclosing hood that requires the least volumetric flow rate. The **high canopy hood**, which is more than 10 ft (3 m) above the process, requires more volumetric flow rate because room air is entrained in the column of hot, contaminated air

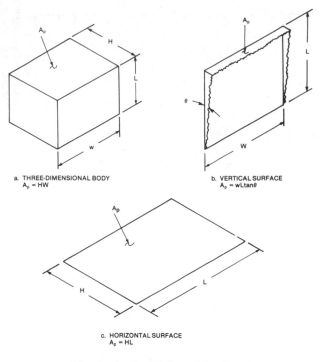

a. THREE-DIMENSIONAL BODY
A_p = HW

b. VERTICAL SURFACE
$A_p = wL\tan\theta$

c. HORIZONTAL SURFACE
A_p = HL

Fig. 6 A_p for Various Situations

rising from the process. This situation should be avoided. Where lateral exhaust must be used, the air flow toward the hood must overcome the tendency of the air to rise and, therefore, generally requires the highest exhaust volumetric flow rate.

Hemeon lists the following equations [(8) through (12)] for determining the volumetric flow rate of hot gases for low canopy hoods. *Canopy hoods located 3 to 10 ft (1 to 3 m) above the process cannot be analyzed by these equations.* Equation (8) can be used to estimate the flow of heated air rising from a hot body if the actual temperature of the hot air leaving the body is approximately the same as the average temperature of the air as it rises past the body (this is normally acceptable):

$$Q_o = (2gRcf/pc_p)^{1/3}(qLA_p^2)^{1/3} \qquad (8)$$

where

Q_o = volumetric flow rate, cfm (L/s)
g = gravitational acceleration, 32.2 ft/s² (9.81 m/s²)
R = air gas constant, 53.352 ft $\cdot$ lb/lb $\cdot$ °R [287 J/(kg $\cdot$ K)]
p = local atmospheric pressure, psf abs (Pa)
c_p = constant pressure specific heat, 0.24 Btu/lb $\cdot$ °R (1004 J/kg $\cdot$ K)
q = convection heat transfer rate, Btu/min (W)
L = vertical height of hot object, ft (m)
A_p = cross-sectional area of air stream at the upper limit of the hot body, ft (m)
cf = 3600 (10^9)

For a standard atmospheric pressure of 2117 psf abs (101.325 kPa), the term $(2gRcf/pc_p)^{1/3}$ becomes 29 (38), and Eq. (8) can be written as:

$$Q_o = cf(qLA_p^2)^{1/3} \qquad (9)$$

where

cf = 29 (38)

For three-dimensional bodies, the area A_p in Eq. (8) is approximated by the plan view area of the hot body (see Figure 6a). For horizontal cylinders, A_p is the product of the length times the diameter of the rod.

For vertical surfaces, the area A_p in Eq. (8) is the area of the air stream (viewed from above) as the flow leaves the vertical surface (see Figure 6b). As the air stream moves upward on a vertical surface, it appears to expand at an angle of approximately 4 to 5 degrees. Thus, A_p is given by:

$$A_p = wL\tan\theta \tag{10}$$

where

  w = width of vertical surface, ft (m)
  L = height of vertical surface, ft (m)
  θ = angle at which the air stream expands

For horizontal heated surfaces, A_p is the surface area of the heated surface and L is the longest length (to be conservative) of the horizontal surface, or its diameter if round (see Figure 6c).

Where the heat transfer is caused by steam from a hot water tank,

$$q = h_{fg}GA_p cf \tag{11}$$

where

  h_{fg} = latent heat of vaporization, Btu/lb (kJ/kg)
  G = steam generation rate, lb/(min · ft²) [kg/(s · m²)]
  A_p = surface area of the tank, ft² (m²)
  cf = 1 (1000)

At 212 °F (100 °C), the latent heat of vaporization is 970.3 Btu/lb (2256.9 kJ/kg). Using this value and Eq. (11), Eq (8) simplifies to

$$Q_o = cfA_p(GL)^{1/3} \tag{12}$$

where

  $\dot{cf}$ = 287 (5000)

The exhaust volumetric flow rate determined by Eq. (8) or (12) is the required exhaust flow rate when: (1) a low canopy hood of the same dimensions as the hot object or surface is used and (2) side and back baffles are used to prevent room air currents from disturbing the rising air column. If side and back baffles cannot be used, increase the canopy hood size and the exhaust flow rate to reduce the possibility of spillage from the hood. A good design provides a low-canopy hood overhang equal to 40% of the distance from the hot process to the hood face on all sides (Industrial Ventilation Manual). The hood flow rate can be increased by using:

$$Q_T = Q_o + V_f(A_f - A_p)cf \tag{13}$$

where

  Q_T = total flow rate entering hood, cfm (L/s)
  Q_o = the flow rate determined by Eq. (8) or (12)
  V_f = the desired indraft velocity through the perimeter area, fpm (m/s)
  A_f = hood face area, ft² (m²)
  A_p = plan view area of Eq. (8) or (12), as discussed above
  cf = 1 (1000)

A minimum indraft velocity of 100 fpm (0.5 m/s) should be used for most design conditions. However, when room air currents are appreciable or if the contaminant discharge rate is high and the design exposure limit is low, higher values of V_f might be required.

Sutton (1950) reported that the volumetric flow rate for a high canopy hood [more than 10 ft. (3 m) above the process] can be predicted empirically from round, square, or nearly square sources by:

$$Q_z = cfZ^{3/2}q^{1/3} \tag{14}$$

where

  Q_z = volumetric flow rate at any elevation Z, cfm (L/s)
  Z = vertical distance (see Figure 7), ft (m)
  cf = 7.4 (8.0)
  q = convection heat transfer rate, Btu/min (W)

Z can be obtained from:

$$Z = Y+2B \tag{15}$$

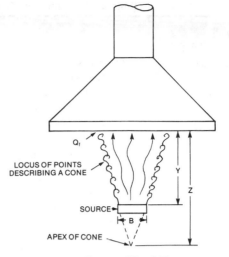

Fig. 7 High Canopy Hood Parameters
NOTE: Y>10 ft (3 m)

where

  Y = distance from the hot process to the hood face (see Figure 7), ft (m)
  B = maximum dimension of the hot process plan view (see Figure 7), ft (m)

At Z, the rising air stream will be nearly round, with a diameter determined by:

$$D_z = cfZ^{0.88} \tag{16}$$

where

  D_z = flow diameter at any elevation Z above the apparent point source, ft (m)
  cf = 0.5 (0.43)

High canopy hoods are extremely susceptible to room air currents. Therefore, they are typically much larger (often twice as large) than indicated by Eq. (16) and are used only if the low canopy hood cannot be used. The total flow rate exhausted from the hood should be evaluated using Eq. (13) *if Q_o is replaced by Q_z.*

Lateral Ventilation Systems

For open vessels, contaminants can be controlled by a lateral exhaust hood, which exhausts air through slots on the periphery of the vessel. Alternatively, air can be blown through one slot and exhausted from another opposite slot. This concept is called "Push-Pull." The inlet is large to accommodate the jet and the room air entrained by the jet. Push-pull systems accommodate wider vessels than do lateral exhaust hoods.

Special Situations

Some operations may require exhaust flow rates different from those developed by the above equations. Typical reasons for different flow rates include the following:

1. Inducted air currents are created whenever anything is projected into an air space. For example, high speed rotating machines such as pulverizers, high speed belt material transfer systems, falling granular materials, and escaping compressed air from pneumatic tools all produce air currents. The size and direction of the air flow should be considered in hood design.
2. Exhaust flow rates that are insufficient to dilute combustible vapor-air mixtures to less than about 25% of the lower explosive limit of the vapor (NFPA 1981).

Table 2 Contaminant Transport Velocities (Industrial Ventilation Manual)

Nature of Contaminant	Examples	Minimum Transport Velocity	
		fpm	m/s
Vapors, gases, smoke	All Vapors, gases and smokes	Any	Any
Fumes	Zinc and aluminum oxide fumes	1400 to 2000	7 to 10
Very fine light dust	Cotton lint, wood flour, litho powder	2000 to 2500	10 to 13
Dry dusts and powders	Fine rubber dust, Bakelite molding powder dust, jute lint, cotton dust, shavings (light), soap dust, leather shavings	2500 to 3500	13 to 18
Average industrial dust	Sawdust (heavy and wet), grinding dust, buffing lint (dry), wool jute dust (shaker waste), coffee beans, shoe dust, granite dust, silica flour, general material handling, brick cutting, clay dust, foundry (general), limestone dust, packaging and weighing asbestos dust in textile industries	3500 to 4000	18 to 20
Heavy dusts	Metal turnings, foundry tumbling barrels and shakeout, sand blast dust, wood blocks, hog waste, brass turnings, cast iron boring dust, lead dust	4000 to 4500	20 to 23
Heavy or moist dusts	Lead dust with small chips, moist cement dust, asbestos chunks from transite pipe cutting machines, buffing lint (sticky), quick-lime dust	4500 and up	23 and up

3. Room air currents caused by cross drafts, compensating air, spot cooling, or motion of the machinery of operators. This is especially significant when designing high canopy hoods for hot process exhaust.

Duct Considerations

The second component of a local exhaust ventilation system is the duct through which contaminated air is transported from the hood(s). Round ducts are preferred because they (1) offer a more uniform air velocity to resist settling of material and (2) can withstand the higher static pressures normally found in exhaust systems. When design limitations require rectangular ducts, the aspect ratio (height to width ratio) should be as close to unity as possible.

Minimum transport velocity is that velocity required to transport particulates without settling. Table 2 lists some generally accepted transport velocities as a function of the nature of the contaminants (Industrial Ventilation Manual). The values listed are typically higher than theoretical and experimental values to account for: (1) damages to ducts, which would increase system resistance and reduce volume and duct velocity, (2) duct leakage, which tends to decrease velocity in the duct system upstream of the leak, (3) fan wheel corrosion or erosion and/or belt slippage, which could reduce fan volume, and (4) re-entrainment of settled particulate caused by improper operation of the exhaust system. Design velocities can be higher than the minimum transport velocities but should never be significantly lower. When particulate concentrations are low, the effect on fan power is negligible.

Standard duct sizes and fittings should be used for economic and delivery time reasons. Information on available sizes and the cost impact of nonstandard sizes should be obtained from the contractor(s).

Duct Size Determination

The size of the round duct attached to the hood can be calculated by using Eq. (1), the volumetric flow rate, and the minimum transport velocity.

Example 2: Suppose the contaminant captured by the hood in *Example 1* requires a minimum transport velocity of 3000 fpm (15 m/s). What diameter round duct should be specified?

Solution: Using Eq. (1), the duct area required is

$$A = 1560/3000 = 0.52 \text{ ft}^2$$

In SI units,

$$A = 702/[(15)(1000)] = 0.0468 \text{ m}^2$$

The area calculated generally will not correspond to a standard duct size. The area of the standard size chosen should be less than that calculated above. For this example, a 9-in. (225 mm) diameter with an area of 0.4418 ft² (0.0398 m²) should be chosen. The actual duct velocity is therefore:

$$V = 1560/0.4418 = 3531 \text{ fpm}$$

In SI units,

$$V = 702/[(0.0398)(1000)] = 17.6 \text{ m/s}$$

Hood Entry Loss

When air enters a hood, there is a loss of total pressure because of dynamic losses. This is called the *hood entry loss* and might have several components. Each component is given by:

$$h_e = C_o P_v \tag{17}$$

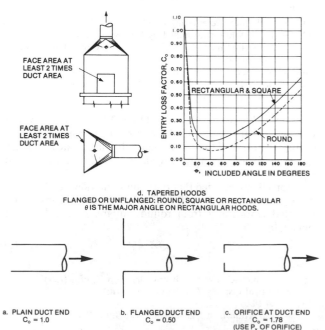

d. TAPERED HOODS
FLANGED OR UNFLANGED: ROUND, SQUARE OR RECTANGULAR
θ IS THE MAJOR ANGLE ON RECTANGULAR HOODS.

a. PLAIN DUCT END
$C_o = 1.0$

b. FLANGED DUCT END
$C_o = 0.50$

c. ORIFICE AT DUCT END
$C_o = 1.78$
(USE P_v OF ORIFICE)

Fig. 8 Entry Losses for Typical Hoods

where

h_e = hood entry loss, in. of water (Pa)
C_o = loss factor, dimensionless
P_v = appropriate velocity pressure, in. of water (Pa)

Loss factors for various hood shapes are given in Figure 8. This graph shows an optimum hood entry angle to minimize the entry losses. However, this total included angle of 45° is impractical in many situations because of the required transition length. A 90° angle, with a corresponding loss factor of 0.25 (for rectangular openings), is standard for most tapered hoods.

Total pressure is very difficult to measure in a duct system, since it varies from point to point across a duct, depending on the local velocity. On the other hand, static pressure remains constant across a straight duct. Therefore, a single measurement of static pressure in a straight duct downstream of the hood can monitor the volumetric flow rate. The absolute value of this static pressure is called the *hood suction*, and is given by:

$$HS = P_v + h_e \qquad (18)$$

where

HS = hood suction, in. of water (Pa)

Simple Hoods

A simple hood has only one dynamic loss. In this situation, the hood suction becomes:

$$HS = (1 + C_o)P_v \qquad (19)$$

where P_v is the duct velocity pressure.

Example 3: Suppose that the hood in *Example 1* was designed with the largest angle of transition between the hood face and the duct equal to 90°. What is the suction for this hood? Assume standard air density.

Solution: The two transition angles cannot be equal. Whenever this is true, then the largest angle is used to determine the loss factor from Figure 8. Because the transition piece originates from a rectangular opening, the curve marked "rectangular" must be used. This corresponds to a loss factor of 0.25. The duct diameter and the velocity required were determined in *Example 2*. Equation (3) can be used to determine the duct velocity pressure because the air is standard air, or:

$$P_v = (3531/4005)^2 = 0.78 \text{ in. of water}$$

In SI units,

$$P_v = (17.6/1.29)^2 = 193 \text{ Pa}$$

Equation (19) then gives:

$$HS = (1 + .25)(.78) = 0.98 \text{ in. of water}$$

In SI units,

$$HS = (1 + .25)(193) = 241 \text{ Pa}$$

Compound Hoods

The losses for multi-slotted hoods (see Figure 9) or single-slot hoods with a plenum are called *compound hoods* and must be analyzed somewhat differently. The slots distribute air over the hood face and *do not influence capture efficiency*. The slot velocity should be approximately 2000 fpm (10 m/s) to provide the required distribution at the minimum energy cost. Higher velocities dissipate more energy.

Losses occur when air passes through the slot and when air enters the duct. Because the velocities, and, therefore, the velocity pressures, can be different at the slot and at the duct entry locations, the hood suction must reflect both losses and is given by:

$$HS = P_v + (C_oP_v)_s + (C_oP_v)d \qquad (20)$$

where the first P_v is generally the higher of the two velocity pressure, *s* refers to the slot, and *d* refers to the duct entry location.

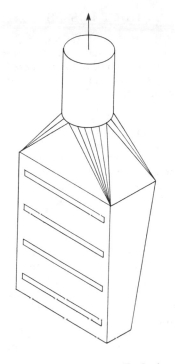

Fig. 9   Multi-Slotted Non-Enclosing Hood

Example 4: A multi-slotted hood has 3 slots, each 1 by 40 in. (25 mm by 1 m). At the top of the plenum is a 90° transition into the 10 in. (250 mm) duct. The volumetric flow rate required for this hood is 1650 cfm (780 L/s). Determine the hood suction. Assume standard air.

Solution: The slot velocity (V_s) from Eq. (1) is:

$$V_s = (1650)(144)/[(3)(1)(40)] = 1980 \text{ fpm}$$

In SI units,

$$V_s = (780/1000)/[(3)(0.025)(1)] = 10.4 \text{ m/s}$$

Substituting this velocity in Eq. (3) gives:

$$P_v = (1980/4005)^2 = 0.24 \text{ in. of water (65 Pa)}$$

The duct area is 0.5454 ft² (0.0491 m²). Therefore, the duct velocity is given by Eq. (1) as:

$$V_d = 1650/0.5454 = 3025 \text{ fpm}$$

In SI units,

$$V_d = 780/[(1000)(0.0491)] = 15.9 \text{ m/s}$$

Substituting the velocity in Eq. (3) gives:

$$P_v = (3028/4005)^2 = 0.57 \text{ in of water (152 Pa)}$$

For a 90° transition into the duct, the loss factor is 0.25. For the slots, the loss factor is 1.78 (see Figure 8). Therefore, using Eq. (20):

$$HS = 0.57 + (1.78)(0.24) + (0.25)(0.57) = 1.14 \text{ in. of water}$$

In SI units,

$$HS = 152 + (1.78)(65) + (0.25)(152) = 306 \text{ Pa}$$

Hood suction is the negative static pressure measured 1 to 3 duct diameters downstream of the hood, the larger distance required for included angles of 180° or larger. Note that the duct velocity pressure is added to the sum of the two losses because it is the larger.

Exhaust volume requirements, minimum duct velocities, and entry loss factors for many specific operations are in Section 5 of the *Industrial Ventilation Manual*.

DUCT LOSSES

Chapter 33 of the 1985 FUNDAMENTALS Volume describes friction losses and how to calculate them, and presents loss coefficients for many fitting types. Many of these fittings do not apply to exhaust systems and should not be used. Table 3 lists the fitting shown in Chapter 33, 1985 FUNDAMENTALS, that apply to industrial exhaust systems.

Elbows with a large centerline radius-to-diameter (R/D) ratio (greater than 1.5) are the most suitable. If the R/D is 1.5 or less, abrasion in dust-handling systems can reduce the life of the fitting. The data in 1985 FUNDAMENTALS are limited to an R/D of 2 for gored elbows. A more complete compilation of the elbow loss data, especially for larger R/D elbows, is given in Table 4. Elbows are often made of 7 or more gores, especially in larger diameters. The loss data for 5-gore elbows applies to these elbows.

Sepsy and Pies (1973) recommend an entry angle of 30° because it has less loss than a 45° entry, and there is less abrasion in dust-handling systems. Table 6.1 and 6.4 in Appendix B of Chapter 33 of the 1985 FUNDAMENTALS Volume includes loss data on converging fittings with 30° angles.

Expansion or contraction losses depend on the conditions both upsteam and downstream of the fitting. Chapter 33 also presents data for contractions and expansions both within a duct segment and at the end of a system (an evase).

Table 4 Elbow Losses
(expanded from Table B-3.1, Chapter 33, 1985 FUNDAMENTALS)

R/D	Smooth	5-gore
0.5	0.71	0.98
0.75	0.33	0.46
1.0	0.22	0.33
1.25	0.17	0.27
1.5	0.15	0.24
1.75	0.14	0.22
2.00	0.13	0.19
2.25	0.13	0.17
2.50	0.12	0.16
2.75	0.12	0.15

Notes:
1. The loss date for 5-gore elbows applies to elbows with more than 5 gores.
2. R is the centerline radius of the elbow.

A system can be designed by calculating either the static pressure or the total pressure through the system. Chapter 33 calculates total pressure, while the *Industrial Ventilation Manual* calculates static pressure. Both use the same technique (but with different numerical values) for calculating fitting losses. The total pressure method is probably easier, but the static pressure method is more frequently used.

Where exhaust systems handling particulates must allow for a substantial increase in future capacity, the required transport

Table 3 Classification of Fittings for Industrial Exahust Systems

This table lists some of the fittings in Appendix B of Chapter 33 in the 1985 FUNDAMENTALS Handbook. They are classified here by their applicability to industrial exhaust systems. Note that "FIG. 1-1" Refers to the figure accompanying Table 1-1 in Appendix B of Chapter 33.
Codes are as follows: F = Freqently used; O = Occasionally used; N/A = Not Applicable; A = Avoid

Figure	Code	Notes	Figure	Code	Notes	Figure	Code	Notes	Figure	Code	Notes
1-1	F	1	3-6	A	5,7,8	5-3	N/A		6-25	N/A	
1-2	O	2	3-7	A	9				6-26	N/A	
1-3	O	2	3-8	A	9	6-1	O	7, 15	6-27	N/A	
1-4	N/A		3-9	A	9	6-2	O	7,14,15	6-28	N/A	
1-5	N/A		3-10	N/A		6-3	A	4,6,7,14	6-29	N/A	
1-6	N/A		3-11	A	4,5,6,8	6-4	F		6-30	N/A	
1-7	F		3-12	A	4,5,7,8	6-5	O	14	6-31	N/A	
1-8	F		3-13	O		6-6	A	8,14	6-32	N/A	
			3-14	O		6-7	N/A		6-33	N/A	
2-1	F	18	3-15	A	8	6-8	N/A		6-34	F	8
2-2	A	5				6-9	N/A		6-35	O	8
2-3	A	5	4-1	O	10,11	6-10	N/A		6-36	N/A	
2-4	A	5	4-2	A		6-11	N/A				
2-5	A	5	4-3	A	8	6-12	N/A		7-1	A	6,16,17
2-7	A	3	4-4	A	8	6-13	N/D		7-2	A	6,8,16,17
2-8	A	3	4-5	A	8	6-14	N/D		7-3	O	16,17
2-9	A	3	4-6	A	8	6-15	N/A		7-4	A	8,16,17
2-10	A	4,5	4-7	O	8	6-16	N/A		7-5	A	6,8,16,17
2-11	F		4-8	O	12	6-17	O	14,20	7-6	N/A	
			4-9	A	7,12	6-18	N/A		7-7	N/A	
3-1	F	(See Table 4)	4-10	A	7,12	6-19	N/A		7-8	N/A	
3-2	F	(See Table 4)	4-11	A	7,12	6-20	N/A		7-9	N/A	
3-3	A	4,6	4-12	0	12	6-21	N/A		7-10	O	Try to avoid
3-4	O					6-22	N/A		7-11	A	7
3-5	O	9	5-1	O	8,13	6-23	N/A		7-12	A	7,8
			5-2	N/A	19	6-24	N/A				

Notes for Table 3

1. Hood data if wall is considered as a flange.
2. Expensive to build
3. Can be used if discharge is vertical
4. High loss
5. Re-entrainment of contaminants probable with its use
6. High wear for systems carrying particulate
7. Poor design
8. Round duct and fitting preferred
9. Elbows with vanes are not recommended due to plugging in dust handling systems and corrosion in some vapor/mist systems
10. Use $\theta < = 20°$

11. Do not use sudden change (see also notes 3 and 5)
12. Keep $\theta < = 20°$
13. Keep $\theta < = 20°$
14. Recommended entry angle is 30°
15. $A_s = A_c$ recommended only for A_b very much less than A_s
16. Use only for off-on applications
17. Dampers must have no leakage at design pressure
18. If vertical with no wall and total pressure is used to design system, this is the loss for a stackhead. If static pressure is used, ignore loss coefficient
19. With $\theta = 180°$, fitting is sometimes used as exhaust from a plenum behind multi-slotted hood
20. Used when multiple inlets to a collector are required

velocities can be maintained by providing open-end stub branches in the main through which air is admitted into the systems at the proper pressure and volumetric flow rate until the future connection is installed. Figure 10 shows such an air bleed-in. The use of outside air minimizes compensating air requirements. The size of the opening can be calculated by first determining the pressure drop required across the orifice from the duct calculations. Then the orifice velocity pressure can be determined from:

$$P_{v,o} = \Delta P_{t,o}/C_o \qquad (21a)$$

or

$$P_{v,o} = \Delta P_{s,o}/(C_o + 1) \qquad (21b)$$

where

$P_{v,o}$ = orifice velocity pressure, in. of water (Pa)
$\Delta P_{t,o}$ = total pressure that must be dissipated across the orifice, in. of water (Pa)
$\Delta P_{s,o}$ = static pressure that must be dissipated across the orifice, in. of water (Pa)
C_o = orifice loss coefficient referenced to the velocity at the orifice cross-sectional area, dimensionless (see Figure 8)

Equation (21a) must be used if the total pressure is calculated through the system; use Eq. (21b) if the static pressure is calculated through the system. Once the velocity pressure is know, Eq. (2) or (3) can be used to determine the orifice velocity. Equation (1) can then be used to determine the orifice size.

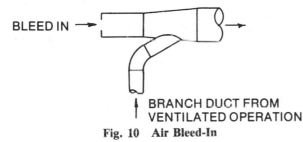

Fig. 10   Air Bleed-In

EXHAUST STACKS

The exhaust stack must be designed and located to prevent the re-entrainment of discharged air into supply system inlets. The building's shape and surroundings determine the atmospheric air flow over it. Chapter 14, 1985 FUNDAMENTALS, has more details on exhaust stack design. The following guidelines can be used:

1. For many one- or two-story industrial or laboratory buildings, 16 ft. (5 m) stacks are adequate for discharging above the roof cavity.
2. When the effluents are highly toxic or their odors are perceived at very low concentrations, there will probably be a pollution problem. The discharge should be above the point where wind flow in unaffected by the building.

If shorter stacks must be used, the stack discharge velocity should be high enough to project the contaminant-laden air above the roof recirculation zone. This usually requires wastefully high velocities [up to 8000 fpm (41 m/s)], however.

If rain protection is important, stackhead design is preferable to weathercaps. Weathercaps, which are not recommended, have three disadvantages:

1. They deflect air downward, increasing the chance that contaminants will recirculate into air inlets.
2. They have high friction losses; losses in the straight duct form of stackheads (Figure 13 F or G, Chapter 14, 1985 FUNDAMENTALS) are balanced by the pressure regain at the expansion to the larger diameter stackhead.

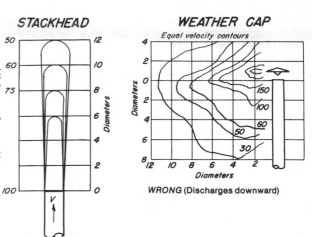

RIGHT (Discharges upward)

Fig. 11   Comparison of Flow Patterns for Stackheads and Weathercaps

3. They provide less rain protection than a properly designed stackhead.

Figure 11 contrasts the flow patterns of weathercaps and stackheads. Loss data for weathercaps are in Chapter 33, 1985 FUNDAMENTALS.

INTEGRATING DUCT SEGMENTS

Most sysems have more than one hood. If the pressures are not designed to be the same for merging parallel air streams, the system will adjust by itself to achieve pressure equality at the common point; however, the flow rates of the two merging air streams will not necessarily be the same as designed. As a result, the hoods can fail to control the contaminant adequately, and expose workers to potentially hazardous contaminant concentrations.

Two design methods ensure that the two pressures will be equal. The preferred method is a design that will self-balance without external aids. The second method uses adjustable balance devices, such as blastgates or dampers. *This method is not recommended, especially when conveying abrasive material.*

AIR CLEANERS

Air-cleaning equipment is usually selected to: (1) conform to federal, state, or local emission standards and regulations; (2) prevent re-entrainment of contaminants to work areas, where they may become a health or safety hazard; (3) reclaim usable materials; (4) permit cleaned air to recirculate to work spaces and/or processes; and (5) prevent annoying neighbors and/or physically damaging adjacent property.

Factors to consider when selecting air-cleaning equipment include type of contaminant (number of components, particulate versus gaseous, and concentration), contaminant removal efficiency required, disposal method, and air or gas stream characteristics. Chapter 11, 1983 EQUIPMENT, covers industrial gas cleaning and air pollution control equipment such as dry centrifugal collectors, fabric collectors, electrostatic precipitators, and wet collectors. Consult a qualified applications engineer when selecting equipment.

The collector's pressure loss must be added to the overall system pressure calculations. In some collectors, specifically some forms of fabric filters, the loss varies as operation time increases. The system should be designed with the maximum pressure drop of the collector, or hood flow rates will be lower than designed during most of the duty cycle. Also, fabric collector losses are usually given only to the clean air plenum. A re-acceleration to the duct velocity, with the associated entry losses, must be calculated in the design phase. Most other collectors are rated *flange-to-flange* and include this re-acceleration in the loss.

AIR-MOVING DEVICES

The type of air-moving device used depends on the type and concentration of contaminant, the pressure rise required, and allowable noise levels. Fans are usually selected. Chapter 3 of the 1983 EQUIPMENT Volume describes available fans and refers the reader to the Air Movement and Control Association (AMCA) *Publication 201, "Fans and Systems,"* for proper connection of the fan(s) to the system. The fan should be located downstream of the air cleaner whenever possible to (1) reduce possible abrasion of the fan wheel blades and (2) create a negative pressure in the air cleaner so air will leak into it and maintain positive control of the contaminant. In some instances, however, the fan is located upstream from the cleaner to help remove dust. This is especially true when using cyclone collectors, such as in the woodworking industry.

If explosive, corrosive, flammable, or sticky materials are handled, an *injector* can transport the material to the air-cleaning equipment. Injectors create a shear layer that induces air flow into the duct. The *Industrial Ventilation Manual* and Hemeon discuss injectors. Injectors are a last resort because their efficiencies seldom exceed 10%.

ENERGY RECOVERY

Transferring energy from exhausted air to makeup air may be economically feasible, depending on (1) the location of the exhaust and makeup air ducts, (2) the temperature of the exhausted gas, and (3) the nature of the contaminants being exhausted.

DUCT CONSTRUCTION

Elbows and converging flow fittings should be made of thicker material than the straight duct, especially if abrasives are conveyed. Some cases require elbows constructed with a special wear strip in the heel of the elbow.

When corrosive material is present, alternatives such as special coatings or different duct materials (fiberglass, stainless steel, or special coatings) can be used. Industrial duct construction is described in Chapter 1 of the 1983 EQUIPMENT Volume in the "Industrial Duct Construction" section. Construction details are given in the Sheet Metal and Air-Conditioning Contractor's National Assoiation's (SMACNA) *Round and Rectangular Duct Construction Standards.*

SYSTEM TESTING

After installation, every exhaust system should be tested to ensure that it operates properly with the require, flow rates through each hood. If the actual installed flow rates are different from the design values, correct the errant volumetric flow rates before using the system. Chapter 37 of this volume, Chapter 13 in 1985 FUNDAMENTALS, AMCA Bulletin 203, "Field Performance Measurements," and the *Industrial Ventilation Manual* contain detailed information on the preferred methods of testing systems. Testing is also necessary to obtain baseline data to determine (1) compliance with federal, state, and local codes; (2) by periodic inspections, whether maintenance on the system is needed to ensure design operation; (3) if a system has sufficient capacity for additional air flow; and (4) whether or not system leakage is acceptable.

OPERATION AND MAINTENANCE

Periodic inspection and maintenance is required for proper operation. Systems are often changed or damaged after installation, resulting in low duct velocities and/or incorrect volumetric flow rates. Low duct velocities can cause the contaminant to settle and plug the duct, which reduces volumes at the affected hoods. Installing additional hoods in an existing system can change volumetric flow at the original hoods. In both cases, changed hood volumes can increase worker exposure and health risks.

The maintenance program should include: (1) ductwork inspection for particulate accumulation and damage to the ductwork by erosion or physical abuse, (2) checking exhaust hoods for proper volumetric flow rates and physical condition, (3) checking fan drives, and (4) maintaining air-cleaning equipment according to manufacturer's guidelines.

REFERENCES

Alden, J.L., and Kane, J.M. 1982. *Design of Industrial Ventilation Systems*, 5th Edition. New York: Industrial Press, Inc., p. 21.

ACGIH. *Industrial Ventilation—A Manual of Recommended Practice.* Committee on Industrial Ventilation, 17th Edition, American Conference of Governmental Industrial Hygienists, Section 2.

Brandt, A.D.; Steffy, R.J.; and Huebscher, R.G. 1947. Nature of Air Flow at Suction Openings. *ASHRAE Transactions*, Vol. 53, p. 55.

Caplan, K.J., and Knutson, G.W. 1977. The Effect of Room Air Challenge on the Efficiency of Laboratory Fume Hoods. *ASHRAE Transactions*, Vol. 83, Part I, p. 141.

DallaValle, J.M. 1952. *Exhaust Hoods.* New York: Industrial Press, Inc., p. 22.

Flynn, M.R., and Ellenbecker, M.J. 1985. The Potential Flow Solution for Air Flow into a Flanged Circular Hood. *American Industrial Hygiene Journal*, Vol. 46, No. 6, pp. 318-322.

Heinsohn, R.J.; Hsieh, K.C.; and Merkle, C.L. 1985. Lateral Ventilation Systems for Open Vessels. *ASHRAE Transactions*, Paper CH-85-08, No. 1.

Hemeon, W.C.L. *Plant and Process Ventilation.* New York: Industrial Press, Inc., p. 77.

Huebener, D.J., and Hughes, R.T. 1985. Development of Push-Pull Ventilation. *American Industrial Hygiene Association Journal*, Vol. 46, No. 5, pp. 262-267.

SMACNA. 1980. *Rectangular Industrial Duct Construction Standards.* Vienna, VA: Sheet Metal and Air Conditioning Contractors' National Assn., Inc.

SMACNA. 1977. *Round Industrial Duct Construction Standards.* Vienna, VA: Sheet Metal and Air Conditioning Contractors' National Assn., Inc.

Sepsy, C.F., and Pies, D.B. 1973. An Experimental Study of the Pressure Losses in Converging Flow Fittings used in Exhaust Systems. Prepared by Ohio State University for National Institute for Occupational Health, Document PB 221 130.

Shibata, M.; Howell, R.H.; and Hayashi, T. 1982. Characteristics and Design Method for Push-Pull Hoods: Part 1—Cooperation Theory of Air Flow. *ASHRAE Transactions*, Vol. 88.

Shibata, M.; Howell, R.H.; and Hayashi, T. 1982. Characteristics and Design Method for Push-Pull Hoods: Part 2—Streamline Analysis of Push-Pull Flow. *ASHRAE Transactions*, Vol. 88.

Silverman, L. 1942. Velocity Characteristics of Narrow Exhaust Slots. *Journal of Industrial Hygiene and Toxicology*, Vol. 24, Nov., p. 267.

NFPA. 1981. *Standard for Ovens and Furnaces—Design, Location and Equipment.* National Fire Protection Association, Standard 86A, Item 4-2.1.

Sutton, O.G. 1950. The Dispersion of Hot Gases in the Atmosphere. *Journal of Meteorology*, Vol. 7, No. 5, p. 307.

Zarouri, M.D.; Heinsohn, R.J.; and Merkle, C.L. 1983. Computer-Aided Design of a Grinding Booth for Large Castings. *ASHRAE Transactions*, Paper No. 2767, Part 2A, pp. 95-118.

Zarouri, M.D.; Heinsohn, R.J.; and Merkle, C.L. 1983. Predicting Trajectories and Concentrations of Particles in a Grinding Booth. *ASHRAE Transactions*, Paper No. 2768, Part 2A, pp. 119-135.

CHAPTER 44

INDUSTRIAL DRYING SYSTEMS

DRYING removes water and other liquids from gases, liquids, or solids. Drying is most commonly used, however, to describe removing water or solvent from solids by thermal means. *Dehumidification* describes drying gases, usually by condensation or absorption by drying agents. (See Chapter 19 of the 1985 FUNDAMENTALS Volume.) *Distillation,* particularly *fractional distillation,* refers to drying liquids.

It is more economical to separate as much water as possible from solid materials before drying. Mechanical methods such as filtration, screening, pressing, centrifuging, or settling require less power and less capital outlay per unit mass of water removed.

This chapter describes systems used for industrial drying and their advantages, disadvantages, relative energy consumption, and applications.

MECHANISM OF DRYING

When a solid dries, two simultaneous processes occur: (1) the transfer of heat to evaporate the liquid and (2) the transfer of mass as vapor and internal liquid. Factors governing the rate of each process determine drying rate.

A principal objective in commercial drying is to supply the required heat most efficiently. Heat transfer can occur by convection, conduction, radiation, or by a combination of the three.

The preparation of this chapter is assigned to TC 9.2, Industrial Air Conditioning.

Types of industrial driers differ in the method used for transferring heat to the solid. In general, heat must flow first to the outer surface of the solid and then into the interior. An exception is drying with high frequency electrical currents, where heat is *generated within the solid,* producing a higher temperature at the interior than at the surface and causing heat to flow from inside the solid to the outer surfaces.

APPLYING HYGROMETRY TO DRYING

In many drying applications, recirculating the medium improves thermal efficiency. Determining the optimum recycled air proportion requires balancing the lower heat loss with more recirculation and the higher drying rate with less recirculation.

Since the recycle ratio affects the humidity of drying air, air humidity throughout the drier must be analyzed to determine whether the predicted moisture pickup of the air is physically attainable. The maximum ability of air to absorb moisture corresponds to the difference between saturation moisture content at wet-bulb (or adiabatic cooling) temperature and moisture content at supply air dew point. Actual moisture pickup of air is determined by heat and mass transfer rate and is always less than the maximum attainable.

The psychrometric chart in Figure 1 can be used for most drying calculations. ASHRAE Psychrometric Chart No. 2 may also be used. Psychrometric charts in SI units are also available. In Figure 1, adiabatic cooling lines indicate paths along which changes in air humidity occur in adiabatic drying. The process

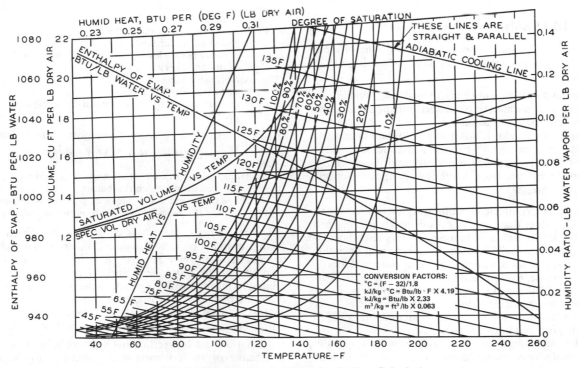

Fig. 1 Psychrometric Chart for Drying Calculations

will not follow exactly the adiabatic cooling line, since some heat is transferred to the material by direct radiation or by conduction from the metal tray or conveyor.

Using the psychrometric chart to analyze drying problems is illustrated by *Example 1.* (Note: Calculations are in inch-pound units; SI is included with given data and answer.)

Example 1: Assume a drier having a capacity of 90.5 lb (41.0 kg) of bone-dry gelatin per hour. Initial moisture content is 228% bone-dry basis and final moisture content is to be 32% bone-dry basis. For optimum drying, supply air is to be at 120 °F (48.9 °C) dry-bulb and 85 °F (29.4 °C) wet-bulb in sufficient quantity so condition of exhaust air is 100 °F (37.8 °C) dry-bulb and 84.5 °F (29.2 °C) wet-bulb. Makeup air is available at 80 °F (26.7 °C) dry-bulb and 65 °F (18.3 °C) wet-bulb.

Find (1) the required amount of makeup and exhaust air and (2) the percentage of recirculated air.

Solution: In this example, humidity in each of the three airstreams is fixed; hence, recycle ratio is also determined. Refer to psychrometric chart (Figure 1), and obtain the humidity ratio of makeup air and exhaust air. To maintain a steady-state condition in the drier, water evaporated from the material must be carried away by exhaust air. Therefore, the difference between the humidity ratio of exhaust air and that of makeup air (known as pickup) is equal to water evaporated from the material divided by the pounds per hour of dry air in exhaust.

Step 1: The moisture in exhaust air at 100 °F (37.8 °C) dry-bulb and 84.5 °F (29.2 °C) wet-bulb is found to be 0.022 lb per lb of dry air. The moisture in makeup air at 80 °F (26.7 °C) dry-bulb and 65 °F (18.3 °C) wet-bulb is found to be 0.010 lb per lb of dry air. Moisture pickup is $0.022 - 0.010$, or 0.012 lb per lb of dry air (0.012 kg/kg).

The amount of water evaporated in the drier $= 90.5 (2.28 - 0.32) = 177$ lb/h (0.0223 kg/s).

Weight of dry air, makeup, and exhaust required to remove the water of evaporation $= 177/0.012 = 14,750$ lb/h (1.858 kg/s) dry air.

Step 2: Let $x =$ percentage of recirculated air and $100 - x =$ percentage of makeup air.

Then $x/100$ (= humidity ratio of exhaust and recirculated air) $+ (100 - x/100)$ (= humidity ratio of makeup air) = humidity ratio of supply air. Hence, $(x/100)(0.022) + [(100 - x)/100](0.010) = 0.018$ at 120 °F (48.9 °C) dry-bulb, 85 °F (29.4 °C) wet-bulb, or $x = 66.7\%$ recirculated air and, therefore, the required makeup air $= 33.3\%$.

DETERMINING DRYING TIME

Drying problems require finding the drying time of a particular material. Three methods are listed below, in order of preference.

1. Conduct tests in a laboratory drier simulating conditions in the commercial machine, or obtain performance data directly from the commercial machine.
2. If the specific material is not available, obtain drying data on similar material by either of the above methods. This is subject to the investigator's experience and judgement.
3. Estimate drying time from theoretical equations. (See texts in the Bibliography.)

When designing commercial equipment, tests are conducted in a laboratory drier that simulates commercial operating conditions. Sample materials used in the laboratory tests should be identical to the material found in the commercial operation. Results from several tested samples should be compared for consistency. Otherwise, the test results may not reflect the drying characteristics of the commercial material accurately.

When laboratory testing is impractical, commercial drying data can be based on the equipment manufacturer's experience—an important source of data.

Method 3, estimating drying time from theoretical equations, should be used with caution, because it only yields approximate values.

Commercial Drying Time

When selecting a commercial drier, the estimated drying time determines what size machine is needed for a given capacity. If the drying time has been derived from laboratory tests, consider the following:

1. In a laboratory drier, considerable drying may be the result of radiation and heat conduction. In a commercial drier, these factors are usually negligible.
2. In a commercial drier, humidity conditions may be higher than in a laboratory drier. In drying operations with controlled humidity, this factor can be eliminated by duplicating the commercial humidity condition in the laboratory drier.
3. Operating conditions are not as uniform in a commercial drier as in a laboratory drier.
4. Because of the small sample used, the test material may not be representative of the commercial material.

Thus, the designer must use experience and judgement to correct the test drying time to suit commercial conditions.

DRIER CALCULATIONS

For preliminary cost estimates for a commercial drier, determine the following:

Circulating Air. The required circulating or supply air flow rate is established by the optimum air velocity relative to the material and can be obtained from laboratory tests or previous experience, keeping in mind that the air also has an optimum moisture pickup. (See the section on "Applying Hygrometry to Drying.")

Makeup and Exhaust. The makeup and exhaust air flow rate required for steady-state conditions within the drier is also discussed under "Applying Hygrometry to Drying." In a *continuously operating* drier, the relation between the moisture content of the material and the quantity of makeup air is given by Equation (1):

$$G_T(W_2 - W_1) = M(w_1 - w_2), \text{ in which } W_2 \text{ is constant} \quad (1)$$

where

G_T = dry air supplied as makeup air to the drier, lb/h (kg/s).
M = stock dried in a continuous drier, lb/h (kg/s).
W_1 = humidity ratio of entering air, pounds of water vapor per pound of dry air (kg/kg).
W_2 = humidity ratio of leaving air, pounds of water vapor per pound of dry air (kg/kg).
w_1 = moisture content of entering material dry basis, pounds of water per pound (kg/kg).
w_2 = moisture content of leaving material dry basis, pounds of water per pound (kg/kg).

In *batch* driers, the drying operation is given by Equation (2) as:

$$G_T(W_2 - W_1) = M_1 (dw/d\theta) \quad (2)$$

where

M_1 = weight of material charged in a discontinuous drier, pounds per batch (kg/batch).
$dw/d\theta$ = the instantaneous rate of evaporation corresponding to w. W_2 varies during a portion of the cycle.

The makeup air quantity is constant and is based on the average evaporation rate. Equation (2) then becomes identical to Equation (1), where $M = M_1/\theta$. Under this condition, the humidity in the *batch drier* varies from a maximum to a minimum during the drying cycle, whereas in the *continuous drier,* the humidity is constant with constant load.

Heat Balance. To estimate the fuel requirements of a drier, a heat balance consisting of the following is needed:

1. Radiation and convection losses from the drier.
2. Heating of the commercial dry material to the leaving temperature (usually estimated).

3. Vaporization of the water being removed from the material (usually considered to take place at the wet-bulb temperature).
4. Heating of the vapor from the wet-bulb temperature in the drier to the exhaust temperature.
5. Heating of the total water in the material from the entering temperature to the wet-bulb temperature in the drier.
6. Heating of the makeup air from its initial temperature to the exhaust temperature.

The energy absorbed must be supplied by the fuel. The selection and design of the heating equipment is an essential part of the overall design of the drier.

DRYING SYSTEM SELECTION

A general procedure consists of the following:

1. Survey of suitable driers.
2. Preliminary cost estimates of various types.
   a. Initial investment
   b. Operating cost
3. Drying tests conducted in prototype or laboratory units of the most promising equipment available. Sometimes a pilot plant is justified.
4. Summary of tests to evaluate quality and samples of the dried products.

Some items can overshadow the operating or investment cost, such as the following:

1. Product quality, which should not be sacrificed.
2. Dusting, solvent, or other product losses.
3. Space limitation.
4. The product's bulk density, which can affect packaging cost.

Friedman (1951) and Parker (1963) discuss additional aids to drier selection.

TYPES OF DRYING SYSTEMS

Radiant Infrared Drying

Thermal radiaton may be applied by infrared lamps, gas-heated incandescent refractories, steam-heated sources, and, most often, by electrically heated surfaces. Since infrared heats only near the receiver's surface, it is best used to dry material in thin sheets.

Using infrared heating to dry webs of material, such as uncoated material, has been relatively unsuccessful because of process control problems. Thermal efficiency can be low, since heat transfer depends on the emitter's characteristics and configuration, and on the properties of the material to be dried.

Radiant heating is used for drying ink or other coatings on paper, textile fabrics, paint films, and lacquers. The development of inks specifically formulted to react with tuned or narrow wavelength infrared radiation has revived infrared drying. Flammable material must not get too close to the heat source.

Ultraviolet Radiation Drying

Ultraviolet (UV) drying uses electromagnetic radiation. Inks and other coatings based on monomers are cure dried when exposed to UV radiation. Ultraviolet drying of inks (Chatterjee and Ramaswamy 1975) has been justified because of superior final printing properties. The print resists scuff, scratch, acid, alkali, and some solvents. Web printing can be done at higher speeds without damage to the web.

A major barrier to wider acceptance of UV drying is the high capital installation cost and increased ink cost. The cost and frequency of replacing UV lamps are greater than for infrared oven maintenance.

Overexposure to radiation and ozone, formed by UV radiation's effect on atmospheric oxygen, can cause severe sunburn and possibly blood and eye damage. Safety measures include fitting the lamp housings with screens, shutters, and exhausts.

Conduction Drying

Drying rolls or drums (Figure 2), flat surfaces, open kettles, and immersion heaters are examples of direct-contact drying. The heating surface *must* have close contact with the material, and agitation may increase uniform heating or prevent overheating.

Conduction drying is used to manufacture and dry paper products. It (1) does not provide a high drying rate, (2) does not furnish uniform heat and mass transfer conditions, (3) usually results in a poor moisture profile across the web, (4) lacks proper control, (5) is costly to operate and install, and (6) usually creates undesirable working conditions in areas surrounding the machine. Despite these disadvantages, replacing existing systems with other forms of drying is expensive. For example, Joas and Chance (1975) report that RF (dielectric) drying of paper compared to steam cylinder conduction drying is approximately four times the captial cost, six times the operating (heat) cost, and five times the maintenance cost. However, augmenting conduction drying with dielectric drying sections offsets the high cost of RF drying and may produce savings and increased profits from greater production and higher final moisture content.

Further use of large conduction drying systems depends on reducing heat losses from the drier, improving heat recovery, and incorporating other drying techniques to improve final product quality.

Dielectric Drying

When wet material is placed in a strong, high frequency (2 to 100 MHz) electrostatic field, heat is generated within the material. More heat is developed in the wetter areas than in the drier areas, resulting in automatic moisture profile correction. Water is evaporated without unduly heating the substrate. Therefore, in addition to its leveling properties, dielectric drying provides uniform heating throughout the web thickness.

Dielectric drying is controlled by varying field or frequency strength; varying field strength is easier and more effective. Response to this variation is quick, with no time nor thermal lag in heating. The dielectric heater is a sensitive moisture meter.

There are several electrode configurations. The platen type (Figure 3) is used for drying and baking foundry cores, heating plastic preforms, and drying glue lines in furniture. The rod or stray field types (Figure 4) are used for thin web material such as paper and textile products. The double-rod types (over and under material) are used for thicker webs or flat stock such as stereotype matrix board and plywood.

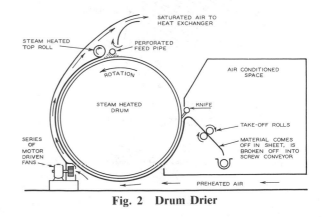

Fig. 2   Drum Drier

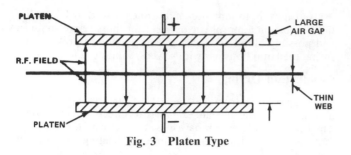

Fig. 3   Platen Type

Dielectric drying is becoming increasingly popular in the textile industry. Because air is entrained between fibers, convection drying is slow and uneven. This can be overcome by dielectric drying after yarn drying. Because the yarn is usually transferred immediately to large packages after drying, even and correct moisture content can be obtained by dielectric drying. Knitting wool seems to benefit from internal steaming in hanks and shows improved "handle."

Warping caused by nonuniform drying is a serious problem for plywood and linerboard. Dielectric drying yields warp-free products.

Dielectric drying is uneconomical for overall paper drying, but has advantages when used at the dry end of a conventional steam drum drier. It corrects moisture profile problems in the web without overdrying. This conventional/dielectric combination is synergistic; the effect of adding the two is greater than the sum of the two effects achieved independently. This is more pronounced in thicker web materials, accounting for as much as a 16% line speed increase and a corresponding 2% energy input increase.

Microwave Drying

Microwave drying or heating uses ultra high frequency (900 to 5000 MHz) power. It is a form of dielectric heating, since it is applied to heating nonconductors. Because of its higher frequency, microwave equipment is capable of generating extreme power densities.

Microwave drying is applied to thin materials in strip form by passing the strip through the gap of a split wave guide. Entry and exit shielding requirements make continuous process ap-

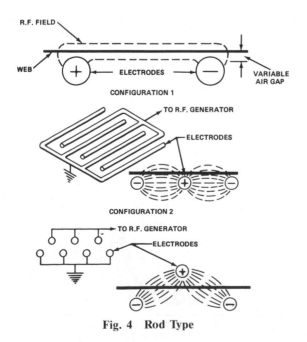

Fig. 4   Rod Type

plications difficult. Its many safety concerns make microwave drying more expensive than dielectric drying. Control is also difficult because microwave drying lacks the self-compensating properties of dielectrics.

Convection Drying (Direct driers)

Some convection drying occurs in almost all driers. True convection driers, however, use circulated hot air or other gases as the principle heat source. Each means of mechanically circulating air or gases has some virtue. Some important convection driers are listed below:

Rotary Driers. These cylindrical drums cascade the material being dried through the airstream. (See Figure 5) The driers are heated directly or indirectly and air circulation is parallel or counterflow. A variation is the rotating-louver drier, which introduces air beneath the flights, achieving close contact.

Cabinet and Compartment Driers. These batch driers range from the heated loft (with only natural convection and usually poor and nonuniform drying) to self-contained units with forced draft and properly designed baffles. Several systems may be evacuated to dry delicate or hygroscopic materials at low temperatures. These driers are usually loaded with material spread in trays to increase the exposed surface. Figure 6 shows a drier that can dry water-saturated products.

When designing driers to process products saturated with solvents, special features must be included to prevent explosive gases from forming. Safe operation requires exhausting 100% of the air circulated during the initial drying period or during any part of the drying cycle when the solvent is evaporating at a high rate. At the end of the purge cycle, the air is recirculated and heat is gradually applied. The amount of air circulated, the cycle lengths, and the rate that heat is applied to prevent circulated air from becoming explosive is determined in the laboratory drier for each product. Recirculating air as soon as feasible in the drying cycle is economical when using costly dehumidified air. The air *must not* recirculate when cross-contamination of products is prohibited.

Driers must have special safety features in case any part of the drying cycle fails. Factory Mutual Insurance Company Bulletin No. 14.15, *Industrial Ovens and Driers,* is one source of information listing safety features to use when designing driers; for example:

1. Each compartment must have separate supply and exhaust fans and an explosion-relief panel.
2. The exhaust fan blade tip speed should be 5000 fpm (25.3 m/s) for a forward-inclined blade, 6800 fpm (34.5 m/s) for a radial-tip blade, and 7500 fpm (38.1 m/s) for a backward-inclined blade. These speeds produce high static pressures at the fan, ensuring constant air exhaust volumes under conditions such as negative pressures in the building or downdrafts in the exhaust stacks.
3. An air flow failure switch in the exhaust duct must shut off both fans and the heating coil, and sound an alarm.
4. An air flow failure switch in the air supply system must shut off both fans and the heating coil, and sound an alarm.

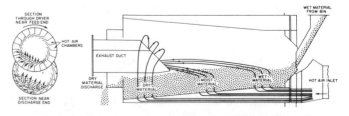

Fig. 5   Cross Section and Longitudinal Section of Rotary Drier

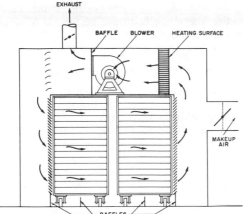

Fig. 6 Compartment Drier, Showing Trucks with Air Circulation

5. A high temperature limit controller in the supply duct must shut off the heat to the heating coil and sound an alarm.
6. An electric interlock on the drier door must cause the drying cycle to repeat if the door is opened beyond a set point, such as wide enough for a man to enter for product inspection.

Tunnel Driers. Tunnel driers are modified compartment driers that operate continuously or semicontinuously. Heated air or combustion gas is circulated by fans. The material is handled on trays or racks on trucks and moves through the drier either intermittently or continuously. The air flow may be parallel, counterflow, or a combination obtained by center exhaust (Figure 7). Air may also flow across the tray surface, vertically through the bed, or in any combination of directions. By reheating the air in the drier or recirculating it, a high degree of saturation is reached before air is exhausted, reducing sensible heat loss.

A variation is the strictly continuous drier having one or more mesh belts that carry the product through the drier, as in Figure 8. Many combinations of temperature, humidity, air direction,

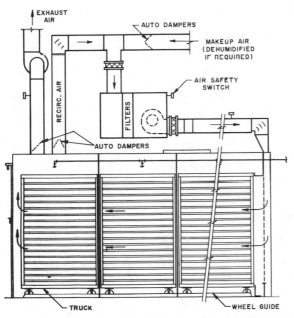

Fig. 7 Explosionproof Truck Drier Showing Air Circulation and Safety Features

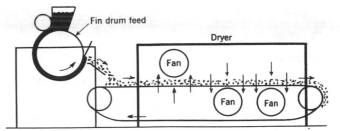

Fig. 8 Section of Continuous Drier, Blow-Through Type

and velocity are possible. Hot air leaks at the entrance and exit can be minimized by baffles or inclined ends, where the material enters and leaves from the bottom.

High Velocity Driers. High velocity hoods or driers have been tried as supplements to conventional cylinder driers for drying paper. When used with conventional cylinder driers, web instability and lack of process control result. Applications such as thin permeable webs, where internal diffusion is not the controlling factor in the drying rate, offer more promise.

Spray Driers. Spray driers have been used in the production of dried milk, coffee, soaps, and detergents. Because the dried product is uniform (in the form of small beads) and the drying time is short (5 to 15 s), this drying method has become more important. When a liquid or slurry is dried, the spray drier has high production rates.

Spray drying involves the atomization of a liquid feed in a hot-gas drying medium. The spray can be produced by a two-fluid nozzle, a high pressure nozzle or a rotating disk. Inlet gas temperatures range from 200 to 1400°F (93 to 760°C), with the high temperatures requiring special construction materials. Since thermal efficiency increases with the inlet gas temperature, high inlet temperatures are desirable. Even heat-sensitive products can be dried at higher temperatures because of the short drying time. Hot-gas flow may be either concurrent or countercurrent to the falling droplets. Dried particles settle out by gravity. Fines in the exhaust air are collected in cyclone separators or bag filters. Figure 9 shows a typical spray drying system.

The bulk physical properties of the dried product, such as particle size, bulk density, and dustiness, are affected by atomization characteristics and the temperature and direction of flow of the drying gas. The product's final moisture content is controlled by the humidity and temperature of the exhaust gas stream.

Currently, pilot-plant or full-scale production operating data are required for design purposes. The drying chamber design is determined by the nozzle's spray characteristics and heat and mass transfer rates. There are empirical expressions that approximate mean particle diameter, drying time, chamber volume, and inlet and outlet gas temperatures. These formulas and further

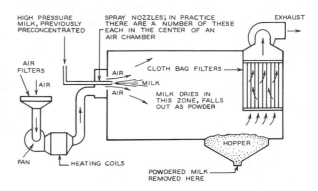

Fig. 9 Spray Drier of the Pressure-Spray Rotary Type

theory are found in the "Reference" section (Friedman, Gluckert and Marshall 1952; Perry and Chilton 1978; and Brown and Associates 1950).

Freeze Drying

Freeze-drying has been applied to pharmaceuticals, serums, bacterial and viral cultures, vaccines, fruit juices, vegetables, coffee and tea extracts, seafoods, meats, and milk.

The material is frozen, then placed in a high vacuum chamber connected to a low temperature condenser or chemical desiccant. Heat is applied slowly to the frozen material by conduction or infrared radiation, allowing the volatile constituent, usually water, to sublime and condense or be absorbed by the desiccant. Most freeze-drying operations occur between 14 and −40°F (−10 and −40°C) under minimal pressure. It is expensive and slow but has advantages for heat-sensitive materials. (See Chapter 9 of the 1986 REFRIGERATION Volume and Perry and Chilton 1978.)

Vacuum Drying

Vacuum drying takes advantage of the lowered boiling point of water as the pressure is lowered. Vacuum drying of paper has been partially investigated. Serious complications arise if the paper breaks, and massive sections must be removed to gain access. Vacuum drying is used successfully for pulp drying where lower speeds and higher weights make breakage relatively infrequent.

Fluidized-Bed Drying

A fluidized bed system contains solid particles through which a gas flows with a velocity higher than the incipient fluidizing velocity but lower than the entrainment velocity. Heat transfer between the individual particles and the drying air is efficient, since there is close contact between powdery or granular material and the fluidizing gas. This contact makes it possible to dry sensitive materials without danger of large temperature differences.

The dry material is free-flowing and not encrusted on trays or other heat-exchanging surfaces, unlike convection-type driers. Automatic charging and discharging are possible, but the greatest advantage is reduced process time. Only simple controls are important, i.e., control over fluidizing air or gas temperatures and the drying time of the material.

All fluid-bed driers should have explosion-relief flaps. Both the pressure and flames of an explosion are dangerous. Also, when toxic materials are used, uncontrolled venting to the atmosphere is impossible. Explosion suppression systems, such as pressure-actuated ammonium-phosphate extinguishers, have been used instead of relief venting. An inert drier atmosphere is preferable to suppression systems because it prevents explosive mixtures from forming.

When organic and inflammable solvents are used in the fluid-bed system, the closed system offers advantages other than explosion protection. A portion of the fluidizing gas is continuously run through a condenser, which strips the solvent vapors and greatly reduces air pollution problems, thus making solvent recovery convenient.

Materials dried in fluidized bed installations include coal, limestone, cement rock, shales, foundry sand, phosphate rock, plastics, medicinal tablets, and foodstuffs. Leva (1959) and Othmer (1956) discuss the theory and methods of fluidization of solids. Clark (1967) and Vanecek et al. (1966) develop design equations and cost estimates.

Agitated-Bed Drying

Uniform drying is ensured by periodically or continually agitating a bed of preformed solids with a vibrating tray or conveyor, a mechanically operated rake, or, in some cases, by partial fluidization of the bed on a perforated tray or conveyor through which recycled drying air is directed. Drying and toasting cereals is an important application.

Drying in Superheated Vapor Atmospheres

When drying solids with air or another gas, the vaporized solvent (water or organic liquid) must diffuse through a stagnant gas film to reach the bulk gas stream. Since this film is the main resistance to mass transfer, the drying rate depends on the solvent vapor diffusion rate. If the gas is replaced by solvent vapor, resistance to mass transfer in the vapor phase is eliminated, and the drying rate depends only on the heat transfer rate. Drying rates in solvent vapor, such as superheated steam, are greater than in air for equal temperatures and mass flow rates of the drying media (Chu, Lane, and Conklin 1953).

This method also has higher thermal efficiency, easier solvent recovery, a lower tendency to overdry, and eliminates oxidation or other chemical reactions that can occur when air is present. In drying cloth, superheated steam reduces the migration tendency of resins and dyes. Superheated vapor drying cannot be applied to heat-sensitive materials because it requires high material temperatures.

Commercial drying equipment having recycled solvent vapor as the drying medium is available. Installations have been built to dry textile sheeting and organic chemicals.

Flash Drying

Finely divided solid particles that are dispersed in a hot gas stream can be dried by *flash drying*, which is rapid and uniform. Commercial application are drying pigments, synthetic resins, food products, hydrated compounds, gypsum, clays, and wood pulp.

SOLUTIONS TO TYPICAL DRYING PROBLEMS

Since many types of driers can be used and special conditions surround each particular problem, it is necessary to consult those experienced with the drier used. The following examples, however, serve as a guide for typical drier calculations.

Example 2: Magnesium hydroxide is to dried from 82% moisture on a bone-dry basis to 4% moisture content on a bone-dry basis. The production rate is to be 3000 lb/h (0.38 kg/s) on a 4% bone-dry basis. Previous experience indicates that a continuous single-conveyor through-circulation drier with a fin-drum feed as illustrated in Figure 8 should be used. The drier is to be heated with steam at 50 psig (345 kPa). The optimum circulating air temperature is 160°F (71.1°C), which is not limited by the steam pressure.

Step 1: Laboratory tests or previous experience indicates that the material enters the drier at a temperature of 60°F (15.6°C) with an initial moisture content of 82% bone-dry basis. The test drying time is 25 min and the final moisture content is 4% bone-dry basis. The temperature of makeup air is 70°F (21.1°C) dry-bulb and 60°F (15.6°C) wet-bulb. The temperature of circulating air is 160°F (71.1°C) dry-bulb and 100°F (37.8°C) wet-bulb. The air velocity down through the preformed bed is 250 fpm (1.27 m/s), and the static pressure drop through the bed is 0.4 in. of water (1.0 kPa). The drier bed is to be loaded with 6.82 lb/ft² (33.3 kg/m²) of bone-dry material. Bed depth is to be 4 in. (100 mm).

Step 2: Previous experience indicates that the commercial drying time is 70% greater than the test time obtained in the laboratory setup used. Therefore, the commercial drying time = 1.7 × 25 = 42.5 min.

Step 3: To dry the desired 3000 lb/h (0.38 kg/s) of material, the holding capacity of the drier is 3000 × (42.5/60) = 2125 lb (964 kg) at 4% bone-dry basis.

The required conveyor area is (2125/6.82) = 312 ft² (29.0 m²). Assuming that a perforated plate conveyor with an 8 ft (2.44 m) effective width is used, the length of the drying zone is (312/8) = 39 ft (11.6 m).

Step 4: The amount of water entering the drier is $(3000/1.04) \times (82/100) = 2370$ lb/h (0.299 kg/s), while the amount of water leaving the drier is $(3000/1.04) \times (4/100) = 115$ lb/h (0.015 kg/s). Thus, the evaporation rate in the drier is $2370 - 115 = 2255$ lb/h (0.284 kg/s).

Step 5: Since the air circulation is perpendicular to the perforated plate conveyor, the total quantity of air that must be circulated equals the air velocity (based on the face area) multiplied by the conveyor area. Thus, supply air $= 250 \times 312 = 78,000$ cfm (36 816 L/s).

From Figure 1, the humidity ratio of the supply air at 160°F (71.1°C) dry-bulb, 100°F (37.7°C) wet-bulb is 0.0285 lb per lb (28.5 g/kg) of dry air. The specific volume of the supply air is 16.33 ft³ (7.71 L/s) of moist air per lb of dry air, from Table 2 in Chapter 6 of the 1985 FUNDAMENTALS Volume.

The quantity of dry air circulated is $(78,000 \times 60)/16.33 = 286,500$ lb/h (36.1 kg/s).

Step 6: The amount of moisture pickup is $(2255/286\,500) = 0.0079$ lb per lb (7.9 g/kg) of dry air. The humidity ratio of the exhaust air is $0.0079 + 0.0285 = 0.0364$ lb per lb (36.4 g/kg) of dry air.

Substitute in Equation (1) and solve for G_T, the required quantity of makeup air. The humidity ratio of the makeup air is 0.0086 lb per lb (8.6 g/kg) of dry air, from Figure 1.

$G_T(0.0364 - 0.0086) = (3000/1.04)[(82 - 4)/100] = 81,000$ lb/h (10.21 kg/s) of dry air. Therefore, makeup air $= (81,000/286,500) = 28.2\%$. Recirculated air $= 71.8\%$.

Step 7: Heat Balance

$$\text{Sensible heat of material} = M(t_{m2} - t_{m1})c_m$$
$$= (3000/1.04)(100 - 60)\,0.3$$
$$= 34,600 \text{ Btu/h (10.1 kW)}$$

$$\text{Sensible heat of water} = M_{w1}(t_w - t_{m1})\,c_w$$
$$= 2370\,(100 - 60)\,1.0$$
$$= 94,800 \text{ Btu/h (27.8 kW)}$$

$$\text{Latent heat of evaporation} = M(w_1 - w_2)\,H$$
$$= 2255 \times 1037$$
$$= 2,338,400 \text{ Btu/h (685 kW)}$$

$$\text{Sensible heat of vapor} = M(w_1 - w_1)(t_2 - t_w)\,c_v$$
$$= 2255\,(160 - 100)\,0.45$$
$$= 60,900 \text{ Btu/h (17.8 kW)}$$

Required heat for material $= 2,528,700$ Btu/h (741 kW)

The temperature drop $(t_2 - t_3)$ through the bed is:

$$\frac{\text{Required heat}}{\text{Supplied air, lb/h} \times C_a} = \frac{2,528,700}{286,500 \times 0.24} = 37°F \ (21°C)$$

Therefore, the exhaust air temperature is $160 - 37 = 123°F$ (50.6°C). Required heat for makeup air $= G_T\,(t_3 - t_1 c_a)$
$$= 81,000\,(123 - 70)\,0.24$$
$$= 1,030,000 \text{ Btu/h (302 kW)}$$

The total heat required for material and makeup air is $2,528,700 + 1,030,000 = 3,559,000$ Btu/h (1043 kW).

Additional heat must be provided for the radiation and convection losses, which can be calculated from the known construction of the drier surfaces.

Example 3: Examine the economic justification of adding a dielectric drier to this linerboard machine (Haley 1976).

width, 220 in. (5.6 m) trim; speed, 1400 fpm (7.1 m/s); basis wt, 42 lb/1000 ft² (0.205 kg/m²); reel moisture, 5%; and moisture on first drier can, 62%

The first six steps involve calculations for current production data.

Step 1: Linerboard production in the process at 5% moisture is:
$$220 \text{ in./}(12 \text{ in. per ft}) \times 1400 \text{ fpm} \times 42 \text{ lb/1000 ft}^2$$
$$= 1078 \text{ lb/min (0.136 kg/s)}$$

Step 2: Bone-dry fiber production in the process is:
$$1078 \text{ lb/min} \times 0.95 = 1024 \text{ lb/min (0.129 kg/s)}$$

Step 3: Average daily production on a 21.5-h basis at 5% moisture is:
$$1078 \text{ lb/min} \times 60 \text{ min/h} \times 21.5 \text{ h/day}$$
$$\times 1 \text{ ton/2000 lb} = 695 \text{ ton/day (630 Mg/day)}$$

Step 4: Water on the first drier is:
$$1024 \text{ lb/min} \times 62/38 = 1671 \text{ lb/min (0.211 kg/s)}$$

Step 5: Water at the reel is:
$$1078 - 1024 = 54 \text{ lb/min (0.007 kg/s)}$$

Step 6: Water evaporated by the machine is:
$$1671 - 54 = 1617 \text{ lb/min (0.204 kg/s)}$$

The next seven steps find the increased production after the dielectric drier is installed, assuming a 6% increase in bone-dry fiber and 7.5% reel moisture.

Step 7: Bone-dry fiber production in the process is:
$$1024 \text{ lb/min} \times 1.06 = 1085 \text{ lb/min (0.137 kg/s)}$$

Step 8: Water at the reel is:
$$1085 \text{ lb/min} \times 7.5/92.5 = 88 \text{ lb/min (0.111 kg/s)}$$

Step 9: Linerboard production in the process at 7.5% moisture is:
$$1085 + 88 = 1173 \text{ lb/min (0.198 kg/s)}$$

Step 10: Average daily production on a 21.5-h basis at 7.5% moisture is:
$$1173 \text{ lb/min} \times 60 \text{ min/h} \times 21.5 \text{ h/day} \times 1 \text{ ton/2000 lb}$$
$$= 757 \text{ ton/day (687 Mg/day)}$$

Step 11: Water on the first drier is:
$$1085 \text{ lb/min} \times 62/38 = 1770 \text{ lb/min (0.223 kg/s)}$$

Step 12: Water to be evaporated is:
$$1770 \text{ (on first drier)} - 88 \text{ (at reel)} = 1682 \text{ lb/min (0.212 kg/s)}$$

Step 13: Water to be removed by the dielectric units is:
$$1682 \text{ (to be evaporated)} - 1617 \text{ (evaporated by linerboard unit)}$$
$$= 65 \text{ lb/min (0.008 kg/s)}$$

The remaining steps pinpoint operating expense and return on investment for the dielectric unit.

Step 14: Average power load for the dielectric unit is:

$$\frac{65 \text{ lb/min} \times 970 \text{ Btu/lb}}{57 \text{ Btu/kW} \cdot \text{min}} = 1106 \text{ kW}$$

Step 15: The value of increased production, assuming an incremental gross profit of $180/ton ($163/Mg), is:
Average daily increase $= 757 - 695 = 62$ ton/day (56.2 Mg/day)
Average annual increase in gross profit $=$
62 ton/day $\times 350$ day/yr $\times$ $180/ton $= $3,906,000$

Step 16: Power cost of the dielectric unit, assuming 75% efficiency and a 5¢ per kWh electric utility rate, is:
Hourly $= 1106/0.75 \times$ $0.05/kWh $= 73.75
Annually $=$ $73.73/h $\times 24$ h/day $\times 350$ day/yr $= $619,500$

Step 17: Other expenses are:
Tube replacement (1/yr), $90,000+ capacitors, $40,000+ other maintenance, $108,000, (3% × $3,600,000) $= $238,000$

Step 18: Total annual high frequency operating expense is:
$619,500 + $238,000 $= $857,500$

Thus, the return on investment is:

Annual increase in gross profit	$3,906,000
Annual H.F. unit operating expense	857,500
Annual incremental profit	$3,048,500
Estimated price of H.F. unit	$3,600,000
Estimated installation cost	800,000
Estimated total investment	$4,400,000

Recover investment in $4,400,000/$3,048,500 = 1.44 years, or 17.3 months.

REFERENCES

Brown, G.G., and Associates. 1950. *Unit Operations*. John Wiley & Sons, New York, NY, p. 564.

Chatterjee, P.C.; and Ramaswamy, R. 1975. Ultraviolet Radiation Drying of Inks. *British Ink Maker*, Vol. 17, No. 2, February, p. 76.

Chu, J.C.; Lane, A.M.; and Conklin, D. 1953. Evaporation of Liquids into their Superheated Vapors. *Industrial and Engineering Chemistry*, Vol. 45, p. 1586.

Clark, W.E. 1967. Fluid Bed Drying. *Chemical Engineering*, Vol. 74, March 13, p. 177.

Friedman, S.J. 1951. Steps in the Selection of Drying Equipment. *Heating and Ventilating*, February, p. 95.

Friedman, S.J.; Gluckert, R.A.; and Marshall, W.R., Jr. 1952. Centrifugal Disk Atomization. *Chemical Engineering Progress*, Vol. 48, p. 181.

Haley, N.A. 1976. High Frequency Heating on a Linerboard Machine.

Tappi Papermakers Conference (Atlanta) Preprint, April 26 to 29, p. 217.

Heating and Ventilating. 1942. What the Air Conditioning Engineer Should Know about Drying, December.

Joas, J.G.; and Chance, J.L. 1975. Moisture Leveling with Dielectric, Air Impingement and Steam Drying—A Comparison. *Tappi,* Vol. 58, No. 3, March, p. 112.

Leva, M. 1959. *Fluidization.* McGraw-Hill Book Co., New York, NY.

Othmer, D.F. 1956. *Fluidization.* Reinhold Publishing Corp., New York, NY.

Parker, N.H. 1963. Aids to Drier Selection. *Chemical Engineering,* Vol. 70, June 24, p. 115.

Perry, R.H.; Chilton, C.H. (ed.) 1978. *Chemical Engineers' Handbook.* McGraw-Hill Book Co., New York, NY, 5th ed., Section 17, Sublimination, and Section 20, Gas-Solid Systems.

Simon, E. Containment of Hazards in Fluid Bed Technology. *Manufacturers of Chemical Aerosol News,* Vol. 49, No. 1, p. 23.

Vanecek, Markvart, and Drbohlav. 1966. *Fluidized Bed Drying.* Chemical Rubber Company, Cleveland, OH.

BIBLIOGRAPHY

[NOTE: In the following items, ABIPC stands for Abstract Bulletin of the Institute of Paper Chemistry Appleton, WI.]

Alt, C. 1964. A Comparison Between Infrared and Other Ink Drying Methods. *Polygraph,* Vol. 17, No. 4, February 20, p. 200; ABIPC 34: 1455.

Appel, D.W.; Hong, S.H. 1969. Condensate Distribution and Its Effect on Heat Transfer in Steam Heated Driers. *Pulp and Paper Canada* Vol. 70, No. 4, February 21, p. 66, T51; ABIPC 39:943.

Balls, B.W. 1970. The Control of Drying Cylinders. *Paper Technology.* Vol. 1, No. 5, October, p. 483. ABIPC 31: 1119.

Bell, J.R.; and Grosberg, P. 1962. The Movement of Vapor and Moisture During the Falling Rate Period of Drying of Thick Textile Materials. *Journal of the Textile Institute,* Transactions Vol, 53, No. 5, May, p. T250; ABIPC 33: 72.

Booth, G.L. 1970. Factors in Selecting an Air Heating System for Drying Coatings. *Paper Trade Journal,* Vol. 154, No. 23, June 8, Graphic Arts p. 47; Abstr. 24, no. 7:71.

Booth, G.L. 1970. General Principles in the Drying of Paper Coatings. *Paper Trade Journal,* Vol. 154, No. 17, April 27, p. 48; Graphic Arts Abstr. 24, no. 7:72.

Chu, J.C.; Finelt, S.; Hoerrner, W.; and Lin, M.S. 1959. Drying with Superheated Steam-Air Mixtures. *Industrial and Engineering Chemistry,* Vol. 51, p. 275.

Church, F. 1968. How Dielectric Heating Helps to Control Moisture Content. *Pulp and Paper International,* Vol. 10, No. 2, February, p. 50; ABIPC 39:202.

Daane, R.A.; and Han, S.T. 1961. An Analysis of Air-Impingement Drying. *Tappi,* Vol. 44, No. 1, January, p. 73; C.A. 55:8855, ABIPC 31:1120.

Dooley, J.A.; and Vieth, R.D. 1965. High Velocity Drying Gives New Impetus to Solution Coatings. *Paper, Film, Foil Converter,* Vol. 39, No. 4, April, p. 53; ABIPC 36.

Dyck, A.W.J. 1969. Focus on Paper Drying. *American Paper Industry,* Vol. 51, No. 6, June, p. 49; ABIPC 40: 458.

Foust, A.S., *et. al.* 1962. Simultaneous Heat and Mass Transfer 11: Drying. *Principles of Unit Operations.* John Wiley & Sons, New York, NY.

Gardner, T.A. 1964. Air Systems and Yankee Drying. *Tappi,* Vol. 47, No. 4, April, p. 210; ABIPC 34:1787.

Gardner, T.A. 1968. Pocket Ventilation and Applied Fundamentals Spell Uniform Drying. *Paper Trade Journal,* Vol. 152, No. 4, January 22, J. 152, No. 4:46, 48, 51-2, Jan. 22; ABIPC 39:115.

Gavelin, G. 1970. New Heat Recovery System for Paper Machine Hood Exhaust. *Paper Trade Journal,* Vol. 154, No. 8, February 23, p. 38; ABIPC 41:1225.

Gavelin, G. 1964. Paper and Paperboard Drying—Theory and Practice (monograph). *Lockwood Trade Journal Co., Inc.,* New York, NY, 85 pp.; ABIPC 35:480.

Hoyle, R. 1963. Thermal Conditions in a Steam Drying Cylinder. *Paper Technology,* Vol. 4, No. 3, June, p. 259; ABIPC 34:341.

Janett, L.G.; Schregenberger, A.J.; and Urbas, J.C. 1965. Forced Convection Drying of Paper Coatings. *Pulp and Paper Canada* Vol. 66, January, p. T20; ABIPC 35:1433.

Larsson, T. 1962. Comparing High Velocity Driers—Aspects of Theory and Design. *Paper Trade Journal,* Vol. 146, No. 38, September 17, p. 36; ABIPC 33:547.

Marshall, W.R., Jr. Drying Section in *Encyclopedia of Chemical Technology.* Interscience Publishers, New York, 2nd ed., Vol. 7, p. 326.

Metcalf, W.K. 1970. What Pocket Ventilation Systems Can Do and What They Cannot. *Pulp and Paper,* Vol. 44, No. 2, February, p. 95: No. 2:95-7, Feb.; ABIPC 41:3231.

Mill, D.N. 1961. High Velocity Air Drying. *Paper Technology,* Vol. 2, No. 4, August, ABIPC 32:588.

Nissan, A.H. 1968. Drying of Sheet Materials. *Textile Research Journal,* Vol. 38, p. 447.

Nissan, A.H.; and Hansen, D. 1962. Fundamentals of Drying of Porous Materials. Errata. *Tappi,* Vol. 45, No. 7, July, p. 608; ABIPC 33:395.

Olmedo, E.B. 1966. Steam Control in Paper Machine Driers. *ATCP* Vol. 6, No. 2, March/April, p. 142.

Priestly, R.J. 1962. Where Fluidized Solids Stand Today. *Chemical Engineering,* July 9, p. 125.

Scheuter, K.R. 1968. Drier Theory and Dryer Systems. *Druckprint,* Vol. 105, No. 12, December, p. 939; ABIPC 40:24.

Sloan, C.E.; Wheelock, T.D.; and Tsao, G.T. 1967. Drying. *Chemical Engineering,* Vol. 74, June 19, p. 167.

Spraker, W.A.; Wallis, G.B.; and Yaros, B.R. 1969. Analysis of Heat and Mass Transfer in the Yankee Drier. *Pulp and Paper Canada,* Vol. 70, No. 1, January 3, p. 55; T1-5, Jan. 3; ABIPC 39:947.

Stangl, K. 1966. Progress in Flash Drying. *Pulp and Paper National,* Vol. 8, No. 6, June, p. 65; ABIPC 37:305.

Streaker, W.A. 1968. Drying Pigmented Coatings with Infrared Heat. *Tappi,* Vol. 51, No. 10, October, p. 105; ABIPC 39: 659.

Tarnawski, Z. 1962. Drying of Paper and Calcultion of the Drying Surface of the Paper Machine. *Przeglad Papier,* Vol. 18, No. 7, July, p. 218; ABIPC 34:639.

Wen, C.Y.; and Loos, W.E. 1969. Rate of Veneer Drying an a Fluidized Bed. *Wood Science and Technology,* Vol. 3.

Wilhoit, D.L. 1968. Theory and Practice of Drying Aqueous Coatings with a High Velocity Air Drier. *Tappi,* Vol. 51, No. 1, January, ABIPC 38:803, C.A. 68:4969, Pkg. Abstr. 35:360.

Yoshida, T.; and Hyodo, T. 1963. Superheated Vapor as a Drying Agent in Spinning Fiber. *Industrial and Engineering Chemistry,* Process Design and Development, January, p. 52.

CHAPTER 45

GEOTHERMAL ENERGY

EMPHASIS on the use of geothermal energy has been directed toward production of electricity, although efforts have also been directed toward the use of geothermal energy for space and domestic water heating, industrial processing, and cooling.

An overall geothermal system considers the resource, user system, and disposal. The resource location and its characteristics (temperature, allowable fluid flow rate, fluid quality, etc.) are important because (1) geothermal energy is not available at all localities and geothermal fluids cannot be economically transmitted over more than a few tens of kilometers and (2) the characteristics of the available resource may or may not be appropriate for the particular application for which an energy supply is being sought. For the most economical and satisfactory operation, the system should be specially designed for use of geothermal fluids. The equipment is off-the-shelf equipment but different from that which has been traditionally used in the same application operated with conventional energy supplies. This is the area in which thermal system design for geothermal energy use is substantially different from the designs for conventional fueled systems. For geothermal energy systems, the design must consider (1) the available resource temperature and flow rate, (2) an appropriate temperature drop of the fluid that is normally much greater than that specified for fluid loops in conventional systems, and (3) the fluid composition. The transmission and distribution system and the peaking/backup system are designed by conventional techniques to provide economical and reliable operation. The main concerns in disposal are that the fluid be disposed of in an environmentally acceptable manner and injected into the reservoir, as necessary, to maintain production.

This chapter illustrates how geothermal energy can be used for space heating and cooling, domestic water heating, and industrial processing. It does this by (1) describing the types of geothermal resources and their general extent in the United States; (2) considering the potential market that may be served with geothermal energy; and (3) illustrating the evaluation considerations, special design aspects, and application approaches for geothermal energy use in each of the applications. The emphasis is on engineering applications of the use of geothermal energy.

THE RESOURCE

Description

Geothermal energy is the thermal energy within the earth's crust: the thermal energy in rock and the fluid (water, steam, or water with large amounts of dissolved solids in it) that fills the pores and fractures within the rock. Calculations have shown that the earth, starting from a completely molten state, would have cooled and become completely solid many thousands of

The preparation of this chapter is assigned to TC 6.8, Geothermal Energy Utilization.

years ago, had there not been an additional energy input other than from the sun. It is believed that the ultimate source of geothermal energy is radioactive decay, which occurs within the earth (Bullard 1973). Through plate motion and vulcanism, some of this energy is concentrated at high temperatures near the surface of the earth. In addition, energy transfer from the deeper parts of the crust to the earth's surface by conduction (and also by convection in regions where geological conditions and the presence of water permit) results in the general condition of thermal energy of elevated temperature at depth.

Because of variation in volcanic activity, radioactive decay, rock conductivities, and fluid circulation, various regions have different heat flows (through the crust to the surface), as well as different temperatures at a particular depth. The *normal* increase of temperature with depth (the normal geothermal gradient) is about 13.7 °F/1000 ft (25 °C/km) of depth with gradients of about 5 to 27 °F/1000 ft (10 to 50 °C/km) being common. The areas that have the higher temperature gradients and/or higher-than-average heat flow rates are of the most interest as economic resources. However, with the presence of certain geological features, areas with normal gradients may be valuable resources.

Geothermal resources of the United States are categorized into the following five basic types:

1. Igneous point sources
2. Deep convective circulation in areas of high regional heat flow
3. Geopressure
4. Concentrated radiogenic heat sources
5. Deep regional aquifers in areas of near normal gradient

Igneous point resources are associated with magma bodies, which result from volcanic activity. These bodies heat the surrounding and overlying rock by conduction and convection, as permitted by the rock permeability and fluid content in the rock pores.

Deep circulation of water in areas of high regional heat flow can result in hot fluids near the surface of the earth. Such resources are called *hydrothermal convection systems*. This is the type of geothermal resource in widespread use. The fluids near the surface have risen from natural convection circulation between the hotter, deeper formation and the cooler formations near the surface. The passageway that provides for this deep circulation must consist of fractures and faults of adequate permeability.

The geopressure resource, present over a wide region in the Gulf Coast area, consists of regional occurrences of confined hot water in deep sedimentary strata: 11,000 psi (76MPa) are common. This resource also contains methane dissolved in the geothermal fluid.

Radiogenic heat sources exist in various regions as granitic plutonic rocks that are relatively enriched in uranium and thorium. These plutons have a higher heat flow than the surrounding rock, and if the plutons are blanketed by sediments of low thermal conductivity, elevated temperatures can result at the base of the sedimentary section. This resource has been identified in the eastern United States. Such systems also have been identified in the western United States, but there they are of secondary importance to both igneous point sources and regions of high heat flow.

Deep regional aquifers of commercial value can occur in deep sedimentary basins, even in areas of only normal temperature gradient. The requirements are that the basins be deep enough to allow usable temperature levels at the prevailing gradient and that the permeabilities within the aquifer be adequate for flow in the aquifer.

The thermal energy in geothermal resource systems exists primarily in the rocks and only secondarily in the fluids that fill the pores and fractures within them. Presently, for the most part, thermal energy is extracted by bringing to the surface the hot water or steam that occurs naturally in the open spaces in the rock. Where rock permeability is low, the energy extraction rate is low. To extract the thermal energy from the rock itself, a recharge of water into the system must occur as the initial water is extracted. In permeable aquifers, or where natural fluid conductors occur, the produced fluid may be injected back into the aquifer some distance from the production hole to pass through the aquifer again and recover some of the energy in the rock; such a system is termed a *stimulated* or *forced geoheat recovery system* (Bodvarsson and Reistad 1976). This type of system is presently in operation in France (BRGM 1978). For recovering energy from impermeable rock, research is now underway to evaluate the feasibility of creating artificial permeability by fracturing (hydraulic and thermal stress) and then extracting the thermal energy by injecting cold water into the fractured system through one well and removing the heated fluid through a second well. This technology is referred to as *hot dry rock* because it is directed at hot rock bodies containing little or no water (Brown et al. 1979).

Temperatures

The temperature of fluids produced from the earth's crust and used for their thermal energy content vary from about 60 to 680 °F (15 to 360 °C). The lower value represents the fluids used as the low temperature energy source for heat pumps, and the higher temperature represents an approximate value for the hottest system in development (for electrical power generation).

Figure 1 shows examples of the temperature as a function of depth for the several cases of A, near normal gradient of 13.7 °F/1000 ft (25 °C/km); B, high gradient of 37.3 °F/1000 ft (68 °C/km); and C and D, convective systems (Combs et al. 1980). In conductive systems, the temperature is relatively constant with depth throughout the permeable horizon but increases with depth above and below this. To achieve high temperatures, either deep drilling or convective systems that originate at depth and provide circulation to shallower regions are necessary.

The following classification of resources by temperature level are used in this chapter:

High temperature $T \geqslant 300$ °F (150 °C)

Intermediate
    temperature 194 °F (90 °C) $\leqslant T \leqslant 300$ °F (150 °C)

Low temperature 60 °F (15 °C) $< T < 194$ °F (90 °C)

Electricity generation is generally not economically feasible for resources with temperatures below about 300 °F (150 °C), which is the reason for the division between high temperature and intermediate temperature systems. However, binary power plants, with the proper set of circumstances, have demonstrated that it is possible to generate electricity economically above 230 °F (110 °C).

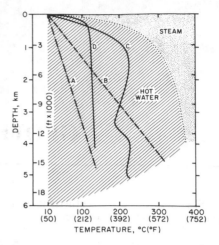

A. Near normal temperature gradient
B. High conductive gradient
C. and D. Temperature depth relations resulting from convective flow

Fig. 1   Representative Temperature-Depth Relations in the Earth's Crust (Combs et al. 1980)

The 194 °F (90 °C) division between intermediate and low temperatures is common in resource inventories but is somewhat arbitrary. However, at 194 °F (90 °C) and above, applications such as district heating can be readily implemented with equipment used in conventional applications of the same type, while at lower temperatures, such applications require redesign to take the greatest advantage of the geothermal resource.

The geothermal systems at the lower temperature levels are more common. Figure 2 shows the percent of frequency of identified convective systems by reservoir temperature for temperatures above 194 °F (90 °C). For resources below 194 °F (90 °C) (Figure 3), a quantitative estimation has been completed of thermal energy recoverable from low temperature geothermal systems within the United States (Reed 1982).

Geothermal Fluids

Geothermal energy is extracted from the earth through some fluid medium. This medium is the naturally occurring fluids in rock pores and fractures, but in the future, it may also be an additional fluid that is introduced into the geothermal system and circulated through it to recover the energy. The fluids being produced are either steam, hot liquid water, or a two-phase

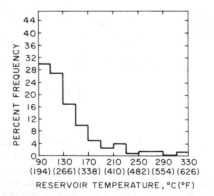

Fig. 2   Percent Frequency of Identified Hydrothermal Convection Systems by Reservoir Temperature in 20 °C Classes (Muffler et al. 1980)

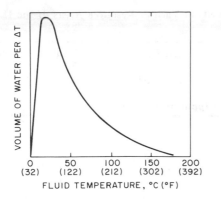

Fig. 3   A Probable Distribution for Geothermal Fluids

mixture of both. These may contain various amounts of impurities. Dissolved gases and dissolved solids are of principal concern.

Geothermal systems that produce essentially dry steam are referred to as *vapor dominated*. These systems are valuable resources, but they are rare. Hot water systems (referred to as liquid dominated) are much more common than vapor-dominated systems. They can be produced either as hot water or as a two-phase mixture of steam and hot water, depending on the pressure maintained on the production system. If the pressure in the production casing or in the formation around the casing is reduced below the saturation pressure at that temperature, some of the fluid will flash, and a two-phase fluid will result. If the pressure is maintained above the saturation pressure, the fluid will remain as a single phase. In these water-dominated systems, both dissolved gases and dissolved solids are significant. For such fluids, the quality varies from site to site and varies from water of potable quality to fluids that have over 300,000 ppm dissolved solids. The U.S. Geological Survey classifies the degree of salinity of mineralized waters as follows:

Dissolved Solids, ppm	Classification
1,000 to 3,000	Slightly saline
3,000 to 10,000	Moderately saline
10,000 to 35,000	Very saline
More than 35,000	Brine

Thus, geothermal fluids range all the way from nonsaline to brine, depending on the particular resource.

Table 1 presents the composition of fluids from a number of geothermal wells in the United States. The list illustrates the types of substances and the range of concentrations that can be expected in the fluids. Although there is great site dependency, the harshness of the fluid increases with increasing temperature. This chapter concentrates on systems produced as a single-phase hot liquid.

Life of the Resource

Although the radioactive decay that appears to be the ultimate source of geothermal energy continues, geothermal energy in a specific locality is limited. The limiting factor is usually thermal water, the medium used to transfer the energy from the rocks to the surface. If production rates of thermal water exceed natural recharge rates, water levels can decline and the resource should be developed with a reservoir management plan that includes injection wells to maintain reservoir pressure. Reservoir life is difficult to determine and involves expensive reservoir engineering techniques. The usual procedure is to expand the area to be developed in stages, monitoring the water levels in wells, then apply proper reservoir management methods as additional

capacity is required and/or initial energy production rates start to drop.

Environmental Aspects

Geothermal resources directly coupled to the production must consider the overall environmental aspects of the use and production of geothermal energy. The primary environmental issues and a very brief discussion of each are presented in Table 2. Willard *et al.* (1980), considers the concerns regarding direct applications.

PRESENT USE AND POTENTIAL DEVELOPMENT

Recent discoveries of concentrated radiogenic heat sources and deep regional aquifers in areas of near normal temperature gradient indicate that most states have geothermal resources that may be economically exploitable. The Interagency Geothermal Coordinating Council (1980) indicates that 37 states have such resources (see Figure 4).

The Geysers resource area in northern California, where electricity is being produced at a rate of 1792 MW in 1985, is the largest single geothermal development in the world. The total electricity generated in the world was 4764 MW in 1985. The annual percentage growth rate from 1978 to 1985 was 16.5%. The direct application of geothermal energy for space heating and cooling, water heating, agricultural growth-related heating, and industrial processing represents over 7000 MW worldwide by the end of 1984. The thermal energy used was found to be 81.7×10^{12} Btu (86.2 PJ) in most instances above a reference temperature of 95 to 104°F (35 to 40°C).

The major uses of geothermal energy in agricultural growth applications are for the heating of greenhouses and aquaculture facilities. The main industrial uses of geothermal energy in this country are for food processing. It is presently used in vegetable dehydration. Worldwide, the main applications include space and water heating, space cooling, agricultural growth, and food processing. The exceptions are diatomaceous earth processing in Iceland and pulp and paper processing in New Zealand.

Potential Impact

Geothermal energy, in terms of the fluids produced, is restricted to temperature levels substantially lower than those from fossil fuels. The maximum temperature of a producing field is 680°F (360°C), and the usual resource is expected at much lower temperatures. Figure 5 presents approximate temperature required for many applications. Space heating and cooling, as well as sanitary water heating, represent uses that are both significant in scale (representing a total of about 25% of U.S. energy consumption) and readily accommodated by the low and intermediate temperature geothermal resources. Many process heat requirements occur at such temperature levels. A number of estimates of the amount of energy consumed at various temperature levels in the process industries are summarized in Figure 6. The figure is a cumulative plot of energy use at or below a particular temperature. Industrial heating consumes 25% of the U.S. energy; so that requirement, together with the space heating, cooling, and sanitary water heating energy requirements, indicate that a significant portion of the total energy use in the United States lies in a temperature range for which geothermal energy is applicable.

DIRECT APPLICATION SYSTEMS

Because many processes require thermal energy at a temperature level compatible with geothermal energy and, furthermore, because geothermal energy can be exploited in most

Table 1   Representative Fluid Compositions from Geothermal Wells in Various Resource Areas of the U.S.[a]

Location	Boise[b] ID	Klamath Falls[c] OR	Beowave[d] NV	Raft River[e] ID	Baca[f] NM	Salton Sea CA
Temperature, °F (°C)	176 (80)	192 (89)	270 (132)	295 (132)	340 (171)	482 (250)
Species in Fluid			Concentration (ppm or mg/kg)			
Total Dissolved Solids	290	795	855	1319	6898	(220,000)
SiO_2	160	48	329	91.8	835	(350)
Na	90	205	214	368	2010	(5100)
K	1.6	4.3	9	65	541	(12,500)
Li	0.05		trace	1.1		(220)
Ca	1.7	26		52	36	(23,000)
Mg	0.05			1.9		(150)
Cl	10	51	50	611	3,770	(133,000)
F	14	1.5	6	5.5		
Br				2.5		
I				0.035		
SO_4	23	330	89	63	58	
S				0.2	2.2	
NO_3		4.9		0.19		
P				0.003		
NH_4		1.3		4.53		
NH_3			3			
H_2S	trace	1.5	6.1			
HCO_3	70	20	41	86.6	118	
CO_3	4	15	168		0	
CO_2	0.2					
Al	minor		0.2			(0.04)
As	0.05					(1)
B	0.14		1	0.3		(350)
Ba	0.2			0.4		(270)
Cr	minor					(0.6)
Cu	0.08		trace			(8)
Fe	0.13	0.3		3.2		(1300)
Mn	0.01		trace	0.08		
Ni	trace			3.5		(2.4)
Sr	0.01			1.3		(500)
Ti	trace		trace			
V			trace			
Zn	trace minor					
Hg	0.02					
Si				44		
H_2	0.0054					
He	0.0016					
CH_r	0.065					
N_2	18.51					
O_2	0.0029	0.02				
Ar	0.62					

NOTES:
[a] All data except Klamath Falls from Cosner and Apps (1978). Klamath Falls data is from Ellis and Conover (1981).
[b] Well name unknown. Near old penitentiary.
[c] Wendling Well. Data from Lund et. al. (1976).
[d] Vulcan Well 2.
[e] Well RRGE I.
[f] Well Baca II. Flashed fluid sample.

states, it is a good choice of energy for many applications. However, an evaluation of using geothermal energy, as well as the proper design for its use, in specific applications, requires consideration of the characteristics of geothermal systems and the interaction with specific equipment. This section explains the geothermal system characteristics and the use of geothermal energy in residential, commercial, and industrial applications.

General Systems

Figure 7 schematically illustrates the direct use of a geothermal resource in Reykjavik, Iceland. Such a system may consist of five subsystems: (1) the production system, consisting of the producing wellbore and associated wellhead equipment; (2) the transmission and distribution system that transports the geothermal energy from the resource site to the user site and then

Table 2   Primary Environmental Issues That May Arise in Specific Applications of Geothermal Resources

Issue	Potential Environmental Impact	Comments
Ecological	Damage to plants and animals.	Many geothermal resources are located in sensitive areas. With proper planning and design, this problem can be minimal.
Air Quality	Emission of various gases into the atmosphere.	Certain resources have some H_2S, radon, or other non-condensable gases, which require proper design.
Noise	Noise pollution.	Primarily a problem during drilling or testing. Proper noise abatement procedures should be followed.
Surface water quality	Degradation of water quality from thermal, chemical, or natural radioactive properties of disposed fluids.	Proper disposal system design and planning for accidental releases are required.
Land use	Conflict of geothermal use of land with uses such as agriculture, recreation, etc.	Since surface area required for geothermal development is relatively small, this issue can usually be resolved.
Geological alteration	Subsidence and/or induced seismic activity.	Subsidence can occur in sedimentary resource areas when fluid injection is not used. Induced seismicity is not a major concern, except for cases of deep high pressure fluid injection.
Water supply and hot springs alteration	Alteration of existing and potential water supplies or hot springs activities because of withdrawal of geothermal fluid and/or energy or injection of geothermal fluids.	Geothermal development near water supplies and hot springs may be restricted or prohibited because hydrological information is inadequate to predict the impact of the development.
Archaeological and cultural resources	Destruction of archaeological areas and/or infringement on cultural resources (historical, paleontological).	May restrict areas to which development is possible. Conduct archaeological survey of prospective development area and do not develop problem areas.
Socioeconomic	Change in existing economic structure, population, and social patterns.	Primarily a concern for large labor intensive developments in sparsely populated areas. Can be controlled with adequate planning.

Fig. 4   States with Known or Potential Low Temperature Geothermal Resources

distributes it to the individual user loads; (3) the user system; (4) the disposal system, which can be either surface disposal or injection back into a formation, which may or may not be the same as that from which it was originally produced; and (5) a peaking/backup system.

In a typical system of this type, the geothermal fluid will be produced from the production borehole by using a lineshaft multistage centrifugal pump. (Some wells may freeflow adequate quantities of fluid and a pump will not be required. However, the more common commercial size operation is expected to require pumping to provide the required flow rate.) When the geothermal fluid reaches the surface, it is sent to an accumulator from which it is pumped, with standard circulating pumps, through the transportation and distribution systems to the application site. To meet short-term load increases that may occur on a daily basis, it is common to store the geothermal fluid near the application site. It is also usual to have the geothermal system designed to meet only the base load of the application and incorporate a peaking station for satisfying the peak loads. The peaking station is most commonly a fossil-fueled unit that will allow the higher loads to be met in either of two ways: (1) by increasing the temperature of the fluid supplied to the application by directly heating the geothermal fluid coming from the transportation system or (2) by increasing the flow rate of fluid supplied to the application (at constant temperature) by heating fluid recirculated from the application and mixing it with fluid coming from the transportation system.

Figure 8 shows a different system from that illustrated in Figure 7. In the system of Figure 8, the geothermal production and disposal system are closely coupled, and they are both separated from the remainder of the system by a heat exchanger. The reason for isolating the production and disposal systems from the rest of the system is to limit the contact of the geothermal fluid with system equipment, thereby reducing corrosion and scaling caused by the geothermal fluid. A secondary loop fluid is heated by the geothermal fluid in the heat exchanger. This secondary fluid, usually treated water, is the medium for transferring the energy to the application. The rest of the system in Figure 8 remains the same as in Figure 7, except that the equipment designs can be based on the properties of the secondary loop fluid for equipment in Figure 8, but they must be based on the geothermal fluid properties for application as illustrated in Figure 7. The desirability of this secondary loop is obvious when the geothermal fluid is particularly harsh in terms of corrosion and/or scaling. Such a system arrangement is also advantageous when the geothermal fluid is clean and the application requires direct use of the heated fluid in a process where water quality is of utmost concern, such as in the food processing industry. There is an additional environmental advantage for this type of system because the geothermal fluid is pumped directly back into the ground without loss to the surrounding surface environment.

General Characteristics of Geothermal Systems

Geothermal energy systems have several characteristics that greatly influence their applicability and the design for their use. These characteristics arise from (1) the resource, (2) the application, and (3) the interaction between both the resource and the application. The characteristics take the form of either constraints or design variables. The constraints are fixed for a particular resource and application, and although they cannot be varied for the application under construction, they influence the feasibility of using the geothermal resource in the particular ap-

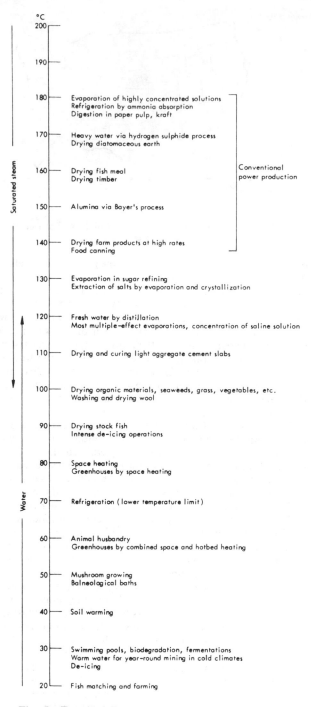

Fig. 5   Required Temperatures (Approximate) of Geothermal Fluids for Various Applications[a]

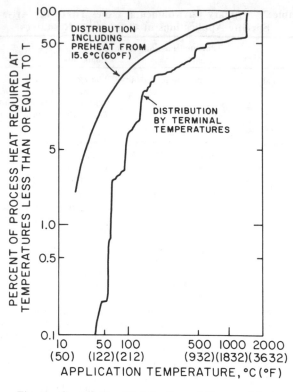

Fig. 6   Cumulative Distribution of Process Heat Requirements (Intertechnology Corp. 1977)

9. Composition of fluid
10. Ease of disposal
11. Resource life

Many of these characteristics have a major influence because the costs of geothermal systems are primarily front-end capital costs, and the annual operating costs are relatively low.

Depth of the Resource. The well cost is usually one of the larger items in the overall cost of a geothermal system, and as

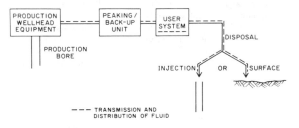

Fig. 7   Basic Geothermal Direct Use System

plication. The design variables are those parameters varied to improve the feasibility of geothermal energy use.

The characteristics that have a major influence on the cost of energy delivered from geothermal systems are as follows:

1. Depth of the resource
2. Distance between resource location and application site
3. Cost of capital
4. Well flow rate
5. Temperature of resource
6. Allowable temperature drop
7. Load size
8. Load factor

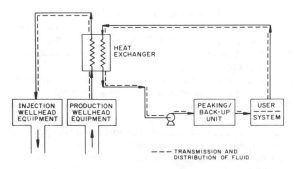

Fig. 8   Geothermal Direct Use System with Wellhead Heat Exchanger and Injection Disposal

the depth of the resource increases, so does the cost of the overall system. This is illustrated in Figure 9. Consequently, the economic upper limit of well depth appears to be about 10,000 ft (3 km) for developments in the near future.

Distance Between Resource Location and Application Site. The direct use of geothermal energy must occur near the resource location. The reason is primarily economic, because although the geothermal fluid (or a secondary fluid) could be transmitted over moderately long distances, greater than 60 mi (97 km), without having a great temperature loss, such transmission would not be economically feasible unless there were very special circumstances. The economic limit for the separation distance between the application and the resource depends on many factors attributable to both the application and the geothermal resource, so that an accurate specification cannot be made. However, it is generally considered that under favorable conditions, economic viability can be achieved for separation distances as great as several tens of kilometers.

Cost of Capital. In a system where the costs are primarily due to capital costs, an increase in the interest rate that is paid for borrowed capital has nearly the same influence as an equal percentage increase in the capital costs. Consequently, as the interest rate increases, the economic position of a particular geothermal system is decreased.

Well Flow Rate. The energy output from a production well varies directly with the flow rate of fluid. Thus, the energy cost at the wellhead varies inversely with the well flow rate. Typical good resources have production rates of about 400 to 800 gpm (25 to 50 L/s) per production well.

Temperature. In geothermal systems, the available temperature is associated with the prevailing resource. This temperature is an approximately fixed value for a given resource. Although the temperature should increase with deeper drilling, natural convection that occurs in the fluid dominated systems (which are the only ones used at this time) keeps the temperature relatively uniform throughout the depth of the resource (see Figure 1). If drilling is continued through the producing region into a region that is not permeable enough to permit natural convection, the temperature may increase or decrease, but usually inadequate flow occurs to yield an economic resource. Deeper drilling at the same area can, however, result in recovery of energy at a higher temperature if deeper separate aquifers (producing zones) occur. Such an increase in temperature is also theoretically possible in the yet unproved hot dry-rock-type systems.

The temperature limitation can present a severe restriction on potential applications. Quite often, it requires a reevaluation of the accepted application temperatures, since these have been developed in systems fueled by conventional fuels where the application temperature could be selected at any value within a relatively broad range (without a major change in the overall system design or energy efficiency). In the use of geothermal energy, the application temperature must be lower than the produced fluid temperature, except in the use of heat pumps, where the application temperature may be somewhat greater than the produced fluid temperature.

Allowable Temperature Drop. The power output from the geothermal well is directly proportional to the temperature drop of the geothermal fluid effected by the user system, since the well flow rate is limited. Consequently, a larger temperature drop means a decreased energy cost at the wellhead. If there is a loop fluid such as in Figure 8 and the maximum loop fluid temperature approaches the geothermal supply fluid temperature, the loop fluid must also have a reasonably large temperature drop across the user system. This is in great contrast to many conventional and solar systems that circulate a heating fluid with a small temperature drop. Consequently, a different design philosophy and different equipment are required.

Although it is important to have a goal of a large ΔT, the maximum ΔT in a single application is not always the most desirable because of the expense of heat exchange equipment at low approach temperatures. For this reason, cascading the geothermal fluid to uses with lower temperature requirements can be advantageous in achieving a large ΔT.

Load Size. It is advantageous to have large-scale applications because of the gain from economy of scale, particularly in regard to reduction in resource development and transmission system costs. However, in many instances, the applications are not extremely large and the more usual application has one to several production wells. For these smaller developments, it is important to match the size of the application with the production rate from the geothermal system because the output from the geothermal resource comes in discrete sizes corresponding to one well increments. Figure 10 shows a schematic diagram of initial

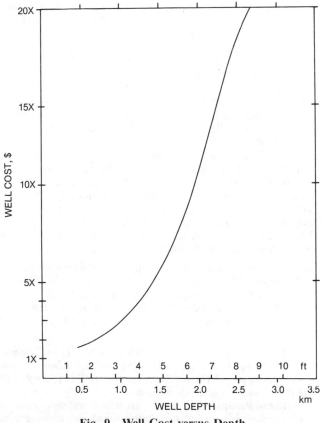

Fig. 9   Well Cost versus Depth

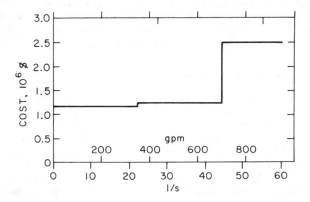

Fig. 10   Cost of the Geothermal Water Investment at the Wellhead in Terms of Yield—Dogger Aquifer, Parisian Region (Coulbois and Herault 1976)

investment, at the wellhead, as a function of production rate illustrating the step costs for one well, one well being pumped, and two wells (Coulbois and Herault 1979). The lowest priced energy, for the range of production illustrated, occurs for an application sized to use a production rate just less than that which would require the second well.

Load Factor. The load factor, defined as the ratio of the average load to the designed capacity of the installed system, effectively reflects the fraction of time that the initial investment in the system is working. Again, because the geothermal system costs are primarily initial investment rather than operating, this factor significantly affects the viability of a geothermal system. As this factor increases, so does the economic position of using geothermal energy. The two main ways of increasing it are to select applications where it is naturally high and to use peaking equipment so that the load that the geothermal system is designed for is not the application peak load, but rather a reduced load that occurs over a longer period.

Composition of Fluid. The quality of the produced fluid is site specific and may vary from potable to heavily brined. The quality of the fluid influences two aspects of the system design: (1) fluid treatment and material selection to avoid corrosion and scaling effects and (2) disposal or ultimate end use of the fluid.

For fluids that are particularly harsh, the best way of handling them is to isolate them from most of the system equipment by the use of heat exchangers of specially selected materials located near the resource, as illustrated in Figure 8. To protect the environment, harsh fluids must be disposed of by injection. On the other hand, milder fluids may be dealt with by material selection for application equipment. In addition, they may be used in a consumption end use such as agricultural irrigation, if they are of sufficiently good quality.

Thus, the quality of the fluid may necessitate extra equipment or special disposal systems, which increase the cost of the geothermal system, or it may allow additional end uses of the fluid, possibly decreasing the cost of the geothermal energy for a particular application.

Ease of Disposal. Depending on the particular resource and applicable environmental regulations, special systems such as cooling, treatment, and/or injection disposal may be required. The ease with which this can be accomplished directly influences the economics of the applications. For example, when injection of the fluid is required, if the local geological structure is such that this can be accomplished with shallow wells and small pumping requirements, the economics are much better than when deep wells and/or large pumping requirements occur.

Resource Life. The life of the resource has a direct bearing on the economic viability of a particular geothermal application. There is little experience in the United States on which to base projections of resource life for heavily developed geothermal resources. However, present experience suggests that the resources can readily be developed in a manner that will allow resource lives of 30 to 50 years and greater.

Equipment and Materials

The primary equipment used in geothermal systems are pumps, heat exchangers, storage vessels, and piping. Some aspects of these components are unique to geothermal applications, but many of them are of routine design. However, the great variability and general tendency of the geothermal fluid requires that particular attention be directed to limiting corrosion and scale buildup, rather than system cleanup. Corrosion and scaling can be limited by (1) proper system and equipment design and (2) treatment of the geothermal fluid. The first of these methods is routinely used in geothermal applications while the second method is in the development stage.

Fluid treatment is the addition of corrosion and/or scaling inhibitors to the geothermal fluid, usually as it comes from the production system. Because very large quantities of geothermal fluid are used in most applications and, therefore, large quantities of the chemical additives are also required, such treatment is expensive. Treatment to prevent corrosion has the additional disadvantage that the added substances are of such a nature that environmental regulations may require removal of all the added chemicals from the effluent prior to disposal. The chemicals added for scale control need not be removed prior to disposal. Philips *et al.* (1977) discusses the primary aspects of brine treatment in geothermal systems and includes an extensive literature listing.

In the proper system and equipment design for limiting corrosion and scaling, there are three primary concepts:

1. Restricting the number of equipment components that come in contact with the geothermal fluid, particularly for the harsher geothermal fluids.
2. Selecting component designs that can either be easily cleaned or that provide continuous cleaning during operation for those equipment items particularly sensitive to corrosion deposits and scale buildup.
3. Selecting proper materials for those components that come in contact with the geothermal fluid.

The first two of these concepts are illustrated by specific examples. The system shown in Figure 8 limits corrosion and scaling problems in surface equipment by limiting the contact of the geothermal fluid to the production well, the injection well, and a wellhead heat exchanger. A following section on heat exchangers depicts various heat exchanger designs where a major feature is either the ease of cleaning or the continuous cleaning of the heat transfer surface on the geothermal fluid side.

Materials Selection. The proper selection of materials requires knowledge of the chemical composition of the geothermal fluid under consideration. Unfortunately, the composition of the fluid varies from resource to resource and from well to well within the same resource. This variation, along with the fact that minor amounts of certain substances can influence the amount of corrosion or scaling that can ocur, limits applying generalized rules for material selection. The technology for selection of materials for use with geothermal fluids is still under development. Chemicals that present the most problems regarding corrosion and scaling from geothermal fluids are listed in Table 3. Table 4 presents general guidelines, based on experience, for the use of various metallic materials in geothermal applications (DeBerry et al. 1978).

Pumps. Pumps are used for production, circulation, and disposal. For circulation and disposal, whether surface disposal or injection, standard state-of-the-art hot water circulating pumps, almost exclusively of the centrifugal design, are used. These are routine engineering design selections with the only special consideration being the selection of appropriate materials. The production pumps, on the other hand, are not a routine selection because of the following factors:

1. There is usually only one production pump per production borehole so that pump redundancy is not easily built into the system and, therefore, a most reliable unit is desired.
2. There is substantial development work being devoted to production pumping systems, particularly at the higher temperatures.

The production well pumps fall into two classifications: *wellhead pumps* and *downhole pumps*. Both classifications have the pump located in the wellbore, but the *wellhead pumps* have the driver located at the wellhead.

Wellhead Pumps. These pumps are usually referred to as *vertical lineshaft pumps* (or *lineshaft pumps*). An above-ground

Table 3   Major Corrosion and Scaling Substances Contained in Geothermal Fluids (DeBerry et al. 1978)

Substance	Major Impact (Corrosion or Scaling)	Form
Hydrogen	Corrosion	Ion
Chlorides	Corrosion	Ion
Hydrogen Sulfide	Corrosion	Gas
Carbon Dioxide	Corrosion	Gas
Ammonia	Corrosion	Gas
Sulphates	Corrosion	Ion
Oxygen	Corrosion	Gas
Transition Metals	Corrosion	Ion
Silicates	Scaling	Solid
Carbonates	Scaling	Solid
Sulfides	Scaling	Solid
Oxides	Scaling	Solid

General concerns of the corrosive effects are as follows:

Hydrogen ion (pH). The general corrosion rate of carbon steels increases rapidly with decreasing pH, especially below pH 7. Passivity of many alloys is pH dependent. Breakdown of passivity at local areas can lead to serious forms of attack, *e.g.,* pitting, crevice corrosion, and stress corrosion cracking.

Chloride. Chloride causes local breakdown of passive films that protect many metals from uniform attack. Local penetration of this film can cause pitting, crevice corrosion, or stress corrosion cracking. Uniform corrosion rates can also increase with increasing chloride concentration, but this action is generally less serious than local forms of attack.

Hydrogen Sulfide. Probably the most severe effect of H_2S is its attack on certain copper and nickel alloys. These metals have performed well in sea water, but are practically unusable in geothermal fluids containing H_2S. The effect of H_2S on iron-based materials is less predictable. Accelerated attack occurs in some cases and inhibition in others. High strength steels are often subject to sulfide stress cracking. H_2S may also cause hydrogen blistering of steels. Oxidation of H_2S in aerated geothermal process streams increases the acidity of the stream.

Carbon Dioxide. In the acidic region, CO_2 can accelerate the uniform corrosion of carbon steels. The pH of geothermal fluids and process streams is largely controlled by CO_2. Carbonates and bicarbonates can display mild inhibitive effects.

Ammonia. Ammonia can cause stress corrosion cracking of copper alloys. It may also accelerate the uniform corrosion of mild steels.

Sulfate. Sulfate plays a minor role in most geothermal fluids. In some low chloride streams, sulfate is the main aggressive anion. Even in this case, it rarely causes the same severe localized attack as chloride.

Oxygen. The addition of small quantities of oxygen to a high temperature geothermal system can greatly increase severe localized corrosion of normally resistant metals. The corrosion of carbon steels is sensitive to trace amounts of oxygen.

Transition Metal Ions. Heavy or transition metal ions might also be included as key species. Their action at low concentrations on most construction materials is ill-defined. However, the poor performance of aluminum alloys in geothermal fluids may be in part because of low levels of copper or mercury in these fluids. In Salton Sea, California, geothermal fluids contain many transition metal ions greater than trace concentrations. Some oxidized forms of transition metal ions (Fe^{+3}, Cu^{+2}), etc. are corrosive, but these ions are present in the lowest oxidation state (most reduced form) in geothermal fluids. Oxygen can convert Fe^{+2} to Fe^{+3}, which is another reason to exclude oxygen from geothermal streams.

Table 4   General Guidelines for Material Use in Geothermal Systems (DeBerry et al. 1978)

Mild steel
By taking appropriate precautions, mild steels can be used for thick-walled applications in contact with most geothermal fluids. Thin-walled applications will be limited by the susceptibility of these materials to localized attack such as pitting and crevice corrosion. High salinity geothermal fluids cause high uniform corrosion, as well as localized corrosion and severely limit the use of low carbon steels. The application of mild steels to geothermal environments requires that precautions be taken for aeration, flow rate, scaling, galvinic coupling, exterior surfaces, and steel specifications.

Stainless steel
The uniform corrosion rate of most stainless steels is low in geothermal fluids, but many are subject to the more serious forms of corrosion: pitting, crevice corrosion, stress corrosion cracking, sulfide stress cracking, intergranular corrosion, and corrosion fatigue. Stainless steels have been used in geothermal environments, but care must be taken in their selection and application.

Titanium and tinanium alloys
Titanium and its alloys have given good results in all but the most extreme environments when tested for geothermal applications. Titanium was used successfully for hydrogen and oil coolers exposed to aerated cooling water/condensate at the Cerro Prieto, Mexico, geothermal facility. Two other heat exchanger materials had failed in this environment.

Nickel based alloys
High nickel alloys are frequently used to combat severe corrosion problems. The Ni-Cr-Mo alloys appear to be the most applicable to high temperature geothermal fluids. Similar alloys containing iron in place of molybdenum face competition from the most resistant stainless steels, but may find application when their mechanical properties are desirable. Cupronickels have limited usefulness in geothermal streams containing even trace quantities of H_2S.

Copper based alloys
The use of copper alloys is severely limited by the relatively high concentrations of sulfide found in most geothermal sources. The Raft River KGRA (Known Geothermal Resource Area), with a low sulfide concentration of 0.1 ppm, appears to be an exceptional case. However, even in this fluid, the performance of copper-nickel alloys (Monel 400, 70Cu/30 Ni, and 90 Cu/10 Ni) was very poor. Dealloying of some copper alloys was observed. However, some nickel-free brasses and bronzes gave acceptable performance.

Cobalt alloys
Cobalt alloys may find application in services requiring high strength combined with resistance to sulfide stress cracking and in services requiring wear resistance.

Zirconium and tantalum
Zirconium and tantalum may be considered for severe, hot acid chloride service such as injection nozzles for acidifying fluid with hydrochloric acid.

Aluminum alloys
Aluminum alloys have not shown good resistance in tests conducted in direct contact with geothermal fluids. Low levels of transition metal ions, especially copper and mercury, greatly increase localized attack of aluminum alloys. These ions are present in most liquid dominated geothermal fluids.

driver, typically an electric motor, rotates a vertical shaft extending down the well the length of the pump. The shaft rotates the pump impellers within the pump bowl assembly, which is positioned at such a depth in the wellbore that adequate net pump static head (NPSH) is available when the unit is operating. Lineshaft pumps have their long vertical shafts supported two ways. One way, called *enclosed lineshaft pump,* places bearings inside a tube concentric to the shaft and of slightly larger diameter. The other way (*open lineshaft*) supports the bearings from the column pipe and no tube encloses the shaft.

In the enclosed lineshaft pump, a lubricating fluid is pumped or gravity fed through the tube to lubricate the bearings. Oil has been used successfully in this application for some geothermal systems, but there has been little experience with its use in systems that have temperatures greater than 300°F (150°C). In some higher temperature systems, water has been pumped through the tube to provide lubrication. Water can lead to mineral deposits on the bearings, and should be treated to minimize deposits.

The bearings in open lineshaft pumps are lubricated by the production fluid as it moves up the column pipe. Such pumps are widely used in domestic water supply systems but have been used with little success in geothermal application. The reliability of lineshaft pumps decreases as the pump-setting depth increases because of the lineshaft bearings. Nichols (1978) indicates that at depths greater than about 800 ft (240 m), reliability is questionable, even under good pumping conditions.

Downhole Pumps. The primary downhole pump, the *electrical submersible pump,* is commercially available and can be readily used for geothermal resources at temperatures below about 250°F (120°C). Units to operate at resource temperatures above this value are presently being tested.

The electrical submersible pump system consists of three primary components located downhole: the pump, the drive motor, and the motor protector. The pump is a vertical multistage centrifugal type. The motor is usually a three-phase induction type that is oil filled for cooling and lubrication. The motor is cooled by heat transfer to the pumped fluid moving up the well. The motor protector is located between the pump and the motor and isolates the motor from the well fluid while allowing for pressure equalization between the pump intake and the motor cavity.

The electrical submersible pump has several advantages over lineshaft pumps, particularly for wells requiring greater pump bowl setting depths. As the well gets deeper, the submersible becomes less expensive to purchase and easier to install. Moreover, it is less sensitive to vertical well deviation and the poor assembly conditions that normally exist at the wellhead. It is reported that the breakover point is at a pump depth of about 800 ft (240 m), with the submersible desirable at pump depths greater than this and the lineshaft preferred at shallower pump settings. The lineshaft has been more widely used for geothermal applications than the electrical submersible, with lineshaft pumps being used for depths of as much as 300 to 500 ft (90 to 150 m).

A development that permits easy removal of the pump without removing the wellhead discharge pipes improves the desirability of the submersible units. In this unit, the submersible pump assembly is suspended in the wellbore with a cable. The pump is serviced by lifting the unit with the cable and removing it from the well piping through a stripper valve. This procedure allows the pump to be removed without the use of well *kill fluids* to hold back the flow, as would be required in the usual pump service operations.

Another type of downhole geothermal pumping system has a turbine and pump located downhole, with a condenser at the surface and piping serving as a steam generator. It uses thermal energy from the geothermal fluid to drive the turbine, which drives the pump (Sperry Research Center 1977).

Heat Exchangers

The systems in Figures 7 and 8 use heat exchangers in contact with the geothermal fluid. For the system of Figure 8, one or more large heat exchangers are located near the wellhead, whereas in the system of Figure 7, air and/or a process fluid is heated by the geothermal fluid in a heat exchanger. The trend is to isolate the geothermal fluid coming in contact with either complicated systems or systems that cannot readily be designed to be compatible with the geothermal fluids. For instance, the geothermal fluid is used directly to heat processing water in many industries, but would not usually be used directly in the evaporator of a heat pump (because of the complicated and expensive system) or in the extended surface coils of a building heat system (because the extended surface coils are made of copper-based materials that are not compatible with most geothermal fluids and also because the building system is complex and expensive).

The principal types of heat exchangers used in transferring energy from the geothermal fluid are (1) plate, (2) shell and tube, (3) downhole, (4) direct contact, and (5) plastic tube. The first three types are used in many geothermal installations.

Plate Heat Exchangers. This exchanger, as illustrated in Figure 11, consists of a series of stamped plates placed one behind the other with seals between consecutive plates. A few or many plates can be stacked together. They are held in place by long bolts that extend through header plates and, when tightened, press the plates against one another to compress the seals.

In use, the geothermal fluid is routed along one side of each plate and the heated fluid is routed along the other side. The plates can be readily manifolded for various combinations of series and parallel flow. These heat exchangers have been widely used for many years in the food processing industry and in marine applications. They have two main characteristics that make them desirable for many geothermal applications:

1. They are readily cleaned. By loosening the main bolts, the header plate and the individual heat exchanger plates can be removed and cleaned.
2. The stamped plates are very thin and may be made of a wide variety of materials. When expensive materials are required, the thinness of the plates keeps this type of heat exchanger much less expensive than other types.

These heat exchangers have additional characteristics that influence their selection in specific applications:

1. Approach temperature differences are usually smaller than those for shell-and-tube heat exchangers; particularly important in low temperature geothermal applications.
2. Pressure drops can be smaller than those for shell-and-tube heat exchangers since, for a given duty, fewer passes are required through a plate exchanger and less entrance and exit losses result.
3. Heat transfer per unit volume is usually larger than for shell-and-tube heat exchangers.
4. Applications are restricted for temperatures less than 500°F (260°C) because of limitations on elastomeric gaskets.
5. Increased capacity can be accommodated easily; only the addition of plates is required.

Shell-and-Tube Heat Exchangers. This commonly applied heat exchanger is used in a limited number of geothermal applica-

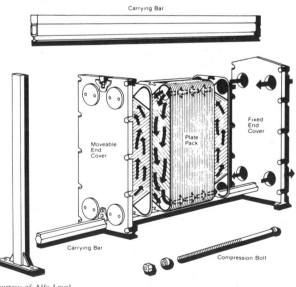

[a]Courtesy of Alfa-Laval

Fig. 11   Plate Heat Exchanger[a]

tions. It has limited application because the plate heat exchanger has economic advantage when specialized materials are required to minimize corrosion. However, when mild steel shells and copper or silicon bronze tubes can be used, the shell-and-tube heat exchangers are more economical. When these units are used, with the geothermal fluid passing through the tube side, the tubes should be in a straight configuration to facilitate mechanical cleaning.

There are two specialized designs of shell-and-tube heat exchangers for geothermal energy use with geothermal fluids that have a high potential for scaling. These are the *fluidized bed* and Advanced Geothermal Energy Primary Heat Exchanger (APEX) concepts. Figure 12 illustrates the type of fluidized bed heat exchanger for geothermal applications. Its primary application is in use with fluids with high scaling potential. It consists of a shell-and-tube heat exchanger with the geothermal fluid (the scaling fluid) passing through the shell side. The fluid passes up through a bed of particles, such as sand, which surrounds

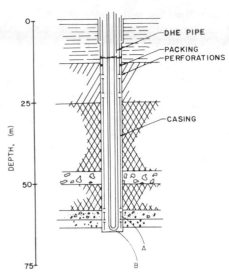

Fig. 13   Typical Downhole Heat Exchanger (DHE) Installation

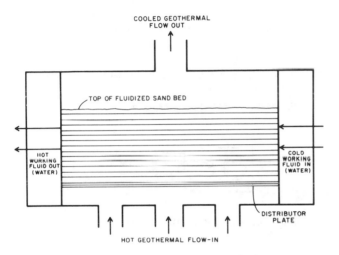

Fig. 12   Schematic of Horizontal Arrangement of a Liquid-Fluidized-Bed Heat Exchanger (Allen and Grimmett 1978)

the tube bundle. The bed is fluidized by the fluid flow. This provides a constant scrubbing action against the tubes, keeping them from scaling and, as a side benefit, increasing the heat transfer rate. The configuration can accommodate either horizontal or vertical tube bundle assemblies. Because of the rapid mixing in the fluidized bed, the shell side temperature distribution approaches isothermal and thus, to get the energy out of the geothermal fluid, such exchangers must operate with series staging. The APEX type of heat exchanger is similar to the fluidized bed design in that a scouring agent (such as sand) is used to help keep the heat transfer surface clean. But in the APEX design, the abrasive material is injected into the geothermal stream before the geothermal stream enters the tubes of a shell-and-tube heat exchanger. As the geothermal stream leaves the heat exchanger, it enters a disengaging zone and the abrasive material and any precipitated solid material is removed (Adams and Gracey 1977).

Downhole Heat Exchangers. In shallow geothermal resource areas, heat exchangers located within the wellbore can work for relatively small-scale direct applications (Culver and Reistad 1978). Figure 13 shows a typical installation. The exchanger consists of pipes or tubes suspended in the cased wellbore. A secondary fluid circulates from the user system through the exchanger. Geothermal fluid passes by the exchanger because of thermosiphoning caused by cooling from the heat exchanger. The systems with higher outputs have perforations in the well cas-

ing near the bottom and just below the water level to promote thermosiphoning.

These systems have not been tested in a large number of resource areas. In resource areas such as at Klamath Falls, Oregon, where over 400 downhole heat exchanger systems are in operation, it appears that economic desirability relative to surface heat exchanger systems exist when a single well output, typically less than 0.8 MW, is adequate for the application and the wells are relatively shallow, up to about 650 ft (200 m).

Direct Contact Heat Exchangers. As another approach to cope with corrosion and scaling tendencies of some geothermal fluids, direct contact heat exchangers are being developed. In these, the geothermal fluid is brought into direct contact with another fluid that vaporizes at the desired recovery temperature and then separates from the geothermal fluid. Similar direct contact heat exchange is very common in oil refineries, but there the exchange is between relatively clean fluids. Figure 14 shows schematics of various configurations of direct contact heat exchange systems. The use of these systems is still in the development stage, but they do appear to have a good potential for application if the particular application can readily make use of a vapor heating medium. One such application is the binary cycle power plant, which is the main application for which these units have been investigated. The systems do have the difficulty that the dissolved gases in the geothermal fluid end up mixed with the secondary vapor and must still be dealt with.

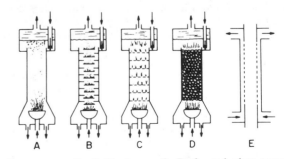

A. Spray tower; B. Baffle tower; C. Perforated plate tower; D. Packed tower; E. Wetted wall tower

Fig. 14   Schematic of Various Types of Direct Contact Counterflow Devices (Jacobs 1977)

Plastic Tube Heat Exchangers. Plastic tubes, developed for heat recovery from corrosive sources, have good potential for application in geothermal systems of a limited temperature range. Because commonly used fan coils have copper-based tubes, they are unsatisfactory for most geothermal fluids. Commercial plastic tube heat exchangers with an upper temperature limit of 122°F (50°C) and designed for air heating are used to a limited extent, but more importantly, it appears that developing products will have a higher allowable temperature (of about 200°F or 93°C) and, consequently, should have much greater applicability. Such units will be substantially larger than the present fan coil units, but the corrosion and scaling resistance appear to outweigh the increase in size (Lienau et al. 1980).

Piping

Standard low-carbon steel pipe is the most common type of pipe used for transmission and distribution lines in geothermal applications. This type of pipe has been the least costly for many installations and, when selected with adequate corrosion allowances, has given acceptable life. Because the mild steel is subject to severe corrosion when free oxygen is present, it is necessary to maintain a tightly sealed system.

Other types of piping, particularly those made of non-metallic materials, appear to have applicability in geothermal systems. However, many of the available ones have only been used in limited geothermal applications or are in the development stage.

Fiberglass reinforced plastic (FRP) pipe is being increasingly used for geothermal applications at temperatures up to about 250°F (120°C). The primary advantage responsible for its use is its noncorrosive nature (particularly in regard to external corrosion in direct buried lines). FRP pipe also has some advantage over steel pipe in that expansion considerations are not so severe and there is less pressure drop for a given flow rate in the FRP pipe. Disadvantages of the FRP pipe are its temperature limitation and its pressure limitation in the larger sizes, particularly at the higher end of the temperature range. The use of PVC plastic pipe in geothermal applications is more restricted because of the temperature limitation, with the maximum recommended temperature being about 125°F (52°C). Polybutylene has been used in district heating pipes up to 6 in. and in many applications of radiant floor pipes. Heat fusion bonding is the preferred method where cyclic heating and cooling is expected [i.e. heat in the winter and the system off (cool) in the summer].

Asbestos cement pipe has been used in a number of geothermal applications, primarily disposal lines, with good success. Studies have presented different conclusions regarding the economy of using asbestos cement piping. Lund *et al.* (1984) found that an asbestos cement based transmission line was the most expensive of the various acceptable alternatives, while Costello *et al.* (1980) reported that its use is more economical than carbon steel for transmission lines with diameters less than 16 in. (400 mm).

A variety of nonmetallic materials, particularly concrete polymer composites, plastics, and refractories, have been evaluated for their use in geothermal applications by Kukack et al. (1976-8). The concrete polymer composites have shown exceptional promise for use as liner material, even at temperatures up to about 464°F (240°C).

The types of piping specified for the main distribution lines in a recent district heating development are illustrated in Figure 15. Figure 15a illustrates a steel pipe in a concrete tunnel with removable lids. This system (widely used in Europe) is desirable because (1) there is good access to the pipe for future development, maintenance, and repair; (2) there is good assurance that the exterior of the pipe will remain dry; and (3) the concrete duct may be oversized to reduce overall cost with future expen-

sion of the system. The primary disadvantage of this type of system is its high cost. The system illustrated in Figure 15b is a direct buried FRP pipeline. It was selected for that portion of the overall development where no future pipe installations were envisioned. The primary reason for selecting this system is that the first cost of a direct buried system is much lower than that for a concrete tunnel system. With the direct buried system, FRP pipe, rather than steel, is selected to minimize external corrosion.

Typical small business or residence piping connections in geothermal district heating systems will probably follow the experience in Europe or Iceland, where steel or FRP piping insulated with urethane foam covered with a plastic jacket is direct buried at a depth just below the frostline.

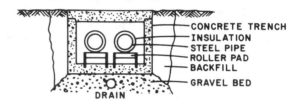

a. Steel pipe in a concrete tunnel with removable lids.

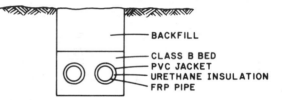

b. Direct buried insulated FRP pipe.

Fig. 15   Main Distribution Lines in a Geothermal District Heating System (Lund et al. 1979)

RESIDENTIAL AND COMMERCIAL APPLICATIONS

The primary applications for the direct use of geothermal energy in the residential and commercial area are space heating, sanitary water heating, and space cooling. Space and sanitary water heating is widespread, while space cooling is used in few instances. Sanitary water heating, or at least preheating, is accomplished almost universally when space heating is accomplished.

Space and Sanitary Water Heating

Figure 16 illustrates the use of geothermal fluid at 170°F (77°C) (Austin 1978). This geothermal fluid is used in two main equipment components for heating of the structures: a plate heat exchanger that supplies energy to a closed heating loop previously heated by a natural gas boiler (the natural gas boiler remains as a standby unit), and a water-to-air coil used for preheating ventilation air.

In this system, proper control is crucial for economical operation, and a major goal of control is to extract a large amount of energy from each unit of geothermal fluid by discharging at the lowest feasible temperature at part load conditions, as well as at the design point (Phillips et al. 1977). After leaving the heat transfer equipment, the geothermal fluid goes to a storm drain that leads to a spray cooling pond and fluid discharge to the river.

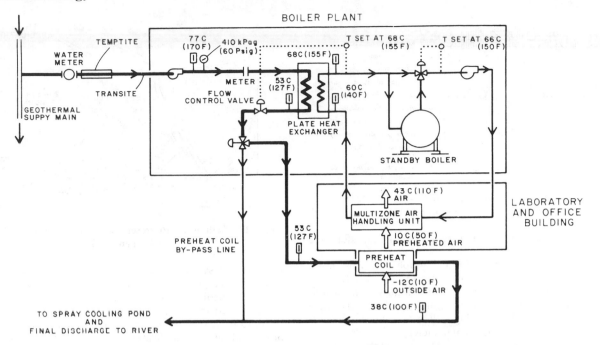

Fig. 16 Heating System Schematic

The average temperature of the discharged fluid is 120 to 130°F (49 to 54°C). The geothermal fluid is used directly in the terminal equipment within the buildings, which would probably not be applied if the system were being designed today. A fair number of corrosion problems have arisen in this direct use, mainly because of the action of hydrogen sulfide on copper-based equipment parts (Mitchell 1980). Even with these difficulties, the geothermal system appears highly cost effective (Lienau 1979).

Individual residence systems in the Klamath Falls area use downhole heat exchangers, as illustrated in Figure 13. The use for a typical residence is illustrated in Figure 17. Water from the community supply system circulates in a closed loop for the space heating, with makeup through a pressure-reducing valve. The sanitary hot water is supplied by connecting the city water supply to one leg of a downhole heat exchanger and the other leg of the downhole heat exchanger to the hot water supply piping within the residence. The space heating loop is constructed of 2 in. (50 mm) pipe and the water heating loop is made with 1 in. (25 mm) pipe. These systems have the advantage of being simple, requiring a minimal amount of wellhead equipment, and avoiding any disposal-associated problems. Such systems, however, are limited in overall applicability, with their best application being for shallow resources and applications that have a thermal power requirement less than the output of a one-well installation (Reistad et al. 1979).

At Reykjavik, Iceland, about 16,000 houses are connected, serving over 100,000 people. The system is schematically illustrated in Figure 18. The fluid is pumped out of the boreholes with deep well pumps set at about 390 ft (120 m) depth, through collecting pipelines to the area's main pumphouse. Fluids at or above 212°F (100°C) pass through a deaerator at the main pumphouse to remove dissolved gases. The fluid is then pumped through the high temperature mains to the various district stations within the city. Fluids below 212°F (100°C) are held in open cisterns at the main pumphouse before being pumped into distribution mains. Since the system uses resources with different temperatures, two types of final distribution systems have developed. In the oldest part of the system, which was designed for a fluid supply temperature of about 185°F (85°C), a single-

pipe design is used where warm water is supplied to the house for heating and domestic use and then drained to the sewer. The fluids at temperatures too high for safe direct use are led to a two-pipe design whereby a sufficient quantity of cooled water from the residences is collected in return water storage tanks for subsequent mixing with the high temperature water to achieve

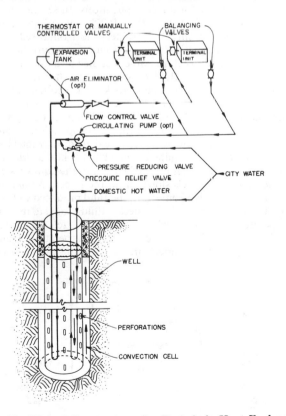

Fig. 17 Typical Connection of a Downhole Heat Exchange System for Space and Sanitary Water Heating (Reistad et al. 1979)

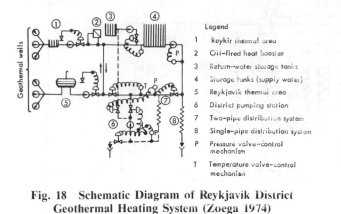

Fig. 18   Schematic Diagram of Reykjavik District Geothermal Heating System (Zoega 1974)

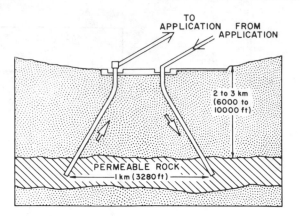

Fig. 20   Schematic Representation of the Doublet System (Rybach 1979)

the desired distribution temperature for heating and domestic use.

Standard house connections for a two-pipe system are shown in Figure 19. The supply solenoid valve (6) is controlled by a room thermostat, and a high temperature limit switch controls the solenoid valve in the return line from the radiators. Demand is limited by a sealed regulating valve, and consumption is measured with an integrating water meter.

The piping is all-welded black steel pipe laid underground. Piping of 3 in. (80 mm) diameter or larger is laid in concrete channels and insulated with rock wool insulation. Smaller pipe is insulated with polyurethane foam and has an outside protective coating of high density polyethylene. The peak heating requirements of this system are met by increasing the temperature of the supply water in an oil-fired boiler plant.

The development of apartment heating from low temperature geothermal resources in France has widened the interest in geothermal energy for direct applications. In several locations around Paris, fluid in the 120 to 160°F (49 to 71°C) range is being withdrawn from relatively deep horizontal sedimentary horizons. After use, the fluid is injected back into the aquifer through a second borehole some distance away from the production well, and the fluid passes through the aquifer again, drawing energy from the aquifer rocks. The geothermal system is referred to as a *doublet*. Figure 20 illustrates a schematic of the typical system. The wellbores may be either nearly vertical or slanted, and systems of both types are in operation. Regardless of the way in which the wellbores are drilled, they intersect the permeable horizontal aquifer about 3280 ft (1 km) apart. In these systems, the fluid that is injected back into the aquifer is heated by the rock as it travels slowly from the injection point to the production point. For some time, the fluid produced will be constant in temperature, with the injected fluid heated to the original temperature of the permeable rock; then, the temperature of the produced fluid will start decreasing in temperature. Figure 21 shows the predicted temperature decrease for a typical system.

Because such systems have a constant temperature output long before the temperature starts decreasing, it will be some time yet before predictions such as that illustrated in Figure 21 can be confirmed from present operations.

Because the temperature of the resource is at the lower end of the scale in these applications, a number of different systems have been considered (BRGM 1978). Figure 22 shows one system that separates the geothermal fluid from the buildings and the major equipment components by a surface heat exchanger, typically a plate heat exchanger and a closed loop heating circuit. A heat pump reduces the return temperature of the closed loop heating fluid so the geothermal fluid can be cooled before injection. In this application, the apartment buildings have two different types of terminal equipment: one group of buildings has radiant floor panels and the other group of buildings has conventional wall radiators. The group of buildings that has the wall radiators also has the domestic water heated with the geothermal system, whereas the other group does not. The buildings with the floor panels are supplied with heating fluid at about 131°F (55°C) with a return temperature of about 86°F (30°C), while the other group of buildings is supplied with heating fluid at about 140°F (60°C) that returns at about 104°F (40°C). Many other geothermal heating installations are in existence (USDOE 1979), but the ones described illustrate a representative cross section of the types of systems.

Types of Terminal Heating Equipment. The types of heating equipment used in geothermal space heating installations are (1) radiant panel, (2) baseboard or wall convectors, (3) forced air, and (4) heat pump. All of these, except for the radiant panel systems, are used in geothermal systems in the United States. The selection of one type over the other is dependent on the

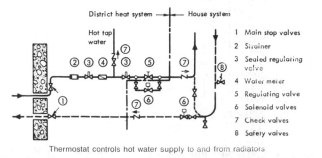

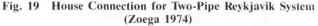

Fig. 19   House Connection for Two-Pipe Reykjavik System (Zoega 1974)

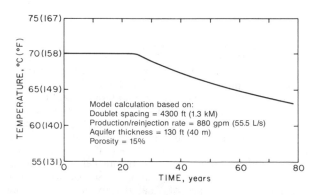

Fig. 21   Temperature Drawdown for a Doublet System (Rybach 1979)

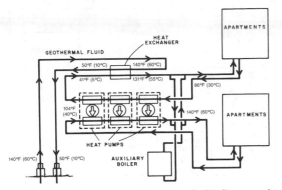

The upper block (2,000 apartments) is equipped with floor panels; the lower block, where domestic hot water is supplied as well (2,000 apartments), has conventional radiators; temperatures in °C

Fig. 22 Simplified Flow Diagram of the Geothermal Heating Installation of Creil (Rybach 1979)

supply fluid temperature. Studies by Culver (1976), Engen (1978), and Bodvarsson and Reistand (1979) of the relative economic position of the various types of terminal systems lead to the following characterization:

1. The heat pump system is economically preferred for fluid supply temperatures up to about 110 to 120 °F (43 to 49 °C).
2. Forced air units are probably the most desirable type of residential heating system in the United States because of the general acceptance of these units and the ease of adapting filtration, humidity control, or cooling. These systems have applicability for fluid supply temperatures ranging from about 120 °F (49 °C) (the top end of where the heat pump is applicable) upward.
3. Baseboard convector systems appear to be the most economical at supply temperatures above about 140 °F (60 °C).
4. Radiant floor panel systems can use water at supply temperatures as low as about 100 °F (38 °C), but they are quite expensive.

Feasibility of Space Heating. In addition to the general characteristics of geothermal applications discussed previously, several factors have a major influence on the feasibility of space heating from geothermal resources. These factors are listed as follows:

Major Factors that Influence District Heating Feasibility

Type of terminal unit	Density of units
Alternative energy costs	Total number of units
Climate	Financing for distribution system
Type of residential unit	

The first of these, the type of terminal unit and its interaction with temperature, has been discussed. The second, the alternative energy cost factor, is explained that as the competing energy costs rise, the feasibility of the geothermal application increases, if all other factors remain constant. The remaining factors affect the costs of the distribution system and the load characteristics. Factors that affect the distribution system costs are important because in district heating systems, whether based on geothermal, solar, or conventional energy supplies, it represents a significant part of the heating cost. These distribution costs, like the geothermal production system costs, are, to a large extent, due to initial capital expenses, and several factors that influence the production system capital costs also apply to the the distribution system capital costs. The load characteristics influence the feasibility of geothermal space heating. In general, the feasibility increases as both the peak requirement and the load duration

(*i.e.,* load factor) increase. It increases as the peak requirement increases because the average has increased and the system can benefit from economy of scale, which is particularly important in the user lines of the distribution system. The feasibility increases as the load factor increases because an increase in load factor improves the economics of such primarily capital cost systems as both the geothermal production and distribution systems.

For space heating, the prevailing climate dictates the peak design and the load duration throughout the year. Figure 23 shows the temperature versus duration curve for temperatures at which space heating is required for a particular location. The residence heating system is designed not for the minimum temperature, but for the ASHRAE 97.5 percentile design point; the resulting load represents the peak design load. Unless auxiliary heating within the space is provided (not usual), the district heating system must also meet this peak load. Since the energy requirement is approximately proportional to the difference in temperature between the inside and outside temperatures, a power scale can be superimposed on Figure 23, as illustrated. As presented, the power curve also includes a contribution for the yearly average water heating rate. The geothermal system may be designed to meet only about 60% of the peak design load, which, as illustrated in Figure 23 (crosshatched area), satisfies about 85 to 90% of the yearly energy requirements. Designed in such a manner, the distribution system operates with a load factor dictated by the climate and system served, with representative values being 0.25 to 0.35 for locations like New York City, Portland, Oregon, and Boise, Idaho. The geothermal production system operates with a load factor of $1/0.6 = 1.67$ times that of the distribution system.

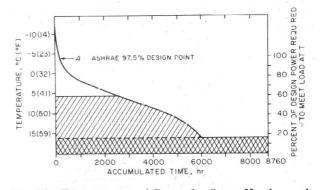

Fig. 23 Temperature and Power for Space Heating and Sanitary Water Heating versus Accumulated Time at or below the Given Temperature for a Particular Location

The type of residential unit served influences the feasibility of the geothermal application because it determines the amount of energy delivered to each site. As the load at a point increases, the cost to deliver the energy, per unit of energy, decreases. For developments of a fixed housing density (number of housing units per unit of area), those developments with high energy requirements per housing unit have greater feasibility for district heating than those with small energy requirements. Also, as the density of housing units increases, so does the feasibility of district heating. The feasibility of district heating is much better for apartments than for suburban residence heating.

Figures 24, 25, 26, and 27 from a study of district heating feasibility illustrate the influence of load factor, heat demand density, load size, and method of financing on distribution system costs. The specific values of the distribution costs, as illustrated, are not significant, since they depend on many factors; rather, they are presented here to illustrate the relative influence of the major factors.

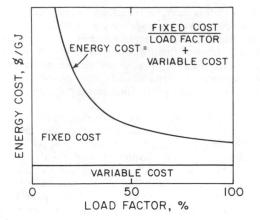

Fig. 24   **Effect of Load Factor on Cost (McDonald 1977)**

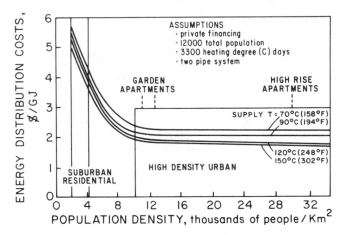

Fig. 25   **Effects of Density and Distribution Temperature on Costs (McDonald 1977)**

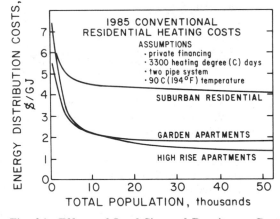

Fig. 26   **Effects of Load Size and Density on Costs (McDonald 1977)**

Peaking and Energy Storage. District heating systems have substantial load variations, and the overall system design must meet them. In addition to the basic geothermal district heating system, peaking and energy storage systems are incorporated to meet these load variations. The load variations arise from three main causes: (1) annual cycles of temperature, (2) daily cycles of temperature, and (3) personal habits such as the lowering of thermostats at night, different working hours, shower times, etc.

The annual and daily temperature variations result in the temperature duration curve considered previously in the discus-

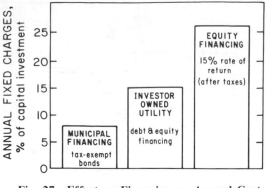

Fig. 27   **Effect on Financing on Annual Costs (McDonald 1977)**

sion of the climate. Because a significant daily temperature variation cannot be relied on during periods when the design condition is approached, and the design condition may occur for an extended period, peaking methods, rather than storage, have been used to meet the primary load variations resulting from temperature change. The two main ways of supplying this peaking are by (1) a fossil-fired peaking station and (2) variable pumping of the geothermal resource with consequent large draw-down of the geothermal reservoir (Bodvarsson and Reistad 1979).

Storage has, on the other hand, been used mainly to meet short-term load increases that occur on a daily basis, primarily because of personal habits. The storage is in large tanks, which, using the geothermal experience in Iceland, are designed to hold about 20% of the peak flow over a 24-hour interval (Olson et al. 1979).

Inclusion of Domestic Water Heating. Domestic water heating in a district space heating system is beneficial because it increases the overall size of the energy load, the energy demand density, and the load factor (see Figure 23). For those resources where domestic water heating to the required temperature is not feasible, preheating is usually desirable.

Space Cooling. There has been little use of geothermal energy for cooling, although emphasis on solar energy and waste heat has created interest in systems that cool with thermal energy. Table 5 lists systems that have received the most attention. The table also indicates the state of development of the various systems. The absorption units are the most developed, with widespread commercial production and application. These units perform reasonably well with heating fluid supply temperatures as low as about 180°F (82°C).

Absorption cooling from geothermal energy requires resource temperatures somewhat higher than 180°F (82°C), which is about the minimum temperature at which reasonable performance can be expected from the absorption units themselves. For the same reasons as for space heating, the economics of operation improves as the temperature of the resource increases above this value.

Space cooling with absorption units from the same geothermal resource used for space heating has the potential to improve the overall economics of the geothermal energy use. The potential for improvement primarily comes from an increased load factor. However, whether or not space cooling actually improves the load factor depends on the temperature of the geothermal resource and the ratio of cooling load to heating load. The load factor increases if the peak thermal energy required to operate the cooling system (cooling load divided by the cooling unit coefficient of performance, which is usually about 0.65 for a single-stage absorption unit for the recommended range of operation) divided by the temperature drop that the cooling unit can extract from the geothermal fluid is less than the heating load

Table 5 Thermal Energy Driven Space Cooling Systems That Are the Primary Candidates for Using Solar and Geothermal Energy for Space Cooling

Absorption: Lithium bromide/water is commercially produced and widely used; new designs allow operation at lower thermal energy input temperature.

Adsorption: Cooling is accomplished by dehumidifying air and then cooling it by adiabatic humidification. Thermal energy reactivates the dessicant used to dehumidify the air. Presently experimental.

Rankine-Cycle Engine/Vapor-Compression Refrigeration: Thermal energy drives a Rankine cycle engine, which drives a vapor compression refrigeration system. Organic working fluids are normally used in the engines at low resource temperatures. A small number of applications and demonstration installations exist.

Other Systems: Many possible systems can produce cooling from thermal energy. The steam jet and Stirling cycle are two examples. However, the steam jet system is less efficient and the Stirling cycle is less developed than the systems listed above.

divided by the temperature drop that the heating system can extract from the geothermal fluid. Otherwise, the size of the geothermal system must be increased for the space cooling requirement. Since the minimum temperature for absorption cooling is greater than that for space heating, the greatest load factor improvement occurs when the cooling load is less than the heating load and the resource temperature is above the minimum required to operate the absorption unit. Large scale district systems require geothermal source temperatures of 176 °F (80 °C) or greater and they must extract a relatively large temperature drop from the geothermal fluid.

INDUSTRIAL APPLICATIONS

The term *industrial* denotes agricultural growth, as well as the usual industrial applications, as listed in the standard industrial classification codes (SIC).

The use of geothermal energy in industrial applications requires design philosophies similar to those for space conditioning. However, they have the potential for much more economical use of the geothermal resource, primarily because of three factors: (1) many industrial applications with year-round operation have the potential for greater load factors than do most space conditioning applications; (2) industrial applications do not require an extensive (and expensive) distribution system to dispersed energy consumers, as is common in district heating; and (3) industrial applications occur at various temperature levels and, consequently, may be able to make greater use of a particular resource than space conditioning restricted to a specific temperature level. Recent studies have tried to take advantage of this last factor by combining several industrial applications into an integrated or *cascaded* system, wherein the geothermal fluid is used in successive processes at lower and lower temperatures until it is finally discarded from the last process with the lowest temperature requirements.

Because the design aspects of the use of geothermal energy in industrial applications are basically the same as for space conditioning, the presentation here for industrial applications concentrates on (1) illustrating those applications and basic processes that have temperature requirements such that they are potential candidates for geothermal heating and (2) presenting examples of the use of geothermal energy in various existing and proposed applications.

Potential Applications

From an engineering viewpoint, a primary prerequisite is that the temperature of the geothermal resource match the applica-

tion. Thus, for a direct use, the temperature of the geothermal resource must be greater than the temperature requirement of the process. However, with the use of heat pumps, the geothermal resource temperature may be below the required temperature of the application. Because the temperature requirement is so important, it provides an initial screening parameter for considering potential processes.

Table 6 lists the temperature and magnitude of use for thermal energy in industrial applications in the United States. Those applications with major requirements below about 300 °F (150 °C) have the most applicability for geothermal energy for two main reasons: (1) above this temperature, the geothermal resource has potential for generation of electrical power and any direct use will face stiff competition from such use and (2) the higher temperature applications are more efficiently met with conventional fuels than are the lower temperature applications, while the reverse is true for geothermal resources over a wide temperature range. The various uses listed in Table 6 can be categorized as occuring in the following basic processes: (1) washing; (2) cooking, blanching, and peeling; (3) sterilization; (4) evaporation and distillation; (5) drying; (6) preheating; (7) miscellaneous heating; and (8) refrigeration.

Table 6 Required Temperature and Energy Use in Industrial Processes (Peterson 1979)

Industry—SIC Group	Temperature °F	°C	Q[c]
Iron ore—1011 pelletizing of concentrates	2350 to 2500	1288 to 1370	39.2
Copper concentrate—1021 drying	250[a]	121	1.8
Bituminous coal—1211 drying (including lignite)	150 to 220[a]	66 to 104	19.0
Sand and gravel—1442			
Potash—1474 drying filter cake	250[a]	121[a]	1.09
Phospate rock—1475 calcining	1400 to 1600	760 to 870	0.75
drying	450[a]	232[a]	11.1
Sulfur—1477 Frasch mining	325 to 340	163 to 171	63.0
Meat packing—2011 Sausages and prepared Meats—2013 scalding, carcass wash, and cleanup	140	60	46.1
singeing flame	500	260	1.12
edible rendering	200	93	0.55
smoking, cooking	155	68	1.22
Poultry dressing—2016 scalding	140	60	3.33
Natural cheese—2022 pasteurization	170	77	1.35
starter vat	135	57	0.02
make vat	106	41	0.50
finish vat	100	38	0.02
whey condensing	160 to 200	71 to 93	10.8
process cheese blending	165	74	0.07
Condensed and evaporated milk—2023 stabilization	200 to 212	93 to 100	3.09
evaporation	160	71	5.48
spray drying	350 to 400	177 to 204	3.78
sterilization	250	121	0.57
Fluid milk—2026 pasteurization	162 to 170	72 to 77	1.52

Table 6　Required Temperature and Energy Use in Industrial Processes (Peterson 1979) (continued)

Industry—SIC Group	Temperature °F	°C	Q^c
Canned specialties—2032			
Beans			
precook (blanch)	180 to 212	82 to 100	0.42
simmer blend	170 to 212	77 to 100	0.25
sauce heating	190	88	0.21
processing	250	121	0.40
Canned fruits and vegetables—2033			
blanching/peeling	180 to 212	82 to 100	1.98
pasteurization	200	93	0.16
brine syrup heating	200	93	1.08
commercial sterilization	212 to 250	100 to 121	1.76
sauce concentration	212	100	0.46
Dehydrated fruits and vegetables—2034			
Fruit and vegetable drying	165 to 185	74 to 85	6.16
Potatoes			
peeling	212	100	0.35
precook	160	71	0.50
cook	212	100	0.50
flake drier	350	177	1.15
granule flash drier	550	288	1.15
Frozen fruits and vegetables—2037			
Citrus juice concentration	190	88	1.40
Juice pasteurization	200	93	0.28
blanching	180 to 212	82 to 100	2.38
cooking	170 to 212	77 to 100	1.49
Wet corn milling—2046			
steep water evaporator	350	177	3.86
starch drier	120	49[a]	0.17
germ drier	350	177	2.03
fiber drier	1000	538	3.09
gluten drier	350	177	1.39
steepwater heater	120	49	0.81
sugar hydrolysis	270	132	1.99
sugar evaporator	250	121	2.89
sugar drier	120	49[a]	0.17
Prepared feeds—2048			
pellet conditioning	180 to 190	82 to 88	2.40
alfalfa drying	400	204[a]	17.7
Bread and baked goods—2051			
proofing	100	38	0.89
baking	420 to 460	216 to 238	6.75
Cane sugar refining—2062			
mingler	125 to 165	52 to 74	0.62
melter	185 to 195	85 to 91	3.48
defecation	160 to 185	71 to 85	0.46
revivifaction	750 to 1110	399 to 599	4.18
granulator		43 to 54	0.46
evaporator		129	27.84
Beet sugar—2063			
extraction	140 to 185	60 to 85	4.88
thin juice heating	185	85	3.25
lime calcining	1000	538	3.14
thin syrup heating	212	100	7.05
evaporation	270 to 280	132 to 280	32.5
granulator	150 to 200	66 to 93	0.16
pulp drier	230 to 280	110 to 138	17.4
Soybean oil mills—2075			
bean drying	160	71	4.27
toaster desolventizer	215	102	6.41
meal drier[a]	350	177[a]	4.60
evaporator	225	107	1.71
stripper	212	100	0.32
Animal and marine fats—2077			
continuous rendering of inedible fat	330 to 350	166 to 177	17.4
Shortening and cooking oil—2079			
oil heater	160 to 180	71 to 82	0.76
washer water	160 to 180	71 to 82	0.13
drier preheat	200 to 270	93 to 132	0.63
cooking oil reheat	200	93	0.34
hydrogenation preheat	300	149	0.39
vacuum deodorizer	300 to 400	149 to 204	0.37
Malt beverages—2082			
cooker	212	100	1.61
water heater	180	82	0.56
mash tub	170	77	0.63
grain drier	400	204[a]	9.68
brew kettle	212	100	4.20
Distilled liquor—2085			
cooking (whiskey)	212	100	3.33
cooking (spirits)	320	160	6.61
evaporation	250 to 290	121 to 143	2.45
drier (grain)	300 to 400	149 to 204	2.05
distillation	230 to 400	110 to 204	8.11
Soft drinks—2986			
bulk container washing	170	77	0.22
returnable bottle washing	170	77	1.34
nonreturnable bottle washing	75 to 85	24 to 29	0.45
can warming	75 to 85	24 to 29	0.55
Cigarettes—2111			
drying	220	104[a]	0.45
rehumidification	220	104[a]	0.45
Tobacco stemming and redrying—2141			
drying	220	104	0.26
Finishing plants, cotton—2261			
washing	212	100	16.2
dyeing	212	100	4.7
drying	275	135	23.4
Finishing plants, synthetic—2262			
washing	200	93	37.9
dyeing	212	100	16.0
drying and heat setting	275	135	24.5
Logging camps—2411			
Sawmills and planing mills—2421			
kiln drying of lumber	300	149	66.9
Plywood—2435			
plywood drying	250	121	53.4
Veneer—2436			
veneer drying	212	100	61.0
Wooden furniture—2511			
makeup air and ventilation	90	21	6.0
kiln drier and drying oven	150	66	4.0
Upholstered furniture—2512			
makeup air and ventilation	70	21	1.5
kiln drier and drying oven	150	66	0.9
Pulp mills—2611			
Paper mills—2621			
Paperboard mills—2631			
Building paper—2661			
pulp digestion	370	188	267
pulp refining	150	66	185

Industry—SIC Group	°F	°C	Q[c]
black liquor treatment	280	138	173
chemicals recovery—			
calcining	1900	1038	101
pulp and paper drying	290	143	404
Solid and corrugated fiber Boxes—2653			
corrugating and glue setting	300 to 350	149 to 177	22.8
Alkalies and chlorine—2812			
mercury cell (to be phased out by 1983)			6.8
diaphragm cell	350	177	86.6
Cyclic intermediates—2865			
ethylbenzene	350	177	3.0
styrene	250 to 350	121 to 177	37.0
phenol	250	121	0.47
Alumina—2819			
digesting, drying, heating	280	138	119.4
calcining	2200	1204	37.2
Plastic materials and resins—2821			
polystyrene, suspension process			
polymerizer preheat	200 to 220	93 to 102	0.107
heating wash water	190 to 200	88 to 93	0.068
Synthetic rubber—2822			
cold SBR latex crumb			
bulk storage	80 to 100	27 to 38	0.189
emulsification	80 to 100	27 to 38	0.091
blowdown vessels	130 to 145	54 to 63	0.912
monomer recovery by flashing and stripping	120 to 140	49 to 60	4.319
drier air temperature	150 to 200	66 to 93	3.864
cold SBR, oil-carbon black masterbatch			
drier air temperature	150 to 200	66 to 93	0.534
oil emulsion holding tank	80 to 100	27 to 38	0.030
cold SBR, oil masterbatch			
drier air temperature	150 to 200	66 to 93	1.15
oil emulsion holding tank	80 to 100	27 to 38	0.095
cold SBR, oil masterbatch			
drier air temperature	150 to 200	66 to 93	1.15
oil emulsion holding tank	80 to 100	27 to 38	0.095
Cellulosic man-made fibers—2823			
polyester	550	288	51.6
nylon	535	279	44.0
acrylic	250	121	24.8
polypropylene	540	282	4.1
Noncellulosic fibers—2824			
rayon	212	100	39.9
acetate	212	100	39.7
Pharmaceutical preparations—2834			
autoclaving and cleanup	250	121	19.88
tablet and dry-capsule drying	250	121	1.05
wet capsule formation	150	66	0.05
Soaps and detergents—2841			
Soaps:			
various processes in soap manufacturer	180	82	0.53
high temperature processes	490	254	0.002
spray drying	500	260[a]	0.001
Detergents:			
various low temperature processes	180	82	0.38

Industry—SIC Group	°F	°C	Q[c]
high temperature processes	500	260	0.38
spray dried detergents	350	177[a]	0.33
spray dried detergents	500	260[a]	0.020
Organic chemicals NEC—2869			
ethanol	200 to 250	93 to 121	6.0
isopropanol	200 to 350	93 to 177	12.0
cumene	250	121	1.0
vinyl chloride monomer	250 to 350	121 to 177	9.0
Urea—2873215			
high pressure steam-heated stripper	375	191	5.35
low pressure steam-heated stripper	290	143	0.94
Explosives—2892			
dope (inert ingredients) drying	300	149	0.006
wax melting	200	93	0.12
nitric acid concentrator	250	121	0.07
sulfuric acid concentrator	200	93	0.02
nitric acid plant	200	93	0.23
blasting cap manufacture	200	93	0.01
Petroleum refining—2911			
crude distillation			
atmospheric topping	650	343	290
vacuum distillation	440 to 800	227 to 427	193
thermal operations	555 to 1010	291 to 543	162
catalytic cracking	1125	607	471
delayed coking	900	482	237
hydrocracking	515 to 810	268 to 432	96
catalytic reforming	925	496	525
catalytic hydrorefining	700	371	55
hydrotreating	700	371	131
alkylation	45 to 340	7 to 171	62
hydrogen plant	1600	871	131
olefins and aromatics	1200	649	131
lubricants			26
asphalt			101
butadiene	250 to 350	121 to 177	63
Paving mixtures—2951			
aggregate drying	275 to 325	135 to 163[a]	92.9
heating asphalt	325	163	5.20
Asphalt felts and coatings—2952			
satuator	400 to 500	204 to 260	1.60
asphalt coating	400 to 500	204 to 260	1.60
drying (steam)	350	177	3.50
sealant	300 to 400	140 to 204	0.60
Tires and inner tubes—301			
vulcanization	250 to 340	121 to 171	6.52
Plastics products—3079			
blow-molded bottles			
high density polyethylene	425	218	3.71
Leather tanning and finishing—3111			
bating	90	32	0.099
chrome tanning	85 to 130	29 to 54	0.063
retan, dyeing, fat liquor	120 to 140	49 to 60	0.16
wash	120	49	0.036
drying	110	43[a]	2.16
finishing drying	110	43[a]	0.14
Flat glass—3211			
melting	2300 to 2700	1260 to 1482	52.8
fabrication (including tempering and laminating)	1470 to 200	799 to 1093	3.7
annealing	930	499	6.2

Table 6 Required Temperature and Energy Use in Industrial Processes (Peterson 1979) *(continued)*

Industry—SIC Group	Temperature °F	°C	Q[c]
Glass containers—3221			
melting-firing	2700 to 2900	1482 to 1593	104.0
conditioning	1500 to 2000	816 to 1093	44.56
annealing	1200	649	13.51
post forming	1200	649	1.50
Hydraulic cement—3241			
drying	275 to 325	135 to 163[a]	8.0
calcining	2300 to 2700	1260 to 1482	494.0
Brick and structural tile—3251			
brick kiln	2500	1371	74.2
Clay refractories—3255			
refractories firing	3300	1816	9.5
Concrete block—3271			
low pressure curing	165	74[a]	12.96
autoclaving	360	182	5.72
Ready-mix concrete—3273			
hot water for mixing concrete	120 to 190	49 to 88	0.36
Lime—3274			
calcining	1800	982	137.0
Gypsum—3275			
kettle calcining	330	166	10.5
wallboard drying	300	149	11.79
Treated minerals—3295			
expanded clay and shale bloating process	1800	982	30.7
Fuller's earth			
drying and calcining	1100	593	6.72
Kaolin			
calcining	1900	1040	1.5
drying	230	110[a]	13.4
Expanded perlite			
drying	160	71[a]	0.23
expansion process	1600	871	1.8
Barium			
drying	230	110[a]	0.36
Blast furnaces and steel mills—3312			
high temperature uses	2700	1482	3480
Ferrous castings			
Gray iron foundries—3321 (73% of heat)			
Malleable iron foundries—3322 (10% of heat)			
Steel foundries—3323 (17% of heat)			
melting in cupola furnaces	2700	1482	154
mold and core preparation	300 to 475	149 to 246	124.1
heat treatment and finishing	900 to 1800	482 to 982	17
pickling	100 to 212	38 to 100	160
Primary copper—3331			
smelting and fire refining	2000 to 2500	1095 to 1371	34.37
Primary zinc—3333			
pyrolytic reduction	2370	1300	1.1
Primary aluminum—3334			
prebaking anodes	2000	1093	8.59
Galvanizing—3479			
cleaning, pickling	130 to 190	54 to 88	0.012
galvanizing (melting zinc)	850	454	0.015
Motors and generators—3621			
drying and preheat	150	66	0.045
baking-prime and paint ovens	350	177	0.140
oxide coat laminations	1500 to 1700	816 to 927	0.76
annealing	1500	816	0.71

Table 6 Required Temperature and Energy Use in Industrial Processes (Peterson 1979) *(continued)*

Industry—SIC Group	Temperature °F	°C	Q[c]
Motor vehicles—3711			
baking prime and paint ovens	250 to 300	121 to 149	0.31
casting foundry	2650	1454	24.0
Inorganic pigments—2816			
drying chrome yellow	200	93	0.079

[a]No special temperature required; requirement is simply to evaporate water or to dry the material
[b]Required application temperature.
[c]Process heat used for application, 10^{12} kJ/yr. Divide by 1.055 to convert to Btu/yr.

Washing. Considerable low temperature thermal energy in the temperature range of about 100 to 200°F (38 to 93°C) is used for washing. The principal users are the food processing, textile, and metal-fabricating industries. The plastics and leather industries represent smaller consumers of such energy. Washing may either consume or not consume the washing fluid. In the consumption use (usual in the food processing and textile industries), fresh wash water is heated from the temperature of the available water supply to the required wash temperature. Such a requirement allows efficient use of the geothermal resource, since a large temperature drop of the geothermal resorce can be realized. For the nonconsumption use of the wash fluid (usual in the metal-fabricating industry), the fluid is recirculated for heating with a 10 to 20°F (5 to 11°C) temperature change being representative of the reheating process. Such a restricted heating temperature change requires either that the resource temperature be greater than the required temperature or that additional measures be taken to achieve a wide temperature change for the geothermal fluid.

Cooking, Blanching, and Peeling. The food processing industry uses thermal energy to cook, blanch, and aid in the peeling of many foods. These processes are done in either a batch or continuous-flow mode. In the blanching or peeling operation, the produce comes in direct contact with a hot fluid. The hot fluid must have closely controlled properties and has to be heated through a heat exchanger if geothermal energy were to be used as the energy source. These processes occur at temperatures in the range of 170 to 220°F (77 to 104°C). Cooking is accomplished both where the product comes in direct contact with the hot fluid and where the product is in containers, which are in turn heated by the hot fluid. Cooking occurs over the temperature range of 170 to 220°F (77 to 104°C), with most of the cooking occurring at about 212°F (100°C).

Sterilization. Thermal energy is required at temperatures ranging from 220 to 250°F (104 to 121°C) for sterilization in a wide range of processes. These processes can use geothermal energy to heat the sterilizing water. Much of the sterilization occurs continuously, but equipment washdown and sterilization often occur periodically.

Evaporation and Distillation. Many industries use evaporators and distillers for concentrating solutions or separating various products. The temperature requirements vary over a wide range, depending on the products involved and the specific designs chosen. In many applications, water is the fluid being evaporated. In these instances, the typical operating temperatures lie in the range of 180 to 250°F (82 to 121°C).

For geothermal application, optional economical operation requires that more stages of evaporation at lower temperatures be designed as compared to designs based on conventional fuels. Applications of evaporation and distillation that appear to have potential for geothermal energy use are sugar and organic liquor processing.

Drying. The drying of products occurs in many industries and is a large consumer of thermal energy in the temperature range appropriate for direct applications of geothermal resources. In most drying applications, heated air is passed around or through the product to achieve the desired drying rate. Major products that require large amounts of drying energy are pulp and paper, textiles, farm products (grain, beet pulp, beverage malt, alfalfa, tobacco, and soybean meal), lumber and plywood, and food products (sugar and dehydrated foods).

Preheating. Many industries consume large quantities of steam or high temperature water that has been heated from the local water supply temperature to the required use temperature. Geothermal energy can preheat this water and thereby decrease the load on the conventionally fueled heating equipment.

Miscellaneous Heating. Thermal energy is used to maintain a space or product at a temperature elevated relative to the surroundings. Examples of such heating are space heating in industrial and agricultural applications (greenhouses and livestock housing), warming of plant beds (open field soil warming and mushroom growing), and maintaining sewage digester tanks at operating temperatures.

Refrigeration. Industrial cooling can be accomplished with geothermal energy by several methods. The required refrigeration temperature strongly influences the type of system that will be selected. For refrigeration temperatures above the freezing point of water, the situation is analogous to space cooling, and the lithium bromide/water system appears to have the most applicability. For refrigeration temperatures below about 32 °F (0 °C), either the Rankine engine/vapor compression system or an absorption system with a refrigerant other than water is the logical choice. Breindel *et al.* (1979) evaluated absorption refrigeration systems for refrigeration temperatures of 32 to −40 °F (0 to −40 °C) with geothermal resource temperatures of 212 to 300 °F (100 to 149 °C).

REFERENCES

Anderson, D.A. and Lund, J., eds. 1980. *Direct Utilization of Geothermal Energy: Technical Handbook.* Geothermal Resources Council *Special Report* No. 7.

Adams, J.F. and Gracey, C.F. 1977. Wellsite Verification Testing of an Advanced Geothermal Primary Heat Exchanger. APEX, Aerojet Liquid Rocket Company Report 2146-102-F.

Allen, E. 1980. Preliminary Inventory of Western U.S. Cities with Proximate Hydrothermal Potential. Report, Elliot Allen and Associates, Inc., Salem, OR.

Allen, C.A.; and Grimmett, E.S. 1978. Liquid-Fluidized-Bed Heat Exchanger Design Parameters. DOE Report, ICP-1153, Allied Chemical, Idaho Chemical Programs, Idaho National Engineering Laboratory.

Barton, D.B. 1970. Current Status of Geothermal Power Plants at The Geysers, Sonoma County, CA. *Geothermics*, Special Issue, Vol. 2, No. 2, Part 2.

Bodvarsson, G.; and Reistad, G.M. 1979. Performance and Feasibility of Forced Geoheat Recovery for Low Temperature Applications. Final Report to U.S. DOE, Report No. RLO-2227-T36-4.

Bodvarsson, G.; and Reistad, G.M. 1976. Econometric Analysis of Forced Geoheat Recovery for Low-Temperature Uses in the Pacific Northwest. *Proceedings* of the Second United Nations Symposium on the Development and Use of Geothermal Resources, San Francisco. Published by Lawrence Berkeley Laboratory, Berkeley, CA, Vol. 3.

Bodvarsson, G. 1974. Geothermal Resource Energetics. *Geothermics*, Vol. 3.

Breindel, B.; Harris, R.L.; and Olson, G.K. 1979. Geothermal Absorption Refrigeration for Food Processing Industries. ASHRAE *Transactions*, Vol. 85, Part 1.

BRGM. 1978. La Geothermie en France. Orleans, France.

Brown, M.C.; Duffield, R.B.; Siciliana, C.L.B.; and Smith, M.C. 1979. Hot Dry Rock Geothermal Energy Development Program, Annual Report, Fiscal Year 1978. DOE Report LA-7807-HDR, Los Alamos Scientific Laboratory, University of California.

Bullard, E. 1973. Basic Theories (Geothermal Energy; Review of Research and Development), UNESCO, Paris, France.

Chappell, R.N.; Prestwich, S.J.; Miller, L.G.; and Ross, H.P. 1979. Geothermal Well Drilling Estimates Based on Past Well Costs. Geothermal Resources Council *Transactions*, Vol. 3.

Combs, J.; Applegate, J.K.; Fournier, R.O.; Swanberg, C.A.; and Nielson, D. 1980. Exploration, Confirmation and Evaluation of the Resource. Geothermal Resources Council, Special Report No. 7, *Direct Utilization of Geothermal Energy: Technical Handbook.*

Cosner, S.R.; and Apps, J.A. 1978. A Compilation of Data on Fluids from Geothermal Resources in the United States. DOE Report LBL-5936, Lawrence Berkeley Laboratory, Berkeley, CA.

Costain, J.K.; Keller, G.V.; and Crewdson, R.A. 1976. Geological and Geophysical Study of the Origin of the Warm Springs in Bath County, Virginia. DOE Report TID-28271, Virginia Polytechnic Institute and State University, Blacksburg, VA.

Costain, J.K.; Glover III, L.; and Sinha, A.K. 1979. Evaluation and Targeting of Geothermal Energy Resources in the United States. DOE Report VPI-SU-5648, 1 through 5, Virginia Polytechnic Institute and State University, Blacksburg, VA, December 1977-March 1979.

Costain, J.K.; Glover III, L.; and Sinha, A.K. 1977. Evaluation and Targeting of Geothermal Energy Resources in the Southeastern United States. DOE Report VPI-SU-5103-5, Virginia Polytechnic Institute and State University, Blacksburg, VA.

Costain, J.K. 1979. Geothermal Exploration Methods and Results—Atlantic Coastal Plain. Geothermal Resources Council, Special Report No. 5, A Symposium of Geothermal Energy and Its Direct Uses in the Eastern United States.

Coulbois, P.; and Herault, J. 1976. Conditions for the Competitive Use of Geothermal Energy in Home Heating. *Proceedings* of the Second United Nations Symposium on the Development and Use of Geothermal Resources, San Francisco, May 1975, published by Lawrence Berkeley Laboratory, Berkeley CA, Vol. 3.

Culver, G.G.; and Reistad, G.M. 1978. Evaluation and Design of Downhole Heat Exchangers for Direct Applications. U.S. DOE Report No. RLO-2429-7.

Culver, G.G. 1976. Optimization of Geothermal Home Heating Systems. Geoheat Utilization Center, Oregon Institute of Technology, Klamath Falls, OR.

Dan, F.J.; Hersam, D.E.; Khoa, S.K.; and Krumland, L.R. 1975. Development of a Typical Generating Unit at The Geysers Geothermal Project-A Case Study. *Proceedings* of the Second United Nations Symposium on the Development and Use of Geothermal Resources, San Francisco, CA.

DeBerry, D.W.; Ellis, P.F.; and Thomas, C.C. 1978. Material Selection Guidelines for Geothermal Power Systems. DOE Report ALO-3904-1, Radian Corporation, Austin, TX. Contains Extensive Literature of Materials Selection Citations.

DiPippo, R. 1985. Geothermal Electric Power, The State of the World—1985. Geothermal Resources Council *Proceedings*, 1985 International Symposium on Geothermal Energy, International Volume, Davis, CA.

Einarsson, S.S. 1973. Geothermal District Heating. Geothermal Energy: Review of Research and Development, UNESCO, Paris.

Ellis, P.F. and Conover, M.F. 1981. Material Selection Guidelines for Geothermal Energy Utilization Systems. DOE Report RA/27026-1, Radian Corporation, Austin, TX.

Engin, I.A. 1978. Residential Space Heating Cost: Geothermal vs Conventional Systems. TREE-1182, Idaho National Engineering Laboratory.

Grim, P.J.; Nichols, C.R.; Wright, P.N.; Berry, G.W.; and Swanson, J. 1978. State Maps of Low-Temperature Geothermal Resources. Geothermal Resources Council *Transactions*, Vol. 2.

Gudmundsson, J.S. 1985. Direct Uses of Geothermal Energy in 1984. Geothermal Resources Council *Proceedings*, 1985 International Symposium on Geothermal Energy, International Volume, Davis, CA.

Interagency Geothermal Coordinating Council. Geothermal Energy, Research, Development and Demonstration Program. DOE Report RA—0050, IGCC—5, U.S. Department of Energy, Washington, D.C.

Intertechnology Corporation. 1977. Analysis of the Economic Potential of Solar Thermal Energy to Provide Industrial Process Heat. Final Report, Vols. 1, 2, and 3, Col. 28-29-1 NTIS, Springfield, VA.

Jacobs, H.R. 1977. Evaluation and Design Considerations for Liquid-Liquid Direct Contact Heat Exchangers for Geothermal Applications. ASME Publication, 77-HT-2.

Kubacka, L.E.; et al. 1976-1978. Alternate Materials of Construction for Geothermal Applications. Brookhaven National Laboratory Progress Reports.

Kunze, J.F.; Richardson, A.S.; Hollenbaugh, K.M.; Nichols, C.R.; and Mind, L.L. 1976. Nonelectric Utilization Project, Boise, Idaho. *Proceedings* of the Second United Nations Symposium on the Development and Use of Geothermal Resources, San Francisco, May 1975. Published by Lawrence Berkeley Laboratory, Berkeley, CA. Vol. 3.

Lienau, P.J. 1984. Geothermal District Heating Projects. District Heating, Vol. 70, No. 1 and 2, The International District Heating Association, Washington, D.C.

Lienau, P.J. 1979. Materials Performance Study of the OIT Geothermal Heating System. Geo-Heat Utilization Center Quarterly Bulletin, Oregon Institute of Technology, Klamath Falls, OR.

Lund, J.W.; Lienau, P.J.; Culver, G.G.; and Higbee, C.V. 1979. Klamath Falls Geothermal Heating District. Geothermal Resources Council *Transactions*, Vol. 3.

McDonald, C.L. 1977. An Evaluation of the Potential for District Heating in the United States. *Proceedings* of the Miami International Conference on Alternative Energy Sources, Clean Energy Research Institute, University of Miami, Coral Gables, FL.

Mitchell, D.A. 1980. Performance of Typical HVAC Materials in Two Geothermal Heating Systems. ASHRAE *Transactions*, Vol. 86, Part 1.

Muffler, L.J.P., ed. 1979. Assessment of Geothermal Resources of the United States-1978. U.S. Geological Survey Circular No. 790.

Nichols, K.E. and Malgieri, A.J. 1978. Technology Assessment of Geothermal Pumping Equipment. DOE Report ALO-4162-2, Barber-Nichols Engineering Company, Arvada, CO.

Nichols, C.R. 1978. Direct Utilization of Geothermal Energy: DOE's Resource Assessment Program. Direct Utilization of Geothermal Energy: A Symposium, Geothermal Resources Council.

Olson, G.K.; Benner-Drury, D.L.; and Cunnington, G.R. 1979. Multi-Use Geothermal Energy System With Augmentation for Enhanced Utilization: A Non-Electric Application of Geothermal Energy in Susanville, California. Final Report DOE-ET-248447-1, Aerojet Energy Conversion Company, Sacramento, CA.

Peterson, Eric A. 1979. Possibilities for Direct Use of Geothermal Energy. ASHRAE *Transactions*, Vol. 85, Part 1.

Phillips, S.L.; Mathur, A.K.; and Doebler, R.E. 1977. A Study of Brine Treatment. EPRI Report ER-476, Lawrence Berkeley Laboratory, Berkeley, CA. Contains Literature Search of 348 Citations.

Reed, M.J., ed. 1983. Assessment of Low-Temperature Geothermal Resources of the United States—1982. Geological Survey Circular 892, United States Department of Interior, Alexandria, VA.

Reistad, G.M.; Culver, G.G.; and Fukuda, M. 1979. Downhole Heat Exchangers for Geothermal Systems: Performance, Economics and Applicability. ASHRAE *Transactions*, Vol. 85, Part 1.

Rybach, L. 1979. Geothermal Resources: An Introduction With Emphasis on Low-Temperature Reservoirs. Geothermal Resources Council, Special Report No. 5, A Symposium of Geothermal Energy and Its Direct Uses in the Eastern United States.

Sperry Research Center. 1977. Feasibility Demonstration of the Sperry Down-Well Pumping System. DOE Report COO-2838-1, Sperry Research Center, Sudbury, MA.

U.S. DOE. 1979. Direct Heat Application Summary. Geothermal Resources Council Annual Meeting.

Zoega, J. 1974. The Reykjavik Municipal Heating System. *Proceedings* of the International Conference on Geothermal Energy for Industrial, Agricultural and Commercial-Residential Uses, Oregon Institute of Technology, Klamath Falls, OR.

BIBLIOGRAPHY

Anderson, D.A.; and Lund, J., eds. 1980. Direct Utilization of Geothermal Energy: Technical Handbook (Geothermal Resources Council, Special Report No. 7).

Armstead, H.C.H. ed. 1973. Geothermal Energy: Review of Research and Development. UNESCO Press, Paris.

Bloomster, C.H.; Fassbender, L.L.; and McDonald, C.L. 1977. Geothermal Energy Potential for District and Process Heating Applications in the U.S.: An Economic Analysis. BNWL-2311, Battelle Pacific Northwest Laboratories, Richland, WA.

Geothermal Resources Council. 1979. Expanding the Geothermal Frontier. Reno, NV, Vol. 3.

Geothermal Resources Council. 1978. Geothermal Energy: A Novelty Becomes a Resource. Geothermal Resources Council *Transactions*, Vol. 2, Sections 1 and 2, Hilo, Hawaii.

Geothermal Resources Council. 1977. Geothermal: State of the Art. Geothermal Resources Council *Transactions*, Vol. 1, San Diego, CA.

Howard, J.H., ed. 1975. Present Status and Future Prospects for Non-Electrical Uses of Geothermal Resources. ERDA Report UCRL-51926, Lawrence Livermore Laboratory, University of California, Livermore, CA.

Kruger, P.; and Ott, C., eds. 1972. *Geothermal Energy*. Stanford University Press.

Lienau, P.J. and Lund, J.W., eds. 1974. Multipurpose Use of Geothermal Energy. *Proceedings* of the International Conference on Geothermal Energy for Industrial, Agricultural and Commercial-Residential Uses, Published by the Geo-Heat Utilization Center, Klamath Falls, OR.

Reistad, G.M. 1980. Direct Application of Geothermal Energy. ASHRAE SP No. 26.

United Nations. 1961. *Proceedings* of the United Nations Conference on New Sources of Energy. Vols. 2 and 3, Rome.

United Nations. 1970. Proceedings of the Second United Nations Symposium on the Development and Utilization of Geothermal Resources. United Nations, Pisa, Italy. Published in Special Issue of *Geothermics*, Vols. 1 and 2.

United Nations. 1975. Proceedings of the Second United Nations Symposium on the Development and Use of Geothermal Resources. Published by Lawrence Berkeley Laboratory, Berkeley, CA, Vols. 1, 2, and 3.

CHAPTER 46

THERMAL STORAGE

INTRODUCTION

OVERVIEW

Thermal storage is the temporary storage of high or low temperature energy for later use. It bridges the time gap between energy availability and energy use. Most thermal storage applications involve a 24-hour storage cycle, although weekly and seasonal storage is also used. While the output of thermal storage is always thermal energy, the input energy may be thermal or electrical. Examples of thermal storage are the storage of solar energy for night heating, the storage of summer heat for winter use, the storage of winter ice for space cooling in the summer, and the storage of heat or coolness generated electrically during off-peak hours for use during subsequent peak hours.

When the period of energy availability is longer than the period of energy use, thermal storage also permits the installation of smaller heating or cooling equipment than would otherwise be required. In many cases, storage can provide benefits for both heating and cooling, either simultaneously, or at different times of the year. Conditions favoring thermal storage include high loads of relatively short duration; high electric power demand charges; low-cost electrical energy during off-peak hours; need for cooling backup in case of a refrigeration plant failure (only the chilled water pump must be powered by the emergency generator); need to provide cooling for small after hour loads such as cooling of restaurants, mid-height elevator equipment rooms, individual offices, and computer rooms; building expansion (installation of storage may eliminate the need for heating/cooling plant expansion); need to provide a fire fighting reservoir (water stored in a water or ice system is available for fire fighting in an emergency); need to supplement a limited-capacity cogeneration plant; and others.

This chapter consists of three parts. The "Introduction" presents an overview of thermal storage, defines frequently used terms, and describes economic considerations. The "Technology" section describes different types of storage devices. Major applications are covered in the final section.

Definitions

In **sensible heat storage**, storage is accomplished by raising or lowering the temperature of the storage medium usually water, rock beds, bricks, sand or soil.

In **latent heat storage**, storage is accomplished by a change in the physical state of the storage medium, usually from liquid to solid (heat of fusion) or vice versa. Typical materials are water/ice, salt hydrates, and certain polymers. Energy densities for latent heat storage are greater than for sensible heat storage, which results in smaller and lighter storage devices and lower storage losses.

The preparation of this chapter is assigned to TC 6.9, Thermal Storage.

Storage efficiency, defined as the ratio of energy that can be withdrawn divided by the amount put into storage, is a major consideration in deciding whether to install thermal storage. Storage efficiencies up to 90% can be achieved in well-stratified water tanks that are fully charged and discharged on a daily cycle. Weekly duty cycling of storage results in lower efficiency than daily cycling. Generally, all storage devices suffer standby losses, although latent heat devices suffer smaller losses than sensible heat devices. Therefore, storage should usually not be charged earlier or to a higher degree than required.

Storage Media

For HVAC and refrigeration purposes, water and phase change materials (PCM's) constitute the principal storage media. Soil, rock, and other solids are also used. Water has the advantage of universal availability, low cost, and transportability through other system components. Phase change materials have the advantage of approximately 80% less volume than that of water for a **temperature swing** of 18 °F (10 °C), which is the difference in temperature between full and empty storage. On the other hand, they are usually viscous and corrosive and must be segregated within the container from the heat transfer medium. This tendency to separate adds a heat transfer penalty, which decreases the temperature swing available for thermal storage. If heating and cooling storage is required, two phase change materials must be provided, unless heat pumping is used.

Storage Strategies

In **full storage systems**, the entire heating (or cooling) load for the design day is generated off-peak and store for use during the following peak period. In **partial storage systems**, only a portion of the daily load is generated during the previous off-peak period and put it in storage; during the peak period, the load is satisfied by simultaneous operation of the heating (or cooling) equipment and withdrawal from storage.

Table 1 (Tamblyn 1977) illustrates different strategies for cooling storage. A conventional system without storage requires a chiller with 1000-kW input. Alternately, operating the chiller around the clock on the design day with partial chilled water storage results in the smallest chiller size: 385 kW. It requires 330,000 gallons (1250 m^3) of storage. Reducing the chiller size helps pay for the storage, although a complete cost trade-off is unlikely, except in very large systems. The last row of Table 1 illustrates full storage: 550,000 gallons (2100 m^3) of thermal storage and a 800-kW chiller are required to take the cooling load entirely off the peak period. Even though both chiller and storage are larger than for the partial storage strategy, such a system may still be appropriate when electric demand charges are very high or when the plant is designed for future expansion. The full-storage system also has the advantage of simple control and operation (see below).

With water as the storage medium, the storage size is inversely proportional to the temperature swing, which should not be

Table 1 Strategies for a Typical Cooling Storage

	Operating Mode	Chiller Load Profile	Chiller Size	Storage Size
1. Conventional	Follows load with no storage		284 ton (1000 kW)	none
2. Partial Storage	Constant operation at full load		109 ton (385 kW)	330,000 gal (1250 m³)
3. Full Storage	Full load operation with storage off electrical demand		227 ton (800 kW)	550,000 gal (2100 m³)

less than 18°F (10°C) for economical design. Tamblyn (1977) derived Figure 1 from typical office building analyses in a cold climate of 5850 degree F days (3900 degree C days). The figure shows the fraction of energy that could be recovered for heating different volumes of water storage with a temperature swing of 18°F (10°C). The "heels" of the curves lie near 0.25 gal/ft² (10 L/m²). As buildings increase in bulk and in envelope insulation, the need for heating storage declines.

Storage can be divided into multiple tanks to permit simultaneous storage for heating and cooling. Thus, some storage is available even when one module is out. In Japan, which has many of the world's thermal storage installations, storage is commonly divided into two equal parts. In summer, both store chilled water; in winter, one is converted to storing warm water.

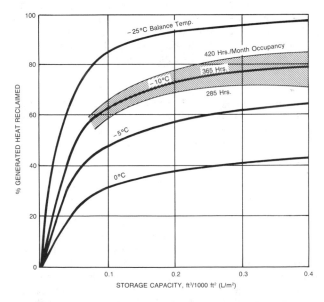

Fig. 1 Heat Reclamation versus Storage Capacity as a Function of Balance Temperature

Design Considerations

Ice storage modules and most PCM modules are manufactured items. As such, they carry a manufacturer's warranty of performance and follow-up during and after installation. No similar guarantees are available with water tanks. Innovative designs allow wide water temperature swings necessary to make

chilled water storage cost effective, and they avoid three-way mixing valves or other hardware unsuitable for such conditions. Ice is affected little by chilled water temperature swings and the various types of control used on chilled water coils, because ice melts and absorbs the design value of heat almost as readily with 2 gpm (126 mL/s) returning from the coils at 50°F (10°C) as 1 gpm (63 mL/s) returning at 60°F (16°C).

Storage Containers

Storage for one- or two-story buildings can often be "in-line" with the circuits served, because the cost premium for the storage container to withstand 7 psi (1 kPa) is negligible. Higher pressures may require the use of steel tanks with reinforced dished ends, which significantly raise costs. For this reason, many storage installations are vented to the atmosphere. Concrete has been the preferred construction material for vented chilled water containers because of its universal availability, adaptability to underground conditions, and cost advantage over steel in sizes over 30,000 gallons (110 m³). Prefabricated steel tanks are available at lower cost for smaller tanks. Plastic tanks are often used for ice and PCM storage media, or the PCM material may be encased in plastic containers which, in turn, are immersed in chilled water or glycol tanks.

Storage Location

In high-rise buildings, water tanks are usually located at ground level or below and are used as a secondary water supply for fire protection. The storage should be near the machine room, although that is neither necessary nor always feasible. Installation outside the building above grade is usually not acceptable, except for industrial facilities, because of economic and aesthetic considerations. If storage is located below grade, the units must be anchored to secure them against uplift from ground water. The anchors must counteract uplift on an empty storage unit because it may be drained for maintenance, repair, or inspection. Such units must have drain pumps for this purpose.

Pumping Strategy

Pumping energy in high-rise buildings is reduced to a minimum by locating storage topside. As an alternative, a heat ex-

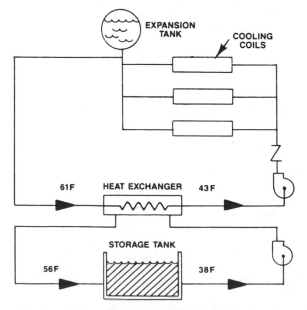

Fig. 2 Bottom-Side Storage With Heat Exchanger

changer can be placed between a bottom storage and the building loop (Figure 2). The temperature drop across the heat exchanger, however, decreases the temperature swing available for storage and thus causes an increase in storage size and in water circulation. In Japan, few heat exchangers are used. Pressurizing a bottomside storage tank is undesirable and can be avoided by pressure-sustaining valves (Figure 3). However, they waste the pumping energy expended to elevate the water to the top of the building. Recovery turbines coupled to the building loop pump or installed separately can be installed to recover that energy, but they are expensive.

There is a trade-off between energy cost and first cost when a heat exchanger is used. Typically, a building may have to have 15 stories before the energy costs due to direct pumping equal or exceed the energy costs due to the heat exchanger losses. Buildings may have to have 40 stories before the costs of energy losses due to direct pumping exceed the combined costs of amortization and energy losses associated with the heat exchanger. One technique for reducing the energy costs of direct pumping is to stage the building circuits according to floor location (Figure 4).

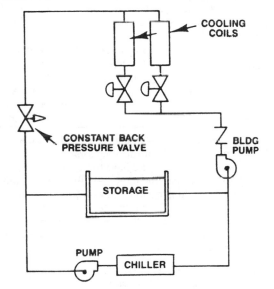

Fig. 3   High-Rise Building Loop With Pressure-Sustaining Valve

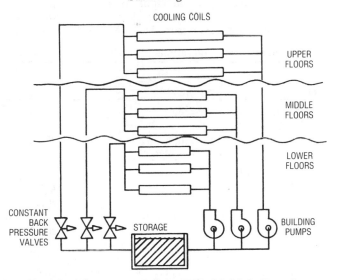

Fig. 4   Bottom-Side Storage With Multiple Pumping Loops to Different Building Floor Heights

Controls

Full-storage controls are simpler than the controls required for partial storage. In full-storage plants, the chilling plant is either on or off and always operates at full power. In partial-storage plants, the chilling plant and the storage unit share the load, and the fraction of the load supplied by either requires more control than a simple on-off device.

Time clocks are frequently used to shut down the heating/cooling plant during on-peak periods. Malfunction of mechanical clocks has caused unwanted plant operation during on-peak periods, so electronic time clocks, which are more reliable, should be installed instead. The seemingly less expensive alternative of requiring the operator to switch compressors on and off manually is not recommended because, if the operator forgets to shut off the compressor before the beginning of the on-peak period even once, it could result, under certain utility tariffs, in a billing penalty for an entire year.

Sensors

Monitoring sensors require regular maintenance and frequent recalibration. Proper sensor performance is more important in thermal storage installations than in other HVAC systems, since the advantages of storage can only be realized through exact timing (to prevent compressor operation during on-peak periods) and accurate sensing of storage water temperature or ice thickness and other system operating data. Although ice is a better heat conductor than water, too much ice on the evaporator coils will cause the compressor to operate at excessively low suction temperatures and pressures, which requires more energy for the same amount of cooling. It could also eventually lead to a complete freeze-up of the unit, preventing water circulation and discharge.

Water Treatment

Water treatment is essential in both open and closed water systems. Treatment is especially necessary for open systems subject to atmospheric pollutants and poor-quality makeup water. Ice storage tanks and evaporator coils are subject to corrosion and require proper cleaning and water treatment, especially if the tank is emptied during the off-season. Both open and closed ice and water storage systems should have automatic water makeup, sight glasses, and corrosion inhibitors. Brine systems require specially treated ethylene glycol. Chapter 53 covers this subject in detail.

Operator Training

Operator training is more critical with thermal storage systems than with conventional HVAC systems, because the systems are more complicated and unfamiliar to most operators. Some storage systems have not saved money because either the original operators had left and were replaced by new, unskilled operators, or the original operators had not been properly trained in how to manage these systems.

Operators should be carefully trained by personnel who understand the system fully (designer, contractor, factory representative), and their performance should be closely monitored for at least one full season. Some ice storage installations may require longer operating training periods than chilled water systems, because they may contain elements unfamiliar to most HVAC system operators. It is important to instill in all operators the fact that, for best economy, storage should be charged only as much as necessary.

THERMAL STORAGE ECONOMICS

The viability of thermal storage depends almost entirely upon favorable economics. The capital cost of refrigeration equipment is closely associated with local bidding practices, manufacturing evolution, and the uniqueness of the job. However, the basic principles can be demonstrated by an example of the design of a water chilling plant to cool a new convention and sports complex. Located in a southern climate, at least 50% of maximum cooling demand occurs in every electric utility billing period. The building has two functions that occur on different days. The first function is as a convention facility, which requires a maximum of 1000 tons (3520 kW) of cooling for 12 hours a day. Note that here 1 kW denotes a cooling load of 3412 Btu/h, not a chiller electrical load. The second function requires 2000 tons (7030 kW) of cooling to maintain comfortable conditions for 25,000 spectators watching a basketball game for four hours. Figure 5 shows the two idealized load profiles.

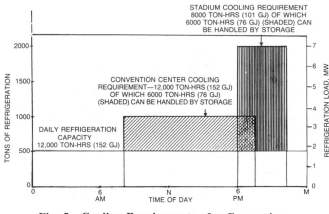

Fig. 5   Cooling Requirements of a Convention and Sports Complex

The convention activity requires 12,000 ton-hours (152 GJ) of cooling, which can be satisfied with a 1000-ton (3520-kW) chiller operating for 12 hours a day or a 500-ton (1760-kW) chiller operating for 24 hours a day. In the latter case, the chiller requires the assistance of 6000 ton-hours (76 GJ) of storage from 8 A.M. to 8 P.M. For the basketball game, a 2000-ton (7030-kW) cooling load occurs during those 4 hours. This load can be handled with a 2000-ton (7030-kW) chiller operating for four hours or the 500-ton (1760-kW) unit cited above operating for 16 hours. The 500-ton (1760-kW) chiller again requires 6000 ton-hours (76 GJ) of storage. In summary, a 500-ton (1760-kW)

refrigeration machine and 6000 ton-hours (76 GJ) of storage can substitute on either load for the 1000-ton (3520-kW) or the 2000-ton (7030-kW) chiller required by conventional design.

To perform a comparative economic analysis, the refrigeration equipment and the storage medium must be selected. In this case, it is assumed that the refrigeration equipment uses centrifugal chillers and that the storage medium is chilled water located in a concrete tank under the building. Table 2 presents costs for centrifugal chillers together with their heat rejection equipment. The table, based on 1986 manufacturers quotations with a 62% premium to cover freight, rigging, sales tax, design fees, contractor markups, electrical transformation and base wiring, and contingencies, gives a representation of real owner cost. From that table the cost of chillers can be determined as follows:

$$500 \text{ tons } (1758 \text{ kW}) - \$259,000$$
$$1000 \text{ tons } (3516 \text{ kW}) - \$414,000$$
$$2000 \text{ tons } (7032 \text{ kW}) - \$598,000.$$

Figure 6 presents a sizing and average costing table for buried concrete tanks. For a 19°F (10.6°C) temperature swing, 6000 ton-hours (76 GJ) of storage require 450,000 gallons (1705 m³) at a cost of $230,000. An average cost for a 500-ton (1758-kW) interface is estimated as $72,000. The cost comparison for serving only the 1000-ton (3520-kW) conventional duty then becomes:

	Non Storage	**Chilled Water Storage**
Refrigeration	$414,000	$259,000
	(1000 tons)	(500 tons)
Chilled Water Storage	-	$230,000
		(450,000 gallons)
Storage Interface	-	$72,000
TOTAL	$414,000	$561,000

To receive further consideration, the storage system, which is more expensive to build, would have to produce operating savings in the cost of electric demand. Assuming the cooling demand load in each billing period is always 50% or more of maximum, it is possible to reduce it by 500 kW, roughly equivalent to 500 tons, in every month through optimal use of storage. Hence, a three-year payback for storage can be achieved if the cost of electric demand is equal to or greater than

$$\frac{(\$561,000 - \$414,000)}{500 \text{ kW} \times 12 \text{ months} \times 3 \text{ years}} = \$8.16 \text{ kW/month}$$

This payback period might be lengthened by a year to pay for the energy to pump in and out of storage and the static head penalty for pumping chilled water directly to the system from storage at atmospheric pressure. However, the chiller costs less

Table 2   Cost of Centrifugal Water Chillers (1986 manufacturers' quotations plus 62%)

Item	Tons			
	250	**500**	**1000**	**1500**
Chiller	$97,000	$162,000	$238,000	$324,000
Condensing Water Pump at 3 gpm/ton	5,000	9,000	16,000	22,000
Water Tower	22,000	40,000	75,000	112,000
Wiring of Tower & Pump Motors	5,000	8,000	15,000	20,000
Condensing Water Lines	12,000 (200 ft @ 8 in.)	24,000 (300 ft @ 10 in.)	40,000 (400 ft @ 12 in.)	80,000 (500 ft @ 8 in.)
Automatic Controls	5,000	8,000	15,000	20,000
Misc. Including Tower Base, Plumbing, Water Treatment, etc.	5,000	8,000	15,000	20,000
TOTAL	$151,000	$259,000	$414,000	$598,000

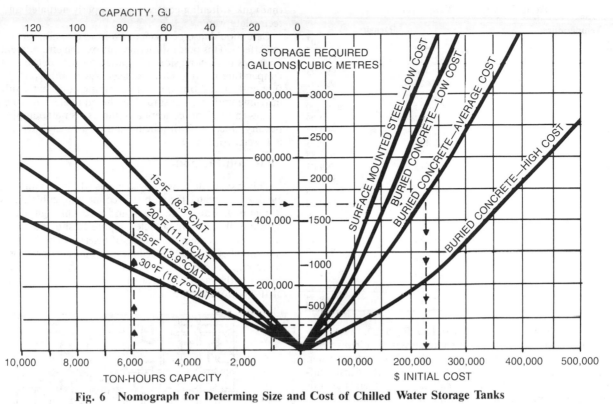

CAPACITY, GJ

TON-HOURS CAPACITY

$ INITIAL COST

Fig. 6   Nomograph for Determing Size and Cost of Chilled Water Storage Tanks

to operate at night during periods of lower wet-bulb temperature. In addition, in areas where electric utilities offer "time-of-use" rates, the cost of electrical energy is significantly lower during off-peak periods (generally at night and on week-ends) than during peak periods. Also, the demand charge is generally lower (or non-existent) during off-peak periods than during peak periods.

Some utilities also offer subsidies for installing storage. Only a careful analysis of all the initial and operating cost factors that relate to a particular design will permit an accurate economic comparison. For payback periods longer than three years, life-cycle costing should be performed, because the simple payback calculations similar to the ones shown here ignore the cost of money over time, which becomes significant as the payback period lengthens. Chapter 49 covers methods of economic analysis.

While storage systems are typically more expensive initially, it is possible that they can be lower in first cost as a result of short cooling load duration. The example of the sports facility cited above illustrates this point. The conventional system required to serve the basketball game load requires a 2000-ton (7030-kW) chiller costing $598,000. This is $37,000 more than the storage system, which can also handle this narrow peak load and provide additional electrical demand savings, as well.

THERMAL STORAGE TECHNOLOGIES

WATER TANKS

Conceptually, the simplest thermal storage is a water tank. During off-peak periods, hot or cold water is generated and stored in the tank, and it is withdrawn during peak periods when needed. Water has the highest specific heat of all common materials: 1 Btu/lb (4180 J/kg), which makes it well suited for thermal storage. The introduction of solid materials, such as rocks, into a water tank decreases its thermal storage capacity.

ASHRAE *Standard* 94.3-1986 gives procedures for measuring the thermal performance of water tanks.

Tanks may be vertical or horizontal cylinders, or they may be rectangular in shape. Steel is the most common material for above-ground tanks, and concrete for buried tanks. Metal tanks, especially cylinders with dished ends, can withstand hydraulic pressure exerted by the building piping circuits. The cost and size limitations of dished ends, however, restrict most tank installations to unpressurized water storage.

Water stored in tanks may be stratified thermally with the lighter, warmer water on top. The buoyancy differential becomes smaller, however, as water reaches its densest condition at 39 °F (4 °C) (Figure 7 and Table 3). In chilled water storage, which com-

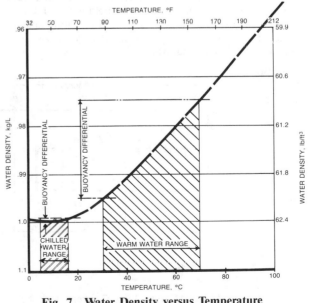

Fig. 7   Water Density versus Temperature

Table 3 Chilled Water Density

Temperature		Density	
°F	°C	lb/ft³	kg/m³
32.0	0	62.420	999.87
33.8	1	62.424	999.93
35.6	2	62.426	999.97
37.4	3	62.427	999.99
39.2	4	62.428	1000.00
41.0	5	62.427	999.99
42.8	6	62.426	999.97
44.6	7	62.424	999.93
46.4	8	62.420	999.88
48.2	9	62.416	999.81
50.0	10	62.411	999.73
51.8	11	62.405	999.63
53.6	12	62.398	999.52
55.4	13	62.391	999.40
57.2	14	62.382	999.27
59.0	15	62.374	999.13
60.8	16	62.364	998.97
62.6	17	62.353	998.80
64.4	18	62.342	998.62
66.2	19	62.330	998.43
68.0	20	62.317	998.23

monly swings between 41°F (5°C) and 59°F (15°C), the density differential is small enough that some care is required to prevent mixing of stored chilled water with warmer return water. Mixing is less critical in hot water storage where the density differential is much larger. Tamblyn (1980) describes several methods for achieving temperature separation in water storage.

Empty Tank

One method for obtaining complete separation of stored and return water temperature is to pump from one tank to another. If only two tanks were used, this practice would double the cost and space required for storage, so in a modified arrangement the chilled water is pumped back and forth among a number of compartments (Figure 8). In this scheme, where up to 14 compartments have been used, the equivalent of one tank must be empty at all times. In schemes where warm and chilled water storage are required simultaneously, the equivalent of two empty compartments is needed. The empty tank concept can achieve an excellent separation of temperature, if a minimum volume of water is left in each compartment to prevent air binding of the pumps. If mixing losses are to be held within 1°F (0.6°C), this remaining volume should be limited to approximately 5% of the volume of each compartment. It may be wise to allow slightly more than the equivalent of one empty tank to ensure

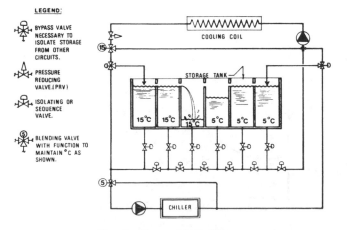

Fig. 8 Empty Tank Concept

that tank switching controls are properly actuated and do not recirculate water.

Care should also be taken to avoid water agitation and waterfall effects. This precaution prevents oxygen entrainment, which increases both corrosion of piping and turbulence that causes temperature mixing. Other concerns with this concept are the first cost of additional concrete, piping, automatic valves, and instrumentation to ensure that the equivalent of one tank is always empty. This concept also incurs a small pumping energy penalty, since the hydraulic head decreases as the level of water is lowered (Figure 8).

Labyrinth Method

This system, developed by Japanese designers and used since 1950, moves water through interconnecting cubicles, as shown in Figure 9. Water flows back and forth through high and low apertures in adjacent cubicles. Figure 10 shows a more sophisticated arrangement consisting of a series of weirs. A string of horizontal cylindrical buried tanks is another variation that has been tried. These have been arranged either with internal baffles or with warm pipe headers on top and cold pipe headers at the bottom of the tank.

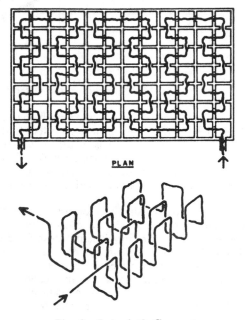

Fig. 9 Labyrinth Concept

Temperature Stratification

Water returning from cooling coils at 59°F (15°C) can float quite successfully above stored chilled water at 41°F (5°C). It is much easier to make hot water stored at 120°F (49°C) float above water returning from heating coils at 90°F (32°C), since the density difference is much larger (Figure 7). A **thermocline**, or zone with a steep temperature gradient, is present between the lighter water on top and the denser water below. Stratified storage tries to keep the thermocline as thin as possible to maintain the maximum effective storage capacity of the tank (Figure 11). Wildin and Truman (1985a) have shown that a thermocline approximately 18-in. (0.5-m) thick develops at the start when charging a chilled water tank. This may expand to two or three times that thickness at the end of the charge period, depending primarily upon inlet and outlet water turbulence and upon heat exchange between the stored water and the walls of the enclosure.

Several methods for introducing and retrieving the warm water at the top and the cold water at the bottom of the tank have

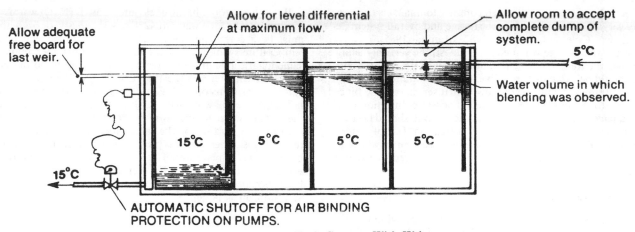

Allow adequate free board for last weir.

Allow for level differential at maximum flow.

Allow room to accept complete dump of system.

5°C

Water volume in which blending was observed.

15°C   5°C   5°C   5°C

15°C

AUTOMATIC SHUTOFF FOR AIR BINDING PROTECTION ON PUMPS.

Fig. 10   Empty Tank Concept With Weirs

been devised. One method uniformly distributes water across the top and bottom of the tank with a piping grid (Figure 12). Care must be taken to ensure even distribution of water at any flow rate by arranging equal flow resistance to every opening into the tank, as illustrated. Another type of diffuser uses concentric pipes (Figure 11). The inner pipe is connected at its center to the supply or return line, and a row of small holes perforates its entire length. A horizontal slot cut in the outer pipe is opposite these holes when viewed in cross section. The diffusers supply or extract water in a thin, evenly distributed stream. For vertical cylindrical tanks, radial diffusers may be used.

The inlet and outlet streams must be kept at a sufficiently low velocity so that buoyancy forces predominate over inertia forces to produce a gravity current (also called density current) across the bottom or the top of the tank. For this purpose, the diffuser dimensions should be selected to create an inlet Froude number equal to or less than two (Wildin and Truman 1985a, 1985b; Yoo and Wildin 1986). The inlet Froude number, F, is defined in Eq. (1).

$$F = Q/\sqrt{gh^3(\Delta\varrho/\varrho)} \qquad (1)$$

where

Q = volume flow rate per unit length of diffuser, ft³/s · ft (m³/s · m)
g = gravitational acceleration, ft/s² (m/s²)
h = inlet opening height, ft (m)
ϱ = inlet water density, lb/ft³ (kg/m³)
$\Delta\varrho$ = difference in density between stored water and incoming or outflowing water, lb/ft³ (kg/m³).

Since the density difference, $\Delta\varrho$, is always very small, it is preferable to obtain its value from Table 3 rather than from Figure 7. Yoo and Wildin (1986) give more information concerning the design of stratified storage hardware.

Example: Find the slot height for a 15-ft long diffuser supplying a flow rate of 90 gpm of water at 41 °F to a tank with water stored at 59 °F.
Solution
From Eq. (1), $h = (Q/F)^{2/3} (g\,\Delta\varrho/\varrho)^{1/3}$. Choosing a Froude number of one, the opening height becomes

$$h = \frac{90 \text{ gpm}/(60 \text{ s/min.} \times 7.48 \text{ gal/ft}^3 \times 15 \text{ ft})^{2/3}}{\{32.2 \text{ ft/s}^2 \times ([62.427 - 62.374]/62.374)\}^{1/3}}$$

$$= 0.187 \text{ ft} = 2.24 \text{ in.}$$

Several factors are vital to the success of stratified storage systems. Whether square, rectangular, free form, or cylindrical, the cross section of the tank should be constant or nearly constant in the direction of the water flow. This constraint permits sloped walls but eliminates horizontal cylinders. Deeper tanks are preferred to shallow tanks. Since the thermocline may increase to a depth of 7 ft (2 m) or so with partial charge and

discharge cycles, it makes little sense to use this system where only 7 ft (2 m) of tank depth is available. When charging a chilled water tank, the chilled water supply temperature should always decrease from the initial charging temperature; a rising temperature during charging tends to deepen the thermocline. Conversely, when charging a hot water tank, the charging temperature should increase with time. In the case of variable energy sources, such as the sun, this implies varying the flow rate through the

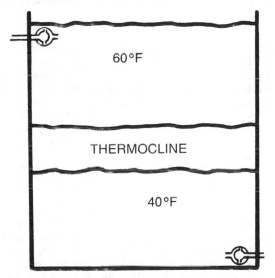

60°F

THERMOCLINE

40°F

Fig. 11   Thermally Stratified Storage With Concentric Pipe Diffusers

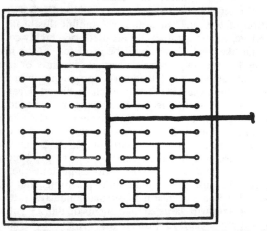

Fig. 12   Plan View of Distributed Nozzle Inlet/Outlet

collectors and storage. Although contrary to much current practice, varying flow improves both storage and overall system performance (Cole and Bellinger 1982, Mumma 1985).

To use the storage volume to the fullest, the vertical distance between the free water surface and the top of the diffuser opening should be as small as possible, yet large enough to be flooded at all times. Similarly, the lower diffusers should be placed as close to the bottom of the tank as possible. Injection of air into a tank, whether at the top or at the bottom, should be avoided, since it can destroy the tank stratification. Use of water at less than 392°F (4°C) is not desirable because it mixes with water below and up to that temperature due to its reduced density (Figure 7 and Table 3).

Flexible Diaphragm

Another system of temperature stratification within storage systems is available under license (Engineering Interface, Toronto). A sheet of coated fabric, is anchored securely at the midpoint of the tank, floats up and down as the volume of stored and return water in the tank is varied. The diaphragm improves the storage efficiency of simple stratification for partial charge and discharge cycles, which are typical of most daily operation. It does not improve the efficiency of simple stratification for full charge and discharge cycles in storage compartments of 50,000 gallons (200 m³) or less, but is best used in tanks that are very large, very shallow, or store water at less than 39°F (4°C).

Storage Efficiency

Well-stratified storage tanks have storage efficiencies of 90% and higher under daily complete charge/discharge cycles, and between 80% and 90% under partial charge/discharge cycles. To achieve high efficiency, the full design temperature swing must be maintained. Heat gains or losses through the tank enclosure decrease the effective temperature swing. For this reason, surface-mounted tanks have always been insulated. It may also be cost effective to insulate buried chilled water tanks where the ground is warm and wet, as in some parts of Florida. To date, however, it has not been viable to insulate buried tanks, except on exposed walls and within partitions separating 104°F (40°C) and 41°F (5°C) compartments.

Heat transfer between the stored water and the tank walls is the primary source of thermal losses. To counter it, water storage should not be charged sooner than necessary. Not only does the stored fluid lose (or gain) heat to the ambient by conduction through the walls, but there is also a vertical heat flow along the tank walls from the warmer to the cooler region. This heat flow is larger, the higher the conductivity of the tank wall material and the thicker the walls. Thus, walls should not be made thicker than necessary for structural strength. Exterior insulation of the tank walls does not inhibit this heat transfer. Therefore, when the tank walls are made of a highly conductive material like steel, they should be insulated on the inside.

Thus far, the only materials suitable for interior insulation with completely closed cell construction, such as foamed glass, have been too expensive for the results achieved. Heat transfer to the ambient is inhibited by either exterior or interior insulation, though somewhat more effectively by interior insulation. Heat loss or gain through the container walls is especially important in storage compartments smaller than 50,000 gallons (200 m³) because the ratio of enclosure area to stored volume is high. It is also a greater problem with empty tank and labyrinth concepts, because they contain more partitions, and with steel tank walls because of their high thermal conductivity. It becomes less important with large compartments of 100,000 gallons (400 m³) or more. Heat is also transferred across the thermocline by conduction.

When heat stored in the enclosure at 59°F (15°C) warms the incoming 41°F (5°C) water to 42°F or 43°F (5.5°C or 6°C), there must be a corresponding reduction in the upper end of the temperature swing because a cooling coil must operate on the same logarithmic mean temperature difference to do the same work (see Chapter 6 in the 1983 EQUIPMENT Volume). Thus, a coil that performs on a 41°F to 59°F (5°C to 15°C) range cannot duplicate the work with 43°F (6°C) entering water, unless the leaving water temperature is dropped to 57°F (14°C) and the flow rate is raised by the same ratio by which the temperature swing is decreased. This problem is less severe in heat storage because the temperature difference between supply and return water tends to be larger. However, ambient losses are usually larger because the temperature difference between storage water and ambient is larger.

Other Factors

The cost of chemicals for water treatment becomes a significant budget item, especially if the tank is filled more than once. A filter system to provide complete filtration of the storage system at least once every 48 hours is a useful accessory to keep the stored water clean. Atmospheric exposure of the storage tank may require occasional addition of biocides.

Many large concrete installations leak initially, and because some localities are short of water, it has been good practice to include at least one partition in the storage tank. This feature gives extra security against the need for complete drainage in all cases and the opportunity to store chilled and hot water simultaneously for greater energy savings in colder climates. Leaks in water tanks have been fixed with pressure grouting, sealants, or liners. The storage pumps should be below the lowest water level of storage for flooded suction. It is equally important not to place equipment between the tank and the suction side of the pumps to avoid stalling of the water flow.

PACKED ROCK BEDS

A packed bed, pebble bed, or rock pile storage uses the heat capacity of a bed of loosely packed particles through which a fluid, usually air, is circulated to add heat to, or remove heat from, the bed. A variety of solids may be used, rock of 0.75 to 2 in. (2 to 5 cm) in size being most prevalent. Well-designed packed rock beds have several desirable characteristics for energy storage. The heat transfer coefficient between the air and the solid is high, the cost of the storage material is low, the conductivity of the bed is low when air flow is not present, and a large heat transfer area is achieved at low cost by using small storage particles. Figure 13 shows a schematic of a packed bed storage

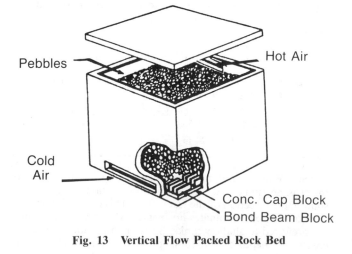

Fig. 13 Vertical Flow Packed Rock Bed

unit. Essential features include a container, a porous structure (such as a wirescreen) to support the bed, and air plenums at both inlet and outlet. The container can be made of wood, concrete blocks, or poured concrete. Insulation requirements outside the bed are small for short-term storage, because the thermal conductivity of the bed in the lateral direction is low. For a rock bed used for daily cycling, the 24-hour heat loss should not exceed 5%, and preferably be only 2%.

Fluid flows through the bed in one direction during the addition of heat and in the opposite direction during the removal of heat. Therefore, heat cannot be added to and removed from these storage devices at the same time. Packed bed storage devices operated in this manner thermally stratify naturally. For good efficiency, it is preferable to raise the bed temperature during downward heat flow and to lower it during upward heat flow. This flow (hot top, cool bottom) inhibits convection currents during standby periods, which would decrease storage efficiency. To prevent channeling (in which a narrow jet of heat transfer fluid travels from inlet to outlet without sweeping through the entire bed), both the inlet and outlet should have plenum chambers. To further equalize pressure drops along all flow paths, it is best to arrange inlet and outlet on opposite sides of the storage bed (see Figure 13).

The plenum chambers distribute the flow over the entire cross section of the bed. Tests by Jones and Loss (1982) on a packed bed like the one in Figure 13 showed that the inlet jet shoots across the rock top, hits the far wall, and forms two counter-rotating flow cells along the side walls. The flow distribution is improved by placing a block slightly larger than the inlet opening inside the top plenum at a distance of one-and-a-half times the vertical inlet dimension.

While rock beds store either heat or coolness, the overwhelming number of applications in North America is for heat storage in solar heating systems. When they store coolness in a humid climate, fungus growth can occur in the bed, which can cause major indoor environmental problems. While they have been used successfully to store coolness in Australia (Close et al. 1968) this application is not recommended for North America except in dry regions like the Southwest.

Because of the large surface areas of the pebbles exposed to the air passing through the bed, pebble beds exhibit good heat transfer between the air and the storage medium. An empirical relation for the volumetric heat transfer coefficient, h_v, is given by the following equation (Löf and Hawley 1948):

$$h_v = 16,000 \ (G/D)^{0.7}, \ \text{Btu/h} \cdot \text{ft}^2 \cdot \text{°F} \qquad (2)$$

$$h_v = \ \ \ 650 \ (G/D)^{0.7}, \ \text{W/(m}^2 \cdot \text{K)} \qquad (2\ \text{SI})$$

where G is the superficial mass velocity in $\text{lb/ft}^2 \cdot \text{h}$ ($\text{kg/m}^2 \cdot \text{s}$), and D is the equivalent spherical diameter of the particles in ft (m) defined as:

$$D = \frac{6}{\pi} \left(\frac{\text{net volume of particles}}{\text{number of particles}} \right)^{1/3} \qquad (3)$$

The superficial mass velocity is the velocity of the heat transfer fluid through the empty container.

The particle size in a packed bed should be uniform to obtain a large void fraction and thus minimize the pressure drop through the bed. Figure 14 (Cole et al. 1980) shows the variation of that pressure drop as a function of face velocity and particle size diameter, $2D$. Analytical or numerical methods can be used to evaluate the performance of packed bed storage devices, but the calculations for an arbitrary time dependent inlet air temperature variation is laborious. Hughes et al. (1976) and Mumma and Marvin (1976) give methods of solution.

ICE STORAGE

Thermal energy can be stored in the latent heat of fusion of ice. Water has the highest latent heat of fusion among all common materials on a weight basis: 144 Btu/lb (80 cal/g or 4180 J/kg). This has an advantage over sensible heat storage in which the temperature of the storage material must be lowered or raised during the charge or discharge process.

Water/Ice Storage on Refrigerant Coils

Several types of ice storage units are available. The type in longest use is the direct expansion (DX) ice builder, which consists of refrigerant coils inside a storage tank filled with water. A compressor and evaporative condenser freeze the tank water on the outside of the coils to a thickness of up to 2.5 in. (63 mm). Ice is melted from the outside of the formation by circulating return water through the tank whereby it again becomes chilled. Stirrers or air bubblers agitate the water to promote uniform ice build-up. One or more ice thickness sensors shut the unit off when it is fully charged. This occurs when approximately one-half of the water in the tank has been frozen. These ice storage units are manufactured in sizes from 100 to 1200 ton-hours (13 to 157 MJ) capacity and shipped to the site in complete assemblies. The largest unit made contains 100,000 lb (45 Mg) of ice; its 40 by 10 by 10 ft (12 by 3 by 3 m) size is governed by road transport limitations.

Water/Ice Storage on Brine Coils

Instead of passing refrigerant through the coils inside the storage tank, brine can be pumped through them. Brine has the advantage of greatly decreasing the refrigerant inventory. However, a refrigerant-to-brine heat exchanger is required between the chiller and the storage tank.

Brine-Type Solid Ice Builders

In this type of storage device, plastic mats containing brine coils are tightly rolled and placed inside a cylindrical water tank (Figure 15). The mats occupy approximately one-tenth of the tank volume; another tenth of the volume is left empty to allow

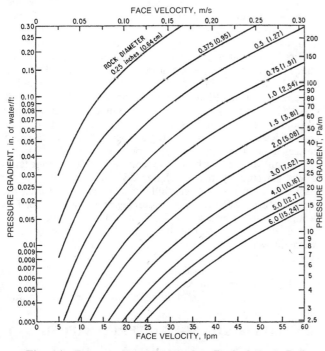

Fig. 14   Pressure Drop Through a Packed Rock Bed
(Cole et al. 1980)

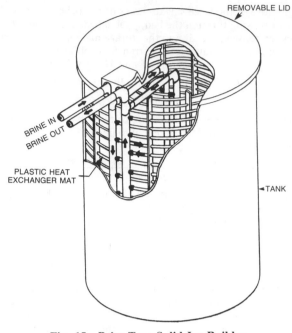

Fig. 15   Brine-Type Solid Ice Builder
(Courtesy: Calmac Manufacturing Corporation)

for the expansion of the water upon freezing, and the rest is filled with water. A brine solution, e.g. 25% ethylene glycol and 75% water, cooled by a liquid chiller circulates through the coils and freezes the water in the tank. Ice is built up to a thickness of 0.4 to 0.5 in. (10 to 13 mm) on the coils, until all of the water is frozen in a solid block of ice. During discharge, the cool brine solution circulates to fan coils and returns to the storage to be cooled again. If it is undesirable to pipe the brine through the entire building, an intermediate brine-to-chilled water heat exchanger can be added. Temperature and rate of ice build-up within the tank are relatively uniform because supply and return coils alternate in the mat structure. The units are designed for multiple modular use with central chillers, but they may also be coupled to packaged unitary cooling units and heat pumps.

Plate Ice Makers

Plate ice makers are direct expansion refrigeration systems whose evaporators consist of vertical refrigerated plates mounted above a water/ice storage tank. Water is pumped from the storage tank to the top of the plates and flows in a thin film down the plates and back to the tank. When the water is near 32 °F (0 °C), some of it freezes on the plates to a thickness of 0.18 to 0.25 in. (4 to 6 mm). It is periodically broken off by passing hot gas through the plates, causing it to fall in flakes or chunks into the tank below. With warmer water, the unit operates as a chiller. Ice forms in 20 to 30 minutes and is harvested in 20 to 40 seconds. Plates are usually grouped in sets of three or more so that the heat of rejection from the ice-building plates can be used to provide the heat for the plate being harvested. The ice accumulates with a void ratio of 45% and is stopped by a water level sensor. The resultant large contact area between chilled water and ice particles permits the device to be discharged very rapidly, i.e., at a rate exceeding ten times its charging rate. By keeping the ice build-up thin, suction pressures are kept high, and the units operate at 0.95 kW/ton (0.27 kW thermal/kW electrical) in the ice building mode and at 0.70 kW/ton (0.2 kW thermal/kW electrical) in the chilling mode (Knebel 1986). Since the ice maker plates must be located above the ice storage bin, more head room is required for plate ice makers than for other ice storage types.

However, where sufficient space is available, the storage bin can be made as large as desirable at low cost, because its size is independent of the size of the refrigerating plant. Chapter 33 of the 1986 REFRIGERATION Volume has further details.

Ice Slurry

In the ice slurry system, a binary solution of water and ethylene glycol is pumped from storage to the top of an ice generator (Figure 16). From there, it flows as a thin film down the inside surfaces of tubes whose outer surfaces are cooled by evaporating a refrigerant. As the solution cools, discrete ice crystals form in the fluid film. The resultant slurry is pumped to storage where the ice crystals form a floating porous ice pack, while the concentrated solution is recirculated to the ice generator. The tank is fully charged when approximately 45% by weight of the solution has been frozen. During discharge, the cold binary solution is pumped from storage to the refrigeration load. Upon return to storage, the warm solution is sprayed into the top of the tank and is cooled again by the melting ice crystals. Due to the large surface area of the ice crystals, the cold solution is near freezing. That temperature can be adjusted by varying the composition of the binary solution. This type of storage device is primarily used for refrigeration storage. Like the plate ice maker, it can also be discharged very rapidly.

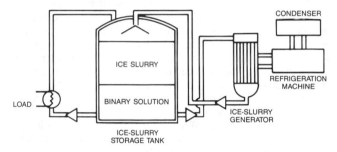

Fig. 16   Ice Slurry Storage (Courtesy: CBI Industries, Inc.)

Performance

All ice storage units suffer a compressor performance penalty, because lower evaporator temperatures are required to make ice than to make chilled water. As ice builds up on the coils, it forms an insulating layer which, in turn, further lowers the required evaporator temperature. Thus, in a typical DX ice builder, the evaporating temperature may vary from 25 °F (−4 °C) at the beginning to 15 °F (−9 °C) or even lower at the end of the charge period. Plate ice makers operate at 20 °F to 22 °F (−6.7 °C to −5.5 °C) and brine-type ice builders at slightly higher evaporator temperatures, because these devices build up a thin layer of ice only. The evaporating temperature of the ice slurry devices depends on the slurry temperature desired.

The chilled water discharge temperature from ice storage tanks is less affected by partial charge/discharge cycles than the discharge temperature from chilled water tanks. However, the storage efficiency of the water/ice storage devices is lowered. This occurs because a cylinder of ice forms "from the inside out" on the refrigerant coils. But the ice melts "from the outside in" where the water contacts the ice. During partial charge/discharge cycles, heat travels from the chilled water, through the layer of ice (which acts as an insulator), through the coil wall, and to the refrigerant. This indirect heat transfer exacts an energy penalty, and it is inefficient to charge and discharge an ice storage unit simultaneously.

PHASE CHANGE MATERIALS (PCMs)

The latent heat of phase change in certain materials can be used to store heat or coolness. The phase change most frequently

Table 4 Properties of Commercially Available Phase Change Materials (Lane 1985)

Material	Type	Melting Point, °F	Melting Point, °C	Heat of Fusion Btu/lb	Heat of Fusion kJ/kg	Latent Heat Btu/ft³	Latent Heat MJ/m³	Cost
$MgCl_2 \cdot 6H_2O$	Quasi Congruent	243	117	72.5	168.6	6500	242	medium
$Na_4P_2O_7 \cdot 10H_2O$	Incongruent	158	70	—	—	—	—	medium
Sodium Acetate $\cdot 3H_2O$	Incongruent	136	58	97.0	225.6	7700	287	medium
$MgCl_2 \cdot 6H_2O/Mg(NO_3)_2 \cdot 6H_2O$	Eutectic	136	58	56.9	132.2	5400	201	medium
Paraffin Wax	Congruent	122	50	114.3	265.9	5500	205	low
$Na_2S_2O_3 \cdot 5H_2O$ (Hypo)	Semi-congruent	118	48	86.4	201.0	9000	335	medium
Neopentyl Glycol	Congruent[a]	110	43	56.3	131.0	—	—	very high
$CaBr_2 \cdot 6H_2O$	Congruent	93	34	49.7	115.6	6000	224	high
$Na_2SO_4 \cdot 10H_2O$	Incongruent	89	32	108.0	251.2	9000	335	low
$Na_2SO_4 \cdot 10H_2O$ (with admixtures)	Incongruent	89	32	89.0	207.0	7300	272	low
$CaCl_2 \cdot 6H_2O$	Semi-congruent	82	28	74.0	172.1	7000	261	low
$CaCl_2 \cdot 6H_2O$ (modified)	Congruent	81	27	82.0	190.7	7800	291	low
PE Olycol	Congruent	74	23	64.7	150.5	4500	177	high
Glauber's salt with various percentages of NaCl, NH_4Cl and KCl	Incongruent	70 to 38	21 to 3	70 to 41	163 to 95	7000 to 4000	260 to 150	low
$CaBr_2 \cdot 6H_2O/CaCl_2 \cdot 6H_2O$	Congruent[b]	57	14	61.0	141.9	6800	253	high
Water/Ice	Congruent	32	0	144.0	335.0	9000	335	very low

[a]Phase change is solid/solid [b]Isomorphous

used is the heat of fusion between solid and liquid phases, although solid/solid or liquid/gas transformations can also be used. The materials used for latent heat storage are generally called *Phase Change Materials* (PCMs) although this is a misnomer since all materials can be made to change phase. The advantages of latent heat storage over sensible heat storage are smaller size, constant temperature during charge and discharge, and lower standby losses.

PCM technology appears simple, yet only recently has PCM technology become a commercial reality. The simplicity of the water/ice phase change at 32°F (0°C) with a very high heat of fusion has induced a great deal of research to find other low-cost materials that would melt and freeze at other temperatures, from cooling storage around 45°F (7°C) to solar heat storage in the 80°F to 130°F (27°C to 54°C) range to off-peak storage of electric heat at up to 1400°F (760°C). Salt hydrates, organics, and clathrates are most frequently used. Tables 4 and 5 (Lane 1985) list currently commercially available PCMs and some of their significant characteristics.

Salt hydrates, which are compounds of salt and water, are frequently tried. Their high heat of fusion is largely due to their high water content. Some have volumetric heats of fusion similar to ice, are non-toxic, non-flammable, and inexpensive. Although some salt hydrates supercool, this can be remedied through the addition of a nucleating agent, which is a small amount of material that never melts. Their major disadvantage is that many melt **incongruently** or **semi-congruently,** i.e., they melt to a saturated aqueous phase and a solid phase, which is the anhydrous salt (incongruent melting) or a lower hydrate of the same salt (semi-congruent melting).

During melting, the heavier solid salt settles out (**phase segregation**). Upon freezing, this salt at the bottom of the container does not recombine with the saturated solution to form the original hydrate, and the latent heat of the bulk material is reduced. The process is progressive and irreversible, unless special provisions are made to counteract this phase segregation. Therefore, a highly desirable property of PCMs is congruent melting, i.e., melting at a well-defined temperature, with the composition of the melt and the solid being identical. Some semi-congruently melting materials behave well enough to be used as PCMs (see below).

Eutectics, another class of materials of interest, are mixtures of two or more materials mixed in a ratio such that their melting point is a minimum. The mixtures melt completely at that point, and they have the same overall composition in the liquid and solid phases, which also makes them suitable PCMs. The first

Table 5 Properties of Selected Phase Change Materials[a]

Material	Melting Point °F	Melting Point °C	Specific Gravity	Specific Heat Btu/lb·°F	Specific Heat kJ/kg	Thermal Conductivity Btu·in. h·ft²·°F	W/(m²·K)
$MgCl_2 \cdot 6H_2O$	243	117	1.57	0.41	1.71		—
	—		1.44	0.67	2.80	—	—
$(MgNO_3)_2 \cdot 6H_2O$	192	89	1.64	0.44	1.84	10.6	0.63
			1.56	0.60	2.51	8.2
Paraffin Wax[b]	122	50	0.79	0.69	2.88	2.3	0.14
$Na_2S_2O_3 \cdot 5H_2O$	118	48	1.73	0.35	1.46	4.0	0.24
			1.67	0.57	2.38	—
$Na_2SO_4 \cdot 10H_2O$	89	32	1.46	0.46	1.92	8.6	0.51
			1.33	0.78	3.26	—
$CaCl_2 \cdot 6H_2O$	82	28	1.71	0.35	1.46	16.8	1.1
			1.50	0.52	2.17	9.1	0.54
H_2O	32	0	0.91	0.5	2.09	15.3	2.2
			1.0	1.0	4.18	9.2	0.6

[a]For each material, the first line lists the properties of the solid, the second line the properties of the liquid.
[b]A representative sample out of a family of many paraffin waxes.

building that relied on a PCM for its space heating system was a solar-heated house constructed in 1947 in Dover, MA (Telkes 1947). The heat store contained 21 tons of Glauber's salt, a salt hydrate chosen for its low cost and high heat of fusion. Unfortunately, it is difficult to work with because it melts incongruently. Many methods to thicken the material or prevent phase separation have not achieved commercial success. However, polymeric additives are available that form a gel matrix to keep the solid phase that separates from incongruent or semi-congruent hydrates in contact with the saturated solution (Page et al. 1981). Alternately, thickening agents using clay or thixotropic gels permit commercial application of Glauber's salt at reduced storage capacity (Calmac 1982). Mixtures of Glauber's salt and various chlorides melt in the 45 to 50°F (7 to 10°C) range and are suitable for cooling storage. While their heat of fusion is lower than that of some other materials, their cost is also low. Their volumetric storage density is 45 to 75% of that of ice, but their higher melting point (see Table 4) reduces the compressor work required for freezing the material.

Another PCM suitable for heat storage is the storage grade hypo salt (sodium thiosulfate pentahydrate, $Na_2S_2O_3 \cdot 5H_2O$) because of its favorable melting point (118°F or 48°C), high density, and medium cost. Hypo can be stabilized by a cross-linked polymer or by stirring it in the liquid state to prevent formation of the undesirable dihydrate. Calcium chloride hexahydrate ($CaCl_2 \cdot 6H_2O$) is commercially available with soluble additives that render it congruently melting (Lane 1982). Due to its relatively low melting point, it is primarily suitable for passive solar heating (Kohler and Lewis 1983).

Sodium hydroxide has proven technically feasible for the storage of electric resistance heat (Comstock and Wescott 1962, DiLauro and Rice 1981). Anhydrous sodium sulfate has a solid/solid phase change at 465°F (240°C) with a low heat of transition. However, combining high specific heat of 0.33 Btu/lb °F (1.4 kJ/kg·K) and high specific gravity (2.7), its total storage of sensible plus latent heat is higher than that of any other common material over a wide range and it may be useful for storing high temperature solar heat (Chubb et al. 1980).

Organics, such as paraffin, have low density, low thermal conductivity, high volume change (they contract upon freezing), and they are expensive and combustible. Their low density requires large storage volumes in spite of their high heats of fusion. Their low thermal conductivity requires packaging them in small (hence expensive) containers. On the other hand, they have few problems of thermal stratification, incongruent melting, or subcooling. They are commercially available as PCMs.

Clathrates are inclusion compounds in which one chemical species is bound inside the cage-like structure of another. Water forms the bonding structure for the clathrates of interest to thermal storage. Among the commonly used refrigerants that can form clathrates with water are R-ll, R-12, and R-22 (Tomlinson 1985). Some of these melt in the 40 to 56°F (5 to 13°C) range and promise to be of value for heat pump storage applications (Carbado 1985). Recently, a gas clathrate PCM with a heat of fusion of 122 Btu/lb (58 kJ/kg) and melting points between 32 and 48°F (0 and 9°C) has become available.

Since PCMs change from liquid to solid during their operating cycle, they must either be encapsulated with the heat transfer fluid passing over the outside of the container or placed inside bulk storage tanks with internal tube heat exchangers distributed throughout the PCM. Encapsulation is generally better when air is the heat transfer fluid; liquid systems may be used with either type. Most salt hydrates are highly corrosive, and special attention must be paid to their containerization. The results of corrosion tests on some common salt hydrate PCMs are shown in Table 6 (Abhat 1978).

Table 6 Corrosion Resistance of Metals to Different Phase Change Materials (Abhat 1978)

PCM	Al	Mg	Cu	Stainless Steel	Mild Steel
$Na_2S_2O_3 \cdot 5H_2O$	o	+	−	+	+
$Na_2HPO_4 \cdot 12H_2O$	−	−	+	+	o
$CaCl_2 \cdot 6H_2O$	−	−	+	+	+
Paraffin	o	+	+	+	+
Lauric Acid	o	−	+	+	−

LEGEND: + resistant − non-resistant o not tested

If a suitable nonsegregating PCM cannot be found, a stabilized non-congruent material may be chosen. Stabilization techniques that appear to be proved so far are: mechanical agitation, microencapsulation, and gelation including use of cross-linked polymers. Each of the stabilization methods has inherent penalties. While thickening or gelling additives decrease the latent heat of fusion and add to the cost, they permit the use of the cheap Glauber's salt and its many low-temperature mixtures. Because of their solid/solid form, they will not expand upon melting and rupture the container seals through crystal growth. Mechanical agitating equipment adds expense, reduces reliability, and requires power to operate.

PCM storage devices can be tested according to procedures of ASHRAE *Standard* 94.1-1985, "Methods of Testing Latent Heat Storage Devices Based on Thermal Performance."

ELECTRICALLY CHARGED HEAT STORAGE DEVICES

Thermal energy can also be stored in electrically charged, thermally discharged storage devices. The size of this equipment is usually specified by the nominal power rating (to the nearest kW) of the internal heating elements, and the nominal storage capacity is taken as the amount of energy supplied (to the nearest kWh) during an 8-hour full-power charge period. For example, a 5-kW heater would have a nominal storage capacity of 40 kWh. ASHRAE *Standard* 94.2-1981 gives methods of testing these devices.

Room Storage Heaters

Room storage heaters have olivine or magnesite brick cores encased in shallow metal cabinets that can fit under windows (Figure 17). The core is heated to 1400°F (760°C) during off-peak hours by resistance heating elements located throughout the cabinet. Storage heaters are discharged either by natural convection, radiation and conduction (static heaters); or by a fan controlled thermostatically, manually, or by a time clock (dynamic heaters). The air flowing through the core is mixed with room air to limit the outlet air temperature to a comfort-

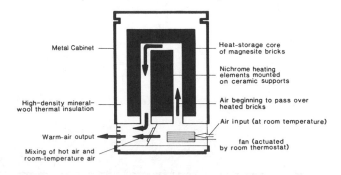

Fig. 17 Room Storage Air Heater (Courtesy: Control Electric Corporation)

able range. Room storage heaters tend to overheat on mild winter days unless equipped with a controller that adjusts the thermal charge dependent on the outdoor temperature. Millions of these room heaters are in use in European homes, and many units of European manufacture have been installed in the United States. These heaters have storage capacities of 14 to 50 kWh with a power draw of 2 to 6 kW, respectively.

Central Storage Air Heaters

Central storage heaters operate on the same principle as room storage heaters; they contain a brick core that is heated to 1400 °F (760 °C) during off-peak hours. They are suitable for buildings with forced air systems since they are discharged by a fan through the building's warm air ducts. They also contain a night heating section, which provides thermal comfort during the off-peak period when the core is being charged. A damper section mixes return air with the heated air circulating through the core section to maintain a comfortable outlet air temperature. A charge controller senses outdoor air temperature as well as core temperature to determine the required charge and to prevent overheating. The units store from 112 to 240 kWh and have a charging draw of 14 to 30 kW, respectively, in addition to the power required for night heating. The core heating elements are activated in steps to prevent current surges. A manual override permits activating the night section during the on-peak period in case the storage is exhausted.

Small Domestic Water Storage Heaters

The hot water heater prevalent throughout the United States is a storage heater because it contains a storage tank. Some electric utilities offer reduced electric rates to customers willing to charge their tanks during off-peak hours only. The charge time is controlled by a time clock or by a signal sent by the utility either over its power lines (ripple control) or by radio. Depending on the nature of the hot water draw by the individual user (see Chapter 13), a tank larger than the one normally used is recommended. Most solar systems use a hot water tank as their storage system. These can be conventional electric hot water heaters, either with or without the heating element or somewhat larger stone-lined tanks. (See Chapter 47, "Solar Energy Use.")

Pressurized Water Storage Heaters

This storage device consists of a cylindrical steel tank containing submersed electrical resistance elements near its bottom and a water-to-water heat exchanger near its top (Figure 18). The tank is surrounded by insulation and enclosed in an aluminum

outer jacket. During off-peak periods, the resistance elements are sequentially energized until the storage water reaches a maximum temperature of 280 °F (138 °C) corresponding to a gage pressure of 35 psi (240 kPa). The ASME Boiler Code considers such vessels "unpressurized", and they are not required to meet the provisions for pressurized vessels. The heaters are controlled by a pressure sensor, which eliminates problems that could be caused by unequal temperature distributions. A thermal controller gives high-limit temperature control protection. Heat is withdrawn from storage by running service water through the heat exchangers and a tempering device that controls the output temperature to a predetermined level. The storage capacity of the device is the sensible heat of water between 280 °F (138 °C) and 20 °F (11 °C) above the desired output water temperature. The output water can be used for space heating or as service hot water. The water in the storage tank is permanently treated and sealed, requires no make-up water, and does not interact with the service water. The units are custom-made in sizes from 240 gallons (0.9 m³) to 18,000 gallons (68 m³) with input power from 20 kW to 5200 kW.

Under-Floor Storage Heaters

This storage consists of mats of electric resistance cables buried in a bed of sand 1 to 3 ft (0.3 to 0.9 m) below the floor of a building. It is suitable for single-story commercial buildings, such as factories and warehouses, where accurate control of temperature is not required. A high water table is acceptable, but the water must not be flowing. This type of storage acts as a flywheel; while it is charged only during the nightly off-peak, it maintains the top of the floor slab at a constant temperature slightly higher than the desired space temperature. Since the heat from the mats spreads in all directions, they do not have to cover the entire slab area. For example, 3-ft (0.9-m) wide mats preformed in long lengths can be placed 6 ft (1.8 m) on centers. The deeper the mats are placed, the larger is the storage capacity of the sand bed, the slower is its response to varying heating needs, and the larger are its heat losses to the ground. For most buildings, a mat location of 18 in. (0.45 m) below the floor elevation is optimum. One manufacturer recommends at least 2 in. (50 mm) of sand below the mats to prevent damage from protruding stones in the subgrade. The remaining sand bed is then placed on top of the mats and the building floor slab placed on top of the bed. When tracked vehicles spread

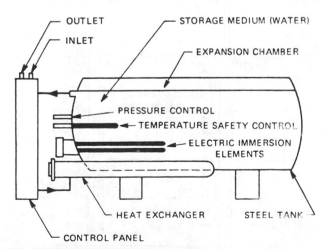

Fig. 18 Pressurized Water Storage Tank (Courtesy: Megatherm Corporation)

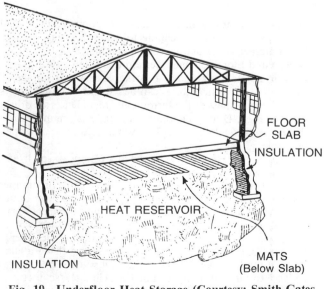

Fig. 19 Underfloor Heat Storage (Courtesy: Smith-Gates Corporation)

the sand, a minimum depth of 12 in. (0.3 m) above the mats is recommended to avoid damage to the mats. The sand bed should be insulated along its perimeter with 2 in. (50 mm) of rigid closed-cell foam insulation to a depth of 4 ft (1.2 m) (see Figure 19). Even with a well-designed storage system of this type, 10% or more of the input heat may be lost to the ground.

GROUND COUPLED STORAGE

Ground coupling uses the earth as a storage medium or heat source/sink, usually for space conditioning. There are two types of ground coupled systems: direct heating/cooling systems and heat pump systems. In direct heating/cooling systems, heat or coolness is stored in a buried vessel or in a localized volume of earth and removed when needed to heat or cool the load directly. In heat pump systems, a heat pump removes heat from, or rejects heat to, the ground for space heating and cooling, respectively (Bose et al. 1985).

A large, closed-loop heat exchanger, buried either vertically or horizontally, couples these systems to the ground. Ground-coupled storage is well-suited to heat recovery using either method, but it is usually applied with the first method. Ground coupling can also increase the capacity of underground thermal storage tanks. In such cases, the tanks are not insulated, and the surrounding soil acts as an extension of the storage tank (Metz 1982). Metz (1983) gives a method of analysis for such systems and comparison with experimental results.

Seasonal Storage

Seasonal thermal storage over prolonged periods, ideally from summer to winter and vice versa, requires large quantities of energy; therefore, the energy sources must be inexpensive. Recovered heat, waste incineration, industrial reject heat, nuclear cooling water, solar heat, and winter chill are examples of suitable energy sources. Because large storage masses are involved, the storage media must be relatively inexpensive. To reduce the cost of the containment structure and to take advantage of the insulating properties of soil, seasonal storage is usually located below ground. Large building or a number of buildings such as shopping centers, university campuses, and hospital complexes are examples of suitable candidates that can take advantage of economies of scale. Some storage options include the following, which are described in greater detail in the resources listed in the bibliography.

Storage in Mines. Mined caverns, abandoned mines, and quarry pits are favorable locations for seasonal storage because the container construction cost is eliminated.

Open Pond Storage. Under certain conditions, open ponds with insulated covers make a workable seasonal storage.

Rock Storage. Vertical ducts can be used as heat exchangers for the storage mass of the surrounding rock. Ducts are drilled into the rock. During charging, hot water is pumped down the holes through a pipe. The water returns in an open borehole, giving up its heat to the rock.

Storage in Soil. Heat can be stored in a volume of soil by circulating warm water through buried pipes.

Seasonal Ice Storage. Ice can store winter chill for summer cooling. Thin sheets of water are sprayed on a growing ice block indoors, or commercial snow-making equipment forms a pile of snow/ice during the winter. The ice can then be used for summer air conditioning. The Annual Cycle Energy System (ACES) design alternately freezes and thaws a large underground ice bank to act as the heat source and sink for a glycol-to-air heat pump. In northern climates, solar collectors can be used to collect additional heat in the winter and reject heat in the summer. In southern climates, only a cool-

ing tower is needed for heat rejection. Energy use is lower than for other types of heating/cooling systems; however, the initial installation is expensive.

STORAGE IN AQUIFERS

Aquifers have a potential for storing large quantities of thermal energy. Here nature provides storage, container, and insulation. Aquifers are water-bearing rocks found near or at nominal depths below the earth's surface. The rocks may be solid porous media or a combination of smaller rocks, such as sand or gravel. To be an aquifer, the rock must be saturated with water. Many aquifers, especially near the surface, consist of a mixture of sand and gravel, saturated with water. Approximately 60% of the surface of the continental United States is underlain by aquifers adequate for thermal energy storage. Many urban areas are concentrated in valleys and near rivers where extensive aquifers exist.

Aquifer storage is best for large systems, mainly communities and major buildings. A large volume is required to ensure reasonable energy recovery and, to be economical, the well cost should be distributed over a large system. Aquifer storage in North America is limited; however, systems are being implemented in other countries. The primary application has been for annual storage, but projects using daily and weekly storage are also being developed and installed. Technically, water in the temperature range of 40 to 500°F (5 to 300°C) can be stored.

Aquifer storage systems are charged and discharged by transferring warm or cold water to and from the aquifer. Figure 20 shows the primary method used to store and retrieve thermal energy. In this system, water is chilled during cold weather in cooling towers or ponds, injected into storage, and retrieved for air conditioning, as required. During charging, cold water is injected in one well, and warm water is withdrawn from the other well. During discharge, the direction of water flow is reversed. Depending on withdrawal and injection rates, a spacing of a few hundred feet between wells is sufficient. More than a

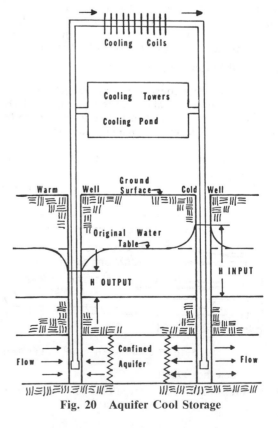

Fig. 20   Aquifer Cool Storage

single pair of wells in the same aquifer may be used. Water loss or gain on an annual basis is negligible, since injected and recovered water quantities are equal. A single well may be used for injecting and recovering water; but very economical sources and means of disposal for water are required. Pressure losses due to flow in the aquifer are larger with a single well, but the capital costs are smaller.

Well diameters range from 4 to 15 in. (100 to 380 mm) and depths from 20 to a few hundred feet (6 to 100+ m). Size and number of wells are a function of water demand and aquifer characteristics—primarily permeability, porosity, and thickness. Well piping must be surrounded by a screen over the entire height of the aquifer; otherwise, nonuniform flow patterns will be created and the system will not perform as expected. System reliability and environmental requirements must also be considered. Well costs vary widely, and bids on a particular well can vary by more than a factor of ten. The American Water Well Association issues reports that are periodically updated for approximate well costs and regulations for every state. Single well costs have varied from $3,000 to over $50,000.

The flow inside aquifers approximates potential flow patterns for a homogeneous system. Figure 21 shows the pattern and the extent of the water front as it reaches the withdrawal well (Schaetzle et al. 1980). The area within the outline is available for thermal storage; it is given by $A = 1.05 R^2$. The area per well pair for a number of pairs is $A = C \cdot R \cdot D$, where R is the distance between rows of injection wells and withdrawal wells, D is the distance between wells in a row, and C is the area constant that can be obtained from Figure 22 for homogenous aquifers. The volume available for energy storage is this area, A, multiplied by the height of the aquifer.

Natural groundwater velocities range from 3 to 300 ft (1 to 100 m) per year. Computer simulations have shown that velocities up to 8 in. (200 mm) per week with well separations of 300 ft (100 m) have no effect on aquifer performance. Strategies to neutralize natural flow consist of injecting and withdrawing water from wells as a function of water movement, or drilling extra wells upstream of the flow and ejecting water to stagnate the flow field. Placing the cold wells on the downstream side of the natural flow and rejecting the water after chilling usage rather than re-injecting it is another possibility. Thermal storage capacity is a function of porosity and type of rock. Most rock has a specific gravity of approximately 2.6 (2600 kg/m³) and a specific heat of approximately 0.2 Btu/lb·°F (0.84 kJ/kg·°C). Porosity can range from less than 5% to more than 50%, with 10 to 30% as general averages for most aquifers. The thermal storage capacity per unit volume of aquifer per degree of temperature change is:

$$q = C_{p,\,rock}\, \varrho_{rock}\, (1 - \phi) + \phi C_{p,\,water} \qquad (6)$$

where

q = specific thermal storage capacity, Btu/ft³·°F (kJ/m³·K)
C_p = specific heat, Btu/lb·°F (kJ/kg·K)
ϱ = density, lb/ft³ (kg/m³)
ϕ = aquifer porosity

The total storage capacity of an aquifer is the above quantity multiplied by the aquifer volume and the useful temperature swing. A typical storage capacity is just over 83 Btu/ft³·°F

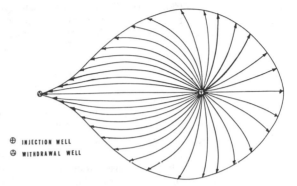

⊕ INJECTION WELL
⊘ WITHDRAWAL WELL

Fig. 21   Water Distribution Pattern for a Well Pair in a Homogeneous Aquifer

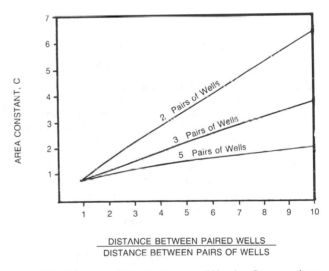

Fig. 22   Constant C to Determine Effective Storage Area

Table 7   Laboratory Coefficient of Permeability, Modified after Todd (1963)

Flow Rate, m³/day·m² at a hydraulic gradient of 1 m/m

10^4	10^3	10^2	10	1	10^{-1}	10^{-2}	10^{-3}	10^{-4}	10^{-5}

Soil Class	Clean gravel	Clean sands; mixtures of clean sands and gravels		Very fine sands; silts, mixtures of sand, silt, and clay; glacial till; stratified clays; etc.			Unweathered clay
Flow Characteristics	Good aquifers			Poor aquifers			Impervious

10^6	10^5	10^4	10^3	10^2	10^1	1	10^{-1}	10^{-2}	10^{-3}	10^{-4}

Flow Rate, gal/day per ft² at a hydraulic gradient of 1 ft/ft

(5000 kJ/m³·K), varying with porosity. At this value, a rock volume of 130 by 200 by 31 ft (40 by 60 by 10 m) has a total storage capacity of approximately 1.2×10^9 Btu (1.2 TJ), with an 18°F (10°C) temperature swing.

The pressure loss in an aquifer for a single withdrawal well is $h_o - h_w = Q \ln (r_o/r_w)/(2\pi Kb)$, where h is the water level, Q is the flow rate, r is the radius from the center of the well, K is the aquifer permeability, b is the aquifer thickness, "o" is the aquifer outer limit where water level changes are not affected by the well, and "w" is the outside well radius (hole radius including gravel packing) (Todd 1963). The effect of r_o can reach for thousands of feet in a confined aquifer. By using pairs of wells in an aquifer, the value of r_o can be limited. The equation shows that the pressure loss strongly depends on the permeability of the aquifer (Table 7). Aquifer systems have been installed into the poor aquifer region listed in the table.

Aquifers require several seasons before achieving their full potential. Storage efficiency can be greater than 80% for aquifers 50-ft (15-m) thick with zero natural flow. However, most aquifer storage systems can be expected to be 40 to 60% efficient.

In a conventional hydraulic system, the water supply is limited in case of a water line break, because only the water in the lines and a trickle replacement flow can cause damage. In an aquifer system, a line break can cause flooding of a few hundred gallons per minute and thousands of gallons total. Therefore, such a system must be designed so that the damage from broken water lines is limited.

THERMAL STORAGE APPLICATIONS

GENERAL CONSIDERATIONS

Figure 23 from Engineering Interface (1986) shows a water storage and building circuit in its simplest form. The "chiller" in the figure may produce hot or cold water, depending on the side to which the storage device is connected. During recharge, only the lower loop is operative. During on-peak operation with full storage, only the upper loop is operative. With partial storage, both loops may operate in parallel, part of the flow passing through storage and part through the chiller. A temperature modulating valve (not shown) adjusts the flow to the load to achieve the desired supply temperature.

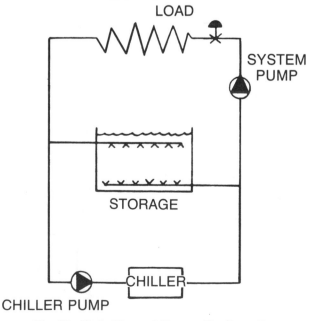

Fig. 23   Basic Thermal Storage Configuration

Storage of Heat in Cool Storage Units

Cool storage installations can also store heat. Since most commercial buildings require cooling some time during the day even in the winter, the refrigeration plant may be in operation all year. When cool storage is charged during the off-peak period, the compressor heat of water-cooled condensers can be stored for use during morning warm-up on the following day. For small buildings, the maximum cooling load during the heating season is likely to be small, even in the middle of the day, so there may be no need for cool storage to reduce demand charges.

If more than one storage unit is installed, one or more of these units can be switched from summer cool storage to winter heat storage in the fall and switched back in the spring. In such an installation, both heat and cool storage can be accomplished simultaneously by operating the compressor during nighttime off-peak periods. The stored heat can be used for morning warm-up (and late afternoon and evening heating, if required), and the stored coolness can provide midday cooling. If both chiller and storage are large enough, all compressor operation can be avoided during the on-peak period, and the required heating or cooling can be satisfied from storage. This method of operation replaces the air side "economizer cycle," which consists of using outside air to cool the building when its enthalpy is lower than that of the return air. Heat and cool storage is usually lower in first cost than the equipment required for an economizer cycle.

Cool storage with heat pumps or heat-recovery equipment may also be used during the heating season. Cooling is withdrawn from storage, as needed. When heat is demanded, the cool storage is recharged by using it as the heat source for the heat pump. Additional heat, if needed, can be obtained from off-peak heating, from solar collectors, from exhaust air, or from other waste heat sources. Excess energy can be rejected through a cooling tower if more cooling than heating is required. The cooling portion of this cycle is usually referred to as "free cooling."

The extra cost of equipping a cool storage facility for heat storage is small. The necessary plant additions are: a partition in the storage tank to convert some portion to storing warm water, some additional controls, and a chiller equipped for heat reclaim duty. The additional cost may be readily offset by savings in heating energy. In fact, adding heat storage capability may increase the economic attractiveness of cool storage systems.

Heat and Cool Storage Capacities

The above methods of applying storage equipment can be used with either water or ice storage. For water storage, capacity is directly proportional to the temperature swing: $Q = mC_p\Delta T$, where Q is the storage capacity in Btu (kJ), m is the storage mass of water in lb (kg), C_p is the specific heat of water (1 Btu/lb or 4.18 kJ/kg), and ΔT is the temperature swing in °F (°C). For heating applications, T is typically 50°F (28°C) or more with operation between 140°F (60°C) and 90°F (32°C) for a dual-temperature hot water/chilled water change-over system.

For cooling applications, typical temperature swings are 15 to 25°F (8 to 14°C), the limitation being the ability to control space humidity at the higher return water conditions. The required water storage mass per unit of cooling stored is given by Eq. (7).

$$m = 12,000/\Delta T, \text{ lb per ton-hour} \qquad (7)$$

$$m = 1000/(4.18 \ \Delta T), \text{ kg per MJ} \qquad (7 \text{ SI})$$

Thermal storage in water has many advantages: it is easily interfaced with heating and cooling plants, can be stored above grade in tanks and below grade in concrete pits, can provide uniform discharge temperature when properly stratified, has lowest operating cost, and is easily controlled. It does, however, require careful design to avoid temperature blending, and it needs a large storage volume.

For ice storage, capacity is related to the latent heat of fusion of water, or 144 Btu/lb (335 kJ/kg). For operation at 32°F (0°C), the storage capacity is equal to that value. For operation at 50°F (10°C), the storage capacity is increased by the sensible heat between that temperature and the freezing point of water. In practice, however, only about one-half of the water in a direct expansion ice storage tank is actually frozen when it is fully charged; therefore, the effective cool storage capacity of ice storage is $0.5 \cdot 144 + 1.0 \cdot (50 - 32) = 90$ Btu/lb (209 kJ/kg).

Ice storage has the advantage of smaller volume and lower standby losses than water and is, therefore, often available in packaged units. Care, however, must be taken to control the exit water temperature, which varies with the discharge rate. Brine/ice storage systems have very small storage volumes because all of the storage water can be frozen. They can be readily coupled to existing packaged refrigeration units, which is especially advantageous in retrofit applications. However, the packaged storage modules are limited in capacity and are difficult to control to produce a uniform discharge temperature. PCMs for thermal storage have the advantage of small volume and low standby loss, and they do not incur a penalty for lower evaporating temperatures when used for cool storage. However, only limited operating experience exists with these systems, and they usually have a higher first cost than other systems.

OFF-PEAK COOLING

Operating and Sizing Storage

At present, the most prevalent use of thermal storage in commercial buildings is for off-peak cooling to reduce the maximum electrical demand of the building during peak daytime hours. Table 8 illustrates the methods by which this can be achieved. The electric utility "billing demand" may be the highest demand at any time, the highest demand during peak hours, or another

Table 8 Storage Methods and Corresponding Operating Strategies

Storage Method		Operating Strategy
Full Storage		All heating/cooling is generated during off-peak hours; the heating/cooling plant is shut down during peak hours.
Partial Storage	Load Leveling	The heating/cooling plant operates at full capacity during 24 hours on the design day
	Demand Limiting	The heating/cooling plant operates to minimize the electric utility billing demand

type of demand defined by the electric utility. The operating strategy to minimize it depends on that definition. Detailed information should be obtained from the electric utility so the designer can design a storage system and an operating strategy to produce maximum cost savings. The designer should also consider the effect of on-peak and off-peak energy charges ($1 kWh) if different charges as a function of time of use (TOU) are offered by the utility.

The sizing of compressors and storage for the different storage operating systems defined in Table 8 is illustrated by the following example (Donovan). Figure 24 shows the building load profile; the daily load is 3984 ton-hours, the average load is 166 ton-hours, and the peak demand is 260 tons. During the peak hours from 9 a.m. to 6 p.m. the cooling load is 2180 ton-hours, while 1804 ton-hours occur during off-peak hours. Figure 25 illustrates full storage, which shows that the entire daily cooling load of 3984 ton-hours is satisfied by chiller operation during 15 off-peak hours. In this instance, a chiller with a capacity of $3984/15 = 265.6$ tons is needed. A fraction of the chiller out

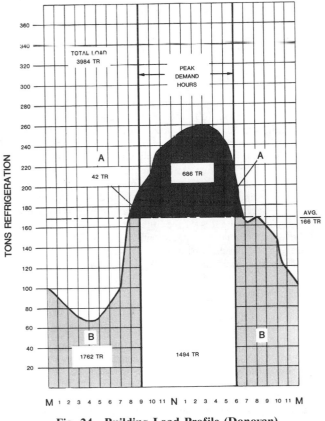

Fig. 24   Building Load Profile (Donovan)

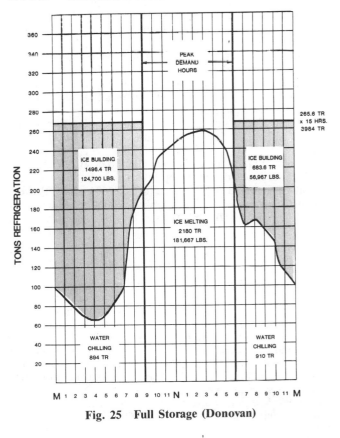

Fig. 25   Full Storage (Donovan)

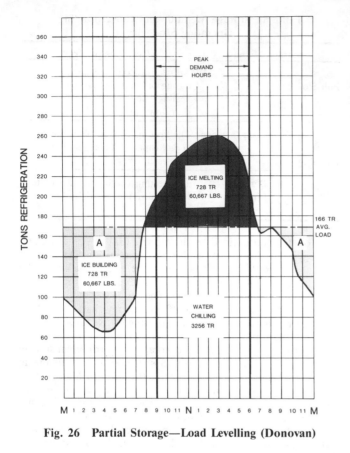

Fig. 26   Partial Storage—Load Levelling (Donovan)

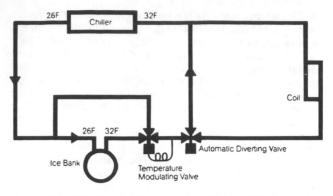

Fig. 27   Partial Storage—Ice Making Mode

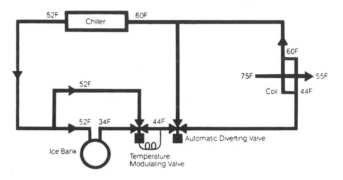

Fig. 28   Partial Storage—Cooling Mode With Water Tempered to Standard Coil Temperatures

put during the 15 off-peak hours is used to cool the building directly, while the rest goes into storage.

Figure 26 shows load leveling in which the required chiller capacity for 24-hour operation is 3984/24 = 166 tons, the average cooling load for the design day. The integrated daily cooling demand that exceeds this value equals 728 ton hours, which is the amount of storage that must be provided. Between 7 p.m. and 8 a.m. the chiller cools the building, and its excess capacity is used to charge storage; between 8 a.m. and 7 p.m. the cooling load is met by the full chiller output augmented by withdrawal from storage.

Demand limiting operation is somewhat more complicated than load leveling. Design procedures are given in GPU *et al.* (1985).

To take full advantage of storage and to determine the most economical system design and operation, hour-by-hour computer calculations should be performed for all 8760 hours of the year. Manual and computer aided methodologies are discussed in detail by Ayres (1980) and Ayres *et al.* (1984).

Circuitry

Figures 27 and 28 (Tamblyn 1977) show charge and discharge operation for ice storage devices suitable for partial storage. During off-peak periods, the building loop containing the cooling coils is bypassed, and the chiller charges the ice storage unit. Since the outlet water from an ice storage unit is usually 34 °F (1 °C) and most building loops are designed for 42 to 48 °F (6 to 9 °C) chilled water supply, the return water from the building loop is only partially cooled in the chiller. A part of that flow is then passed through the ice storage unit where it is cooled to 34 °F (1 °C). In this case, the remainder of the flow bypasses storage, and a downstream modulating valve maintains the

desired chilled water supply temperature to the building loop, 44 °F (6 °C). If demand limiting is desired, the chiller electrical demand must also be controlled. It is set for the maximum permissible electrical demand and provides chilled water at constant temperature but variable volume. The rest of the chilled water flow is provided from storage. Individual cooling coil demand is controlled by thermostats, and the total pump flow is controlled either through a variable speed pump or through a bypass.

The low supply air temperature achievable with ice storage can be advantageous to reduce air flows and duct sizes throughout a building. To achieve a satisfactory level of air movement, part of the return air can be recirculated through terminal air blenders and mixed with the supply air. GPU Service Corporation et al. (1985) discuss the influence of chilled water and air supply temperatures on coil selection and fan power.

The low supply air temperature, coupled with the ability for rapid discharge of ice brine/ice builders, is used to cool aircraft at many terminal gates where high cooling loads occur during the relatively short passenger loading and unloading periods. Storage is recharged during periods when the gate is not occupied. Air temperatures of 26 °F (−3 °C) are required because of the small aircraft duct sizes.

With brine/ice builders, it may be advisable to use closer tube spacing or to locate the glycol chiller downstream of the storage to maintain a low temperature, because the output temperature of a brine/ice unit rises gradually as the unit is discharged (Figure 29). This rise is due to the insulating effect of the water layer between coil and ice after the ice next to the coil has melted. The same arrangement should be used with PCM storage devices having melting point temperatures above those required for full dehumidification. In such cases, storage acts as a pre-cooler for the warm return water, and the PCM storage supplies sensible cooling while the chiller supplies latent cooling.

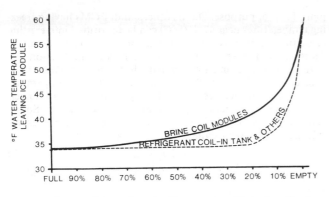

Fig. 29 Chilled Water Supply Temperature Variation During Discharge of Ice Storage

Multiple Storage Units

It is sometimes advantageous to subdivide large storage installations into several units. Particularly in the case of ice units, it is advisable to install multiple compressors as well, because it permits disconnecting some of the compressor units during periods of light loads. The resulting larger evaporating area and thinner ice thickness (causing higher evaporating temperatures) and relatively larger condensing capacity (causing lower condensing temperatures) decrease the required lift and increase compressor efficiency. Only small savings result from disconnecting some of the ice storage units during light loads, because even a partially charged ice storage unit provides 34°F (1°C) water. In multiple chilled water installations, however, it is preferable to disconnect some storage units during periods of light loads and to charge and discharge the remaining units fully during each cycle, because partial recharge of water units tends to decrease temperature stratification.

Each ice unit operating in parallel should have shut-off valves at both inlet and outlet so it can be separately taken out of service for maintenance. In cases where water is pumped, a water equalizing line should also be installed between adjacent units to prevent undesirable high or low flow conditions in any unit. Table 9 (GPU et al. 1985) lists the size of the required equalizer line.

If ice storage units require a minimum water flow rate to avoid excessive ice melting in the entrance compartment, the ice water supply pump and control valves serving the HVAC cooling coils must be arranged to maintain this minimum flow rate. If a three-way temperature control valve serving the cooling coil is located at the pump suction side, the flow through the coil is constant and the flow through the ice storage unit is variable. Under light loads, little or no ice water is required, and the flow through the ice storage unit may drop below the minimum rate. To avoid this problem, either an additional pump is required, or the system must be designed to provide constant flow through the ice storage unit and variable flow through the cooling coils. The latter solution is preferable because it avoids the installation and operating cost of an additional pump (Ayres Associates 1985).

**Table 9 Required Sizes for Equalizer Connections
(GPU et al. 1985)**

Ice Builder Flow Rate, GPM	(L/s)	Equalizer Pipe Size, in.	(mm)
Up to 120	(Up to 7.5)	3	(75)
121 to 240	(7.6 to 15)	4	(100)
241 to 630	(15 to 40)	6	(150)
631 to 1170	(40 to 75)	8	(200)
1171 to 1925	(75 to 120)	10	(250)
1926 to 2820	(120 to 180)	12	(300)

Refrigerant Flow

Thermal expansion valves are usually set for 5 to 7°F (2.7 to 3.9°C) superheat, leaving the evaporator tubes to ensure that liquid refrigerant is not carried over into the compressor (liquid slugging). Thus, they are not well-suited to operating at two different suction temperatures and pressures required for off-peak ice making and on-peak water chilling, as shown in Figures 27 and 28. Under such conditions, they may operate erratically. Admitting too much refrigerant causes refrigerant droplets to enter the compressor (liquid slugging), which damages the compressor, while admitting too little refrigerant causes refrigerant starvation and reduced heat transfer in the downstream coils of the evaporator, decreasing compressor efficiency.

To guard against liquid slugging, suction line accumulators should be provided—especially for positive displacement machines, such as reciprocating and screw compressors. Centrifugal compressors are able to pass relatively large amounts of liquid refrigerant without damage. Liquid receivers in ice storage systems should be sized to hold the full refrigerant charge. Undersized receivers can cause the refrigerant to back up into the condenser tubes, reducing the available heat transfer surface and thus the overall system performance. The refrigerant then tends to remain in the large evaporator tubes, and pump-down controls are required to return the liquid to the receiver when the system is shut off.

Oil Return

Refrigerant lines should be arranged to prevent the trapping of large amounts of oil anywhere in the system and to ensure its return to the compressor under all operating conditions, especially during periods of light compressor loads. All suction lines should slope toward the suction line accumulators, and all discharge lines should pitch toward the oil separators. Oil tends to accumulate in the evaporator coils of the storage units, since that is the location of lowest temperature and pressure. Since refrigerant accumulators trap oil in addition to liquid refrigerant, the larger accumulators required for ice-storage systems necessitate special provisions to ensure adequate oil return to the compressor.

The capacity of an ice storage unit using direct expansion valves to meter the liquid to the evaporator and to avoid liquid slugging may be 8 to 10% less than that of a system that fully floods all of the evaporator tubes (Ayres Associates 1985). The industrial refrigeration practice of using liquid overfeed and low-pressure receivers to prevent liquid refrigerant from reaching the compressor is more reliable than the use of direct expansion coils and thermal expansion valves in connection with ice systems. The difficulties experienced with thermal expansion valves can be avoided by using electronically controlled refrigerant feed valves, which are available from several manufacturers.

On initial start-up of an ice storage system with warm water in the tank and no ice on the evaporator coils, the compressor will encounter high suction pressures. Suction pressure regulators, such as hold-back valves or crank-case pressure regulators, limit the pressure to avoid motor overloads and frequent high-pressure safety shutdowns.

Part Load Operation

During mild spring and fall days, full ice-storage capacity is not needed. If the electric tariff is based on a monthly demand charge that is independent of the demand in any previous month, it may be possible to operate a partial storage system as a full storage system and save money. If, however, a "ratchet" clause is in effect (in which the monthly billing demand is not less than a certain fraction of the highest billing demand during a preceding specified period), the building operator does not benefit from reducing electrical demand during spring and fall by more than a certain amount. In such cases, the use of storage should be reduced as much as possible without raising the on-peak demand above that of the highest summer month.

Suitability of Storage Devices to Retrofits

The smaller volume required for latent heat storage (ice and PCM) compared to water storage favors them for retrofit installations where space is limited. Latent heat storage is also preferred for building sites where rock or a high water table make deep excavation for a tank expensive. The small module size of brine/ice units is an advantage in instances where access to the equipment room is limited or where the storage units can be distributed throughout the building and located near the cooling coils. Chilled water tanks incur external thermal losses of 2 to 5% per day, while latent heat storage tanks, because of their smaller size, lose less. Existing installations that already contain chilled water piping and conventional water chillers are more easily and cheaply retrofitted to accept chilled water storage than latent heat storage. The requirement for brine in some ice storage systems complicates pumping and heat exchange for existing equipment.

Ice storage has generally been used with positive displacement compressors because they are more easily modified for ice making. Centrifugal chillers, with their low cost for large sizes and reputation for reliability, are more suited to chilled water generation than to ice making. To equip a centrifugal compressor for ice making requires a change of compressor wheel because a higher pressure ratio is needed to make ice than to chill water. This greater pressure also increases the required compressor power, making it necessary either to derate the compressor or to replace the motor with a higher kilowatt motor. Valves and other components of the cooling plant may also require replacement because of the higher power. In many cases, it may be more economical to replace the entire cooling plant with one designed for ice storage than to attempt to retrofit a centrifugal chiller

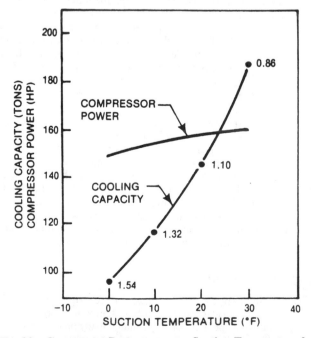

Fig. 30   Compressor Performance vs. Suction Temperature for Constant Condensing Temperature (Ayres Sowell Assoc. 1982) (Numbers in figure denote hp/ton)

plant for that purpose. On the other hand, PCMs having freezing temperatures near 47 °F (8 °C) can be retrofitted into existing centrifugal chiller systems without modification or derating. Thus, these devices are well-suited to retrofit applications.

All compressors must be derated when making ice instead of chilled water. The 15 to 20 °F (-9 to -6 °C) suction temperature required to make ice decreases COP by about 30% and capacity by an even larger amount, as shown in Figure 30 (Ayres Sowell Associates 1982). Suction temperature drops linearly as ice thickness increases by the following relationship:

$$t_s = 20 - 4x \qquad (8)$$
$$t_s = -0.192x \qquad (8\ SI)$$

where

t_s = suction temperature, °F (°C)
x = ice thickness, in. (mm)

The chilling plant consumes between 0.75 and 1.25 kW/ton (0.21 to 0.36 kW electrical/kW thermal) while making ice. This may be partly offset during the on-peak phase of partial storage by the lower demands of 0.5 to 0.75 kW/ton (0.14 to 0.21 kW electrical/kW thermal) for cooling the upper range of return chilled water, which is at a lower temperature than the return coolant of conventional systems. However, the overall energy consumption is likely to be at least 15% higher than the 0.6 to 0.8 kW/ton (0.17 to 0.23 kW electrical/kW thermal) generally used for chilling water (Engineering Interface 1986).

OFF-PEAK HEATING

Service Water Heating

The tank-equipped service water heater, which is the standard water heater in North America, is a thermal storage device—in contrast to the instantaneous tankless water heater frequently found in Europe. Some electric utilities provide incentives for off-peak water heating. The heater is then equipped with a time clock that locks out the circuit during peak hours, or a signal is sent from the utility, either by radio or over the power lines, that turns the heater off or permits it to be turned on when requested by the thermostat. The financial incentive for off-peak water heating is relatively small, because most domestic water heating occurs during off-peak hours anyway. It is advisable to increase the tank size of off-peak water heaters over the size chosen for conventional heaters, although the need for that depends on the habits of the users.

An alternate method of off-peak water heating connects two tanks in series such that the hot water outlet of the first tank supplies water to the second tank (Oak Ridge 1985). This arrangement minimizes the mixing of hot and cold water in the second tank, because that tank benefits from stratification in the first tank. Tests performed on this configuration show that it can supply 80 to 85% of its rated capacity at temperatures suitable for domestic needs, compared to 70% for single-tank configurations. The wiring of the four heating elements in the two water heaters must be modified to accommodate the dual tank configuration. The upper element in the second tank must be locked out, and the other three elements must be prevented from operating simultaneously.

Solar Space and Water Heating

Either rock beds, water tanks, or PCMs can be used, depending on the type of solar system. Various applications are described in Chapter 47, "Solar Energy Use."

Space Heating

Thermal storage in small buildings can be carried out by (1) radiant floor heating, (2) brick storage heaters, or (3) water storage heaters. The first is generally applicable to single-story buildings only. The choice of the other two depends on the type of heating system in the building, with air systems using brick and water systems using water or a PCM. Water systems can be charged either electrically or thermally.

Popular locations for storage in residential applications include basements, crawl spaces, garages, and outdoors or indoors below grade. Basements have few unfavorable conditions, but installation can be difficult if the storage unit must be assembled in place in an area with limited access. The same drawback applies to crawl spaces, which, because of their cooler ambient temperature, require more insulation than basements. In severe climates, freeze protection may be needed. Garages impose insulation problems similar to those of crawl spaces, but complete tanks can easily pass through their doors. Outdoor storage above grade requires additional insulation, which must also be protected from the weather.

Ground water is the main problem with outdoor storage below grade. Porous insulation should not be used below grade, and even closed-cell foams may have their insulating value reduced by one-half in the presence of ground water. Drainage tiles and a sump pump may be required where the soil drains poorly. Wood, unless it is pressure treated for ground contact, should not be used in contact with the ground or with water, because it rots. Considerations for storage tank locations in commercial buildings are discussed in the introduction of this chapter.

Insulation is more important for hot storage than for cool storage because the difference in temperatures between storage and occupied space is much larger. Methods of determining the economic thickness of insulation are given in Chapter 20 of the 1985 FUNDAMENTALS Volume. The relation between nominal rock size, face velocity (volumetric flow rate divided by cross-sectional area of the bed), and pressure gradient through rock bed storage units is shown in Figure 14. The rock bed cover is a potentially serious source of leakage in an air system, since the force on a 6 by 8 ft (1.8 by 2.4 m) cover pressurized to one inch of water (250 Pa) is approximately 250 lb (1100 N). Covers should be sealed with silicone sealants or a soft rubber gasket and should be screwed and bolted to the container sides.

Figure 31 shows the operating characteristics of electrically charged room storage heaters. Curve 1 represents their theoretical performance. In reality, heat is continually transferred to the room during charging by radiation and convection from the exterior surface of the device. This *static discharge* is shown in curve 2. When the thermostat calls for heat, the internal fan is started, and the resulting faster *dynamic discharge* corresponds to curves 3 and 4.

The operating characteristics of these devices differ from conventional electric heaters in two important respects. First, since the heating elements are energized only during the off-peak period, they must supply the total daily heating requirement during that period, typically 8 or 10 hours. Second, the rate at which heat can be delivered to the heated space decreases as the charge level decreases. Thus, the heaters are less able to meet the building heat load toward the end of the discharge period, which often coincides with a period of high heating demand. This applies primarily to room heaters and less to central heaters that contain tempering dampers.

A rational design procedure requires an hourly simulation of design heat load and discharge capacity of the storage device. A tentative selection of the storage device is made. Starting with a fully charged storage device, the energy required to meet the heating load during the first hour of the discharge period is subtracted from storage, and the maximum possible dynamic discharge rate of the device is calculated for the second hour. This procedure is repeated for each hour of the discharge period. The first criterion for satisfactory performance is that this discharge rate is no less than the design heating load at any hour. When the off-peak period commences, energy is added to storage at the rate determined by the connected load of the resistance elements, while the design heating load is subtracted from storage. At the end of a 24-hour period, the second criterion of satisfactory performance, the daily energy balance, is checked. Assuming that the design day is preceded and followed by similar days, the storage energy level at the end of the simulated day should equal the starting level. If the chosen device cannot meet these conditions, a device with a larger storage capacity, a higher charge rate, or both must be chosen, and the calculations must be repeated.

A simpler procedure is recommended by Hersh et al. (1982) for typical residential heating system designs. For each zone of the building, the design heat loss is calculated in the usual manner and multiplied by the selected sizing factor. The resulting value is rounded to the next higher kilowatt and designated as the required storage heater capacity. Sizing factors in the United States have ranged between 2.0 and 2.5 for an 8-hour charge period and between 1.6 and 2.0 for a 10-hour charge period. The lower end of the range is marginal for the northeastern United States.

Central ceramic brick storage heaters usually have a night heating section that supplies heat to the occupied space during the off-peak period while storage is being charged. Thus, the amount of heat that must be put into storage is equal to the space heating needs during the peak period only. For best efficiency, the unit should not be charged to a higher temperature than required to satisfy the heating needs of the following day. Therefore an outdoor anticipatory temperature sensor is recommended. Electrically charged pressurized water storage tanks must recharge the full daily heating and hot water requirement during the off-peak period, since they do not have a night heating section. Their heat exchanger design allows them to discharge at a constant rate, which does not decrease near the end of the cycle.

Thermally charged hot water storage tanks are similar in design to that of cool storage tanks described under the section on off-peak cooling; most of these tanks are also used for cooling during part of the year. Contrary to off-peak cooling, off-peak heating seldom permits a reduction in the size of the heating plant. The size of storage used for both heating and cooling depends more on cooling than on heating for lowest life cycle cost, except in some residential applications.

Care should be taken to avoid thermal shock of concrete tanks. Tamblyn (1985) showed that "the seasonal change from hot to cool storage caused sizable leaks to develop if the cooldown

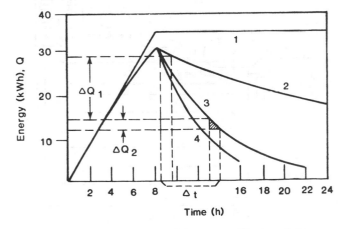

Fig. 31 Storage Heater Performance Characteristics (Hersh 1981)

period was accelerated below five days." Raising a concrete tank's temperature does not cause problems, since this generates compressive stresses, which concrete is well able to sustain. Cooldown, on the other hand, causes tensile stresses, under which concrete has low strength.

OFF-PEAK REFRIGERATION

Ice is the usual storage medium for refrigeration. Such systems are generally controlled by a liquid refrigerant recirculation system. The circulation rate can be as high as three times the evaporation rate, which results in excellent heat transfer. Figure 32 shows a multiple coil storage unit. A positive level control device usually controls the flow of high-pressure liquid from the receiver by operating a solenoid valve in the interconnecting line. The refrigerant pump pumps liquid from the low-pressure receiver through control solenoid valves into the liquid feed manifolds of the ice makers themselves. Downstream of the liquid manifold are orifice plates that are predrilled based on an accurate assessment of design conditions with respect to both liquid flow and pressure differentials, thus ensuring uniform flow of liquid refrigerant across the entire coil. The spent gases, together with the remaining liquid, continue into the low-pressure receiver where the liquid portion is recirculated as the suction gas is drawn into the compressor and continues into the condenser (Donovan).

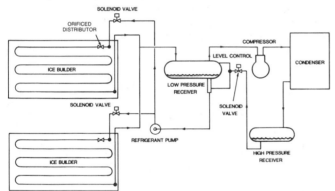

Fig. 32   Typical Refrigeration System Using Liquid Refrigerant and Ice Storage (Donovan)

A variation of the liquid refrigeration recirculation technique uses a series of vessels instead of the liquid pump (Figure 33). Hot gas passes through the oil separator on its way to the condenser. Prior to entering the condenser, a portion of the hot gas is directed into one or the other of two pumper drums through a series of control valves. In Figure 33 the right-hand solenoid valve is shown in the open position, so the hot gas pressurizes the right-hand pumper drum and forces liquid refrigerant into the intercooler. A modified back-pressure regulator shown in the line between the intercooler and the low-pressure receiver controls the operating steam pressure and forces liquid refrigerant into the supply headers of the ice makers.

The liquid flow across the ice storage coils is balanced by orifice plates. The spent gas, together with the remaining liquid, continues into the low-pressure receiver. At this point, the two components are separated and the gas is drawn off to the compressor. The liquid from the low-pressure receiver then flows into the nonpressurized pumper drum to the left of the intercooler. While liquid is entering the pumper drum, venting takes place through a 3-way valve connected to the low-pressure receiver near its top. Either time- or temperature-control automatically switches the hot gas control solenoids when one pumper drum becomes empty and the other filled, thus reversing the process. Liquid make-up from the high-pressure receiver is usually con-

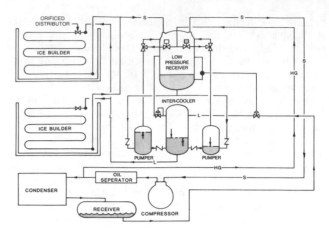

Fig. 33   Liquid Refrigerant Recirculation System Using Pumper Drums (Donovan)

trolled by a float arrangement located in the low-pressure receiver. This arrangement has a higher first cost than that using the mechanical pump, but it does avoid the use of a pump and has other operational benefits for large, multiple evaporator systems (Donovan).

For single-coil systems, a flooded ammonia system can be used. Figure 34 shows such an arrangement with liquid refrigerant entering at the bottom of the coil through a header and the vapor passing into the surge drum through a suction manifold. From there it is drawn off by the compressor, passes through a suction accumulator, and is directed into the condenser. While the valve in the line between the surge drum and the suction accumulator is shown as a solenoid valve, it would more likely be a back-pressure regulator with auxiliary stop feature or an expansion valve. The stop feature can be wired together with the liquid line solenoid valve and the ice thickness control to isolate the storage unit completely from the rest of the system. Liquid level in the surge drum is maintained by the external electric float device controlling the solenoid valve in the liquid line (Donovan).

For single-coil fluorocarbon systems, an ice storage unit charged by direct expansion can be used (Figure 35). The coil is charged from the top through a thermal expansion valve or a series of valves with the gas being drawn off from the bottom header. The controlling thermal bulb is fixed to the suction line and modulates the thermal valve to ensure entry of the proper amount of liquid refrigerant from the high-pressure receiver. The

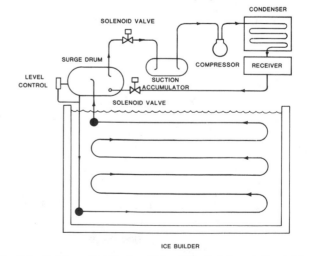

Fig. 34   Refrigeration System Using Flooded Ammonia and Ice Storage (Donovan)

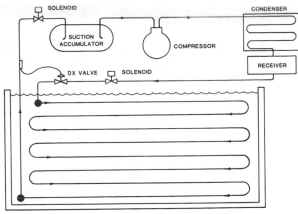

SOLENOID
SUCTION ACCUMULATOR
COMPRESSOR
CONDENSER
RECEIVER
DX VALVE SOLENOID
ICE BUILDER

Fig. 35 Refrigeration System Using Liquid Refrigerant and Direct Expansion Ice Storage (Donovan)

ice thickness control operates the solenoid valve in the liquid line and provides a simple way to start and stop the ice making cycle. It also stops the flow of liquid refrigerant from the receiver during shutdown, which otherwise could result in overcharging the ice unit.

Another thermal storage system well suited to storage for refrigeration is the ice slurry previously described under "Ice Storage."

REFERENCES

Abhat, A. 1978. Performance Studies of a Finned Heat Pipe Latent Heat Thermal Energy Storage System. SUN, Mankind's Future Source of Energy, Pergamon Press, Elmsford, NY, Vol. I, pp. 541-546.

ASHRAE. 1981. Methods of Testing Thermal Storage Devices with Electrical Input and Thermal Output Based on Thermal Performance. ASHRAE Standard 94.2 1981.

ASHRAE. 1985. Methods of Testing Active Latent Heat Storage Devices Based on Thermal Performance. ASHRAE Standard 94.1-1985.

ASHRAE. 1986. Methods of Testing Active Sensible Heat Thermal Energy Storage Devices Based on Thermal Performance. ASHRAE Standard 94.3-1986.

Ayres Associates. 1980. A Guide for Off-Peak Cooling in Buildings. Southern California Edison Company, Rosemead, CA.

Ayres Associates. 1985. Performance of Commercial Cool Storage Systems. Vol 1: Early Case Histories; Vol. 2: Cipher Data Products Ice Storage System Improvements. EPRI EM 4044, June.*

Ayres, J.M.; Lau, H.; and Scott, J.R. 1984. Sizing of Thermal Storage Systems for Cooling Buildings with Time-of-Use Electric Rates. ASHRAE Transactions, Vol. 90, Part 1.

Ayres Sowell Associates. 1982. Field Performance of an Ice Storage Off-Peak Cooling Installation. Southern California Edison Company, Rosemead, CA.

Bose, J.E.; Parker, J.D.; and McQuiston, F.C. 1985. Design/Data Manual for Ground-Coupled Heat Pumps. ASHRAE *Publication* GCHP.

Calmac Manufacturing Corporation. 1982. Bulk Storage of PCM. Report to Argonne National Laboratory, NTIS PB82-805862, National Technical Information Service, Springfield, VA.

Carbado, J. J. 1985. A Direct-Contact Charged, Direct-Contact Discharged Cool Storage System Using Gas Hydrate. ASHRAE Transactions, Vol. 91, Part 2.

Chubb, T.A., et al. 1980. DOE Conf. 801055, October, p. 68.

Close, D.J.; Dunkle, R.V.; and Robeson, K.A. 1968. Design and Performance of a Thermal Storage Air Conditioning System. Mechanical and Chemical Engineering Transactions, Inst. of Civil Engineers, Australia, Vol. MC4, p. 45.

Cole, R.T. et al. 1980. Design and Installation Manual for Thermal Energy Storage. ANL-79-15, 2d ed., Argonne National Laboratory.

Cole, R.L.; and Bellinger, F.O. 1982. Natural Thermal Stratification in Tanks, Phase I, Final Report. Argonne National Laboratory ANL-82-5.

Comstock and Wescott, Inc. 1962. Promising Heat Storage Material Found Through Research. EEI Bulletin, February, pp. 49-50.

di Lauro, G.F.; and Rice, R.E. 1981. Conceptual Design of a Latent Heat Thermal Energy Storage Subsystem for a Saturated Steam Solar Receiver and Load. Proc. 6th Annual Thermal and Chemical Storage Contractors' Review Meeting, DOE Conf-810940, Sept.

Donovan, J.F. The Ice Builder, An Off-Peak Approach. Chester-Jensen Company, Chester, PA.

Engineering Interface, Ltd. 1986. Commercial Cool Storage: Presentation Material. Vol. 1, Seminar Handbook; Vol. 2, Slide Package. EPRI EM 4405, February.*

GPU Service Corporation and Enviro-Management & Research Co. 1985. Commercial Cool Storage Design Guide. EPRI EM 3981, Electric Power Research Institute, Palo Alto, CA. Also available from GPU Service Corporation, 100 Interpace Parkway, Parsippany, NJ 07054.

Hersh, H.N. 1981. Optimal Sizing of Heating Systems that Store and Use Thermal Energy. ANL/SPG-18, Argonne National Laboratory, June.

Hersh, H.; Mirchandani, G.; and Rowe, R. 1982. Evaluation and Assessment of Thermal Energy Storage for Residential Heating. ANL SPG-23, Argonne National Laboratory, April.

Hughes, P.J.; Klein, S.A.; and Close, D.A. 1976. Packed Bed Thermal Storage Models for Solar Air Heating and Cooling Systems. J. of Heat Transfer, ASME, Vol. 98, p. 336.

Jones, D.E.; and Loss, W. 1982. Flow Distribution Improvements in Vertical Rock Beds for Solar Energy Thermal Storage. ASHRAE Transactions, Vol. 88, Part 2.

Knebel, D.E. 1986. A Showcase on Cost Savings. ASHRAE Journal, May, p. 28.

Kohler, J.; and Lewis, D. 1983. Phase Change Products for Passive Homes. Solar Age, Vol. 65.

Lane, G.A. 1982. Congruent-Melting Phase-Change Heat Storage Materials. ASHRAE Transactions Vol. 88, Part 2.

Lane, G.A. 1985. PCM Science and Technology: The Essential Connection. ASHRAE Transactions, Vol. 91, Part 2.

Löf, G.O.G.; and Hawley, R.W. 1948. Unsteady Heat Transfer Between Air and Loose Solids. Industrial and Engineering Chemistry, Vol. 40, p. 1061.

Metz, P.D. 1982. The Use of Gound-Coupled Tanks in Solar-Assisted Heat Pump Systems. ASME Transactions, J. of Solar Energy Engineering, Vol. 104, p. 366.

Metz, P.D. 1983. A Simple Computer Program to Model Three-Dimensional Underground Heat Flow with Realistic Boundary Conditions. ASME Transactions, J. of Solar Energy Engineering, Vol. 105, p. 42.

Mumma, S.M. 1985. Field Testing of Systems Using Controls to Enhance Thermal Stratification During Solar Collection. ASHRAE Transactions, Vol. 91, Part 2.

Mumma, S.A.; and Marvin, W.C. 1976. A Method of Simulating the Performance of a Pebble Bed Thermal Storage and Recovery System. ASME Paper 76-HT-13.

Oak Ridge National Laboratory. 1985. Field Performance of Residential Thermal Storage Systems. EPRI EM 4041, May.*

Page, J.K.R., et al. 1981. Thermal Storage Materials and Components for Solar Heating. International Solar Energy Society, Solar World Forum, Brighton, U.K., August.

Schaetzle, W.J., et al. 1980. Thermal Energy Storage in Aquifers: The Design and Applications. Pergamon Press, Elmsford, NY.

Tamblyn, R.T. 1977. Thermal Storage, A Sleeping Giant. ASHRAE Journal, June.

Tamblyn, R.T. 1985. College Park Thermal Storage Experience. ASHRAE Transactions, Vol. 91, Part 1.

Tamblyn, R.T. 1980. Thermal Storage, Resisting Temperature Blending. ASHRAE Journal, January, p. 65.

Telkes, M. 1947. Solar House Heating—A Problem of Heat Storage. Heating and Ventilating, Vol. 44, pp. 68-75.

Todd, D.K. 1963. Groundwater Hydrology. John Wiley & Sons.

Tomlinson, J. J. 1985. Clathrates and Conjugating Binaries: New Materials for Thermal Storage. ASHRAE Transactions, Vol. 91, Part 2.

Wildin, M.W.; and Truman, C.R. 1985. Evaluation of Stratified Chilled Water Storage Techniques. EPRI EM 4352, Electric Power Research Institute, December.*

Wildin, M.W.; and Truman, C.R. 1985. A Summary of Experience with Stratified Chilled Water Tanks. ASHRAE Transactions, Vol. 91, Part 1.

Yoo, J.; and Wildin, M.W. 1986. Initial Formation of a Thermocline in Stratified Thermal Storage Tanks. ASHRAE Transactions, Vol. 92, Part 2.

BIBLIOGRAPHY

Phase Change Materials

Abhat, A. 1983. Low Temperature Latent Heat Thermal Energy Storage: Heat Storage Materials. Solar Energy, Vol. 30, No. 4, pp. 313-332.

Altman, M.; Yeh,H; and Lorsch, H.G. 1973. Conservation and Better Utilization of Electric Power by Means of Thermal Energy Storage and Solar Heating. University of Pennsylvania Report, NTIS PB 210359, National Technical Information Service, Springfield, VA.

Böer, K.W.; Higgins, J.H.; and O'Connor, J.H. 1975. Solar One, Two Years Experience. Proc. 10th IECEC, p. 7.

Hale, D.V.; Hoover, M.J; O'Neill, M.J. 1971. Phase Change Materials Handbook. NASA CR-61363.

Herrick, C.S. 1982. Melt-Freeze Cycle Life Testing of Glauber's Salt in a Rolling Cylinder Heat Store. Solar Energy, Vol. 28, pp. 99-104.

Jones, D.E.; and Hill, J.E. 1979. An Evaluation of ASHRAE Standard 94-77 for Testing Pebble Bed and Phase Change Thermal Energy Storage Devices. Transactions ASHRAE, Vol. 85, Part 2, p. 607.

Janz, G.J., et al. 1976. Eutectic Data. Molten Salts Data Center, Rensselaer Polytechnic Institute, Troy, NY, ERDA TID-27163.

Kauffman, K.W.; and Gruntfest, I.J. 1973. Congruently Melting Materials for Thermal Energy Storage. Report NCEMP-20, National Center for Energy Management and Power, University of Pennsylvania.

Lane, G.A.; and Rossow, H.E. 1976. Encapsulation of Heat of Fusion Storage Materials. Proc. 2nd Southeastern Conf. on Applications of Solar Energy, O.A. Arnas (ed.), Baton Rouge, LA, p. 442.

Lane, G.A. 1983. Solar Heat Storage: Latent Heat Materials, Vol. I, Background and Scientific Principles. CRC Press, Boca Raton, FL.

Lane, G.A. 1986. Solar Heat Storage: Latent Heat Materials, Vol. II, Technology. CRC Press, Boca Raton, FL.

MacCracken, C.D. 1984. Design Considerations for Modular Glycol-Ice Storage Systems. ASHRAE Transactions, Vol. 90, Part 1.

MacCracken, C.D. 1984. Solid State Phase Change for Passive Solar Applications. 9th National Passive Solar Conference, American Solar Energy Society, Columbus, OH, September.

MacCracken, C.D. 1985. Control of Brine-Type Ice Storage Systems. ASHRAE Transactions, Vol. 91, Part 1.

Marks, S.B. 1983. The Effect of Crystal Size on the Thermal Energy Storage Capacity of Thickened Glauber's Salt. Solar Energy, Vol. 30, pp. 45-49.

Rueffel, P.G. 1980. U.S. Patent 4,211,885.

Schröder, J. Some Materials and Measures to Store Latent Heat. Philips GmbH Forschungslaboratorium, Aachen, West Germany (in English).

Telkes, M. 1974. Solar Heat Storage. ASHRAE Journal, Vol. 16, p. 38.

Telkes, M. 1980. U.S. Patent 4,187,189.

Ground Coupled Storage

ASTM. 1985. Classification of Soils for Engineering Purposes. ASTM 2487. American Society for Testing and Materials, Philadelphia.

Biehl, R. A. 1977. The Annual Cycle Energy System: A Hybrid Heat Pump Cycle. ASHRAE Journal, July, p. 20.

Bose, J.E. 1982. Earth Coil/Heat Pump Research at Oklahoma State University. 6th Heat Pump Technology Conference, Oklahoma State University, Stillwater, OK.

Buies, S. 1984. The "Fabrikaglace" Process to Make and Store Natural Ice. Third International Workshop on Ice Storage for Cooling Applications, Argonne National Laboratory, ANL/CNSV-TM-77, p. 4.

Foster, L.J. 1985. A Review of the Design and System Performance. ASHRAE Transactions, Vol. 91, Part 1.

Francis, C.E. 1985. The Production of Ice With Long-Term Storage. ASHRAE Transactions, Vol. 91, Part 1.

Hansen, K.K.; Hansen, P.N.; and Ussing, V. 1985. Stratified Operation of a 500 m³ Test Pit. Proceedings, Enerstock '85, 3rd Intl. Conf. on Energy Storage for Building Heating and Cooling, Public Works Canada, Ottawa K1A 0M2, p. 157.

Kusuda, T.; and Achenbach, P.R. 1965. Earth Temperatures and Thermal Diffusivity at Selected Stations in the United States, Part I. ASHRAE Transactions, Vol. 71, pp. 61-75.

McGarity, A.E.; Kirkpatrick, D.L.; and Norford, L.K. 1987. Design and Operation of an Ice Pond for Cooling a Large Commercial Office Building. ASHRAE Transactions, Vol. 92, Part 1.

Metz, P.D. 1983. Ground Coupled Heat Pump System Experimental Results. ASHRAE Transactions, Vol. 89, Part 2B.

Nordell, B., et al. 1985. The Borehole Heat Store at Lulea. Proceedings, Enerstock '85, 3rd Intl. Conf. on Energy Storage for Building Heating and Cooling, Public Works Canada, Ottawa, Canada K1A 0M2, pp. 70, 71, 131.

Ostensson, B. A. 1985. HVAC System Based on Seasonal Storage. Proceedings, Enerstock '85, 3rd Intl. Conf. on Energy Storage for Building Heating and Cooling, Public Works Canada, Ottawa, K1A 0M2, p. 132.

Proceedings of the Nordic Symposium on Earth Heat Pump Systems, Chalmers University of Technology, Göteborg, Sweden, October 16-17, 1979.

Wijsman, A.J.; and Havings, J. 1986. The Groningen Project: 96 Solar Houses with Seasonal Heat Storage in the Soil. Proc. Annual Meeting, American Solar Energy Society, Boulder, CO, p. 530.

Aquifers

Brett, C.E.; and Schaetzle, W.J. Experience with Chilled Water Storage in a Water Table Aquifer. Proceedings, Enerstock '85, 3rd Intl. Conf. on Energy Storage for Building Heating and Cooling, Public Works Canada, Ottawa, Canada K1A OM2.

DOE. 1981-83. Proc. DOE Physical and Chemical Energy Storage Annual Contractors' Review Meetings, Conf-810940, 1981; Conf-820827, 1982; Conf-830974, 1983, available from NTIS, Springfield, VA.

Ebeling, L., et al. 1979. The Effect of System Size on the Practicality of Aquifer Storage. Proc. Silver Jubilee Congress, Int'l. Solar Energy Society. Available from American Solar Energy Society, Boulder, CO.

LBL. 1978. Thermal Energy Storage in Aquifers Workshop, LBL Report No. 8431. Lawrence Berkeley Laboratory, Berkeley, CA.

Trinity University. 1975. Proceedings, Solar Energy Storage Options.

Vail, L.W. 1983. Numerical Model for Analysis of Multiple Well Aquifer Thermal Energy Storage Systems. DOE Physical and Chemical Energy Storage Annual Contractors Review Meeting, Conf-830974.

Applications

ASHRAE. 1985. Thermal Storage. ASHRAE TDB-TH-1.

Electric Power Research Institute. 1983. Issues in Residential Load Management. EM 2991, April.*

Hersh, H.N. 1985. Current Trends in Commercial Cool Storage. EPRI, EM 4125, July.*

Lorsch, H. G.; and Baker, M. A. 1984a. Survey of Thermal Energy Storage Installations in the United States and Canada. ASHRAE.

Lorsch, H. G.; and Baker, M. A. 1984b. A Description of Six Representative Thermal Storage Installations." Oak Ridge National Laboratory, ORNL/Sub/83-28915/1, May.

PEPCO/DOE/EPRI. 1984. Thermal Energy Storage: Cooling Commercial Buildings Using Off-Peak Energy. Seminar Proceedings, EPRI EM 2244, February.*

San Diego Gas and Electric Company. 1984. Thermal Energy Storage-Inducement Program for Commercial Space Cooling. San Diego, CA, April.

*Available from Research Reports Center, POB 50490, Palo Alto, CA 94303; phone (415) 965-4081. Additional bibliographic references on thermal storage are in Chapter 6.

CHAPTER 47

SOLAR ENERGY UTILIZATION

SOLAR water heaters first appeared in the United States in the early 1900's. However, the introduction of low-cost water heaters using fossil fuels and electricity ended their use except for a few applications where conventional fuels were not available or expensive. In the 1920's and 1930's, interest increased in the use of solar radiation for space heating. Early solar houses used large expanses of south-facing glass to admit winter sunshine. While the extra glass admitted large amounts of solar radiation, it also lost so much heat at night and on cloudy days that there was little actual energy savings.

Since the oil boycott of 1973, the cost of fossil fuels and electricity has risen to the point that the economics of solar energy utilization has become more favorable. Recent passive solar homes use movable insulation and efficient glazing systems to minimize the heat loss when the sun is not shing. Installing solar energy collectors on south-facing roofs or walls, and using water or air as a heat transfer medium with rock beds or heat of fusion materials for energy storage has received equal interest.

The major obstacles encountered in solar heating and cooling are economic, resulting from the high cost of the equipment needed to collect and store solar energy. In most cases, the cost of owning solar equipment is greater than the resulting saving in fuel cost. Some problems that must be overcome are inherent in the nature of solar radiation.

1. It is relatively low in intensity, rarely exceeding 300 Btu/h·ft² (945 W/m²). Consequently, when large amounts of energy are needed, large collectors must be used.
2. It is intermittent, because of the inevitable variation in solar radiation intensity from zero at sunrise to a maximum at noon and back to zero at sunset. Some means of energy storage must usually be provided at night and during periods of low solar irradiation.
3. It is subject to unpredictable interruptions because of clouds, rain, snow, hail, or dust.
4. A failure to choose systems that make maximum use of the solar energy input by effectively using the energy at low temperatures.

This chapter covers the use of solar energy for space heating and cooling and for providing service hot water. It combines information prior to the 1973 oil embargo with developments since then and lists new references from ASHRAE and other sources.

QUALITY AND QUANTITY OF SOLAR ENERGY

The Solar Constant, I_{sc}

Solar energy approaches the earth as electromagnetic radiation extending from X rays 0.1 μm in wavelength to 100 metre-long radio waves. The earth maintains a thermal equilibrium between the annual input of shortwave (0.3 to 2.0 μm) radiation from the sun and the outward flux of longwave radiation (3.0 to 30 μm). This equilibrium is global rather than local, because at any given time, some places are too cold for human existence while others are too hot.

Only a limited band need be considered in terrestrial applications, because 99% of the sun's radiant energy is contained between 0.28 and 4.96 μm. The most probable value of the *solar constant* (defined as the intensity of solar radiation on a surface normal to the sun's rays, beyond the earth's atmosphere at the average earth-sun distance) is 429.5 Btu/h·ft² (1353 W/m²) ±1.5%. Current information suggests that the radiation scale in use since 1956 is 2% too low and that it varies slightly because of changes in the sun's output of ultraviolet radiation.

The major variations in solar radiation intensity and air temperature are the results of the slightly elliptical nature of the earth's orbit around the sun (see Figure 1) and the tilt, with respect to the orbital plane, of the axis about which the earth rotates. The sun is located at one focus of the earth's orbit and is 91.5 × 10⁶ miles (14.7.2 Gm) away in late December and early January, while the earth-sun distance on July 1 is about 94.4 × 10⁶ miles (152.0 Gm). Because radiation follows the inverse square law, the normal incidence intensity on an extraterrestrial surface varies from 444.1 Btu/h·ft² (1399 W/m²) on January 1 to 415.6 Btu/h·ft² (1309 W/m²) on July 5.

Solar Angles

The axis about which the earth rotates is tilted (see Figure 1) at an angle of 23°27.14′ (23.45°) to the plane of the ecliptic that contains the earth's orbital plane and the sun's equator. The

---

The preparation of this chapter is assigned to TC 6.7, Solar Energy Utilization.

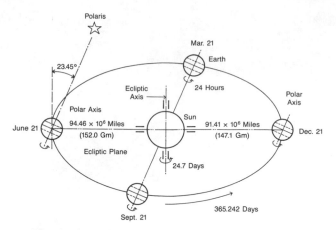

Fig. 1   Annual Motion of the Earth about the Sun

earth's tilted axis results in a day-by-day variation of the angle between the earth-sun line and the earth's equatorial plane, called the *solar declination*, (δ). This angle varies with the date, as shown in Table 1A, for the year 1964 and in Table 1B for 1977. For other dates, the declination may be estimated by:

$$\delta = 23.45 \sin [360 (284 + N)/365] \qquad (1)$$

where

N = year day, with January 1 = 1 (for values of N, see Tables 1A and 1B).

The relationship between δ and the date varies to an insignificant degree. The daily change in the declination is the primary reason for the changing seasons, with their variation in the distribution of solar radiation over the earth's surface and the varying number of hours of daylight and darkness.

The earth's rotation causes the sun's apparent motion (Figure 2). The position of the sun (Figure 3) can be defined in terms of its altitude β above the horizon (angle HOQ) and its azimuth φ, measured as angle HOS in the horizontal plane.

At solar noon, the sun is, by definition, exactly on the meridian, which contains the south-north line and, consequently, the solar azimuth φ is 0.0°. The *noon altitude* (β_N) is:

$$\beta_N = 90° - LAT + \delta \qquad (2)$$

where

LAT = latitude
δ = solar declination

Because the earth's daily rotation and its annual orbit around the sun are regular and predictable, the solar altitude and azimuth may be readily calculated for any desired time of day

as soon as the latitude, longitude, and date (declination) are specified. *Apparent Solar Time, AST,* must be used, expressed in terms of the *hour angle (H)*, where:

$$H = \text{(Number of hours from solar noon)} \cdot 15° \qquad (3)$$
$$= \text{(Number of minutes from solar noon)}/4 \qquad (3.1)$$

Solar Time

Apparent Solar Time generally differs from Local Standard Time (LST) or Daylight Saving Time (DST), and the difference can be significant, particularly when DST is in effect. Because the sun appears to move at the rate of 360° in 24 h, its apparent rate of motion is 4 min per degree of longitude. The procedure for finding AST is shown in Eq. (4) as follows:

$$AST = LST + \text{Equation of Time}$$
$$+ \text{(4 min.)(LST Meridian} - \text{Local Longitude)} \qquad (4)$$

The longitudes of the seven Standard Time Meridians that affect North America are Atlantic ST, 60°; Eastern ST, 75°; Central ST, 90°; Mountain ST, 105°; Pacific ST, 120°; Yukon ST, 135°; and Alaska-Hawaii ST, 150°.

Equation of Time is the measure, in minutes, of the extent by which Solar Time, as told by a sundial, runs faster or slower than Local Standard Time (LST), as determined by a clock that runs at a uniform rate. Table 1A gives values of the declination of the sun and the Equation of Time for the 21st day of each month for the year 1964 (when the ASHRAE solar radiation tables were first calculated), while Table 1B gives values of δ and the equation of time for six days in each month for the year 1977.

Example 1: Find AST at noon DST on July 21 for Washington, DC, longitude = 77°, and for Chicago, longitude = 87.6°.

Solution: Noon DST is actually 11:00 A.M., LST. For Washington, in the Eastern Time Zone, the LST Meridian is 75°; for July 21, the Equation of Time = −6.2 minutes. Thus noon, Washington DST, is actually:

$$11:00 - 6.2 + 4 (75 - 77) = 10:45.8 \text{ AST} = 10.76 \text{ h}$$

For Chicago, in the Central Time Zone, the LST Meridian is 90°, so noon, Central Daylight Saving Time, is:

$$11:00 - 6.2 + 4 (90 - 87.6) = 11.03.4 \text{ AST} = 11.06 \text{ h}$$

The hour angles, *H*, for these two examples (see Figure 3) are:

for Washington, H = (12.00 − 10.76) 15 = 18.6° east
for Chicago,   H = (12.00 − 11.06) 15 = 14.10° east

To find the solar altitude β and the azimuth φ when the hour angle H, the latitude LAT, and the declination δ are known, the following equations may be used:

Table 1A   Year Date, Declination, and Equation of Time for the 21st day of Each Month; with Data* (A, B, C) Used to Calculate Direct Normal Radiation Intensity at the Earth's Surface

Month	Jan	Feb	Mar	Apr	May	June	July	Aug	Sept	Oct	Nov	Dec
Day of the year	21	52	80	111	141	172	202	233	264	294	325	355
Declination, degrees	−19.9	−10.6	0.0	+11.9	+20.3	+23.45	+20.5	+12.1	0.0	−10.7	−19.9	−23.45
Equation of time, minutes	−11.2	−13.9	−7.5	+1.1	+3.3	−1.4	−6.2	−2.4	+7.5	+15.4	+13.8	+1.6
Solar noon		late			early			late			early	
A, Btu·h/ft²	390	385	376	360	350	345	344	351	365	378	387	391
B, Dimensionless	0.142	0.144	0.156	0.180	0.196	0.205	0.207	0.201	0.177	0.160	0.149	0.142
C, Dimensionless	0.058	0.060	0.071	0.097	0.121	0.134	0.136	0.122	0.092	0.073	0.063	0.057

*A is the apparent solar irradiation at air mass zero for each month; B is the atmospheric extinction coefficient; C is the ratio of the diffuse radiation on a horizontal surface to the direct normal irradiation.

Table 1B Solar Position Data for 1977*

Month		Jan	Feb	Mar	Apr	May	June	July	Aug	Sept	Oct	Nov	Dec
Date													
1	Year Day	1	32	60	91	121	152	182	213	244	274	305	335
	Declination	−23.0	−17.0	−7.4	+4.7	+15.2	+22.1	+23.1	+17.9	+8.2	−3.3	−14.6	−21.9
	Eq of Time	−3.6	−13.7	−12.5	−4.0	+2.9	+2.4	−3.6	−6.2	+0.0	+10.2	+16.3	+11.0
6	Year Day	6	37	65	96	126	157	187	218	249	279	310	340
	Declination	−22.4	−15.5	−5.5	+6.6	+16.6	+22.7	+22.7	+16.6	+6.7	−5.3	−16.1	−22.5
	Eq of Time	−5.9	−14.2	−11.4	−2.5	+3.5	+1.6	−4.5	−5.8	+1.6	+11.8	+16.3	+9.0
11	Year Day	11	42	70	101	131	162	192	223	254	284	315	345
	Declination	−21.7	−13.9	−3.5	−8.5	+17.9	+23.1	+22.1	+15.2	+4.4	−7.2	−17.5	−23.0
	Eq of Time	−8.0	−14.4	−10.2	−1.1	+3.7	+0.6	−5.3	−5.1	+3.3	+13.1	+15.9	+6.8
16	Year Day	16	47	75	106	136	167	197	228	259	289	320	350
	Declination	−20.8	−12.2	−1.6	+10.3	+19.2	+23.3	+21.3	+13.6	+2.5	−8.7	−18.8	−23.3
	Eq of Time	−9.8	−14.2	−8.8	+0.1	+3.8	−0.4	−5.9	−4.3	+5.0	+14.3	+15.2	+4.4
21	Year Day	21	52	80	111	141	172	202	233	264	294	325	355
	Declination	−19.6	−10.4	+0.4	+12.0	+20.3	+23.4	+20.6	+12.0	+0.5	−10.8	−20.0	−23.4
	Eq of Time	−11.4	−13.8	−7.4	+1.2	+3.6	−1.5	−6.2	−3.1	+6.8	+15.3	+14.1	+2.0
26	Year Day	26	57	85	116	146	177	207	238	269	299	330	360
	Declination	−18.6	−8.6	+2.4	+13.6	+21.2	+23.3	+19.3	+10.3	−1.4	−12.6	−21.0	−23.4
	Eq of Time	−12.6	−13.1	−5.8	+2.2	+3.2	−2.6	−6.4	−1.8	+8.6	+15.9	+12.7	−0.5

*From ASHRAE *Standard* 93-1986. Units for declination are angular degrees; units for Equation of Time are minutes of time. Values of declination and *Equation of Time* will vary slightly for specific dates in other years.

$$\sin \beta = \cos (LAT) \cos \delta \cos H + \sin (LAT) \sin \delta \quad (5)$$

$$\sin \phi = \cos \delta \sin H / \cos \beta \quad (6)$$

or $\quad \cos \phi = [\sin \beta \sin (LAT) - \sin \delta]/\cos \beta \cos (LAT) \quad$ (6a)

Values of β and ϕ are given in Table 2 for the daylight hours of the 21st day of each month at 40° north latitude. Similar values are given in Tables 2 to 10 in Chapter 27 of the 1985 FUNDAMENTALS Volume for latitudes from 0 to 64° north. For any other date or latitude, interpolation between the tabulated values will give sufficiently accurate results. More precise values, with azimuths measured from the north, are given in U.S. Hydrographic Office Bulletin No. 214 (1958).

The Incident Angle

The incident angle, θ, between the line normal to the irradiated surface (OP′ in Figure 3) and the earth-sun line, OQ, is important in solar technology because it affects the intensity of the direct component of the solar radiation striking the surface and the ability of the surface to absorb, transmit, or reflect the sun's rays.

To determine ϕ, it is necessary to know the surface azimuth, ψ, and the surface solar azimuth, γ. The surface azimuth (angle POS in Figure 3) is the angle between the south-north line, SO, and the normal PO to the intersection of the irradiated surface with the horizontal plane, shown as line OM. The surface-solar azimuth, angle HOP, is designated by γ and is the angular difference between the solar azimuth, ϕ, and the surface azimuth, ψ. For surfaces facing *east* of south, $\gamma = \phi - \psi$ in the morning and $\gamma = \phi + \psi$ in the afternoon. For surfaces facing *west* of south, $\gamma = \phi + \psi$ in the morning and $\gamma = \phi - \psi$ in the afternoon. For south-facing surfaces, $\psi = 0°$, so $\gamma = \phi$ for all conditions. The angles, δ, β, and ϕ, are always positive.

For a surface with a tilt angle Σ (measured from the horizontal), the angle of incidence θ between the direct solar beam and the normal to the surface (angle QOP in Figure 3) is given by:

$$\cos \theta = \cos \beta \cos \gamma \sin \Sigma + \sin \beta \cos \Sigma \quad (7)$$

For any vertical surface, $\Sigma = 90°$, $\cos\Sigma = 0$, $\sin \Sigma = 1.0$, thus:

$$\cos \theta = \cos \beta \cos \gamma \quad (8)$$

For horizontal surfaces, $\Sigma = 0°$, $\sin \Sigma = 0$, and $\cos \Sigma = 1.0$, thus:

$$\theta_H = 90 - \beta \text{ deg} \quad (9)$$

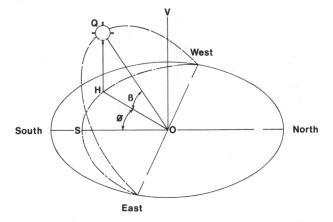

Fig. 2 Apparent Daily Path of the Sun across the Sky from Sunrise to Sunset, Showing the Solar Altitude (β) and the Solar Azimuth (ϕ)

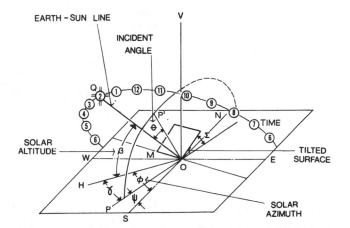

Fig. 3 Solar Angles with Respect to a Tilted Surface

Table 2 Solar Position and Irradiation Values for 40 deg North Latitude[a]

Date	Solar Time AM	Solar Time PM	Solar Position ALT	Solar Position AZM	Direct Normal Irrad.	South-Facing Surface Angle with Horizontal 0	30	40	50	60	90
Jan 21	8	4	8.1	55.3	142	28	65	74	81	85	84
	9	3	16.8	44.0	239	83	155	171	182	187	171
	10	2	23.8	30.9	274	127	218	237	249	254	223
	11	1	28.4	16.0	289	154	257	277	290	293	253
		12	30.0	0.0	295	164	270	291	303	306	263
		Surface Daily Totals			2,182	948	1,660	1,810	1,906	1,944	1,726
Feb 21	7	5	4.8	72.7	69	10	19	21	23	24	22
	8	4	15.4	62.2	224	73	114	122	126	127	107
	9	3	25.0	50.2	274	132	195	205	209	208	167
	10	2	32.8	35.9	295	178	256	267	271	267	210
	11	1	38.1	18.9	305	206	293	306	310	304	236
		12	40.0	0.0	308	216	306	319	323	317	245
		Surface Daily Totals			2,640	1,414	2,060	2,162	2,202	2,176	1,730
Mar 21	7	5	11.4	80.2	171	46	55	55	54	51	35
	8	4	22.5	69.6	250	114	140	141	138	131	89
	9	3	32.8	57.3	282	173	215	217	213	202	138
	10	2	41.6	41.9	297	218	273	276	271	258	176
	11	1	47.7	22.6	305	247	310	313	307	293	200
		12	50.0	0.0	307	257	322	326	320	305	208
		Surface Daily Totals			2,916	1,852	2,308	2,330	2,284	2,174	1,484
Apr 21	6	6	7.4	98.9	89	20	11	8	7	7	4
	7	5	18.9	89.5	206	87	77	70	61	50	12
	8	4	30.3	79.3	252	152	153	145	133	117	53
	9	3	41.3	67.2	274	207	221	213	199	179	93
	10	2	51.2	51.4	286	250	275	267	252	229	126
	11	1	58.7	29.2	292	277	308	301	285	260	147
		12	61.6	0.0	293	287	320	313	296	271	154
		Surface Daily Totals			3,092	2,274	2,412	2,320	2,168	1,956	1,022
May 21	5	7	1.9	114.7	1	0	0	0	0	0	0
	6	6	12.7	105.6	144	49	25	15	14	13	9
	7	5	24.0	96.6	216	214	89	76	60	44	13
	8	4	35.4	87.2	250	175	158	144	125	104	25
	9	3	46.8	76.0	267	227	221	206	186	160	60
	10	2	57.5	60.9	277	267	270	255	233	205	89
	11	1	66.2	37.1	283	293	301	287	264	234	108
		12	70.0	0.0	284	301	312	297	274	243	114
		Surface Daily Totals			3,160	2,552	2,442	2,264	2,040	1,760	724
June 21	5	7	4.2	117.3	22	4	3	3	2	2	1
	6	6	14.8	108.4	155	60	30	18	17	16	10
	7	5	26.0	99.7	216	123	92	77	59	41	14
	8	4	37.4	90.7	246	182	159	142	121	97	16
	9	3	48.8	80.2	263	233	219	202	179	151	47
	10	2	59.8	65.8	272	272	266	248	224	194	74
	11	1	69.2	41.9	277	296	296	278	253	221	92
		12	73.5	0.0	279	304	306	289	263	230	98
		Surface Daily Totals			3,180	2,648	2,434	2,224	1,974	1,670	610
July 21	5	7	2.3	115.2	2	0	0	0	0	0	0
	6	6	13.1	106.1	138	50	26	17	15	14	9
	7	5	24.3	97.2	208	114	89	75	60	44	14
	8	4	35.8	87.8	241	174	157	142	124	102	24
	9	3	47.2	76.7	259	225	218	203	182	157	58
	10	2	57.9	61.7	269	265	266	251	229	200	86
	11	1	66.7	37.9	275	290	296	281	258	228	104
		12	70.6	0.0	276	298	307	292	269	238	111
		Surface Daily Totals			3,062	2,534	2,409	2,230	2,006	1,728	702

[a]Based on data from ASHRAE Handbook (Table 1, p. 27.2, 1985 FUNDAMENTALS Volume), 0% ground reflectance, 1.0 clearness factor.

Table 2 Solar Position and Irradiation Values for 40 deg North Latitude[a] (continued)

Date	Solar Time AM	Solar Time PM	Solar Position ALT	Solar Position AZM	Direct Normal Irrad.	0	30	40	50	60	90
Aug 21	6	6	7.9	99.5	81	21	12	9	8	7	5
	7	5	19.3	90.0	191	87	76	69	60	49	12
	8	4	30.7	79.9	237	150	150	141	129	113	50
	9	3	41.8	67.9	260	205	216	207	193	173	89
	10	2	51.7	52.1	272	246	267	259	244	221	120
	11	1	59.3	29.7	278	273	300	292	276	252	140
		12	62.3	0.0	280	282	311	303	287	262	147
	Surface Daily Totals				2,916	2,244	2,354	2,258	2,104	1,894	978
Sept 21	7	5	11.4	80.2	149	43	51	51	49	47	32
	8	4	22.5	69.6	230	109	133	134	131	124	84
	9	3	32.8	57.3	263	167	206	208	203	193	132
	10	2	41.6	41.9	280	211	262	265	260	247	168
	11	1	47.7	22.6	287	239	298	301	295	281	192
		12	50.0	0.0	290	249	310	313	307	292	200
	Surface Daily Totals				2,708	1,788	2,210	2,228	2,182	2,074	1,416
Oct 21	7	5	4.5	72.3	48	7	14	15	17	17	16
	8	4	15.0	61.9	204	68	106	113	117	118	100
	9	3	24.5	49.8	257	126	185	195	200	198	160
	10	2	32.4	35.6	280	170	245	257	261	257	203
	11	1	37.6	18.7	291	199	283	295	299	294	229
		12	39.5	0.0	294	208	295	308	312	306	238
	Surface Daily Totals				2,454	1,348	1,962	2,060	2,098	2,074	1,654
Nov 21	8	4	8.2	55.4	136	28	63	72	78	82	81
	9	3	17.0	44.1	232	82	152	167	178	183	167
	10	2	24.0	31.0	268	126	215	233	245	249	219
	11	1	28.6	16.1	283	153	254	273	285	288	248
		12	30.2	0.0	288	163	267	287	298	301	258
	Surface Daily Totals				2,128	942	1,636	1,778	1,870	1,908	1,686
Dec 21	8	4	5.5	53.0	89	14	39	45	50	54	56
	9	3	14.0	41.9	217	65	135	152	164	171	163
	10	2	20.7	29.4	261	107	200	221	235	242	221
	11	1	25.0	15.2	280	134	239	262	276	283	252
		0612	26.6	0.0	285	143	253	275	290	296	263
	Surface Daily Totals				1,978	782	1,480	1,634	1,740	1,796	1,646

Column group headers: **Btu/h · ft² Total Irradiation on Surfaces Designated below[b]** — **South-Facing Surface Angle with Horizontal** (0, 30, 40, 50, 60, 90)

[a]Based on data from ASHRAE Handbook (Table 1, p. 27.2, 1985 FUNDAMENTALS Volume), 0% ground reflectance, 1.0 clearness factor.

See also Equations 13 and 14 in ASHRAE's *Solar Collector Performance Manual.*

Example 2: Find θ for a south-facing surface tilted upward at 30° to the horizontal at 40° north latitude at 4:00 P.M., AST, on August 21.

Solution: At 4:00 P.M. on August 21, Table 2 gives $\beta = 30.7°$ and $\phi = 79.9°$. From Table 1A, $\delta = +12.1°$. Since the surface is south-facing, $\psi = 0°$ and $\gamma = \phi = 79.9°$. Using Eq 7:

$\cos\phi = \cos 30.7 \cdot \cos 79.9 \cdot \sin 30 + \sin 30.7 \cdot \cos 30$
$= 0.860 \cdot 0.175 \cdot 0.500 + 0.511 \cdot 0.866$
$= 0.075 + 0.443 = 0.518$
$\theta = 58.80°$

Tabulated values of θ are given in Tables A-7 through A-12 of ASHRAE *Standard* 93-86, *Methods of Testing to Determine the Performance of Solar Collectors,* for horizontal surfaces and for south-facing surfaces tilted upward at angles equal to the latitude − 10°, the latitude, the latitude + 10°, and the latitude + 20°. The tables cover the latitudes from 24° to 64° north, by 8° intervals.

The Solar Spectrum

Beyond the earth's atmosphere, the effective black body temperature of the sun is 10,372°R (5,762 K). The maximum spectral intensity occurs at 0.48 μm in the green portion of the visible spectrum (see Figure 4). Thekaekara (1973) has prepared tables and charts of the sun's extraterrestrial spectral irradiance from 0.120 to 100 μm, the range where, for practical purposes, all of the sun's radiant energy is contained. The ultraviolet portion of the spectrum below 0.40 μm contains 8.73% of the total, another 38.15% is contained in the visible region between 0.40 and 0.70 μm, and the infrared region contains the remaining 53.12%.

Solar Radiation at the Earth's Surface

In passing through the earth's atmosphere, some of the sun's direct radiation, I_D, is scattered by nitrogen, oxygen, and other molecules, which are small compared to the wavelength of the radiation; and by aerosols, water droplets, dust, and other par-

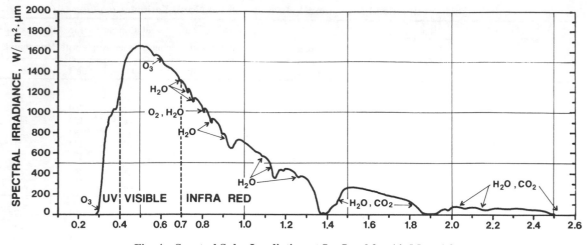

Fig. 4 Spectral Solar Irradiation at Sea Level for Air Mass 1.0

ticles with diameters comparable to the wavelength (Gates 1966). This scattered radiation causes the sky to be blue on clear days, and some of it reaches the earth as diffuse radiation, I_d.

Attenuation of the solar rays is also caused by absorption, first by the ozone in the outer atmosphere, which causes a sharp cutoff at 0.29 μm of the ultraviolet radiation reaching the earth's surface. In the longer wavelengths, a series of absorption bands exists, caused by water vapor, carbon dioxide, and ozone. The total amount of attenuation at any given location is determined by the length of the atmospheric path, which the rays traverse, and by the composition of the atmosphere. The path length is expressed in terms of the air mass m, which is the ratio of the mass of atmosphere in the actual earth-sun path to the mass that would exist if the sun were directly overhead at sea level ($m = 1.0$). For all practical purposes, at sea level, $m = 1.0/\sin \beta$. Beyond the earth's atmosphere, $m = 0$.

Prior to 1967, solar radiation data was based on an assumed solar constant of 419.7 Btu/h $\cdot$ ft^2 (1322 W/m^2) and on a standard sea level atmosphere containing the equivalent of 2.8 mm of ozone, 20 mm of precipitable moisture, and 300 dust particles per cm^3. Threlkeld and Jordan (1958) considered the wide variation of water vapor in the atmosphere above the United States at any given time, and particularly the seasonal variation, which finds three times as much moisture in the atmosphere in midsummer as in December, January, and February. The basic atmosphere was assumed to be at sea level barometric pressure, with 2.5 mm of ozone, 200 dust particles per cm^3, and an actual precipitable moisture content that varied throughout the year from 8 mm in midwinter to 28 mm in mid-July. Figure 5 shows the variation of the direct normal irradiation with solar altitude, as estimated for clear atmospheres and for an atmosphere with variable moisture content.

Stephenson (1967) shows that the intensity of the direct normal irradiation at the earth's surface on a clear day can be estimated by:

$$I_{DN} = A/\exp (B/\sin \beta) \text{ Btu/h} \cdot \text{ft}^2 \qquad (10)$$

where A, the apparent extraterrestrial irradiation at $m = 0$, and B, the atmospheric extinction coefficient, are functions of the date which take into account the seasonal variation of the earth-sun distance and the air's water vapor content.

The values of the parameters A and B given in Table 1A were selected so that the resulting value of I_{DN} would be in close agreement with the Threlkeld and Jordan values on *average cloudless days*. The values of I_{DN}, given in Tables 19 through 27 in Chapter 27 of the 1985 FUNDAMENTALS Volume, were obtained by using Equation (10) and data from Table 1A. The values

of the solar altitude, β, and the solar azimuth, ϕ, were obtained by using Equations (5) and (6).

A similar program was developed by Morrison and Farber (1974) to prepare Tables 2 and 3 of this chapter. For these tables, the atmosphere is assumed to be at sea level and moderately dusty, and the amounts of precipitable water are the average values for the continental United States for each month. Because local values of atmospheric water content and elevation can vary markedly from the sea level average, the concept of *clearness number* was introduced to express the ratio between the actual clear-day direct radiation intensity at a specific location and the

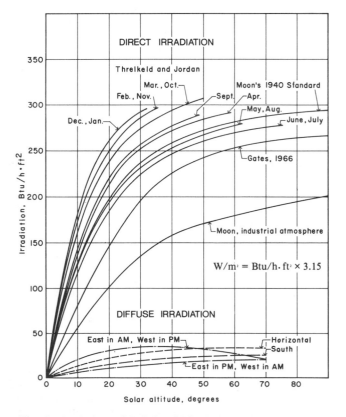

Fig. 5 Variation with Solar Altitude and Time of Year for Direct Normal Irradiation; Typical Values of Clear Day Diffuse Irradiation versus Solar Altitude for Horizontal and Vertical Surfaces

Table 3 Daylong Direct Solar Irradiation in Btu/ft² for the 21st Day of Each Month at Latitudes from 24 to 64 deg North, on Surfaces Normal to the Sun's Rays; Total Irradiation on Horizontal Surfaces and South-Facing Surfaces Tilted at the Following Angles above the Horizontal: L − 10 deg; L deg; L + 10 deg; L + 20 deg; 90 deg*

Date	Deg Lat	I_{DN}	Total Solar Irradiation, $I_{D\theta} + I_d$					
			Horiz	L − 10	L	L + 10	L + 20	Vertical
Jan 21	24	2,766	1,622	1,984	2,174	2,300	2,360	1,766
δ = − 20 deg	32	2,458	1,288	1,893	2,008	2,118	2,166	1,779
	40	2,182	948	1,660	1,810	1,906	1,944	1,726
	48	1,710	596	1,360	1,478	1,550	1,578	1,478
	56	1,126	282	934	1,010	1,058	1,074	1,044
	64	306	45	268	290	302	306	304
Feb 21	24	3,036	1,998	2,276	2,396	2,446	2,424	1,476
δ = − 10.6 deg	32	2,872	1,724	2,188	2,300	2,345	2,322	1,644
	40	2,640	1,414	2,060	2,162	2,202	2,176	1,730
	48	2,330	1,080	1,880	1,972	2,024	1,978	1,720
	56	1,986	740	1,640	1,716	1,792	1,716	1,598
	64	1,432	400	1,230	1,286	1,302	1,282	1,252
Mar 21	24	3,078	2,270	2,428	2,456	2,412	2,298	1,022
δ = 0.0 deg	32	3,012	2,084	2,378	2,403	2,358	2,246	1,276
	40	2,916	1,852	2,308	2,330	2,284	2,174	1,484
	48	2,780	1,578	2,208	2,228	2,182	2,074	1,632
	56	2,586	1,268	2,066	2,084	2,040	1,938	1,700
	64	2,296	932	1,856	1,870	1,830	1,736	1,656
Apr 21	24	3,036	2,454	2,458	2,374	2,228	2,016	488
δ = + 11.9 deg	32	3,076	2,390	2,444	2,356	2,206	1,994	764
	40	3,092	2,274	2,412	2,320	2,168	1,956	1,022
	48	3,076	2,106	2,358	2,266	2,114	1,902	1,262
	56	3,024	1,892	2,282	2,186	2,038	1,830	1,450
	64	2,982	1,644	2,776	2,082	1,936	1,736	1,594
May 21	24	3,032	2,556	2,447	2,286	2,072	1,800	246
δ = + 20.3 deg	32	3,112	2,582	2,454	2,284	2,064	1,788	469
	40	3,160	2,552	2,442	2,264	2,040	1,760	724
	48	3,254	2,482	2,418	2,234	2,010	1,728	982
	56	3,340	2,374	2,374	2,188	1,962	1,682	1,218
	64	3,470	2,236	2,312	2,124	1,898	1,624	1,436
June 21	24	2,994	2,574	2,422	2,230	1,992	1,700	204
δ = + 23.45 deg	32	3,084	2,634	2,436	2,234	1,990	1,690	370
	40	3,180	2,648	2,434	2,224	1,974	1,670	610
	48	3,312	2,626	2,420	2,204	1,950	1,644	874
	56	3,438	2,562	2,388	2,166	1,910	1,606	1,120
	64	3,650	2,488	2,342	2,118	1,862	1,558	1,356

intensity calculated for the standard atmosphere for the same location and date.

Figure 6 shows the Threlkeld-Jordan map of winter and summer clearness numbers of the continental United States. Irradiation values given in Tables 2 and 3 should be adjusted by the clearness numbers applicable to each particular location.

Design Values of Total Solar Irradiation

The total solar irradiation of a terrestrial surface of any orientation and tilt, with an incident angle θ designated as $I_{t\theta}$, is the sum of the direct component, $I_{DN} \cos \theta$ plus the diffuse component coming from the sky, $I_{d\theta}$, plus whatever amount of reflected shortwave radiation, I_r, may reach the surface from the earth or from adjacent surfaces:

$$I_{t\theta} = I_{DN} \cos \theta + I_{d\theta} + I_r \qquad (11)$$

The diffuse component is difficult to estimate because of its nondirectional nature and its wide variations. Figure 5 shows typical values of diffuse irradiation of horizontal and vertical surfaces. For clear days, Threlkeld (1963) has derived a dimensionless parameter (designated as C in Table 1A) that depends on the dust and moisture content of the atmosphere and thus varies throughout the year.

$$C = I_{dH}/I_{DN} \qquad (12)$$

where I_{dH} is the diffuse radiation falling on a horizontal surface under a cloudless sky.

To estimate the amount of diffuse radiation, $I_{d\theta}$, which reaches a tilted or vertical surface, Eq 13 may be used:

$$I_{d\theta} = C \cdot I_{DN} \cdot F_{ss} \qquad (13)$$

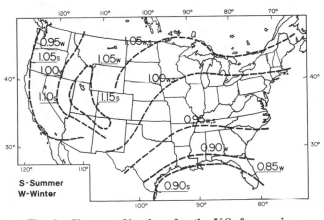

S-Summer
W-Winter

Fig. 6 Clearness Numbers for the U.S. for use in Summer (S) and Winter (W)

Table 3 (*continued*)

Date	Deg Lat	I_{DN}	Total Solar Irradiation, $I_{D\theta} + I_d$					
			Horiz	L − 10	L	L + 10	L + 20	Vertical
July 21	24	2,932	2,526	2,412	2,250	2,036	1,766	246
δ = +20.5 deg	32	3,012	2,558	2,442	2,250	2,030	1,754	458
	40	3,062	2,534	2,409	2,230	2,006	1,728	702
	48	3,158	2,474	2,386	2,200	1,974	1,694	956
	56	3,240	2,372	2,342	2,152	1,926	1,646	1,186
	64	3,372	2,248	2,280	2,090	1,864	1,588	1,400
Aug 21	24	2,864	2,408	2,402	2,316	2,168	1,958	470
δ = +12.1 deg	32	2,902	2,352	2,388	2,296	2,144	1,934	736
	40	2,916	2,244	2,354	2,258	2,104	1,894	978
	48	2,898	2,086	2,300	2,200	2,046	1,836	1,208
	56	2,850	1,883	2,218	2,118	1,966	1,760	1,392
	64	2,808	1,646	2,108	1,008	1,860	1,662	1,522
Sept 21	24	2,878	2,194	2,432	2,366	2,322	2,212	992
δ = 0.0 deg	32	2,808	2,014	2,288	2,308	2,264	2,154	1,266
	40	2,708	1,788	2,210	2,228	2,182	2,074	1,416
	48	2,568	1,522	2,102	2,118	2,070	1,966	1,546
	56	2,368	1,220	1,950	1,962	1,918	1,820	1,594
	64	2,074	892	1,726	1,736	1,696	1,608	1,532
Oct 21	24	2,868	1,928	2,198	2,314	2,364	2,346	1,422
δ = −10.7 deg	32	2,696	1,654	2,100	2,208	2,252	2,232	1,588
	40	2,454	1,348	1,962	2,060	2,098	2,074	1,654
	48	2,154	1,022	1,774	1,860	1,890	1,866	1,626
	56	1,804	688	1,516	1,586	1,612	1,588	1,480
	64	1,238	358	1,088	1,136	1,152	1,134	1,106
Nov 21	24	2,706	1,610	1,962	2,146	2,268	2,324	1,730
δ = −19.9 deg	32	2,405	1,280	1,816	1,980	2,084	2,130	1,742
	40	2,128	942	1,636	1,778	1,870	1,908	1,686
	48	1,668	596	1,336	1,448	1,518	1,544	1,442
	56	1,094	284	914	986	1,032	1,046	1,016
	64	302	46	266	286	298	302	300
Dec 21	24	2,624	1,474	1,852	2,058	2,204	2,286	1,808
Δ = −23.45 deg	32	2,348	1,136	1,704	1,888	2,016	2,086	1,794
	40	1,978	782	1,480	1,634	1,740	1,796	1,646
	48	1,444	446	1,136	1,250	1,326	1,364	1,304
	56	748	157	620	678	716	734	722
	64	24	2	20	22	24	24	24

*Adapted from Morrison and Farber (1974).

where F_{ss} is the angle factor between the surface and the sky and:

$$F_{ss} = (1 + \cos \Sigma)/2 \qquad (14)$$
$$F_{sg} = (1 - \cos \Sigma)/2 \qquad (15)$$

where F_{sg} is the angle factor between the surface and the earth. The reflected radiation I_r from the foreground is:

$$I_r = I_{tH} \cdot \varrho_g \cdot F_{sg} \qquad (15.1)$$

where ϱ_g is the reflectance of the foreground.

The intensity of the reflected radiation that reaches any surfaces depends on the nature of the reflecting surface and on the incident angle between the sun's direct beam and the reflecting surface. Many measurements made of the reflection (*albedo*) of the earth under varying conditions show clean, fresh snow has the highest reflectance (0.87) of any natural surface.

Threlkeld (1963) gives values of reflectance for commonly encountered surfaces at solar incident angles from 0 to 70°. Bituminous paving generally reflects less than 10% of the total incident solar irradiation; bituminous and gravel roofs reflect from 12 to 15%; concrete, depending on its age, reflects from 21 to 33%. Bright green grass reflects 20% at $\theta = 30°$ and 30% at $\theta = 65°$.

In Table 2, ground reflection is omitted. Among the reasons for omission are (1) the extremely wide variation in foreground surfaces, (2) the fact that most solar collectors are tilted so that their angle factors are low and the influence of reflected radiation are small, and (3) the decision to provide conservative design

values. The maximum daily amount of solar irradiation that can be received at any given location is that which falls on a flat plate with its surface kept normal to the sun's rays so it receives both direct and diffuse radiation. (The values given in Chapter 27 of the 1985 FUNDAMENTALS Volume for normal irradiation include the diffuse component.)

For fixed, flat-plate collectors, the total amount of clear day irradiation depends on the orientation and slope. As shown by Figure 7 for 40 degree north latitude, the total irradiation of horizontal surfaces reaches its maximum in midsummer, while vertical south-facing surfaces experience their maximum irradiation during the winter. These curves show the combined effects of the varying length of days and changing solar altitudes.

In general, flatplate collectors are mounted at a fixed tilt angle Σ (above the horizontal) to give the optimum amount of irradiation for each particular purpose. Collectors intended for winter heating benefit from higher tilt angles than those used in summer to operate cooling systems. Solar water heaters, which should operate satisfactorily throughout the year, require an angle that is a compromise between the optimal values for summer and winter. Figure 7 shows the monthly variation of total day-long irradiation on the 21st day of each month at 40° north latitude for flat surfaces with varying tilt angles.

Table 3 gives the day-long total solar irradiation for the 21st day of each month, at latitudes 24 to 64° north on surfaces with the following orientations: normal to the sun's rays (direct normal, DN, data *do not* include diffuse irradiation); horizontal;

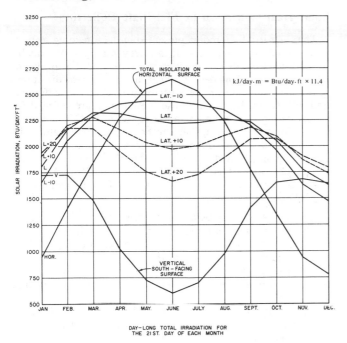

Fig. 7 Total Daily Irradiation for the 21st Day of Each Month for Horizontal, Tilted, and Vertical Surfaces at 40° North Latitude

south-facing, tilted at (LAT − 10), L, (LAT + 10), (LAT + 20), and 90° from the horizontal. The day-long total irradiation for fixed surfaces is highest for those that face south, but a deviation in azimuth of 15 to 20° causes only a small reduction.

Solar Energy for Flat-Plate Collectors

The preceeding data apply to clear days. The irradiation for average days may be estimated for any specific location by referring to publications of the U.S. Weather Service and to articles by Jordan and Lieu (1977) and Duffie and Beckman (1974). The Climatic Atlas of the United States gives maps of monthly and annual values of percentage of possible sunshine, total hours of sunshine, mean solar radiation, mean sky cover, wind speed, and wind direction.

The total daily horizontal irradiation data reported prior to 1964 by the U.S. Weather Bureau for approximately 100 stations shows that the percentage of total clear-day irradiation is approximately a linear function of the percentage of possible sunshine. The irradiation is not zero for days when the percentage of possible sunshine is reported as zero, because substantial amounts of energy reach the earth in the form of diffuse radiation. Instead, the following relationship exists:

$$\frac{\text{Daylong actual } I_{tH}}{\text{Clear day } I_{tH}} \, 100 = a + b \, (\text{possible sunshine percent}) \tag{16}$$

where a and b are constants for any specified month at any given location.

Longwave Atmospheric Radiation

In addition to the shortwave (0.3 to 2.0 μm) radiation that it receives from the sun, the earth also receives longwave radiation (4 to 100 μm, with maximum intensity near 10 μm) from

the atmosphere. A surface on the earth in turn emits longwave radiation in accordance with the *Stefan-Boltzmann Law:*

$$q_{Rs} = e_s \, \sigma \, (T_s/100)^4 \tag{17}$$

where

e_s = surface emittance
σ = constant, 0.1713 (5.67)
T_s = absolute temperature of the surface, °R (K)

For most nonmetallic surfaces, the longwave hemispheric emittance is high, ranging from 0.84 for glass and dry sand, to 0.95 for black builtup roofing. For highly polished metals and certain selective surfaces (see Chapter 39, 1985 FUNDAMENTALS), e_s may be as low as 0.05 to 0.20.

Atmospheric radiation comes primarily from water vapor, carbon dioxide, and ozone (Bliss 1961); very little comes from oxygen and nitrogen, although they make up 99% of the air.

Approximately 90% of the incoming atmospheric radiation comes from the lowest 300 ft (90 m). Thus, the air conditions at ground level determine, in large measure, the magnitude of the incoming radiation. The downward radiation from the atmosphere may be expressed as:

$$q_{Rat} = e_{at}\sigma \, (T_{at}/100)^4 \tag{18}$$

The emittance of the atmosphere is a complex function of air temperature and moisture content. The dew point temperature of the atmosphere near the ground determines the total amount of moisture in the atmosphere above the place where the dry-bulb and dew point temperatures of the atmosphere are determined (Reitan 1963). Bliss (1961) found that the emittance of the atmosphere is related to the dew point temperature, as shown by Table 4.

If the apparent sky temperature is defined as that temperature that, radiating as a black body, emits radiation at the rate actually emitted by the atmosphere at ground level temperature with its actual emittance, e_{at}, then:

$$\sigma \, (T_{\text{sky}}/100)^4 = e_{at} \, \sigma \, (T_{at}/100)^4 \tag{19}$$

or

$$T_{\text{sky}}^4 = e_{at} \, T_{at}^4 \tag{20}$$

Example 3: Consider a summer night condition when the ground level temperatures are 65 °F dew point and 85 °F dry bulb. By interpolation from Table 4, e_{at} at 65 °F dew point is 0.87 and the apparent sky temperature becomes:

$$T_{\text{sky}} = 0.87^{0.25} \, (85 + 459.6) = 526.0 \, °R$$

Thus, $T_{\text{sky}} = 526.0 - 459.6 = 66.4 °F$, which is 18.6 °F below the ground level dry-bulb temperature.

For a winter night in Arizona when the temperatures at ground level are 60 °F dry bulb and 25 °F dew point, the emittance of the atmosphere would be 0.78 by interpolation from Table 4, and the apparent sky temperature would be 488.3 °R or 28.7 °F.

Table 4 Sky Emittance and Amount of Precipitable Moisture versus Dew Point Temperature

Dew point Temperature		Sky Emittance	Precipitable Water	
°F	°C	e_a	mm	in.
−20	−28.9	0.68	3.0	0.12
−10	−23.3	0.71	4.0	0.16
0	−17.8	0.73	4.5	0.18
10	−12.2	0.76	5.5	0.22
20	−6.7	0.77	7.3	0.29
30	−1.1	0.79	10.5	0.41
40	4.4	0.82	14.5	0.57
50	10.0	0.84	20.5	0.81
60	15.6	0.86	29.0	1.14
70	21.1	0.88	41.0	1.61

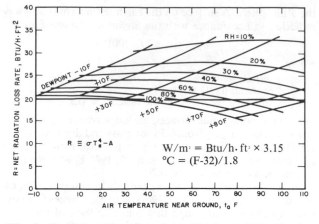

Fig. 8   Radiation Heat Loss from Horizontal Blackbody to the Sky

There are other ways to estimate the apparent sky temperature, including a very simple relationship, which ignores vapor pressure of the atmosphere to give:

$$T_{sky} = 0.0552 \, (T_{at})^{1.5} \qquad (21)$$

where T is in K.

If the temperature of the radiating surface is assumed to equal the atmospheric temperature, the loss of heat from a black surface ($e_s = 1.00$) may be found from Figure 8.

Example 4: For the conditions used in the foregoing summer example, 85 °F dry bulb and 65 °F dew point, the rate of radiative heat loss would be about 23 Btu/h · ft² (72 W/m²). For the winter example with 60 °F dry bulb and 25 °F dew point, the heat loss would be about 27 Btu/h · ft² (85 W/m²).

Where a bare, blackened roof is used as a heat dissipater, the rate of heat loss rises rapidly as the surface temperature goes up. For the summer example, a black-painted metallic roof, $e_s = 0.96$, at 100 °F will have a heat loss rate of:

$$q_{RAD} = 0.1713 \cdot 0.96 \, [(560/100)^4 - (526/100)^4]$$
$$= 35.8 \; \text{Btu/h} \cdot \text{ft}^2 \; (113 \; \text{W/m}^2)$$

This analysis shows that radiation alone is not a potent means of dissipating heat under summer conditions of high dew point and high ambient temperature. In spring and fall, when both dew point and dry-bulb temperatures are relatively low, radiation becomes much more effective.

On overcast nights, when the cloud cover is low, the clouds act much like black bodies at ground level temperature, and virtually no heat can be lost by radiation. The exchange of longwave radiation between the sky and terrestrial surfaces occurs in the daytime, as well as at night, but the much greater magnitude of the solar irradiation masks the longwave effects. Chapter 25 of the 1985 FUNDAMENTALS Volume addresses this phenomenon as it applies to building surfaces.

SOLAR ENERGY COLLECTION

Solar energy can be used by (1) heliochemical, (2) helioelectrical, and (3) heliothermal processes. The first, through photosynthesis, produces food and converts CO_2 to O_2. The second process, using photovoltaic converters, powers spacecraft and is useful for many terrestrial applications. The third process, the primary subject of this chapter, provides thermal energy for space heating and cooling, domestic water heating, power generation, distillation, and process heating.

Solar Heat Collection by Flat-Plate Collectors

The solar irradiation data presented in the foregoing sections may be used to estimate how much energy is likely to be available for collection at any specific location, date, and time of day by either a concentrating device, which can use only the direct rays of the sun, or by a flat-plate collector, which can use both direct and diffuse irradiation. Because the temperatures needed for space heating and cooling do not exceed 200 °F (90 °C), even for absorption refrigeration, they can be attained by carefully designed flat-plate collectors. Single-effect absorption systems can, depending on the load and ambient temperatures, use energizing temperatures of 110 to 230 °F (43 to 110 °C).

A flat-plate collector generally consists of the following components shown in Figure 9:

Glazing, which may be one or more sheets of glass or other diathermanous (radiation-transmitting) material.

Tubes, fins, or **passages** for conducting or directing the heat transfer fluid from the inlet to the outlet.

Absorber plate, which may be flat, corrugated, or grooved, to which the tubes, fins, or passages are attached. The plate may be integral with the tubes.

Headers or **manifolds** to admit and discharge the fluid.

Insulation, which minimizes heat loss from the back and sides of the collector.

Container or **casing,** which surrounds the foregoing components and keeps them free from dust, moisture, etc.

Flat-plate collectors have been built in a wide variety of designs from many different materials (see Figure 10). They have been used to heat fluids such as water, water plus an anitfreeze additive, or gases such as air. The major objective has been to collect as much solar energy as possible at the lowest possible total cost. The collector should also have a long effective life, despite the adverse effects of the sun's ultraviolet radiation; corrosion or clogging because of acidity, alkalinity, or hardness of the heat-transfer fluid; freezing or air-binding in the case of water, or deposition of dust or moisture in the case of air; and breakage of the glazing because of thermal expansion, hail, vandalism, or other causes. (These problems can be minimized by the use of tempered glass.)

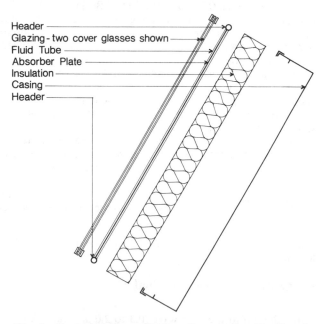

Header
Glazing - two cover glasses shown
Fluid Tube
Absorber Plate
Insulation
Casing
Header

Fig. 9   Exploded Cross Section through Double-Glazed Solar Water Heater

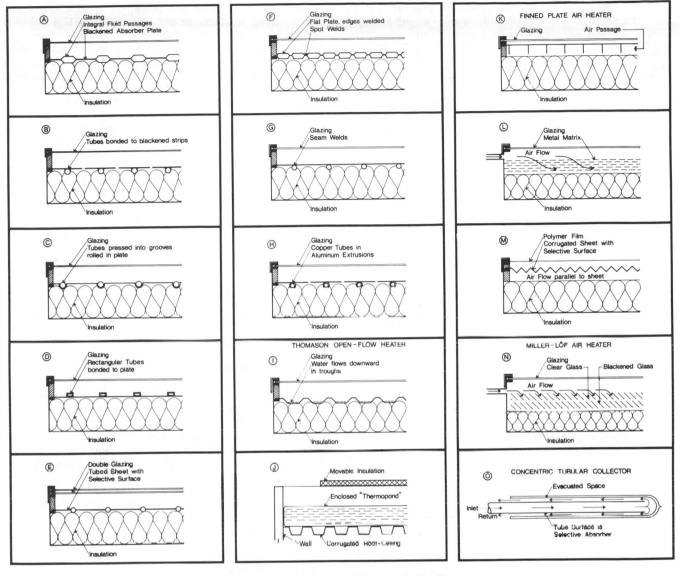

Fig. 10 Variations of Solar Water and Air Heaters

Glazing Materials

Glass has been widely used to glaze solar collectors because it can transmit as much as 90% of the incoming shortwave solar irradiation while transmitting virtually none of the longwave radiation emitted by the absorber plate outward. Glass with low iron content has a relatively high transmittance for solar radiation (approximately 0.85 to 0.90 at normal incidence), but its transmittance is essentially zero for longwave thermal radiation (5.0 to 50 μm) emitted by sun-heated surfaces.

Plastic films and sheets also possess high shortwave transmittance, but because most usable varieties also possess transmission bands in the middle of the thermal radiation spectrum, they may have longwave transmittances as high as 0.40.

Plastics are also generally limited in the temperatures they can sustain without deteriorating or undergoing dimensional changes. Only a few can withstand the sun's ultraviolet radiation for long periods. They can withstand breakage by hail and other stones, and in the form of thin films, they are completely flexible and light in weight.

The glass that is generally used in solar collectors may be either single-strength [0.085 to 0.100 in. (2.2 to 2.5 mm) thick] or double-strength [0.115 to 0.133 in. (2.9 to 3.4 mm) thick]. The commercially available grades of window and greenhouse glass have normal incidence transmittances of about 0.87 and 0.85, respectively. For direct radiation, the transmittance varies markedly with the angle of incidence, as shown by Table 5, which gives transmittances for single- and double-glazing using double-strength clear window glass.

The 4% reflectance from each glass-air interface is the most important factor in reducing transmission, although a gain of about 3% in transmittance can be obtained by the use of water-white glass. Anti-reflection coatings and surface texture can also improve transmission significantly. The effect of dirt and dust on collector glazing may be quite small, and the cleansing effect of occasional rain is adequate to maintain the transmittance with 2 to 4% of its maximum value.

The function of the glazing is to admit as much solar irradiation as possible and to reduce the upward loss of heat to the lowest attainable value. Although glass is virtually opaque to the longwave radiation emitted by the collector plate, the absorption of that radiation causes the glass temperature to rise and thus to lose heat by radiation and convection to the surrounding atmosphere. This type of heat loss can be reduced by

Table 5 Variation with Incident Angle of Transmittance for Single and Double Glazing and Absorptance for Flat Black Paint

Incident Angle, Deg	Transmittance		Absorptance for Flat Black Paint
	Single Glazing	Double Glazing	
0	0.87	0.77	0.96
10	0.87	0.77	0.96
20	0.87	0.77	0.96
30	0.87	0.76	0.95
40	0.86	0.75	0.94
50	0.84	0.73	0.92
60	0.79	0.67	0.88
70	0.68	0.53	0.82
80	0.42	0.25	0.67
90	0.00	0.00	0.00

using an infrared-reflecting coating on the underside of the glass; but such coatings are costly, and they also reduce the effective solar transmittance of the glass by as much as 10%.

In addition to serving as a heat trap by admitting shortwave solar radiation and retaining longwave thermal radiation, the glazing also reduces heat loss by convection. The insulating effect of the glazing is enhanced by the use of several sheets of glass, or glass plus plastic. The upward heat loss may be expressed by:

$$Q_{up} = A_p U_L (t_p - t_{at}) \qquad (22)$$

where

Q_{up} = heat loss upward from the absorber, Btu/h (W)
A_p = absorber plate area, ft^2 (m^2)
U_L = upward heat loss coefficient, Btu/h $\cdot$ ft^2 $\cdot$ °F [W/(m$^2 \cdot$ K)]
t_p = absorber plate temperature, °F (°C)
t_{at} = ambient air temperature, °F (°C)

The loss from the back of the plate rarely exceeds 10% of the upward loss.

Collector Plates

The collector plate absorbs as much as possible of the irradiation reaching it through the glazing while losing as little heat as possible upward to the atmosphere and downward through the back of the casing, and transfers the retained heat to the transport fluid. The absorptance of the collector surface for shortwave solar radiation depends on the nature and color of the coating and on the incident angle, as shown in Table 5 for a typical flat black paint.

By suitable electrolytic or chemical treatments, surfaces can be produced with high values of solar radiation absorptance, α, and low values of longwave emittance, e_s. Essentially, typical selective surfaces consist of a thin upper layer, which is highly absorbent to shortwave solar radiation but relatively transparent to longwave thermal radiation, deposited on a substrate that has a high reflectance and a low emittance for longwave radiation. Selective surfaces are particularly important when the collector surface temperature is much higher than the ambient air temperature.

For fluid-heating collectors, passages must be integral with or firmly bonded to the absorber plate. A major problem is obtaining a good thermal bond between tubes and absorber plates without incurring excessive costs for labor or materials. Materials most frequently used for collector plates are copper, aluminum, and steel. UV-resistant plastic extrusions are used for low temperature application. If the entire collector area is in contact with the heat transfer fluid, the thermal conductance of the material is not important.

Whillier (1964) concluded that steel tubes are as effective as copper if the bond conductance between tube and plate is good.

Potential corrosion problems should be considered for any metals. Bond conductance can range from a high of 1000 Btu/h $\cdot$ ft^2 $\cdot$ °F [5700 W/(m$^2 \cdot$ k)] for a securely soldered or brazed tube to a low of 3 (17) for a poorly clamped or badly soldered tube. Plates of copper, aluminum, or stainless steel with integral tubes are among the most effective types available.

Figure 10, adapted from Van Straaten (1961) and other sources, shows a few of the large number of solar water and air heaters that have been used with varying degrees of success. Figure 10A shows a bonded sheet design, in which the fluid passages are integral with the plate, thus ensuring good thermal contact between the metal and the fluid. Figures 10B and 10C show fluid heaters with tubes soldered, brazed, or otherwise fastened to upper or lower surfaces of sheets or strips of copper, steel, or aluminum. The tendency is to use copper tubes because of their superior resistance to corrosion.

Thermal cement, clips, clamps, or twisted wires have been tried in the search for low-cost bonding methods. Figure 10D shows the use of extruded rectangular tubing to obtain more heat transfer area between tube and plate. Mechanical pressure, thermal cement, or brazing may be used to make the assembly. Soft solder must be avoided because of the high plate temperatures encountered at stagnation conditions.

Figure 10E shows a double-glazed collector with a tubed copper sheet, while 10F shows the use of thin parallel sheets of malleable metal (copper, aluminum, or stainless steel) that are seam-welded along their edges and spot-welded at intervals to provide fluid passages that are developed by expansion. The nontubular types are limited in the internal pressure that they can sustain; they are more adapted to space heating than to domestic hot water heating because of the relatively high city water pressures used in the United States.

Figure 10G shows a seam-welded stainless steel absorber with integral tubes. Figure 10H shows copper tubes pressed into appropriately shaped aluminum extrusions. Differential thermal expansion may break the thermal bond.

Figure 10I shows a proprietary open-flow collector, which uses black-painted corrugated aluminum sheets, generally mounted on steeply pitched south-facing roofs. Water is distributed to the channels by perforated copper or plastic piping running along the peak of the roof. The sun-warmed water is collected at the bottom of the channels by a galvanized or plastic trough and conducted through plastic pipe to the basement storage tank.

Figure 10J shows another proprietary collector that consists of horizontally arranged transparent plastic bags filled with treated water. A corrugated metal roof-ceiling with a black waterproof liner supports these *thermoponds*. The water is thus essentially in thermal contact with the ceiling. Movable horizontal insulating panels cover the ponds on winter nights; during winter days, they are opened to admit solar radiation. In summer, the operation is reversed: the panels are opened at night to dissipate heat but are closed during the day to keep out unwanted solar radiation.

Air or other gases can be heated with flat-plate collectors, particularly if some type of extended surface, Figure 10K, is used to counteract the low heat-transfer coefficients between metal and air. Metal or fabric matrices, Figure 10L, or thin corrugated metal sheets, Figure 10M, may be used, with selective surfaces applied to the latter when a high level of performance is required. The principal requirement is a large contact area between the absorbing surface and the air. The Miller-Löf air heater, Figure 10N, provides this area by overlapping glass plates, the upper being clear and the lower blackened to absorb the incoming solar radiation.

Reduction of heat loss from the absorber can be accomplished either by a selective surface to reduce radiative heat transfer or by suppressing convection. Francia (1961) showed that a honeycomb made of transparent material, placed in the air space between the glazing and the absorber, was beneficial.

Tubular collectors, Figure 10O, with evacuated jackets have demonstrated that the combination of a selective surface and an effective convection suppressor can result in good performance at temperatures higher than a flat-plate collector can attain.

Concentrating Collectors

Temperatures far above those attainable by flat-plate collectors can be reached if a large amount of solar radiation is concentrated upon a relatively small collection area. Simple flat reflectors can markedly increase the amount of direct radiation reaching a flat-plate collector, as shown in Figure 11A.

Because of the apparent movement of the sun across the sky, conventional concentrating collectors must follow the sun during its daily motion. There are two methods by which the sun's motion can be readily tracked. The *altazimuth method* requires the tracking device to turn in both altitude and azimuth; when it is done properly, this method enables the concentrator to follow the sun exactly. Paraboloidal solar furnaces, Figure 11B, generally use this system. The polar, or equatorial, mounting points the axis of rotation at the North Star, tilted upward at the angle of the local latitude. By rotating the collector 15°/h, it follows the sun perfectly (on March 21 and September 21). If the collector surface or aperture must be kept normal to the solar rays, a second motion is needed to correct for the change in the solar declination. This motion is not essential for most solar collectors.

The maximum variation in the angle of incidence for a collector on a polar mount will be ±23.5° on June 21 and December 21; the incident angle correction would then be cos 23.45° = 0.917.

Horizontal reflective parabolic troughs, oriented east and west, as shown in Figure 11C, require continuous adjustment to compensate for the changes in the sun's declination. There is inevitably some morning and afternoon shading of the reflecting surface if the concentrator has opaque end panels. The necessity of moving the concentrator to accommodate the changing solar declination can be reduced by moving the absorber or by using a trough with two sections of a parabola facing each other, as shown in Figure 11D. Called a *compound parabolic concentrator* and designated usually by its initials (CPC), this design can accept incoming radiation over a relatively wide range of angles. By using multiple internal reflections, any radiation that is accepted finds its way to the absorber surface located at the bottom of the apparatus. By filling the collector shape with a highly transparent material with an index of refraction greater than 1.4 the acceptance angle can be increased. By shaping the surfaces of the array properly, total internal reflection is made to occur at the medium-air interfaces, which results in a high concentration efficiency. Called the *dielectric compound parabolic concentrator* (DCPC), this device has been applied to photovoltaic generation of electricity (Cole *et al.* 1977).

The parabolic trough of Figure 11C can be simulated by many flat strips, each adjusted at the proper angle so that all reflect onto a common target. By supporting the strips on ribs with parabolic contours, a relatively efficient concentrator can be produced with less tooling than the complete reflective trough.

Another Fresnel concept applied this segmental idea to flat and cylindrical lenses. A modification is shown in Figure 11F, in which a linear Fresnel lens, curved to shorten its focal distance, can concentrate a relatively large area of radiation onto an elongated receiver. Using the equatorial sun-following mounting, this type of concentrator has come into wide use as a means of attaining temperatures well above those that can be reached with flat-plate collectors.

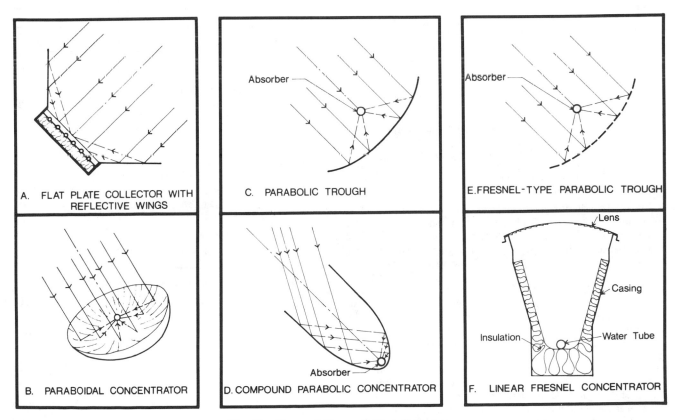

A. FLAT PLATE COLLECTOR WITH REFLECTIVE WINGS

B. PARABOIDAL CONCENTRATOR

C. PARABOLIC TROUGH

D. COMPOUND PARABOLIC CONCENTRATOR

E. FRESNEL-TYPE PARABOLIC TROUGH

F. LINEAR FRESNEL CONCENTRATOR

Fig. 11   Types of Concentrating Collectors

Concentrating collectors have both bad and good features: (1) except at low concentration ratios, they can use only the direct component of the solar radiation, since the diffuse component cannot be concentrated by most types; and (2) in summer, when the sun rises and sets well to the north of the east-west line, the sun-follower, with its axis oriented north-south, can begin to accept radiation directly from the sun long before a fixed, south-facing flat plate can receive anything other than diffuse radiation from the portion of the sky that it faces. Thus, at 40° north latitude, for example, the cumulative *direct* radiation available on a clear day to a sun-follower is 3180 Btu/ft^2 (36.3 MJ/m^2) while the *total* radiation falling on the flat plate tilted upward at an angle equal to the latitude is only 2220 Btu/ft^2 (25.3 MJ/m^2) each day. Thus, in relatively cloudless areas, the concentrating collector may capture more radiation per unit of aperture area than a flat-plate collector.

For extremely high inputs of radiant energy, a multiplicity of flat mirrors, called *heliostats,* using altazimuth mounts, can be used to reflect their incident direct solar radiation onto a common target. Using slightly concave mirror segments on the heliostats, large amounts of thermal energy can be directed into the cavity of a steam generator to produce steam at high temperature and pressure.

Collector Performance

The performance of collectors may be analyzed by a procedure originated by Hottel and Woertz (1942) and extended by Whillier (ASHRAE 1977). The basic equation is:

$$q_u = I_{t\theta}(\tau \cdot \alpha)_\theta - U_L(t_p - t_{at}) \qquad (23)$$

$$= \dot{m} \, c_p \, (t_{f,e} - t_{f,i})/A_{ap} \qquad (23A)$$

Eq 23 also may be used with concentrating collectors:

$$q_u/A_{ap} = I_{DN}(\tau \cdot \alpha)_\theta \, (\varrho \cdot \Gamma) - U_L \, (A_{abs}/A_{ap}) \, (t_{abs} - t_a) \qquad (24)$$
where

q_u = heat usefully gained by collector, Btu/h·ft^2 (W/m^2)
$I_{t\theta}$ = total irradiation of collector, Btu/h·ft^2 (W/m^2)
I_{DN} = direct normal irradiation, Btu/h·ft^2 (W/m^2)
$(\tau,\alpha)_\theta$ = transmittance of cover, absorptance of plate at prevailing incident angle, θ
U_L = loss factor, Btu/h·ft^2·°F [W/(m^2·K)]
t_p, t_{at} = temperatures of the absorber plate and the atmosphere, °F (°C)
$\dot{m}$ = fluid flow rate 1bm/h (kg/s)
$t_{f,e}, t_{f,i}$ = temperatures of the fluid leaving and entering the collector, °F (°C)
ϱ, Γ = reflectance of the concentrator surface, fraction of reflected or refracted radiation that reaches the absorber
A_{abs}, A_{ap} = areas of absorber surface and of aperture that admit or receive radiation, ft^2 (m^2)

The total irradiation and the direct normal irradiation for clear days may be taken from Table 3 for 40° north latitude and for other latitudes or from ASHRAE *Standard* 93-1986. The transmittance for single- and double-glazing and the absorptance for flat black paint may be found in Table 5 for incident angles from 0 to 90°. These values, and the products of τ and α, are also in Figure 12. Little change occurs in the solar-optical properties of the glazing and absorber plate until θ exceeds 30°, but, since all values reach zero when $\theta = 90°$, they drop off rapidly for values of θ beyond 40°.

For nonselective absorber plates, U_L varies with the temperature of the plate and the ambient air, as shown in Figure 13. For selective surfaces, which effect major reductions in the emittance of the absorber plate, U_L will be much lower than the values shown there. Manufacturers of such surfaces should be asked for values applicable to their products, or test results should be consulted that give the necessary information.

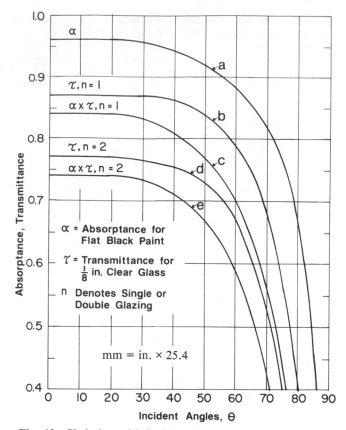

Fig. 12   Variation with Incident Angle of: a. Absorptance of Flat Black Paint; b. Transmittance of 1/8 in. Clear Glass; c. Product of a × b; d. Transmittance of Double 1/8 in. Clear Glass; e. Product of a × d

Example 5: A flat-plate collector is operating in Denver, latitude = 40° north, on July 21 at noon solar time. The atmospheric temperature is assumed to be 85 °F and the average temperature of the absorber plate is 140 °F. The collector is single-glazed with flat black paint on the absorber. The tilt angle is 30° from the horizontal and the collector faces south. Find the rate of heat collection and the collector efficiency. Neglect the back and side losses from the collector.
Solution: From Table 2, Total Irradiation = 307 Btu/h·ft^2
Solar ALT = 70.6°
By geometry $\theta = 10.6°$
From Figure 12, $\tau = 0.87$, and $\alpha = 0.96$.
From Figure 13, $U_L = 1.3$ Btu/h·ft^2·°F.
Then from Eq. (23)

$$q_u = 307 \, (0.87 \cdot 0.96) - 1.3 \, (140 - 85)$$
$$= 185 \text{ Btu/h·ft}^2$$

The collector efficiency, η, is

$$\eta = 185/307 = 0.60$$

The general expression for collector efficiency is:

$$\eta = (\tau \cdot \alpha)_\theta - U_L \, (T_P - t_{at})/I_{t\theta} \qquad (25)$$

For incident angles below about 35°, the product τ times α is essentially constant and Eq (25) is linear with respect to the parameter $(t_p - t_{at})/I_{t\theta}$ as long as U_L remains constant.

Whillier (ASHRAE 1977) suggested that an additional term, F_R, be introduced to permit the use of the fluid inlet temperature in Eqs 23 and 25 to give:

$$q_u = F_R I_{t\theta} \, (\tau \cdot \alpha)_\theta - U_L \, (t_{f,i} - t_{at}) \qquad (26)$$

$$\eta = F_R \, (\tau \cdot \alpha)_\theta - F_R U_L \, (t_{f,i} - t_{at})/I_{t\theta} \qquad (27)$$

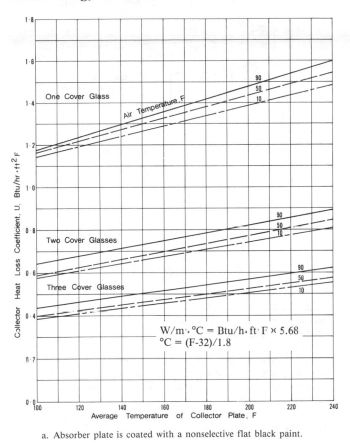

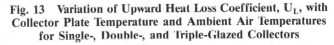

a. Absorber plate is coated with a nonselective flat black paint.

Fig. 13   Variation of Upward Heat Loss Coefficient, U_L, with Collector Plate Temperature and Ambient Air Temperatures for Single-, Double-, and Triple-Glazed Collectors

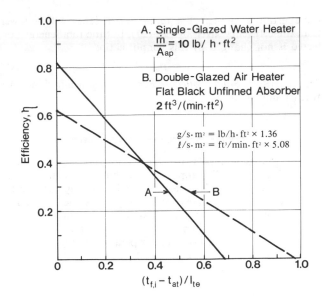

Fig. 14   Efficiency versus Parameter $(t_{f,i} - t_{at})/I_{t\theta}$ for Single-Glazed Solar Water Heater and Double-Glazed Solar Air Heater

where F_R = heat actually delivered by collector/heat that would be delivered if the absorber were actually at $t_{f,i}$. F_R is called the *Collector Heat Removal Factor* and its value is found from the results of a test performed in accordance with ASHRAE *Standard* 93-1986.

The results of such a test are plotted in Figure 14. When the parameter is zero, because there is no temperature difference between the fluid entering the collector and the atmosphere, the value of the Y-intercept equals $F_R (\tau \cdot \alpha)$. The slope of the efficiency line equals the heat loss factor, U_L, multiplied by F_R. For the single-glazed, nonselective collector with the test results shown in Figure 14, the Y-intercept is 0.82, and the X-intercept is 0.69. This collector used high transmittance single-glazing, $\tau = 0.91$, and the black paint has an absorptance of 0.97, so $F_R = 0.82/(0.91 \cdot 0.97) = 0.93$.

Assuming that the relationship between η and the parameter is actually linear, as shown, the slope is $-0.82/0.69 = -1.19$; thus $U_L = 1.19/F_R = 1.19/0.93 = 1.28$. The tests for which the results are shown in Figure 14 were run indoors. Factors that affect the measured efficiency are wind speed and fluid velocity.

Figure 14 also shows the efficiency for a double-glazed air heater with an unfinned absorber coated with flat black paint. The Y-intercept for the air heater, *B*, is considerably lower than it is for the water heater, *A*, because (1) transmittance of the double-glazing used in *B* is lower than the transmittance of the single-glazing used in *A*; and (2) F_R is lower for *B* than for *A* because of the lower heat-transfer coefficient between the air and the unfinned metal absorber.

The X-intercept for air heater *B* is higher than it is for the water heater *A* because the upward loss coefficient U_L is much

lower for the double-glazed air heater than for the single-glazed water heater. The data for both *A* and *B* were taken at near-normal incidence with high values of $I_{t\theta}$. For Example 5, using a single-glazed water heater, the value of the parameter would be close to $(140 - 85)/307 = 0.18$, and the expected efficiency, 0.60, agrees closely with the test results.

As ASHRAE *Standard* 93-1986 shows, the incident angles encountered with south-facing tilted collectors vary widely throughout the year. Considering a surface located at 40° north latitude with a tilt angle $\Sigma - 40°$, the incident angle θ will depend on the time of day and the declination, δ. On December 21, $\delta = 23.456°$; at four hours before and after solar noon, the incident angle is 62.7° and it remains close to this value for the same solar time throughout the year. The total irradiation at these conditions varies from a low of 45 Btu/h·ft² (142 W/m²) on December 21 to approximately 140 Btu/h·ft² (441 W/m²) throughout most of the other months.

When the irradiation is below about 100 Btu/h·ft² (315 W/m²), the losses from the collector may exceed the heat that can be absorbed. This situation varies with the temperature difference between the collector inlet temperature and the ambient air, as suggested by Eq (26).

When the incident angle rises above 30°, the product of the transmittance of the glazing and the absorptance of the collector plate begins to diminish and thus the heat absorbed also drops. The losses from the collector generally are higher as the time moves farther from solar noon and consequently the efficiency also drops. Thus, the daylong efficiency is lower than the near-noon performance. During the early afternoon hours, the efficiency is slightly higher than at the comparable morning time because ambient air temperatures are lower in the morning than in the afternoon.

ASHRAE *Standard* 93-1986 describes the *incident angle modifier,* which may be found by tests run when the incident angle is set at 30, 45, and 60°. Simon (1976) showed that for many flat-plate collectors, the incident angle modifier is a linear function of the quantity $(1/\cos \theta - 1)$. For evacuated tubular collectors, the incident angle modifier may grow with rising values of θ.

ASHRAE *Standard* 93-1986 specifies that the efficiency be reported in terms of the gross collector area, A_g, rather than the aperture area, A_{ap}. The reported efficiency will be lower than the efficiency given by Eq. (27), but the total energy collected is not changed by this simplification:

$$\eta \cdot A_g = \eta_{ap} \cdot A_{ap}/A_g \qquad (28)$$

The ASHRAE *Solar Collector Performance Manual* includes further information.

HEAT STORAGE SYSTEMS

Storage may be a part of solar heating, cooling, and power generating system. For approximately half of the 8,760 hours per year, any location is in darkness, so heat storage is necessary if the system must operate continuously. For some applications such as swimming pool heating, daytime air heating, and irrigation pumping, intermittent operation is acceptable, but most other uses of solar energy require operating at night and when the sun is obscured by clouds. Chapter 46 provides further information.

SERVICE AND DOMESTIC WATER HEATING BY SOLAR ENERGY

This section introduces methods for determining water heating requirements, available insolation, component efficiencies, system performance, energy savings, and economic feasibility for solar heating of domestic and service hot water. It also explains installation, operation, and maintenance procedures. A more complete treatment is in the ASHRAE *Solar Domestic and Service Hot Water Manual* (1983), which has examples corresponding to the calculation methods presented here.

SYSTEMS

A solar water heater includes a solar collector array that absorbs solar radiation and converts it to heat. This heat is then absorbed by a heat transfer fluid (water, a non-freezing liquid, or air) that passes through the collector. The heat transfer fluid's heat can be stored or used directly.

Since portions of the solar energy system are exposed to the weather, they must be protected from freezing. The systems must also be protected from overheating caused by high insolation levels during periods of low energy demand.

In solar water heating systems, potable water is heated directly in the collector or indirectly by a heat transfer fluid that is heated in the collector, passes through a heat exchanger, and transfers its heat to the domestic or service water. The heat transfer fluid is transported by either natural or forced circulation. Natural circulation occurs by natural convection (thermosiphoning), whereas forced circulation uses pumps or fans. Except for thermosiphon systems, which need no control, solar domestic and service hot water systems are controlled using differential thermostats.

Six types of solar energy systems are used to heat domestic and service hot water: thermosiphon, recirculation, drain-down, drain-back, indirect water heating, and air. The ASHRAE *Solar Domestic and Service Hot Water Manual* describes each, along with its advantages and disadvantages.

Thermosiphon Systems

Thermosiphon systems (Figure 15) heat potable water directly and use natural convection to transport it from the collector to storage. They are applicable in climates where freezing is infrequent, or for summer only use. Pressure-reducing valves are

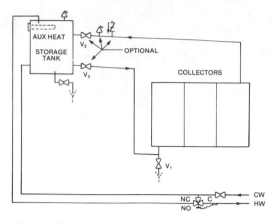

Fig. 15　Thermosiphon System

required when city water pressure is greater than the working pressure of the collectors. In a thermosiphon system, the storage tank must be elevated above the collectors, which sometimes requires designing the upper level floor and ceiling joists to bear this additional weight. Also, extremely hard or acidic water can cause scale deposits that clog or corrode the absorber fluid passages.

Since thermosiphon flow is induced whenever there is sufficient sunshine, these systems do not need pumps. Reverse thermosiphoning must be eliminated either by draining the collector or with thermal traps.

Recirculation Systems

Recirculation systems (Figure 16) are direct water heating systems that pump potable water from storage to the collectors when there is enough solar energy available to warm it, and then return it to the storage tank until needed. Since a pump circulates the water, the collectors can be mounted either above or below the storage tank. Recirculation systems are practical only in areas where freezing is infrequent. Freeze protection for extreme weather conditions is provided either by recirculating warm water from the storage tank or by flushing the collectors with cold water. Direct water heating systems should not be used in areas where water is extremely hard or acidic. Scale deposits may quickly clog or corrode the absorber fluid passages, rendering the system inoperable.

This type of system is exposed to city water line pressures and must be assembled to withstand test pressures, as required by

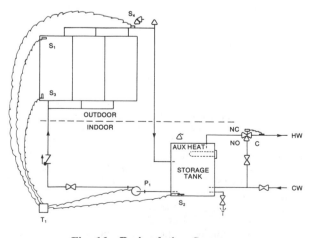

Fig. 16　Recirculation System

local code. Pressure-reducing valves and pressure relief valves are required when the city water pressure is greater than the working pressure of the collectors. Recirculation systems often use a single storage tank for both solar energy storage and the auxiliary water heater, but two-tank storage systems can be used.

Drain-Down Systems

Drain-down systems (Figure 17) are pumped circulation, direct water heating systems that circulate potable water from storage to the collector array where it is heated. Circulation continues until usable solar heat is no longer available. When a freezing condition is anticipated or a power outage occurs, the system drains automatically by isolating the collector array and exterior piping from city water pressure and draining it using one or more valves. The solar collectors and associated piping *must* be carefully sloped to drain the collector's exterior piping.

This type of system is exposed to city water pressures and must be assembled to withstand test pressures, as required by local code. Pressure-reducing valves and pressure relief valves are required when city water pressure is greater than the working pressure of the collectors. One- or two-tank storage systems can be used. Scale deposits and corrosion can occur in the collectors with hard or acidic water.

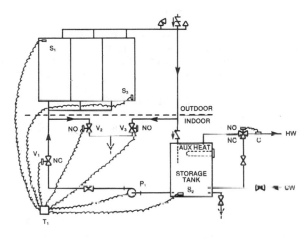

Fig. 17   Drain-Down System

Drain-Back Systems

Drain-back systems (Figure 18) are generally indirect water heating systems that circulate treated or untreated water through the closed collector loop to a heat exchanger, where its heat is transferred to the potable water. Circulation continues until usable energy is no longer available. When the pump stops, the collector fluid drains by gravity to a storage tank or drain-back tank. In a pressurized system, the tank also serves as an expansion tank when the system is operating and must be protected from excessive pressure with a temperature and pressure relief valve. In an unpressurized system, the tank is open and vented to the atmosphere.

Since the collector loop is isolated from the potable water, valves are not needed to actuate draining, and scaling is not a problem. The collector array and exterior piping must be sloped to drain completely.

Indirect Water Heating Systems

Indirect water heating systems (Figure 19) circulate a freeze-protected heat transfer fluid through the closed collector loop

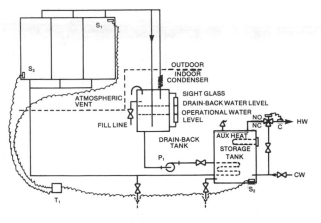

Fig. 18   Drain-Back System

to a heat exchanger, where its heat is transferred to the potable water. The most commonly used heat transfer fluids are water/ethylene glycol and water/propylene glycol solutions, although other heat transfer fluids such as silicone oils, hydrocarbons, or refrigerants can also be used (ASHRAE 1983). These fluids are non-potable, sometimes toxic, and normally require double wall heat exchangers. The double wall heat exchanger can be located inside the storage tank, or an external heat exchanger can be used. The collector loop is closed and therefore requires an expansion tank and a pressure relief valve. A one- or two-tank storage system can be used. Additional over-temperature projection may also be needed to protect the collector fluid from decomposing or becoming corrosive.

Designers should avoid automatic water makeup in systems using water/antifreeze solutions because a significant leak may induce enough water into the system to raise the freezing temperature of the solution above the ambient temperature, causing the collector array and exterior piping to freeze. Also, antifreeze systems with large collector arrays and long pipe runs may need a time-delayed bypass loop around the heat exchanger to avoid freezing the heat exchanger on startup.

Air Systems

Air systems (Figure 20) are indirect water heating systems that circulate air through the collectors via ductwork to an air-to-liquid heat exchanger. There, heat is transferred to the potable water, which is pumped through the tubes of the exchanger and

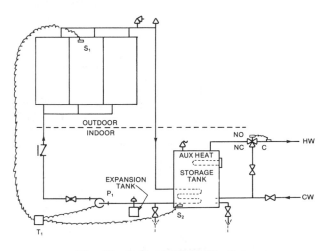
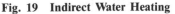

Fig. 19   Indirect Water Heating

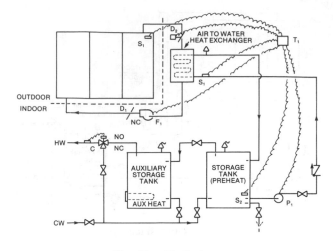

Fig. 20 Air System

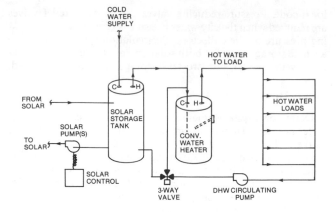

Fig. 22 DHW Recirculation System With Makeup Preheat

returned to the storage tank. Circulation continues as long as usable heat is available. Air systems can use single or double storage tank configurations. The two-tank storage system is used most often, since air systems are generally used for preheating domestic hot water and may not be capable of reaching 120 to 160°F (50 to 70°C) delivery temperatures.

Air does not need to be protected from freezing or boiling, is noncorrosive, and is free. However, air ducts and air handling equipment need more space than piping and pumps. Ductwork is very laborious to seal, and air leaks are difficult to detect. Power consumption is generally higher than that of a liquid system because of high collector and heat exchanger static pressure loss. All dampers installed in air systems must fit tightly to prevent leakage and heat loss.

In areas with freezing temperatures, tight dampers are needed in the collector ducts to prevent reverse thermosiphoning at night, which could freeze the water in the heat exchanger coil. No special precautions are needed to control overheating conditions in air systems.

DOMESTIC HOT WATER RECIRCULATION SYSTEMS

Domestic hot water recirculation systems (Figures 21 and 22), which continuously circulate domestic hot water throughout a building, are common in motels, hotels, hospitals, dormitories,

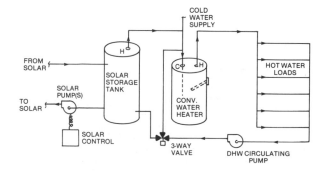

Fig. 21 DHW Recirculation System

office buildings, and other commercial buildings. The recirculation heat losses in these systems are usually a significant part of the total water heating load. A properly integrated solar energy system can make up much of this heat loss.

SYSTEM COMPONENTS

A solar domestic hot water system has a variety of components. The parts are combined depending on function, component compatibility, climate conditions, required performance, site characteristics, and architectural requirements. For optimum system performance, the components of the solar energy system must fit and function together satisfactorily. The system must also be properly integrated into the conventional domestic or service hot water system. The major components involved in the collection, storage, transportation, control, and distribution of solar energy are discussed in this section.

Collectors

Flat plate collectors are the most commonly used collectors in water heating applications because of the year-round load requiring temperatures between 80 and 180°F (27 and 82°C). For discussions of other collectors and applications, see ASHRAE *Standard* 93-1986, the ASHRAE *Solar Collection Performance Manual,* and previous sections of this chapter. Collectors must withstand extreme weather conditions (such as freezing, stagnation, and wind), as well as system pressures.

Heat Transfer Fluid

Heat transfer fluids transport heat from the solar collectors to the domestic water. Potential safety problems exist in the transfer of heat energy from solar collectors to potable hot water supplies. The problems are both chemical and mechanical in nature and apply primarily to liquid transfer and storage systems in which a heat exchanger interface exists with the potable water supply. Both the chemical compositions of the heat transfer fluids (pH, toxicity, and chemical durability), as well as their mechanical properties (specific heat and viscosity) must be considered (see ASHRAE *Solar Domestic and Service Hot Water Manual*).

Except in unusual cases or when potable water is being circulated, the energy transport fluid is non-potable and has the potential for contaminating potable water during the heat transfer process. Even potable or "non-toxic" fluids in closed systems are likely to become non-potable because of contamination from metal piping, solder joints and packing, or by inadvertent installation of a toxic fluid at a later date.

Trade-offs between thermal efficiency, cost effectiveness, and risk for both heat transfer fluids and heat exchangers may be necessary to provide acceptable safety. Existing codes regulate the need and design of heat exchangers (Hall 1979).

Thermal Energy Storage

Thermal energy (heat) storage in hydronic solar domestic and service heating systems is virtually always liquid stored in tanks. All storage tanks and bins should be well insulated so that the collected heat is not lost to the tanks' or bins' surroundings, which are normally not occupied.

Thermal energy in domestic hot water systems is usually stored in one or two tanks. The hot water outlet is at the top of the tank and cold water enters the tank through a dip tube that extends down to within 4 to 6 in. (100 to 150 mm) from the tank bottom. The outlet on the tank to the collector loop should be approximately 4 in. (100 mm) above the tank bottom to prevent scale deposits from being drawn into the collectors. Water from the collector array returns to the upper portion of the storage tank. This plumbing arrangement may take advantage of thermal stratification, depending on the delivery temperature from the collectors and the flow rate through the storage tank.

Single tank electric auxiliary systems often incorporate storage and auxiliary heating within the same vessel. Conventional electric water heaters commonly have two heating elements: one near the top and one near the bottom. If a dual element tank is used in a solar energy system, the bottom element should be disconnected and the top left functional to take advantage of fluid stratification. Standard gas- and oil-fired water heaters should not be used in single-tank arrangements. In gas and oil water heaters, heat is added to the bottom of the tanks, which reduces both stratification and collection efficiency in single-tank systems.

Dual-tank systems often use the solar domestic hot water storage tank as a preheat tank. The second tank is normally a conventional domestic hot water system tank and contains the auxiliary heat source. Multiple tank systems are sometimes used in large institutions, where they operate similarly to dual-tank systems. Using a two-tank system increases collector efficiency and the fraction of the total heating load supplied by the solar energy system (solar fraction), and reduces the auxiliary heating requirement. However, it increases tank heat losses. The water inlet to these tanks is usually a dip tube that extends close to the bottom of the tank, as noted above. To stratify the second tank, the "cool" water inlet should be close to the top, particularly if the backup energy source is electricity.

Rule-of-thumb estimates for sizing storage tanks usually range from 1 to 2.5 gal/ft^2 (40 to 100 L/m^2) of the solar collector area. The most often used figure is 1.8 gal/ft^2 (75 L/m^2) of collector area, which will usually provide enough heat for a sunless period of a day or so. Storage volume should be analyzed and sized according to the project water requirements and draw schedule.

Heat Exchangers

Heat exchangers transfer thermal energy (heat) between two fluids. All solar energy systems using indirect water heating require one or more heat exchangers. Potential contamination problems exist in the transfer of heat energy from solar collectors to potable hot water supplies.

Heat exchangers influence the effectiveness with which collected energy is made available to heat domestic water. They also separate and protect the potable water supply from contamination when non-potable heat transfer fluids are used. Like transport fluid selection, heat exchanger selection considers thermal performance, cost effectiveness, reliability and safety, and the following characteristics:

1. Heat exchange effectiveness
2. Pressure drop, operating power, and flow rate
3. Physical design, design pressure, configuration, size, materials, and location in the system
4. Cost and availability
5. Reliable protection of the potable water supply from contamination by the heat transfer fluids
6. Leak detection, inspection, and maintainability
7. Material compatibility with other system elements such as metals and fluids
8. Thermal compatibility with system design parameters such as operating temperatures, flow rate, and fluid thermal properties

Heat exchanger selection depends on the characteristics of the fluids that pass through the heat exchanger and the properties of the exchanger itself. Fluid characteristics to consider are the fluid type, temperature, specific heat, and mass flow rate. Physical properties of the heat exchanger are the overall heat transfer coefficient of the heat exchanger and the heat transfer surface area. When these variables are known, the heat transfer rate can be determined. The heat transfer fluid temperatures of interest are the hot and cold fluid inlet temperatures and the hot and cold fluid outlet temperatures.

For most solar domestic hot water system designs, only the hot and cold inlet temperature are known and the other temperatures must be calculated, which requires knowing the physical properties of the heat exchanger.

This information can be used to evaluate two quantities that are useful in determining the heat transfer in a heat exchanger and the performance characteristics of the collector when combined with a given heat exchanger. These quantities are (1) the fluid capacitance rate, which for a given fluid is the product of the mass flow rate and the specific heat of the fluid passing through the heat exchanger, and (2) heat exchanger effectiveness, which relates the capacitance rate of the two fluids to the fluid inlet and outlet temperatures. The effectiveness is equal to the ratio of the actual heat transfer rate to the maximum heat transfer rate theoretically possible. Generally, a heat exchanger effectiveness of 0.4 or greater is recommended. The ASHRAE *Solar and Domestic and Service Hot Water Manual* has further information.

Expansion Tanks. An expansion tank is necessary to control system pressure in a solar domestic hot water system having closed circulation in the collector loop (see Chapter 13). The maximum operating temperature should be the collector stagnation temperature, if the collectors remain full during stagnation.

Pumps. Pumps circulate heat transfer liquid through collectors and heat exchangers. The two most commonly used fluid circulators are centrifugal pumps and positive displacement pumps. In solar domestic hot water systems, the pump is usually a centrifugal circulator driven by a small fractional horsepower motor. The flow rate for collectors generally ranges from 0.015 to 0.04 gpm/ft^2 [0.036 to 0.84 L/(s $\cdot$ m^2)].

Pumps used in drain-back systems must provide the lift head up to the collectors in addition to the friction head. These heads must be added for systems with open return piping, and the pump should be able to satisfy both head requirements individually for systems with siphon return piping.

System Piping. Piping can be plastic, copper, galvanized steel, or stainless steel. The most widely used is sweat-soldered L-type copper tubing. M-type copper is also acceptable if permitted by local building codes. If water/glycol is the heat transfer fluid, galvanized pipes or tanks must not be used because unfavorable chemical reactions will occur; copper piping is recommended instead. Also, if glycol solutions or silicone fluids are used, they may leak through joints where water would not. System piping should be compatible with the collector fluid passage material, e.g., copper or plastic piping should be used when using collectors with copper fluid passages.

Piping that carries potable water can be plastic, copper, galvanized steel, or stainless steel. In indirect systems, corrosion inhibitors must be checked and adjusted routinely, preferably every three months, as well as any time after that the system reaches stagnation conditions. If dissimilar metals are joined, use dielectric or nonmetallic couplings. The best protection is sacrificial anodes or getters in the fluid stream. Their location depends on the material to be protected, the anode material, and the electrical conductivity of the heat transfer fluid. Sacrificial anodes consisting of magnesium, zinc, or aluminum are often used to reduce corrosion in storage tanks. Because there are so many possibilities, each combination must be evaluated on its own merits. A copper-aluminum or copper-galvanized steel joint is unacceptable because of severe galvanic corrosion. Systems containing aluminum, copper, and iron metals have a greatly increased potential for corrosion.

Insufficient consideration of air elimination requirements, pipe expansion control, and piping slope can cause serious system failures. Collector pipes (particularly manifolds) should be designed to allow expansion from stagnation temperatures to extreme cold weather temperatures. Expansion control can be achieved with offset elbows in piping, hoses, or expansion couplings. Expansion loops should be avoided unless installed horizontally, particularly in systems that must drain for freeze protection. The collector array piping should slope 0.06 in. per foot (5 mm/m) for drainage (DOE 1978).

Air can be eliminated by placing air vents at all piping high points and by air purging during filling. Flow control, isolation, and other valves in the collector piping must be chosen carefully so these components do not restrict drainage significantly or back up water behind them. The collectors must drain completely.

Valves and Gauges. Valves in solar domestic hot water systems must be located to ensure system efficiency, satisfactory performance, and the safety of equipment and personnel. Drain valves must be ball type; gate valves may be used if the stem is installed horizontally.

Check valves or other valves used for freeze protection or for reverse thermosiphoning must be reliable to avoid significant damage.

Auxiliary Heat Sources. On sunny days, a typical solar energy system should supply water at a predetermined temperature, and the solar storage tank should be large enough to hold sufficient water for a day or two. Because of the intermittent nature of solar radiation, an auxiliary heater must be installed to handle hot water requirements. Operation of the auxiliary heater can be timed to take advantage of off-peak utility rates, if a utility is the source of auxiliary energy. The auxiliary heater should be carefully integrated with the solar energy system to obtain maximum solar energy use. For example, the auxiliary heater should not destroy any stratification that may exist in the solar-heated storage tank, which would reduce collector efficiency.

Fans. Fans circulate air in air systems by forcing air that has been heated in the solar collectors through ductwork to an air-to-water heat exchanger. The heat from the air is then transferred to the water that is pumped through the coil section of the heat exchanger. For detailed information on fan performance and selection, refer to Chapter 3 of the 1983 EQUIPMENT Volume.

Ductwork, particularly in systems with air-type collectors, must be sealed carefully to avoid leakage in duct seams, damper shafts, collectors, and heat exchangers. Duct sizing should be done by using conventional air duct design methods contained in other chapters in this volume.

Control Systems. Control systems regulate solar energy collection by controlling fluid circulation, activate system protection against freezing and overheating, and initiate auxiliary heating when it is required.

The three major control components are sensors, controllers, and actuated devices. Sensors detect conditions or measure quantities such as temperatures. Controllers receive output from the sensors, select a course of action, and signal a system component to adjust the condition. Actuated devices are components such as pumps, valves, dampers, and fans that execute controller commands and regulate the system.

Temperature sensors measure the temperature of the absorber plate near the collector outlet and near the bottom of the storage tank. The sensors send signals to a controller, such as a differential temperature thermostat, for interpretation.

The differential thermostat compares the signals from the sensors with adjustable set points for high and low temperature differentials. The controller performs different functions, depending on which set points are met. In liquid systems, when the temperature difference between the collector and storage reaches a high set point, usually 20°F (11°C), the pump starts, automatic valves are activated, and circulation begins. When the temperature difference reaches a low set point, usually 4°F (2°C), the pump is shut off and the valves are de-energized and returned to their normal positions. To restart the system, the high temperature set point must again be met. If the system has either freeze or overtemperature protection, the controller opens or closes valves or dampers and starts or stops pumps or fans to protect the system when its sensors detect either a freezing or an overheating condition is about to occur.

Collector loop sensors can be located on the absorber plate, in a pipe above the collector array, on a pipe near the collector, or in the collector outlet passage. Sensors must be selected to withstand high temperatures, such as those that may occur during collector stagnation. Although any of these locations may be acceptable, attaching the sensor on the collector absorber plate is recommended. When attached properly, it gives accurate readings, can be installed easily, and is basically not affected by ambient temperature, as are sensors mounted on exterior piping.

A sensor installed on an absorber plate reads temperatures 3 to 4°F (2°C) higher than the temperature of the fluid leaving the collector. However, such temperature discrepancies can be compensated for in the differential thermostat settings.

The sensor must be attached with good thermal contact to the absorber plate. If a sensor access cover is provided on the enclosure, it must be gasketed for a watertight fit. Adhesives and adhesive tapes should not be used to attach the sensor to the absorber plate.

The storage temperature sensor should be near the bottom of the storage tank to detect the temperature of the fluid before it is pumped to the collector or the heat exchanger. The storage fluid is usually coldest at that location because of thermal stratification and the location of the makeup water supply. The sensor should be either securely attached to the tank and well insulated, or immersed inside the tank near the collector supply.

The freeze-protection sensor, if required, should be located so that it will detect the coldest liquid temperature when the collector is shut down. The two most common locations are the back of the absorber plate at the bottom of the collector and the collector intake manifold. The absorber plate location is recommended because reradiation to night sky will freeze the collector heat transfer fluid, even though the ambient temperature is above freezing. Some systems, such as the recirculation system, require two sensors for freeze protection, while others, such as the drain-down, require only one.

The auxiliary heater temperature sensor should be located at the top of the auxiliary heating tank near the hot water outlet. Control on-off temperature differentials affect system efficiency. The turn-on temperature differential must be selected properly because if the differential is too high, the system starts later than it should, and if it is too low, the system starts too soon. The turn-on differential for liquid systems usually ranges from 15 to 30 °F (8 to 17 °C) and is most commonly 20 °F (11 °C). For air systems, the range is usually 25 to 45 °F (14 to 25 °C).

The turn-off temperature differential is more difficult to estimate. Selection depends on a comparison between the value of the energy collected and the cost of collecting it. It varies with individual systems, but a value of 4 °F (2 °C) is typical.

Water temperature in the collector loop depends on ambient temperature, solar radiation, radiation from the collector to the night sky, and collector loop insulation. Freeze-protection sensors should be set to detect temperatures of 40 °F (4 °C) to provide adequate protection.

Sensors are an important but often overlooked control system component. They must be selected and installed properly because no control system can produce accurate outputs from unreliable sensor inputs. Sensors are used in conjunction with a differential temperature controller and are usually supplied by the controller manufacturer. Sensors must survive the anticipated operating conditions without physical damage or loss of accuracy. Low-voltage sensor circuits must be located away from 120/240 VAC lines to avoid electromagnetic interference. Any sensors attached to the collector should be able to withstand stagnation temperatures.

Sensor calibration, which often is overlooked by installers and maintenance personnel, is critical to system performance; a routine calibration maintenance schedule is essential.

System Performance Evaluation Methods

The performance of any solar energy system is directly related to (1) the heating load requirements, (2) the amount of solar radiation available, and (3) the solar energy system characteristics. Various calculation methods use different procedures and data when considering available solar radiation. Some simplified methods may consider only average annual incident solar radiation, while complex methods may use hourly data.

Solar energy system characteristics, as well as individual component characteristics, are required to evaluate performance. The degree of complexity with which these systems and components are described varies from system to system. Some common characteristics of selected components (such as collectors) that are required for many evaluation methods are discussed in this chapter.

The cost effectiveness of a solar domestic and service hot water heating system depends on initial cost and energy cost savings. A major task is to determine how much energy is saved. The *annual solar fraction,* which is the annual solar contribution to the water heating load divided by the load, can be used to estimate these savings. It is expressed as a decimal fraction or percent and generally ranges from 0.3 to 0.8 (30 to 80%), although more extreme values are possible.

Analysis and Economic Evaluation Methods

System performance and economic evaluation methods are generally categorized according to complexity and include (1) hand calculation methods, (2) simplified computer methods, and (3) complex hour-by-hour computer methods. The ASHRAE *Solar Domestic and Service Hot Water Manual* covers these methods in detail.

Water Heating Load Requirements

The amount of water required must be estimated as accurately as possible because it affects system component selection. Chapter 54 gives methods to determine the load.

Oversized storage may result in low temperature water that requires auxiliary heating to reach a desired supply temperature. Undersizing can prevent the collection and use of available solar energy.

Integration of the solar energy system into a recirculating hot water system, if one is used, must also be considered carefully to maximize solar energy use (see Figures 21 and 22).

COOLING BY SOLAR ENERGY

A review of solar-powered refrigeration by Swartman (1974) emphasizes various absorption systems tried during the past several decades. Newton (ASHRAE 1977) discusses commercially available water vapor/lithium bromide absorption refrigeration systems. Standard absorption chillers are generally designed to give rated capacity for activating fluid temperatures well above 200 °F (90 °C) at full load and design condenser water temperature. Few flat-plate collectors can operate efficiently in this range; therefore, lower hot fluid temperatures are used when solar energy provides the heat. Both the temperature of the condenser water and the percentage of design load are determinants of the optimum energizing temperature, which can be quite low, sometimes below 120 °F (50 °C). Proper control can raise the Coefficient of Performance (COP) at these part load conditions.

Many large commercial or institutional cooling installations must operate year-round, and Newton (Chapter 8, ASHRAE 1977) has shown that the low temperature cooling water available in winter enables the LiBr − H$_2$O to function well with hot fluid inlet temperatures below 190 °F (88 °C). The Japanese report successful operation of residential chillers in sizes as low as 1.5 tons (5.3 kW), with inlet temperatures in the range of 175 °F (80 °C).

COOLING BY NOCTURNAL RADIATION AND EVAPORATION

Bliss (1961) used unglazed tube-in-strip collectors mounted on south-facing roofs to collect solar heat in winter and to reject heat in summer by radiation to the night sky. He used radiant ceilings with water tanks for storage and heat pumps to raise or lower the temperature of the circulating water as needed. Nocturnal radiation can produce cooling at the rate of 20 to 30 Btu/h·ft^2 (63 to 95 W/m^2) during nights when the dew point temperature is low. Radiation cooling effectiveness is greatly reduced when the dew point temperature is high and little radiant cooling can be accomplished under overcast skies. Evaporation must be used when high rates of heat dissipation are needed.

In Australia, school cooling systems that evaporate water in the discharge air to chill the rocks in a switched-bed rock-filled recuperator have operated successfully. The incoming fresh air required for ventilation in Australian schools is generally 20 to 25 cfm (9 to 12 L/s) per person, the higher figure for infant and primary schools. With the RBR (rock bed regenerator) system, 100% makeup air is used during the summer months, and the ventilation rate per pupil ranges from 28 to 85 cfm (13 to 40 L/s).

In the evaporative RBR (rock bed regenerator), the incoming air cools as it passes through rocks chilled by the evaporatively-cooled exhaust air that flows through the RBR. The airflow is switched every 10 minutes. Water sprays for only 10 seconds at the beginning of each cycle, and this is adequate to provide the necessary cooling. Power for the two fans used in the 2000 cfm (940 L/s) system is only 600 W, because the pressure drop through the 5-in. (125-mm) deep pebble bed (0.25 in. or 6 mm mesh screen) is only 0.13 in. of water (32 Pa). The power consumption per unit of floor area is 0.75 to 1.0 W/ft^2 (95 W/m^2) for mechanical refrigeration.

The conventional evaporative cooler is used to cool industrial buildings and low-cost housing, but the high indoor humidities caused by direct evaporative cooling produce nearly as much discomfort as the high temperatures with which it contends.

SOLAR HEATING AND COOLING SYSTEMS

The components and subsystems discussed earlier in this chapter may be combined to create a wide variety of solar heating and cooling systems. There are two principal categories of such systems: *passive* and *active*. Passive systems require little if any nonrenewable energy to make them function (Yellott 1977, Yellott *et al*. 1976). Active systems must have continuous availability of nonrenewable energy, generally in the form of electricity, to operate pumps and fans. *Hybrid systems* require some nonrenewable energy, but the amount is so small that they can maintain a coefficient of performance of about 50. Passive systems antedate active systems by a wide margin, since every building is passive in the sense that the sun tends to warm it by day and cool it at night in the absence of the sun.

Passive Systems

Passive systems may be divided into several categories. The first residence to which the name *solar house* was applied used a large expanse of south-facing glass to admit solar radiation into the house; it would be called a *direct gain* passive system.

Indirect gain solar houses use the south-facing wall surface or the roof of the structure to absorb solar radiation, which causes a rise in temperature; this, in turn, conveys heat into the building in several ways. This principle was applied with good effect to the pueblos and cliff dwellings of the southwest. Glass has led to modern adaptations of the indirect gain principle (Trombe 1977, Balcomb *et al*. 1977).

By glazing a large south-facing, massive masonry wall, solar energy can be absorbed during the day, and conduction of heat to the inner surface provides radiant heating at night. The mass of the wall and its relatively low thermal diffusivity delays the arrival of the heat at the indoor surface until it is needed. The glazing reduces the loss of heat from the wall back to the atmosphere and increases the collection efficiency of the system.

Openings in the wall, near the floor, and near the ceiling allow convection to transfer heat to the room. The air in the space between the glass and the wall warms as soon as the sun heats the outer surface of the wall. The heated air rises and enters the building through the upper openings. Cool air flows through the lower openings, and convective heat gain can be established as long as the sun is shining.

In another indirect gain passive system, a metal roof-ceiling supports transparent plastic bags filled with water (Hay and Yellott 1969). Moveable insulation above these *thermoponds* is rolled away during the winter day to allow the sun to warm the stored water. The water then transmits heat indoors by convection and radiation. The insulation remains over the *thermoponds* at nights or during overcast days.

During the summer the water bags are exposed at night to cool them by: (1) convection to the cool night air, (2) radiation cooling to the night sky, and (3) evaporative cooling from exposed water added to the thermoponds. The insulation covers the water bags during the day to protect them from unwanted irradiation.

Pittenger *et al*. (1978) tested a building where water rather than insulation was moved to provide summer cooling and winter heating.

Add-on greenhouses can be used as solar attachments when the orientation and other local conditions are suitable. The greenhouse can provide a buffer between the exterior wall of the building and the outdoor conditions. During daylight hours, warm air from the greenhouse can be introduced into the house by natural convection or a small fan.

Control, in most passive systems, is accomplished by moving a component that regulates the amount of solar radiation admitted into the structure. Window shades or venetian blinds, manually operated, are the most widely used and simplest controls, but these can be automated if the user chooses to pay for this convenience.

Active Systems

Active systems absorb solar radiation with collectors and convey it by a suitable fluid to storage. As heat is needed, it is obtained from storage via heated air or water. Control is exercised by several types of thermostats, the first being a differential device that starts the flow of fluid through the collectors when they have been sufficiently warmed by the sun. It also stops the fluid flow when the collectors no longer gain heat. In locations where freezing conditions occur only rarely, a low temperature sensor on the collector controls a circulating pump when freezing impends. This process wastes some of the stored heat, but it prevents costly damage to the collector panels. This system is not suitable for northern regions where subfreezing temperatures persist for long periods.

The space heating thermostat is generally the conventional double-contact type that calls for heat when the temperature in the controlled space falls to a predetermined level. If the temperature in storage is adequate to meet the heating requirement, a pump or fan is started to circulate the warm fluid. If the temperature in the storage subsystem is inadequate, the thermostat calls on the auxiliary or standby heat source.

Space Heat and Service Hot Water

Figure 23 shows one of the many systems for service hot water and space heating. In this case, a large, atmospheric-pressure storage tank is used, from which water is pumped to the collectors by pump P1 in response to the differential thermostat T1. The drainback system is used to prevent freezing, since the amount of antifreeze required in such a system would be prohibitively expensive. Service hot water is obtained by placing a heat exchanger coil in the tank near the top, where, if stratification is encouraged, the hottest water will be found.

An auxiliary water heater boosts the temperature of the sun-heated water when required. Thermostat T2 senses the indoor temperature and starts P2 when heat is needed. If the water in the storage tank becomes too cool to provide enough heat, the second contact on the thermostat calls for heat from the auxiliary heater.

Standby heat becomes increasingly important as heating requirements increase. The heating load, winter availability of solar radiation, and cost and availability of the auxiliary energy must be determined. It is rarely cost effective to do the entire heating job for either space or service hot water by using the solar heat collection and storage system alone.

Electric resistance heaters have the lowest first cost, but may have high operating costs. Water-to-air heat pumps, which use the sun-heated water from the storage tank as the evaporator energy source, are an alternative auxiliary heat source. The heat

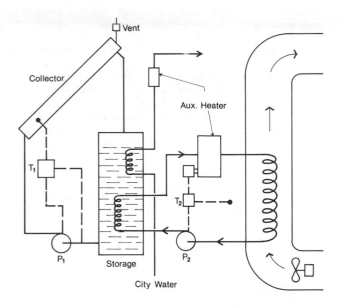

Fig. 23   Solar Collection, Storage, and Distribution System for Domestic Hot Water and Space Heating

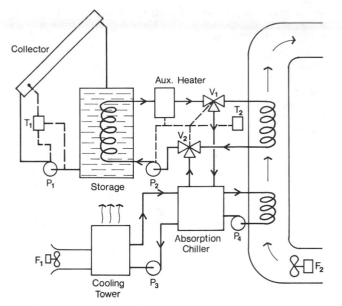

Fig. 24   Space Heating and Cooling System Using Lithium-Bromide-Water Absorption Chiller

pump's coefficient of performance is high enough to yield 10,000 to 14,000 Btu (10.6 to 14.8 MJ) of heat for each kWh of energy supplied to the compressor. When summer cooling is needed as well as winter heating, the heat pump becomes a logical solution, particularly in large systems where a cooling tower is used to dissipate the heat withdrawn from the system.

The system shown in Figure 23 may be retrofitted into a warm air furnace. In such systems, the primary heater is deleted from the space heating circuit and the coil is located in the return duct of the existing furnace. Full backup is thus obtained and the auxiliary heater provides only the heat not available at the storage temperature of the solar system.

Solar Cooling with Absorption Refrigeration

When solar energy is used for cooling as well as for heating, the absorption system shown in Figure 24, or one of its many modifications, may be used. The collector and storage sub systems must operate at temperatures approaching 200°F (90°C) on hot summer days when the water from the cooling tower exceeds 80°F (27°C), but considerably lower operating water temperatures may be used when cooler water is available from the tower. The controls for the collection, cooling, and distribution subsystems are generally separated, with the circulating pump P1 operating in response to the collector thermostat T1, which is located within the air-conditioned space. When T2 calls for heating, valves V1 and V2 direct the water flow from the storage tank through the unactivated auxiliary heater to the fan coil in the air distribution system. The fan F1 in this unit may respond to the thermostat also, or it may have its own control circuit so that it can bring in outdoor air when suitable temperature conditions are present.

When thermostat T2 calls for cooling, the valves direct the hot water into the absorption unit's generator, and pumps P3 and P4 are activated to pump the cooling tower water through the absorber and condenser circuits and the chilled water through the cooling coil in the air distribution system. A relatively large hot water storage tank allows the unit to operate when no sunshine is available. A chilled water storage tank (not shown) may

be added so that the absorption unit can operate during the day whenever water is available at a sufficiently high temperature to make the unit function properly. The coefficient of performance of a typical absorption unit of the lithium-bromide-water type may be as high as 0.75 under favorable conditions, but frequent on-off cycling of the unit to meet a high variable cooling load may cause significant loss in performance because the unit must be heated to operating temperature after each shutdown. Modulating systems are analyzed differently than on-off systems.

Water-cooled condensers are required with the absorption cycles, since the lithium-bromide-water cycle operates with a relatively delicate balance among the temperatures of the three fluid circuits—cooling tower water, chilled water, and activating water. The steam-operated absorption systems, from which today's solar cooling systems are derived, customarily operate at energizing temperatures of 230 to 240°F (110 to 116°C), but these are above the capability of most flat-plate collectors. The solar cooling units are designed to operate at considerably lower temperatures, but unit ratings are also lowered.

Smaller domestic units may operate with natural circulation (*percolation*), used to carry the lithium-bromide-water solution from the generator (to which the activating heat is supplied) to the separator and condenser; there, the reconcentrated Li-Br is returned to the absorber while the water vapor goes to the condenser before being returned to the evaporator where the cooling takes place. Larger units use a centrifugal pump to transfer the fluid.

SIZING OF COLLECTOR AND STORAGE SUBSYSTEMS

The basic approach to sizing solar water heating and space heating and cooling systems is to find the monthly heat requirements by using Weather Service temperature data and the standard ASHRAE procedure for estimating heating loads. For service water heating, the daily and monthly requirements and the delivery temperatures are first established, and the probable temperature of the supply water is found from local records for each month.

The availability of solar radiation for any specific location must next be determined and the clear-day data (given in ASHRAE *Standard* 93-1986; and, for 40° north latitude, in Tables 2 and 3 of this chapter) form a good starting point. Multiplication of the clear-day irradiation for the selected surface tilt angle by the number of days in the month and the probable percentage of possible sunshine will give an estimated amount of the solar radiation that reaches the collector on average days. Collector performance can be estimated for each month by using an average daylight ambient air temperature, insolation data, and the characteristics of the proposed collector. The slope-intercept method is outlined earlier in the chapter.

If only a hand calculator is available, one day per month is about the limit of the calculating capability of the average engineer, but when higher powered computation facilities are available, then hour-by-hour estimates can be made, using weather data available on tapes from the National Weather Service at Asheville, North Carolina. (ASHRAE developed bin and degree hour summaries of these tapes are available on floppy disks for microcomputers.) A *standard year* is sometimes employed, for which the average horizontal irradiation and the average ambient air temperatures come close to matching the Weather Bureau averages for that location. This method must be approached with care, however, because of changing weather patterns and the absence of really long-term solar irradiation data for most locations.

Methods of estimating solar system performance have been proposed that greatly simplify the tasks of selecting the most economical combinations of collector orientation tilt and area with storage subsystems of varying capacity. Beckman *et al.* (1977) describes the f-chart method validated by many computer simulations based on data established by the Weather Bureau for many locations around the United States.

Installation Guidelines

Most solar system components are the same as those in present HVAC and hot water systems (pumps, piping, valves, and controls), and their installation is not much different from conventional system installation.

The solar collectors are the most unfamiliar component used in a solar energy system. They are located outdoors, which necessitates penetration of the building envelope. They also require a structural element to support them at the proper tilt and orientation toward the sun.

Site considerations must be taken into account. The collectors should be located so that shading is minimized and installed so that they are attractive on and off site. They should be located to minimize vandalism and avoid a safety hazard.

Collectors should be placed as near to the storage tank as possible to reduce piping cost and heat losses. The collector and piping must be installed so that they can be drained without trapping fluid within the system.

For best annual performance, collectors should be installed at a tilt angle above the horizontal that is appropriate for the local latitude. They should be oriented toward true south, not magnetic south. Small variations in tilt ($\pm 10°$) and orientation ($\pm 20°$) are acceptable without significant performance degradation. (See the section on control systems and the ASHRAE *Solar Domestic and Service Hot Water Manual* for control sensor installation in domestic hot water systems.)

Collector Mounting

Solar collectors are usually mounted on the ground or on flat or pitched roofs. A roof location necessitates the penetration of the building envelope by mounting hardware, piping, and control wiring. Ground or flat roof-mounted collectors are generally rack mounted.

Pitched roof mounting can be done several ways. Collectors can be mounted on structural *standoffs,* which support them at an angle other than that of the roof to optimize solar tilt. In another pitched roof-mounting technique called *direct mounting,* collectors are placed on a waterproof membrane on top of the roof sheeting. The finished roof surface together with the necessary collector structural attachments and flashing are then built up around the collector. A weatherproof seal between the collector and the roof must be maintained to prevent leakage, mildew, and rotting.

Integral mounting can be done for new pitched roof construction. The collector is attached to and supported by the structural framing members. The top of the collector then serves as the finished roof surface. Weather tightness is crucial to avoid damage and mildew.

Collectors should support the snow loads that occur on the roof area they cover. The collector tilt usually expedites snow sliding with only a small loss in efficiency. The roof structure should be free of objects that could impede snow sliding, and the collectors should be raised high enough to prevent snow buildup over them.

The mounting structure should be built to withstand winds of at least 100 mph (0.45 m/s), which impose a wind load of 40 lb/ft^2 (195 kg/m^2) on a vertical surface or an average of 25 lb/ft^2 (122 kg/m^2) on a tilted roof (HUD 1977). Flat-plate collectors mounted flush with the roof surface should be constructed to withstand the same wind loads.

When mounted on racks, the collector array becomes more vulnerable to wind gusts as the angle of the mount increases. Collectors can be uplifted by wind striking the undersides. This wind load, in addition to the equivalent roof-area wind loads, should be determined according to accepted engineering procedures.

Expansion and contraction of system components, material compatibility, and the use of dissimilar metals must be considered. Collector arrays and mounting hardware (bolts, screws, washers, angles) must be well protected from corrosion. Steel-mounting hardware in contact with aluminum and copper piping in contact with aluminum hardware are both examples of high corrosion-potential combinations.

Dissimilar metals can be separated by washers made of fluoro-carbon polymar (such as Teflon), phenolic (such as Bakelite), or neoprene rubber.

Freeze Protection

Freeze protection is important and is often the determining factor when selecting a system. Freezing can occur at ambient temperatures as high as 42°F (6°C) because of night-sky radiation.

One simple way to protect against freezing is draining the fluid from the collector array and interior piping when a potential freezing condition exists. The drainage may be automatic, as in drain-down and drain-back systems, or manual, as in the thermosiphon systems. Automatic systems should be capable of fail-safe drainage operation—even in the event of pump failure or power outage. Special pump considerations may also be required to permit water to drain back through the pump and to permit system refilling without causing cavitation.

In areas where freezing in infrequent, recirculating water from storage to the collector array can be used as freeze protection.

Freeze protection can be provided by using fluids that resist freezing. Fluids such as water/glycol solutions, silicone oils, and hydrocarbon oils are circulated by pumps through the collector array and double wall heat exchanger. Draining the collector fluid is not required, since these fluids have a freezing point well below the coldest anticipated outdoor temperature.

In mild climates where recirculation freeze protection is used, a second level of freeze portection can be provided by flushing the collector with cold supply water when the collector approaches near-freezing temperatures. This can be accomplished with a temperature-controlled valve that is set to open a small port at near-freezing temperature of about 40 °F (4.5 °C) and then closes at a slightly higher temperature.

Overtemperature Protection

During periods of high insolation and low hot water demand, overheating can occur in the collectors or storage tanks. Protection against overheating must be considered for all portions of the solar hot water system. Liquid expansion or excessive pressure can burst piping or storage tanks. Steam or other gases within a system can restrict liquid flow, making the system inoperable.

The most common methods of overheat protection stop circulation in the collection loop until the storage temperature decreases, discharge the overheated water from the system and replace it with cold makeup water, or use a heat exchanger as a means of heat rejection. Some freeze-protection methods can also provide overheat protection.

For non-freezing fluids such as glycol antifreezes, overtemperature protection is needed to limit fluid degradation at high temperatures during collector stagnation.

Safety

Safety precautions required for installing, operating, and servicing a solar domestic hot water system are essentially the same as those required for a conventional domestic hot water system. One major exception is that some solar systems use non-potable heat transfer fluids. Local codes may require a double wall heat exchanger for potable water installations.

Pressure relief must be provided in all parts of the collector array that can be isolated by valves. The outlet of these relief valves should be piped to a container or drain and not where workers could be affected.

Startup Procedure

After completing the installation, certain tests must be performed before charging or filling the system. The system must be checked for leakage, and pumps, fans, valves, and sensors must be checked to see that they are functional. Testing procedures vary with system type.

Closed-loop systems should be hydrostatically tested. The system is filled and pressurized to one and a half times the operating pressure for one hour and inspected for leaks and any appreciable pressure drop.

Drain-down systems should be tested to be sure that all water drains from the collectors and piping located outdoors. All lines should be checked for proper pitch so that gravity drains them completely. All valves should be verified to be in working order.

Drain-back systems should be tested to ensure that the collector fluid is draining back to the reservoir tank when circulation stops and that the system refills properly.

Air systems should be tested for leaks before insulation is applied by starting the fans and checking the ductwork for leaks.

Pumps and sensors should be inspected to verify that they are in proper working order. Proper cycling of the system pumps can be checked by a running time meter. A sensor that is suspected of being faulty can be dipped alternately in hot and cold water to see if the pump starts or stops.

Following system testing and before filling or charging it with heat transfer fluid, the system should be flushed to remove debris.

System Maintenance

All systems should be checked at least once a year in addition to any periodic maintenance that may be required for specific components. A log of all maintenance performed should be kept, along with an owner's manual that describes system operational characteristics and maintenance requirements.

The collectors' outer glazing should be cleaned periodically by hosing. Leaves, seeds, construction dirt, and other debris should be carefully swept from the collectors. Care should be taken not to damage plastic covers.

Without opening up a sealed collector panel, the absorber plate should be checked for surface coating damage caused by peeling, crazing, or scratching. Also, the collector tubing should be inspected to ensure that it is not loose and no longer contacting the absorber. If it is, the manufacturer should be consulted for repair instructions.

Heat transfer fluids should be tested and replaced at intervals suggested by the manufacturer. Also, the solar energy storage tank should be drained about every six months to remove sediment.

Performance Monitoring/Minimum Instrumentation

Temperature sensors and temperature differential controllers are required to operate most solar systems. However, additional instruments should be installed for system monitoring, check out, and troubleshooting.

Thermometers should be located on the collector supply and return lines so that the temperature difference in the lines can be determined visually.

A pressure gauge should be inserted on the discharge side of the pump. The gauge is used to monitor the pressure that the pump must work against and to indicate if the flow passages are blocked.

Running time meters on pumps and fans may be installed to determine if the system is cycling properly.

DESIGN, INSTALLATION, AND OPERATION GUIDE

The following checklist is for those designing solar heating and cooling systems. Specific values have not been included because these vary for each application. The designer must decide whether design figures are within acceptable limits for any particular project (see DOE 1978 for further information). The review order listed does not reflect their precedence or importance during design.

Collectors

1. Check flow rate for compliance with manufacturer's recommendations.
2. Check that collector area matches application and claimed solar participation.
3. Review collector instantaneous efficiency curve and check match between collector and system requirements.
4. Relate collector construction to end use; two cover plates are not required for low temperature collection in warm climates and may, in fact, be detrimental. Two cover plates are more efficient when the temperature difference between absorber plate and outdoor air is high, such as in severe

winter climates or when collecting at high temperatures for cooling. Radiation losses only become significant at relatively high absorber plate temperatures. Selective surfaces should be used in these cases. Flat black surfaces are acceptable and sometimes more desirable for low collection temperatures.

5. Check match between collector tilt angle, latitude, and collector end use.
6. Check collector azimuth.
7. Check collector location for potential shading and exposure to vandalism or accidental damage.
8. Review provisions made for high stagnation temperatures. If not used, are liquid collectors drained or left filled in the summer?
9. Check for snow hang-up and ice formation. Will casing vents become blocked?
10. Review precautions, if any, against outgassing.
11. Check access for cleaning covers.
12. Check mounting for stability in high winds.
13. Check for architectural integration. Do collectors on roof present rain-water drainage or condensation problems? Do roof penetrations form potential leak problems?
14. Check collector construction for structural integrity and durability. Will materials deteriorate under operating conditions? Will any pieces fall off?
15. Are liquid collector passages organized in such a way as to allow natural fill and drain? Does mounting configuration affect this?
16. Does air collector duct connection configuration promote a balanced airflow and an even heat transfer? Are connections potentially leaky?

Hydraulics

1. Check that the flow rate through the collector array matches system parameters.
2. If antifreeze is used, check that flow rate has been modified to allow for viscosity and specific heat.
3. Review properties of proposed antifreeze. Some fluids are highly flammable. Check toxicity, vapor pressure, flash point, and boiling and freezing temperatures at atmospheric pressure.
4. Check means of make-up into antifreeze system. An automatic water makeup system can result in freezing.
5. Check that provisions are made for draining and filling the system. (Air vents at high points, drains at low points, pipes correctly graded in between, drainback systems vented to storage or expansion tank.)
6. If system uses draindown freeze protection, check that:
   a. Provision is made for draindown volume and back venting.
   b. Pipes are graded for draindown.
   c. Solar primary pump is sized for lift head.
   d. Pump should be self-priming and meet NPSH requirements if tank is below pump.
7. Check that collector pressure drop for drainback system is slightly higher than static pressure between the supply and return headers.
8. Optimum pipe arrangement is reverse return with collectors in parallel. Series collectors reduce flow rate and increase head. A combination of parallel/series can sometimes be beneficial, but check that equipment has been sized and selected properly.
9. Cross connections under different operating modes sometimes result in pumps operating in opposition or tandem, causing severe hydraulic problems.
10. If heat exchangers are used, check that approach temperature differential has been recognized in the calculations.

11. Check that adequate provisions are made for water expansion and contraction. Use specific volume/temperature tables for calculation. Each unique circuit must have its own provision for expansion and contraction.
12. Three-port valves tend to leak through the closed port. This, together with reversed flows in some modes, can give potential hydraulic problems. As a general rule, simple circuits and controls are better.

Airflow

1. Check that the flow rate through the collector array matches the system design parameters.
2. Check temperature rise across collectors using air mass flow and specific heat.
3. Check that duct velocities are within the system parameters.
4. Check that cold air or water cannot flow from collectors by gravity under "no-sun" conditions.
5. Verify duct material and construction methods. Duct work must be sealed to reduce losses.
6. Check duct configuration for balanced flow through collector array.
7. More than two collectors in series can reduce collection efficiency.

Thermal Storage

1. Check that thermal storage capacity matches parameters of collector area, collection temperature, utilization temperature, and system load.
2. Verify that thermal inertia does not impede effective operation.
3. Check provisions made to promote temperature stratification during both collection and use.
4. Check that pipe and duct connections to storage are compatible with the control philosophy.
5. If liquid storage is used for high temperatures (above 200 °F or 90 °C), check that tank material and construction can withstand the temperature and pressure.
6. Check that storage location does not promote unwanted heat loss or gain and that adequate insulation is provided.
7. Verify that liquid storage tanks are treated to resist corrosion. This is particularly important in tanks that are partially filled.
8. Check that provision is made to protect liquid tanks from overpressure and vacuum.

Utilization

1. *Domestic Hot Water*
   a. Characteristics of domestic hot water loads include short periods of high draw interspersed with long dormant periods. Check that domestic hot water storage matches solar heat input.
   b. Check that provisions have been made to prevent reverse heating of the solar thermal storage by the domestic hot water backup heater.
   c. Check that system allows cold make-up water preheating on days of low solar input.
   d. Verify that tempering valve limits domestic hot water supply to a safe temperature during periods of high solar input.
   e. Depending on total dissolved solids, city water heated above 150 °F (65 °C) may precipitate a calcium carbonate scale. If collectors are used to heat water directly, check provisions made to prevent scale formation in absorber plate waterways.

f. Check if the system is required to have a double wall heat exchanger and that it conforms to appropriate codes, if the collector uses non-potable fluids.

2. *Heating*

a. Warm air heating systems have the potential of using solar energy directly at moderate temperatures. Check that air volume is sufficient to meet the heating load at low supply temperatures and that the limit thermostat has been reset.

b. At times of low solar input, solar heat can still be used to meet part of the load by preheating return air. Check location of solar heating coil in system.

c. Baseboard heaters require relatively high supply temperatures for satisfactory operation. Their output varies as the 1.5 power of the log mean temperature difference and falls off drastically at low temperatures. If solar is combined with baseboard heating, check that supply temperature is compatible with heating load.

d. Heat exchangers imply an approach temperature difference that must be added to the system operating temperature to derive the minimum collection temperature. Verify calculations.

e. Water-to-air heat pumps rely on a constant solar water heat source for operation. When the heat source is depleted, the backup system must be used. Check that storage is adequate.

3. *Cooling*

a. Solar activated absorption cooling with fossil fuel back-up is currently the only commercially available active cooling. Be assured of all design criteria and a large amount of solar participation. Verify calculations.

b. Storing both hot water and chilled water may make better use of available storage capacity.

Controls

1. Check that control philosophy matches the desired modes of operation.

2. Verify that collector loop controls recognize solar input, collector temperature, and storage temperature.

3. Verify that controls allow both the collector loop and the utilization loop to operate independently.

4. Check that control sequences are reversible and will always revert to the most economical mode.

5. Check that controls are as simple as possible within the system requirements. Complex controls increase the frequency and possibility of breakdowns.

6. Check that all controls are "fail safe."

Performance

1. Check building heating, cooling, and domestic hot water loads as applicable. Verify that building thermal characteristics are acceptable.

2. Check solar energy collected on a monthly basis. Compare with loads and verify solar participation.

REFERENCES

ASHRAE. 1983. Solar Domestic and Service Hot Water Manual.

ASHRAE. 1986. Methods of Testing to Determine the Thermal Performance of Solar Collectors. ANSI/ASHRAE *Standard* 93-1986.

Angstrom, A. 1915. A Study of the Radiation of the Atmosphere. Smithsonian Misc. Coll., Vol. 65, No. 3.

Balcomb, D.; et al. 1977. Thermal Storage Walls in New Mexico. Solar Age, Vol. 2, No. 8, p. 20.

Beckman, W.A.; Klein, S.A.; and Duffie, J.A. 1977. Solar Heating Design by the F-Chart Method. John Wiley, New York.

Bennett, I. 1965. Monthly maps of Daily Insolation in the U.S. Solar Energy, Vol. 9, No. 3, p. 145.

Bennett, I. 1967. Frequency of Daily Insolation in Anglo North America during June and December. Solar Energy, Vol. 11, No. 1, January-March, p. 41.

Bliss, R.W. 1961. Atmospheric Radiation Near the Surface of the Earth. Solar Energy, Vol. 5, No. 3, p. 103.

Butler, C.P.; et al. 1964. Surfaces for Solar Spacecraft Power. Solar Energy, Vol. 8, No. 1, January-March, p. 2.

Climatic Atlas of the U.S. 1968. U.S. Government Printing Office, Washington, DC.

Cole, R.L.; et al. 1977. Applications of Compound Parabolic Concentrators to Solar Energy Conversion. Argonne National Laboratory, Chicago, Report No. AML-77-42.

Duffie, J.A., and Beckman, W.A. 1974. Solar Energy Thermal Processes. John Wiley, New York.

Edwards, D.K.; et al. 1962. Spectral and Directional Thermal Radiation Characteristics of Selective Surfaces. Solar Energy, Vol. 6, No. 1, January-March, p. 1.

Francia, G. 1961. A New Collector of Solar Radiant Energy. U.N. Conference on New Sources of Energy, Rome, Vol. 4, p. 572.

Gates, D.M. 1966. Spectral Distribution of Solar Radiation at the Earth's Surface. Science, Vol. 151, No. 3710, p. 523.

Gier, J.T., and Dunkle, R.V. 1958. Selective Spectral Characteristics as an Important Factor in the Efficiency of Solar Energy Collectors. Transactions of the Conference on Scientific Uses of Solar Energy, 1955, Vol. 2, Part 1-A, p. 41.

Hall, I.J.; Prairie, R.R.; Anderson, H.E.; and Boes, E.C. 1979. Generation of Typical Meteorological Years: 426 Solmet Stations. ASHRAE *Transactions*, Vol. 85, Part 2, p. 507.

Hay, H.R., and Yellott, J.I. 1969. Natural Air Conditioning with Roof Ponds and Movable Insulation. ASHRAE *Transactions*, Vol. 75, Part 1, p. 165.

Hottel, H.C., and Woertz, B.B. 1942. The Performance of Flat-Plate Solar Collectors. Transactions of ASME, Vol. 64, p. 91.

HUD. 1977. Intermediate Minimum Property Standards Supplement for Solar Heating and Domestic Hot Water Systems. U.S. Dept. of Housing and Urban Development, SD Cat. No. 0-236-648.

Jordan, R.C., and Liu, B.Y.H. (eds.) 1977. Applications of Solar Energy for Heating and Cooling of Buildings. ASHRAE Publication GRP 170.

Morrison, C.A., and Farber, E.A. 1974. Development and Use of Solar Insolation Data for South Facing Surfaces in Northern Latitudes. ASHRAE *Transactions*, Vol. 80, Part 2. p. 350.

Mumma, S.A. 1985. Solar Collector Tilt and Azimuth Charts for Rotated Collectors on Sloping Roofs. Proceedings Joint ASME-ASES Solar Energy Conference, Knoxville, TN.

Newton, A.B., and Gilman, S.F. 1982. Solar Collector Performance Manual. ASHRAE Pub. SP 32.

Newton, A.B. U.S. Patents 2,343,211 and 2,396,338.

Parmalee, G.V., and Aubele, W.W. 1952. Radiant Energy Transmission of the Atmosphere. ASHVE Transactions, Vol. 58, p. 85.

Pittenger, A.L.; White, W.R.; and Yellott, J.I. 1978. A New Method of Passive Solar Heating and Cooling. Proceedings, Second National Passive Systems Conference, Philadelphia, ISES and DOE.

Reitan, C.H. 1963. Surface Dew Point and Water Vapor Aloft. Journal of Applied Meteorology, Vol. 2, No. 6, p. 776.

Simon, F.F. 1976. Flat-Plate Solar Collector Performance Evaluation. Solar Energy, Vol. 18, No. 5. p. 451.

Stephenson, D.G. 1967. Tables of Solar Altitude and Azimuth; Intensity and Solar Heat Gain Tables. Technical Paper No. 243, Division of Building Research, National Research Council of Canada, Ottawa.

Tables of Computed Altitude and Azimuth. 1958. Hydrographic Office Bulletin No. 214, Vols. 2 and 3, U.S. Superintendent of Documents, Washington, DC.

Tables of Radiation Powers. Paper No. 105, Division of Building Research, National Research Council of Canada, Ottawa.

Tabor, H. 1958. Selective Radiation. I. Wavelength Discrimination. Transactions of the Conference on Scientific Uses of Solar Energy, 1955, Vol. 2, Part 1-A, p. 1, University of Arizona Press.

Telkes, M. 1949. A Review of Solar House Heating. Heating and Ventilating, p. 68.

Thekaekara, M.P. 1973. Solar Energy Outside the Earth's Atmosphere. Solar Energy, Vol. 14, No. 2, January, p. 109.

Threlkeld, J.L. 1963. Solar Irradiation of Surfaces on Clear Days. ASHRAE *Transactions*, Vol. 69, p. 24.

Threlkeld, J.L., and Jordan, R.C. 1958. Direct Radiation Available on Clear Days. ASHRAE *Transactions*, Vol. 64, p. 45.

Trombe, F.; et al. 1977. Concrete Walls for Heat. Solar Age, Vol. 2, No. 8, p. 13.

Van Straaten, J.F. 1961. Hot Water from the Sun. Ref. No. D-9, National Building Research Institute of South Africa, Council for Industrial and Scientific Research, Pretoria.

Whillier, A. 1964. Thermal Resistance of the Tube-Plate Bond in Solar Heat Collectors. Solar Energy, Vol. 8, No. 3, p. 95.

Yellott, J.I. 1977. Passive Solar Heating and Cooling Systems. ASHRAE *Transactions*, Vol. 83, Part 2, p. 429.

Yellott, J.I.; Aiello, D.; Rand, G.; and Kung, M.Y. 1976. Solar-Oriented Architecture. Arizona State University Architecture Foundation, Tempe, AZ.

Zarem, A.M., and Erway, D.D. 1963. Introduction to the Utilization of Solar Energy. McGraw-Hill, New York.

BIBLIOGRAPHY

ASHRAE. 1977. Applications of Solar Energy for Heating and Cooling of Buildings.

Barley, C.D., and Winn, C.B. 1978. Optimizing Sizing of Solar Collectors by the Method of Relative Areas. Solar Energy, Vol. 21, No. 4.

Bennett, I. 1967. Frequency of Daily Insolation in Anglo North America during June and December. Solar Energy, Vol. 11, No. 1, January-March, p. 41.

DHW System Efficiency Nomograph. 1980. Economic Analysis of Residential Solar Water Heaters. Mueller Associates, Inc.

DOC. 1977. Solar Heating and Cooling of Residential Buildings. U.S. Dept. of Commerce.

DOE. 1978. Solar Heating and Cooling Project Experiences Handbook. U.S. Dept. of Energy.

DOE. 1978. State-of-the-Art Study of Heat Exchangers Used with Solar-Assisted Domestic Hot Water Systems. Potential Contamination of Potable Water Supply. U.S. Dept. of Energy.

DOE. 1979. Active Solar Energy System Design Practices Manual. U.S. Dept. of Energy, Solar/0802/79/01.

DOE. 1981. Recommended Requirements to Code Officials for Solar Heating, Cooling and Hot Water Systems U.S. Dept. of Energy, DOE/CS/342 81-01.

Daniels, F. 1964. Direct Use of the Sun's Energy. Yale University Press, New Haven, CT.

Foster, William M. 1977. Design Options for Residential Solar Hot Water Heating Systems. Solar Engineering Magazine, 2:10, Oct.

HUD. 1979. Solar Domestic Hot Water. U.S. Dept. of Housing and Urban Development, HUD 000-1230.

HUD. 1980. Installaton Guidelines for Solar DHW Systems in One- and Two-Family Dwelling. U.S. Dept. of Housing and Urban Development, 2nd edition, May.

HUD. 1980. Solar Terminology. U.S. Dept. of Housing and Urban Development, HUD-PDR-465(2), March.

ITT 1976. Solar Heating Systems Design Manual. International Telephone and Telegraph Corp.

Lameiro, G.F., and Bendt, P. 1978. The GFL Method for Designing Solar Energy Space Heating and Domestic Hot Water Systems. Vol. 2.1. Proceedings at the 1978 Annual Meeting of the American Section of the International Solar Energy Society, Inc., Denver, CO.

Lewis, T. 1978. Solar System Controls. International Solar Energy Society.

Lewis, T. 1978. Solar Thermal Storage. International Solar Energy Society. 1978.

Mumma, S.; Milnarist, L.; and Rodriquez-Anza, J. 1973. Innovative Double Walled Heat Exchanger for Use in Solar Water Heating. EW-78-G-03.

Pacific Regional Solar Heating Handbook. 1976. Los Alamos Scientific Laboratory.

Ward, Dan S., and Oberoi, Harjinder S. 1980. Handbook of Experience in the Design and Installation of Solar Heating and Cooling Systems. ASHRAE, July.

CHAPTER 48

ENERGY MANAGEMENT

ENERGY conservation can be defined as *more efficient or effective use of energy.* Moreover, technology alone cannot produce sufficient results without a continuing management effort. Energy management begins with the commitment and support of an organization's top management. A suggested flow chart for developing an energy management program is shown in Figure 1.

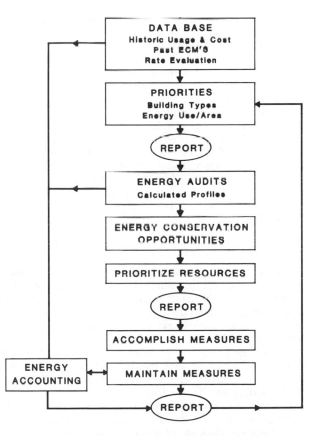

Fig. 1   Energy Management Program

ORGANIZING FOR ENERGY MANAGEMENT

Since energy management is performed in existing facilities, most of this chapter is devoted to these facilities. Information on energy conservation in new design can be found throughout all volumes of the ASHRAE Handbook. However, a true energy conserving design allows the principles of Energy Management to be applied within the facility without modification. The area most likely to be overlooked in new design is the ability to measure and monitor energy consumption and trends for each energy use category.

To be effective, energy management must be given the same emphasis as management of any other cost/profit center. In this regard, the functions of top management are as follows:

1. To establish the energy cost/profit center
2. To assign direct responsibility for the program
3. To hire or assign an energy manager
4. To allocate resources
5. To ensure that the energy is promulgated to all departments and provide necessary support to achieve effective results
6. To monitor the cost effectiveness of the program

An effective energy management program requires that the manager act (supported by a suitable budget) and be held *accountable* for those actions. It is common for a facility to allocate 3 to 10% of the annual energy cost for the administration of an energy management program. In addition to salaries and other administrative expenses, the budget should include continuing education for the energy manager and staff. However, other resources are needed. In fact, money is often the least constraining factor, since properly managed energy conservation activities soon pay for themselves. The necessary resources are management attention, skills (both inside and outside the organization), manpower, and money.

If it is not possible to add a full-time, first-line manager to the staff, an existing employee should be considered for either a full- or part-time position. Energy management should not be an alternate or collateral duty of a person who is already fully occupied.

Figure 2 shows the organizational functions for effective energy management. The solid lines indicate normal reporting relationships within the organization. The dotted lines indicate new relationships created by energy management. The arrows indicate the primary directions in which initiatives related to energy conservation normally occur. This chart shows the ideal organization. In actuality, however, the functions shown may overlap, especially in smaller organizations. For example, the

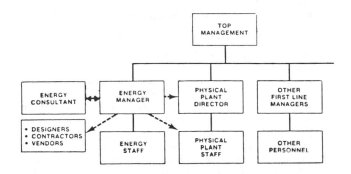

Fig. 2   Organizational Relationships

The preparation of this chapter is assigned to TC 9.6, Systems Energy Utilization.

assistant principal of a high school may also serve as the energy manager and physical plant director. However, the important point is that all functions are covered.

The Energy Manager

The functions of an energy manager fall into the following four broad categories:

1. Technical
2. Policy-related
3. Planning and purchasing
4. Public relations

Technical functions include:

1. Conducting energy audits and identifying energy conservation opportunities (ECOs)
2. Acting as an in-house technical consultant on new energy technologies, alternative fuel sources, and energy-efficient practices
3. Evaluating the energy efficiency of proposed new construction, building expansion, remodeling, and new equipment purchases
4. Setting performance standards for efficient operation and maintenance of machinery and facilities
5. Reviewing state-of-the-art energy management hardware
6. Selecting the most appropriate technology
7. Reviewing operation and maintenance
8. Implementing energy conservation measures (ECMs)
9. Establishing an Energy Accounting Program for continuing analysis of energy use and the results of energy conservation measures
10. Maintaining the effectiveness of energy conservation measures

Policy-related functions include the following:

1. Fulfilling energy policy established by top management
2. Monitoring federal and state legislation and regulatory activities, and recommending policy/response on such issues
3. Representing the organization in energy associations
4. Administering government-mandated reporting programs

Planning and Purchasing functions include the following:

1. Monitoring energy supplies and costs to take advantage of fuel-switching opportunities
2. Ensuring that energy-using systems and equipment are purchased based on economics and ability to perform the required functions, not simply on the lowest initial cost
3. Negotiating or advising on major utility contracts
4. Developing contingency plans for supply interruptions or shortages
5. Forecasting the organization's short- and long-range energy requirements and costs
6. Developing short- and long-range energy conservation plans and budgets
7. Periodic reporting to top management

Public Relations functions include the following:

1. Making fellow employees aware of the benefits of efficient energy use
2. Establishing a mechanism to elicit and evaluate energy conservation suggestions from employees
3. Recognizing successful energy conservation projects through awards to plants or employees
4. Establishing an energy communications network within the organization, including bulletins, manuals, and conferences
5. Making the community aware of the energy conservation achievements of the organization with press releases and appearances at civic groups

General qualifications of the staff energy manager include the following:

1. A technical background, preferably in engineering, including experience in energy-efficient design of building systems and processes
2. Practical, hands-on experience with systems and equipment
3. Goal orientation
4. Ability to work with people at all levels—from operations and maintenance personnel to top management

Specific educational and professional qualifications of the staff energy manager should be as follows:

1. Bachelor of Science degree from an accredited four-year college, preferably in mechanical, electrical, industrial or chemical engineering
2. Thorough knowledge of the principles and practices of energy resource planning and conservation
3. Familiarity with the administrative governing organization
4. Ability to analyze and compile technical and statistical information and reports with particular regard to energy usage
5. Knowledge of resources and information relating to energy conservation and planning
6. Ability to develop and establish effective working relationships with other employees and to motivate people to act without direct control
7. Ability to function as a goal-oriented manager
8. Ability to interpret plans and specifications for buildings facilities
9. Knowledge of the basic types of automatic controls and systems instrumentation
10. Knowledge of energy-related metering equipment and practices
11. Knowledge of the organization's manufacturing processes
12. Knowledge of (a) building systems design and (b) operation and/or maintenance of building systems
13. Personal qualities of (a) interest and enthusiasm for efficient energy use and (b) ability to present ideas to all organization levels

The Energy Consultant

In many instances, the energy manager needs outside assistance to conduct the entire energy management program. An energy consultant may be called on to assist in any of the energy manager's functions and, in addition, may be responsible for training the energy management, operations, and maintenance staffs.

The basic qualifications of an energy consultant should be similar to those of the energy manager. The consultant should be an objective party or engineer with no connections with the sale of product equipment or systems.

Specialists with narrow areas of expertise may not contribute effectively to the system interaction of a comprehensive and integrated energy management program. For example, a lighting engineer could develop methods to reduce lighting energy while simultaneously causing other systems that interact with the lighting system to increase their energy consumption. Optimum energy conservation can only be accomplished if system interaction is thoroughly understood and accounted for by the energy consultant and manager.

Motivation

The success of an energy management program depends on the interests and motivation of the people implementing it (Turner 1982). Participation and communication are key ingredients. Employees can also be stimulated to support an energy management program through awareness, by informing them of the following:

1. The amount of energy they are using
2. Costs
3. The critical part energy has in the continued viability of their jobs
4. What energy saving means in their operations
5. The relationship between the production rate and energy consumption
6. Benefits such as greater comfort, if they participate

To the extent that it is practical, energy management activities can be made a part of each supervisor's performance or job standards. If the supervisor knows that top management is solidly behind the energy management program and the overall performance rating depends, to some extent, on the energy savings the department or group achieves, the supervisor will motivate employee interest and cooperation.

IMPLEMENTING THE ENERGY MANAGEMENT PROGRAM

The following are five basic stages in implementing an energy management program:

1. Develop a thorough understanding of how energy is used.
2. Conduct a planned, comprehensive search to identify all potential opportunities for energy conservation activities.
3. Identify, acquire, allocate, and prioritize the resources necessary to implement and maintain energy conservation opportunities.
4. Accomplish the energy conservation measures in rational order. This is usually a series of independent activities taking place over a period of years.
5. Maintain the energy conservation measures that have been taken. Reevaluate as building functions change over time.

Energy efficiency and/or energy conservation efforts should not be equated with discomfort, nor should they interfere with the primary function of the organization or facility. Energy conservation activities that disrupt or impede normal function of workers and/or processes and adversely affect productivity constitute false economies.

Database

In developing an energy management program, a base of past energy usage and cost should be developed. Any reliable utility data that is applicable should be examined. Generally, this is monthly data and should be analyzed over several years. A base year should be established to be used as a reference point for future energy conservation and energy cost avoidance activities. In tabulating such data, the actual dates of meter readings should be recorded; any periods during which consumption was estimated rather than measured should be noted.

If energy is available for more than one building and/or department within the authority of the energy manager, each of these should be tabulated separately. Initial tabulations should include both Btu (kJ) and cost per unit area. (In an industrial facility, this may be Btu (kJ) and cost per unit of goods produced.) Available information on variables that may have affected past energy use should also be tabulated. These might include heating or cooling degree-days, percent occupancy for a hotel, or quantity of goods produced in a production facility. Since such variables may not be directly proportional to energy use, it is best to plot information separately or superimpose one plot over another, rather than developing values as Btu per square foot per degree day, for example. As such data are tabulated, energy accounting procedures for regular collection and use of future data should be developed.

Table 1   1983 Building Characteristics

| Type | Size—Square Feet* | | | % Buildings Less than 50% | |
| | Per Building | | Avg. Per | | |
	Average	Median	Worker	Heated	Cooled
Assembly	12,000	5,900	914	5	53
Educational	34,200	18,100	986	0	52
Food Sales/Service	5,400	2,800	362	10	37
Health Care	37,600	4,700	413	0	33
Mercantile/Services	9,700	3,500	749	24	68
Lodging	21,100	6,800	944	0	33
Office	14,700	4,100	323	8	27
Residential	10,400	4,400	1,790	0	66
Warehouse	16,000	4,800	1,261	64	89
Other	15,400	3,400	762	41	66
Vacant	11,900	3,300	2,199	67	85

*Multiply values by 0.0929 to convert sizes to square metres.

SOURCE: EIA-246 (83) Figures 3 and 6, Tables 27 and 28. Based on 7140 buildings.

The data in this section provides a basis for comparison. The data presented are obtained from a survey of several thousand buildings in 1983. They are the largest existing consistent collection of data for non-residential buildings. These data are statistically representative of the existing stock of buildings. Caution should be used when comparing other than "typical" or "representative" buildings with these data.

Tables 1 and 2 show physical characteristics of the buildings surveyed. Table 3 shows measured energy consumption data by building type.

Table 2   1983 Building Characteristics

Heating Fuel	Percent	A/C System *(Cont.)*	Percent
Gas	51	Heat Pump	4
Electric	28	Well Water	1
Oil/Kerosene	14	None	33
LPG	4		
Wood	3	**Percent Heated**	
Steam	1	1-50	13
Coal	1	51-99	14
Other	1	100	61
None	11	None	11
Cooling Fuel		**Percent Cooled**	
Electric	64	1-50	25
Gas	4	51-99	13
None	33	100	29
		None	33
Water Heating Fuel		**Floors**	
Gas	36	One	58
Electric	35	Two	23
Oil/Kerosene	4	Three	12
Other	3	Four Plus	7
None	26		
		Year Built	
Cooking Fuel		Before 1900	7
Electric	22	1901-20	10
Gas	17	1921-45	18
LPG	2	1946-60	24
None	63	1961-70	18
		1971-73	5
Heating System		1974-79	13
Self Contained	15	1980-83	4
Combination	74		
Heat Pump	4	**Number of Fuels Used**	
Passive Solar	1	One	20
None	11	Two	61
		Three	5
A/C System		None	4
Window	21	Other	10
Wall	10		
Central	44		

SOURCE: EIA-246 (83) Tables 21,22,23,24,27,28,30,33. Based on 7140 Buildings.

Table 3　1983 Commercial Building Energy Use in the United States

Building Type	Percent		Thousand Btu per Square Foot per Year*						
	Bldg.	Sq. ft.	All Buildings Elec.	Gas	Total	Elec. Heat	Elec. HVAC	Elec. AC	Gas Heat
Assembly	12	11	22	49	69	22	24	25	50
Educational	5	12	26	55	80	32	35	24	63
Food Sales/Service	10	4	108	134	213	131	145	108	145
Health Care	2	4	65	107	204	65	68	62	111
Lodging	3	4	67	99	163	104	108	51	155
Mercantile/Services	28	20	42	42	81	40	40	48	47
Office	15	16	62	66	123	77	77	55	81
Residential	6	5	17	48	73	38	35	13	63
Warehouse	10	13	31	57	76	43	47	30	61
Other	4	5	55	62	101	—	—	47	71
Vacant	5	5	35	57	73	40	31	44	63

*Multiply values by 11.4 to convert to megajoules per square meter per year.
SOURCE: DIA-0318(83) Tables 6, 10, 11, 20, 21, 22, 23. Based on 6345 buildings.

ANSI/ASHRAE *Standard* 105-1984, "Standard Methods of Measuring and Expressing Building Energy Performance," contains information that allows uniform, consistent expressions of energy consumption, both in proposed buildings and in existing buildings. Its use is recommended. However, the data presented here are not in accordance with this standard.

The quality of energy consumption data for buildings published here and elsewhere varies because they are collected for many different purposes by many people with different levels of technical knowledge of buildings. Also, these are national data, so there are regional and local variations.

At this point in the development of an energy management program, it is useful to compile a list of previously accomplished energy conservation measures and the actual energy and/or cost savings of such measures. These items should be targeted for attention during subsequent energy audits to determine their present effectiveness and the effort(s) necessary to maintain and/or improve it.

Since most energy management activities are dictated by economics, the energy manager must understand the utility rates that apply to each facility. Special rates are commonly applied for such variables as interruptible service, on peak/off peak, summer/winter, and peak demand, to name a few. There are more than 1000 electric rate variations in the United States. The energy manager should work with local utilities to develop the most cost effective methods of metering and billing and to enable energy cost avoidance to be calculated effectively.

For example, it is common for electric utilities to meter both electric consumption (kWh) and demand (kWd). Demand is the peak rate of consumption, typically integrated over a 15-minute or 30-minute period. Electric utilities may also establish a "ratchet" billing procedure for demand. A simplified example of ratchet demand billing would state that the "billing demand" is established as either the *actual demand* for the month in question or 85% of the *highest demand* during the previous 11 months, whichever is greatest. Figure 3 illustrates a gas heated, electrically cooled building with the highest electric demands occurring in the summer, and shows actual demand versus billing demand under an 85% "ratchet." The winter demand is approximately 700 kWd each month, with chiller operation causing the August demand to peak at 1000 kWd. Since an 85% "ratchet" applies, all months following August with actual demand lower than 850 kWd are billed at 850 kWd. Therefore, the following can be concluded:

1. Energy conservation that reduces winter demand would not reduce the billed cost of demand, unless it also reduced summer demand; and if such an opportunity was implemented

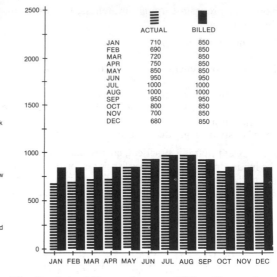

Fig. 3　Actual Demand versus Billing Demand (85%, 11-Month Ratchet)

in September, it would not produce savings in demand billings for the first 11 months.

2. Energy conservation that reduces peak demand in each of the summer months (for example, 50 kWd reduction in chiller peaks) results in savings in demand billings throughout the year.

There are many variations of the above billing methods, and it is important to understand applicable rates.

Priorities

Having established a data base, the energy manager should assign priorities to future work efforts. If there is more than one building or department under the energy manager's care, the data base for energy use and cost for each should be compared on an overall basis and on the basis of energy use and cost per unit area, cost per unit of production, or some other index that demonstrates an acceptable level of accuracy. Comparisons should also be made with realistic energy targets, if they are known. From such comparisons, it is often possible to set priorities that use the available resources most effectively.

At this point, a report should be prepared for top management outlining the data collected, the priorities assigned, and plans for continued development of the energy management program and projected budget needs. This should be the beginning of a regular monthly, quarterly, or semi-annual reporting procedure.

Energy Audits

Three levels of energy audits have been defined (Stewart and Pavlak 1980):

Level I—An energy report that records information on energy use patterns, design characteristics, equipment, systems, and modes of operation and that establishes one or more energy use indices (such as Btu (kJ) and cost per unit area, meal served, guest day, patient day, and product produced).

Level II—A cursory on-site audit that identifies and estimates energy and energy cost savings for no cost/low cost operating and maintenance (O & M) energy-saving measures and indicates the opportunity for capital modification measures. A Level II audit could benefit from the use of a Level II audit workbook/

manual that contains a checklist of O & M and capital modification measures. Level II audits include all Level I requirements.

Level III—A detailed on-site audit that identifies and quantifies the cost effectiveness of operation and maintenance and capital modification energy-saving measures. A Level III audit may benefit from the use of a Level III audit workbook/manual that contains a checklist of O & M and capital intensive modification measures and standard calculation procedures to determine the energy savings for specific measures. Level III audits include all of the Level I and Level II requirements. Level III audits also may require the use of special diagnostic equipment such as flue gas analyzers and airflow measurement devices.

In the complete development of an energy management program, Level III audits should be performed on all facilities, while Level I and Level III audits are useful in establishing the program. Figure 4 illustrates Level III energy audit input procedures in which the following data are collected:

1. General building data
2. Historic energy consumption data
3. Energy systems data

The collected data is used to calculate an energy use profile that includes all end-use categories. From the energy use pro-

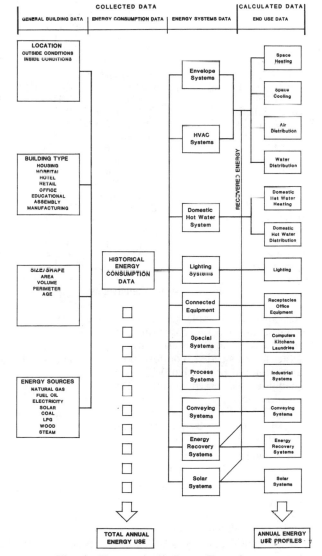

Fig. 4   Energy Audit Input Procedures

files, it is then possible to develop and evaluate Energy Conservation Opportunities.

In conducting an energy audit, a thorough *systems* approach produces the best results. One energy manager has defined the systems approach as beginning at the end rather than at the beginning. As an example of this approach, consider a factory with steam boilers in constant operation. An expedient (and often cost-effective) approach would be to measure the combustion efficiency of each boiler and to take steps to improve boiler efficiency. However, beginning at the end would require observing all or most of the end uses of steam in the plant. It is possible that this would result in the discovery of considerable quantities of steam being wasted by venting to the atmosphere, venting through defective steam traps, uninsulated lines, and passing through unused heat exchangers. Elimination of such end use waste could produce greater savings than those easily and quickly developed by improving boiler efficiency. When using this approach, care must be taken to make cost-effective use of the energy auditor's time. It may not be cost-effective to track down every end use.

When conducting an energy audit, it is important to become familiar with operating and maintenance procedures and personnel; the energy manager can then recommend, through the appropriate departmental channels, energy-saving operating and maintenance procedures. The energy manager should determine, through continued personal observation, the effectiveness of the recommendations and work with the affected personnel in attaining the desired results.

Stewart *et al.* (1984) tabulated 139 different energy audit input procedures and forms for 10 different building types, in each of which 62 factors are used. They discuss features of selected audit forms and can help in developing or obtaining an audit procedure.

To calculate the energy cost avoidance of various energy conservation opportunities, it is helpful to develop an energy cost distribution chart similar to that shown for a hospital in Figure 5. Preliminary information of this nature can be developed from monthly utility data by calculating end use energy profiles (Shchadi *et al.* 1984).

Base load energy use is the amount of energy consumed independent of weather. When a building has electric cooling and no electric heating, the base load energy use is normally the energy consumed during the winter months. The opposite is true for heating. The annual estimated base load energy consump-

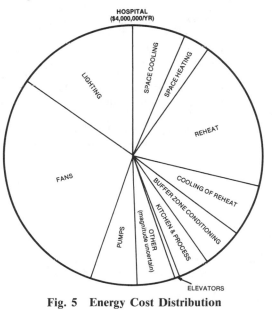

Fig. 5   Energy Cost Distribution

tion can be obtained by establishing the average monthly consumption during the non-heating or cooling months and multiplying by 12. Then, by subtracting the base load energy consumption from the total annual energy consumption, an accurate estimate of the heating or cooling energy consumption can be obtained for many buildings. This approach is not valid when building use differs from summer to winter; when there is cooling in operation 12 months of the year; or when there is space heating use during the summer months, as for reheat.

Although it is difficult to relate heating and cooling energy used in commercial buildings directly to severity of weather, Shehadi *et al.* (1984) suggested that this is possible, using a curve fitting method to calculate the balance point of a building. The pitfalls of such an analysis are estimated, rather than actual, utility usage data; the necessity for using the actual dates of the metered information; and non-regularity of building use and/or operation.

Having used only monthly data, a more detailed breakdown of energy usage requires some metered data to be collected on a daily basis (winter days versus summer days, weekdays versus weekends) and some hourly information to be collected to develop profiles for night (unoccupied), morning warmup, day (occupied), and the shutdown period. For large facilities, some submetering may also be desirable. For relatively constant loads, routine indications may be acceptable. For variable loads, kWh meters will be necessary.

Energy Conservation Opportunities

It is possible to quantitatively evaluate various energy conservation opportunities from the end use energy profiles. Important considerations in this process are as follows:

1. System interaction
2. Utility rate structure
3. Comprehensiveness
4. Quality of energy

Accurate energy savings calculations can be made only if system interaction is understood fully, and proper allowances are made for such interaction. The resultant remaining energy use calculated should be verified against a separately calculated zero-based energy target.

Further, the actual energy cost avoidance may not be proportional to the energy saved, depending on the method of billing for energy used. Using average costs per unit of energy in calculating the energy cost avoidance of a particular measure is likely to result in incorrect values.

Figure 6 is one example of a comprehensive list of potential energy conservation opportunities. The references listed at the end of this chapter also contain such lists. An example of the quality of energy is the analysis of equipment requiring steam at various pressures; that is, steam at higher pressures is intrinsically more valuable.

In addition, previously accomplished energy conservation measures should be evaluated—first to ensure that they have remained effective, and second to consider revising them to reflect changing technology and/or building use.

Prioritize Resources

After establishing a list of energy conservation opportunities, the necessary resources should be evaluated, prioritized, and implemented.

In establishing priorities, the capital cost, cost effectiveness, and resources available must be considered. Factors involved in the desirability of a particular energy conservation retrofit measure are as follows:

BOILERS	OUTSIDE AIR VENTILATION
BOILER AUXILIARIES	VENTILATION LAYOUT
CONDENSATE SYSTEMS	ENVELOPE INFILTRATION
WATER TREATMENT	WEATHERSTRIPPING
FUEL ACQUISITION	CAULKING
FUEL SYSTEMS	VESTIBULES
CHILLERS	ELEVATOR SHAFTS
CHILLER AUXILIARIES	SPACE INSULATION
STEAM DISTRIBUTION	VAPOR BARRIER
HYDRONIC SYSTEMS	GLAZING
PUMPS	INFRARED REFLECTION
PIPING INSULATION	WINDOWS
STEAM TRAPS	WINDOW TREATMENT
DOMESTIC WATER HEATING	SHADING
LAVATORY FIXTURES	VEGETATION
WATER COOLERS	TROMBE WALLS
FIRE PROTECTION SYSTEMS	THERMAL SHUTTERS
SWIMMING POOLS	SURFACE COLOR
COOLING TOWERS	ROOF COVERING
CONDENSING UNITS	LAMPS
CITY WATER COOLING	FIXTURES
AIR HANDLING UNITS	BALLASTS
COILS	SWITCH DESIGN
OUTSIDE AIR CONTROL	PHOTO CONTROLS
BALANCING	INTERIOR COLOR
AIR VOLUME CONTROL	DEMAND LIMITING
SHUTDOWN	CURRENT LEAKAGE
AIR PURGING	POWER FACTOR
MINIMIZING REHEAT	TRANSFORMERS
AIR HEAT RECOVERY	POWER DISTRIBUTION
FILTERS	COOKING PRACTICES
DAMPERS	HOODS
HUMIDIFICATION	REFRIGERATION
DUCT RESISTANCE	DISHWASHING
SYSTEM AIR LEAKAGE	LAUNDRY
DIFFUSERS	VENDING MACHINES
SYSTEM INTERACTION	CHILLER HEAT RECOVERY
SYSTEM RECONFIGURATION	HEAT STORAGE
SPACE SEGREGATION	TIME-OF-DAY RATES
EQUIPMENT RELOCATION	COMPUTER CONTROLS
FAN-COIL UNITS	COGENERATION
HEAT PUMPS	ACTIVE SOLAR SYSTEMS
RADIATORS	STAFF TRAINING
SYSTEM INFILTRATION	OCCUPANT INDOCTRINATION
RELIEF AIR	DOCUMENTATION
SPACE HEATERS	MANAGEMENT STRUCTURE
CONTROLS	FINANCIAL PRACTICES
THERMOSTATS	BUILDING GEOMETRY
SETBACK	SPACE PLANNING
INSTRUMENTATION	

Fig. 6   Comprehensiveness

1. Rate of return (simple payback, life cycle cost)
2. Total savings (energy, cost avoidance)
3. Initial cost (required investment)
4. Other benefits (safety, comfort, improved system reliability and improved productivity)
5. Liabilities (increased maintenance costs and potential obsolescence)
6. Risk of failure (confidence in predicted savings, rate of increase in energy costs, maintenance complications, and success of others with the same measures)

The resources available to accomplish an energy conservation retrofit measure should include the following:

1. Management attention, commitment and follow-through
2. Skills
3. Manpower
4. Investment capital

Energy conservation measures may be financed with the following:

1. Profit/investment
2. Borrowing
3. Rearranging budget priorities
4. Energy savings
5. Shared savings plans with outside firms and investors

When all of the above considerations have been weighed and a prioritized list of recommendations is developed, a report should be prepared for management. Each recommendation should include the following information:

1. The present condition of the system or equipment to be modified
2. The recommended action
3. Who should accomplish the action
4. The necessary documentation or follow-up required
5. Interferences
6. Staff effort required
7. Risk of failure
8. Interactions
9. Economic analysis (including payback, investment cost, and estimated savings figures) using corporate economic evaluation criteria

The energy manager must be prepared to "sell" the plans. Every organization has limited funds available and must use these funds in the most effective way. Energy conservation measures generally must be financially justified if they are to be adopted. In this regard, the energy manager is competing with others in the organization for the same funds. A successful plan is presented in a form easily understood by the decision makers. It must be presented in their language, with the case built around their reference points, rather than those of the energy manager. Finally, it is important that the energy manager present benefits other than the financial ones, such as improved quality of product or the possibility of postponing other expenditures by implementing a particular measure.

Accomplish Measures

From the above prioritized list, and following approval of management, the energy manager directs the completion of selected energy conservation retrofit measures. Certain measures will require that an engineer prepare plans and specifications for the retrofit work. As such, the "package" of services required from the engineer usually includes drawings, specifications, assistance in obtaining competitive bids, evaluation of bids, selection of the best bid, construction observation, final checkout, and assistance in training of personnel in the proper use and application of the revisions.

Maintain Measures

Once energy conservation measures have begun, it is necessary to establish procedures to record, on a frequent and regular basis, energy consumption and costs for each building and/or end use category, in a manner consistent with functional cost accountability. Additional metering may be needed to accomplish this work accurately. Metering can be in the form of devices that automatically read and transmit data to a central location or in the form of less expensive metering devices that require routines for building maintenance and/or security personnel to assist in a regular meter-reading program. Many energy managers find it beneficial to collect energy consumption information as often as daily or twice daily (i.e., shift changes). However, if the energy manager is not able to evaluate data as frequently as it is collected, it may be more practical to collect the data less frequently. The energy manager must review data while it is current and take immediate action if profiles indicate that a trend is in the wrong direction. Such trends could be caused by control systems requiring recalibration, changes in operating practices, or failures of mechanical systems that should be isolated and corrected as soon as possible.

Energy Accounting

The energy manager continues the meter reading, monitoring, and tabulation of facility energy use and profiles. These tabulations indicate the cost of energy management efforts and the resulting energy cost avoidance. In conjunction with this effort, the energy manager periodically reviews pertinent utility rates, rate structures, and their trends as they affect the facility. The energy manager provides periodic reports of the energy management efforts to top management, summarizing the work accomplished, the cost effectiveness of such work, the plans and suggested budget for future work, and projections of future utility costs. If energy conservation measures are to retain their cost effectiveness, continued monitoring and periodic re-auditing is necessary, since many energy conservation measures become less effective if they are not carefully monitored and maintained.

BUILDING ENERGY USE REDUCTION

The need for occasional reductions in energy use during specific periods has become more common due to rising energy costs and sometimes due to supply reductions or equipment failures. Emergency periods include a "short-term" shortage of a particular energy source or sources brought about by factors such as natural disasters, extreme weather conditions, labor strikes, world political activities, or other forces beyond the control of the building owner and operator; by failures in building systems or equipment; or because of self-imposed cutbacks in energy use. This section provides information for building owners and operators to help maintain "near normal" operation of facilities during energy emergencies.

The following terms are applicable to such programs.

Energy Emergency—A period where energy supply reductions and/or climatic and natural forces or equipment failures preclude the "normal" operation of a building and necessitate a reduction in building energy use.

Level of Energy Emergency—A measure of the emergency severity that calls for the implementation of various energy use reduction measures. Typical levels include the following:

1. Green (Normal)—All occupant or building functions maintained and systems operating under the normal operating circumstances for the building
2. Blue—All or most of the occupant or building functions maintained with reductions in building system output that may result in borderline occupancy comfort
3. Yellow—A minor reduction of occupant or building functions with reductions in output
4. Red—A major reduction of occupant or building functions and systems that barely maintains building occupancy capability
5. Black—The orderly shutdown of systems and occupancy that maintains the minimum building conditions needed to protect the building and its systems

Implementation

Each building owner, lessor, and operator should use the energy team approach and identify an individual with the necessary authority who will review and fit recommendations into a plan for the particular building. For each class of emergency, the responsible party recommends a specific plan to reduce building energy use that still maintains the best building environment under the given circumstances. Implementation of the particular recommendations should then be coordinated through the building operator with assistance from the responsible party and the building occupants, as necessary. The plan should be tested occasionally.

Depending upon the type of building, its use, the form of the energy source(s) for each function, and local conditions such as climate and availability of other similar buildings, the following steps should be taken in developing a building energy plan:

1. Develop a list of measures similar to the list below that are applicable to the building.
2. Estimate the amount and type of energy savings for each of the measures and appropriate combination of measures (e.g., account for air-conditioning savings that result from reducing lighting and other internal loads). Tabulate demand and usage savings separately for response to different types of emergencies.
3. For the various levels of energy emergency, develop a plan that would maintain the best building environment under the circumstances. Include both short- and long-term measures in the plan. Operational changes may be implemented quickly and prove adequate for short-term emergencies.
4. Experiment with the plan developed above, record energy consumption and demand reduction data, and revise the plan, as necessary. Much of the experimentation may be done on weekends to minimize disruptive effects.
5. Meet with local utility company(s) to review the plan.

Depending upon the level of energy emergency and the building priority, the following actions are some examples that may be considered in developing the plan for emergency energy reduction in the building:

1. Change operating hours.
2. Move personnel into other building areas (consolidation).
3. Shut off nonessential equipment.

Thermal Envelope

1. Use all existing blinds, draperies, etc., during summer.
2. Install interior window insulation.
3. Caulk and seal around unused exterior doors and windows.
4. Install solar shading devices in summer.
5. Seal all unused vents and ducts to outside.

Heating, Ventilating, and Air Conditioning Systems and Equipment

1. Modify controls or control set points to raise and lower temperature and humidity, as necessary.
2. Shut off or isolate all nonessential equipment.
3. Tune up equipment.
4. Lower thermostat set points in winter.
5. Reduce the level of reheat or eliminate it in winter.
6. Reduce or eliminate ventilation and exhaust airflow.

7. Raise thermostat set points in summer.
8. Reduce the amount of recooling in summer.

Lighting Systems

1. Remove lamps or reduce lamp wattage.
2. Use task lighting, where appropriate.
3. Move building functions to exterior or daylight areas.
4. Turn off electric lights in areas with adequate natural light.
5. Lower luminaire height, where appropriate.
6. Wash all lamps and luminaires.
7. Replace fluorescent ballasts with high efficiency or multilevel ballasts.
8. Revise building cleaning and security procedures to minimize lighting periods.
9. Consolidate parking and turn off unused parking security lighting.

Special Equipment

1. Take transformers off line during periods of nonuse.
2. Shut off or regulate the use of vertical transportation systems.
3. Shut off unused or unnecessary equipment such as duplication equipment, music, typewriters, computers, etc.
4. Reduce or turn off hot water supply.

Building Operation Demand Reduction

1. Sequence heating or air-conditioning systems.
2. Disconnect or turn off all nonessential loads.
3. Turn off some lights.
4. Pre-heat or pre-cool prior to the emergency period.

REFERENCES

Shehadi, Cowan, Spielvogel, and Wulfinghoff. 1984. Energy Use Evaluation. Symposium AT84-8, ASHRAE *Transactions*, Vol. 90, Part 1B, pp. 401-450.

Stewart, R.; Stewart, S.; and Joy, R. 1984. Energy Audit Input Procedures and Forms. ASHRAE *Transactions*, Vol. 90, Part 1A, pp. 350-362.

Stewart, S., and Pavlak, A. 1980. *Model Energy Audit Program Guidelines*. U.S.D.O.E. Agreement DE-FG45-80R510197, p. 24.

Turner, W.C. 1982. *Energy Management Handbook*. John C. Wiley & Sons, Inc., New York, NY, p. 11.

BIBLIOGRAPHY

Freand, J.K. 1980. Selling Energy Management To An Owner's Engineer's Management. *Heating, Piping and Air-Conditioning,* September.

Guide to a Successful Project Energy Conservation & Management, Model Competitive Procurement Procedure and *Professional Selection of Professoinal Engineers.* NSPE-PEPP, 2029 K Street, N.W., Washington, DC 20006.

Landsberg, D., and Stewart, R. 1980. *Improving Energy Efficiency in Buildings.* State University of New York Press, Albany, NY.

Total Energy Management. 1979. National Electrical Contractors Association, Washington, DC.

CHAPTER 49

OWNING AND OPERATING COSTS

A PROPERLY engineered system must also be economical. Economics are difficult to assess because of the complexities that surround the effective management of money and the inherent difficulty of predicting operating and maintenance expenses far into the future. Complex tax structures and the time value of money can affect the final engineering decision. This does not imply the use of either the cheapest or the most expensive system: instead, it demands an intelligent analysis of financial objectives and engineering requirements of the owner. Therefore, the engineer is responsible for evaluating the proper use of money, as dictated by the specific circumstances.

Although intangible factors may alter the final decision between otherwise equal alternatives, the normal choice should be the alternative with the lowest overall cost. This overall cost may be divided into two main categories, owning costs and operating costs, which may be further subdivided as follows:

Owning Costs: (1) Capital Recovery and Interest, (2) Taxes, and (3) Insurance.
Operating Costs: (1) Energy and Fuel, (2) Operating and Maintenance Services, and (3) Materials and Supplies.

A representative form for assembling and tabulating these costs is shown as Table 1.

OWNING COSTS

Three elements must be established to calculate the annual owning cost: (1) initial cost, (2) service life, and (3) the rate of return on the investment.

Initial Cost of System

Major decisions affecting annual owning and operating costs for the life of the building must generally be made prior to the complete development of contract drawings and specifications. Comparisons between alternate methods of solving the engineering problems peculiar to each project must be made in the early stages of architectural design to achieve the best performance and economics. Oversimplified estimates can lead to substantial errors in evaluating the system.

A thorough understanding of the installation costs and accessory requirements must be established. Detailed lists of materials, controls, space and structural requirements, services, installation labor, etc., can be prepared to reduce the inaccuracy in preliminary cost estimates. A reasonable estimate of the cost of components may be derived from the cost records of recent installations of comparable design or from quotations submitted by manufacturers and contractors. Table 2 is a representative checklist for initial cost items.

Amortization and Depreciation

Amortization is the periodic payment of money to discharge a debt; depreciation is the allocation of the first cost of a capital asset over the estimated life of the asset. Depreciation may be deducted from income in calculating income taxes.

Interest and Return on Investment

Money to be invested in a mechanical system must either be borrowed, obtained from equity investors, or diverted from other uses. In any case, it has value. Its minimum value is the rate of interest on invested money. This cost to the owner is a proper part of the total cost of the installation. That cost (interest on debt, return on equity, or a combination of interest and return) varies widely.

Every investor has a minimum acceptable rate of return on investments. This is the rate below which the investment would not be made. The prospective building owner should be consulted to establish the desired rate of return.

Capital Recovery Factor (CRF) is calculated using interest (i) and an amortization period (n) that determines the uniform annual cost needed to repay a debt or initial cost. The factor is determined by:

$$CRF = i\,(1 + i)^n/[(1 + i)^n - 1] \qquad (2)$$

Table 3 gives abbreviated CRF values; some business or engineering calculators include function keys to calculate these values.

Example 1: If a $1000 expenditure is to be amortized over 20 yr at 8%, the CRF factor [by Eq.(2) or from Table 3] is 0.10185. Multiplying the expenditure by the CRF factor gives $101.85. This is the uniform annual owning cost necessary when 20 yr is required to repay the debt.

Insurance

Insurance reimburses a property owner for a financial loss so that equipment can be repaired or replaced. Financial recovery may also include replacing the loss of income, rents, or profits resulting from the property damage.

Some government authorities regulate the activities of insurance companies doing business within their jurisdiction and determine the premium rates that may be charged for various forms of insurable property. Some of the principal factors that influence the total annual premium are building size, construction material, amount and size of mechanical equipment, policy limits of liability, nature of the owner's business, and applied deductibles. The property owner should consult an insurance specialist to select an appropriate insurance program.

OPERATING COSTS

Operating costs result from the actual operation of the system. They include fuel and electrical costs, wages, supplies, water,

---

The preparation of this chapter is assigned to TC 1.8, Owning and Operating Costs.

Table 1   Owning and Operating Cost Data and Summary

OWNING COSTS	
I. Initial Cost of System	
A. Equipment (see Table 2 for items included)....	
B. Control Systems—Complete.................	
C. Wiring and piping costs attributable to system .	
D. Any increase in building construction cost attributable to system........................	+ _____
E. Any decrease in building construction cost attributable to system........................	− _____
F. Installation Costs	
G. Miscellaneous............................	
TOTAL INITIAL COST (IC)	
II. Annual Fixed Charges	
A. Amortization period, n (number of years during which initial cost is to be recovered).......	
B. Interest rate, i	
C. Capital Recovery Factor (CRF); from Table 4 ..	
D. Equivalent uniform annual cost: (CRF) (IC) ...	
E. Income Taxes	
F. Property Taxes	
G. Insurance	
H. Rent	
TOTAL ANNUAL FIXED CHARGES (AFC)	

OPERATING COSTS	
III. Annual Maintenance Allowances	
A. Replacement or servicing of oil, air, or water filters	
B. Contracted maintenance service	
C. Lubricating oil and grease	
D. General housekeeping costs	
E. Replacement of worn parts (labor and material)	
F. Refrigerant	
TOTAL ANNUAL MAINTENANCE ALLOWANCE:	
IV. Annual Energy and Fuel Costs	
A. Electric Energy Costs	
1. Chiller or compressor	
2. Pumps	
a. Chilled water	
b. Heating water........................	
c. Condenser or tower water	
d. Well water...........................	
e. Boiler auxiliaries (including fuel oil heaters).............................	
3. Fans	
a. Condenser or Tower	

IV. Annual Energy and Fuel Costs (*continued*)	
A. Electric Energy Costs (*continued*)	
b. Inside Air Handling	
c. Exhaust	
d. Make-up air	
e. Boiler auxiliaries and equipment room ventilation	
4. Resistance heaters (primary or supplementary)	
5. Heat pump.........................	
6. Domestic water heating	
7. Lighting	
8. Cooking and food service equipment	
9. Miscellaneous (elevators, escalators, computers, etc.)	
B. Gas, Oil, Coal, or Purchased Steam Costs	
1. On-Site generation of the electrical power requirements under *A* this section.......	
2. Heating	
a. Direct heating.....................	
b. Ventilation.......................	
1. Preheaters	
2. Reheaters	
c. Supplementary Heating (i.e., oil preheating).......................	
d. Other	
3. Domestic water heating	
4. Cooking and food service equipment	
5. Air Conditioning	
a. Absorption	
b. Chiller or compressor	
1. Gas and Diesel engine driven........	
2. Gas turbine driven	
3. Steam turbine driven..............	
5. Miscellaneous	
C. Water	
1. Condenser make-up water	
2. Sewer charges	
3. Chemicals.........................	
4. Miscellaneous	
TOTAL ANNUAL FUEL AND ENERGY COSTS:	
V. Wages of engineers and operators	

SUMMARY	
II. Total Annual Fixed Charges	
III. Total Annual Maintenance Costs	
IV. Total Annual Fuel and Energy Costs..........	
V. Annual Wages for Engineers and Operators.....	
TOTAL ANNUAL OWNING AND OPERATING COSTS:...........	

Table 2   Initial Costs

1. **Energy and Fuel Service Costs**
   a. Fuel service, storage, handling, piping, and distribution costs
   b. Electrical service entrance and distribution equipment costs
   c. Total energy plant (See Chapter 10 of this volume.)
2. **Heat-Producing Equipment**
   a. Boilers and furnaces
   b. Steam-water converters
   c. Heat pumps or resistance heaters
   d. Make-up air heaters
   e. Heat-producing equipment auxiliaries
3. **Refrigeration Equipment**
   a. Compressors, chillers, or absorption units
   b. Cooling towers, condensers, well water supplies
   c. Refrigeration equipment auxiliaries
4. **Heat Distribution Equipment**
   a. Pumps, reducing valves, piping, piping insulation, etc.
   b. Terminal units or devices
5. **Cooling Distribution Equipment**
   a. Pumps, piping, piping insulation, condensate drains, etc.
   b. Terminal units, mixing boxes, diffusers, grilles, etc.
6. **Air Treatment and Distribution Equipment**
   a. Air heaters, humidifiers, dehumidifiers, filters, etc.
   b. Fans, ducts, duct insulation, dampers, etc.
   c. Exhaust and return systems
7. **System and Controls Automation**
   a. Terminal or zone controls
   b. System program control
   c. Alarms and indicator system
8. **Building Construction and Alteration**
   a. Mechanical and electric space
   b. Chimneys and flues
   c. Building insulation
   d. Solar radiation controls
   e. Acoustical and vibration treatment
   f. Distribution shafts, machinery foundations, furring

material, and maintenance parts and services. Chapter 28 in the 1985 FUNDAMENTALS Handbook, "Energy Estimating Methods," outlines how to estimate fuel and electrical requirements. Note that total energy consumption cannot generally be multiplied by a per unit energy cost to arrive at annual utility costs.

Electrical Energy

Even the simplest of utility rates have step rate schedules for consumption and the cost of the last unit of energy consumed may be substantially different from the first. The last unit may be cheaper than the first because the fixed costs to the utility have already been recovered from early consumption costs. Alternatively, the last unit of energy may be sold at a higher rate to encourage conservation.

To reflect the time-varying operating costs, some utilities charge different rates for consumption according to the time of use and season, typically rising toward the peak period of use. This may justify the cost of shifting the load to alternate periods. Rates may also vary because of taxes and long-term contracts.

Allowances may be available because of transformer ownership and the voltage provided by the utility. A special rate may be available for specific interruptable loads such as domestic water heaters. Due to substantial variations in fuel prices, electrical utilities may apply a fuel adjustment charge to customers' bills to recover costs. This adjustment may not be reflected in the rate schedules. The utilities should be asked to provide detailed cost estimates for various consumption levels. This should include special rates, allowances, taxes, prompt payment discounts, and fuel adjustments.

Electrical systems may experience low power factor. In this condition, the utility must supply more current and their costs increase. The power factor is the ratio of active (real) power kW to apparent (reactive) power kVA. It is measured as the cosine of the angle, which represents the lead or lag of the current relative to the voltage. Levels close to unity are ignored by most utilities, but severe penalties may be imposed for lower power factors.

Demand. Electric rates may have demand charges based on the customer's peak kW demand, energy charges based on actual kW consumption, and consumer monthly charges for each meter to reflect its hookup cost. While consumption costs tend to cover the utility's operating costs, demand charges cover the utility's owning costs.

Where demand charges are applied, they may be formulated in a variety of ways:

1. Straight charge—$/kW per month, which is charged for the peak demand of the month,
2. Excess charge—$/kW above a basic demand (i.e. 50 kW), which may be established each month.
3. Maximum demand (ratchet)—$/kW for the maximum annual demand, which may be reset only once per year. This established demand may either benefit or penalize the owner.
4. Combination demand—In addition to a basic demand charge, utilities may include further demand charges as demand-related consumption charges in cents per hour of operation of the demand.

Table 3   Capital Recovery Factors

Years	Rate of Return or Interest Rate, %								
	3.5	4.5	6	8	10	12	15	20	25
2	0.52640	0.53400	0.54544	0.56077	0.57619	0.59170	0.61512	0.65455	0.69444
4	0.27225	0.27874	0.28859	0.30192	0.31547	0.32923	0.35027	0.38629	0.42344
6	0.18767	0.19388	0.20336	0.21632	0.22961	0.24323	0.26424	0.30071	0.33882
8	0.14548	0.15161	0.16104	0.17401	0.18744	0.20130	0.22285	0.26061	0.30040
10	0.12024	0.12638	0.13587	0.14903	0.16275	0.17698	0.19925	0.23852	0.28007
12	0.10348	0.10967	0.11928	0.13270	0.14676	0.16144	0.18448	0.22526	0.26845
14	0.09157	0.09782	0.10758	0.12130	0.13575	0.15087	0.17469	0.21689	0.26150
16	0.08268	0.08902	0.09895	0.11298	0.12782	0.14339	0.16795	0.21144	0.25724
18	0.07582	0.08224	0.09236	0.10670	0.12193	0.13794	0.16319	0.20781	0.25459
20	0.07036	0.07688	0.08718	0.10185	0.11746	0.13388	0.15976	0.20536	0.25292
25	0.06067	0.06744	0.07823	0.09368	0.11017	0.12750	0.15470	0.20212	0.25095
30	0.05437	0.06139	0.07265	0.08883	0.10608	0.12414	0.15230	0.20085	0.25031
35	0.05000	0.05727	0.06897	0.08580	0.10369	0.12232	0.15113	0.20034	0.25010
40	0.04683	0.05434	0.06646	0.08386	0.10226	0.12130	0.15056	0.20014	0.25006

5. Some utilities may waive demand charges as encouragement for an "all electric" building.

The actual level of demand represents the peak energy use averaged over a specific period, usually 15, 30, or 60 minutes. Accordingly, high electrical loads of only a few minutes duration may never be recorded at the full instantaneous value. Alternatively, demands may be established during a short period (i.e. 5 minutes out of each hour), where peak demand is recorded as the average of several consecutive short periods.

The particular method of demand metering and billing is an important factor when considering load shedding or shifting devices. The portion of the total bill attributed to demand may vary widely from 0% to as high as 70%, depending on the duration of the demand (i.e., the electrical load factor).

Analytical Methods

Analysis of electrical operating costs starts with the recording of data from the bills on a form similar to that in Table 4. By dividing the consumption by the days between readings, the average daily consumption can be calculated. This consumption should be plotted to detect errors in meter readings or reading dates and to detect consumption variances (see Figure 1). For this example, 312 kWh/day is chosen as the "Base Electrical Consumption" to cover year-round electrical needs such as lighting, business machines, domestic hot water, terminal reheat, security, and safety lighting. At this point, consumptions or spans that appear to be in error should be reexamined and corrected, as necessary. If the reading date for the 10Nov86 bill in Table 4 was 05Nov86, the curve in Figure 1 would be more continuous. On the basis of a 05Nov86 reading, the minimum daily consumption of 312 kWh on the continuous curve (Figure 1) occurred in the February billing.

To start the analysis, the monthly base consumption is calculated (base daily consumption times billing days) and is subtracted from each monthly total to obtain the difference. These differences fall under either summer excess or winter excess, depending upon the season. Excess consumption in the summer is primarily due to the air-conditioning load.

A similar analysis is made of the actual monthly demand. In Table 4, the base demand is 33.0 kW, and it is usually found in the same or adjacent months as the month with the base consumption.

The base consumption can be further analyzed by calculating the electrical load factor (ELF) associated with this consumption. If the base demand had operated 24 hours a day, then base consumption would be:

$$33.0 \text{ kW} \cdot 24 \text{ h/day} = 792 \text{ kWh/day} \tag{1}$$

But if the daily base consumption is 312 kWh/day, then the electrical load factor is:

$$\text{ELF} = \frac{\text{Base Consumption}}{\text{Base Demand} \cdot 24 \text{ h}} = \frac{312}{792} = 0.394 \text{ or } 39.4\% \tag{2}$$

The example indicates that this electrical load factor (39.4%) is higher than the occupancy factor (29.8%).

$$\frac{\text{Occupancy}}{\text{Factor}} = \frac{\text{Occupied Hours}}{24 \text{ hrs} \cdot 7 \text{ days}} = \frac{50}{168} = 0.298 = 29.8\% \tag{3}$$

One reason for this difference may be that the lights are left illuminated beyond the occupied hours.

Because of the extra air conditioning demand, summer demand is 46.8 kW. If this additional demand of 13.8 kW had operated 24 hours each day, the summer extra would equal $13.8 \cdot 24$ or 331.2 kWh/day. The ratio of each summer month's excess as a percent of 331.2 kWh yields the summer electrical load factor. Summer ELFs higher than the occupancy factor indicate that air conditioning is not shut off as early as possible in the evening. Winter excess demand and consumption are analyzed in the same way to yield winter monthly electrical load factors.

Fuels

Natural gas consists of about 96% methane with varying amounts of other gases such as ethane, butane, nitrogen, and carbon dioxide. The thermal content varies from well to well or even from day to day from the same well. Unless the gas is treated to a constant thermal value such as 1000 Btu/ft^3 (37.26 MJ/m^3), the utility may charge according to the thermal value by applying a thermal multiplier to the consumption volume, usually close to unity.

Larger natural gas customers may enjoy a lower rate structure, depending upon the annual volume consumed (it usually must be guaranteed) and upon the interruptability of supply.

Table 4 Analytical Method

Billing Date	Billing Days	Consumption Total Actual	Consumption Actual Per Day	Consumption Base[b]	Air Conditioning Diff.	Air Conditioning ELF	Air Conditioning Excess	Demand Actual	Demand Winter Excess	Demand Summer Excess
12Aug86								46.2		0.6
11Sep86	30	14,700	490	9,360	5,340	53.7	1,859	46.8		1.2
10Oct86	29	10,860	374.5	9,048	1,812	18.9		46.8		1.2
10Nov86	31	9,120	294.2	8,112	1,008[a]	12.8		45.6		0.0
06Dec86	26	10,680	410.8	9,672	1,008[a]			33.0[c]	0.0	
09Jan87	34	10,860	319.4	8,736	252			33.0	0.0	
13Feb87	35	10,920	312[b]	10,920	000			33.6	0.6	
11Mar87	27	8,700	322.2	8,424	276			33.0	0.0	
10Apr87	30	10,140	338	9,360	780			33.6	0.6	
12May87	32	11,020	342.4	9,984	1,036	9.8		45.6[d]		0.0
12Jun87	31	11,760	379.4	9,672	2,088	20.3		46.8		1.2
13Jul87	31	14,160	456.8	9,672	4,488	43.7	893	46.8		1.2
11Aug87	29	14,340	494.5	9,048	5,292	55.2	1,937	46.8		1.2
10Sep87	30	13,740	458	9,360	4,380	42.1	904	46.2		0.6
14Oct87	34	12,120	356.5	10,608	1,512	13.4		45.6		0.0
10Nov87	27	9,360	346.7	8,424	936			33.6		

[a]Estimated from corrected monthly consumption from Figure 1
[b]Base electrical consumption = 312 kW h/day
[c]Base winter demand = 33 kW
[d]Base summer demand = 45.6 kW. Base summer excess demand = (45.6 − 33) = 12.6

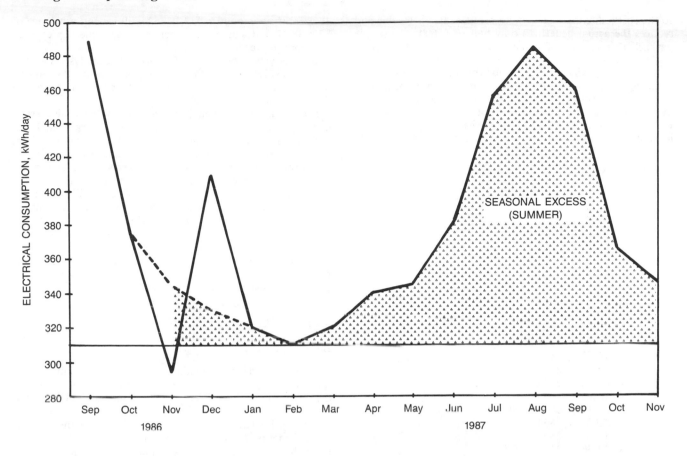

Fig. 1 Average Daily Electrical Consumption (from Table 5)

Where boilers and steam generators have dual fuel capabilities (both natural gas and fuel oil), the natural gas distributor may allow a lower rate, since they can shed a large customer under peak load conditions, such as during severely cold weather.

Future Costs

Future costs of fuels and electricity are only an estimate. These forecasts are often done in "constant dollars," and may require adjustment before use. Forecasts of future costs can be obtained from utilities, governments, or private sources. This cost can have an important effect on an economic analysis.

Maintenance

Dohrmann and Alereza (1986) determined the annual maintenance cost of HVAC systems including wages, supplies, materials, parts, and payments to maintenance service firms. The annual cost in 1983 to maintain a 10-year old system, in a 100,000 square foot building, consisting of a centrifugal chiller, fire-tube gas fired boiler, and a VAV distribution system, was about $0.358 US per square foot ($3.85/m²). The study also indicated that the cost would change with the substitution of other HVAC equipment.

Chapter 59 covers the maintenance, maintainability, and reliability of systems. The quality of maintenance and maintenance supervision can be a major factor in the energy cost of a building. The extent of the maintenance is, in itself, a substantial operating cost to the building owner.

Other Factors

The various options available to the designer may impact other cost factors. The owner should be advised of the following:

1. Equipment rooms, electric meter and switchgear rooms, and duct and/or pipe chases may impact upon the leasable space and the realizable income of the owner.
2. Taxes and/or tax credits may vary from time to time. These must be investigated thoroughly.
3. Depreciation rates may be straight line or accelerated. Consult the owner and local authorities before proceeding with any economic analysis to avoid unreasonable assumptions.

Tangible and certain non-tangible **future costs and benefits**, which may stem from proposed **capital expenditures**, must be considered. Such non-tangible items as aesthetics, acoustics, specific comfort, security, and flexibility must be considered. Energy management or control methods may increase utility costs and/or shorten service life.

ECONOMIC ANALYSIS TECHNIQUES

For any proposed capital investment, the primary future consequences lie in the area of energy costs, maintenance costs, and interest charges on money borrowed to finance the project. Current marginal costs of the last unit of energy, including all local taxes, fuel adjustments, and prompt payment discounts, establish the changes in the operating cost during the first year. If the proposed capital expenditure is $18,000 and the annual savings is estimated at $5000, the simple payback would be in 3.6 years (18,000/5000). Corporate income taxes are usually about 50%, so the cost reduction means more profit, which is taxable and reduces the actual benefit to only half of $5000. The simple payback after taxes therefore increases from 3.6 years to 7.2 years (18,000/2500).

Discounted payback accounts for the time value of money. If management require a 15% rate of return on investments, savings beyond the current year must be discounted at 15%, since they are not available now. The present value of a $2500 saving, which will not be realized until next year, is only $2173.91. If it is not realized until the third year, then it is worth only $1890.36 now.

Present Worth Discounted Benefits

$$PW = BENEFIT/(1 + i)^n$$

$2173.91 = 2500/1.15
$1890.36 = 2500/(1.15 \cdot 1.15)$
$1643.79 = 2500/(1.15 \cdot 1.15 \cdot 1.15)$
$1429.38 = 2500/1.15^4$
$1242.94 = 2500/1.15^5$
$1080.82 = 2500/1.15^6$
$ 939.84 = 2500/1.15^7$
$ 817.25 = 2500/1.15^8$
$ 710.65 = 2500/1.15^9$
$ 617.96 = 2500/1.15^{10}$
$ 537.35 = 2500/1.15^{11}$
$ 467.27 = 2500/1.15^{12}$
$ 406.32 = 2500/1.15^{13}$
$ 353.32 = 2500/1.15^{14}$
$ 307.23 = 2500/1.15^{15}$
$ 267.16 = 2500/1.15^{16}$
$ 232.31 = 2500/1.15^{17}$
$ 202.01 = 2500/1.15^{18}$
$ 175.66 = 2500/1.15^{19}$
$ 152.75 = 2500/1.15^{20}$

The total of all the discounted future costs and benefits is the **net present value**. For this example, the present value of the benefits after 20 years is only $15,648.33, and the investment of $18,000.00 is still not matched. The net present value is −2351.67 (negative).

Capital investments decrease in value over time due to wear and tear. Such a decrease is allowed in computing the value for tax purposes. This decrease is called depreciation. The allowable annual **depreciation rate and term** on the original capital investment must be known and deducted from the "before tax" benefit before the tax rate is applied.

$$ATB = BTB - RATE (BTB - DEPR) \quad (5)$$

where

ATB = After Tax Benefit
BTB = Before Tax Benefit
RATE = Corporate Tax Rate
DEPR = Depreciation Allowed

If the depreciation rate is 10% per year or $1800 and the tax rate is 50%, then the after-tax benefit in the first year is:

$$ATB = 5000 - 0.50 (5000 - 1800) = \$3400$$

By applying management's required rate of return by discounting the first year after-tax benefit at the rate of 15% present values are:

2nd year $2956.52 = 3400/1.15,
3rd year $2570.88 = 3400/1.15 × 1.15,
4th year $2235.56 = 3400/1.15 × 1.15 × 1.15,
5th year $1943.96 = 3400/1.15^4,
7th year $1469.91 = 3400/1.15^6,
nth year $ ATB = 3400/1.15^{(n-1)}.

If the discounted, after tax benefits are accumulated, after

11 years they amount to $17,794.62, still leaving a balance of $205.38, So a discounted payback after taxes and depreciation is slightly more than 11 years.

In cases where the period of an economic analysis is greater than the expected life of the building components, the replacement of such components must be calculated as a negative cash flow.

Service life is the median time during which a particular system or component remains in its original service application and then is replaced. Replacement may occur for any reason including, but not limited to, failure, general obsolescence, reduced reliability, excessive maintenance cost, and changed system requirements due to such influences as building characteristics or energy prices.

Table 5 lists representative estimates of service life of various system components. The service life may not be the same as the depreciation period or the study period.

A number of other factors must be considered in the life cycle costing technique of **cash flow analysis**.

The **present worth** of an annual cost over a selected time period (*n*), using interest on money (*i*) and a cost escalation (*j*), is called **Present Worth Escalation Factor** (PWEF). For constant rates, the suggested formula is:

$$PWEF = \frac{[(1 + j)/(1 + i)]^n - 1}{j - 1} \quad \text{for } j \neq 1$$

$$PWEF = n \quad \text{for } j = 1 \quad (7)$$

During periods of substantial inflation, savings estimated during the first year will escalate in future years. In addition, depreciation may be accelerated by applying a higher rate, but on the declining balance. Finally, portions of the project may be financed where interest to be paid will reduce the value of future benefits. The principal portion of the loan must be paid throughout the term of the loan and is part of present value calculations. At the end of the study period, the initial investment may have some salvage value, for which the asset may be sold. This value must be considered in the complete analysis.

Consider the following assumptions in conjunction with the cash flow analysis in Table 6:

$18,000 project cost
$16,000 cash outlay
5% inflation rate on future benefits
20% depreciation allowance on the declining balance
7.5% interest rate for 10 years on $2000 to be financed
20-year study period
$2000 estimated salvage value (in current dollars)

Various analysis techniques and their required data can have an important impact upon the results. When they are applied to the sample assumptions in Table 6 and previous examples, the payback results vary as follows:

Analysis Considerations	Payback Period
Simple payback	3.6 years
Tax effects at 50%	7.2 years
Future benefits discounted	20+ years
Asset depreciated	11+ years
First-year benefits escalated, project partially debt financed, asset has salvage value	7.4 years

SHARED SAVINGS

This contractual arrangement, whereby savings are shared for a limited time between the owner and the consultant-contractor, can mean substantially less initial investment on the owner's part. For a relatively low initial cost, the owner receives a portion of the future savings. The contractor, who finances the bulk of the

Table 5 Equipment Service Life[a]

Equipment Item	Median Years	Equipment Item	Median Years	Equipment Item	Median Years
Air conditioners		Air terminals		Air-cooled condensers	20
Window unit	10	Diffusers, grilles, and registers	27	Evaporative condensers	20
Residential single or split package	15	Induction and fan-coil units	20	Insulation	
Commercial through-the-wall	15	VAV and double-duct boxes	20	Molded	20
Water-cooled package	15	Air washers	17	Blanket	24
Heat pumps		Duct work	30	Pumps	
Residential air-to-air	15[b]	Dampers	20	Base-mounted	20
Commercial air-to-air	15	Fans		Pipe-mounted	10
Commercial water-to-air	19	Centrifugal	25	Sump and well	10
Roof-top air conditioners		Axial	20	Condensate	15
Single-zone	15	Propeller	15	Reciprocating engines	20
Multizone	15	Ventilating roof-mounted	20	Steam turbines	30
Boilers, hot water (steam)		Coils		Electric motors	18
Steel water-tube	24 (30)	DX, water, or steam	20	Motor starters	17
Steel fire-tube	25 (25)	Electric	15	Electric transformers	30
Cast iron	35 (30)	Heat Exchangers		Controls	
Electric	15	Shell-and-tube	24	Pneumatic	20
Burners	21	Reciprocating compressors	20	Electric	16
Furnaces		Package chillers		Electronic	15
Gas- or oil-fired	18	Reciprocating	20	Valve actuators	
Unit heaters		Centrifugal	23	Hydraulic	15
Gas or electric	13	Absorption	23	Pneumatic	20
Hot water or steam	20	Cooling towers		Self-contained	10
Radiant heaters		Galvanized metal	20		
Electric	10	Wood	20		
Hot water or steam	25	Ceramic	34		

[a]Obtained from a nation-wide survey conducted by ASHRAE TC 1.8 (Akalin 1978). Data changed by TC 1.8 in 1986.
[b]See Lovvorn and Hiller (1985) and Easton Consultants (1986) for further information.

Table 6 Cash Flow Analysis

End of Year	(1) Elec. Saving	(2) Fuel Saving	(3) Main-tenance Saving	(4) Interest (If De-ductible)	(5) Net Benefits Before Taxes (1+2+3+4)	(6) Depre-ciation Allowance	(7) Taxable Benefits (5 + 6)	(8) Taxes (50%) of 7)	(9) Net Benefits After Taxes (5 - 8)	(10) Non Deductible Part of Loan (Princ.)	(11) Cash Outlay/ Salvage	(12) Total Benefits (9 − 10 + 11)	(13) Present Value (15% Disc on 12)
0	$0	$0	$0	$0	$0	$0	$0	$0	$0	$0	$ − 16,000	$ − 16,000	$ − 16,000
1	$5,000	$0	$0	$ − 150	$4,850	$ − 3,600	$1,250	$625	$4,225	$141		$4,084	$3,551
2	$5,250	$0	$0	$ − 139	$5,111	$ − 2,880	$2,231	$1,115	$3,995	$152		$3,843	$2,906
3	$5,512	$0	$0	$ − 128	$5,385	$ − 2,304	$3,081	$1,540	$3,844	$163		$3,681	$2,420
4	$5,788	$0	$0	$ − 116	$5,672	$ − 1,843	$3,829	$1,915	$3,758	$176		$3,582	$2,048
5	$6,078	$0	$0	$ − 103	$5,975	$ − 1,475	$4,500	$2,250	$3,725	$189		$3,536	$1,758
6	$6,381	$0	$0	$ − 88	$6,293	$ − 1,180	$5,113	$2,557	$3,736	$203		$3,533	$1,528
7	$6,700	$0	$0	$ − 73	$6,627	$ − 944	$5,684	$2,842	$3,786	$218		$3,567	$1,341
8	$7,036	$0	$0	$ − 57	$6,979	$ − 755	$6,224	$3,112	$3,867	$235		$3,632	$1,187
9	$7,387	$0	$0	$ − 39	$7,348	$ − 604	$6,744	$3,372	$3,976	$252		$3,724	$1,059
10	$7,757	$0	$0	$ − 20	$7,736	$ − 483	$7,253	$3,627	$4,110	$271		$3,839	$949
11	$8,144	$0	$0	$0	$8,144	$ − 387	$7,758	$3,879	$4,266	$0		$4,266	$917
12	$8,552	$0	$0	$0	$8,552	$ − 309	$8,242	$4,121	$4,430	$0		$4,430	$828
13	$8,979	$0	$0	$0	$8,979	$ − 247	$8,732	$4,366	$4,613	$0		$4,613	$750
14	$9,428	$0	$0	$0	$9,428	$ − 198	$9,230	$4,615	$4,813	$0		$4,813	$680
15	$9,900	$0	$0	$0	$9,900	$ − 158	$9,741	$4,871	$5,029	$0		$5,029	$618
16	$10,395	$0	$0	$0	$10,395	$ − 127	$10,268	$5,134	$5,261	$0		$5,261	$562
17	$10,914	$0	$0	$0	$10,914	$ − 101	$10,813	$5,407	$5,508	$0		$5,508	$512
18	$11,460	$0	$0	$0	$11,460	$ − 81	$11,379	$5,690	$5,771	$0		$5,771	$466
19	$12,033	$0	$0	$0	$12,033	$ − 65	$11,968	$5,984	$6,049	$0		$6,049	$425
20	$12,635	$0	$0	$0	$12,635	$ − 52	$12,583	$6,291	$6,343	$0	$5,307	$11,650	$712

Assumptions:
Annual inflation rate is 5% for the entire analysis.
Electrical cost increase is the same as inflation

Net present value is	$9,217
Internal rate of return is	24.25%
Years to payback	7.38 years

initial cost, receives the largest portion of the cost savings, as determined by the agreement. The shared savings technique is a new method of financing. As a result, local tax laws must be investigated because they affect the benefits and costs. This form of financing is primarily for the building owner who may have reservations about future benefits and, therefore, is unwilling or unable to provide all the financing.

In the cash flow analysis example in Table 7, the owner's financial viewpoint where there are five buildings to be retrofitted can be considered in the following manner. If the initial cost

Table 7 Owner's Cash Flow Analysis With Shared Savings

End of Year	(1) Elec. Saving	(2) Fuel Saving	(3) Maintenance Saving	(4) Interest (If Deductible)	(5) Net Benefits Before Taxes (1+2+3+4)	(6) Capital Cost Allowance	(7) Taxable Benefits (5 + 6)	(8) Taxes (50% of 7)	(9) Net Benefits After Taxes (5 - 8)	(10) Non Deductible Part of Loan (Princ.)	(11) Cash Outlay/ Salvage	(12) Total Benefits (9 - 10 + 11)	(13) Present Value (15% Disc on 12)
0	$0	$0	$0	$0	$0	$0	$0	$0	$0	$0	$ - 16,000	$ - 16,000	$ - 16,000
1	$5,000	$0	$0	$ - 150	$4,850	- $18,000	- $13,150	$ - 6,575	$11,425	$141		$11,284	$9,812
2	$5,250	$0	$0	$ - 139	$5,111	$0	5,111	$2,555	$2,555	$152		$2,403	$1,817
3	$5,512	$0	$0	$ - 128	$5,385	$0	$5,385	$2,692	$2,692	$163		$2,529	$1,663
4	$5,788	$0	$0	$ - 116	$5,672	$0	$5,672	$2,836	$2,836	$176		$2,661	$1,521
5	$30,388	$0	$0	$ - 103	$30,285	$0	$30,285	$15,143	$15,143	$189		$14,954	$7,435
6	$31,907	$0	$0	$ - 88	$31,819	$0	$31,819	$15,909	$15,909	$203		$15,706	$6,790
7	$33,502	$0	$0	$ - 73	$33,429	$0	$33,429	$16,715	$16,715	$218		$16,496	$6,202
8	$35,178	$0	$0	$ - 57	$35,121	$0	$35,121	$17,560	$17,560	$235		$17,326	$5,664
9	$36,936	$0	$0	$ - 39	$36,897	$0	$36,897	$18,449	$18,449	$252		$18,196	$5,173
10	$38,783	$0	$0	$ - 20	$38,763	$0	38,763	$19,381	$19,381	$271		$19,110	$4,724
11	$40,722	$0	$0	$0	$40,722	$0	$40,722	$20,361	$20,361	$0		$20,361	$4,376
12	$42,758	$0	$0	$0	$42,758	$0	$42,758	$21,379	$21,379	$0		$21,379	$3,996
13	$44,896	$0	$0	$0	$44,896	$0	$44,896	$22,448	$22,448	$0		$22,448	$3,648
14	$47,141	$0	$0	$0	$47,141	$0	$47,141	$23,571	$23,571	$0		$23,571	$3,331
15	$49,498	$0	$0	$0	$49,498	$0	$49,498	$24,749	$24,749	$0		$24,749	$3,042
16	$51,973	$0	$0	$0	$51,973	$0	$51,973	$25,987	$25,987	$0		$25,987	$2,777
17	$54,572	$0	$0	$0	$54,572	$0	$54,572	$27,286	$27,286	$0		$27,286	$2,536
18	$57,300	$0	$0	$0	$57,300	$0	$57,300	$28,650	$28,650	$0		$28,650	$2,315
19	$60,165	$0	$0	$0	$60,165	$0	$60,165	$30,083	$30,083	$0		$30,083	$2,114
20	$63,174	$0	$0	$0	$63,174	$0	$63,174	$31,587	$31,587	$0	$5,307	$36,893	$2,254

Assumptions:
Annual inflation rate is 5% for the entire analysis.
Electrical cost increase is the same as inflation

Net present value is	$65,189
Internal rate of return is	51.1%
Years to payback	4.16 years

is 20% of the $90,000 cost to implement the recommended actions, the investment is still $18,000. If the total investment is depreciated, for tax purposes, in the first year and the owner receives 20% of the savings for the first four years and 100% thereafter, the cash flow is shown in Table 7. The discounted payback is 4.2 years in this example.

REFERENCES

Akalin, M.T. 1978. Equipment Life and Maintenance Cost Survey. ASHRAE *Transactions,* Vol. 84, Part 2, pp. 94-106.

Dohrmann, D.r.; and Alereza, T. 1986. Analysis of Survey Data on HVAC Maintenance Costs. ASHRAE *Transactions,* Vol. 92, Part 2A.

Easton Consultants. 1986. Survey of Residential Heat Pump Service Life and Maintenance Issues. Available from American Gas Association, Arlington, VA (Catalog No. S-77126).

Lovvorn, N.C.; and Hiller, C.C. 1985. A Study of Heat Pump Service Life. ASHRAE *Transactions,* Vol. 91, Part 2B, pp. 573-588.

BIBLIOGRAPHY

ASTM. 1985. Definition of Terms Relating to Building Economics. (Rev. A). ASTM *Standard* E833-85. American Society for Testing and Materials, Philadelphia.

Kurtz, M. 1984. *Handbook of Engineering Economics: Guide for Engineers, Technicians, Scientists, and Managers.* McGraw-Hill, New York.

Quirin, D.G. 1967. *The Capital Expenditure Decision.* Richard D. Irwin, Inc., Homewood, IL.

Van Horne, J.C. 1980. *Financial Management and Policy.* Prentice Hall, Inglewood, NJ.

CHAPTER 50

CONTROL OF GASEOUS CONTAMINANTS

THIS chapter concerns designing and using commercially available equipment and techniques to control gaseous contaminants and odors in occupied or conditioned space. Although some of the techniques apply to industrial emissions or processes, other chapters deal more specifically with those objectives. (See Chapter 11 of the 1983 EQUIPMENT Volume.) The fundamentals and control of air contaminants are in Chapters 11 and 12 of the 1985 FUNDAMENTALS Volume.

Several advances relating to gas filtration (i.e., removing gaseous contaminants from an airstream) have been made. ASHRAE *Standard* 62-1981 lists health standards established by law and government agencies, such as the Occupational Safety and Health Administration (OSHA) and the Environmental Protection Agency (EPA). Gas-measuring equipment has become more accurate and dependable, and the performance and application of control methods are better understood (Csermely and Bosworth 1964). Also, field performance data augment laboratory data to provide more reliable system design factors (Dravnicks and Whitfield 1971).

Reducing makeup air, which increases recirculation, lowers the thermal energy required to condition the air but increases the concentration of gaseous contaminants. These factors make the gaseous environment as important as the heating, cooling, and humidity aspects of comfort engineering.

DEFINING THE PROBLEM

To deal with gaseous contamination, the engineer must consider the source, nature, concentration, applicable standards, air dynamics, any special related conditions, and economics. Designers should define these factors thoroughly to make selecting control devices and media easier.

Source. Defining the source (e.g., polluted makeup or ventilation air, high peak occupancy, or process emissions) is probably the most significant and difficult aspect in defining the contamination problem. Studying the source may enable the problem to be treated at the point of generation or isolated by exhaust.

Nature. The nature of the contaminants helps determine the urgency of the problem and the selected control strategy. Gaseous contaminants may cause stuffiness or odor, be toxic or irritating, or have carcinogenic potential.

All ambient airstreams contain a mixture of trace contaminants, yet only one or a small number of contaminants may cause a problem in a particular case. The mixture should be characterized as precisely as possible by measurement or by calculation from generation rates. Nevertheless, characterizing the active constituents in any mixture often presents formidable problems for the analytical chemist. The capacity and maintenance costs of the control device can be determined by considering generation rates of the contaminants characterized in whatever terms possible.

Applicable standards, together with the nature of the contaminant, dictate the control levels. In an odor problem, the desired control level may be below the odor threshold or at some other level prescribed by appropriate guidelines. For example, formaldehyde causes discomfort at 0.1 ppm or lower, but occupational regulations describe it as a health hazard at 3 ppm. The sulfur dioxide limit for workers is set at 5 ppm, but it causes electronic apparatus to corrode at 0.05 ppm. The engineer must determine whether the control motive is legal compliance, comfort, or protection. These factors determine the design criteria for the equipment and control devices. The standards of the American Conference of Governmental Industrial Hygienists, The American Industrial Hygiene Association, and the Occupational Safety and Health Administration are widely known and used.

Air dynamics affect the designer's ability to isolate contaminants or capture contaminated air for concentration and treatment. Relevant factors include dilution, mixing, appropriate air change rates, and pressurization.

Special related conditions include the effect of neighboring emissions, inadvertent recycling of untreated exhaust, changes in standards, abrupt changes in humidity and temperature, changes in manufacturing processes, and coincident loads of airborne particulates.

Economics can be an overriding consideration since the cost of air-cleaning systems can vary greatly, depending on the performance requirements imposed. Studying these considerations should help in selecting the system with the best cost/value relationship.

APPLICATIONS

General applications of gas and odor filtering equipment include the following (starred (*) items have energy conservation implications):

1. Treatment of ventilation or makeup air to remove ambient pollutants or contaminants to protect the occupant or contents of the space.
2. Treatment of makeup air to reach acceptable ventilation air quality as defined by ASHRAE *Standard* 62-1981.
*3. Treatment of industrial exhaust air (subsequent to use of pollution abatement equipment) for use as recycled air in the conditioned space.
*4. Treatment and recirculation of toilet exhaust.
*5. Treatment of recirculated air to relieve stuffiness and odor as a substitute for ventilation air. ASHRAE *Standard* 62-1981 permits such recirculation under conditions that insure adequate indoor air quality.
6. Treatment of in-plant air to reduce hazardous gas concentrations below levels specified by standards or agencies.
*7. Treatment of in-plant air to eliminate exposure to harmful gases, e.g., carcinogens.

The preparation of this chapter is assigned to TC 2.3, Air Contaminants: Gaseous and Particulate.

8. Treatment of breathing air for isolated booths, control suites, single respirators, or closed-loop hyperbaric systems.

*9. Treatment of captured exhaust from localized processes and procedures, e.g., safety cabinets, for recycling.

10. Treatment of air contaminants generated by mechanical equipment, i.e., ozone from electrostatic grids or off-odor from heat exchange equipment.

11. Treatment of air made hostile to delicate electronic apparatus (i.e., computers) or mechanical equipment (i.e., air compressors) by process-generated acid gas fumes (i.e., sulfur and chlorine compounds).

*12. Treatment of highly objectionable localized odors, generally the decay products of proteins from organic waste (e.g., morgues, animal rooms).

ENERGY CONSERVATION

Ventilation is traditionally used to control gaseous odors by diluting them with outdoor air or by exhausting contaminated air and introducing makeup air to the space. Since air within occupied space represents an energy investment in heating or cooling, it can be wasteful to throw away conditioned air for contaminant or odor control. The designer should examine the cost of each aspect of environmental control. Suitable treatment and reuse of air saves almost all heating and cooling energy, unlike heat exchange devices. Economics and conservation have thrust gaseous contamination control into fields of application formerly solved by exhaust and ventilation.

Energy savings can be calculated using the temperature bin method. If repetitive calculations are planned, the bin method can be upgraded to a computer program. Extensive computer programs generally are not required for these calculations because the only unknown in the procedure is the supply air temperature, which may be predicted for each 5 °F (3 °C) temperature bin.

When treated recirculation air systems replace exhaust air systems using 100% outside air, they should have "economizer ventilation" cycles that can use up to 100% outside air when it is beneficial. Economizer cycles generally use 100% outside air when temperatures are between 55 and 70 °F (13 and 21 °C); therefore, no energy is saved in this range of outside temperatures. If the economizer cycle is not used, there could be a penalty in using treated recirculated air in this temperature range.

The momentary savings from reduced ventilation can be estimated using the information and methods in Chapter 28 of the 1985 FUNDAMENTALS Volume. A useful estimate of ventilation savings can be made by the bin method. An instantaneous energy calculation is performed at many different outdoor dry-bulb temperatures. The results are multiplied by the number adjusted to accommodate other energy consumption factors such as humidification and dehumidification.

Example: Assume the following conditions for a ventilation system in Little Rock, Arkansas.

1. Comfort conditioning is achieved using a heat pump with the performance coefficient listed in Table 6 of Chapter 28 of the 1985 FUNDAMENTALS Volume.
2. The indoor temperature is 72 °F throughout the heating season.
3. Energy for humidification/dehumidification is neglected.
4. Electricity cost is $0.08/kWh.

Solution: Applicable equations are:

$$q = 60 \varrho \dot{V} c_p (t_i - t_o)$$
$$= 1.08 \dot{V} (t_i - t_o)/COP \text{ and } Q = \Sigma q\tau$$

where

q = rate of heat transfer to the ventilation air, Btu/h
ϱ = density of Standard dry air, 0.075 lb/ft^3

$\dot{V}$ = volumetric flow rate of Standard ventilation air, 1.0 scfm
c_p = Specific heat at a constant volume of Standard dry air, Btu/(lb °F)
t_i = indoor design temperature, 72 °F
t_o = outdoor temperature, °F
COP = heat pump coefficient of performance
Q = energy used to condition ventilation air, Btu
τ = hours of occurrence of each t_o (from weather data)

The table below illustrates the bin method to calculate the cost of ventilation air.

t_o (Outdoor Temp) °F	Coefficient of Performance (COP)	$q = \dfrac{1.08 \dot{V} (t_i - t_o)}{COP}$ (Btu/h)	τ (hours)	$q\tau$ (Btu)
72	2.60	0	940	0
67	2.63	2.05	803	1650
62	2.66	4.06	725	2940
57	2.66	6.09	672	4090
52	2.64	8.18	638	5220
47	2.59	10.4	669	6970
42	2.53	12.8	605	7750
37	2.45	15.4	509	7850
32	2.36	18.3	363	6640
27	2.25	21.6	172	3720
22	2.12	25.5	50	1270
17	1.97	30.2	25	754
12	1.81	35.8	5	179
7	1.65	42,5	1	43

$Q = \Sigma q\tau = 49,100$ Btu/scfm
Cost/scfm $= 49,100/3414$ Btu/kWh $\cdot \$0.08$/kWh $= \$1.151$ per scfm

---

Table 1 summarizes energy savings for 16 cities in the United States. Suprisingly, annual savings for all U.S. cities are about $1.00 per cfm ($0.50 per L/s), with the exception of California and Arizona, which have moderate dry-bulb temperatures and low wet-bulb temperatures. Gulf coast cities have high cooling season savings and small heating season savings. The opposite is true for the eastern seaboard and upper midwest cities.

In general HVAC practice, using odor control equipment with particulate filters to reduce outdoor air requirements is acceptable, though not widely used. Figure 1 illustrates the theoretical decay rate of a contaminant using ventilation dilution (lower curve) and recirculation with a contamination control device with 50% efficiency. Similiar curves may be plotted using equations derived by Turk (1963) and Yocum and Cote (1971). Although gaseous contamination control devices may not be 100% efficient for all gaseous airborne pollutants, the engineer can combine ventilation and recirculation with treatment to provide air of acceptable quality while conserving energy.

ASHRAE *Standard* 62-1981 lists ventilation rates, minimum standards for ventilation air quality, minimum standards for recirculated air quality, and permits greatly reduced levels of ventilaiton air through the use of appropriate gas and particulate filtration. Table 2 lists the ventilation air quality standards acceptable under ASHRAE *Standard* 62-1981, accepted by many state and local code groups, and recognized in energy-related legislation.

In addition to ventilation reduction, forced exhaust, hoods, or toilet exhaust should be reduced to a minimum. These areas impose a demand for makeup air, far in excess of that prescribed by ASHRAE *Standard* 62-1981. Where permitted by code, filtering and recirculating air exhausted from toilets can save energy. Furthermore, highly contaminated industrial exhaust air that would normally be treated for emission control can be treated secondarily to meet health and comfort standards.

Table 1   Annual Savings per 10,000 cfm Treated Exhaust Air

	Cooling		Heating		Humidification	
	Ton Hours	Plant Reduction, Tons	Energy, Million Btu	Plant Output Reduction, 1000 Btu/h	Energy, Million Btu	Plant Output Reduction, 1000 Btu/h
Phoenix	44,565	30	670	389	268	153
Los Angeles	8,978	20	822	292		
Sacramento	14,228	27	1117	410		173
San Diego	22,973	23	826	281		110
San Francisco		6	1202	346		145
Denver			2097	745	839	242
Washington	49,178	40	1564	572	326	214
Tampa	178,106	51	333	324		138
Atlanta	78,270	40	1069	518	124	207
Chicago	31,444	40	2107	799	494	248
St. Louis	58,331	44	1582	691	378	235
New York	38,393	37	1654	572	405	214
Charlotte	65,070	40	1161	518	185	207
Nashville	68,156	40	1363	605	181	221
Houston	166,365	51	604	410		173
Seattle	4,395	9	1702	475	147	193

Operating basis:

24-h, 365-day operation

Cooling above 27.0 Btu/lb dry air (72°F db, 50% rh or 75°F db, 45% rh)

Heating to 70°F supply air

Humidification to 36 grain/lb dry air (72°F db, 30% rh, 40°F dp)

Cooling and heating plant reductions based on ASHRAE 2.5% and 97.5% design

Humidification plant reduction based on 50% rh at 97.5% design

Based on Air Force Manual AFM 88-29 Engineering weather data

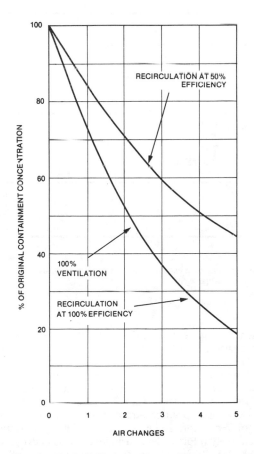

Fig. 1   Typical Gaseous Decay Phenomenon

DESIGN CONSIDERATIONS AND TECHNIQUES

Gaseous filtration presents many physical and chemical uncertainties. Each contaminant has unique properties affecting its control, such as molecular weight, polarity, partial pressure, diffusivity, thermal conductivity, acidity/basicity, and various other physical and chemical properties. Though general rules can be drawn, each contaminant behaves individually. Nevertheless, the control device or system must handle a complex mixture of many contaminants.

Efficient particulate filtration is not related to concentration, whereas gas filter efficiency is (Stankavich 1969). Dry sorption devices, the most common gas filters, vary in efficiency at high and low concentrations, with the performance curve peak varying from one control medium to another (see Figure 2).

Sorption devices are temperature- and humidity-sensitive (Sleik and Turk 1953). Lower temperatures usually increase efficacy and capacity; elevated temperatures decrease both (Barneby 1958). For activated charcoal a fall-off has been observed in the 110 to 125°F range (40 to 50°C) where increased molecular energy can override relatively weak attractive forces. For some substances high humidity can reduce capacity because potentially active sites become occupied by water molecules. On the other hand, humidity, short of saturation, is imperative to the performance of oxidizing agents such as potassium permanganate impregnated alumina, which rely on ionic chemical reaction to modify gaseous pollutants (Keuhner and Hopkins 1959, and Bamson and Keuhner 1962).

Odor Control Considerations

Engineers face special problems when contaminants are odorous, but not otherwise harmful. This can occur when ven-

Table 2 Air Quality Data: Applicable Standards on Gaseous Contaminants

Pollutant	Averaging Time	California Standards[a] Concentration	National Standards[b] Primary	ASHRAE 62-81
Oxidants (ozone)	1 hour	0.10 ppm (200 μg/m^3)	(0.12 ppm) 245 μg/m^3	0.050 ppm (100 μg/m^3)
Carbon Monoxide	12 hour	10 ppm (11 mg/m^3)	—	17.2 ppm (20 mg/m^3)
	8 hour	—	9 ppm 10 mg/m^3	
	1 hour	40 ppm (46 mg/m^3)	(35 ppm) 40 mg/m^3	
Nitrogen Dioxide	Annual Average	—	(0.05 ppm) 100 μg/m^3	0.1 ppm (200 μg/m^3)
	1 hour	0.25 ppm (470 μg/m^3)	—	
Sulfur Dioxide	Annual Average	—	(0.03 ppm) 80 μg/m^3	0.03 ppm (80 μg/m^3)
	24 hour	0.04 ppm (105 μg/m^3)	(0.14 ppm) 365 μg/m^3	
	3 hour	—	—	
	1 hour	0.5 ppm (1310 μg/m^3)	—	
Suspended Particulate Matter	Annual Geometric Mean	60 μg/m^3	75 μg/m^3	
	24 hour	100 μg/m^3	260 μg/m^3	260 μg/m^3
Sulfates	24 hour	25 μg/m^3	—	—
Lead	30 Day Average	1.5 μg/m^3	1.5 μg/m^3	—
Hydrogen Sulfide	1 hour	0.03 ppm (42 μg/m^3)	—	—
Hydocarbons[c] (Other than methane)	3 hour (6 to 9 a.m.)	—	160 μg/m^3	1800 μg/m^{3c}
Ethylene	8 hour	0.1 ppm	—	—
	1 hour	0.5 ppm		
Visibility Reducing Particles	1 observation	In sufficient amount (8) to reduce the prevailing visibility to less than 10 miles (16 km) when the relative humidity is less than 70%	—	—
Odor				Essentially unobjectionable
Other Contaminants				d

Notes:
[a]California standards are values that are not to be equaled or exceeded.
[b]National standards, other than those based on annual averages or annual geometric means, are not to be exceeded more than once per year.
[c]Ppm information is not translatable because of the variety of contaminants having different molecular weights.
[d]Not to exceed 10% the Current Threshold Limit Value (CTLV).

tilation rates are reduced to save energy. Decreased reliance on ventilation air and increased reliance on recirculated air often cause a buildup of contaminants like body odor, tobacco smoke odor and cooking odors. The olfactory response cannot be predicted merely from the mass of contaminant in the air. For instance, the effluent from normal, healthy bodies contains many chemicals, some odor-relevant and some not. Some become odorous at concentrations less than 1 ppb when present alone, and may increase or decrease in odor potency when others are present.

When the engineer must deal with a particular, specifiable odorous substance and can determine the rate of generation, then threshold tables can reveal the amount of air cleaning needed to produce relatively odorless conditions (Leonardos *et al.* 1969, Engen 1970, Van Gemert and Nettenbreyer 1977, Fazzalari 1978, ASTM 1968, Cain 1978). Engineers dealing with complex, poorly specified odorous contaminants can measure the amount of odorless air necessary to dilute the contaminant to a relatively odorless level using psychophysical procedures (ASTM 1975, 1978; Hellman and Small 1974; Cain 1978). This

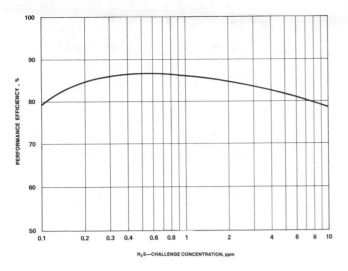

Fig. 2 Typical Performance (Efficiency) of a 3 in. (75 mm) Deep Chemisorbent Bed at an Approach Velocity of 62.5 fpm (0.313 m/s) and a Superficial Residence Time of 0.25 seconds

procedure gives some idea of the efficiency necessary for an air-cleaning device to produce the same relatively odorless conditions as simple dilution with pure air. ASHRAE *Standard* 62-1981 provides information on needs for fresh-air equivalents. (See Chapter 12 of the 1985 FUNDAMENTALS Volume on "Odors.")

CONTROL METHODS

Controlling gaseous contaminants involves reducing their concentration to acceptable or prescribed levels by: (1) dilution (ventilation), (2) elimination from the airstream (filtration), or (3) a combination of the first two.

Ventilation is the most accepted method of controlling gaseous contaminants within conditioned spaces (see Chapter 22 of the 1985 FUNDAMENTALS Volume).

Proper carbon dioxide and oxygen levels can be maintained with a ventilation rate of approximately 4 cfm (1.9 L/s) per person. Odor control often requires many times this air change rate, and thus can determine ventilation rates. Once metabolic requirements based on occupancy levels are met, additional contamination control can be designed on the basis of value engineering of energy cost and consumption. (See "Energy Conservation" section.)

Ventilation air deliberately introduced into a building must meet air quality levels prescribed by ASHRAE *Standard* 62-1981. Several contaminants are components of smog, which the designer must consider to ensure that the air contacting occupants will not cause them health hazards or discomfort. Local air quality agencies are reliable sources of information about the ambient conditions prevailing in outside air.

Odor Control. Controlling odorous contaminants differs from controlling other contaminants only in that malodors can be modified by using deodorizing chemicals (Von Bergen 1957, Pollution Engineering 1973). This strategy should be used carefully because it increases the concentration of organic gases in the air, which defeats the goal of gaseous contamination control and may pose an additional air pollution hazard. Deodorizers can cope with episodic odor problems (e.g., spills of odorous materials) or with problems that resist control by other means (e.g., tobacco smoke odor in smoking areas). Chapter 11 of the 1985 FUNDAMENTALS Volume gives further caution regarding the use of odor modifiers or perfumes.

It is generally preferable to remove odorous contaminants from the air the same way other contaminants are removed. The only difference between odorous and other contaminants is that odorous contaminants often cause considerable discomfort at barely measureable concentrations. Furthermore, the occupant, rather than an instrument, is the final judge of when control procedures are sufficient.

An uncertain area in odor control concerns the contribution of particulates to odors, especially to tobacco smoke odor. High efficiency (80 to 90%) filters (both strainer and electrostatic types) reduce odors, because the submicrometre particles act as host vectors for adsorbed odorants (See ASHRAE *Standard* 52-76). Unless particulate filters are maintained properly, the collection point can become a secondary source of odor, however.

Washing or Scrubbing

The term air scrubber or air washer is applied to many pieces of equipment that remove particulates or gaseous vapors from the air by liquid washing, including spray towers, packed towers, vortex contractors, and venturi scrubbers (Bosworth and Barduhn 1964). Chapter 11 of the 1983 EQUIPMENT Volume has information on industrial air and gas cleaners used predominantly for air emission treatment. This equipment uses absorption (the dissolution of molecules into a liquid) as its means of control (Perry and Chilton 1973, Calvert). The equipment can use clear water or other solvents or a variety of reagents to control specific contaminants, i.e., caustics, hypochlorites, and permanganates (Posselt and Reidies 1965). See Chapter 11 of the 1983 EQUIPMENT Volume for liquid chemical reaction control.

Traditionally, water scrubbing apparatus has not been used for HVAC applications because it yields moisture-laden air. Scrubbers have been applied predominantly in industrial and process emission and pollution control. This control is mentioned because fuel costs may make recycling of industrial exhaust air within occupied factory space cost-effective. An appropriate scrubber can be used in the initial stage or exhaust air treatment with subsequent control systems to improve air quality sufficiently for reuse. If secondary dry filters stages are used, proper moisture control is essential.

Dry Sorbent Systems

The dry sorbent system, available in an array of applicable hardware, is widely used. The capacities of sorbent materials vary for different contaminants. Commercially available materials include activated charcoal, silica gel, molecular sieves, porous clay minerals and special impregnated substrates such as permanganate-treated alumina. Regardless of the sorbent type, the contaminant must migrate from the gas stream to the sorbent surface. This removal process is influenced by: (1) the velocity of the gas through the sorbent bed, (2) the mean particle size and distribution of sizes in the bed, (3) physical and chemical properties of the gas and sorbent, (4) bed depth, and (5) filter container configuration.

This section covers only the more well-known media.

Activated Charcoals. The terms charcoal, activated charcoal and activated carbon are synonymous and represent a family of carbonaceous substances manufactured by various processes to develop highly adsorptive properties. An array of raw materials, manufacturing process and impurities can have significance in surface area, density, pore structure, hardness, retentivity and activity of the end product (Barneby 1958). These factors affect performance. Since charcoal used adsorption to capture contaminants, the effectiveness of the control system depends on surface area in the form of minute pores throughout the structure. In activated charcoal, these pores generally have a diameter less than 9 nanometre.

Because of its nonpolar characteristics, activated charcoal can adsorb a variety of gasses and vapors including a broad spectrum of organic substances. Generally, the carbons are highly responsive toward molecules of moderate molecular weight and gases with high boiling points, such as naphthalene, carbon tetrachloride, benzene and butyric acid. Lighter gases, such as ammonia, sulfur dioxide, ethylene and formaldehyde, are not adsorbed effectively by standard charcoal (Sleik and Turk 1953). Furthermore, activated charcoal tends to be more effective at high concentrations, which encourages its use in solvent recovery. Although activated charcoal has been successful in many applications, it must be used cautiously in airstreams with elevated temperatures, high humidity levels, or involving flammability problems.

If a gaseous contaminant is chemically reactive, the adsorption capacity of the charcoal can be improved by using specific impregnating agents like halogenation or caustic impregnation. Impregnation usually increases both the efficacy and capacity of charcoal for the specific contaminant (Lee 1965).

These remarks refer to virgin carbons and may not apply to reactivated or recycled carbon because inadequate reactivation can compromise properties.

Permanganated Alumina. Permanganated alumina consists of potassium permanganate on aluminum oxide. Its properties have been documented, and it has been applied commercially in HVAC applications (Keuhner and Hopkins 1959, Bamson and Keuhner 1959). Alumina alone is an adsorbent, while potassium permanganate is a strong oxidizing agent. Although it has a smaller surface area than active carbon, alumina is more polar and adsorbs the water necessary in the ionic oxidation process. The activated surface adsorbs both odorants and water, yielding oxidation products.

As contaminants are adsorbed from the airstream and oxidized, the permanganate is reduced to MnO_2 and the color of the substrate changes from purple to brown. This chemical change does not appreciably reduce the ability of the substrate to adsorb gases. Furthermore, the MnO_2 still oxidizes some sulfur compounds. Thus, the alumina/permanganate system is extremely effective in treating sulfur-bearing airstreams at room temperatures. Generally, the alumina/permanganate media are effective for readily oxidizable lighter gases, which are not controlled well by activated carbon. The system has low effectiveness and capacity for substances that are not rapidly oxidizable.

COMMERCIAL EQUIPMENT

Containment devices in HVAC systems can accept any dry pelletized media. The pellet sizes usable for gas purification are limited by efficiency and pressure drop requirements. Normally, the pelletized or granular media are held between metal sheets having perforations somewhat smaller than the least particle size for the adsorber media. The perforated metal and screens are usually aluminum, stainless steel, painted steel, or steel with chemical conversion coatings. Gaskets are a vital part of a dry sorbent cleanser because the very high removal efficiencies possible with many media cannot be obtained is there is any appreciable bypass around the media cannot be obtained if there is any appreciable bypass around the media beds. A small margin of unperforated support material around each tray is also needed to prevent edge bypass. These margins are typically 0.5 to 1 in. (13 to 25 mm). Each device should be judged according to control media characteristics and installation demands. (See ''Design Considerations and Techniques'' and ''Defining the Problem'' sections.)

Available equipment (Figure 3) can be categorized as follows:

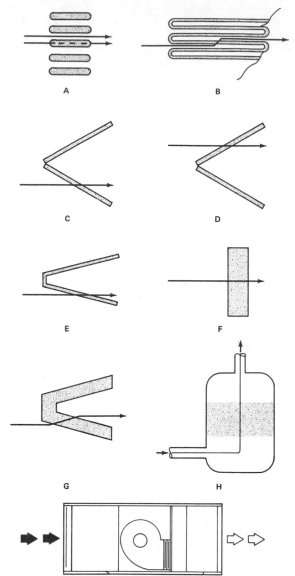

Fig. 3   Typical Equipment Configurations

Partial Bypass. Available in 1-, 2-, and 4-in. (25-, 50-, and 100-mm) configurations, this sorption filter is designed predominantly for occupancy odor control is residential or light commercial applications. Its low efficiency, 5 to 15%, prevents its use in engineered installations, and it should be used only for light-duty, recirculation systems for nominal or cosmetic control.

Serpentine. A thin bed [3/8 to 1/2 in. (9 to 13 mm)] convoluted configuration usually used for medium duty recirculation applications, such as commercial ventilation reduction and occupancy odor control.

Thin-Bed Tray. This configuration [a flat tray usually 1/2 to 5/8 in. (13 to 16 mm) in bed thickness] uses multiple trays to attain extended surface area to maximize dwell time of the air in the sorption media, and to reduce pressure drop across the filter. (See Figure 4.)

Intermediate Bed Depth Trays. As described above, but having nominal thickness of 7/8 to 1 in. (23 to 25 mm) depth, designed for higher efficiency and longer system life with higher media content.

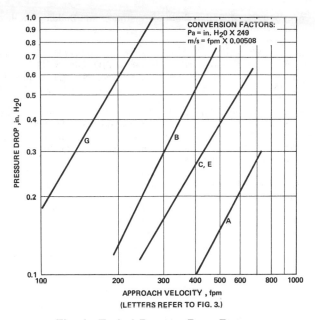

CONVERSION FACTORS:
Pa = in. H_2O X 249
m/s = fpm X 0.00508

Fig. 4 Typical Pressure Drop Ranges

Intermediate Bed Depth V Module. In this module, extended surface area is attained in a V-shaped configuration that has an average bed depth of 1 to 1 1/8 in. (25 to 28 mm) and offers easier field media servicing.

Thick-Bed Tray. A flat tray that has an average bed depth of 2 in. (50 mm) or more and is used in a flat configuration with low duct velocities. It generally has a higher pressure drop.

Thick-Bed Extended Surface Area Module. This unit has a 3-in. (75-mm) average bed depth, and attains lower bed velocity and lower pressure loss by extended surface area techniques. It is used in high efficiency, single-pass applications with high media consumption.

Packed Column. This system is a deep bed tower, usually manufactured of FRP (Fiberglass Reinforced Plastic), and has deep beds of sorption media from 1 to 4 ft (0.3 to 1.2 m). It controls extremely high concentrations to yield large reductions in a single pass. Normally used for emission abatement, the deep bed provides a very effective initial stage in industrial air reuse systems, if its high air flow resistance can be tolerated.

Self-Contained Equipment. While the above cells, modules or trays can be incorporated into side-access housing or other standardized equipment for installation, they can also be used with an array or pre-engineered recirculating equipment, each with a containment device in a self-contained housing with appropriate air volume sizing. Such apparatus is used mainly to supplement pre-existing air-conditioning or heating equipment, to treat localized containment problems or to handle contaminants independently of the HVAC system.

The choice of equipment depends on the required results and economics. The total cost of the system includes initial cost, labor cost for replacing filters, cost of replacement media, and operating cost. Operating cost is essentially the fan power required for air flow through the media. Figure 4 shows typical pressure drops for the configurations in Figure 3. Since fan power is directly proportional to system pressure loss, overall operating costs can be calculated.

SYSTEMS DESIGN

Using the variety of media containment devices available, the engineer can design appropriate gas containment control specific to the problem being considered. Factors such as concentration, humidity, temperature, and contaminant nature influence control strategies, so there is no generalized performance standard or rating system for gas filters. The engineer may need to rely on specific performance data from the manufacturer or from laboratory or on-site testing for performance and capacity.

Design alternatives can be divided into two categories, the first dealing with relatively low concentrations and the second dealing with heavier ones (see Figure 5). For low concentrations, partial bypass systems are used. They are applicable to situations where contaminant loads are nominal or intermittent, and where high air change rates can provide adequate contaminant control. This is typical of ventilation reduction applications where high single-pass efficiencies are not needed because the filtration system is replacing only fractional quantities of equivalent fresh air. Partial bypass causes small pressure drop, thus reducing the energy impact of the system.

System (A) (Figure 5) has a light-duty partial bypass flat filter in the HVAC system to provide low levels of equivalent fresh air. System (B) illustrates the use of thin-to-intermediate bed-depth filters in a standby filter bank used only where high levels of return air are indicated. System (C) treats all air, but used interspersed modules or trays in the containment frame.

In heavier, more demanding situations, systems (D) through (I), all of which require total containment systems, no bypass of air, and medium-to-deep bed-type containers, can be used. System (D) shows gaseous filtration used to treat makeup air to eliminate harmful pollutants or ambient contaminants, or to comply with ASHRAE *Standard* 62-1981. System (E) shows makeup and return air used separately to attain high levels of control and reduction within the space. System (F) illustrates treatment of the mixed air only, which also typifies treatment of recirculation only in a closed space. System (G) shows gaseous filtration added to exhaust air for recirculation within the space or retreatment at the air handler. This is typical of hood exhaust or toilet exhaust treatment for recycling. System (H) shows double banking used for high single-pass performance when high challenge concentrations are expected or when very low contaminant levels are demanded. Different media combinations

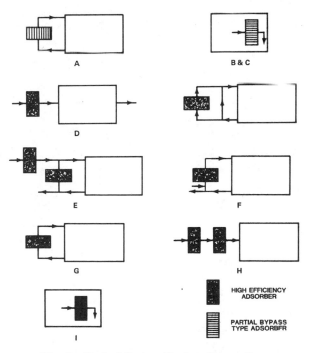

HIGH EFFICIENCY ADSORBER

PARTIAL BYPASS TYPE ADSORBER

Fig. 5 Typical System Design Alternatives

can be used with this technique to achieve greater efficacy, longer filter life or other advantages. System (I) shows engineered self-contained equipment used to provide recirculation within the space, independent of HVAC air handlers.

BIBLIOGRAPHY

NTIS Publications can be obtained from the National Technical Information Service, 5285 Port Royal Road, Springfield, VA 22161.

ASHRAE. 1981. Ventilation for Acceptable Indoor Air Quality. ASHRAE *Standard* 62-1981.

ASHRAE. 1980. Energy Conservation in New Building Design. ANSI/ASHRAE/IES *Standard* 90A-1980.

ASHRAE. 1976. Method of Testing Air-Cleaning Devices Used in General Ventilation for Removing Particulate Matter. ASHRAE *Standard* 52-76.

EPA. *Survey of Indoor Air Quality Health Criteria and Standards.* EPA Publication 6007-78-027. Available NTIS.

EPA. *Indoor Air Pollution in the Residential Environment.* EPA Contract No. 68-02-2294.

NIOSH. 1976. *Recirculation of Exhaust Air.* NIOSH-66-186, Available NTIS.

National Primary and Secondary Ambient Air Quality Standards. U.S. Environmental Protection Agency, Code of Federal Regulations Title 40 Part 50, 40 CFR 50.

Williams-Steiger Occupational Safety Act of 1970. 84 Stat. of Title 29, Labor Code of Federal Regulations, 29 CFR 1910.1000.

REFERENCES

ACGIH. 1977. Documentation of Threshold Limit Values for Substances in Workroom Air. American Conference of Governmental Industrial Hygienists.

ASTM. 1968. Manual on Sensory Testing Methods. American Society for Testing and Materials. ASTM Special Technical Publication 434, Washington, DC.

ASTM. 1975. Practice for Referencing Suprathreshold Odor Intensity. American Society for Testing and Materials, ASTM E544-75.

ASTM. 1978. Test Method for Measurement of Odor in Atmospheres. (Dilution Method). American Society for Testing and Materials, ASTM D1391.

Bamson, B.W.; and Keuhner, R.L. 1962. Composition and Method for Deodorizing Air. U.S. Patent 3,049,399. August 14.

Barnebey, H.L. 1958. Activated Charcoal for Air Purification. ASHRAE Transactions, Vol. 64, p. 481.

Bosworth, C.M.; and Barduhn, A.J. 1964. Recent Advances in Odor Control by Air Washing. Annals of the New York Academy of Sciences, Vol. 116, Art. 2, p. 638.

Cain, W. 1978. Minimum Rates of Air Intake into Buildings: Role of Odors. Energy Conservation Strategies in Buildings, John B. Pierce Foundation, New Haven, CT.

Calvert, S. Wet Scrubber System Study. Vol. 1: Scrubber Handbook and Vol. 2: Final Report and Bibliography, PB213016, NTIS.

Csermeley, T.J.; and Bosworth, C.M. 1964. New Techniques for Evaluating Odor Control Methods. ASHRAE Transactions, Vol. 70, p. 354.

Dravnieks, A.; and Whitfield, J. 1971. Gas Chromatographic Study of Air Quality in Schools. ASHRAE Transactions, Vol. 77, Part 1, p. 113.

Engen, T. 1970. Man's Ability to Perceive Odors. Advances in Chemoreception; Vol. 1: Communication by Chemical Signals. Appleton-Century-Crofts, New York, p. 361.

Fazzalari, F.A. 1978. Compilation of Odor and Taste Threshold Values Data. ASTM Data Series Publication D 548A, Philadelphia, PA.

Hellman, T.; and Small, F. 1974. Characterization of the Odor Properties of 101 Petrochemicals Using Sensory Methods. Journal of the Air Pollution Control Association, October, Vol. 24, No. 10, p. 979.

Keuhner, R.L.; and Hopkins, N.E. 1959. Method of Deodorizing and Sterilizing Air in Enclosed Spaces. U.S. Patent 2,876,507. March 10.

Lee, D.R. 1965. Using Impregnated Activated Carbon. Journal of the American Association for Contamination Control, Vol. 4, No. 12, December, p. 18.

Leonardos, G.; Kendall, D.; and Barnard, N. 1969. Odor Threshold Determinations of 53 Odorant Chemicals. Journal of the Air Pollution Control Association, Vol. 19, p. 91.

Perry, R.; and Chilton, C.(eds.). 1973. Chemical Engineer's Handbook. McGraw-Hill Book Co., New York, NY.

Pollution Engineering. 1973. Odor Modification. July, p. 27.

Posselt, H.S.; and Reidies, A.H. 1965. Odor Abatement with Potassium Permanganate Solutions. Industrial and Engineering Chemistry, Product Research and Development, Vol. 4, March, p. 48.

Sleik, H.; and Turk, A. 1953. Air Conservaton Engineering. Connor Engineering Corp., Danbury, CT.

Stankavich, A.J. 1969. The Capacity of Activated Charcoals Under Dynamic Conditions for Selected Atmospheric Contaminants in the Low Parts Per Million Range. ASHRAE Symposium Bulletin, Odors and Odorants: An Engineering View.

Turk, A. 1963. Measurements of Odorous Vapors in Test Chambers: Theoretical. ASHRAE Journal, Vol. 5, No. 10. October p. 55.

Van Gemert, L.; and Nettenbreyer, A. 1977. Compilaton of Odor Threshold Values in Air and Water. National Institute for Water Supply, Voorburg, Netherlands, p. 79.

Von Bergen, J. 1957. Industrial Odor Control. Chemical Engineering, Vol. 64. August, p. 239.

Yocum, J.E.; and Cote, W.A. 1971. Transactions, Vol. 77, p. 61-71. Indoor Outdoor Air Pollutant Relationships for Air Conditioned Buildings.

CHAPTER 51

AUTOMATIC CONTROL

AUTOMATIC control of HVAC systems and equipment usually includes temperature control and may also include humidity, pressure, and flow rate control. Automatic control primarily modulates the equipment capacity to meet the load requirements and provides safe operation of the equipment. It requires mechanical, electrical, and electronic control devices, and implies that human intervention is limited to starting and stopping equipment, and adjusting control set points.

This chapter focuses on controls that are normally custom-designed by a control system designer. The controls normally supplied internally as part of the equipment by the manufacturer are covered in the chapters on equipment. The chapter covers the following: (1) control fundamentals, including terminology; (2) the different types of control components; (3) the methods of connecting these components together to form various types of individual control loops or subsystems; (4) the synthesis of these subsystems into a complete control system; and (5) the important areas of commissioning, operation, and maintenance.

CONTROL FUNDAMENTALS

CONTROL

An **open loop** control system does not have a direct link between the value of the controlled variable and the controller. An example of an open loop control system is a furnace that has a fixed cycle of on and off times regardless of the space temperature or outdoor air temperature (Kuo 1975). The open loop control system is unaffected by the controlled variable, which is the space temperature. A **closed loop** control, or feedback control system, measures the actual changes in the controlled variable and actuates the control device to bring about a change. The corrective action continues until the variable is brought to a desired value within the design limitations of the controller. This system of transmitting the value of the controlled variable back to the controller is known as **feedback**.

Feedforward control anticipates how an external variable will affect the system. An outdoor thermostat arranged to control heat flow to a building in proportion to the load caused by

changes in outdoor temperature is an example. In essence, the designer of this system presumes a fixed relationship between outside air temperature and the heat requirement of the building and takes control action based on the outdoor air temperature. The actual space temperature has no effect on this controller. Because there is no feedback of the controlled variable (space temperature) in this case, the control is called open loop. Feedforward control can also be used effectively on a feedback controller to change the characteristics of the control based on both the feedback variable and an external variable that affects the control loop. The controller is then a feedback controller with feedforward compensation.

TERMINOLOGY

The **control loop**, shown in Figure 1, is comprised mainly of (1) a **sensor** that measures the controlled variable and conveys values to the controller and (2) a **controller** that compares the value of the controlled variable with setpoint and generates a signal to the controlled device for corrective action. Thermostats, humidistats, and pressure controls are examples of controllers.

The **setpoint** is the desired value of the controlled variable. The controller seeks to maintain this setpoint.

The **controlled device** reacts to signals received from the controller to vary the flow of the control agent. It may be a valve, damper, electric relay, or a motor driving a pump or a fan.

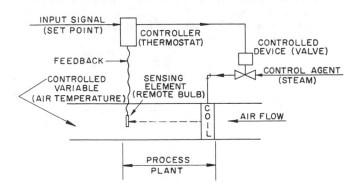

Fig. 1 Discharge Air Temperature Control—An Example of a Feedback Control System

The preparation of this chapter was assigned to TC 1.4, Control Theory and Application.

The **control agent** is the medium manipulated by the controlled device. It may be air or gas flowing through a damper; gas, steam, or water flowing through a valve; or an electric current.

The **process plant** is the air conditioning apparatus being controlled. It reacts to the output of the control agent and affects the change in the controlled variable. It may include a coil, air duct, fan, or occupied space of the building.

The **controlled variable** is the variable such as temperature, humidity, or pressure that is being controlled.

ANALOG CONTROL AND DIRECT DIGITAL CONTROL

Traditionally, HVAC control has been performed by analog devices. A common analog HVAC controller is the pneumatic controller. The principle behind pneumatic controllers is that the sensor sends a pneumatic signal whose pressure is proportional to the value of the variable being measured. The controller contains circuitry that compares this air pressure from the sensor to the desired value of air pressure, and outputs a control signal based on this comparison. The pneumatic controller receives and acts upon data continuously.

Recently, direct digital controllers have entered the HVAC control arena. A direct digital controller receives electronic signals from the sensors, converts the electronic signals to numbers, and performs mathematical operations on these numbers inside the computer. The output from the computer takes the form of a number, and can be converted to a voltage or pneumatic signal to operate the actuator. The digital controller must sample its data because the computer must have time for other operations besides reading data. If the sampling interval for the digital controller is chosen properly, no significant degradation in control performance will be seen due to sampling.

BLOCK DIAGRAMS

A control loop can be represented in the form of a block diagram. In a block diagram, shown in Figure 2, each component of the control loop is modeled and represented in its own block. The flow of information from one component to the next is shown by lines between the blocks. The figure shows the setpoint being compared to the feedback of the controlled variable. This difference, or error, is fed into the controller, which sends a control signal to the controlled device. In this case, the controlled device is a valve. The valve can change the amount of steam flow through the coil of Figure 1. The amount of steam flow is the input to the next block, which represents the process plant. From the process plant block comes the controlled variable, which is temperature. The controlled variable is sensed by the sensing element and fed to the controller as feedback, completing the loop.

Each component of Figure 2 can be represented by a transfer function, which is an idealized mathematical representation of the relationship between the input and output variables of the component. The transfer function is sufficiently detailed to cover both the dynamic and static characteristics of the device. The dynamics of the component are represented in the time domain by a differential equation. For the purposes of a transfer function, the differential equation is converted to its *LaPlace transform* or *z-transform*.

In environmental control systems, the transfer function of many of the components can be adequately described by a first order differential equation, implying that the dynamic behavior is dominated by a single dominant capacitance factor. For such elements, the time constant is defined as the time it takes for the output to reach 63.2% of its final value when a step change in the input is effected. When the time constant of the component is small, its output will react rapidly to reflect changes in the input; conversely, components with a larger time constant will be sluggish in responding to changes in the input.

Deadtime is a nonlinearity, which can cause control and modeling problems. Deadtime is the time between a change in the process input and when that change affects the output of the process. Deadtime can occur in the control loop of Figure 1 due to the transportation lag of the air. The temperature that the sensor sees represents the conditions at the coil some time in the past, because the air it is sensing went through the coil some time in the past. Deadtime can also occur due to a slow sensor, a time lag in the signal from the controller, or the transportation lag of the control agent. If the deadtime is small, it can be ignored in the model of the control system but must be considered if it is significant. The designer must make the judgment.

The gain of a transfer function is the amount by which the output of the component will change for a given change of input under steady-state conditions. If the element is linear, its gain remains constant. However, many control system components are nonlinear and have varying gains, depending on the operating conditions.

Figure 3 shows the response of a first order plus deadtime process to a step change of the input signal. Notice that the process shows no reaction during the deadtime, followed by a response that looks like a first order exponential.

PERFORMANCE REQUIREMENTS OF CONTROL SYSTEMS

The control system performance in an air-conditioning application is evaluated in terms of the speed of response and its stability. If a control loop is stable, the value of the controlled variable will remain at its setpoint. A control loop that responds quickly will reject disturbances and quickly return the controlled variable to its setpoint. The two requirements of speed and stability are often contradictory, i.e., a change made in one of the component parameters to improve speed of response could adversely affect stability. Hence, the performance level of such

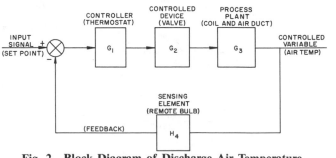

Fig. 2   Block Diagram of Discharge Air Temperature Control System

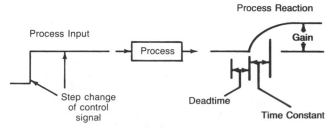

Fig. 3   Process Subjected to a Step Input

systems must be selected to suit the application and must be evaluated in terms of control, comfort, and energy conservation.

TYPES OF CONTROL ACTION

Closed loop control systems are commonly classified by the type of corrective action the controller is programmed to take when it senses a deviation of the controlled variable from the setpoint. Following are the six most common types of control action.

1. **Two-position action.** The controlled device shown in Figure 4 can be positioned only to a maximum or minimum state, or can be either on or off. A typical home thermostat that starts and stops a furnace is a good example of two-position action.

    Controller differential, as it applies to two-position control action, is the difference between a setting at which the controller operates to one position and a setting at which it operates to the other position. Thermostat ratings usually refer to the differential in degrees that will become apparent by raising and lowering the dial setting. This differential is usually called the manual differential of the thermostat. When the same thermostat is applied to an operating system, the total change in temperature that occurs between a call for more heat and a call for less heat is usually greater than the manual differential caused by thermostat lag. The differential encountered on the job under control is called operating differential. For example, a thermostat with a 2°F (1°C) differential when raising and lowering the dial setting may actually produce temperature variations of 3°F (1.7°C) between the "system on" and "system off" states.

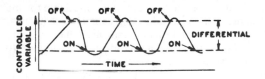

Fig. 4   Two-Position Control

2. **Timed two-position action** is a common variation of straight two-position action that is often used on room thermostats to reduce operating differential. In heating thermostats, a heater element is energized during "on" periods, prematurely shortening the on-time as the heater falsely warms the thermostat. This is called heat anticipation. The same anticipating action can be obtained in cooling thermostats by energizing a heater during thermostat "off" periods. In either case, the percentage of on-time is varied in proportion to the system load, while the total cycle time remains relatively constant.

    Electronic thermostats lend themselves easily to timed two-position action. The electronic thermostat is a small computer that can include a clock to keep track of time. It is then a programming task to program the minimum on-time and minimum off-time of the thermostat. Means to vary the minimum on-time and minimum off-time can be given to the user.

3. In **floating action**, the controller can perform only two operations—moving the controlled device toward either its open or closed position, usually at a constant rate (see Figure 5). Generally, a neutral zone between the two positions allows the controlled device to stop at any position whenever the controlled variable is within the differential of the controller. When the controlled variable gets outside the differential of the controller, the controller moves the controlled device in the proper direction.

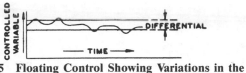

Fig. 5   Floating Control Showing Variations in the Controlled Variable as the Load Changes

4. In **proportional action**, the controlled device is positioned proportionally, in response to slight changes in the controlled variable (see Figure 6). A proportional controller can be described by:

$$V_p = K_p e$$

where

V_p = the output of the proportional controller
K_p = the proportional gain (proportional to 1/throttling range)
e = the error signal, or offset

The output of the controller is proportional to the error of the control signal from its setpoint. An example of proportional control is a thermostat in a fan discharge duct actuating an automatic valve in the steam supply to a coil to regulate the air temperature leaving the coil. This control is similar to that shown in Figure 1.

Throttling range is the amount of change in the controlled variable required for the controller to move the controlled device from one extreme to the other. It can be adjusted to meet job requirements. Throttling range is inversely proportional to proportional gain.

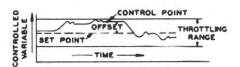

Fig. 6   Proportional Control Showing Variations in the Controlled Variable as the Load Changes

Control point is the actual value of the controlled variable at which the instrument is controlling. It varies within the throttling range of the controller and changes with changing load on the system and other variables.

Offset is the difference between the setpoint and the actual control point under stable conditions. This is sometimes called drift, deviation, droop, or stead-state error.

5. **Proportional plus integral** (PI) control improves upon simple proportional control by adding another component to the control action that eliminates the offset typical of proportional control (see Figure 7). The reset action is most easily shown by the equation:

$$V_p = K_p e + K_i \int e \, dt$$

where

V_p = output of the controller
K_i = integral gain
t = time
e = error

The second term in the equation implies that the longer the period during which the error (e) exists, the greater the controller output will become in attempting to eliminate the error.

Selecting the proportional and integral gain constants is critical to system stability. Proper selection essentially eliminates offset, obtaining greater control accuracy. Also, energy efficiency is improved by PI control in applications such as VAV fan control, chiller control, and hot and cold deck control.

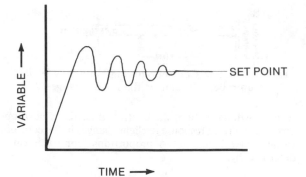

Fig. 7   Proportional Plus Integral (PI) Control

6. **Proportional-integral-derivative** (PID) control is PI control with a term added to the controller, which varies with the value of the derivative of the error. The equation for PID control is:

$$V_p = K_p e + K_i \int e\,dt + K\,de/dt$$

where

K = the derivative gain of the controller
de/dt = the derivative of the error

The other terms are defined above. Adding the derivative term gives some anticipatory action to the controller, which will result in a faster response and greater stability. However, the addition of the derivative term also makes the controller more sensitive to noisy signals and harder to tune than a PI controller. Most HVAC control loops perform satisfactorily with PI control, without the need for adding the derivative term.

ENERGY SOURCES FOR CONTROL SYSTEMS

Control components can be classified into the following three main groups according to the primary source of energy:

1. **Pneumatic** components use compressed air, usually at a pressure of 15 to 35 psi (100 to 250 KPa) gauge, as an energy source. The air is generally supplied to the controller, which regulates the pressure supplied to the controlled device.
2. **Electric** components use electrical energy, either low or line voltage, as the energy source. The electric energy supplied to the controlled device is regulated by the controller. Controlled devices in this category include relays, contactors, electro-mechanical and hydraulic actuators, and solid-state regulating devices. The components that include signal conditioning and amplification in their operation are classified as electronic.
3. **Self-Powered** components apply the power of the measured system to induce the necessary corrective action. The measuring system derives its energy from the process under control, or any auxiliary source of energy. Temperature changes at the sensor result in pressure or volume changes of the enclosed media, which are transmitted directly to the operating device of the valve or damper. A component using a thermopile in a pilot flame to generate electrical energy is also self-powered.

This method of classification can be extended to individual control loops and to complete control systems. For example, the room temperature control for a particular room that includes a pneumatic room thermostat and a pneumatically actuated reheat coil would be referred to as a pneumatic control loop. Most complete control systems use a combination of some or all of the above components and are more accurately called *hybrid systems.* As an example, the control system for an air handler could include electric components for on/off control of the fan, pneumatic components for control of the heating and cooling coils, and self-powered safety controls (e.g., a freezestat).

CONTROL COMPONENTS

This section describes the various types and categories of control devices commonly found in HVAC control systems. While control components may be clarified several ways, this section considers the grouping of components by their function within a complete control system. The first subsection considers the controlled device or final control element. Examples are relays, valves, dampers, and VAV boxes (which contain a damper or damper-like mechanism). Actuators, which are used to drive the valve or damper assembly, are also covered.

The next subsection considers the sensing element that measures changes in the controlled variable. (Chapter 13 of the 1985 FUNDAMENTALS Volume has further information.) Specific examples of sensor types included are temperature, humidity, water and air pressure, and water and airflow rate. While many other kinds of special sensors are available, these types represent the majority of those found in the HVAC control systems and subsystems described in Section IV.

In the third subsection, various types of controllers are reviewed. Controllers are classified according to the control action they cause to maintain the desired conditon (set point); such as, whether they are two-position, floating control, proportional control, proportional plus integral (PI) control, or proportional plus integral plus derivative (PID) control. In addition, this section describes the various techniques available for making the control decision in a modulating control system, such as pneumatic, electronic, and digital controllers. Thermostats (devices that combine a temperature sensor and controller into a single unit) are also described and listed.

Many control systems can be constructed using only the three types of components described in the first three sections. In practice, however, a fourth group is sometimes necessary. The members of this group are neither sensing elements nor controlled devices or controllers, but are referred to as auxiliary control components, which include transducers, relays, switches, power supplies, and air compressors. A brief description and example for each is included.

CONTROLLED DEVICES

The controlled device is most frequently used to regulate or vary the flow of steam, water, or air within an HVAC system. Water and steam flow regulators are called **valves** and airflow control devices are called **dampers**, although both types perform essentially the same function. Both types of devices—valves and dampers—must be properly sized and selected for the particular application for the control systems to control the controlled variable properly. The control system's link to the valve or damper is a component referred to as an **operator** or **actuator**. This device uses electricity, compressed air, or hydraulic fluid to power the motion of the valve stem or damper linkage through its operating range.

Valves

An **automatic valve** is designed to control the flow of steam, water, gas, and other fluids, and may be considered as a variable orifice positioned by an electric or pneumatic operator in response to impulses from the controller. It may be equipped with

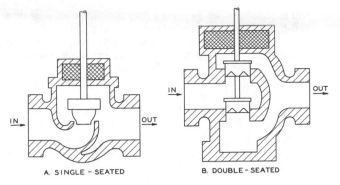

Fig. 8   Typical Single- and Double-Seated Two-Way Valves

a throttling plug or V-port specially designed to provide desired flow characteristics.

Renewable composition disks are common. They are made of materials best suited to the media handled by the valve, the operating temperature, and the pressure. For high pressures or for superheated steam, metal disks are often used. Internal parts of valves, such as the seat ring, throttling plug or V-port skirt, disk holder, and stem, are sometimes made of stainless steel or other hard and corrosion-resistant metals for use in severe service.

Various types of automatic valves include the following:

A **single-seated valve** (Figure 8A) is designed for tight shutoff. Appropriate disk materials for various pressures and media are used.

A **double-seated** or **balanced valve** (Figure 8B) is designed so that the media pressure acting against the valve disk is essentially balanced, reducing the operator force required. It is widely used where fluid pressure is too high to permit a single-seated valve to close. It cannot be used where tight shutoff is required.

A **three-way mixing valve** (Figure 9A) has two inlet and one outlet connection and a double-faced disk operating between two seats. It is used to mix two fluids entering through the inlet connections and leaving through the common outlet, according to the position of the valve stem (and disk).

A **three-way diverting valve** (Figure 9B) has one inlet and two outlet connections, and two separate disks and seats. It is used to divert the flow to either of the outlets or to proportion the flow to both outlets.

A **butterfly valve** consists of a heavy ring enclosing a disk that rotates on an axis at or near its center and is similar to a round single-blade damper in principle. The disk seats against a ring machined within the body or a resilient liner in the body. Two butterfly valves can be used together to act like a 3-way valve for mixing or diverting.

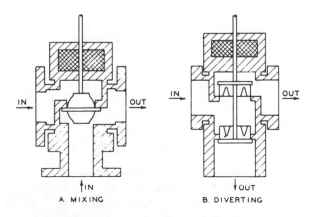

Fig. 9   Typical Three-Way Mixing and Diverting Valves

Characteristics

The performance of a valve is expressed in terms of its flow characteristics as it operates through its stroke, based on a **constant pressure drop**. Three common characteristics are shown in Figure 10 and are defined as follows:

Quick Opening. Maximum flow is approached rapidly as the device begins to open.
Linear. Opening and flow are related in direct proportion.
Equal Percentage. Each equal increment of opening increases the flow by an equal percentage over the previous value.

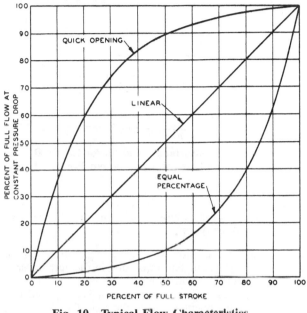

Fig. 10   Typical Flow Characteristics

Since the pressure drop across a valve seldom remains constant as its opening changes, actual performance usually deviates from the published characteristic curve. The magnitude of the deviation is determined by the overall system design. For example, in a system arranged so that control valves or dampers can shut off all flow, the pressure drop across a controlled device increases from a minimum at design conditions to the total system pressure drop at no flow. Figure 11 shows the extent of the resulting deviations for a valve or damper designed with a linear characteristic, when selection is based on various percentages of total system pressure drop. To approximate the designed characteristic of the valve or damper, the design pressure drop should be a reasonably large percentage of the total system pressure drop, or the system should be designed and controlled so that this pressure drop remains relatively constant.

Higher pressure drops for controlled devices are obtained by using smaller sizes with a possible increase in size of other equipment in the system. Since sizing techniques are different for steam, water, and air, each is discussed separately.

OPERATORS

Valve operators are of the following four general types:

1. A **solenoid** consists of a magnetic coil operating a movable plunger. Most are for two-position operation, but modulating solenoid valves are available with a pressure equalization bellows or piston to achieve high resolution. Solenoid valves are generally limited to relatively small sizes [up to 4 in. (100 mm)].

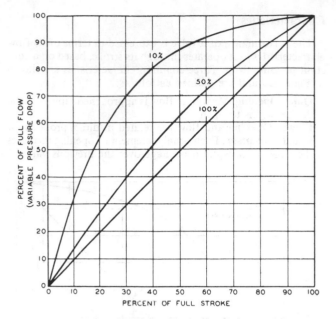

Fig. 11   Typical Performance Curves for Linear Devices at Various Percentages of Total System Pressure Drop

2. An **electric motor** operates the valve stem through a gear train and linkage. Electric motor operators are classified in the following three types:

   a. **Unidirectional**—for two-position operation. The valve opens during one-half revolution of the output shaft and closes during the other one-half revolution. Once started, it continues until the half revolution is completed, regardless of subsequent action by the controller. Limit switches built into the operator stop the motor at the end of each stroke. If the controller has been satisfied during this interval, the operator will continue to the other position.

   b. **Spring-return**—for two-position operation. Electric energy drives the valve to one position and holds it there. When the circuit is broken removing the energy, the spring returns the valve to its normal position.

   c. **Reversible**—for floating and proportional operation. The motor can run in either direction and can stop in any position. It is sometimes equipped with a return spring. In proportional control applications, a feedback potentiometer for rebalancing the control circuit is also driven by the motor.

3. A **pneumatic operator** consists of a spring-opposed, flexible diaphragm or bellows attached to the valve stem. An increase in air pressure, above the minimum point of the spring range, compresses the spring and simultaneously moves the valve stem. Springs of various ranges, in terms or air pressure required to compress the spring completely, can sequence the operation of two or move devices by proper selection or adjustment of the springs. For example, a chilled water valve operator may modulate the valve from fully closed to fully open over a spring range of 3 to 8 psi (21 to 55 kPa) gauge, while a sequenced steam valve may operate from 8 to 13 psi (55 to 90 kPa) gauge.

4. **Springless pneumatic operators**, using two opposed diaphragms or two sides of a single diaphragm, are also used, but they are generally limited to special applications involving large valves or high pressures. Pneumatic operators are used primarily for proportional control. Two-position con-

trol is accomplished by using a two-position controller or a two-position pneumatic relay to apply either full air pressure or no pressure to the valve operator. Pneumatic valves and valves with spring-return electric operators can be classified as normally open or normally closed.

   a. A **normally open** valve will assume an open position, providing full flow, when all operating force is removed.

   b. A **normally closed** valve will assume a closed position, stopping flow, when all operating force is removed.

5. An **electric-hydraulic** actuator is similar to a pneumatic one, except it uses an incompressible fluid, which is circulated by an internal electric pump.

Selection and Sizing

Steam Valves. Steam-to-water and steam-to-air heat exchangers are typically controlled through regulation of steam flow rate using a two-way throttling valve. One-pipe steam systems require a line-size two-position valve for proper condensate drainage and steam flow, while two-pipe steam systems can be controlled by two-position or modulating (throttling) valves.

Water Valves. Valves used for water service may be two- or three-way and two-position or proportional. Proportional valves are used most often, but two-position valves are not unusual and are sometimes essential (e.g., on steam preheat coils). Two-position valves are normally the quick opening type, while proportioning valves are normally the linear or equal percentage type.

The **flow coefficient** Cv (Kv) is generally used to compare valve capacities. Cv is defined as the volume of water flow in gpm (L/s) at 60°F (16°C) through a control valve in the fully open position with a 1 psi (6.9 kPa) differential across the valve.

While it is possible to design a water system in which the pressure differential from supply to return is kept constant, it is seldom done. It is safer to assume that the pressure drop across the valve will increase as it modulates from fully open to fully closed. Figure 12 shows the effect in a simple system with one pump and one two-way control valve with its heat exchanger. The **system curve** represents the pressure or head loss in the piping system and heat exchanger at various flow rates. The **pump curve** is the typical curve for a centrifugal pump. At design flow rates, the valve is selected for a specific pressure drop, A-A'. At part load the valve must partially close to provide a higher pressure drop, B-B'. The ratio between the design pressure drop A-A' and the zero flow pressure drop C-C' influences the control capability of the valve.

Better control at part load is obtained by using equal percentage valves. This is particularly true for hot water coils where

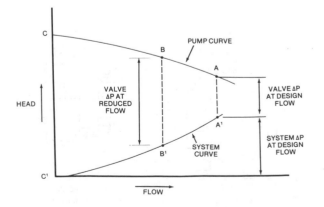

Fig. 12   Pump and System Curves with Valve Control

the heat output of the coil is not linearly related to flow. As flow is reduced, a greater amount of heat is transferred from each unit volume of water, counteracting the reduction in flow. Reset of the supply water temperature with the outdoor temperature can partially correct this.

DAMPERS

Types and Characteristics

Automatic dampers are used in air-conditioning and ventilation systems to control airflow. They may be used for modulating control to maintain a controlled variable such as mixed air temperature or supply air duct static pressure, or a two-position controller to initiate system operation (such as opening minimum outside air dampers when a fan system is started).

Two damper arrangements are used for air-handling system flow control parallel-blade and opposed-blade (see Figure 13). Parallel-blade dampers are adequate for two-position control. Parallel-blade dampers can be used for modulating control in special situations, but opposed-blade dampers are preferable, since they normally provide better control, as shown in Figures 14 and 15. In these figures, the parameter α is the ratio of the system pressure drop to the drop across the damper at maximum (fully open) flow.

Damper leakage is an important factor, particularly where tight shut-off is required. For example, an outdoor air damper must close tightly to prevent coils and pipes from freezing. Low leakage dampers are more costly and require larger operators because of the friction of the seals in the closed position; therefore, they should be used only when necessary, including any location where the tight closing damper will reduce energy consumption significantly.

Operators

Like valve operators, damper operators are available using either electricity or compressed air as a power source.

1. **Electric damper operators** (or **actuators**, as they are sometimes called) can be either unidirectional, spring return, or reversible. The reversible type is frequently used for accurate control in modulating damper applications. A reversible electric

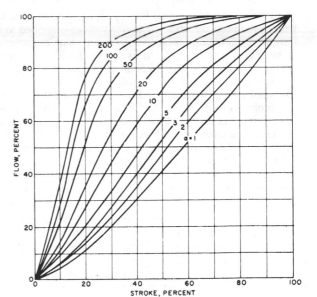

Fig. 14   Installed Characteristic Curves of Parallel Blade Dampers

actuator has two sets of motor windings within the unit's housing. Energizing one set of windings moves the actuator output shaft in a clockwise direction, and energizing the other causes the shaft to turn in a counterclockwise direction. When neither set of windings is energized, the shaft remains in its last position. The simplest form of control for this actuator is a floating point controller, which causes a contact closure to drive the motor in a clockwise and counterclockwise direction. This type of actuator is available with a wide range of options for rotational shaft travel (expressed in degrees of rotation) and timing (expressed in the number of seconds to move through the rotational range). In addition, a variety of standard electronic signals from electronic controllers (such as 4-20 milliamps dc or 0-10 volts dc) can be used to drive

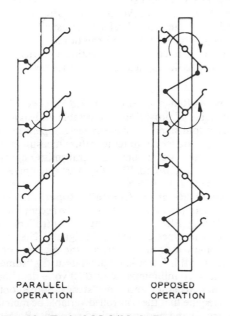

Fig. 13   Typical Multiblade Dampers

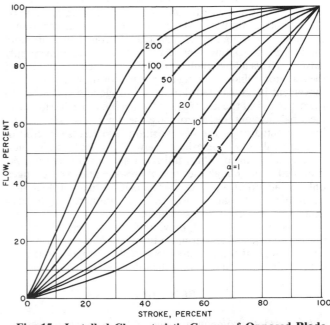

Fig. 15   Installed Characteristic Curves of Opposed Blade Dampers

this type of modulating actuator. A spring return actuator will move in one direction whenever voltage is applied to its internal windings, and, when no power is present, the actuator is returned via spring force to its normal position. Depending on how the actuator is connected to the dampers, this will open or close the dampers.

2. **Pneumatic damper operators** are similar to pneumatic valve operators, with the exception that they have a longer stroke, or the stroke is increased by a multiplying lever. Increasing the air pressure produces a linear motion of the shaft, which, through a linkage, moves the crank arm to open or close the dampers. Normally open or normally closed operation refers to the position of the dampers when no air pressure is applied at the operator. This position depends on how the operator is mounted and how the linkage is connected.

Mounting. Damper operators are mounted in several different ways, depending on the damper size, accessibility, and power required to move the dampers. They can be mounted in the air flow on the damper frame and connected by a linkage directly to a damper blade, or they can be mounted outside the duct and connected to a crank arm attached to a shaft extension of one of the blades. On large dampers, two or more operators may be needed. In this case, they are usually mounted at separate points on the damper. An alternative is to install the damper in two or more sections, with each section being controlled by a single damper operator for outside air control; however, proper airflow control is easier with a single modulating damper. Positive positioners may be required for proper sequencing (see below). A small damper with two-position operator may be used for minimum outside flow, with a large damper being independently controlled for economy cycle cooling.

POSITIVE POSITIONERS

A pneumatic operator may not respond quickly or accurately enough to small changes in control pressure, due to friction in the actuator or load, or to changing load conditions such as wind acting on a damper blade. Where accurate positioning of a modulating damper in response to load is required, positive positioners should be used.

A positive positioner provides up to full main control air pressure to the actuator for any change in position required by the controller. This is achieved by the sample arrangement shown schematically in Figure 16. An increase in branch pressure from the controller (A) moves the relay lever (B), opening the supply valve (C). This allows main air to flow to the relay chamber and the actuator cylinder, moving the piston (not shown). The piston movement is transmitted through a linkage and spring (D) to the other end of the lever (B), and when the force due to movement balances out the control force, the supply valve closes, leaving the actuator in the new position. A decrease in control pressure will allow the exhaust valve (E) to open until a new balance is obtained. Thus, full main air pressure is available, if needed, even though the control pressure may have changed only a fraction of a psi. The movement feedback linkage may be mounted internally or externally. Positioners may be connected for direct- or reverse-action.

A positive positioner (1) provides finite and repeatable positioning change and (2) permits adjustment of the control range (spring range of the actuator) to provide a proper sequencing control of two or more controlled devices.

SENSORS

A sensor is the component in the control system that measures the value of the controlled variable. The change in the controlled

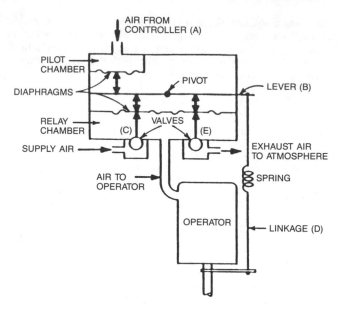

Fig. 16   Positive Positioner

variable (such as the temperature of water flowing in a pipe) produces a change in some physical or electrical property of the primary sensing element, which is then available for translation or amplification by mechanical or electrical signal. When the sensor makes use of a conversion from one form of energy (such as mechanical or thermal) to another (such as electrical), the device is called a transducer. In some cases, the sensing element is a transducer, such as a thermistor, in which a change in electrical resistance occurs as a direct result of a change in temperature.

With the trend toward electronic miniaturization and solid-state sensing elements, sensor selection has become a specialty. New measurement technologies and manufacturers are emerging regularly, expanding the options available to the control system designer and outdating older texts on sensor application. This section does not describe all of the various technologies for measurement and transmission of even the common variables of temperature, humidity, pressure, and flow rate. Chapter 13 of the FUNDAMENTALS Volume, manufacturers' catalogs and tutorials, and the general references listed in the bibliography give specific applications information.

Some things to consider in selecting a particular sensor product for a specific application are as follows:

1. **Operating Range of the Controlled Variable.** The sensor must be capable of providing a detectable and significant change in its output signal over the expected operating range. In the case of an office room temperature measurement, for example, the output of a pneumatic transmitter may change from 3 to 15 psig (20.7 to 103 kPa) over a temperature range of 55 to 85 °F (13 to 20 °C).

2. **Compatibility of the Controller Input.** Pneumatic receiver controllers for HVAC will typically accept input signals of 3 to 15 psig. Electronic and digital controllers accept various ranges and types of electronic signals. The selection of an electronic sensor must consider the specific controller to be used, or, if this is not known, an industry "standard" signal, such as 4-20 milliamps dc or 0-10 volts dc, should be used.

3. **Setpoint Accuracy and Consistency.** Some control applications require that the controlled variable be maintained within a narrow band about a desired setpoint. Both the accuracy

and sensitivity of the sensor selected must reflect this requirement, although an accurate sensor alone cannot maintain the setpoint if the controller is unable to resolve the input signal, the controlled device cannot be positioned accurately, or the controlled device exhibits excessive hysteresis.

4. **System Response Time (or Process Dynamics).** Associated with a sensor/transducer arrangement is a response curve, which describes the response of the sensor output to a change in the controlled variable. If the time constant of the process being controlled is short, and stable accurate control is important, the sensor selected must have a fast response time.

5. **Control Agent Properties and Characteristics.** The control agent is the medium to which the sensor is exposed, or with which it comes in contact, for the purpose of measuring a variable such as temperature or pressure. If the agent acts on the sensor so as to corrode or otherwise degrade its performance, a different sensor should be selected, or the sensor must be isolated or protected from direct contact with the agent.

6. **Ambient Environment Characteristics.** When isolated from direct contact with the control agent, the ambient environment in which the sensor's components are located must be considered. The temperature and humidity range of the ambient environment must not adversely affect the sensor or its accuracy. Likewise, the presence of certain gases, chemicals, and electromagnetic interference (EMI) can cause component degradation. In such cases, a special sensor or transducer housing can be used to protect the element while ensuring a true indication of the control variable.

Temperature Sensors

Temperature-sensing elements fall into three general categories: those that use a change in relative dimension due to differences in thermal expansion, those that use a change in state of a vapor or liquid-filled bellows, and those that make use of a change in some electrical property. Within each category, there are a variety of sensing element configurations to measure room, duct, water, and surface temperatures.

The specific types of temperature-sensing technologies commonly used in HVAC applications are as follows:

1. A **bimetal** element is composed of two thin strips of dissimilar metals fused together. Because the two metals have different coefficients of thermal expansion, the element bends as the temperature varies, and produces a change in position. Depending on the space available and the movement required, it may be a straight strip, U-shaped, or wound into a spiral. This element is commonly applied in room, insertion, and immersion thermostats.

2. A **rod-and-tube** element consists of a high expansion metal tube containing a low expansion rod with one end attached to the rear of the tube. The tube changes length with changes in temperature, causing the free end of the rod to move. This element is commonly used on certain types of insertion and immersion thermostats.

3. A **sealed bellows** element is either vapor-, gas-, or liquid-filled after being evacuated of air. Temperature changes cause changes in pressure or volume of the gas or liquid, resulting in a change in force or movement. This element is often used in room thermostats.

4. A **remote bulb** element is a sealed bellows or diaphragm to which a bulb or capsule is attached by means of a capillary tube; the entire system is filled with vapor, gas, or liquid. Temperature changes at the bulb result in volume or pressure changes that are communicated to the bellows or diaphragm through the capillary tube. The remote bulb element is useful

where the temperature measuring point is remote from the desired thermostat location. It usually is provided with fittings suitable for insertion into a duct, pipe, or tank. **Averaging bulbs** are used in large ducts where a single sensing point may not be representative.

5. A **thermistor** makes use of the change of electrical resistance of a semiconductor material for a representative change in temperature. The characteristic curve of a thermistor is non-linear over a wide range. It has a negative temperature coefficient, meaning that the resistance decreases as the temperature increases. For electronic control systems, a variety of techniques are available to provide a linear change over a particular temperature range. In a digital control system, one technique to linearize the curve over certain ranges is to store a computer "look-up table" that maps the temperatures corresponding to the measured resistance. Thermistors are used because of their relatively low cost and the large change in resistance possible for a small change in temperature.

6. A **resistance temperature detector** (RTD) is another sensor that changes electrical resistance with temperature. Most metallic materials increase in resistance with increasing temperature. Over limited ranges, this variation is linear for certain metals such as platinum, copper, tungsten, and some nickel/iron alloys. Platinum, for example, is linear within ± 0.3 percent from 0 to 300°F (-17 to 149°C). The RTD sensing element is available in several different forms for surface or immersion mounting. For direct measurement of fluid temperatures, the winding of resistance wire is encased in a stainless-steel bulb to protect it from corrosion. Flat grid windings are used for measurements of surface temperatures. The RTD measurement circuit typically consists of three wires to correct for line resistance. In many cases, the three-wire RTD is mated to an electronic circuit to produce a 4 to 20 milliamp current signal over a finite temperature range.

7. A **thermocouple** is formed by the junction of two wires of dissimilar metals. An electromotive force dependent upon the wire materials and junction temperature exists between the wires. When the wires are joined at two points, a thermocouple circuit is formed. As long as one junction is kept at a constant temperature, different from the other junction, an electric current flows through the circuit as a result of the difference in voltage potential developed by the two junctions. The constant temperature junction is called the cold junction. Various systems are used to provide cold junction compensation. Advances in solid-state circuitry have produced thermocouple transmitters with built-in cold junction and linearization circuits. Attaching the proper thermocouple to this circuit is all that is required to provide a linearized signal (such as 4 to 20 milliamp dc) to a controller or indicating digital meter.

Humidity Sensors

Humidity sensors or hygrometers can be used to measure the relative humidity or dew point of ambient or moving air. Materials that respond directly to atmospheric moisture detect relative humidity directly. Two basic types are available for use in central systems—mechanical hygrometers and electronic hygrometers. A mechanical hygrometer operates on the principle that a hygroscopic material, when exposed to water vapor, retains moisture and expands. This change in size or form is detected by a mechanical linkage and converted to a pneumatic or electronic signal. The most direct indicator of relative humidity is the change in length of an untampered human hair. Human hair will exhibit a total change of about 2.5% of original length as the relative humidity changes from 0 to 100% RH. A human hair hygrometer can measure relative humidity from 5 to 100%

to within 5% at temperatures above 32°F (0°C). Other materials used in humidity sensors include organic materials (such as wood fibers, paper, cotton) and manufactured materials (such as nylon).

Electronic hygrometers can be of the capacitance- or resistance-type. The resistance-type uses a conductive grid coated with a hygroscopic (or water-absorbent) substance. The conductivity of the grid varies with the water retained, so the resistance varies according to the relative humidity. Two popular sensors are the Dunmore and Pope units. In both instruments, the conductive element is arranged in an AC-excited wheatstone bridge, and both respond to humidity changes quickly. The capacitance-type is commonly based on thin film, plastic foils that change the capacitance with relative humidity. The sensor is a stretched membrane of nonconductive foil coated on both sides with gold electrodes and is mounted within a perforated plastic capsule. The change of the sensor's capacity versus relative humidity is nonlinear with progressive characteristics, i.e., with rising relative humidity. The output voltage to the converter rises proportionately more than the humidity. The capacitance of the relative humidity sensor varies positively with increasing temperature and increasing relative humidity, as well. The signal is linearized and temperature compensated in the amplifier circuit to provide an output voltage signal as the RH changes from 0 to 100%.

Pressure Transducers, Transmitters, and Controllers

A pneumatic pressure transmitter converts a change in absolute, gauge, or differential pressure to a mechanical motion using a bellows, diaphragm, or Bourdon tube mechanism. This mechanical motion, when corrected through appropriate linkage, produces a change in the air pressure to a controller. In some instances, the sensing and control functions are combined in a single component called a *pressure controller.*

Electronic pressure transducers may use the mechanical actuation of a diaphragm or Bourdon tube device to produce a displacement detected by a potentiometer or differential transformer. The change in resistance, in the form of a potentiometer, is then converted using electronic circuitry to a voltage or direct current compatible with the input of the controller. Another type of transducer uses a strain gauge bonded to a diaphragm. The strain gauge detects the displacement resulting from the force applied to the diaphragm. Electronic circuitry for temperature compensation and amplification produces a standard output signal.

Flow Rating Sensing

The following basic sensing principles and devices are used to sense water or fluid flow: orifice plate, Pitot tube, venturi, turbine meter, magnetic flow meter, vortex shedding meter, and doppler effect meter. Each of these has characteristics of rangeability, accuracy, cost, and suitability for use with clean or dirty fluids that make it appropriate for a particular application. In general, the pressure differential devices (orifice plates, venturi, and Pitot tubes) are less expensive and simpler to use but have limited range, so their accuracy depends on how they are applied and where they are located in a system.

More sophisticated flow devices, such as turbine, magnetic, and vortex shedding meters, usually have better range and are more accurate over a wide range. In the case of a flowmeter being retrofit into an existing piping system, the expense of shutting down a system and cutting into a pipe must sometimes be considered. In this case, a non-invasive meter, such as a doppler effect meter, can be cost-effective.

CONTROLLERS

Controllers take the sensor effect, compare it with the desired control condition (set point), and regulate an output signal to cause a control action on the controlled device. The controller and sensor can be combined in a single instrument, such as a room thermostat, or they may be two separate devices. When separate pneumatic units are used, the pneumatic controller is usually called a **receiver-controller**.

Electric/Electronic Controllers

For two-position control, the controller output may be a simple electrical contact that starts a burner or pump, or that actuates a spring-return valve or damper operator. Single-pole, double-throw (SPDT) switching circuits are used to control a three-wire unidirectional motor operator. SPDT circuits also are used for heating-cooling applications. Either single-pole, single-throw (SPST), or SPDT circuits can be modified for times two-position action.

For floating control, the controller output is a SPDT switching circuit with a neutral zone where neither contact is made. This control is used with reversible motor operators.

Proportional control gives continuous or incremental changes in output signal to position an electrical actuator or controlled device.

Indicating or Recording Controllers

Controllers can be of the indicating or recording type.

The nonindicating controller is most common in HVAC work, and includes all types in which the sensing element does not provide a visual indication of the value of the controlled variable. For an indication, a separate thermometer, relative humidity indicator or pressure gauge is required. With room thermostats, for example, a separate thermometer is often attached to the cover.

1. An *indicating* controller has a pointer added to the sensing element or attached to it by a linkage, so that the value of the controlled variable is indicated on a suitable scale.
2. A *recording* controller is similar to an indicating controller, except that the indicating pointer is replaced by a recording pen that provides a permanent record on a special recorder chart paper.
3. *Proportional band* is a term used in connection with modulating controllers and means the same as throttling range. It is usually expressed in percent of the scale or chart range of the controller.

Pneumatic Receiver Controllers

Pneumatic receiver controllers are normally combined with sensing elements with a force or position output to obtain a variable air pressure output. The control mode is usually proportional, but other modes such as proportional-integral can be used. These controllers are generally classified as nonrelay, relay direct, or reverse-acting type.

1. The **nonrelay** pneumatic controller uses a restrictor in the air supply and a bleed nozzle. The sensing element positions an air exhaust flapper that varies the nozzle opening, causing a variable air pressure output applied to the controlled device, usually a pneumatic operator. The response time is increased, since all air must flow through the small orifice to position the actuator.

2. A **relay-type** pneumatic controller, directly or indirectly through a restrictor, nozzle, and flapper, actuates a relay device that amplifies the air volume available for control. This arrangement provides quick response to a measured variable change.

Controllers are further classified by construction as direct- or reverse-acting.

1. **Direct-acting** controllers increase the output signal as the controlled variable increases. For example, a direct-acting pneumatic thermostat increases output pressure when the sensing element detects a temperature rise.
2. **Reverse-acting** controllers increase the output signal as the controlled variable decreases. A reverse-acting pneumatic thermostat increases output pressure when the temperature drops.

Direct Digital Controllers

A direct digital controller uses a digital computer (such as a microprocessor or mini-computer) to implement control algorithms on one or multiple control loops. It is fundamentally different from pneumatic or electronic controllers in that the control algorithm is stored as a set of program instructions in memory (referred to as software or firmware). The controller itself calculates the proper control signals digitally rather than using an analog circuit or mechanical change.

A digital controller can be either a single loop or multi-loop controller. Interface hardware allows the digital computer to process signals from various "input" devices such as electronic temperature, humidity, or pressure sensors described in the previous section on sensors. Based on the digitized equivalents of the voltage or current signals produced by the inputs, the control software calculates the required state of the "output" devices such as valve and damper actuators and fan starters. The output devices are then positioned to the calculated state via interface hardware that converts the digital signal from the computer to an analog voltage or current required to position the actuator or energize a relay.

The operator enters parameters such as setpoints, proportionals or integral gains, minimum on and off times, or high and low limits. The control algorithms stored in the computer's memory in conjunction with actual input values make the control decisions. The computer scans the input devices, executes the control algorithms, then positions the output device(s) in a time-multiplex scheme. Digital controllers can be classified with regard to the way control algorithms are in memory.

1. **Pre-programmed control** routines are typically stored in permanent memory, such as PROM (programmable read only memory). To prevent unauthorized alteration, the operator can modify parameters such as set points, limits, and minimum off times within the control routines, but the program logic cannot be changed without replacement of the memory chips.
2. **User-programmable controllers** allow the algorithms to be changed by the user. A programming language, provided with the controller, can vary from a derivation of a standard language (such as Pascal or Basic) to a custom language developed by the controller's manufacturer. Pre-programmed routines for proportional, proportional plus integral, Boolean logic, timers, etc., are typically included in the language. Standard energy management routines may also be pre-programmed and interact with other control loops where appropriate.

A terminal allows the user to communicate with and, where applicable, modify the program in the controller. These terminals can range from hand-held units with an LCD display and several buttons or a full-size console with a CRT (Cathode-ray tube) and typewriter-style keyboard. The terminal can be limited in function to allow only the display of sensor and parameter values or powerful enough to allow changing or reprogramming the control strategies. In some instances, an operator's terminal can communicate remotely with one or more controllers, thus allowing centralized system displays, alarms, and commands.

Thermostats

Thermostats combine the control and sensing function into a single device. Because they are so prevalent in pneumatic control systems, this section describes the various types and operating characteristics.

1. The **day-night** or **dual-temperature room** thermostat controls at a reduced temperature at night. It may be indexed (changed from day to night operation) individually or in groups from a remote point by a manual or time switch. Some electric types have an individual clock and switch built into the thermostat.

   The **pneumatic day-night** thermostat uses a two-pressure air supply system—the two pressures often being 13 and 17 psi (89.6 and 117 kPa) gauge, or 15 and 20 psi (103.35 and 137.8 kPa) gauge. Changing the pressure at a central point from one value to the other actuates switching devices in the thermostat and indexes it from day to night or vice versa. Supply-air mains are often divided into two or more circuits so that switching can be done in various areas of the building at different times. For example, a school building may have separate circuits for classrooms, offices and administrative areas, the auditorium, the gymnasium, and locker rooms.
2. The **heating-cooling** or **summer-winter** thermostat can have its action reversed and its set point changed by indexing. It is used to actuate controlled devices, such as valves or dampers, that regulate a heating source at one time and a cooling source at another. Often it is indexed manually in groups by a switch, or automatically by a thermostat sensing the temperature of the control agent (outdoor temperature or another suitable variable).

   The **pneumatic heating-cooling** thermostat uses a two-pressure air supply, as described for day-night thermostats.
3. **Multistage** thermostats are arranged to operate two or more successive steps in sequence.
4. A **submaster** thermostat has its set point raised or lowered over a predetermined range, in accordance with variations in output from a master controller. The master controller can be a thermostat, manual switch, pressure controller, or similar device. For example, a master thermostat measuring outdoor air temperature can be used to readjust a submaster thermostat controlling the water temperature in a heating system. Master-submaster combinations are sometimes designated as single-cascade action. When such action is accomplished by a single thermostat having more than one measuring element, it is known as *compensated control*.
5. A **wet-bulb** thermostat is often used for humidity control with proper control of the dry-bulb temperature. A wick, or other means for keeping the bulb wet with pure (distilled) water, and rapid air motion to ensure a true wet-bulb measurement are essential. Because of maintenance problems, wet-bulb thermostats are seldom used.
6. A **dew point** thermostat is a device designed to control from dew point temperatures. Dew point is measured in several ways—the most accurate is to measure the temperature of a hydroscopic solution maintained by an equilibrium vapor pressure with its surroundings.

7. A **dead band** thermostat has a wide differential over which the thermostat remains neutral, requiring neither heating nor cooling. This differential may be adjustable up to 10°F (5.5°C). The thermostat then controls to maximum or minimum output over a small differential at each end of the dead bank, as shown in Figure 17.

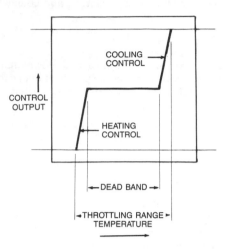

Fig. 17   Dead Band Thermostat

AUXILIARY CONTROL DEVICES

In addition to the conventional controllers and controlled devices described, many control systems require auxiliary devices to perform various functions.

Auxiliary controls for electric control systems include the following:

1. **Transformers** to provide current at the required voltage.
2. **Electric relays** to control electric heaters or to start and stop oil burners, refrigeration compressors, fans, pumps, or other apparatus for which the electrical load is too large to be handled directly by the controller. Other uses include time-delay and circuit-interlocking safety applications.
3. **Potentiometers** for manual positioning of proportional control devices, for remote set point adjustment of electronic controllers, and for feedback.
4. **Manual switches** for performing several operations. These can be two-position or multiple-position with single or multiple poles.
5. **Auxiliary switches** on valve and damper operators for providing a selected sequence of operation.

Auxiliary control equipment for pneumatic system includes the following:

1. **Air compressors** and accessories, including driers and filters, to provide a source of clean, dry air at the required pressure.
2. **Electropneumatic relays**, which are electrically actuated air valves for operating pneumatic equipment in accordance with variations in electrical input to the relay.
3. **Pneumatic-electric switches**, which are actuated by air pressure to make or break an electrical circuit.
4. **Pneumatic relays**, which are actuated by the pressure from a controller to perform numerous functions. They may be divided into two groups:
   a. **Two-position relays**, which permit a controller actuating a proportional device to also actuate one or more two-position devices.
   b. **Proportional relays**, which are used to reverse the action of a proportional controller, select the higher or lower of two or more pressures, average two or more pressures, respond to the difference between two pressures, add or subtract pressures, and amplify or retard pressure changes.
5. **Positive Positioning relays**, which are devices for ensuring accurate positioning of a valve or damper operator in response to changes in pressure from a controller. They are affected by the position of the operator and the pressue from the controller; and, whenever the two are out of balance, these relays will use full control air pressure to change the pressure applied to the operator until balance is restored.
6. **Switching relays**, which are pneumatically operated air valves for diverting air from one circuit to another, or for opening and closing air circuits.
7. **Pneumatic switches**, which are manually operated devices for diverting air from one circuit to another or for opening and closing air circuits. They can be two-position or multiple-position.
8. **Gradual switches**, which are proportional devices for manually varying the air pressure in a circuit.
9. **Logic networks and square root extractors.**

Auxiliary control devices common to both electric and pneumatic systems include the following:

1. **Step controllers** for operating a number of electric switches in sequence by means of a proportional electric or pneumatic operator. They are commonly used for controlling several steps of refrigeration capacity and may be arranged to prevent simultaneous starting of compressors and to alternate the sequence to equalize wear. They may also be used for se-

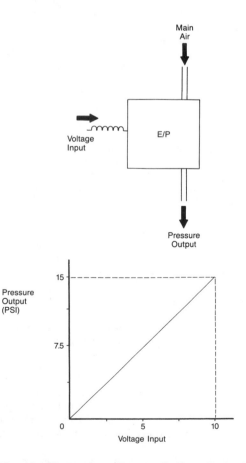

Fig. 18   Electronic-to-Pneumatic Transducer (E/P)

quence operation of electric heating elements and other equipment.

2. **Power controllers** for controlling electrical power input to resistance-type electric heating elements. The final controlled device may be a variable autotransformer, a saturable-core reactor, or a solid-state power controller. They are commonly available with various ratings for either single- or three-phase heater loads. Normally they are arranged to regulate power input to the heater in response to demands of proportional electronic or pneumatic controllers. However, solid-state controllers may also be used in two-position control modes.

3. **Clocks or timers** for turning apparatus on and off at predetermined times, for switching control systems from day to night operation, and for other time sequence functions.

4. **Transducers**, which consist of combinations of electric or pneumatic control devices, may be required. For these applications, devices commonly called transducers are used to convert electric signals to pneumatic output or vice versa. Transducers may convert proportional input to either proportional or two-position output.

One transducer that has come into widespread use is the electronic-to-pneumatic (E-to-P) transducer (Figure 18). The E-to-P converts a proportional elecctronic output signal into a proportional pneumatic signal. It can be used to combine electronic and pneumatic control components to form a control loop, as illustrated in Figure 19. Electronic components are used for sensing and signal conditioning, while pneumatics are used for actuation. The electronic controller can be either an analog or a digital controller.

The E-to-P transducer presents a special option for retrofit applications. As illustrated in Figure 20, an existing HVAC system with pneumatic controls can be retrofit with electronic sensors and controllers while retaining the existing pneumatic actuators. One advantage of this approach is that the retrofit can be accomplished with only a minor interruption to the operation of the control system.

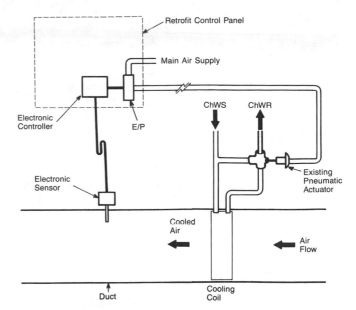

Fig. 20   Retrofit of an Existing Pneumatic System with Electronic Sensors and Controllers

ing and the pressure difference between the mixed air plenum and outdoor air conditions.

Fixed minimum outdoor air control for VAV systems *with* return fans has two variations. Minimum outdoor air is determined by the airflow difference between the supply and return fans (Figure 21B), as well as by the outdoor air damper minimum position.

If the *outdoor air supplied is greater than the difference between the supply and return fan airflows*, a variation of Economizer Cycle Control is used (Figure 21C).

With this method of control, all outdoor air goes to the fan

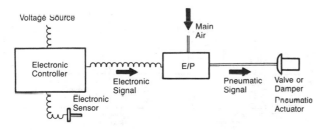

Fig. 19   Example of Electronic and Pneumatic Control Components Combined with an Electronic-to-Pneumatic (E/P) Transducer

CONTROL OF CENTRAL SUBSYSTEMS

CONTROL OF OUTDOOR AIR QUANTITY

Fixed minimum outdoor air control provides ventilation air, space pressurization (exfiltration), and make-up for exhaust fans.

For systems *without* return fans, the outdoor air damper (Figure 21A) is interlocked to open only when the supply fan operates. The outdoor air damper should open quickly when the fan turns on to prevent excessive negative duct pressurization. Rate of outdoor airflow is determined by damper open-

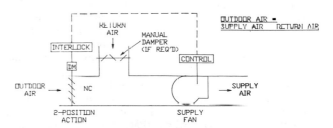

Fig. 21A   Fixed Minimim Outdoor Air for Systems Without Return Fans

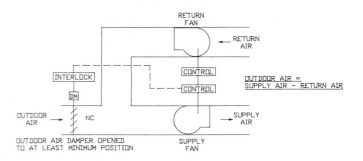

Fig. 21B   Fixed Minimim Outdoor Air for Systems With Return Fans

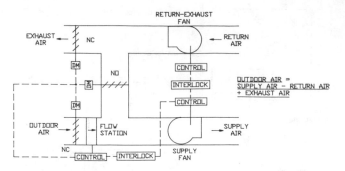

Fig. 21C Fixed Minimim Outdoor Air for Systems With Return-Exhaust Fans—Outdoor Air is Greater than the Difference Between Supply and Return Air Flows

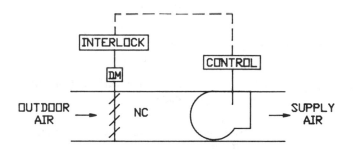

Fig. 22 100% Outdoor Air Control

and no air is returned. The outdoor air damper (Figure 22) is interlocked and opens before the fan starts.

Economizer cycle control reduces cooling costs when outside conditions are suitable. If outdoor air is below a high temperature limit, typically 65°F (18°C), the return, exhaust, and outdoor air dampers (Figure 23) modulate to maintain a ventilation cooling setpoint, typically 55 to 60°F (13 to 16°C). The relief dampers are interlocked to close and the return air dampers to open when the supply fan is not operating. When outdoor air exceeds the high temperature limit setpoint, the outdoor air damper is maintained at a fixed minimum while the outdoor air temperature interlock causes the relief and return air dampers to close and open respectively.

Enthalpy economizer control replaces the high temperature limit of the Economizer Cycle to further reduce energy costs when latent loads are significant. The interlock function (Figure 23) can be based on (1) a fixed enthalpy high limit, (2) a comparison with return air so as not to exceed return air enthalpy, or (3) a combination of enthalpy and temperature high limits.

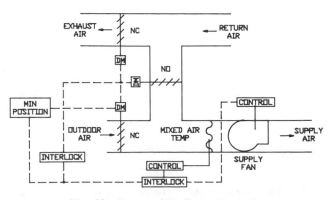

Fig. 23 Economizer Cycle Control

VAV warm-up control during unoccupied periods requires no outdoor air. Typically, outdoor and exhaust dampers remain closed. However, systems with a return fan (Figure 24) should position the outdoor air damper at its minimum position to prevent excessive positive or negative duct pressurization. The section "Control System Design and Application" has information on fan control during warm-up. Normally, the return fan is off during this cycle.

Night cool-down control (also called "night purge") provides 100% outdoor air for cooling during unoccupied periods (Figure 25). The space is cooled to a space setpoint, typically 9°F (5°C) above outdoor air temperature. Limit controls prevent operation if outdoor air is above space dry-bulb or dew point temperature or if outdoor air dry-bulb temperature is too cold, typically 50°F (10°C). The night cool-down cycle is initiated before sunrise, when overnight outside temperatures are usually the coolest, prior to the beginning of the optimum start program—typically four hours before occupancy.

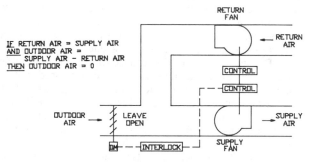

Fig. 24 VAV Warm-up Control

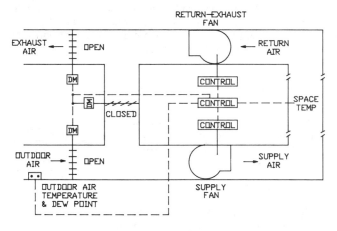

Fig. 25 Night Cool Down Control

FAN CONTROL

Fan modulation is provided by the following methods:

Fan inlet or discharge dampers
Fan scroll dampers
Variable speed
Fan runaround or scroll bypass
Controllable pitch
Fan inlet vanes

Constant Volume Control

Constant volume control fixes the airflow rate when duct resistances vary (Figure 26).

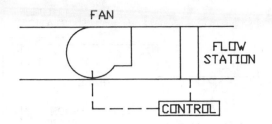

Fig. 26   Constant Volume Control

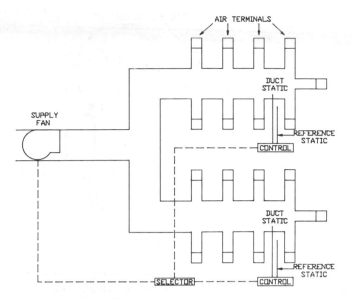

Fig. 27B   Multiple Static Sensors

Duct Static Control

Duct static control for VAV systems maintains a static pressure at a location of measurement. The location (based on duct layout) is typically between 75% and 100% of the distance between the first and last air terminal (Figure 27A).

The pressure selected provides minimum static pressure to all air terminal units during all supply fan design conditions.

Multiple static sensors (Figure 27B) are required when more than one duct runs from the supply fan. The sensor having the lowest static requirement controls the fan. Since duct run-outs may vary, a control that uses individual setpoints for each measurement is recommended.

Duct static limit control protects from excessive duct pressures—usually at the discharge of the supply fan. Two variations are used: (1) a **fan shutdown**, which is a safety high-limit control that turns the fans off and (2) a **controlling high limit**, which is used in systems having zone fire dampers. When the zone fire damper closes (Figure 27C), duct pressure drops, causing the duct static control to increase fan modulation; however, the controlling high limit will override.

Supply fan warm-up control for systems having a return fan prevents the supply fan from delivering more airflow than the return fan can produce during warm-up mode (Figure 27D). If supply fan airflow exceeds return fan airflow maximum capacity, excessive negative duct pressurization can occur.

Return fan static control from returns having local (zoned) flow control is identical to the supply fan static control concept (Figure 27E).

Return Fan Control

Return fan control for VAV systems provides proper building pressurization and minimum outdoor air.

Duct static control to the supply-fan-modulation means is sent

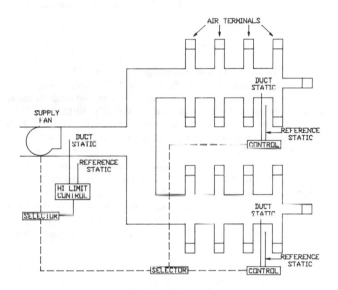

Fig. 27C   Duct Static Limit Control: Controlling High Limit Type

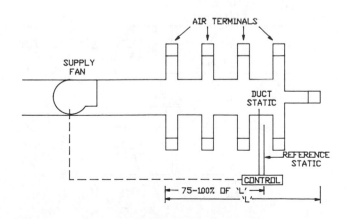

Fig. 27A   Duct Static Control

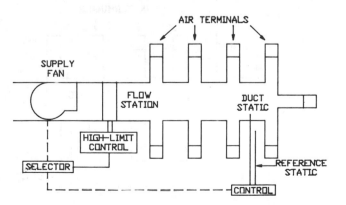

Fig. 27D   Supply Fan Warm-Up Control

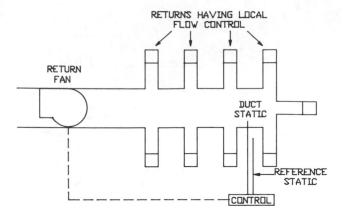

Fig. 27E Return Fan Static Control

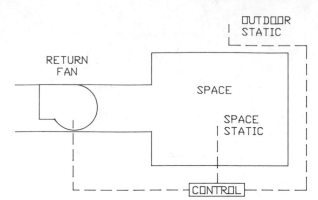

Fig. 28B Direct Building Pressurization Control

to the return-fan-modulation means (Figure 28A). This open loop (without feedback) control requires similar supply and return fan airflow modulation characteristics. The return fan airflow is adjusted at minimum and maximum airflow conditions. System airflow turndown should not be excessive, typically a maximum of 50%. Provisions for warm-up and exhaust fan switching are impractical.

Direct building pressurization control of the return fan is accomplished by measuring the space and outdoor static pressures (Figure 28B). The indoor static location must be selected carefully: away from doors and openings to an outside, away from elevator lobbies, and in a large representative area using a sensor shielded from air velocity effects. Likewise, the outdoor static location must be selected carefully: typically 10 to 15 ft (3 to 4.6 m) above the building and oriented to minimize wind effects from all directions. The amount of minimum outdoor air varies with building permeability and exhaust fan switching. During the warm-up mode, the building static pressure is reset to zero differential pressure, and all exhaust fans are turned off.

Airflow tracking uses duct airflow measurements (Figure 28C) to control the return air fans. Sensors called flow stations are typically multiple point, pitot tube, and averaging. To maintain pressurization of the building, provisions must account for ex-

haust fan switching. Warm-up is accomplished by setting the return airflow equal to the supply fan airflow—usually with exhaust fans turned off.

During night cool-down, the return fan operates in the normal mode (see three previous paragraphs).

Sequencing Fans

Sequencing of fans for VAV systems gives greater airflow reduction. The results are greater operating economy and stable fan operation, if airflow reductions are significant. Alternation of fans usually provides greater system reliability.

Centrifugal fans are controlled to keep system disturbances to a minimum when additional fans are started. The added fan is started and slowly brought up to capacity while the capacity of operating fans is reduced *simultaneously*. The output of all fans combined then equals the output before fan addition.

Vane axial fans usually cannot be sequenced in the same manner as centrifugal fans. To avoid "stall," operating fans must be reduced to some minimum level. Hence, additional fan may be started and modulated to achieve equilibrium.

Unstable Fan Operation

Fan instability for VAV systems can usually be avoided by proper fan sizing. However, if airflow reduction is large (typically over 60%) a technique for maintaining airflow within the fan's stable range is usually required, such as:

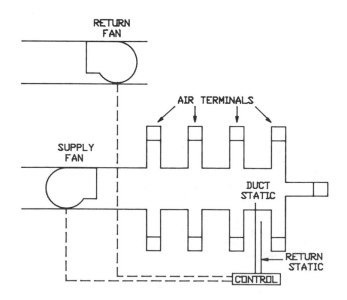

Fig. 28A Duct Static Control of Return Fan

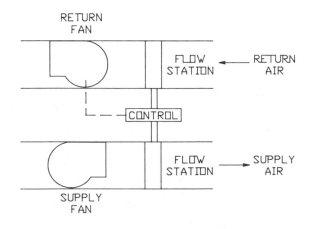

Fig. 28C Airflow Tracking Control

Sequencing of fans, as discussed in a preceding paragraph.

Coil reset avoids fan instability by resetting the cooling coil discharge temperature higher (Figure 29A) so that the building cooling loads require greater airflow. Since a time lag occurs between temperature reset and demand for more airflow, the value at which reset starts should be selected on the safe side of the fan instability point. When this technique is used, dehumidification requirements should be checked to be sure they can be maintained.

Fan bypass allows airflow to "short circuit" around the fan so that a minimum airflow can be maintained (Figure 29B). This technique uses constant volume control to limit the low airflow.

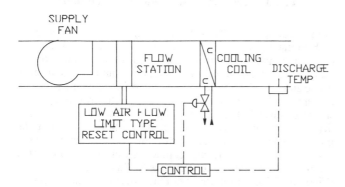

Fig. 29A   Coil Reset Control to Prevent Supply Fan Instability

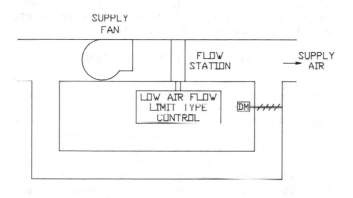

Fig. 29B   Fan Bypass Control to Prevent Supply Fan Instability

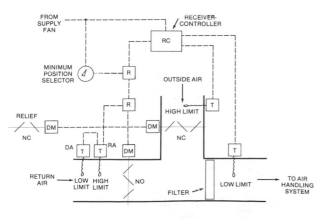

Fig. 29C   Warm-Up/Cool Down Cycle for Outside Air Control

CONTROL OF HEATING COILS

Heating coils in central air-handling units *preheat, reheat,* or *heat,* depending on the climate and amount of minimum outdoor air needed.

Preheating Coils

Control of steam or hot water preheating coils must include protection against freezing unless the minimum outdoor air quantity is small enough to keep the mixed air temperature above freezing and there is enough mixing to prevent stratification. Even though the average mixed air temperature is above freezing, inadequate mixing may allow a freezing air stratum to impinge on the coil.

Steam preheat coils should have two-position valves and vacuum breakers to prevent a buildup of condensate in the coil. The valve should be fully open when outdoor air (or mixed air) temperature is below freezing. This causes unacceptably high coil discharge temperatures at times, so face and bypass dampers are required for final temperature control (Figure 30). The bypass damper should be sized to provide the same pressure drop at full bypass airflow as the combination of face damper and coil at full airflow.

Hot water preheat coils must maintain a minimum water velocity of 3 fps (0.9 m/s) in the tubes to prevent freezing. A two-position valve combined with face and bypass dampers can usually be used to control the water velocity. More commonly, a secondary pump control in one of two configurations (Figures 31 and 32) is used. The control valve modulates to maintain the desired coil air discharge temperature, while the pump operates to maintain the minimum tube water velocity when outdoor air is below freezing. The system in Figure 32 uses less pump power, allows variable flow in the hot water supply main, and is preferred for energy conservation. The system in Figure 31 may be

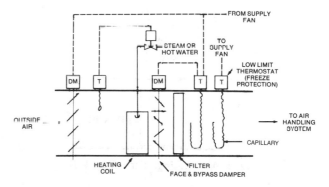

Fig. 30   Preheat With Face and Bypass Dampers

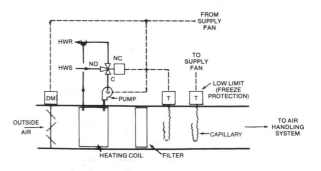

Fig. 31   Preheat-Secondary Pump and Three-Way Valve

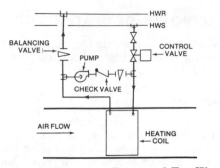

Fig. 32   Preheat-Secondary Pump and Two-Way Valve

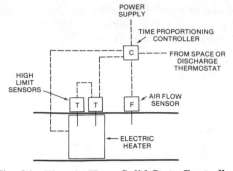

Fig. 34   Electric Heat: Solid-State Controller

required on small systems with only one or two air handlers or where constant main water flow is required.

Reheat and Heating Coils

Steam or hot water reheat and heating coils not subject to freezing can be controlled by simple two- or three-way modulating valves (Figure 33A and B). Steam distributing coils are required to ensure proper steam coil control. The valve is controlled by coil discharge air temperature or by space temperature, depending on the HVAC system. Valves are normally open to allow heating if control power fails. Load analyzer control resets discharge temperature controllers to satisfy a representative zone with the greatest demand. On many systems, outdoor air temperature resets the heating discharge controller, but this is not as cost-effective as load analyzer control.

Electric heating coils are controlled in either a two-position

or modulating mode. Two-position operation uses power relays with contacts sized to handle the power required by the heating coil. Timed two-position control requires a timer and contactors. The timer can be electro-mechanical, but it is usually electronic and provides a time base of one to five minutes. Step controllers provide cam-operated sequencing control of up to 10 stages of electric heat. Each stage may require a contactor, depending on the step controller contact rating. Thermostat demand determines the percentage of "on" time. Since rapid cycling of mechanical or mercury contactors can cause maintenance problems, solid-state controllers like SCRs (silicon control rectifiers) or Triacs are preferred. These devices make cycling so rapid that the control is proportional. For safety (and code requirements), an electric heater must have a minimum airflow switch and high-temperature limit sensors—one with manual reset and one with automatic reset. Therefore, face and bypass dampers are not used. Figure 34 shows the control system with a solid-state controller and safety controls.

CONTROL OF COOLING COILS

Cooling coils in central air-handling units can use chilled water, brine, glycol, or refrigerant (direct expansion) as the cooling medium. Most cooling processes involve some dehumidification. The amount of dehumidification that occurs is a function of the effective coil surface temperature and is limited by the freezing point of water or other coolant. If water condensing out of the air stream freezes on the coil surface, airflow is restricted and, in severe cases, may be shut off. The practical limit is about 40 °F (4 °C) dew point on the coil surface. As Figure 35 shows, this results in a relative humidity of about 30% at a space temperature of 75 °F (24 °C), which is adequate for most industrial processes. When lower humidities are required, chemical dehumidifiers are necessary (see "Humidity Control").

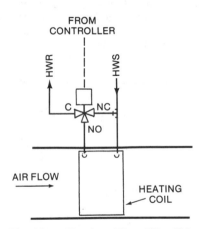

Fig. 33A   Heating: Three-Way Valve

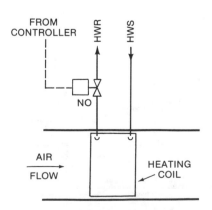

Fig. 33B   Heating: Two-Way Valve

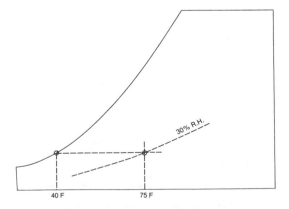

Fig. 35   Cooling and Dehumidifying—Practical Low Limit

Chilled water or brine cooling coils are controlled by two- or three-way valves (Figures 36A and B). Valves are similar to those used for heating control but are normally closed to prevent cooling when the fan is off. The valve typically modulates in response to coil air discharge temperature or space temperature. A load analyzer can reset discharge temperature controllers. Outdoor air reset is sometimes used, but it is not as cost-effective as a load analyzer.

When maximum relative-humidity control is required, a space or return air humidistat is provided with the space thermostat. To limit maximum humidity, a control function selects the higher of the two output signals and controls the cooling coil valve accordingly. A reheat coil must maintain space temperature (see Figure 37).

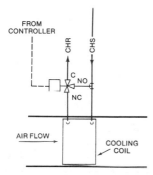

Fig. 36A   Chilled Water Control: Three-Way Valve

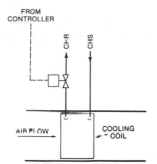

Fig. 36B   Chilled Water Control: Two-Way Valve

Direct expansion (DX) cooling coils are usually controlled by solenoid valves in the refrigerant liquid line (Figure 38). Face and bypass dampers are not recommended because ice tends to form on the coil when airflow is reduced. Control can be improved by using two or more stages, with the solenoid valves controlled in sequence with a differential of 1 or 2°F (0.6 or 1.1°C) between stages (Figure 39). The first stage should be the first coil row on the entering air side with the following rows forming the second and succeeding stages. Side-by-side stages tend to generate icing on the stage in use, with reduction of airflow and loss of control. Modulating control is achieved using a variable suction pressure controller (Figure 40). This type of control is uncommon but necessary if accurate control of discharge or space temperature is needed.

Evaporative cooling can also provide sensible cooling using standard evaporative coolers or air washers (Figure 41). Process efficiency is described by the ratio of dry-bulb temperature difference between inlet and outlet divided by the difference between inlet dry-bulb and the inlet wet-bulb temperature. Air washers are usually 90 to 95% efficient, while evaporative coolers vary from 50 to 90%. (See Chapter 4 in the 1983 EQUIPMENT Volume.) The space temperature controls the spray pump (Figure 42), which causes high relative humidity in the space; humidity

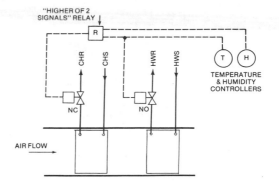

Fig. 37   Cooling and Dehumidifying With Reheat

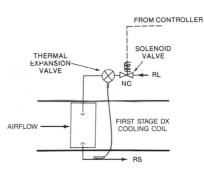

Fig. 38   Direct Expansion—Two-Position Control

cannot be controlled, since it is primarily a function of outdoor wet-bulb temperature.

HUMIDITY CONTROL

While simple cooling by refrigeration maintains an upper limit to space humidity, it does not control humidity without additional equipment.

Dehumidification

A formerly used method of dehumidification is the **sprayed coil dehumidifier** (Figure 43). The systems in Figures 42 and 43 have essentially the same effect (Figure 44). Space relative humidities ranging from 35 to 55% at 75°F (24°C) can be obtained with these systems; however, maintenance and operating costs caused by reheat and solid deposition on the coil make this system undesirable.

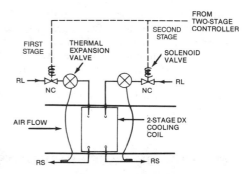

Fig. 39   Two-Stage Direct Expansion Cooling

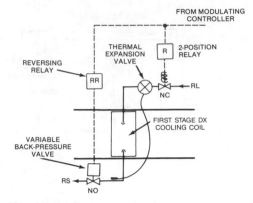

Fig. 40   Modulating Direct Expansion Cooling

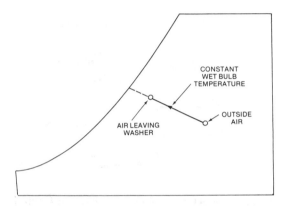

Fig. 41   Psychrometric Chart: Evaporative Cooling

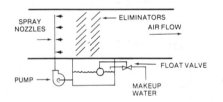

Fig. 42   Evaporative Cooling: Air Washer

Chemical dehumidifiers can develop space humidities below those possible with cooling/dehumidifying coils. These devices adsorb moisture using silica gel or similar material. For continuous operation, heat is added to regenerate the material. The adsorption process also generates heat (Figure 45). Figure 46 shows a typical control system.

Humidification

Evaporative pans (usually heated), **steam jet,** and **atomizing spray tubes** are all used to humidify a space. A space or return air humidistat is used for control. A high-limit duct humidistat should also be used to minimize moisture carryover or condensation in the duct (Figure 47). Proper use and control of humidifiers can achieve high space humidity, though humidifiers more often maintain design minimum humidity during the heating season.

CONTROL OF SPACE CONDITIONS

Single-Zone HVAC. A space thermostat controls single zone

heating and cooling directly. If used, a humidifier is controlled by the space humidistat.

Multizone and Dual-Duct units have mixing dampers controlled by the zone space thermostat for each zone (Figure 48). If used, humidifiers are usually controlled by a return air humidistat. Some states no longer permit mixing hot and cold air to provide simultaneous heating and cooling. A three-deck unit may be used as an alternative in a multizone system (Figure 49). Zone dampers in this unit operate with sequenced damper motors (DM) either (1) to mix hot supply air with bypass air when the cold deck damper is closed or (2) to mix cold supply air with bypass air when the hot deck damper is closed.

Variable Air Volume units have motorized dampers in each zone supply duct. A related zone space thermostat controls each

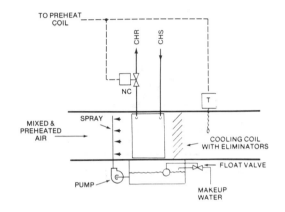

Fig. 43   Sprayed Coil Dehumidifier

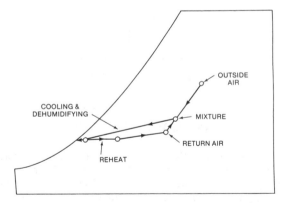

Fig. 44   Psychrometric Chart for Air Washer Evaporative Cooling and Sprayed Coil Dehumidification

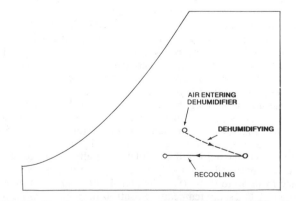

Fig. 45   Psychrometric Chart: Chemical Dehumidification

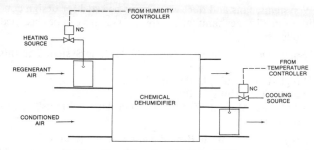

Fig. 46   Chemical Dehumidifier

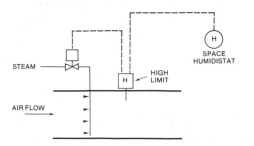

Fig. 47   Steam Jet Humidifier

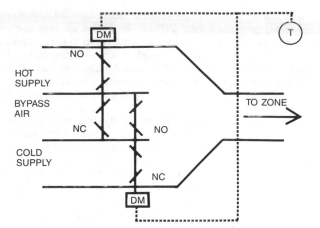

Fig. 49   Zone Mixing Dampers—Three-Deck Multizone System

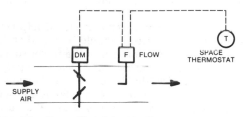

Fig. 50   Zone Variable Air Volume Damper

damper by a flow sensor/controller that is reset by the thermostat (Figure 50). Humidifiers, if used, are controlled by a return air humidistat or a humidistat in a representative critical zone.

The system layout can make the control of economizers and static pressure difficult. The interaction of the return exhaust fan and the static pressure and volume control is a particular concern in the control system layout.

Pressure Control

The most common application for static pressure controls is fan capacity control in VAV systems. The control maintains a constant static pressue at a selected point in the supply duct by varying supply fan or motor speed, or by modulating dampers at the fan supply or return. A typical system uses inlet vane dampers. Fan speed control, either by motor speed control or by a variable speed clutch, is similar, except that the speed control is the controlled device. Considerable fan energy can be conserved by either method. Modulating dampers in the duct require more energy than other methods.

Static pressure controls can also be used to pressurize a building or space relative to adjacent spaces or outdoors. Typical applications include clean rooms (positive to prevent infiltration), laboratories (positive or negative, depending on use), and various manufacturing processes, such as spray-painting rooms. The pressure controller usually modulates dampers in the supply ducts to maintain desired pressures as exhaust volumes change.

CONTROL SYSTEM DESIGN AND APPLICATION

CENTRAL AIR-HANDLING SYSTEMS

Variable Air Volume

Variable Air Volume systems vary the amount of air supplied by terminal units in individual zones as the load varies in those zones. Hybrid systems that use bypass terminal units to vary air volume to the space while handling a constant air volume from the central fan are treated as Constant Volume (CV) systems.

From a control standpoint, central systems can further be classified as:

1. Single-Duct Cooling Only
2. Single-Duct Heating/Cooling
3. Dual-Duct (see "Dual-Duct Systems" in this section)
   a. Dual-Duct Single Supply Fan
   b. Dual-Duct Dual Supply Fan

Single-Duct Cooling Only Fan Control (Figure 51). In a VAV

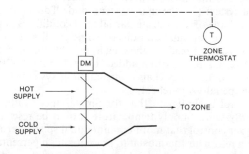

Fig. 48   Zone Mixing Dampers—Multizone System

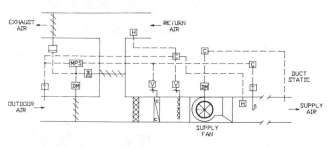

Fig. 51   VAV, Single-Duct Cooling Only

system having a supply fan with no means of modulation, as terminal units reduce total airflow, the duct static pressure increases as the fan moves up its operating curve. If uncontrolled, this pressure can damage duct work. Even in strong ducts, terminal unit dampers must work against a higher pressure, which results in poor control, increased noise, and increased fan energy when compared to reducing the pressure. Therefore, supply fan volume controls should be used.

Fan volume control is based on supply duct static pressure. To conserve fan energy, the static pressure controller should be set at the lowest point that permits proper air distribution at design conditions, yet high enough to allow terminal units to function properly. The controller requires Proportional-Integral (PI) control because Proportional-Only (P) control allows static pressure to drift upward as cooling load decreases, thus imposing more terminal unit pressure and consuming more fan energy.

The pressure sensor must be placed properly to maintain optimum pressure throughout the supply duct. Experience indicates that most systems perform satisfactorily with the sensor located at 75 to 100% of the distance from the first to the most remote terminal.

In addition to the remote static pressure controllers, a high-limit static pressure controller should be placed at the fan discharge to override the remote sensor if a fire or smoke damper closes between the fan and the remote sensor. Supply fan static pressure control devices should be interlocked to go to the minimum flow or closed position when the fan is not running; this precaution prevents fan overload or damage to duct work on start-up.

Temperature and Ventilation Control. These systems generally supply constant temperature air at all times. To conserve central plant energy, supply temperature can be raised in response to demand from the zone with the greatest load (load analyzer control). However, since more cool air must then be supplied to match a given load, mechanical cooling energy saved by raising the supply temperature may be offset by an increase in fan energy. Equipment operating efficiency should be studied closely before using temperature reset on cooling-only VAV systems.

Ventilation dampers (Outside Air, Return Air, and Exhaust Air) are controlled for free cooling as a first-stage cooling in sequence with a cooling coil from the discharge temperature controller. When outdoor air temperature rises to the point that it can no longer be used for cooling, an outdoor air limit (economizer) control overrides the discharge controller and moves ventilation dampers to the minimum ventilation position. An enthalpy control system can replace outdoor air limit economizer control for climatic areas, where applicable.

Single-Duct Heating/Cooling. Single duct VAV systems, which supply warm air to all zones when heating is required and cool air to all zones when cooling is required, have limited application and are used where heating is required only for morning warm-up. They are not recommended if some zones require heating and others require cooling simultaneously. These systems commonly are controlled during occupancy like Single-Duct Cooling Only systems.

During warmup periods, as determined by a time clock or manual switch, a constant heating supply air temperature is maintained. Since the terminal unit may be fully open, uncontrolled overheating can result. It is preferable to allow unit thermostats to maintain complete control of their terminal units by reversing their action to the unit. During warmup and unoccupied cycles, outdoor air dampers should be closed.

Constant Volume

Constant Volume systems supply a constant amount of variable temperature air to individual zones. In all single-duct

CV systems, fans and duct work must be sized for design conditions in all zones simultaneously. CV systems can be classified as follows:

Single-Duct Single Zone (see "Single-Zone Systems" in this section)
Single-Duct Multiple Reheat Zones
Single-Duct Multiple Bypass Terminal Zones
Dual-Duct Multiple Zone (see "Dual-Duct Systems" in this section)

Single-Duct Multiple Reheat Zone systems (Figure 52) use a single central Constant Volume fan system to serve multiple zones. All air delivered to zones is cooled to satisfy the greatest cooling load. Air delivered to other zones is then reheated with heating coils in individual zone ducts. Because these systems consume more energy than VAV systems, they are generally limited to those applications that have larger ventilation needs, such as hospitals and special process or laboratory applications. Some states no longer permit simultaneous heating and cooling.

No **fan control** is required, since the design, selection, and adjustment of fan system components determine system air volume and duct static pressure.

These systems generally supply **constant temperature** air at all times. To conserve energy, supply temperature can rise in response to demand from the greatest cooling load (load analyzer control) for less than design loads.

Humidity control is commonly from a representative zone humidistat or a return air humidistat and is interlocked with the humidifying system to operate only during the heating season. A high-limit humidistat in the supply air duct prevents excessive duct moisture.

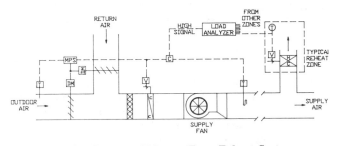

Fig. 52   Constant Volume, Zone Reheat System

Ventilation dampers (OA, RA, and EA) are controlled for free cooling as a first-stage cooling in sequence with the cooling coil from the discharge temperature controller. When outdoor air temperature rises to the point that it can no longer be used for cooling, an outdoor air limit control overrides the discharge controller and moves ventilation dampers to minimum ventilation position, as determined by the Minimum Positioning Switch. An enthalpy control system can replace outdoor air limit control for applicable areas.

Single-Duct Multiple Bypass Terminal Zone systems (Figure 53) are a compromise between single-duct VAV systems and CV reheat systems. The primary systems and all ducts supply a constant volume of air. During partial load conditions in the space, however, the terminal unit diverts some air directly back to the return system instead of reheating it, thus "bypassing" the space. These terminals are often added to single-zone CV systems to provide zoning to packaged air-handling systems without the energy penalty for reheat.

Control is similar to that for Single-Duct Multiple-Reheat Zone Systems. Supply temperature should be reset from load analyzer control that monitors individual space thermostats or from a return air thermostat to prevent a high percentage of the air bypassing the space, reducing air circulation and comfort.

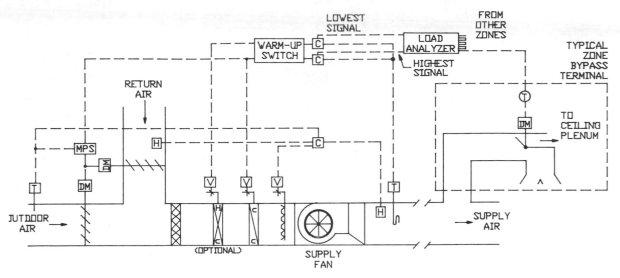

Fig. 53 Variable Constant Volume System

To provide unoccupied heating or warm-up, the central fan system can include a heating coil. During warm-up or unoccupied periods, a constant supply-duct heating temperature is maintained with all bypass terminal units closed to the bypass. An unoccupied mode zone thermostat can cycle the fan, or the terminal unit thermostat action can be reversed to prevent overheating.

Dual-Duct

Dual-Duct systems may be either CV or VAV, depending upon whether terminal mixing box units operate their dampers together or dampers operate individually, thus allowing zone air volume to vary with variations in load conditions.

VAV Dual-Duct Single Supply Fan Systems (Figure 54) use a single supply fan into separate heating and cooling ducts. Terminal mixing box units in which the heating and cooling dampers operate in sequence are used to satisfy space load requirements. Frequently, the space thermostat provides for Zero Energy Band operation for greater energy savings.

Fan Control. Static control is similar to VAV Single-Duct Systems, except it is necessary to use static pressure sensors in each supply duct. Through a comparator control, the sensor sensing the lowest pressure controls the fan volume control system, thus ensuring adequate static pressure under all load conditions to supply the necessary air for all zones, whether they are supplied from the hot or cold duct.

If the system includes a Return Air Fan, its volume control considerations are similar to those described under "Fan Control." To sense total supply airflow, flow stations are usually located in each supply duct, and a signal corresponding to the sum of the two airflows is transmitted to the RA fan volume controller for reset purposes.

Temperature Control. The hot deck has its own heating coil, and the cold deck has its own cooling coil. Each coil is controlled from its own discharge air temperature controller. Controller setpoint is usually reset from the greatest representative demand zone thermostat (load analyzer control): the hot deck from the thermostat with greatest heating demand and the cold deck from the thermostat with greatest cooling demand. An alternative to greatest-demand reset is reset from a parameter that predicts load, such as OA temperature, duct air volume, or RA temperature. In any case, positive control is required to

prevent simultaneous heating and cooling of the air (a code mandate in many states).

Control from the zone requiring the most heating or cooling increases operation economy, since it reduces the energy level delivered at less-than-maximum load conditions. Figure 54 shows this as reset control of duct temperatures. However, the expected economy is lost if air quantity to a zone is undersized, thermostats in some spaces are reset to an extreme value by occupants, the thermostat is placed so it senses spot loads (i.e., coffee pots, solar, copier), or if the thermostat malfunctions. In these cases, a weighted average of zone signals can regain the benefit at the expense of some comfort in specific zones.

In specific applications, it may not be wise to let the highest-demand heating thermostat dictate supply air temperature because the highest demand may come from a temporarily unoccupied zone. Additional heating savings are generated when the user selects which thermostats are in the group from which the highest-demand thermostat is determined.

Ventilation Control. Ventilation dampers (OA, RA, and EA) are controlled for cooling, with outside air as the first-stage of cooling in sequence with the cooling coil from the cold deck discharge temperature controller. When outdoor air temperature rises to the point that it can no longer be used for cooling, an outdoor air limit control overrides a discharge controller and moves the ventilation dampers to the minimum ventilation position, as determined by the Minimum Positioning Switch. An enthalpy control system can replace OA limit control for applicable areas. A more accurate OA flow measuring system can replace the Minimum Positioning Switch.

Humidity is commonly controlled by a return air humidity sensor. It is coordinated with the OA temperature sensor so that the humidifying system only operates during the heating season. In addition, a high-limit humidistat in the supply air duct prevents excessive duct moisture.

VAV Dual-Duct Dual Supply Fan Systems (Figure 55) use separate supply fans for the heating and cooling ducts. Static pressure control is similar to that for VAV Dual-Duct Single Supply Fan Systems, except that each supply fan has its own separate static pressure sensor and control system. If the system has a Return Air Fan, its volume control considerations are similar to those described under "Fan Control" in the section on "Control of Outdoor Air Quantity." Temperature, ventilation, and humidity control considerations are similar to those for VAV Dual-Duct Single Supply Fan Systems.

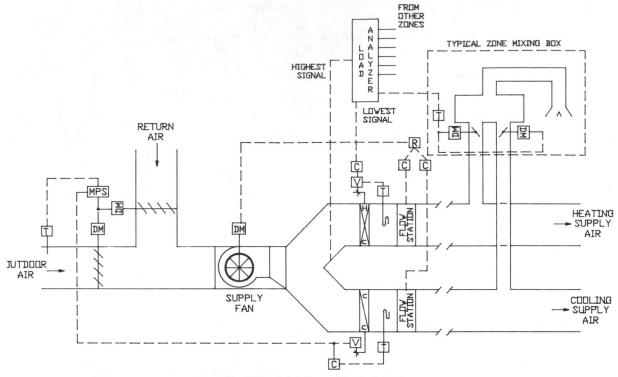

Fig. 54   VAV, Dual-Duct, Single Fan System

CV Dual-Duct Multiple Zone Systems (Figure 56) use a single CV supply fan and multiple zone mixing dampers in terminal units that supply a constant volume of air to individually controlled zones. They require no automatic control of duct static pressure nor fan volume as these operating characteristics are set by system design and component selection and adjustment. Considerations for temperature, ventilation, and humidity control are similar to those for VAV Dual-Duct Single Supply Fan Systems.

Multizone Units

Multizone units are the same as CV Dual-Duct Multiple-Zone Systems, except for the location of zone mixing dampers. These dampers are at the central air-handling unit and feed individual zone supply ducts that extend to the conditioned spaces. Fan, temperature, ventilation, and humidity control considerations are the same as those for CV Dual-Duct Multiple Zone Systems.

Single Zone

Single-Zone systems (Figure 57) use a CV air-handling unit (usually factory packaged) and are controlled from a single space thermostat. No fan control is required because fan volume and static pressure in the ducts are set by system design and component selection.

Temperature and Ventilation Control. A single space thermostat controls the heating coil, ventilation dampers, and cooling coil in sequence, as thermal load varies in the conditioned space. Ventilation dampers (OA, RA, and DA) are controlled for outside air cooling as a first-stage cooling. When outdoor air temperature rises to the point that it can no longer be used for cooling, an outdoor air limit control overrides the signal to the ventilation dampers and moves them to the minimum ventilation position, as determined by the Minimum Positioning Switch. Where applicable, an enthalpy control system can replace the OA limit control for climatic areas. A Zero Energy Band thermo-

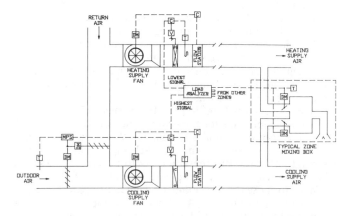

Fig. 55   VAV, Dual-Duct, Dual-Supply Fan System

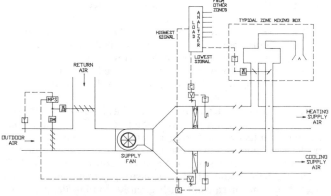

Fig. 56   Constant Volume, Dual Duct, or Multizone Single-Fan System

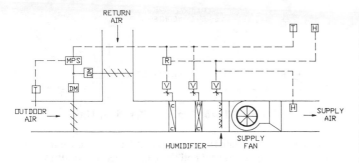

Fig. 57   Single-Zone Fan System

stat can separate the heating and cooling control ranges, thus saving energy.

Humidity control is from either a space or return air humidistat. It controls a moisture-adding device (steam jet or pan type) for winter operation and can also override space thermostat control of the cooling coil for dehumidification during summer operation. In the latter case, the space thermostat brings on the heating coil for reheat. The high-limit humidistat in the supply air duct prevents excessive duct moisture.

Makeup Air Systems

Makeup air systems (Figure 58) replace air exhausted from the building through exfiltration or by laboratory or industrial processes. Air must enter the space at or near space conditions to minimize uncomfortable air currents. The fan is usually turned on, either manually or automatically, as exhaust fans are turned on.

The two-position outdoor air damper is closed, except when the makeup fan is in operation. The outdoor air limit control opens the preheat coil valve when outdoor air temperature drops to the point where the air requires heating to raise it to the desired supply air temperature. The discharge temperature controller then positions the face and bypass dampers to maintain the desired supply air temperature. A capillary element thermostat located adjacent to the coil shuts the fan down for freeze protection should air temperature approach freezing at any spot along the sensing element.

HYDRONIC SYSTEMS

Proper control of hot and chilled water flow rates in hydronic systems must consider both the hydraulic and thermal requirements of the distribution system. Failing to consider hydraulic principles in piping network design and pump and control valve selection can make the hydronic system uncontrollable. Proper location and use of the compression tank, dynamic separation

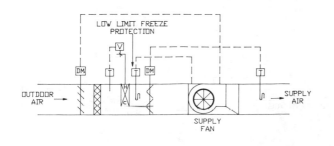

Fig. 58   Makeup Air System

of primary and secondary pump circuits, design allowance for adequate pressure drop through the automatic control valves, and stable system pressures are important for stable system control.

Of the load control methods used in larger systems, valve control for variable flow in the load circuit is the most popular. Heating or cooling coil capacity in air systems can be controlled using a three-way or two-way throttling valve. The three-way valve is usually a mixing valve located in the coil outlet piping. As the valve mixes two flow streams, total flow rate through the branch piping is essentially constant. Figure 59 is an example of three-way valve control for a central chilled water plant system.

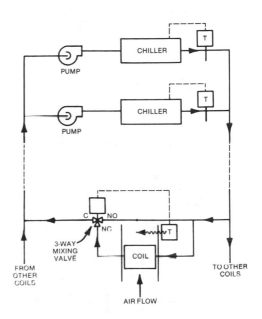

Fig. 59   Three-Way Valve Control of a Coil

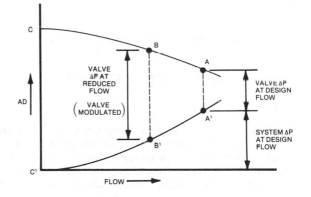

Fig. 60   Pump and System Curves with Valve Control

A two-way throttling valve reduces the flow rate and increases the pressure differentials across the pump and load circuits. Throttling requires more attention to valve and pump selection because the pump operating point moves as the valves reduce system flow rate (Figure 60). Because of the more exacting design requirements of two-way valve control at terminal units, the three-way valve has been widely used until recently. Three-way valve control requires more energy because the flow rate is constant, so pump horsepower is constant, regardless of cooling load. With constant flow, there are many operating hours when temperature difference across the chiller is 2 to 3 °F (1 to 2 °C) relative to design chilled water ranges of 10 to 12 °F (5 to 6 °C).

The scheme in Figure 61 solves the problem of variable water flow to terminal units and constant flow through the chiller while operating the chiller plant efficiently. Any number of chillers can be used, though only two are shown. At full load, both chillers are on-line and full flow goes to the terminal units. As terminal unit valves modulate from decreased load, flow decreases and the pressure drop from supply to return mains increases. The pressure differential controller senses this change and partially opens the bypass valve to compensate. The bypass valve is sized to match the flow through one chiller, enabling one chiller and pump to shut down when the bypass is fully open. As load increases to a point where the bypass is closed completely, the second chiller and pump can restart.

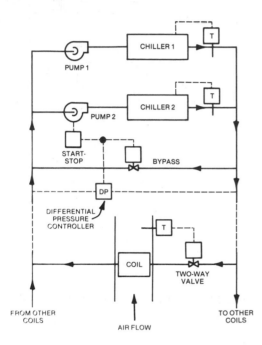

Fig. 61   Two-Way Valve with Pump Bypass

SPACE CONTROL SYSTEMS

VAV Terminal Units

VAV Terminal Units are used in conjunction with VAV central air-handling fan systems to vary the volume of air into individual zones as required by thermal load on the area. They are available in several configurations; therefore, control considerations vary. VAV terminal unit controls are discussed in the following categories:

Single-Duct VAV	Dual-Duct VAV
Throttling	Variable Constant Volume
Variable Constant Volume	Variable Constant Volume (ZEB)
Bypass	
Induction	
Fan-Powered	

Throttling VAV Terminal Units (Figure 62) are sometimes called "pressure dependent;" that is, the volume of air entering the conditioned space at any given space temperature varies as static pressure in the supply duct varies. The space thermostat controls the damper directly.

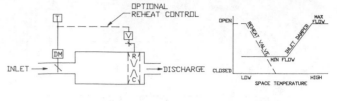

Fig. 62   Throttling VAV Terminal Unit

As an option, a reheat coil can be added. The space thermostat also controls the reheat coil valve in sequenced mode to open the valve after the damper has closed to its minimum flow position.

For perimeter areas, convectors or radiation with automatic control valves can meet reheat need. Functionally, these are controlled similar to the reheat coil valves.

Variable Constant Volume Terminal Units (Figure 63) are sometimes called "pressure independent"; that is, with varying supplying duct static pressure, the unit continues to deliver the same volume of air to the conditioned space at the same space temperature. Either a mechanical or receiver-controller-type airflow controller in the unit provides this function (Figure 63).

A flow sensor in the box airflow stream controls air volume. The room sensor resets airflow controller setpoint as thermal load on the area changes. The airflow controller can be set with a minimum flow condition to ensure comfortable distribution of supply air into the space under light loading. Maximum flow can be set to limit flow to that required for design conditions.

This unit can also have a reheat coil or separate convection, or radiation can provide the reheat function. Reheat control is similar to that for Throttling VAV Terminal Units.

Bypass VAV Terminal Units (Figure 64) have a space thermostat-controlled diverting damper that proportions the amount of entering supply air between the discharge duct and the bypass opening into the return plenum. A manual balancing damper in the bypass is adjusted to match the resistance in the discharge duct. In this way, the supply air from the primary system remains at a constant volume.

Induction VAV Terminal Units (Figure 65) provide return air reheat by routing air through the unit to induce air from the

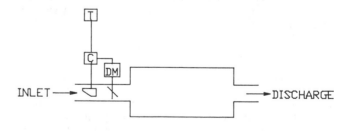

Fig. 63   Variable Constant Volume, VAV Terminal Unit

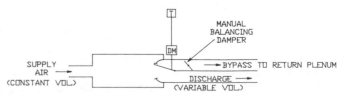

Fig. 64   Bypass VAV Terminal Unit

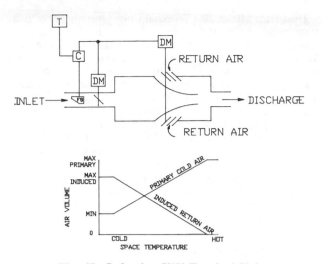

Fig. 65   Induction VAV Terminal Unit

return air plenum into the stream of air being delivered to the conditioned space. In addition to the inlet damper, there is also a damper on the return air inlet. Both dampers are controlled simultaneously so that as the primary air opening decreases, the return air opening increases.

An airflow controller in the unit controls the volume of air coming through the primary air damper. The space thermostat resets the setpoint of this controller, as required by thermal load on the conditioned space.

Fan-Powered VAV Terminal Units (Figure 66) are similar to Throttling VAV Terminal Units, except that they include an integral fan that recirculates space air at a constant volume. In addition to enhancing air distribution in the space, they also provide a reheat coil and a means of maintaining a lowered unoccupied temperature in the space when the primary system is off.

Figure 66 shows a typical control sequence. A space thermostat resets an integral airflow controller as it senses space load changes. As primary air decreases, the fan comes on to ensure adequate air circulation. The units serving the perimeter area of a building usually include a reheat coil, which is sequenced with the primary air damper to supply heat when required. When the primary air system is not operating (night time or unoccupied control mode), the "night" operating mode of the thermostat

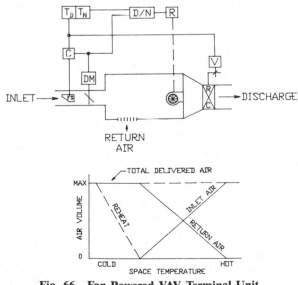

Fig. 66   Fan-Powered VAV Terminal Unit

cycles the fan with the reheat coil valve open to maintain the lowered temperature in the space.

Bypass Fan Induction Terminal Units (Figure 67) are similar to the Fan-Powered VAV Terminal Units, except that the fan pulls air from the return plenum only. An alternate location for the reheat coil is in the return plenum opening. The control sequence is the same as the Fan-Powered VAV Terminal Unit.

Variable Constant Volume, Dual-Duct Terminal Units (Figure 68) have inlet dampers on the heating and cooling supply ducts. They are interlinked to operate in reverse of each other and require a single control actuator. There is also a total airflow volume damper with its own actuator.

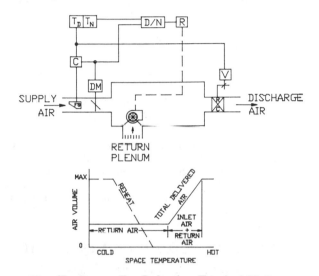

Fig. 67   Bypass Fan Induction Terminal Unit

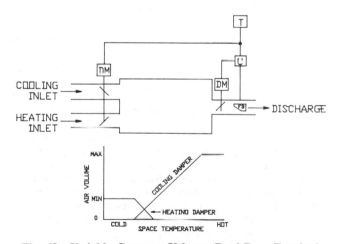

Fig. 68   Variable Constant Volume, Dual-Duct Terminal Unit

The space thermostat controls inlet mixing dampers directly, and the airflow controller controls the volume damper. The space thermostat resets the airflow controller from maximum to minimum flow as thermal load on the conditioned area changes. Figure 68 shows the control schematic and damper operation. Note that in a portion of the control range there is a mixing of the heating and cooling supply air.

Variable Constant Volume (ZEB) Dual-Duct Terminal Units (Figure 69) have inlet dampers on the cooling and heating supply ducts with individual damper actuators and airflow controllers and no total airflow volume damper. The space thermostat (ZEB) resets airflow controller setpoints in sequence as space

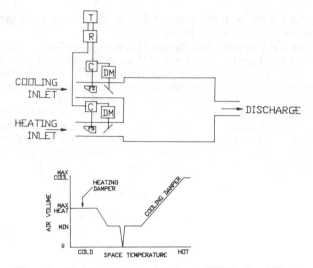

Fig. 69 Variable Constant Volume (ZEB), Dual-Duct Terminal Unit

load changes. The airflow controllers maintain adjustable minimum flows for ventilation, with no overlap of damper operations, during the zero energy band when neither heating or cooling is required. Figure 69 shows the control schematic and damper operation. Energy consumption of Variable Constant Volume Dual-Duct Terminal units with and without ZEB is essentially the same.

CONSTANT VOLUME TERMINAL UNITS

Multiple zone systems using CV air distribution can be classified as:

Single-Duct VAV	Dual-Duct VAV
Zone reheat	Mixing Box
Positive Constant Volume	Constant Volume Mixing Box

Single-Duct Zone Reheat systems have a heating coil (hot water, steam, or electric) in the branch supply duct to each zone. The central air-handling unit supplies constant-temperature air. The space thermostat positions the reheat coil valve (or electric heating elements) as required to maintain space condition (Figure 70).

Single-Duct Positive Constant Volume terminal units supply a constant volume of distribution air to the space, even though static pressure varies in the supply duct system. This is accomplished by an integral mechanical constant volume regulator or an airflow constant volume control furnished by the terminal unit manufacturer. If a reheat coil comes with the unit, a space thermostat controls the reheat coil valve as required to maintain space condition (Figure 71).

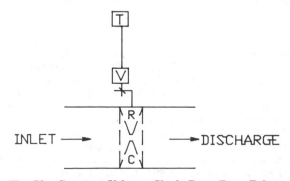

Fig. 70 Constant Volume, Single-Duct Zone Reheat

Dual-Duct Mixing Box Terminal Units generally apply to low-static-pressure systems that require large amounts of ventilation. The warm duct damper and the cool duct damper are linked to operate in reverse of each other. A space thermostat positions the mixing dampers through a damper actuator to mix warm and cool supply air to maintain space condition. Discharge air quantitiy depends on static pressure in each supply duct at that location. Static pressures in the supply ducts vary because of the varying airflow in each duct (Figure 72).

Dual-Duct Constant Volume Mixing Box Terminal Units are typically used on high-static-pressure systems where the airflow quantity served into each space is more critical. The units are the same as those described above, except that they include either an integral mechanical constant volume regulator or an airflow constant volume control furnished by the unit manufacturer (Figure 73).

PERIMETER RADIATION AND CONVECTION

Radiators or convectors can provide either the total room heat or supplemental heat of the perimeter to offset building transmission losses. Control strategy depends on which function the radiation performs.

For a total room heating application, rooms are usually controlled individually. With individual room control, each radiator and convector is equipped with an automatic control valve. Depending on room size, one thermostat may control one valve or several valves is unison.

The thermostat can be located in the return air to the unit or on a wall at the occupant level. Return air control is generally the least accurate and results in the widest space temperature fluctuations. When space is controlled for comfort of seated occupants, wall-mounted thermostats give the best results.

For supplemental heating applications, where perimeter radiation is used to offset perimeter heat losses only (with a zone or space load handled separately by a zone air system), outdoor reset of the water temperature to the radiation should be considered. Radiation can be zoned by exposure and the compensating outdoor sensor can be located to sense compensated indoor (outdoor) temperature, solar load, or both.

Fan Coil Units

Fan coils can contain packaged controls for the fan and valves, or they can be field installed. These units can be categorized as follows:

Two-Pipe Heating
Two-Pipe Cooling
Two-Pipe Heating/Cooling
Four-Pipe Heating/Cooling, Split Coil
Four-Pipe Heating/Cooling, Single Coil

Chapters 13, 14, and 15 describe design features and applications for the central plant and distribution systems associated with these fan coil units.

Typically, an integral return air thermostat or a wall-mounted one controls an automatic control valve on the heating (cooling) coil. Frequently, a local fan switch operates the fan, or a central time clock may operate it.

Figure 74 shows typical control of a **Two-Pipe Heating/Cooling** fan coil unit. The single coil is used for heating or cooling, depending on the season, so hot water temperatures can be much lower than with standard heating coils. The unit requires an integral return-air or a wall-mounted heating/cooling thermostat that reverses its action from a remote heating/cooling changeover signal. Alternately, a sensed change in supply water temper-

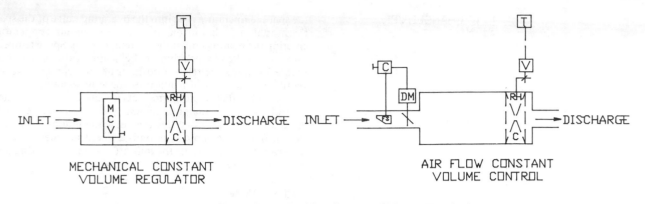

Fig. 71   Single-Duct, Positive Constant Volume Terminal Unit

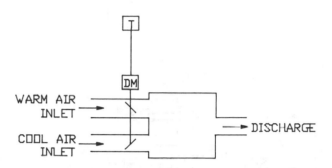

Fig. 72   Dual-Duct Mixing Box Terminal Unit

ature from a pipe-mounted aquastat can cause the heating/cooling changeover. Frequently, a local fan switch operates the fan, or a central time clock can operate it.

Four-Pipe Heating/Cooling Split Coil systems hydraulically separate the heating and cooling systems; control precautions for two-pipe systems do not apply. The four-pipe fan coil unit typically has a "split-coil" with one heating and two cooling rows. Hot water or steam can be used to heat, while direct expansion or chilled water can be used to cool. Figure 75 shows a room thermostat connected to the hot water valve and the chilled water valve. The hot water valve closes if room temperature increases. Further increases begin to open the chilled water valve. Valve ranges should be adjusted to provide a dead band within which both heating and cooling valves are closed. A local fan switch can control the fan, or a central time clock can operate it.

In **Four-Pipe Heating/Cooling Single Coil** systems (Figure 76), special control three-way valves are used on both the supply and the return water side of the coil. The space thermostat controls both valves in the following sequence: when the thermostat senses a need for heat, valves to the chilled water supply and return circuits remain closed while the supply water valve hot water port is throttled to maintain space temperature. When the thermostat senses a need for cooling, valves to the hot water supply and return circuits remain closed and the supply water valve cold water port is throttled to maintain space temperature. The supply water valve is adjusted so both supply ports are closed in the dead band between heating and cooling operations. During this dead band, the return water valve is positively positioned to connect the correct return water circuit to the coil before either supply port opens. A local fan switch can control the fan, or a local time clock can operate it.

Unit Ventilators

Packaged units are designed to heat, ventilate, and cool a space by introducing outdoor air in quantities up to 100%. Optionally, they can also cool and dehumidify with a cooling coil (either chilled water or DX). Heating can be by hot water, steam, or electric resistance. The control of these coils can be by valves or face and bypass dampers. Consequently, control systems applied to unit ventilators are many and varied. This section describes the three most commonly used control schemes: Cycle I, Cycle II, and Cycle III (Figures 77 and 78).

Cycle I supplies 100% outdoor air at all times, except during the warm-up stage (Figure 77). During warm up, the heating valve is open, the OA damper is closed, and the RA damper is open. As temperature rises into the operating range of the space thermostat, the OA damper fully opens and the RA

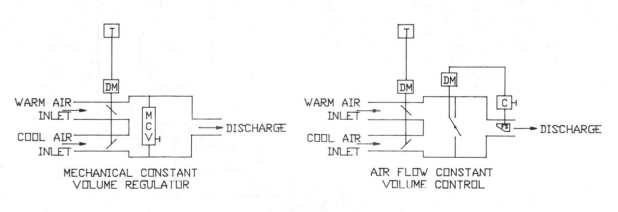

Fig. 73   Dual-Duct, Constant Volume Mixing Box Terminal Units

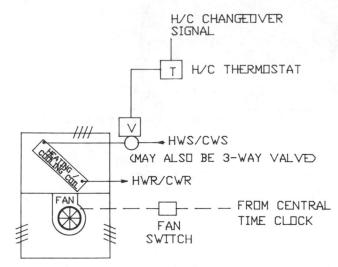

Fig. 74 Two-Pipe Heating/Cooling Fan Coil Unit

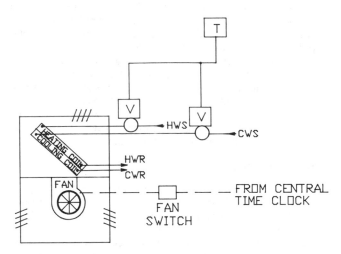

Fig. 75 Four-Pipe Heating/Cooling Split Fan Coil Unit

damper closes. To maintain space temperature, the heating valve is positioned, as required. The air stream thermostat can override space thermostat action on the heating valve to open the valve to maintain a minimum air discharge temperature into the space. Figure 79 shows the relative position of the heating valve and ventilation dampers in relation to space temperature.

Cycle II supplies a set minimum quantity of outdoor air during the heating stage. Outdoor air is gradually increased, as required for cooling. During warm-up, the heating valve is open, the OA damper is closed, and the RA damper is open. As the space temperature rises into the operating range of the space thermostat, ventilation dampers move to their set minimum ventilation position. To maintain space temperature, the heating valve and ventilation dampers are operated in sequence, as required. The air stream thermostat can override space thermostat action of the heating valve and ventilation dampers to prevent discharge air from dropping below a minimum temperature. Figure 79 shows the relative position of the heating valve and ventilation dampers in relation to space temperature.

Cycle III supplies a variable amount of outdoor air during the heating, ventilating, and cooling stages, as required to maintain a fixed temperature [typically 55°F (13°C)] entering the heating coil (Figure 78). When heat is not required, this air is used for cooling. During warm-up, the heating valve is open, the OA air damper is closed, and the RA damper is open. As

the space temperature rises into the operating range of the space thermostat, ventilation dampers control the air temperature entering the heating coil at the set temperature. Space temperature is controlled by positioning the heating valve, as required. Figure 79 shows the relative position of the heating valve and ventilation dampers in relation to space temperature.

Frequently, day/night thermostats are used with any of these control schemes to maintain a lower space temperature during unoccupied periods by cycling the fan with outdoor air damper closed. Another common option is a freeze stat placed next to the heating coil that shuts the unit off when near-freezing temperatures are sensed.

Radiant Panels

Radiant panels combine controlled temperature room surfaces

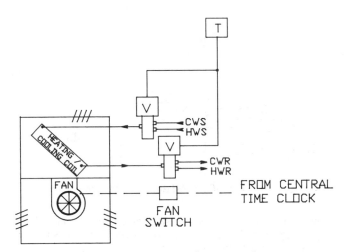

Fig. 76 Four-Pipe Heating/Cooling Single Fan Coil Unit

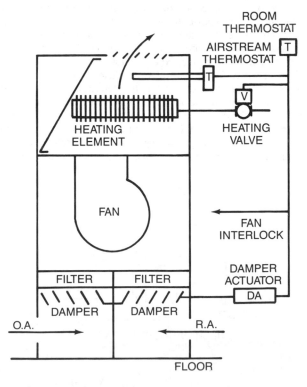

Fig. 77 Cycles I and II Control Arrangements

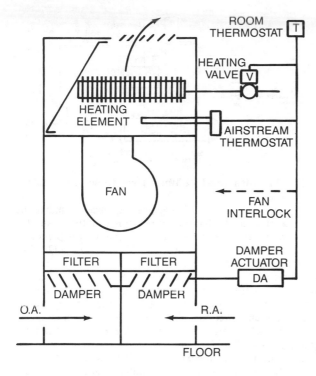

Fig. 78   Cycle III Control Arrangement

with central air conditioning and ventilation. The radiant panel can be in the floor, walls, or ceiling. Panel temperature is maintained by circulating water or air or by electric resistance. The central air system can be a basic one-zone, constant-temperature, CV system with a radiant panel operated by individual room control thermostats; or the central air system can include some or all the features of dual duct, reheat, multizone, or VAV systems, with the radiant panel operated as a one-zone, constant-temperature system. The one-zone radiant heating panel system is often operated from an outdoor temperature reset system to vary panel temperature as outdoor temperature varies.

Radiant panels for both heating and cooling applications require controls similar to that described for the four-pipe heating/cooling single coil fan coil. During the cooling cycle, ventilation air supplied to the space should have a dew point temperature below that of the radiant panel surface to prevent condensation.

CENTRAL PLANT HEATING AND COOLING SOURCES

The term "Central Plant," as used here, refers not only to a plant supplying heating and/or cooling media to multiple buildings, but also to a single building having central chillers and boilers.

Control considerations for a central plant generally consist of the following three broad categories:

1. Control of the individual units (boilers and chillers).
2. Control of the plant (starting, stopping, and adjusting individual units making up the plant, including auxiliaries)
3. Control of the distribution system

Central heating and cooling systems are also covered in the 1983 EQUIPMENT Volume: Chapter 23, "Automatic Fuel-Burning Equipment;" Chapter 24, "Boilers;" Chapter 18, "Liquid Chilling Systems;" and Chapter 12 of this volume, "Heating and Cooling from a Central Plant."

Control of Individual Units

Almost always, a manufacturer supplies boilers (both steam and hot water) and chillers (all types) with an automatic control package installed. Control functions fall in two categories: capacity and safety.

Capacity controls vary the thermal capacity of the unit as a function of the presented load. A designer needs to understand the operation of these controls to integrate them into control system design for a multiple-unit plant.

Safety controls generally shut down the unit and generate an alarm whenever an unsafe condition is detected. When a supervisory control system is used, the alarm should be retransmitted to the control center.

CONTROL OF THE PLANT

Load Control in Hydronic Heating Systems

Load affects the rate of heat input to a hydronic system. Rate control cycles and modulates the flame, and turns boilers on and off. The first two control items are in the boiler control package. The control system designer decides when to add or drop a boiler.

Hot water distribution control must consider both temperature control at the hot water boilers or converter, and the control method for multiple zones. If multiple or alternate heating

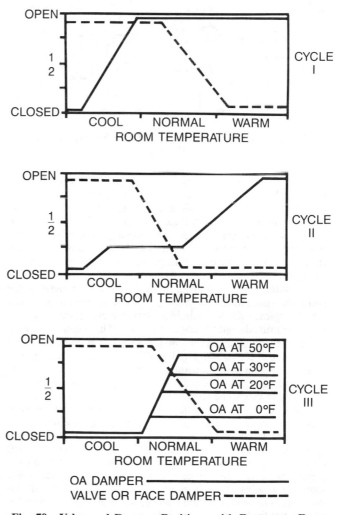

Fig. 79   Valve and Damper Positions with Respect to Room Temperature

sources (such as condenser heat recovery or solar storage) are used, the control strategy must also include the means for sequencing or selecting the most economical hot water source. The section "Control of Central Subsystems" in this chapter describes control of hot water coils at the HVAC system, and this section covers the control of the heating source and distribution system.

Figure 80 shows a system for load control of a gas- or oil-fired boiler. Boiler controls usually include combustion controls (flame failure, high temperature, and other safety cutouts) and capacity controls. Intermittent burner firing usually controls capacity, although fuel input modulation is common in larger systems. In most cases, the boiler is controlled to maintain a constant water temperature, although an outdoor air thermostat can reset temperatures when the boiler is not used for domestic water heating. A master-submaster arrangement resets supply water temperature, with the outdoor master themostat resetting the submaster thermostat according to the reset schedule shown. Water temperature should not be reset below 120 °F (49 °C), because condensation of flue gases and boiler damage can result.

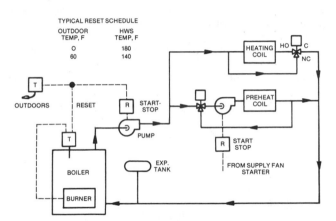

Fig. 80   Load and Zone Control in a Simple Hydronic System

Zone control usually maintains a constant supply temperature from the boiler and varying flow rate to the zone. In Figure 80, a room thermostat controls a three-way valve that varies the preheat coil output. Larger systems with sufficiently high pump operating costs can use variable speed pump drives, pump discharge valves with minimum flow bypass valves, and two-speed drives to reduce secondary pumping capacity to match the load.

Hot water heat exchangers or steam-to-water converters are sometimes used instead of boilers as hot water generators. Converters typically do not include a control package; therefore, the engineer must design the control scheme. The scheme in Figure 81 can be used with either low-pressure steam or boiler water ranging from 200 to 260 °F (93 to 127 °C) as the heating source. The supply water thermostat controls a modulating two-way valve in the steam (or hot water) supply line. An outdoor thermostat usually resets the supply water temperature downward as load decreases. A flow switch interlock should close the two-way valve when the hot water pump is not operating.

Chapter 14 covers the central plant arrangement for a *two-pipe fan coil system*. Figure 82 shows the hot water generator and chiller connected by changeover valves to the distribution piping, with the primary control as the means of changeover from the heating to cooling source. A solar-compensated outdoor thermostat can initiate changeover manually or automatically. Chapter 14 describes calculation of a suitable changeover temperature.

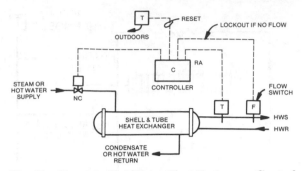

Fig. 81   Steam-to-Hot Water Heat Exchanger Control

Two-pipe central plant changeover sequences from heating to cooling must ensure that the temperature of return water to the chiller does not cause excessively high evaporator pressures. If water temperature to the chiller exceeds about 75 °F (24 °C), the resulting high suction pressure could overload a reciprocating compressor chiller. To avoid this, a return water bypass loop around the chiller can be used to reduce the entering water temperature until system return temperature has cooled down to an acceptable level. In addition, reset of hot water temperature with outdoor temperature can help ensure that water temperature entering the chiller is much lower at changeover than at design heating conditions. A bypass line with a modulating valve controlled by a sensor in the chilled water return line may be installed as an alternative scheme. The bypass ensures that the chiller can quickly lower the chilled water loop temperature without allowing hot water to flow into the chiller (Figure 82).

Changeover from cooling to heating should not allow cold water to enter a hot boiler, as thermal shock to the heat exchanger can occur. A pipe-mounted aquastat can work as a low-limit control of the boiler three-way bypass valve. Although it is simpler and safer to use shell and tube heat exchangers to isolate the boiler and chiller from distribution piping, initial cost is higher. The bypass line control valve can be controlled by the aquastat to shorten the boiler heat-up period and reduce the possibility of thermal shock.

Chapter 14 describes central plant control for a *three-pipe system*. The needs of the most critical space, or changeover settings of an outdoor air thermostat, cause start and stop of the chiller and boiler. Because water flow rate through the chiller decreases as the common return temperature rises, a flow switch in the chiller pipe should shut off the compressor to prevent the possibility of freezing. Heat exchangers or the alternate piping scheme can prevent this problem.

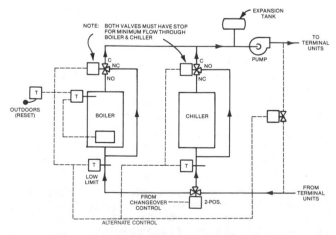

Fig. 82   Central Plant for Two-Pipe System

Control of Chiller Plants

Because each central chiller plant is unique with a wide variety of chiller types, sizes, drives, manufacturers, piping configurations, pumps, cooling towers, distribution systems, and loads, it is almost inevitable that each installation, including its controls, is designed on a custom basis.

Section II (Chapters 12 through 22) of the 1983 EQUIPMENT Volume gives information on various types of chillers (e.g., absorption, centrifugal, and reciprocating). Each type has specific characteristics that must match the requirements of the installation. Chapter 18 of the 1983 EQUIPMENT Volume covers variations in piping configurations (e.g., series and parallel chilled water flow) and some control considerations associated with them.

Chiller plants are generally one of two types: **variable flow** (Figure 83) or **constant flow** (Figure 84). The examples show parallel flow configuration. The determining factor is generally the nature of control of the remote load. Throttling coil valves produce a flow rate at the chillers that varies with load and a temperature differential that tends to remain near the design temperature differential. Chilled water supply temperature typically controls such systems. To improve energy efficiency, the setpoint is reset based on the zone with the greatest load (load reset).

The constant flow system (Figure 84) is actually constant flow under each combination of chillers on line; a major upset always occurs whenever a chiller is added or dropped. The load reset function ensures that the zone with the largest load is satisfied, while supply or return water control treats average zone load.

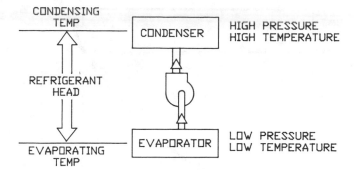

Fig. 85   Refrigerant Head Diagram

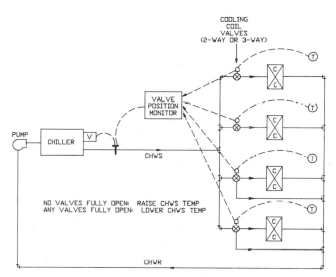

Fig. 86   Chilled Water Load Reset

Optimize Refrigerant Head. Chiller efficiency (kW/ton) is a function of the percent of full load on the chiller and the refrigerant head, which is the refrigerant pressure difference between the condenser and evaporator. In practice, the head is represented by condenser water leaving temperature minus chilled water supply temperature (Figure 85). To reduce the refrigerant head, either the chilled water supply temperature must be increased and/or the condenser water temperature decreased. The gain is 1 to 2% energy saving for each degree F (2 to 3% per °C) reduction in head.

Two effective methods for reducing refrigerant head are as follows:

Use chilled water load reset to raise supply setpoint as load decreases. Figure 86 shows the basic principle of this function. Varying degrees of sophistication are available, especially with computer control.

Lower condenser temperature to the lowest safe temperature (use manufacturer's recommendations) by keeping the cooling tower closed, operating at full pump capacity, and maintaining full airflow in all cells of the cooling tower until water temperature is within about 5 °F (3 °C) of outdoor air wet bulb. However, pumps and fans consume power. Consider all of them and the fan power of the VAV air handlers in calculating net energy savings.

Optimize Operation. Multiple chiller plants should be operated at the most efficient point on the part-load curve. Figure 87 shows a typical part-load curve for a centrifugal chiller operated at design conditions. Figure 88 shows similar curves at different

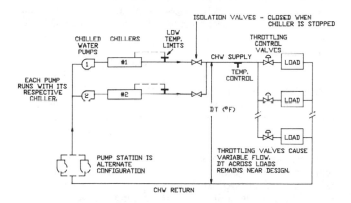

Fig. 83   Variable Flow Chilled Water System

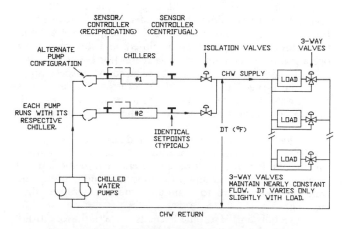

Fig. 84   Constant Flow Chilled Water System

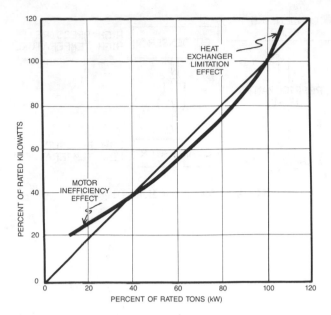

Fig. 87　Chiller Part-Load Characteristics at Design Refrigerant Head

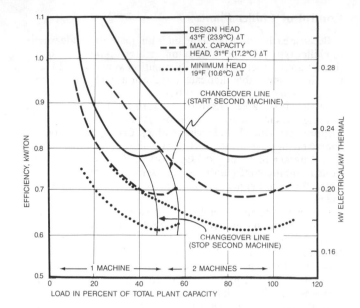

Fig. 89　Multiple Chiller Operation Changeover Point—Two Equal-Sized Chillers

head-limiting conditions. Figure 89 indicates the point at which a chiller should be added or dropped in a two-unit plant. The part-load curves are plotted for all combinations of chillers; then the break-even point between n and $n + 1$ chillers can be determined.

Minimize Run Time. Daily start-up of the chiller plant based on start-up time of the air-handling units should be optimized. Generally, chillers may be started at the same time as the first fan system. Exceptions are: chillers are started early if the water distribution loop has great thermal mass; chillers may be started later when outside air can provide cooling to fan systems at start-up.

Control of Cooling Tower with Water-Cooled Condenser

Control system designers work with liquid chiller control when the equipment package is integrated into the central chiller plant. Typically, cooling tower and chilled and condenser pump's control must be considered if the overall plant is to be stable and energy-efficient. This section considers control of the condenser water circuit and the possible control arrangements for various central plants.

The most common packaged mechanical-draft cooling towers for comfort air-conditioning applications are counterflow induced-draft and forced-draft. Both are controlled similarly, depending on the manufacturer's recommendations. On larger towers, two-speed or variable-speed fans (and associated motor control circuitry) can reduce fan power consumption at part-load conditions.

Figure 90 shows bypass valve control of condenser water temperature. With centrifugal chillers, condenser supply water temperature is allowed to float as long as the temperature remains above a low limit. The manufacturer should specify the minimum entering condenser water temperature required for satisfactory performance of the particular chiller. [Minimum condenser water temperatures for centrifugal chillers usually range from 55 to 65 °F (13 to 18 °C).] The control schematic in Figure 90 works as follows: for a condenser supply temperature [for example, above a setpoint of 75 °F (24 °C)], the valve is open to the tower, the bypass valve is closed, and the tower fan is operating. As water temperature decreases [for example, to 65 °F (18 °C)], the tower fan speed can be reduced to low-speed operation if a two-speed motor is used. On a further decrease in condenser water supply temperature, the tower fan(s) stop and the bypass valve begins to modulate to maintain the acceptable minimum water temperature.

In colder areas that require year-round air-conditioning, cooling towers may require sump heating to prevent heat-up and continuous full flow over the tower to prevent ice formation. In that case, the cooling tower sump thermostat would control a hot water or steam valve to maintain water temperature above freezing.

The section on "Hydronic Systems" covers flow control in hydronic systems.

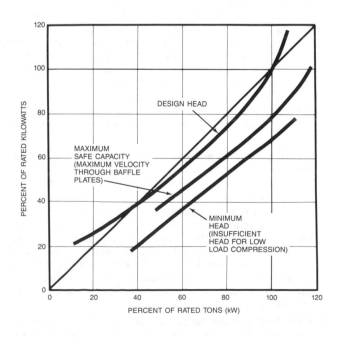

Fig. 88　Chiller Part-Load Characteristics with Variable Head

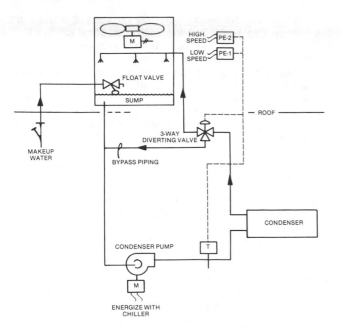

Fig. 90   Condenser Water Temperature Control

Heat Pump, Heat Recovery, and Storage Systems

Heat pumps are refrigeration compressors in which the evaporator is used for cooling and the condenser is used for heating. Many conventional means can control heating and cooling cycles. The unique feature of a heat pump system is the heating/cooling changeover by which the desired evaporator/condenser circuit is selected. Any of three different media (refrigerant, air, or water) can be switched for changeover. Chapter 9 in this volume and Chapter 44 in the 1983 EQUIPMENT Volume have details.

Heat recovery and storage systems are almost always unique, so they require customized control systems to provide the desired sequence. Chapters 6 and 8 in this volume have further details.

DESIGN CONSIDERATIONS AND PRINCIPLES

Total building HVAC system selection and design considers the type and size of the structure and how it is used and operated. Subsystems, such as fan and water supply, are normally controlled by localized automatic control, sometimes called "local loop" control. A local loop control system includes the sensors, controllers, and controlled devices used with a single HVAC system and excludes any supervisory or remote functions such as reset and start-stop. However, extension of local control to a central control point is frequently included in the design when justified by operating economy through reduced labor and energy costs and need to diagnose system malfunction when it occurs, thus reducing any damage that might result from delay.

The growing popularity of distributed processing using microprocessors has extended computer use at many locations besides the central control point. Specifically, the "local loop controller" can be a microprocessor (DDC) instead of a pneumatic or electric thermostat, and some energy management functions may be performed by a local microprocessor.

Because heating or cooling systems are designed to meet maximum design conditions, they nearly always function at partial

capacity. It is important to be able to control the system at all times; therefore, the HVAC system must facilitate control operation. Because the system must be adjusted and maintained in operation for many years, the simplest system that produces the necessary results is usually best.

Coordination Between Mechanical and Electrical Systems

The control system designer knows what controls are needed and how they function. However, even when the system is basically pneumatic, the electrical engineer must design wiring, conduit, switchgear, and electrical distribution for many electrical devices involved.

The mechanical designer must tell the electrical designer the total electrical requirements of the control system if the controls are to be wired by the electrical contractor. These include the devices to be furnished, connected, or both; loads in watts or horsepower; location of electrical items; and a description of each control function. Proper coordination should develop a schematic control diagram that interfaces properly with other control elements to form a complete and usable system. As an option, the control engineer may develop a complete performance specification and require the control system contractor to perform all related wiring required to perform the specified sequence.

Coordination is essential. The control system designer must take the initiative and make the final checks of drawings and specifications. Both mechanical and electrical specifications must be checked to ensure compatability and uniformity of all documents.

Building and System Subdivision

Building and mechanical system subdivision considers the following:

1. Heating and cooling loads as they vary—they may require the ability to heat or cool interior or exterior areas of a building at any time.
2. Occupancy schedules and the flexibility to meet needs without undue initial and/or operating costs.
3. Fire safety smoke control and possible compartmentation that matches the air-handling system layout and operation.

Control Principles for Energy Conservation

After the general needs of a building have been established and the building and system subdivision has been made based on similar needs, the mechanical system and its control approach can be considered. Designing systems that conserve energy requires (1) knowledge of the building, (2) its operating schedule, (3) the systems to be installed, and (4) a good knowledge of ASHRAE *Standard* 90A-1980, "Energy Conservation in New Building Design." Five principles or approaches that conserve energy are as follows:

1. **Run equipment only when needed.** Schedule HVAC unit operation for occupied periods. Run heat at night only to maintain internal temperature between 50 and 55°F (10 and 13°C) to prevent freezing. Start morning warm-up as late as possible to achieve design internal temperature by occupancy time (optimum start control), considering residual temperature in space, outdoor temperature, and equipment capacity. Under most conditions, equipment can be shut down some time before the end of occupancy, depending on internal and external load and space temperatue (optimum stop control). Calculate shutdown time so that space temperature

does not drift out of the selected comfort zone before the end of occupancy.

2. **Sequence heating and cooling.** Do not supply heating and cooling simultaneously. Central fan systems should use cool outdoor air in sequence between heating and cooling. The zoning and system selection should eliminate, or at least minimize, simultaneous heating and cooling. Also, humidification and dehumidification should not occur concurrently.

3. **Provide only the heating or cooling actually needed.** Generally, reset the supply temperature of hot and cold air (or water) according to actual need. This is especially important on systems or zones that allow simultaneous heating and cooling.

4. **Supply heating and cooling from the most efficient source.** Use free or low-cost energy sources first, then use higher-cost sources, as necessary.

5. **Apply outdoor air control.** Do not use outdoor air for ventilation until the building is occupied, and then use psychrometrically proper outdoor air quantities. When on minimum outdoor air, use no more than that recommended by ASHRAE *Standard* 62-1981, "Standards for Natural and Mechanical Ventilation." In cooling mode (in cost-effective areas), use enthalpy rather than dry bulb to determine whether outdoor or return air is the most energy efficient air source.

Automatic Control

System Selection. The mechanical system significantly affects how zones and subsystems can be controlled. The system selected and the number and location of zones further influence the amount of simultaneous heating and cooling that occurs. Systems for exterior building sections should control heating and cooling in sequence to *minimize simultaneous heating and cooling*. In general, the control system must be designed to accomplish this, since only a few mechanical systems have this inherent ability (e.g., two-pipe systems and single-coil systems). Systems that require engineered control systems to minimize simultaneous heating and cooling include the following:

1. **Cooling variable air volume with zone reheat.** Reduce cooling energy and/or air volume to a minimum before applying reheat.
2. **Four-pipe heating and cooling for unitary equipment.** Sequence heating and cooling.
3. **Double-duct systems.** Condition only one duct (either hot or cold) requiring one thermal energy at a time. The other duct should supply a mixture of outdoor and return air.
4. **Single-zone heating/cooling systems.** Sequence heating and cooling.

Some exceptions will always exist, as in the case of dehumidification with reheat; therefore, the preceding principles are considered objectives.

Control zones are determined by location of the thermostat or temperature sensor that sets the requirements for heating and cooling supplied to the space. Typically, these control zones are for a room or an open area portion of a floor.

Many states no longer permit systems that reheat cold air or that mix heated and cooled air to heat and cool simultaneously. Such systems should be avoided. If selected, they should be designed for minimal use of the reheat function by zoning to match actual dynamic loads and reset cold and warm air temperatures based on the zone(s) with the greatest demand. Control details are shown later in this chapter. Heating and cooling supply zones should be structured to cover only areas of similar load. Different exterior exposures should have different supply zones.

Systems that provide changeover switching between heating and cooling prevent simultaneous heating and cooling. They include hot or cold secondary water for fan coils or single-zone fan systems. They usually require small operational zones, which have low load diversity, to permit changeover from warm to cold water without occupant dissatisfaction.

Systems for building interiors usually require year-round cooling and are somewhat simpler to control than exterior systems. These areas normally use all-air systems with constant supply air temperature, with or without variable air volume control. Proper control techniques and operational understanding can reduce the energy used to treat these areas. Reheat should be avoided.

General load characteristics of different parts of a building may lead to selecting different types of systems for each.

Load Matching. When individual room control is used, it is possible to control space more accurately and conserve energy if the whole system can be controlled in response to the major factor influencing system load. Thus, water temperature in a hot water heating system, steam temperature or pressure in a steam heating system, or delivered air temperature in a central fan system can be varied as building load varies. This puts a reasonable control on the whole system, relieves individual space controls of part of their burden, and allows more accurate space control. Also, modifying the basic rate of heating or cooling input to the system in accordance with system load reduces losses in the distribution system.

The system must always satisfy the area or room with the greatest demand. Individual controls handle demand variations within the area the system serves. The more accurate the system zoning, the greater the control by the overall system, the smaller the system distribution losses, and the more effectively space conditions are maintained by individual controls.

Design Considerations

Size of Controlled Area. No individually controlled area should exceed about 5000 square feet, because the difficulties of obtaining good distribution and of finding a representative location for the space controls increase with zone area. Each individually controlled area must have similar load characteristics throughout. For uniform conditions throughout an area, equitable distribution must be provided by competent engineering design, careful equipment sizing, and proper system balancing. The control can measure conditions only at its location; it cannot compensate for variable conditions throughout the area caused by improper distribution or inadequate design. Areas or rooms having dissimilar load characteristics, or different conditions to be maintained, should be individually controlled. The smaller the controller area, the better the control obtained and the more optimal the system performance and flexibility.

Location of Space Sensors. Space sensors and controllers must be located where they accurately sense the variables they control and where the condition is representative of the whole area (zone) they serve. In large open areas that have more than one zone, thermostats should be in the middle of their zone to prevent being affected by conditions in surrounding zones. There are three common locations for space temperature controllers or sensors.

1. **Wall-mounted thermostats or sensors** are usually placed on inside walls or columns in the occupied space they serve. Avoid outside wall locations. Mount thermostats where they will not be affected by heat from sources such as direct sun rays; wall pipes or ducts; convectors; and direct air currents from diffusers or equipment such as copy machines, coffee makers, or refrigeration cases. Air circulation should be ample and unimpeded by furniture or other obstructions, and there should be protection from mechanical injury. Thermo-

stats located in spaces such as corridors, lobbies, or foyers should be used to control only those areas.

2. **Return air thermostats** can control floor-mounted unitary conditioners such as induction or fan-coil units and unit ventilators. On induction and fan-coil units, the sensing element is behind the return air grille. On classroom unit ventilators that use up to 100% outdoor air for natural cooling, however, a forced flow sampling chamber should be provided for the sensing element.

   If return air sensing is used with central fan systems, locate the sensing element as near the space being controlled as possible to eliminate influence from other spaces and the effect of any heat gain or loss in the duct. Where combination supply/return light fixtures are used to return air to a ceiling plenum, the return air sensing element can be located in the return air opening of a light fixture. (Be sure to offset the setpoint to compensate for the heat from the light fixtures.)

   The sensing element should be located carefully to avoid radiant effect and to ensure adequate air velocity across the element.

3. **Diffuser-mounted thermostats** usually have sensing elements mounted on circular or square ceiling supply diffusers and depend on aspiration of room air into the supply air stream. They should be used only on high-aspiration diffusers adjusted for a horizontal air pattern. The diffuser in which the element is mounted should be in the center of the occupied area of the controlled zone.

Cost Analysis

Due to the rising cost of energy, it has been popular to promote various types of control equipment by "months to payback" based on projected energy savings. While this is one appropriate measure of the value of a purchase, it may be risky to rely solely on it, since many other factors can affect the true value. For example, if the estimated payback of an energy management system is 24 months, it does not necessarily mean an annual rate of return of 50%. For a detailed explanation of life cycle costing, see Chapter 49.

CONTROL APPLICATION LIMITATIONS AND PRECAUTIONS

Controls for Mobile Units

The operating point of any control that relies on pressure to operate a switch or valve varies as atmospheric pressure changes. Normal variations in atmospheric pressure do not noticeably change the operating point, but a change in altitude affects the control point to an extent governed by the change in absolute pressure. This is especially important when controls are selected for use in land and aerospace vehicles which, in normal use, are subject to wide variations in altitude. This effect can be substantial; for example, barometric pressure decreases by nearly one-third as the altitude increases from sea level to 10,000 feet.

In mobile applications, three detrimental factors are always present in varying degrees: vibration, shock, and G-forces. Controls selected for such service must qualify for the specific environment expected in the installation. In general, devices containing mercury switches, slow-moving or low-force contacts, or mechanically balanced components are unsuitable for mobile applications, while electronic solid-state devices are generally less susceptible to mobile forces.

Explosive Atmospheres

Sealed-in-glass contacts are not considered explosion-proof;

therefore, other means must be provided to eliminate any possible spark within the atmosphere.

When using electric control systems, the designer can use an explosion-proof case to surround the control case and contacts, permitting only the capsule and the capillary tubing to extend into the conditioned space. It is often possible to use a long capillary tube and mount the instrument case in a nonexplosive atmosphere. The latter method can be duplicated in an electronic control system by placing an electonic sensor in the conditioned space and feeding its signal to an electronic transducer placed in the nonexplosive atmosphere.

Because a pneumatic control system uses compressed air as its energy source, it is safe in otherwise hazardous locations. However, many pneumatic systems include E/P or P/E interfaces to electrical components. All electrical components require appropriate explosion-proof protection.

Sections 500 to 503 of the National Electrical Code include detailed information on electrical installation protection requirements for various types of hazardous atmospheres.

Limit Controls

When selecting automatic controls, it is important to consider the type of operation needed to control high or low limit (safety). This control may be inoperative for days, months, or years, and then operate immediately to prevent serious damage to equipment or property. Separate operating and limit controls are always recommended, even for the same functions.

Steam or hot water exchangers tend to be self-regulating and, in that respect, differ from electrical resistance heat transfer devices. For example, if airflow through a steam or hot water coil stops, coil surfaces approach the temperature of the entering steam or hot water, but cannot exceed it. Only convection or radiation losses from the steam or hot water to the surrounding area take place, and the coil is not usually damaged. Electric coils and heaters, on the other hand, can be damaged when no air flows around them. Therefore, control and power circuits must interlock with heat transfer devices (pumps and fans) to shut off the electrical energy when the device shuts down. Flow or differential pressure switches may be used for this purpose, however, they should be calibrated to energize only when airflow exists. This precaution shuts off power in case a fire damper closes or some duct lining blocks the air passage. Limit thermostats should also be installed to de-energize the heaters when temperatures exceed safe operating conditions.

Safety for Duct Heaters

The current in individual elements of electric duct heaters is normally limited to a maximum safe value established by the National Electric Code or local codes. In addition to the airflow interlock device, an automatic reset high-limit thermostat and a manual reset backup high-limit safety device are usually applied to duct heaters (Figure 91). The auto-reset high limit normally de-energizes the control circuit; however, if the control circuit has an inherent time delay or uses solid-state switching devices, a separate safety contactor may be desirable. The manual reset backup limit is generally arranged to interrupt all current to the heater independently, in case other control devices fail.

Cooling/Heating Changeover

With automatic changeover between heating and cooling, the control system should prevent operation of both modes for a time to prevent cycling between the two functions and/or unnecessary energy consumption. A controller with an adjustable dead band (differential) between heating and cooling easily accomplishes this function.

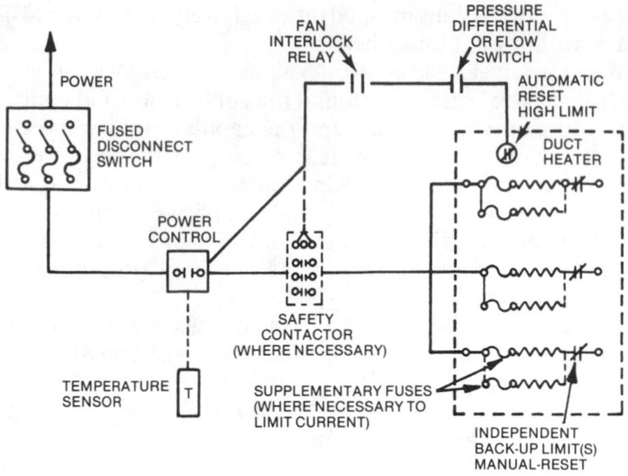

Fig. 91   Duct Heater Control

Lowered Night Temperature

When temperatures during unoccupied periods are lower than normally maintained during occupied periods, an automatic timer often establishes the proper day and night temperature time cycle. Allow sufficient time in the morning to pick up the conditioning load well before there is any heavy load increase in conditioned spaces. Night setback temperatures are often monitored and controlled more closely with supervisory control systems (see "Control of Central Subsystems" section). These supervisory systems take into account variables such as outdoor temperature, system capacity, and building mass to determine the optimal start-up and shutdown times.

Multiple Thermostats per Zone

Buildings or zones arranged in a modular arrangement can be designed for subdividing to meet occupant needs. Until subdividing is done, operating inefficienceis can occur if a zone has more than one thermostat. If a system allows one thermostat to turn on heating while another turns on cooling, control the two zones or terminals from a single thermostat until the area is subdivided properly.

USING COMPUTERS IN AUTOMATIC CONTROL

Computers can perform the control schemes described in this chapter. Chapter 60 covers the computer components and some of the ways computers are being used for HVAC. Other technical publications are available that describe the application of computers in the HVAC control industry.

COMMISSIONING, OPERATION, AND MAINTENANCE

An HVAC control system should be one that can be successfully operated and maintained. Historically, proper maintenance and operation of HVAC control systems has been neglected, and control engineers should educate the owner about the importance of operation and maintenance and ensure that the owner's personnel have effective operating manuals and adequate training.

Commissioning

A successful control system receives a proper start-up and

testing (commissioning) and not merely the adjustment of a few parameters (such as setpoints and throttling ranges) and a few quick checks of the system. However, the controls used for many efficient HVAC systems present a formidable challenge for proper commissioning and require the services of experienced professionals. In general, the increased use of VAV systems and digital controls have increased the importance and complexity of commissioning.

The design and construction specifications should include specific commissioning procedures to be followed. In addition, commissioning should be coordinated with testing and balancing (see Chapter 57), since each affects the other. The commissioning procedure begins by checking each control device to see that it is installed and connected according to approved shop drawings. Each electrical and pneumatic connection is verified, and all interlocks to fan and pump motors and primary heating and cooling equipment is checked.

Tuning—General Considerations

The systematic tuning of controllers improves the performance of all control systems and is particularly important for digital control. As a first step, the controlled process should be controlled manually between various setpoints to evaluate the following questions.

1. Is the process noisy (rapid fluctuations in controlled variable)?
2. Is there appreciable hysteresis (backlash) in the actuator?
3. How easy or difficult is it to maintain and change setpoint?
4. In which operating region is the process most sensitive (highest gain)?

If the process cannot be controlled manually, the reason should be identified and corrected before tuning the controller.

Tuning selects one or more control parameters that determine the steady-state and transient characteristics of the control system. HVAC processes are nonlinear, and characteristics change on a seasonal basis. Controllers tuned under one operating condition may become unstable as conditions change. A well-tuned controller will (1) minimize the steady-state error from setpoint, (2) respond quickly to disturbances, and (3) remain stable under all operating conditions. Tuning of proportional controllers is a compromise between minimizing steady-state error and maintaining margins of stability. Proportional plus Ingetral (PI) control minimizes this compromise because the integral action reduces steady-state error as the proportional term determines the controller's response to disturbances.

Control loops should be tuned under conditions of highest process gain to ensure stability over a wide range of process conditions.

Tuning PI Controllers

Popular methods of determining PI controller tuning parameters include closed-loop and open-loop process identification methods (Kinney 1983) and trial-and-error methods (Nesler and Stoecker 1984). The closed-loop method increases the gain of the controller in a proportional-only mode until the system continuously cycles after a setpoint change (Figure 92). Proportional and integral terms are then computed from the loops period of oscillation and the proportional gain value that caused cycling. The open-loop method introduces a step change in input into the opened control loop using a graphical technique. Proportional and integral terms are calculated from the estimated process parameters using a series of equations.

The trial-and-error method involves adjusting the gain of the proportional-only controller until the desired response to a setpoint change is observed. Conservative tuning dictates that this response should have a small initial overshoot and quickly damp

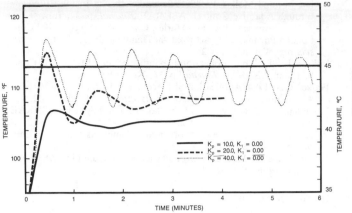

Fig. 92 Response of Discharge Air Temperature to a Step Change in Setpoints at Various Proportional Constants and No Integral Action

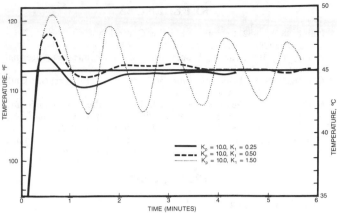

Fig. 93 Response of Discharge Air Temperature to a Step Change in Setpoints at Various Integral Constants with a Fixed Proportional Constant

to steady-state conditions (Nesler and Stoecker 1984). Setpoint changes should be made in a range where controller saturation is avoided. The integral term is then increased until changes in setpoint produce the same dynamic response as the controller under proportional-only control, but with the response now centered about the setpoint (Figure 93).

Tuning Digital Controls

In tuning digital controllers, additional parameters may need to be specified. The selection of a digital controller sampling interval is a compromise between computational resources and control requirements. A controller sampling interval about half of the time constant of the controlled process usually provides adequate control. Many digital control algorithms include an error deadband to eliminate unnecessary control actions when the process is near setpoint. Hysteresis compensation is possible with digital controllers, but it must be carefully applied as overcompensation can cause continuous cycling of the control loop.

OPERATION AND MAINTENANCE

Operation

Proper operation requires trained operators, but most operating budgets do not provide for training. Many owners of small- and medium-sized buildings turn operation over to the custodial staff. Large facilities may also have inadequately trained operating staffs. The control system designer can compensate for this by making control systems as simple and automatic as possible and by providing detailed operating manuals. Fortunately, energy costs are making owners more receptive to the need for proper operation.

Maintenance

For smaller facilities whose budgets do not allow for full-time maintenance personnel, a maintenance contract with a control manufacturer or independent service organization is usually established. Sometimes, an annual contract is made part of the bid package. Larger facilities usually have an in-house maintenance group who must be properly trained. (See Chapter 59.)

Control systems with maintenance requirements that exceed those allocated by the building owner can occur in modern HVAC system designs and can undermine the effectiveness of

the total system. Factors that can lead to excessive maintenance requirements include (1) overly complex system design; (2) hardware components, such as sensors and controllers, which require frequent recalibration or adjustment; and (3) the absence of reliable indicating devices to enable personnel to diagnose malfunctions properly. Since these factors are affected by the design, designers can minimize maintenance requirements by keeping designs simple and specifying the appropriate hardware.

Training

Training of maintenance and operating personnel must include the following:

1. Technical information about the control system and the individual control devices, including theory of operation and maintenance manuals.
2. An understanding of the control system philosophy and intent, so that the effect of adjustments and changes can be appreciated.
3. An understanding of the limits of the HVAC and control systems, and the knowledge that retrofitting may be possible if these limits make the system inadequate.
4. Periodic formal retraining of existing personnel, plus formal training of new personnel. On-the-job training without some formal curriculum can result in large knowledge gaps.

The designer must convince the owner that training and retraining programs are necessary to preserve the control system and provide satisfactory control.

Retrofitting

Many HVAC systems designed in the 1950's and 60's can be retrofitted to save energy while maintaining the needed environment. Haines (1982) gives some suggestions for retrofit. Each project is unique, and the control designer must reject "cookbook" or "canned" solutions.

Systems with excessive maintenance requirements can also be retrofitted to reduce maintenance costs and restore energy-efficient operation. This can be done by (1) replacing older equipment with low-maintenance (virtually "drift-free") sensors and controllers, (2) eliminating unnecessary complexity (for example, replace enthalpy economizer cycles with simple dry-bulb designs with drift-free sensors), and (3) incorporating the appropriate monitoring capability, such as gauges and meters, to check system operation.

REFERENCES

Haines, R.W. 1982. Retrofit of Existing Control Systems. Heating/Piping/Air Conditioning, Parts I and II, March and April.

Kinney, T.B. 1983. Turning Process Controllers. Chemical Engineering, September 19.

Kuo, B.C. 1975. *Automatic Control Systems*, 3rd Ed. Prentice Hall, Englewood Cliffs, NJ.

Nesler, C.G., and Stoecker, W.F. 1984. Selecting the Proportional and Integral Constants in the Direct Digital Control of Discharge Air Temperature. ASHRAE *Transactions*, Vol. 90, Part 2.

Ziegler, J.G., and Nichols, N.B. 1942. Optimal Settings for Automatic Controllers. ASME *Transactions*, Vol. 64, pp. 759-765.

BIBLIOGRAHPY

Interfacing Sensors and Actuators

Baker, D.W., and Hurley, C.W. 1984. On-site Calibration of Flow Metering Systems Installed in Buildings. National Bureau of Standards (NBS) Science Series Report 159, Washington, D.C.

Coad, W.J. 1985. Variable Flow in Hydronic Systems for Improved Stability, Simplicity and Energy Economics. ASHRAE *Transactions*, Vol. 91, Part 1B.

Hurley, C.W., and Schooley, J.F. 1984. Calibration of Temperature Measurement Systems Installed in Buildings. National Bureau of Standards (NBS) Science Series Report 153, Washington, D.C. 20234.

Hyland, R.W., and Hurley, C.W. 1983. General Guidelines for the On-site Calibration of Humidity and Moisture Control Systems in Buildings. National Bureau of Standards (NBS) Science Series Report 157, Washington, D.C.

Johnson, G.A. 1985. Retrofit of a Constant Volume Air System for Variable Speed Fan Control. ASHRAE *Transactions*, Vol. 91, Part 1.

Kao, J.Y., and Snyder, W.J. 1982. Application Information on Typical Hygrometers Used in Heating, Ventilating, and Air Conditioning (HVAC) Systems. National Bureau of Standards Report NBSIR 81-2460, Washington, D.C. 20234.

Treichler, W.W. 1985. Variable Speed Pumps for Water Chillers, Water Coils, and Other Heat Transfer Equipment. ASHRAE *Transactions*, Vol. 91, Part 1.

Zell, B.P. 1985. Design and Evaluation of Variable Speed Pumping Systems. ASHRAE *Transactions*, Vol. 91, Part 1.

Automatic Computer Control Applications

Chapman, W.F. 1980. Microcomputers Hail New Era in Controls. ASHRAE *Journal*, p. 38, July.

Coggan, D.A. 1986. Control Fundamentals Apply More Than Ever to DDC. ASHRAE *Transactions*, Vol. 92, Part 1.

Doucet, P. 1982. Direct Digital Control: Next Generation for Building Automation. Specifying Engineer, August.

Edwards, H.J. 1980. *Automatic Controls for Heating and Air Conditioning*. McGraw Hill, Inc.

Haines, R.W. 1983. *Control Systems for Heating, Ventilating and Air Conditioning*, 3rd Edition. Van Nostrand Reinhold.

Kirts, R.E. 1985. Users Guide to Direct Digital Control of Heating, Ventilating, and Air Conditioning Equipment. Naval Civil Engineering Laboratory Report UG-0004, Port Hueneme, CA 93043.

Lau, A.S.; Beckman, W.A.; and Mitchell, J.W. 1985. Development of Computerized Control Strategies for Large Chilled Water Plants. ASHRAE *Transactions*, Vol. 91, Part 1B.

Levine, M., and Moll, L.W. 1981. Beyond Setback: Energy Efficiency through Adaptive Control. ASHRAE *Journal*, p. 37, July.

May, W.B.; Borresen, B.A.; and Hurley, C.W. 1982. Direct Digital Control of a Pneumatically Actuated Air-Handling Unit. ASHRAE *Transactions*, Vol. 88, Part 2.

Mills, S.J. 1983. The Application Flexibility of the EMCS-DDC Combination. ASHRAE *Journal*, p. 36, November.

Walker, C.A. 1984. Application of Direct Digital Control to a Variable Air Volume System. ASHRAE *Transactions*, Vol. 90, Part 2.

Wichman, P.E. 1984. Improved Local Loop Control Systems. ASHRAE *Transactions*, Vol. 90, Part 2.

Williams, V.A. 1982. Better Control through Computers. ASHRAE *Transactions*, Vol. 88, Part 1.

Yaeger, G.A. 1986. Flow Charting and Custom Programming. ASHRAE *Transactions*, Vol. 92, Part 1.

Communications

Davies, D.W., *et al.*, 1979. *Computer Networks and Their Protocols*. John Wiley and Sons, Chichester.

Digital Equipment Corp. 1981. *Terminals and Communications Handbook*. Maynard, MA.

Freeman, R.L. 1980. *Telecommunication System Engineering*. John Wiley and Sons, New York.

Martin, J. 1981. *Computer Networks and Distributed Processing*. Prentice-Hall, Englewood Cliffs, NJ.

Martin, J. 1976. *Telecommunications and the Computer,* 2nd ed. Prentice-Hall, Englewood Cliffs, NJ.

McNamara, J.E. 1977. Technical Aspects of Data Communications. Digital Equipment Corp., Maynard, MA.

Newman, H.M. 1983. Data Communications in Energy Management and Control Systems: Issues Affecting Standardization. ASHRAE *Transactions*, Vol. 89, Part 1.

Roden, M.S. 1982. *Digital and Data Communication Systems*. Prentice-Hall, Englewood Cliffs, NJ.

Sapienza, G.R. 1986. The Effect of EMCS Architecture on Direct Digital Controllers. ASHRAE *Transactions*, Vol. 92, Part 1.

Operator-Machine Interface

Dressel, L.J. 1982. Improved Operator Interface Techniques. ASHRAE *Transactions*, Vol. 88, Part 1.

Schaefer, R.J. 1982. A Technique for the Use of Color Graphics and Light Pens in Energy Management Applications. ASHRAE *Transactions*, Vol. 88, Part 1.

Westphal, 1982. Human Engineering: the Man/System Interface. ASHRAE *Transactions*, Vol. 88, Part 1.

Review of Basic Control Theory

Deshpande, P.B., and Ash, R.H. 1981. *Elements of Computer Process Control*. Instrument Society of America, Research Triangle Park, NC.

McMillan, G.K. 1983. *Tuning and Control Loop Performance*. Instrument Society of America, Research Triangle Park, NC.

Murrill, P.W. 1981. *Fundamentals of Process Control Theory*. Instrument Society of America, Research Triangle Park, NC.

Ogata, K. 1970. *Modern Control Engineering,* Prentice-Hall, Englewood Cliffs, NJ.

Ogata, K. 1978. *System Dynamics*. Prentice Hall, Englewood Cliffs, NJ.

Williams, T.J. 1984. *The Use of Digital Computers in Process Control*, Instrument Society of America, Research Triangle Park, NC.

CHAPTER 52

SOUND AND VIBRATION CONTROL

A PROPER acoustical environment is as important for human comfort as other environmental factors controlled by air-conditioning systems. The objective of sound control is to achieve an appropriate sound level for all activities and people involved, *not* the lowest possible level. Because of the wide range of activities and privacy requirements, appropriate indoor acoustical design levels may vary considerably from room to room. Appropriate outdoor levels depend on local ambient sound conditions.

Sound and vibration are the result of a disturbance that propagates through an elastic medium. What most people think of as sound is a pressure pulsation in air. What most people think of as vibration is a feelable or visible oscillatory motion of a structure. HVAC systems require energy to do work, and inevitably some of this energy converts to acoustic energy as well as mechanical energy. HVAC noise and vibration control methods assess the amount of acoustic energy, and convert controlled amounts of this acoustic energy to mechanical energy, such as vibration isolation, or to thermal energy, such as much of duct system noise control.

This chapter is divided into six separate but interrelated parts, and has been organized in much the same order in which mechanical systems are designed. Section topics included are the following: (1) Acoustical Design Goals, (2) Sound Control for Indoor Mechanical Systems, (3) Mechanical Equipment Room Noise Isolation, (4) Sound Control for Outdoor Equipment Installations, (5) Vibration Isolation and Control, and (6) Troubleshooting. Successful design procedure requires understanding the fundamentals of and the definitions used in sound control. Chapter 7 of the 1985 FUNDAMENTALS Volume includes a discussion of the fundamental concepts required for use of this chapter.

ACOUSTICAL DESIGN GOALS

The designer's fundamental concern is how humans respond to sound. Frequently this concern is only generally related to the variation of sound energy. Humans will say one sound is louder than another, higher pitched or lower pitched and so forth. These are subjective reactions to changes in sound pressure level and in the spectral content and temporal variation of sound. Under carefully controlled experimental conditions, humans can detect small changes in sound level. But the human reaction describing *halving* or *doubling* of loudness requires changes in sound pressure level of about 10 dB. In a typical environment for broadband sounds, 3 dB is a minimum perceptible change. This means that halving the power output of the source results in a barely noticeable change in sound pressure level, and the power output must be reduced by a factor of 10 before humans determine that loudness has been halved. Subjective changes are shown in Table 1.

Table 1 Subjective Effect of Changes in Sound Pressure Level, Broadband Sounds

Change in Sound Pressure Level	Apparent Change in Loudness
3 dB	Just noticeable
5 dB	Clearly noticeable
10 dB	Twice (or half) as loud

The preparation of this chapter is assigned to TC 2.6, Sound and Vibration Control.

The Quality of Sound

The way in which humans react to the quality of sound is as important to the design engineer as their reaction to the loudness. Sound quality is a function of the relative intensities of sound levels in each region of the audible spectrum and it is important to achieve appropriate levels of sound throughout the audible spectrum. Figure 1 shows an indoor sound spectrum and the manner in which fan and diffuser noise contribute to that spectrum at various frequencies. The fan noise has been attenuated to a degree that it approaches the sound criteria (in this case an RC-35 contour) only in the lower octave bands. If this was the only noise present in the space, it would be considered rumbly by most listeners. However, the diffusers have been selected to balance the spectrum by filling in the higher frequencies so that the quality of the sound is more pleasant. Unfortunately, achieving a balanced sound spectrum is not usually this easy—there may be a multiplicity of sound sources to consider. As a guide to the designer, Figure 2 shows the more common mechanical and electrical noise sources and frequencies that control the indoor noise spectrum.

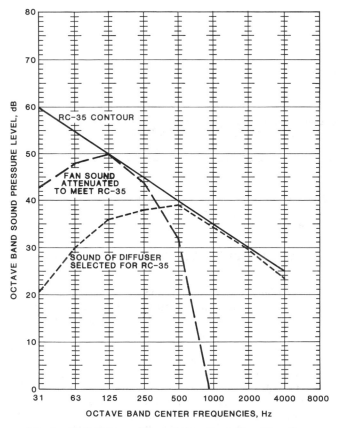

Fig. 1 Well-Balanced Sound Spectrum Resulting from Proper Selection of Air Outlets and Adequate Fan Noise Attenuation

Establishing Design Goals

The recommended acoustical design goal for air-conditioning systems is the achievement of a level of *background sound* that is unobtrusive in quality and low enough in level that it does not interfere with the occupancy requirements of the space being served.

For example, large conference rooms, auditoriums, and recording studios can tolerate a low level of background sound before interference problems develop. On the other hand, higher levels

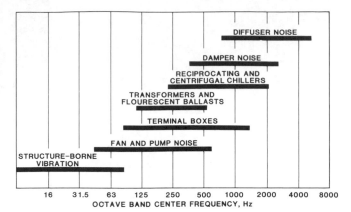

Fig. 2 Frequencies at Which Various Types of Mechanical and Electrical Equipment Generally Control Sound Spectra

of background sound are acceptable and even desirable in certain situations, such as in open-plan offices or music practice rooms, where a certain amount of speech and activity masking is essential. Therefore, it is important to recognize that the system noise control goal is a variable that depends closely on space-use requirements.

It is also important to recognize that the degree or occupancy satisfaction achieved with a given level of background sound is multidimensional. To be unobtrusive, it should have the following properties:

1. A balanced distribution of sound energy over a broad frequency range.
2. No audible tonal characteristics such as a whine, whistle, hum, or rumble.
3. No noticeable time-varying levels from *beats* or other system-induced aerodynamic instability.

In other words, the background sound should be steady in level, bland in character, and free of identifiable machinery noises.

ACOUSTICAL DESIGN CRITERIA

Three types of acoustical design criteria are used by the air-conditioning industry: A-Weighted Sound Level (dBA), Noise Criteria (NC) Curves, and Room Criteria (RC) Curves.

A-Weighted Sound Level

A-Weighted Sound Level (dBA) is one of the most widely used methods of stating design goals in terms of a single number, but its usefulness is limited because it gives no information on spectrum content needed for engineering. The measuring method is simple since the A-weighted sound level is obtained by a single reading. The standard sound level meter includes an electronic weighting network that de-emphasizes the low frequency portions of the noise spectrum, automatically compensating for the lower sensitivity of the human ear to low frequency sounds. Figure 3 shows the characteristic of the A-weighting network (ANSI).

The A-weighted sound level has the advantage of identifying the desirable level as a single-valued number that correlates well with human judgment of *relative loudness*. However, it has the disadvantage of not correlating well with human judgment of the relative noisiness or the subjective quality of the sound.

The A-weighted level comparison is best used with noises that sound alike but differ mainly in level. It should not be used for comparison of sounds with distinctly different spectral characteristics. In other words, two sounds at the same dBA level, but

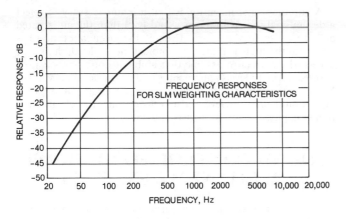

Fig. 3 Curves Showing A-Weighting Networks

with different spectral content, may be judged differently by the listener for an acceptable background sound in his environment. One of these noises might be completely acceptable, while the other could be objectionable because its spectrum shape resulted in a sound which was rumbly, hissy, or tonal in character.

NC Curves

The NC (Noise Criteria) Curves (Figure 4) have been widely used for many years (Beranek 1957). In practice, these curves define the limits that the octave-band spectrum of a noise source must not exceed to achieve a level of occupant acceptance. For example an NC-35 design goal is commonly used for private office; the background noise level meets this goal provided no portion of its spectrum lies above the designated NC-35 curve.

There are two problems in using the NC design goal: (1) If the NC-level is determined by a singular tangent peak, the actual level of resulting background sound may be quieter than desired for masking unwanted speech and activity noises, because the spectrum on either side of the tangent peak drops off too rapidly. (2) If the shape of the NC-Curve is matched approximately, the resulting sound will be either rumbly or hissy, depending on where the match occurs.

In other words, the shape of the NC-Curve is not that of a well balanced, bland sounding noise. Therefore, NC-Curves should be used with caution in critical noise situations where the background sound of the air-conditioning system is required to mask speech and activity noise.

RC Curves

RC (Room Criteria) Curves (Figure 5) are preferred for establishing HVAC system design goals (Blazier 1981). The shape of these curves differs from that of the NC curves at both low and high frequencies.

The shape of the RC Curve is a close approximation to a well balanced, bland-sounding spectrum. It provides guidance whenever the space requirements dictate that a certain level of background sound be maintained for masking or other purposes. Generally, it is desirable to approximate the shape of the curve within ± 2 dB over the entire frequency range to achieve an optimum balance in sound quality. If the low frequency levels (31.5 to 250 Hz) exceed the design curve by as much as 5 dB, the sound is likely to be rumbly; exceeding the design curve by 5 dB at high frequencies (2000 to 4000 Hz) causes the sound to be hissy.

Recommended NC and RC design levels are given in Table 2. The values for each type of room are justifiable for buildings in quiet locations or where sound transmission is reduced through exterior walls. An increase of 5 dB in NC or RC levels

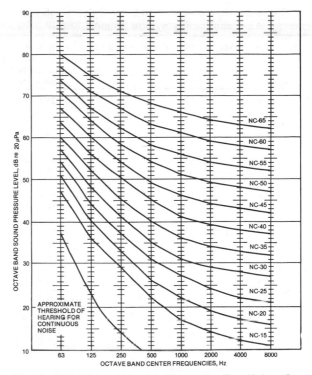

Fig. 4 NC (Noise Criteria) Curves for Specifying the Design Level in Terms of the Maximum Permissible Sound Pressure Level for Each Frequency Band

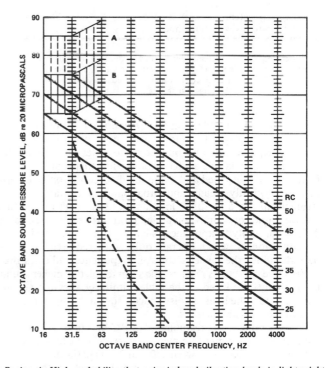

Region A: High probability that noise-induced vibration levels in lightweight wall and ceiling constructions will be clearly feelable; anticipate audible rattles in light fixtures, doors, windows, etc.

Region B: Noise-induced vibration levels in lightweight wall and ceiling constructions may be moderately feelable; slight possibility of rattles in light fixtures, doors, windows, etc.

Region C: Below threshold of hearing for continuous noise.

Fig. 5 RC (Room Criterion) Curves for Specifying Design Level in Terms of a Balanced Spectrum Shape

Table 2　Recommended Indoor Design Goals for Air-Conditioning System Sound Control[a]

(Note: These are for *unoccupied* spaces, with all systems operating.)

Type of Area	Recommended RC or NC Criteria Range
1. Private residences	25 to 30
2. Apartments	25 to 30
3. Hotels/motels	
a. Individual rooms or suites	30 to 35
b. Meeting/banquet rooms	25 to 30
c. Halls, corridors, lobbies	35 to 40
d. Service/support areas	40 to 45
4. Offices	
a. Executive	25 to 30
b. Conference rooms	25 to 30
c. Private	30 to 35
d. Open-plan areas	35 to 40
e. Computer equipment rooms	40 to 45
f. Public circulation	40 to 45
5. Hospitals and clinics	
a. Private rooms	25 to 30
b. Wards	30 to 35
c. Operating rooms	35 to 40
d. Corridors	35 to 40
e. Public areas	35 to 40
6. Churches	25 to 30[b]
7. Schools	
a. Lecture and classrooms	25 to 30
b. Open-plan classrooms	30 to 35[b]
8. Libraries	35 to 40
9. Concert halls	b
10. Legitimate theaters	b
11. Recording studios	b
12. Movie theaters	30 to 35
13. Laboratories with fume hoods	c

[a]Design goals can be increased by 5 dB when dictated by budget constraints or when noise intrusion from other sources represents a limiting condition.
[b]An acoustical expert should be consulted for guidance on these critical spaces.
[c]See section on "Laboratory Fume Hood Exhaust" in this chapter.

is permissible for buildings in relatively noisy locations without adequate exterior-wall sound-transmission loss, or where the owner's requirements and budget make lower costs desirable.

The ranges of Table 2 are based on the fact that sound radiated from properly designed and maintained air-conditioning equipment is typically steady and broadband in character. More stringent limits, 5 to 10 dB lower, should be specified for impulsive sounds or sounds containing prominent pure tones. Table 2 does not apply to appliances such as dishwashers and room air conditioners, which operate only when required for short periods under the owner's control. Experience indicates that under these conditions most people seem to tolerate higher sound levels than those listed in the table. Similarly, they are not intended to rate the level in noisy spaces, such as computer rooms or word processing centers.

To determine if the recommended RC design levels listed in Table 2 have been met, the measured levels of at least three of the four octave bands between 250 and 2000 Hz should lie within the indicated 5 dB RC range. Should the levels in the octave bands below 250 Hz be greater than the RC range established at higher frequencies, a potential rumble problem is indicated.

In mechanical systems having variable air volume, it may not be possible to fill in the higher frequencies when the quantity of air supplied is moderate to low. If acoustic privacy is important in these cases, it may be necessary to provide controlled amounts of electronic masking noise or to advise the building designer that improved sound-isolating construction is needed.

A common misconception is that it is unnecessary to select a design goal that is lower in sound level than the anticipated activity noise in the space. Even if the occupancy noise is significantly higher than the ambient noise level, it is not necessarily correct to assume that ambient noise levels can be allowed to rise to levels approaching that of the occupancy noise. Where speech contributes heavily to the occupancy noise, raising the ambient noise levels raises the occupancy levels until the point of physical discomfort is reached.

SOUND CONTROL FOR INDOOR MECHANICAL SYSTEMS

The air-conditioning system serving a room or space is frequently the major determinant of background noise level in the room. The system noise level must be evaluated and then controlled to achieve a satisfactory acoustical environment in the room. There are several paths by which system noise reaches a listener. These paths include airborne transmission of equipment noise to adjacent areas through the mechanical room construction; structureborne transmission of equipment vibration through the building structure; and ductborne noise created and transmitted by air-handling systems and their components.

If all noise transmission paths are not evaluated and controlled, excessive noise and/or vibration levels are likely to result. The evaluation process should take place in the design phase of a project and is as important to the project as thermal load calculations. Remedial measures to reduce ductborne noise are often expensive and only marginally effective. For this reason, noise control must be integrated into the system during the design phase. System noise calculations are the responsibility of the mechanical engineer designing the system, unless an acoustical consultant is involved. While the terminology and procedures for system noise control may be unfamiliar initially, their repeated use familiarizes the designer with conditions and systems that warrant detailed analyses and those that do not.

RELATIONSHIP BETWEEN SOURCE SOUND POWER LEVEL, L_w, AND ROOM SOUND PRESSURE LEVEL, L_p

General Case

The sound pressure level (L_p) that occurs at a chosen point in a room when a given source sound power level (L_w) is introduced depends on (1) room volume, (2) furnishings, (3) source strength, and (4) distance of the sound source(s) from the point of observation.

Schultz (1985) updated previous prediction methods of the relationship between sound power and sound pressure levels in typical furnished rooms of various sizes and shapes contained in previous ASHRAE Handbooks. Previous assumptions are only valid when dealing with empty rooms with "hard" acoustic surfaces, such as a laboratory reverberation chamber used for source sound power level determinations. Once any amount of distributed acoustical absorption is introduced, the behavior of the sound field is altered significantly.

Most typical rooms have distributed acoustical absorption and scattering elements such as furniture present. Although the amount of absorption and scattering varies from space to space (e.g., hospital rooms versus executive offices), the effect does not drastically change the relationship between sound power and sound pressure levels, as earlier Handbook volumes predicted.

The following empirical equation can be used to estimate the sound pressure level at a chosen distance from a sound source in "normal" rooms, as a function of the source sound power level, room size and frequency. Predictions should be accurate to ±2 dB.

$$L_p - L_w - 5 \log V - 3 \log f - 10 \log r + 25 \text{ dB} \qquad (1)$$

For SI units,

$$L_p - L_w - 5 \log V - 3 \log f - 10 \log r + 12 \text{ dB} \qquad (1\text{ SI})$$

where

L_p = room sound pressure level at the chosen reference point in dB re 20 μPa
L_w = source sound power level in dB re 10^{-12} W
V = room volume in ft^3 (m^3)
f = octave-band center frequency in Hz
r = distance from the source to the reference point in ft (m)

Equations (1) and (1 SI) apply directly when there is a *single* sound source in the room. When there is more than one source, the total sound pressure level at the reference point is obtained by adding (on an energy basis) the contribution of each source, using the corresponding L_w and r for each source.

Special Case: Distributed Ceiling Array

In most field applications, the air supply terminal diffusers are located in the ceiling of the conditioned space. The number of outlets within a given room are generally established by the floor area to be served by each terminal, which in turn varies as a function of the ceiling height and the load requirements. These considerations frequently lead to a more or less geometric distribution of air diffusers in the ceiling plane of the room, and whose individual sound power levels are nominally the same.

The total sound pressure level, L_{pt}, at a given reference point in the room that results from the combination of individual sources can be determined by using Equation (1) to compute the L_p due to each source, and then summing these on an energy basis. However, for the frequently encountered situation, in which the number and spacing of diffusers is strongly influenced by the room geometric proportions and results in a more or less "regular" ceiling array, the use of Equation (2) is recommended.

Equation (2) may be used to estimate the resulting room sound pressure level, L_{pt}, in a plane 5 ft (1.5 m) above the floor (standing head-height) due to a distributed ceiling array of nominally similar diffusers. For diffuser spacings on the order of the ceiling height, the variation in sound pressure level at any point within the reference plane above the floor should be on the order of about 1 dB, provided that there are at least four diffusers in the ceiling array. These equations also may be used for an array of linear diffusers, by taking the source sound power level as that due to a single section and the number of sources as the number of sections in the array.

$$L_{pt}, 5 \text{ ft,} = L_{ws} - 5 \log X - 28 \log h + 1.3 \log N -$$
$$3 \log f + 31 \text{ dB} \qquad (2)$$

$$L_{pt}, 1.5 \text{ m,} = L_{ws} - 5 \log X - 28 \log h + 1.3 \log N -$$
$$3 \log f + 17 \text{ dB} \qquad (2\text{ SI})$$

where

L_{pt} = average sound pressure level in a plane 5 ft (1.5 m) above the floor, in dB re 20 μPa
L_{ws} = sound power level of a *single* outlet in the array (This is the combined soundpower of that delivered by the distribution duct and that generated at the air terminal) in dB re 10^{-12} watt
X = ratio of the floor area served by each outlet to the square of the ceiling height ($X = 1$ if the area served equals h^2)
h = ceiling height in ft (m)
N = number of ceiling outlets in the room (N should be at least four)
f = octave-band center frequency in Hz

Example 1: Calculate the average sound pressure level for the 500 Hz octave-band in a plane 5 ft above the floor in an open-plan office served by a distributed array of ceiling outlets. The ceiling height is 9 ft and the outlets are spaced on 9 ft centers. The total area served is 2000 ft^2 and each outlet serves approximately 133 ft^2. The sound power level of a single outlet at 500 Hz is 45 dB re 10^{-12} watt.

1. Each outlet serves 133 ft^2. Therefore,

$$N = \frac{2000}{133} = 15$$

2. The area served by each outlet is 133 ft^2; the ceiling height is 9 ft. Therefore,

$$133/9^2 = 1.64$$

3. From Eq. (2):

$$L_{pt} = 45 - 5 \log 1.64 - 28 \log 9 + 1.3 \log 15$$
$$-3 \log 500 + 31 = 41 \text{ dB}$$

NOISE LIMIT SPECIFICATIONS FOR AIR-DISTRIBUTION SYSTEMS

The distribution system, via supply and return openings, determines airborne sound level in a room. In some cases, air valves and other devices radiate sound through the ceiling. Knowing this, the design can specify components that do not exceed the design criterion. However, the judgement of the acoustical acceptability of the overall final design is made by the occupants of the conditioned spaces. For this reason, the noise limits for components of the system should be established by working backwards from the selected room criterion. Each component is chosen based on how much of the total sound power it is allowed to contribute to the room.

For example, the attenuation required between the fan inlet or discharge can be determined by starting with the number of outlets or inlets in each conditioned space and computing what level of sound power must not be exceeded in the main supply or return ductwork ahead of the branch takeoffs. The difference between this sound power level and that computed for the fan represents the amount of attenuation required on the inlet and discharge sides of the equipment, or in the main ductwork and branches. A limit specification can then be developed for the sound power output of the fan equipment by accounting for the amount of attenuation that can be incorporated external to the fan.

A similar procedure can be used to develop a limit specification for air terminal devices such as VAV valves and fan-powered boxes. Adding up the sound powers delivered at each outlet or inlet determines the total for the device.

Sound power limits for air diffusers can be determined by starting with the room criterion and the number of diffusers serving the space to calculate the sound power per diffuser that should not be exceeded. Example 2 illustrates such a procedure.

Example 2: Using the data given in *Example 1*, calculate the sound power level spectrum of a single ceiling outlet that will allow the array not to exceed a room sound pressure level criterion of RC-40 at a level 5 ft above the floor.

Solution:

1. Determine $[L_{ws} - L_{pt}(5 \text{ ft})]$, the difference in dB between the sound power level of a single source in the array and the average sound pressure level at the 5 ft elevation. This is done by rearranging the terms in Eq. (2):

$$L_{ws} - L_{pt}(5 \text{ ft}) = 5 \log 1.64 + 28 \log 9 - 1.3 \log 15 + 3 \log f - 31$$
$$= 3 \log f - 4.7$$

2. Determine $[L_{ws} - L_{pt}(5 \text{ ft})]$ for each frequency band using the general result of Step 1.

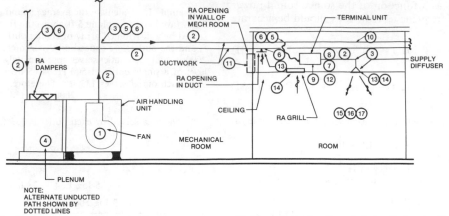

1. *Fan generated sound power level*
2. *Attenuation in straight, lined and unlined duct*
3. *Attenuation in lined and unlined fittings*
4. *Attenuation through plenum*
5. *Regenerated noise at fittings, etc.*
6. *Branch and outlet power division*
7. *Terminal unit discharge sound power level*
8. *Attenuation through terminal unit*
9. *Terminal unit casing radiated sound power level*
10. *Transmission loss through duct walls (breakout)*
11. *Transmission loss through return air opening in wall*
12. *Transmission loss through ceiling construction*
13. *End reflection loss*
14. *Air distribution device sound power level*
15. *Effect of multiple air distribution devices*
16. *Room effect*
17. *Room criterion*

Fig. 6 System Noise Schematic

@ 125 Hz: $L_{ws} - L_p(5 \text{ ft}) = 3 \log \ \ 125 - 4.7 = 1.6$ dB
@ 250 Hz: $\qquad\qquad\qquad = 3 \log \ \ 250 - 4.7 = 2.5$ dB
@ 500 Hz: $\qquad\qquad\qquad = 3 \log \ \ 500 - 4.7 = 3.4$ dB
@ 1000 Hz: $\qquad\qquad\qquad = 3 \log \ 1000 - 4.7 = 4.3$ dB
@ 2000 Hz: $\qquad\qquad\qquad = 3 \log \ 2000 - 4.7 = 5.2$ dB
@ 4000 Hz: $\qquad\qquad\qquad = 3 \log \ 4000 - 4.7 = 6.1$ dB

3. The permissible sound power level spectrum of the single source, L_{ws}, is equal to the values of the RC-40 criterion curve (see Figure 5) plus the power/pressure level differences determined in Step 2:

$$L_{ws} \ (\text{re RC-40}) = L_{pt} \ (\text{re RC-40}) + [L_{ws} - L_{pt} \ (5 \text{ ft})]_{(f)}$$

The result is tabulated below in Column 4, rounded to the nearest dB:

1	2	3	4
Frequency (Hz)	RC-40 (dB re 20 μPa)	$L_{ws} - L_{pt}$(5 ft) (dB)	L_{ws} re RC-40 (dB re 10^{-12} watt)
125	55	2	57
250	50	3	53
500	45	3	48
1000	40	4	44
2000	35	5	40
4000	30	6	36

RECOMMENDED SOUND CONTROL PROCEDURE

Figure 6 schematically illustrates a typical variable volume air-handling system. The numbers in the figure indicate the noise generating and attenuating elements that may need consideration or evaluation. Not all paths shown in Figure 6 exist in every system; however, with the methodology presented in this section, the designer can apply the appropriate procedures to the specific system design.

The following assumptions have been made in developing this procedure:

1. This procedure is predicated on obtaining adequate attenuation to achieve the design goals at the first critical outlet near the noise source. Inherent is the assumption that if this is achieved, then all outlets further from the noise source will also have adequate attenuation, unless the design goal for subsequent outlets is less than the first one.

2. The major noise source in an air-conditioning system is the fan. The procedure allows the designer to determine the attenuation required to eliminate fan noise to the desired degree. However, the designer must be aware of other noise sources in the system—regenerated noise created by fittings, terminal devices, and sound attenuators. Methods for evaluating these sources are also given in this chapter.

3. All prediction schemes and manufacturer's data assume uniform flow conditions. For example, for air distribution device sound power levels, manufacturers base their data on uniform velocity profile conditions and duct connection configurations. Corrections must be made and recognized where uniform flow conditions do not exist.

The system noise procedure follows these basic steps:

1. Determine the noise generated by the source.
2. Determine the attenuation provided by all supply ductwork, fittings and so forth. In doing this, calculate the resultant sound power level at each point of interest in the system. Determine if regeneration noise is a problem.
3. Calculate the resulting sound pressure level and compare it to the chosen design criteria.
4. Increase the attenuation in the system to eliminate deficiencies.
5. Determine if breakout noise is a problem and incorporate corrective measures.
6. Repeat the procedure for the return side of the system.

It is important to include all system components in the procedure. Unlined ductwork, branch take-offs, and elbows all provide attenuation. Failure to consider the contribution of these components can result in too little background noise generated by the system.

System-noise procedure demonstrates several useful facts. First, systems designed for low pressure and low velocities are less likely to have noise problems because of the lower sound power level of the fan, less regenerated noise at the fittings, etc. Second, location of the lining in a duct system is important. Lining in small ductwork provides more attenuation than lining in large ductwork. However, if only branch ductwork is lined for attenuation, spaces served by or located under major duct

Table 3 Typical Noise Levels Produced by Mechanical Room Equipment

Noise Source	Typical Noise Level[a] TR = Tons Refrig. hp = Horsepower	Comments	Standard Error of Estimate[b]	Estimated Uncertainty	Reference
Centrifugal chillers[c]	L_p (1 m) = 60 + 11 Log (TR) dB(A)	See table below for typical octave band spectrum shape.	4 dB	—	Blazier (1972)
Reciprocating chillers	L_p (1 m) = 71 + 9 Log (TR) dB(A)		5 dB	—	Blazier (1972)
Absorption machines	L_p (1 m) < 85 dB(A)	Noise produced by solution pump and auxiliary equipment.	—	± 5 dB	Blazier (1972)
Circulating pumps	L_p (1 m) = 77 + 10 Log (hp) dB(A)			± 5 dB	Heinter (1968), Kugler et al. (1973)
Boilers	L_p (1 m) < 88 dB(A)	Forced draft type.	—	± 5 dB	Blazier (1972)
Casing radiation, vane axial fans	L_w (case) = L_w (fan) − 10 dB	L_w (case) = A-weighted sound power of fan case.	—	± 5 dB	
Casing radiation, central station centrifugal fans	L_w (case) = L_w (fan) − 15 dB	L_w (fan) = A-weighted sound power of fan inlet.	—	± 5 dB	

Octave band levels in dB referred to A-weighted levels	63	125	250	500	1000	2000	4000	Sessler (1973), Miller (1970)
Centrifugal chiller, internal geared, medium to full load	−8	−5	−6	−7	−8	−5	−8	
Centrifugal chiller, direct drive, medium to full load	−8	−6	−7	−3	−4	−7	−12	
Centrifugal chiller, >1000 ton, medium to full load	−11	−11	−8	−8	−4	−6	−13	
Reciprocating chiller, all loads	−19	−11	−7	−1	−4	−9	−14	

[a]Equations give the mean value to be anticipated for equipment of current manufacture at full load.

[b]The standard error of estimate is a measure of the variation to be anticipated from machine to machine due to differences in design, size, and point of operation. Statistically, two of the three machines sampled over a range of sizes among different manufacturers would be expected to have noise level differences lying within the range of ±1 standard error about the mean.

[c]During light load operation, centrifugal chiller noise levels can be expected to increase about 5 dB in all octave bands not containing either the compressor shaft frequency or the final stage blade passage frequency. These bands typically increase 10 to 13 dB (shaft frequency band) and 8 to 10 dB (blade pass frequency band).

runs may be subjected to excessive noise because of unattenuated fan noise and subsequent breakout.

Source Noise Levels

Source noise levels are often available from the equipment manufacturers in the form of Sound Power Level, L_w, or Sound Pressure Level, L_p, at a specified distance from the noise source. In using these data, it is important to understand the test method used to gather the data and to assess its relevance to the particular application. Where source noise levels are unavailable or are irrelevant, Table 3 presents values which can be used to predict noise levels from selected types of equipment. The section below presents a method for predicting fan sound power level.

PREDICTION OF FAN SOUND POWER

The sound power generation of a given fan performing a given duty is best obtained from the fan manufacturer's test data taken under approved test conditions. However, if such data are not readily available, the octave band sound power levels for various fans can be estimated by the procedure described below.

Fan noise can be rated in terms of the specific sound power level, which is defined as the sound power level generated by a fan operating at a capacity of 1 cfm (or 1 L/s) and a pressure of 1 in. of water (or 1 Pa). By reducing all fan noise data to this common denominator, the specific sound power level serves as a basis for direct comparison of the octave band levels of various fans and as a basis for a conventional method of calculating the noise levels of fans at actual operating conditions.

A study shows that on a specific sound power level basis, small fans are somewhat noisier than large fans. While size division

is necessarily arbitrary, the size divisions indicated are practical for estimating fan noise. Fans generate a tone at the blade passage frequency, and the strength of this tone depends, in part, on the type of fan. To account for this blade passage frequency, an increase should be made in the octave band into which the blade frequency falls. The number of decibels to be added to this band is called the *blade frequency increment* (BFI). Blade frequency (B_f) is:

$$B_f = \text{rps} \times \text{no. of blades or } [(\text{rpm} \times \text{no. of blades})/60] \quad (2)$$

The number of blades and the fan rpm (rps) can be obtained from the fan selection catalog. If this catalog is unavailable, Table 4 can be used for estimation. Table 5 lists specific sound power levels and blade frequency increments. For a more complete description of fan types, construction and applications, see

Table 4 Octave Band in which Blade Frequency Increment (BFI) Occurs[a]

Fan Type	Octave Band in which BFI Occurs
Centrifugal	
Airfoil, backward curved backward inclined	250 Hz
Forward curved	500 Hz
Radial blade, pressure blower	125 Hz
Vaneaxial	125 Hz
Tubeaxial	63 Hz
Cooling Tower	
Propeller	63 Hz

[a]Use for estimating purposes. For speeds of 1750 rpm (29 rps) or more, move the BFI to the next higher octave band. Where actual fan is known, use manufacturers' data.

Table 5   Specific Sound Power Levels (dB re 1pW) for Inlets or Outlets and Blade Frequency Increments (BFI) for Various Types of Fans (see Note)

Fan Type	Wheel Size	Octave Band Center Frequency, Hz							BFI
		63	125	250	500	1000	2000	4000	
Centrifugal									
Airfoil, backward	Over 36 in. (900 mm)	32	32	31	29	28	23	15	3
curved, backward inclined	Under 36 in. (900 mm)	36	38	36	34	33	28	20	
Forward curved	All	47	43	39	36	34	32	28	2
Radial blade,	Over 40 in. (1000 mm)	45	39	42	39	37	32	30	8
Pressure blower	40 in. (1000 mm) to 20 in. (500 mm)	55	48	48	45	45	40	38	8
	Under 20 in. (500 mm)	63	57	58	50	44	39	38	8
Vaneaxial	Over 40 in. (1000 mm)	39	36	38	39	37	34	32	6
	Under 40 in. (1000 mm)	37	39	43	43	43	41	28	6
Tubeaxial	Over 40 in. (1000 mm)	41	39	43	41	39	37	34	7
	Under 40 in. (1000 mm)	40	41	47	46	44	43	37	7
Propeller									
Cooling tower	All	48	51	58	56	55	52	46	5

NOTE: Add 3 dB to the above values for the total sound power level being radiated.

Chapter 3 of the 1983 EQUIPMENT Volume. Sound power levels at actual operating conditions can be estimated by the actual fan-volume flow rate and fan pressure, as:

$$L_w = K_w + 10 \log \frac{Q}{Q_1} + 20 \log \frac{P}{P_1} + C \tag{4}$$

where

L_w = estimated sound power level of fan (dB re 1pW)
K_w = specific sound power level (see Table 2)
Q = flow rate, cfm (L/s)
Q_1 = 1 when flow is in cfm (0.472 when flow is in L/s)
P = pressure drop, in. of water (Pa)
P_1 = 1 when pressure is in in. of water (249 when pressure is in Pa)
C = correction factor in dB, for point of fan operation

Values of the estimated sound power level are calculated for all seven bands, and the BFI is added to the octave band in which the blade passage frequency falls.

Example 3: A forward curved fan is selected to supply 8800 cfm at 1.5 in. of water. Sized for efficient operation, it has 24 blades and operates at 1170 rpm.
  Solution:
  Step 1. The specific sound power levels are obtained from the second line of Table 5 and are entered on Line 1 of Table 6.
  Step 2. The additional sound power levels due to the volume flow rate and pressure are found using Eq. (4), as $L_w = K_w + 10 \log 8800 + 20 \log 1.5 + 0 = K_w + 39.5 + 3.6 = K_w + 43$.
  Step 3. Since the fan has 24 blades and operates at 1170 rpm, $B_f = 19.5 \times 24 = 468$ Hz, which falls in the 500 Hz octave band.
  Step 4. Combining these steps results in Line 4 of Table 6.

Point of Operation

The specific sound power levels given in Table 5 are for fans operating at or near the peak efficiency point of the fan performance curve. This conforms with the recommended practice of selecting fan size and speed so that operation falls at or near this point; it is advantageous for energy conservation and corresponds to the lowest noise levels for that fan. If, for any reason, a fan is not or cannot be selected optimally, the noise level produced will increase and correction factor C in Eq. (4) accounts for this. This correction factor should be applied to all octave bands.

Table 6   Sample Calculation for Example 3

Reference	Octave Band Center Frequency, Hz						
	63	125	200	500	1000	2000	4000
Table 5	47	43	39	33	28	25	23
Eq. (4)	43	43	43	43	43	43	43
Eq. (3) and Table 5	—	—	—	2	—	—	—
Total (dB re 1pW)	90	86	82	78	71	68	66

Example 4: A fan will handle 27,000 cfm at 2.5 in. of water. For lower first cost and space requirements, the engineer selects a 27-in. double-width air foil fan. Catalog performance data for this show a peak efficiency of 78%; however, for this selected duty, the fan curve shows an efficiency of only 49%. Percentage of peak static efficiency is $(49/78) \times 100 = 62\%$. According to Table 7, this will result in a 12 dB increase in the sound power level generated by the fan.
  If operating cost optimization and mechanical efficiency were considered, the fan choice might be a 36-in. double-width unit. In this case, the efficiency is $(71/78) \times 100 = 91\%$ and there is no increase in sound level; the fan is operating near its peak efficiency.

Table 7   Correction Factor, *C*, for Off-Peak Operation

Static Efficiency % of Peak	Correction Factor dB
90 to 100	0
85 to 89	3
75 to 84	6
65 to 74	9
55 to 64	12
50 to 54	15

Fan Sound Test Accuracy

In the present state of the art, the accuracy in determining sound power is of the order ±2 dB in the octave bands centered at 250, 500, 1000, 2000, and 4000 Hz. The 63 Hz octave band presents some very difficult measuring problems, and variations of 6 to 8 dB can be expected. Lesser problems exist in the 125 and 8000 Hz octave bands, and variations of 3 to 4 dB can occur in these octave bands.

Implications of VAV on Fan Noise

The preceding discussion focused on predicting fan sound power levels for fans serving constant volume systems. There are two additional areas to consider when fans serve variable air volume (VAV) systems: (1) the efficiency and stability of the fan through the entire range of modulation and (2) the acoustic impact of the means by which fan output is modulated.

The fan must be selected for its efficiency and stability through the entire range of modulation. A fan selected for peak efficiency at full output may surge at a normal operating point of 50% of maximum output. Similarly, a fan selected to operate at the 50% point may be so inefficient at full output that its noise levels are unacceptable. In general, fan selection for VAV systems is a compromise between fan surge and fan inefficiency, and the narrower the range of modulation, the more acceptable the compromise will be.

How delivered air quantities are modulated is also important. Fan output is usually modulated in one of three ways: (1) through variable inlet vanes, which add resistance to the fan system, altering the operating point by doing so; (2) through variable speed fan motors and mechanical drives, which slow the fan to match the operating requirements without altering the point of operation on the fan curve; and (3) by using variable pitch fan blades, which change the fan geometry to increase or decrease fan output.

While the fan modulation system is often selected based on non-acoustic factors such as initial cost of equipment, operating costs or space requirements, there are important acoustical factors to consider when analyzing fan modulation systems. The first system, variable inlet vanes, may generate significant low-frequency noise as the vanes shut down. Additional attenuation with a corresponding additional pressure drop is required to attenuate the noise generated by the inlet vanes. Consequently, payback cost analysis must include the additional sound attenuation and energy costs to move the air through this sound attenuation.

The other two systems, variable speed motors and drives and variable pitch fan blades, are actually quieter at reduced air output than at full output. The designer has the option of designing for maximum output as if the system were constant volume, or selecting the sound attenuation for a more normal operating point and allowing fan noise to exceed the design criteria during the rare occasions when the fan operates at full output. In this case, the reduced cost of sound attenuation and corresponding pressure drop reduction is a trade-off against initial equipment costs.

General Discussion of Fan Sound

To minimize the required duct sound attenuation, the proper selection and installation of the fan (or fans) are vitally important. Some factors to consider are as follows:

1. The air distribution system should be designed for minimum resistance, since fan sound generation, regardless of fan type, increases with static pressure.
2. The specific sound power levels of the practical fan designs for any given job should be examined by the design engineer. Different types of fans generate different levels of sound and produce different octave band spectra. The engineer should select a fan that will generate the lowest possible sound level, commensurate with other fan selection parameters.
3. Fans with relatively few blades (less than 15) tend to generate pure tones, which may dominate the spectrum. These occur at the blade passage frequency [Eq. (3)] and its harmonics. The intensity of these tones depends on resonances within

the duct system, on fan design, and on inlet flow distortions.
4. Duct connections at both the fan inlet and outlet should be designed for uniform and straight air flow. Gusty and swirling inlet air flow should be avoided. Variations from accepted application arrangements can severely degrade both the aerodynamic and acoustic performance of any fan type and invalidate manufacturers' ratings or other performance predictions.
5. In variable-volume systems, specific attention should be paid to the effect of changes in volume on the fan sound power. Reducing volume flow by changes in inlet vane settings may substantially increase the fan sound power.

NOISE CONTROL ALONG DUCT PATHS

Natural Attenuation in Ducts

Even if the ductwork contains no sound attenuators (acoustical linings or sound traps), only a fraction of the acoustic energy generated by the fan, the duct fittings, etc. reaches any one room because of the combined effects of energy division at branch takeoffs, as well as energy losses because of duct wall vibration and wave reflections at elbows and duct outlets.

To avoid overdesigning the acoustic duct treatment, credit should be given for this natural attenuation.

The natural attenuation for round ducts with or without external thermal insulation is about 0.03 dB/ft (0.1 dB/m) below 1000 Hz, rising irregularly to 0.1 dB/ft (0.3 dB/m) at high frequencies. The natural attenuation in unlined rectangular sheet metal ducts is given in Table 8.

Selection of Absorptive Material

Sound-absorbing material can be arranged in a duct system in the following ways:

1. Line all fan suction and discharge plenums to get economical sound absorption in systems.
2. Line ducts with sound-absorbing material, which also serves as thermal insulation. Note: Duct dimensions must be increased to compensate for area lost due to lining.
3. Locate lined duct sections close to elbows to take advantage of the interaction of sound absorption and sound reflection.
4. Install prefabricated attenuators, which contain specially shaped perforated baffles filled with sound absorbing material.

Usually, several arrangements are combined to achieve the required amount of sound attenuation.

When a sound wave impinges on the surface of a porous material, the air within the small pores of the material is set into a vibrating motion. The flow resistance within the pores of the material converts a portion of the sound energy to heat. The decimal fraction representing the absorbed portion of the energy of the incident sound wave is called the absorption coefficient. Considerable absorption may also result, particularly in the low frequency range, from the flexural vibrations of duct

Table 8 Approximate Natural Attenuation in Unlined Rectangular Sheet-Metal Ducts (Ver 1978)

P/A Ratio in/in²	mm/mm²	Octave Band Center Frequency, Hz		
		63	125	250 and Over
		Attenuation, dB/ft (dB/m)[a]		
Over 3.1	Over 0.012	0 (0)	0.3 (0.98)	0.1 (0.33)
3.1 to 0.13	0.012 to 0.005	0.3 (0.98)	0.1 (0.33)	0.1 (0.33)
Under 0.13	under 0.005	0.1 (0.33)	0.1 (0.33)	0.1 (0.33)

[a]Double these values if the duct is externally insulated.

walls. In the selection and application of the absorptive material, remember that thin materials, particularly when mounted on hard, solid surfaces, do not absorb low frequency sound. For significant sound absorption at frequencies below 500 Hz, the material must be 2 in. (50 mm) or thicker.

Sound-absorbing materials suitable for use in air ducts are available in blankets and semirigid boards. Consult manufacturers' literature for their selection and use. The following additional properties should be evaluated in the selection of acoustical materials: (1) adequate strength to avoid breakage and crumbling, (2) fire resistance and compliance with national and local code requirements, (3) resistance to erosion at high air velocities, and (4) freedom from odor when either dry or wet.

Attenuation of Sound from Lined Plenums

Sound absorption provided by a plenum on the fan discharge, as shown in Figure 7, is often an economical arrangement. Both experiment and ray theory acoustics have led to the following approximate expression for acoustic plenum attenuation in dB (Wells 1958).

$$\text{Attenuation} = 10 \log \left[\frac{1}{S_e\{(\cos \theta / 2\pi d^2) + (1 - \alpha)/\alpha S_w\}} \right] \quad (5)$$

where

α = absorption coefficient of the lining, dimensionless
S_e = plenum exit area, ft^2 (m^2)
S_w = plenum wall area, ft^2 (m^2)
d = distance between entrance and exit, ft (m) (see Figure 7)
θ = the angle of incident at the exit, i.e., the angle that the direction d makes with the normal to the exit opening, degrees

For frequencies high enough to make the wave length less than the plenum dimensions, Eq. (5) is accurate to within a few decibels. At lower frequencies, Eq. (5) is conservative, and the actual attenuation exceeds the calculated value by 5 to 10 dB because of sound reflection by the plenum.

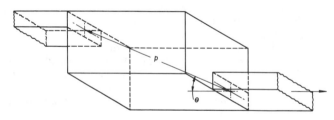

Fig. 7   Diagram of Sound Absorbing Plenum

Attenuation of Sound in Lined Ducts

Duct linings can be designed both to absorb sound and to insulate thermally. Thicknesses between 0.5 and 2 in. (13 and 50 mm) are usually adequate for thermal insulation. The sound absorption of such relatively thin linings is limited, especially at low frequencies.

The theory of sound attenuation in internally lined ducts has been investigated extensively (Ver 1978); because of measurement difficulties, however, the experimental work has lagged considerably. Kuntz (1987), under ASHRAE sponsorship, measured the attenuation of sound in lined rectangular ducts. The methodology shown below is taken from this review.

The attenuation of sound in round ducts has not been investigated at this time. Until such data are available, Table 9 is recommended as the best available.

To determine the attenuation of lined rectangular or square ducts, use the following two equations. These equations are not applicable to ducts with very low sound transmission walls, such as flexible ducts or ducts covered with thin plastic or metal foil. Since most calculations of attenuation are for octave bands of noise rather than for specific tones, the designer should be aware that the attenuation is frequency dependent. To compensate for this frequency dependence, Eq. (6) can be evaluated one-third octave below and Eq. (7) one-third octave above the center frequency of the octave.

At low frequencies (800 Hz and below), Eq. (6) may be used to calculate the total attenuation or insertion loss for any duct length.

$$a = \frac{t^{1.08} \, h^{0.356} \, (P/A) L f^{(1.17 + K_2 d)}}{K_1 d^{2.3}} \quad \text{dB,} \quad (6)$$

where

K_1 = 1190 (5.46 $\cdot$ 10^{-3}) [I-P units (SI units)]
K_2 = 0.19 (0.0119)
d = nominal density, lb/ft^3 (kg/m^3)
t = material thickness, in. (mm)
h = smallest inside cross dimension of the lined duct, in. (mm)
f = frequency, Hz
P = inside duct perimeter, in. (mm)
L = duct length, ft (m)
A = inside duct area, in^2 (mm^2)

At high frequencies (800 Hz and above), Eq. (7) may be used to calculate the total attenuation or insertion loss for duct lengths of 10 ft (3 m) or less. For ducts longer than 10 ft (3 m), the 10 ft (3 m) total attenuation values should be used.

$$a = \frac{K_4 \, (P/A) \, L \, f^{[K_5 - 1.61 \log (P/A)]}}{w^{2.5} \, h^{2.7}} \quad \text{dB,} \quad (7)$$

where

w = largest inside cross dimension of the duct, in. (mm)
L = duct length, ft (m) [limited to 10 ft and 3 m]
K_4 = 2.11 $\cdot$ 10^9 (3.32 $\cdot$ 10^{18})
K_5 = -1.53 (-3.79)

(When lined ducts are used before and after turns, the high-frequency equation may be used for each section. This assumption has not been supported by research.)

In one-third octave band calculations the smallest value calculated at 800 Hz should be taken. To prevent the prediction of excessive values, the insertion loss in any straight, lined section should be limited to 40 dB at any frequency. This limitation is due to structure-borne sound in the duct walls. Tables

Table 9   Round Duct Attenuation (United Sheet Metal 1973)

Diameter Size, in. (mm)	Approximate Attenuation, dB/ft (dB/m) for 1 in. (25 mm) duct liner[a] Octave Band Center Frequency, Hz						
	63	125	250	500	1000	2000	4000
6 (150)	0.2 (0.66)	0.5 (1.6)	1.0 (3.3)	1.8 (5.9)	2.2 (7.2)	2.2 (7.2)	2.0 (6.6)
12 (300)	0.15 (0.49)	0.3 (0.98)	0.7 (2.3)	1.5 (4.9)	2.2 (7.2)	2.2 (7.2)	1.5 (4.9)
24 (600)	0.1 (0.33)	0.2 (0.66)	0.5 (1.6)	1.0 (3.3)	1.7 (5.6)	0.9 (3.0)	0.5 (1.6)
48 (1200)	0.04 (0.13)	0.1 (0.33)	0.3 (0.1)	0.6 (2.0)	0.6 (2.0)	0.8 (2.6)	0.5 (1.6)

[a]Test data based on 26 to 22 gauge (0.55 to 0.85 mm) spiral wound duct with perforated spiral wound steel liner 24-ft (7.2-m) long. Diameter shown is free area. Data are for no airflow circumstance.

Table 10 Sound Attenuation in Straight Lined Sheet Metal Ducts of Rectangular Cross-Section in dB/ft (dB/0.3 m) Lining Thickness: 1 in. (25 mm)[a]; No Airflow

Internal Cross-Sectional Dimensions		Octave Band Center Frequency (Hz)						
in.	(mm)	63	125	250	500	1000	2000	4000
4 × 4	(100 × 100)	.16	.44	1.21	3.32	9.10	10.08	3.50
4 × 6	(100 × 150)	.13	.37	1.01	2.77	7.58	8.26	3.13
4 × 8	(100 × 200)	.12	.33	.91	2.49	6.82	6.45	2.57
4 × 10	(100 × 250)	.11	.31	.85	2.32	6.37	5.02	2.07
6 × 6	(150 × 150)	.12	.34	.93	2.56	7.01	7.50	3.17
6 × 10	(150 × 250)	.10	.27	.75	2.04	5.61	5.67	2.67
6 × 12	(150 × 300)	.09	.26	.70	1.92	5.26	4.80	2.33
6 × 18	(150 × 460)	.08	.23	.62	1.70	4.67	2.95	1.51
8 × 8	(200 × 200)	.10	.28	.77	2.12	5.82	6.08	2.95
8 × 12	(200 × 300)	.09	.24	.65	1.77	4.85	4.98	2.64
8 × 16	(200 × 410)	.08	.21	.58	1.59	4.37	3.89	2.17
8 × 24	(200 × 610)	.07	.19	.52	1.42	3.88	2.39	1.41
10 × 10	(250 × 250)	.09	.24	.67	1.84	5.04	5.17	2.79
10 × 16	(250 × 410)	.07	.20	.55	1.49	4.10	4.04	2.41
10 × 20	(250 × 510)	.07	.18	.50	1.38	3.78	3.30	2.05
10 × 30	(250 × 760)	.06	.16	.45	1.23	3.36	2.03	1.34
12 × 12	(300 × 300)	.08	.22	.60	1.64	4.48	4.52	2.67
12 × 18	(300 × 460)	.07	.18	.50	1.36	3.74	3.71	2.39
12 × 24	(300 × 610)	.06	.16	.45	1.23	3.36	2.89	1.97
12 × 36	(300 × 910)	.05	.15	.40	1.09	2.99	1.78	1.28
15 × 15	(380 × 380)	.07	.19	.52	1.42	3.88	3.84	2.53
15 × 22	(380 × 560)	.06	.16	.43	1.19	3.27	3.20	2.29
15 × 30	(380 × 760)	.05	.14	.39	1.06	2.91	2.46	1.86
15 × 45	(380 × 1140)	.05	.13	.34	.94	2.17	1.51	1.21
18 × 18	(460 × 460)	.06	.17	.46	1.26	3.45	3.37	2.42
18 × 28	(460 × 710)	.05	.14	.38	1.03	2.84	2.69	2.13
18 × 36	(460 × 910)	.05	.13	.34	.94	2.59	2.15	1.78
18 × 54	(460 × 1370)	.04	.11	.31	.84	1.65	1.32	1.16
24 × 24	(610 × 610)	.05	.14	.38	1.05	2.87	2.73	2.26
24 × 36	(610 × 910)	.04	.12	.32	.87	2.39	2.24	2.02
24 × 48	(610 × 1220)	.04	.10	.29	.78	1.90	1.75	1.66
24 × 72	(610 × 1830)	.03	.09	.25	.70	1.06	1.07	1.08
30 × 30	(760 × 760)	.04	.12	.33	.91	2.49	2.32	2.14
30 × 45	(760 × 1140)	.04	.10	.28	.76	1.88	1.90	1.91
30 × 60	(760 × 1520)	.03	.09	.25	.68	1.35	1.48	1.57
30 × 90	(760 × 2290)	.03	.08	.22	.60	.76	.91	1.02
36 × 36	(910 × 910)	.04	.11	.29	.81	2.01	2.03	2.04
36 × 54	(910 × 1370)	.03	.09	.25	.67	1.42	1.66	1.83
36 × 72	(910 × 1830)	.03	.08	.22	.60	1.02	1.30	1.50
36 × 108	(910 × 2740)	.03	.07	.20	.54	.57	.80	.98
42 × 42	(1070 × 1070)	.04	.10	.27	.73	1.59	1.81	1.97
42 × 64	(1070 × 1630)	.03	.08	.22	.60	1.11	1.47	1.75
42 × 84	(1070 × 2130)	.03	.07	.20	.55	.81	1.16	1.45
42 × 126	(1070 × 3200)	.02	.06	.18	.49	.45	.71	.94
48 × 48	(1220 × 1220)	.03	.09	.24	.67	1.30	1.65	1.90
48 × 72	(1220 × 1830)	.03	.07	.20	.56	.92	1.35	1.70
48 × 96	(1220 × 2440)	.02	.07	.18	.50	.66	1.05	1.40
48 × 144	(1220 × 3660)	.02	.06	.16	.45	.37	.65	.91

[a]Based on measurements of surface-coated duct liners of 1.5 lb/ft^3 (24 kg/m^3) density. For the specific materials tested, liner density had a minor effect over the nominal range of 1.5 to 3 lb/ft^3 (24 to 48 kg/m^3).

10 and 11 present the attenuation of random noise per 1-ft (0.3-m) length of duct for frequently used clear cross-sectional dimensions, in octave bands from 63 to 4000 Hz. Data are presented for 1 in. (25 mm) lining thickness in Table 10 and for 2-in. (50-mm) liner thickness in Table 11. The dark line in each table indicates the separation between the low and high-frequency attenuation values. The high-frequency attenuation values are applicable to a maximum of 10 ft (3 m). Because of the differences between the manufacturers' materials, the calculated values might be reduced by 10% for critical applications. The attenuation values listed apply when flow effects are negligible, as is usually the case of air flow below 2000 fpm (10 m/s).

Table 11   Sound Attenuation in Straight Lined Sheet Metal Ducts of Rectangular Cross-Section in dB/ft (dB/0.3 m)
Lining Thickness: 2 in. (50 mm)[a]; No Airflow

Internal Cross-Sectional Dimensions		Octave Band Center Frequency (Hz)						
in.	(mm)	63	125	250	500	1000	2000	4000
4 × 4	(100 × 100)	.34	.93	2.56	7.02	19.23	10.08	3.50
4 × 6	(100 × 150)	.28	.78	2.13	5.85	16.03	8.26	3.13
4 × 8	(100 × 200)	.26	.70	1.92	5.26	14.42	6.45	2.57
4 × 10	(100 × 250)	.24	.65	1.79	4.91	13.46	5.02	2.07
6 × 6	(150 × 150)	.26	.72	1.97	5.40	14.81	7.50	3.17
6 × 10	(150 × 250)	.21	.58	1.58	4.32	11.85	5.67	2.67
6 × 12	(150 × 300)	.20	.54	1.48	4.05	11.11	4.80	2.33
6 × 18	(150 × 460)	.17	.48	1.31	3.60	8.80	2.95	1.51
8 × 8	(200 × 200)	.22	.60	1.64	4.49	12.31	6.08	2.95
8 × 12	(200 × 300)	.18	.50	1.36	3.74	10.26	4.98	2.64
8 × 16	(200 × 410)	.16	.45	1.23	3.37	9.23	3.89	2.17
8 × 24	(200 × 610)	.15	.40	1.09	2.99	5.68	2.39	1.41
10 × 10	(250 × 250)	.19	.52	1.42	3.89	10.66	5.17	2.79
10 × 16	(250 × 410)	.15	.42	1.15	3.16	8.66	4.04	2.41
10 × 20	(250 × 510)	.14	.39	1.06	2.92	7.22	3.30	2.05
10 × 30	(250 × 760)	.13	.34	.95	2.59	4.04	2.03	1.34
12 × 12	(300 × 300)	.17	.46	1.26	3.46	9.48	4.52	2.67
12 × 18	(300 × 460)	.14	.38	1.05	2.88	7.62	3.71	2.39
12 × 24	(300 × 610)	.13	.35	.95	2.59	5.47	2.89	1.97
12 × 36	(300 × 910)	.11	.31	.84	2.31	3.06	1.78	1.28
15 × 15	(380 × 380)	.15	.40	1.09	2.99	7.64	3.84	2.53
15 × 22	(380 × 560)	.12	.34	.92	2.52	5.55	3.20	2.29
15 × 30	(380 × 760)	.11	.30	.82	2.25	3.89	2.46	1.86
15 × 45	(380 × 1140)	.10	.27	.73	2.00	2.17	1.51	1.21
18 × 18	(460 × 460)	.13	.35	.97	2.66	5.79	3.37	2.42
18 × 28	(460 × 710)	.11	.29	.80	2.19	3.95	2.69	2.13
18 × 36	(460 × 910)	.10	.27	.73	2.00	2.94	2.15	1.78
18 × 54	(460 × 1370)	.09	.24	.65	1.78	1.65	1.32	1.16
24 × 24	(610 × 610)	.11	.29	.81	2.21	3.73	2.73	2.26
24 × 36	(610 × 910)	.09	.25	.67	1.84	2.65	2.24	2.02
24 × 48	(610 × 1220)	.08	.22	.61	1.66	1.90	1.75	1.66
24 × 72	(610 × 1830)	.07	.20	.54	1.48	1.06	1.07	1.08
30 × 30	(760 × 760)	.09	.25	.70	1.92	2.65	2.32	2.14
30 × 45	(760 × 1140)	.08	.21	.58	1.60	1.88	1.90	1.91
30 × 60	(760 × 1520)	.07	.19	.52	1.44	1.35	1.48	1.57
30 × 90	(760 × 2290)	.06	.17	.47	1.28	.76	.91	1.02
36 × 36	(910 × 910)	.08	.23	.62	1.70	2.01	2.03	2.04
36 × 54	(910 × 1370)	.07	.19	.52	1.42	1.42	1.66	1.83
36 × 72	(910 × 1830)	.06	.17	.47	1.28	1.02	1.30	1.50
36 × 108	(910 × 2740)	.06	.15	.41	1.14	.57	.80	.98
42 × 42	(1070 × 1070)	.07	.21	.56	1.54	1.59	1.81	1.97
42 × 64	(1070 × 1630)	.06	.17	.47	1.28	1.11	1.47	1.75
42 × 84	(1070 × 2130)	.06	.15	.42	1.16	.81	1.16	1.45
42 × 126	(1070 × 3200)	.05	.14	.38	1.03	.45	.71	.94
48 × 48	(1220 × 1220)	.07	.19	.52	1.42	1.30	1.65	1.90
48 × 72	(1220 × 1830)	.06	.16	.43	1.18	.92	1.35	1.70
48 × 96	(1220 × 2440)	.05	.14	.39	1.06	.66	1.05	1.40
48 × 144	(1220 × 3660)	.05	.13	.34	.94	.37	.65	.91

[a]Based on measurements of surface-coated duct liners of 1.5 lb/ft^3 (24 kg/m^3) density. For the specific materials tested, liner density had a minor effect.

Duct Silencers

Another method of obtaining duct attenuation either alone or with lined ducts, is the use of prefabricated silencers, sometimes called *sound traps,* which are available in various sizes, both rectangular and circular. The rectangular units are available in 3-ft (0.9-m), 5-ft (1.5-m), and 7-ft (2.1-m) lengths. The lengths of circular units are a function of diameter. These interrelated factors should be considered when selecting silencers: (1) required insertion loss, (2) static pressure drop, and (3) *self-noise,* i.e., the noise generated by air moving through the silencer passages. All three are related to the air velocity through the silencer; the insertion loss is inversely related to the velocity; the pressure drop and self-noise are directly related. Manufacturers' literature have further details.

Table 12   Estimated Attenuation of Elbows in Lined Duct Systems

Diameter		Octave Band Frequency, Hz							
Inches	(mm)	63	125	250	500	1000	2000	4000	8000
5 to 10	(125 to 250)	0	0	1	2	3	4	6	8
11 to 20	(260 to 510)	0	1	2	3	4	6	8	10
21 to 40	(520 to 1020)	1	2	3	4	5	6	8	10
41 to 80	(1030 to 2030)	2	3	4	5	6	8	10	12

Attenuation of Duct Fittings

Sound is attenuated by lined or unlined elbows and branch take-offs only when they are followed and/or preceded by at least three duct diameters of duct lining. Virtually no data are available on the attenuation at branch take-offs, and data available on the attenuation of elbows is based on limited testing.

Table 12 presents empirical data on the attenuation provided by duct elbows in lined duct systems.

Branch Power Division

At branch takeoffs, acoustic energy is distributed between the branch and the main duct in accordance with the ratio of the cross-sectional area of the branch to the total cross-sectional area of all of the ducts following the take-off. It can be assumed that the branch power division that occurs at a branch takeoff is proportional to the decimal equivalent of the ratio of the area of the branch to the area of all ducts leaving the takeoff and can be expressed by:

Branch Power Division (dB) =   (8)
10 log Branch Area/Total Area of all Ducts After Takeoff

Table 13 presents the branch power division for a number of branch area ratios.

Duct End Reflection Loss

When plane wave sound passes from a small space such as a duct into a large space the size of a room, a certain amount of sound is reflected back into the duct, significantly reducing low frequency sound. Unpublished research indicates, however, that this only occurs when the duct termination is preceded by a straight section of ductwork, 3 to 5 duct diameters long and without a diffuser or grille. Any terminal device directly attached to the duct and effective in diffusing the airflow reduces the end reflection loss.

End reflection loss should not be included in the attenuation of any system where linear diffusers are tapped directly into plenums, or where diffusers are connected to primary ductwork with curved elements (flexible ductwork), or where the distances between diffusers and the primary duct are short.

The attenuation available through end reflection loss may be

Table 13   Power Level Division at Branch Takeoffs

B/T	Division (dB)	B/T	Division (dB)
1.00	0	0.10	10
0.80	1	0.08	11
0.63	2	0.063	12
0.50	3	0.05	13
0.40	4	0.04	14
0.32	5	0.032	15
0.25	6	0.025	16
0.20	7	0.02	17
0.16	8	0.016	18
0.12	9	0.012	19

Table 14   End Reflection Loss[a]

Mean Duct Width		Octave-Band Center Frequency (Hz)				
in.	(mm)	63	125	250	500	1000
6	(150)	18dB	12dB	8dB	4dB	1dB
8	(200)	16	11	6	2	0
10	(250)	14	9	5	1	0
12	(300)	13	8	4	1	0
16	(400)	11	6	2	0	0
20	(500)	9	5	1	0	0
24	(600)	8	4	1	0	0
28	(700)	7	3	1	0	0
32	(800)	6	2	0	0	0
36	(900)	5	1	0	0	0
48	(1200)	4	1	0	0	0
72	(1800)	1	0	0	0	0

[a]Do not apply for linear diffusers or diffusers tapped directly into primary ductwork. If duct terminates in a diffuser, deduct at least 6 dB.

enough in critical situations to warrant designing the duct layout to maximize the loss. For instance, air can be dumped out of open ducts onto plaques suspended at least one duct diameter beneath the duct; a duct 3 to 5 diameters long can be connected to bar-type return air grilles (opposed blade dampers behind the bar grille will probably negate end reflection); straight ductwork 3 to 5 diameters long can be connected to architectural openings.

Low frequency attenuation from end reflection loss can easily equal 50 to 75 ft (15 to 23 m) of lined ductwork or a 7-ft (2-m) long standard pressure drop silencer at low frequencies. Expense and space is conserved when it is part of the total building design. Table 14 presents the optimal reflection losses for the configuration shown.

AIRFLOW NOISE

Aerodynamic Noise Generated at Duct Fittings (Ver 1984)

Although fans are a major source of the sound to be considered when designing quiet duct systems, they are not the only source. Aerodynamic noise is generated at elbows, dampers, branch take-offs, air modulation units, sound traps and other duct elements. The sound power levels in each octave band depend on the geometry of the device, the turbulence of the airflow and the airflow velocity. The intensity of flow-generated noise is proportional to between the fifth and sixth power of the local flow velocity in the duct. Therefore, a small inaccuracy in predicting the local flow velocity can result in a serious noise problem. Aerodynamic noise problems can be avoided by sizing ductwork so that velocities are very low, avoiding abrupt changes in area or direction and attenuating noise generated at the fittings with sufficient sound attenuation between the fitting and the terminal device.

Sizing ductwork for low velocities is both expensive and space-consumptive. In actual practice, there is often insufficient space to allow smooth airflow, abrupt changes in area and direction and ideal duct lengths between fittings and terminal devices. There is an unlimited number of geometries for duct elements and attempts to develop a universal law for aerodynamic noise generation have proven futile. Estimating procedures for *certain* types of elements are presented below.

Sound Generated at Dampers, Elbows and Junctions

Octave band sound power levels generated at single- and multi-blade dampers, with and without turning vanes, and at junctions can be predicted by following this generalized equation:

$$PWL_{f_o} = K + 10 \log f_o + 50 \log U +$$
$$10 \log S + 10 \log D + Special\ Parameters \quad (9)$$

where

f_o = octave band center frequency, Hz
K = characteristic spectrum of the fitting, based on Strouhal Number
U = velocity factor; the velocity in the constricted part of the flow field or the velocity in the branch duct, fpm (m/s)
S = cross-sectional area of the duct in which the dampers are installed, cross-sectional area of the elbow or cross-sectional area of the branch duct at a junction, ft^2 (m^2)
D = duct height normal to the damper axis, the cord length of a typical turning vane, height of the elbow or in the case of junctions, $D = \sqrt{4\ s/\pi}$, ft (m)

Special Parameters have the following values:

Dampers: -107 (-18 for SI calculations) dB

Elbows with Turning Vanes: $10 \log n -107$ (-18 for SI calculations) dB

where n = the number of turning vanes

For **Elbows Without Turning Vanes and Junctions:** -107 (0 for SI calculations) $+ \Delta r + \Delta T$

where Δr is a correction for rounding, and ΔT is a correction for upstream turbulence

Prior to solving Eq. (9), it is necessary to perform the following preliminary calculations.

Preliminary Calculations for Dampers and Elbows With Turning Vanes

1. Determine Pressure Loss Coefficient, C

$$C = 15.9 \cdot 10^6 \frac{\Delta P}{(Q/S)^2} \quad (10)$$

For SI units,

$$C = 1.67 \frac{\Delta P}{(Q/S)^2} \quad (10\ SI)$$

where

ΔP = pressure drop across fitting, in. of water (Pa)
Q = volume flow rate, cfm (m^3/s)

2. Determine Blockage Factor, BF

For multi-blade dampers and elbows with turning vanes

$$BF = 0.5\ \text{if}\ C = 1$$

$$BF = \frac{\sqrt{C} - 1}{C - 1}\ \text{for}\ C \neq 1$$

for single blade dampers

$$BF = \frac{\sqrt{C} - 1}{C - 1}\ \text{if}\ C < 4$$

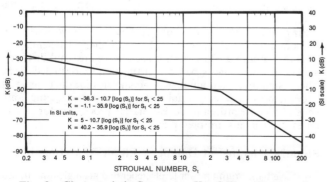

Fig. 8   Characteristic Spectrum, K, of Flow-Generated Noise of Dampers to be Used with Eq. (7)

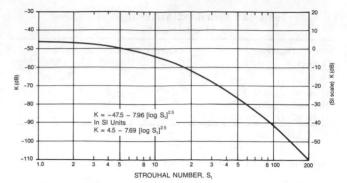

Fig. 9   Characteristic Spectrum, K, of Flow-Generated Noise for Bends Fitted with Curved-Blade Turning Vanes

$$BF = 0.68C^{-0.15} - 0.22\ \text{if}\ C > 4$$

3. Determine Velocity Term, U

$$U = Q/S\ (BF) \quad (13)$$

4. Determine Strouhal Number, S_t

$$S_t = 60\ f_o D/U \quad (14)$$

For SI units,

$$S_t = f_o D/U \quad (14\ SI)$$

5. Enter Figure 8 to determine the characteristic spectrum for dampers. Enter Figure 9 to determine the characteristic spectrum for elbows with turning vanes.

Preliminary Calculations for Elbows and Junctions Without Splitter Dampers

1. Determine Velocity Factor, M

$$M = U_M/U_B \quad (15)$$

where

U_M = velocity in main duct, fpm (m/s)
U_B = velocity in branch duct, fpm (m/s)

2. Determine Strouhal Number

$$S_t = 60\ f_o D/U_B \quad (16)$$

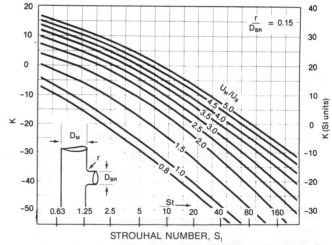

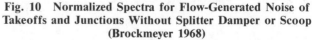

Fig. 10   Normalized Spectra for Flow-Generated Noise of Takeoffs and Junctions Without Splitter Damper or Scoop (Brockmeyer 1968)

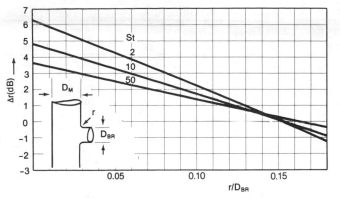

Fig. 11   Rounding Correction (Brockmeyer 1968)

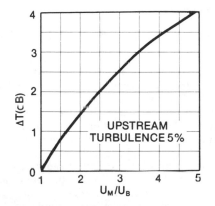

**Fig. 12   Correction for Upstream Turbulence
(Brockmeyer 1968)**

For SI units,

$$S_t = f_0 D/U_B \qquad (16\ SI)$$

3. Enter Figure 10 to determine the characteristic spectrum, K.

4. Determine the rounding correction from Figure 11. If the elbow is not rounded, then $r/D_B = 0$.

5. Determine the correction for upstream turbulence, T, from Figure 12. This correction should be applied only if duct upstream has dampers, turns or takeoffs within a length of 5 main duct diameters.

Prediction of Noise Along Other Branches at Junctions

Knowing the octave band sound power level at a specific branch of a junction makes it possible to predict the flow generated noise along other branches or in the main duct, using the relationships shown in Table 15.

Table 15   Prediction of Flow Generated Noise for Junctions and Turns

X Junction	$PWL_{BRANCH} = PWL_U(m = U_{m_1}/U_B)$ $PWL_{MAIN} = PWL_{BRANCH} + 20\log\dfrac{D_M}{D_B} + 3$ D_M = Equivalent diameter of Main Duct D_B = Equivalent diameter of Branch Duct
T Junction	$PWL_{BRANCH} = PWL_U(m = 1)$ $PWL_{MAIN} = PWL_U(m = 1) + 3$
90° Bend	$PWL = PWL_U(m = 1)$
90° Branch Takeoff	$PWL_{BRANCH} = PWL_U(m = U_{m_1}/U_B)$ $PWL_{MAIN} = PWL_{BRANCH} + 20\log\dfrac{D_M}{D_B}$

Example 5: Determine the sound power level of a multi-blade damper positioned in a 12-in. by 12-in. duct that drops the pressure by 0.5 in. of water at a volume flow rate of 4000 cfm.

1. Total pressure loss coefficient, C

$$C = 15.9 \cdot 10^6 \frac{0.5}{\left(\frac{4000}{1}\right)^2} = 0.5$$

2. Blockage Factor, BF

$$BF = \frac{\sqrt{0.5} - 1}{0.5 - 1} = 0.586$$

3. Velocity Factor, U

$$U = \frac{4000}{1\,(0.586)} = 6826\ fpm$$

4. The remaining steps are tabulated in Table 16a.

Example 6: Predict the octave band sound power levels in the branch duct and main duct described below. The rectangular main duct is 12 in. by 36 in., and the volume flow rate in the main duct is 12,000 cfm. The branch duct is 10 in. by 10 in. and its flow rate is 1200 cfm. The 90 degree turn from the main duct to the branch duct has no rounding.

1. Area Ratio $\dfrac{S_M}{S_B} = \dfrac{1 \cdot 3}{(10 \cdot 10)/144} = 4.32$

Table 16a   Sample Calculations for Example 5 (Multi-Blade Damper)

f_o	Octave Band Center Frequency (Hz)								
	31	**63**	**125**	**250**	**500**	**1K**	**2K**	**4K**	**8K**
S_t	0.276	0.55	1.1	2.2	4.4	8.8	17.6	35.3	70.6
K	−30.3	−33.5	−36.7	−40	−43.2	−46.4	−49.6	−57.6	−67.5
$10\log f_o$	15	18	21	24	27	30	33	36	39
$50\log U$	191.8	191.8	191.8	191.8	191.8	191.8	191.8	191.8	191.8
$10\log S$	0	0	0	0	0	0	0	0	0
$10\log D$	0	0	0	0	0	0	0	0	0
Constant Factor (I-P units)	−107	−107	−107	−107	−107	−107	−107	−107	−107
$PWL(f_o)$	69.5	69.3	69.1	68.8	68.6	68.4	68.2	63.2	56.3

Table 16b   Sample Calculations for Example 6 (Junction)

	Octave Band Center Frequency, f/Hz								
	31	63	125	250	500	1K	2K	4K	8K
S_t	1	2	4	8	16	32	64	128	256
$10 \log f_o$	15	18	21	24	27	30	33	36	39
K	+1.0	−3.0	−8.0	−14.5	−21	−28	−36.5	−44	−53.5
$50 \log U_B$	162	162	162	162	162	162	162	162	162
$10 \log S_B D_B$	−1.8	−1.8	−1.8	−1.8	−1.8	−1.8	−1.8	−1.8	−1.8
Δr	7	6.5	6	5	4.5	4	3.5	0	0
ΔT	—	—	—	—	—	—	—	—	—
Constant Factor	−107	−107	−107	−107	−107	−107	−107	−107	−107
Branch Duct PWL (f_o)	76.2	74.7	72.2	67.7	63.7	59.2	53.2	45.2	38.7
Correction to Branch PWL to get to Main Duct PWL, $10 \log S_M/S_B$	+6.3	+6.3	+6.3	+6.3	+6.3	+6.3	+6.3	+6.3	+6.3
Main Duct PWL	82.5	81.0	78.5	74.0	70.0	65.5	59.5	51.5	45.0

2. Velocity Ratio = M = $\dfrac{U_M}{U_B} = \dfrac{12{,}000/3}{1200\,(144)/(10 \cdot 10)} = 2.3$

3. Velocity in Branch = $U_B = \dfrac{1200}{(10 \cdot 10)/144} = 1728$ ft/min

4. Strouhal Number (Eq. 14)

$$= S_t = 60\, f_o 0.94/1728 = 0.0326\, f_o$$

5. The remaining steps are tabulated in Table 16b.

Aerodynamically Generated Duct Rumble

Aerodynamic noise generated in ductwork near fans can result in duct-radiated rumble. The most troublesome frequency region is usually below 250 Hz, often extending down through the 31.5 and 16 Hz octave bands. Once generated, sound energy in these low frequencies is not easily attenuated, and it is readily transmitted up and down the airstream and through the duct walls. Add-on devices such as silencers or lagging are inefficient at low frequencies, and have limited effectiveness. The most effective treatment is to increase the duct stiffness, by using circular ductwork. Rectangular ductwork is troublesome because it is less stiff than circular ductwork. Further information is available in the section on "Transmission Loss Through Duct Walls."

Providing good airflow conditions at or near the fan is the most effective method of avoiding possible rumble conditions. Figure 13 shows various outlet conditions and their classifications with regard to possible rumble development. Ebbing et al. (1978) and Harold (1986) have more details on the subject.

Noise and turbulence inside a duct also cause the walls to vibrate and radiate noise to surrounding spaces. Rectangular ducts are more susceptible to this than are round ducts, and the problem is a function of both duct size and velocity. To prevent excessive noise radiation from duct walls, all fittings should be smooth and designed to avoid abrupt changes of direction or velocity. Whenever possible, medium- and high-velocity ducts and terminal boxes should be located in non-critical areas (e.g., above corridors).

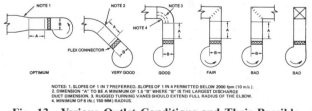

NOTES: 1. SLOPES OF 1 IN 7 PREFERRED. SLOPES OF 1 IN 4 PERMITTED BELOW 2000 fpm (10 m/s).
2. DIMENSION "A" TO BE A MINIMUM OF 1.5 "B" WHERE "B" IS THE LARGEST DISCHARGE DUCT DIMENSION. 3. RUGGED TURNING VANES SHOULD EXTEND FULL RADIUS OF THE ELBOW.
4. MINIMUM OF 6 IN.(150 MM) RADIUS.

Fig. 13   Various Outlet Conditions and Their Possible Rumble Developments

NOISE GENERATED BY AIR TERMINALS

Air terminals, devices used to deliver air into a space and to control air volume and/or temperature by directional vanes, dampers or valves, heat exchange, and fan control fall into two categories. The first category, *air terminal devices*, consists of diffusers, grilles, and registers that radiate sound directly into an air-conditioned space. They allow no opportunity for sound attenuation along the duct path, thus requiring selection for noise generation that meets the established room criterion values as well as other factors. The second category, terminal valves, consists of terminal boxes and air valves that are separated from the space they serve by ductwork, ceiling plenums, or ceilings. These devices are selected so that their sound power ratings do not exceed the sum of the established room criterion and the attenuation provided between the air-conditioned room and the device.

While fan-generated noise is most critical in the low frequency bands, many air terminals such as diffusers, registers, grilles, and terminal boxes without fans do not contribute greatly to low frequency noise levels. In these cases, an allowance for fan noise may be unnecessary in selecting the terminals. However, both fan and terminal unit noise must be considered to obtain the balanced sound spectrum implied by the RC curves.

Air Terminal Device Installation Factors

The sound level output of an air diffuser or grille depends not only on the air quantity and the size and design of the outlet, but also on the air approach configuration (Waeldner 1975). Manufacturers' ratings apply only to outlets installed as recommended, i.e., with a uniform air velocity distribution throughout the neck of the unit. Poor approach conditions can easily increase sound levels by 10 to 20 dB above the manufacturer's ratings (see Figures 14 and 15). Poor approach conditions can sometimes be overcome with properly adjusted accessories such as turning vanes or equalizing grids. However, using these in critical, low noise level projects should be avoided.

Flexible duct is often used to correct misalignment between the supply duct and the diffuser ceiling location. A misalignment or offset that exceeds one-fourth of a diffuser diameter in a diffuser collar length of two diameters significantly increases the diffuser sound level (see Figure 15). There is no appreciable change in diffuser performance with an offset less than one-eighth the length of the collar.

When a volume control damper is installed close to an air outlet to achieve system balance, the acoustic performance of the air outlet must be based not only on the air volume han-

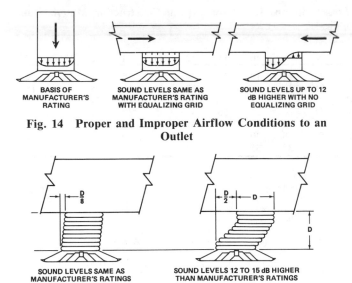

Fig. 14 Proper and Improper Airflow Conditions to an Outlet

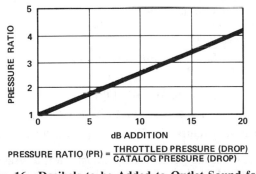

Fig. 15 Effect of Proper and Improper Alignment of Flexible Duct Connector

dled, but also on the magnitude of the pressure drop across the damper. The sound level change is proportional to the Pressure Ratio (PR) of the throttled pressure drop to the catalog pressure drop of the outlet, as shown in Figure 16.

In acoustically critical spaces (such as concert halls), it is almost always necessary to avoid using balancing dampers, equalizers and so forth directly behind terminal devices or open end ducts. They should be located five to 10 duct diameters from the opening, followed by lined duct to the terminal or open duct end.

Linear diffusers are often installed in distribution plenums that permit installing the damper at the plenum entrance. The further a damper is installed from the outlet, the lower the resultant sound level will be (see Table 17).

Fig. 16 Decibels to be Added to Outlet Sound for Throttled Damper Close to the Outlet

$$\text{PRESSURE RATIO (PR)} = \frac{\text{THROTTLED PRESSURE (DROP)}}{\text{CATALOG PRESSURE (DROP)}}$$

Terminal Valve Selection and Installation

Acoustic concerns for terminal valves include noise from the device that radiates through the ceiling material, and sound that discharges into the ductwork upstream and downstream from the device, arriving at the occupied space by way of the plenum and/or intervening ductwork. Most manufacturers provide radiated and discharge noise data, and use of ARI/ADC Standard 880 should improve the reliability of these data. However, until a reliable applications standard is widely adopted, this chapter can help to predict terminal valve noise levels in typical rooms (Blazier 1981).

Table 17 Decibels to be Added to Diffuser Sound Rating to Allow Throttling of Volume Damper

Pressure Ratio (PR) = Throttled Pressure / Minimum Pressure						
Location of Volume Damper	1.5	2	2.5	3	4	6
(A) OB damper in neck of linear diffuser	5	9	12	15	18	24
(B) OB damper in plenum side inlet	2	3	4	5	6	9
(C) Damper in supply duct at least 5 ft (1.5 m) from plenum	0	0	0	2	3	5

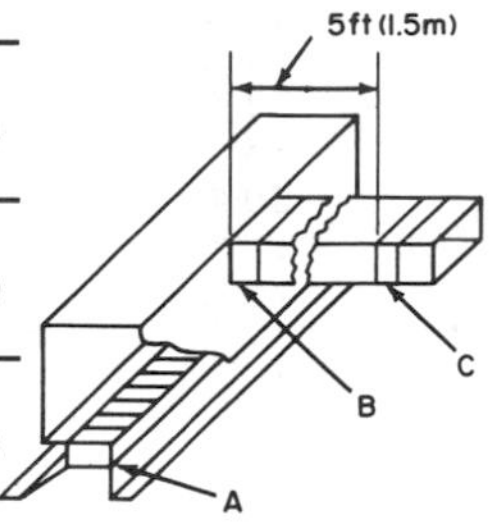

Fan-Powered Terminal Valves

A special terminal valve cycles an internal fan to modulate temperature by cycling. In this way, heated air from the ceiling plenum mixes with the primary air to control the delivered air temperature. In addition to the potential acoustic problems described in the preceding section, these devices can transmit excess fan noise into the occupied space by radiating noise into the ceiling plenum as well as along the duct path. The lack of a standard for testing fan-powered terminal valves makes evaluation of their sound characteristics especially difficult, but the following general guidelines can be used in selection and installation to lessen the problems.

1. It is difficult to achieve NC or RC levels below 40 where fan-powered terminal valves are located immediately above or in a ceiling plenum shared by an air-conditioned space. These units should not be placed above or near noise-sensitive spaces. If this cannot be done, the system designer should consider inherently quieter VAV system concepts.
2. Return air openings in acoustical ceilings should not be located near fan-powered terminal valves. This precaution prevents the sound radiated from the valve from having a direct acoustical path to the listener.
3. Where possible, fan-powered terminal valves should be located above non-sensitive spaces such as corridors, utility rooms, toilets, and service closets.
4. Intermittent fan operation of parallel fan-powered terminal valves is often more annoying than a design with constant fan operation.
5. Fan speeds should be the minimum for required airflow. However, the system designer should use judgment in the catalog data as it pertains to fan speed.
6. Static pressure at the valve should be as low as possible.
7. Installing lined duct elbows (boots) on the return air openings to fan-powered terminal valves can attenuate some fan noise, especially when the boots point up toward the structural deck.
8. It may be possible to reduce sound levels radiated by the bottoms of the boxes by damping or stiffening the large radiating surfaces.
9. Where fan-powered terminal valves are located above noise-sensitive spaces such as conference rooms, private offices, and classrooms, it may be necessary to control noise radiated by the valves with drywall ceilings.

DUCTBORNE CROSSTALK

Sound transmitted between rooms by way of the duct system is called ductborne crosstalk, and is controlled by using duct

Table 18 Transmission Loss (Columns 1-15) and Insertion Loss (Columns 16,17) for Typical Construction Materials and Assemblies[a]

Octave Band Center Frequency, Hz	1	2	3	4	5	6	7	8	9	10	11	12	13	14	15	16	17
63[b]	32	34	29	31	32	12	25	25	11	12	25	23	17	15	15	1	9
125	34	36	32	33	34	17	36	36	16	16	41	29	23	18	18	2	15
250	35	38	33	35	36	34	43	47	23	23	47	31	33	21	24	4	20
500	37	43	34	36	39	35	50	51	27	27	56	31	35	39	35	8	25
1000	42	50	37	41	45	42	50	57	32	32	65	31	35	38	45	9	31
2000	49	56	42	48	46	38	44	57	28	30	68	39	33	49	53	9	33
4000	55	61	49	54	40	44	55	62	32	35	69	43	37	55	58	14	27

Transmission Loss:

1 = 4 in. (100 mm) dense concrete or solid concrete block [48 lb/ft² (235 kg/m²)]
2 = 8 in. (200 mm) dense concrete or solid concrete block [96 lb/ft² (475 kg/m²)]
3 = 4 in. (100 mm) hollow core dense aggregate concrete block [28 lb/ft² (135 kg/m²)]
4 = 8 in. (200 mm) hollow core dense aggregate concrete block [44 lb/ft² (215 kg/m²)]
5 = 12 in. (300 mm) hollow core dense aggregate concrete block [60 lb/ft² (300 kg/m²)]
6 = Standard drywall partition, 5/8 in. (16 mm) gypsum board on both sides of 2 × 4 in. (600 × 1200 mm) wood studs
7 = Standard drywall partition, two layers of 5/8 in. (16 mm) gypsum board on each side of 3-5/8 in. (90 mm) metal studs
8 = Standard drywall partition, two layers of 5/8 in. (16 mm) gypsum board on each side of 3-5/8 in. (90 mm) metal studs, 1-1/2 sound attenuation blanket in wall cavity

9 = 1/2 in. (13 mm) plate glass
10 = Double glazing, two 1/2 in. (13 mm) panes, 1/2 in. (13 mm) air space
11 = Roof construction, 6 in. (150 mm) thick, 20 gauge [0.0396 in.(1.006 mm)] steel deck with 4 in. (100 mm) lightweight concrete topping, 5/8 in. (16 mm) gypsum board ceiling on resilient hangers
12 = 1-3/4 in. (45 mm) thick solid core wood door
13 = 1-3/4 in. (45 mm) thick insulated hollow 16 gauge [0.0635 in. (1.613 mm)] steel door with weatherstripping
14 = Acoustic equipment housing, 20 gauge [0.0396 in. (1.006 mm)] steel outer shell, 2 in. (50 mm) thick acoustic insulation, 22 gauge [0.0336 in. (0.8534 mm)] perforated inner shell
15 = Acoustic equipment housing, 20 gauge [0.0396 in. (1.006 mm)] steel outer shell, 4 in. (100 mm) thick acoustic insulation, 22 gauge [0.0336 in. (0.8534 mm)] perforated inner shell
Insertion Loss:
16 = Typical mineral fiber lay-in acoustical ceiling
17 = Typical gypsum board ceiling

[a]Compiled from several literature sources.

[b]Some of the values for this octave band are extrapolated.

linings, splitters, prefabricated silencers, and devious duct routings. Generally, the requisite duct attenuation to prevent crosstalk is about 5 dB greater than the transmission loss (TL) of the intervening architectural construction, but if ceiling heights, sound-absorbing treatments, or background noise levels are radically different between source and receiving rooms, the needed duct attenuation may be even greater. U.S. Gypsum (1971) and Hedeen et al. (1980) list transmission loss ratings for typical architectural constructions, and Table 18 shows a few ratings for more frequently encountered materials or construction.

In addition to duct paths, crosstalk can also occur through air plenums, underwindow units (fan coil, induction), or enclosures that extend from one room to another. Therefore, such devices should not be designed to extend through partitions, and all openings around pipes and ducts should be tightly sealed to prevent sound leakage between rooms. In some cases, it may be necessary to extend walls full-height or provide barriers above the ceiling.

TRANSMISSION LOSS THROUGH DUCT WALLS

Noise radiated through duct walls can be a problem if the noise traveling in the duct (usually fan or flow noise) is not adequately attenuated before the duct runs over an occupied space (Cummings 1985). This transmission path is called "breakout." Noise can also be transmitted into the duct in one space and radiated from the duct to another space. Transmission into a duct is called "breakin."

Transmission Loss of Rectangular Ducts

Breakout Transmission Loss. The breakout transmission loss (TL_{out}) of duct walls is defined as:

$$TL_{out} = 10 \log \left(\frac{W_i}{A_i} \frac{A_o}{W_r} \right) \text{ dB} \qquad (17)$$

for a duct of length L and cross-section ab (a being the larger dimension) as shown in Figure 17. In Eq. (17), W_i is the sound power in the duct and W_r is the sound power radiated from the walls. In this case,

$$A_i = ab \qquad (18)$$

$$A_o = 2L(a + b) \qquad (19)$$

The cross-sectional area of the inside of duct (A_i) is associated with W_i and the surface area of the outside of the duct (A_o) is associated with W_r. TL_{out} in Eq. (17) is a normalized value of transmission loss that accounts for the ratio A_o/A_i associated with W_r and W_i. To obtain W_r, Eq. (17) may be rewritten as follows:

$$L_{w_r} = L_{w_i} + 10 \log (A_o/A_i) - TL_{out} \qquad (19 \text{ a})$$

where

$$L_{w_r} = 10 \log (W_r \cdot 10^{12}) \qquad (19 \text{ b})$$

and

$$L_{w_i} = 10 \log (W_i \cdot 10^{12}) \qquad (19 \text{ c})$$

Table 19 lists values for TL_{out} in Eq. (19a) for selected duct sizes.

Since the sound power within the duct slowly decreases along the length of the duct, the actual TL_{out} (as defined above) will

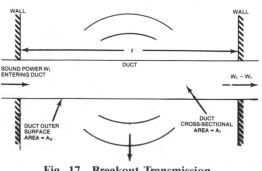

Fig. 17 Breakout Transmission

Table 19 TL_{out} versus Frequency for Various Rectangular Ducts

Duct Size			Octave Band Center Frequency, Hz							
in. (mm)	Guage (mm)		63	125	250	500	1K	2K	4K	8K
12 × 12 (300 × 300)	24 ga (0.7)		21	24	27	30	33	36	41	45
12 × 24 (300 × 600)	24 ga (0.7)		19	22	25	28	31	35	41	45
12 × 48 (300 × 1200)	22 ga (0.85)		19	22	25	28	31	37	43	45
24 × 24 (600 × 600)	22 ga (0.85)		20	23	26	29	32	37	43	45
24 × 48 (600 × 1200)	20 ga (1.0)		20	23	26	29	31	39	45	45
48 × 48 (1200 × 1200)	18 ga (1.3)		21	24	27	30	35	41	45	45
48 × 96 (1200 × 2400)	18 ga (1.3)		19	22	25	29	35	41	45	45

NOTE: The data are from tests on 20 ft (6 m) long ducts, but the TL values are for ducts of the cross section shown regardless of length.

increase slightly, for any type of duct, as the length increases. This effect does not apply to the prediction method and is usually minimal.

The transmission loss curve can be divided into two regions: one where the plane mode transmission within the duct predominates and another where multi-mode transmission is dominant. The limiting frequency between these two regions is given by:

$$f_L = \frac{24134}{(ab)^{1/2}} \tag{20}$$

where a and b are in inches. Or in SI units:

$$f_L = \frac{6.13 \cdot 10^5}{(ab)^{1/2}} \tag{20 SI}$$

where a and b are in mm.

For $f < f_L$, the plane mode breakout TL may be calculated from the formula

$$TL_{out} = 10 \log \left(\frac{fq^2}{a+b} \right) + 17 \text{ dB} \tag{21}$$

where q is the mass/unit area of the duct walls in lb_m/ft^2 or kg/m^2 and f is the frequency in Hz; here, a and b are in inches or mm. The minimum possible value of TL_{out} occurs where $W_r = W_i$ and a lower limit is thus imposed on TL_{out}:

$$TL_{out}(\text{min}) = 10 \log [24L(1/a + 1/b)] \tag{22}$$

where L is in feet and a,b are in inches. Or in SI units:

$$TL_{out}(\text{min}) = 10 \log [1000L (1/a + 1/b)] \tag{22 SI}$$

where L is in metres and a and b are in mm.

When $f \geqslant f_L$, the multimode TL may be found from the formula

$$TL_{out} = 20 \log [qf] \quad 31 \text{ dB} \tag{23}$$

where again q is in lb_m/ft^2 and f is in Hz. Or is SI units:

$$TL_{out} = 20 \log [qf] - 45 \text{ dB} \tag{23 SI}$$

To plot TL_{out} over the entire frequency range of interest on semi-log paper, draw a base line of TL_{out}(min) from Eq. (22) parallel to the (logarithmic) frequency axis. Next, draw a curve of Eq. (24) down to the base line and up to a frequency f_L.

Erase the portion of the base line to the right of the point where it meets this curve. Draw a curve of Eq. (23), from f_L upward. The curves from Eq. (21) and (23) generally do not meet at f_L and they should be joined by a vertical line. The wave coincidence effect and acoustic "leaks" at seams and joints combine to limit the high frequency TL to about 45 dB, so finally the upper portion of the curve should be leveled off at this value, in a horizontal line. Figure 18 shows the general form of the resultant curve.

Table 19 shows some values of TL_{out}, calculated according to the above scheme for a range of duct sizes.

This method is based on a mass law impedance for the duct walls and is only valid for $f > 28,570 \sqrt{t}/a$ (144 000 $\sqrt{t}/a$) [t being the duct wall thickness in inches (mm) and a the larger transverse wall dimension in inches (mm)]; this frequency limit applies to galvanized steel ducts. Below this frequency, the actual TL will exhibit damped resonances, which produce progressively more pronounced maxima and minima in the TL curve as the frequency falls. The present method still predicts the overall behavior however, and generally gives somewhat conservative predictions at low frequencies. The effects of "wave coincidence" are not explicitly included in the prediction scheme (aside from the 45 dB limit on TL_{out}) but these would occur, for ordinary ductwork, at frequencies above the range of interest.

Duct fittings such as elbows will not materially affect the TL, but should be included in the effective radiating surface area when the actual sound power radiated from a length of ductwork is being calculated.

Breakin Transmission Loss. Figure 19 shows the breakin configuration. The incident sound power from the surrounding space is W_i, and sound power W_t travels out along the duct in *both* directions, as shown. The breakin TL can be defined as

$$TL_{in} = 10 \log \left(\frac{W_i}{2 W_t} \right) \tag{24}$$

which is the logarithmic ratio of the total incident sound power, W_i, to the total transmitted power, $2 W_t$. To obtain sound power, W_t, transmitted down a duct in a specified direction, Eq. (24) must be rewritten as follows:

$$L_{w_t} = L_{w_i} - TL_{in} - 3 \tag{24a}$$

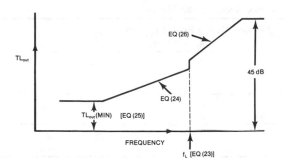

Fig. 18 Composite Curve of TL_{out} for a Rectangular Duct

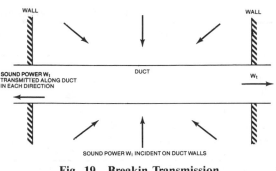

Fig. 19   Breakin Transmission

This definition is more in line with the common definition of the TL of a partition than that of the breakout TL. An equivalent definition cannot be used in the latter case because there is no well-defined "incident"—as opposed to "reflected"—sound power. The incident sound power level (L_w^i) may be related to the sound pressure level in the reverberant field (L_p^i) as follows,

$$L_w^i = 10 \log \left(\frac{W_i}{10^{-12}} \right) = L_p^{rev} + 10 \log A_o - 16 \text{ dB} \qquad (25)$$

where W_i is in watts and A_o is in ft². Or in SI units:

$$L_w^i = L_p^{rev} + 10 \log A_o - 6 \text{ dB} \qquad (25 \text{ SI})$$

where A_o is in m².

The breakin TL may be calculated in terms of TL_{out} (since it is difficult to calculate directly) by one of two formulae. The first of these applies at frequencies below the "cut-off" frequency, f_1, for the lowest acoustic cross-mode in the duct, and the second at frequencies above f_1. For rectangular ducts this cut-off frequency is given by

$$f_1 = 6764/a \qquad (26)$$

where a (the larger duct dimension) is in inches. Or in SI units:

$$f_1 = 1.718 \cdot 10^5/a \qquad (26 \text{ SI})$$

where a is in mm.

For $f \lesssim f_1$, TL_{in} equals the larger of the following:

$$TL_{out} - 4 - 10 \log \left(\frac{a}{b} \right) + 20 \log \left(\frac{f}{f_1} \right) \qquad (27a)$$

or

$$10 \log [12L(1/a + 1/b)] \qquad (27b)$$

where L is in feet and a, b in inches. In SI units for $f \lesssim f_1$, TL_{in} equals the larger of the following:

$$TL_{out} - 4 - 10 \log (a/b) + 20 \log (f/f_1) \qquad (27a \text{ SI})$$

or

$$10 \log [1000L (1/a + 1/b)] \qquad (27b \text{ SI})$$

where L is in metres and a and b are in mm.

For $f > f_1$, TL_{in} is given by

$$TL_{in} = TL_{out} - 3 \text{ dB} \qquad (28)$$

Table 20 shows a series of calculated values of TL_{in}, corresponding to the ducts listed in Table 19.

Transmission Loss of Circular Ducts

Breakout Transmission Loss. Simple prediction methods for the TL of circular ducts can disagree with actual measurements by 20 to 30 dB at low frequencies and are not considered accurate enough to be discussed in this chapter. As an alternate to a prediction scheme, general comments and data on selected ducts are given.

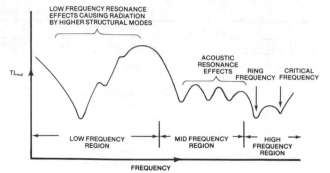

Fig. 20   General Form of TL_{out} Curve for a Circular Duct

An ideal circular duct has a high TL at low frequencies because uniform internal sound pressure fluctuations cause a uniform "breathing" mode in the pipe walls that present a high impedence to the sound waves. Measurements of actual ducts show a much lower TL than that predicted for ideal ducts at low frequencies, although the difference decreases at high frequencies.

This TL deficit can be explained by small departures from circularity in the ducts, which cause higher structural modes to be excited in the duct walls, even with plane wave transmission within the duct. Spiral wound ducts are more nearly circular than long seam ducts and may have a significantly higher TL at low frequencies. However, both types of duct exhibit similar behavior at high frequences. Figure 20 shows the general form of the TL curve for typical circular air conditioning ducts. At very low frequencies, the TL continues to rise as the frequency falls. This frequency region is of little interest since it is below 50 Hz. At frequencies below 100 Hz, there is low frequency resonance controlled region where the higher structural modes radiate sound. As the frequency rises, however, these modes radiate with decreasing efficiency as the mode order increases and the TL rises to a peak. The TL then begins to fall and has a series of peaks and troughs corresponding to the acoustic modal resonances in the duct. This continues until the *ring frequency* is reached. At this point, the entire duct cross-section exhibits a resonance phenomenon of almost uniform expansion and contraction. At an even higher frequency, the wave coincidence effect causes a further dip. The TL rises above this in a manner similar to that of a flat plate of the same material.

Although the TL curve has a complicated structure, it is highest at "low" frequencies. The region where the TL has its maximum value (discounting the very low frequency rise) is between 50 and 300 Hz, depending on the duct size; here the TL can be 30 dB or more higher than that of a rectangular duct. It is also in this region that internal sound power levels tend to be highest. In this important respect, circular ducts are far superior to either rectangular or flat oval ducts.

Table 20 TL_{in} versus Frequency for Various Rectangular Ducts

Duct Size			Octave Band Center Frequency, Hz							
in.	(mm)	Gauge (mm)	63	125	250	500	1K	2K	4K	8K
12 × 12	(300 × 300)	24 ga (0.7)	16	16	16	25	30	33	38	42
12 × 24	(300 × 600)	24 ga (0.7)	15	15	17	25	28	32	38	42
12 × 48	(300 × 1200)	22 ga (0.85)	14	14	22	25	28	34	40	42
24 × 24	(600 × 600)	22 ga (0.85)	13	13	21	26	29	34	40	42
24 × 48	(600 × 1200)	20 ga (1.0)	12	15	23	26	28	36	42	42
48 × 48	(1200 × 1200)	18 ga (1.3)	10	19	24	27	32	38	42	42
48 × 96	(1200 × 2400)	18 ga (1.3)	11	19	22	26	32	38	42	42

NOTE: The data are from tests on 20 ft (6 m) long ducts, but the TL values are for ducts of the cross section shown regardless of length.

Table 21 TL_{out} versus Frequency for Various Circular Ducts[a]

Duct Size and Type	Octave Band Center Frequency, Hz							
	63	125	250	500	1K	2K	4K	8K
8 in.(200 mm) dia., [26 ga (0.022 in.)(0.55 mm)] long seam, length = 15 ft (4.5 m)	>45	(53)	55	52	44	35	34	26
14 in.(350 mm) dia., [24 ga (0.028 in.)(0.7 mm)] long seam, length = 15 ft (4.5 m)	>50	60	54	36	34	31	25	38
22 in.(550 mm) dia., [22 ga (0.034 in.)(0.85 mm)] long seam, length = 15 ft (4.5 m)	>47	53	37	33	33	27	25	43
32 in.(800 mm) dia., [22 ga (0.034 in.)(0.85 mm)] long seam, length = 15 ft (4.5 m)	(51)	46	26	26	24	22	38	43
8 in.(200 mm) dia., [26 ga (0.022 in.)(0.55 mm)] spiral wound, length = 10 ft (3 m)	>48	>64	>75	>72	56	56	46	29
14 in.(350 mm) dia., [26 ga (0.022 in.)(0.55 mm)] spiral wound, length = 10 ft (3 m)	>43	>53	55	33	34	35	25	40
26 in.(650 mm) dia., [24 ga (0.028 in.)(0.7 mm)] spiral wound, length = 10 ft (3 m)	>45	50	26	26	25	22	36	43
26 in.(650 mm) dia., [16 ga (0.064 in.)(1.6 mm)] spiral wound, length = 10 ft (3 m)	>48	>53	36	32	32	28	41	36
32 in.(800 mm) dia., [22 ga (0.034 in.)(0.85 mm)] spiral wound, length = 10 ft (3 m)	>43	42	28	25	26	24	40	45
14 in.(350 mm) dia., [24 ga (0.028 in.)(0.7 mm)] long seam with two 90° elbows length = 15 ft (4.5 m) plus elbows	>50	54	52	34	33	28	22	34

[a]In cases where background noise swamped the noise radiated from the duct walls, a lower limit on the TL is indicated by a > sign. Parentheses indicate measurements in which background noise has produced a greater uncertainty than usual in the data.

Table 22 TL_{in} versus Frequency for Various Circular Ducts[a]

Duct Size and Type	Octave Band Center Frequency, Hz							
	63	125	250	500	1K	2K	4K	8K
8 in.(200 mm) dia., [26 ga (0.022 in.)(0.55 mm)] long seam, length = 15 ft (4.5 m)	>17	(31)	39	42	41	32	31	23
14 in.(350 mm) dia., [24 ga (0.028 in.)(0.7 mm)] long seam, length = 15 ft (4.5 m)	>27	43	43	31	31	28	22	35
22 in.(550 mm) dia., [22 ga (0.034 in.)(0.85 mm)] long seam, length = 15 ft (4.5 m)	>28	40	30	30	30	24	22	40
32 in.(800 mm) dia., [22 ga (0.034 in.)(0.85 mm)] long seam, length = 15 ft (4.5 m)	(35)	36	23	23	21	19	35	40
8 in.(200 mm) dia., [26 ga (0.022 in.)(0.55 mm)] spiral wound, length = 10 ft (3 m)	>20	>42	>59	>62	53	53	43	26
14 in.(350 mm) dia., [26 ga (0.022 in.)(0.55 mm)] spiral wound, length = 10 ft (3 m)	>20	>36	44	28	31	32	22	37
26 in.(650 mm) dia., [24 ga (0.028 in.)(0.7 mm)] spiral wound, length = 10 ft (3 m)	>27	38	20	23	22	19	33	40
26 in.(650 mm) dia., [16 ga (0.064 in.)(1.6 mm)] spiral wound, length = 10 ft (3 m)	>30	>41	30	29	29	25	38	33
32 in.(800 mm) dia., [22 ga (0.034 in.)(0.85 mm)] spiral wound, length = 10 ft (3 m)	>27	32	25	22	23	21	37	42
14 in.(350 mm) dia., [24 ga (0.028 in.)(0.7 mm)] long seam with two 90° elbows length = 15 ft (4.5 m) plus elbows	>27	37	41	29	30	25	19	31

[a]In cases where background noise swamped the noise radiated from the duct walls, a lower limit on the TL is indicated by a > sign. Parentheses indicate measurements in which background noise has produced a greater uncertainty than usual in the data.

Duct fittings such as elbows appear to reduce the *TL* somewhat, but not enough information is currently available to form the basis of a quantitative prediction scheme. The effect of elbows is to reduce the *TL* at all frequencies, though this effect appears (from the limited data available) to be most severe at low frequencies.

Table 21 gives measured *TL* data on a range of duct sizes and indicates the effect of elbows in reducing the *TL*. The *TL* definition is expressed in Eq. (17), with appropriate expression for A_o and A_i.

Breakin Transmission Loss. The definition of Eq. (24) still applies for the breakin *TL* of circular ducts, and Eq. (25) can still be used to relate W_i to the reverberant field sound pressure level if the correct value of A_o is inserted.

In the case of circular ducts, the cut-off frequency for the lowest acoustic cross-mode is given by:

$$f_1 = 7929/d, \tag{29}$$

$$f_1 = 201\,400/d \tag{29 SI}$$

where d is the duct diameter in inches (mm), and the breakin *TL* can be found, as before, in terms of TL_{out}.

Where $f \leqslant f_1$, TL_{in} is given by

$$TL_{in} = \text{the larger of} \begin{cases} TL_{out} - 4 + 20 \log \left(\dfrac{f}{f_1}\right) \\ 10 \log (2L/d) \end{cases} \tag{30}$$

where L and d are in inches (mm); for $f > f_1$, TL_{in} is given by Eq. (28).

Table 22 gives TL_{in} values for the ducts listed in Table 21.

Transmission Loss of Flat-Oval Ducts

Breakout Transmission Loss. Vibration measurements currently available indicate that at low to mid frequencies most of the acoustic radiation emanates from the flat duct sides while at high frequencies the duct radiates uniformly. Evidently the

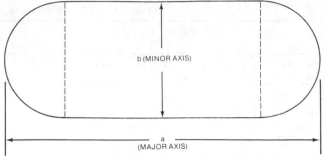

Fig. 21 Cross Section of a Flat-Oval Duct

flat sides vibrate in much the same way as the walls of rectangular ducts at low frequencies, with the curved ends acting like springs. Resonant behavior, probably related to the ring frequency phenomenon of circular ducts, prevails at high frequencies. In the available data, the minimum in the *TL* curve is at the ring frequency of the "equivalent" circular duct, the diameter of which is equal to the smaller dimension of the flat oval duct.

Although flat oval ducts seem to combine the worst features of rectangular and circular ducts, this is not true, since at low to mid frequencies only the flat sides are responsible for significant radiation. This means that these ducts tend to have a higher *TL* than rectangular ducts in the important low frequency region, resulting in a difference of 8 to 10 dB in some cases. However, circular ducts are superior to both flat oval and rectangular ducts at low frequencies.

The cross-sectional geometry of flat-oval ducts is illustrated in Figure 21 with *a* as the major axis and *b* as the minor axis. The breakout *TL* is defined by Eq. (17) but A_i and A_o are now given by the expressions

$$A_i = b(a - b) + \pi b^2/4 \tag{31}$$

$$A_o = L[2(a - b) + \pi b] \tag{32}$$

Table 23 TL_{out} versus Frequency for Various Flat-Oval Ducts

Duct Size (a × b)			Octave Band Center Frequency, Hz							
in.	(mm)	Gauge (mm)	63	125	250	500	1K	2K	4K	8K
12 × 6	(300 × 150)	24 ga (0.7)	31	34	37	40	43	—	—	—
24 × 6	(600 × 150)	24 ga (0.7)	24	27	30	33	36	—	—	—
24 × 12	(600 × 300)	24 ga (0.7)	28	31	34	37	—	—	—	—
48 × 12	(1200 × 300)	22 ga (0.85)	23	26	29	32	—	—	—	—
48 × 24	(1200 × 600)	22 ga (0.85)	27	30	33	—	—	—	—	—
96 × 24	(2400 × 600)	20 ga (1.0)	22	25	28	—	—	—	—	—
96 × 48	(2400 × 1200)	18 ga (1.3)	28	31	—	—	—	—	—	—

NOTE: The data are from tests on 20 ft (6 m) long ducts, but the *TL* values are for ducts of the cross section shown regardless of length.

Table 24 TL_{in} versus Frequency for Various Flat-Oval Ducts

Duct Size (a + b)			Octave Band Center Frequency, Hz							
in.	(mm)	Gauge (mm)	63	125	250	500	1K	2K	4K	8K
12 × 6	(300 × 150)	24 ga (0.7)	18	18	22	31	40	—	—	—
24 × 6	(600 × 150)	24 ga (0.7)	17	17	18	30	33	—	—	—
24 × 12	(600 × 300)	24 ga (0.7)	15	16	25	34	—	—	—	—
48 × 12	(1200 × 300)	22 ga (0.85)	14	14	26	29	—	—	—	—
48 × 24	(1200 × 600)	22 ga (0.85)	12	21	30	—	—	—	—	—
96 × 24	(2400 × 600)	20 ga (1.0)	11	22	25	—	—	—	—	—
96 × 48	(2400 × 1200)	18 ga (1.3)	19	28	—	—	—	—	—	—

NOTE: The data are from tests on 20 ft (6 m) long ducts, but the *TL* values are for ducts of the cross section shown regardless of length.

The duct perimeter P is given by

$$P = 2(a - b) + \pi b \qquad (33)$$

and the fraction, σ, of P taken up by the flat duct sides is given by

$$\sigma = 1/\left[1 + \frac{\pi b}{2(a - b)}\right] \qquad (34)$$

To estimate TL_{out} for flat-oval ducts at low to mid frequencies, draw a base line of TL_{out} (min), where

$$TL_{out}(min) = 10 \log (A_o/A_i) \qquad (35)$$

where A_o and A_i (in the same units) are given by Eq. (32). Next, plot a curve of

$$TL_{out} = 10 \log \left(\frac{q^2 f}{\sigma^2 P}\right) + 20 \text{ dB} \qquad (36)$$

(where q is the mass/unit area of the duct walls in lb_m/ft^2 or kg/m^2 and f the frequency in Hz), from the base line up to a frequency of

$$f_L = 8115/b, \qquad (37)$$
$$f_L = 206\,120/b \qquad (37 \text{ SI})$$

where b is the minor axis of the duct cross section in inches. [The frequency f_L is the upper limit of applicability of Eq. (36), and is equal to one-eighth of the ring frequency of the equivalent circular duct.] Finally, erase the portion of the base line to the right of the point where it meets this curve.

The comments on the low frequency TL_{out} of rectangular ducts should also apply to flat-oval ducts; low frequency resonance effects may be expected, but Eq. (35) and (36) should still predict the overall behavior or give conservative predictions. The effects of fittings can be expected to be small at low frequencies but, as in the case of rectangular ducts, should be included in calculating the surface area of the duct.

Table 23 gives some values of TL_{out} for flat oval ducts of various sizes. The upper frequency limit on TL_{out} is imposed by Eq. (37).

Breakin Transmission Loss. The breakin TL of flat-oval ducts is defined by Eq. (24); again, Eq. (25) relates the reverberant field sound pressure level to W_i.

While there are no exact solutions for the cut-off frequency for the lowest acoustic cross-mode in flat oval ducts, an approximate solution exists as follows:

$$f_1 = \frac{C}{(a - b)\left[1 + \frac{\pi b}{2(a - b)}\right]^{\frac{1}{2}}} \qquad (38)$$

where a and b are in inches (mm), and $C = 6764$ (171 800). Eq. (38) is valid where $a/b \geqslant 2$; for $a/b < 2$, and deteriorates progressively as a/b approaches unity. Again, TL_{out} may be found in terms of TL_{in}, as follows.

Where $f \leqslant f_1$, TL_{in} is given by

$$TL_{in} = \text{the larger of} \begin{cases} TL_{out} + 10 \log (f^2 A_i) - 81 \text{ dB} \\ 10 \log \left(\frac{6PL}{A_i}\right), \end{cases} \qquad (39)$$

where A_i is in square inches and is given by Eq. (31), P is in inches and is given by Eq. (33) and L is in feet. In SI units:

$$TL_{in} = \text{the larger of} \begin{cases} TL_{out} + 10 \log (f^2 A_i) - 109 \text{ dB} \\ 10 \log (PL/A_i) + 27 \text{ dB} \end{cases} \qquad (39 \text{ SI})$$

where A_i is in square mm, P is in mm, and L is in metres.

If $f > f_1$, TL_{in} is given by Eq. (28). Table 24 gives TL_{in} values for the ducts listed in Table 23.

Insertion Loss of External Acoustic Wall Lagging on Rectangular Ducts

External acoustic lagging is sometimes applied to ductwork to reduce low frequency noise radiation from the walls. This is common in rectangular ducts, since both flat-oval and circular ducts have a higher TL at low frequencies than rectangular ducts.

Prediction methods for noise reduction effected by external lagging have not been developed for flat-oval and circular duct geometries. However, methods are given for estimating the insertion loss (TL) of lagging on rectangular ducts. Lagging consists of a layer of soft, flexible, porous material such as glass fiber blanket covered with an outer impervious layer, i.e. a relatively rigid material such as gypsum board or a limp material such as sheet lead. The absorbent thickness is h and the duct cross section measures $a \times b$, as shown in Figure 22. The insertion loss is defined as

$$IL = 10 \log \left[\frac{W_r \text{ (without lagging)}}{W_r \text{ (with lagging)}}\right] \qquad (40)$$

Two prediction methods are required: the first is for rigid outer covering materials and the second is for limp materials. In the case of rigid materials, there is a pronounced resonance effect between the duct walls and the outer covering. With the limp materials however, the variation in the separation of the duct and its outer covering causes a "spreading" of this resonance so that it is no longer well-defined, and the two cases must be treated separately.

1. **Rigid Covering Materials.** This category includes any type of outer covering (sheet metal, gypsum board and so forth) that maintains a relatively constant distance between the duct and covering.

Data Required:
perimeter of duct = $P_1 = 2(a + b)$, in inches
perimeter of outer covering = $P_2 = 2(a + b + 4h)$, in inches
mass/unit area of duct = M_1, in lb/ft^2
mass/unit area of outer covering = M_2, in lb/ft^2
cross sectional area of absorbent material = $S = 2h(a[\,b + 2h)$, in square inches

a. Calculate the low frequency insertion loss,

$$IL(lf) = 20 \log \left(1 + \frac{M_2}{M_1} \cdot \frac{P_1}{P_2}\right) \text{ dB} \qquad (41)$$

On semi-log graph paper, draw a horizontal line parallel to the frequency axis (see Figure 23 for an example of a composite IL curve) representing a constant IL equal to $IL(lf)$.

b. Calculate the resonance frequency

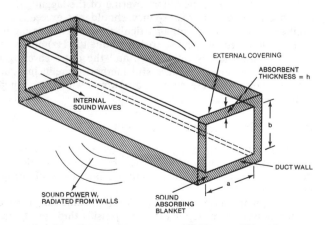

SOUND POWER W,
RADIATED FROM WALLS

INTERNAL SOUND WAVES

EXTERNAL COVERING

ABSORBENT THICKNESS = h

b

DUCT WALL

a

SOUND ABSORBING BLANKET

Fig. 22 Rectangular Duct with External Lagging

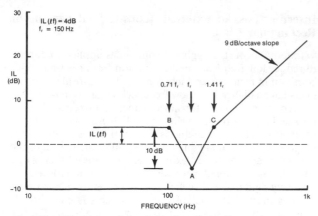

Fig. 23   Example of the Insertion Loss Curve for Duct Lagging with a Rigid Outer Covering

$$f_r = 156 \left[\left(\frac{P_2}{P_1} + \frac{M_2}{M_1} \right) P_1 / M_2 S \right]^{1/2} \text{Hz} \qquad (42)$$

c. Mark point A at $IL(lf) - 10$ dB and frequency f_r. Mark point B at 0.71 f_r and point C at 1.41 f_r on the $IL(lf)$ line; join each of these to point A (see Figure 23). From point C draw a line to the right with a slope of $+9$ db/octave. The $IL(lf)$ line should be truncated, at its right hand end, in point B. The resulting curve, consisting of four straight-line segments, represents the IL of the duct lagging.

2. **Limp Covering Materials.** This category includes any material such as sheet lead, sheet vinyl and so forth that does not retain its shape and sags, producing a variation in the separation of the duct and outer covering. (Data required are the same as for rigid covering materials.)

a. Calculate $IL(lf)$ from Eq. (41) and plot on semi-log graph paper as before.
b. Calculate f_r from Eq. (42).
c. Mark a point on the $IL(lf)$ line at f_r and from this draw a line to the right at $+9$ dB/octave. Truncate the right hand end of the $IL(lf)$ line at the point marked. This two line segment curve represents the IL of the duct lagging.

Comments on the Method

The IL predictions should be fairly reliable up to about 1 kHz for most ducts. Accurate predictions are not normally required above this frequency.

At low frequencies, some discrepancies can occur between the predicted and actual IL because of structural resonance effects in the duct and/or in the outer covering of the lagging, if the covering is rigid. The discrepancy should not exceed a few decibels. Duct lagging is not a particularly effective measure for reducing low frequency noise (below about 100 Hz) unless the absorbent thickness is quite large and the outer covering is substantial. A far more successful method of reducing duct radiated noise is to use circular ductwork, which has a high transmission loss at low frequencies.

Acoustically Generated Duct Rumble

Any low frequency noise that breaks out of ductwork can result in low frequency noise, or rumble. The noise might be due to one or a combination of aerodynamic conditions or fan noise.

Rectangular ductwork does a poor job of containing low frequency noise. The reduction of energy passing through a typical rectangular duct wall is less than the Sound Transmission Loss

of the duct. The measure of the breakout is the duct breakout noise insertion loss, and can be estimated from the tabulated Sound Transmission Loss and the duct dimensions as follows:

$$\text{Breakout Noise Reduction} = TL - 10 \log (S/A), \text{dB}$$

where

    TL = Sound Transmission Loss in Table 19 for rectangular ducts
    S = Surface area of length of duct being considered
    A = Cross-sectional area of duct

If the sound power level entering the duct is L_{wd}, the sound power radiated through the duct surface is

$$L_{wr} = L_{wd} - \text{Breakout Noise Reduction (dB)}$$

For example, the value for a 20,000 cfm fan might be 100 dB at 63 Hz for L_{wd}. Sound Transmission Loss might be 20 dB, with a breakout noise reduction of 12 dB for a 15 ft (4.6 m) duct. The sound power radiated from the section is 88 dB (Harold 1986).

Rectangular Versus Round or Flat-Oval Ductwork

Table 19 compared with Table 21 shows that round ductwork is much more effective in containing low-frequency noise than rectangular ductwork, regardless of whether the noise is flow-generated or is due to acoustic excitation. In tight spaces, multiple round ducts in parallel can be used where space is not available for a single round duct of equivalent cross-sectional area. Flat-oval ductwork falls between round and rectangular, and its breakout noise reduction depends on the area of flat surface.

MECHANICAL EQUIPMENT ROOM NOISE ISOLATION

Mechanical equipment is inherently noisy. Pumps, chillers, cooling towers, boilers, and fans create noise that is difficult to contain. Noise-sensitive spaces must be isolated from these sources. One of the best precautions is to locate mechanical spaces away from acoustically critical spaces. Buffer zones (e.g., storage rooms, corridors, or less noise-sensitive spaces) can be placed between mechanical equipment rooms and rooms requiring quiet. Noise transmission through roofs and exterior walls is usually less of a problem, making corner rooms and top-floor spaces less of a problem for housing mechanical equipment.

Construction enclosing a mechanical equipment room should be poured concrete or masonry units having enough surface weight to provide adequate sound transmission loss capability. Walls must be airtight and caulked at the edges to prevent sound leaks. Floors and ceilings should be concrete slabs, except for the ceiling or roof deck above a top-floor mechanical space.

Penetrations of the mechanical equipment room enclosure create potential paths for noise to escape into adjacent spaces. Therefore, wherever ducts, pipes, conduits, etc. penetrate the walls, floor, or ceiling of a mechanical equipment room, it is necessary to acoustically treat the opening for adequate noise control. A 1/2- to 5/8-in. (12- to 16-mm) clear space should be left all around the penetrating element and filled with fibrous material for the full depth of the penetration. Both sides of the penetration should be sealed airtight with a nonhardening resilient sealant (see Figure 24).

Doors into mechanical equipment rooms are frequently the weak link in the enclosure. Where noise control is important, they should be as heavy as possible, gasketed around the perimeter, have no grilles or other openings and be self-closing. If such doors lead to sensitive spaces, two doors separated by a 3- to 10-ft (1- to 3-m) corridor may be necessary.

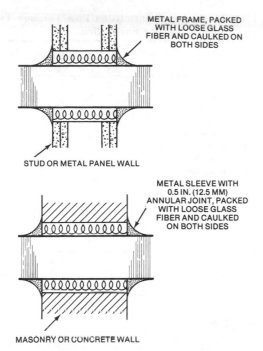

Fig. 24   Typical Duct, Conduit, and Pipe Wall Penetrations

Penetration of Walls by Ducts

Ducts passing through the mechanical equipment room enclosure pose an additional problem. Noise can be transmitted via the duct walls to either side of the wall. Airborne noise in the mechanical room can be transmitted into the duct and enter an adjacent space by reradiating from the duct walls, even if the duct contains no grilles, registers, diffusers, or other openings. These ducts may require lagging or enclosures fabricated from materials that provide a resilient wrap (fibrous glass or open cell foam) over which a dense outer skin can be applied. This outer skin may be 1-in. (25-mm) thick dense plaster, gypsum board layers with equivalent surface weight, heavy-gauge sheetmetal, loaded or leaded vinyl, lead, or other material with similar characteristics.

Noise levels in ducts close to fans are usually high. Noise can come not only from the fan but also from pulsating duct walls, excessive air turbulence and air buffeting caused by tight or restricted airflow entrance or exit configurations. Control of low frequency noise propagation from these sources can be very difficult. Thus, duct layout and air flow conditions when there are nearby noise sensitive areas should be carefully considered.

Mechanical Chases

Mechanical chases and shafts should be treated the same way as mechanical equipment rooms, especially if they contain any noise-producing equipment. The shaft should be closed at the mechanical equipment room and shaft walls should have a surface weight sufficient to reduce sound transmission to noise-sensitive areas to acceptable levels. Chases should not be allowed to become *speaking tubes* between spaces requiring different acoustical environments. Any vibrating piping, ducts, conduits, or equipment should be isolated so that vibration is not transmitted to the shaft walls and the general building construction.

If mechanical equipment rooms are to be used as supply or return plenums, all openings into the equipment room plenum space may require noise control treatment. This is especially true if the ceiling space just outside the equipment room is used as

a return air plenum and the ceiling is acoustical tile. Most acoustical tile is almost transparent acoustically, particularly at low frequencies, so sound passes through practically unimpeded, in either direction.

Special Wall Construction

When mechanical equipment rooms must be placed adjacent to offices, conference rooms, secretarial pools, or other noise-sensitive areas, the building construction around the equipment space should reduce the noise enough to satisfy the acoustical requirements of the nearby spaces. Depending on the degree of noise sensitivity, it may be necessary to consider one of the following treatments.

For walls, an additional skin that is totally separate and resiliently isolated from the heavy and dense inner wall may be provided outside the mechanical room wall. This outer skin may be similar to metal studs with two layers of 5/8 in. (16 mm) or equivalent surface weight gypsum board attached and with all joints staggered and sealed airtight. Two to 4 in. (50 to 100 mm) of fibrous glass insulation may be placed between studs. It is necessary to provide an air cavity, at least 2 to 4 in. (50 to 100 mm) in depth, between the inner wall and the outer resilient skin. Optimum sound reduction can be achieved only if the outer skin resilient isolation is complete and can not transmit structure-borne vibration or airborne sound from the mechanical equipment and the equipment room enclosure itself.

Other situations may require the use of double-wall construction consisting of two heavy, dense, masonry walls separated by an air cavity. Where floating floor construction is used, it is advantageous to support the inner wall on the floating slab.

Floating Floors

Typical floating floor construction can be used to further reduce noise between the mechanical room and noise-sensitive areas above or below. It is composed of two reinforced concrete slabs: the floating or isolated wearing slab and the structural floor slab. The floating floor slab is designed with a minimum 4 in. (100 mm) thickness and with a 1- to 4-in. (25- to 100-mm) separation between the structural and the floating slabs. A 2-in. (50-mm) separation is most common. The connection between the slabs is made by supporting the floating slab on permanent load-bearing resilient material. The edges of the floating slab are isolated from the structure with resilient material, and the joint is resiliently caulked.

The isolation material supporting the floating slab must be resilient, have permanent dynamic and static properties and safely support both the floating slab and the imposed live load for the life of the building. Isolation material for the floating slab should (1) have a natural frequency in the range of 7 to 15 Hz under the load conditions that exist in the building, (2) be tested for load versus deflection and for natural frequency with known aging properties and a history of applications in similar floating floor installations, (3) be tested in service for impact insulation class (IIC) and sound transmission class (STC) by an independent testing laboratory, and (4) be designed for the loads imposed on the isolator in service and during construction.

Following are two common methods for constructing floating floors:

1. Individual pads are spaced on 1 to 2 ft (0.3 to 0.6 m) centers each way and covered with plywood or sheet metal. Low density absorption material can be placed between the pads to reduce the tunneling effect. Reinforced concrete is placed directly on the waterproofed panels and cured. Then, the equipment is set (Figure 25a).

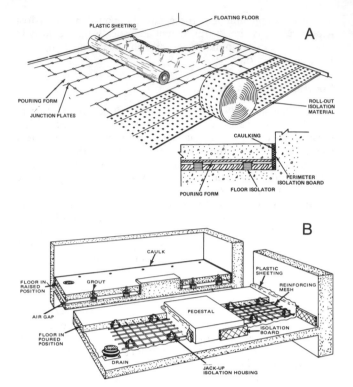

Fig. 25 Typical Floating Floor Constructions

Table 25 Sound Transmission Loss Through Typical Floor Construction, dB[a]

	Frequency, Hz					
	125	250	500	1000	2000	4000
6 in. (150 mm) concrete structural floor	35	36	40	46	53	58
6 in. (150 mm) floor slab, 2 in. (50 mm) air space, 4 in. (100 mm) floating floor, equipment noise impinging on walls and ceiling	44	47	58	68	75	87
6 in. (150 mm) floor slab, 2 in. (50 mm) air space, 4 in. (100 mm) floating floor, equipment noise contained to avoid flanking	52	64	78	90	96	73

[a]A change in slab thickness, concrete weight, isolator stiffness, or flanking control will result in corresponding changes in the acoustical performance of the system.

2. Cast-in-place canisters are placed on 2 to 4 ft (0.6 to 1.2 m) centers each way on the structural floor. Reinforced concrete is poured over the canisters; after curing, the entire slab is raised into operating position, the canister access holes are grouted, and the equipment is set (Figure 25b).

With either system, mechanical equipment with vibration isolators can be placed on the floating slab unless the equipment operates at shaft rotation speeds, in revolutions per second, that are 0.7 to 1.4 times the resonance frequency of the floating slab system. In that case, the equipment should be supported with isolators on structural slab extensions that penetrate through the floating slab. This type of installation does require careful attention to details to avoid acoustical flanking caused by improper direct contact between the floating slab and the structural penetrations. Floating floors primarily control airborne sound transmission. They are not intended to be used in place of vibration isolators.

The actual resonant frequency of the floated slab is determined by both the stiffness of the resilient elements used to support the floated slab, and the stiffness of the air space between the structural and floated slabs. With a 2 in. (50 mm) airspace and a 4 in. thick (100 mm) floating slab, the resonance frequency can be expected to be near 18 Hz. Thus, equipment operating between about 12.5 and 25 rps (750 to 1500 rpm) should be supported on structural slab extensions, unless the equipment is rated at about 5 hp or less.

Resilient material inserted between the floating and structural slabs results in a very resilient upper concrete slab. This slab must be designed to operate within the safe bending limits of the concrete. While floating floor tests have shown transmission loss ratings exceeding STC 75, these can only be realized in field installations where all flanking sound transmission paths or short circuits have been minimized. Table 25 is included to show improvement of sound transmission loss by floating floor slabs, with or without flanking noise control.

Enclosed Air Cavity

If acoustically critical spaces are located over a mechanical equipment room, it may be necessary either to install a floating floor in the space above or to form a totally enclosed air cavity between the spaces by installing a dense plaster or gypsum board ceiling resiliently suspended in the equipment room. Ideally, such a ceiling can be positioned between building beams, leaving the beam bottoms available for hanging equipment, piping, ducts and so forth without penetrating the ceiling with hanger rods or other devices. In the case of barjoist-type construction, it may be easier to resiliently attach the ceiling to the underside of the joists and support all equipment, ducts and pipes from the mechanical room floor or from wall supports, properly vibration isolated.

TRANSMISSION LOSS THROUGH CEILING CONSTRUCTION

When terminal units, fan-coil units, air handling units, or ductwork are in a ceiling plenum above an occupied room, noise transmission through the ceiling construction can be high enough to cause excessive noise levels in that room. Since there are no standard tests relating to the direct transmission of sound through ceiling construction (insertion loss), ceiling product manufacturers do not regularly publish data that can be used in calculations. Published data is usually room-to-room sound transmission loss through a common ceiling plenum. Acoustical ceilings are rarely homogeneous surfaces; they usually have light fixtures, diffusers and grilles, speakers and so forth. These elements reduce the transmission loss of the ceiling and must be considered.

To estimate the noise level in a room from sound transmission through a ceiling, the sound power level in the ceiling plenum must be reduced by the insertion loss of the ceiling material before applying Eq. (1). In the absence of a recognized test standard, the values in Table 18 may be used as an estimate. This calculation should be repeated for each octave band of interest, and the results compared to the room noise criterion.

If increased insertion loss is required, consider the following options:

1. Using a different type of ceiling with higher insertion loss, i.e., gypsum board, high *TL* acoustical tile, and so forth.

2. Increasing the insertion loss of the ceiling by applying gypsum board, sheet lead or other secondary barrier material on top of the ceiling.
3. Treating the source by lagging.

LABORATORY FUME HOOD EXHAUST

Fume hood exhaust systems frequently are the major noise source in a laboratory, and as such, require noise control (Sessler and Hoover 1983). The exhaust system may consist of individual exhaust fans ducted to separate fume hoods, or a central exhaust fan connected through a distribution system to a large number of hoods. In either case, the noise levels produced in the laboratory space can be estimated using procedures described in this section.

Recommended noise level design criteria for laboratory spaces using fume hoods are as follows:

Laboratory Type	Noise Criteria (NC) or Room Criteria (RC)
Testing or research with little requirement for speech or study	45-55
Research, with some communication, telephone, and study	40-50
Teaching	35-45

Noise control measures that have been successfully applied to a variety of fume hood systems consist of the following:

Fan Selection.
1. Use backward inclined or forward curved, rather than radial blade fans where conditions permit.
2. Select fan to operate at a low tip speed and maximum efficiency.

Sound Attenuation. Use prefabricated silencers or sections of lined ductwork where conditions permit.

All potential noise control measures should be carefully evaluated for compliance with applicable codes, safety requirements and corrosion resistance requirements of the specific system. In addition, vibration isolation for fume hood exhaust fans is generally required. As a guide, see Table 27, for centrifugal fans. However, for some laboratory facilities, particularly those having electron microscopes, vibration control can be critical and a vibration specialist should be consulted.

SOUND CONTROL FOR OUTDOOR EQUIPMENT INSTALLATIONS

Outdoor equipment such as air-cooled condensers, condensing units and cooling towers should be carefully selected, installed and maintained so that the radiated sound is not annoying to people outdoors or in nearby buildings. Whether or not a particular source of sound is annoying depends mostly on the difference in the sound levels existing at the listening location when the particular source is (1) operating or (2) not operating (i.e., the outdoor ambient noise level).

Outdoor ambient noise is a complex phenomenon. It is primarily a function of traffic and fluctuates with time; it depends on the proximity of various types of roads, the traffic involved, shielding by buildings and so forth. A complete description of the outdoor ambient noise in a given community requires statistical evaluation of noise levels occurring at many different locations. While approximations still must be made

for equipment selection purposes at specific locations, techniques are available to assess or predict such noise levels (Harris 1979).

ACOUSTICAL DESIGN PROCEDURES

If the equipment sound power level spectrum and ambient sound pressure level spectrum are known, the contribution of the equipment to the sound level at any location can be estimated by analyzing the sound transmission paths involved. Outdoors, when there are no intervening barriers, the principal factors are reflections from buildings near the equipment and the distance to the specific location [see Figure 26 and Eq. (43)].

The following equation may be used to estimate the decibel differences between the sound power level of the equipment and the sound pressure level at any distance from it, at any frequency:

$$L_p = L_w + 10 \log Q - 20 \log d - C \qquad (43)$$

where

L_p = sound pressure level at a distance d from the source, ft (m)
L_w = sound power level of the source
C = correction factor, 0 dB when d is in ft (11 dB when d is in m)
Q = determined from Figure 26.

Note: Equation does not apply where d is less than twice the maximum dimension of the equipment; results may be low by up to 5 dB where d is between two and five times maximum equipment dimension.

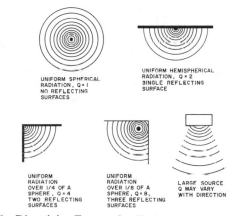

Fig. 26 Directivity Factors for Various Radiation Patterns

ROOFTOP CURB-MOUNTED EQUIPMENT

This equipment usually becomes part of the roof deck construction and is frequently used on lightweight roof structures in schools, small hospital and office facilities and so forth that are also sensitive to sound and vibration problems. Large roof openings, within the periphery of the curb, are required for the supply and return duct connections. These ducts run directly from the noise-generating equipment to the building interior and permit little or no room to apply adequate noise control treatment. Typical acoustical tile ceilings are not adequate noise barriers; some combination of duct silencers, lagged ducts or impervious ceilings is frequently required to reduce the noise level to acceptable levels underneath the units.

Equipment that transmits objectionable noise through the roof opening must be mounted on a raised steel frame (commonly called dunnage) above the roof. The duct openings no longer must be directly below the unit and can be as far away as necessary for adequate noise control. For roof construction without adequate airborne sound transmission loss, additional treatment can be installed in the steel framework or intervening air space.

VIBRATION ISOLATION AND CONTROL

Vibration and vibration-induced noise, major sources of occupant complaint, are increasing in modern buildings. Lighter weight construction and equipment located in penthouses or intermediate level mechanical rooms increase structure-borne vibration and noise transmission. Not only is the physical vibration disturbing, but the regenerated noise from structural movement can be heard in other remote sections.

This section discusses vibration produced by mechanical equipment and the most effective control of vibration transmission to the building structure. It also covers the basis of vibration control and a description and tabulation of vibration levels that can be expected with modern mechanical equipment.

Two sections follow: (1) the theory of vibration isolation for rigid and non-rigid floor systems and (2) an applied approach to vibration isolation. In the second section, Table 27 shows appropriate isolation systems for most mechanical equipment in actual buildings. The references cover special cases, describe the isolation system in detail and identify possible problem areas. Piping and duct isolation and seismic protection are covered in separate sections.

The final section identifies common problems encountered in the isolation of mechanical equipment for buildings.

UNDERSTANDING VIBRATION AND ITS CONTROL

Rigidly mounted pieces of HVAC equipment transmit their full vibrational force to the building structure. This can result in disturbing physical vibration felt by the occupant, damaging structural vibration, and annoying noise when the vibration excites the structure at frequencies within the normal hearing range.

The vibration can be isolated or reduced to a fraction of the original force with resilient mounts between the equipment and the supporting structure. The following sections give the basic information necessary to understand vibration isolation, to properly select and specify vibration isolators and to analyze and correct field problems. Harris and Crede (1976) and Den Hartog (1956) provide more detailed information on the subject.

Criteria should be established for equipment vibration to determine the excessive forces that must be isolated or that adversely affect the performance or life of the equipment. Figures 27 and 28 show the significance and interrelationship of equipment vibration levels and vibration isolation systems where the isolators provide a fixed efficiency as determined by Eq. (44), and where the magnitude of transmission to the building is a function of the magnitude of the vibration force. Theoretically, an isolation system could be selected to isolate forces of extreme magnitude; however, isolators should not be used to mask a condition that should be corrected before it damages the equipment. Rather, isolators should be selected to isolate the vibratory forces of equipment operation, and if transmission occurs, to indicate a faulty operating condition that should be corrected.

Ideally, vibration criteria should (1) measure rotor unbalance as a function of type, size, mass and stiffness of equipment; (2) consider the vibration generated by system components such as bearing and drives, as well as installation factors such as alignment, and (3) be verifiable by field measurement. Figure 29 shows some commonly used criteria that do not meet all the requirements above, but are generally satisfactory. A simpler approach is to use the criteria in Table 26, which have been developed by individuals and firms experienced in vibration testing of HVAC equipment. Table 26 shows the maximum allowable vibration levels for steady state movement taken on the bearing or machine structure if it is sufficiently rigid. These criteria can be met by any properly operating equipment, will determine reasonable vibration levels to be isolated and will make the equipment acceptable. These values are practical levels that allow for misalignment, drive eccentricities, belt vibration and similar factors affecting the overall vibration level. These levels can be maintained throughout the life of the equipment.

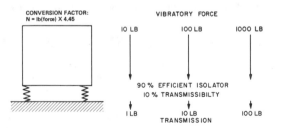

Fig. 27   Transmission to Structure Varies as Function of Magnitude of Vibratory Forces

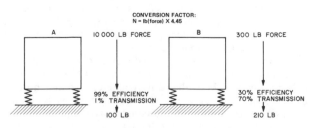

Fig. 28   Interrelationship of Equipment Vibration, Isolation Efficiency and Transmission

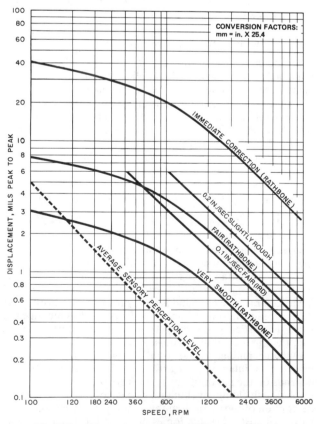

Fig. 29   Currently Available Vibration Criteria

Table 26 Equipment Vibration Criteria

Equipment	Maximum Allowable Vibration Peak-to-Peak Displacement,	
	mil	mm
Pumps		
1800 rpm	2	0.05
3600 rpm	1	0.025
Centrifugal compressors	1	0.025
Fans (vent sets, centrifugal, axial)		
Under 600 rpm	4	0.1
600 to 1000 rpm	3	0.075
1000 to 2000 rpm	2	0.05
Over 2000 rpm	1	0.025

1 mil = 0.001 inch

THEORY OF VIBRATION ISOLATION

Chapter 7 of the 1985 FUNDAMENTALS Volume gives a more complete coverage of the theory of vibration isolation. Basic equations from Chapter 7 are repeated here to review the theory of vibration isolation, properly select and specify isolators as indicated in Table 27, and analyze and correct field problems as discussed in the sections on Vibration Problems and Trouble Shooting.

For a single degree of freedom system (as shown in Figure 30), which is approximated when equipment is installed on grade,

Transmission T to building structure is:

$$T = \left| \frac{1}{1 - (f_d/f_n)^2} \right| \qquad (44)$$

Equipment displacement X is:

$$X = \left| \frac{F/k}{1 - (f_d/f_n)^2} \right| \qquad (45)$$

A simple, single degree of freedom seldom exists because all equipment room floors, especially upper floor locations, deflect under load. This results in a complex system, but for purposes of simplication it can be visualized as a two degree of freedom system as shown in Figure 31. For such a system.:

Transmission to building structure is:

$$T_c = \left| \frac{1}{[1 - (f_d/f_n)^2] \, [1 \, [\, (k/k_f) - (f_d/f_f)^2] - k/k_f} \right| \qquad (46)$$

Equipment displacement X is:

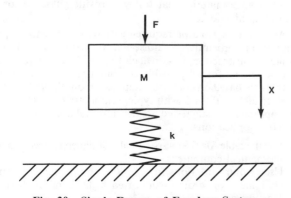

Fig. 30 Single Degree of Freedom System

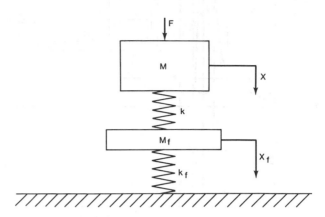

Fig. 31 Two Degree of Freedom System

$$X = \left| \frac{(F/k) \, [1 + (k/k_f) - (f_d/f_f)^2]}{[1 - (f_d/f_n)^2][1 + (k/k_f) - (f_d/f_f)^2] - k/k_f} \right| \qquad (47)$$

Floor displacement X_f is:

$$X_f = \frac{(F/k_f)}{[1 - (f_d/f_n)^2][1 + (k/k_f) - (f_d/f_f)^2] - k/k_f} \qquad (48)$$

The following terms are used in Eq. (44) through (48):

T = transmissibility
F = vibratory force, lbs (N)
f_d = frequency of vibratory force (disturbing frequency), Hz
f_n = natural frequency of isolator, Hz
f_f = natural frequency of floor, Hz
k = isolator stiffness, lb/in (N/mm)
k_f = floor stiffness, lb/in. (N/mm)
X = equipment displacement (single amplitude), in. (mm)
X_f = floor displacement (single amplitude), in. (mm)

The following conclusions can be derived from the study of Eq. (44) through (48):

1. In spring isolators commonly used for HVAC equipment, the natural frequency of the isolator, f_n, is a function of isolator deflection, as shown in Figure 32. (This relationship is not true of some other isolation materials and is further discussed in the Types of Vibration Isolators section.) Note that it takes large increases in deflection to significantly change natural frequency, e.g., quadrupling deflection only reduces natural frequency by half.

2. Isolation efficiency is a function of the ratio of disturbing frequency, f_d, to isolator natural frequency, f_n. As shown in Figure 33 for Single Degree of Freedom System, when $f_d = f_n$ resonance occurs, resulting in theoretically infinite transmission and excessive equipment movement. As isolator natural frequency, f_n, becomes lower than disturbing fre-

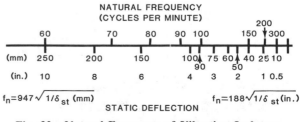

Fig. 32 Natural Frequency of Vibration Isolators

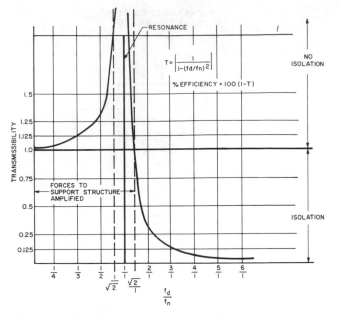

Fig. 33   Vibration Transmissibility as Function of Ratio, f_d/f_n

quency, f_d, the isolation range is entered when f_d/f_n becomes $\geqslant \sqrt{2}$. Note that the transmissibility curve in Figure 33 becomes asymptotic above a f_d/f_n ratio of about 6:1 and, above this point as explained in conclusion 1, it takes very large increases in static deflection to reduce isolator natural frequency and further reduce transmission.

3. The mass or weight of equipment has no effect on isolation efficiency. Figure 34 shows that the transmissibility to the structure is the same for both "heavy" and "light" systems, assuming isolator deflection is the same. Increased mass does affect the movement of equipment itself and is discussed in the section "Inertia Blocks."

4. The ratio of isolator stiffness to floor stiffness, k/k_f, is important in most upper story equipment locations. If isolators are very much *less* stiff than the floor, k/k_f becomes very small and is not a significant factor. As a general rule, isolator stiffness should be kept to a maximum of 1/10 floor stiffness. This has been accomplished in Table 27 by increasing isolator deflection as floor span increases. It is important to note that k_f is floor stiffness, not total floor deflection. For example, if a 1000 lb (454 kg) piece of equipment causes its isolators to deflect 1 in. (25 mm) and the floor to deflect an "additional" 0.1 in. (2.54 mm): $k = 1000$ lb/in (175 N/mm) $k_f = 10,000$ lb/in (1750 N/mm) and $k/k_f = 0.1$ regardless of the amount of total floor deflection. Table 27 takes k/k_f into consideration by increasing isolator deflection as the floor span increases.

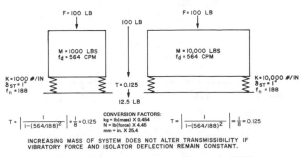

Fig. 34   Effect of Mass on Transmissibility

5. The ratios of disturbing frequency, f_d, to isolator natural frequency, f_n, and floor natural frequency, f_f, are important. If f_d is equal or close to f_n or f_f, a resonant condition can occur, causing excessive equipment movement and transmission to the structure.

It is easy to select isolators so their natural frequency, f_n, is not the same or close to disturbing frequency, f_d. This has been accomplished in Table 27 by varying isolator deflection as a function of equipment operating speed.

It is extremely difficult to determine floor natural frequency, f_f, as part of the isolator selection process because f_f can only be calculated with a complex computer analysis. Design engineers dealing with long floor spans, low equipment, operating speeds, and/or lightweight structures should seek expert assistance in the selection of vibration isolation. When resonance problems occur it is usually desirable to seek expert assistance; however, the "Troubleshooting" section provides information on how to evaluate and correct some of the more commonly encountered resonance problems.

INSTRUCTIONS TO THE DESIGNER/SPECIFIER

Vibration isolators must be selected to compensate for the floor deflection. Longer spans also allow the structure to be more flexible, permitting the building to be more easily set into motion. By using the Selection Guide, building spans, equipment operating speeds, equipment horsepower, damping, and other factors are taken into consideration.

By Specifying Isolator Deflection, rather than isolation efficiency, transmissibility, or other theoretical parameters, the designer can compensate for floor deflection and building resonances by selecting isolators that are satisfactory to provide minimum vibration transmission, and that have more deflection than the supporting floor.

When the specifier permits equipment suppliers to provide "appropriate" isolators, a satisfactory job is not ensured, since different brands of isolators with varying deflections may be furnished, and no one supplier can carry the full responsibility for a building free of vibration and noise as specified.

To apply the information from the Selection Guide, base type, isolator type, and minimum deflection, columns are added to the equipment schedule, and the isolator specifications are incorporated into mechanical specifications for the project. Then, for each piece of mechanical equipment, base type, isolator type, and minimum deflection are entered, as tabulated in the Selection Guide.

Table 27 recommends deflections based on the experience of acoustical and mechanical consultants and vibration control manufacturers. Recommended isolator type, base type and minimum static deflection are reasonable and safe recommendations for 70 to 80% of HVAC installations. Footnotes for the table and reference material that follows provide guidance for less typical applications.

As vibration isolator requirements depend on the type of equipment, proximity to noise-sensitive areas, and type of building construction, it is difficult to provide recommendations and selections for all possible combinations. The recommendations are based on concrete equipment room floors 4- to 12-in. (100- to 300-mm) thick with typical floor stiffness. The following approach is suggested to develop isolator selections for specific applications:

1. Use the table for floors specifically designed to accommodate mechanical equipment.
2. Use recommendations for the 20 ft (6 m) span column for equipment on ground-supported slabs adjacent to noise-sensitive areas.

Table 27 Vibration Isolator Selection Guide

Equipment Type	Notes[a]	Grade Supported Slab Base Type[b]	Iso-lator Type[c]	Min. Defl. in. (mm)	20 ft (6 m) Floor Span Base Type[b]	Iso-lator Type[c]	Min. Defl. in. (mm)	30 ft (9 m) Floor Span Base Type[b]	Iso-lator Type[c]	Min. Defl. in. (mm)	40 ft (12 m) Floor Span Base Type[b]	Iso-lator Type[c]	Min. Defl. in. (mm)	50 ft (15 m) Floor Span Base Type[b]	Iso-lator Type[c]	Min. Defl. in. (mm)
Refrigeration Machines	12,13															
Reciprocating Compressors	2,3,13	C	3	0.75 (19.05)	C	3	0.75 (19.05)	C	3	1.50 (38.1)	C	3	1.50 (38.1)	C	3	2.50 (63.5)
Reciprocating Condensing Units & Chilling Units	2,3	A	2	0.25 (6.35)	A	4	0.75 (19.05)	A	4	1.50 (38.1)	A	4	2.50 (63.5)	A	4	2.50 (63.5)
Hermetic Centrifugal Chillers	2,3,4,12	A	1	0.25 (6.35)	A	4	0.75 (19.05)	A	4	1.50 (38.1)	A	4	1.50 (38.1)	A	4	1.50 (38.1)
Open Centrifugal Chillers	2,3,12	C	1	0.25 (6.35)	C	4	0.75 (19.05)	C	4	1.50 (38.1)	C	4	1.50 (38.1)	C	4	2.50 (63.5)
Absorption Chillers	—	A	1	0.25 (6.35)	A	4	0.75 (19.05)	A	4	0.75 (19.05)	A	4	1.50 (38.1)	A	4	1.50 (38.1)
Air Compressors																
Tank Mounted	3,15	A	3	0.75 (19.05)	A	3	0.75 (19.05)	A	3	1.50 (38.1)	A	3	2.50 (63.5)	A	3	2.50 (63.5)
Base Mounted																
Up to 500 rpm	8,13,14,15	C	3	0.75 (19.05)	C	3	0.75 (19.05)	C	3	1.50 (38.1)	C	3	1.50 (38.1)	C	3	2.50 (63.5)
501 rpm & Over	13,14,15	C	3	0.75 (19.05)	C	3	0.75 (19.05)	C	3	1.50 (38.1)	C	3	1.50 (38.1)	C	3	2.50 (63.5)
Pumps																
Close coupled, to 7½ hp (6 kW)	16	B/C	2	0.25 (6.35)	C	3	0.75 (19.05)	C	3	0.75 (19.05)	C	3	0.75 (19.05)	C	3	0.75 (19.05)
Close coupled, 10 hp (7.5 kW) & over Flexible coupled, to 40 hp (30 kW)	16	C	3	0.75 (19.05)	C	3	0.75 (19.05)	C	3	1.50 (38.1)	C	3	1.50 (38.1)	C	3	1.50 (38.1)
Flexible coupled, 50 to 125 hp (37 to 93 kW)	10,16	C	3	0.75 (19.05)	C	3	0.75 (19.05)	C	3	1.50 (38.1)	C	3	2.50 (63.5)	C	3	2.50 (63.5)
Flexible coupled, 150 hp (110 kW) & over	10,16															
Packaged Rooftop Air Conditioning Units	5,6,8,17	(Not Applicable)			D	3	0.75 (19.05)	A/B	3	1.50 (38.1)	A/B	3	2.50 (63.5)	A/B	3	3.5 (88.9)
Ducts	7															
Piping	7															
Cooling Towers & Closed Circuit Coolers	5,18															
Up to 300 rpm	8															
301 to 500 rpm	—	A	1, 2	0.25 (6.35)	A	4	2.50 (63.5)	A	4	2.50 (63.5)	A	4	2.50 (63.5)	A	4	3.50 (88.9)
501 rpm & over	—	A	1, 2	0.25 (6.35)	A	4	0.75 (19.05)	A	4	1.50 (38.1)	A	4	1.50 (38.1)	A	4	2.50 (63.5)
Fans and Air Handling Equipment	19															
Axial, tubular, & fan heads	4,9															
Up to 22 in. (550 mm) wheel dia.	9	A/B	2	0.25 (6.35)	A/B	3	0.75 (19.05)	A/B	3	0.75 (19.05)	A/C	3	0.75 (19.05)	A/C	3	1.50 (38.1)
24 in. (60 mm) wheel dia. & over	9															
Up to 50 hp (37 kW)	9															
Up to 300 rpm	8															
301 to 500 rpm	8	B/C	3	0.75 (19.05)	C	3	1.50 (38.1)	C	3	2.50 (63.5)	C	3	2.50 (63.5)	C	3	2.50 (63.5)
501 rpm & over		B/C	3	0.75 (19.05)	C	3	1.50 (38.1)	C	3	1.50 (38.1)	C	3	1.50 (38.1)	C	3	2.50 (63.5)
Centrifugal Fans & Vent Sets	4,9,19															
Up to 22 in. (550 mm) wheel dia.	9	A/B	2	0.25 (6.35)	A/B	3	0.75 (19.05)	A/B	3	0.75 (19.05)	A/C	3	0.75 (19.05)	A/C	3	0.75 (19.05)
24 in. (600 mm) wheel dia. & over	9															
Up to 50 hp (37 kW)	9															
Up to 300 rpm	8															
301 to 500 rpm	8	B	3	1.50 (38.1)	B	3	1.50 (38.1)	B	3	1.50 (38.1)	B	3	2.50 (63.5)	B	3	2.50 (63.5)
501 rpm & over		B	3	0.75 (19.05)	B	3	0.75 (19.05)	B	3	0.75 (19.05)	B	3	1.50 (38.1)	B	3	2.50 (63.5)
50 hp (37 kW) & over	2,3,9															
Up to 300 rpm	8															
301 to 500 rpm	8	B/C	3	0.75 (19.05)	C	3	1.50 (38.1)	C	3	2.50 (63.5)	C	3	2.50 (63.5)	C	3	3.50 (88.9)
501 rpm & over		B/C	3	0.75 (19.05)	C	3	1.50 (38.1)	C	3	1.50 (38.1)	C	3	2.50 (88.9)	C	3	2.50 (88.9)
Packaged Air Handling Equipment	4,19															
Up to 10 hp (7.5 kW)	4	A	2	0.25 (6.35)	A	3	0.75 (19.05)	A	3	0.75 (19.05)	A	3	0.75 (19.05)	A	3	1.50 (38.1)
15 hp (11 kW) & over	2,3,4,9															
Up to 500 rpm	8	A	2	0.25 (6.35)	A	3	0.75 (19.05)	A	3	1.50 (38.1)	A	3	1.50 (38.1)	A	3	2.50 (63.5)
501 rpm & over		A	2	0.25 (6.35)	A	3	0.75 (19.05)	A	3	1.50 (38.1)	A	3	1.50 (38.1)	A	3	2.50 (63.5)

[a]See Notes for Use with Table 27 section of text for explanation.

[b]*Base Types:*
   A. No base, isolators attached directly to equipment (Note 27)
   B. Structural steel rails or base (Notes 28 & 29)
   C. Concrete inertia base (Note 30)
   D. Curb-mounted base (Note 31)

[c]*Isolator Types:*
   1. Pad, rubber or glass fiber (Notes 20 & 21)
   2. Rubber floor isolator or hanger (Notes 20 & 25)
   3. Spring floor isolator or hanger (Notes 22, 23 & 25)
   4. Restrained spring isolator (Notes 22 & 24)
   5. Thrust restraint (Note 26)

3. For roofs and for floors constructed with open web joists, thin long span slabs, wooden construction and any unusual light construction, evaluate all equipment weighing more than 300 lbs (135 kg), to determine the additional deflection of the structure caused by the equipment weight. Isolator deflection should be 15 times the additional deflection or the deflection shown in the table, whichever is greater. If the required spring isolator deflection exceeds commercially available products, consider air springs, stiffen the supporting structure or change the equipment location.

4. When mechanical equipment is adjacent to noise sensitive areas, Mechanical Equipment Room Noise Isolation should be implemented.

NOTES FOR USE WITH TABLE 27

The notes in this section are keyed to the numbers listed in the second column, headed "Notes," in Table 27, and to other reference numbers throughout the table.

While the guide is conservative, cases may arise where the vibration transmission to the building is still excessive. If the problem persists after all short circuits have been eliminated, it can almost always be corrected by increasing isolator deflection, using low frequency air springs, changing operating speed, reducing vibratory output by additional balancing or, as a last resort, changing floor frequency by stiffening or adding more mass.

Note 1. Isolator deflections shown are based on a floor stiffness that can be reasonably expected for each floor span and class or equipment.

Note 2. For large equipment capable of generating substantial vibratory forces and structure-borne noise, increase isolator deflection, if necessary, so isolator stiffness is at least 0.10 floor stiffness.

Note 3. For noisy equipment adjoining or near noise-sensitive areas, see Mechanical Equipment Room Noise Isolation section.

Note 4. Certain designs cannot be installed directly on individual isolators (Type A) and the equipment manufacturer or a vibration specialist should be consulted on the need for supplemental support (Base Type).

Note 5. Wind load conditions must be considered. Restraint can be achieved with restrained spring isolators, Type 4, supplemental bracing or limit stops.

Note 6. Certain types of equipment require structural support base curb-mounted base, Type D. Airborne noise must be considered.

Note 7. See text for hanger locations adjoining equipment and in equipment rooms.

Note 8. To avoid isolator resonance problems, select isolator deflection from Figure 32 so that natural frequency is 40% or less than the lowest operating speed of equipment.

Note 9. To limit undesirable movement, thrust restraints (Type 5) are required for all ceiling suspended units and floor-mounted units operating at 2 in. (50 mm) and up total static pressure.

Note 10. Pumps over 75 hp (56 kW) may require extra mass and restraining devices.

Note 11. See text for full discussion.

Isolation for Specific Types of Equipment

The following notes, which are also keyed to Table 27, will assist in selecting isolation systems for specific types of equipment.

Note 12. Refrigeration Machines. Large centrifugal, hermetic and reciprocating refrigeration machines generate very high noise levels and special attention is required when such equipment is installed in upper-story locations or near noise-sensitive areas. If such equipment is to be located near extremely noise-sensitive areas, confer with an acoustical consultant.

Note 13. Compressors. The two basic types of reciprocating compressors are (1) single- and double-cylinder vertical, horizontal or L-head, which are usually air compressors; and (2) "Y," "W" and multihead or multicylinder air and refrigeration compressors. Single- and double-cylinder compressors generate high vibratory forces requiring large inertia bases (Type C) and are generally not suitable for upper-story locations. If such equipment must be installed in an upper-story location or grade locations near noise-sensitive areas, unbalanced forces should always be obtained from the equipment manufacturer and a vibration specialist consulted for design of the isolation system.

Note 14. When using "Y," "W," and multihead and multicylinder compressors, obtain the magnitude of unbalanced forces from the equipment manufacturer so that the necessity for an inertia base can be evaluated.

Note 15. Base-mounted compressors through 5 hp (3.7 kW) and horizontal tank-type air compressors through 10 hp (7.5 kW) can be installed directly on spring isolators (Type 3) with structural bases (Type B) if required, and compressors 15 to 100 hp (10 to 75 kW) on spring isolators (Type 3) with inertia bases (Type C) weighing one to two times the compressor weight.

Note 16. Pumps. Concrete inertia bases (Type C) are preferred for all flexible-coupled pumps and are desirable for most close-coupled pumps, although steel bases (Type B) can be used. Close-coupled pumps should not be installed directly on individual isolators (Type A) because the impeller usually overhangs the motor support base, causing the rear mounting to be in tension. The primary requirement for Type C bases are strength and shape to accommodate base elbow supports. Mass is not usually a factor except for pumps over 75 hp (56 kW) where extra mass helps limit excess movement due to starting torque and forces. Concrete bases (Type C) should be designed for a thickness one-tenth the longest dimension with minimum thickness as follows: (1) for up to 30 hp (22 kW), 6 in. (152 mm); (2) for 40 to 75 hp (30 to 56 kW), 8 in. (203 mm); and (3) for 100 hp (75 kW) and higher, 12 in. (304 mm).

Pumps over 75 hp (56 kW) and multistage pumps may exhibit excessive motion at startup; supplemental restraining devices can be installed if this proves necessary. Pumps over 125 hp (93 kW) may generate high starting forces, and it is recommended that a vibration specialist be consulted.

Note 17. Packaged rooftop air-conditioning equipment. This equipment is usually on lightweight structures that are susceptible to sound and vibration transmission; the noise problem is further compounded by curb-mounted equipment, which requires large roof openings for supply and return air.

The table shows Type D vibration isolator selections for all spans up to 20 ft (6 m), but extreme care must be taken for equipment located on spans over 20 ft (6 m), especially if construction is open web joists of thin lightweight slabs. The recommended procedure is to determine the additional deflection that equipment weight causes in the roof. If additional roof deflection is 0.25 in. (6.4 mm) or under, the isolator can be selected for 15 times additional roof deflection. If additional roof deflection is over 0.25 in. (6.4 mm), supplemental stiffening should be installed or the unit relocated.

For units capable of generating high noise levels, especially larger units, consider mounting the unit on a platform above the roof deck to provide an air gap (buffer zone) and locating the unit away from the roof penetration, which permits acoustical treatment of ducts before entering the building.

Some rooftop equipment has compressors, fans and other equipment isolated internally. Experience has shown this isolation is not always reliable because of internal short circuiting, inadequate static deflection or panel resonances. It is recommended that rooftop equipment be isolated externally, as if internal isolation was not used.

Note 18. Cooling Towers. These are normally isolated with restrained spring isolators (Type 4) directly under the tower or tower dunnage. Occasionally, high deflection isolators are proposed for use directly under the motor-fan assembly, but this arrangement must be used with extreme caution.

Note 19. Fans and Air Handling Equipment. The following should be considered in selecting isolation systems for fans and air handling equipment:

a. Fans with wheel diameters 22 in. (560 mm) and under and all fans operating at speeds to 300 rpm (5 r/s) do not generate large vibratory forces. For fans operating under 300 rpm (5 r/s), select isolator deflection so the isolator natural frequency is 40%

or less than the fan speed. For example, for a fan operating at 275 rpm, 0.4 × 275 = 110 cpm. Therefore, an isolator natural frequency of 110 cpm (2 cps) or lower is required. This can be accomplished with a 3 in. (75 mm) deflection isolator (Type 3).

b. Flexible duct connectors should be installed at the intake and discharge of all fans and air handling equipment to reduce transmission to duct work.

c. Inertia bases (Type C) are recommended for all Class 2 and 3 fans and air handling equipment because extra mass permits using stiffer springs, which limit movement.

d. Thrust restraints (Type 5) that incorporate the same deflec-

tion as isolators should be used for all fan heads, all suspended fans and all base-mounted and suspended air-handling equipment operating at 2 in. (50 mm) and over total static pressure.

Vibration Isolators: Materials, Types, and Configurations

The following notes (20 through 31) are included in Figure 35 to assist in the evaluation of isolators commercially available for HVAC equipment. The isolator selected for an application depends on the required deflection, but life, cost, and suitability must also be considered.

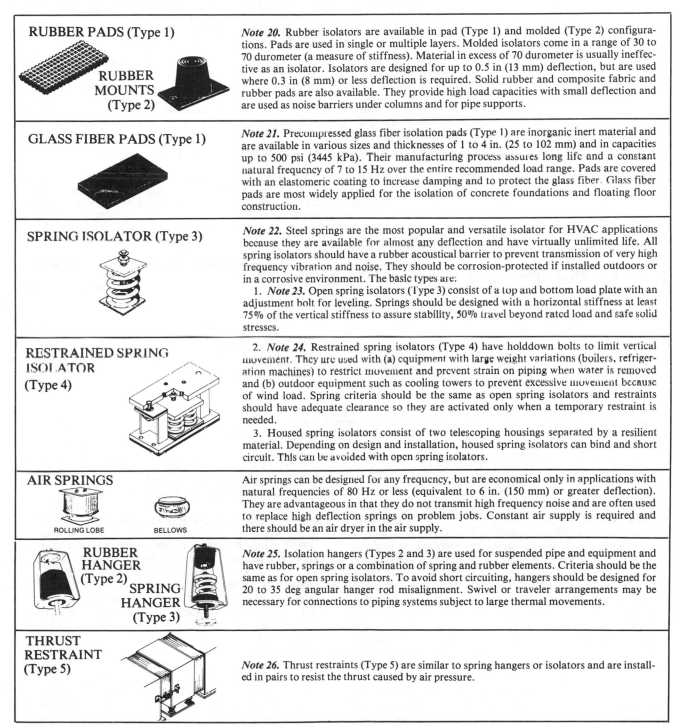

RUBBER PADS (Type 1)
RUBBER MOUNTS (Type 2)

Note 20. Rubber isolators are available in pad (Type 1) and molded (Type 2) configurations. Pads are used in single or multiple layers. Molded isolators come in a range of 30 to 70 durometer (a measure of stiffness). Material in excess of 70 durometer is usually ineffective as an isolator. Isolators are designed for up to 0.5 in (13 mm) deflection, but are used where 0.3 in (8 mm) or less deflection is required. Solid rubber and composite fabric and rubber pads are also available. They provide high load capacities with small deflection and are used as noise barriers under columns and for pipe supports.

GLASS FIBER PADS (Type 1)

Note 21. Precompressed glass fiber isolation pads (Type 1) are inorganic inert material and are available in various sizes and thicknesses of 1 to 4 in. (25 to 102 mm) and in capacities up to 500 psi (3445 kPa). Their manufacturing process assures long life and a constant natural frequency of 7 to 15 Hz over the entire recommended load range. Pads are covered with an elastomeric coating to increase damping and to protect the glass fiber. Glass fiber pads are most widely applied for the isolation of concrete foundations and floating floor construction.

SPRING ISOLATOR (Type 3)

Note 22. Steel springs are the most popular and versatile isolator for HVAC applications because they are available for almost any deflection and have virtually unlimited life. All spring isolators should have a rubber acoustical barrier to prevent transmission of very high frequency vibration and noise. They should be corrosion-protected if installed outdoors or in a corrosive environment. The basic types are:

1. *Note 23.* Open spring isolators (Type 3) consist of a top and bottom load plate with an adjustment bolt for leveling. Springs should be designed with a horizontal stiffness at least 75% of the vertical stiffness to assure stability, 50% travel beyond rated load and safe solid stresses.

RESTRAINED SPRING ISOLATOR (Type 4)

2. *Note 24.* Restrained spring isolators (Type 4) have holddown bolts to limit vertical movement. They are used with (a) equipment with large weight variations (boilers, refrigeration machines) to restrict movement and prevent strain on piping when water is removed and (b) outdoor equipment such as cooling towers to prevent excessive movement because of wind load. Spring criteria should be the same as open spring isolators and restraints should have adequate clearance so they are activated only when a temporary restraint is needed.

3. Housed spring isolators consist of two telescoping housings separated by a resilient material. Depending on design and installation, housed spring isolators can bind and short circuit. This can be avoided with open spring isolators.

AIR SPRINGS
ROLLING LOBE   BELLOWS

Air springs can be designed for any frequency, but are economical only in applications with natural frequencies of 80 Hz or less (equivalent to 6 in. (150 mm) or greater deflection). They are advantageous in that they do not transmit high frequency noise and are often used to replace high deflection springs on problem jobs. Constant air supply is required and there should be an air dryer in the air supply.

RUBBER HANGER (Type 2)
SPRING HANGER (Type 3)

Note 25. Isolation hangers (Types 2 and 3) are used for suspended pipe and equipment and have rubber, springs or a combination of spring and rubber elements. Criteria should be the same as for open spring isolators. To avoid short circuiting, hangers should be designed for 20 to 35 deg angular hanger rod misalignment. Swivel or traveler arrangements may be necessary for connections to piping systems subject to large thermal movements.

THRUST RESTRAINT (Type 5)

Note 26. Thrust restraints (Type 5) are similar to spring hangers or isolators and are installed in pairs to resist the thrust caused by air pressure.

Fig. 35   Vibration Isolators

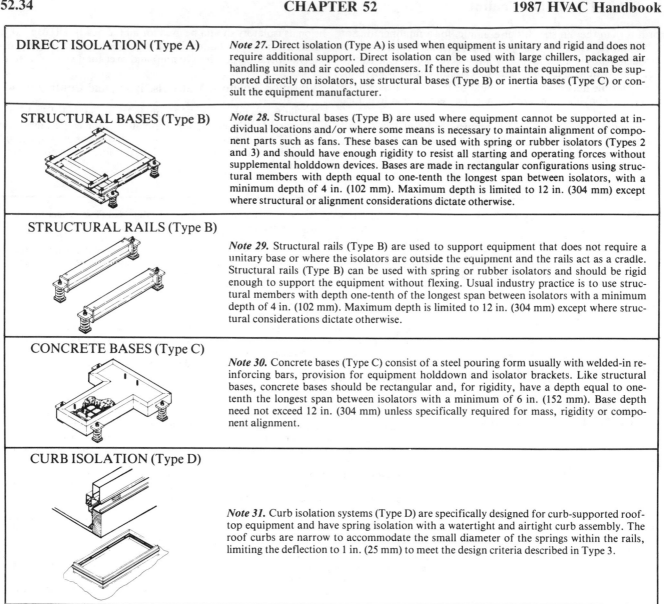

DIRECT ISOLATION (Type A)	*Note 27.* Direct isolation (Type A) is used when equipment is unitary and rigid and does not require additional support. Direct isolation can be used with large chillers, packaged air handling units and air cooled condensers. If there is doubt that the equipment can be supported directly on isolators, use structural bases (Type B) or inertia bases (Type C) or consult the equipment manufacturer.
STRUCTURAL BASES (Type B)	*Note 28.* Structural bases (Type B) are used where equipment cannot be supported at individual locations and/or where some means is necessary to maintain alignment of component parts such as fans. These bases can be used with spring or rubber isolators (Types 2 and 3) and should have enough rigidity to resist all starting and operating forces without supplemental holddown devices. Bases are made in rectangular configurations using structural members with depth equal to one-tenth the longest span between isolators, with a minimum depth of 4 in. (102 mm). Maximum depth is limited to 12 in. (304 mm) except where structural or alignment considerations dictate otherwise.
STRUCTURAL RAILS (Type B)	*Note 29.* Structural rails (Type B) are used to support equipment that does not require a unitary base or where the isolators arc outside the equipment and the rails act as a cradle. Structural rails (Type B) can be used with spring or rubber isolators and should be rigid enough to support the equipment without flexing. Usual industry practice is to use structural members with depth one-tenth of the longest span between isolators with a minimum depth of 4 in. (102 mm). Maximum depth is limited to 12 in. (304 mm) except where structural considerations dictate otherwise.
CONCRETE BASES (Type C)	*Note 30.* Concrete bases (Type C) consist of a steel pouring form usually with welded-in reinforcing bars, provision for equipment holddown and isolator brackets. Like structural bases, concrete bases should be rectangular and, for rigidity, have a depth equal to one-tenth the longest span between isolators with a minimum of 6 in. (152 mm). Base depth need not exceed 12 in. (304 mm) unless specifically required for mass, rigidity or component alignment.
CURB ISOLATION (Type D)	*Note 31.* Curb isolation systems (Type D) are specifically designed for curb-supported rooftop equipment and have spring isolation with a watertight and airtight curb assembly. The roof curbs are narrow to accommodate the small diameter of the springs within the rails, limiting the deflection to 1 in. (25 mm) to meet the design criteria described in Type 3.

Fig. 35   Vibration Isolators (continued)

ISOLATION OF VIBRATION AND NOISE IN PIPING SYSTEMS

All piping systems have mechanical vibration generated by the equipment and impeller-generated and flow-induced vibration and noise, which is transmitted by the pipe wall and the water column. In addition, equipment installed on vibration isolators exhibits some motion or movement from pressure thrusts during operation. It has even greater movement during start up and shut down when the equipment goes through the resonant frequency of the isolators. The piping system must be flexible enough to (1) reduce vibration transmission along the connected piping, (2) permit equipment movement without reducing the performance of vibration isolators, and (3) accommodate equipment movement or thermal movement of the piping at connections without imposing undue strain upon the connections and equipment.

Flow noise in piping can be minimized by sizing pipe so that velocities are 4 fps (1.2 m/s) maximum for pipe 2 in. (50 mm) and smaller and using a pressure drop limitation of 4 ft/100 ft (1 m/30 m) with a maximum velocity of 10 fps (3 m/s) for larger pipe sizes. Flow noise and vibration can be reintroduced by turbulence, sharp pressure drops, and entrained air. Care should be taken to avoid these conditions.

Resilient Pipe Hangers and Supports

Resilient pipe hangers and supports are necessary to prevent vibration and noise transmission from the piping system to the building structure and to provide flexibility in the piping.

Suspended Piping. Isolation hangers described in the vibration isolation section should be used for all piping in equipment rooms or for 50 ft (15 m) from vibrating equipment, whichever is greater. To avoid reducing the effectiveness of equipment isolators, at least three of the first hangers from the equipment should provide the same deflection as the equipment isolators, with a maximum limitation of 2 in. (50 mm) deflection; the remaining hangers should be spring or combination spring and rubber with 0.75 in. (20 mm) deflection. It is good practice to require the first two hangers adjacent to the equipment to be the positioning or precompressed type to prevent load transfer to the equipment flanges when the piping system is filled. The positioning hanger aids in installing large pipe and many engineers specify this type for all isolated pipe hangers for piping 8 in. (200 mm) and over. While isolation hangers are not often specified for branch piping or piping beyond the equipment room for economic reasons, they should be used for all piping over 2 in. (50 mm) in diameter and for any piping suspended below or near noise sensitive areas. Hangers adjacent to noise sensitive areas should be the spring and rubber combination.

Floor Supported Piping. Floor supports for piping in equipment rooms and adjacent to isolated equipment should use vibration isolators as described in the vibration isolation section. They should be selected according to the guidelines for hangers. The first two adjacent floor supports should be the restrained spring type with a blocking feature that prevents load transfer to equipment flanges as the piping is filled or drained. Where pipe is subjected to large thermal movement, a slide plate (Teflon, graphite or steel) should be installed on top of the isolator, and a thermal barrier should be used when rubber products are installed directly beneath steam or hot water lines.

Riser Supports, Anchors and Guides. Many piping systems have anchors and guides, especially in the risers, to permit expansion joints, bends or pipe loops to function properly. Anchors and guides are designed to eliminate or limit (guide) pipe movement and must be rigidly attached to the structure, which

is inconsistent with the resiliency required for effective isolation. The engineer should try to locate the pipe shafts, anchors and guides in non-critical areas such as by elevator shafts, stairwells and toilets, rather than adjoining noise-sensitive areas. Where a concern about vibration transmission exists, some type of vibration isolation support or acoustical support is required for the pipe support, anchors and guides.

Since anchors or guides must be rigidly attached to the structure, the isolation cannot deflect in the sense previously discussed and the primary interest is an an acoustical barrier. Such acoustical barriers càn be provided by heavy-duty rubber and duck and rubber pads that can accommodate large loads with minimal deflection. Figures 36, 37, and 38 show some arrangement for resilient anchors and guides. Similar resilient type suports can be used for the pipe.

The resilient supports for the pipe, anchors, and guides can attenuate noise transmission but do not provide the resiliency required to isolate vibration. Vibration must be controlled in an anchor guide system by designing ample flexibility into the piping system before the anchors with flexible pipe connectors and resilient isolation hangers or supports.

Completely spring isolated riser systems that eliminate the anchors and guides have been used successfully in many instances and give effective vibration and acoustical isolation. In this type of isolation system the springs are sized to accommodate thermal growth as well as guide and support the pipe. Such systems require careful engineering to accommodate the movements encountered not only in the riser but also in the branch takeoff to avoid overstressing the piping.

Piping Penetrations. Most HVAC systems have many points at which piping must penetrate floors, walls and ceilings. If such penetrations are not properly treated, they provide a path for airborne noise, which can destroy the acoustical integrity of the occupied space. Seal the openings in the pipe sleeves between noisy areas such as equipment rooms and occupied spaces with an acoustical barrier such as fibrous material and caulking or with engineered pipe penetration seals as shown in Figure 39.

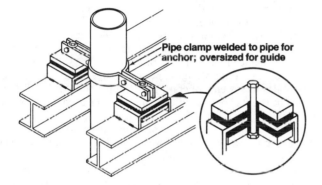

Fig. 36   Acoustical Barriers for Pipe Anchors and Guides

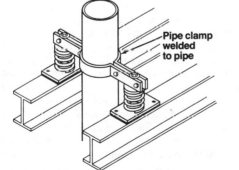

Fig. 37   Spring Isolated Riser System

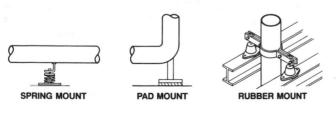

Fig. 38   Conventional Isolators as Pipe Supports for Lines with Expansion Joints

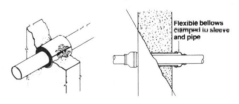

Fig. 39   Acoustical Pipe Penetration Seals

FLEXIBLE PIPE CONNECTORS

Flexible pipe connectors (Figure 40): (1) provide piping flexibility to permit isolators to function properly, (2) protect equipment from strain from misalignment and expansion or contraction of piping, and (3) attenuate noise and vibration transmission along the piping. Connectors are available in two basic configurations: (1) hose type, a straight or slightly corrugated wall construction of either rubber or metal and (2) the arched or expansion joint type, a short length connector with one or more large radius arches, of either rubber, Teflon, or metal. Metal expansion joints are seldom used in HVAC systems for vibration and sound isolation and their use is not recommended. All flexible connectors require end restraint to counteract the pressure thrust, which is either (1) added to the connector, (2) incorporated by its design, (3) added to the piping system (anchoring), or (4) built in by the stiffness of the system. Connector

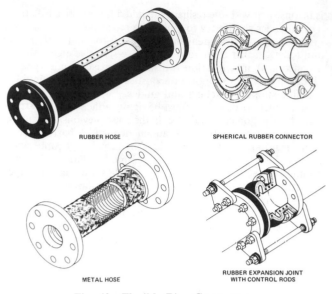

Fig. 40   Flexible Pipe Connectors

extension caused by pressure thrust on isolated equipment should also be considered when flexible connectors are used. Over-extension will cause failure; manufacturers' recommendations on restraint, pressure and temperature limitations should be adhered to strictly.

Hose Connectors

Hose Connectors accommodate lateral movement perpendicular to the length and have very limited or no axial movement capability.

Rubber Hose connectors can be of molded or handwrapped construction with wire reinforcing and are available with metal-threaded end fittings or integral rubber flanges. Application of threaded fittings should be limited to 3 in. (76 mm) and smaller pipe diameter. The fittings should be the mechanically expanded type to minimize the possibility of pressure thrust blow-out. Flanged types are available in larger pipe sizes. Although rubber hose has some built in thrust restraint, isolated control rod assemblies are recommended when hose is attached to spring-isolated equipment and where piping is not anchored to resist pressure thrust. Table 28 provides recommended lengths.

Table 28   Recommended Live[a] Length of Flexible Rubber and Metal Hose

Nominal Diameter		Length,[b]	
in.	(mm)	in.	(mm)
0.75	(20)	12	(300)
1	(25)	12	(300)
1.5	(40)	12	(300)
2	(50)	12	(300)
2.5	(65)	12	(300)
3	(80)	18	(450)
4	(100)	18	(450)
5	(125)	24	(600)
6	(150)	24	(600)
8	(200)	24	(600)
10	(250)	24	(600)
12	(300)	36	(900)

[a]Live Length is end-to-end length for integral flanged rubber hose and is end-to-end less total fitting length for all other types.
[b]Based upon recommendatons of Rubber Expansion Joint Division, Fluid Sealing Association.

Metal Hose is constructed with a corrugated inner core and a braided cover, which helps attain a pressure rating and provides end restraints that eliminate the need for supplemental control assemblies. Short lengths of metal hose or corrugated metal bellows, commonly called "pump connectors," are available without braid and have built-in control assemblies. Metal hose is used to control misalignment and vibration rather than noise and is used primarily where temperature or the pressure of flow-media preclude the use of other material. Table 28 provides recommended lengths.

Expansion Joint or Arched Type Connectors

Expansion joint or arched-type connectors have one or more convolutions or arches and can accommodate all modes of axial, lateral and angular movement and misalignment. These connectors are available in flanged rubber and Teflon construction. When made of rubber, they are commonly referred to as expansion joints, spool joints or spherical connectors, and in Teflon, as couplings or expansion joints.

Rubber expansion joints or spool joints are available in two basic types: (1) handwrapped with wire and fabric reinforcing and (b) molded with fabric and wire or with high strength fabric only instead of metal for reinforcing. The handmade type is available in a variety of materials and lengths for special applications. Most rubber expansion joints have limited or no built-in thrust restraints and their control assemblies must be used as described for rubber hose joints.

Rubber spherical connectors are molded with high strength fabric or tire cord reinforcing instead of metal. Their distinguishing characteristic is a large radius arch. The shape and construction of some designs permit usage without control assemblies in systems operating to 150 psi (1000 kPa). Where thrust restraints are not built in, they must be used as described for rubber hose joints.

Teflon expansion joints and couplings are similar in construction to rubber expansion joints with reinforcing metal rings. They usually have built-in control assemblies.

In evaluating these devices, consider the temperature, pressure, and service conditions as well as each device's ability to attenuate vibration and noise. Metal hose connections can accommodate misalignment and attenuate mechanical vibration transmitted through the pipe wall but do little to attenuate noise. This type of connector has superior resistance to long-term temperature effects. Rubber hose, expansion joints and spherical connectors attenuate vibration and impeller-generated noise transmitted through the pipe wall. Because the rubber expansion joint and spherical connector walls are flexible, they have the ability to grow volumetrically and attenuate noise and vibration at blade passage frequencies. This is a particularly desirable feature in uninsulated piping systems such as condenser water and domestic water, which may run adjacent to noise-sensitive areas. However, high pressure has a detrimental effect on the ability of the connector to attenuate vibration and noise. In addition, where control assemblies must be used, the pressure thrust in the system causes the resilient washers to become "solid," thereby diminishing their isolation capability. Because none of the flexible pipe connectors will control flow or velocity noise nor completely isolate vibration and noise transmission to the piping system, resilient pipe hangers and support should be used; these are shown in Table 27 and described in the "Resilient Pipe Hangers and Supports" section.

ISOLATING DUCT VIBRATION

Flexible canvas and rubber duct connections should be used at fan intake and discharge. However, they are not completely

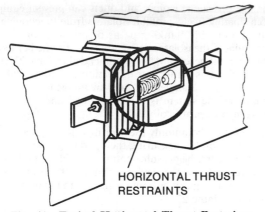

Fig. 41   Typical Horizontal Thrust Restrainer

effective since they become rigid under pressure and allow the vibrating fan to pull on the duct wall. Thrust restraints as shown in Figure 41 should be used on all equipment as indicated in Table 27 and in the Vibration Isolator Selection section to maintain a slack position of the flexible duct connections.

While vibration transmission from ducts, which are isolated by flexible connectors, is not a common problem, flow pulsations within the duct can cause mechanical vibration in the duct walls, which can be transmitted through rigid hangers. Spring or combination spring and rubber hangers are recommended wherever ducts are suspended below or near a noise sensitive area. These hangers are especially recommended for large ducts with velocities above 1500 fpm (7.6 m/s) and for all size ducts when duct static pressures are 2 in. of water (500 Pa) gauge and over.

SEISMIC PROTECTION

Seismic protection of resiliently mounted equipment poses a unique problem not found in vibration isolation selection application (Mason and Lama 1976). If a seismic snubber is incorrectly selected it would not become apparent until an earthquake occurred. This deficiency could then manifest itself in a loss of life or property. Since resiliently-mounted systems are much more susceptible to earthquake damage due to resonances inherent in the vibration isolators, a professional engineer should evaluate these systems. Seismic history in both Alaska and California shows improperly designed seismic snubber systems have failed with seismic inputs as low as 0.2 G.

Seismic snubbers can be designed to hold equipment in place without regard to internal damage or to keep the equipment operational during and after a seismic event. Static analysis techniques are acceptable in many codes, but may not point out serious design deficiencies, nor relieve the designer of legal

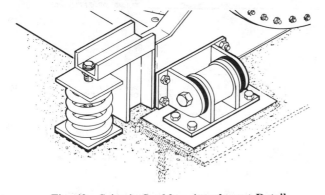

Fig. 42   Seismic Snubber Attachment Detail

responsibility. A dynamic analysis is preferred to help prevent failures.

Because of the potential for catastrophic failure, it is suggested that seismic snubbers be tested to verify their characteristics. Note that both the attachment to the equipment as well as to the structure is critical since a failure at these interfaces will be just as serious as a failure of the snubber itself. There are several snubbing systems presently in use that have proven adequate or acceptable to professional societies. The engineer should take every precaution to ensure he uses one of the proven systems where required. Figure 42 shows a typical all-directional seismic snubber.

TROUBLESHOOTING

In spite of all efforts taken by specifying engineers, consultants, and installing contractors, situations arise where there is disturbing noise and vibration. While this chapter is not a comprehensive guide to troubleshooting, many problems can be readily identified and corrected by (1) determining which equipment or system is the source of the problem, (2) determining if the problem is one of airborne sound, vibration and structure-borne noise, or a combination of both, and (3) applying appropriate solutions.

DETERMINING PROBLEM SOURCE

The system or equipment that is the source of the problem can often be determined without instrumentation. The vibration and noise levels are usually well above the sensory level of perception and are readily felt or heard. A simple and accurate method is to turn on and off individual pieces of equipment until the vibration or noise is eliminated. Often, the source of the problem is more than one piece of equipment or the interaction of two or more systems, so it is always a good idea to double check by shutting off the system and operating the equipment individually.

DETERMINING PROBLEM TYPE

The next step is to determine if the problem is one of noise or vibration.

1. If vibration is perceptible, vibration transmission is usually the major cause of the problem. The possibility that light weight wall or ceiling panels are excited by airborne noise should be considered. If vibration is not perceptible, the problem may still be one of vibration transmission causing structure-borne noise, which can be checked by following the procedure below.
2. If a sound level meter is available, check C-scale and overall scale readings. If the difference is greater than 6 dB, or if the slope of the curve is greater than 5 to 6 dB/octave in the low frequencies, vibration is probably the problem.
3. If the affected area is remote from source equipment, there is no problem in intermediary spaces and noise does not appear to be coming from the duct system or diffusers, structure-borne noise is probably the problem.

SOUND PROBLEMS

Sound problems are more complex than vibration problems and usually require the services of an acoustical engineer or consultant.

If the affected area adjoins the room where the source equipment is located, structure-borne noise must be considered as part of the problem and the vibration isolation systems should be checked. A simple but reasonably effective test is to have one person listen in the affected area while another person shouts loudly in the equipment room. If the voice cannot be heard, the problem is likely one of structure-borne noise. If the voice can be heard, check for openings in the wall or floor separating the areas. If no such openings exist, the structure separating the areas does not provide adequate transmission loss. In such situations, refer to the "Mechanical Equipment Room Noise Isolation" section of this chapter for possible solutions.

If duct-borne sound—noise from grilles or diffusers and noise emanating from duct walls (breakout noise)—is the problem, measure the sound pressure levels and compare them with the RC curves in Figure 5. Where the measured curve differs from the RC curve, the potential noise source can be narrowed down by comparing it with Figure 2. Once the noise sources have been identified, the engineer can determine whether sufficient attenuation has been provided by analyzing each sound source using the procedures presented in this chapter.

If the sound source is a fan, pump or similar rotating equipment, determine if it is operating at the most efficient part of its operating curve. This is the point at which most equipment operates smoothest. Excessive vibration and noise can occur if a fan or pump is trying to move too little or too much air or water. In this respect, make sure to check that vanes, dampers and valves are in the correct operating position and that system has been balanced properly.

VIBRATION PROBLEMS

Vibration and structure-borne noise problems can occur from:

1. Equipment operating with excessive levels of vibration, usually caused by unbalance.
2. Lack of vibration isolators.
3. Improperly selected or installed vibration isolators that do not provide the required isolator deflection.
4. Flanking transmission paths such as rigid pipe connections or obstructions under the base of isolated equipment.
5. Floor flexibility.
6. Resonances in equipment, the vibration isolation system or the building structure.

Most field-encountered problems are the result of improperly selected or installed isolators and flanking paths of transmission, which can be simply evaluated and corrected.

Floor flexibility and resonance problems are seldom encountered and usually required analysis by outside experts. However, the information provided below will identify such problems.

If the equipment lacks vibration isolators, isolators recommended in Table 27 can be added by using structural brackets without altering connected ducts or piping.

Testing Vibration Isolation Systems

Improperly functioning vibration isolation systems are the cause of most field encountered problems and can be evaluated and corrected by the following procedures.

1. Ensure that the system is "free floating" by bouncing the base, which should cause the equipment to move up and down freely and easily. On floor mounted equipment, check that there are no obstructions between the base and floor, which would "short circuit" the isolation system. This is best accomplished by passing a rod under the equipment. A small obstruction might permit the base to "rock" giving the impression that it is "free floating" when it is not. On suspended equipment, make sure that rods are not touching the hanger box. Rigid

connections such as pipes and ducts can prevent equipment from floating freely, prohibit isolators from functioning properly and provide flanking paths of transmission.
2. Determine if the isolator deflection is as specified or required, changing it if necessary, as recommended in Table 27. A common problem is inadequate deflection caused by underloaded isolators. Overloaded isolators are not generally a problem as long as the system is "free floating" and there is space between the spring coils.

With the most commonly used spring isolators, determine the spring deflection by measuring the operating height and comparing it to the free height information available from the isolator manufacturer. Once the actual isolator deflection is known, determine its adequacy by comparing it with the recommended deflection in Table 27.

Except in situations where heavy equipment is installed on extremely long span floors or very "flexible" floors, if the natural frequency of the isolator is 1/4 or less than the disturbing frequency (usually considered the operating speed of the equipment), the isolators should be amply efficient. If a transmission problem exists, it may be caused by (1) excessively rough equipment operation, (2) the system not being "free floating" of flanking paths of transmission as described above, or (3) a resonance or floor stiffness problem as described below.

While it is easy to determine the natural frequency of spring isolators by height measurements, such measurements are difficult with pad and rubber isolators and are not accurate in determining their natural frequencies. Although such isolators theoretically can provide natural frequencies as low as 260 Hz (approximately 0.5 in. [13 mm] deflection), they actually provide higher natural frequencies and generally do not provide the desired isolation efficiencies for upper floor equipment locations.

Isolation efficiency cannot be checked by comparing the vibration amplitude level of the equipment to that of the structure as shown in Figure 43 (top). These levels seem to show 10% transmission (90% isolator efficiency) when, actually, the isolators might be in resonance, resulting in higher levels of vibration than if no isolators were installed. The only accurate way to measure isolator efficiency is to compare two sets of measurements on the structure: one having the equipment operating *with* isolators and one *without* isolators, as shown in Figure 43 (bottom).

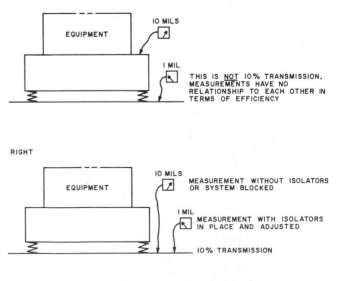

Fig. 43   Testing Isolation Efficiency

Floor Flexibility Problems

Floor flexibility is not a problem with most equipment and structures; however, such problems can occur with heavy equipment installed on long span floors or thin slabs and with rooftop equipment installed on "light" structures of open web joist construction. If floor flexibility is suspected, the isolators should be 1/10 or less as stiff as the floor to eliminate the problem. Floor stiffness can be determined by calculating the additional deflection in the floor caused by a specific piece of equipment.

For example, if a 10,000 lb (4500 kg) piece of equipment causes floor deflection of an additional 0.1 in. (2.5 mm), floor stiffness is 100,000 lb/in. (17 500 N/mm) and an isolator of 10,000 lb/in (1750 N/mm) must be used. Note that the floor stiffness or spring rate, *not* the total floor deflection, is determined. In this example the total floor deflection might be 1 in. (25 mm), but if the problem equipment causes 0.1 in. (2.5 mm) of that deflection, 0.1 in. (2.5 mm) is the important figure and floor stiffness k is 100,000 lb/in. (17 500 N/mm).

Resonance Problems

Resonance problems occur when the operating speed of the equipment is the same or close to the natural frequency of (1) an equipment component such as a fan shaft or bearing support pedestal, (2) the vibration isolation system, or (3) the natural frequency of the floor or other building component such as a wall. Resonance can cause excessive equipment vibration levels as well as objectionable and possibly destructive vibration transmission. These conditions must always be determined and corrected.

Vibration Isolation System Resonance

Vibration isolation system resonance is always characterized by excessive equipment vibration and usually results in objectionable transmission to the structure. However, transmission might not occur if the equipment is on-grade or on a stiff floor. Vibration isolation system resonance can be measured with instrumentation or, more simply, by determining the isolator natural frequency as described in the section "Testing Vibration Isolation Systems" and comparing this figure to the operating speed of the equipment.

When vibration isolation system resonance exists, the isolator natural frequency must be changed using the following guidelines:

1. If the equipment is installed on pad or rubber isolators, isolators with the deflection recommended in Table 27 should be installed.
2. If the equipment is installed on spring isolators and there is no objectionable vibration or noise transmission to the structure, determine if the isolator is providing maximum deflection. For example, an improperly selected or installed nominal 2 in. (50 mm) deflection isolator could be providing only 1/8 in. (3 mm) deflection, which would be in resonance with equipment operating at 500 rpm (8 Hz). If this is the case, the isolators should be replaced with ones having enough capacity to provide 2 in. (50 mm) deflection. Since there was no transmission problem with the "resonant" isolators, it is not necessary to use greater deflection isolators than can be conveniently installed.
3. If the equipment is installed on spring isolators and there is objectional noise or vibration transmission, replace the isolators with spring isolators with the deflection recommended in Table 27.

Building Resonance

Building resonance problems occur when some part of the structure has a natural frequency the same as the disturbing frequency or the operating speed of some of the equipment. These problems can exist even if the isolator deflections recommended in Table 28 are used. The resulting objectionable noise or vibration should be evaluated and corrected. Often, the resonant problem is in the floor on which the equipment is installed, but can also occur in a remotely located floor, wall, or other building component. If a noise or vibration problem is from a remote source, such as equipment installed several floors away, that cannot be associated with piping or ducts, resonance must be suspected.

Resonance problems can be resolved by the following:

1. *Reducing the vibratory force F by balancing the equipment.* This is not a practical solution for a true resonant problem, but is viable when the disturbing frequency equals the floor natural frequency, as evidenced by the equal displacement of the floor and the equipment, especially when the equipment is operating with excessive vibration.
2. *Changing the isolator natural frequency, f_n, by increasing or decreasing the deflection.* Only small changes are necessary to "detune" the system. Generally, increasing the deflection is preferred; If the initial deflection was 1 in. (25 mm), a 2 or 3 in. (50 or 75 mm) deflection isolator should be installed. However, if the initial isolator deflection was 4 in. (100 mm), it would be more practical and economical to replace it with 2 or 3 in. (50 or 75 mm) deflection isolators. Changing the natural frequency is only practical for true resonant conditions, *not* when the disturbing frequency equals the floor natural frequency ($f_d = f_f$). In such situations, the floor and equipment displacement are the same. Assuming that an effective isolation system is $f_d/f_n = 4$, it occurs in the asymptotic portion of the displacement curve and requires a tremendous increase in isolator deflection for even a small reduction in equipment displacement. In such situations, methods 1, 3, or 4 provide a more practical and economical solution.
3. *Changing the structure stiffness, k_f, or the structure natural frequency, f_f.* A change in structure stiffness changes the structure natural frequency; the greater the stiffness, the higher the frequency. However, the structure natural frequency can also be changed by increasing or decreasing the floor deflection without changing the floor stiffness. While this is an impractical approach and is not recommended, it may be the only solution in certain cases.
4. *Changing the disturbing frequency, f_d, by changing the equipment operating speed.* This is practical only for belt-driven equipment such as fans.

Trouble-shooting is time consuming, expensive, and often difficult. In addition, once a transmission problem exists, the occupants become more sensitive and require lower reduction of the sound and vibration levels than initially would have proved satisfactory. Therefore, the need for trouble shooting should be avoided by carefully designing, installing and testing the system as soon as it is operational and before the building is occupied.

REFERENCES

ASA. 1983. Specification for Sound Level Meters. Acoustical Society of America *Standard* 47-83 (ANSI S1.4-83), New York, NY.

Beranek, L.L. 1957. Revised Criteria for Noise in Buildings. *Noise Control,* January, p. 19.

Blazier, W.E. 1972. Chiller Noise: Its Impact on Building Design. ASHRAE Symposium Bulletin No. 3.

Blazier, W.E. 1981. Noise Rating of Variable Air-Volume Terminal Devices. ASHRAE *Transactions*, Vol. 87, Part 1.

Blazier, W.E. 1981. Revised Noise Criteria (RC Curves) for Application in the Acoustical Design of HVAC Systems. *Noise Control Engineering,* Vol. 16, No. 2, March-April.

Brockmeyer, H. 1968. Stromungsakustische Untersuchungen an Kanalnetzelementen von Hochgeschwindigkeits-Klimaanlagen. Dissertation, Technischen Universitat Carolo Wilhelmina, Braunschweig.

Cummings, A. 1985. Acoustic Noise Transmission Through Duct Walls. ASHRAE *Transactions*, Vol. 91, Part 2A, pp. 48-61.

Den Hartog, J.P. 1956. *Mechanical Vibrations*. McGraw-Hill, New York, NY.

Ebbing, C.E.; Fragnito, D.; and Inglis, S. 1978. Control of Low Frequency Duct-Generated Noise in Building Air Distribution Systems. ASHRAE *Transactions*, Vol. 84, Part 2, p. 191.

Harold, R.G. 1986. Round Duct Can Stop Rumble Noise in Air Handling Installations. ASHRAE *Transactions*, Vol. 92, Part 2.

Harris, C.M., ed. 1979. *Handbook of Noise Control,* Chapter 35. McGraw-Hill, New York, NY.

Harris, C. M.; and Crede, C.E., eds. 1976. *Shock & Vibration Handbook*. McGraw-Hill, New York, NY.

Hedeen, R.A. *et al.* 1980. *Compendium of Materials for Noise Control*. U.S. Dept. of Health, Education and Welfare, NIOSH, Cincinnati.

Heinter, I. 1968. How to Estimate Plant Noises. *Hydrocarbon Processing*, Vol. 47, No. 12, December, p. 67.

Kugler, B.A.; *et al.* 1973. Noise Study of Proposed SOCAL El Segundo Refinery Project. Bolt, Beranek & Newman, Inc., Report No. 2426.

Mason, N.J.; and Lama, P.J. 1976. Seismic Control for Floor Mounted Equipment. *Heating, Piping & Air Conditioning,* March.

Miller, L.N. 1970. Acquisition and Study of the Noise Data of Certain Electrical and Mechanical Equipment Used in Buildings. Bolt, Beranek & Newman, Inc., Report No. 1778.

Schultz, T.J. 1983. Relationship Between Sound Power Level and Sound Pressure Level in Dwellings and Offices. ASHRAE *Transactions*, Vol. 91, Part 1A, pp. 124-153.

Sessler, S.M. 1973. Acoustical and Mechanical Considerations for the Evaluation of Chiller Noise. ASHRAE *Journal*, Vol. 15, October, p. 39.

Sessler, S.M.; and Hoover, R.M. 1983. Laboratory Fume Hood Noise. *Heating/Piping/Air Conditioning.* September.

United Sheet Metal Co. 1973. Bulletin 40-1-672-B. Westervill, OH. (From DAL Test Reports NO. DAL-985-1,2,3-70 and Kal 1507-7-73.

United States Gypsum. 1971. *Drywall Construction Handbook*. Chicago.

Ver, I.L. 1984. Noise Generation and Noise Attenuation of Duct Fittings—A Review: Part I and Part II. ASHRAE *Transactions*, Vol. 90, Part 2A, pp. 354-390.

Ver, I.L. 1978. A Review of the Attenuation of Sound in Straight Lined and Unlined Ductwork of Rectangular Cross Section. ASHRAE *Transactions*, Vol. 84, Part 1, p. 122.

Waeldner, W.J. 1975. Acoustical Considerations in Air Distribution. ASHRAE *Transactions*, Vol. 81, Part 2, p. 504.

Wells, R.J. 1958. Acoustical Plenum Chambers. *Noise Control*, July, p. 9.

CHAPTER 53

WATER TREATMENT

THIS chapter covers the fundamentals of corrosion, its prevention and control, and some of the common problems arising from corrosion in heating and air-conditioning equipment. Further information can be obtained from the references listed in the bibliography and in publications of the National Association of Corrosion Engineers and the American Water Works Association.

DEFINITIONS

Some terms commonly used in the field of water treatment are defined as follows:

Alkalinity. The sum of the bicarbonate, carbonate and hydroxide ions in water. Other ions, such as borate, phosphate, or silicate, can also contribute to alkalinity.

Anion. A negatively charged ion of an electrolyte, which migrates towards the anode under the influence of a potential gradient.

Anode. The electrode of an electrolytic cell at which oxidation occurs.

Biological Deposits. Water-formed deposits of biological organisms or the products of their life processes, such as barnacles, algae, or slimes.

Cathode. The electrode of an electrolytic cell at which reduction occurs.

Cation. A positively charged ion of an electrolyte, which migrates toward the cathode under the influence of a potential gradient.

Corrosion. The deterioration of a material, usually a metal, by reaction with its environment.

Corrosivity. The capacity of an environment to bring about destruction of a specific metal by the process of corrosion.

Electrolyte. A solution through which an electric current can be made to flow.

Galvanic Corrosion. Corrosion resulting from the contact of two dissimilar metals in an electrolyte or from the contact of two similar metals in an electrolyte of nonuniform concentration.

Hardness. The sum of the calcium and magnesium ions in water.

Inhibitor. A chemical substance that reduces the rate of corrosion or of scale formation.

Ion. An electrically charged atom or group of atoms.

Passivity. The tendency of a metal to become inactive in a given environment.

pH. The logarithm of the reciprocal of the hydrogen ion concentration of a solution. *pH* values below 7 are increasingly acid, and those above 7 are increasingly alkaline.

Polarization. The deviation from the open circuit potential of an electrode resulting from the passage of current.

ppm. Parts per million by weight. In water, ppm are essentially the same as milligrams per litre (mg/L); 10 000 ppm (mg/L) − 1%.

Scale. The formation at high temperature of thick corrosion product layers on a metal surface. The deposition of water insoluble constituents on a metal surface.

Sludge. A sedimentary water-formed deposit.

Tuberculation. The formation of localized corrosion products scattered over the surface in the form of knob-like mounds.

Water-formed Deposit. Any accumulation of insoluble material derived from water or formed by the reaction of water on surfaces in contact with it.

BASIC THEORY—MECHANISM

Corrosion is defined as destruction of a metal or alloy by chemical or electrochemical reaction with its environment. In most instances, this reaction is electrochemical in nature, much like that in an electric dry cell. The basic nature of corrosion is almost always the same; a flow of electricity between certain areas of a metal surface through a solution capable of conducting an electric current. This electrochemical action causes destructive alteration (eating away) of a metal at areas, called anodes, where the electric current enters the solution. It is the critical step in a series of reactions associated with corrosion.

For corrosion to occur, there must be a release of electrons at the anode and a formation of metal ions through oxidation and disintegration of the metal. At the cathode, there must be a simultaneous acceptance of ions or formation of negative ions. Action at either electrode does not occur independently. According to Faraday's law, the two reactions must be at the same time at equivalent rates. Corrosion, or disintegration of the metal, occurs only at the anodes. Anode and cathode areas may shift from time to time as the corrosion process proceeds, resulting in uniform corrosion.

Reactions at the cathode surface most often control the rate of corrosion. Depending on the nature of the electrolyte, the hydrogen generated at the cathode surface may (1) accumulate to coat the surface and slow down the reaction (cathodic polarization), (2) form bubbles and be swept away from the surface, thus allowing the reaction to proceed, and (3) react with oxygen in the electrolyte to form water or a hydroxyl ion.

At the anode, the metal ion entering the solution may react with a constituent in the electrolyte to form a corrosion product. With iron or steel, the ferrous ion may react with the hydroxyl ion in water to form ferrous hydroxide and then with oxygen to produce ferric hydroxide (rust). These corrosion products may accumulate on the anode surface and slow down the reaction rate (*anodic polarization*).

ACCELERATING OR INTENSIFYING FACTORS

Moisture

Corrosion does not occur in dry air. However, in most natural atmospheres, some moisture is present as water vapor. In pure air, almost no iron corrosion occurs at relative humidities up to 99%. But with contaminants such as sulfur dioxide or solid particles of charcoal present, corrosion could proceed at relative humidities of 50% or above. Pure air is seldom encountered in practice. During rains, exposed metal surfaces are completely wetted, allowing the corrosion reaction to proceed as long as the metal remains wet. This applies to iron and unalloyed steel. Many alloys develop thin corrosion product films or oxide coatings and are unaffected by moisture.

Oxygen

With electrolytes consisting of water solutions of salts or acids, the presence of oxygen in the media accelerates the corrosion rate of ferrous metals by depolarizing the cathodic areas through reaction with hydrogen generated at the cathode. This allows the anodic reaction to proceed. In many ferrous systems used for handling water, such as boiler systems or hot water heating systems, oxygen is removed to reduce the corrosion rate. This is done by adding oxygen scavenging chemicals, such as sulfites, to the system, or by using deaeration equipment to expel the dissolved oxygen.

The presence of oxygen in the media does not affect all alloys in the manner described above. In alloys that develop protective oxide films, such as stainless steels, oxygen can reduce corrosion by maintaining the oxide film. The media, free of oxygen, might cause some corrosion of the alloy; but with oxygen present, the oxide film becomes reinforced and prevents corrosion.

Solutes

In ferrous materials such as iron and steel, mineral acids accelerate the corrosion rate, whereas alkalies reduce it. Since the corrosion reaction at the cathode is related to the concentration of hydrogen ions present, the higher the concentration (the more acid the media), the less likely the cathode area will become polarized. Alkaline solutions, containing a much higher concentration of hydroxyl ions than hydrogen, promote polarization of the cathode areas, thus reducing the rate of dissolution at the anode. Relative acidity or alkalinity of a solution is defined as pH; a neutral solution has a pH of 7. Solutions increase in acidity as the pH decreases and increase in alkalinity as pH increases.

The corrosivity of most salt solutions depends on whether they are neutral, acid, or alkaline when dissolved in water. For example, aluminum sulfate is the salt of a strong acid (sulfuric

acid) and a weak alkali (aluminum hydroxide). When dissolved in water, a solution of aluminum sulfate is acid in nature and reacts with iron as would a dilute acid. Since alkaline solutions are generally less corrosive to ferrous systems, it is practical in many *closed* water systems to minimize corrosion by adding an alkali or alkaline salt, to raise the pH to 9 or higher.

Differential Solute Concentration

A potential difference between anode and cathode areas is necessary for the corrosion reaction to proceed. Such a potential difference can be established at different locations on a metal surface because of differences in concentration of a solute in the media at these locations. Corrosion caused by these circumstances is commonly called *concentration cell corrosion*. Such cells can be metal ion or oxygen concentration cells.

In the metal ion cell, the metal surface in contact with the higher concentration of dissolved metal ion becomes the cathodic area, and the surface in contact with the lower concentration becomes the anode. The metal ions involved may be a constituent of the media or may result from the corroding surface itself. The differences in concentration in the media may be caused by flow of the media sweeping away the dissolved metal ions at one location and not at another. Such differences could occur at crevices or be caused by deposits of one sort or another. The anodic area is outside the crevice or deposit where the metal ion concentration is least.

In the oxygen concentration cell, the surface area in contact with the media of higher oxygen concentration becomes the cathodic area, and the surface in contact with the media of lower oxygen concentration becomes the anode. Crevices or foreign deposits on the metal surface can produce conditions favorable to corrosion. The anodic area, where corrosion proceeds, will be in the crevice or under the deposit. Although they are actually manifestations of concentration cell corrosion, *crevice corrosion* and *deposit attack* are sometimes referred to as different types of corrosion.

Galvanic or Dissimilar Metal Corrosion

Another factor that can accelerate the corrosion process is the difference in potential of dissimilar metals coupled together and immersed in an electrolyte. The following factors control the severity of corrosion resulting from such dissimilar metal coupling:

1. The relative differences in position (potential) in the galvanic series, with reference to a standard electrode. The greater the difference, the greater the driving force of the reaction. The galvanic series for metals in flowing aerated sea water is shown in Table 1.
2. The relative area relationship between anode and cathode areas. Since the amount of current flow and, therefore, total metal loss is determined by the potential difference and resistance of the circuits, a small anodic area corrodes more rapidly; it is penetrated at a greater rate than a large anodic area.
3. Polarization of either the cathodic or anodic area can reduce the potential difference, and thus reduce the rate of attack of the anode.

It is inadvisable to couple a small exposed area of a less noble metal with a large area of a more noble metal in media where the less noble material may tend to corrode by itself. If such couples cannot be avoided, but one of the dissimilar metals can be painted or coated with a nonmetallic coating, the cathodic material should be coated, rather than the anodic one. If the

Table 1 Galvanic Series of Metals and Alloys in Flowing Aerated Sea Water at 40 to 80°F (4.4 to 26.7°C)

Corroded End (Anodic or Least Noble)

Magnesium Alloys (1)
Zinc (1)
Beryllium
Aluminum Alloys (1)
Cadmium
Mild Steel, Wrought Iron
Cast Iron, Flake or Ductile
Low Alloy High Strength Steel
Ni-Resist, Types 1 & 2
Naval Brass (CA464), Yel. Brass (CA268), Al. Brass (CA687), Red Brass (CA230), Admlty Brass (CA443) Mn Bronze
Tin
Copper (CA102, 110), Si Bronze (CA655)
Lead-Tin Solder
Tin Bronze (G & M)
Stainless Steel, 12 to 14% Cr (AISI Types 410,416)
Nickel Silver (CA 732, 735, 745, 752, 764, 770, 794)
90/10 Copper-Nickel (CA 706)
80/20 Copper-Nickel (CA 710)
Stainless Steel, 16 to 18% Cr (AISI Type 430)
Lead
70/30 Copper-Nickel (CA 715)
Nickel Aluminum Bronze
INCONEL[a] Alloy 600
Silver Braze Alloys
Nickel 200
Silver
Stainless Steel, 18 Cr, 8 Ni (AISI Types 302, 304, 321, 347)
MONEL[a] Alloys 400, K-500
Stainless Steel, 18 Cr, 12 Ni-Mo (AISI Types 316, 317)
Carpenter 20[c] Stainless Steel, INCOLOY[a] Alloy 825
Titanium, HASTELLOY[b] Alloys C & C 276, INCONEL[a] Alloy 625
Graphite, Graphitized Cast Iron

Protected End (Cathodic or Most Noble)

[a]International Nickel Trademark
[b]Union Carbide Corp. Trademark
[c]The Carpenter Steel Co. Trademark

two materials can be insulated from each other by using an insulated joint in piping systems, the galvanic couple can be avoided. Where this is not possible, a *waster* heavy wall nipple section of the less noble material can be used and readily replaced when it fails.

In piping systems handling natural waters, galvanic corrosion is not likely to extend more than three to five pipe diameters down the ID of the less noble pipe material. In metal components exposed to the atmosphere, galvanic effects are likely to be confined to the area immediately adjacent to the joint.

Stray Current Corrosion

Stray current corrosion is a form of galvanic corrosion. The electrical potential driving the corrosion reaction is from stray electrical currents of an electric generator. This phenomenon can occur on buried or submerged metallic structures. The soil or submergence media provide the electrolyte. The anode, or structure suffering accelerated corrosion, may be located some distance from the cathode structure. The corrosion attack by stray currents is usually restricted to the structure surface in contact with the soil or other submergence media.

Effects of Stress

Stresses in metallic structures rarely have significant effects on the uniform corrosion resistance of metals and alloys. There have been a few instances of stress accelerating corrosion with some materials, the more highly stressed areas usually being anodic to the less severely stressed areas. But such mechanisms are usually a laboratory curiosity rather than a practical reality. On the other hand, stresses in specific metals and alloys can cause corrosion cracking when exposed to specific corrosive environments. The cracking can have catastrophic effects on the usefulness of the particular metal.

Almost all metals and alloys exhibit susceptibility to stress-corrosion cracking in one or more specific environments. Common examples are steels in hot caustic solutions, high zinc content brasses in ammonia, and stainless steels in hot chlorides. Metal producers' data has more details on specific materials. Stress-corrosion cracking frequently can be prevented by using the susceptible alloy in the annealed or stress-relieved condition, or by selecting a material resistant to attack by the specific media.

Temperature

Some think that corrosion rates double for every 18°F (10°C) rise in temperature. This idea comes from studies of chemical reaction rates where this ratio is a valid approximation. Such a ratio cannot necessarily be applied to corrosion reactions, and the effect of temperature cannot be generalized.

In systems where the presence of oxygen in the media promotes corrosion, temperature increase may increase the corrosion rate to a point. Oxygen solubility will decrease as temperature increases and may approach zero at boiling in an open system. Therefore, the corrosion rate may decrease beyond a critical temperature level because of a decrease in oxygen solubility. However, in a closed system, from which oxygen cannot escape, the corrosion rate may continue to increase with temperature rise. For those alloys that depend on oxygen in the media for maintaining a protective oxide film, an increase in temperature and the corresponding reduction in oxygen content can accelerate the corrosion rate by preventing oxide film formation.

Temperature also can affect corrosion behavior by causing a dissolved salt in the media to precipitate on the surface as a scale, which can be protective. An example is calcium carbonate scale in hard waters. Temperature can affect the nature of the corrosion product, which may be relatively stable and protective in certain temperature ranges, and unstable and nonprotective in other temperature ranges. An example is zinc in distilled water; the corrosion product is nonprotective from 140 to 190°F (60 to 88°C) but reasonably protective at other temperatures. Thus, the effect of temperature on a particular system is difficult to predict without specific knowledge of the characteristics of the metals involved and the constituents of the media.

Pressure

As with temperature, it is difficult to predict the effects of pressure on corrosion. Where dissolved gases such as oxygen and carbon dioxide affect the corrosion rate, pressure on the system may increase their solubility and thus increase corrosion. Similarly, a vacuum on the system reduces dissolved gas solubility and thus also reduces corrosion. In a heated system, pressure may raise the boiling point of the media, and thereby affect the corrosion rate with temperature. It is seldom possible or practical to control metallic system corrosion by pressure control alone.

Velocity

The effects of flow velocity (Copson 1952) of the media in a system depend on the characteristics of the particular metal

Table 2 Composite Reference of Materials for Equipment Components[11]

Equipment	Casings and Support		Grids, Fill and Eliminators		Pipes		Pans or Basins		Ducts		Heat Transfer Surfaces		Valves and Pumps		Fans	
Cooling Towers	Al	W	Al		Al	Ct	Al	SS					Al		Al	S
	S	Ct	SS		S	SS	S	W					S		Cu	
	SS		P		Cu		Cu	C					Cu		Ct	
	P		W		P		Ct									
Evaporative Condensers	Al	P	Al	P	Al	P	Al	Ct	Al	Ct	Al		Al		Al	SS
	S	W	SS	Ct	S	Ct	S	SS	S	SS	Cu		S		S	Ct
	SS	Ct	Cu		Cu	SS	Cu		Cu		SS		Cu		Cu	
Cooling Coils (Condensation)	Al	P			Al	P	Al				Al		Al			
	S	W			S	Ct	S				Cu		S			
	Cu	Ct			Cu		Ct				SS		Cu			
	SS				SS								SS			
Air Washers	Al	P	Al		Al	P	Al		Al	S	Al		Al		Al	
	S	W	SS		S	Ct	S		Cu		Cu		S		SS	
	Cu	Ct	P		Cu		Ct		SS		SS		Cu		Ct	
	SS		Ct		SS				Ct		Ct					
Room Air Conditioners	Al	P	Al	W	Al	Ct	Al				Al		Al	P	Al	Ct
	S	W	Cu	Ct	Cu		S				Cu		S		Cu	
	Cu	Ct	SS		SS		Ct				SS		Cu		SS	
	SS		P		P						Ct		SS		P	
Air-Cooled Condensers	Al	P	Al	P	Al	P			Al	W	Al	Ct	Al		Al	Ct
	S	W	S	W	S	Ct			S	Ct	S		S		S	
	Cu	Ct	Cu	Ct	Cu				Cu		Cu		Cu		Cu	
	SS		SS		SS				SS		SS		SS		SS	
Heating Coils	Al	SS	Al	SS	Al	Ct					Al	Ct	Al			
	S	Ct	S	Ct	S						S		S			
	Cu		Cu		Cu						Cu		Cu			
	P(<65 °C)		P (<65 °C)		SS						SS					

Al: Aluminum— aluminum in contact with water of high pH or containing certain dissolved salts, particularly those of copper, is subject to rapid localized attack. Special precautions in equipment design and water treatment may permit its use when this is desirable because of its low density or other considerations.

Ct: Coatings—galvanizing, plating or protective coatings may be used over appropriate base material.

C: Concrete; Cu: Copper and alloys; P: Plastics; S: Steel; SS: Stainless steel; W: Wood.

or alloy. In media where oxygen increases the corrosion rate, e.g., iron or steel in water, flow velocity can increase the rate by making more oxygen available to the metal surface for reaction. Under the same circumstances, the films of alloys dependent on thin oxide films for corrosion resistance can be enhanced because of velocity, and maintain resistance up to high velocities. This is frequently true of stainless steels.

In metal systems where corrosion products retard corrosion by acting as a physical barrier, velocity of media flow may sweep away these products, permitting corrosion to proceed at its initial rate. In specific media and for a specific metal, there may be a critical velocity below the point that the corrosion product film is adherent and protective.

Turbulent media flow may cause uneven attack, involving localized erosion and corrosion. This attack is called *erosion-corrosion,* and can occur in piping systems at sharp bends if the designed flow velocity is high. Copper and some of its alloys are subject to this type of attack.

Very high velocity can cause localized cavitation, which forms bubbles that collapse and literally tear out particles of metal. This can occur in pump impellers and mixer propeller blades. This effect is further aggravated by the presence of suspended solids in the medium that impinge on the metal surface.

Low velocities can allow suspended solids to precipitate on a metal surface, which initiates concentration cell corrosion.

PREVENTIVE AND PROTECTIVE MEASURES

Materials Selection

It is possible to construct almost any piece of heating or air-conditioning system equipment with materials that will not cor-rode significantly under service conditions. However, this is rarely possible in reality because of economic and physical limitations.

When selecting construction materials for a piece of equipment, consider (1) the corrosion resistance of each proposed metal or other material to the service environment, (2) the nature of the corrosion products that may be formed and their effects on equipment operation, (3) the suitability of the materials to handling by standard fabrication methods, and (4) the effects of design and fabrication limitations on tendencies toward local corrosion (as discussed in the preceding section). The overall economic balance during the projected life of the equipment should also be considered. It may be less expensive in the long run to pay more for a corrosion-resistant material and avoid regular painting or other corrosion-control measures, than to use a less expensive material that requires regular corrosion control maintenance throughout the life of the equipment.

Other considerations include selection of materials used during fabrication and the methods of fabrication. For example, if acid fluxes are not properly removed from a piece of equipment, they can aggravate localized corrosion after the product goes into service. Construction materials (metallic or nonmetallic) frequently used for components of air-conditioning and refrigeration equipment are summarized in Table 2. The following design and material selection considerations are required for optimum performance:

1. Use of dissimilar metals in any system should be avoided or minimized. Where dissimilars are used, insulating gaskets and/or organic coatings must be used to prevent galvanic couples.
2. Temperature and pressure-measuring equipment using mercury should be forbidden, since accidental breakage and mercury spillage into the system can cause severe damage.

Table 3 Typical Field-Applied Paint Systems

Systems	Advantages	Disadvantages
Alkyd	1. Good adhesion to most substrates. 2. Skill required for application is minimal. 3. Reasonably high solids allow for maximum mil thickness in a minimum number of coats. High solids facilitate covering the anchor pattern so that proper protection is achieved. In general, alkyd formulations will take continuous operating temperatures of about 200°F (93°C).	1. Minimum resistance to acid or alkali contamination.
Vinyls	1. Excellent gloss and color retention. 2. The best known air-dry, thin film, acid resistant coating. 3. Excellent moisture resistance, both immersion and splash.	1. Relatively low operating temperature limit in ranges of 130 to 140°F (54 to 60°C). 2. In relation to other coatings, relatively low solids with the high in the range of 30% by volume. 3. Need for better surface preparation than other coatings because of poor ability to wet.
Converted or Catalyzed Epoxy	1. Excellent alkali resistance. 2. High film build with minimum number of coats. 3. Chemical conversion ensuring a better cure. 4. Excellent abrasion resistance.	1. Chalks readily, although not a degrading type of chalk, as is experienced in oil films. 2. Always a two component system, necessitating a relatively short pot life.

3. Stagnation or sluggish fluid flow, unnecessarily high fluid velocities, impingement, and erosion should be eliminated through design of equipment and accessories.
4. Corrosion inhibitors and biological control additives must be compatible with the materials chosen for any given system.

Protective Coatings

The environment in which system components eventually operate largely determines the type of coating system needed. Even with a coating suited for the environment, the protection provided depends on the adhesion of the coating to the base material, which is decided by both surface preparation and application technique. Consult several reliable manufacturers of industrial coatings before choosing a coating system for any exposure and follow the manufacturer's recommendations for both surface preparation and application technique.

Although many types of protective coatings are available, only three basic types of environments and three generic types of coatings need be considered.

Normal mild atmospheric corrosion can be effectively prevented by alkyd resin systems. These systems can undergo less-than-perfect cleaning and still give reasonably good service. A vinyl resin system, along with the best surface preparation, is recommended when exposure to acid conditions is anticipated. If the equipment is to be used under severe alkali conditions, the best type of coating is a catalyzed epoxy. Table 3 lists some of the advantages and disadvantages for each of the broad classifications.

For severe exposures, an initial coat of a high zinc primer with an organic or inorganic vehicle often can greatly extend the life of the coating and the equipment being protected. Table 4 is a guide for coatings based on Federal Specification materials by end use.

Surface Preparation

An important factor in corrosion control is the condition of the substrate prior to coating. Therefore, surface preparation should be considered carefully. The environment in which the system components will eventually operate largely determines the type of coating needed. Each coating has a particular tolerance for surface contamination that determines the degree of surface preparation necessary. Coatings that require the removal of all contaminants are not necessary in some environmental conditions.

Rust and mill scale often present a problem in surface preparation. Mill scale is a source of trouble because it does not have the same coefficient of expansion as the steel; thus, it may become cracked and loosened during fabrication and shipping or during expansion and contraction of the metal. Moisture and contaminants may reach exposed areas and cause corrosion. Surface preparation is generally divided into the following two types:

Mechanical cleaning methods are generally described as follows, and are listed in descending order of effectiveness:

1. *Hand cleaning* is the oldest and most common cleaning method, accomplished using a wire brush, scraper or chipping hammer.
2. *Power tool cleaning* is done with rotary wire brushes, descalers, and rotary scalers.
3. *Flame cleaning* involves using a torch played on the steel to take advantage of the difference in the rate of expansion between the base metal and the mill scale. An advantage of this type of cleaning, in some cases, is that the steel can be painted

Table 4 Guide for Coatings Based on Federal Specification Materials by End Use

Exposure	Primers	Intermediate and Finish
Dry interior use	TT-P-636-B synthetic alkyd primer	TT-E-489-B gloss synthetic enamel TT-E-509 semigloss synthetic enamel TT-P-51D flat alkyd enamel
Exterior exposure (normal weather conditions)	TT-P-615-B basic lead silico chromate alkyd primer TT-P-636-B synthetic alkyd primer	TT-E-489-B gloss synthetic enamel
Interior-exterior heavy moisture or acid conditions	MIL-P-15328-A vinyl wash primer (m.c. primer) MIL-P-15929-A vinyl red lead (primer)	MIL-P-15929-A vinyl red lead (Intermediate)
Interior-exterior alkali conditions	MIL-P-23377 primer epoxy polyamide	MIL-C-22750-A coating epoxy polyamide (Intermediate) MIL-C-2275-A coating epoxy polyamide (Finish)

while it is still warm, eliminating the problem of adsorbed moisture.

4. *Blast cleaning* involves abrading surfaces with high velocity impact of abrasive particles.

Chemical Cleaning. Many types of chemical surface preparations are available; selection depends on the type and degree of contamination. A brief description of each follows.

1. *Solvent wiping and vapor degreasing* is the least effective of all types of chemical surface preparation, but it is still one of the most widely used. In solvent wiping, the surface is wiped with a suitable solvent such as naphtha or toluol. In vapor degreasing, the item to be cleaned is exposed to the solvent in its vapor phase. The solvent condenses on the metal surface and washes off the contaminant. This method is more satisfactory than wiping because it can clean irregular surfaces better and solvent contamination is not a factor. Solvent wiping is sometimes used initially in other cleaning methods.

2. *Alkali cleaning* is generally preferred over solvent cleaning. The solution can be applied by spray or soaking, depending on the size of the article. Alkaline cleaners are water soluble and are generally used at high temperature, although cold types are also available.

3. *Emulsifiable solvent cleaning* removes oils and greases. Emulsifiable solvents offer the advantage of flushing the soil away during the rinsing operation, leaving only a very thin film of solvent on the surface, which can later be removed if necessary. The emulsifiable solvents are either used in dip tanks or are sprayed or brushed on the surface and allowed to stand for a few minutes. The loosened and dissolved matter is then rinsed with water.

4. *Steam cleaning* abrades surfaces with high velocity steam impact. This type of cleaning is very effective but must often be augmented with wire brushing or sandblasting.

5. *Acid cleaning* treats the metal with an acid containing oil solvents such as alcohols, ethers, or ketones to help remove oil and oil-type products. Detergents and wetting agents are incorporated to help wet the surface and remove soils. Acid cleaners of this type effectively remove grease, oil, and other surface contaminants, but acids alone are not effective on greases. This method differs from alkali or emulsion cleaning in that it removes light rust and minutely etches the surface of the metal, thus improving the adhesion properties of the coatings by providing a good mechanical base. The use of a phosphoric acid cleaner has the added advantage of reacting with the steel to produce a thin film of insoluble iron phosphate, which enhances paint adhesion. If mill scale is too heavy, phosphoric acid solutions may require too much time; in which case, sulfuric acid pickling may be used where practical.

Shop applied coatings offer the best results because better conditions for controlled surface preparation and coating application usually exist in the shop.

Field applied coatings can be the same types as shop-applied coatings. The limiting factor is accessibility. Once equipment is in place, obstructions can make it difficult to use the type of surface preparation that will do the best job.

Maintenance of Protective Coatings. Defects in a coating are virtually inescapable. These defects can be caused either by coating flaws in the film during application or by mechanical damage after coating; the damage must be repaired to eliminate premature failure at these points. Depending on the severity of the service, an inspection should be scheduled after installation to detect mechanical damage. Damaged areas should be noted and repaired.

Cathodic Protection

Cathodic protection reduces or prevents corrosion by making the metal the cathode in a conducting medium by means of direct electric current that is impressed or galvanic. It is widely used to control corrosion in water storage tanks; heat exchange water boxes; water and chemical processing equipment such as filters, reactors and clarifiers; and the external surfaces of submerged and underground tanks, piping, and piling. Cathodic protection may be used with iron, aluminum, lead, and stainless steel. On new steel structures, optimum corrosion-control design is often achieved by applying cathodic protection in combination with coatings, environment conditioning, or both.

The cathodic protection principle is unique in that protective effects can be directed from distantly positioned anode current sources onto existing submerged or buried structures. Corrosion control can generally be accomplished by cathodic protection without taking the facilities out of service, exposing the surfaces for coating, or specially treating the surrounding environment.

Since this process superimposes an applied current onto an existing electrochemical corrosion system, its design must be adapted to meet the varying needs of the specific corrosion problem. The electrochemical corrosion mechanisms to which cathodic protection can be applied fall into the following two broad classifications:

1. Corrosion of a metal surface by *stray* direct currents, which flow in circuits grounded at more than one point or in subsurface structures purposely made part of a direct current circuit.

2. Corrosion of a metal surface in an electrolyte by *galvanic* currents originating between discreet areas of oxidation and reduction reactions. Galvanic currents are the effect rather than the cause of corrosion.

Complete corrosion control by cathodic protection is approached when the net current flow at any point on the metal surface either measures zero or is flowing from the corroding media into the metal. It generally is not feasible to measure current flow directly at all points on a metal surface. Full cathodic protection requires polarizing the cathode areas to the open circuit potential of the anodes. The criterion for cathodic protection of iron is met when all points on the metal surface are polarized to a potential of -0.85 V or more negative, measured against a copper sulfate reference electrode positioned on the metal surface.

The protective current requirements generally vary with factors influencing corrosion rates. Increasing oxygen concentration, temperature, and velocity increases protective current requirements. Resistive coatings, precipitated calcareous salts, adherent zinc or aluminum flocs, silt, and electrophoretically deposited particles all reduce the protective current requirements.

Adequate protective current flow onto a surface from sacrificial or impressed current sources is equally effective.

Sacrificial Anodes. Coupling a more active metal to a structure results in galvanic current flow through the corroding electrolyte, providing a protection effect on the cathode surface. In providing the galvanic protective current flow, the more active metal is electrochemically consumed (sacrificed) and must be replaced. No outside power is required for protection.

The properties of the more commonly used sacrificial galvanic anode materials are tabulated below.

Material (and Specification)	Theo. lb/A • yr (kg/A • yr)	Actual lb/A • yr (kg/A • yr)	Potential (Cu-CuSO$_4$) V
Magnesium (AZ-63A)	8.5 (3.9)	17 (7.7)	− 1.55
Zinc (MIL-A-18001)	23.0 (10.4)	25 (11.4)	− 1.10[a]
Aluminum (B-605)	6.5 (3.0)	12 (5.4)	− 1.05[a]
Aluminum (ERP-HP7)	6.5 (3.0)	8 (3.6)	− 1.20[a]

[a]Sea Water.

The sacrificial anode consumption is greater than the theoretical electrochemical equivalent of its protective current output. This is attributable to the self-corrosion current flow superimposed on the protective current output. Sacrificial anode system design is limited by the available driving voltage between the sacrificial anode and the structure to be protected. The resistance of the circuit between the anodes and the structure mainly determines the protective current flow. A high resistivity electrolyte requires a larger number of anodes than a more conductive electrolyte to obtain the same amount of protective current flow.

Sacrificial anodes are cast in various forms and weights for optimum design and service life. Special backfills around the anodes are used in soils to maintain moisture at the anode surface and increase efficiency. In condenser water boxes and similar exposures, sacrificial anodes are sometimes encased in perforated plastic containers for optimum service life and performance.

The zinc on galvanized iron protects the underlying metal until it is consumed in the protective process. Zinc and aluminum anodes can usually be used in combination with well-coated surfaces without accelerating coating damage.

Impressed Current. An external voltage source can be used to impress protective current flow from anodes through the conducting medium onto the corroding surface. Alternating current power, converted to direct current by an adjustable output selenium or silicon rectifier, is most commonly used.

Sacrificial anodes, such as scrap iron or aluminum, are sometimes used with impressed current. Non-sacrificial anodes (those not consumed by the electrochemical process) such as graphite, high silicon cast iron alloy, platinum or platinum plated or clad on titanium or tantalum, and silver-lead alloys in sea water are more widely used in impressed current systems. The distribution of protective current on the cathode, power costs, and stray current effects on neighboring structures should be considered when selecting number, form, and arrangement of anodes.

One method of impressed current cathodic protection is automatic potential control (Sudrabin 1963). In this system, the potential of the structure is continuously measured against a reference electrode by a monitoring system that regulates the protective current applied to maintain the structure at a preselected protective potential value. Since the protective current requirements vary from place to place and time to time, an automatic potential control system protects at all times and prevents excessive cathodic protection, which would accelerate (1) coating damage by electroendosmotic effect, (2) cathodic attack on amphoteric metals such as aluminum, and (3) power wastage.

Limitations. Full cathodic protection depends on adequate current flow reaching all surfaces to be protected. On bare surfaces, the relation between an anode and cathode configuration determines, in large part, the distribution of protective current. For example, relatively simple anode systems adequately distribute protective current on the outside of storage tanks, well-coated pipelines, tank interiors, and water boxes of heat exchangers. However, the protective current received on the interior of a condenser tube from anodes in the water box diminishes rapidly within a very short distance of the tube entrance.

Rapid attenuation of the protective effect occurs on the exterior of bare pipelines in conductive media. Therefore, protective current sources must be applied at more frequent intervals. Harmful effects of stray currents from a cathodic protection system on neighboring utilities or other isolated metallic systems must be considered. All underground cathodic protection installations should be reported to, and examined in cooperation with, local electrolysis committees.

Economics. Since the cathodic protection principle must be adapted to meet the specific needs of each corrosion problem, the costs vary.

Environmental Change

Another approach to corrosion protection is to change the environment so that it is less aggressive to the equipment. A familiar example is the use of solid desiccants such as silica gel to maintain a low moisture level in refrigerant lines. Desiccants are applied to minimize atmospheric corrosion by maintaining a low relative humidity. The *mothballing* technique for preserving decommissioned ships and other heavy equipment is an example of this.

Vapor phase corrosion inhibitors can minimize atmospheric corrosion in certain cases. For example, dicyclohexylammonium nitrite is sometimes used to protect steel parts within sealed containers. A related compound, cyclohexylamine bicarbonate, is used in Great Britain to protect idle boilers.

Adding alkali to water to raise the pH and using corrosion inhibitors, such as chromates, are other examples of reducing corrosive attack by changing the environment. Corrosion inhibition in water systems is discussed more fully in the next section. Inhibitors for corrosion control are added to glycol antifreeze solutions, lubricants, lithium bromide absorption refrigeration brines, and other liquids.

The local environment at a metal surface can be made less corrosive by adding filming amines to steam to protect condensate lines and certain additives to fuel oil to reduce fireside corrosion in boilers.

Finally, equipment design modifications that reduce the likelihood of corrosion are also environmental changes. They include eliminating crevices and providing weep holes to prevent water accumulation.

WATERSIDE CORROSION AND DEPOSITS

Since the occurrence and correction of corrosion in water systems are so closely related to the occurrence and correction of other water-caused pollution, it is impossible to consider them separately. The most common of these water problems in heating and cooling systems is one or more of the following: (1) corrosion, (2) scale formation, (3) biological growths and (4) suspended solid matter.

Some knowledge of these problems is important because each of them can reduce the cooling or heating efficiency of a system and can lead to premature equipment failure and widespread damage to persons in the vicinity.

Controlling waterside problems, particularly in heating and cooling systems, is complex. Handling these problems involves water chemistry, engineering, economics, and personnel administration during each stage of the system development, design, construction, installation, and operation. This chapter

Table 5   Analyses of Typical Public Water Supplies

Substance	Unit	(1)	(2)	(3)	(4)	(5)	(6)	(7)	(8)	(9)
		\multicolumn{9}{c}{Location or Area[a],[b]}								
Silica	SiO_2	2	6	12	37	10	9	22	14	—
Iron	Fe^2	0	0	0	1	0	0	0	2	—
Calcium	Ca	6	5	36	62	92	96	3	155	400
Magnesium	Mg	1	2	8	18	34	27	2	46	1 300
Sodium	Na	2	6	7	44	8	183	215	78	11 000
Potassium	K	1	1	1	—	1	18	10	3	400
Bicarbonate	HCO_3	14	13	119	202	339	334	549	210	150
Sulfate	SO_4	10	2	22	135	84	121	11	389	2 700
Chloride	Cl	2	10	13	13	10	280	22	117	19 000
Nitrate	NO_3	1		0	2	13	0	1	3	—
Dissolved Solids		31	66	165	426	434	983	564	948	35 000
Carbonate Hardness	$CaCO_3$	12	11	98	165	287	274	8	172	125
Noncarbonate Hardness	$CASO_4$	5	7	18	40	58	54	0	295	5 900

[a]All values are ppm (mg/L) of the unit cited to nearest whole number (Collins 1944).
[b]Numbers indicate location or area as follows:
(1) Catskill supply—New York City
(2) Swamp water (colored) Black Creek, Middleburg, FL
(3) Niagara River (filtered) Niagara Falls, NY
(4) Missouri River (untreated) average
(5) Well waters—public supply—Dayton, OH—30 to 60 ft (9 to 18 m)
(6) Well water—Maywood, IL—2090 ft (637 m)
(7) Well water—Smithfield, VA—330 ft (100 m)
(8) Well water—Roswell, NM
(9) Ocean water—average

Table 6   Variations in Composition of Schuylkill River Water at Belmont Filter Plant, Philadelphia, PA

Sample Date[a]	pH	Total Hardness	Total Alkalinity	Chloride	Sulfate	Total Dissolved Solids
		\multicolumn{5}{c}{parts per million (mg/L)}				
January	7.0	73	32	5	48	123
February	6.7	93	38	6	59	155
March	7.2	105	42	6	52	145
April	7.3	106	43	7	60	169
May	6.9	102	39	7	66	187
June	6.9	137	49	10	89	218
July	6.9	176	65	15	114	282
August	7.3	166	67	14	87	235
September	7.2	175	63	16	109	268
October	6.9	205	70	21	135	341
November	7.6	181	61	8	121	289
December	6.7	184	58	18	121	286
Minimum	6.7	73	32	5	48	123
Maximum	7.6	205	70	21	135	341

[a]1949. Samples were composites for the first 10 days of each month.

provides a background for better understanding the causes and handling of water problems in heating and cooling systems. However, it omits many water problems and treatment methods not usually encountered in these systems. The bibliography lists sources of additional information.

Water Characteristics

Between the time that water falls as rain, sleet, or snow and the time that it is pumped into a user's premises, it dissolves a small amount of almost every gas and solid substance with which it comes in contact. These dissolved impurities, rather than the water itself, are the primary causes of various water problems.

Table 5 indicates the complexity of water chemistry. Water received at a given location can vary widely from time to time, either because supplies from different sources are being used or because the composition of a single supply fluctuates, as in the case of river water (Table 6).

Another often overlooked characteristic affecting water-caused problems is the change in composition of the water added to a system after the system starts to operate. Changes in chemical composition result from evaporation, aeration, corrosion, and scale formation. These chemical changes, temperature changes, formation of biological growths, and the accumulation of suspended matter all tend to produce operating results that can differ from those based on the chemical analysis of the makeup water.

Chemical Characteristics. The type and amount of dissolved inorganic materials, including gases, define the chemical characteristics of any water. Typical water analyses, such as those shown in Table 5, are not complete but give the major important constituents for municipal and average industrial water use. The many minor constituents present in most water supplies have little or no importance in most water uses.

In water analyses, all values except pH are usually given as parts per million (mg/L). [*Note:* To obtain ppm, multiply gr/gal by 17.] When water analyses are reported in ppm (mg/L), the chemical species must also be given. Thus, the same calcium concentration in a single water sample might be variously expressed as 100 ppm (mg/L) as $CaCO_3$, 56 ppm (mg/L) as *CaO*, or 40 ppm (mg/L) as *Ca*. Generally, lower pH water tends to be more corrosive and higher pH water tends to be more scale-forming, although many other factors affect both properties.

Most water analyses include only dissolved solids and omit the dissolved gases that are also present. Certain of these, such as nitrogen, have virtually no effect on any water use. Others, such as oxygen, carbon dioxide, and hydrogen sulfide, produce important effects in water systems. Carbon dioxide either can be measured directly or estimated from the pH and total alkalinity by using one of the many available variations of Tillmann's curves (Figure 1).

Oxygen and hydrogen sulfide must be measured by special techniques at the time the sample is collected to be meaningful. Oxygen is important in the corrosion of metals and is readily dissolved upon contact with air in many water systems. Thus, the water chemist often makes the conservative assumption that any water supply that contacts air will be saturated with oxygen according to its partial pressure in air and the water temperature.

Of the chemical constituents usually reported in a water analysis, the most commonly recognized is *total hardness*, which is a measure of the dissolved substances. In most cases, it corresponds to the calcium and magnesium content of the water. The hardness, particularly the calcium, is one of the factors that influence scale formation.

Alkalinity is a measure of the capacity of a water to neutralize strong acids. In natural waters, the alkalinity almost always consists largely of bicarbonate, although there may also be some carbonate present. In treated waters, borate, hydroxide, phosphate, and other constituents, if present, will be included in the alkalinity measurement. Alkalinity also contributes to scale formation. In water chemistry, factors that increase scale formation decrease corrosion, and vice versa.

Alkalinity is measured using two different end-point indicators. The *phenolphthalein alkalinity* (or *P* alkalinity) measures the strong alkali present. The *methyl orange alkalinity* (or *M* alkalinity), also called the *total alkalinity,* measures all of the alkalinity present in the water. Note that the total alkalinity includes the phenolphthalein alkalinity. For most

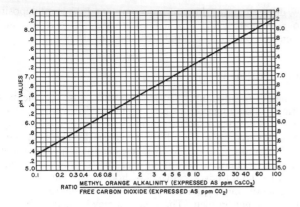

Fig. 1 Relationship Between Bicarbonate Alkalinity, Free Carbon Dioxide, and pH

Table 7 Alkalinity Interpretation for Natural Waters

P Alk[a]	Carbonate	Bicarbonate	Free Carbon Dioxide
0	0	= M Alk	Present
< 0.5M Alk[b]	= 2 P Alk	= M Alk − 2 P Alk	0
= 0.5M Alk	= 2 P Alk = M Alk	0	0
> 0.5M Alk[c]	= 2 (M Alk − P Alk)	0	0

[a]P Alk = Phenolphthalein Alkalinity.
[b]M Alk = Methyl Orange (Total) Alkalinity.
[c]Treated waters only. Hydroxide also present.

natural waters, in which the concentration of phosphates, borates, and other noncarbonate alkaline materials is small, the actual chemical species present can be estimated from the two alkalinity measurements, as shown in Table 7.

Alkalinity or acidity is often confused with pH. Such confusion may be avoided by keeping in mind that the pH is a measure of the hydrogen ion concentration, in moles per litre, expressed as the logarithm of its reciprocal.

The *total dissolved solids* content of a water also affects corrosion and scale formation. Higher dissolved solids tend to increase scale formation. The effects on corrosive tendencies are ambivalent. Since low solids waters have less tendency to deposit scale, they are generally corrosive. On the other hand, a high solids water that is nonscaling tends to produce more intensive corrosion because of its high conductivity.

Sulfates also contribute to scale formation in high calcium waters. Calcium sulfate scale, however, forms only at much higher concentrations than the more common calcium carbonate scale. High sulfates also contribute to increased corrosion because of their high conductivity.

Chlorides have no effect on scale formation but do contribute to corrosion because of their conductivity and because the small size of the chloride ion permits the continuous flow of corrosion current when surface films are porous. Chlorides are a useful measuring tool in evaporative systems. Virtually all other constituents in the water increase or decrease as a result either of the addition of common treatment chemicals or of chemical changes that take place in the normal operation of the water system. With few exceptions, chlorides are changed only by evaporation, so that the ratio of chlorides in a water sample from an operating system to those of the makeup water provides a measure of the number of times that the water has been concentrated in the system.

Soluble Iron can arise from metallurgy corrosion within the cooling water systems or as a contaminant in the makeup water supply. The iron can form heat-insulating deposits by precipitation as iron hydroxide or iron phosphate (if a phosphate-based water treatment product is used or if phosphate is present in the makeup water).

Silica can form particularly hard-to-remove scales if permitted to concentrate sufficiently. Fortunately, silicate scales are far less common than others. In addition to dissolved solids, waters (particularly unpurified waters from surface sources or those that have been circulating in open equipment) frequently contain *suspended solids,* both organic and inorganic. Organic matter in surface supplies may be present as colloidal solutions. Natural coloring matter is usually in this form. At high velocities, hard suspended particles can abrade equipment. Settled suspended matter of all types can contribute to concentration cell corrosion.

Biological Characteristics. Bacteria, algae, and fungi are present in many waters and their growth can cause operating problems. The usual microbiological examination of water for sanitary purposes establishes the probable presence or absence of pathogens. In cooling systems, nonpathogenic organisms are more important as causes of operating difficulties. Living organisms are rarely a problem in heating systems because of the sterilizing action of higher temperatures. Microbiological tests of the water are useful diagnostic tools for problem solving in industrial and commercial systems. Relatively simple and inexpensive methods are available for performing these tests. One accepted method uses membrane filter counts obtained with "dip-sticks" (Cotton, Sladek, and Sohn 1975). Preventive measures can be selected by examining the deposits taken from the equipment.

Heating and Cooling Water Systems

To evaluate the probable effects of the water supply or the boiler or recirculating water, the treatment specialist needs more information than the actual or anticipated water analysis. This includes data on the size, construction, operating pattern, and other characteristics of the system. All heating and cooling systems involve a temperature change, and this influences the rates at which water-caused problems can develop.

In steam heating systems, the concentration of dissolved solids in the boiler water increases as boiler water is converted to steam. In the ordinary space heating system, this change is limited because all of the steam is condensed and returned to the boiler. On the other hand, the nature of the water changes taking place within the boiler are drastically altered if the percentage of condensate returning to the boiler is reduced. The condensate has characteristics quite different from those of the boiler water, because it is substantially free of dissolved solids but can create different problems because of the presence of dissolved oxygen or carbon dioxide.

In hot water heating and other closed circulating systems, there should be few water-caused problems because there should be virtually no makeup water and no opportunity for significant changes in the composition of the water within the system. Experience has shown, however, that a substantial proportion of such systems do not operate according to this theory (Sussman and Fullman 1953), and the need for water treatment in both ordinary hot water heating systems and high temperature hot water systems is now commonly accepted by engineers.

Like hot water heating systems, closed cooling systems (chilled water, chilled-hot water, brine, or glycol) require more makeup in practice than in theory. As a result, treatment of the circulating water or solution in these systems is desirable.

Condensers and other heat exchangers in refrigeration and air-conditioning systems can be cooled by water passing through the equipment and going to waste. In such cases, the water-caused problems are directly related to the chemical composition of the cooling water. As a result of increasing water shortages, such once-through cooling is becoming less common and is being replaced by open circulating systems that use cooling towers, evaporative condensers, or spray ponds. In these, the makeup water composition is drastically changed by evaporation, aeration, and other chemical and physical processes that depend on the contaminants present in the air to which the water is exposed in the open circuit.

Humidification and dehumidification equipment presents several types of water problems. During humidification, water circulating in the equipment is subjected to the same exposure conditions and composition changes as those that take place in open circulating systems. During dehumidification, however, there is a combination of dilution that can result in a water as low in dissolved solids as is steam condensate, plus exposure to aeration and the scrubbing of contaminants from air.

Materials of Construction. The seriousness of corrosion in heating and cooling systems depends, in part, on the nature of the materials of construction present, their degree of proximity, their relative areas, and other physical factors, as well as the chemical composition of the water. Table 2 summarizes the common materials used for construction.

Water-Caused Troubles

The operator of a heating or cooling system can recognize water-caused troubles by the appearance of one or more of three symptoms, each of which can be produced by causes other than the water. Several different conditions can act together in the production of any given symptom, such as (1) reduction in heat transfer rate, in which case the formation of an insulating deposit on a heat transfer surface significantly reduces the cooling or heating efficiency of the equipment; (2) reduced water flow, which results from a partial or complete blockage of pipe lines, condenser tubes, or other openings; and (3) damage to or destruction of the equipment. This can result from corrosion of metals or deterioration of wood or plastics. It can also be caused by excessively rapid wear rates of moving parts such as pumps, shafts, or seals.

Corrosion contributes to all three symptoms. Heat transfer rates can be reduced and water flow blockages can be created by deposits of corrosion products. The damage or destruction of equipment is most often the result of metallic corrosion and the somewhat parallel phenomenon of wood delignification.

Scale formation also contributes to all three symptoms. Even a small buildup of scale on a heat exchange surface reduces heating or cooling efficiency. Further buildup reduces water flow. Finally, scale buildup in boilers may continue until it reaches the point at which heat transfer is so low that the metal overheats, permitting the tubes to rupture under the operating pressure. Scale particles can also accelerate the wear of moving parts.

Biological growths, such as slime, can act as insulators to reduce cooling efficiency. Algae growths often accumulate to the point where they interfere with water flow in cooling towers. The poultice effect created by accumulations of organic matter can cause localized corrosive attack resulting in premature equipment failure. Wood destruction can also occur as a result of fungus action.

Suspended solid matter, such as dirt scrubbed from the air or finely divided mill scale, can also contribute to all three symptoms. These deposits can reduce heat transfer or reduce water flow, depending on where they accumulate. Like local deposits of organic matter, dirt deposits tend to localize corrosion, and suspended solids cause rapid wear of moving parts.

Water Treatment

General Considerations. Correcting water-caused problems in heating and cooling systems is complicated. Therefore, it is important to consult a water treatment specialist early in the design stage of any system and regularly thereafter during design, construction, and operation. Such factors as the improper use of water treatment chemicals can cause problems more serious than those that would have occurred without treatment.

Frequently, more than one solution is possible for the same water treatment problem. The selection may be dictated by such considerations as economics, available space, or labor. A water treatment program selected for any given system should be based on the various factors mentioned in this chapter. The selected treatment program must be followed diligently because it is only as effective as the consistency and control with which it is applied.

Using chemicals for water treatment requires certain safety precautions with which building, operating, and maintenance personnel are not ordinarily familiar. It is important that (1) the potential hazards associated with any particular water treatment chemical or program be well understood beforehand, (2) suitable safety rules be formulated, (3) appropriate safety equipment be supplied, and (4) the safety program be enforced at all times to avoid injury or equipment damage. Also, contamination of drinking water by nonpotable treated or untreated waters must be prevented by eliminating crossconnections between systems or providing approved backflow preventers. Disposal of waters treated with some chemicals into municipal sewers or into streams or lakes may be restricted. Pollution control regulations should be consulted when selecting water treatment. Non-polluting chemicals may not be as effective as those used in the past. In some cases, removal of treatment chemicals prior to discharging blowdown or drainage can be economically justified.

With very few exceptions, the proper control of water treatment programs that involve the addition of chemicals to the water depends on proportional feeding of the chemicals to maintain a desired concentration level at all times. Particularly in systems that have appreciable makeup rates, intermittent batch or slug feeding of water treatment chemicals cannot be relied on to produce satisfactory results.

Because sound water treatment programs require care and consistent attention, devices appear on the market that allegedly prevent scale and corrosion without requiring the operator's attention. Various natural forces, such as electricity, magnetism, or catalysis, generally behaving in some new way, are said to be responsible for the effects claimed. However, independent investigations of these devices have found them to produce no significant effect in preventing or correcting corrosion and scale formation (Eliassen, Skrinde, and Davis 1958; and Welder and Partridge 1954).

Corrosion Control. Corrosion damage to water systems can be minimized by using corrosion-resistant construction materials, providing protective coatings to separate the water from the metal surfaces of the equipment, removing oxygen from the water, or altering the water composition by adding corrosion inhibitors and pH control chemicals. Two or more of these methods are often used in the same system.

Corrosion control by the selection of corrosion-resistant materials of construction is within the province of the equipment or system designer. Although it is technically possible to build equipment that shows no significant corrosion under

Table 8 Solubility of Oxygen from Air in Water at Different Temperatures (Nordell 1961)

Temperature		Millilitres per Litre (mL/L)				
°C	°F	Air	=	Oxygen	+	Nitrogen
0	32	28.64	=	10.19	+	18.45
5	41	25.21	=	8.91	+	16.30
10	50	22.37	=	7.87	+	14.50
15	59	20.11	=	7.04	+	13.07
20	68	18.26	=	6.35	+	11.91
25	77	16.71	=	5.75	+	10.96
30	86	15.39	=	5.24	+	10.15
40	104	13.15	=	4.48	+	8.67
50	122	11.40	=	3.85	+	7.55
60	140	9.78	=	3.28	+	6.50
80	176	6.00	=	1.97	+	4.03
100	212	0.00	=	0.00	+	0.00

almost any operating conditions, economic limitations usually make this impossible. On the other hand, investigation of corrosion failures in air-conditioning and heating equipment sometimes reveals design errors that show that elementary principles of corrosion control have been ignored.

Protective coatings are essential for controlling corrosion on external and other surfaces not reached by treated water, but can also be helpful as adjuncts to water treatment for controlling corrosion at particularly vulnerable locations. For example, metal pans of cooling towers or evaporative condensers operated in areas, such as larger cities, in which the air contains considerable amounts of dust or other solid matter, should be coated with paint or other suitable protective coating to minimize localized pitting of the bottom resulting from a layer of dirt. This attack can take place even when the circulating water is adequately treated with corrosion inhibitors.

When controlling corrosion by water treatment, oxygen removal is effective for closed systems in which opportunities for the pickup of additional oxygen are small. Thus, boiler feedwater can be deaerated mechanically in an open heater or deaerating heater. This process is based on the reduced solubility of oxygen in water at higher temperatures (Table 8) and is made more effective by equipment design features that reduce the partial pressure of oxygen in the gas above the water. The last traces of oxygen are removed chemically by adding sodium sulfite or, at higher temperatures, hydrazine.

$$\text{Sulfite: } 2\,Na_2SO_3 + O_2 \rightarrow 2\,Na_2SO_4$$

$$\text{Hydrazine: } N_2H_4 + O_2 \rightarrow N_2 + 2H_2O$$

Undesirable side reactions can occur at higher temperatures, leading to acidic gases when sulfite is used, or to ammonia when hydrazine is used.

Chemical removal of oxygen is used less often for cold water circuits because of the slow rate of reaction of the sodium sulfite with the dissolved oxygen, although the addition of a small amount of a cobalt salt acts as a catalyst to speed the reaction (Pye 1947). In open-spray systems, chemical removal of oxygen would be too expensive because the circulating water is thoroughly oxygenated again with each passage through the spray equipment.

Oxygen removal by vacuum deaeration can be used to minimize corrosion in once-through cooling systems. It is particularly applicable for an appreciable carbon dioxide concentration because it, as well as the oxygen, is removed.

Corrosion control treatment of heating and cooling waters is most often a combination of pH control and the maintenance of a corrosion inhibitor in the water. Adjustment of the pH to 7.0 is not sufficient to stop corrosion, however. When the oxygen is removed, control of pH at certain levels is frequently

adequate, as in the case of low pressure heating boilers maintained at a pH above 10.5. In most other cases, the adequate minimization of corrosion requires an inhibitor in addition to pH control.

Chromates are the most effective and universal corrosion inhibitors known for the variety of metals used in water systems. Depending on the water temperature and the effectiveness of treatment control, the minimum concentration required may be from 200 (as sodium chromate) to 2000 ppm (mg/L). The minimum concentration must be maintained carefully because with chromates, as with other anodic inhibitors, pitting can develop if the inhibitor concentration is allowed to drop very low. Higher-than-minimum concentrations are maintained in closed systems because the small water losses keep the cost low and an extra safety factor is provided. The chromates are effective inhibitors over a very wide pH range from about 6.5 up. An upper pH limit is frequently established for scale control. Disposal of chromate-treated waters is subject to increasingly stringent pollution control regulations. State and federal regulations require chromate to be removed from the water before it is discharged to sewers or public waterways. The appropriate regional office of the Environmental Protection Agency has these guidelines.

When economy of treatment is of primary importance, as in large cooling towers, it is possible to use several low concentration mixtures of several different inhibitors. Some of the combination treatment products used are chromate-zinc, chromate phosphate, zinc-phosphate, phosphonate-phosphate, phosphonate-molybdate, and phosphonate-silicate. These blends may also contain sodium tolyltriazole for nonferrous corrosion inhibition and low molecular weight polymers for scale control. Close pH control may be essential for good corrosion control. Each of these blends cover a portion of the pH range from 6.0 to 9.0. When selecting a treatment product, consult local, state, and federal environmental guidelines.

In closed systems, chromates are becoming increasingly unacceptable because of their yellow color, disposal problems, and potential hazard if used carelessly. Sodium nitrite has been used as an inhibitor in place of chromate. With ferrous metals, it is nearly as effective as chromate but must be maintained at a pH above 7.0 to avoid breakdown and at a minimum concentration of about 500 ppm (mg/L). It is also necessary to check for both nitrite and nitrate concentrations at frequent intervals because the nitrite is subject to rapid bacterial oxidation and conversion to nitrate, which has essentially no corrosion inhibiting properties. Sodium nitrite has little or no protective effect on nonferrous metals, and other inhibitors must be added with it to provide protection. A commonly used nitrite-base inhibitor includes borax as a pH buffer and sodium tolyltriazole as an inhibitor for nonferrous metals. Other nonchromate inhibitors including organic inhibitors and hydrazine-organic combinations have often been found to be less objectionable in view of the microbiological problems associated with nitrites.

Under the proper conditions, polyphosphates reduce tuberculation and pitting. For this purpose, polyphosphate concentrations higher than those used for scale control must be provided, as must close pH control, in the 6.0 to 7.0 range. In addition, polyphosphates must be combined with other inhibitors to control pitting corrosion of copper and steel.

Corrosion-control treatment of once-through cooling water is practical only with very inexpensive chemicals. Sodium silicate (water glass) or phosphate-silicate mixtures control corrosion in once-through systems, including potable water systems. Sufficient silicate is fed to increase the silica content of the water by about 8 ppm (mg/L).

Other chemicals used for corrosion control in closed heating and cooling systems include volatile amines (such as morpholine and cyclohexylamine) and filming amines (such as octade-cylamine) used for steam condensate line protection. Various proprietary chemical mixtures are used for glycol or alcohol antifreeze solutions in chilled water or snow-melting systems, where the inhibitor must be chemically compatible with the antifreeze agent.

The delignification of wood in cooling towers, while not strictly corrosion, is a related deterioration of construction materials. Several distinct types of failure have been noted, one of which is biological in nature and another chemical. This deterioration can be prevented by treating the wood, either prior to construction or when in place.

Solutions of copper salts and of chromates are among those used for this purpose. Chemical delignification by chlorine, usually a significant problem where the circulating water is high in alkalinity and low in hardness, can be minimized by keeping the circulating water pH low (about 7.0) and by limiting chlorine to a maximum of 1.0 ppm (mg/L).

Scale Control. The methods used for scale control in heating and cooling systems include a variety of internal and external treatment procedures. The selection of an appropriate method for any one system requires evaluating many factors. Smaller systems tend to use internal treatment methods in which the chemicals are added directly to the water, whereas larger systems may use external treatment if financially justifiable.

Each of these scale control methods attempts to minimize the opportunity for precipitation of calcium carbonate, the least soluble common constituent of waters. The solubility of calcium carbonate depends on the pH, temperature, and total solids content of a water, in addition to the calcium and alkalinity (bicarbonate or carbonate). Using these items and one of several nomographs (such as that in Figure 2) the pH_s, which is the pH at which any given water is in equilibrium with calcium carbonate, can be calculated. This pH_s can be used with the actual pH of the water in either of two calculations that indicate whether the water tends to precipitate calcium carbonate or to dissolve it. The older of these is the Langelier Saturation Index (1936).

$$\text{Saturation Index} = pH - pH_s$$

A positive Saturation Index shows a scale-forming tendency. The larger the index, the greater this tendency, but it is a tendency only. Other factors may inhibit scale formation under some circumstances. Usually, calcium carbonate precipitates, generally as a scale, when the Saturation Index exceeds +0.5 to +1.0. A negative Saturation Index indicates that calcium carbonate will dissolve and that bare metal will remain bare and thus accessible for corrosion.

Ryznar (1944) suggested a modified method for predicting scale formation based on operating performance. He called this the Stability Index.

$$\text{Stability Index} = 2\,pH_s - pH$$

The Stability Index is always positive. When it falls below 6.0, scale formation is possible, and it becomes more probable the lower the numerical value of the index.

Similar but more difficult methods for estimating the scale-forming tendencies of calcium sulfate (Denman 1961) and calcium phosphate (Green and Holmes 1947) have been published but are not as commonly used. At cooling water temperatures and lower pressure boiler temperatures, calcium sulfate is far more soluble than calcium carbonate, as shown in Figure 3.

The most foolproof method for preventing scale formation is softening the water by passage through an ion exchange water softener. This external treatment process removes all but 2 to 5 ppm (mg/L) of hardness. It is usually carried out in a closed vertical tank about two-thirds filled with small beads of a cation exchange resin that has unique chemical properties. At low con-

centrations, it preferentially absorbs calcium and magnesium ions from the water, yielding, in return, a chemically equivalent amount of sodium ion that is not scaleforming.

The calcium and magnesium content of the resin ultimately rise to the point where they are no longer completely absorbed from the water passing through the resin. The flow of water is then reversed, backwashing the resin to remove any dirt particles, and the resin is then regenerated by passing a much higher concentration of salt through it. The sodium ions of the strong salt solution displace the absorbed calcium and magnesium ions, restoring the resin to its initial sodium form. After rinsing out excess salt, the resin is ready for another softening cycle.

$$Na_2R + Ca^{++} \text{ (or } Mg^{++}) \; \underset{\text{Regeneration}}{\overset{\text{Softening}}{\rightleftharpoons}} \; CaR + 2Na^+$$

Regenerated Resin   Exhausted Resin

When it is possible to accept and control the presence of suspended matter in the water, hardness may be eliminated by precipitation within the operating equipment. This is commonly done in lower pressure process steam boilers. Alkalis are commonly used to precipitate calcium carbonate in accordance with Eq. (1). Phosphates are added to remove the last of the hardness, by virtue of the lower solubility of calcium phosphate, as shown in Eq. (2). Magnesium is most commonly precipitated as the hydroxide, as shown in Eq. (3).

$$Ca(HCO_3)_2 + 2\,NaOH \rightarrow CaCO_3 + Na_2CO_3 + 2\,H_2O \quad (1)$$

$$3\,Ca(HCO_3)_2 + 6\,NaOH + 2\,Na_3PO_4$$
$$\rightarrow Ca_3(PO_4)_2 + 6\,Na_2CO_3 + 6\,H_2O \quad\quad\quad (2)$$

$$Mg(HCO_3)_2 + 4\,NaOH$$
$$\rightarrow Mg(OH)_2 + 2\,Na_2CO_3 + H_2O \quad\quad\quad\quad (3)$$

There are situations in which it is economically or otherwise impossible to remove the hardness from water. In these cases, other measures can be taken to control scale formation. One common method is to reduce the alkalinity of the water. This substantially reduces scale formation as the solubility of calcium carbonate is much less than that of other calcium salts.

Most of the alkalinity can be removed by an anion exchange resin, in a process analogous to softening. In this case, the alkalinity (bicarbonate) is retained by the resin, which gives up to the water equivalent amounts of chloride. When the resin begins to pass larger amounts of alkalinity than desired, it is backwashed and regenerated by a salt solution, as described above. Usually, this salt solution contains a small percentage of alkali.

$$R'CL + HCO_3 \; \underset{\text{Regeneration}}{\overset{\text{Dealkalizing}}{\rightleftharpoons}} \; R'HCO_3 + Cl$$

Regenerated Resin   Exhausted Resin

Inasmuch as the hardness of the water remains unchanged but the alkalinity is reduced, this process is called dealkalizing, rather than softening. Particularly, in large cooling towers, sulfuric acid is commonly used to eliminate most of the alkalinity. The solubility of calcium sulfate is about 2000 ppm (mg/L), in contrast to 35 ppm (mg/L) for calcium carbonate, thus permitting a much higher hardness to be present in the circulating water before scale can form. The acid feeding procedure involves a considerable risk without careful controls. The alkalinity of the circulating water is reduced to such a low figure that a slight overdose of acid produces a low pH, causing corrosive circulating water. Accordingly, it is good practice to restrict acid feed to systems that operate under constant conditions of makeup water composition and evaporation, or to use automatic pH control equipment.

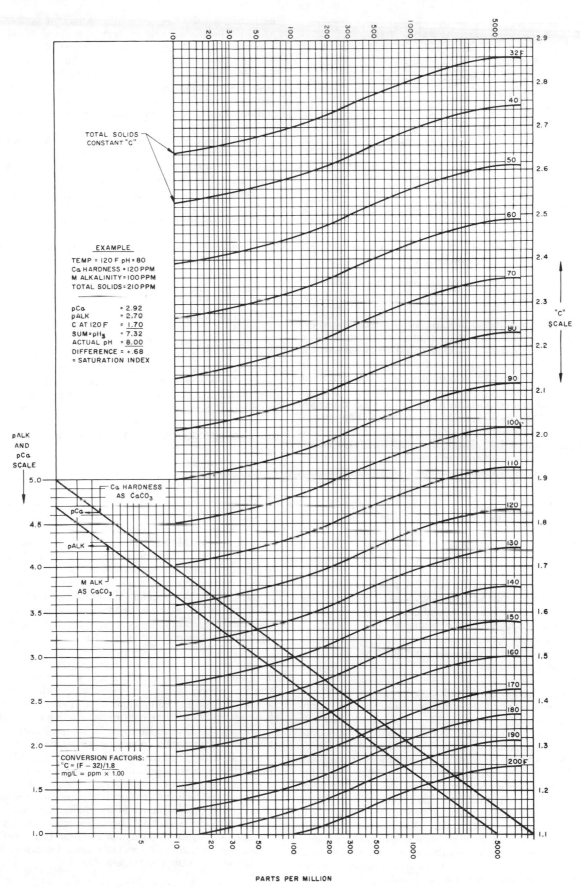

PARTS PER MILLION

Fig. 2 Langelier Saturation Index Nomograph

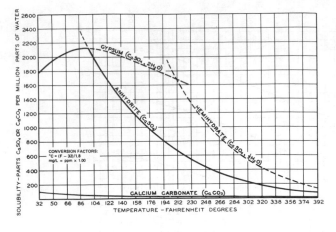

Fig. 3   Solubility of Calcium Sulfate and of Calcium Carbonate for Comparison

(CaCO$_3$ in Equilibrium with Normal CO$_2$ Content of the Atmosphere)

For cooling waters that cannot use the above measures, two other measures are used in conjunction to minimize scale formation in cooling systems. First, the total dissolved solids in the circulating water are controlled by a continuous bleed or bleedoff to a maximum value proportional to the concentration of hardness, silica, or other limited-solubility constituent. Second, scale control adjuncts are added to the water to increase the apparent solubility of the calcium carbonate. Low concentrations [2 to 5 ppm (mg/L)] of sodium polyphosphates, organic dispersing agents such as various lignin derivatives, synthetic polymer polyelectrolytes, organic phosphates, or mixtures of these are used. These measures are also used with acid feeding.

Biological Growths. Algae, bacterial slimes, and fungi are important bacterial growths because they are able to interfere with the functioning of cooling systems. Heating systems do not generally suffer from the effects of biological growths, because their operating temperatures are sufficient to kill the organisms involved.

Algae, which require light for their life processes, are likely to cause difficulty in cooling tower head pans, spray ponds, and other areas where sunlight is abundant. Algae growths can become copious enough in a short time to cause blocking of water distribution piping, nozzles, and troughs. In smaller equipment, blocking off sunlight by using opaque head pan covers can effectively control algae. Where this is not possible, biocidal chemicals can be used.

Most waters contain slime-producing organisms, but significant amounts of slime are produced only when the conditions favor their life processes. These conditions include sufficient food material from the water or from airborne material, combined with optimum temperature conditions, such as often exist on cooling surfaces and in air washers. Equipment near sources of nutrients is particularly susceptible to slime formation. Two common examples are air washers in printing plants that have fine paper dust in the air and refrigeration cooling towers located in food storage areas of markets. Slimes can be formed from bacteria, yeasts, or molds. Generally, the bacteria form thick, soft slimes; the latter two tend to form tough, rubbery slimes. In any case, wherever slimes or other microbiological growths threaten to interfere with the efficient functioning of a cooling system, the use of biocidal materials is indicated.

In large systems, particularly once-through cooling systems using river, estuarian, or sea water, macroorganisms such as bar-

nacles and mussels may accumulate. Although antifouling paints can prevent the growth of such macroorganisms on large diameter pipe surfaces, they must be renewed at frequent intervals and are not applicable to inaccessible areas such as the insides of smaller diameter piping. Generally, chlorine is used to destroy such organisms. In once-through systems, intermittent feeding of chlorine in the form of chlorine gas or hypochlorite solutions most effectively and economically control microorganisms and slimes.

In other systems, the effective control of slime and algae frequently requires a combination of mechanical and chemical measures. For example, when a system already contains a considerable accumulation of slime, a preliminary mechanical or detergent cleaning will make the subsequent application of a microbiocidal chemical more effective in killing the growths and more enduring in the prevention of further growths. Similarly, periodic mechanical removal of slimes from readily accessible areas reduces the chemical microbiocide requirements and makes them more effective.

Chlorine and chlorine-yielding compounds, such as sodium hypochlorite and calcium hypochlorite, are among the most effective microbiocidal chemicals. However, they do not always apply to the control of organic materials in cooling systems. In air washers, for instance, their odor may become offensive; in wood cooling towers, excessive concentrations of chlorine can cause rapid deterioration of wood construction, and in metal equipment, higher concentrations of chlorine can accelerate corrosion. In systems large enough to justify equipment for the controlled feeding of chlorine, its use may be both safe and economical. Some of its disadvantages can be avoided by combining the chlorine with isocyanuric acid, which minimizes the free chlorine concentration. Most chlorine programs can benefit from surfactant (chlorine helper) products or non-oxidizing, organic microbiocides.

When selecting a microbiocide, consider the pH of the circulating water and the chemical compatibility with the corrosion/scale inhibitor product. Many organic microbiocides are available to allow for flexibility in these areas. Typical products include quarternary ammonium compounds, tributyl tin oxide, methylene bis (thiocyanate), isothiazolones, and many proprietary blends. All microbiocides must be handled with care to ensure personal safety; always follow product labeling instructions. Cooling water microbiocides are approved and regulated through the Environmental Protection Agency.

Copper sulfate, which is used widely to control algae in lakes and reservoirs, should not be used in cooling systems, because the copper can *plate out* on ferrous surfaces, causing accelerated pitting. In alkaline waters, it precipitates out and is ineffective. Proprietary compounds in which copper is chemically combined in complexes of much greater stability are available; these are safe for cooling system equipment and in all waters.

The manner of feeding slime control chemicals to a system is important. Often, the continuous feeding of low dosages is neither effective nor economical. Better results can be obtained by shock feeding larger concentrations to the system to achieve a toxic level of the chemical in the water for a sufficient time to kill the organisms present. Alternate shock feeding of two different types of microbiocides usually gives the most effective results. Much larger biocide dosages are required when growths have been permitted to accumulate than when they have been kept under control. At times, organisms appear to build up an immunity to the particular chemical being used, making it necessary to change the biocidal chemical occasionally to keep the organic growths under control.

Suspended solids are undesirable in heating and cooling water systems. Settling out on heat exchange surfaces, they can be as effective as scale or slime in reducing heat transfer. They may accumulate enough to interfere with water flow, and localized corrosive attack can occur beneath such accumulations. Abrasive dirt particles can cause excessively rapid wear of such moving parts as pump shafts and mechanical seals.

Treatment with polyelectrolytes, together with blowdown, will prevent most harmful effects of suspended solids. In larger cooling towers, the suspended solids content can be kept to an acceptably low level by the use of side stream filters. These are ordinary sand filters or other filters through which 1 to 5% of the circulating water is continuously passed. Before any new system is put into operation, it is important to flush it thoroughly, to remove as much suspended material as possible. A chemical detergent cleaning is also desirable.

Localized areas frequently can be protected by special methods. Thus, pump-packing glands or mechanical shaft seals can be protected by fresh water makeup or by circulating water from the pump casing, through a cyclone separator or filter, into the lubricating chamber.

Gross solid contaminants are kept out of large once-through cooling systems by trash screens. Recirculating systems use strainers. In closed recirculating systems, particles of mill scale and of some iron oxide corrosion products can be removed with magnetic separators or strainers in which the screens are either made of a magnetic alloy or have permanent magnets fastened to them.

In smaller equipment, a good dirt-control measure is the installation of backflush connections and shutoff valves on all condensers and heat exchangers, so that they can be readily backflushed with makeup water or detergent solutions to remove accumulated settled dirt. These connections can also be used for acid cleaning to remove calcium carbonate scale.

Selection of Water Treatment

Many methods are available for the correction of almost any water-caused difficulty. However, no one treatment method applies to all cases. Selection of the proper water treatment method and the details of the chemicals and equipment necessary to apply that method depend on many factors. The chemical characteristics of the water, which change with the operation of the equipment, are important. Other factors contributing to a lesser degree to the selection of proper water treatment are economics and other nonchemical influences. Among these nonchemical factors are the design of individual major system components such as the cooling tower or boiler, equipment operation, and human factors such as the quantity and quality of operating personnel available.

Once-Through Systems. Economics is the overriding consideration in the treatment of water in once-through systems. The quantities of water to be treated are usually so large that any treatment other than simple filtration or the addition of a few ppm (mg/L) of a polyphosphate, silicate, or other inexpensive chemical would not be feasible. Intermittent treatment with polyelectrolytes can help to maintain clean conditions when the cooling water is sediment-laden. In such systems, it is generally less expensive to invest more in corrosion-resistant construction materials rather than to attempt to treat the water.

Open Recirculating Systems. The selection of water treatment for open recirculating systems is affected considerably by the size of the system. At one extreme, large industrial cooling tower systems use such huge quantities of water that it is necessary to minimize the concentration of any treatment chemical used. In these systems, sizable expenditures for chemical treatment and control equipment can be justified, as can the use of com-

petent operating personnel. At the other extreme, in small air-conditioning and refrigeration cooling towers, the total amount of water used is so small that multiplying chemical concentrations by a factor of 10 can mean the expenditure of only a few more dollars per month, whereas the cost of the entire system is such that little or nothing can be justified by chemical feeding or automatic control equipment, and only part-time, unskilled operating personnel can be employed.

Therefore, a typical water treatment scheme for a large industrial cooling tower system operating above a 10,000 gpm (630 L/s) circulation rate might include scale control by a controlled bleed and alkalinity reduction via automatically pH-controlled sulfuric acid feed combined with corrosion control. The latter is obtained by feeding a mixed inhibitor with a concentration on the order of 50 to 100 ppm (mg/L), with efficacy depending both on the maintenance of pH within a narrow range and on periodic controlled chlorination with chlorine gas for slime control.

Available cooling tower controllers can monitor this and other programs by controlling acid feed via pH, total dissolved solids via conductivity, inhibitor concentration via direct or indirect measurement, and corrosion rate via test probes.

On the other hand, in a small air-conditioning or refrigeration cooling tower circulating at 100 gpm (6.3 L/s), treatment might consist of a controlled bleed to minimize scale formation, and the maintenance of 200 to 500 ppm (mg/L) of an inhibitor for corrosion control, plus the occasional application of a shock dose of microbiocide to control organic growths.

Air Washers and Sprayed Coil Units. A water treatment program for an air washer or a sprayed coil unit is usually complex and depends on the purpose and function of the system. Some systems, such as sprayed coils in office buildings, are used primarily for the control of temperature and humidity, while other air washer systems are intended to remove dust, oil vapor, and other airborne contaminants from an airstream, in addition to supplying temperature and humidity control. Without proper chemical treatment, the fouling characteristics of the contaminants removed from the air will cause operational problems in the circulating water of the system. For proper system operation, it is imperative that a suitable water treatment program be initiated when the system is put into operation.

Scale control is important in air washers or sprayed coil systems providing humidification, since the minerals present in the water may concentrate through the process of water evaporation to such a degree that they become a problem. Where scale control is necessary, it is usually obtained either by alkalinity reduction or by the use of phosphates or organic scale inhibitors. Corrosion protection may be conveniently afforded by the use of organic corrosion inhibitor blends.

Using suitable dispersants and surfactants is often necessary to control oil and dust removed from the airstream. The type of dispersant depends on the nature of the contaminant and the degree of system contamination. The dispersants should produce a minimal amount of foam in the system for maximum operating efficiency.

Control of slime and bacterial growth is also an important part of the treatment of air washers and sprayed coil systems. Because these systems are constantly exposed to airborne spores and bacteria, the potential for biological growth is enhanced, especially if the water contains any contaminants that are nutrients for the microorganisms. Because of the wide variations in conditions and applications of air washing installations and the possibilities of toxicity problems, individual cases should be studied by a knowledgeable chemical consultant before a water treatment program is started. All microbiocides applied in air washers must have specific Environmental Protection Agency label approval for that use.

Ice Machines. Lime scale formation, cloudy or "milky" ice, objectionable taste and odor, and sediment comprise the bulk of water problems encountered in ice machines. Lime scale formation is probably the most serious problem because it interferes with the harvest cycle by forming on the freezing surfaces where it prevents the smooth release of ice from the surface to the harvest bin.

Scale is caused by dissolved minerals in the water. Because water tends to freeze in a pure state, these dissolved minerals concentrate in the unfrozen water and some eventually deposit on the machine's freezing surfaces as a lime scale. Two main factors contributing to the problem are calcium hardness and total alkalinity (carbonate and bicarbonate).

The probability of scale formation in an ice machine varies directly with the concentrations of calcium hardness and total alkalinity in the water circulating in the ice machine. Table 9 shows how the problem can vary when using water with different hardness and alkalinity contents.

To prevent dissolved minerals in the water from depositing on freezing surfaces during normal operation, the use of a slowly soluble food-grade polyphosphate is recommended. These products keep hardness minerals in solution and thereby inhibit scale formation.

Dirty or scaled-up icemakers should be thoroughly cleaned before starting the water treatment program. Water distributor holes should be cleared and all loose sediment and other material flushed from the system. Existing scale formations can be removed by circulating an acceptable acid solution through the system. Several of these products are available from air-conditioning and refrigeration parts wholesalers throughout the country.

Although polyphosphates can inhibit lime scale in the icemaking section and help prevent sludge deposits in the sump caused by loose particles of lime scale, they do not eliminate the soft, milky, or white ice caused by high concentrations of dissolved minerals in the water.

Even with proper chemical treatment, the maximum mineral content that can be carried in the recirculating water and still produce clear ice is about 500 to 1000 ppm (mg/L). Increased bleedoff or reducing the thickness of the ice slab or the size of the cubes may help correct this condition. However, demineralizing or distillation equipment is needed to prevent this problem completely. Such equipment is expensive and usually not economical for use with small ice machines.

Another problem frequently encountered in servicing ice machines is objectionable taste or odor. When water containing an offensive taste or odor is used in an ice machine, the material causing the taste or odor is trapped in the ice. An activated carbon filter on the makeup water line can remove the objectionable taste or odor from the water. However, carbon filters need to be serviced or replaced regularly to avoid organic buildup in the carbon-bed itself.

Occasionally, slime growth is the cause of an odor problem in an ice machine. This problem can be controlled by cleaning the machine regularly with a food-grade acid. If the slime deposits persist, sterilization of the ice machine is helpful.

Feedwater often contains suspended solids such as mud, rust, silt, and dirt. To remove these contaminants, a sediment filter of appropriate size can be installed in the feed lines. In addition to improving the quality of the ice, installing a suspended solids filter protects solenoid valves in the machine.

Closed recirculating systems are often defined as systems requiring less than 5% makeup per year. The need for water treatment in such systems (i.e., hot water heat, chilled water, combined cooling and heating, and closed loop condenser water) is often ignored because the total amount of scale that could be deposited from the water initially filling the system would be insufficient to interfere significantly with heat transfer. This

Table 9 Scale Formation in an Ice Machine

Total Alkalinity as Bicarbonate	Hardness as Calcium Carbonate			
ppm (mg/L)	0 to 49	50 to 99	100 to 199	200 and up
0 to 49	No scale	Very light scale	Very light scale	Very light scale
50 to 99	Very light scale	Moderate scale	Moderate scale	Moderate scale
100 to 199	Very light scale	Troublesome scale	Troublesome scale	Heavy scale
200 and up	Very light scale	Troublesome scale	Heavy scale	Very heavy scale

rationalization leads to the erroneous conclusion that damage resulting from the corrosive factors of water required for the initial fill would not be serious. However, operating experience and tracer studies in many systems have shown that appreciable water losses are the rule, not the exception (Sussman and Fullman 1953). Losses of 25% of system volume per month are fairly common. Therefore, all systems should be adequately treated for corrosion control, and scale-forming waters should be softened before use as makeup. Many closed loop systems contain glycol or alcohol solutions, and the inhibitor products chosen for corrosion control must be chemically compatible.

The selection of a treatment program for closed systems is often influenced by factors other than degree of corrosion protection offered. Chromates are the most effective corrosion inhibitors; however, the toxicity of the chromate ion may rule out its use in locations where drainage water can cause pollution or where the yellow color may be objectionable. Leaks cause staining of carpet or other furnishings. In such cases, alternative inhibitor systems, such as buffered nitrites containing organic inhibitors for nonferrous metals, sulfites in hot systems, and other proprietary organic inhibitors, may be used.

Before treating new systems, they must be cleaned and flushed. Grease, oil, construction dust, dirt, and mill scale are always present in varying degrees and must be removed from the metallic surfaces to ensure adequate heat transfer and reduce the opportunity for localized corrosion. Detergent cleaners with organic dispersants are available for proper cleaning and preparation of new closed systems.

Chilled water systems without such bimetallic couples as steel and copper should maintain a minimum concentration of 200 ppm (mg/L) chromate as sodium chromate, with higher concentrations sometimes being required, depending on the chloride concentration of the recirculating water. Generally, an additional 1 ppm (mg/L) of sodium chromate is required for each ppm (mg/L) of chloride as chloride ion (Cl^-). Sodium chromate levels of 500 to 1000 ppm (mg/L) are usually maintained to reduce unexpected or unknown water losses reducing inhibitor concentration below the minimum. The pH value of the system water should be maintained above 6.5 for maximum ferrous metal protection and below 9.0 for maximum nonferrous metal protection. Unless nonconductive couplings of different metals are used throughout the system, treatment levels should be 2000 ppm (mg/L) or more. The presence of aluminum or its alloys, along with other metals, makes corrosion prevention more difficult and usually requires supplementary additives such as nitrates or silicates, in addition to the chromate inhibitor.

With buffered sodium nitrite inhibitors, a minimum of 500 ppm (mg/L) as sodium nitrite is required, along with maintaining pH in the range of 8.0 to 10.0. Other proprietary inhibitors, free of chromate, borate, and nitrite ions, are available. These include organic inhibitors and dispersants that can provide adequate corrosion and deposit control.

Water Treatment

53.17

Low Temperature Secondary and Hot Water Heating Systems.
Closed chilled water systems, which are usually converted to hot
water heating during winter, and primary low temperature hot
water heating systems, all of which usually operate in the
temperature range of 140 to 250°F (60 to 120°C), require higher
concentrations of inhibitors than does chilled water. Due to heat
stresses and higher corrosion rates. For example, the typical low
temperature hot water heating system [180 to 250°F (80 to
120°C)] requires a minimum of 1500 ppm (mg/L) sodium
chromate with pH at 6.5 to 9.0, or 2500 ppm (mg/L) sodium
nitrite with pH at 8.0 to 10.0. Organic proprietary inhibitors containing no chromates or nitrites are also available for such
systems.

**Medium Temperature and High Temperature Hot Water
Heating Systems.** Medium temperature hot water heating systems
[250 to 350°F (120 to 177°C)] and high temperature, high
pressure hot water systems [above 350°F (177°C)] require careful
consideration of treatment for corrosion and deposit control.
Makeup water for such systems should be demineralized or
softened to prevent scale deposits. For corrosion control, oxygen scavengers such as sodium sulfite or hydrazine should be
introduced to remove dissolved oxygen, and neutralizing amines
plus enough caustic soda should be used to maintain pH in the
8.0 to 10.0 range.

Electrode boilers are sometimes used to generate low or high
temperature hot water. Such systems operate through heat
generated because of the electrical resistance of the water between electrodes. The conductivity of the recirculating water is
an important factor with specific requirements depending on
the voltage used. Treatment of this type of system for corrosion and deposit control varies. In some cases, sodium sulfite
and caustic soda are used to maintain the desired specific conductance, sulfite residual, and pH value from 7.0 to 9.0. In other
applications, hydrazine and neutralizing amines (which do not
add to the conductivity) can remove dissolved oxygen and maintain the pH value at 7.0 to 9.0. The choice depends on the required conductivity of the electrode boiler and the conductivity
of the makeup water. Before selecting the water treatment for
an electrode boiler, consult the boiler manufacturer or the
operating manual for the boiler concerned.

Brines. Brine systems must be treated to control corrosion and
deposits. The standard chromate treatment program is the most
effective. Calcium chloride brines require a minimum of 1800
ppm of sodium chromate with pH 6.5 to 8.5. Sodium chloride
brines require a minimum of 3600 ppm (mg/L) of sodium
chromate and also pH 6.5 to 8.5. Sodium nitrite at 3000 ppm

(mg/L) in calcium brines or 4000 ppm (mg/L) in sodium brines
while controlling pH between 7.0 and 8.5 should provide adequate protection. Organic inhibitors are available that may provide adequate protection where neither chromates nor nitrites
can be used.

Ethylene glycol or propylene glycol are used instead of brine
systems and as antifreeze in chilled or secondary hot water
systems. Such glycols are available commercially with inhibitors
such as sodium nitrite, potassium phosphate, and organic inhibitors for nonferrous metals added by the manufacturer. These
require no further treatment, but softened water should be used for all filling and makeup requirements. Samples from the
systems should be checked periodically to ensure that the inhibitor has not been depleted. Analytical services are available
from the glycol manufacturers and others for this purpose.

Boilers. The bibliography lists some of many volumes written about boiler water treatment. The most important observations are that a wide range of treatment procedures can be used
for boiler waters, and that the method selected must depend on
the composition of the makeup water, the operating pressure
of the boiler, and the makeup rate, as well as other
considerations.

Minimum makeup water pretreatment for low pressure boilers
should consist of ion exchange softening with further consideration given to dealkalizers, desilicizers, or demineralizers.

In low pressure systems where steam is used for cooking,
heating, and humidification, some makeup is required, and the
use of inhibitors is paramount. In these cases, it is necessary
to remove dissolved oxygen from the feedwater through the use
of a deaerator or feedwater heater. This is then followed by treatment to raise the pH value above 10.5 and sodium sulfite or
hydrazine to remove the last traces of dissolved oxygen (Blake
1968). Scale control may also be required.

As operating pressures and makeup rates go up, the corrosion problem does not decrease, but the scale problem becomes
more important. Corrosion is controlled by using an open heater
or, at higher operating pressures, a deaerating heater to remove
oxygen from the boiler feedwater; the maintenance of a sulfite
or hydrazine residual as an oxygen scavenger in the boiler water;
and the maintenance of a sufficiently high pH in the boiler water.
Scale is controlled by external softening and by internal treatment, usually with phosphates and organic dispersants, to
precipitate residual traces of calcium, generally as a phosphate
(hydroxy apatite), and magnesium (as magnesium hydroxide or
a basic silicate). The ASME standards for boiler water quality
are given in Table 10.

Table 10   ASME Standards[a]

Boiler Water Quality					
Drum Pressure		**Silica,**	**Total Alkalinity,[c]**	**Neutralized Specific Conductance,**	**Suspended Solids,**
psig	**(kPa)**	**ppm SiO$_2$**	**ppm CaCO$_3$**	**micromhos/cm**	**ppm[e]**
0-300	(0-2.1)	150	700[b]	7000	300
301-450	(2.1-3.1)	90	600[b]	6000	250
451-600	(3.1-4.1)	40	500[b]	5000	150
601-750	(4.1-5.2)	30	400[b]	4000	100
751-900	(5.2-6.2)	20	300[b]	3000	60
900-1000	(6.2-6.9)	8	200[b]	2000	40
1001-1500	(6.9-10.3)	2	0[d]	150	20
1501-2000	(10.3-13.8)	1	0[d]	100	10

[a]Source—ASME Research Committee on Water in Thermal Power Systems. (ASME Standards were proposed at the conclusion of 1978.)
[b]Alkalinity not to exceed 10% of specific conductance.
[c]Minimum level of OH alkalinity in boilers below 1000 psi must be individually specified with regard to silica solubility and other components of internal treatment.
[d]Zero in these cases refers to free sodium or potassium hydroxide alkalinity. Some small variable amount of total alkalinity will be present and measurable with the assumed coordinated control or volatile treatment employed at these high pressure ranges.
[e]American Boiler and Affiliated Industries Manufacturers Association's maximum limits for boiler-water concentrations in units with a steam drum.

Treatment of the boiler water is often affected by the end use of the steam. This may range from reduction of alkalinity so it can minimize condensate line corrosion by keeping carbon dioxide low in the steam, to silica removal for the protection of steam turbines against siliceous turbine blade deposits. Antifoam agents are used for improved operation and steam quality.

Return Condensate Systems. Three approaches are used to minimize corrosion in condensate systems: (1) eliminating alkalinity from all water entering the boiler to minimize the amount of carbon dioxide in the condensate lines, (2) the use of volatile amines, such as morpholine and cyclohexylamine, to neutralize carbon dioxide and thus raise the pH of the condensate, and (3) the introduction of filming amines, such as octadecylamine, into the steam to form a thin, hydrophobic film on the condensate line surfaces. The latter is particularly effective in minimizing corrosion by oxygen. The need for chemical treatment can be minimized by designing return systems so that the condensate is still very hot when it reaches the boiler feed pump.

UNDERGROUND CORROSION

Corrosion activity on subsurface structures must always be anticipated. In addition to the economic loss when the underground facilities are destroyed by corrosion, loss of valuable fluids and continuity of service, and creation of hazards to life and property must be considered. Corrosion-control devices should be designed into new subsurface structures. These control measures must be selected and adapted to meet the specific conditions in which the structure will exist. A corrosion survey is usually necessary before corrosion control measures can be designed for underground structures (Peabody 1963).

Protective Coatings—Electrically Insulating

Protective coatings are applied to underground structures to isolate them from the soil environment and insulate them from electrical effects. Such coating materials must possess long-term qualities of high electrical resistance, inertness to the environment, low water absorption, high resistance to deformation by soil pressures and the temperatures at which they are operated, and good adhesion. Most coatings require reinforcing and/or shielding to resist soil stresses. The performance of all coating systems, even those of the best material specifications, depends on the metal surface preparation, application procedure and conditions, backfilling, and the physical, chemical, biological, and electrical stresses that occur in service.

The coatings most commonly used on underground structures include (1) hot-applied coal tar enamel, (2) hot-applied petroleum base coatings, such as asphalt enamels and waxes, (3) polyethylene or polyvinyl (tapes and extruded polyethylene), (4) coal tar epoxy resin, and (5) cold-applied bituminous and asphalt emulsions, cutback solvents, and greases. The performance of cold-applied coatings is generally least effective. Each of the coatings is formulated by its manufacturers for specific application and service conditions. The National Association of Corrosion Engineers (NACE) has prepared statements on minimum requirements for coal tar coatings, asphalt-type protective coatings, and prefabricated plastic films.

Cathodic Protection

Although cathodic protection can be applied to bare structures underground, it is most widely used to provide corrosion control for exposed metal at the coating flaws that inevitably occur on the coating during and after installation. The rate of metal penetration at coating flaws is often greater than that on bare surfaces. Galvanic anodes (magnesium or zinc) or impressed current systems can be used for cathodic protection of underground pipelines and tanks. Impressed current may be applied from anodes distributed alongside the structure, from remote anodes, or from deep well anodes.

The method used depends on the economics and the site conditions affecting the cathodic protection design requirements. Full cathodic protection is achieved when enough current is applied to the structure to prevent current flow into the soil from any and all points on the surface of the structure. Specifically, this protective current must be applied to the structure in an amount sufficient to maintain its external surface negative at every point by at least 0.85 V to a copper-saturated copper sulfate half cell in the immediate proximity thereof.

Types of Soils

The corrosivity of a soil is affected by its porosity (aeration), electrical resistivity, dissolved salts (depolarizers and inhibitors), moisture, and acidity or alkalinity. Although corrosion rates and characteristics cannot be related exactly to the individual factor, the attack on a metallic structure buried in nonuniform soil will be greatest on those surfaces in contact with the least porous (air-free), least resistive, most saline, moistest, or the most acidic soil. The National Bureau of Standards conducted a comprehensive, long-term study of underground corrosion. These studies (Romanoff 1957) were conducted from 1910 until 1955 and cover soil corrosivity, materials, coatings, cathodic protection, and stray currents.

Bacterial

High rates of corrosion in some air-free environments are associated with the presence of sulfate-reducing bacteria (*sporovibrio desulfuricans*). Bacterial activity is not a special and new form of corrosion. The conventional use of well-applied coatings and cathodic protection will control corrosion on underground metallic structures in the presence of these bacteria. Coatings that disbond, allowing water and corrodent to reach the metal surface, will shield the exposed metal from the effects of applied cathodic protection.

Insulation Failures

Most thermal insulation does not provide corrosion protection in soils or water. Catastrophic corrosion occurs on hot pipe surfaces when intermittently contacted by water (Sudrabin 1956). This corrosion process cannot be controlled by cathodic protection. Insulation, such as glass fiber or magnesia-asbestos, must be kept dry in underground runs through conduits. Severe corrosion has been experienced within a few months after construction on magnesia-asbestos insulated, snow melting pipe manifolds extending below the slab into the soil (Sudrabin and LeFebvre 1953). Natural asphalt materials used for underground pipe heat insulation exhibit some corrosion protective effect. However, they are relatively permeable to water, and repeated heating and cooling initiates attack under the insulation. Similarly, corrosion has occurred at locations of fluctuating water table.

Radiant heat and snow-melting pipe embedded in slabs constructed with open expansion joints and vermiculite-filled concrete, brick, or concrete block supports has been subject to severe corrosion (Sudrabin and LeFebvre 1953). Severe corrosion of radiant heating pipe embedded in sand or porous concrete under terrazzo flooring has also been experienced. It is good construction practice, in such heating systems, to avoid severe corrosion problems by using a minimum thickness of 1.5 in. (40 mm) of cement-rich concrete to surround the piping, a waterproof membrane under the slab, and steel saddle pipe supports. The piping should be coated at expansion joints, and pipe should not contact the reinforcing steel. Lightweight or insulating concrete produces local cell activity at the nonuniformities in contact with the piping. The piping should be insulated from all other metallic structures. Magnesium anodes buried in the adjoining soil may be attached to the piping for protection.

Although cathodic protection has been applied to radiant heating piping, it is not always possible to direct adequate amounts of protective current to corroding surfaces. The best corrosion-control measures are those integrated into the original design and construction of the heating system.

FIRESIDE CORROSION AND DEPOSITS

The surfaces of flues and boilers that are contacted by combustion products are seldom corroded while the equipment is operating, unless halogenated hydrocarbons, such as certain degreasing solvents, are present in the combustion air. Chimney connectors, smoke hoods, and canopies in contact with flue gas may, however, be subject to attack during warm up periods or when the rate of operation is so low that the temperature of the flue gas is below its dew point. In stack sections where flue gas temperatures drop below the dew point during operations, corrosion is inevitable.

It is common to use cast iron or acid-resistant, vitreous enameled steel in flue gas connections to appliances to prolong the life of these parts. Metal surfaces with temperatures that do not exceed 400 °F (200 °C) can be protected by periodic applications of paints. Protective coatings with organic binders are destroyed rapidly above 400 °F (200 °C) because of the decomposition of the organic materials. Stacks and other surfaces that reach higher temperatures can be protected with special coatings, such as silicones, resistant to these higher surface temperatures.

Corrosion on the fireside of boilers is common, and certain precautions must be taken to prevent it. It has been reported that 15% of boiler tube failures have been caused by fireside attack (Hinst 1955). The most common cause of fireside corrosion is the condensation of sulfuric acid at cold ends of the furnace. All fossil fuels contain varying amounts of sulfur. Even low sulfur fuel oil containing less than 1.0% sulfur forms gaseous oxides of sulfur when burned. Sulfur dioxide has no particularly corrosive effect on the boiler when it remains in the gaseous state and is emitted from the stack, but it pollutes the atmosphere. However, in boilers that operate with fluctuating loads and varying amounts of excess air present in the combustion chamber, the sulfur dioxide can further oxidize to sulfur trioxide, which is corrosive to the metallic surfaces of the boiler. Metals such as vanadium and iron act as catalysts, encouraging oxidation of sulfur dioxide to sulfur trioxide.

The sulfur trioxide combines with moisture, forming sulfuric acid. The condensation point of sulfuric acid is 330 °F (165 °C). Where a boiler has a variable load, the metal surface temperature in the furnace may drop below 330 °F (165 °C) at low firing rates and condense sulfuric acid, causing serious corrosion. This may happen regularly throughout the normal operating period but is most likely to occur when the boiler is shut down for some period. Furthermore, moisture may condense on the metallic surfaces during shutdown because of the high relative humidity. In the presence of moisture, as well as acidic soot deposits, fireside corrosion will continue.

Fireside corrosion can be reduced by modifying the firing cycle to minimize the number of times the flue gas temperature drops below its dew point. Other methods include using low sulfur content fuel oils, regulating excess air, and using fuel oil additives that neutralize acidic condensate and deposits on fireside surfaces. Good maintenance practices are essential. A boiler should be fired to maintain a constant temperature. A boiler let down at the end of a day and left at low is not only conducive to condensation of sulfuric acid, causing corrosion, but also encourages soot and slag formation and stress corrosion cracking around the tube ends.

Additives, such as magnesium and calcium oxide slurries, have effectively neutralized sulfuric acid formed on firesides. Certain manganese-bearing compounds inhibit the formation of sulfur trioxide significantly and thereby are effective in reducing sulfuric acid corrosion. These compounds also reduce smoke, soot, and deposits (Belyea 1966). Some additives contain detergents, which are surface-active agents, and dispersants that prevent fuel from adhering to burner nozzles, a cause of sticking, fuel dribbling, improper spray pattern, smoking, and soot deposits (Bausch and MacPherson 1965). The resulting deposits absorb acid gases and cause serious corrosion and combustion inefficiency.

Care after shutdown is equally important in preventing fireside corrosion. The fireside of a boiler should always be thoroughly brushed and cleaned to remove accumulations of soot and other deposits (Hinst 1955). This should be followed by air drying.

Moisture absorbents, such as silica gel and quicklime, can be spread on trays on top of the tubes or in the bottom of the boiler drum or shell. This will reduce the condensation of moisture and the resulting corrosion during idle periods. (See Chapter 24 of the 1983 EQUIPMENT Volume.)

REFERENCES

Belyea, A.R. 1966. Manganese Additive Reduces SO₃. *Power*, November.

Blake R.T. 1968. Cure for Pitting in Low Pressure Boiler Systems. *Air Conditioning, Heating and Ventilating*, November, p. 45.

Copson, H.R. 1952. Effect of Velocity on Corrosion by Water. *Industrial Engineering & Chemistry*, Vol. 44.

Cotton, R.A.; Sladek, K.J.; and Sohn, B.I. 1975. Evaluation of a Single-step Bacterial Pollution Monitor. *Journal of the American Water Works Association*, Vol. 67, p. 449.

Eliassen, R.; Skrinde, R.T.; and Davis, W.B. 1958. Experimental Performance of "Miracle" Water Conditioners. American Water Works Association *Journal*, Vol. 50, p. 1371.

Hinst, H.F. 1955. Eleven Ways to Avoid Boiler Tube Corrosion. *Heating, Piping and Air Conditioning*, January.

Nordell, E. 1961. *Water Treatment for Industrial and Other Uses*. Reinhold Publishing Co., New York, NY.

Peabody, A.W. 1963. Pipeline Corrosion Survey Techniques. *Materials Protection*, Vol. 2, No. 4, p. 62.

Pye, D. Chemical Fixation of Oxygen. *Journal of the American Water Works Association*, Vol. 39, p. 1121.

Romanoff, M. 1957. Underground Corrosion. National Bureau of Standards *Circular*, No. 579.

Sudrabin, L.P. 1963. Designing Automatic Controls for Cathodic Protection. *Materials Protection*, Vol. 2, No. 2.

Sudrabin, L.P. 1956. An Anomaly in Pipe Line Corrosion Diagnosis. *Corrosion*, Vol. 12, No. 3, p. 17.

Sudrabin, L.P. and LeFebvre, F.J. 1953. External Corrosion of Piping in Radiant Heating and Snow Melting Systems. Heating, Piping and Air-Conditioning Contractors National Association *Official Bulletin*, Vol. 60, July.

Sudrabin, L.P. 1963. A Review of Cathodic Protection Theory and Practice. *Materials Protection*, Vol. 2, No. 5.

Sussman, S. and Fullman, J.B. 1953. Corrosion in Closed Circulating Water Systems. *Heating and Ventilating*, October, p. 77.

Weider, B.Q. and Partridge, E.P. 1954. Practical Performance of Water Conditioning Gadgets. *Industrial and Engineering Chemistry*, Vol. 46, p. 954.

BIBLIOGRAPHY

ARI. 1958. *Corrosion and Its Prevention*. Air-Conditioning and Refrigeration Institute, Arlington, VA.

American Society for Testing Materials. 1969. Manual on Water. *Special Technical Publication*, No. 442, 3rd Ed., Philadelphia, PA.

Berk, A.A. 1962. *Handbook—Questions and Answers on Boiler Feed Water Conditioning*. Bureau of Mines, U.S. Department of the Interior, Washington, DC.

Carrier Corp. 1963. System Design Manual—Part 5—Water Conditioning. Syracuse, NY.

Evans, U.R. 1963. *An Introduction to Metallic Corrosion*, 2nd ed. Edward Arnold, Ltd., London.

Evans, U.R. 1960. *The Corrosion and Oxidation of Metals*. Edward Arnold, Ltd., London.

Hamer, P.; Jackson, J.; and Thurston, E.F. 1961. *Industrial Water Treatment Practice*. Butterworth & Co., Ltd., London.

McCoy, J.W. 1980. *Microbiology of Cooling Water*. Chemical Publishing Company, New York, NY.

McCoy, J.W. 1974. *The Chemical Treatment of Cooling Water*. Chemical Publishing Company, New York, NY.

NACE. 1969. Control of External Corrosion on Underground or Submerged Metallic Piping Systems. NACE-RP-1-69. National Association of Corrosion Engineers, Houston, TX.

NACE. 1980. *NACE Corrosion Engineer's Reference Book*. National Association of Corrosion Engineers, Houston, TX.

Nalco. 1979. *Nalco Water Handbook*. The Nalco Chemical Company, Oak Brook, IL.

Powell, S.T. 1954. *Water Conditioning for Industry*. McGrawHill, New York, NY.

Rosa, F. 1985. *Water Treatment Specification Manual*. McGrawHill, New York, NY.

CHAPTER 54

SERVICE WATER HEATING

A SERVICE water heating system has (1) a heat energy source, (2) heat transfer equipment, (3) distribution system, and (4) terminal hot water usage devices.

1. **Heat Energy Sources** may be (1) fuel combustion, (2) solar energy collection, (3) electrical conversion, and (4) recovered waste heat from such sources as flue gases, ventilation and air-conditioning systems, refrigeration cycles, or process waste discharge.
2. **Heat Transfer Equipment** is of either the direct or indirect type.
3. **Distribution Systems** transport the hot water produced by the water heating equipment to plumbing fixtures and other terminal points. The amount of water consumed must be replenished in the water heating equipment and piping system under pressurized conditions from the building water service main. For locations where constant supply temperatures are desired, circulation piping must be provided from remote fixtures.
4. **Terminal Hot Water Usage Devices** are plumbing fixtures and equipment requiring hot water for specific use. They typically exhibit intermittent periods of irregular, constant, or no-flow conditions. These patterns and their related water usage requirements vary for different building and process applications.

SYSTEM REASONING

Flow rate is the primary factor to be determined in the hydraulic and thermal design of the water heating and piping systems. Operating temperatures, pressures, and water quality are also mandatory considerations to be interrelated with system flow rate requirements. Separate procedures are used to select water heating equipment and design the piping system.

Water heating equipment, storage facilities, and piping should have enough capacity to (1) provide the required hot water without wasting energy or water and (2) allow economical system installation, maintenance, and operation.

Hot water can be provided in various ways because of (1) the variety of types and designs of water heating equipment available and (2) the application of equipment at various points along the piping distribution in relation to the overall design of the system. The service water heating system for a given application must be selected considering the overall design and energy usage demand for both the building's hot water and mechanical systems.

Water heating equipment types and designs are based on (1) the heat energy source, (2) application of the developed energy to heating the water, and (3) the control method used to deliver the necessary hot water at the required temperature under all water demand flow conditions. Application of this equipment within the overall design of the hot water system is based on (1) location within the system, (2) related temperature requirements, and (3) the volume of water to be used.

The choice of central or point of use water heating systems should be made after evaluating both initial costs and the differences in operating costs. Similarly, the choice of energy source

should consider operating costs and equipment life cycle costs. In making energy conservation choices, the current editions of the following energy conservation guides should be consulted: ANSI/ASHRAE/IES Standard 90 or the ANSI/ASHRAE/IES Standard 100 Series sections on Service Water Heating (see also Design Considerations).

METHOD OF HEAT DEVELOPMENT

Direct. Heat from the combustion of fuels, collection of solar energy, or direct conversion of electrical energy into heat may be applied directly in water heating equipment.

Indirect. Heat energy can also be developed from remote heat sources such as boilers, solar, cogeneration, refrigeration, waste heat, etc. and then transferred to the water.

DIRECT HEAT TRANSFER EQUIPMENT

Gas-Fired

Residential gas-fired water heating equipment is usually the automatic storage type. For industrial and commercial use, common gas-fired heaters are (1) automatic storage, (2) circulating tank, (3) instantaneous, (4) hot water supply boilers.

Automatic Storage Heaters incorporate the burner(s), storage tank, outer jacket, insulation, and controls in a single unit. They are installed without dependence upon other water storage equipment.

Circulating Tank Heaters are classified in two types: (1) automatic, in which the thermostat is located in the water heater and (2) non-automatic, where the thermostat is located within the storage tank proper. This type of heater has a practically unlimited range of size.

Instantaneous Heaters have little water storage capacity, are self-contained, and are often similar to a circulating tank heater. They usually include a flow switch as part of the control system. Instantaneous heaters may have a modulating gas valve that varies gas flow as water flow changes.

Hot Water Supply Boilers are capable of providing high temperature hot water and are operated with a pressure vessel philosophy. They are typically applied as an alternative to a circulating tank or instantaneous heaters.

The National Fuel Gas Code, NFPA Standard 54-84 (ANSI Z223.1) covers the installation of gas-fired water heaters. This code also covers the installation of venting equipment and controls available for gas-fired water heaters.

Oil-Fired

Oil-fired heaters are generally the automatic storage type with high recovery rates. They use Grade No. 1 or No. 2 fuel and have pressure atomizing, aspirating, or vaporizing burners. Oil-fired heaters can also be hot water supply boilers, circulating tank, and instantaneous type. Installation of oil-fired water heaters is covered in NFPA Standard 31-83, *Standard for the Installation of Oil Burning Equipment* (ANSI Z95.1).

The preparation of this chapter is assigned to TC 6.6, Service Water Heating.

Electric

Electric water heaters are generally the automatic storage type, consisting of a tank with one or more immersion heating elements attached to line voltages of 120, 208, 240, 277, or 480 V. Element wattages are selected to meet recovery requirements. Electric water heating elements consist of resistance wire embedded in refractories having good heat conduction properties and electrical insulating values. Heating elements are generally sheathed in copper or alloy tubes, and are fitted into a threaded or flanged mounting for insertion into the tank. Thermostats controlling heating elements may be the immersion or surface-mounted type. State and local regulatory agencies may require listing by a recognized testing laboratory.

Residential Storage Water Heaters range up to 120 gallons (450 L) with input up to 12,000 W. They have a primary resistance heating element near the bottom and possibly a secondary element located in the upper portion of the tank. In twin element heaters, the thermostats are usually interlocked so that the primary heating element cannot operate if the top of the tank is cold.

Commercial Electric Water Heaters are available in vertical or horizontal models. Many combinations of power, voltage, and storage capacity are available. Instantaneous electric water heaters are commonly used for swimming pool or booster applications.

Heat Pump Water Heater models either include a storage tank or are meant to be connected to an existing storage water heater. They use a refrigeration cycle to extract heat from the air to heat water.

Electric Energy Demand Control. Several peak demand controls are available. These are used to avoid adding water heating loads to building peak electrical demands. These devices operate on the principle that a building's peak electrical demand exists for a short period during which heated water can be supplied from storage rather than continuing electrical demand for hot water recovery. Avoidance of electrical use for service water heating during peak demand hours allows water heating at the lowest electric energy cost in many electric rate schedules. Wiring costs may also be reduced where the water heater load is positively prevented from loading the building service during other peak electrical use.

The essential functions of load detection and control involve sensing the building electrical load and comparing it with peak demand data. When the load is below peak demand, the device allows the water heater to operate. Some devices can program deferred loads in steps as capacity is available. This priority sequence may involve each of several banks of elements in a water heater, multiple water heaters, or water heating and other deferrable loads, such as pool heating and snow melting. When load controllers are used, storage heaters must be used.

Sizing recommendations apply only to water heating systems without load-limiting devices. When load-limiting devices are used, the storage and recovery rate must be increased. Manian and Chackeris (1974) include a detailed discussion on load limited storage heating system design.

INDIRECT HEAT TRANSFER EQUIPMENT

Indirect water heating uses steam, hot water, or other fluid, heated in a separate generator or boiler, as the heating medium. The water heater extracts its heat through either an external or internal heat exchanger. Systems are classified as storage type, semi-instantaneous, or instantaneous.

When using an indirect system, serious concern must be given to prevent contamination of the service water by leakage of the heating medium through the heat transfer surface. Some national, state, and local codes require double wall, vented tubing in indirect water heaters to preclude the possibility of cross contamination.

When high or low pressure steam is used as the heating medium, high condensation rates will occur, particularly when a sudden demand causes an inflow of cold water. The steam and condensate return pipes should be of ample size. Condensate should be drained by gravity without lifts to a vented condensate receiver located below the level of the heater. Otherwise, water hammer, reduced capacity, and heater damage may result. The condensate may be cooled by preheating the cold water supply to the heater.

Storage Type

Storage water heaters are designed for service conditions where hot water requirements are not constant or when a large volume of heated water must be held in storage for periods of peak load. The tank heating surface may consist of a tube bundle, usually copper tubing, attached to a tube sheet. The bundle is inserted into the tank through a flanged opening to which the bundle and bonnet are securely attached. The heating fluid is circulated through the tubes of the bundle to transfer heat to the water in the tank. Adequate clearance is needed to remove the bundle for cleaning or replacement. When the heater is in use, cold water enters the storage tank beneath the heating coil. As it absorbs heat by natural convection, it warms and rises to the upper portion of the tank, where it can be drawn off.

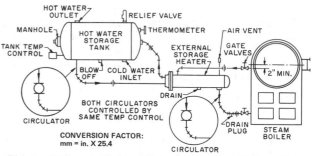

Fig. 1   External Storage Water Heater Installation Used Below the Water Line on a Steam Boiler

Figure 1 shows an indirect, external water heater designed for connection to a separate tank. The boiler water circulates through the heater shell, while domestic water from the storage tank circulates through the tubes and back to the tank. The storage tank should be installed as far above the boiler as possible. Where headroom is limited or faster recovery is desired, circulating pumps can be installed in both the boiler water and domestic water piping circuits. Steam can also be used as the heating medium in a similar scheme.

Indirect Immersion Storage Type

This heater (Figure 2) has a power gas or oil burner firing into a horizontal tube containing a finned tube bundle. An intermediate heat transfer fluid, usually water, is pumped through the finned bundle and then to the water heating bundle located

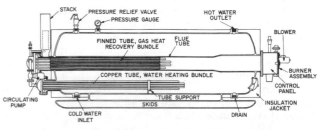

Fig. 2   Indirect Immersion-Fired Water Heater

below the fire tube in the shell or storage tank. The heat transfer fluid, continuously circulated at a controlled velocity, is the basic source of heat to the stored water, even though the firing tube is immersed in the water and serves as additional heat surface. The heat transfer fluid is circulated at a maximum temperature of 250°F (121°C), and the closed system is operated under pressure to prevent boiling.

Corrosion and scale formation are minimized on the heating medium side because no makeup water, and hence no oxygen, is brought into the circulating fluid system. The metal temperature of the domestic water side of the water heating bundle is usually less than direct fired water heaters, which minimizes scale formation from hard water on that side.

Instantaneous Type

The instantaneous indirect water heater is used for a steady, continuous supply of hot water. In this unit, the water is heated as it flows through the tubes. The heating medium (steam or hot fluid) flows through the shell, yielding a small ratio of hot water volume to heating medium volume resulting in uncertain temperature control. Instantaneous water heaters are designed to provide sufficient capacity to heat the required quantity of water at the time the hot water draw occurs. A thermostatic mixing valve could maintain a more uniform temperature of the hot water supply to the plumbing fixtures and limit the danger of scalding.

Some indirect instantaneous water heaters are located inside a boiler. A special opening through which the coil can be inserted is provided in the boiler. While the coil can be placed in the steam space above the water line of a steam boiler, it is usually placed below the water line. Coils of tubing, often with integral fins, are immersed in the boiler water and are used without storage tanks. The flow rate through the coil is affected by the friction loss in the coil and by fittings and restrictions. The water attains the desired temperature in passing through the coil.

Because the water heater transfers heat from the boiler water to the domestic water, gross output of the boiler must be considered when selecting the desired flow rate and outlet temperature of the heater. This method of heating water is frequently found in automatically fired installations where either steam or hot water boilers supply hot water during the summer.

Semi-Instantaneous Type

Semi-instantaneous water heaters have limited storage, determined by manufacturers to meet the average momentary surges of hot water. They usually consist of a heating element and control assembly devised for the close control of the leaving hot water temperature.

For surge loads in water flow rates (as in laundry and secondary school gym shower applications) the heat input peak can be reduced by adding a hot water storage tank and a circulating pump. With this arrangement, the tank acts as a "flywheel" to the surge in water flow, while the recirculating pump governs the heat input.

Blending Type

Steam or hot water developed from indirect or separate heating equipment can be injected directly into the process or volume of water to be heated. This is often associated with point-of-use applications, e.g., certain types of commercial laundry, food, and process equipment.

Solar Water Heaters

Availability of solar energy at the building site, the efficiency and cost of solar collectors, and the availability and cost of alternate fuels determine whether or not solar energy collection units should be used as a heat energy source. To conserve fuel or electrical energy, solar energy equipment can be included to supplement primary energy sources.

The basic elements of a solar water heater are solar collectors, a storage tank, piping, and controls. The system may use natural convection or forced circulation. Auxiliary heat energy sources may also be added to the (1) storage tank, (2) water leaving the tank, or (3) incoming supply feed bypassing the solar heater. Adding auxiliary energy to the lower part of the tank as in method (1) can lead to higher mean collector temperature, poorer collector performance, and higher auxiliary energy use. Any supplemental energy should be added to the upper part of the tank. In method (3), failure to use some of the collected solar energy may result. A modulated auxiliary heat energy source as in method (2) improves solar collector performance by operating at a lower mean collector temperature.

Collector design must allow operation in below freezing conditions where applicable. Antifreeze solutions in a separate collector piping circuit arrangement are often used, as well as systems that allow water to "drain back" to heated areas when low temperatures occur. Uniform flow distribution in a collector or in a bank of collectors is important for good performance. Storage tanks and piping must be well insulated and must be arranged for minimum pressure drop. It is desirable to maintain stratification in the storage tank for better system performance.

The application, design, and sizing of solar water heaters will depend on: auxiliary energy requirements; collector orientation; temperature of the cold water; general site, climatic, and solar conditions; installation requirements; area of collectors; and amount of storage. Successful design of solar water heating systems depends on empirically verifying manufacturer's data and water usage assumptions.

Waste Heat

Waste heat can be recovered by inserting heat exchange elements into gaseous or fluid streams. Heat recovered from this separate equipment is used frequently to preheat cold water entering the service water heater. Heat also can be recovered from equipment, such as air-conditioning or refrigeration compressors. Waste heat recovery is an energy conservation method that can reduce (1) energy costs, (2) energy requirements of the building heating and service water heating equipment, or (3) cooling requirements of applicable air-conditioning systems.

DISTRIBUTION SYSTEMS

Pipe Sizing

The water distribution system must be properly designed for the total hot water system to function properly. Hot water needed in any building varies with the type of establishment, usage, occupancy, and time of day. Piping should be capable of meeting peak demand.

Supply Piping System

Sizing of hot water supply pipes involves the same principles as those of sizing of cold water supply pipes. Table 1 and manufacturer's specifications for fixtures and appliances allow hot water demands to be determined. These demands, together with procedures given in Chapter 34 of the 1985 FUNDAMENTALS Volume, are used to size the mains, branches, and risers.

Allowance for pressure drop through the heater may be needed

Table 1   Hot Water Demands and Use for Various Types of Buildings

Type of Building	Maximum Hour	Maximum Day	Average Day
Men's dormitories	3.8 gal (14.4 L)/student	22.0 gal (83.4 L)/student	13.1 gal (49.7 L)/student
Women's dormitories	5.0 gal (19 L)/student	26.5 gal (100.4 L)/student	12.3 gal (46.6 L)/student
Motels: No. of units[a]			
20 or less	6.0 gal (22.7 L)/unit	35.0 gal (132.6 L)/unit	20.0 gal (75.8 L)/unit
60	5.0 gal (19.7 L)/unit	25.0 gal (94.8 L)/unit	14.0 gal (53.1 L)/unit
100 or more	4.0 gal (15.2 L)/unit	15.0 gal (56.8 L)/unit	10.0 gal (37.9 L)/unit
Nursing homes	4.5 gal (17.1 L)/bed	30.0 gal (113.7 L)/bed	18.4 gal (69.7 L)/bed
Office buildings	0.4 gal (1.5 L)/person	2.0 gal (7.6 L)/person	1.0 gal (3.8 L)/person
Food service establishments:			
Type A—full meal	1.5 gal (5.7 L)/max	11.0 gal (41.7 L)/max	2.4 gal (9.1 L)/avg
restaurants and cafeterias	meals/h	meals/h	meals/day[b]
Type B—drive-ins, grilles,	0.7 gal (2.6 L)/max	6.0 gal (22.7 L)/max	0.7 gal (2.6 L)/avg
luncheonettes, sandwich	meals/h	meals/h	meals/day[b]
and snack shops			
Apartment houses: No. of apartments			
20 or less	12.0 gal (45.5 L)/apt.	80.0 gal (303.2 L)/apt.	42.0 gal (159.2 L)/apt.
50	10.0 gal (37.9 L)/apt.	73.0 gal (276.7 L)/apt.	40.0 gal (151.6 L)/apt.
75	8.5 gal (32.2 L)/apt.	66.0 gal (250 L)/apt.	38.0 gal (144 L)/apt.
100	7.0 gal (26.5 L)/apt.	60.0 gal (227.4 L)/apt.	37.0 gal (140.2 L)/apt.
200 or more	5.0 gal (19 L)	50.0 gal (195 L)/apt.	35.0 gal (132.7 L)/apt.
Elementary schools	0.6 gal (2.3 L)/student	1.5 gal (5.7 L)/student	0.6 gal (2.3 L)/student[b]
Junior and senior high schools	1.0 gal (3.8 L)/student	3.6 gal (13.6 L)/student	1.8 gal (6.8 L)/student[b]

[a]Interpolate for intermediate values.   [b]Per day of operation.

when sizing hot water lines, particularly where instantaneous water heaters are used and the available pressure is low.

Return Piping System

For hot water systems in which piping from the heater to the fixture or appliance is 100 ft (30 m) or less, circulation systems are not generally used. However, circulation piping is commonly provided in any hot water supply system in which it is desirable to have hot water available continously at the fixtures. This includes cases where the hot water piping system exceeds 100 ft (30 m). The water circulation pump may be controlled by a thermostat (in the return line) set to start and stop the pump over an acceptable temperature range. Since hot water is corrosive because of its high oxygen content and high temperature, circulating pumps should be made of bronze or other corrosion-resistant material. For small installations, a simplified pump sizing is to allow 1 gpm (63 mL/s) for every 20 fixture units in the system; 0.5 gpm (32 mL/s) for each 0.75 or 1 in. (20 or 25 mm) riser; 1 gpm (63 mL/s) for each 1.25 or 1.5 in. (32 or 40 mm) riser; and 2 gpm (126 mL/s) for each riser 2 in. (50 mm) or larger.

Where multiple risers or horizontal loops are used, balancing valves in the return lines are recommended. A check valve should be placed in each return to prevent entry of cold water or reversal of flow, particularly during periods of hot water demand.

The circulation hot water supply may be an up-feed or down-feed piping system. Three common methods of arranging circulation lines are shown in Figure 3. Although the diagrams apply to multi-story buildings, arrangements (A) and (B) are also used in residential designs.

In circulation systems, air venting, pressure drops through the heaters and storage tanks, balancing, and line losses should be considered. In Figures 3A and 3B, air is vented by connecting the circulating line below the top fixture supply. With this arrangement, air is eliminated from the system each time the top fixture is opened. Generally, for small installations, a 0.5 or 0.75 in. (13 or 20 mm) hot water return is ample. Werden and

Spielvogel (1969), Dunn *et al.* (1959), and NSF Standard 5-83 cover heat loss calculations for large systems.

For larger installations, heat losses of lines become significant. A quick method to size the return follows:

1. Determine total length of all hot water supply and return piping.
2. Multiply this total by 30 Btu/h·ft (28.8 W/m) to obtain approximate total heat loss in Btu/h (W) for covered pipe. For uninsulated pipe, use 60 Btu/h·ft (57.7 W/m). Actual heat losses in pipes as given in Table 2 for 140°F (60°C) water in pipe and 70°F (21°C) ambient temperature of 30 and 60 Btu/h·ft (28.8 and 57.7 W/m) are recommended for ease in calculation.
3. Divide total heat loss by 10,000 (40 000) to obtain total pump capacity in gpm (L/s). Required circulating pump capacity based on 8.33 lb. water/gal (1 kg water/L)·60 min/h (3600 s/h)·20°F (11.1°C) allowable temperature drop = 10,000 (40 000).
4. Select a pump to provide the required gpm (L/s) and obtain from the pump curves the head created at this flow.
5. Multiply the head by 100 and divide by the total length of hot water return piping to determine the allowable friction loss per 100 ft (100 m) of pipe.
6. Determine the required gpm (L/s) in each circulating loop and size the hot water return pipe based on this gpm (L/s) and the allowable friction loss from Step 5.

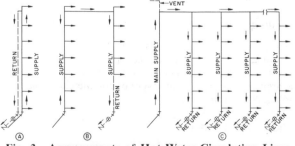

Fig. 3   Arrangements of Hot Water Circulation Lines

Table 2 Heat Loss of Pipe
[At 70°F (39°C) Temperature Difference]

Pipe Size in.	(mm)	Bare Copper Tubing Btu/h·ft	(W/m)	0.5-in. (13-mm) Glass Fiber Insulated Copper Tubing Btu/h·ft	(W/m)
0.75	(20)	30	(28.8)	17.7	(17.0)
1	(25)	38	(36.5)	20.3	(19.5)
1.25	(32)	45	(43.2)	23.4	(22.5)
1.5	(40)	53	(50.9)	25.4	(24.4)
2	(50)	66	(63.4)	29.6	(28.4)
2.5	(65)	80	(76.9)	33.8	(32.5)
3	(80)	94	(90.4)	39.5	(38.0)
4	(100)	120	(115.4)	48.4	(46.5)

All storage tanks and piping on recirculating systems should be insulated as recommended by ASHRAE *Standard* 90A.

Special Piping—Commercial Kitchens

Adequate flow rates and pressures must be maintained for automatic dishwashers in commercial kitchens. To reduce operating difficulties, piping for automatic dishwashers should be installed according to the following recommendations:

1. The supply line for 180°F (82°C) water from the water heater to the dishwasher should not be less than 0.75 in. (20 mm) ID pipe size.
2. No auxiliary feed lines should connect to the 180°F (82°C) supply line to the dishwasher.
3. The cold water feed line to the water heater should be no less than 1 in. (25 mm) ID pipe size.
4. A return line should be installed when the water heater is more than 5 ft (1.5 m) from the dishwasher.
5. Forced circulation by a pump should be used if the water heater is installed on the same level as the dishwasher, if the length of return piping is more than 60 ft (18 m), or if the water lines are trapped.
6. If a circulating pump is used, it is generally installed in the return line. It may be controlled by (a) the dishwasher wash switch, (b) a manual switch located near the dishwasher, (c) an immersion thermostat built as an integral part of the pump, or (d) an immersion thermostat located in the return line.
7. A pressure-reducing valve should be installed in the low temperature supply line to a booster water heater, but external to a recirculating loop. It should be adjusted, with the water flowing, to the value stated by the washer manufacturer [typically 20 psi (140 kPa)].
8. A check valve should be installed in the return circulating line.
9. If a check valve type of water meter is installed in the cold water line ahead of the heater, it is necessary to install an expansion tank between the water meter and heater.
10. National Sanitation Foundation (NSF) standards require the installation of a 0.25 in. (6 mm) IPS connection and pressure gauge mounted adjacent to the supply side of the control valve. They also require a water line strainer ahead of any electrically operated control valve (Figure 4).
11. NSF standards do not accept copper water lines not under constant pressure, except for the line downstream of the solenoid valve on the rinse line to the cabinet.

Water Pressure—Commercial Kitchen

Proper flow pressure must be maintained to achieve efficient dishwashing. The standards of the National Sanitation Foundation for dishwasher water flow pressures are 15 psi (100 kPa) gauge minimum, 25 psi (170 kPa) gauge maximum, and 20 psi (140 kPa) gauge ideal. Flow pressure is the line pressure measured

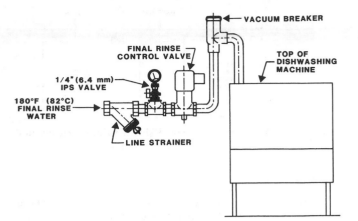

Fig. 4 National Sanitation Foundation (NSF) Plumbing Requirements for a Commercial Dishwasher

when water is flowing through the rinse arms of the dishwasher. Low flow pressure can be caused by undersized water piping, stoppage in piping, or excess pressure drop through heaters. Low water pressure causes an inadequate rinse, resulting in poor drying and sanitizing of the dishes. If flow pressure in the supply line to the dishwasher is below 15 psi (100 kPa) gauge, a booster pump should be installed to provide supply water at 20 psi (140 kPa) gauge.

A flow pressure in excess of 25 psi (170 kPa) gauge will cause atomization of the 180°F (82°C) rinse water, resulting in an excessive temperature drop. Between the rinse nozzle and the dishwasher, the temperature drop can be as much as 15°F (8°C). A pressure regulator should be installed in the supply water line adjacent to the dishwasher and external to the return circulating loop. The regulator should be set to maintain a pressure of 20 psi (140 kPa) gauge.

Two Temperature Service

Where multiple temperature requirements are met by a single system, the system temperature is determined by the maximum temperature needed. Lower temperatures can be obtained by mixing water from hot and cold water supplies. Automatic blending to reduce hot water temperature available at certain outlets may be necessary to prevent injury or damage from excessive water temperatures (Figure 5). Where predominant usage is at lower temperatures, the common approach is to heat all water to the lower temperature, then use a separate booster heater to further heat the water for the higher temperature services (Figure 6). This method offers better protection against scalding. A third method uses separate heaters for the higher temperature service (Figure 7). It is common practice to cross-connect the two heater, so that one heater can serve the complete installation temporarily while the other is valved off for maintenance. Each heater should be sized for the total load.

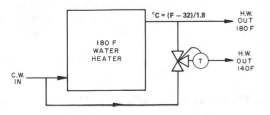

Fig. 5 Two-Temperature Service Using a Three-Way Control Valve

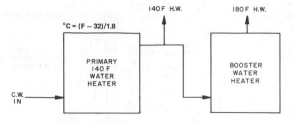

Fig. 6 Two-Temperature Service Using a Primary Heater and Booster Heater in Series

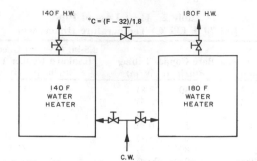

Fig. 7 Two-Temperature Service with Separate Heater for Each Service

Manifolding

Where one heater does not have the capacity to supply both needs, two or more self-contained storage heaters may be installed in parallel. With such an installation, one mixing valve of adequate capacity should be used, not two. It is difficult to obtain even flow through parallel mixing valves.

Heaters installed in parallel must be identical, i.e., have the same input and storage capacity, with inlet and outlet piping arranged so that an equal flow is received from each heater under all demand conditions.

DESIGN CONSIDERATIONS

WATER HEATING EFFICIENCIES

The following definitions apply to water heating systems.

Recovery Efficiency. Heat absorbed by the water divided by heat input to the heating unit during the period that water temperature is raised from inlet temperature to final temperature.

Thermal Efficiency. Heat in the water delivered at the heater outlet divided by the heat input of the heating unit over a specific period.

Energy Factor. A measure of the overall efficiency of a residential storage water heater representing heat in the daily delivered water divided by the estimated daily energy consumption of the water heater, as measured by the U.S. Department of Energy test procedures.

Hot Water Distribution Efficiency. Heat contained in the water at points of use divided by the heat delivered at the heater outlet.

Heater System Efficiency. Heat contained in the water at points of use divided by the heat input to the heating unit at a given flow rate.

Overall System Efficiency. Heat in the water delivered at points of use divided by the heat supplied to the heater for any selected time period.

Hot water system design should consider the following points:

1. Water heaters of different sizes and insulation have different standby losses.
2. A properly designed, sized, and insulated distribution system is necessary to deliver minimum water temperatures satisfactory for the uses served.
3. Heat traps between recirculation mains and infrequently used branch lines reduce convection losses to these lines.
4. Control of circulating pumps to operate only as needed to maintain proper temperature at the end of the main reduces losses on return lines.
5. Provision for shutdown of circulators during building vacancy reduces circulating losses.

WATER QUALITY, CORROSION, AND SCALE

A complete water analysis and an understanding of system requirements are needed to protect water heating systems from scaling and corrosion. Soft waters may aggravate corrosion problems, while hard waters may cause scale (fouling or liming of the surface). Scale from mineral-bearing waters increases with film temperatures and, for a given temperature, decreases with velocity because of the decreasing heating surface temperature and shearing action of the flow. Corrosion problems increase with temperature because of the release of corrosive gases such as oxygen and carbon dioxide (CO_2) and the increase in electrical conductivity of the water (Toaborek et al. 1972.)

Oxygen and CO_2 in the water supply are major factors in corrosion with some relationship between organic content and certain types of corrosion. Hard waters tend to deposit scale, which acts as a protective shield against corrosion but reduces the heat transfer rate. Hardness and alkalinity give a rough indication of the scale and corrosion properties of water, respectively.

Cathodic protection reduces corrosion problems in many water heaters. An anode, which is typically a rod of magnesium metal immersed in the tank (cathode). The active metal serves as a sacrificial material to reduce or prevent corrosion of the basic tank materials. Higher temperatures or softened waters may cause rapid anode consumption. Routine replacement is recommended to prolong heater life.

Corrosion and scaling usually increase with temperature, so water temperature should be kept as low as possible. Figure 8 illustrates the effect of increased temperature on scaling tendencies. When high temperature is required, water heaters capable of providing satisfactory results at that temperature level should be selected. Less active materials are necessary at elevated temperatures. Steel storage tanks can be protected to varying degrees by galvanizing or by lining with copper, glass, or cement.

Tanks constructed of stainless steel, copper, aluminum, monel,

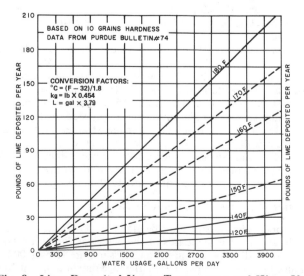

Fig. 8 Lime Deposited Versus Temperature and Water Use

or nonferrous alloys may be considered but should be compatible with the elements in the water. Extreme caution should be taken with stainless steel in the presence of chlorides or with copper in the presence of ammonia or CO_2. Many water heating applications (such as a laundry or car wash) require water supplies relatively low in hardness. If water is naturally hard, water treatment is recommended for satisfactory final results (see Chapter 53).

SPECIAL CONCERNS

Legionella Pneumophila (Legionaires' Disease)

The bacteria that causes Legionaires' Disease has been discovered in the service water systems of various buildings in this country and abroad. Infection has often been traced to Legionella Pneumophila colonies in shower heads. Ciesielki *et al.* (1984) determined that the Legionella Pneumophila can colonize in hot water systems maintained at 115°F (46°C) or less. Unrecirculated segments of the service water systems provide ideal breeding locations, e.g., shower heads, faucet aerators, and uncirculated sections of storage type water heaters.

To limit the potential of Legionella Pneumophila growth, service water temperatures in the 140°F (60°C) range are recommended. This high temperature, however, increases the potential for scalding, so care must be taken. Supervised periodic flushing of fixture heads with 170°F (76.6°C) water is recommended in hospitals and health care facilities, since already weakened patients are generally more susceptible to infection.

Utilization Temperatures

Typical temperature requirements for some services are shown in Table 3. In some cases, slightly lower temperatures may be satisfactory.

Table 3   Representative Hot Water Utilization Temperatures

Use	Temperature °F	Temperature °C
Lavatory		
Hand washing	105	40
Shaving	115	45
Showers and tubs	110	43
Therapeutic baths	95	35
Commercial and institutional laundry	180	82
Residential dishwashing and laundry	140	60
Surgical scrubbing	110	43
Commercial Spray Type Dishwashing as required by N.S.F.		
Single or multiple tank hood or rack type		
Wash	150 min.	65 min.
Final rinse	180 to 195	82 to 90
Single tank conveyor type		
Wash	160 min.	71 min.
Final rinse	180 to 195	82 to 90
Single tank rack or door type		
Single temperature wash and rinse	165 min.	74 min.
Chemical sanitizing types (see Manufacturer for actual temp. required)	140	60
Multiple Tank Conveyor Type		
Wash	150 min.	65
Pumped rinse	160 min.	71 min.
Final rinse	180 to 195	82 to 90
Chemical Sanitizing Glasswasher		
Wash	140	60
Rinse	75 min.	24 min.

Hot Water from Tanks and Storage Systems

With storage heaters, it is common to assume that 60 to 80% of the hot water in a tank is usable before dilution by cold water lowers the temperature below an acceptable level. Thus, the hot water available from a self-contained storage heater is usually considered to be:

$$Q_t = R + MS_t/d \qquad (1)$$

where

Q_t = available hot water, gph (L/s)
R = recovery rate at the required temperature, gph (L/s)
M = ratio of usable water to storage tank capacity
S_t = storage capacity of the heater tank, gal (L)
d = duration of peak hot water demand, h (s)

Usable hot water from an unfired tank in gal (L) is calculated from:

$$Q_a = MS_a \qquad (2)$$

where

Q_a = usable water available from an unfired tank, gal (L)
S_a = capacity of unfired tank, gal (L)
NOTE: Assumes tank water at required temperature.

Hot water obtained from a water-heating system using a storage heater with an auxiliary storage tank can be determined by:

$$Q_z = dQ_t + Q_a = R \cdot d + M(S_t + S_a) \qquad (3)$$

where

Q_z = total hot water available from system during one peak, gal (L)

CODES AND STANDARDS

Codes and standards that have special significance to water heating applications follow.

ANSI Z-21.10.1-84.   American National Standard for Gas Water Heaters, Volume I: Automatic Storage Water Heaters with Inputs of 75,000 Btu per Hour or Less. (Also AGA 1631-0008.)

ANSI Z-21.10.3-84.   Gas Water Heaters, Volume III: Circulating Tank, Instantaneous and Large Automatic Storage Water Heaters. (Also AGA 1631-0110.)

ANSI Z-21.56-83.   Gas-Fired Pool Heaters.

ANSI Z-21.22-79.   Relief Valve and Automatic Gas Shutoff Devices for Hot Water Supply Systems.

UL 174-83.   Household Electric Storage Tank Water Heaters.

UL 1453-82.   Electric Booster and Commercial Storage Tank Water Heaters.

UL 1261-81.   Electric Water Heaters for Pools and Tubs.

UL 732-74.   Oil-Fired Water Heaters.

ASME Boiler and Pressure Vessel Code Section IV (H and HLW) Code Construction. H label governs low pressure heating boilers, and HLW label governs low pressure, fired, potable hot water heaters.

ASME Boiler and Pressure Vessel Code Section VIII. U label governs unfired water heaters and pressure vessels. (Note: Some states, cities, and counties require ASME-stamped equipment.)

NFPA Standard 54-84   (ANSI Z223.1-1984). National Fuel Gas Code. Governs installation of gas-fired water heaters.

NFPA 31-83.   Installation of Oil Burning Equipment.

ANSI Standard 119 governs water heating installation in mobile homes and recreational vehicles.

ASHRAE Standard 90 and 100 series provide recommended guidelines for energy conserving design for service water heating.

ASPE publishes a data book on plumbing and service water heating.

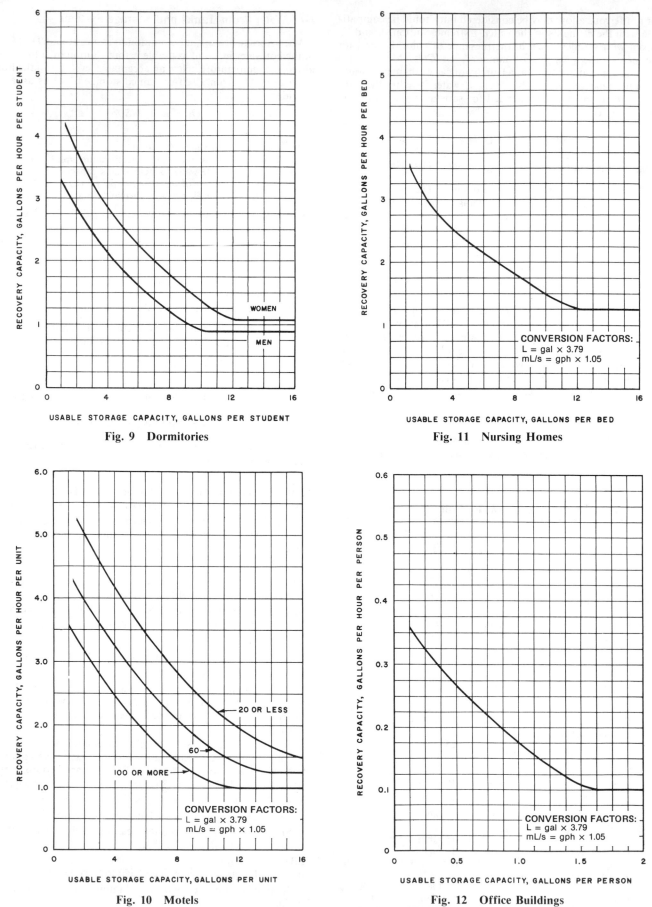

Fig. 9   Dormitories

Fig. 11   Nursing Homes

Fig. 10   Motels

Fig. 12   Office Buildings

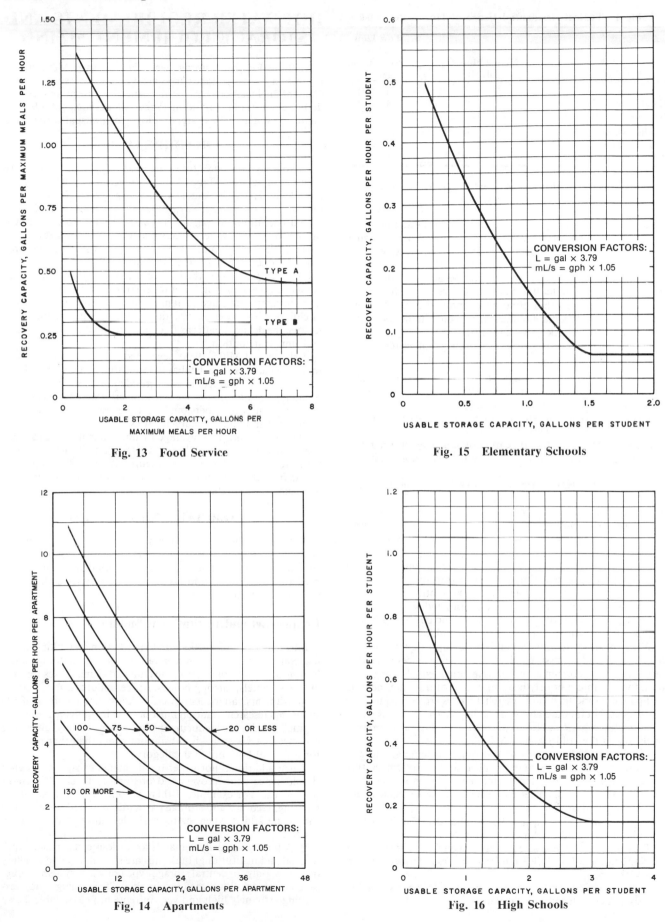

Fig. 13   Food Service

Fig. 15   Elementary Schools

Fig. 14   Apartments

Fig. 16   High Schools

Table 4 Typical Residential Usage of Hot Water/Task

Use	High Flow gal	High Flow L	Low Flow (Water Savers Used) gal	Low Flow (Water Savers Used) L
Food preparation	5	(19)	3	(11)
Hand dishwashing	4	(15)	4	(15)
Automatic dishwasher	15	(57)	15	(57)
Clothes washer	32	(121)	21	(80)
Shower or bath	20	(76)	15	(57)
Face and hand washing	4	(15)	2	(7.2)

SAFETY DEVICES FOR HOT WATER SUPPLY SYSTEMS

A water heater storage tank is under a certain water pressure, depending on the static pressure in the system. When the water in the tank is heated, it expands and causes tank pressure to rise rapidly if backflow cannot occur because of a check valve or pressure reducing valve in the line or because of temporary shutoff of the cold water line. Such a pressure rise, if the heating continues for any length of time, may rupture the tank. Systems can be protected by a diaphram expansion tank in the cold water line between the check valve and heater.

The following three devices also protect hot water supply systems from damage.

Energy Cutoff Device (high limit) prevents stored water temperatures from exceeding 210°F (99°C) for residential water by stopping the flow of fuel or energy.

Temperature relief valve opens when stored water temperature exceeds 210°F (99°C). This should comply with the current applicable American National Standards and have a water discharge capacity equal to or exceeding the heat input rating of the water heater.

Pressure relief valve opens at its pressure setting. It should have a discharge capacity sufficient to relieve excess fluid pressure in the water heater. It can be the thermal expansion or water rated type and should comply with current applicable American National Standards or the ASME *Boiler and Pressure Vessel Code*.

Some difference of opinion exists among various regulatory agencies as to the selection of these protective devices and methods of installation. As a result, it is essential to check and comply with the manufacturer's instructions and applicable local codes. In the absence of such instructions and codes, the following recommendations may be used as a guide.

Water heating systems should be equipped with both a temperature and a pressure relief valve. These devices can either be separate or in combination and have ratings equal to or greater than the maximum hourly heat input rate of the water heating equipment. Sometimes pressure relief valves are not required by local codes, but they are always essential in closed systems where water meters, check valves, or pressure reducing valves prevent backflow in the cold water supply line.

Temperature relief valves or combination temperature and pressure relief valves should be installed so that the temperature sensitive element is located in the top 6 in. (150 mm) of the tank.

Safety devices should meet the current applicable requirements and be certified as follows:

1. Energy cutoff devices, listed and labeled by Underwriters' Laboratories and/or American Gas Association.
2. Pressure relief valves, listed by American Gas Association or National Board of Boiler and Pressure Vessel Inspectors, and so labeled.
3. Temperature or combination temperature and pressure relief valve, A.G.A. listed and labeled.

HOT WATER REQUIREMENTS AND STORAGE EQUIPMENT SIZING

Methods for sizing storage water heaters vary. Methods using recovery versus storage curves are based on extensive research. Conventional methods have been retained because other methods do not cover as many building types. All methods provide adequate hot water if the designer allows for unusual conditions.

RESIDENTIAL

Estimating procedures for sizing residential water heaters vary with manufacturers. Table 4 shows typical hot water usage in a residence. HUD-FHA in its *Minimum Property Standards for One and Two Family Living Units*, No. 4900.1-1982, has established minimum permissible water heater sizes, as shown in Table 5. Storage water heaters may vary from the sizes shown in the table if combinations of recovery and storage that produce the one hour draw required are used.

Over the last decade, the structure and lifestyle of the family has altered the household's hot water consumption. Due to variations in family size, age of family members, presence and age of children, hot water use volumes and temperatures, and other factors, the demand patterns fluctuate widely in both magnitude and time distribution.

Perlman and Mills (1985) developed average residential hot water use patterns. The database for this study consisted of direct measurements conducted on 58 residential installations. For broad representation, the site selection criteria required an adequate geographical dispersion, both rural and urban, and a wide range of demographic characteristics.

The overall and peak average of hot water use volumes are shown in Table 6. Average hourly patterns and 95% confidence level profiles are illustrated in Figures 17 and 18. Samples of results from the analysis of similarities in hot water use are given in Figures 19 and 20.

COMMERCIAL AND INDUSTRIAL

Hot or warm water is used by most industrial and commercial establishments. The specific requirements vary in total volume, flow rate, duration of peak load period, and temperature needed. Water heaters and systems should be selected based on these requirements.

Commercial and Institutional Buildings

Information in this section, up to the section on multiple housing, consists of sizing recommendations for central storage water heating systems. Hot water usage data and sizing curves for dormitories, motels, nursing homes, office buildings, food service establishments, apartments, and schools are based on EEI-sponsored research. Caution must be used in applying these data to small buildings or reducing the hot water capacity, unless the expected hot water use is substantially less than that required for a typical building in a category.

When additional hot water requirements exist, the designer should increase the recovery and/or storage capacity to account for this use. For example, if there is food service in an office building, recovery and storage capacities required for each use should be added when sizing a single central water heating system.

Peak hourly and daily demands for various categories of commercial and institutional buildings are shown in Table 1. These demands, only for central storage-type hot water systems, represent maximum flows metered in this 129 building study, excluding extremely high and very infrequent peaks. Table 2 also

Table 5   HUD—FHA Minimum Water Heater Capacities for One- and Two-Family Living Units

Number of Baths	1 to 1.5			2 to 2.5				3 to 3.5			
Number of Bedrooms	1	2	3	2	3	4	5	3	4	5	6
GAS[a]											
Storage, gal (L)	20 (76)	30 (114)	30 (114)	30 (114)	40 (150)	40 (150)	50 (190)	40 (150)	50 (190)	50 (190)	50 (190)
1000 Btu/h (kW) input	27 (7.9)	36 (10.5)	36 (10.5)	36 (10.5)	36 (10.5)	38 (11.1)	47 (13.8)	38 (11.1)	38 (11.1)	47 (13.8)	50 (14.6)
1-h draw, gal (L)	43 (163)	60 (227)	60 (227)	60 (227)	70 (265)	72 (273)	90 (341)	72 (273)	82 (311)	90 (341)	92 (350)
Recovery, gph (mL/s)	23 (24)	30 (32)	30 (32)	30 (32)	30 (32)	32 (36)	40 (42)	32 (34)	32 (34)	40 (42)	42 (44)
ELECTRIC[a]											
Storage, gal (L)	20 (76)	30 (114)	40 (150)	40 (150)	50 (190)	50 (190)	66 (250)	50 (190)	66 (250)	66 (250)	80 (300)
kW input	2.5	3.5	4.5	4.5	5.5	5.5	5.5	5.5	5.5	5.5	5.5
1-h draw, gal (L)	30 (114)	44 (167)	58 (220)	58 (220)	72 (273)	72 (273)	88 (334)	72 (273)	88 (334)	88 (334)	102 (387)
Recovery, gph (mL/s)	10 (10)	14 (15)	18 (19)	18 (19)	22 (23)	22 (23)	22 (23)	22 (23)	22 (23)	22 (23)	22 (23)
OIL[a]											
Storage, gal (L)	30 (114)	30 (114)	30 (114)	30 (114)	30 (114)	30 (114)	30 (114)	30 (114)	30 (114)	30 (114)	30 (114)
1000 Btu/h (kW) input	70 (20.5)	70 (20.5)	70 (20.5)	70 (20.5)	70 (20.5)	70 (20.5)	70 (20.5)	70 (20.5)	70 (20.5)	70 (20.5)	70 (20.5)
1-h draw, gal (L)	89 (337)	89 (337)	89 (337)	89 (337)	89 (337)	89 (337)	89 (337)	89 (337)	89 (337)	89 (337)	89 (337)
Recovery, gph (mL/s)	59 (62)	59 (62)	59 (62)	59 (62)	59 (62)	59 (62)	59 (62)	59 (62)	59 (62)	59 (62)	59 (62)
TANK-TYPE INDIRECT[b, c]											
I-W-H rated draw, gal (L) in 3-h, 100°F (55.6°C) rise		40 (150)	40 (150)			66 (250)[d]	66 (250)	66 (250)	66 (250)	66 (250)	66 (250)
Manufacturer-rated draw, gal (L) in 3-h, 100°F (55.6°C) rise		49 (186)	49 (186)			75 (284)[d]	75 (284)	75 (284)	75 (284)	75 (284)	75 (284)
Tank capacity, gal (L)		66 (250)	66 (250)			66 (250)[d]	82 (310)	66 (250)	82 (310)	82 (310)	82 (310)
TANKLESS-TYPE INDIRECT[c, e]											
I-W-H-rated, gpm (mL/s) 100°F (55.6°C) rise		2.75 (170)	2.75 (170)	3.25 (200)		3.25 (200)[d]	3.75 (200)	3.25 (200)	3.75 (200)	3.75 (200)	3.75 (200)
Manufacturer-rated draw, gal (L) in 5 min, 100°F (55.6°C) rise		15 (57)	15 (57)	25 (95)		25 (95)[d]	35 (133)	25 (95)	35 (133)	35 (133)	35 (133)

[a]Storage capacity, input and recovery requirements indicated in the table are typical and may vary with each individual manufacturer. Any combination of these requirements to produce the stated 1-h draw will be satisfactory.

[b]Boiler-connected water heater capacities [180°F (82.2°C) boiler water, internal, or external connection].

[c]Heater capacities and inputs are minimum allowable. Variations in tank size are permitted when recovery is based on 4 gph/kW (4.2 mL/s · kW) @ 100°F (55.5°C) rise for electrical, A.G.A. recovery ratings for gas heaters and IBR ratings for steam and hot water heaters.

[d]Also for 1 to 1.5 baths and 4 B.R. for indirect water heaters.

[e]Boiler-connected heater capacities [200°F (93°C) boiler water, internal, or external connection].

shows average hot water consumption figures for these types of buildings. Averages for schools and food service establishments are based on actual days of operation, while all others are based on total days. These averages can be used to estimate monthly consumption of hot water.

Dormitories

Hot water requirements for college dormitories generally include showers, lavatories, service sinks, and washing machines. Peak demand usually results from the use of showers. Load profiles and hourly consumption data indicate that peaks may last one or two hours and then taper off substantially. These peaks occur predominantly in the evening, mainly around midnight. The figures do not include hot water used for food service.

Motels

Domestic hot water requirements are for tubs and showers, lavatories, and general cleaning purposes. Recommendations are based on tests at low- and high-rise motels located in urban, suburban, rural, highway, and resort areas. Peak demand, usually from shower use, may last one or two hours and then drop off sharply. Food service, laundry, and swimming pool requirements are not included.

Nursing Homes

Hot water is required for tubs and showers, wash basins, service sinks, kitchen equipment with food service for patients, and for general cleaning. These figures include hot water for kitchen use. When other equipment, such as for heavy laundry and hydrotherapy purposes, is to be used, its additional hot water requirement should be added to those recommended.

Office Buildings

Hot water requirements are primarily for cleaning and lavatory use by occupants and visitors. Hot water use for food service within office buildings is not included.

Food Service Establishments

Hot water requirements are primarily for dishwashing. Other uses include food preparation, cleaning pots and pans and floors, and hand washing for employees and customers. The recommendations of hot water requirements are for establishments serving food at table, counter and booth seats, and to parked cars. Food service establishments that use disposable service exclusively are not included.

Dishwashing, as metered with other hot water requirements in these tests, is based on the normal practice of dishwashing after meals but not on indiscriminate or continuous use of machines irrespective of the flow of soiled dishes. The recommendations include hot water supplied to dishwasher booster heaters.

Apartments

Hot water requirements for both garden-type and high-rise apartments are for one- and two-bath apartments, showers, lavatories, kitchen sinks, dishwashers, clothes washers, and general cleaning purposes. Clothes washers can be either in individual apartments or centrally located. These data apply to central water heating systems only.

Elementary Schools

Hot water requirements are for lavatories, cafeteria and kitchen use and general cleaning purposes. When showers are used,

Table 6   Overall (OVL) and Peak Average Hot Water Use Volumes

Group	Hourly		Daily		Weekly		Monthly	
	OVL avg	Peak avg	OVL avg	Peak avg	OVL avg	Peak avg	OVL avg	Peak avg
All Families, gal	2.6	4.6	62.4	67.1	436	495	1897	2034
(L)	(9.8)	(17.3)	(236)	(254)	(1652)	(1873)	(7178)	(7700)
"Typical" Families, gal	2.6	5.8	63.1	66.6	442	528	1921	2078
(L)	(9.9)	(21.9)	(239)	(252)	(1673)	(1981)	(7270)	(7866)

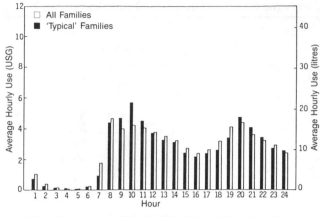

Fig. 17   Average Hourly Hot Water Use—By Hour

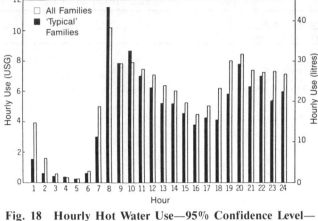

Fig. 18   Hourly Hot Water Use—95% Confidence Level—
By Hour

their additional hot water requirements should be added to those recommended. The recommendations include hot water for dishwashing machines, but not for extended school operation, such as evening classes.

High Schools

Senior high schools, grades 9 or 10 through 12, require hot water for showers, lavatories, dishwashing machines, kitchens, and general cleaning. Junior high schools, grades 7 through 8 or 9, have requirements similar to those of the senior high schools. Where no showers are included, junior high schools would follow the recommendations made for elementary schools.

Requirements for high schools are based on daytime use. The recommendations do not include hot water usage for additional activities, such as night school. In such cases, the maximum hourly demand remains the same, but the maximum daily and average daily usage is increased, usually by the number of additional people using showers and, to a lesser extent, eating and washing facilities.

SIZING EXAMPLES

Figures 9 to 16 show relationships between recovery and storage capacity for the various building categories. Any combination of storage and recovery capacity that falls on the proper curve will satisfy the building requirements. Using the minimum recovery rate and the maximum storage capacity on the curves yields the smallest hot water capacity capable of satisfying the building requirement. The higher the recovery capacity, the greater the 24-hour heating capacity and the smaller the storage capacity required.

These curves can be used to select water heaters that have fixed storage or recovery capacities, by adjusting recovery and storage requirements. Where hot water demands are not coincident with peak electric, steam, or gas demands, greater heater inputs can be selected if they do not create additional energy system demands, and the corresponding storage tank size can be selected from the curves.

Recovery capacities in Figures 9 to 16 represent the actual hot water required without considering system heat losses. Heat losses from storage tanks and recirculating hot water piping should be calculated and added to the recovery capacities shown. With large uninsulated storage tanks and extensive lengths of uninsulated hot water piping, it is necessary to either substantially increase the recovery capacity or insulate the equipment.

The storage capacities shown are net usable requirements. On the assumption that 60 to 80% of the hot water in a storage tank is usable, the actual storage tank size should be increased by 25 to 66% to compensate for unusable hot water.

Examples

The following examples are worked in conventional units only. Answers and given quantities are in dual units.

Example 1: Determine the required water heater size for a 300-student women's dormitory for the following criteria:

a. Storage system with minimum recovery rate.

b. Storage system with recovery rate of 2.5 gph (2.6 mL/s) per student.

c. With the additional requirement for a cafeteria to serve a maximum of 300 meals per hour for minimum recovery rate combined with item *a,* and for a recovery rate of 1.0 gph (1.1 mL/s) per maximum meal per hour combined with item *b.*

Solution:

a. The minimum recovery rate from Figure 9 for women's dormitories is 1.1 gph per student, or a total of 330 gph recovery is required. Storage required is 12 gal per student or 3600 gal storage. On a 70% net usable basis, the necessary tank size is 1.43 · 3600 = 5150 gal (19.5 m³).

b. The same curve also shows 5 gal storage per student at 2.5 gph recovery, or 300 · 5 = 1500 gal storage with recovery of 300 · 2.5 = 750 gph. The tank size will be 1.43 · 1500 = 2150 gal (8140 L).

c. The additional requirement for a cafeteria can be determined from Figure 13, with the storage and recovery capacity added to that for the dormitory.

For the case of minimum recovery rate, the cafeteria requires 300 · 0.45 = 135 gph recovery rate and 300 · 7 · 1.43 = 3000 gal of additional storage. The entire building then requires 330 + 135 = 465 gph (488 mL/s) recovery and 5150 + 3000 = 8150 gal (30.9 m³) of storage.

With one gal recovery per maximum meal hour, the recovery required is 300 gph, with 300 · 2.0 · 1.43 = 860 gal of additional storage. Combining this with item *b,* the entire building requires 750 + 300 = 1050 gph (1.1 L/s) recovery and 2150 + 860 = 3010 gal (11.4 m³) of storage.

Note: Recovery capacities shown are for heating water only. Additional capacity must be added to offset the system heat losses.

Example 2: Determine the water heater size and monthly hot water consumption for an office building to be occupied by 300 people:

a. Storage system with minimum recovery rate.

b. Storage system with 1.0 gal (3.8 L) per person storage.

c. Additional minimum recovery rate requirement for a luncheonette, open 5 days a week, serving a maximum of 100 meals in one hour, and an average of 200 meals per day.

d. Monthly hot water consumption.

Solution:

a. With minimum recovery rate of 0.10 gph per person from Figure 12 for office buildings, 30 gph recovery is required, while the storage is 1.6 gal per person, or 300 · 1.6 = 480 gal storage. The tank size will be 1.43 · 480 = 690 gal (2620 L).

b. The curve also shows 1.0 gal storage per person at 0.175 gph per person recovery, or 300 · 0.175 = 52.5 gph. The tank size will be 1.43 · 300 = 430 gal (1630 L).

c. The hot water requirements for a luncheonette are contained in Figure 13. The recovery versus storage curve shows that with minimum

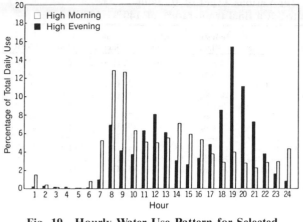

**Fig. 19 Hourly Water Use Pattern for Selected
"High Morning" and "High Evening" Users—By Hour**

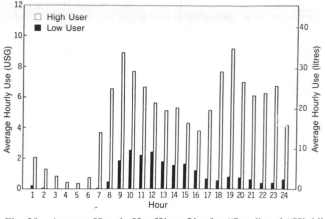

**Fig. 20 Average Hourly Hot Water Use for "Low" and "High"
Users—By Hour**

recovery capacity of 0.25 gph per maximum meals per hour, 100 meals would require 25 gph recovery, while the storage would be 2.0 gal per meal, or $100 \cdot 2.0 \cdot 1.43 = 286$ gal (1080 L) storage. The combined requirements with item *a* would then be 55 gph recovery and 976 gal (3700 L) storage.

Combined with item *b*, the requirement will be 77.5 gph recovery and 716 gal (2710 L) storage.

d. From Table 1, the office building will consume an average of 1.0 gal per person per day $\cdot$ 30 days $\cdot$ 300 people = 9000 gal per month, while the luncheonette will consume 0.7 gal per meal $\cdot$ 200 meals per day $\cdot$ 22 days per month = 3080 gal per month, for a total of 12,080 gal (45.8 m³) per month.

Note: Recovery capacities shown are for heating water only. Additional capacity must be added to offset the system heat losses.

Example 3: Determine the water heater size for a 200-unit apartment house:

a. Storage system with minimum recovery rate, with a single tank.

b. Storage system with 4 gph (4.2 mL/s) per apartment recovery rate, with a single tank.

c. Storage system for each of two 100-unit wings.
   1. Minimum recovery rate.
   2. Recovery rate of 4 gph (4.2 mL/s) per apartment.

Solution:

a. The minimum recovery rate, from Figure 14, for apartment buildings with 200 apartments is 2.1 gph per apartment, or a total of 420 gph recovery required. The storage required is 24 gal per apartment, or 4800 gal. Based on 70% of this hot water being usable, the necessary tank size is $1.43 \cdot 4800 = 6860$ gal (26.0 m³).

b. The same curve also shows 5 gal storage per apartment at 4 gph recovery, or $200 \cdot 4 = 800$ gph. The tank size will be $1.43 \cdot 1000 = 1430$ gal (5410 L).

c. Alternate solution for a 200-unit apartment house with two wings, each with its own hot water system. In this instance, the solution for each 100-unit wing would be:

1. With minimum recovery rate of 2.5 gph per apartment, from the curve, a 250 gph recovery is required, while the necessary storage is 28 gal per apartment, or $100 \cdot 28 = 2800$ gal. The required tank size is $1.43 \cdot 2800 = 4000$ gal (15.2 m³) for each wing.

2. The curve also shows that for a recovery rate of 4 gph per apartment, the storage would be 14 gal, or $100 \cdot 14 = 1400$ gal, with recovery of $100 \cdot 4 = 400$ gph. The necessary tank size is $1.43 \cdot 1400 = 2000$ gal (7570 L) in each wing.

Note: Recovery capacities shown are for heating water only. Additional capacity must be added to offset the system heat losses.

Example 4: Determine the water heater size and monthly hot water consumption for a 2000-student high school.

a. Storage system with minimum recovery rate.

b. Storage system with 4000-gal (15.2 m³) maximum storage capacity.

Solution:

a. With the minimum recovery rate of 0.15 gph per student from Figure 16 for high schools, 300 gph recovery is required. The storage required

is 3.0 gal per student, or $2000 \cdot 3.0 = 6000$ gal storage. The tank size is $1.43 \cdot 6000 = 8600$ gal (32.6 m³).

b. The net storage capacity will be $0.7 \cdot 4000 = 2800$ gal, or 1.4 gal per student. From the curve, 0.37 gph per student recovery capacity is required, or $0.37 \cdot 2000 = 740$ gph (777 mL/s).

c. From Table 1, hot water consumed monthly is 2000 students $\cdot$ 1.8 gal per student per day $\cdot$ 22 days = 79,200 gal (300 m³).

Note: Recovery capacities shown are for heating water only. Additional capacity must be added to offset the system heat losses.

Table 7 can be used to determine the size of water heating equipment from the number of fixtures. To obtain the probable maximum demand, multiply the total quantity for the fixtures by the demand factor in line 19. The heater or coil should have a water heating capacity equal to this probable maximum demand. The storage tank should have a capacity equal to the probable maximum demand multiplied by the storage capacity factor in line 20.

Example 5: Determine heater and storage tank size for an apartment building from a number of fixtures.

60 lavatories	$\times$ 2 gph	(2.1 mL/s)	=	120 gph (126 mL/s)
30 bathtubs	$\times$ 20 gph	(21 mL/s)	=	600 gph (630 mL/s)
30 showers	$\times$ 30 gph	(31.5 mL/s)	=	900 gph (945 mL/s)
60 kitchen sinks	$\times$ 10 gph	(10.5 mL/s)	=	600 gph (630 mL/s)
15 laundry tubs	$\times$ 20 gph	(21 mL/s)	=	300 gph (315 mL/s)
Possible maximum demand			=	2520 gph (2646 mL/s)

Solution:

Probable maximum demand = $2520 \cdot 0.30 = 756$ gph (2646 $\times$ 0.30 = 794 mL/s)

Heater or coil capacity = 756 gph (794 mL/s)

Storage tank capacity = $756 \cdot 1.25$
                       = 945 gal (3580 L)

Showers

In many housing installations such as motels, hotels, military barracks, and dormitories, the peak hot water load usually results from the use of showers. Table 1 indicates the probable hourly hot water demand and the recommended demand and storage capacity factors applied to various types of buildings. Hotels will normally have a 3- to 4-hour peak shower load. Motels require similar volumes of hot water, but the peak demand may last for only a 2-hour period. In some types of housing, such as barracks, fraternities, or dormitories, all occupants may take showers within a very short period. In this case, it is best to find the peak load by determining the number of shower heads, the rate of flow per head, and estimating the length of time that the showers will be on.

The flow rate from a shower head varies depending on the type, size, and water pressure. At 40-psi (280-kPa) water pressure, available shower heads have nominal flow rates from about 2.5 to 10 gpm (160 to 630 mL/s). In multiple shower installations,

Table 7   Hot Water Demand per Fixture for Various Types of Buildings
[Gallons (litres) of water per hour per fixture, calculated at a final temperature of 140 °F (60 °C)]

	Apartment House	Club	Gym- nasium	Hospital	Hotel	Industrial Plant	Office Building	Private Residence	School	YMCA
1. Basins, private lavatory	2 (7.6)	2 (7.6)	2 (7.6)	2 (7.6)	2 (7.6)	2 (7.6)	2 (7.6)	2 (7.6)	2 (7.6)	2 (7.6)
2. Basins, public lavatory	4 (15)	6 (23)	8 (30)	6 (23)	8 (30)	12 (45.5)	6 (23)	—	15 (57)	8 (30)
3. Bathtubs	20 (76)	20 (76)	30 (114)	20 (76)	20 (76)	—	—	20 (76)	—	30 (114)
4. Dishwashers[a]	15 (57)	50-150 (190-570)	—	50-150 (190-570)	50-200 (190-760)	20-100 (76-380)	—	15 (57)	20-100 (76-380)	20-100 (76-380)
5. Foot basins	3 (11)	3 (11)	12 (46)	3 (11)	3 (11)	12 (46)	—	3 (11)	3 (11)	12 (46)
6. Kitchen sink	10 (38)	20 (76)	—	20 (76)	30 (114)	20 (76)	20 (76)	10 (38)	20 (76)	20 (76)
7. Laundry, stationary tubs	20 (76)	28 (106)	—	28 (106)	28 (106)	—	—	20 (76)	—	28 (106)
8. Pantry sink	5 (19)	10 (38)	—	10 (38)	10 (38)	—	10 (38)	5 (19)	10 (38)	10 (38)
9. Showers	30 (114)	150 (568)	225 (850)	75 (284)	75 (284)	225 (850)	30 (114)	30 (114)	225 (850)	225 (850)
10. Service sink	20 (76)	20 (76)	—	20 (76)	30 (114)	20 (76)	20 (76)	15 (57)	20 (76)	20 (76)
11. Hydrotherapeutic showers				400 (1520)						
12. Hubbard baths				600 (2270)						
13. Leg baths				100 (380)						
14. Arm baths				35 (130)						
15. Sitz baths				30 (114)						
16. Continuous-flow baths				165 (625)						
17. Circular wash sinks				20 (76)	20 (76)	30 (114)	20 (76)		30 (114)	
18. Semicircular wash sinks				10 (38)	10 (38)	15 (57)	10 (38)		15 (57)	
19. DEMAND FACTOR	0.30	0.30	0.40	0.25	0.25	0.40	0.30	0.30	0.40	0.40
20. STORAGE CAPACITY FACTOR[b]	1.25	0.90	1.00	0.60	0.80	1.00	2.00	0.70	1.00	1.00

[a]Dishwasher requirements should be taken from this table or from manufacturers' data for the model to be used, if this is known.
[b]Ratio of storage tank capacity to probable maximum demand/h. Storage capacity may be reduced where an unlimited supply of steam is available from a central street steam system or large boiler plant.

flow control valves are recommended, since they reduce the flow rate and maintain it regardless of fluctuations in water pressure. The manufacturer's maximum flow rating can usually be reduced up to 50% without adversely affecting the spray pattern of the shower head. Flow control valves are commonly available in sizes from 1.5 to 4.0 gpm (94 to 250 mL/s).

If the manufacturer's flow rate for a shower head is not available and a flow control valve is not used, the following will serve as a guide for sizing the water heater:

Small shower head: 2 to 3 gpm (130 to 190 mL/s).
Medium shower head: 4 to 6 gpm (250 to 380 mL/s).
Large shower head: 7 to 9 gpm (440 to 570 mL/s).

Food Service

In a restaurant, bacteria are usually killed by rinsing the washed dishes with 180 to 195 °F (82 to 90 °C) water for several seconds. In addition, an ample supply for general purpose hot water, usually 140 to 150 °F (60 to 65 °C), is required for the wash cycle of dishwashers. Although a water temperature of 140 °F (60 °C) in private dwellings is reasonable for dishwashing, in public places, sanitation regulations by the National Sanitation Foundation make 180 to 195 °F (82 to 90 °C) water mandatory in the rinsing cycle. However, the National Sanitation Foundation allows lower temperatures when certain types of machines and chemicals are used. Because of the two-temperature need, the hot water requirements for food service establishments present special problems. The lower temperature water is distributed for general use, but the 180 °F (82 °C) water should be confined to the equipment requiring it and should be obtained by boosting the temperature. It would be dangerous to distribute 180 °F (82 °C) water for general use. NSF Standard 26-80 covers the design of dishwashing machines and water heaters used by restaurants.

The American Gas Association has published a recommended procedure for sizing gas-fired water heaters for restaurants that consists of determining the following:

1. Types and sizes of dishwashers used.
2. Required quantity of general purpose hot water (manufacturers' data should be consulted to determine the initial fill requirements of the wash tanks).
3. Duration of peak hot water demand period.
4. Inlet water temperature.
5. Type and capacity of existing water-heating system.
6. Type of water-heating system desired.

Equation (4) may be used to size the required heater(s) after allowing for the quantity of hot water withdrawn from the storage tank each hour. The general purpose and 180 to 195 °F (82 to 90 °C) water requirements are determined from Tables 8 and 9.

To determine the quantity of usable hot water from storage, the duration (in hours) of consecutive peak demand must be calculated. This peak demand period will usually coincide with the dishwashing period during and after the main meal and may last for 3 hours or more.

$$\text{Input (Btu/h)} = \frac{(\text{gph})(\Delta t)(8.33)}{\text{Thermal Efficiency}} \quad (4)$$

$$\text{Input (W)} = \frac{(\text{mL/s})(\Delta t)(4.18)}{\text{Thermal Efficiency}} \quad \text{(4 SI)}$$

Table 8   NSF Final Rinse Water Requirements for Dishwashing Machines[a]

Type and Size of Dishwasher	Flow Rate gpm	(L/s)	Hot Water Requirements at 180 °F (82 °C) to 195 °F (95 °C) Max.			
			Heaters Without Internal Storage gph	(mL/s)	Heaters With Internal Storage to Meet Flow Demand[c], gph	(mL/s)
Door Type:						
16 × 16 in. (406 × 406 mm)	6.94	(0.438)	416	(437)	69	(72.5)
18 × 18 in. (457 × 457 mm)	8.67	(0.547)	520	(546)	87	(91.4)
20 × 20 in. (508 × 508 mm)	10.4	(0.656)	624	(655)	104	(109.2)
undercounter type	5	(0.316)	300	(315)	70	(73.5)
Conveyor type:						
single tank	6.94	(0.438)	416	(437)	416	(436.8)
multiple tank (dishes flat)	5.78	(0.365)	347	(364)	347	(364.4)
multiple tank (dishes inclined)	4.62	(0.292)	277	(291)	277	(291)
Silver washers	7	(0.44)	420	(441)	45	(47)
Utensil washers	8	(0.50)	480	(504)	75	(79)
Makeup water requirements	2.31	(0.146)	139	(146)	139	(146)

Note: Values are extracted from NSF Standard 5-83.
[a]Flow pressure at dishwashers is assumed to be 20 psi (140 kPa) gauge pressure.
[b]Based on the flow rate in gpm (L/s)
[c]Based on dishwasher operation at 100% of mechanical capacity.

Table 9   General Purpose Hot Water [140°F (60°C)] Requirement for Various Kitchens Uses[a,b]

Equipment	gph	(mL/s)
Vegetable sink	45	(47)
Single pot sink	30	(32)
Double pot sink	60	(63)
Triple pot sink	90	(95)
Prescrapper (open type)	180	(189)
Preflush (hand operated)	45	(47)
Preflush (closed type)	240	(252)
Recirculating preflush	40	(42)
Bar sink	30	(32)
Lavatories (each)	5	(5.3)

Note: Values are extracted from Dunn et al. (1959).
[a]Supply water pressure at equipment is assumed to be 20 psi (140 kPa) gauge.
[b]Dishwasher operation at 100% of mechanical capacity.

Any hour in which the dishwasher is used at 70% of mechanical capacity or more should be considered as a peak hour. If the peak demand lasts for four hours or more, the value of a storage tank is reduced unless very large tanks are used. Some storage capacity is desirable to meet momentary high draws.

The National Sanitation Foundation *Standard No.* 5-83 recommendations for hot water rinse demand are based on 100% mechanical operating capacity of the machines. The data provided in Table 8 are also based on 100% operating capacity. NSF 5-83 states that 70% of operating rinse capacity is all that is normally attained, except for rackless-type conveyor machines.

Examples 6, 7, and 8 demonstrate the use of Eq. (4) and Tables 8 and 9. The calculations assume a heater efficiency of 75%.

Example 6: Determine the hot water demand for a new water-heating system in a cafeteria kitchen with one vegetable sink, five lavatories, one prescrapper, one utensil washer, and one two-tank conveyor dishwasher (dishes inclined) with makeup device. The initial fill requirement for the tank of the utensil washer is 85 gph at 140°F (89.3 mL/s at 60°C). The initial fill requirement for the dishwasher is 20 gph (21 mL/s) for each tank, or a total of 40 gph (42 mL/s), at 140°F (60°C). The maximum period of consecutive operation of the dishwasher at or above 70% capacity is assumed to be 2 h. The supply water temperature is 60°F (15.6°C).

Solution: The required quantities of general purpose [140°F (60°C)] and rinse [180°F (82°C)] water for the equipment, from Tables 8 and 9, are shown in the following tabulation:

Item	Quantity Required[a] at 140°F, gph	(mL/s)	Quantity Required[b] at 180°F, gph	(mL/s)
Vegetable sink	45	(47)	—	
Lavatories (5)	25	(26)	—	
Prescrapper	180	(189)	—	
Dishwasher	—		277	(291)
Initial tank fill	40	(42)		
Makeup water	—		139	(146)
Utensil washer	—		75	(79)
Initial tank fill	85	(89)	—	
Total requirements	375	(393)	491	(516)

[a]General purpose hot water consumption, from Table 9.
[b]Water consumption when dishwasher is operated at 100% of mechanical capacity, from Table 8.

The total consumption of 140°F (60°C) water is 375 gph. The total consumption 180°F (82°C) depends on the type of heater to be used. For a heater that has enough internal storage capacity to meet the flow demand, the total consumption, based on the recommendation of the NSF, is 70% of the total calculated from Table 9, or approximately 350 gph (0.70·491 = 344 gph). For an instantaneous heater without internal storage capacity, the total quantity of 180°F (82°C) water consumed must be based on the flow demand. From Table 8, the quantity required for the dishwasher is 277 gph; for the makeup, 139 gph; and for the utensil washer, 480 gph. The total consumption of 180°F (82°C) water is 277 + 139 + 480 = 896 gph, or approximately 900 gph (945 mL/s).

Example 7: Determine gas input requirements for heating water in the cafeteria kitchen described in Example 6, by the following systems, which are among many possible solutions:

  a. Separate self-contained storage-type heaters.

  b. Single instantaneous-type heater, having no internal storage to supply both 180 and 140°F (82 and 60°C) water through a mixing valve.

  c. Separate instantaneous-type heaters, having no internal storage.

  d. Combination of heater and external storage tank for 140°F (60°C) water, plus a booster heater for 180°F (82°C) water. The heater and external storage are to supply 140°F (60°C) water for both the general purpose requirement and the booster heater. The booster heater is to have sufficient storage capacity to meet the flow demand of 180°F (82°C) rinse water.

Solution a: The temperature rise for 140°F water is 140 − 60 = 80°F. From Eq. (4), the gas input required to produce 375 gph of 140°F water with an 80°F temperature rise is 334,000 Btu/h (98 kW). One or more heaters with this total requirement may be selected.

From Eq. (4), the gas input required to produce 350 gph of 180°F water with a temperature rise of 120°F (180 − 60) is 467,000 Btu/h (137 kW). One or more heaters with this total requirement may be selected from manufacturers' catalogs.

Solution b: The correct sizing of instantaneous-type heaters depends on the flow rate of the 180°F rinse water. From Example 6, the hourly consumption of 180°F water based on the flow rate is 900 gph. Hourly consumption of 140°F water is 375 gph.

Gas input required to produce 900 gph of 180°F water with a 120°F temperature rise is 1,200,000 Btu/h. Gas input to produce 375 gph of 140°F water with a temperature rise of 80°F deg is 334,000 Btu/h. Total heater requirement is 1,200,000 + 334,000 = 1,534,000 Btu/h (449 kW). One or more heaters meeting this total input requirement can be selected from manufacturers' catalogs.

Solution c: Gas input required to produce 140°F water is the same as for Solution b, 334,000 Btu/h (98 kW). One or more heaters meeting this total requirement can be selected.

Gas input required to produce 180°F water is also the same as in Solution b, 1,200,000 Btu/h (352 kW). One or more heaters meeting this total requirement can be selected.

Solution d: The *net* hourly hot water requirement must be determined to size the heater required to supply 140°F water. From Eq. (2), the quantity of usable water in storage Q_a is 0.7 500 = 350 gal. The total quantity of 140°F water required for the two hours is 2(375 + 350) = 1450 gal. From Eq. (3), $Q_t = (1450 − 350)/2 = 550$ gph from the heater.

From Eq. (4), the gas input required to produce 550 gph of 140°F water with an 80°F deg temperature rise is 489,000 Btu/h (143 kW).

For systems involving storage tanks, it is assumed that water in the tanks has been brought up to temperature prior to the peak dishwashing period, and that enough time will elapse before the next peak period to permit recovery of the water temperature in the storage tank.

The booster heater is sized to heat 350 gph from 140 to 180°F, a 40°F rise. From Eq. (4), the gas input required is 156,000 Btu/h (46 kW).

Example 8: A luncheonette has purchased a door-type dishwasher that will handle 16 × 16-in. (400 × 400-mm) racks. The existing hot water system is capable of supplying the necessary 140°F (60°C) water to meet all requirements for general purpose use, plus supply to a booster heater that is to be installed. Determine the size of booster heater required to heat 140°F (60°C) water to provide sufficient 180°F (82°C) rinse water for the dishwasher, using the following:

  a. Booster heater with no storage capacity.

  b. Booster heater with enough storage capacity to meet flow demand.

Solution a: Since the heater is the instantaneous type, it must be sized to meet the 180°F water demand at a rated flow. From Table 8, this rated flow is 6.94 gpm, or 416 gph. From Eq. (4), the required gas input, with a 40°F temperature rise, is 85,000 Btu/h (4.2 kW). A heater meeting this input requirement can be selected from manufacturers' catalogs.

Solution b: In designing a system with a booster heater having storage capacity, hourly flow demand of the dishwater can be used instead of the flow demand used in Solution a. The flow demand from Table 8 is 69 gph when the dishwasher is operating at 100% mechanical capacity. However, the NSF states that 70% of operating rinse capacity is all that is normally attained for this type of dishwasher. Therefore, the hourly flow demand is 0.70·69 = 48 gph. From Eq. (4), with a 40°F temperature rise, the gas input required is 22,000 Btu/h (6.4 kW). A booster heater with this input can be selected from manufacturers' catalogs.

Estimating Procedure. Hot water requirements for kitchens are sometimes estimated on the basis of the number of meals served (assuming eight dishes per meal). Dishwashing demand is either

$$R_1 = C_1 N/\Theta \qquad (5)$$

where

R_1 = 180°F (82°C) water for dishwasher gph (mL/s)
N = number of meals served
Θ = hours of service
C_1 = 0.8 (0.84) for single-tank dishwasher
C_1 = 0.5 (0.53) for two-tank dishwasher

or

$$Q_2 = C_2 V \qquad (6)$$

where

R_2 = Water for sink with gas burners, gph (mL/s)
C_2 = 3 (3.2)
V = sink capacity [15 in. (380 mm) depth], gal. (L)

General purpose hot water at 140°F (60°C) is

$$R_3 = C_3 N/(\Theta + 2) \qquad (7)$$

where

R_3 = General purpose water, gph (mL/s)
C_3 = 1.2 (1.3)

Total demand is

$$R = R_1 + R_2 + R_3$$

For soda fountains and luncheonettes, use 75% of the total demand. For hotel meals or other elaborate meals, use 125%.

Schools

Service water heating in schools is needed for janitorial work, lavatories, cafeterias, shower rooms, and sometimes swimming pools.

Hot water used in cafeterias is about 0.7 of that usually required in a commercial restaurant serving adults, and can be estimated by the method used for restaurants. Where NSF sizing is required, follow *Standard No. 5-83.*

Shower and restaurant loads will not ordinarily be concurrent. Each should be determined separately, and the larger load should determine the size of the water heater(s) and the tank. Provision must be made to supply 180°F (82°C) sanitizing rinse. Where feasible, the same water heating system can be used for both needs. Where the distance between the two points of need is great, different water heating systems should be used.

A separate water heating system for the swimming pool can be sized as outlined in the section on swimming pools.

Domestic Coin-Operated Laundries

Small domestic machines in coin laundries or apartment house laundry rooms have a wide range of draw rates and cycle times. Domestic machines provide wash water temperatures (normal) as low as 120°F (49°C). Some manufacturers recommend temperatures of 160°F (71°C). The average appears to be 140°F (60°C). The hot water sizing calculations must assure a supply to both the instantaneous draw requirements of a number of machines filling at one time and the average hourly requirements.

The number of machines that will be drawing at any one time varies widely; the percentage is usually higher in smaller installations. One or two customers starting several machines at about the same time has a much sharper effect in a laundry with 15 or 20 machines than in one with 40 machines. Simultaneous draw may be estimated as:

1 to 11 machines: 100% of possible draw
12 to 24 machines: 80% of possible draw
25 to 35 machines: 60% of possible draw
36 to 45 machines: 50% of possible draw
Possible peak draw can be calculated from:

$$F = N \cdot P \cdot Q/T \qquad (8)$$

where

F = peak draw, gpm (L/s)
N = number of washers installed
P = number of machines drawing hot water divided by N
Q = quantity of hot water supplied to machine during hot wash fill, gal (L)
T = wash fill period, minute (s)

Recovery rate can be calculated from:

$$R = C_4 \cdot N \cdot P \cdot Q/(\Theta + 10) \qquad (9)$$

where

R = total quantity of hot water (per machine) used for entire cycle (machine adjusted to hottest water setting).
Θ = actual machine cycle time, minute (hour).
C_4 = units conversion, 60 (60 000)

Note: ($\Theta + 10$) is the cycle time plus 10 min. for loading and unloading

Commercial Laundries

Commercial laundries generally use a storage water heating system. The water is softened to reduce soap use and improve quality. The trend is toward installation of high capacity washer-extractor wash wheels, resulting in high peak demand. Hot water lines should be sized for this peak demand, and the normal velocity used is 10 fps (3.0 m/s). Tanks and pipes must be lined properly or made of non-ferrous materials to prevent rust spots on the laundry.

Sizing Data. Laundries normally come under five classifications. The required hot water is determined by the weight of material processed. Average hot water requirements at 180°F (82°C) are:

Institutional:	2 gal/lb	(16.7 L/kg)
Commercial:	2 gal/lb	(16.7 L/kg)
Linen supply:	2.5 gal/lb	(20.9 L/kg)
Industrial:	2.5 gal/lb	(20.9 L/kg)
Diaper:	2.5 gal/lb	(20.9 L/kg)

Total weight (mass) of the material times the above values give the average hourly hot water requirements. The designer must consider peak requirements; for example, a 600-lb (270-kg) machine may have 20 gpm (1.3 L/s) average requirement, but the peak requirement could be 350 gpm (22 L/s).

In a multiple machine operation, it is not practicable to fill all machines at the momentary peak rate. Diversity factors can be estimated by using 100% of the largest machine plus the following percentage balance:

Total No. of Machines	2	3 to 5	6 to 8	9 to 11	12 & over
100% +		60%	45%	40%	35%	30%

Types of Systems. Service water-heating systems for laundries are pressurized or vented. The pressurized system uses city water pressure, and the full peak flow rates are received by the softeners, reclaimer, condensate cooler, water heater, and the lines to the wash wheels. The flow surges and stops at each operation in the cycle. A pressurized system is satisfactory for quantities up to 400 gpm (25 L/s) if the lines from the city to the washroom are large enough for this flow.

The vented system uses pumps from a vented (open) hot water heater or tank to supply hot water. This system is based on the principle of a fluctuating water level in the tank, from about

6 in. (150 mm) above the heating element to a point 12 in. (300 mm) from the top of the tank, the working volume. The level will drop for each machine fill and makeup continuously at the average flow rate under city pressure during the complete washing cycle. The tank is sized to have full working volume at the beginning of each cycle. Lines and softeners can be sized for this flow rate from the city to the tank, not the peak machine fill rate as with a closed pressurized system. The waste heat exchangers have a continuous flow across the heating surface at this low flow rate, with continuous heat reclamation from the waste water and flash steam. Automatic flow regulating valves on the inlet water manifold will control this low flow rate.

A vented system allows smaller water makeup lines from the city through the heat reclaiming equipment to the storage tank, since the continuous makeup is based on flow rate. Softeners can be sized on this low basis. Rapid fill of machines will increase production (more batches processed).

Heat Recovery. Commercial laundries are ideally suited for heat recovery because 135 °F (57 °C) waste temperature is discharged to the sewer. Fresh water can be conservatively preheated to within 15 °F (8.3 °C) of the waste water temperature for the next operation in the wash cycle. Regions with an annual average temperature of 55 °F (13 °C) can increase to 120 °F (49 °C) the initial temperature of fresh water going into the hot water heater. For each 1000 gph (1050 mL/s) or 8340 lb (3780 kg) of water preheated 65 °F (36 °C) [55 to 120 °F (13 to 49 °C)], heat reclamation will be 540,000 Btu/h (158 kW). This saves 655 ft^3 (18.5 m^3) of natural gas per hour or 3.92 gal (14.8 L) of oil per hour.

Flash steam from a condensate receiving tank is often wasted to the atmosphere. The heat in this flash can be reclaimed with a suitable heat exchanger. Makeup water to the heater can be preheated 10 to 20 °F (5.5 to 11 °C) above existing makeup temperature with the flash steam.

Industrial Plants

Hot water is used in industrial plants for cafeterias, showers, lavatories, gravity sprinkler tanks, and industrial processes. If the same hot water system is used only for the cafeteria, employee cleanup, laundry, and small miscellaneous uses, the water heater can be sized to meet employee cleanup load (with additional provision for the sanitizing rinse needs of the cafeteria). Employee cleanup load is usually heaviest and not concurrent with other uses. The other loads should be checked, however, to be certain that this is true.

The employee cleanup load consists of one or more of the following: (1) wash troughs or standard lavatories, (2) multiple wash sinks, and (3) showers. Hot water requirements for employees using standard wash fixtures can be estimated at 1 gal (3.8 L) of hot water for each clerical and light industrial employee per work shift and 2 gal (7.6 L) for each heavy industrial worker.

The number of workers using multiple wash fountains is disregarded for sizing purposes. Hot water demand is based on full flow for the entire cleanup period. Table 10 indicates this usage for a 10-minute period. The shower load depends on the flow rate of shower heads, total number of showers, and length of use. Table 10 also may be used, based on a 15-minute shower period. Water heaters used to prevent freezing in gravity sprinkler tanks should be part of a separate system. The load depends on tank heat loss, tank capacity, and winter design temperature.

Process hot water load must be determined separately. Volume and temperature vary with the specific process. If the process load occurs at the same time as the shower or restaurant load, the system must be sized to reflect this total demand. Separate systems can also be used, depending on the size of the various loads and the distance between them.

Table 10 Hot Water Usage for Industrial Wash Fountains and Showers

Multiple Wash Fountains			Showers		
Type in. (mm)		Gal of 140 °F (L of 60 °C) Water Required for 10-min Period[a]	Flow Rate, gpm (L/s)	Gal of 140 °F (L of 60 °C) Water Required for 15-min Period[b]
36 (910)	Circular	40 (152)	3 (0.19)	29.0 (110)
36 (910)	Semicircular	22 (83)	4 (0.25)	39.0 (148)
54 (1370)	Circular	66 (250)	5 (0.32)	48.7 (185)
54 (1370)	Semicircular	40 (152)	6 (0.38)	58.0 (220)

[a]Based on 110 °F (43 °C) wash water and 40 °F (4 °C) cold water at average flow rates.
[b]Based on 105 °F (40 °C) shower water and 40 °F (4 °C) cold water.

Ready-Mix Concrete

In cold weather, ready-mix concrete plants need hot water to mix the concrete so that it will not be ruined by freezing before it sets. Operators prefer to place the mix at about 70 °F (21 °C). With the cold aggregate, hot water must be used. Usually, about 150 °F (65 °C) water is considered proper for cold weather. When the water temperature is too high, some of the cement will flash set.

Thirty gallons of hot water per cubic yard (150 L./m^3) of concrete mixed is generally used for sizing. To obtain the total hot water load, the number of trucks loaded each hour and the capacity of the trucks is calculated. The hot water is dumped into the mix as fast as possible at each loading, and ample hot water storage is required. If storage is not used, large heat exchangers must be used for the high draw rate. Table 11 shows a method of sizing for concrete plants.

Part of the heat may be obtained by heating the aggregate bin. This is done by circulating hot water through pipe coils in the walls or sides of the bin. If aggregate is warmed, the temperature of the mixing water may be lower and the aggregate will flow easily from the bins. When aggregate is not heated, it often freezes into chunks, which must be thawed to go through the dump gates. If hot water is used for thawing, too much water would accumulate in the aggregate, and control of the final product might vary beyond allowable limits. Therefore, jets of steam supplied by a small gas-fired boiler and directed on the large chunks are often used for thawing.

Swimming Pools/Health Clubs

The desirable temperature for swimming pools is about 80 °F (27 °C). Maintaining this temperature usually requires a water heating system to compensate for heat losses to the ground and air. General practice is to use independent heating equipment for showers and steam rooms, a standard water heater for the showers, and a small boiler or central steam supply for the steam room.

Special pool heating equipment is available from most manufacturers of water heaters or boilers. Some manufacturers offer packaged units that include a pool temperature controller and a water bypass to prevent condensation. The water heating system is usually installed in the normal circulation system of the pool, prior to the return of treated water to the pool. Circulation rates generally complete a change of water every 8 hours for residential pools and every 6 hours for commercial pools. Indirect systems using hot water piping imbedded in the walls or floor of the pool can also be used. Since pool water does not pass through the heater, corrosion, scaling, and condensation problems are reduced greatly. However, the initial cost of this system is relatively high, and direct heating is more common.

In addition to the safety controls normally used, pool heaters should be equipped with a pool temperature control and a water

Table 11 Water Heater Sizing for Ready-Mix Concrete Plant [Input and Storage Tank Capacity To Supply 150°F (65.6°C) Water at 40°F (4.4°C) Inlet Temperature]

Time Interval between Trucks[a]	Capacity	Truck Capacity			
		6 yards (4.6 m³)	7.5 yards (5.7 m³)	9 yards (6.8 m³)	11 yards (8.4 m³)
50 min (0.83 h)	Btu/h (kW)	458,200 (134.3)	526,900 (154.4)	595,600 (174.5)	687,200 (201.3)
	gal (L)	430 (1630)	490 (1860)	560 (2120)	640 (2430)
35 min (0.58 h)	Btu/h (kW)	612,000 (179.3)	700,000 (205.1)	792,000 (232.1)	915,000 (268.1)
	gal (L)	430 (1630)	490 (1860)	560 (2120)	640 (2430)
25 min (0.42 h)	Btu/h (kW)	785,000 (230.0)	900,000 (263.7)	1,020,000 (298.9)	1,175,000 (344.3)
	gal (L)	430 (1630)	490 (1860)	560 (2120)	640 (2430)
10 min (0.17 h)	Btu/h (kW)	1,375,000 (402.9)	1,580,000 (462.9)	1,790,000 (524.5)	2,060,000 (603.6)
	gal (L)	430 (1630)	490 (1860)	560 (2120)	640 (2430)
5 min (0.08 h)	Btu/h (kW)	1,830,000 (536.2)	2,100,000 (615.3)	2,380,000 (697.3)	2,740,000 (802.8)
	gal (L)	430 (1630)	490 (1860)	560 (2120)	640 (2430)
0 min (0 h)	Btu/h (kW)	2,760,000 (808.7)	3,150,000 (923.0)	3,580,000 (1048.9)	4,120,000 (1207.2)
	gal (L)	430 (1630)	490 (1860)	560 (2120)	640 (2430)

[a]This table assumes that there is 10-min loading time for each truck. Thus, for a 50-min interval between trucks, it is assumed that one truck/h is served. For 0-min between trucks, it is assumed that one truck loads immediately after the truck ahead has pulled away. Thus, 6 trucks/h are served.

It is also assumed that each truck carries a 120-gal (455-L) storage tank of hot water for washing down at the end of dumping the load. This hot water is drawn from the storage tank and must be added to the total hot water demands. This has been included in the sizing table given above.

pressure or flow safety switch. The temperature control is usually installed in the return line from the pool to the heater, preferably at the inlet to the heater. The pressure or flow switch is mounted in either the heater inlet or outlet, depending on the manufacturer's instructions. This installation protects the heater against inadequate water flow.

Several methods for sizing pool water heating systems are occasionally recommended. Some are estimates based on pool area or water volume. Others are more complex and involve many factors, including calculation of heat loss from the water surface to the air. Unless unusual conditions exist, the A.G.A. recommends sizing the equipment on the amount of heat necessary to raise the temperature of the volume of water the desired number of degrees in a specified time, plus an allowance for losses.

Pool use is one of the most important considerations in sizing the water heater. Some pools are used only periodically, as on weekends. For economical operation, the heater should be on only during, and just prior to, the period of pool use. It should be capable of heating the required volume of water during the specified use period, and handling heat losses from conduction and surface evaporation during the 24-hour period. The rate of evaporation depends on air and water temperatures and wind velocity. Conduction losses between the pool and the surrounding ground are generally so small that they can be neglected. Chapter 20 gives an equation to estimate evaporation.

A high input heater is most desirable in reducing heatup time. The maximum time recommended for this purpose is 24 h for pools used only periodically; however, most pools are used continuously during the swimming season. These require heating the pool water above a maximum temperature rise only once a season. When pool heaters are sized for this use, a greater period is allowed to reach the desired pool temperature. A practical maximum is 48 h. The longer the pickup period selected, the lower the initial cost of heating equipment. In some areas, air source heat pumps have been used successfully. They are usually used to extend the swimming season rather than allow year-round operation, and to sustain temperature rather than allow intermittent use with rapid pickup.

Electric boilers have also been used. A variation of the electric boiler is the tankless electric circulation water heater, available in both single-phase and three-phase.

To size a heater for an outdoor pool, proceed as follows:

1. Obtain pool water capacity in gallons (m³). If not known, multiply the length in feet (m) by the width in feet (m) by a 5.5-ft (1.7-m) assumed average depth, to determine the con-

tents. Each cubic foot of volume equals 7.5 gal (28.4 L) of water.

2. Determine the desired heat pickup time in hours.
3. Determine the required pool water temperature desired by the owner. If uncertain, assume a pool temperature of 80°F (27°C).
4. Determine the average temperature of the coldest month in which the pool will be used.
5. Determine the average wind velocity in mph (km/h). For pools under 900 ft² (85 m²) in built-up areas where the pool is sheltered from the prevailing wind by nearby fences, buildings or shrubs, an average wind velocity of less than 3.5 mph (5.6 km/h) can be assumed. For these pools, use 75% of the values calculated by Eq. (11). For more exposed locations or higher wind velocities, see the notes for Eq. (11).

With this information, the following equations give the required heater output.

$$q_1 = 8.33V \, (t_f - t_i)/\Theta \tag{10}$$

in SI units

$$q_1 = 4170V \, (t_f - t_i)/3600\Theta \tag{10 SI}$$

where

q_1 = Pool heat-up rate, Btu/h (kW)
V = Pool volume, gal (m³)
t_f = final temperature [usually 80°F (27°C)]
t_i = initial pool temperature, °F (°C)
Θ = pool heat-up time, h

Eq. (11) calculates heat loss from the pool surface.

$$q_2 = 10.5A \, (t_p - t_a) \tag{11}$$

or in SI units

$$q_2 = 60A \, (t_p - t_a) \tag{11 SI}$$

where

q_2 = **Heat loss from pool surface, Btu/h · ft² (W/m²)**
A = pool surface area, ft² (m²)
t_p = **pool temperature, °F (°C)**
t_a = **ambient temperature, °F (°C)**

Notes: These heat losses assume a wind velocity of 3.5 mph (5.6 km/h). For a velocity of 5 mph (8.1 km/h), multiply these values by 1.25; for 10 mph (16.1 km/h), multiply by 2.0.

The required heater output then equals half the surface loss obtained from Eq. (11) plus the heat-up value obtained from Eq. (10). The heater input then equals the output divided by the fuel conversion efficiency.

Table 12   Hot Water Demand in Fixture Units [140°F (60°C) Water]

	Apartment House	Club	Gymnasium	Hospital	Hotels and Dormitories	Industrial Plant	Office Bldg	School	YMCA
Basins, private lavatory	0.75	0.75	0.75	0.75	0.75	0.75	0.75	0.75	0.75
Basins, public lavatory	—	1	1	1	1	1	1	1	1
Bathtubs	1.5	1.5	—	1.5	1.5	—	—	—	—
Dishwashers	1.5			Five (5) Fixture Units per 250 Seating Capacity					
Therapeutic bath	—	—	—	5	—	—	—	—	—
Kitchen sink	0.75	1.5	—	3	1.5	3	—	0.75	3
Pantry sink	—	2.5	—	2.5	2.5	—	—	2.5	2.5
Service sink	1.5	2.5	—	2.5	2.5	2.5	2.5	2.5	2.5
Showers[a]	1.5	1.5	1.5	1.5	1.5	3.5	—	1.5	1.5
Circular wash fountain	—	2.5	2.5	2.5	—	4	—	2.5	2.5
Semicircular wash fountain	—	1.5	1.5	1.5	—	3	—	1.5	1.5

[a]In applications where the principal use is showers, as in gymnasiums or at end of shift in industrial plants, use conversion factor of 1.00 to obtain design water flow rate in gpm (L/s).

SIZING INSTANTANEOUS AND SEMI-INSTANTANEOUS HEATERS

The methods for sizing storage water heating equipment should *not* be used for instantaneous and semi-instantaneous heaters. The following is based on the Hunter Method for sizing hot and cold water piping, with diversity applied for hot water and various building types.

Fixture units (Table 12) are selected for each fixture using hot water and are totalled. Maximum hot water demand in gpm (L/s)

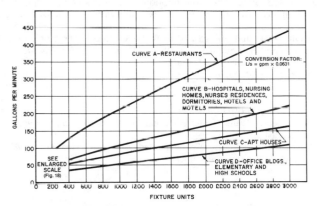

Fig. 21   Modified Hunter Curve for Hot Water Flow Rate (Corrected for Type of Building Use)

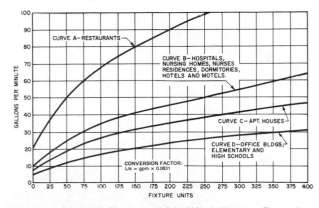

Fig. 22   Enlarged Section of Modified Hunter Curve for Hot Water Flow Rate (Corrected for Type of Building Use)

is obtained from Figure 21 or 22 by matching total fixture units to the curve for the type of building and reading gpm (L/s). Hot water for fixtures and outlets that have constant flows should be added to demand.

The heater can then be selected with the total demand and temperature rise required. (See the information on hot water supply temperature elsewhere in this chapter.) For critical applications such as hospitals, using multiple heaters with 100% standby is recommended. Consider multiple heaters for buildings in which continuity of service is important.

The minimum recommended size for the semi-instantaneous heater is 10 gpm (0.6 L/s), except for restaurants, in which it is 15 gpm (1.0 L/s). When the flow for a system having equipment for which the flows or diversity are not easily determined, the heater may be sized for the full flow of the piping system. Caution must be used when sizing heaters with low flows, and careful judgment should be applied to estimate diversities.

Unusual hot water requirements in a building should be analyzed to determine if additional capacity is required. An example is a dormitory in a military school where all showers and lavatories can be used simultaneously when students return from a drill. In such a case, the heater and piping should be sized for the full flow of the system.

While the fixture count method bases heater size on the diversified system hot water flow, hot water piping should be sized for the full flow to the fixtures. Recirculating hot water systems are adaptable to this type of heater. When these systems are installed, the heater capacity should be checked and increased if necessary to offset heat losses of the recirculating system.

To make preliminary estimates of hot water demand when the fixture count is not known, use Table 13 with Figure 21 or 22. The results will usually be higher than the demand determined from the actual fixture count. Actual heater size should be determined from Table 12. Hot water consumption over time can be assumed the same as that in the section on sizing storage heaters.

Table 13   Preliminary Hot Water Demand Estimate

Type of Building	Unit	Fixture Units Per Unit
Hospital or nursing home	Bed	2.50
Hotel or motel	Room	2.50
Office building	Person	0.15
Elementary school	Student	0.30
Jr. and Sr. high school	Student	0.30[a]
Apartment house	Apartment	3.00

[a]Plus shower load.

Example 9: Determine the hot water flow rate for sizing a semi-instantaneous heater for a 600-student elementary school with the following fixture count: 60 public lavatories, 6 service sinks, 4 kitchen sinks, 6 showers, and 1 dishwasher at 8 gpm (0.5 L/s).

Solution: For a preliminary estimate, use Table 13 to find estimated flow. The basic flow is determined from curve D of Figure 22, at 600 students • 0.3 fixture units per student = 180 fixture units, plus 6 showers • 1.5 fixtures units = 9, or 189 fixture units, for a total flow of 23 gpm (1.45 L/s).

To size the unit based on actual fixture count and Table 12, the calculation is as follows:

60 public lavatories	× 1	F.U. =	60 F.U.
6 service sinks	× 2.5	F.U. =	15 F.U.
4 kitchen sinks	× 0.75	F.U. =	3 F.U.
6 showers	× 1.5	F.U. =	9 F.U.
Subtotal			87 F.U.

At 87 fixture units, curve D of Figure 22 shows 16 gpm (1.0 L/s), to which must be added the dishwasher requirement of 8 gpm (0.5 L/s). Thus, the total flow is 24 gpm (1.5 L/s).

Comparing the flow based on actual fixture count to that obtained from the preliminary estimate shows the preliminary estimate to be slightly lower. It is possible that the preliminary estimate could have been as much as twice the final fixture count result. To prevent oversizing the equipment, it is imperative to use the actual fixture count method to select the unit.

BOILERS FOR INDIRECT WATER HEATING

Section 7.3.2 of ANSI/ASHRAE/IES Standard 90A discusses Combination Service Water Heating/Space Heating Boilers. Also the ANSI/ASHRAE/IES 100 series standards section "Service Water Heating" has information on this topic.

REFERENCES

AGA. Sizing and Equipment Data for Specifying Swimming Pool Heaters. American Gas Association, Catalog No. R-00995.

Ciesielki, C.A.; et al. 1984. Role of Stagnation and Obstruction of Water Flow in Isolation of Legionella Pneumophila From Hospital Plumbing. Applied and Environmental Microbiology, Nov., p. 984-987.

Dunn, T.Z.; Spear, R.N.; Twigg, B.E.; and Williams, D. 1959. Water Heating for Commercial Kitchens. *Air Conditioning, Heating and Ventilating*, May, p. 70. Also published as a bulletin titled *Enough Hot Water—Hot Enough*. American Gas Association, 1959.

Manian, V.S.; and Chackeris, W. 1974. Off Peak Domestic Hot Water Systems for Large Apartment Buildings. ASHRAE *Transactions*, Vol. 80, Part 1, p. 147.

NSF. 1983. Hot Water Generating and Heat Recovery Equipment. National Sanitation Foundation Standard 5-83, Ann Arbor, MI.

Perlman, M., and Mills, B. 1985. Development of Residential Hot Water Use Patterns. ASHRAE *Transactions*, Vol. 91, Part 2.

Toaborek, J. *et al.* 1972. Fouling—The Major Unresolved Problem in Heat Transfer. *Chemical Engineering Progress*, Feb., p. 59.

Werden, R.G., and Spielvogel, L.G. 1969. Sizing of Service Water Heating Equipment in Commercial and Institutional Buildings, Part 1. ASHRAE *Transactions*, Vol. 75, p. 81.

BIBLIOGRAPHY

AGA. Comprehensive on Commercial and Industrial Water Heating. American Gas Association, Catalog No. R-00980.

AGA. 1965. *Gas Engineers Handbook*. American Gas Association, Cleveland, OH.

AGA. 1962. Water Heating Application in Coin Operated Laundries. American Gas Association, Catalog No. C-10540.

Brooks, F.A. Use of Solar Energy for Heating Water. Smithsonian Institution, Washington, D.C.

Coleman, J.J. 1974. Waste Water Heat Reclamation. ASHRAE *Transactions*, Vol. 80, Part 2, p. 370.

Dawson, F.M., and Kalinski, A.A. Water-Supply Piping for Plumbing Systems. National Association of Master Plumbers, Technical Bulletin No. 3.

Hebrank, E.F. 1956. Investigation of the Performance of Automatic Storage-Type Gas and Electric Domestic Water Heaters. University of Illinois, Engineering Experiment Bulletin No. 436.

Jones, P.G. 1982. The Consumption of Hot Water in Commercial Building. *Building Services Engineering, Research and Technology*, Vol. 3, pp. 95-109.

Schultz, W.W., and Goldschmidt, V.W. 1978. Effect of Distribution Lines on Stand-By Loss of Service Water Heater. ASHRAE *Transactions*, Vol. 84, Part 1, pp. 256-265.

Smith, F.T. 1965. Sizing Guide For Gas Water Heaters For In-Ground Swimming Pools. American Gas Association, Catalog No. R-00999.

Talbert, S.G.; Stickford, G.H.; Newman, D.C.; and Stiegelmeyer, W.N. 1986. Effect of Hard Water Scale Buildup and Water Treatment on Residential Water Heater Performance. ASHRAE *Transactions*, Vol. 92, Part 2.

Wetherington, T.I., Jr. 1975. Heat Recovery Water Heating. *Building Systems Design*, December/January.

CHAPTER 55

SNOW MELTING

THE practicality of melting snow with heated coils has been demonstrated in a large number of installations including sidewalks, roadways, ramps, and runways. Melting eliminates the need for snow removal, provides greater safety for pedestrians and vehicles, and reduces the labor of slush removal.

There are three types of heated-slab snow melting systems:

1. Hot fluid circulated in embedded pipes
2. Embedded electric heating resistance cable or wire
3. Overhead high intensity infrared radiant heating

System design must determine and satisfy two primary requirements: (1) heating and (2) hot fluid hydraulic layout or electrical layout.

HOT FLUID SYSTEM DESIGN

Heating Requirement

The heating requirement for snow melting is affected by four atmospheric factors: (1) rate of snowfall, (2) air temperature, (3) wind velocity, and (4) humidity. The effects of these factors can be evaluated by considering the action of snow falling on a warmed surface.

The first flakes fall on a dry, warm surface, where they are warmed to 32°F (0°C) and melted. The water from the melted snow forms a film over the entire area and starts to evaporate. This evaporation is a mass heat transfer from the surface to the atmosphere. In addition, there is heat transfer from the film to the ambient air and surfaces.

Mass transfer by evaporation. The evaporation rate of the melted snow from the snow melting slab is affected by the wind speed and the vapor pressure difference between air and melted snow. The air vapor pressure, however, is fixed by the relative humidity and temperature of the air. If the slab surface temperature is fixed, the evaporation loss varies with changes in air temperature, relative humidity and wind speed.

Heat transfer by convection and radiation from the melted snow to the ambient air and surfaces. A combined film coefficient is sufficiently accurate to determine the combined convection and radiation loss. This coefficient is based on heat transfer from a wetted surface, such as the film of melted snow, to the air. The coefficient is a function of wind speed alone. The heat transfer depends on the film coefficient and the temperature difference between the surface and the air. Since the surface temperature is fixed, the convection and radiation losses vary with changes in air temperature and wind speed.

To determine evaporation and heat transfer from the melted snow to the air, three of these four climatic factors must be known: (1) wind speed, (2) air temperature, (3) relative humidity, and (4) rate of snowfall. Rate of snowfall determines the heat required to warm the snow to 32°F (0°C) to melt it.

The preparation of this chapter is assigned to TC 6.1, Hot Water and Steam Heating Equipment and Systems, and TC 6.4, In-Space Convective Heating.

Before deriving equations to give quantitative values for the effects of these four factors, consider the insulating effect of the unmelted snow. The first flakes fall on a dry, warm surface, and are then warmed to 32°F (0°C) and melted. While the flakes are being warmed and before they are completely melted, they act as tiny blankets or insulators. The effect of this insulation when measured can be very large. Since the snowflakes cover a fraction of the surface area, it is convenient to think of the insulating effect as an area ratio. The area covered by snowflakes is the insulated area, and the uncovered area is the uninsulated area. The term *free area ratio* (A_r) represents the ratio of the uncovered, or free, area to the total area, and is expressed as:

$$A_r = A_f/A_t \tag{1}$$

where

A_r = free area ratio
A_f = free area, ft² (m²)
A_t = total area, ft² (m²)

therefore,

$$0 \leqslant A_r \leqslant 1$$

For $A_r = 1$, the system must melt the snow so rapidly that accumulation would be absolutely zero. This is impossible theoretically, but for practical purposes, it is permissible to have $A_r = 1$ as a maximum. For $A_r = 0$, the surface must be completely covered with snow to a depth sufficient to prevent evaporation and heat transfer losses. Research on the insulating effects of snow indicates that there are only three practical values for the free area ratio: 0, 0.5, and 1. This is discussed in greater detail in a later section.

Chapman (1952) derives and explains equations for the heating requirements of a snow melting system. Chapman and Katunich (1956) derive the general equation for slab output, q_o, as:

$$q_o = q_s + q_m + A_r (q_e + q_h) \tag{2}$$

where

q_r = sensible heat transferred to snow, Btu/h·ft² (W/m²).
q_m = heat of fusion, Btu/h·ft² (W/m²).
A_r = ratio of snow-free area to total area, dimensionless.
q_e = heat of evaporation, Btu/h·ft² (W/m²).
q_h = heat transfer by convection and radiation, Btu/h·ft² (W/m²).

The sensible heat, q_s, to bring the snow to 32°F (0°C) is:

$$q_s = 2.6s (32 - t_a) \tag{3}$$

In SI, $\quad\quad q_s = 0.578s (0 - t_a) \tag{3 SI}$

where

s = rate of snowfall, in. (mm) of water equivalent per hour.
t_a = air temperature, °F (°C).

The heat of fusion, q_m, to melt the snow is:

$$q_m = 746s \tag{4}$$

In SI, $\quad\quad q_m = 92.6s \tag{4 SI}$

The heat of evaporation, q_e, (mass transfer) is:

$$q_e = h_{fg} (0.0201v + 0.055)(0.185 - p_{av}) \qquad (5)$$

In SI, $\qquad q_e = h_{fg} (0.005v + 0.022)(0.625 - p_{av}) \qquad (5\ SI)$

where

h_{fg} = heat of evaporation at the film temperature, Btu/lb (kJ/kg).
v = wind speed, mph (km/h).
p_{av} = vapor pressure of moist air, in. of mercury (kPa).

The heat transfer, q_h, (convection and radiation) is:

$$q_h = 11.4 (0.0201v + 0.055)(t_f - t_a) \qquad (6)$$

In SI, $\qquad q_h = 188.2 (0.005v + 0.022)(t_f - t_a) \qquad (6\ SI)$

where

t_f = water film temperature, °F (°C), usually taken as 33 °F (0.6 °C).

In addition to determining the four heating requirements, it is necessary to allow for back and edge losses. These losses vary from 30 to 50%, depending on the slab construction and fluid temperature.

Chapman (1952) derived the equation for the required fluid temperature to provide an output, q_o. For construction similar to Figure 1, the equation is:

$$t_m = 0.5q_o + t_f \qquad (7)$$

In SI, $\qquad\qquad t_m = 0.089q_o + t_f \qquad (7\ SI)$

where

t_m = mean fluid temperature (antifreeze solution), °F (°C).

Equation (7) applies to 1 in. (25 mm) as well as ¾ in. (20 mm) IPS pipe (see Figure 1). Equation (7) does not apply to embedded electric cable or wire systems or high intensity electric infrared systems, since electric heat output can be chosen to match q_o by exact choice of system wattage input.

The designer can use Equations (2) through (7) to determine the heating requirement of a snow melting system. The solutions of these equations, however, require the simultaneous consideration of the four climatic factors: (1) wind speed, (2) air temperature, (3) relative humidity, and (4) rate of snowfall. Annual averages or maximums should not be used for the climatic factors, since there is no assurance that they will ever occur simultaneously. It is necessary, therefore, to make a frequency analysis of the solutions to Equation (2) for all the occurrences of snow fall for several years.

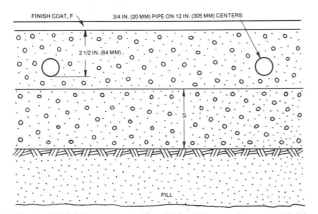

FINISH COAT, F   3/4 IN. (20 MM) PIPE ON 12 IN. (305 MM) CENTERS

2 1/2 IN. (64 MM)

S

FILL

F = Depth of Finish Coat—Assumed as 0.5 in. (13 mm) of concrete. Finish Coat may be asphalt, but then cover slab should be reduced from 3 in. (75 mm). Depth of slab should always keep thermal resistance equal to 3 in. (75 mm) of concrete.
S = Depth required by structural design [should be a minimum of 2 in. (50 mm) of concrete].

Fig. 1   Detail of Snow Melting Panel Using Hot Fluid System

Table 1 shows analyses of 33 cities and operating information for applicable snow melting systems. In freezing temperatures (32 °F or 0 °C and below), without snowfall the system may be idling, which means that some heat is supplied to the slab so that there will be immediate melting when snow starts to fall. Column 4 of Table 1 gives the mean temperature during freezing periods. This temperature together with wind speed is used to calculate the *idling load*. The column headed "Hours of Snowfall" indicates the number of hours that snow is falling at rates equal to or greater than 0.01 in. (0.25 mm) of water equivalent per hour. There are snowfalls of trace quantities about twice as often as there are for measurable quantities of 0.01 in. (0.25 mm) or more. Light falls can normally be handled by idling loads.

The remaining columns of Table 1 represent the frequency distribution of required heat output. This distribution is based on the solution to the basic equation for two values of the free area ratio, A_r. This distribution represents the basis of the analyses and is also the basis for Tables 2 and 3.

For specific conditions, or for cities other than those given in Table 1, Equations (2) and (7) are used. Table 4 gives solutions to these equations for relative humidities of 80%. For other values of relative humidity, Equations (8) and (9) can be used to determine the corrections.

$$dq_o/dp_{av} = -A_r (0.0201v + 0.055)h_{fg} \qquad (8)$$

In SI, $\qquad dq_o/dp_{av} = -A_r (0.005v + 0.022)h_{fg} \qquad (8\ SI)$

$$dt_m/dp_{av} = -(A_r/2)(0.0201v + 0.055)h_{fg} \qquad (9)$$

In SI, $\qquad dt_m/dp_{av} = -(A_r/2)(0.005v + 0.022)h_{fg} \qquad (9\ SI)$

It is necessary to determine values for the appropriate climatic variables before solving Equation (2). The best procedure is probably to contact the local National Weather Service office and examine the *Local Climatological Summary*. An approximation can be made by using Table 5 for values of s, and solutions for Equation (2) taken from Table 4, with the following qualifications:

1. When designing a Class I system, use:
   $A_r = 1.0$, $t_a = 30°F (-1.1°C)$, and $v = 15$ mph (24 km/h)
2. When designing a Class II system, use:
   $A_r = 1.0$, $t_a = 20°F (-6.7°C)$, and $v = 15$ mph (24 km/h)
3. When designing a Class III system, use:
   $A_r = 1.0$, $t_a = 0°F (-17.8°C)$, and $v = 15$ mph (24 km/h)

Snow melting installations are classified in Table 2 according to types as Class I, II, or III. Chapman (1957) discusses these classes, which are defined in the footnotes to Table 2. Snow melting systems are generally classified (as to the urgency for melting) as follows:

Class I (minimum): Residential walks or driveways and interplant areaways.
Class II (moderate): Commercial (stores and offices) sidewalks and driveways, and steps of hospitals.
Class III (maximum): Toll plazas of highways and bridges, and aprons and loading areas of airports.

These classifications depend on the allowable rate of snow melting. For example, a residential system does not have to melt snow as rapidly as does a commercial system. A depth of snow of an inch (25 mm) for an hour during a heavy storm might not be objectionable for a residential system. On the other hand, a store manager might consider the system inadequate if half an inch (13 mm) of snow accumulated on the sidewalk in front of the store. The difference between a Class I System and a Class II System is in the required ability of each system to melt snow. All classes must be adequate for some combination of weather factors. If equipment is selected with the capacity to melt snow

Table 1 Data for Determining Operating Characteristics of Snow Melting Systems[a,b]

	Period of No Snowfall							Period of Snowfall[d]										
	Air Temperature[c]		Mean during freezing period[g] F (°C)	Wind speed freezing period[g] mph (km/h)	Hours of Snowfall[c]		Free area ratio, A_r	Required Output,[e] Btu/h·ft² (W/m²)									Maximum Output Btu/h·ft² (W/m²)
City	Over 32 F (0°C)	Below or Equal to 32 F (0°C)			%	Hour per year		0 to 49 (0 to 156)	50 to 99 (157 to 313)	100 to 149 (314 to 471)	150 to 199 (472 to 629)	200 to 249 (630 to 787)	250 to 299 (788 to 944)	300 to 349 (945 to 1102)	350 to 399 (1103 to 1259)	400 up (1260 up)	
	% of winter hours with no snow at above temperatures							Frequency distribution of snowfall hours at above outputs, %[f]									
Albuquerque, NM	74.7	24.7	26.2 (-3.3)	8.5 (13.7)	0.6	22	1	62.0	25.4	7.6	4.2	0.0	0.8	—	—	—	259 (817)
							0	94.1	5.9	—	—	—	—	—	—	—	82 (259)
Amarillo, TX	73.1	26.0	24.6 (-4.1)	13.3 (21.4)	0.9	33	1	33.7	35.4	15.4	10.7	3.0	1.8	—	—	—	260 (820)
							0	88.1	10.1	1.8	—	—	—	—	—	—	143 (451)
Boston, MA	64.6	31.4	24.7 (-4.1)	14.2 (22.9)	4.0	145	1	51.5	30.0	12.3	4.3	1.2	0.6	0.1	—	—	320 (1009)
							0	83.2	14.0	2.0	0.3	0.3	0.1	—	0.2	—	370 (1167)[h]
Buffalo-Niagara Falls, NY	46.5	46.9	23.9 (-4.5)	10.8 (17.4)	6.6	240	1	50.7	32.6	11.2	3.7	1.4	0.2	0.2	—	—	309 (975)
							0	95.9	3.4	0.2	0.5	—	—	—	—	—	192 (606)
Burlington, VT	39.0	54.5	19.6 (-6.9)	10.8 (17.4)	6.5	236	1	53.7	29.9	13.2	2.5	0.6	0.1	—	—	—	280 (883)
							0	91.8	7.6	0.6	—	—	—	—	—	—	142 (448)
Caribou-Limestone, ME	21.4	70.6	16.5 (-8.6)	10.0 (16.1)	8.0	290	1	35.0	39.7	16.0	5.7	2.0	1.0	0.5	0.1	—	378 (1192)
							0	92.0	7.5	0.5	—	—	—	—	—	—	138 (435)
Cheyenne, WY	46.4	49.8	21.5 (-5.9)	15.3 (24.6)	3.8	138	1	16.5	26.2	19.4	13.1	8.6	4.7	4.2	4.7	2.6	499 (1574)
							0	94.3	5.4	0.3	—	—	—	—	—	—	129 (498)
Chicago, IL	45.4	50.9	21.4 (5.9)	11.5 (18.5)	3.7	134	1	45.8	37.4	11.4	3.1	1.4	0.6	0.2	0.1	—	368 (1161)
							0	91.5	8.1	0.3	0.1	—	—	—	—	—	165 (520)
Col. Springs, CO	54.3	43.6	22.1 (-5.5)	11.5 (18.5)	2.1	76	1	26.8	36.3	19.0	7.5	4.4	5.5	0.5	—	—	311 (981)
							0	98.4	1.6	—	—	—	—	—	—	—	63 (199)
Columbus, OH	59.0	38.1	24.5 (-4.2)	10.0 (16.1)	2.9	105	1	65.8	22.4	8.0	1.7	1.7	0.4	—	—	—	261 (823)
							0	97.7	2.3	—	—	—	—	—	—	—	72 (227)
Detroit, MI	47.0	49.3	24.1 (-4.4)	10.6 (17.1)	3.7	134	1	60.4	27.7	9.3	1.5	0.8	0.3	—	—	—	278 (877)
							0	95.9	3.5	0.6	—	—	—	—	—	—	140 (442)
Duluth, MN	12.6	80.5	14.5 (-9.8)	12.0 (19.3)	6.9	250	1	23.7	32.9	20.6	13.7	4.3	2.5	1.7	0.6	—	382 (1205)
							0	94.8	4.7	0.0	0.3	0.2	—	—	—	—	206 (650)
Falmouth, MA	68.5	29.5	25.5 (-3.6)	12.8 (20.6)	2.0	73	1	50.0	33.9	14.2	1.6	0.3	—	—	—	—	204 (643)
							0	91.5	7.4	1.1	—	—	—	—	—	—	144 (454)
Great Falls, MT	49.0	46.2	16.5 (-8.6)	14.4 (23.2)	4.8	174	1	26.2	27.6	16.7	16.4	7.5	4.6	0.3	0.5	0.2	451 (1422)
							0	94.6	4.8	0.6	—	—	—	—	—	—	138 (435)
Hartford, CT	56.4	38.9	24.4 (-4.3)	8.2 (13.2)	4.7	171	1	48.4	34.6	11.2	4.3	0.8	0.7	—	0.1	—	396 (1249)
							0	80.4	16.7	2.2	0.5	—	0.1	—	0.1	—	383 (1208)
Lincoln, NB	45.0	52.5	20.8 (-6.3)	10.1 (16.3)	2.5	91	1	32.7	26.2	20.0	13.9	5.7	1.5	—	—	—	293 (924)
							0	97.2	2.6	0.0	0.0	0.2	—	—	—	—	202 (637)
Memphis, TN	87.2	12.5	27.0 (-2.8)	11.5 (18.5)	0.3	11	1	48.4	28.3	6.7	13.3	3.3	—	—	—	—	227 (716)
							0	85.0	8.3	6.7	—	—	—	—	—	—	144 (454)
Minneapolis-St. Paul, MN	23.6	70.8	16.9 (-8.4)	11.1 (17.9)	5.6	203	1	28.4	31.4	21.7	14.1	3.5	0.6	0.3	—	—	313 (987)
							0	96.5	3.1	0.3	0.1	—	—	—	—	—	155 (489)
Mt. Home, ID	56.3	42.6	24.9 (-4.0)	9.5 (15.3)	1.1	40	1	74.2	21.9	3.9	—	—	—	—	—	—	143 (451)
							0	98.1	1.9	—	—	—	—	—	—	—	90 (284)
New York, NY	55.7	42.2	24.2 (-4.4)	11.8 (19.0)	2.1	76	1	53.1	31.8	9.4	2.2	1.5	1.7	—	0.3	—	385 (1214)
							0	87.6	9.6	1.5	0.7	0.3	0.3	—	—	—	298 (940)
Ogden, UT	50.0	45.6	24.3 (-4.3)	9.4 (15.1)	4.4	160	1	64.6	29.2	5.8	0.3	0.1	—	—	—	—	216 (681)
							0	88.8	9.4	1.4	0.3	0.1	—	—	—	—	216 (681)[h]
Oklahoma City, OK	79.0	19.8	24.6 (-4.1)	15.8 (25.4)	1.2	44	1	27.8	18.7	17.0	12.6	14.3	5.9	2.7	1.0	—	394 (1243)
							0	95.7	4.3	—	—	—	—	—	—	—	81 (255)
Philadelphia, PA	75.8	22.6	26.7 (-3.0)	9.7 (15.6)	1.6	58	1	62.3	23.6	10.4	2.3	0.9	0.5	—	—	—	296 (934)
							0	84.3	14.0	1.1	0.2	0.4	—	—	—	—	229 (722)
Pittsburgh, PA	55.2	39.8	24.3 (-4.3)	11.6 (18.7)	5.0	182	1	53.6	30.8	8.4	4.6	1.9	0.7	—	—	—	282 (889)
							0	93.3	5.9	0.7	0.1	—	—	—	—	—	157 (495)
Portland, OR	92.9	6.1	28.9 (-1.8)	8.4 (13.5)	1.0	36	0	78.0	16.9	5.1	—	—	—	—	—	—	125 (394)
							0	91.5	8.5	—	—	—	—	—	—	—	97 (306)
Rapid City, SD	45.2	51.6	19.3 (-7.1)	12.9 (20.8)	3.2	116	1	29.7	29.0	16.0	8.4	6.3	3.6	1.9	2.0	3.1	581 (1832)
							0	97.6	2.2	0.2	—	—	—	—	—	—	102 (322)
Reno, NV	56.0	41.6	24.3 (-4.3)	5.6 (9.0)	2.4	87	1	82.6	15.4	1.8	0.2	—	—	—	—	—	152 (479)
							0	90.2	8.0	1.6	0.2	—	—	—	—	—	154 (486)[h]
St. Louis, MO	68.7	30.4	25.0 (-3.9)	11.5 (18.5)	0.9	33	1	42.9	31.4	16.7	7.1	1.9	—	—	—	—	225 (710)
							0	85.2	11.6	2.6	0.6	—	—	—	—	—	152 (479)
Salina, KS	60.0	38.5	23.3 (-4.9)	10.9 (17.5)	1.5	54	1	44.9	31.9	12.7	7.6	2.2	0.7	—	—	—	286 (902)
							0	93.5	6.2	0.3	—	—	—	—	—	—	120 (378)
Sault Ste. Marie, MI	21.3	69.2	18.6 (-7.5)	9.4 (15.1)	9.5	345	1	45.7	32.8	14.3	5.7	1.4	0.1	—	—	—	262 (826)
							0	97.9	2.0	0.1	—	—	—	—	—	—	144 (454)
Seattle-Tacoma, WA	88.0	10.8	28.5 (-2.0)	5.9 (9.5)	1.2	44	1	86.3	12.3	1.4	—	—	—	—	—	—	137 (432)
							0	91.0	8.1	0.9	—	—	—	—	—	—	128 (404)
Spokane, WA	48.5	46.1	25.7 (-3.5)	10.7 (17.2)	5.4	196	1	62.6	28.7	7.4	1.1	2.0	—	—	—	—	205 (647)
							0	92.0	7.8	0.2	—	—	—	—	—	—	127 (401)
Washington, DC	77.9	21.2	26.8 (-2.9)	9.6 (15.5)	0.9	33	1	59.0	29.8	10.6	0.6	—	—	—	—	—	154 (486)
							0	85.7	11.8	2.5	—	—	—	—	—	—	121 (382)

[a] From *Air Conditioning, Heating and Ventilating*, August, 1957, p. 87.

[b] The period covered by this table is from Nov. 1 to March 31, including February taken as a 28.25 day month. Total hours in period = 3630.

[c] The percentage in Columns 2 and 3 plus the percent under hours of snowfall total 100%. Note that *Hours of Snowfall* does not include idling time, and is not actual operating time. See text.

[d] Snowfalls of trace amounts are not included; hence, *Hours of Snowfall* includes only those hours of 0.01 in. water (0.25 mm) equivalent per hour snowfall.

[e] Output does not include allowance for back or edge losses since these depend on slab construction.

[f] Percentages total 100% of the number of hours of snowfall.

[g] *Freezing Period* is that during No Snowfall when the air temperature is 32 F (0°C) or below.

[h] When heat output for A_r = 0 equals or exceeds the heat output for A_r = 1, the heat transfer q_h is from the air *to* the slab. This occurs when snowfall is at temperatures above 32 F (0°C).

Table 2　Design Data for Three Classes of Hot Fluid Snow Melting System[a]

City	Design Output, Btu/h · ft^2			Design Output, W/m^2		
	Class I System[b]	Class II System[c]	Class III System[d]	Class I System[b]	Class II System[c]	Class III System[d]
Albuquerque, NM	71	82	167	224	259	527
Amarillo, TX	98	143	241	309	451	760
Boston, MA	107	231	255	338	729	804
Buffalo-Niagara Falls, NY	80	192	307	252	606	968
Burlington, VT	90	142	244	284	448	770
Caribou-Limestone, ME	89/93	138	307	281/293	435	968
Cheyenne, WY	83	129	425	262	407	1340
Chicago, IL	89	165	350	281	520	1104
Colorado Springs, CO	49/63	63	293	154/199	199	924
Columbus, OH	52	72	253	164	227	798
Detroit, MI	69	140	255	218	442	804
Duluth, MN	83/114	206	374	262/360	650	1180
Falmouth, MA	93	144	165	293	454	520
Great Falls, MT	84/112	138	372	265/353	435	1173
Hartford, CT	115	254	260	363	801	820
Lincoln, NB	64/67	202	246	202/211	637	776
Memphis, TN	134	144	212	423	454	669
Minneapolis-St. Paul, MN	63/95	155	254	199/300	489	807
Mt. Home, ID	50	90	140	158	284	442
New York, NY	121	298	342	382	940	1079
Ogden, UT	98	216	217	309	681	684
Oklahoma City, OK	66	81	350	208	256	1104
Philadelphia, PA	97	229	263	306	722	830
Pittsburgh, PA	89	157	275	281	495	867
Portland, OR	86	97	111	271	306	350
Rapid City, SD	58/86	102	447	183/271	322	1410
Reno, NV	98	154	155	309	486	489
St. Louis, MO	122	152	198	385	479	624
Salina, KS	85	120	228	268	378	719
Sault Ste. Marie, MI	52/78	144	213	164/246	454	672
Seattle-Tacoma, WA	92	128	133	290	404	420
Spokane, WA	87	127	189	274	401	596
Washington, DC	117	121	144	369	382	454

From *Air Conditioning, Heating and Ventilating,* August 1957, p. 92.

[a]Where idling rate is greater than Class I design rate, idling rate value follows slash and should be used as Class I design output.

[b]For Class I (residential) Systems, the design output is set at the required heat output (see Table 1) when $A_r = 0$ at the 98th percentile of the frequency distribution; that is, where 98% of the hours have this output or less.

[c]For Class II (commercial) Systems, the design output is the maximum output when $A_r = 0$ in Table 1 (last column).

[d]For Class III (industrial) Systems, the design output is determined by the following four requirements: (1) Output is never exceeded for two consecutive hours; (2) Output for $A_r = 1$, Table 1, is at least 1 Btu/h · ft^2 (3.15 W/m^2) greater than maximum output for $A_r = 0$; (3) A_r is greater than or equal to 0.5 maximum requirement shown in Table 1 for $A_r = 1$; that is, $q_o = q_s + q_m + 0.5 (q_e + q_h)$ for the conditions where $q_t = q_s + q_m + q_h + q_e$ are a maximum, and (4) the free area ratio A_r is unity for at least 98% of the hours listed in Table 1.

whenever the conditions are milder than some of the critical values, it will be inadequate a fraction of the time. In a residential system where initial cost must be kept at a minimum, the designer may have to accept more frequent snow accumulations.

Table 2 contains the design heat requirements for all classes of snow melting systems. Under Class I systems, the values in parentheses are idling rates and, since they exceed the Class I design rates, should be taken as design output for this classification. The designer can alter design rates if a particular job should have different design criteria from those given in the footnotes of Table 2. Any change in design conditions used should be based on the frequency distribution given in Table 1.

Use of Tables 1, 2, and 3 is illustrated by Example 1.

Example 1: An engineer has been retained to design snow melting systems for the service areas of a turnpike running from the eastern edge of the Wisconsin-Illinois border northwest to the Wisconsin-Minnesota border just east of St. Paul. He decides that Chicago data will be adequate for the southern terminus and that Minneapolis-St. Paul data will be adequate for the northern terminus. His problem is to determine the heat and hydraulic requirements of the systems for service areas between Chicago and St. Paul.

Solution: Assume, for this example, that the city in question is Madison, Wisconsin. Weather bureau records indicate that the annual average number of days with snow cover of an inch (25 mm) or more would be 100, and that the engineer can assume an average snowfall of 40 in. (1 m). In addition, he can estimate about 11 days per year with a snowfall of an inch (25 mm) or more (Chapman 1957).

For the walkways to the restaurant from the parking area, a Class I design rate could be used. This rate could be taken as 90 Btu/h · ft^2 (284 W/m^2). This agrees with data in Tables 2 and 3, which give the design rate at 89 (281) for Chicago and idling rate at 95 (300) for Minneapolis.

The lanes leading from the turnpike to the gasoline pumps and parking areas should be rated as Class II areas. A check of Tables 1 and 2 indicates that 160 Btu/h · ft^2 (505 W/m^2) would be adequate.

If an emergency area is included for a wrecking truck, ambulance or police garage, it would be wise to consider a Class III rate for this area. An inspection of Table 1 for Chicago shows that a rate of 275 Btu/h · ft^2 (867 W/m^2) would be adequate for $A_r = 1$ for 99.4% of the time. Similarly, 275 (867) would be adequate 99.4% of the time in St. Paul. Therefore, 275 Btu/h · ft^2 (867 W/m^2) seems sufficient for the emergency areas. Table 2 in the Class III column lists 350 Btu/h · ft^2 (1104 W/m^2) for Chicago and 254 Btu/h · ft^2 (801 W/m^2) for St. Paul, but for uses similar to the areas here, 275 Btu/h · ft^2 (867 W/m^2) should be adequate.

Table 3 Yearly Operating Data[a]

City	Idling			Melting			
	Time,[b] h/yr (W/m²)	Rate,[c] Btu/h·ft²	Annual Output,[d] Btu/ft² (kJ/m²)	Time,[e] h/yr	Annual Output,[g] Btu/ft² (kJ/m²) Class I[f]	Class II[f]	Class III[f]
Albuquerque, NM	897	32.5 (102.5)	29,100 (91.9)	22	908 (2.9)	969 (3.1)	1150 (3.6)
Amarillo, TX	944	51.1 (161.2)	48,200 (152.2)	33	2150 (6.8)	2520 (7.9)	2770 (8.7)
Boston, MA	1140	52.1 (164.3)	59,400 (187.3)	145	8000 (25.2)	9080 (28.6)	9100 (28.7)
Buffalo-Niagara Falls, NY	1702	50.2 (158.3)	85,500 (269.4)	240	11,800 (37.2)	14,600 (46.0)	14,900 (47.0)
Burlington, VT	1978	76.9 (242.5)	152,000 (479.7)	236	11,800 (37.2)	13,500 (42.6)	13,800 (43.5)
Caribou-Limestone, ME	2563	93.0 (293.3)	238,000 (751.7)	290	17,800 (56.1)[h]	20,600 (65.0)	22,500 (71.0)
Cheyenne, WY	1808	77.7 (245.1)	140,000 (443.1)	138	9730 (30.7)	13,200 (41.6)	20,200 (63.7)
Chicago, IL	1848	67.8 (213.8)	125,000 (395.1)	134	7200 (22.7)	8390 (26.5)	8700 (27.4)
Colorado Springs, CO	1583	63.4 (200.0)	100,000 (316.6)	76	3960 (12.5)[h]	3960 (12.5)	7390 (23.3)
Columbus, OH	1383	45.0 (141.9)	62,200 (196.2)	105	3590 (11.3)	4180 (13.2)	5350 (16.9)
Detroit, MI	1790	49.0 (154.5)	87,600 (276.6)	134	5540 (17.5)	6850 (21.6)	7070 (22.3)
Duluth, MN	2922	113.8 (358.9)	332,000 (1048.7)	250	33,200 (104.7)[h]	38,100 (120.2)	39,500 (124.6)
Falmouth, MA	1071	44.2 (139.4)	47,400 (149.3)	73	3830 (12.1)	4250 (13.4)	4290 (13.5)
Great Falls, MT	1677	111.6 (352.0)	187,000 (590.3)	174	13,700 (43.2)[h]	15,400 (80.1)	19,100 (60.2)
Hartford, CT	1412	41.9 (132.2)	59,200 (186.7)	171	9830 (31.0)	10,800 (34.1)	10,810 (34.1)
Lincoln, NB	1906	67.2 (211.9)	128,000 (403.9)	91	4750 (15.0)[h]	8350 (26.3)	8520 (26.9)
Memphis, TN	454	32.0 (100.9)	14,500 (45.8)	11	702 (2.2)	721 (2.3)	792 (2.5)
Minneapolis-St. Paul, MN	2570	95.1 (299.9)	244,000 (770.7)	203	14,200 (44.8)[h]	17,600 (55.5)	18,400 (58.0)
Mt. Home, ID	1546	41.9 (132.2)	64,800 (204.4)	40	1260 (4.0)	1530 (4.8)	1590 (5.0)
New York, NY	1532	50.7 (159.9)	77,700 (245.0)	76	4180 (13.2)	4690 (14.8)	4710 (14.9)
Ogden, UT	1655	44.6 (140.7)	73,800 (232.9)	160	7050 (22.2)	7370 (23.2)	7370 (23.2)
Oklahoma City, OK	719	56.2 (177.3)	40,400 (127.5)	44	2380 (7.5)	2800 (8.8)	5400 (17.0)
Philadelphia, PA	820	31.4 (99.0)	25,700 (81.2)	58	2710 (8.5)	3100 (9.8)	3110 (9.8)
Pittsburgh, PA	1445	49.5 (156.1)	71,500 (225.6)	182	9050 (28.5)	10,700 (33.7)	11,100 (35.0)
Portland, OR	221	17.4 (54.9)	3840 (12.1)	36	1300 (4.1)	1330 (4.2)	1360 (4.3)
Rapid City, SD	1873	86.4 (272.5)	162,000 (510.4)	116	7450 (23.5)[h]	8250 (26.0)	13,400 (42.3)
Reno, NV	1510	36.9 (116.4)	55,700 (175.8)	87	2970 (9.4)	3030 (9.6)	3030 (9.6)
St. Louis, MO	1104	44.8 (141.3)	4950 (156.0)	33	2190 (6.9)	2290 (7.2)	2380 (7.5)
Salina, KS	1398	53.9 (170.0)	75,400 (237.7)	54	2920 (9.2)	3370 (10.6)	3810 (12.0)
Sault Ste. Marie, MI	2512	77.7 (245.1)	195,000 (615.7)	345	17,600 (55.5)[h]	22,200 (70.0)	23,200 (73.2)
Seattle-Tacoma, WA	392	17.2 (54.2)	6750 (21.2)	44	1410 (4.4)	1430 (4.5)	1430 (4.5)
Spokane, WA	1673	39.1 (123.3)	65,500 (206.3)	196	8650 (27.3)	9350 (29.5)	9560 (30.2)
Washington, DC	770	30.6 (96.5)	23,600 (74.3)	33	1650 (5.2)	1660 (5.2)	1690 (5.3)

[a] From *Air Conditioning, Heating and Ventilating*, August 1957, p. 94.
[b] From Table 1, Column 3 × 3630 (hour per year).
[c] Rate when idling, Btu/h·ft² = $(0.27 v + 3.3)(32 - t)$ or W/m² = $(1.143 v + 15.4)(0 - t)$, where v = wind speed from Column 5, Table 1, and t = air temperature from Column 4, Table 1.
[d] Product of the preceding columns.
[e] Hours of Snowfall, from Column 7, Table 1.
[f] See footnote for Table 4.
[g] Based on the condition that surface temperature is maintained at 33 deg F (18.3°C) until required output exceeds designed output, at which time design output is used regardless of required output. Distribution of required output based on Table 1.
[h] Based on Idling Rate rather than Design Rate.

Table 4 Heat Output and Fluid Temperature[a] for Snow Melting System

s Rate of Snowfall in./h (mm/h)	A_r		$t_a = 0$ F (−17.8°C) Speed v, mph (km/h)			$t_a = 10$ F (−12.2°C) Speed v, mph (km/h)			$t_a = 20$ F (−6.7°C) Speed v, mph (km/h)			$t_a = 30$ F (−1.1°C) Speed v, mph (km/h)		
			5 (8)	10 (16.1)	15 (24.1)	5 (8)	10 (16.1)	15 (24.1)	5 (8)	10 (16.1)	15 (24.1)	5 (8)	10 (16.1)	15 (24.1)
0.08 (2.0)	1.0	q_o	151 (4-76)	205 (647)	260 (820)	127 (401)	168 (530)	209 (659)	102 (322)	128 (404)	154 (486)	75 (237)	84 (265)	94 (296)
		t_m	108 (42.2)	135 (57.2)	162 (72.2)	97 (36.1)	117 (47.2)	138 (58.9)	85 (29.4)	97 (36.1)	110 (43.3)	70 (21.1)	75 (23.9)	79 (26.1)
	0.0	q_o	66 (208)	66 (208)	66 (208)	64 (202)	64 (202)	64 (202)	62 (196)	62 (196)	62 (196)	60 (189)	60 (189)	60 (189)
		t_m	66 (18.9)	66 (18.9)	66 (18.9)	65 (18.3)	65 (18.3)	65 (18.3)	64 (17.8)	64 (17.8)	64 (17.8)	63 (17.2)	63 (17.2)	63 (17.2)
0.16 (4.1)	1.0	q_o	218 (686)	273 (861)	327 (1031)	193 (609)	233 (735)	274 (864)	165 (520)	191 (602)	217 (684)	135 (426)	144 (454)	154 (486)
		t_m	142 (61.1)	169 (76.1)	198 (92.2)	129 (53.4)	149 (65.0)	170 (76.6)	117 (47.2)	129 (53.9)	142 (61.1)	100 (37.8)	105 (40.5)	109 (42.8)
	0.0	q_o	133 (419)	133 (419)	133 (419)	129 (407)	129 (407)	129 (407)	125 (394)	125 (394)	125 (394)	121 (382)	121 (382)	121 (382)
		t_m	99 (37.2)	99 (37.2)	99 (37.2)	97 (36.1)	97 (36.1)	97 (36.1)	95 (35.0)	95 (35.0)	95 (35.0)	93 (33.9)	93 (33.9)	93 (33.9)
0.25 (6.35)	1.0	q_o	292 (921)	347 (1094)	401 (1265)	265 (836)	305 (962)	346 (1091)	235 (741)	261 (823)	287 (905)	203 (640)	212 (669)	221 (697)
		t_m	179 (81.7)	206 (96.7)	234 (112.2)	165 (73.9)	186 (85.6)	206 (96.7)	151 (66.1)	163 (72.8)	176 (80.0)	134 (56.1)	139 (59.4)	144 (62.2)
	0.0	q_o	208 (656)	208 (656)	208 (656)	202 (637)	202 (637)	202 (637)	195 (615)	195 (615)	195 (615)	188 (593)	188 (593)	188 (593)
		t_m	137 (58.3)	137 (58.3)	137 (58.3)	134 (56.7)	134 (56.7)	134 (56.7)	131 (55.0)	131 (55.0)	131 (55.0)	127 (52.8)	127 (52.8)	127 (52.8)

[a] Not applicable to electric snow-melting systems.

Note: This table is based on a relative humidity of 80% for all air temperatures.

s = rate of snowfall, inches of water equivalent per hour (mm/h)
A_r = free area ratio
q_o = slab output, Btu/h·ft² (W/m²)
t_a = air temperature, F (°C)
t_m = fluid temperature, F (°C). Based on construction as shown in Fig. 1[a]
v = wind speed, mph (km/h)

Table 5 Snowfall Data for Various Cities[a]

City	Number of Readings with Maximum Temperature in 6-Hour Period Below Freezing at Various Snowfall Rates				Total Readings Taken	Assumed Design Rate of Snowfall[b] S in./h (mm/h)
	Snowfall Rate in Equivalent Inches (mm) of Water per 6 Hour					
	0.00 to 0.24 (0 to 6.3)	0.25 to 0.49 (6.35 to 12.5)	0.50 to 0.75 (12.6 to 19)	0.75 to 0.99 (19.1 to 25.1)		
Col. 1	Col. 2	Col. 3	Col. 4	Col. 5	Col. 6	Col. 7
Albany, NY	2052	29	5	1	3720	0.16 (4.1)
Asheville, NC	463	5	1	0	3536	0.08 (2.0)
Billings, MT	1640	4	0	0	3532	0.08 (2.0)
Bismarck, ND	2838	0	0	0	3720	0.08 (2.0)
Cincinnati, OH	1045	3	0	0	3720	0.08 (2.0)
Cleveland, OH	1569	2	0	0	3720	0.08 (2.0)
Evansville, IN	916	5	1	1	3720	0.08 (2.0)
Kansas City, MO	1189	12	2	1	3720	0.16 (4.1)
Madison, WI	2370	5	2	0	3720	0.08 (2.0)
Portland, ME	2054	33	4	1	3720	0.16 (2.0)

[a] Data from U.S. Weather Bureau. Based on readings taken 1:30 a.m., 7:30 a.m., 1:30 p.m. and 7:30 p.m. daily from November 15 to February 15 from 1940 to 1949. Where the total readings are less than 3720, the period of record is less than 10 years. The difference between Col. 6 and the sum of readings in Col. 2, 3, 4 and 5 is the number of readings with a maximum temperature (in the 6-h period) above freezing.

[b] The design rate is found as follows: Proceed to left (on line from any city) from Col. 5 until the column containing the tenth reading is found. Assume that the larger value in the heading of the selected column is an *average maximum* value, and should be multiplied by 2 to obtain the maximum rate for a 6-h period. This maximum rate divided by 6 is the design rate per hour. This is equivalent to dividing the larger value in the heading of the selected column by 3.

For example: For Albany, N.Y., Col. 5 and 4 total six readings, and consequently the tenth reading is in Col. 3, which has the larger value of 0.49 (12.5) in the column heading. Dividing 0.49 (12.5) by 3, the design water equivalent of 0.16 in. (4.1 mm) per hour is found, as listed in Col. 7.

Hydraulic Requirement

When the heating requirements are known, the hydraulic requirements of the system should be calculated by following the procedures outlined in Chapter 13. Since snow melting systems use an antifreeze solution (usually ethylene glycol in water), the hydraulic design must consider its effect on the components (pumps, piping, and heat exchangers), which are detailed in Chapter 13 of this volume and Chapter 18 of the FUNDAMENTALS Volume.

INSTALLATION

Gordon (1950) discusses precautions to be taken during the installation of hot fluid piping systems concerning internal corrosion, flammability, toxicity, cleaning, joints, and hookup.

Safety

Since ethylene glycol and petroleum distillates are slightly toxic, the system should be installed and maintained independently. No permanent connection should be installed between the snow melting system and the drinking water supply. Ethylene glycol is not flammable. In fact, aqueous solutions of less than 60% glycol are used for fire sprinkler systems; they do not freeze and are effective fire extinguishing agents.

Petroleum distillates suitable for fluids in snow melting systems are classified as nonflammable but have fire points between 300 and 350 °F (150 and 177 °C). When using fluids of this type, any oil dripping from the seals on the pump should be collected. It is good practice to place a barrier between the oil lines and the boiler so a flashback from the boiler will not ignite a possible oil leak.

Other nonflammable fluids, such as those used in some transformers, can be used as the antifreeze. These fluids are three or four times more expensive than the glycols with the corrosion protection of the oils.

An ASME pressure relief valve of adequate capacity should be installed on a closed system.

Internal Corrosion

Since ethylene glycol solutions become corrosive in service, rust inhibitors are generally included. Even with an inhibitor,

the solution should be tested annually to determine any change in acidity. If the test indicates that the inhibitor has been exhausted, the entire system should be drained and a fresh solution installed. To increase the life of the inhibitor, the heat exchanger surfaces should be kept below 285 °F (140 °C), which corresponds to about 40 psig (280 kPa above atm.) steam. Temperatures above 300 °F (150 °C) accelerate the deterioration of the inhibitors.

A strainer, sediment trap, or other means for cleaning the piping system must be provided. It should be in the return line ahead of the heat exchanger, and must be cleaned frequently during the initial system operation to remove scale and sludge.

Slab Construction

It is satisfactory to use ¾-in. (20-mm) pipe or tube on 12-in. (300-mm) centers as a standard coil. If pumping loads require reduced friction, the pipe size can be increased to 1 in. (25 mm), but the slab depth must be increased accordingly.

The piping should be supported by a minimum of 2 in. (50 mm) of concrete above and below the pipe. This requires a 5-in. (125-mm) slab for ¾-in. (20-mm) pipe and 5.4-in. (137-mm) for 1-in. (25-mm) pipe.

A moisture barrier should be placed between any insulation and the fill. The joints in the barrier should be mopped and the fill made smooth enough to eliminate holes or gaps for moisture transfer. Also, the edges of the barrier should be flashed to the surface of the slab so that the ends are sealed. If the piping must pass through a concrete expansion joint, stress in the tubing must be avoided. Figure 2 shows a method of protecting the tubing from stress under normal conditions.

To prevent external corrosion, all portions of the tube not totally embedded in concrete must be kept dry at all times. These sections can be protected with waterproof tape and flexible foam plastic insulation. All joints in the covering of the tube must be watertight and the ends of the insulation sealed to the tube to prevent moisture from entering.

Thermal Stresses

Chapman (1955) discusses the problems of thermal stress. In general, there will be no ill effects from the thermal stresses if the following installation and operation rules are observed.

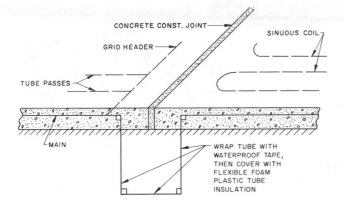

Fig. 2 Piping Detail for Concrete Construction Joints

1. Minimize the temperature difference between the fluid and the slab surface by:
   a. Close pipe spacing (see Figure 1)
   b. Low temperature drop in fluid, $\Delta t \leqslant 20\,°F$ ($11\,°C$)
   c. Continuous operation (if economically feasible)
2. Keep pipe near surface to obtain about 2-in. (50-mm) cover.
3. Use reinforcing steel designed for thermal stress if high structural loads are expected (such as on highways).

Testing

After installation but before pouring concrete, all piping should be tested to about 100 psig (700 kPa above atm.). This pressure should be maintained until all welds and connections have been checked for leaks. If an oil is used as an antifreeze, the test should be performed with air or some gas only 50 psi (350 kPa) required with an air test but *not with water*. Using water is dangerous because the pipe may not be thoroughly dried when the oil is introduced. The water will tend to collect, and when the temperature falls below $32\,°F$ ($0\,°C$), the collected water can freeze and cause damage.

Draining and Venting

The slab surface and the coil require proper drainage. The slab must be sloped to allow the water from the melted snow to run off. Puddles are objectionable on sidewalks and drives because they cause splashing and retard heat flow from the embedded pipes.

The pipes must be positioned to allow drainage. If the antifreeze becomes corrosive it must be drained; blowing air through the system is not completely reliable.

Coils must be installed so that the air is completely vented during filling. Air must be continuously eliminated during operation. (See Chapter 13.)

Drifting Snow

Because some drifting will occur on every system adjacent to a wall or vertical surface, extra piping should be added in these areas. If possible, coils should also be added in the vertical surface. Drainage carried to the area expected to be drifted tends to wash away some snow.

ELECTRIC SNOW MELTING SYSTEMS

General Design

Snow melting systems using electricity as an energy source include the use of (1) either mineral insulated (MI) cable, (2) resistance wire assembly to be embedded in the paving materials, or (3) high intensity infrared.

Heat Density

The basic load calculations for electric systems are the same as presented earlier in this chapter. However, electric system output is determined by installed resistance and the voltage impressed, and it cannot be overfired or altered by flow rates of fluid. Consequently, safety factors are not applied to requirements, nor are marginal capacity systems applied.

Table 6 indicates electric snow melting intensity values similar to Table 2, but they have been modified and converted to conform with recognized electric snow melting practice.

Heat intensity can be varied within a slab by altering the cable or wire spacing to compensate for anticipated drift areas or other high heat loss areas.

Slab Design

Concrete slabs containing electric heating cable or wire must be designed and constructed with subbase, expansion-contraction joints, reinforcement, and drainage to prevent slab cracking; otherwise, crack-induced shearing or tensile forces would break the heating cable or wire. Cable must not run through expansion-contraction joints, keyed construction joints, or control joints (dummy grooves); however, cable or wire may be run under 0.12-in. (3 mm) score marks (block and other patterns).

Control joints must be placed wherever the slab changes size or direction. The maximum dimension between control joints for ground-supported slabs should be less than 15 ft (4.6 m), and the length should be no greater than twice the width, except for ribbon driveways or sidewalks. In ground-supported slabs, most cracking occurs during the early cure. Depending upon the amount of water used in a concrete mix, shrinkage during cure will be up to 0.75 in. per 100 ft (60 mm per 100 m). During the early cure period, concrete does not have sufficient strength to overcome friction between the slab and under the bed while shrinking, if the slab is more than 15 ft (4.6 m) in length.

If the slabs containing heating cables are to be poured in two separate layers, the top layer containing the heating cables does not contribute toward total slab strength; therefore, the lower slab must be designed to provide total slab strength.

The concrete mix of the top layer of concrete should give maximum *weatherability*. Compressive strength should be 4000 to 5000 psi (27 600 to 34 500 kPa); recommended slump 3 in. (75 mm) maximum, 2 in. (50 mm) minimum. Air content and aggregate size should be as follows:

Maximum Size Crushed Rock Aggregate[a], in. (mm)	Air Content (%)
2.5 (64)	5 ± 1
1 (25)	6 ± 1
0.5 (13)	7.5 ± 1

[a]Do not use river gravel or slag.

Snow melting systems should have good surface drainage. When the ambient air temperature is freezing, run-off from melting snow immediately freezes upon leaving the heated area. Any water able to get under the slab also freezes when the system is de-energized, causing extreme frost heaving. Run-off water should be piped away in heated or below frost line drains.

When cable must be run around obstacles such as a storm sewer grate, the cable spacing should be reduced uniformly. MI cable spacing is held with copper spacing strips.

Cable or wire may be placed in contact with an existing sound pavement (either concrete or asphalt) and then covered with 1.25

Table 6 Electric Snow Melting System Design Data

Design heat density installed in slab, watts per square foot (0.0929 m^2) of heated area

Location	Residential[a] Theoretical[d] Class I	Residential[a] Common[e] densities actually installed	Commercial-Industrial[b] Theoretical[d] Class II	Commercial-Industrial[b] Common[e] densities actually installed	Critical[c] Theoretical[d] Class III	Critical[c] Common[e] densities actually installed	Location	Residential[a] Theoretical[d] Class I	Residential[a] Common[e] densities actually installed	Commercial-Industrial[b] Theoretical[d] Class II	Commercial-Industrial[b] Common[e] densities actually installed	Critical[c] Theoretical[d] Class III	Critical[c] Common[e] densities actually installed
Arkansas							**Michigan**						
Ft. Smith		20		40		45	Detroit	28	40-60	57	60	105	60
Little Rock		20		30		50	Sault Ste. Marie	21		59		87	
							Jackson		40		60		80
Colorado													
Colorado Springs	20		26		120		**Minnesota**						
Denver		42		50		60	Duluth	34		85		153	
Pueblo				45		60	Minneapolis-St. Paul	26	42-75	64	60-75	104	70-75
Connecticut							**Missouri**						
Hartford	47	30	104	50	107	70	Kansas City		42		40-50		60-70
Middletown		40-60		40-60		60-70	St. Joseph		42		42		
New Haven		40		40		60	St. Louis	50	40-60	62	40-60	81	60
Delaware							**Montana**						
Wilmington		30		40		50	Great Falls	34		57		153	
District of Columbia							**Nebraska**						
Washington	48	30-40	50	40-55	59	55-60	Lincoln	26	40-50	83	40-50	101	60
Idaho							Omaha		40-45		60		60
Mt. Home	21		37		57		**Nevada**						
Illinois							Reno	40		63		64	
Chicago	37	40	68	50	144	60	**New Hampshire**						
Peoria		40		45-50		55-60	Concord		50		50		75
Rockford		42		40-60			Manchester						
Springfield		40		45-50		55-60	**New Jersey**						
Indiana							Atlantic City		30		40		60
Elkhart				42			Morristown		40		50		60
Hartford City				35			**New Mexico**						
Indianapolis		40		40		40-60	Albuquerque	29		34		69	
South Bend				52		50-55	**New York**						
Iowa							Buffalo-Niagara Falls	33		79	60	126	
Dubuque		40		40-60			New York City	50	35-50	122	40-50	140	50-60
Kansas							Poughkeepsie		40		70		100
Kansas City		40		50		60	Syracuse		40-60		60		60
Salina	35		49		94		**North Carolina**						
Topeka		40		40		60	Charlotte		42		30-42		42
Wichita		50		50		50	**Ohio**						
Kentucky							Canton		30		36		
Ashland				42			Cincinnati		40		50		60
Maine							Cleveland		40				45-55
Caribou-Limestone	37		57		126		Columbus	21	30	30	40	104	50
Bangor		40		40		60	Findlay				40		60
Portland		40		40		60	Ironton		30		40		
Maryland							Lima		40		40		70
Baltimore	44	30-45	95	45-55	105	50-70	Portsmouth		30-40		40		
Massachusetts							Steubenville		40		45		
Boston	44	40-45	95	50-60	105	60-75	**Oklahoma**						
Falmouth	38		59		68		Oklahoma City	27	25	33	40	144	45
Fall River		40		40		60	Tulsa		20		30		40
Springfield		40		40		80							

[a] *RESIDENTIAL:* Residential walks or driveways and interplant areaways—allow snow to cover area temporarily, but do not accumulate for worst conditions of 98% of snow frequency. Minimum recommended intensity, 30 W/ft^2 (320 W/m^2).

[b] *COMMERCIAL-INDUSTRIAL:* Commercial sidewalks, steps, and driveways—allow snow to cover area temporarily, but do not accumulate for worst conditions of 100% of snow frequency. Minimum recommended intensity, 40 W/ft^2 (430 W/m^2).

[c] *CRITICAL:* Toll plazas of highways and bridges, and aprons and loading areas of airports—melt snow immediately for 98% of snow frequency. (Modified definition of Table 2, Class III

design.) Minimum recommended intensity, 60 W/ft^2 (650 W/m^2). (Article 422-74(b), National Electric Code). Installed heating intensity of embedded cable or wire systems shall not exceed 120 W/ft^2 (1300 W/m^2).

[d] Based on values of Table 2, including adjustment for assumed 40% heat loss through edge and bottom of slab.

[e] Based on survey of actual practice, as reported by 66 electric utilities. Survey made by TC 3.3 during Spring 1966.

Table 6　Electric Snow Melting System Design Data (Continued)

Design heat density installed in slab, watts per square foot (0.0929 m^2) of heated area

Location	Residential[a] Theoretical[d] Class I	Common[e] densities actually installed	Commercial-Industrial[b] Theoretical[d] Class II	Common[e] densities actually installed	Critical[c] Theoretical[d] Class III	Common[e] densities actually installed	Location	Residential[a] Theoretical[d] Class I	Common[e] densities actually installed	Commercial-Industrial[b] Theoretical[d] Class II	Common[e] densities actually installed	Critical[c] Theoretical[d] Class III	Common[e] densities actually installed
Oregon							**Vermont**						
Portland	35	42	40	42	46	60	Bennington		50		50		75
							Burlington	37	50	58	50	100	75
Pennsylvania													
Allentown		40		44-55		60	**Virginia**						
Johnstown		30		40		70	Richmond		30		40		
Philadelphia	40	40	94	40-60	108	40-100	Abingdon		30		30		
Pittsburgh	37	30-40	65	30-60	113	60							
							Washington						
Rhode Island							Seattle	38		53		55	
Providence		45		65			Spokane	36	30-40	52	30-45	78	
So. Dakota							**West Virginia**						
Rapid City	24		42		183		Wheeling		35		35-50		
							Bluefield				40		80
Tennessee							Parkersburg		30		45		60
Memphis	55		59		87		Beckley		40		40		
Kingsport				42			Charleston		40		45		50
Nashville		40		40		60	Morgantown		30		45		60
Texas							**Wisconsin**						
Amarillo	40		59		99		Milwaukee		45		50-65		65
Utah							**Wyoming**						
Ogden	40		89		89		Cheyenne	34		53		174	

to 1.5 in. (32 to 38 mm) of asphalt. If there are signs of cracking or heaving, the pavement should be replaced. Cable or wire should not be placed over existing expansion-contraction, control, or construction joints. The finest grade of asphalt possible is best for the top course; no stone should exceed 0.38 in. (10 mm) diameter.

Area Layout

The area to be protected by electric snow melting must first be measured and planned. For total snow removal, heaters must cover the entire area. In larger installations, it may be desirable to melt snow and ice from only the most frequently used areas, such as walkways and wheel tracks for trucks and autos. Planning for separate circuits should be considered so that individual areas within the system can be heated, as required.

Switchgear and Conduit

Double-pole, single-throw switches or tandem circuit breakers to open both sides of the line should be used. The switchgear may be in any protected, convenient location. It is also advisable to include a pilot lamp on the load side of each switch so that there is a visual indication when the system is energized.

The power supply conduit is run underground, outside the slab, or in a prepared base. For concrete, this should be done before the reinforcing mesh is installed.

MINERAL INSULATED (MI) CABLE

Mineral Insulated (MI) heating cable is a copper or copper alloy sheath, magnesium oxide (MgO)-filled, die-drawn cable with one or two copper or copper alloy conductors. Although it is heavy-duty cable, its use is practical in any snow melting installation.

MI Cable Layout

To determine the MI heating cable needed for a specific area, it is necessary to know the following:

1. heated area size
2. watts per ft^2 (W/m^2) area required
3. voltage or voltages available
4. the approximate cable length needed

To find approximate MI cable length, estimate 2 linear ft of cable per ft^2 (6.6 m/m^2) of area for concrete, and 3 linear ft of cable per ft^2 (10 m/m^2) of area for asphalt. This corresponds to a 6-in. (150-mm) on-center spacing in concrete and 4-in. (100-mm) on-center spacing in asphalt.

Cable spacing is dictated primarily by the heat conducting ability of the material in which it is embedded. Concrete has a higher heat transmission coefficent, which permits wider cable spacing. A procedure to determine the proper MI heating cable as follows:

1. Determine total wattage (W_t).

$$W_t = Aw$$

2. Determine total resistance (R).

$$R = E^2/W_t$$

3. Determine calculated cable resistance per foot (m) (r_1).

$$r_1 = R/L_1$$

where

W_t = total wattage needed, W.
A = heated area of each heated slab, ft^2 (m^2).
w = desired watt density input, W/ft^2 (W/m^2).

E = voltage available, V.
r_1 = calculated cable resistance, ohms per ft (m) of cable.
L_1 = estimated cable length, ft (m).
R = total resistance of heater cable, ohms.
L = actual cable length needed, ft (m).
r = actual cable resistance, ohms per ft (m).
S = cable center to center spacing, in. (mm).
I = total current per MI cable, amperes.

MI heating cables commercially available have actual total resistance values (r) per ft (m) of cable (total of two, if two conductor) ranging from 0.0016 to 0.6 ohm/ft (0.0052 to 1.97 ohm/m). Manufacturing tolerances are ±10% on these values. Mineral insulated cables are die-drawn, with the internal conductor drawn to size indirectly via pressures transmitted through the mineral insulation. Special cables are not economical unless the quantity needed is 100,000 ft (30 000 m) or more.

4. From manufacturer's literature, choose a cable closest in resistance (r) to the calculated r_1. Table 7 illustrates typical cable resistances.
5. Determine actual cable length needed to give wattage desired.
6. Determine cable spacing within heated area.

$$S = 12A/L$$

Cable spacing for optimum performance should be within the following limits: in concrete, 3 in. (75 mm) minimum to 9 in. (229 mm) maximum; in asphalt, 3 in. (75 mm) minimum to 6 in. (150 mm) maximum.

Because the manufacturing tolerance on cable length is ±1%, and installation tolerances on cable spacing must be compatible with field conditions, it is usually necessary to adjust the installed cable as the end of the heating cable is rolled out. Cable spacing of the last several passes may have to be altered to give a uniform heat distribution.

The installed cable within the heated areas is a serpentine shape originating from a corner of the heated area (see Figure 3). Since heat is evenly conducted from all sides of the heating cable, cables in a concrete slab can be run within half the spacing dimension of the heated area perimeter. However, in asphalt, heating cables must be kept well

Table 7   Typical Heating Cable Resistances

ohm/ft (m) Total at 77 F (25°C)		Volt Rating	Conductor		Sheath		OD		lb/ft (kg/m)
			E,C[a]	A.W.G.	E,C[a]		in.	mm	
Single Conductor									
0.610	(2.001)	300	E	26	E		0.120	3.048	15 (22)
0.391	(0.119)			25			0.128	3.251	20 (30)
0.300	(0.984)			23			0.145	3.683	34 (51)
0.200	(0.656)			21			0.150	3.810	38 (57)
0.100	(0.328)			18			0.165	4.191	45 (67)
0.050	(0.164)			15			0.175	4.445	56 (83)
0.030	(0.098)			13			0.200	5.080	72 (107)
0.020	(0.066)			11			0.215	5.461	85 (127)
0.010	(0.033)			8			0.246	6.248	120 (179)
0.200	(0.656)	600	E	21	E		0.183	4.648	53 (79)
0.105	(0.344)			18			0.205	5.207	69 (103)
0.060	(0.197)			16			0.210	5.334	74 (110)
0.035	(0.115)			16			0.215	5.461	85 (127)
0.025	(0.082)			12			0.240	6.096	100 (149)
0.020	(0.066)			11			0.253	6.426	112 (167)
0.013	(0.043)			9			0.277	7.036	143 (213)
0.006	(0.020)			6			0.240	6.096	202 (301)
0.00651	(0.021)	600	C	18	C		0.199	5.055	65 (97)
0.00409	(0.013)			16			0.215	5.461	73 (109)
0.00258	(0.008)			14			0.230	5.842	90 (134)
0.00162	(0.005)			12			0.246	6.248	105 (156)
0.00102	(0.003)			10			0.277	7.036	135 (201)
Two Conductor									
0.800	(2.625)	300	E	25	E		0.165	4.191	50 (75)
0.400	(1.312)			21			0.183	4.648	67 (100)
0.125	(0.410)			18			0.246	6.248	96 (143)
0.070	(0.230)	600	E	16	E		0.340	8.636	182 (271)
0.044	(0.144)		E	14	E		0.371	9.423	220 (328)
0.028	(0.092)		E	12	E		0.402	10.211	260 (387)
0.00818	(0.027)		C	16	C		0.340	8.636	182 (271)
0.00516	(0.017)		C	14	C		0.371	9.423	220 (328)

[a]E = Everdur; C = Copper.

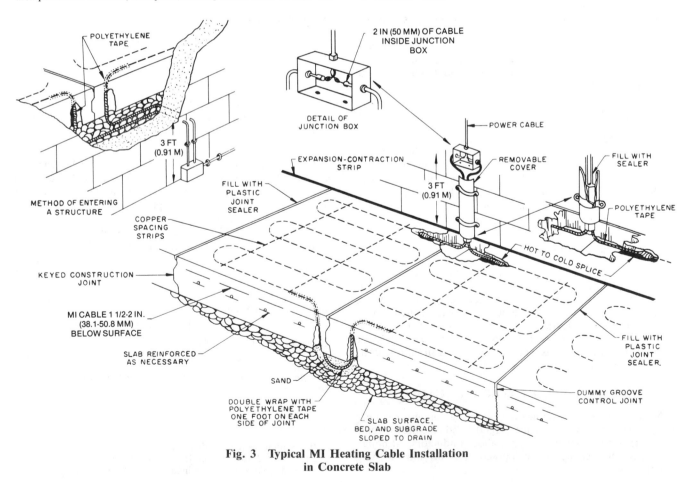

Fig. 3 Typical MI Heating Cable Installation in Concrete Slab

Table 8 MI Cold Lead Cables (Maximum Voltage - 600 V)

Single-Conductor Cable Current Capacity, A	A.W.G.	Two-Conductor Cable Current Capacity, A	A.W.G.
30	14	25	14/2
40	12	30	12/2
55	10	40	10/2
70	8	50	8/2
100	6	70	6/2
135	4	90	4/2
155	3		
180	2		
210	1		

in from the edge approximately 12 in. (305 mm) unless provisions have been made to prevent possible collapse of the edge.

7. Determine current (I) required for cable.

$$I = E/R, \text{ or } I = W/E$$

8. Choose *cold lead* cable as dictated by current requirements (see Table 8).

MI Cable Cold Lead

Every MI heating cable is factory fabricated with a non-heat-generating cold lead cable attached to the heating cable. The cold lead cable must be long enough to reach a dry location for termination, and of sufficient wire guage to comply with local and National Electric Code standards. Underwriters' Laboratories requires a minimum cold lead length of 7 in. (180 mm). Table 7 indicates the National Electric Code ratings of cold lead cables available.

MI cable junction boxes must be in a location where the box will remain dry, and where at least 3 ft (0.9 m) of cold lead cable is available at the end for any necessary future service (see Figure 3). Preferred junction box locations are indoors, on the side of a building, utility pole or wall, or inside a manhole on the wall. Boxes should have a hole in the bottom to drain condensation. Outdoor boxes should be completely watertight, except for the condensation drain hole. Where junction boxes are mounted below grade, the cable end seals must be coated with an epoxy to prevent moisture entry. Cable end seals should extend into the junction box far enough to allow removal of the end seal, if necessary.

Magnesium oxide, used as insulation in MI cable, is very hygroscopic. The only vulnerable part of the MI cable is the end seal. However, should moisture get into this end, it can be easily detected with a megohm meter, and driven out by applying a torch 2 to 3 ft (0.6 to 0.9 m) from the end and working the flame towards the end.

Installation

MI electric heating cable is installed in a concrete slab by pouring the slab in one or two pours. In single-pour application, the cable is hooked on top of the reinforcing mesh before the pour is started. In two-layer application, the cable is laid on top of the bottom structural slab and embedded in the finish layer. For a proper bond between the layers, the finish slab should be poured within 24 hours of the first, and a bonding grout should be applied. The finish slab should be at least 1.5 in. (38 mm) and not more than 2 in. (50 mm) thick.

The cable is uncoiled from reels back and forth in a sinuous fashion with pre-calculated spacing between passes. Prepunched copper spacing strips, nailed to the lower slab, are often used for uniform spacing.

The least expensive way to protect the MI cable that is installed in concrete from slab movement is to apply a film of silicone grease. Another method that increases the cost by 10 or 15% is a glass tape applied with an overlap of 0.25 to 0.5 in. (6 to 13 mm). This glass tape, which can be factory applied, gives the cable additional protection against puncture by sharp aggregate. A more expensive method is to nylon jacket the heat cable. This provides excellent physical protection to the cable without adding excessive insulation. Protective coatings also safeguard the cable from chemical corrosion that might be a problem in some areas.

Calcium chloride or other chloride additives should not be added to a concrete mix in winter, since chlorides are destructive to copper. Cinder or slag fill should also be avoided under snow melting panels. Where the *cold lead* cable is brought from the slab, it should be taped with polyvinyl chloride or polyethylene tape to protect it from corrosion from fertilizers and other ground attack. Within 2 ft (0.6 m) of the heating section, only polyethylene should be used, since heat may break down the polyvinyl chloride tapes. Underground, the leads should be installed in suitable conduits to protect them from physical damage.

To install MI cable in asphalt slabs, the cable is fixed in place on top of the base pour, a coat of bituminous binder is applied over the base and the cable, and a 6 in. (150 mm) × 6 in. (150 mm) × 20 guage mesh of material inert to copper and asphalt is laid over the cables to prevent them from floating in the topping. The top layer of asphalt over the cable should be 1.25 to 1.5 in. (32 to 38 mm) thick (see Figure 4).

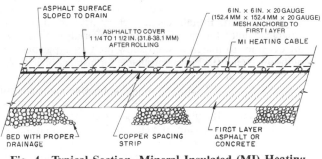

Fig. 4 Typical Section, Mineral Insulated (MI) Heating Cable in Asphalt

Testing

MI heating cables should be thoroughly tested before, during, and after installation to ensure they have not been damaged, either in transit or installation.

Because of the very hygroscopic nature of the magnesium oxide insulation, damage to the cable sheath is easily detectable with a 500-V field megohm meter. Cable insulation resistance should be noted on arrival. Any cable with insulation resistance less than 200 megohm (2×10^8 ohms) should not be used. Any cable that shows a marked loss of insulation resistance at the time of installation should be investigated for probable damage. Cable should also be checked for electrical continuity.

EMBEDDED WIRE SYSTEMS

Types of Wire and Mats

In an embedded system, the resistance elements may consist of a length of copper wire or alloy with a given amount of resistance. This element, when energized, will produce the required amount of heat. Witsken (1965) describes this system in further detail.

Elements are either solid-strand conductors or conductors spirally wrapped around a nonconducting fibrous material core (synthetic fiber, glass fiber, or asbestos). Both types are covered with an exterior layer of insulation such as polyvinyl chloride or silicone rubber.

The heat-generating portion of an element is the conductive core. The resistance is specified in ohms per linear foot of core. Alternately, a manufacturer may specify the wire in terms of watts per foot (W/m) of core, where the power is a function of ohms per foot (ohms/m) of core, applied voltage, and total length of core.

The selection of insulating materials for heating elements is influenced by the watt density, the application, and end use. Physical characteristics and chemical inertness are important qualities for an insulating shield.

Polyvinyl chloride is the lowest cost insulation and is widely used because of its inertness to oils, hydrocarbons, and alkalies. An outer covering of nylon is often added to increase physical strength and to withstand abrasion. Heat output of embedded polyvinyl chloride is limited to 5 watts per linear foot (16 W/m). Silicone rubber is not inert to oils or hydrocarbons. An additional covering—metal braid, conduit, or fiberglass braid—is needed for protection. This material can dissipate up to 10 watts per inear foot (33 W/m).

Lead can be used to encase the resistance element, insulated with glass fiber or asbestos. The lead sheath is then covered with a vinyl material. Output is limited to approximately 10 watts per linear foot (33 W/m) by the polyvinyl chloride jacket.

Teflon has good physical and electrical properties and can be operated at temperatures up to 500°F (260°C).

Low watt density (less than 10 watts per linear foot or 33 W/m) resistance wires may be attached to plastic or fiber mesh to produce a mat unit. Prefabricated factory assembled mats are available to embed in specified paving materials in a variety of watt densities to match desired snow melting capacities. Mat lengths up to 60 ft (18.3 m) are available for installation in asphalt sidewalks and driveways.

Pre-assembled mats are also available for stair steps, with appropriate tread melting section widths. Mats are seldom made larger than 60 ft^2 (5.6 m^2), since larger areas are more difficult to install both mechanically and electrically. Mats can be tailored to follow contours of curves and around objects by making a series of cuts, as shown in Figure 5. Extreme care should be ex-

ercised to prevent damage to the heater wire (or lead) insulation during this operation.

The mats should be installed between 1.25 and 1.5 in. (32 to 38 mm) below the finished surface of asphalt pavement and 1.5 to 2 in. (38 to 50 mm) below the surface of concrete pavement. Mats that are not damaged by hot asphalt compaction should be used for asphalt paving.

Embedded Wire Layout

Heating wires should be long enough to fit between the concrete slab dummy groove control or construction joints. Concrete forms may be inaccurate, so allow 2 to 4 in. (50 to 100 mm) between the edge of the concrete and the heating wire for clearance. Allow approximately 4 in. (100 mm) between the adjacent heating wires at the control or construction joints.

For asphalt, select the longest wire or largest heating mat that can be used on straight runs. Put the mats at least 12 in. (300 mm) in from the pavement edge. Adjacent mats must not overlap. Junction boxes should be located so that the maximum number of mats can be accommodated by each box. Wiring must conform to requirements of the National Electric Code. It is best to position junction boxes adjacent to or above the slab.

Installation

All Types

1. The wire or mats should be checked with an ohmmeter before, during, and after installation to prevent damage.
2. Temporarily lay the mats in position and install conduit feeders and junction boxes. Leave enough slack in the lead wires to permit temporary removal of the mats during the concrete or asphalt first pour. Ground all leads carefully using the grounding braids provided.
3. Secure all splices with approved crimped connectors or setscrew clamps. Tape all the power splices with plastic tape to make them waterproof. All junction boxes, fittings, and snug bushings must be approved for this class of application. The entire installation must be completely waterproof to ensure trouble-free operation.

Concrete

1. Each slab area between the expansion joints must be poured and finished individually. Pour the base slab and rough level to within 1.5 to 2 in. (38 to 50 mm) of the desired finish level. Place the mats in position and check for damage.
2. Pour the top slab over the mats while the rough slab is still wet and cover the mats to a depth of at least 1.5 in. (38 mm) but not more than 2 in. (50 mm).
3. Do not walk on or strike the mats with shovels or other tools.
4. Except for brief testing purposes, do not energize the mats until the concrete is completely cured.

Asphalt

1. Pour and level the base course. If units are to be installed on an existing asphalt surface, clean it thoroughly before placing the mats.
2. Apply a bituminous binder course to the lower base, install the mats, and apply a second binder coating over the mats. The finish topping over the mats should be applied in a continuous pour to a depth of 1.25 to 1.5 in. (32 to 38 mm). Note: do not dump a large mass of hot asphalt on the mats because the heat could damage the insulation.
3. Check all circuits with an ohmmeter to be sure no damage occurred during the installation.
4. Do not energize the system until the asphalt has completely hardened.

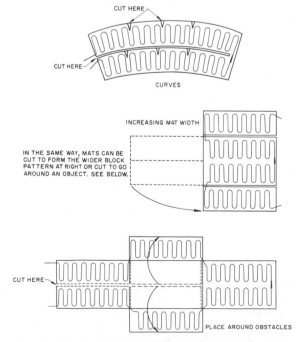

Fig. 5　Shaping Mats Around Curves and Obstacles

Snow Melting

INFRARED SNOW MELTING SYSTEMS

General Application

While overhead infrared systems can be designed specifically for snow melting and pavement drying, they are usually installed for the additional features they offer. Infrared systems provide comfort heating for people, which can be particularly useful at plant, office building, and hospital entrances or on loading docks. Infrared lamps produce higher lighting levels, which can aid in the protection, safety, and attraction of a facility. These additional features sometimes justify the somewhat higher cost of infrared systems.

Infrared fixtures can be installed under entrance canopies, along building facades, and on poles when no structure is near. Approved equipment is available for recess, surface, and pendant mounting.

Infrared Fixture Layout

The same infrared fixtures used for people comfort heating installations can be used for snow melting systems. The major differences in target area design and infrared fixture selection result from *horizontal* surfaces being emphasized in snow melting, whereas personal comfort emphasizes the need of the human body's *vertical* surfaces to be irradiated. When snow melting is the prime design concern, fixtures with narrow beam patterns confine the radiant energy within the target area for more efficient operation. Asymmetric reflector fixtures, which aim the radiation primarily to one side of the fixture center line, are often used near the side lines of the target area.

Infrared fixtures usually have a longer energy pattern parallel to the long dimension of the fixture than at right angles to it (Frier 1965). Therefore, fixtures should be mounted in a row parallel to the longest dimension of the area. Where the target area is 8 ft (2.4 m) or more in width, it is best to locate the fixtures in two or more parallel rows. This arrangement also gives better personnel comfort heating, since radiation is directed from both sides across the target area, providing a more favorable incident angle.

Radiation Spill

In theory, the most desirable energy distribution would be uniform throughout the snow melting target area at a density equal to the design requirement. Heating fixture reflector design determines the percentage of the total fixture radiant output scattered outside of its target area design pattern.

Even the best controlled beam fixture do not have a completely sharp cutoff at the beam edges. Therefore, if uniform distribution is maintained for the full width of the area, a considerable amount of radiant energy falls outside the target area. For this reason, infrared snow melting systems are designed so that the intensity on the pavement begins to decrease before reaching the edge of the area (Frier 1964). This design procedure minimizes stray radiant energy losses.

Figure 6 shows the watts per square foot (W/m²) values obtained in a sample snow melting problem (Frier 1965). The sample design average is 45 watts per square foot (484 W/m²). It is apparent that the central part of the target area has an incident watt density above the design average value and that the peripheral area has radiation densities below the average. Figure 6 shows how the watt density and distribution in the snow melting area depends on the number, wattage, beam pattern, mounting height, and relative position of the heaters to the pavement (Frier 1964).

With distributions similar to the one in Figure 6, snow begins to collect at the edges of the area as the energy requirements

INFRARED INTENSITY ON THE PAVEMENT FROM FOUR FIXTURES — WATTS PER SQ FT —														
14.7	16.0	19.75	23.7	25.5	27.5	28.2	28.0	28.2	27.5	25.5	23.7	19.75	16.0	14.7
23.7	24.8	28.7	31.7	35.7	38.2	38.5	39.4	38.5	38.2	35.7	31.7	28.7	24.8	23.7
25.7	31.7	37.5	42.7	46.4	49.4	52.2	53.0	52.2	49.4	46.4	42.7	37.5	31.7	25.7
28.2	34.3	42.8	46.7	51.2	55.7	58.5	63.0	58.5	55.7	51.2	46.7	42.8	34.3	28.2
28.2	34.3	42.8	46.7	51.2	55.7	58.5	63.0	58.5	55.7	51.2	46.7	42.8	34.3	28.2
25.7	31.7	37.5	42.7	46.4	49.4	52.2	53.0	52.2	49.4	46.4	42.7	37.5	31.7	25.7
23.7	24.8	28.7	31.7	35.7	38.2	38.5	39.4	38.5	38.2	35.7	31.7	28.7	24.8	23.7
14.7	16.0	19.75	23.7	25.5	27.5	28.2	28.0	28.2	27.5	25.5	23.7	19.75	16.0	14.7

Fig. 6 Typical Energy Levels per Unit Area for an Infrared Snow Melting System

for snow melting approach or exceed system capacity. As the snowfall lessens, the snow is melted again to the edges of the area and possibly beyond, if system operation is continued.

Target Area Watt Density

Theoretical target area wattage densities for snow melting with infrared systems are the same as those for commercial applications of embedded element systems; however, it should be emphasized that theoretical density values are for radiation incident to the pavement surface. Multiplying the recommended snow melting wattage density by the pavement area to obtain the total power input for the system does not result in good performance. An estimate, based on actual practice, to help estimate the total input wattage to be installed in the infrared fixtures above the target area is to multiply the commonly used snow melting watt densities shown in Table 6 by the target area; then, further increase the resulting product by a correction factor of 1.6. The resulting wattage compensates not only for the radiant efficiency involved, but also for the radiation falling outside the snow melting area. For small areas, or when the fixture mounting height exceeds 16 ft (4.9 m), the multiplying factor can be as large as 2.0; large areas with sides approaching equal lengths can have a factor of about 1.4.

The point-by-point method is the best way to calculate the heating fixture requirements for an installation. This method involves dividing the target area into a grid pattern of one foot (metre) squares, and cumulatively adding the watt per square foot (W/m²) radiant energy contributed by each infrared fixture on each square foot (metre) of grid (see Figure 6). The recommended radiant energy distribution of a given infrared fixture can be obtained from the equipment manufacturer and should be followed for that fixture size and placement.

System Operation

With infrared energy, the target area can be preheated to snow melting temperatures in 20 to 30 min, unless the air temperature is well below 20 °F (−7 °C), or wind velocity is high (Frier 1965). This fast warm-up time makes it unnecessary to turn on the system until snow begins to fall. The equipment can be turned on either manually or automatically with a snow detector. A timer is sometimes used to turn the system off 4 to 6 hours after the snow stops falling, to allow time to dry the pavement completely.

If the snow is allowed to accumulate before the infrared system is turned on, there will be a delay in clearing the pavement, as is the case with embedded systems. Since the infrared energy is absorbed in the top layer of snow rather than by the pavement surface, the length of time needed depends on the snow depth and atmospheric conditions. Generally, a system that maintains a clear pavement by melting 1 in. (25 mm) of snow an hour as it falls requires, under the same conditions, one hour to clear 1 in. (25 mm) of accumulated snow.

To ensure maximum efficiency, fixtures should be cleaned at least once a year, preferably at the beginning of the winter season. Other maintenance is minimal.

SNOW MELTING IN GUTTERS AND DOWNSPOUTS

Both MI cable and insulated wire are used to prevent heavy snow and ice accumulation on roof overhangs and to prevent ice dams from forming in gutters and downspouts (Lawrie 1966). Figure 7 shows a typical insulted wire layout to protect a roof edge and downspout. Wire or MI cable for this purpose is generally rated approximately 6 to 16 watts per linear foot (65 to 172 W/m²) and about 2.5 ft (0.76 m) of wire is installed per linear foot (m) of roof edge. One foot (m) heated wire length per linear foot (m) of gutter or downspout is usually adequate.

If the roof edge or gutters (or both) are heated, downspouts must also be heated to carry away water from melted snow and ice. A heated length of wire is dropped inside the downspout to the bottom, even if it is underground, using weights, if necessary.

Lead wires should be spliced or plugged into the main power line in a waterproof junction box, and a ground wire should be installed from a downspout or gutter to a good electrical ground.

Manual switch control is generally used, although a protective thermostat, sensing outdoor temperature, should be used to prevent system operation above 40 °F (4.4 °C).

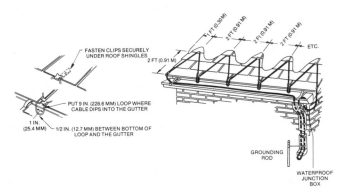

Fig. 7   Typical Insulated Wire Layout to Protect a Roof Edge and Downspout

CONTROL

Hot Fluid Systems

Snow melting systems can be controlled either manually or automatically. Manual operation is strictly two-position control, either 0 to 100% operation, and has the disadvantage of requiring the owner to turn on the system before a snowfall early enough for the system to attain the temperature needed to melt the snow. If the system is not turned on until the snow starts

falling, it may not melt snow effectively for several hours, giving additional snowfall a chance to accumulate and increasing the time needed to melt the area.

Automatic controls are available that either sense the presence of snow or the temperature of the walk or driveway. Systems with automatic snow-sensing controls operate only when snow is present. Systems with temperature-sensing controls operate any time the walk surface temperature approaches freezing.

Electric Systems

A simple on-off switch normally is used to activate electric snow melting equipment, and a pilot light indicates when the system is on. For heavy current loads, the on-off switch controls a magnetic contactor, which, in turn, *makes or breaks* the snow melting circuit. The operator turns the system *on* in anticipation of snow, and *off* when the surface snow is cleared. The control system should have an outdoor thermostat that turns the system off when the outdoor ambient temperature rises above 35 °F (1.7 °C), as automatic protection against accidental operation in summer.

For critical applications (see Table 6), the high watt density capacity is needed only during extreme snow conditions. To limit the energy waste from this excess capacity during normal and light snow conditions, it is common to include a low temperature range thermostat, with a remote slab temperature sensing bulb, in the control circuit. The remote temperature sensing bulb is installed midway between cable or wire runs or between mats in the slab, and the thermostat setting is adjusted above the freezing point, at about 40 °F (4.4 °C). Thus, during mild weather snow conditions, the system is automatically cycled on and off as the slab temperature at the sensing bulb reaches 40 °F (4.4 °C).

General

There are several fully automatic control systems. These systems provide a means of detecting precipitation and simultaneously sensing air temperature. Chapter 51 has basic information on control equipment, such as thermostats, and fundamentals on control circuits.

REFERENCES

Chapman, W.P. 1952. Design of Snow Melting Systems. *Heating and Ventilating,* April, p. 95, and November, p. 88.

Chapman, W.P. 1955. Are Thermal Stresses a Problem in Snow Melting Systems? *Heating, Piping and Air Conditioning,* June, p. 104, and August, p. 92.

Chapman, W.P. 1956. Calculating the Heat Requirements of a Snow Melting System. *Air Conditioning, Heating and Ventilating,* September through August 1957.

Chapman, W.P., and Katunich, S. 1956. Heat Requirements of Snow Melting Systems. ASHRAE *Transactions,* Vol. 62, p. 359.

Frier, J.P. 1964. Design Requirements for Infrared Snow Melting Systems. *Illuminating Engineering,* October, p. 686. Also discussion, December.

Frier, J.P. 1965. Snow Melting with Infrared Lamps. *Plant Engineering,* October, p. 150.

Gordon, P.B. 1950. Antifreeze Protection for Snow Melting Systems. *Heating, Piping and Air Conditioning Contractors National Association Official Bulletin,* February, p. 21.

Hydronics Institute, The. 1968. Snow Melting Calculation and Installation Guide. Berkeley Heights, NJ.

Lawrie, R.J. 1966. Electric Snow Melting Systems. *Electrical Construction and Maintenance,* March, p. 110.

Witsken, C.H. 1965. Snow Melting with Electric Wire. *Plant Engineering,* September, p. 129.

CHAPTER 56

EVAPORATIVE AIR COOLING

EVAPORATIVE cooling, using current technology and available equipment, is an energy-efficient and cost-effective means of cooling. Applications are found for comfort cooling in commercial and institutional buildings, in addition to the traditional industrial applications for improvement of worker comfort in mills, foundries, power plants, and other hot operations. There are several types of apparatus that cool by evaporating water directly in the air stream. These include (1) evaporative coolers, (2) spray-filled and wetted-surface air washers, (3) sprayed coil units, and (4) humidifiers. Interest has increased in equipment (for indirect evaporative cooling) that combine the evaporative cooling effect in a secondary airstream with heat exchange to produce cooling without adding moisture to the primary airstream.

Indirect evaporative cooling equipment was once considered too expensive when compared with assembly line refrigerated equipment, but energy conservation and increasing energy costs have revived interest in both indirect and direct evaporative cooling systems.

Evaporative cooling reduces the dry-bulb temperature and provides a better environment for human occupancy and farm livestock. Evaporative cooling is also used to improve products grown or manufactured by controlling dry-bulb temperatures and/or relative humidity levels.

When temperature or humidity must be controlled within narrow limits, mechanical refrigeration can be combined in stages with evaporative cooling or used as a backup system. Evaporative cooling equipment, including unitary equipment and air washers, is covered in Chapter 4 of the 1983 EQUIPMENT Volume.

SYSTEM DESIGN

Two types of systems use evaporative cooling: (1) systems that improve the environment for people, animals, or processes, without attempting to control ambient temperature or humidity (spot cooling); and (2) systems designed to improve ambient conditions in a space (area cooling).

In a hot environment, where ambient heat control is difficult or impractical, cooling is accomplished by passing below-skin-temperature air over the body. Evaporative coolers are suited to this purpose. The performance of evaporative cooling is directly related to climatic conditions. The entering wet-bulb temperature governs the final dry-bulb temperature of the air discharged from a direct evaporative cooler. The capability of the direct evaporative cooler is determined by how much the dry-bulb temperature exceeds the wet-bulb temperature. The performance of indirect evaporative coolers is also limited by the wet-bulb temperature of the secondary airstream.

Indirect systems that use room exhaust as secondary air or incorporate precooled air in the secondary airstream may produce leaving dry-bulb temperatures approaching the wet-bulb temperature of the secondary airstream.

The direct evaporative cooling process is an adiabatic exchange of heat. For water to evaporate, heat must be added. The heat is supplied by the air into which water is evaporated. The dry-bulb temperature is lowered, and sensible cooling results. The amount of heat removed from the air equals the amount of heat absorbed by the water evaporated as heat of vaporization. If water is recirculated in the evaporative cooling apparatus, the water temperature in the reservoir will approach the wet-bulb temperature of the air entering the process. By definition, an adiabatic process is one during which no heat is added or extracted from the system. The initial and final conditions of an adiabatic process fall on a line of constant total heat (enthalpy), which nearly coincides with a line of constant wet-bulb temperatures.

The maximum reduction in dry-bulb temperature is the difference between the entering air dry-bulb and wet-bulb temperatures. If the air is cooled to the wet-bulb temperature, the air becomes saturated and the process is 100% effective. System effectiveness is the depression of the dry-bulb temperature of the air leaving the apparatus divided by the difference between the dry bulb and wet-bulb temperatures of the entering air. Evaporative cooling is less than 100% effective, although systems may be 85 to 90% effective, or even better.

When a direct evaporative cooling unit cannot provide the desired conditions, there are alternatives that can satisfy system requirements and still be energy effective and economical to operate. The recirculating water that supplies the evaporative cooling unit can be chilled by mechanical refrigeration to provide lower leaving wet-bulb and dry-bulb temperatures and lower humidity. This arrangement will reduce operating costs by as much as 25 to 40% compared with the cost of using mechanical refrigeration only. Indirect evaporative pre-cooling applied as a first stage, upstream from a second direct evaporative cooling stage, makes it possible to reduce both the entering dry-bulb and wet-bulb temperatures before the air enters the direct evaporative cooling unit. Indirect evaporative cooling systems may save as much as 60 to 75% or more of the total cost of operating a mechanical refrigeration system to produce the same cooling effect. Systems may combine indirect evaporative cooling, direct evaporative cooling, and mechanical refrigeration—or any two of these processes.

The psychrometric chart in Figure 1 illustrates what happens when air is passed through a direct evaporative cooling unit. In the example, assume an entering condition of 95 °F dry-bulb and 75 °F wet-bulb. The initial difference is 20 °F (95 − 75 = 20). If the effectiveness is 80%, the depression is 16 °F dry bulb or (0.80 · 20/100). The dry-bulb temperature leaving the evaporative cooler is 79 °F (95 − 16 = 79). In the adiabatic

The preparation of this chapter is assigned to TC 5.7, Evaporative Cooling.

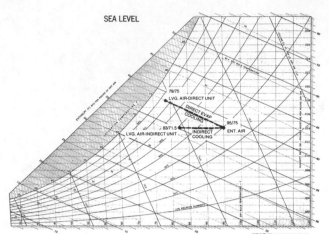

Fig. 1   Effect of Direct Evaporative Cooling System

evaporative cooler, it is assumed that only a portion of the water recirculated is evaporated and that the water supply is recirculated. The recirculated water will reach an equilibrium temperature that is approximately the same as the wet-bulb temperature of the entering air.

The performance of an indirect evaporative cooling system can be shown on a psychrometric chart also. Many manufacturers of indirect evaporative cooling equipment use a similar definition of effectiveness as used for a direct evaporative cooler to describe the cooling effect in the primary airstream. The term Performance Factor (P.F.) is also used. In indirect evaporative cooling, the cooling process in the primary airstream follows a line of constant moisture content (constant dew point). Performance factor (or effectiveness) is the dry-bulb depression in the primary airstream divided by the difference between the entering dry-bulb temperature of the primary airstream minus the entering wet-bulb temperature of the secondary air. Depending on heat exchanger design and relative air quantities of primary and secondary air, effectiveness ratings may be as high as 85%.

Using the previous example, assuming an effectiveness (P.F.) of 60%, and assuming both primary air and secondary air enter the apparatus at the outdoor condition of 95 °F db and 75 °F wb, the dry-bulb depression is 0.60 (95 − 75) = 12 °F. The dry-bulb temperature leaving the indirect evaporative cooling process is (95 − 12) = 83 °F. Since the process cools without adding moisture, the wet-bulb temperature is also reduced. Plotting the psychrometric chart shows the final wet-bulb temperature to be 71.5 °F. Since both the wet-bulb and the dry-bulb temperatures in the indirect evaporative cooling process are reduced, indirect evaporative cooling can be used as a substitute for a portion of the refrigeration load in many applications.

APPLICATIONS

Commercial

Single stage and multi-staged systems can provide evaporative cooling for comfort and for a wide variety of industrial processes and agricultural applications. Indirect cooling does not increase the humidity ratio in the primary air stream, so it can reduce the sensible heat load on a refrigerated coil. This effect allows the size of the refrigeration system to be reduced, which lowers energy use and operating costs.

The temperature within laundries can be reduced to 5 to 10 °F (3 to 6 °C) below the outdoor temperature using a single-stage

evaporative cooler. With only fan ventilation, laundries usually exceed the outdoor temperature by 10 °F (6 °C) or more.

Indoor swimming pools may be cooled effectively using indirect or "regenerative" evaporative cooling. Indoor temperature and humidity are kept high during summer to increase comfort out of the water and to reduce energy loss from the pool water water surface.

Large motors operating at full load in higher-than-rated ambient temperatures require ventilation from external cooling sources. Use of evaporative cooling can reduce the quantity of ventilation air required and can permit overloading within the motor service factor. Transformer capacity can also be increased by using evaporative cooling.

Gas turbine-driven generators have capacity output related to the temperature of the incoming air. A reduction of as much as 20% in output may result from an increase in air temperature of 60 to 100 °F (33 to 56 °C). Evaporative cooling to supply cooler incoming air is widely used in this application. Care must be used to prevent any entrainment of free moisture in the supply air to avoid damage to the turbine.

Agricultural

The outdoor air temperature in animal shelters can be reduced, regardless of the climatic conditions. Farm applications include milking parlors, poultry houses, stalls and stockpens, pig farrowing houses, and other general cooling and ventilation of farm buildings. These applications are discussed in more detail in Chapter 37 of this Volume.

Produce storage can be improved considerably through the use of evaporative cooling. High humidity, lower temperature, and fresh air to provide adequate oxygen for respiration and for carrying away the waste products of living processes can be achieved. Potato storage, apple storage, and citrus storage are all suitable applications for evaporative cooling. Chapters 16, 17, and 18 of the 1986 REFRIGERATION Volume provide detailed information about environmental control during handling and storage of deciduous tree and vine fruits, citrus, bananas, tropical fruits, and vegetables.

Greenhouse cooling during hot weather is essential for developing high quality crops. Temperature and relative humidity can be controlled in the presence of strong radiation with evaporative cooling. Greenhouse design is covered in Chapter 37 of this Volume.

WEATHER CONDITIONS

The effectiveness of evaporative cooling depends on weather conditions. System design is affected by the prevailing outdoor dry-bulb and wet-bulb temperatures, as well as the application of the system. For example, a simple residential direct evaporative cooling system, with an effectiveness of 80%, will provide satisfactory room conditions (given an adequate quantity of outdoor supply air) throughout the cooling season in areas such as Reno, Nevada, where the 1% design dry-bulb and mean coincident wet-bulb temperatures are 96 °F and 61 °F (35.6 °C and 16.1 °C). Supply air temperature can be 68 °F (20 °C) at this condition, which may be satisfactory for a residential application with no internal heat gain. In the same location, additional cooling effect can be gained, if required by the nature of the load, by the addition of an indirect evaporative pre-cooling stage, which lowers the temperature (both dry-bulb and wet-bulb) entering the direct evaporative cooling stage and, consequently, lowers the supply air temperature.

In a geographic location such as Atlanta, Georgia, with design temperatures of 94 °F and 74 °F (34.4 °C and 23.3 °C), the same direct evaporative cooler could supply only 78 °F (25.6 °C). This would be reduced to 72.4 °F (22.4 °C) by the addition of a 65% effective indirect evaporative pre-cooling stage (Supple 1982).

Even in locations with relatively high design wet-bulb temperatures, indirect evaporative pre-cooling added to refrigerated cooling systems can significantly reduce the energy consumed and lower operating cost during intermediate seasons. In systems using large proportions of outside air, it can also lower costs. Size reduction in the refrigeration machinery may also be possible.

ECONOMIC CONSIDERATIONS

Design of evaporative cooling systems and sizing of equipment should be based on the load requirements of the application and local dry-bulb and wet-bulb design conditions, which may be found in Chapter 24 of the 1985 FUNDAMENTALS Volume, "Weather Data and Design Considerations."

Total energy use for a specific application during a set period may be forecast by using annual weather data. Dry-bulb and mean coincident wet-bulb temperatures, with the hours of occurrence, can be summarized and used in a modified bin procedure. The calculations must reflect the hours of occupancy. Results may vary for different types of buildings, even though the same weather station data may be used.

A common source of weather data is the 60-station Test Reference Year (TRY) weather data, published by the National Climatic Weather Center. Other sources of weather data are Air Force Manual 88-29, in which data is tabulated for most major cities and military bases in the United States; and an ASHRAE set of computer floppy disks covering a bin method analysis of weather data titled, "Bin and Degree Hour Weather for Simplified Energy Calculations."

When comparing systems, the cost analysis should include the annual energy reduction at the applicable electrical rate, plus the anticipated energy cost escalation over the expected life of the system.

Reducing air conditioning kilowatt draw is even more important in areas with "racheted" demand rates (Scofield and Deschamps 1980). In these areas, the demand rate is not set monthly. A summer month with a heavy cooling peak energy demand can set the demand rate for the entire year.

Many areas have "time of day" electrical metering as an incentive to use energy during "off-peak" hours when energy rates are the lowest. Thermal storage using ice banks or chilled water storage vessels may be used as part of a multistage evaporative-refrigerated cooling system to combine the energy-saving advantages of evaporative cooling with off-peak savings accomplished using thermal storage. In addition to the cost savings because of off-peak energy rates, thermal storage systems may actually save energy because the refrigeration equipment operates at a time when the ambient temperature and resulting condensing temperatures are lower (Eskra 1980).

PSYCHROMETRICS

Figure 2 shows the two-stage process applied to nine western cities in the United States. The entering conditions to the first-stage indirect unit are at the recommended 1% design dry-bulb/wet-bulb temperatures from the 1985 FUNDAMENTALS Volume. The effectiveness ratings are 60% for the first (indirect) stage and 90% for the second (direct) stage. The leaving air temperatures range from 52 to 70°F (11 to 21°C) and are saturated (80% and higher). Figure 3 projects these second-stage supply temperatures (based on a 95% room sensible heat factor: room sensible heat/room total heat) to a room condition at 78°F (25.6°C) dry-bulb temperature. Given a 1% entering condition in the six cities shown, room conditions are maintained within the comfort zone without a refrigerated third stage.

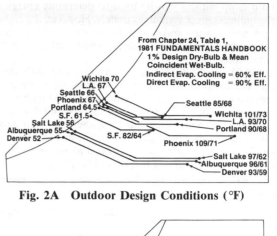

Fig. 2A   Outdoor Design Conditions (°F)

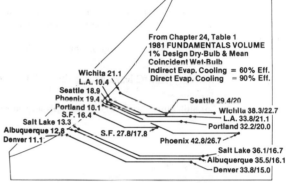

Fig. 2B   Outdoor Design Conditions (°C)

However, Figures 2 and 3 point out the need to consider the following factors carefully:

1. As the room sensible heat factor increases, the required supply air temperature decreases to maintain a given room condition.
2. As the supply air temperature increases, the supply air quantity increases, resulting in higher air-side system initial cost and increased supply air fan power.
3. A decrease in the required room dry-bulb temperature causes an increase in the supply air quantity. At a given room sensible heat factor, a decrease in room dry-bulb temperature may cause the relative humidity to exceed the comfort zone.
4. The suggested 1% entering air (dry bulb/mean wet-bulb) conditions to the system are only one consideration. Partial load conditions must also be considered, along with the effect (extent and duration) of spike wet-bulb temperatures. Mean wet-

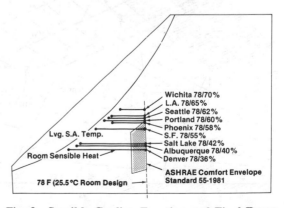

Fig. 3   Sensible Cooling Function and Final Room Design Conditions

bulb temperatures can be used to determine energy use of the indirect/direct system accurately. However, the higher wet-bulb temperature spikes should be considered to determine the operating results and affected room temperatures at these conditions.

An ideal condition for the maximum use with minimum energy consumption of a two- and three-stage indirect/direct system is a room sensible heat factor of 90% and higher, a supply air temperature of 60°F (16°C), and 78°F (26°C) dry-bulb room temperature. In many cases, third-stage refrigeration is required to ensure satisfactory dry-bulb temperature and relative humidity.

Refrigeration capacity is determined as in the following example. The calculations are reflected in Figure 4.

Example: Assume the following:

1. Supply air quantity = 24,000 cfm (11 300 L/s), supply air temperature = 60°F (16°C).
2. Design condition = 99°F (37°C) dry-bulb and 68°F (20°C) wet-bulb
3. Effectiveness of indirect unit = 60%, effectiveness direct unit = 90%
4. Indirect unit performance:

    99 − (99 − 68)(0.60) = 80.4°F leaving dry-bulb (61.8°F wet-bulb)

    In SI:

    37 − (37 − 20)(0.60) = 26.8°C leaving dry-bulb (16.6°C wet-bulb)

    Direct unit performance:
    80.4 − (80.4 − 61.8)(0.90) = 63.7°F dry-bulb supply air temperature

In SI:

26.8 − (26.8 − 16.6)(0.90) = 17.6°C dry-bulb supply air temperature

5. Calculate booster refrigeration capacity to drop the supply air temperature from 63.7°F (17.6°C) to the required 60°F (16°C) supply air temperature.

Coil located ahead of direct unit:

$$\frac{(60)(h_2 - h_1)(\text{Supply Air, cfm})}{\text{Specific volume dry air @ lvg. air (1st stage)}} = \text{Btu/h cooling}$$

With numeric values of enthalpies h_1 and h_2 in Btu/lb and the specific volume of air in ft^3/lb dry air, taken from the ASHRAE Psychrometric Chart No. 1, the cooling load is calculated as follows:

$$\frac{(60)(27.6 - 25.5)(24,000)}{(13.78)} = 219,400 \text{ Btu/h (18.3 tons)}$$

In SI:

$$\frac{(h_2 - h_1)(\text{Supply Air, L/s})}{1000 \cdot \text{Specific volume dry air @ lvg. air (1st stage)}}$$

$$= \text{kW cooling}$$

With the numeric values of enthalpies h_1 and h_2 in kJ/kg and the specific volume of air in m^3/kg dry air, taken from the ASHRAE Psychrometric Chart No. 1 in SI units, the cooling load is calculated as follows:

$$\frac{46.5 - 41.6)(11\ 300)}{(1000)(0.861)} = 64.3 \text{ kW cooling}$$

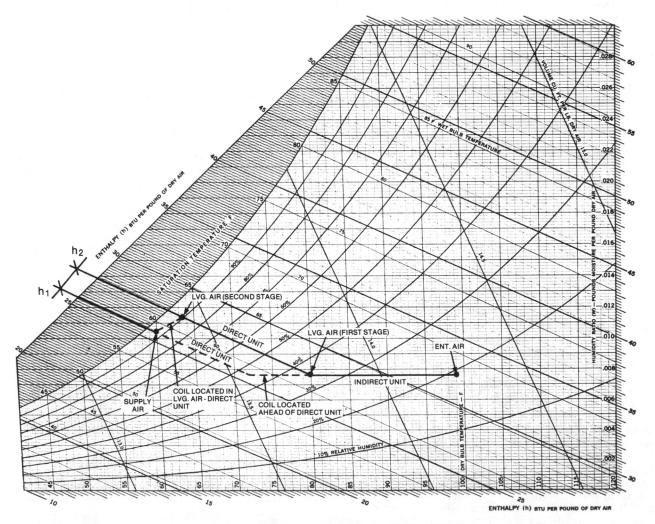

Fig. 4   Calculation of Third-Stage Refrigeration

Coil located in the leaving air of the direct unit:

$$\frac{(60)(27.8 - 25.7)(24,000)}{(13.43)} = 225,000 \text{ Btu/h (18.8 tons)}$$

In SI:

$$\frac{(46.8 - 42.0)(11\ 300)}{(1000)(0.829)} = 65.4 \text{ kW cooling}$$

The above calculations can be used, depending on the location of the booster coil, to determine third-stage refrigeration capacity and the selection of the cooling coil.

By using this example, refrigeration sizing can be compared to a conventional, refrigerated system without staged evaporative cooling. Assuming mixed air conditions to the coil of 81°F (27.2°C) dry-bulb and 66.5°F (19.2°C) wet-bulb, and the same 60°F (15.6°C) dry-bulb supply air as shown in Figure 2, the refrigerated capacity is:

$$\frac{(60)(31.1 - 25.7)(24,000)}{(13.31)} = 584,200 \text{ Btu/h (48.7 tons)}$$

In SI:

$$\frac{(54.6 - 42.0)(11\ 300)}{(1000)(0.832)} = 171.1 \text{ kW cooling}$$

This represents an increase of 30.4 tons (106.8 kW). The staged evaporative effect reduces the required refrigeration by 62.4%.

INDIRECT EVAPORATIVE PRE-COOLING IN THE OUTDOOR AIR SYSTEM

Since there is no increase in absolute humidity in the primary airstream, indirect evaporative cooling is well-suited to pre-cooling the air entering a refrigerated coil. The cooling effect provided by the upstream indirect evaporative equipment is a sensible cooling load reduction to the downstream refrigerated coil and compression apparatus. This reduces the size of the required refrigeration system, as well as reducing energy and operating costs. By contrast, direct evaporative cooling equipment will exchange latent heat for sensible heat, increasing the latent load on the coil in proportion to the sensible cooling achieved. The enthalpy of the air entering the coil is not changed.

The kilowatt per ton (kW cooling/kW power input) of cooling effect is substantially lower with indirect evaporative cooling than with conventional refrigerated equipment. The indirect equipment selected must result in only a minimal addition of static pressure loss in the primary air system. The added static pressure loss increases the primary air-fan motor power, and the total effect on the system must be considered, even when continuous cooling is not required. Static pressure loss for a nominal selection may be as low as 0.2 in. of water (50 Pa), which represents a minimal addition to supply fan power required. In addition, the equipment also may require additional energy for water pumping and for moving secondary air across the evaporative surfaces.

The pre-cooling configuration is shown in Figure 5. The primary air side of the indirect unit is positioned at the intake to the refrigerated cooling coil. The secondary air to the unit can come from outdoor ambient air or room exhaust air. Exhaust air from the space may have a lower wet-bulb temperature than outdoor ambient, depending on climate, time of year, and space latent load. Latent cooling may be possible in the primary air stream using room exhaust air as secondary air. This may occur if the dew point temperature of the primary air is above the exhaust (secondary air) wet-bulb temperature. If this is possible, provision to drain the water condensed from the primary airstream may be necessary.

In many areas, an indirect precooler can satisfy more than one-half of the annual cooling load. For example, a study by

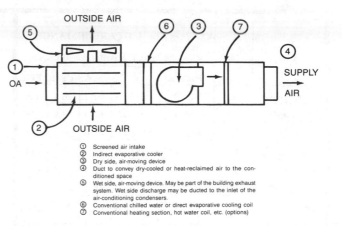

① Screened air intake
② Indirect evaporative cooler
③ Dry side, air-moving device
④ Duct to convey dry-cooled or heat-reclaimed air to the conditioned space
⑤ Wet side, air-moving device. May be part of the building exhaust system. Wet side discharge may be ducted to the inlet of the air-conditioning condensers.
⑥ Conventional chilled water or direct evaporative cooling coil
⑦ Conventional heating section, hot water coil, etc. (options)

Fig. 5   Indirect Evaporative Pre-Cooling Configuration

Supple (1982) showed that 30% of the annual cooling ton-hours for Chicago can be accomplished by indirect evaporative pre-cooling. Indirect evaporative pre-cooling systems using exhaust air as the secondary air may be equally effective in a warm, humid climate as in drier areas.

INDIRECT EVAPORATIVE PRE-COOLING IN THE MIXED AIR SYSTEM

Indirect evaporative cooling can also save energy in systems that use a mixture of return air and outside air. The apparatus configuration is similar to Figure 5, except that a mixing section with outside-air and return-air dampers is added upstream of the indirect pre-cooling section. Outdoor would be used as secondary air for the indirect evaporative cooler.

A typical indirect evaporative pre-cooling stage can reduce the dry-bulb temperature by as much as 60% to 80% of the difference between the entering dry-bulb temperature and the wet-bulb temperature of the secondary air. When the dry-bulb temperature of the mixed air is more than a few degrees above the wet-bulb temperature of the secondary airstream, indirect evaporative pre-cooling of the mixed airstream may reduce the amount of refrigerated cooling required.

The pre-cooling contribution depends on the differential between mixed air dry-bulb temperature and secondary air wet-bulb temperature. As mixture temperature increases, or as secondary air wet-bulb decreases, the pre-cooling contribution becomes more significant. In systems with unducted returns in the ceiling plenum spaces, heat added in the return air by lighting and roof loads can be rejected in the indirect evaporative pre-cooling stage.

In Variable Air Volume Systems, a decrease in supply air volume, during periods of reduced load, results in lower air velocity through the evaporative cooler. This increases the equipment effectiveness. Lower static pressure loss reduces the energy consumed by the supply fan motor.

INDIRECT/DIRECT EVAPORATIVE COOLING SYSTEMS (TWO AND THREE STAGE) WITH BOOSTER REFRIGERATION

Staged evaporative systems can totally cool office buildings, schools, gymnasiums, department stores, restaurants, factory space, and other types of buildings. These systems can control room dry-bulb temperature and relative humidity, even though one stage is a direct evaporative cooling stage. In many cases, booster refrigeration is not required. One study (Supple 1982) showed that even in "higher humidity" areas with a 1% mean wet-bulb design temperature of 75°F (24°C), 42% of the an-

INDIRECT/DIRECT SYSTEM PERFORMANCE

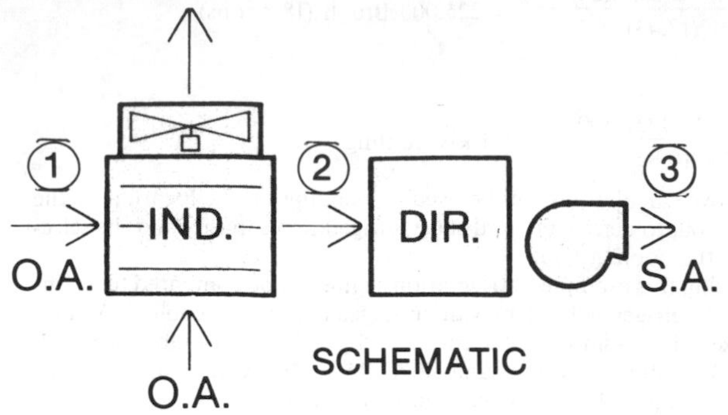

City	Elev. Ft	①O.A. Design Temp. DB/WB	I/D PERFORMANCE 0.733 Watts/CFM (S.A.)			
			② ③S.A.	EER	EUC	
Los Angeles	312	93/70	79.2/65.8	67.1	26.4	30%
San Francisco	8	82/64	71.2/60.2	61.3	34.9	23%
Seattle	14	85/68	74.8/64.5	68.6	24.2	33%
Albuquerque	5310	96/61	75.0/52.9	55.1	44.0	18%
Denver	5283	93/59	72.6/50.5	52.7	47.6	17%
Salt Lake City	4220	97/62	76.0/54.0	56.2	42.4	19%
Phoenix	1117	109/71	86.2/64.0	66.2	27.7	29%
El Paso	3918	100/64	78.4/57.2	59.3	37.8	21%
Santa Rosa	167	99/68	80.4/61.6	63.5	31.7	25%
Spokane	2357	93/64	75.6/57.8	59.6	37.4	21%
Boise	2842	96/65	77.4/58.5	60.4	36.2	22%
Billings	3567	94/64	76.0/57.5	59.4	37.7	21%
Portland, Or.	57	90/68	76.8/63.5	64.8	29.7	27%
Sacramento	17	101/70	82.4/64.0	65.8	28.3	28%
Fresno	326	102/70	82.8/63.8	65.7	28.4	28%
Austin	597	100/74	84.4/69.5	71.0	20.6	39%

SCHEMATIC

①
O.A. → —IND.— → ② → DIR. → ③ → S.A.

O.A.

Outdoor air design condition: 1% dry-bulb/mean coincident wet-bulb,

EER = (Energy Efficiency Ratio) BTU cooling output per watt of electrical input. Comparison base to conventional system 60° S.A.; 25° ΔT.

EUC = Energy Use Comparison to a conventional system with an EER of 8.

SA = Supply Air temperature leaving I/D unit at 1% design condition.

I/D efficiency: indirect = 60% (DB − WB x .6); direct = 90% (DB − WB x .9).

Note: Sea level psychrometric chart used. 5000 ft elev. will increase S.A. temperature 3 to 4%.

Fig. 6   Indirect/Direct Two-Stage System Performance

nual cooling ton-hours can be satisfied by two-stage evaporative cooling. Refrigerated cooling need supply only 58% of the ton-hours.

Figure 6 shows indirect/direct two-stage system performance for 16 cities. Performance is based on 60% effectiveness of the indirect stage and 90% for the direct stage. Supply air temperatures (leaving the direct stage), at the 1% design dry-bulb/mean wet-bulb condition range from 52.7°F (11.5°C) to 71°F (21.7°C). Energy use ranges from 17 to 39% compared to conventional refrigerated equipment. Any of these locations will show significant energy reduction with two- or three-stage systems.

Figure 7 shows the two-stage system configurations with an economizer cycle, optional third-stage cooling, and power return/exhaust fan. In this configuration, the indirect unit is positioned with air pre-cooling (stage one), direct evaporative cooling (stage two), and booster refrigerated cooling coil (stage three). The refrigerated coil can be located upstream or downstream from the direct evaporative cooling stage. The diagram shows the supply fan located upstream of the indirect cooler. This allows fan-generated heat to be removed by the indirect stage.

Figure 4 shows the psychrometric process for the two-stage and three-stage systems; h_2 minus h_1 represents the cooling requirement of the refrigerated third stage.

The economizer section with return air and outside air-mixing dampers would be used for systems that require recirculation of room air. A heating section can be included in the supply air system when required for year-round operation or as a means of control.

System Operation

When cooling is required, the control dampers introduce outdoor air mixing with return air to maintain a mixed air temperature. When the outdoor temperature increases and additional cooling is required, the indirect evaporative cooling stage

is operated to cool the air sensibly (no moisture added), and both the dry-bulb and wet-bulb temperatures are reduced. On further need for cooling, the direct evaporative cooling stage cools the air adiabatically. If a lower supply air temperature is required, or if required by room humidity control, a booster refrigerated third-stage cooling coil can be included. Variations in the sequencing of the stages are sometimes used.

During the heating cycle, the mixing dampers would be set for return of recirculated room air with introduction of a minimum outside air quantity to satisfy ventilation requirements. The heating apparatus is operated when required. The direct evaporative cooling stage pump can be operated during the heating season for humidification.

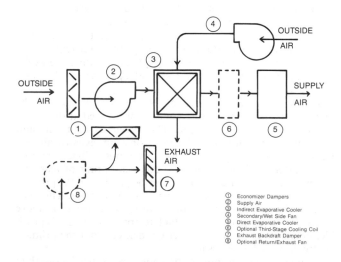

① Economizer Dampers
② Supply Air
③ Indirect Evaporative Cooler
④ Secondary/Wet Side Fan
⑤ Direct Evaporative Cooler
⑥ Optional Third-Stage Cooling Coil
⑦ Exhaust Backdraft Damper
⑧ Optional Return/Exhaust Fan

Fig. 7   Two-Stage System with Third-Stage Option

Table 1 Data for Applying Three-Stage Systems

Bin No.	1	2	3	4	5
1-db/Mean wb, °F (°C)[a]	103/70 (39.4/21.1)	95/68 (35.0/20.0)	85/66 (29.4/18.9)	75/63 (23.9/17.2)	65/58 (18.3/14.4)
2-Operating hours[b]	15	182	367	525	613
3-EAT(db) °F (°C)[c]	103 (39.4)	95 (35.0)	85 (29.4)	75 (23.9)	65 (18.3)
4-LAT(First Stage), °F (°C)[d]	83.2/63.8 (28.4/17.7)	78.8/62.5 (23.8/16.9)	73.6/62 (23.1/16.7)	67.8/60.2 (19.9/15.7)	60.8/56.5 (16/13.6)
5-LAT (Third Stage), °F (°C)[e]	70.5 (21.4)	69.0 (20.6)	65.0 (18.3)	63.5 (17.5)	not req.
6-ΔT(Third Stage), °F (°C)[f]	12.7 (7.1)	9.8 (5.4)	8.6 (4.8)	4.3 (2.4)	0 (0)
7-Third Stage, Cooling Tons (kW)[g]	34.3 (120.6)	26.5 (93.2)	23.7 (83.3)	11.6 (40.8)	0 (0)
8-Third Stage, Ton-Hrs (GJ)[h]	515 (6.5)	4823 (61.0)	8514 (107.8)	6090 (77.0)	0 (0)
9-kWh, Evap. Stages[i]	59	710	1431	2048	1839
10-kWh, Third Stage[j]	618	5788	10,217	7308	0
11 kWh, S.A. Fan[k]	195	2388	4771	6825	7969
12-Total kWh[l]	872	8864	16,419	16,181	9808

Total Annual Cooling Energy Consumption = 52,144 kWh[m]

Notes:
[a]Modified Bin TRY weather data.
[b]System operates 0700-1800, 5 days per week.
[c]Temperature entering indirect unit.
[d]Indirect unit cooling effectiveness is 60%. LAT = EAT − (0.6)(db − wb) Plot on psychrometric chart as total sensible cooling.
[e]For refrigerated coil located upstream of direct unit, determine required third stage leaving temperature by plotting on a psychrometric chart as the intersection of an extension of the indirect stage sensible cooling line with the enthalpy line corresponding to the specified supply air condition of 60°F db/59°F wb. This represents sensible cooling only.
[f]Line 4 minus line 5.
[g]For coil upstream from direct unit:

$$\frac{(cfm)(\Delta T: line~6)(1.08)}{12,000} = tons \qquad in~SI: \qquad \frac{(L/S)(\Delta T)(1.2)}{1000} = kW~cooling$$

[h]Line 8 times line 2.
[i](0.13 kW/1000 cfm)(30,000 cfm)(hrs: line 2). Bin 5 requires first-stage operation only at average of 0.10 kW/1000 cfm.
[j](1.2 kW/ton)(Third stage ton-hours: line 8).
[k](13.0 kW: S.A. fan)(hours: line 2).
[l]Total of lines 9 through 11.
[m]Sum of the five weather bins, line 12.

Typical Control Sequence

Two- and three-stage cooling systems and 100% outdoor air systems (no return air provisions or economizer dampers) using room or supply air duct thermostat control follow this sequence:

1. *First-stage* cooling energizes the indirect unit secondary fan and pump.
2. *Second-stage* cooling energizes the direct unit pump.
3. *Third-stage* cooling (alternative) energizes the conventional cooling coil control valves.

On 100% outdoor air systems, the heating apparatus may be in the supply air downstream of the direct unit, which will require thermostat-controlled heating.

Two- and three-stage systems with economizer dampers (return air and outdoor air proportional damper control) follow this sequence:

With no call for cooling:

1. The return air damper is open 100%.

Table 2 Data for Applying a Conventional Refrigerated System

Bin No.	1	2	3	4	5
1-db/Mean wb, °F (°C)[a]	103/70 (39.4/21.1)	95/68 (35.0/20.0)	85/66 (29.4/18.9)	75/63 (23.9/17.2)	65/58 (18.3/14.4)
2-Operating hours[b]	15	182	367	525	613
3-RA temp. (db) °F (°C)[c]	82.0 (27.8)	82.0 (27.8)	82.0 (27.8)	82.0 (27.8)	82.0 (27.8)
4-Rise-Min. O.A., °F (°C)[d]	3.2 (1.8)	2.0 (1.1)	0.5 (0.3)	0 (0)	0 (0)
5-EAT to coil °F (°C)[e]	85.2 (29.6)	84.0 (28.9)	82.5 (28.1)	75.0 (23.9)	65.0 (18.3)
6-Coil ΔT, °F (°C)[f]	25.2 (14.0)	24.0 (13.3)	22.5 (12.5)	15.0 (8.3)	5.0 (2.8)
7-Sensible Cooling Tons (kW)[g]	68.0 (239)	64.8 (228)	60.8 (214)	40.5 (142)	13.5 (47)
8-Total Cooling Ton (kW)[h]	73.1 (257)	69.7 (245)	65.4 (230)	43.5 (153)	14.5 (51)
9-Ton Hours (GJ)[i]	1097 (14)	12,685 (161)	24,002 (304)	22,838 (290)	8889 (113)
10-kWh Refrigeration[j]	1316	15,222	28,802	27,406	10,667
11-kWh, S.A. Fan[k]	179	2166	4367	6248	7295
12-Total kWh[l]	1495	17,388	33,169	33,654	17,962

Total Annual Cooling Energy Consumption = 103,668 kWh[m]

Notes:
[a]Modified Bin TRY weather data.
[b]System operates 0700-1800, 5 days per week.
[c]Based on an estimated allowance for heat gain in the return plenum due to lighting and roof load.
[d](O.A. − R.A) • (0.15) − temperature rise due to outside air. The system operates on 100% O.A. in bins 4 and 5.
[e]Line 3 plus Line 4. The coil EAT in bins 4 and 5 is the O.A. temperature in the economizer range.
[f]Represents the EAT to the coil minus the required 60°F (15.6°C) supply air temperature.
[g]Calculation of sensible cooling:

$$\frac{(cfm)(\Delta T: line~6)(1.08)}{12,000} = tons \qquad in~SI: \qquad \frac{(L/S)(\Delta T)(1.2)}{1000} = kW~cooling$$

[h]Sensible heat factor = 93%. Estimate total coil load as:

$$\frac{(sensible~load:~line~7)}{0.93} = total~cooling$$

[i]Line 8 times line 2.
[j](1.2 kW/ton)(ton-hours: line 9).
[k](11.9 kW: S.A. fan)(hours: line 2).
[l]Line 10 plus line 11.
[m]Sum of the five weather bins, line 12.

2. The outdoor air damper is in the minimum ventilation position.
3. No pumps or secondary air fans are in operation.
4. The system heating apparatus can be energized.

First-stage cooling:

1. The return air damper is closed.
2. The outdoor air damper is opened 100%. The override thermostat in the supply air duct can modulate the dampers to mixed air if the outdoor air temperature is too low.
3. The first stage control is channeled through the outdoor air thermostat, allowing the indirect unit secondary fan and pump to energize only when the outdoor air temperature is above the set point.

Second-stage cooling:
The direct unit pump is energized.

Third-stage cooling (optional):
The conventional cooling coil control valves are energized.

SYSTEM LOAD EXHAUST

Many system designs employ ceiling return air plenums with recessed light fixtures and ballasts. This design can place a large portion of the total heat gain in the return side of the system.

In many cases, the portion of the load that determines the supply air quantity (room sensible heat gain) represents 60 to 65% of the total load. The remaining cooling load (the roof, the wall above the ceiling line, latent heat gain, outdoor air, and the portion of lighting and ballast heat rejected to the return air plenum) could be as much as 35 to 40% of the total load. The indirect/direct system using 100% outdoor air allows the return air portion of the load to be rejected in the exhaust air. In such cases, these load components would not be included as part of the room load.

To exhaust the return side load, the cooling system operates on the 100% outdoor air inherent in the indirect/direct system. System cooling is an extension of the economizer cycle. The energy used by the evaporative stages to cool the outdoor air is substantially less than required by a refrigerated system that cools mixed air to the equivalent supply air temperature.

Under partial load, as the outdoor ambient dry-bulb temperature decreases, the corresponding wet-bulb temperature also decreases. This causes the supply air temperature of the evaporative stages to decrease, increasing system capacity. As the VAV terminal units respond to the partial load requirement and reduce the air quantity supplied to the respective spaces, the velocity through the central indirect/direct apparatus decreases, causing an additional reduction in supply air temperature. There is also a reduction in the supply air system static pressure drop, motor brake horsepower, and kilowatt consumption. The use of fan speed control or fan variable inlet vane control may permit additional energy savings.

SYSTEM ANALYSIS

The comparisons in Table 1 and Table 2 show a significant reduction in refrigeration load and energy use with a three-stage evaporative system. Table 2 can be used as an example to estimate the annual energy consumption of a conventional system using previously outlined criteria. Since the system is wet-bulb temperature oriented, even coastal areas can be considered candidates for the use of two- and three-stage systems. San Francisco, for example, has a 1% design mean coincident wet-bulb temperature of 64 °F (17.8 °C) and will show a significant reduction in refrigeration load. At higher altitudes, with low design wet-bulb temperatures, little or no refrigeration is required, and annual energy reduction is even more significant.

This analysis compares three-stage systems with systems operating with return air (and minimum outdoor air) at higher temperatures and on an economizer cycle at lower temperatures. If a design requires a 100% outside air system, an evaluation of a staged evaporative system will show both a greater reduction in refrigeration load and in annual energy usage.

The total energy required for this system is shown in Table 1, Line 8. The annual kWh for the third stage is calculated on Line 10, using the appropriate kW/ton (kW/kW) value.

For this example, the annual savings of the evaporative system over the conventional system is 51 524 kWh (103 668 kWh − 52 144 kWh). However, when comparing systems, the cost analysis should include the annual kilowatt reduction at the applicable electrical rate, as well as the anticipated energy cost escalation over the expected life of the system.

In addition, electrical demand charges have become increasingly more important and should be considered. Demand rates are set when the air-conditioning system is operating at peak load. Any reduction in kilowatt demand during these periods can reduce energy costs, since the reduced demand rate applies to total energy use. To evaluate demand costs properly, a minimum of a monthly analysis should be performed.

REFERENCES

Eskra, N. 1980. Indirect/Direct Evaporative Cooling Systems. ASHRAE Journal, Vol. 22, No. 5, p. 22.

Schofield, M., and Deschamps, N. 1980. EBTR Compliance and Comfort Too. ASHRAE Journal, Vol. 22, No. 6, p. 61.

Supple, R.G. 1982. Evaporative Cooling for Comfort. ASHRAE Journal, Vol. 24, No. 8, p. 42.

Watt, J.R. 1986. *Evaporative Air Conditioning Handbook*. Chapman and Hall, London.

CHAPTER 57

TESTING, ADJUSTING, AND BALANCING

THIS chapter develops standardized practices for testing, adjusting, and balancing various types of air-conditioning and refrigeration systems. Material is still being developed through research, since the analytical approach is still in its infancy.

A building is a dynamic entity that changes with time and must be rebalanced accordingly. The designer must consider initial and supplementary testing and balancing requirements. It is essential to have complete and accurate operating and maintenance instructions and manuals that include how to test, adjust, and balance the building systems. Optimum comfort, process results, and economy require in-depth training of building operating personnel or the use of qualified operating service organizations.

This chapter does not dictate which groups or individuals should perform the functions of a complete testing, adjusting, and balancing procedure. However, the procedure must produce results that meet the intent of the designer, which should accurately reflect the requirements of the owner.

The overall concept requires that one source be responsible for testing, adjusting, and balancing all systems. As part of this responsibility, the testing organization should check the performance data of all equipment under field conditions to ensure compliance.

The testing of boilers and other pressure vessels for compliance with safety codes is not performed by testing and balancing firms, whose primary function is to verify operating conditions in relation to design conditions for flow, temperature, pressure drops, noise, and vibration.

DEFINITIONS

System testing, adjusting, and balancing is the process of checking and adjusting all the building environmental systems to produce the design objectives. It includes (1) the balance of air and water distribution, (2) adjustment of total system to provide design quantities, (3) electrical measurement, (4) verification of performance of all equipment and automatic controls, and (5) sound and vibration measurement. These are accomplished by (1) checking installations for conformity to design, (2) measurement and establishment of the fluid quantities of the system, as required to meet design specifications, and (3) recording and reporting the results.

The following definitions are used in this chapter:

Test: To determine quantitative performance of equipment.

Balance: To proportion flows within the distribution system (submains, branches, and terminals) according to specified design quantities.

Adjust: To regulate the specified fluid flow rate and air patterns at the terminal equipment (e.g., reduce fan speed, throttling).

Procedure: Standardized approach and execution of sequence of work operations to yield reproducible results.

Report forms: Test data sheets arranged for collecting test data in logical order for submission and review. These data should also form the permanent record to be used as the basis for any future testing, adjusting, and balancing required.

Terminal: The point where the controlled fluid enters or leaves the distribution system. These are supply inlets on water terminals, supply outlets on air terminals, return outlets on water terminals, and exhaust or return inlets on air terminals such as registers, grilles, diffusers, louvers, and hoods.

Main: Duct or pipe containing the system's major or entire fluid flow.

Submain: Duct or pipe containing part of the system's capacity and serving two or more branch mains.

Branch main: Duct or pipe serving two or more terminals.

Branch: Duct or pipe serving a single terminal.

GENERAL CRITERIA

Effective and efficient testing, adjusting, and balancing require a systematic, thoroughly planned procedure implemented by experienced and qualified staff. All activities, including organization, calibrated instrumentation, and execution of the actual work, should be scheduled. Because many systems function differently on a seasonal basis, and because temperature performance is a significant factor, it is important to coordinate air side with water side work. Preparatory work includes planning and scheduling all procedures, collecting necessary data (including all change orders), reviewing collected data, studying the system to be worked on, preparing forms, and making preliminary field inspections.

It is recommended that low pressure duct systems be tested for air leakage during construction. Air leakage can have a marked effect on testing, adjusting, and balancing. Duct systems must be designed, constructed, and installed to minimize and control air leakage. Accordingly, there is concern in energy conservation endeavors to specify, test, and maintain all duct leakage for all types of duct systems. *HVAC Duct Construction Standards—Metal and Flexible,* published by SMACNA, covers pressure classification and respective duct-sealing requirements.

Design Considerations

Testing, adjusting, and balancing begin as a design function. Designs should be planned carefully because most of the devices required for adjustments are integral parts of the design and installation. To ensure that proper balance can be achieved by the balancing technician, the engineer should show and specify a sufficient number of dampers and flow-control devices.

The testing procedure depends on the system's characteristics. The interaction between individual air terminals (e.g., registers, diffusers, and troffers) and terminal units (e.g., induction units and dual-duct air mixing units) varies with the system static and

The preparation of this chapter is assigned to TC 9.7, Testing and Balancing.

velocity pressure. Accordingly, in low pressure systems, the restriction (adjustment) of one terminal may appreciably change the delivery of adjacent terminals. In a high pressure induction system, the restriction of one unit has relatively little effect on adjacent units.

METHODS FOR VOLUMETRIC MEASUREMENTS

General

The various techniques for measuring the airflow in duct systems and at terminal devices are controversial, and none is universally accepted. It is difficult to measure air velocities and flow rates accurately in the field. Most methods are subject to the ability of the tester. Proper testing is time consuming and requires diligence and expertise.

Laboratory tests, data, and techniques prescribed by equipment and air terminal manufacturers must be reviewed and corroborated for accuracy, applicability, and reproducibility of results. Conversion factors that enable correlation of field data with laboratory results must be developed to predict the equipment's actual field performance.

Terminals

Generally, *K* factors of terminal manufacturers should be checked for accuracy by another method prior to acceptance.

Terminal manufacturers usually base their volumetric test measurements on a deflection vane anemometer. The velocity so obtained is multiplied by an empirical *effective* area (generally not defined) to obtain the terminal's delivery. The accuracy of the results depends on a very exact positioning of the sensing jet of the velocity-measuring instruments. Unless the tester knows this position, the measurements may be wrong.

The methods advocated for measuring the air flow of troffer-type terminals also require extreme care. The use of special probe fittings, requiring precise and impartial positioning to produce unbiased data, is not considered to be practical either in the field or laboratory. Also, measurement of small air quantities, frequently lower than 40 cfm (18.9 L/s) per supply terminal, involves laboratory testing procedures not suitable for field application. The measurement of airflow in return air and heat removal troffers is even more difficult to perform accurately in the field.

None of the existing procedures for rating air and light troffer performance defines specific methods for measuring airflow, nor do they specify the type of instruments to be used. Therefore, the industry still needs information verifying the correlation of laboratory and field test procedure for measuring capacities of air troffers.

Duct Flow

Most procedures for testing, adjusting, and balancing air-handling systems place prime importance on the measurement of volumes in the ducts rather than at terminals. They assume that such measurements are more reliable than those obtained at the terminals, which are based on manufacturer's data. In such procedures terminal measurements are relied on only for balancing the distribution within a space or zone.

The preferred method of duct volumetric flow measurement is by pitot tube average. Care should be taken to obtain the maximum straight run to the traverse station. Test holes should be located as shown in Chapter 13 of the 1985 FUNDAMENTALS Volume to obtain the best duct velocity profile. Where factory fabricated volume measuring stations that have multipitot tubes and egg crate straighteners are used, they should be checked against a pitot tube traverse for calibration in the field.

The power input to a fan's driver as an indicator of its delivery should be used only as a guide. It is useful to verify performance determined by a reliable method (e.g., pitot tube traverse of systems's main). A study of the characteristics of various types of fans shows that the power-to-flow rate relationship is not proportional. In some cases, as with backward curved blade fans, two or more flow values require the same power. The forward curved blade centrifugal fan is the only type with suitable characteristics [i.e., cfm (L/s) varies directly with bhp (kW)] for the power input to indicate what the fan is delivering.

Mixture Plenums

Approach conditions are often so unfavorable that the air quantities comprising a mixture (e.g., outdoor air and return air) cannot be determined accurately by volumetric measurements. In such cases, the temperature of the mixture indicates the balance (proportions) between the component airstreams. The temperature of the mixture can be calculated from Eq. (1).

Pressure Measurements

The pressures involved with air measurements are barometric pressure, static pressure, velocity pressure, total pressure, and differential pressure.

Using pressure measurement for field evaluation of air-handling system performance is not recommended. Where required by specifications, the results should be considered as rough checks or indicators. For various reasons, pressure readings taken in the field do not reflect the pressures associated with the fan's catalog rating. Generally, such readings are misleading and misinterpreted.

Because of this, pressure drops through equipment such as coils, dampers, or filters should not be used as a means for measuring the airflow through them. Pressure is an acceptable means of establishing flow volumes only where it is required by, and performed in accordance with, the manufacturer who certifies the specified equipment. Generally, this is limited to high pressure induction and air-mixing units where it serves to simplify the testing procedure.

Stratification

Normal design practices minimize conditions causing air turbulence to produce the least friction, resistance, and consequent pressure losses in the system. However, under certain conditions, air turbulence is desirable and necessary to promote mixing of air streams of different temperatures, which would otherwise stratify. Stratification primarily occurs in smooth, uninterrupted flow conditions where an invisible barrier occurs between two masses of air of different temperatures. The return and outside air streams at the inlet side of the air-handling unit tend to stratify where enlargement of the inlet plenum or casing size decreases the air velocity. Without a deliberate effect to mix the two air streams, stratification will exist throughout the system (filter, coils, eliminators, fans, ducts, etc.). Stratification can damage equipment by freezing liquids in the coils and rupturing them. It can also affect the performance of temperature control in plenums and/or spaces.

Stratification can be eliminated by adding obstructions to breakup and mix of the two air streams. There is no particular fix to stratification problems, and the predesigned requirements may not necessarily be successful. Each condition must be evaluated by field temperature measurements and experimentation of the arrangement of baffles, nozzles, turbulators, etc.

BALANCING PROCEDURES FOR AIR DISTRIBUTION SYSTEMS

General procedures for testing and balancing are included to assist those who require a conceptual background for this phase. The bibliography lists sources of additional information.

No one established procedure is applicable to all systems. However, there is one point of agreement: air systems should be balanced before hydronic, steam, and refrigerant systems.

Instrumentation for Testing and Balancing

The minimum instruments necessary for air balance are as follows:

1. Micromanometer calibrated in no less than 0.005 in. of water (1 Pa) divisions
2. Combination inclined and vertical manometer [0 to 10 in. of water (0 to 2500 Pa)] is generally the most useful
3. Pitot tubes in lengths, as required
4. A tachometer, which should be the high quality, direct contact, self-timing type
5. Clamp-on ampere meter with voltage scales
6. Deflecting vane anemometer
7. Rotating vane anemometer
8. Thermal-type (hot-wire) anemometer
9. Flow hood
10. Dial and glass stem thermometers

New instrumentation should be evaluated for accuracy and repeatability prior to use in the field.

Preliminary Procedure for Air Balancing

Before operating the system, the following steps should be performed:

1. Obtain design drawings and specifications and become thoroughly acquainted with the design intent.
2. Obtain copies of approved shop drawings of all air-handling equipment, outlets (supply, return, and exhaust), and temperature control diagrams.
3. Compare design to installed equipment and field installation.
4. Walk the system from the air-handling equipment to terminal units to determine variations of installation from design.
5. Check filters and dampers (both volume and fire) for correct and locked position, and temperature control for completeness of installation before starting fans.
6. Prepare report test sheets for both fans and outlets. Obtain manufacturer's outlet factors and recommended procedure of testing. A summation of required outlet volumes permits a crosscheck with required fan volumes.
7. Determine best locations in main and branch ductwork for most accurate duct traverses.
8. Place all outlet dampers in the open position.
9. Prepare schematic diagrams of system as-built ductwork and piping layouts to facilitate reporting.

Equipment and System Check

1. Place all fans (supply, return, and exhaust) in operation, and immediately check the following items:

a. Motor amperage and voltage to guard against possible overload

b. Fan rotation

c. Automatic dampers for proper position

d. Air and water resets operating to deliver required temperatures

e. Air leaks in the casing and in the scarfing around the coils and filter frames should be checked by moving a light along the outside of the joint while observing the darkened interior of the casing. Caulk any leaks. Note points where piping enters the casing to ensure that escutcheons are tight. Do not rely on pipe insulation to seal these openings because the insulation may shrink. In prefabricated units, check that all panel-fastening holes are filled to prevent whistling.

2. Traverse the main supply ductwork whenever possible. All main branches should also be traversed where duct arrangement permits. Selection of traverse points and method of traverse should be as follows:

a. Each main or branch should be traversed after the longest possible straight run for the duct involved.

b. For test hole spacing, refer to Chapter 13 of the 1985 FUNDAMENTALS Volume.

c. Traverse should be made using a pitot tube and manometer where velocities are over 700 fpm (3.56 m/s). Below this velocity, use either a micromanometer and pitot tube or a recently calibrated hot wire anemometer.

d. Note temperature and barometric pressure to determine if they need to be corrected for standard air quantity. Corrections are normally insignificant; however, abnormal conditions where very accurate results are desirable would justify them.

e. After establishing total air being delivered, it may be necessary to adjust the fan speed to obtain design air to allow for normal leakage and additional static pressure imposed by system characteristics. Check power and speed to see that motor power, critical fan speed, or both have not been exceeded.

f. Adjust branch dampers until each has the proper air volume.

g. With all the dampers and registers in the system open and with the supply, return, and exhaust blowers operating at or near design speed, set the minimum outdoor and return air ratio. If duct traverse locations are not available, this can be done by measuring the mixture temperature with thermometers in the return air, outdoor air louver, and the filter section.

As an approximation, the temperature of the mixture may be calculated from Eq. (1).

$$100 \, t_m = X_o t_o + X_r t_r \tag{1}$$

where

t_m = temperature of the mixture of return and outdoor air, °F (°C).

t_o = temperature of outdoor air, °F (°C).

X_o, X_r = percentage of outdoor and return air, respectively.

t_r = temperature of return air, °F (°C).

The larger the temperature difference between hot and cold air, the easier it is to get accurate damper settings. Take the temperature of the mixture at many points in a uniform traverse to be sure there is no stratification. A simple, but effective, traverse is to take a reading at the center of each filter when disposable or washable filters are installed.

After the minimum outdoor air damper has been set for the proper percentage of outdoor air, take another traverse of mixture temperatures and install baffling if the variation from the average is more than ±5% in the critical horizontal plane of a horizontal unit. A wider variation is permissible in the vertical plane of a horizontal unit, if the lowest temperature of the mixture, when referred to the coldest outdoor air temperature in winter, does not drop below freezing when no preheater is used. Remember that stratified air temperatures vary with the outdoor temperature while most of the internal loads on a central system do not.

If no return air fan is used, this adjustment generally will not affect the percentage of outdoor air when the supply fan speed is changed to give the design quantities of air. With a return air fan, the manual return air damper at the mixing plenum may need to be adjusted if the speed of the return fan and supply fan were not changed proportionately.

3. Carefully set the system for balance using the prescribed procedures as follows:

a. Adjust the system with mixing dampers positioned under the minimum outdoor air conditions.

b. When adjusting multizone or double-duct constant volume systems or variable volume systems, establish the ratio of the design volume through the cooling coil to total fan volume to achieve the desired diversity factor. Keep the proportion of cold to total air constant during the balance. However, check each zone or branch with this component on full cooling. If the design calls for full flow through the cooling coil, the entire system should be set to full flow through the cooling side while making tests. (Normally, this will only occur on systems supplying interior areas or 100% outdoor air systems.) Perform the same procedure as above for the hot air side.

4. Terminal Outlet Balance.

a. Start terminal outlet balance from the fan out. Branch dampers should be used for major adjusting and terminal dampers for trim, or minor adjustment only. It may be necessary to install additional sub-branch dampers to decrease the use of terminal dampers that create objectionable noise.

b. Normally, several passes through the entire system are necessary to obtain proper outlet values.

c. Totaling the tested outlet air quantity acts as a possible indicator of duct leakage when compared to duct traverse air quantities.

d. With total air established in the branches and at the outlets, perform the following: (a) take new amperage readings, (b) find static pressure across the fan, and (c) read and record static pressure across each component (intake, filters, coils, and mixing dampers).

Dual-Duct Systems

Most constant volume dual-duct systems are designed to handle a portion of the total system's supply through the cold duct and smaller air quantities through the hot duct. Balancing should be accomplished as follows:

1. Check the leaving air temperature at the nearest terminal to verify that the hot and cold damper inlet leakage is not greater than the maximum allowable leakage established.
2. The apparatus and main trunks should be checked, as outlined in this chapter.
3. Determine if the static pressure at the end of the system (the longest duct run) is at or above the minimum required for mixing box operation. Proceed to the extreme end of the system and check the static pressure drop *across* the box with an inclined draft gauge or magnehelic gauge. The drop *across* the box should equal or exceed the minimum static pressure recommended by the manufacturer of the box. About 0.75 in. (190 Pa) static pressure is common for the mechanical regulator. Additional pressure is required for the low pressure distribution system downstream of the box.
4. Balance diffusers or grilles on the low pressure side of the box, as described for low pressure systems.
5. Change the control settings to full heating and make certain that the controls and dual-duct boxes function properly. Spot check the airflow at several diffusers.
6. If the engineer has included a diversity factor in selecting the main apparatus, it will not be possible to get full flow from all boxes simultaneously, as outlined above.

VARIABLE VOLUME SYSTEMS

Energy conservation has caused the development of a large variety of variable volume systems. These systems can be categorized as *pressure dependent* or *pressure independent*.

The **pressure-dependent** system incorporates air terminal boxes that have a thermostat signal controlling a damper actuator. The air volume to the space varies to maintain the space temperature while the air temperature supplied to the terminal boxes remains constant. The balance of this type of system is constantly changing with loading changes; therefore, any balancing procedure will not produce repeatable data unless changes in system load are simulated by using the same configuration of thermostat settings each time the system is tested (i.e., the same terminal boxes are fixed in the minimum and maximum positions for the test).

The **pressure-independent** system incorporates air terminal boxes that have a thermostat signal used as a master control to open or close the damper actuator and a velocity controller used as a submaster control to maintain the maximum and minimum amounts of air to be supplied to the space. The air volume to the space varies to maintain the space temperature, while the air temperature supplied to the terminal remains constant. The balance of this type of system is constantly changing within the limits of the interior and/or exterior load changes; therefore, any balancing procedure will not produce repeatable data unless changes in the system load are simulated as in a pressure-dependent system. Care should be taken to verify the spring range of the damper actuator as it responds to the velocity controller to prevent dead bands or overlap of control in response to other system components (double duct VAV, fan powered boxes, retrofit systems, etc.). Also, care should be taken to verify the action of the thermostat with regard to the damper position, as the velocity controller can change the control signal ratio or reverse the control signal.

In a pressure-dependent system, volume dampers upstream of each terminal box are required to proportion the system properly. The setting of minimum airflows to the space, other than at no flow, is not suggested unless the terminal box has a normally closed damper and the manufacturer of the damper actuator provides mechanical stops. The pressure-independent system requires no volume dampers upsteam of the terminal box, and minimum and maximum airflows can be set with the velocity controller.

The primary difference between the two systems is that the pressure-dependent system will supply a different amount of air to the space as the pressure upstream of the terminal box changes. If the thermostats are not calibrated properly to meet the space load, several zones may overcool or overheat. When the zones overcool and receive greater amounts of supply air than required, they decrease the amount of air that can be supplied to overheated zones. The pressure-independent system is not affected by improper thermostat calibration in the same way that a pressure-dependent system because the minimum and maximum airflow limits may be set for each zone.

System Static Control

The system pressure on either the pressure-dependent system or the pressure-independent system can be controlled in the following ways:

1. **No Fan Volumetric Control.** With this type of system, pressure and noise should be considered.
2. **System By-Pass Control.** As the systemic pressure increases due to terminal boxes closing, a relief damper bypasses the system air back to the fan inlet. With this type of control, the economy of varied fan output is non-existent, and usually the relief damper is a large source of duct leakage.

3. **Discharge Damper**. System losses and noise should be considered with this system.
4. **Vortex Damper**. System losses due to inlet air conditions are a problem and the vortex damper does not close 100%.
5. **Varying Fan Speed Mechanically**. Slippage loss of belts, cost of belt replacement, and the high initial cost of the electrical components are of concern with this system of control.
6. **Variable Pitch-in-Motion Fans**. This system is comparable to varying fan speed.

In controlling the above fan systems, the location of the static pressure sensors is critical and should be field verified to give the most representative point of operation. After the terminal boxes have been proportioned, the static pressure control can be verified by observing static pressure changes at the fan discharge and the static sensor as the load is simulated from maximum airflow to minimum airflow (i.e., set all terminal boxes to balanced airflow conditions and verify if any changes in static pressure occur by placing one terminal box at a time to minimum airflow unitl all terminals are placed at the minimal airflow setting). Care should be taken to verify that the maximum to minimum air volume changes are within the fan curve performance (rpm or total pressure).

Diversity

Diversity may be used on either type of system where it is assumed that the total system airflow volume is, by design, lower as not all of the system terminal boxes will ever open fully. Care should be taken to avoid any duct leakage. All ductwork upstream of the terminal box should be considered as medium pressure ductwork, whether in a low or medium pressure system. (Refer to Chapter 43.)

The procedure to test the total air on the system should be established by setting terminal boxes to the zero or minimum position nearest to the fan on either type of system. Also, care should be taken during peak load conditions to verify that there is adequate pressure upstream of the terminal boxes to achieve design airflow to the spaces.

Fresh Air Requirements

Maintaining the space under a slight positive or neutral pressure to atmosphere is difficult with all variable volume systems. In most systems, the exhaust requirement for the space is normally constant; hence, the outside air used to equal the exhaust air and meet the minimum fresh air requirements for the building codes must also remain constant. Due to the location of the outside air intake and the varying changes in pressure, this usually does not happen. The outside air should enter the fan at a point of constant pressure (i.e., supply fan volume can be controlled by proportional static pressure control, and that same control can control the volume of the return air fan).

Return Air Fans

If return air fans are required in series with a supply fan, the type of control and sizing of the fans is most important, as serious over and under pressurization can occur, especially during the economizer cycle.

Various Types of VAV Systems

1. **Single Duct VAV**. This system incorporates a pressure dependent or independent terminal and usually has reheat at some predetermined minimal setting on the terminal unit. Because this system uses reheat, it is poor for energy conservation.
2. **Bypass System**. This system incorporated a generally pressure-dependent damper, which, on a demand for heating, closes the damper to the space and opens to the return air plenum. This system sometimes incorporates a constant bypass airflow or a reduced amount of airflow bypassed to the return plenum in relation to the amount supplied to the space. There is no economical value in varying the fan speed with this type of system. A control problem can exist if any return air sensing is done to control a warm-up or cool-down cycle.
3. **VAV System using Single Duct VAV & Fan Powered Terminals—Pressure Dependent**. This system has a primary source of air from the fan to the terminal and a secondary powered fan source, which pulls air from the return air plenum before the additional heat source. This system places additional maintenance of terminal filters, motors, capacitors, etc., on the building owner. In certain fan powered boxes, back draft dampers are a source of system duct leakage when the system has a call for full closing.
4. **Double Duct VAV**. The type of terminal incorporates two single-duct variable terminals and can be controlled by velocity controllers in sequence with one another so that both hot and cold duct will be closed or can be controlled by having either the hot or cold duct use the velocity controller and the other duct use a downstream sensor in the terminal unit to maintain either maximum or minimum airflow. Often, low system pressure, either in the hot duct or cold duct, causes mixing of air in the two ducts, which results in excess energy use or discomfort in the space.

Balancing the VAV System

The general procedure for balancing a VAV system is as follows:

1. Determine the required maximum air volume to be delivered by the supply and return air fans. Diversity of load usually means the volume will be somewhat less than the outlet total.
2. Obtain fan curves on these units and request information on surge characteristics from the fan manufacturer.
3. If an inlet vortex damper control is to be used, obtain the fan manufacturers's data pertaining to the derating of the fan when used with the damper. If speed control is used, obtain information as to maximum and minimum speed that can be be obtained with the drive.
4. Determine from the manufacturer the minimum and maximum operating pressures for terminal or variable volume boxes to be used on the project.
5. Construct a theoretical system curve with approximate surge area included. The system curve initiates at the minimum inlet static of the boxes, plus system loss at minimum flow and terminates at design maximum flow. The operating range using an inlet vane damper is between the surge line intersection with the system curve and the maximum design flow. When variable speed control is used, the operating range is between (a) the minimum speed that can produce the necessary minimum box static at minimum flow still in the fan's stable range and (b) the maximum speed necessary to obtain maximum design flow.
6. The terminal boxes must then be positioned to the proportion of maximum fan air volume to total installed terminal maximum volume.
7. The fan should be set to operate at approximate design speed (increase about 5% for a full open inlet vane damper).
8. A sufficient number of terminal boxes should be checked to be representative of the system. If a wide variation in static pressure is encountered, or a number are below minimum at maximum flow, then every box should be checked.
9. A total air traverse must then be made.
10. A speed increase must be made if either or both static pressure and volume are low. If the volume is correct, but

the static is high, the speed must be reduced. If the static is high or correct, but the volume is low, it is necessary to go over all the terminals and adjust them to the proper volume.

11. Items 7 through 10 should be taken with the return exhaust fan set and traversed and the system set on minimum outdoor air.
12. Set the outlets to design volume with the VAV box on maximum flow setting. Verify the minimum flow setting.
13. Set the return outlets throughout the system.
14. The terminals then should be set to minimum, and the inlet vane or speed controller adjusted until minimum static and volume are obtained.
15. The temperature control and balancing personnel should then cooperate in the final location of the sensor for the static pressure controller. This must be located in the supply duct far enough from the fan discharge to represent the average static pressure in the system.
16. Check the return air fan speed or inlet vane damper to be sure it is tracking with the supply fan to assure proper outside air volume.
17. The system should then be placed on 100% outside air (weather permitting) and supply and return fans checked for power and static pressure.

Induction Systems

Most induction systems use high velocity air distribution. Balancing should be accomplished as follows:

1. Perform steps outlined under the basic procedures common to all systems for apparatus and main trunk capacities.
2. Primary airflow at each terminal unit can be determined by reading the unit plenum pressure with a portable dry-type draft gauge or magnehelic gauge and locating the point on the charts (or curves) of air quantity versus static pressure supplied by the unit manufacturer.
3. Make a spot check of the air distribution by reading the first and last unit on each riser. Do not reset these units. Study these results and then adjust riser dampers to regulate proper flow in each riser. Normally, the high capacity risers should be cut back to improve the airflow in the rest of the system.
4. Beginning on the floor nearest the main supply duct, start the first pass around the system, reading and adjusting as you go. If all unit dampers are open, set the units on the floor nearest the main supply duct about 10% under design capacity.
5. Normally, about three complete passes around the entire system are required for proper adjustment. A final pass without adjustments must be made to record the end result.
6. The noise level of the system must be reasonable. If the fan speed is too high, excess static pressure will be supplied to the induction units and the unit dampers, and riser dampers will have to be closed further to obtain the design nozzle pressures. The increased pressure drop across the unit damper and riser damper generates noise and contributes to a higher room noise level. To provide the quietest possible operation, the fan should be adjusted to the slowest speed that will provide sufficient nozzle pressure to all units with the minimum throttling of all unit and riser dampers.
7. Normally, the flow of water in induction unit coils is automatically controlled to adjust room temperature. Some systems use the primary air source to power the controls and move a secondary air damper for adjusting room temperature. In such a case, it is extremely important that the manufacturer's minimum static pressure in the plenum of each unit be maintained.

After balancing each supply unit on minimum outdoor air, reposition to maximum, then take additional power and static

pressure readings in this position. Comparing power and static pressures in these two positions immediately indicates any changes necessary in the return system to accomplish the design requirements.

Adjust the air terminal outlets for a proper distribution pattern. Make a final trim of air balance after the building is occupied and in normal use.

Report and Report Information

The air-handling system report, in order to be of value to the consulting engineer and owner's maintenance department, should consist of at least the following items:

1. Design
   a. Air quantity to be delivered
   b. Fan static pressure
   c. Motor power
   d. Percent of outside air under minimum conditions
   e. Rpm of the fan
   f. The power required to obtain this air quantity at the design static pressure

2. Installation
   a. Equipment manufacturer
   b. The size unit installed
   c. The arrangement of the air-handling unit
   d. The class fan
   e. Nameplate horsepower, nameplate voltage, phase, cycles, and full load amperes of the motor installed

3. Field tests
   a. Fan rpm
   b. Power readings (voltage, amperes of all *legs* at motor terminals)
   c. Total pressure differential across unit components
   d. Fan suction and fan discharge static pressure (equals fan total pressure)
   e. A plot of actual readings on manufacturer's fan performance curve to show the installed fan operating point

It is important to establish the initial static pressures accurately for the air-treatment equipment and the duct system so that the variation in air quantity because of filter loading can be calculated. It enables the designer to ensure that the total fan quantity will never be less than the minimum requirements. It also serves as a check of dirt loading in coils, since the design air quantity for peak loading of the filters has been calculated.

4. Terminal Outlets
   a. Outlet by room designation and position
   b. Outlet manufacture and type
   c. Outlet size (using manufacturer's designation to ensure proper factor)
   d. Manufacturer's outlet factor (Where no factors are available, or field tests indicate the listed factors are incorrect, a factor must be determined in the field by traverse of a duct leading to a single outlet. A traverse also ensures that no installation air leakage exists.)
   e. Design air quantity and the required velocity in fpm (m/s) to obtain this cfm (L/s)
   f. Test velocities and resulting air quantity
   g. Adjustment pattern for every air terminal

5. Additional Information

The following information is desirable under applicable circumstances:

a. Air-handling units
   (1) Belt number and size
   (2) Drive and driven sheave size

(3) Belt position on adjusted drive sheaves (bottom, middle, and top)
(4) Motor speed under full load
(5) Motor heater size
(6) Filter type and static pressure at initial use and full load (Time to replace.)
(7) Variations of velocity at various points across the face of the coil
(8) Existence of vortex or discharge dampers, or both

b. Distribution system
 (1) Unusual duct arrangements
 (2) Branch duct static readings in double-duct and induction system
 (3) Ceiling pressure readings where plenum ceiling distribution is being used; tightness of ceiling
 (4) Relationship of building to outdoor pressure under both minimum and maximum outdoor air
 (5) Induction unit manufacturer and size (including required air quantity and plenum pressures for each unit) and a test plenum pressures and resulting primary air delivery from the manufacturer's listed curves

c. All equipment nameplates not visible and easily readable

More detailed information on testing, adjusting, and balancing for air systems is available from sources listed in the bibliography. Many independent firms have developed detailed procedures suitable to their own operations and the area in which they function. These procedures are often available for information and evaluation upon request.

PRINCIPLES AND PROCEDURES FOR BALANCING HYDRONIC SYSTEMS

A considerable difference exists between air and water side balance requirements. Air side balance requires a precise flow definition because the air is the prime heating or cooling load conveyance medium. A reduction in airflow to less than the design requirement directly reduces the load ability for given inlet and outlet air conditions across a terminal heat transfer unit. Since water side flow rate is not linearly related to terminal unit heat transfer capability, the flow rates need not be as precisely defined for balance as for the air side. Instead, adequate flow rate is related to the relationship between heat transfer and water flow for water-to-air terminal units.

Heat Transfer at Reduced Flow Rate

The typical *heating only* hydronic system often operates satisfactorily at reduced flow because of the water flow/heat transfer relationship, as shown in Figure 1.

A decrease in terminal unit flow rate to 50% of design requirement still allows about 90% of heat transfer capability. The reason for the relative insensitivity to changing flow rates is that the governing coefficient for heat transfer is the outside or air side coefficient. A change in internal or water side coefficient with flow rate does not materially affect the overall heat transfer coefficient. This means that (1) load ability for water-to-air terminals is basically established by the mean air-to-water temperature difference, (2) a high order of design temperature difference exists between the air being heated and mean water temperature in the coil (a substantial change in mean water temperature is necessary before terminal load ability is measurably changed), and (3) a substantial change in the mean water temperature (load ability) requires a very substantial change in water flow rate.

A secondary safety factor in terms of application also applies to heating terminals. Unlike chilled water, hot water is not bound to a narrow temperature span in terms of supply water temper-

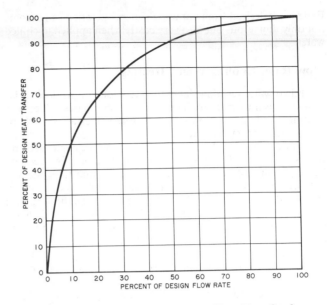

Fig. 1 Effects of Flow Variation on Heat Transfer for a 20°F (11.1°C) Design Δt at 200°F (93.3°C) Supply Temperature

ature. This means that a reduction in terminal heating capacity as caused by inadequate flow rate can often be overcome by simply raising the system supply water temperature. Design for upper temperature limits [250°F (121°C) for low pressure code] does not allow the temperature increase safety factor to be applied.

The previous comments apply to allowable flow variation for heating terminals selected for a 20°F (11°C) temperature drop (Δt) and the general order of 200°F (93°C) supply water temperature. Changes in design supply water temperature and design temperature drop affect permissible flow variation. When 90% terminal capacity is acceptable for a system application, the flow variation can be approximated, as shown in Figure 2.

Note that heating system tolerance to unbalance decreases with increases in the design Δt and with decreases in supply water temperature. As a general rule, however, system tolerance to flow rates less than design is important.

Working experience with hot water systems may have demonstrated to the mechanical contractor that extensive actual mechanical balance is not needed. While generally true, this assumption can become dangerous, since massive short circuiting can and will cause problems, even with the hot water system.

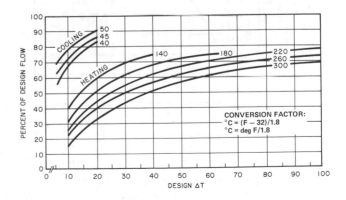

Fig. 2 Percent Variation of Design Flow versus Design Δt to Maintain 90% Terminal Heat Transfer

Experience derived from hot water system operation can become not only dangerous but also very costly when applied to chilled water.

Flow Rate, Cooling versus Heating

Chilled water terminals are much less tolerant to flow variation. This is illustrated in Figure 2, which compares chilled and heating terminals for flow reduction that will establish 90% of design heat transfer capacity.

Many dual-temperature changeover systems are completed and first started during the heating season. Reasonably adequate heating ability in all terminals may suggest that the system is balanced adequately. As shown in Figure 2, 40% of design flow through the terminal provides 90% terminal design heating with about 140°F (60°C) supply water and a 10°F (5.6°C) Δt. Increased supply water temperature establishes the same heat transfer at terminal flow rates of less than 40% design.

The majority of dual-temperature systems establish a decreased flow during the cooling season because of the introduction of chiller pressure drop against the distribution pump.

The flow reduction can reach 25%, meaning that during chiller operation, a terminal that originally heated satisfactorily could receive only 30% of the originally defined design flow rate.

Given these circumstances, a costly balance problem will suddenly appear during spring chilled water startup. Balance procedures must be related to the least tolerant system application to avoid this type of trouble.

The major reason for lessened tolerance of chilled water terminals to decreased flow is that the air-to-water temperature difference is much less that with heating terminals.

Generalized Chilled Water Terminal; Flow versus Heat Transfer

The general change for chilled heat transfer with changes in water flow rate is shown in Figure 3. The curves shown are based on ARI rating points; 45°F (7.2°C) inlet water at a 10°F (5.6°C) rise with air at 80°F (26.7°C) db and 67°F (19.4°C) wb.

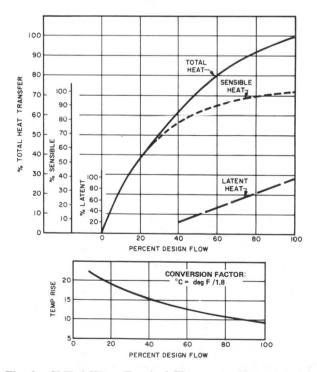

Fig. 3   Chilled Water Terminal Flow versus Heat Transfer

Table 1   Load-Flow Variations

Load Type	% Design Flow at 90% Load	Other Load, Order of %		
		Sensible	Total	Latent
Sensible	65	90	84	58
Total	75	95	90	65
Latent	90	98	95	90

Dual temperature systems are designed to chilled flow requirements and often operate on a 10°F (5.6°C) temperature drop at full-load heating.

The basic curve applies to catalog ratings for lower db temperatures, providing a consistent entering air moisture content or vapor pressure is maintained [e.g., 75°F (23.9°C) db, 65°F (18.3°C) wb]. Deviation from the curves shown is to be expected with changes in inlet water temperature, temperature rise, air velocity, and db and wb conditions. Figure 3 should be considered only as a general representation of variable change, not as a fact that applies to all chilled water applications.

If the chilled water terminal is matched to the load, the load variation to 90% design can be interpreted to three flow variations, as shown in Table 1. Note that load-flow variation for Figure 2 is stated for total load.

Table 1 and Figure 3 illustrate that the first loss with reduced chilled terminal flow rate is latent capability. Table 1 defines that permissible flow variation from design will be related to the following application requirements: (1) when high latent capability is needed, operational terminal flow rate must substantially meet design flow and (2) the application where sensible load control is predominant provides for a much wider terminal flow tolerance.

Flow Tolerance and Balance Procedure

A workable design procedure rests on a *design base* flow rate and a design flow tolerance given as a percentage allowable deviation from base. It is the consultant's responsibility, based on experience and judgment, to define both the base flow rates and allowable flow tolerance. The cost of balance rises with tightened flow tolerance specification. A tight flow tolerance specification should not be made if a high system flow tolerance is present.

Figure 4 outlines suggested flow tolerance as a function of supply water temperature and water temperature drop and is based on achieving from 97% to 101.5% of expected terminal heat transfer. A maximum flow tolerance band of ±10% is suggested, even though some hot water systems can tolerate a higher flow deviation. The ±10% tolerance band is economically achievable, and its use as a maximum tolerance eliminates troublesome side effects caused by low water velocity, air purge problems, etc. Some systems require a tighter flow tolerance than ±10%, however. Heating terminals using low temperature water as from heat recovery may require a ±5% flow tolerance [110°F (43°C) supply at 20°F (11°C) Δt, for example]. Other systems may allow no negative flow tolerance.

BASIC METHODS OF WATER SIDE BALANCE

It is preferable to balance the water side separately by direct flow measurement. This balance approach is very accurate because it eliminates compounding errors introduced by the temperature difference procedures. Balance by direct flow measurement allows the pump to be matched to the actual system requirements (pump impeller trim). The reduction in final operating cost will, in many cases, pay for the cost of water side

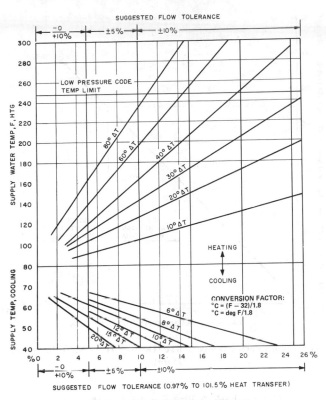

Fig. 4   Flow Tolerance Plot

balance. Proper instrumentation and good preplanning is needed. Water flow instrumentation must be installed during construction of the piping system; they can consist of all or a combination of the following:

1. **System components used as flow meters**—Control valves, terminal units, chillers, etc.
2. **Flow meters**—Venturi, orifice plate, and pitot tube
3. **Pumps**
4. **Flow limiting devices and balancing devices**

System circumstance often dictates a combination of flow and temperature balance. In many cases, it may not be economically sound or even necessary to install flow indicating devices at every terminal. For example, in reheat, induction, and radiation systems, temperature readings can be used to set the flow. Branch piping and risers should still be set with primary flow measuring devices. The water balance is undertaken using all the pressure measuring methods available and verified by total heat transfer using air and water temperature readings. The pressure readings provide the necessary accuracy for a good balance only if verified by a heat balance.

Balance by Temperature Difference

An often-used balance procedure is based on water temperature difference measurement. The consultant selects cooling terminal equipment for a calculated sensible and latent design load. When air-handling coils are selected, the air side load is carried by design load airflow based on design entering and leaving air db and wb conditions. The coil size selected is based on air side requirements projected against a specified inlet water temperature and a selected water temperature rise. The water temperature rise is translated to gpm (L/s) for the applied load. Coil pressure drop is determined based on the selected design gpm (L/s).

Since the coil selection is based on a design water temperature difference, a simple (but often false) balance premise seems evi-

dent: *Design gpm (L/s) will be provided when design water temperature rise is set.* This premise for water side temperature difference balance is generally invalid because it overlooks a basic relationship—load balance.

The measured water side temperature rise across any specific coil must be a function of the water flow rate and the applied air side load at the time of measurement. Water side load must equal air side load. The load balance relationship states the following:

1. Setting of design water temperature rise provides design gpm (L/s) only when air side loading exactly matches design (a very improbable circumstance).
2. Setting of design water temperature rise cannot establish design gpm (L/s) when air side loading differs from design (the usual circumstance).
3. Water side balance by temperature difference measurement can only be established by (a) measuring the true applied load at the time of balance and determining the ratio between the applied and design loads, (b) water temperature difference setting to a ratio adjusted difference [if applied load is 50% design, a design Δt of 10 °F (5.6 °C) would be balance set to 5 °F (2.8 °C) water temperature difference for the design gpm (L/s) balance point].

Temperature Difference Balance Accuracy

While structured from a theoretically sound base, the load-correlated temperature difference balance method has significant limitations. Meaningful results are established only by absolutely precise differential measurements. Since the working differentials are of minor order, minor instrumentation or readout error may invalidate results because errors are compounded. For example, if the actual accuracy of thermometer readout is ±0.5 °F (0.3 °C) the actual temperature rise could be either 4 or 6 °F (2.2 or 3.3 °C) even though a 5 °F (2.8 °C) rise is observed and recorded. Actual flow rate could then vary between 83 to 125% of design, even though the applied load is precisely determined.

It is difficult, however, to estimate the actual applied instantaneous air side load. Actual air side flow rates may have an accuracy order of only +10%, while the necessary wb measurements can be affected by stratification and by instrumentation and readout error.

Temperature difference balance procedures could provide actual flow rates varying from 60 to 175% of design under circumstances of actual 50% load operation when the airflow is estimated at ±10% accuracy with ±0.5 °F (0.3 °C) readout accuracy applied to both the wb and water side thermometers.

The order of accuracy indicated does not represent actual temperature difference procedure accuracy range. The actual accuracy range cannot be defined, since this is a function of both controllable and uncontrollable circumstances, instrument calibration, readout care, stratification, water side thermal bulb resistance, system load stability, etc. Actual accuracy may be more or less than illustrated.

The order of flow balance accuracy finally attained is affected by the compound errors introduced and by precision readout capability and care. Flow balance accuracy is also affected by the interdependence of balance points. Each time a balance valve is adjusted, all other previously balanced coils are affected. This means that each balance point must be adjusted several times. Even so, the order of accuracy is limited because of compounded error introduction.

Procedure and Application

Those concerned with actual water side balance work recognize the inherent inaccuracy of water temperature difference balance procedures and use this method only as a last resort when flow informational and measurement devices are not included in the system piping.

Water temperature difference balance procedure is sometimes integrated with flow measurement. For example, a group of terminals included in a branch circuit may not have means for flow measurement although the branch circuit does. In this case, a water temperature difference balance procedure is applied to the terminals, and results are correlated with actual branch circuit flow rate (total terminal flow rate), as read from the branch circuit flow meter.

Water side temperature difference balance requires a continual load balance reference to the air side. Procedures stated for this principle consequently and necessarily specify that air side balance shall be completed before water side temperature difference balance is started.

Flow Balancing by Rated Differential Procedure

This procedure depends on the derivation of a performance curve for the test coil that compares water temperature difference (Δtw) to entering water temperature (EWT) minus entering air temperature (EAT). One point of the desired curve can be determined from the manufacturer's ratings since these are published in terms of $EWT - EAT$. A second point can be established by observing that the heat transfer from air to water is zero (and consequently $\Delta tw = 0$) when $EWT - EAT$ is zero. With these two points, an approximate performance curve can be drawn. Then, for any other $EWT - EAT$, this curve is used to determine the appropriate Δtw.

Example: From given manufacturer's data,

Capacity = 10,000 Btu/h
EWT = 200°F
EAT = 60°F
Water flow = 1.5 gpm

Solution:

1. Calculate rated $\Delta tw = \dfrac{10,000}{50 \cdot 1.5} = 13.33$°F

2. Construct a performance curve as illustrated in Figure 5.
3. From test data,
   EWT = 180°F
   EAT = 70°F
   $(EWT - EAT)$ = 110°F
4. From the performance curve, Figure 5, read $\Delta tw = 10.5$°F, which is required to balance water flow at 1.5 gpm.

This procedure is recommended for use in balancing terminal devices such as finned tube radiators, where flow measuring devices do not exist and where airflow measurements cannot be made. It may also be used for cooling coils when no latent transfer is involved (coil is dry).

Flow Balancing by Total Heat Transfer

This procedure is based on the determination of water flow by an energy balance about the coil. From field measurements of airflow, wet- and dry-bulb temperatures both upstream and downstream of the coil, and entering and leaving water temperatures (Δtw), water flow can be determined by the following equations:

$$gpm = \frac{\text{Load in Btu/h}}{500 \times \Delta tw} \qquad (2)$$

or, in SI units,

$$(L/s) = \frac{\text{Load in W}}{4000\ \Delta tw} \qquad (2\ SI)$$

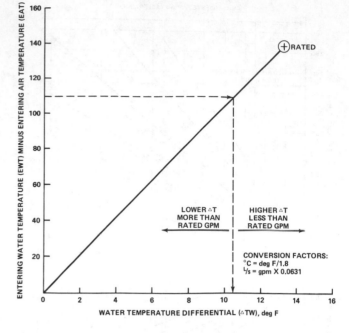

Fig. 5 Coil Performance Curve (Derived from Manufacturers' Data)

$$\text{Cooling load in Btu/h} = 4.5\ \text{cfm}\ (h_1 - h_2)$$
$$\text{(For standard air)} \qquad (3)$$

where

h is in Btu/lb.

or, in SI units,

$$\text{Cooling load in watts} = 1.20\ (L/s)\ (h_1 - h_2) \quad (3\ SI)$$

where

h is in kJ/kg.

$$\text{Heating load in Btu/h} = 1.08\ \text{cfm}\ (t_a) \qquad (4)$$

where

t_a is in °F.

or, in SI units,

$$\text{Heating load in watts} = 1.23\ (L/s)\ (t_a) \qquad (4\ SI)$$

where

t_a is in °C.

For example:

Test Data	Psychrometric Chart or Table
EWBT = 68.5°F (20.3°C)	h_1 = 32.84 Btu/lb, da (76.52 kJ/kg)
LWBT = 53.5°F (11.9°C)	h_2 = 22.32 Btu/lb, da (52.01 kJ/kg)
cfm = 22,000 (10 384 L/s)	
LWT = 59.0°F (15°C)	
EWT = 47.5°F (8.6°C)	

$$gpm = \frac{4.5 \times 22,000 \times (32.84 - 22.32)}{500\ (59.0 - 47.5)} = 181\ gpm$$

$$L/s = \frac{1.2\ (10\ 384)\ (76.12 - 52.01)}{4000\ (15 - 8.6)} = 11.9\ L/s$$

The desired water flow is achieved by successive manual adjustments and recalculations.

Balance by Flow Measurement

All variations of balancing of hydronic systems cannot be listed; however, the generalized procedural approach should balance the system while minimizing operating cost. Excess pump head (excess operating power) should be eliminated by trimming the pump impeller, rather than by allowing the excess head to be absorbed by throttle valves, which adds a lifelong operating cost penalty to system operation.

Balance with lowest cost operation can be achieved either by preset, using calibrated balance valves followed by final adjustment and impeller trim, or by setting of system balance valves while simultaneously maintaining close watch and control of pumped flow by using the pump throttle valve. When final balance valve setting is achieved, excess pump head (pump throttle valve head loss) is eliminated by pump impeller trim.

The following is a general basic procedure based on job setting of the system balance valves:

1. General

  a. Develop a flow diagram if one is not included in the design drawing. Illustrate all balance instrumentation, and include any additional instrumentation requirements.

  b. Compare pumps, primary heat exchangers, and terminal units specified and determine if design diversity factor can be achieved.

  c. Examine control diagrams to determine necessary control adjustments to obtain design flow conditions.

  d. Using the shop drawings and flow diagrams, starting from the pumps, list the required pressure drop of each component including flow stations, and the C_v of control valves, heat exchangers, and coils. Design temperature drops should also be listed.

2. Balance Procedure—Primary and Secondary Circuits

  a. Inspect the system completely to ensure that it has been flushed out and is clean, all manual valves are in the open or operating position, all automatic valves are in their proper position and operative, the expansion tanks are properly charged, and the system is entirely void of air.

  b. Place the controls in position of design flow.

  c. Examine the flow diagram and piping for obvious short circuits; check flow and balance these down.

  d. Take suction, discharge, and differential pressure readings at both full flow and no flow.

  e. Read amperage and voltage and determine approximate brake horsepower (kW).

  f. Establish a pump curve and determine the approximate gpm (L/s) being delivered.

  g. If a total flow station exists, check the pressure differential, determine the flow, and compare with the pump curve flow.

  h. If possible, set the total flow about 10% high; maintain pumped flow to a constant value as balance proceeds by adjusting of the pump throttle valve.

  i. If branch main flow stations exist, these should be tested and set, starting by setting the shortest runs low as balancing proceeds to the longer branch runs.

  j. If the system incorporates primary-secondary pumping circuits, a reasonable balance must be obtained in the primary loop before the secondary loop can be considered. However, the secondary pumps must be running and terminal units open to flow when the primary loop is being balanced.

3. Balancing Water Terminals

  Although a high degree of accuracy in field testing is not possible, as many different sources of flow verification as possible should be used. Pressures can be read more accurately. Temperature, however, reveals improper equipment or faulty installation more readily; therefore, both should be used when possible. Using the composite coil diagram (Figure 6), the following are the possible methods of setting:

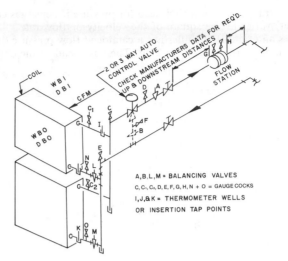

Fig. 6   Composite Coil Diagram

  a. With full flow through the coil, read differential at flow station (Taps G-H) and set A to required water volume.

  b. With full flow through the coil, read differential of Taps C-D and determine flow using Valve C_v.

  c. Take pressure differential readings between Taps C_1-N and C_2-O to verify balance between coil banks.

  d. Take water temperature in and out, air wb on and off, and air volume; by total heat transfer, determine the water volume.

  e. With three-way valves, after flow has been established through the coil, note the differential between Taps D to E and flow through the coil. Change flow to full bypass and adjust balancing Valve B until the same differential exists.

  f. With full flow through the bypass, read differential G to H at the flow station and determine volume.

  g. With full flow through the bypass, read differential F to G and determine flow using valve bypass C_v.

  h. When a coil is on a system using two-way valves, all other valves of the system must be set to achieve design diversity.

  i. A minimum of three passes or readings is necessary to ensure proper balance.

  j. Load balance checks should be made to check equipment performance and verify water flow rates.

SYSTEM COMPONENTS AS FLOW METERS

C_v Relationship

Any system component that is C_v rated or that has an accurate cataloged flow-pressure drop relationship can be used as a flow-indicating device. The use of system components (control valves, terminals, and chillers) requires an understanding of the term C_v (Carlson 1968).

Use of Equipment Manufacturer Data for Flow Measurement

Most hydronic system component manufacturers of terminal units, chillers, boilers, and valves provide flow-pressure drop information for their units. This information may be presented as only a single cataloged rating point. The single flow-pressure drop point can be used, however, to establish a C_v rating for any system component. The Bernoulli equation may be rearranged to show that head (or pressure if density is constant) varies as the square of the velocity or flow rate.

As an example, a chiller has a cataloged flow pressure drop relationship of 100 gpm at 25 ft. The base head of the chiller would be:

$$C_v = \frac{\text{gpm}}{\sqrt{\text{drop in psi}}} = \frac{100}{\sqrt{25/2.3}} = 30.33 \text{ ft}$$

where 2.3 = ft of head per psi

At 30 ft, the flow would be:

$$\text{gpm} = \sqrt{30/2.3} \cdot 30.33 = 109.5$$

In SI units (6.3 L/s at 75 kPa):

$$C_v = \frac{\text{L/s}}{\sqrt{\text{drop in kPa}}} = \frac{6.3}{\sqrt{75}} = 0.727 \text{ kPa}$$

At $\sqrt{90}$ kPa, the flow rate • 0.727 = 6.9 L/s

Accuracy of system components used as flow indicators depends on (1) accuracy of cataloged information concerning flow-pressure drop relationships and (2) accuracy of pressure differential readouts. Unfortunately, many components are rated only to a calculated pressure drop, which may or may not conform to reality. This is especially true for the shell side of shell-and-tube exchangers and some evaporators. Unrealistic data may also be stated for terminals when pressure drop has been calculated. This depends on the tube friction loss and other data used in the calculation.

As a rule, the system component should be laboratory flow tested if it is to be used as a flow indicator. Consult the component manufacturer for the basis of the pressure drop statement. If calculated, derived flow results should be regarded as having limited accuracy.

Pressure Differential Readout—By Gauge

Either gauges or manometers can be used for reading differential pressures. Gauges usually are used for high differential pressures and mercury manometers for lower differentials. The accuracy of gauge readout is diminished when two gauges are used. This is especially true when the gauges used for readout are permanently mounted on the system and, as such, subject to malfunction.

Since a differential reading is sought, a single high quality gauge should be used for readout (Figure 7). This gauge should be alternately valved to the high and low pressure side to establish the differential. Using a single gauge eliminates the usual need for static height correction and virtually eliminates errors caused by gauge calibration.

Differential pressure can also be read from specially constructed differential gauges, thus eliminating the usual need for subtraction of outlet from inlet pressures to establish differential pressure. Differential pressure gauges are usually dual gauges mechanically linked to provide a direct differential pressure readout. The differential pressure gauge readout can be stated in terms of psi (kPa) or feet of head (Pa) of 60°F (15.6°C) water.

Conversion of Differential Pressure to Head

Pressure gauges always work to a pressure registration and that the obtained differential is a pressure differential. This differential can only be restated to fluid head as a function of fluid density.

The commonly used hydronic system conversion factor is related to water density at about 60°F (15.6°C), 1 psi (6.89 kPa) equal to 2.31 ft (6.89 kPa). Pressure gauges can be calibrated

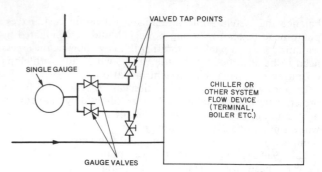

Fig. 7   Single Gauge Best for Reading Differential Pressure

to feet of water head using this conversion. The calibration only applies to water at 60°F (15.6°C), however, and the readout may require correction when a gauge so calibrated is applied to water at a significantly higher temperature.

Conversion factors and correction factors for pressure gauges for various fluid densities are shown in Table 2. The differential gauge readout should only be defined in terms of fluid head of the fluid actually causing the flow pressure differential. When this is done, the resultant fluid head can be applied to the C_v to determine actual flow rate through any flow device, if the manufacturer has correctly stated the flow to fluid head relationship.

For example, a manufacturer may test a boiler or control valve with 100°F (38°C) water. If the test differential pressure is converted to head at 100°F, a C_v independent of test temperature and density may be calculated. Differential pressures from another test made in the field at 250°F (120°C) may be converted to head at 250°F (120°C). The C_v calculated with this head is also independent of temperature. The manufacturer's data can then be directly correlated with the field test to establish flow rate at 250°F (120°C).

It is important that a density correction be made to the gauge reading when differential heads are to be used to estimate pump flows as in Figure 8. This is because of the shape of the pump curve. An incorrect head difference entry into the curve, as caused by an uncorrected gauge reading, can cause a major error in the estimated pumped flow (see Figure 8). In this case, gauge readings for a pumped liquid that has a specific gravity

Table 2   Differential Pressure Conversion to Feet of Head

Fluid specific gravity	Corresponding water temp. °F	Corresponding water temp. °C	Foot fluid head equal to 1 psi (6.89 kPa)[a]	Correction Factor when gauge is stated to ft water head at 60°F (15.6°C)[b]
1.5			1.5	
1.4			1.64	
1.3			1.75	
1.2			1.9	
1.1			2.1	
1.0	60	(15.6)	2.31	1.0
0.98	150	(65.6)	2.35	1.02
0.96	200	(93.3)	2.4	1.04
0.94	250	(121.1)	2.45	1.065
0.92	300	(148.0)	2.5	1.09
0.9	340	(171.1)	2.6	1.13
0.8			2.85	
0.7			3.3	
0.6			3.85	
0.5			4.6	

[a]Differential psi readout is multiplied by this number to obtain ft fluid head when gauge is calibrated in psi.

[b]Differential ft water head (kPa) readout is multiplied by this number to obtain ft fluid head (kPa) when gauge calibration is stated to ft head (kPa) of 60°F (15.6°C) water.

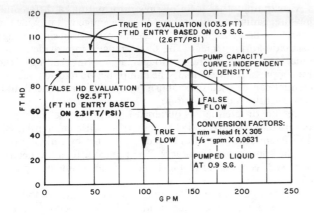

Fig. 8   Effect of Density Correction

Table 3   Conversion Table

Water Temperature		Ft head (kPa) differential
°F	(°C)	per in. Hg (kPa) differential
60	(15.6)	1.046 (0.9253)
150	(65.6)	1.07 (0.9465)
200	(93.3)	1.09 (0.9642)
250	(121.1)	1.11 (0.9819)
300	(148.9)	1.15 (1.0173)
340	(171.1)	1.165 (1.0306)

of 0.9 [2.6 ft (66 mm) liquid/psi (kPa)] were not corrected; the gauge conversion assumed at 2.31 ft (58.7 mm) liquid/psi (kPa). A 50% error in flow estimation is shown.

Use of Mercury Manometers for Differential Head Readout

Mercury manometers are also used for differential pressure readout, especially when very low differentials, great precision, or both, are required. Mercury manometers for field testing is discouraged because of the possibility of mercury blowout into the water system, which will cause rapid deterioration of system components. Mercury manometers must be handled with care. A proposed manometer arrangement is shown in Figure 9.

Reference to Figure 9 and the following instructions provide accurate manometer readings with minimum risk of mercury blowout.

1. Make sure that both legs of the manometer are filled with water and attach across flow device.
2. Open the purge bypass valve.
3. Open valved connections to high and low pressure.
4. Open the bypass vent valve slowly and purge air here.
5. Open manometer block vents and purge air at each point.
6. Close the needle valves. The mercury columns should zero in if the manometer is free of air. If not, vent again.
7. Open the needle valves and begin throttling the purge bypass valve slowly, watching mercury columns. If the manometer

has an adequate available mercury column, the valve can be closed and the differential reading taken. However, if the mercury column reaches the top of the manometer before the valve is completely closed, this indicates insufficient manometer height, and further throttling will blow mercury into the blowout collector. A longer manometer or the single gauge readout method should then be used.

Given that an accurate height of mercury differential is established, an error is often introduced when converting in. (mm) of mercury to ft of water (kPa). Conversion tables almost always state that 1 in. Hg (3.38 kPa) equals 1.13 ft (3.38 kPa) of 60°F (15.6°C), water and this conversion is usually applied. While correct for a mercury column exposed to air, the 1.13 (3.38 kPa) conversion factor is incorrect for liquid differential readout because it disregards the fact that the mercury differential column (H in Figure 9) is partially counterbalanced by an equal height of flow liquid. When a mercury manometer is used to determine differential water head in a water flow test, the conversion factor is 1 in. (25.4 mm) of mercury for 1.046 ft of water (3.13 kPa) when the water is on the order of 60°F (15.6°C).

The conversion factor changes with fluid test temperature, density, or both. Conversion factors, as shown, are to a water base; counterbalance water height H is considered to be at room temperature. Fluid flow density changes, with temperature only, are shown in Table 3.

Other Flow Information Devices, Orifice Plates and Flow Indicators

Manufacturers have provided flow information for several devices used in hydronic system balance. They are classified as (1) orifice flow meters, (2) Venturi flow meters, (3) impact or velocity head flow meters, (4) pilot tube flow meters, and (5) bypass *spring impact* flow meters.

The **orifice flow meter** is probably used most, since it has the lowest cost and has an inherent high order of accuracy. The meter is calibrated, differential head versus gpm (L/s). As a general rule, accuracy increases with increased differential across the meter. The differential pressure readout instrument may be a differential gauge, a single gauge as used in Figure 7, or a manometer. Dual gauges (high and low pressure) are seldom used because of a compounding error introduction.

The **Venturi flow meter** is more expensive than the orifice plate meter but has lower pressure loss, since a carefully formed flow path increases velocity head recovery. The actual merit of a lower pressure drop, as established by the Venturi meter, is debatable for hydronic systems. This is because most, if not all, flow information points will be balance requirement points. The flow information will generally be used for setting a balance valve, the usual requirement being a high balance valve pressure drop. The low Venturi meter pressure drop is then of little value and may be disadvantageous because the balance valve must be more sharply set than an orifice meter.

The Venturi flow meter is advantageous, however, when used in a *main* flow line and where it is to be used for flow information only. Then flow meter head loss is directly chargeable to pumping power requirements.

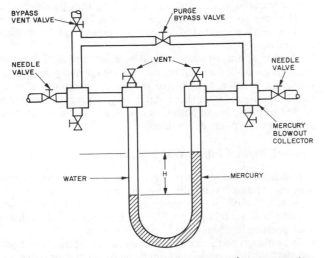

Fig. 9   Proposed Mercury Manometer Arrangement Providing for Accurate Reading and Blowout Protection

Velocity impact meters generally are costly because they need precise construction and calibration. The meters are generally of specially contoured glass or plastics permitting observation of a flow float. As flow increases, the flow float rises in the calibrated tube and indicates flow rate. Velocity impact meters generally have high accuracy, but are so expensive that their major use is in the laboratory. However, a special version of the velocity impact meter is applied to hydronic systems. This version uses the velocity head difference between the pipe side wall and the pipe center to cause flow rate through a small flow meter.

Flow accuracy of the bypass flow impact or differential velocity head flow meter is less than a flow-through type, since meter flow rate depends on meter accuracy, location of the interior impact tube, and on a necessary assurance that interior velocity profile corresponds to theory and the laboratory test calibration base. The velocity head flow meter does not establish head loss as a requirement for operation.

The **pitot tube flow meter** is also used for pipe flow measurement. The pitot is either traversed, or a calibrated averaging tube is used. Since the velocity head differences are low, manometers are generally used for readout.

The **bypass spring impact flow meter** uses a defined piping pressure drop to cause a correlated bypass side branch flow. The side branch flow impacts against a specially designed spring that increases in length with increased side branch flow. Each individual flow meter is calibrated to relate extended spring length position to main flow. The bypass spring impact flow meter has, as its principal merit, a direct readout. However, dirt collection on the spring reduces accuracy. The bypass is accordingly valved open only when a reading is made. Flow readings can be taken at any time.

The **calibrated balance valve** is a variable orifice flow meter. Balance valves can be calibrated so that a flow pressure drop relationship can be obtained for each incremental setting of the valve. A rotating plug valve may have its setting expressed in percent open or degree open; a globe valve, to percent open or number of turns. The calibrated balance valve must be manufactured with precision and care to ensure that each valve of a particular size has the same calibration characteristic.

If the above meters are to be useful, the minimum distance upstream and downstream as recommended by the meter manufacturer must be adhered to closely (Figure 10). To get a minimum pipe diameter, multiply the pipe diameter by 5, 10, 15, or 20 to give a resulting distance from the meter to any obstruction such as an elbow, valve, or tee.

The Pump: Its Use as an Indicator

The pump is not a meter; however, it can be used as an indicator of flow along with the other system components.

Differential head readings across a pump can be correlated with the pump curve to establish the pump flow rate. The order of flow accuracy is dependent on (1) accuracy of readout, (2) pump curve shape, (3) actual conformance of pump to its published curve, (4) pump operation without cavitation, (5) air-free operation, and (6) velocity head correction.

As with any other form of flow information, a differential pressure reading must be taken. A single gauge will provide the greatest accuracy. Figure 11 illustrates an often-used single gauge installation arrangement. The single gauge can provide a continual check against strainer clogging by routine reading of the strainer pressure differential. The pump suction to discharge differential can be used to establish pump differential head and, consequently, pump flow rate.

Pressure differential, as obtained from the gauge reading, is converted to ft (mm) head. The conversion, differential psi (kPa) to differential ft (mm) fluid head, is affected by fluid density. Use the conversions in Table 2. The pump differential head is then used, as in Figure 12 and Table 2, to determine pump flow rate.

As long as the differential head used to enter the pump curve is expressed as ft (mm) fluid head of the fluid being pumped, the pump curve shown by the manufacturer should be used as described. The pump curve may state that the curve was defined by test with 85 °F (29.4 °C) water. This is unimportant, since the same curve applies unchanged to 60 or 250 °F (15 or 120 °C) water, or to any fluid within a broad viscosity range.

As a general rule, pump-derived flow information, as established by differential head readout, is questionable unless the following precautions are observed:

1. The installed pump should be factory calibrated by a test to establish actual flow-head relationship for that particular pump. Production pumps can vary from the cataloged curve because of minor changes in impeller diameter, interior casting tolerances, and machine fits.
2. When a calibration curve is not available for a centrifugal pump under test, the pump could be dead-ended (discharge valve closed) to establish the no-flow shutoff head and then compared to the published curve. If the shutoff head differs from that published, draw a new curve parallel to the published curve. While not exact, the new curve will usually fit the actual pumping circumstance more accurately. Since the clearances between the impeller and casing virtually minimize the danger of damage to the pump during no-flow shutoff heat test, verification with the manufacturer is required.
3. Differential head should be determined as accurately as possible, especially for flat curved pumps.
4. The pump should be operating air-free and without cavitation. A cavitating pump will not operate to its curve, and differential readings will provide false results.
5. Ensure that the pump is operating above the minimum net positive suction head.
6. Power readings can be used as a check for the operating point when the pump is flat curved or as a reference check when the pump is suspected of cavitating or providing false readings because of air.

The power draw reading should be a wattage draw. Ampere readings cannot be trusted because of voltage and power factor problems. When a large motor is checked, a *shunt* wattmeter should be used. Given motor efficiency, wattage draw can be related to pump brake power, as described on the pump curve and operating point determined.

Central Plant Chilled Water Systems

In existing installations, the need for establishing thermal load profiles accurately is of prime importance in establishing proper primary chilled water supply temperature and flow. In new installations, actual load profiles can be compared with design load profiles to obtain valid operating data.

To be able to perform proper testing and balancing, it is essential that all interconnecting points between the primary and secondary system be designed with sufficient temperature,

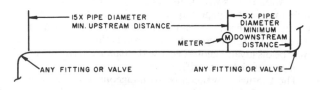

Fig. 10   Diagram Depicting Minimum Installation Dimensions for Flow Meter

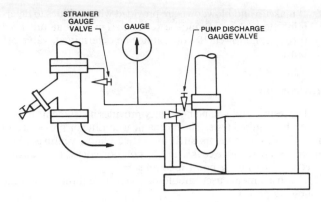

Fig. 11 Single Gauge Provides for Differential Readout Across Pump and Strainer

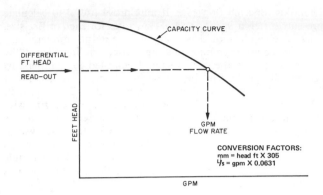

Fig. 12 Differential Head Used to Determine Pump Flow

pressure, and flow connections so that adequate data may be indicated and/or recorded.

Water Flow Instrumentation

As indicated previously, the proper location and use of system instrumentation is vital to the accuracy of the system balance. Table 4 shows a practical approach to locating temperature and pressure test points. With a table of this nature, instrumentation can be tailored to a specific design with ease and accuracy. Flow-indicating devices should be placed in water systems as follows:

1. At each major heating coil bank [10 gpm (0.63 L/s)]
2. At each major cooling coil bank [10 gpm (0.63 L/s) or more]
3. At each bridge in primary-secondary systems
4. At each main pumping station
5. At each water chiller evaporator
6. At each water chiller condenser
7. At each water boiler outlet
8. At each floor takeoff to booster reheat coils, fan coil units, induction units, ceiling panels, and radiation (Do not exceed 25 terminals off any one zone meter probe.)
9. At each vertical riser to fan coil units, induction units, and radiation
10. At the point of tie-in to existing systems

STEAM DISTRIBUTION SYSTEMS

Procedures for Steam Balancing Variable Flow Systems

A steam distribution system cannot be balanced in the same way that air and hydronic systems are adjusted or balanced by adjustable flow regulating devices. Flow regulation is accomplished by fixed restrictions built into the piping system in accordance with carefully designed pipe and orifice sizes.

It is important to have a balanced distribution of steam to all portions of the steam piping system at all load levels. This is best accomplished by the proper design of the steam distribution piping system by carefully considering steam pressure, steam quantities required by each branch circuit, pressure drops, steam velocities, pipe sizes, etc. Just as other flow systems are balanced, steam distribution systems are balanced by ensuring that the pressure drops are equalized at design flow rates for all portions of the piping system. Only marginal balancing can be done by pipe sizing. Therefore, additional steps must be taken to accomplish a balanced performance.

Steam flow balance can be improved by using spring-type packless supply valves equipped with precalibrated orifices. The

valves should have a tight shutoff between 25 in. of Hg. (85 kPa) to 60 psig (410 kPa). These valves have a non-rising stem, are available with a lockshield, and have a replaceable disk. Orifice flanges can also be used to regulate and measure steam flow at appropriate locations throughout the system. The orifice sizes are determined by the pressure drop required to provide a given flow rate at a given location in the system. It is suggested that a schedule be prepared showing (1) orifice sizes, (2) valve or pipe sizes, (3) required flow rates, and (4) corresponding pressure dif-

Table 4 Instrument Guide for Water System

Point of Information	Manifold Gauge	Single Gauge	Thermometer	Test Well	Pressure Tap
Pump—Suction, Discharge	x				
Strainer—In, Out					x
Cooler—In, Out		x	x		
Condensers—In, Out		x	x		
Concentrator—In, Out		x	x		
Absorber—In, Out		x	x		
Tower Cell—In, Out				x	x
Heat Exchanger—In, Out	x		x		
Coil—In, Out				x	x
Coil Bank—In, Out		x	x		
Booster Coil—In, Out					x
Cool Panel—In, Out					x
Heat Panel—In, Out				x	x
Unit Heater—In, Out					x
Induction—In, Out					x
Fan Coil—In, Out					x
Water Boiler—In, Out			x		
3-Way Valve—All Ports					x
Zone Return Main		x			
Bridge—In, Out		x			
Water Makeup		x			
Expansion Tank		x			
Strainer Pump					x
Strainer Main	x				
Zone Three-Way—All Ports				x	x

ferentials for each flow rate. It may prove useful to calculate pressure differentials for several flow rates for each orifice size. Such a schedule should be maintained for future reference.

After the appropriate regulating orifices are installed in the proper locations, the system should be tested for tightness by sealing all openings in the system and applying a vacuum of 20 in. of Hg (500 mm), which should be held for 2 hours. Next, the system should be readied for warm-up and pressurizing with steam following the procedures outlined in Section VI of the *ASME Boiler and Pressure Vessel Code*. After the initial warm-up and system pressurization, evaluate system steam flow and compare with system requirements. The orifice schedule calculated earlier will now be of value should any of the orifices need to be changed.

Steam Flow Measuring Devices

Many devices are available for measuring flow in steam piping systems: (1) steam meters, (2) condensate meters, (3) orifice plates (mentioned above), (4) venturi fittings, (5) steam recorders, and (6) manometers for reading differential pressures across orifice plates and Venturi fittings. Some of these devices are permanently affixed into the piping system to facilitate taking instantaneous readings that may be necessary for proper system operation and control. A surface pyrometer used in conjunction with a pressure gauge is a convenient way to determine steam saturation temperature and the degree of superheat at various locations in the system. Such information can be used to evaluate performance characteristics of the system.

COOLING TOWERS

Field testing cooling towers is a demanding and difficult task. The Cooling Tower Performance Test (AABC), establishes a procedure for these tests. Certain general guidelines for testing cooling towers are as follows.

1. Conditions at Time of Test

a. Water flow within 15% of design flow
b. Heat load within 30% of design heat load and stabilized
c. Entering wet bulb within 12 °F (6.7 °C) of entering design wet bulb
d. Using the above limitations and as accurate field readings as possible, a projection to design conditions produces an accuracy of ±5% of tower performance.

2. Conditions for Performing Test

a. Water circulating system serving the tower should be thoroughly cleaned of all dirt and foreign matter. Samples of water should be clear and indicate clear passage of water through pumps, piping, screens, and strainers.
b. Fans serving the cooling tower should be operating in proper rotation. Foreign obstructions should be removed. Permanent obstruction should be noted.
c. Interior filling of cooling tower should be clean and free of foreign materials such as scale, algae, or tar.
d. Water level in the tower basin should be maintained at the proper level. Visually check the basin sump during full flow to determine that the centrifugal action of the water is not causing entrainment of air, which could cause pump cavitation.
e. Water circulating pumps should be tested with full flow through the tower. If flow exceeds design, it should be valved down until design is reached. The flow finally set should be maintained throughout the test period. All valves, except necessary balancing valves, should be in the full open position.

f. If makeup and blowdown are provided with facilities to determine flow, these should be set to design flow at full flow through the tower. If flow cannot be determined, valve off both.

Instruments

The testing and balancing agency provides instruments to perform the required tests. The mechanical contractor provides and installs all components such as orifice plates, venturis, thermometer wells, gauge cocks, and corporation cocks. The designer specifies measuring point locations.

The instruments used should be recently calibrated from the following group:

1. Temperature

a. Mercury with divisions of 0.2 °F (0.1 °C) in proper well for water should be used.
b. Mercury thermometer with solar shield and 0.2 °F division or thermocouple with 0.2 °F (0.1 °C) reading having mechanical asperation for wet-bulb readings should be used.
c. Sling psychrometer may be used for rough checks.
d. Mercury thermometers with 0.2 °F (0.1 °C) should be used for taking dry-bulb readings.

2. Water Flow

a. Orifice or Venturi drops can be read using a water-over-mercury manometer or a recently calibrated differential pressure gauge.
b. Where corporation cocks are installed, a pitot tube and manometer traverse can be made by trained technicians.

Test Method

The actual test consists of the following steps:

1. Conduct water flow tests to determine volume of water on the tower, volume of makeup, and blowdown water.
2. Conduct water temperature tests, if possible, in suitable wells as close to the tower as possible. Temperature readings at pumps or the condensing element are not acceptable in tower evaluation. If there are no wells, surface pyrometer readings are acceptable.
3. Take makeup water volume and temperature readings at the point of entry to the system.
4. Take blowdown volume and temperature readings at the point of discharge from system.
5. Take inlet and outlet dry- and wet-bulb temperature readings using the prescribed instruments.
   a. Use wet bulb entering and leaving to determine tower actual performance as against design.
   b. Use wet bulb and dry bulb entering and leaving to determine evaporation involved.
6. If the tower has a ducted inlet or outlet, where a reasonable duct traverse can be made, use this air volume as a cross check of tower performance.
7. Take wet- and dry-bulb temperature readings between 3 and 5 ft (0.91 and 1.52 m) from the tower on all inlet sides. These readings shall be taken halfway between the base and the top of the inlet louvers at no more than 5-ft (1.52-m) spacing horizontally, and then they should be averaged. Note any unusual inlet conditions.
8. Note wind velocity and direction at the time of test.
9. Take test readings continually with a minimum of time lapse between readings.
10. If the first test indicates a tower deficiency, perform two additional tests to verify the original readings.

TEMPERATURE CONTROL VERIFICATION

The test and balance technician should work in close cooperation with the temperature control installer to ensure a complete project. The balancing technician need only verify proper operation, not adjust, relocate, or recalibrate any controls.

Upon completing the testing, adjusting, and balancing of all HVAC systems, the automatic control system(s) should be staged to prove its capability of matching system capacity to varying load conditions. In the event all flow balancing is completed in a particular season of operation, such as the cooling cycle, arrangements for the opposite season (heating cycle) control verification should be implemented and completed prior to project acceptance.

1. Suggested procedure

a. Obtain design drawings and specifications and become thoroughly acquainted with the design intent.
b. Obtain copies of approved shop drawings of control diagrams.
c. Compare design to installed equipment and field installation.
d. Obtain manufacturer's recommended operating and testing procedure.
e. Verify that all controllers are calibrated and in control.
f. Check for proper location of transmitters and controllers. Note any adverse conditions that would effect control. Suggest relocation, if necessary.

2. Pneumatic systems

a. Verify main control supply air for proper pressure and observe compressor and dryer operation.
b. Verify calibration of all controllers and sensitivity of each controller and note any overlap in controlled devices.
c. Compare all control terminations with design drawings.
d. Verify operation of all limiting controllers (i.e., firestats, freezestats, preheat thermostats, high and low thermostats).
e. Activate controlled devices, checking for free travel and proper operation of dampers. Verify proper application of N.O. and N.C. positions.
f. Verify operation of pilot positioners, sequence of damper operators, and operation of control valves to ensure proper relationship.
g. Check adjustment of all pressure/electric end switches and mercury switches for proper setting and operation for the seasonal cycle of operation in effect. Simulate conditions to activate sequences used in the opposite season.
h. Check level and zero of inclined gauge or U-tube manometers. Verify proper location of sensors.
i. Verify operation of lockout or interlock system.
j. Verify the span of control from a normally closed position to a normally open position, observing any dead bands, excessive pressures, etc.
k. Verify sequence of operations (i.e., night setback, switchovers, resets, cooling tower control, etc.).

3. Electric systems

For high voltage and low voltage, complete steps (a) through (f) under the "Suggested Procedure" section.

a. With voltmeter, verify control voltage.
b. Set thermostat in cool position and turn to lowest setting. Verify proper operation of contactor, damper motor, etc.
c. Set thermostat to highest setting. Verify proper action of damper motors, end switches, and resistance heat sequences.
d. Activate solenoid valves, low limit thermostats, and lockout devices to verify proper action.

4. Direct Digital Control (DDC)

a. Check software algorithms for each control loop for accuracy and correct application.

b. Check all control loops and their individual field points for correct response.
c. Check calibration of all field sensors.
d. Check calibration and response time on transducers.
e. Check fail safe modes (N.O., N.C., etc.) of all control devices.
f. Manually stroke each damper and control valve.
g. Check lightning protection and system battery backup.
h. Check phone modem.
i. With system in full operation, test each control loop at both ends of control range.

5. Electronic Digital

a. Check all control loops and their individual field points for correct response.
b. Check calibration of all field sensors.
c. Check calibration and response time of all transducers.
d. Check fail safe modes (N.C., N.O., etc.) of all control devices.
e. Manually stroke each damper and control valve.
f. Check lightning protection.
g. With system in full operation, test each control loop at both ends of control range.

6. Energy Management Systems (EMS)

a. The calibration and verification of sequences usually does not include verification of sensors used on the energy management system. After the total system control has been checked and made fully operational, the energy management system contractor should verify that readouts of all sensors and transmitters are within the range of the control scope. The energy management system contractor should contact the control representative and the test balance technician to aid in tracing any sensor problem found after a thorough check.

FIELD SURVEY FOR ENERGY AUDIT

An energy audit is an organized survey of a specific building to identify and measure all energy uses, determine probable sources of energy losses, and list energy conservation opportunities. This is usually performed as a team effort under the direction of a qualified energy engineer. The field data gathering portion of the work can be done by firms employing technicians trained in testing, adjusting, and balancing.

Instruments

To determine a building's energy usage characteristics, an accurate measurement of existing conditions must be made. This requires proper instruments. Accurate measurements not only point out opportunities to reduce waste, but also provide a record of the actual conditions in the building before energy conservation measures were taken. They provide a compilation of data of installed equipment and a record of equipment performance prior to changes.

Remember that judgments will be made based upon the information gathered during the field survey. *That which is not accurately measured cannot be properly evaluated.*

Generally, the instruments required for performing testing, adjusting, and balancing are sufficient for energy conservation surveying. Possible additional instruments include a power factor meter, a light meter, combustion testing equipment, refrigeration gauges, and equipment for recording temperatures, fluid flow rates, and energy use over time. Only high quality instruments should be used.

Observation of system operation and any information the technician can obtain from the operating personnel pertaining to the operation should be included in the report.

Data Recording

Organized record keeping is extremely important. A camera is also helpful. Photographs of building components and mechanical and electrical equipment can be reviewed later when the data is analyzed.

Data sheets needed for energy conservation field surveys contain different and, in some cases, more comprehensive information than those used for testing, adjusting, and balancing. Generally, the energy engineer determines the degree of field work to be performed; data sheets should be compatible with the instructions received.

Building Systems

The most effective way to reduce building energy waste is to identify and define the energy load by building system. This provides an orderly procedure for tabulating the load. Also, the most effective energy conservation opportunities can be achieved more quickly because high priorities can be assigned to systems that consume the most energy.

For this purpose, *load* is defined as the quantity of energy used in a building, or by one of its subsystems, for a given period.

A building can be divided into nonenergized systems and energized systems. Nonenergized systems are those systems that do not require outside energy sources such as electricity and fuel. Energized systems require outside energy sources. Examples might be mechanical systems and the electrical system. Energized and nonenergized systems can be divided into subsystems defined by function. Nonenergized subsystems are (1) building site, envelope, interior, and subsystem, (2) building utilization subsystem, and (3) building operation subsystem.

Building Site, Envelope, and Interior

The site, envelope, and interior are surveyed to determine how they can be changed to reduce the building load that the mechanical and electrical systems must meet without adversely affecting the building's appearance. This requires uncovering energy-wasting items and recording any existing conditions affecting the practicability of making changes to eliminate waste.

It is important to compare actual conditions with conditions assumed by the designer, so that the mechanical and electrical systems can be adjusted to balance their capacities to satisfy the real imposed needs.

Building Use

The functioning of people within the building envelope subsystem is one of the most important subsystems when considering the building load; it must be observed because the action of people affects the energy usage of all other building subsystems.

Building use loads can be classified as (1) people occupancy loads and (2) people operation loads. People occupancy loads are related to schedule, density, and mixing of occupancy types (e.g., process and office). People operation loads are varied, such as (1) operation of manual window shading devices, (2) setting of room thermostats, and (3) such conservation-related habits as turning off lights, closing doors and windows, turning off energized equipment when not in use, and not wasting domestic hot or chilled water.

Building Operation Subsystem

This subsystem consists of the operation and maintenance of all of the building subsystems. The load on the building operation subsystem is affected by such factors as (1) the time that janitorial services are performed, (2) janitorial crew size and time required to do the cleaning, (3) amount of lighting used to perform janitorial functions, (4) quality of the equipment maintenance program, (5) system operational practices, and (6) equipment efficiencies.

Building Energized Systems

The energized subsystems of the building are generally plumbing, heating, ventilating, cooling, space conditioning, control, electrical, and food service. Although these systems are interrelated and often use common components, it is important to evaluate the energy usage of each subsystem independently, as nearly as possible, for a logical organization of data. In this way, proper energy conservation measures for each subsystem can be developed.

Process Loads

In addition to building subsystem loads, the process load in most buildings must be evaluated. The energy field auditor must be able to determine its impact.

Most process tasks not only require energy for performing a service, but they also affect energy consumption of other building subsystems. For example, if a process releases large amounts of heat to the space, the process consumes energy and also imposes a large load on the cooling system.

Guidelines for Making a Field Study Form

A brief checklist that outlines requirements for a field study form needed to conduct an energy audit follows.

1. **Inspection and observation of all systems.** Record the following physical and mechanical conditions:

   a. Fan blades, fan scroll, drives, belt tightness and alignment
   b. Filters, coils and housing tightness
   c. Ductwork (equipment room and space, where possible)
   d. Strainers
   e. Insulation ducts and piping
   f. Makeup water treatment and cooling tower

2. **Interview Physical Plant Supervisor.** Record conditions to the following survey:

   a. Is the system operating as designed? If not, what changes have been made to ensure its performance?
   b. Have there been changes, modifications, or additions to the system?
   c. If the system has been a problem, list problems by frequency of occurrence.
   d. Are any systems cycled? If so, which systems and when, and would building load permit it?

3. **Recording of System Information.** Record the following system/equipment identification:

   a. Type of system—single zone, multizone, double-duct low or high velocity, reheat, variable volume, or other
   b. System arrangement—fixed minimum outside air, no relief, gravity or power relief, economizer gravity relief, exhaust return, or other
   c. Air-handling equipment—fans (supply, return, or exhaust): manufacturer, model and size, type, class; dampers (vortex, scroll, or discharge); motors: manufacturer, hp (kW), full load amperes, voltage, phase, and service factor
   d. Chilled and hot water coils—area in ft² (m²), tubes on face, fins per in. (mm), and number of rows (coil data necessary when shop drawings are not available)

e. Terminals—high pressure mixing box: manufacturer, model, type (reheat, constant volume, variable volume, induction); grilles, registers, and diffusers: manufacturer, model, style, and AK factor

f. Main heating and cooling pumps, over 5 hp (3.7 kW)—manufacturer, pump service and identification, model and size, impeller diameter, rpm, gpm (L/s), head at full flow, head at no flow; motor data: hp (kW), rpm, voltage, amperes, and service factor

g. Refrigeration equipment—chiller manufacturer, type, model, serial number, nominal tons (kW), bhp (kW), total heat rejection, motor [hp (kW), amperes, volts], chiller pressure drop, entering and leaving chilled water temperatures, condenser pressure drop, condenser entering and leaving water temperatures, running amperes and volts, no load running amperes and volts

h. Cooling tower—manufacturer, size, type, nominal tons (kW), range, gpm (L/s), and EWB

i. Heating equipment—boiler (small through medium) manufacturer, fuel, Btu/h (W) input (rated), and Btu/h (W) output (rated)

4. **Recording of Test Data.** Record the following test data:

a. Systems in normal mode of operation (if possible)—fan motor: running amperes and volts and power factor [over 5 hp (3.7 kW)]; fan: rpm, total air (pitot tube traverse where possible), and static pressure (discharge static minus inlet total); static profile drawing (static pressure across filters, heating coil, cooling coil, and dampers); static pressures at ends of runs of the system (identifying locations)

b. Cooling coils—entering dry- and wet-bulb temperatures, leaving dry and wet bulb, entering and leaving water temperature, coil pressure drop (where pressure taps permit and manufacture's ratings can be obtained), cfm (L/s) of coil (when other than fan), outdoor wet and dry bulb, time of day, and conditions (sunny or cloudy)

c. Heating coils—entering and leaving dry-bulb temperature, entering and leaving water temperatures, coil pressure drop (where pressure taps permit and manufacture's ratings can be obtained), and cfm (L/s) of coil (when other than fan)

d. Pumps—no flow head ft (kPa), full flow discharge psi (kPa), full flow suction psi (kPa), full flow differential ft (kPa), motor running amperes and volts, and power factor [over 5 hp (3.7 kW)]

e. Chiller (under cooling load conditions)—chiller pressure drop, entering and leaving chilled water temperatures, condenser pressure drop, entering and leaving condenser water temperature, running amperes and volts, no load running amperes and volts, chilled water on and off, and condenser water on and off

f. Cooling tower—gpm (L/s) on tower, entering and leaving water temperature, entering and leaving wet bulb, fan motor (amperes, volts, power factor [over 5 hp (3.73 kW)] ambient wet bulb)

g. Boiler (full fire)—input Btu/h (W) (if possible), %CO_2, stack temperature, efficiency, and complete Orsat test on large boilers

h. Boiler controls—description of the operation

i. Temperature controls—operating and set point temperatures for mixed air controller, leaving air controller, hot deck controller, cold deck controller, outdoor reset, interlock controls, and damper controls; description of complete control system and any malfunctions.

j. Outside air intake versus exhaust air—total airflow measured by pilot tube traverses of both outside air intake and exhaust air systems obtained where possible. Determine if there is an imbalance in the exhaust system such that it will cause infiltration. Observe the exterior walls of building to determine if outside air can infiltrate into the return air system (record outside air temperature, dry and wet bulb; return air temperature, dry and wet bulb; and return air plenum temperature, dry and wet bulb). The greater the differential between outside and return air, the more evident the problem will appear.

TESTING FOR SOUND AND VIBRATION

Testing for sound and vibration ensures that equipment is operating satisfactorily and that no objectionable noise and vibration are transmitted to the building structure and occupied space. Although sound and vibration are specialized fields that require expertise not normally developed by the HVAC engineer, the procedures to test HVAC systems are relatively simple and can be performed with a minimum of equipment by following the steps outlined in this section. Although useful information is provided for resolving common noise and vibration problems, this section does not provide information on problem solving or the design of HVAC systems. For these purposes, a thorough understanding of the material in Chapter 52 is essential. If the engineer is not experienced in this area, the services of an acoustical consultant should be obtained.

TESTING FOR SOUND

The present state of the art does not permit tests to determine if equipment is operating with desired sound levels. Field tests can determine only sound pressure levels, and equipment ratings are almost always in terms of sound power levels. Until new techniques are developed, the testing engineer can determine only if sound pressure levels are within desired limits and, if not, determine which equipment, systems or components are the source of excessive or disturbing transmission.

Sound-Measuring Instruments

Although an experienced listener can often determine whether or not systems are operating in an acceptably quiet manner, sound-measuring instruments are necessary to determine whether system noise levels are in compliance with specified criteria and, if not, to obtain and report detailed information to evaluate the cause of noncompliance. Basic instruments normally used in field testing are as follows:

The **precision sound level meter** is the instrument used to measure sound pressure level. The most basic sound level meters measure overall sound pressure level and have up to three weighted scales that provide limited filtering capability. The instrument is useful in assessing outdoor noise levels in certain situations and can provide limited information on the low frequency content of overall noise levels, but it provides insufficient for problem diagnosis and solution. Its usefulness in evaluating indoor HVAC sound sources in limited.

Proper evaluation of HVAC sound sources requires a sound level meter capable of filtering overall sound levels into frequency increments of one octave or less.

Sound Analyzers are instruments that provide detailed information about the sound pressure levels at various frequencies through filtering networks. The most popular sound analyzers are the octave band and center frequency types, which break the sound into the eight-octave bands of audible sound. Instruments are also available for 0.33, 0.1, and narrower spectrum analysis; however, these are primarily for laboratory and research applications. Sound analyzers (octave band or center frequency) are required where specifications are based on Noise

Criterion (NC) Curves or similar criteria based on frequency, and for problem jobs where a knowledge of frequency is necessary to determine proper corrective action.

Personal Computers have emerged as a versatile sound-measuring tool. Software systems used in conjunction with portable computers allow all of the functional capabilities described above, plus many that previously required a fully equipped acoustical laboratory. This type of sound-measuring system is many times faster and much more versatile that conventional sound level meters. With suitable accessories, it can also be used to evaluate vibration levels.

A **stethoscope** is an invaluable instrument in measuring sound levels and tracking down problems, as it enables the listener to determine the direction of the sound source.

Regardless of the type of sound-measuring system used, the system should be calibrated prior to each use. Some systems have built-in calibration, and other use external calibrators. Much information is available on the proper application and use of sound-measuring instruments.

Air noise caused by air flowing at a velocity of over 1000 fpm (5.0 m/s) or winds over 12 mph (5.4 m/s) can cause substantial error in sound measurements due to wind effect on the microphone. For outdoor measurements or in places where air movement is prevalent, a wind screen for the microphone or a special microphone is required.

Sound Level Criteria

In the absence of specified values, the testing engineer must determine if sound levels are within acceptable limits. The criteria provided in Chapter 52 is acceptable for most applications. Note that complete absence of noise is seldom a design criterion, except for certain critical locations such as sound and recording studios. In most locations, a certain amount of noise is desirable to mask other noises and provide speech privacy, as well as provide an acoustically pleasing environment, since few people can function effectively in extreme quiet. Chapter 7, Table 2, in the 1985 FUNDAMENTALS Volume lists typical sound pressure levels. In determining allowable HVAC equipment noise, it is as inappropriate to demand 30 dB for a factory where the normal noise level is 75 dB as it is to specify 60 dB for a private office where normal noise level might be 35 dB.

Most field sound measuring instruments and techniques yield an accuracy of ±3 dB, which is about the smallest difference in sound pressure level that the average person can discern. A reasonable tolerance for sound criteria is 5 dB, and, if 35 dBA were to be considered the maximum allowable noise, the design engineer should specify 30 dBA.

The measured sound level of any location is a combination of all sound sources present including sound generated by HVAC equipment, as well as sound from other sources such as plumbing systems and fixtures, elevators, light ballasts, and outside noises. In testing HVAC systems for sound, all sources of sound from other than HVAC equipment are considered background or ambient noise.

Background sound measurements generally have to be made when (1) specification requires determination of sound levels from HVAC equipment only as opposed to the sound level in a space not exceeding a certain specified level, (2) sound level in space exceeds desirable level, in which case it is necessary to determine what part of the noise is contributed by the HVAC system, and (3) for residential locations and space where there is little significant background noise during the evening hours and where generally low allowable noise levels are specified or desired. Because background noise from outside sources such as vehicular traffic can fluctuate widely, sound measurements for residential locations are best made in the normally quiet evening hours.

Sound-Testing Procedures

Ideally, the building should be completed and ready for occupancy before sound level tests are taken. All spaces in which readings will be taken should be furnished with drapes, carpeting, and furniture, as these affect the room absorption and the subjective quality of the sound. In actual practice, since most tests have to be conducted before the space is completely finished and furnished for final occupancy, the testing engineer must make some allowances. Since furnishings increase the absorption coefficient and reduce sound pressure level that can be expected between most *live* and *dead* spaces to 4 dB, the following guidelines should suffice for measurements made in unfurnished spaces. If sound pressure level is 5 dB or more over specified or desired criterion, it can be assumed that criterion will not be met, even with the increased absorption provided by furnishings. If sound pressure level is 0 to 4 dB greater than specified or desired criterion, recheck when the room is furnished to determine compliance.

Follow this general procedure:

1. Obtain a complete set of accurate, as-built drawings and specifications, including duct and piping details. Review specifications to determine sound and vibration criteria and any special instructions for testing.
2. Visually check systems for noncompliance with plans and specifications, obvious errors, and poor workmanship. Turn system on for audible check. Listen for noise and vibration, especially duct leaks and loose fittings that can be the source of disturbing noise.
3. Adjust and balance equipment, as described in other sections of this chapter so that final acoustical tests are made with the system as it will be operating. It is desirable to perform acoustical tests for both summer and winter operation, but where this is not practical, make tests for the summer operating mode, as it usually has the potential for higher sound levels. Tests must be made for all mechanical equipment and systems including standby.
4. Check calibration of instruments.
5. Measure sound levels in all areas as required, combining measurements as indicated in Item 3 if equipment or systems must be operated separately. Before final measurements are made in any particular area, survey the area using an A-weighted scale reading (dBA) to determine the location of highest sound pressure level. Indicate this location on a testing form and use it for test measurements. Restrict the preliminary survey to determine location of test measurements to areas that can be occupied by standing or sitting personnel. For example, measurements would not be made directly in front of a diffuser located in the ceiling, but they would be made as close to the diffuser as standing or sitting personnel might be situated. In the absence of specified sound criteria, the testing engineer shall measure sound pressure levels in all occupied spaces to determine compliance with critieria, as indicated in Chapter 52, and to determine any sources of excessive or disturbing noise.
6. Determine if background noise measurements must be made.
   a. If specification requires determination of sound level from HVAC equipment only, it will be necessary to take background noise readings by turning HVAC equipment off.
   b. If specification requires compliance with a specific noise level or criteria (for example: sound levels in office areas shall not exceed 35 dBA), ambient noise measurements need be made only if the noise level in any area exceeds the specified value.
   c. For residential locations and areas requiring very low noise levels such as sound recording studios and locations that will be used during the normally quieter evening hours,

it is usually desirable to make sound measurements in the evening and/or take ambient noise measurements.

7. For outdoor noise measurements to determine noise as radiated by outdoor or roof-mounted equipment such as cooling towers and condensing units, review information contained in the "Sound Control for Outdoor Equipment Installations" section of Chapter 52 for proper procedure and necessary calculations.

Noise Transmission Problems

Regardless of the precautions taken by the specifying engineer and the installing contractors, situations can occur where the sound level exceeds specified or desired levels and there will be occasional complaints of noise in completed installations. A thorough understanding of Chapter 52 and the "Vibration Testing" section of this chapter is desirable before attempting to resolve any noise and vibration transmission problems. The following is intended as an overall guide rather than a detailed problem-solving procedure.

All noise transmission problems can be evaluated in terms of the source-path-receiver concept. Objectionable transmission can be resolved by (1) reducing the noise at the source by replacing defective equipment, repairing improper operation, proper balancing and adjusting, and replacing with quieter equipment; (2) attenuating the paths of transmission with silencers, vibration isolators, and wall treatment to increase transmission loss, and (3) reducing or masking the objectionable noise at the receiver by increasing room absorption or introducing a nonobjectionable masking sound. The following discussion includes (1) ways to identify actual noise sources, using only simple instruments or without any instruments and (2) possible corrections.

When the engineer is troubleshooting in the field, it is important to listen to the offending sound. The best instruments are no substitute for careful listening, as the human ear has the remarkable ability to identify certain familiar sounds such as bearing squeak or duct leaks and is able to discern small changes in frequency or sound character that might not be apparent from meter readings only. The ear is also a good direction and range finder, as noise generally gets louder as one approaches the source, and direction can often be determined by turning the head. The hands can also identify noise sources. Air jets from duct leaks can often be felt, and the sound of rattling or vibrating panels or parts often changes or stops when these parts are touched.

In trying to locate noise sources and transmission paths, the engineer should consider the location of the affected area. In areas remote from equipment rooms containing significant noise producers (as indicated in Chapter 52, Table 3) but adjacent to shafts, noise is usually the result of structure-borne transmission through pipe and duct supports and anchors. In areas adjoining, above, or below equipment rooms, noise is usually caused by openings (acoustical leaks) in the separating floor or wall or by improper, ineffective, or maladjusted vibration isolation systems.

Unless the noise source or path of transmission is quite obvious, the best way to identify it is by eliminating all sources systematically as follows:

1. Make sure that the objectionable noise is caused by the HVAC system by turning off all equipment. If the noise stops, the HVAC system components (compressors, fans, and pumps) must be operated separately to determine which are contributing to the objectionable noise. Where one source of disturbing noise predominates, the test can be performed starting with all equipment in operation and turning off components or systems until the disturbing noise is eliminated. Tests can also be performed starting with all equipment turned off and operating various component equipment singularly, which permits evaluation of noise from each individual component.

When testing with a sound level meter, any system component can be termed a predominant noise source if, when the equipment is shut off, the sound level drops 3 dBA or, if measurements are taken with equipment operating individually, the sound level is within 3 dBA of the overall objectionable measurement.

When a sound level meter is not used, it is best to start with all equipment operating and shut off equipment one at a time, since the ear can reliably detect differences and changes in noise but not absolute levels.

2. When it has been established that some part of the HVAC system is the source of the objectionable noise, try to further isolate the source. By walking around the room, determine whether the noise is coming from the air outlets or returns, the hung ceiling, or through the floors or walls.

3. If the noise is coming through the hung ceiling, check that ducts and pipes are isolated properly and not touching the hung ceiling supports or electrical fixtures, which would provide large noise radiating surfaces. If ducts and pipes are the source of noise and are isolated properly, the possible remedies are to reduce the noise by changing flow conditions, installing silencers, and/or wrapping the duct or pipe with an acoustical barrier such as a lead blanket.

4. If noise is coming through the walls, ceiling, or floor, check for any openings to adjoining shafts or equipment rooms, and check vibration isolation systems to ensure that there is no structure-borne transmission from nearby equipment rooms or shafts.

5. Noise traced to air outlets or returns usually requires careful evaluation by an engineer or acoustical consultant to determine the source and proper corrective action. Chapter 52 contains much useful information on this subject. In general, air outlets can be selected to meet any acoustical design goal by keeping the velocity sufficiently low. For any given outlet, the sound level increases about 2 dB for each 10% increase in airflow velocity over the vanes, and doubling the velocity increases the sound level by about 16 dB. Also, the sound approach conditions caused by improperly located control dampers or improperly sized diffuser necks can easily increase sound levels by 10 to 20 dB.

A simple yet effective instrument that aids in locating noise sources is a microphone mounted on a pole. It can be used to localize noises in hard-to-reach places, such as hung ceilings and behind heavy furniture.

6. If the noise is traced to an air outlet, measure the A-sound level close to it but with no air blowing against the microphone. Then, remove the inner assembly or core of the air outlet and repeat the reading with the meter and the observer in exactly the same position as before. If the second reading is more than 3 dB below the first, a significant amount of noise is caused by airflow over the vanes of the diffuser or grille. In this case, check whether the system is balanced properly. As little as 10% too much air will increase the sound generated by an air outlet by 2.5 dB. As a last resort, a larger air outlet could be substituted to obtain lower air velocities, and hence less turbulence for the same air quality. Before considering this, however, the air approach to the outlet should be checked.

Noise far exceeding the normal rating of a diffuser or grille is generated when a throttled damper is installed close to it. Air jets impinge upon the vanes or cones of the outlet and produce *edge tones* similar to the hiss heard when blowing against the edge of a ruler. The material of the vanes has no effect on this noise, although loose vanes may cause additional noise from vibration.

When balancing air outlets with integral volume dampers, consider the static pressure drop across the damper, as well as the air quantity. Separate volume dampers should be installed sufficiently upstream from the outlet so that there is no jet impingement. Plenum inlets should be brought in from the side, so that the jets do not impinge on the outlet vanes.

7. If the air outlets are eliminated as sources of excessive noise, inspect the fan room. If possible, change the fan speed by about $\pm 10\%$. If resonance is involved, this small change can make a big difference.

8. Sometimes fans are poorly matched to the system. If a belt-driven fan delivers air at a higher static pressure than is needed to move the design air quantity through the system, reduce the fan speed by changing sheaves. If the fan does not deliver enough air, consider increasing the fan speed only after checking the duct system for unavoidable losses. Turbulence in the air approach to the fan inlet not only increases the fan sound generation, but decreases its air capacity. Other parts that may cause excessive turbulence are dampers, duct bends, and sudden enlargements or contractions of the duct.

When investigating fan noise, assistance can usually be obtained from the supplier or manufacturer of the fan.

9. If additional acoustical treatment is to be installed in the ductwork, obtain a frequency analysis. This involves the use of an octave band analyzer and should generally be left to a trained acoustician.

TESTING FOR VIBRATION

Testing for vibration is necessary to ensure that (1) equipment is operating with satisfactory vibration levels and (2) objectionable vibration and noise are not transmitted to the building structure. Although these two factors are interrelated, they are not necessarily interdependent. A different solution is required for each, and it is essential to test both the isolation system and the vibration levels of the equipment.

General Procedure

The general order of steps in vibration testing are as follows:

1. Make a visual check of all equipment for obvious errors that must be corrected immediately.

2. Make sure all isolation systems are *free floating* and not short circuited by any obstruction between equipment or equipment base and building structure.

3. Turn on the system for an audible check of any obviously rough operation. Check bearings with a stethoscope. Bearing check is especially important because bearings can become defective in transit and/or if equipment was not stored and maintained properly. Defective bearings should be replaced immediately to avoid damage to the shaft and other components.

4. Equipment and systems should be adjusted and balanced, as described in other sections of this chapter, so final vibration tests are made on equipment as it will actually be operating.

5. Test equipment vibration.

Instrumentation

Although instruments are not required to test vibration isolation systems, they are essential to test equipment vibration properly.

Sound level meters and **computer-driven sound measuring systems,** described under "Sound Measuring Instruments," are the most useful instruments for measuring and evaluating vibration. Usually, they are fitted with accelerometers or vibration pickups, which permits a full range of vibration measurement and analysis. Other instruments used for testing vibration in the field are described below.

Reed Vibrometers are relatively inexpensive instruments often used for testing vibration, but relative inaccuracy limits their usefulness.

Vibrometers are moderately priced instruments that measure vibration amplitude by means of a light beam projected on a graduated scale.

Vibration Meters are moderately priced electronic instruments that measure vibration amplitude on a meter scale and are very simple to use.

Vibrographs are moderately priced mechanical instruments that measure both amplitude and frequency. They are useful for analysis and testing because they provide a chart recording showing amplitude, frequency, and actual wave form of vibration. They can be used for simple yet accurate determination of the natural frequency of shafts, components, and systems by a *bump test.*

Vibration Analyzers are relatively expensive electronic instruments that measure amplitude and frequency, usually incorporating a variable filter.

Strobe Lights are often used with many of the above instruments in analysis and balancing of rotating equipment.

Stethoscopes that amplify sound are available as inexpensive *mechanic's* type (basically, a standard stethoscope with a probe attachment); relatively inexpensive types incorporating a tuneable filter; and moderately priced powered types that electronically amplify sound and provide some type of meter and/or chart recording. Also, stethoscopes are often used to determine whether or not bearings are bad.

The choice of instrumentation depends on the test. A stethoscope should be part of every tester's kit as it is one of the most practical, yet least expensive, instruments and one of the best means of checking bearings. The vibrometers and vibration meters can be used to measure vibration amplitude as an acceptance check. Since they cannot measure frequency they cannot be used for analysis and primarily function as a go/no go instrument. The best acceptance criteria consider both amplitude and frequency. However, since vibrometers and vibration meters are moderately priced and easy to use, they are widely used. Anyone seriously concerned with vibration testing should have an instrument that can determine frequency, as well as amplitude, such as a vibrograph or vibration analyzer.

Testing Vibration Isolation Systems

The following steps should be taken to ensure that vibration isolation systems are functioning properly:

1. Assure that system is *free floating* by applying an unbalanced load, which should cause system to move freely and easily. On floor-mounted equipment, check that there are no obstructions between the base or foundation and the building structure that would cause transmission while still permitting equipment to *rock* relatively free because of the application of an unbalance force, as shown in Figure 13. On suspended equip-

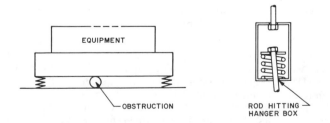

Fig. 13   Obstructed Isolation Systems

ment, check that hanger rods are not touching the hanger. Rigid connections such as pipes and ducts can prohibit mounts from functioning properly and from providing a transmission path. Note that the fact that the system is free floating does not mean that the isolators are functioning properly. For example, a 500 rpm fan installed on isolators having a natural frequency of 500 cpm could be free floating but would actually be in resonance, resulting in transmission to the building and excessive movement.

2. Determine if isolators are adjusted properly and providing desired isolation efficiency. All isolators supporting a piece of equipment should have approximately the same deflection, i.e. compressed the same under the weight of equipment. If not, they have been improperly adjusted, installed, or selected; this should be corrected immediately. Note that isolation efficiency cannot be checked by comparing vibration amplitude on equipment to amplitude on the structure as shown in Figure 14. The only accurate check of isolation efficiencies is to compare vibration measurements of equipment operating with isolators to measurements of equipment operating without isolators. As such tests are usually impractical, it is best to check isolator deflection to determine if deflection is as specified, and if specified or desired isolation efficiency is being provided. Figure 15 shows natural frequency of isolators as a function of deflection and shows the theoretical isolation efficiencies for various frequencies at which the equipment operates.

While it is easy to determine the deflection of spring mounts by measuring the difference between the free heights with a ruler (information as shown on submittal drawings or available from manufacturer), such measurements are difficult with most pad or rubber mounts. Further, most pad and rubber mounts do not lend themselves to accurate determination of natural frequency as a function of deflection. For such mounts, the most practical approach is to check that there is no excessive vibration of the base and no noticeable or objectionable vibration transmission to the building structure.

If isolators are in the 90% efficiency range and there is transmission to the building structure, the equipment is operating roughly or there is a flanking path of transmission, such as connecting piping or obstruction, under the base.

Testing Equipment Vibration

Testing equipment vibration is necessary as an acceptance check to determine if equipment is functioning properly and to ensure that objectionable vibration and noise are not transmitted. Although a person familiar with equipment can determine when it is operating roughly, instrumentation is usually required to determine accurately if vibration levels are satisfactory.

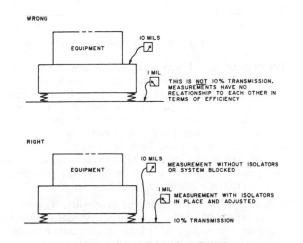

Fig. 14 Testing Isolation Efficiency

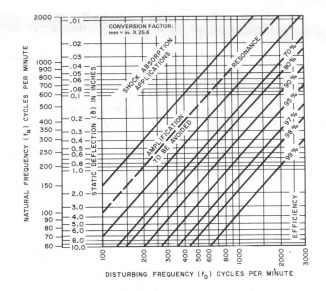

Fig. 15 Isolator Natural Frequencies and Efficiencies

Vibration Tolerances

Table 26 of Chapter 52 provides vibration tolerance criteria (see "Vibration Tolerance" section for complete discussion). These criteria are based on equipment installed on vibration isolators and can be met by any reasonably smoothly running equipment.

Procedure for Testing Equipment Vibration

The following steps should be taken to ensure that equipment vibration is tested properly:

1. Determine operating speeds of equipment from nameplates, drawings, or a speed-measuring device such as a tachometer or strobe, and indicate on test form. For any equipment where the driving speed (motor) is different from driven speed (fan wheel, rotor, impeller) because of belt drive or gear reducers, indicate both driving and driven speeds.
2. Determine acceptance criteria from specifications and indicate on test form. If specifications do not provide criteria, use those shown in Chapter 52.
3. Ensure that the vibration isolation system is functioning properly (see the "Testing Vibration Isolation Systems" section).
4. Operate equipment and make visual and aural checks for any apparent rough operation. Check all bearings with a stethoscope. Any defective bearings, misalignment, or obvious rough operation should be corrected before proceeding further. If not corrected, equipment should be considered *not acceptable*.
5. Measure and record on the test form vibration at bearings of driving and driven components in horizontal, vertical and, if possible, axial directions. There should be at least one axial measurement for each rotating component (fan-motor, pump-motor).
6. Evaluate measurements as described below.

Evaluating Vibration Measurements

Vibration measurements are evaluated in accordance with type of measurements made as follows:

1. Amplitude Measurement. When specification for acceptable equipment vibration is based on amplitude measurements only and measurements are made with an instrument that measures only amplitude, such as a vibration meter or vibrometer:

a. No measurement shall exceed specified values or values shown in Table 26 of Chapter 52, taking into consideration reduced values for equipment installed on inertia blocks

b. No measurement shall exceed values shown in Table 26, Chapter 52, for driving and driven speeds, taking into consideration reduced values for equipment installed on inertia blocks. For example, with a belt-driven fan operating at 800 rpm and having an 1800 rpm driving motor, amplitude measurements at fan bearings must be in accordance with values shown for 800 cpm, and measurements at motor bearings must be in accordance with values shown for 1800 cpm. If measurements at motor bearings exceed specified values, take measurements of motor only with belts removed to determine if there is feedback vibration from fan.

c. No axial vibration measurement should exceed maximum radial (vertical or horizontal) vibration at the same location.

2. Amplitude and Frequency Measurements. When specification for acceptable equipment vibration is based on both amplitude and frequency measurements and measurements are made with instruments that measure both amplitude and frequency such as a vibrograph or vibration analyzer:

a. No amplitude measurements at driving and driven speeds shall exceed specified values or values shown in Table 26, Chapter 52, taking into consideration reduced values for equipment installed on inertia blocks. Measurements that exceed *acceptable* amounts may be evaluated as explained in the "Vibration Analysis" section.

b. No axial vibration measurement shall exceed maximum radial (vertical or horizontal) vibration at the same location.

c. The presence of any vibration at frequencies other than driving or driven speeds is generally reason to rate operation *not acceptable* and such vibration should be analyzed as explained in the "Vibration Analysis" section that follows.

Vibration Analysis

Although this section does not provide a complete analysis of vibration, the following guide covers most problems that may be encountered.

Axial Vibration Exceeds Radial Vibration. When amplitude of axial vibration (parallel with shaft) at any bearing exceeds radial vibration (perpendicular to shaft—vertical or horizontal), it usually indicates misalignment; this should be checked carefully. This is most common on direct-driven equipment because, although flexible couplings that accommodate parallel and angular misalignment of shafts are generally used, such misalignment can generate forces that cause axial vibration. As axial vibration can cause premature bearing failure, misalignment should be corrected promptly. Other possible causes of large amplitude axial vibration are resonance, defective bearings, insufficient rigidity of bearing supports or equipment, and loose hold-down bolts.

Vibration Amplitude Exceeds Allowable Tolerance at Rotational Speed. The allowable vibration limits established by Table 29, Chapter 52 are based on vibration caused by rotor imbalance, which results in vibration at rotational frequency. While vibration caused by imbalance must be at the frequency at which the part is rotating, a vibration at rotational frequency can be, but does not have to be, caused by imbalance. An unbalanced rotating part develops centrifugal force, which causes it to vibrate at rotational frequency, but vibration at rotational frequency can also result from other conditions such as bent shaft, eccentric sheave, misalignment, and resonance. If vibration amplitude exceeds allowable tolerance at rotational frequency, the following

steps should be taken before performing field balancing of rotating parts.

1. Check vibration amplitude as equipment goes up to operating speed and as it coasts to a stop. Any significant peaks at or near operating speed, as shown in Figure 16, indicate a probable condition of resonance, that is, some part having a natural frequency close to the operating speed, resulting in greatly amplified levels of vibration.

A bent shaft or eccentricity will usually cause imbalance, but will also result in significantly higher vibration amplitude at lower speeds, as shown in Figure 17, whereas vibration caused by imbalance generally increases as speed increases.

If bent shaft or eccentricity is suspected, check the dial indicator. A bent shaft or eccentricity between bearings as shown in Figure 18A, can usually be compensated for by field balancing, although some axial vibration might remain. Field balancing cannot correct vibration caused by bent shaft on direct-connected equipment, on belt-driven equipment where the shaft is bent at the location of sheave, or if the sheave is eccentric, as shown in Figure 18B. This is because the center-to-center distance of the sheaves will fluctuate, each revolution resulting in vibration.

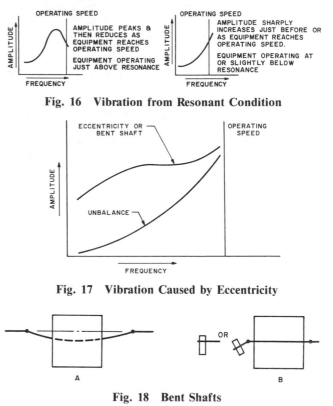

Fig. 16 Vibration from Resonant Condition

Fig. 17 Vibration Caused by Eccentricity

Fig. 18 Bent Shafts

2. For belt- or gear-driven equipment where vibration is at motor driving frequency rather than driven speed, it is usually best to disconnect the drive to perform tests. If the vibration amplitude of the motor operating by itself does not exceed specified or allowable values, then excessive vibration (when connected) is probably a function of bent shaft, misalignment, eccentricity, resonance, or loose hold-down bolts.

3. Vibration caused by imbalance can be corrected in the field by firms specializing in this service or by testing personnel if they have appropriate equipment and experience.

Vibration at other than Rotational Frequency. Vibration at frequencies other than driving and driven speeds is generally considered *not acceptable*. Table 5 shows some common conditions that can cause vibration at other than rotational frequency.

Table 5   Common Causes of Vibration other than Unbalance at Rotation Frequency

Frequency	Source
0.5 × rpm	Vibration at approximately 0.5 rpm can result from improperly loaded sleeve bearings. This vibration will usually suddenly disappear as equipment coasts down from operating speed.
2 × rpm	Equipment not tightly secured or bolted down.
2 × rpm	Misalignment of couplings or shafts usually results in vibration at twice rotational frequency and generally a relatively high axial vibration.
Many × rpm	Defective antifriction (ball, roller) bearings usually result in low amplitude, high frequency, erratic vibration. Since defective bearings usually produce *noise* rather than any significantly measurable vibration, it is best to check all bearings with stethoscope or similar listening device.

Resonance. If resonance is suspected, it is necessary to determine which part of the system is in resonance.

1. *Isolation Mounts.* The natural frequency of the most commonly used spring mounts is a function of spring deflection, as shown in Figure 32, Chapter 52, and it is relatively easy to calculate by determining the difference between the free and operating height of the mount, as explained in the "Testing Vibration Isolation Systems" section. This technique cannot be applied to rubber, pad, or fiberglass mounts, which have a natural frequency in the 300 to 3000 cpm range. Natural frequency for such mounts is determined by a *bump test* as described in the next paragraph. Any resonance with isolators should be immediately corrected as it results in excessive movement of equipment and more transmission to the building structure than if equipment were attached solidly to the building (installed without isolators).

2. *System Component.* Resonance can occur with any system component shaft, structural base, casing, and connected piping. The easiest way to determine natural frequency is to make a *bump test* with a vibrograph. This test consists of bumping the part and measuring with an instrument; the part will vibrate at its natural frequency, which is recorded on instrument chart paper. Similar tests, though not as convenient or accurate, can be made with a reed vibrometer or a vibration analyzer. However, most of these instruments are restricted to frequencies above 500 cpm and, therefore, cannot be used to determine natural frequencies of most isolation systems, which usually have natural frequencies lower than 500 cpm.

Checking For Vibration Transmission. The source of vibration transmission can be checked by determining frequency with a vibration analyzer and tracing back to equipment operating at this speed. However, the easiest and usually best means (even if test equipment is being used) is to shut off equipment one at a time until the source of transmission is located. Most transmission problems cause disturbing noise; listening is the most practical approach to determine a noise source, since the ear is usually better than sound-measuring instruments at distinguishing small differences and changes in character and amount of noise. Where disturbing transmission consists solely of vibration, a measuring instrument will probably be helpful unless vibration is significantly above the sensory level of perception. Vibration below the sensory level of perception generally will not be objectionable.

If equipment is located near the affected area, check isolation mounts and equipment vibration, as previously indicated. If vibration is not being transmitted through the base or if the affected area is remote from equipment, the probable cause is transmission through connected piping and/or ducts. Ducts can usually be isolated by isolation hangers. However, transmission through connected piping, which is very common, presents

numerous problems that should be understood before attempting to correct them.

Vibration and Noise Transmission in Piping Systems

Vibration and noise in connected piping can be caused by mechanical vibration (1) generated by equipment (pump, compressor, etc.) and transmitted through the walls of pipes; (2) generated by mechanical vibration and transmitted by a water column; or (3) generated by flow (velocity) noise and vibration. Flexible pipe connectors, which provide system flexibility to permit isolators to function properly and protect equipment from stress caused by misalignment and thermal expansion, can be very useful in attenuating mechanical vibration transmitted through a pipe wall. However, they rarely suppress flow vibration and noise and only slightly attenuate mechanical vibration as transmitted through a water column.

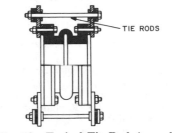

TIE RODS

Fig. 19   Typical Tie Rod Assembly

Tie rods (Figure 19) are often used with flexible rubber hose and rubber expansion joints. While they accommodate thermal movements, they hinder the isolation of vibration and noise. This is because pressure in the system causes the hose or joint to expand until resilient washers under tie rods are virtually rigid. To isolate noise adequately with a flexible rubber connector, tie rods and anchor piping should not be used (see Figure 36, Chapter 52). However, this technique generally cannot be used with pumps that are on spring mounts because they would still permit hose to elongate. Flexible metal hose can be used with spring isolated pumps, since wire braid serves as tie rods; metal hose controls vibration but not noise.

Problems of transmission through connected piping are usually best resolved by changes in the system to reduce noise (improve flow characteristics, turn down impeller) or by completely isolating piping from the building structure. It must be realized, however, that it is almost impossible to isolate piping completely from the structure, as required resiliency is inconsistent with rigidity requirements of pipe anchors and guides. Chapter 52 contains information on flexible pipe connectors and resilient pipe supports, anchors, and guides, which should help resolve any piping noise transmission problems.

BIBLIOGRAPHY

AABC. 1984. *National Standards for Total System Balance,* 4th edition. Associated Air Balance Council.

AABC. 1967. *How to Lick Damper Leakage.* Associated Air Balance Council.

AABC. 1967. *How to Lick the Problem of Adjustable Sheaves.* Associated Air Balance Council.

AABC. 1966. *What You Should Know About Air Diffusion Devices.* Associated Air Balance Council.

ASA. 1983. *Specification for Sound Level Meters.* ANSI *Standard* S1.4-83 or ASA *Standard* 47-83. Acoustical Society of America, New York, NY.

ASHRAE. 1974. Energy Conservation Pumping Systems. ASHRAE *Journal,* Vol. 16, No. 6, June.

Barnhart, J.T. 1974. How Temperature and Altitude Affect Fan Selection. *Plant Engineering,* December 26.

Barrett, J. 1969. Dual Duct Systems. *Heating, Piping and Air Conditioning,* January.

Barrett, J.C. 1964. Instruments and Procedures for Testing Air Distribution Systems. *Air Conditioning, Heating, and Ventilating,* April.

Carlson, G.F. 1974. Liquid Viscosity Effects on Pumping System—Part I and II. ASHRAE *Journal,* Vol. 16, No. 7 and No. 9.

Carlson, G.F. 1974. Pump Energy Savings for Hydronic Systems. *Heating, Piping and Air Conditioning,* July.

Carlson, G.F. 1972. Central Plants Chilled Water Systems. ASHRAE *Journal,* Feb. through April (3 parts).

Carlson, G.F. 1968-69. Hydronic Systems: Analysis and Evaluation. ASHRAE *Journal,* Oct. through March (6 parts).

Carter, H.C. 1971. Testing and Adjusting Air and Water Systems. *Actual Specifying Engineer,* November.

Choat, E.E. 1976. An Evaluation of the Temperature Difference Method for Balancing Hydronic Coils. ASHRAE *Transactions,* Vol. 82, Part 1.

Coad, W.J.; and Sutherlin, P.D. 1974. A New Look at Fan System Curves. *Heating, Piping and Air Conditioning,* November.

Eads, W.G. 1975. *Testing, Balancing and Adjusting of Environmental Systems.* Sheet Metal and Air Conditioning Contractors National Association.

Field Balancing Depends on Dampers. 1967. Associated Air Balance Council, January.

Flanagan, R. 1969. Air Handling Unit Analysis. *Heating, Piping and Air Conditioning,* March.

Gupton, G.W. 1975. Re-adjusting and Rebalancing Air and Water Systems for Energy Savings. *Heating, Piping and Air Conditioning*, February.

Hankins, R. 1969. Applications of Computer to Air Conditioning Duct Systems. *Heating, Piping and Air Conditioning,* February.

Hanna, G.M. 1968. Calibration Wind Tunnel for Air Measuring Instruments. *Air Engineering,* January.

Hanna, G.M. 1967. Instruments for Measuring Low Velocity with a Pitot Tube. *Air Engineering,* December.

Hayes, F.C.; and Stoecker, W.F. 1966. Tables of Application Factors for Flow Measurement at Return Intakes. ASHRAE *Transactions,* Vol. 72, Part 2.

Hayes, F.C.; and Stoecker, W.F. 1966. The Effect of Inlet Conditions on Flow Measurements at Ceiling Diffusers. ASHRAE *Transactions,* Vol. 72, Part 2.

Hightower, G.B. 1971. Testing, Balancing and Adjusting of HVAC Induction Systems. ASHRAE *Journal,* Vol. 13, No. 6, June.

Janisse, N. 1969. How to Control Air Systems. 1969. *Heating, Piping and Air Conditioning,* April.

Jones, E. 1969. Variable Volume Air Systems. *Heating, Piping and Air Conditioning,* January.

Journeyman and Apprentice Program. Carrier Corp, Ventilating and Air Conditioning Contractors Association of Chicago.

Journeyman Extension Program of Air Conditioning and Refrigeration. Ventilating and Air Conditioning Contractors Association of Chicago.

Kahoe, H.T. 1962. Balancing Air Flow in Air Conditioning Systems (three parts). *Air Conditioning, Heating, and Ventilating,* June, July, August.

Kahoe, H.T. 1966. Choose the Right Fan. *Air Conditioning and Refrigeration Business,* October.

Kahoe, H.T. 1975. Effective Energy Management Requires Proper System Balance. *Air Conditioning and Refrigeration Business,* January.

Kahoe, H.T. 1967. Graphs Simplify Field Testing and Balancing. *Air Conditioning and Refrigeration Business,* November.

Kahoe, H.T. 1963. How to Test and Balance Air Conditioning Systems: Part 1—A Practical Guide to Air Balance; Part 2—A Practical Guide to Water Balance; Part 3—Testing and Balancing Instruments. *Air Conditioning and Refrigeration Business,* January, May, August.

Kahoe, H.T. 1967. How to Write Specifications for Balancing Air Systems. *Air Conditioning and Refrigeration Business,* January.

Kahoe, H.T. 1969. Kahoe Finds Fan Ratings Need Overhaul. *Air Conditioning and Refrigeration Business,* January.

Kahoe, H.T. 1966. Partially Occupied Buildings Present Balancing Problems. *Air Conditioning and Refrigeration Business,* August.

Kahoe, H.T. 1968. Take the Trouble Out of Trouble-shooting. *Air Conditioning and Refrigeration Business,* September.

Kahoe, H.T. 1968. Testing/Balancing Lab Makes Producers Tell the Truth. *Air Conditioning and Refrigeration Business,* April.

Kisner, F. 1975. Instrumentation for Testing and Balancing the Plant Air Distribution System. *Plant Engineering,* April 17.

Kisner, F. 1975. Recommended Flow Measurement Procedures for Testing and Balancing the Plant Air Conditioning System. *Plant Engineering,* June 12.

Littmann, S.A. 1960. How to Balance Big Building Air Conditioning Systems. *Air Engineering,* April, May, June.

Lord, G.D. 1973. Fan Problem or System Problem. *Heating, Piping and Air Conditioning,* November.

May, J. 1969. Efficiency Testing and Application of Air Filters. *Heating, Piping and Air Conditioning,* March.

NEBB. 1983. *Procedural Standards for Testing, Balancing and Adjusting of Environmental Systems,* 4th edition. National Environmental Balancing Bureau.

Nevins, R.G., and Ward, E.D. 1968. Room Air Distribution with an Air Distribution Ceiling. ASHRAE *Transactions,* Vol. 74, Part 1.

Otto, G. 1966. How the A.D.C. Test Code Works. *Air Conditioning, Heating and Ventilating,* February.

Reh, H.C. 1960. How to Balance an Air System. *Air Conditioning, Heating and Ventilating,* October.

Ries, L.S. 1967. New Ceiling System Tested in New Air Lab. *Heating, Piping and Air Conditioning,* September.

Rickelton, D. 1967. Terminal Equipment for Air Systems. *Heating, Piping, and Air Conditioning,* April.

Sandberg, C.I. 1972. Testing and Balancing Guide Specs Revised. *Actual Specifying Engineer,* November.

Seibert, R.H. 1968. Fans in HVAC Service. *Air Conditioning, Heating and Ventilating,* September.

SMACNA. 1985. *HVAC Duct Construction Standards—Metal and Flexible.* Sheet Metal and Air Conditioning Contractors' National Association, Vienna, VA.

SMACNA. 1982. *HVAC Systems—Testing, Adjusting, and Balancing.* Sheet Metal and Air Conditioning Contractors' National Association, Vienna, VA.

SMACNA. 1982. *Industrial Ventilation Manual of Recommended Practices.* Sheet Metal and Air Conditioning Contractors' National Association, Vienna, VA.

SMACNA. 1980. *Rectangular Industrial Duct Construction Standards.* Sheet Metal and Air Conditioning Contractors' National Association, Vienna, VA.

SMACNA. 1977. *Round Industrial Duct Construction Standards.* Sheet Metal and Air Conditioning Contractors' National Association, Vienna, VA.

Stockwell, R.E. 1967. The Confusion in Testing and Balancing of Air Conditioning Systems. *Heating, Piping and Air Conditioning,* July.

Straub, H. 1969. Principles of Air Distribution. *Heating, Piping and Air Conditioning,* April.

Straub, H.; and Sylvester, G. 1963. How Air Flow Tests are Performed Under ADC's Test Code. *Heating, Piping and Air Conditioning,* September.

Sturgeon, C. (ed). *Air Balance Procedures.* Ventilating and Air Conditioning Contractors Association of Chicago.

Tamura, G.T., and Wilson, A.G. 1967. Building Pressures Caused by Chimney Action and Mechanical Ventilation. ASHRAE *Transactions,* Vol. 73, Part 2.

Tamura, G.T.; and Wilson, A.G. 1967. Pressure Differences Caused by Chimney Effect in Three High Buildings. ASHRAE *Transactions,* Vol. 73, Part 2.

Tamura, G.T.; and Wilson, A.G. 1968. Pressure Differences Caused by Wind on Two Tall Buildings. ASHRAE *Transactions,* Vol. 74, Part 2.

Tamura, G.T.; and Wilson, A.G. 1966. Pressure Differences for a Nine-story Building as a Result of Chimney Effect and Ventilating System Operation. ASHRAE *Transactions,* Vol. 72, Part 1.

Test, Balance and Adjust Manual for Mechanical Contractors. Mechanical Contractors Association of America.

Testing and Balancing Manual for Ventilating and Air Conditioning Systems. Ventilating and Air Conditioning Contractors Association of Chicago.

Trickler, C.J. 1960. How Much Air is Delivered. *Air Conditioning, Heating, and Ventilating,* August.

Wind, M. 1968. Air Balance and Testing. *Heating, Piping and Air Conditioning,* December.

Wortel, R. 1969. Single Duct Systems. *Heating, Piping and Air Conditioning,* January.

Yerges, L. 1969. Noise Control in Air Systems. *Heating, Piping and Air Conditioning,* March.

Yousoufian, H.H. 1964. Predicting Air Jet Performance. *Air Conditioning, Heating, and Ventilating,* September.

CHAPTER 58

FIRE AND SMOKE CONTROL

IN building fires, smoke often flows to locations remote from the fire, threatening life and damaging property. Stairwells and elevators frequently become smoke-filled, thereby blocking or inhibiting evacuation. Smoke is recognized as the major killer in fires.

Previously, the idea of using pressurization to prevent smoke infiltration of stairwells began to attract attention. This concept was followed by the idea of the "pressure sandwich," that is, venting or exhausting the fire floor and pressurizing the surrounding floors. Frequently, the building's ventilation system is used for this purpose. The term "smoke control" describes such systems that use pressurization produced by mechanical fans to limit smoke movement in fire situations.

This chapter discusses fire protection and smoke control systems in buildings as they relate to the HVAC field. Much of this chapter has been either taken directly or summarized from the ASHRAE manual, *Design of Smoke Control Systems for Buildings* (Klote and Fothergill 1983). The American Society for Testing and Materials (ASTM 1985) and the National Fire Protection Association (NFPA 1985a) state that smoke consists of the airborne solid and liquid particulates and gases evolved when a material undergoes pyrolysis or combustion.

The objectives of fire safety are to provide a degree of protection for a building's occupants, the building and the property inside it, and neighboring buildings. Various forms of system analysis have been used to help quantify protection. The specific life safety objectives differ with occupancy. For example, nursing home requirements can be different from those for office buildings.

Two basic approaches to fire protection are to prevent fire ignition and to manage fire impact. Figure 1 shows a decision tree for fire protection. The building occupants and managers have the primary role in preventing fire ignition. The building design team may incorporate features into the building to assist the occupants and managers in this effort. Because it is impossible to prevent fire ignition completely, managing fire impact has assumed a significant role in fire protection design. Compartmentation, suppression, control of construction materials, exit systems, and smoke management are management examples. The NFPA Fire Protection Handbook (NFPA 1986) contains detailed information about fire safety.

Historically, fire safety professionals have considered the HVAC system as a potentially dangerous penetration of the natural building membranes (wall, floors, etc.) that can readily transport smoke and fire. For this reason, the HVAC systems traditionally have been shut down when fire has been discovered. Although shutting down the HVAC system prevents fans from forcing smoke flow, it does not prevent smoke movement through

ducts due to smoke buoyancy, stack effect, or the wind. As a solution to the smoke problem, the concept of smoke control has developed, and it should be viewed as only one part of the overall building fire-protection system.

SMOKE MOVEMENT

A smoke control system must be designed so that it is not overpowered by the driving forces that cause smoke movement, which include stack effect; bouyancy; expansion; wind; and the heating, ventilating, and air conditioning (HVAC) system. Generally, in a fire, smoke is moved by a combination of these forces. Following are explanations of each driving force.

Stack Effect

When it is cold outside, an upward movement of air often occurs within building shafts, such as stairwells, elevator shafts, dumbwaiter shafts, mechanical shafts, or mail chutes. This phenomenon, referred to as normal stack effect, is caused because the air in the building is warmer and less dense than the outside air. Normal stack effect is great when outside temperatures are low and for tall buildings. However, normal stack effect can exist even in a one-story building.

When the outside air is warmer than the building air, a downward airflow frequently exists in shafts. This downward airflow is called reverse stack effect. At standard atmospheric

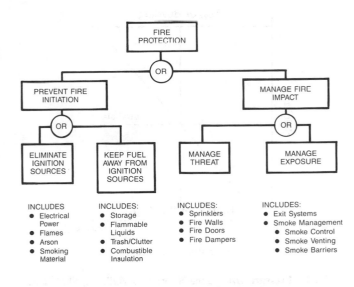

Fig. 1 Simplified Fire Protection Decision Tree

The preparation of this chapter is assigned to TC 5.6, Control of Fire and Smoke.

pressure, the pressure difference due to either normal or reverse stack effect is expressed as:

$$\Delta p = K_s\left(\frac{1}{T_o} - \frac{1}{T_i}\right)h \qquad (1)$$

where

Δp = pressure difference, in. of water (Pa)
T_o = absolute temperature of outside air, °R (K)
T_i = absolute temperature of air inside shaft, °R (K)
h = distance above neutral plane, ft (m)
K_s = coefficient, 7.64 (3460)

For a building 200-ft (60-m) tall with a neutral plane at the mid-height, an outside temperature of 0°F (−18°C) and an inside temperature of 70°F (21°C), the maximum pressure difference due to stack effect would be 0.22 in. of water (55 Pa). This means that at the top of the building, a shaft would have a pressure of 0.22 in. of water (55 Pa) greater than the outside pressure. At the bottom of the shaft, the shaft would have a pressure of 0.22 in. of water (55 Pa) less than the outside pressure. Figure 2 diagrams the pressure difference between a building shaft and the outside. In the diagram, a positive pressure difference indicates that the shaft pressure is higher than the outside pressure, and a negative pressure difference indicates the opposite.

Stack effect usually exists between a building and the outside. The air movement in buildings caused by both normal and reverse stack effect is illustrated in Figure 3. In this case, the pressure difference expressed in Equation (1) refers to the pressure difference between the shaft and the outside of the building.

Figure 4 can be used to determine the pressure difference due to stack effect. For normal stack effect, $\Delta p/h$ is positive, and the pressure difference is positive above the neutral plane and negative below it. For reverse stack effect, $\Delta p/h$ is negative, and the pressure difference is negative above the neutral plane and positive below it.

In unusually tight buildings with exterior stairwells, reverse stack effect has been observed even with low outside air temperatures (Klote 1980). In this situation, the exterior stairwell temperature was considerably lower than the building temperature. The stairwell was the cold column of air, and other shafts within the building were the warm columns of air.

If the leakage paths are uniform with height, the neutral plane is near the mid-height of the building. However, when the leakage

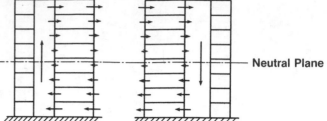

Note: Arrows Indicate Direction of Air Movement

Fig. 3　Air Movement due to Normal and Reverse Stack Effect

paths are not uniform, the location of the neutral plane can vary considerably, as in the case of vented shafts. McGuire and Tamura (1975) provide methods for calculating the location of the neutral plane for some vented conditions.

Smoke movement from a building fire can be dominated by stack effect. In a building with normal stack effect, the existing air currents (as shown in Figure 3) can move smoke considerable distances from the fire origin. If the fire is below the neutral plane, smoke moves with the building air into and up the shafts. This upward smoke flow is enhanced by any buoyancy forces due to the temperature of the smoke. Once above the neutral plane, the smoke flows from the shafts into the upper floors of the building. If the leakage between floors is negligible, the floors below the neutral plane, except the fire floor, is relatively smoke-free until the quantity of smoke produced is greater than can be handled by stack effect flows.

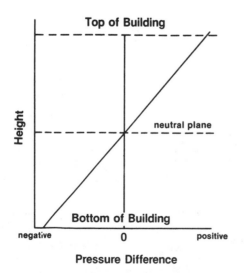

Fig. 2　Pressure Difference Between a Building Shaft and the Outside due to Normal Stack Effect

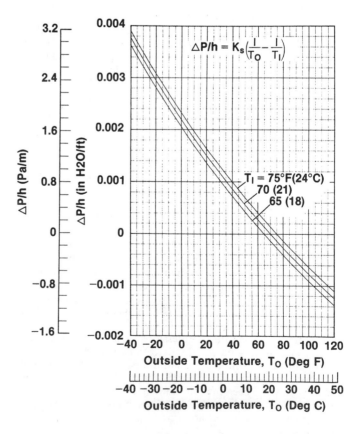

Fig. 4　Pressure Difference Due to Stack Effect

Smoke from a fire located above the neutral plane is carried by the building airflow to the outside through exterior openings in the building. If the leakage between floors is negligible, all floors other than the fire floor remain relatively smoke-free until the quantity of smoke produced is greater than can be handled by stack effect flows. When the leakage between floors is considerable, the smoke flows to the floor above the fire floor.

The air currents caused by reverse stack effect (Figure 3) tend to move relatively cool smoke down. In the case of hot smoke, buoyancy forces can cause smoke to flow upward, even during reverse stack effect conditions.

Buoyancy

High temperature smoke from a fire has a buoyancy force due to its reduced density. The pressure difference between a fire compartment and its surroundings can be expressed as follows:

$$\Delta p = K_s \left(\frac{1}{T_o} - \frac{1}{T_f} \right) h \qquad (2)$$

where

Δp = pressure difference, in. of water (Pa)
T_o = absolute temperature of the surroundings, °R (K)
T_f = absolute temperature of the fire compartment, °R (K)
h = distance above the neutral plane, ft (m)
K_s = coefficient, 7.64 (3460)

The pressure difference due to buoyancy can be obtained from Figure 5 for the surroundings at 68°F (20°C). The neutral plane is the plane of equal hydrostatic pressure between the fire compartment and its surroundings. For a fire with a fire compartment temperature at 1470°F (800°C), the pressure difference 5 ft (1.5 m) above the neutral plane is 0.052 in. of water (13 Pa). Fang (1980) studied pressures caused by room fires during a series of full-scale fire tests. During these tests, the maximum pressure

difference reached was 0.064 in. of water (16 Pa) across the burn room wall at the ceiling.

Much larger pressure differences are possible for tall fire compartments where the distance, h, from the neutral plane can be larger. If the fire compartment temperature is 1290°F (700°C), the pressure difference 35 ft (10.7 m) above the neutral plane is 0.35 in. of water (88 Pa). This causes a large fire, and the pressures produced by it are beyond the present smoke-control methods. However, the example illustrates the extent to which Eq. (2) can be applied.

In a building with leakage paths in the ceiling of the fire room, this buoyancy-induced pressure causes smoke to move to the floor above the fire floor. In addition, this pressure causes smoke to move through any leakage paths in the walls or around the doors of the fire compartment. As smoke travels away from the fire, its temperature drops due to heat transfer and dilution. Therefore, the effect of buoyancy generally decreases with distance from the fire.

Expansion

In addition to buoyancy, the energy released by a fire can move smoke by expansion. In a fire compartment with only one opening to the building, building air will flow in and hot smoke will flow out. Neglecting the added mass of the fuel, which is small compared to the airflow, the ratio of volumetric flows can be expressed as a ratio of absolute temperatures.

$$\frac{Q_{out}}{Q_{in}} = \frac{T_{out}}{T_{in}}$$

where

Q_{out} = volumetric flow rate of smoke out of the fire compartment, cfm (m³/s)
Q_{in} = volumetric flow rate of air into the fire compartment, cfm (m³/s)
T_{out} = absolute temperature of smoke leaving fire compartment, °R (K)
T_{in} = absolute temperature of air into fire compartment, °R (K)

For a smoke temperature of 1290°F (700°C), the ratio of volumetric flows would be 3.32. Note: absolute temperature is used for calculation. In such a case, if the air flowing into the fire compartment is 3180 cfm (1.5 m³/s), then the smoke flowing out of the fire compartment would be 10,600 cfm (5.0 m³/s). In this case, the gas has expanded to more than three times its original volume.

For a fire compartment with open doors or windows, the pressure difference across these openings due to expansion is negligible. However, for a tightly sealed fire compartment, the pressure differences due to expansion may be important.

Wind

In many instances, wind can have a pronounced effect on smoke movement within a building. The pressure, p_w, that the wind exerts on a surface can be expressed as:

$$p_w = \tfrac{1}{2} C_w \varrho_o V^2 \qquad (3)$$

where

C_w = dimensionless pressure coefficient
ϱ_o = outside air density
V = wind velocity

For an air density of 0.075 lb/ft³ (1.20 kg/m³), this relation becomes:

$$p_w = C_w K_w V^2 \qquad (3a)$$

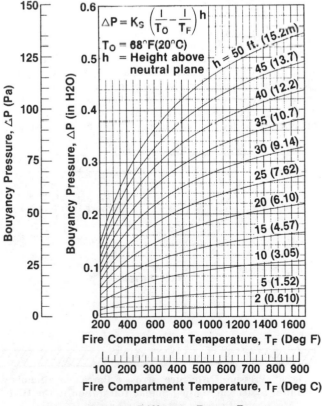

Fig. 5   Pressure Difference Due to Buoyancy

where

p_w = wind pressure, in. of water (Pa)
V = wind velocity, mph (m/s)
K_w = coefficient, 4.82×10^{-4} (0.600)

The pressure coefficients, C_w, are in the range of -0.8 to 0.8, with positive values for windward walls and negative values for leeward walls. The pressure coefficient depends on building geometry and varies locally over the wall surface. In general, wind velocity increases with height from the surface of the earth. Sachs (1972), Houghton and Carruther (1976), Simiu and Scanlan (1978), and MacDonald (1975) give detailed information concerning wind velocity variations and pressure coefficients. Shaw and Tamura (1977) have developed specific information about wind data with respect to air infiltration in buildings.

A 35 mph (15.6 m/s) wind produces a pressure on a structure of 0.47 in. of water (117 Pa) with a pressure coefficient of 0.8. The effect of wind on air movement within tightly constructed buildings with all doors and windows closed is slight. However, the effects of wind can become important for loosely constructed buildings or for buildings with open doors or windows. Usually, the resulting airflows are complicated, and computer analysis is required.

Frequently in fire situations, a window breaks in the fire compartment. If the window is on the leeward side of the building, the negative pressure caused by the wind vents the smoke from the fire compartment. This can reduce smoke movement throughout the building. However, if the broken window is on the windward side, the wind forces the smoke throughout the fire floor and to other floors. This endangers the lives of building occupants and hampers fire fighting. Pressures induced by the wind in this situation can be large and can dominate air movement throughout the building.

HVAC System

The HVAC system frequently transports smoke during building fires. For this reason, before the concept of smoke control developed, HVAC systems were shut down when fires were discovered.

In the early stages of a fire, the HVAC system can aid in fire detection. When a fire starts in an unoccupied portion of a building, the HVAC system can transport the smoke to a space where people can smell it and be alerted to the fire. However, as the fire progresses, the HVAC system transports smoke to every area that it serves, thus endangering life in all those spaces. The HVAC system also supplies air to the fire space, which aids combustion. These are the reasons HVAC systems traditionally have been shut down when fires have been discovered. Although shutting down the HVAC system prevents it from supplying air to the fire, shutting down the HVAC system does not prevent smoke movement through the supply and return air ducts, air shafts, and other building openings due to stack effect, buoyancy, or wind.

SMOKE MANAGEMENT

The term "smoke management," as used in this chapter, includes all methods that can modify smoke movement, either independently or in combination, for the benefit of occupants and fire fighters and for the reduction of property damage. The use of barriers, smoke vents, and smoke shafts are traditional methods of smoke management.

The effectiveness of a barrier in limiting smoke movement depends on the leakage paths in the barrier. Holes where pipes penetrate walls or floors, cracks where walls meet floors, and cracks around doors are a few leakage paths. The pressure difference across these barriers depends on stack effect, buoyancy, wind, and the HVAC system.

The effectiveness of smoke vents and smoke shafts depends on their proximity to the fire, the buoyancy of the smoke, and the presence of other driving forces. In addition, when smoke is cooled due to sprinklers, the effectiveness of smoke vents and smoke shafts is reduced.

Elevator shafts in buildings have been used as smoke shafts. This prevents their use for fire evacuation, and these shafts frequently distribute smoke to floors far from the fire. Specially designed smoke shafts, which have essentially no leakage on floors other than the fire floor, can prevent the smoke shaft from distributing smoke to nonfire floors.

PRINCIPLES OF SMOKE CONTROL

Smoke control uses the barriers (walls, floors, doors, etc.) for traditional smoke management in conjunction with airflows and pressure differences generated by mechanical fans.

Figure 6 illustrates a pressure difference across a barrier acting to control smoke movement. Within the barrier is a door. The high pressure side of the door can be either a refuge area or an escape route. The low pressure side is exposed to smoke from a fire. Airflow through the cracks around the door and through other construction cracks prevents smoke infiltration to the high pressure side. When the door is opened, air flows through the opening. When the air velocity is low, smoke can flow against the airflow into the refuge area or escape route, as shown in Figure 7. This smoke backflow can be prevented if the air velocity is sufficiently large, as shown in Figure 8. The magnitude of the velocity necessary to prevent backflow depends on the energy release rate of the fire, as discussed later.

The two basic principles of smoke control are as follows:

1. Airflow by itself can control smoke movement if the average air velocity is of sufficient magnitude.
2. Air pressure differences across barriers can act to control smoke movement.

Pressurization results in airflow through the small gaps around closed doors and in construction cracks, thereby preventing smoke backflow through these openings. Therefore, in a physical sense, the second principle is a special case of the first principle. However, considering the two principles as separate is advantageous for smoke control design. For a barrier with one or more large openings, air velocity is the appropriate physical quantity for both design considerations and acceptance testing.

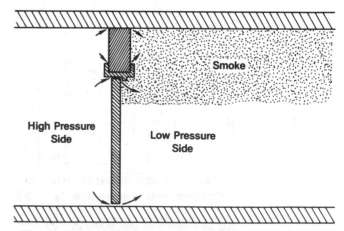

Fig. 6 Pressure Difference Across a Barrier of a Smoke Control System Preventing Smoke Infiltration to the High Pressure Side of the Barrier

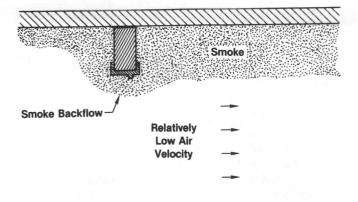

Fig. 7 Smoke Backflow Against Low Air Velocity Through an Open Doorway

However, when there are only small cracks, such as around closed doors, designing to and measuring air velocities is impractical. In this case, the appropriate physical quantity is pressure difference. Consideration of the two principles as separate also emphasizes the different considerations necessary for open and closed doors.

Because smoke control relies on air velocities and pressure differences produced by fans, it has the following three advantages in comparison to the traditional methods of smoke management:

1. Smoke control is less dependent on tight barriers. Allowance can be made in the design for reasonable leakage through barriers.
2. Stack effect, buoyancy, and wind are less likely to overcome smoke control than with passive smoke management. In the absence of smoke control, these driving forces cause smoke movement to the extent that leakage paths allow. However, pressure differences and airflows of a smoke control system act to oppose these driving forces.
3. Smoke control can use airflow to prevent smoke flow through an open doorway in a barrier. Doors in barriers are opened during evacuation and are sometimes accidentally left open or propped open throughout fires. In the absence of smoke control, smoke flow through these doors is common.

Smoke control systems should be designed so that a path exists for smoke movement to the outside; such a path acts to relieve pressures of gas expansion due to the fire heat.

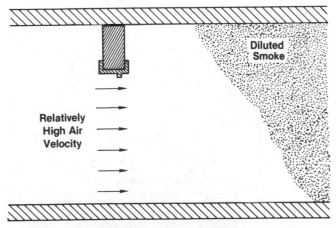

Fig. 8 No Smoke Backflow with High Air Velocity Through an Open Doorway

Dilution (or purging) of smoke in the fire space does not achieve smoke control, i.e., smoke movement cannot be controlled by simply supplying and exhausting large quantities of air from the space or zone in which the fire is located. This supplying and exhausting of air is sometimes called purging the smoke. Because a fire produces large quantities of smoke, purging cannot ensure breathable air in the fire space. In addition, purging cannot control smoke movement because it does not provide the needed airflow at open doors and the pressure differences across barriers. However, for spaces separated from the fire space by smoke barriers, purging can limit the level of smoke significantly.

Airflow

Theoretically, airflow can stop smoke movement through any space. However, the two places where air velocity is most commonly used to control smoke movement are open doorways and corridors. Thomas (1970) developed an empirical relation for the critical velocity to prevent smoke from flowing upstream in a corridor:

$$V_k = K \left(\frac{g\,E}{W\,\varrho\,c\,T} \right)^{1/3} \qquad (4)$$

where

V_k = critical air velocity to prevent smoke backflow
E = energy release rate into corridor
W = corridor width
ϱ = density of upstream air
c = specific heat of downstream gases
T = absolute temperature of downstream mixture of air and smoke
K = constant of the order of 1
g = gravitational constant

The downstream properties are considered to be taken at a point sufficiently far downstream of the fire for the properties to be uniform across the cross section. The critical air velocity can be evaluated at $\varrho = 0.081$ lb/ft³ (1.3 kg/m³), $c = 0.24$ Btu/lb·°F (1.005 kJ/kg·°C), $T = 81$°F (27°C), and $K = 1$.

$$V_k = K_v \left(\frac{E}{W} \right)^{1/3} \qquad (4a)$$

where

V_k = critical air velocity to prevent smoke backflow, fpm (m/s)
E = energy release rate into corridor, Btu/h (W)
W = corridor width, ft (m)
K_v = coefficient, 5.68 (0.0292)

This relation can be used when the fire is located in the corridor or when the smoke enters the corridor through an open door, air transfer grille, or other opening. The critical velocities calculated from the above relation are approximate because only an approximate value of K was used. However, critical velocities calculated from this relation indicate the air velocities required to prevent smoke backflow from fires of different sizes.

Equation (4) can be evaluated from Figure 9. For example, for an energy release rate of 0.512×10^6 Btu/h (150 kW) into a corridor 4.0-ft (1.2-m) wide, the above relation yields a critical velocity of 286 fpm (1.45 m/s). However, for a larger energy release rate of 7.2×10^6 Btu/h (2.1 MW), the relation yields a critical velocity of 690 fpm (3.50 m/s) for a corridor of the same width.

In general, a high air velocity requires a smoke-control system that is expensive and difficult to design. Airflow is most important in preventing smoke backflow through an open doorway that serves as a boundary of a smoke control system. Thomas (1970) indicated that Eq. (4) gives an estimate of the airflow needed to prevent smoke backflow through a door. Many designers feel that it is prohibitively expensive to design systems

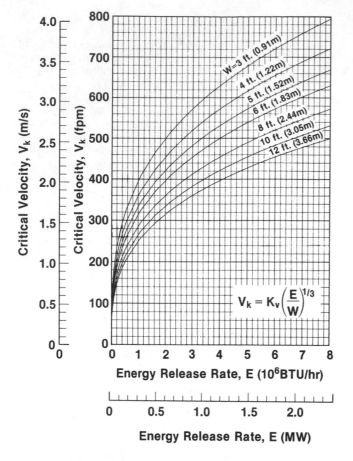

$$V_k = K_v \left(\frac{E}{W}\right)^{1/3}$$

Fig. 9   Critical Velocity to Prevent Smoke Backflow

to maintain air velocities in doorways greater than 300 fpm (1.5 m/s). A discussion of an appropriate design air velocity in a smoke control system is provided later.

Equation (4) is not appropriate for sprinklered fires having small temperature differences between the upstream air and downstream gases. Shaw and Whyte (1974) provide an analysis with experimental verification of a method to determine the velocity needed through an open doorway to prevent backflow of contaminated air. This analysis is specifically for small temperature differences and includes the effects of natural convection. This method calculates for a sprinklered fire where the temperature difference is only 3.6°F (2°C), that an average velocity of 50 fpm (0.25 m/s) would be the minimum velocity needed through a doorway to prevent smoke backflow. This temperature difference is small, and it is possible that larger values may be appropriate in many situations. Further research is needed in this area.

Even though airflow can control smoke movement, it is not the primary method because of the large quantities of air required for such systems to be effective. The primary means is air pressure differences across partitions, doors, and other building components.

Pressurization

The airflow rate through a construction crack, door gap, or other flow path is proportional to the pressure difference across that path raised to the power *n*. For a flow path of fixed geometry, *n* is theoretically in the range of 0.5 to 1. However,

for all flow paths, except extremely narrow cracks, $n = 0.5$, and the flow can be expressed as:

$$Q = CA \sqrt{2\Delta p/\varrho} \qquad (5)$$

where

    Q = volumetric airflow rate
    C = flow coefficient
    A = flow area (also called leakage area)
    Δp = pressure difference across the flow path
    ϱ = density of air entering the flow path

The flow coefficient depends on the geometry of the flow path, as well as on turbulence and friction. In the present context, the flow coefficient is generally in the range of 0.6 to 0.7. For $\varrho = 0.075$ lb/ft³ (1.2 kg/m³) and $C = 0.65$, the flow equation above can be expressed as:

$$Q = K_f A \sqrt{\Delta p} \qquad (5a)$$

where

    Q = volumetric flow rate, cfm (m³/s)
    A = flow area, ft² (m²)
    Δp = pressure difference across flow path, in. of water (Pa)
    K_f = coefficient, 2610 (0.839)

Airflow rate can also be determined from Figure 10. The flow area is frequently the same as the cross sectional area of the flow path. A closed door with a crack area of 0.11 ft² (0.01 m²) and a pressure difference of 0.01 in. of water (2.5 Pa) would have an air leakage rate of approximately 29 cfm (0.013 m³/s). If the pressure difference across the door was increased to 0.30 in. of water (75 Pa), then the flow would be 157 cfm (0.073 m³/s).

Frequently, in field tests of smoke control systems, pressure differences across partitions or closed doors have fluctuated by as much as 0.02 in. of water (5 Pa). These fluctuations have generally been attributed to wind, although they could have been due to the HVAC system or some other source. To control smoke movement, the pressure differences produced by a smoke control system must be sufficiently large so they are not overcome by pressure fluctuations, stack effect, smoke buoyancy, and the forces of the wind. However, the pressure difference produced by a smoke control system should not be so large that door opening problems result.

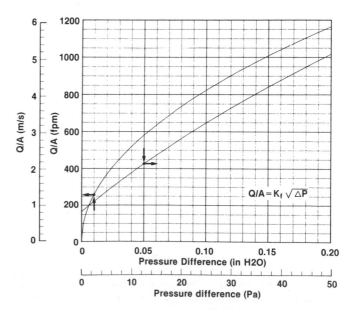

Fig. 10   Airflow due to Pressure Differences

PURGING

As previously stated, purging cannot ensure breathable air in the fire space while the fire is burning and producing smoke. However, purging can remove smoke from the fire space after fire extinction. After-fire purging is needed to allow the fire fighters to inspect and verify that the fire is totally extinguished. Traditionally, fire fighters purge by opening doors and breaking or opening windows. For spaces where these techniques are not appropriate, an HVAC system with a purge mode of operation may be desirable.

In general, the systems discussed in this chapter are based on the two basic principles of smoke control. However, it is not always possible to maintain sufficiently large airflow through open doors to prevent smoke from infiltrating a space that is intended to be protected. Ideally, such occurrences of open doors will only happen for short periods during evacuation. Smoke that has entered such a space can be purged, i.e., diluted, by supplying outside air to the space.

An example is a compartment isolated from a fire by smoke barriers and self-closing doors, so that no smoke enters the compartment when the doors are closed. However, when one or more of the doors is open, the airflow is insufficient to prevent smoke from flowing into the compartment from the fire space. For analysis, it is assumed that smoke is of uniform concentration throughout the compartment. When all the doors are closed, the concentration of contaminant in the compartment can be expressed as:

$$\frac{C}{C_o} = e^{-a\theta} \qquad (6)$$

where

    C_o = initial concentration of contaminant
    C = concentration of contaminant at time, θ
    a = purging rate in number of air changes per minute
    θ = time after doors closed in minutes
    e = exponential base, approximately 2.718

The concentrations, C_o and C, must both be in the same units, and they can be any units appropriate for the particular contaminant being considered. McGuire, Tamura, and Wilson (1970) evaluated the maximum levels of smoke obscuration from a number of tests and a number of proposed criteria for tolerable levels of smoke obscuration. Based on this evaluation, they state that the maximum levels of smoke obscuration are greater by a factor of 100 than those relating to the limit of tolerance. Thus, they indicate that an area can be considered "reasonably safe" with respect to smoke obscuration if its atmosphere will not be contaminated to an extent greater than 1% by the atmosphere prevailing in the immediate fire area. Such dilution would also reduce the concentrations of toxic smoke components. Toxicity is more complex, and no parallel statement has been made regarding the dilution needed to obtain a safe atmosphere with respect to toxic gases.

Equation (6) can be solved for the purging rate.

$$a = \frac{1}{\theta} \ln\left(\frac{C_o}{C}\right) \qquad (7)$$

For example, if the contaminant in a compartment is 20% of the burn room concentration when doors are open, and at six minutes after the door is closed, the contaminant concentration is 1% of the burn room, the Eq. (7) indicates the compartment must be purged at a rate of one air change every two minutes.

In reality, the concentration of the contaminant is not uniform throughout the compartment. Because of buoyancy, it is likely that higher concentrations of contaminant tend to be near the ceiling. Therefore, and exhaust inlet located near the ceiling and a supply outlet located near the floor would probably purge the smoke even faster than the above calculations indicate. Caution should be exercised in the location of the supply and exhaust points to prevent the supply air from blowing into the exhaust inlet and thus short circuiting the purging operation.

DOOR OPENING FORCES

The door-opening forces resulting from the pressure differences produced by a smoke-control system must be considered. Unreasonably high door opening forces can result in occupants having difficulty or being unable to open doors to refuge areas or escape routes.

The force required to open a door is the sum of the forces to overcome the pressure difference across the door and to overcome the door closer. This can be expressed as:

$$F = F_{dc} + \frac{K_d W A \Delta p}{2(W-d)} \qquad (8)$$

where

    F = the total door opening force, lb (N)
    F_{dc} = the force to overcome the door closer, lb (N)
    W = door width, ft (m)
    A = door area, ft^2 (m^2)
    Δp = pressure difference across the door, in. H$_2$O (Pa)
    d = distance from the doorknob to the edge of the knob side of the door, ft (m)
    K_d = coefficient, 5.20 (1.00)

This relation assumes that the door-opening force is applied at the knob. Door-opening forces due to pressure difference can be determined from Figure 11. The force to overcome the door

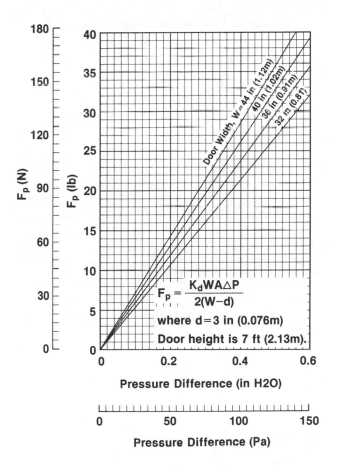

Fig. 11   Door Opening Force Due to Pressure Differences

closer is usually greater than 3 lb (13 N) and, in some cases, can be as large as 20 lb (90 N). For a door that is 7-ft (2.1-m) high and 36-in. (0.9-m) wide, subject to a pressure difference of 0.30 in. of water (75 Pa), the total door-opening force is 30 lb (133 N), if the force to overcome the door closer is 12 lb (53 N).

FLOW AREAS

In the design of smoke-control systems, airflow paths must be identified and evaluated. Some leakage paths are obvious, such as cracks around closed doors, open doors, elevator doors, windows, and air transfer grilles. Construction cracks in building walls are less obvious but no less important.

The flow area of most large openings, such as open windows, can be calculated easily. However, flow areas of cracks are more difficult to evaluate. The area of these leakage paths is dependent on workmanship, i.e., how well a door is fitted or how well weather stripping is installed. A door that is 36 in. by 7 ft (0.9 by 2.1 m) with an average crack width of 1/8 in. (3.2 mm) has a leakage area of 0.21 ft² (0.020 m²). However, if this door is installed with a 3/4 in. (19 mm) undercut, the leakage area is 0.32 ft² (0.030 m²)—a significant difference. The leakage area of elevator doors has been measured in the range of 0.55 to 0.70 ft² (0.051 to 0.065 m²) per door.

For open stairwell doorways, Cresci (1973) found that complex flow patterns exist and that the resulting flow through open doorways was considerably below the flow calculated by using the geometric area of the doorway as the flow area in Eq. (5a). Based on this research, it is recommended that the design flow area of an open stairwell doorway be half that of the geometric area (door height times width) of the doorway. An alternate approach for open stairwell doorways is to use the geometric area as the flow area and use a reduced flow coefficient. Because it does not allow the direct use of Eq. (5a), this alternate approach is not used here.

Typical leakage areas for walls and floors of commercial buildings are tabulated as area ratios in Table 1. These data are based on a relatively small number of tests performed by the National Research Council of Canada (Tamura and Shaw 1976a, 1976b, 1978; Tamura and Wilson 1966). The area ratios are evaluated at typical airflows at 0.30 in. of water (75 Pa) for walls, and 0.10 in. of water (25 Pa) for floors. It is believed that actual leakage areas depend primarily on workmanship rather than construction materials, and, in some cases, the flow areas in par-

Table 1 Typical Leakage Areas For Walls and Floors of Commercial Buildings

Construction Element	Wall Tightness	Area Ratio A/A_w
Exterior Building Walls	Tight	0.70×10^{-4}
(includes construction	Average	0.21×10^{-3}
cracks, cracks around	Loose	0.42×10^{-3}
windows and doors)	Very Loose	0.13×10^{-2}
Stairwell Walls	Tight	0.14×10^{-4}
(includes construction	Average	0.11×10^{-3}
cracks but not cracks	Loose	0.35×10^{-3}
around windows or doors)		
Elevator Shaft Walls	Tight	0.18×10^{-3}
(includes construction	Average	0.84×10^{-3}
cracks but not cracks	Loose	0.18×10^{-2}
around doors)		A/A_f
Floors	Average	0.52×10^{-4}
(includes construction		
cracks and areas around		
penetrations)		

A = leakage area; A_w = wall area; A_f = floor area

ticular buildings may vary from the values listed. Data concerning air leakage through building components is also provided in the 1985 FUNDAMENTALS Volume, Chapter 22.

Because the vent surface is usually covered by a louver and screen, the flow area of a vent is less than its area (vent height times width). Because the slats in louvers are frequently slanted, calculation of the flow area is further complicated. Manufacturers' data should be sought for specific information.

EFFECTIVE FLOW AREAS

The concept of effective flow areas is useful for analysis of smoke-control systems. The paths in the system can be in parallel with one another, in series, or a combination of parallel and series paths. The effective area of a system of flow areas is the area that results in the same flow as the system when it is subjected to the same pressure difference over the total system of flow paths. This concept is similar to the effective resistance of a system of electrical resistances. The effective area for parallel leakage areas is the sum of the individual leakage paths:

$$A_e = \sum_{i=1}^{n} A_i \tag{9}$$

where n is the number of flow areas, A_i, in parallel.

For example, the effective area, A_e, for the three parallel leakage areas of Figure 12 is:

$$A_e = A_1 + A_2 + A_3 \tag{10}$$

If A_1 is 1.08 ft² (0.10 m²) and A_2 and A_3 are 0.54 ft² (0.05 m²) each, then the effective flow area, A_e, is 2.16 ft² (0.20 m²).

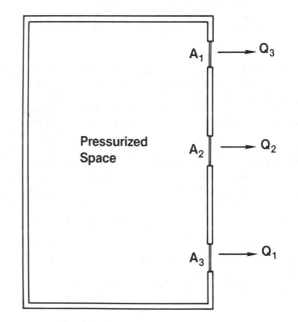

Fig. 12 Leakage Paths in Parallel

Three leakage areas in series from a pressurized space are illustrated in Figure 13. The effective flow area of these paths is:

$$A_e = \left(\frac{1}{A_1^2} + \frac{1}{A_2^2} + \frac{1}{A_3^2} \right)^{-1/2} \tag{11}$$

The general rule for any number of leakage areas in series is:

$$A_e = \left[\sum_{i=1}^{n} \frac{1}{A_i^2} \right]^{-1/2} \tag{12}$$

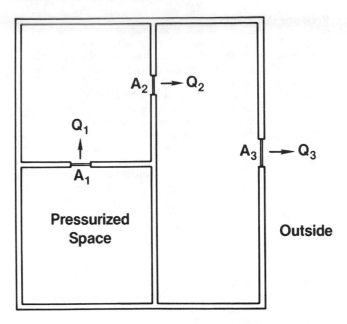

Fig. 13   Leakage Paths in Series

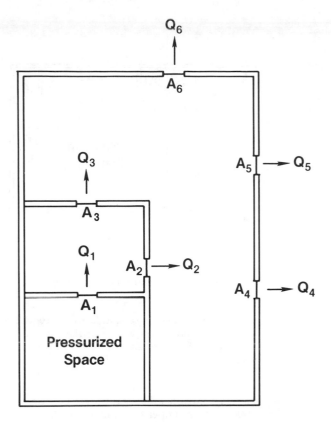

Fig. 14   Combination of Leakage Paths in Parallel and Series

where n is the number of leakage areas, A_i, in series. In smoke-control analysis, there are frequently only two paths in series. For this case, the effective leakage area is:

$$A_e = \frac{A_1 A_2}{\sqrt{A_1^2 + A_2^2}} \qquad (13)$$

Example 1

Calculate the effective leakage area of two equal flow paths in series. Let $A = A_1 = A_2 = 0.22$ ft² (0.02 m²)

$$A_e = \frac{A^2}{\sqrt{2A^2}} = \frac{A}{\sqrt{2}} = 0.15 \text{ ft}^2 \text{ (0.014 m}^2\text{)}$$

Example 2

Calculate the effective area of two flow paths in series, where $A_1 = 0.22$ ft² (0.02 m²) and $A_2 = 2.2$ ft² (0.2 m²).

$$A_e = \frac{A_1 A_2}{\sqrt{A_1^2 + A_2^2}} = 0.219 \text{ ft}^2 \text{ (0.0199 m}^2\text{)}$$

This example illustrates that when two areas are in series, and one is much larger than the other, the effective area is approximately equal to the smaller area.

The method of developing an effective area for a system of both parallel and series paths is to combine groups of parallel paths and series paths systematically. The system illustrated in Figure 14 is analyzed as an example. The figure shows that A_2 and A_3 are in parallel; therefore, their effective area is:

$$A_{23_e} = A_2 + A_3$$

Areas A_4, A_5, and A_6 are also in parallel, so their effective area is:

$$A_{456_e} = A_4 + A_5 + A_6$$

These two effective areas are in series with A_1. Therefore, the effective flow area of the system is given by:

$$A_e = \left[\frac{1}{A_1^2} + \frac{1}{A_{23_e}^2} + \frac{1}{A_{456_e}^2}\right)^{-1/2}$$

Example 3

Calculate the effective area of the system in Figure 14, if the leakage areas are $A_1 = A_2 = A_3 = 0.22$ ft² (0.02 m²) and $A_4 = A_5 = A_6 = 0.11$ ft² (0.01 m²).

$$A_{23_e} = 0.44 \text{ ft}^2 \text{ (0.04 m}^2\text{)}$$
$$A_{456_e} = 0.33 \text{ ft}^2 \text{ (0.03 m}^2\text{)}$$
$$A_e = 0.16 \text{ ft}^2 \text{ (0.015 m}^2\text{)}$$

SYMMETRY

The concept of symmetry is useful in simplifying problems. Figure 15 illustrates the floor plan of a multistory building that can be divided in half by a plane of symmetry. Flow areas on one side of the plane of symmetry are equal to corresponding flow areas on the other side. For a building to be so treated, every floor of the building must be such that it can be divided in the same manner by the plane of symmetry. If wind effects are not considered in the analysis or if the wind direction is parallel to the plane of symmetry, then the airflow is only one half of the building analyzed. It is not necessary that the building be geometrically symmetric, as shown in Figure 15; it must be symmetric only with respect to flow.

DESIGN PARAMETERS: A GENERAL DISCUSSION

Ideally, codes should contain design parameters leading to the design of safe and economical smoke control systems. Unfortunately, because smoke control is a new field, consensus has not been reached as to what constitutes reasonable design parameters. The designer must adhere to any smoke control

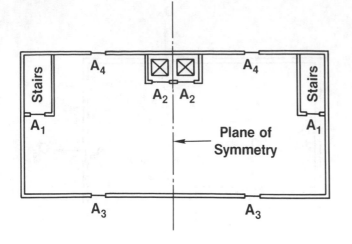

Fig. 15 Building Floor Plan Illustrating Symmetry Concept

criteria existing in appropriate codes or standards. If necessary, however, the designer should seek a waiver of the local codes to ensure an effective smoke-control system. In the absence of code requirements for specific parameters, the following discussion may be helpful to the designer.

Five areas for which design parameters must be established are (1) leakage areas, (2) weather data, (3) pressure differences, (4) airflow, and (5) number of open doors in the smoke-control system.

Leakage areas have already been discussed. Windows, in the fire compartment should be considered because they can affect pressure differences and airflow depending on whether they are broken or not. Further, smoke control systems primarily aid in building evacuation and only need to operate during the time needed for evacuation. These factors are included in the following discussion of these parameters.

Weather Data

Little consideration has been given to weather data specifically for the design of smoke-control systems. A designer may use the design temperatures for heating and cooling found in Chapter 24 of the 1985 FUNDAMENTALS Volume. In a normal winter, approximately 22 hours are at or below the 99% design value, and approximately 54 hours are at or below the 97.5% design value. Furthermore, extreme temperatures can be considerably lower than the winter design temperatures. For example, the 99% design temperature for Tallahassee, Florida, is 27 °F (−3 °C), but the lowest temperature observed there was −2 °F (−19 °C) (NOAA 1979).

Temperatures are generally below the design values for short periods, and because of the thermal lag of building materials, these short intervals of low temperature usually do not cause problems with heating. However, there is no time lag for a smoke-control system; so it is subjected to all the extreme forces of stack effect that exist the moment it is operated. If the outside temperature is below the winter design temperature for which a smoke-control system was designed, then problems from stack effect may result. A similar situation can result with respect to summer design temperatures and reverse stack effect.

Wind data is needed for a wind analysis of a smoke-control system. At present, no formal method of such an analysis exists, and the approach most generally taken is to design the smoke-control system to minimize any effects of wind.

Pressure Differences

Both the maximum and minimum allowable pressure differences across the boundaries of smoke control should be considered. The maximum allowable pressure difference should not result in excessive door-opening forces. Section 5-2.1.4.3 of the National Fire Protection Association (NFPA) Life Safety Code (NFPA 1985b) states that the force required to open any door in a means of egress shall not exceed 30 lb (133 N).

A minimum allowable pressure difference across a boundary of a smoke-control system might be that no smoke leakage occurs during building evacuation. In this case, the smoke-control system must produce sufficient pressure differences to overcome forces of wind, stack effect, or buoyancy of hot smoke. The pressure differences due to wind and stack effect can become large in the event of a broken window in the fire compartment. Evaluation of these pressure differences depends on evacuation time, rate of fire growth, building configuration, and the presence of a fire-suppression system. In the absence of a formal method of analysis, such evaluations must be based on experience and engineering judgment.

Other criteria might maintain smoke-free egress routes or prevent smoke infiltration to a refuge area; these possible alternatives are not discussed here.

A method for determining the pressure difference across a smoke barrier resulting from the buoyancy of hot gases has been covered. For a particular application, it may be necessary to design a smoke-control system to withstand an intense fire next to a door in a boundary of a smoke-control zone. To prevent smoke infiltration, the smoke-control system should maintain a minimum pressure difference under nonfire conditions in the range of 0.08 to 0.10 in. of water (20 to 25 Pa).

If boundary is exposed to hot smoke from a remote fire, a lower pressure difference due to buoyancy will result. For a smoke temperature of 750 °F (400 °C), the pressure difference caused by the smoke 5.0 ft (1.5 m) above the neutral plane would be 0.04 in. of water (10 Pa). In this situation, it is suggested that the smoke-control system be designed to maintain a minimum pressure in the range of 0.06 to 0.08 in. of water (15 to 20 Pa).

Water spray from fire sprinklers cools smoke from a building fire and reduces the pressure differences due to buoyancy. In such a case, it is wise to allow for pressure fluctuations. Accordingly, a minimum pressure difference in the range of 0.02 to 0.04 in. of water (5 to 10 Pa) is suggested.

Windows in the fire compartment can break due to exposure to high temperature gases. In such cases, the pressure due to the wind on the building exterior can be determined from Eq. (3). If this window is the only opening to the outside on the fire floor and the window faces into the wind, the boundary of the smoke-control system could be subjected to higher pressures. One possible solution is to vent the fire floor on all sides to relieve such pressures. For a building that is much longer than it is wide, it may be necessary to vent only on the two longer sides.

In addition to wind effects, stack effect can be increased in the event of a broken fire compartment window. With a fire on a lower floor during cold weather, stack effect will increase pressures of the fire floor above surrounding spaces. Even though little research has been done on the subject, the chances of a window breaking in the fire compartment are reduced by the operation of fire sprinklers.

Airflow

When the doors in the boundaries of smoke-control systems are open, smoke can flow into refuge areas or escape routes unless there is sufficient airflow through the open door to prevent smoke backflow. One criterion for selecting a design velocity through an open door is that no smoke backflow should occur during building evacuation. Other criteria might include limited smoke leakage into areas to be protected. Under such criteria, the toxicity of the smoke is a factor that must be considered. Selection of this velocity depends on evacuation time, rate of fire growth, building configuration, and the presence of a fire-suppression system. In the absence of a formal method of analysis, such an evaluation must be based on experience and engineering judgment.

At present, little is known about the critical velocity needed to stop smoke backflow through an open door. In the absence of a specific relationship for doorways, the analysis presented for corridors can yield approximate results. The width of the doorway may be used in place of the width of the corridor. This technique is based on the assumption that smoke properties are uniform across the cross section. As previously illustrated, for a particular application, it may be considered necessary to design for an intensive fire, such as one with an energy release rate of 8×10^6 Btu/h (2.4 MW). In this case, a critical velocity of approximately 800 fpm (4 m/s) would be required to stop smoke.

In another application, it may be estimated that the building would be subjected to a much less intense fire with an energy release rate of 427,000 Btu/h (125 kW). To protect against smoke backflow during evacuation, the critical velocity would be 300 fpm (1.5 m/s).

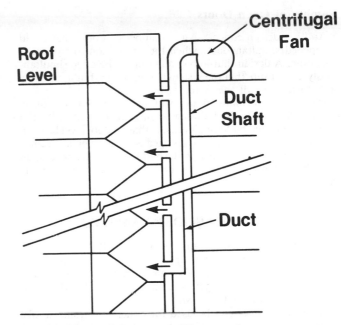

Fig. 17 Stairwell Pressurization by Multiple Injection with a Roof-Mounted Fan

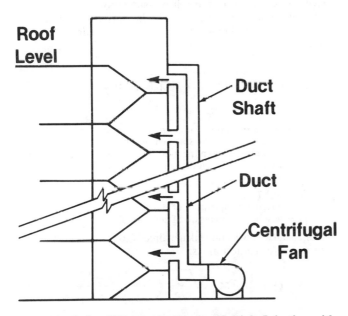

Fig. 16 Stairwell Pressurization by Multiple Injection with Fan Located at Ground Level

For tall stairwells, supply air can be supplied at a number of locations over the height of the stairwell. Figures 16 and 17 are two examples of many possible multiple injection systems that can be used to overcome the limitations of single injection systems. In these figures, the supply duct is shown in a separate shaft. However, systems have been built that have eliminated the expense of a separate duct shaft by locating the supply duct in the stairwell itself. In such a case, care must be taken that the duct does not become an obstruction to orderly building evacuation.

STAIRWELL COMPARTMENTATION

An alternative to multiple injection is compartmentation of the stairwell into a number of sections, as illustrated in Figure

18. When the doors between compartments are open, the effect of compartmentation is lost. For this reason, compartmentation is inappropriate for densely populated buildings where total building evacuation by the stairwell is planned in the event of fire. However, when a staged evacuation plan is used and when the system is designed to operate successfully when the maximum number of doors between compartments are open, compartmentation can be an effective means of providing stairwell pressurization for tall stairwells.

In a sprinklered building, the smoke away from the immediate fire area might be considered cooled to near ambient temperature by the water spray from the sprinklers. In this case, a design velocity in the range of 50 to 250 fpm (0.25 to 1.25 m/s) may be used.

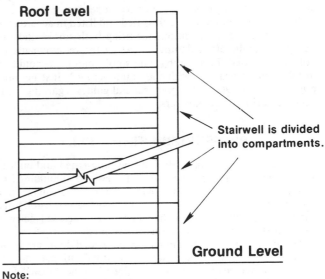

Note:
Each four-floor compartment has at least one supply air injection point.

Fig. 18 Compartmentation of a Pressurized Stairwell. Each Compartment of Four Floors Has at Least One Supply Air Injection Point

Number of Open Doors

Another design concern is the number of doors that could be opened simultaneously when the smoke-control system is operating. A design that allows all doors to be open simultaneously may ensure that the system always works, but it probably adds to the cost of the system.

Deciding how many doors will be open simultaneously depends largely on the building occupancy. For example, in a densely populated building, it is likely that all doors will be open during evacuation. However, if a staged evacuation plan or refuge area concept is incorporated in the building fire emergency plan or if the building is sparsely occupied, only a few of the doors may be open during a fire.

FIRE AND SMOKE DAMPERS

Openings for ducts in walls and floors with fire resistance ratings should be protected by fire dampers and ceiling dampers, as required by local codes. Also, air transfer openings should be protected. These dampers should be classified and labeled in accordance with UL 555-81.

A smoke damper can be used for either traditional smoke management (smoke containment) or for smoke control. In smoke management, a smoke damper inhibits the passage of smoke under the forces of buoyancy, stack effect, and wind. Generally, for smoke management, smoke dampers should have low leakage characteristics at elevated temperatures. However, smoke dampers are only one of many elements (partitions, floors, doors, etc.) intended to inhibit smoke flow. In smoke management applications, the leakage characteristics of smoke dampers should be selected to be appropriate with the leakage of the other elements of the system.

In a smoke-control system, a smoke damper inhibits the passage of air that may or may not contain smoke. Low leakage characteristics of a damper are not necessary when outside (fresh) air is on the high pressure side of the damper, as is the case for dampers that shut off supply air from a smoke zone or that shut off exhaust air from a nonsmoke zone. In these cases, moderate leakage of smoke-free air through the damper does not adversely affect the control of smoke movement. It is best to design smoke-control systems so that only smoke-free air is on the high pressure side of a smoke damper.

Smoke dampers should be classified and listed in accordance with UL 555S-85. At locations requiring both smoke and fire dampers, combination dampers meeting the requirements of both can be used. Fire, ceiling, and smoke dampers should be installed in accordance with the manufacturer's instructions. NFPA Standard 90-A-1985 gives general guides regarding locations requiring these dampers.

PRESSURIZED STAIRWELLS

Many pressurized stairwells have been designed and built to provide a smoke-free escape route in the event of a building fire. A secondary objective is to provide a smoke-free staging area for fire fighters. On the fire floor, a pressurized stairwell must maintain a positive pressure difference across a closed stairwell door so that smoke infiltration is prevented.

During building fire situations, some stairwell doors are opened intermittently during evacuation and fire fighting, and some doors may even be blocked open. Ideally, when the stairwell door is opened on the fire floor, airflow through the door should be sufficient to prevent smoke backflow. Designing such a system is difficult because of the many combinations of open stairwell doors and weather conditions that affect the airflow.

Stairwell pressurization systems are divided into single and multiple injection systems. A single injection system has pressurized air supplied to the stairwell at one location—most commonly at the top. Associated with this system is the potential of smoke entering the stairwell through the pressurization fan intake. Therefore, automatic shutdown during such an event should be considered.

For tall stairwells, single injection systems can fail when a few doors are open near the air supply injection point. Such a failure is especially likely with bottom injection systems when a ground level stairwell door is open.

STAIRWELL ANALYSIS

This section presents an analysis for a pressurized stairwell in a building without vertical leakage. The performance of pressurized stairwells in buildings without elevators may be closely approximated by this method. It is also useful for buildings with vertical leakage in that it yields conservative results. Only one stairwell is considered in the building; however, the analysis can be extended to any number of stairwells by the concept of symmetry. For evaluation of vertical leakage through the building or with open stairwell doors, computer analysis is recommended. The analysis is for buildings where the leakage areas are the same for each floor of the building and where the only significant driving forces are the stairwell pressurization system and the temperature difference between the indoors and outdoors.

The pressure difference, Δp_{sb}, between the stairwell and the building can be expressed as:

$$\Delta p_{sb} = \Delta p_{sbb} + \frac{B\,y}{1 + \left(\dfrac{A_{sb}}{A_{bo}}\right)^2} \tag{14}$$

where

Δp_{sbb} = the pressure difference, Δp_{sb}, at the stairwell bottom
y = distance above the stairwell bottom
A_{sb} = flow area between the stairwell and the building (per floor)
A_{bo} = flow area between the building and the outside (per floor)
$B = \dfrac{gp}{R}\left(\dfrac{1}{T_o} - \dfrac{1}{T_s}\right)$
T_o = absolute temperature of outside air
T_s = absolute temperature of stairwell air

For a stairwell with no leakage directly to the outside, the flow rate of pressurization air is:

$$Q = \frac{2}{3}\, NCA_{sb} \sqrt{\frac{2}{\varrho}}\left(\frac{\Delta p_{sbt}^{3/2} - \Delta p_{sbb}^{3/2}}{\Delta p_{sbt} - \Delta p_{sbb}}\right) \tag{15}$$

where

N = number of floors
C = flow coefficient, see Eq. (19)
Δp_{sbt} = the pressure difference, Δp_{sb}, at the stairwell top

---

Example 4

Each story of a 20-story stairwell is 10.8 ft (3.3 m) in height. The stairwell has a single-leaf door at each floor leading to the occupant space and one ground-level door to the outside. The exterior of the building has a wall area of 6030 ft² (560 m²) per floor. The exterior building walls and stairwell walls are of average leakiness. The stairwell wall area is 560 ft² (52 m²) per floor. The area of the gap around each stairwell door to the building is 0.26 ft² (0.024 m²). The exterior door is well gasketed, and its leakage can be neglected when it is closed.

For this example, the following design parameters are used: outside design temperatures, $t_o = 14\,°F\ (-10\,°C)$; stairwell temperature, $t_s = 70\,°F\ (21\,°C)$; minimum design pressure differences when all stairwell doors are closed of 0.551 in. of water (137 Pa).

Using the leakage ratios for an exterior building wall of average tightness from Table 1, A_{bo} = 6030 (0.21 • 10^{-3}) = 1.27 ft^2 (0.118 m^2). Using leakage ratios for a stairwell wall of average tightness from Table 1, the leakage area of the stairwell wall is 560 (0.11 • 10^{-3}) = 0.06 ft^2 (0.006 m^2). A_{sb} equals the leakage area of the stairwell wall plus the gaps around the closed doors. A_{sb} = 0.06 + 0.26 + 0.32 ft^2 (0.030 m^2). The temperature factor, B, is calculated at 0.00170 in. of water/ft (1.39 Pa/m). The pressure difference at the stairwell bottom is selected as Δp_{sbb} = 0.080 in. of water (20 Pa) to provide an extra degree of protection above the minimum allowable value of 0.052 in. of water (13 Pa). The pressure difference Δp_{sbt} is calculated from Eq. (14) at 0.426 in. of water (106 Pa) using y = 217 ft (66.1 m). Thus, Δp_{sbt} does not exceed the maximum allowable pressure. The flow rate of pressurization air is calculated from Eq. (15) at 8200 cfm (3.9 m^3/s).

The flow rate is highly dependent on the leakage area around the closed doors and upon the leakage area that exists in the stairwell walls. In practice, these areas are difficult to evaluate and even more difficult to control. If the flow area, A_{sb}, in Example 4 were 0.54 ft^2 (0.050 m^2) rather than 0.32 ft^2 (0.030 m^2), then a flow rate of pressurization air of 13,800 cfm (6.5 m^3/s) would have been calculated from Eq. (15). A fan with a sheave is one approach to allow adjustment of supply air to offset for variations in actual leakage from the values used in design calculations.

STAIRWELL PRESSURIZATION AND OPEN DOORS

The simple pressurization system discussed previously has two limitations regarding open doors. First, when a stairwell door to the outside and doors to the building are open, the simple system cannot provide sufficient airflows through doorways to prevent smoke backflow. Second, when stairwell doors are open, the pressure difference across the closed doors can drop to low levels. Two common systems used to overcome these problems are overpressure relief and supply fan bypass.

Overpressure Relief

The total airflow rate is selected to provide the minimum air velocity when a specific number of doors are open. When all the doors are closed, part of this air is relieved through a vent to prevent excessive pressure buildup, which could cause excessive door-opening forces. This excess air can be vented either to the building or to the outside. Exterior vents can be subject to adverse effects of the wind, so wind shields are recommended.

Barometric dampers that close when the pressure drops below a specified value can minimize the air losses through the vent when doors are open. Figure 19 illustrates a pressurized stairwell with overpressure relief vents to the building at each floor. In systems with vents between the stairwell and the building, the vents typically have one or more fire dampers in series with the barometric damper. As an energy conservation feature, these fire dampers are normally closed but open when the pressurization system is activated. This arrangement also reduces the possibility of annoying damper chatter that frequently occurs with barometric dampers.

An exhaust duct can provide overpressure relief in a pressurized stairwell. This system is designed so that the normal resistance of a nonpowered exhaust duct acts to maintain pressure differences that are within the design limits.

Exhaust fans also can relieve excessive pressures when all stairwell doors are closed. The fan should be controlled by a differential pressure sensor, so that it will not operate when the pressure difference between the stairwell and the building falls below a specific level. This control should prevent the fan from pulling smoke into the stairwell when a number of open doors have reduced stairwell pressurization. Such an exhaust fan should

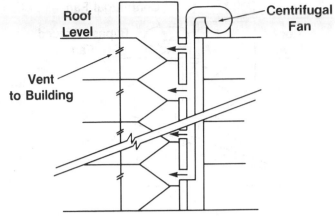

Notes:
1. Vents to the building have a barometric damper and one or two fire dampers in series.
2. A roof-mounted supply fan is shown; however, the fan may be located at any level.
3. A manually operated damper may be located at the stairwell top for smoke purging by the fire department

Fig. 19   Stairwell Pressurization with Vents to the Building at Each Floor

be specifically sized so that the pressurization system will perform within design limits. Because an exhaust fan can be adversely affected by the wind, a wind shield is recommended.

An alternate method of venting a stairwell is through an automatically opening stairwell door to the outside at ground level. Under normal conditions, this door would be closed and, in most cases, locked for security reasons. Provisions need to be made so that this lock does not conflict with the automatic operation of the system.

Possible adverse wind effects are also a concern with a system that uses an open outside door as a vent. Occasionally, high local wind velocities develop near the exterior stairwell door, and such winds are difficult to estimate without expensive modeling. Local objects on a wall can act as wind breaks (or wind shields).

Supply Fan Bypass

In this system, the supply fan is sized to provide at least the minimum air velocity when the design number of doors are open. Figure 20 illustrates such a system. The flow rate of air into the stairwell is varied by modulating bypass dampers, which are controlled by one or more static pressure sensors that sense the pressure difference between the stairwell and the building. When all the stairwell doors are closed, the pressure difference increases and the bypass damper opens to increase the bypass air and decrease the flow of supply air to the stairwell. In this manner, excessive stairwell pressures and excessive pressure differences between the stairwell and the building are prevented.

ELEVATORS

Elevator smoke-control systems intended for use by firefighters should keep elevator cars, elevator shafts, and elevator machinery rooms smoke free. Small amounts of smoke in these spaces is acceptable, provided that the environment is nontoxic and that the operation of the elevator equipment is not affected. Elevator smoke-control systems intended for fire evacuation of the handicapped or other building occupants should also keep elevator lobbies smoke free or nearly smoke free. The long-standing obstacles to fire evacuation by elevators are logistics of evacua-

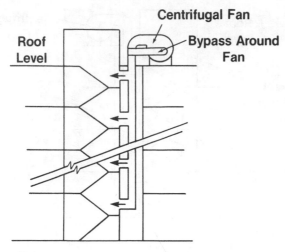

Notes:
1. Fan bypass controlled by one or more static pressure sensors located between the stairwell and the building.
2. A roof-mounted supply fan is shown; however, the fan may be located at any level.
3. A manually operated damper may be located at the stairwell top for smoke purging by the fire department.

Fig. 20   Stairwell Pressurization with Bypass Around Supply Fan

tion, reliability of electrical power, elevator door jamming, and fire and smoke protection. All of these obstacles, except smoke protection, can be addressed by existing technology, as discussed by Klote (1984).

Klote and Tamura (1986) studied conceptual elevator smoke-control systems for handicapped evacuation. The major problem was maintaining pressurization with open doors, especially doors on the ground floor. Of the systems evaluated, only one with a supply fan bypass with feedback control maintains adequate pressurization with any combination of open or closed doors. There are probably other systems capable of providing adequate smoke control, and the procedure used by Klote and Tamura can be viewed as an example of how to evaluate the performance of a system to meet the particular characteristics of a building under construction.

The transient pressures due to "piston effect" when an elevator car moves in a shaft have been a concern with regard to elevator smoke control. Piston effect is not a concern for slow-moving cars in multiple car shafts. However, for fast cars in single car shafts, the piston effect can be considerable.

ZONE SMOKE CONTROL

Pressurized stairwells are intended to prevent smoke infiltration into stairwells. However, in a building with just stairwell pressurization, smoke can flow through cracks in floors and partitions and through shafts to damage property and threaten life at locations remote from the fire. The concept of zone smoke control is intended to limit such smoke movement.

A building is divided into a number of smoke-control zones, each zone separated from the others by partitions, floors, and doors that can be closed to inhibit the smoke movement. In the event of a fire, pressure differences and airflows produced by mechanical fans limit the smoke spread from the zone in which the fire initiated. The concentration of smoke in this zone goes unchecked and accordingly, in zone smoke-control systems, the

building occupants should evacuate the smoke zone as soon as possible after fire detection.

A smoke-control zone can consist of one floor, of more than one floor, or a floor can be divided into more than one smoke-control zone. Some arrangements of smoke-control zones are illustrated in Figure 21. All of the non-smoke zones in the building may be pressurized. The term *pressure sandwich* describes cases where only adjacent zones to the smoke zone are pressurized, as in Figures 21 (b) and (d).

Zone smoke control is intended to limit smoke movement to the smoke zone by the two principles of smoke control. Pressure differences in the desired direction across the barriers of a smoke zone can be achieved by either supplying outside (fresh) air to non-smoke zones, by venting the smoke zone, or by both methods.

Venting of smoke from a smoke zone prevents significant over-pressures due to thermal expansion of gases caused by the fire. However, venting results in only slight reduction of smoke concentration in the smoke zone. This venting can be accomplished by exterior wall vents, smoke shafts, and mechanical venting (exhausting).

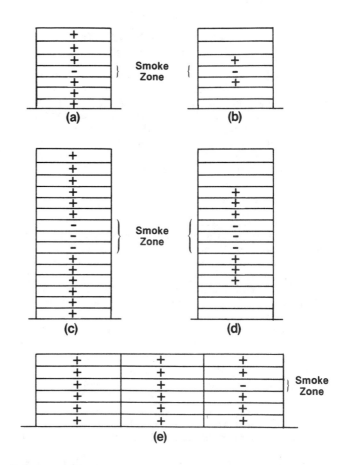

Note:
In the above figures, the smoke zone is indicated by a minus sign, and pressurized spaces are indicated by a plus sign. Each floor can be a smoke control zone as in (a) and (b), or a smoke zone can consist of more than one floor as in (c) and (d). All the non-smoke zones in a building may be pressurized as in (a) and (c) or only non-smoke zones adjacent to the smoke zone may be pressurized as in (b) and (d). A smoke zone can also be limited to a part of a floor as in (e).

Fig. 21   Some Arrangements of Smoke Control Zones

COMPUTER ANALYSIS

Some design calculations associated with smoke control are appropriate for hand calculation. However, other calculations involve time consuming, trial and error solutions that are more appropriately left to a computer. The National Bureau of Standards has developed a computer program (Klote 1982) specifically for analysis of smoke-control systems. A number of other programs applicable to smoke control have been developed. Some calculate steady state airflow and pressures throughout a building (Sander 1974, Sand, and Tamura 1973). Other programs go beyond this to calculate the smoke concentrations that would be produced throughout a building in the event of a fire (Yoshida et al. 1979, Evers and Waterhouse 1978, Wakamatsu 1977, Rilling 1978).

Each of these programs differs from the others; however, the basic concepts behind these programs are essentially the same. A building is represented by a network of spaces or nodes, each at a specific pressure and temperature. The stairwells and other shafts are modeled by a vertical series of spaces, one for each floor. Air flows through leakage paths from regions of high pressure to regions of low pressure. These leakage paths are doors and windows that may be opened or closed. Leakage can also occur through partitions, floors, and exterior walls and roofs. The airflow through a flow path is a function of the pressure difference across the path, as presented in Eq. (5).

Air from outside the building can be introduced by a pressurization system into any level of a shaft or even into other building compartments. This allows simulation of stairwell pressurization. In addition, any building space can be exhausted. This allows simulation of zoned smoke-control systems. The pressures throughout the building and flow rates through all the flow paths are obtained by solving the airflow network, including the driving forces such as wind, the pressurization system, or an inside-to-outside temperature difference.

ACCEPTANCE TESTING

Regardless of the care, skill, and attention to detail with which a smoke-control system is designed, an acceptance test is needed as assurance that the system, as built, operates as intended.

An acceptance test should be composed of two levels of testing. The first level is of a functional nature to determine if everything in the system works as it is supposed to work, i.e., an initial checkout of the system components. The importance of the initial checkout has become apparent because of the problems that have been encountered during tests of smoke control systems. These problems include fans operating backward, fans to which no electrical power was supplied, and controls that did not work properly.

The second level of testing is of a performance nature to determine if the system, as a system, performs adequately under all required modes of operation. This can consist of measuring pressure differences across barriers under various modes of smoke-control system operation. In cases where airflows through open doors are important, these should be measured. Chemical smoke from smoke candles (sometimes called smoke bombs) is not recommended for performance testing because it normally lacks the buoyancy of hot smoke from a real building fire. Smoke near a flaming fire has a temperature in the range of 1000 to 2000 °F (540 to 1100 °C). Heating chemical smoke to such temperatures to emulate smoke from a real fire is not recommended unless precautions are taken to protect life and property. These same comments about buoyancy apply to tracer gases. Thus, it seems that pressure difference testing is the most practical performance test. A guide specification for acceptance testing is available from the Smoke Control Association (1985).

REFERENCES

ASTM. 1985. Terminology Relating to Fire Standards (Rev. B). Standard E176-85. American Society for Testing and Materials, Philadelphia.

Cresci, R.J. 1973. Smoke and Fire Control in High-Rise Office Buildings—Part II, Analysis of Stair Pressurization Systems. Symposium on Experience and Applications on Smoke and Fire Control, ASHRAE Annual Meeting, June.

Evers, E., and Waterhouse, A. 1978. A Computer Model for Analyzing Smoke Movement in Buildings. Building Research Est., Fire Research Station, Borehamwood, Herts, England.

Fang, J.B. 1980. Static Pressures Produced by Room Fires. National Bureau of Standards (U.S.), NBSIR 80-1984.

Houghton, E.L., and Carruther, N.B. 1976. *Wind Forces on Buildings and Structures.* John Wiley & Sons, New York.

Klote, J.H. 1980. Stairwell Pressurization. ASHRAE *Transactions*, Vol. 86, Part 1, pp. 604-673.

Klote, J.H. 1982. A Computer Program for Analysis of Smoke Control Systems. National Bureau of Standards (U.S.), NBSIR 82-2512.

Klote, J.H. 1984. Smoke Control for Elevators. ASHRAE *Journal*, Vol. 26, No. 4, April, pp. 23-33.

Klote, J.H., and Fothergill, J.W. 1983. *Design of Smoke Control Systems for Buildings.* ASHRAE Publication.

Klote, J.H., and Tamura, G.T. 1986. Smoke Control and Fire Evacuation by Elevators. ASHRAE *Transactions*, Vol. 92, Part 1.

MacDonald, A.J. 1975. *Wind Loading on Buildings.* John Wiley & Sons, New York.

McGuire, J.H., and Tamura, G.T. 1975. Simple Analysis of Smoke Flow Problems in High Buildings. *Fire Technology*, Vol. 11, No. 1, pp. 15-22, February.

McGuire, J.H.; Tamura, G.T.; and Wilson, A.G. 1970. Factors in Controlling Smoke in High Buildings, Symposium on Fire Hazards in Buildings. ASHRAE Semi-Annual Meeting, January.

NFPA. 1986. *Fire Protection Handbook.* 16th Ed. National Fire Protection Association, Quincy, MA.

NFPA. 1985a. Installation of Air-Conditioning and Ventilating Systems. NFPA 90A-1985. National Fire Protection Association, Quincy, MA.

NFPA. 1985b. *Code for Safety to Life from Fire in Buildings and Structures.* NFPA 101-1985, National Fire Protection Association.

NOAA. 1979. *Temperature Extremes in the United States.* National Oceanic and Atmospheric Administration (U.S.), National Climatic Center, Asheville, NC.

Rilling, J. 1978. Smoke Study, 3rd Phase, Method of Calculating the Smoke Movement between Building Spaces. Centre Scientifique et Technique du Batiment (CSTB), Champs Sur Marne, France, September.

Sachs, P. 1972. *Wind Forces in Engineering.* Pergamon Press, New York.

Sander, D.M., and Tamura, G.T. 1973. FORTRAN IV Program to Simulate Air Movement in Multi Story Buildings. National Research Council, Canada, DBR Computer Program No. 35.

Sander, D.M. 1974. FORTRAN IV Program to Calculate Air Infiltration in Buildings, National Research Council, Canada, DBR Computer Program No. 37, May.

Shaw, B.H., and Whyte, W. 1974. Air Movement through Doorways—The Influence of Temperature and its Control by Forced Airflow, *Building Services Engineer*, Vol. 42, pp. 210-218, December.

Shaw, C.Y., and Tamura, G.T. 1977. The Calculation of Air Infiltration Rates Caused by Wind and Stack Action for Tall Buildings. ASHRAE *Transactions*, Vol. 83, Part 2, pp. 145-158.

Simiu, E., and Scanlan, R.H. 1978. *Wind Effects on Structures: An Introduction to Wind Engineering.* John Wiley & Sons, New York.

Smoke Control Association. 1985. Smoke Control System Testing. Box 421, Buckingham, PA 08912.

Tamura, G.T., and Shaw, C.Y. 1976a. Studies on Exterior Wall Air Tightness and Air Infiltration of Tall Buildings, ASHRAE *Transactions*, Vol. 83, Part 1, pp. 122-134.

Tamura, G.T., and Shaw, C.Y. 1976b. Air Leakage Data for the Design of Elevator and Stair Shaft Pressurization Systems, ASHRAE *Transactions*, Vol. 83, Part 2, pp. 179-190.

Tamura, G.T., and Shaw, C.Y. 1978. Experimental Studies of Mechanical Venting for Smoke Control in Tall Office Buildings, ASHRAE *Transactions*, Vol. 86, Part 1, pp. 54-71.

Tamura, G.T., and Wilson, A.G. 1966. Pressure Differences for a 9-Story Building as a Result of Chimney Effect and Ventilation System Operation. ASHRAE *Transactions*, Vol. 72, Part 1, pp. 180-189.

Thomas, P.H. 1970. Movement of Smoke in Horizontal Corridors against an Airflow. *Institution of Fire Engineers Quarterly*, 30 (77), pp. 45-53.

UL. 1981. Fire Dampers and Ceiling Dampers, UL *Standard* 555, Underwriters Laboratories, Northbrook, IL.

UL. 1985. Leakage Rated Dampers for Use in Smoke Control Systems. UL *Standard* 555S, Underwriters Laboratories.

Wakamatsu, T. 1977. Calculation Methods for Predicting Smoke Movement in Building Fires and Designing Smoke Control Systems. *Fire Standards and Safety*, ASTM STP 614, American Society for Testing and Materials, Philadelphia, PA, pp. 168-193.

Yoshida, H.; Shaw, C.Y.; and Tamura, G.T. 1979. A FORTRAN IV Program to Calculate Smoke Concentrations in a Multi-Story Building. National Research Council, Canada, DBR Computer Program No. 45.

CHAPTER 59

MECHANICAL MAINTENANCE

THE design engineer should play a major role in formulating the discipline and defining the essential concepts of a maintenance program. Any successful program depends on the support of the peripheral elements of management. Sound economic and conceptual awareness are the foundations of that support.

While mechanical maintenance was once the responsibility of trained technical personnel, increasingly sophisticated systems and equipment require overall management programs to handle organization, staffing, planning, and control. These programs should meet present and future energy management requirements, upgrade management skills, and increase communication among the beneficiaries of cost-effective maintenance. Chapter 48 covers comprehensive energy management programs.

The following terms are commonly used to communicate fundamental concepts of maintenance.

DEFINITIONS

The **maintenance program** defines the maintenance concept in terms of time and resource allocation. It documents the objectives and establishes the criteria for evaluation and commits the maintenance department to basic areas of performance such as (1) prompt response to mechanical failure and (2) attention to planned functions that protect a capital investment and minimize the down time or failure response.

Failure response classifies maintenance department resources expended or reserved for dealing with interruptions in the operation or function of a system or equipment under the maintenance program. This classification has two types of responses: repair and service.

Repair is defined as "to make good, or to restore to good or sound condition," with the following constraints: (1) operation must be fully restored without embellishment and (2) failure must trigger the response.

Service is the provision of what is necessary to effect a maintenance program short of repair. It is usually based on manufacturer's recommended procedures.

Planned maintenance classifies maintenance department resources that are invested in prudently selected functions at specified intervals. All functions and resources attributed to this classification must be planned, budgeted, and scheduled. It embodies two concepts: preventive and corrective maintenance.

The **preventive maintenance** concept classifies resources allotted to ensure proper operation of a system or equipment under the maintenance program. Durability, reliability, efficiency, and safety are the principal objectives.

Corrective maintenance classifies resources, expended or reserved, for predicting and correcting conditions of impending failure. Corrective action is strictly remedial and always performed before failure occurs. An identical procedure performed in response to failure is classified as a repair. Corrective action may be taken during a shutdown caused by failure, providing it is optional and unrelated.

Predictive maintenance is a function of corrective maintenance. Statistically supported objective judgment is implied. Nondestructive testing, chemical analysis, vibration and noise monitoring, as well as routine visual inspection and logging are all classified under this function, providing that the item tested or inspected is part of the planned maintenance program.

ECONOMICS

The economic merit of every system or facility is a function of its durability, reliability, and maintainability. It is difficult to focus on true cost when future qualitative values must be equated with the immediate initial cost. These qualities can be quantified as follows:

Durability is the average expected **service life** of a system or facility. Table 1 in Chapter 49 shows the service life of various equipment in terms of median years. It is more specifically quantified by individual manufacturers as **design life**, which is the average number of hours of operation before failure, extrapolated from accelerated life tests and stressing critical components to economic destruction.

Reliability implies that a system or facility will perform its intended function for a specified period of time without failure.

Maintainability compliments reliability by defining the specific time that a system or facility can operate to an economically fully restored condition.

LIFE CYCLE COSTING

Low initial cost does not necessarily lead to lower overall cost. Advances in engineering technology allow products to be manufactured at lower operating cost without sacrificing comfort, security, durability, maintainability, or reliability. While these advances are beneficial and are generally accepted by the profession, the engineer should be aware of systems and components that have been stripped of valuable features because of cost escalation. Effective life cycle costing analysis (Kempf 1967) requires awareness, insight, and experience. (Refer to Chapter 49 for further information.)

RESPONSIBILITIES

The responsibility of implementing the foregoing concepts and protecting the economic plan extends beyond the maintenance department. Others that influence the effectiveness are described below.

The preparation of this chapter is assigned to TC 1.7, Maintenance, Maintainability and Reliability.

Design Engineer

The design engineer performs the following:
1. Designs in accordance with the following principles.
   a. Selects systems with minimal mechanical components requiring service and maintenance.
   b. Locates the components requiring service and maintenance in equipment rooms or service areas; avoids locating components above hung ceilings or in occupied spaces.
   c. Provides access for servicing, removal, and replacement.
   d. Specifies sufficient instrumentation for measuring, indicating, monitoring, operating, and servicing at part load, as well as full load.
   e. Selects equipment for durability, reliability, maintainability, and serviceability.
   f. Selects equipment with stable operating points at full- and part-load conditions but below the maximum limits of capacity, speed, temperature, and pressure.
   g. Prepares a suitable energy consumption budget.
   h. Prepares a sequence of controls.
2. Advises the owners as to the minimal training and experience for the operating personnel. Specifies that these personnel have adequate instruction by the manufacturers' representatives for major apparatus and complex system components.
3. Prepares graphic system flow diagrams indicating air flows, water flows, temperatures, and pressures at full- and part-load operating conditions.
4. Prepares operation and maintenance manuals.
5. Instructs the contractors and owners as to the design intent of the system performance and operations, as well as the system's capabilities and limitations.
6. Obtains performance feedback on the equipment and systems, with periodic follow-up surveys after the building is occupied.
7. Considers future costs, including analyses of energy costs with conservation concepts.
8. Supervises total construction of the system.
9. Supervises the commissioning of all the systems, including all balance reports, design performance versus actual performance, as-built drawings, operation and maintenance manuals, and settings of all valves and controls.
10. Provides consistency of nomenclature for equipment and controls.

Equipment Manufacturer or Supplier

The equipment manufacturer performs the following:
1. Designs equipment for durability, reliability, maintainability, serviceability, and stability of performance.
2. Publishes comprehensive data on capacity ratings, performance characteristics, sound level generation, applications and limitations, control diagrams, optional accessories and their functions, and spare parts lists.
3. Provides installation, operation, service, and maintenance instructions.
4. Provides a trained staff to assist engineers and contractors and provide instructions to operating personnel, as well as factory training for operating personnel.
5. Develops an adequate and reliable service organization or service agency network.
6. Stocks an adequate supply of spare parts.
7. Maintains production facilities that will ensure delivery of products in phase with building construction schedules so that systems and equipment can be tested for defects before building occupancy.
8. Maintains quality control facilities to minimize replacement, reorders, premature breakdowns, and major overhauls.
9. Maintains research and development facilities to improve products, develop new products, and devise better means to service and maintain equipment.
10. Submits comprehensive shop drawing data to facilitate proper hookup of related building systems.
11. Provides proper information regarding full- and part-load performance of equipment.

Contractor

The contractor performs the following activities to contribute to effective operation and maintenance:
1. Furnishes specified products and conforming to specified installation, workmanship, servicing, and testing requirements.
2. Maintains and services equipment according to the manufacturer's instructions from the time of installation until final acceptance.
3. Protects materials and equipment until final acceptance; cleans piping, ductwork, and equipment.
4. Conducts trial runs before acceptance testing to detect equipment and system faults and to adjust and balance components. Also, the contractor should retest and balance equipment after occupancy.
5. Tests all equipment and systems in the present of the engineer and owners' representatives to prove performance of controls and equipment capacity.
6. Provides for the instruction of operating personnel on the attendance, operation, and maintenance of equipment and
7. Furnishes charts, graphic flow, and control diagrams and compiles classified and indexed information and data for operation and maintenance manuals.
8. Furnishes as-built drawings.
9. Operates equipment at part load, as well as full load to determine proper system operation in the presence of the engineer and owner's representatives.
10. Establishes warranty dates and turns over warranty certificates from manufacturers.

Owner or Building Manager

As the principal, the building owner or manager performs the following:
1. Establishes a policy on the quality of mechanical equipment, materials, and systems, with respect to performance, economic life, operation, service, maintenance, and repairs. The project program should guide the design engineer in the planning and construction of buildings.
2. Determines the following as part of this policy:
   a. What type of maintenance program to adopt.
   b. Whether to provide for operation and maintenance by contract, in-house services, or both.
   c. What type of an operation and maintenance manual to prepare, how comprehensive the manual is to be, and whether it is to be prepared by the design engineer, the construction contractor, a service contractor, an operation and maintenance consultant, or an in-house operation and maintenance staff.
3. Develop an organizational structure commensurate in its extent, arrangement, manageability, and adequacy to meet the needs of the program objectives and the type of program.
4. Staffs according to the time and skills required to perform scheduled tasks with some reserve for unpredicted service and repair.
5. Maintains a **system of records** in a central file, including the following:
   a. Inventory data.

b. Operating, inspection, and servicing instructions; procedures; and schedules.

c. Records and reports on work performed, time expended, and parts and supplies used.

d. Operation logs and operating data.

e. All meter readings.

6. Becomes involved throughout the project with the design engineer to determine if equipment can be serviced with a minimum of field problems.

Air Conditioning and Refrigeration Institute Form 260 is an example of the information needed to determine the type and frequency of inspection. Parker and Skidmore (1968) show sample refrigeraion logs and Scruggs (1969) shows sample inventory data and record of repair cards.

Director of Maintenance

A skilled manager is needed to organize, staff, train, plan, and control maintenance. The manager should have the cooperation of management and all departments influencing maintenance. The manager's responsibilities include administering the maintenance budget and protecting the life cycle objectives. The manager should also use the **least alternative cost** criteria to control the program resources and analyze failures to determine the consequential effect on durability and prevention potential (Loveley 1973).

Maintenance Program Requirements

Maintenance programs include the following:

1. **Management maintenance policy,** which defines the objectives and type of program; provides for organizing and staffing; and directs and controls its effectiveness, performance, and cost.

2. **Inventories and records** of the systems, system components, equipment, and controls, including the following:

a. Construction drawings and specifications, including design and commissioning data referred to previously.

b. Records of as-built drawings.

c. Microfilms of as-built drawings and specifications.

d. Documentation of system changes or enhancements into "as-is" drawings and specifications.

e. Shop drawings and equipment catalogs.

f. Equipment installation, service, and maintenance instructions; troubleshooting check lists; and spare parts lists.

g. Service organizations and spare parts sources.

h. Inventory of spare parts.

i. Valve charts and system flow diagrams.

3. **Procedures and Schedules.** This is the action part of the program, relating to operation, inspection, service, repair, and replacement. It involves the following minimal requirements:

a. **Operating Instructions**

(1) Starting and stopping procedures, sequences, and frequency.

(2) Adjustment and regulation.

(3) Seasonal start-up and shutdown.

(4) Seasonal changeover.

(5) Logging and recording.

NOTE: Log sheets should be prepared regularly (hourly in large systems), including the following:

(a) Energy consumption and demand.

(b) All air, fuel, and water temperatures, including ambient.

(c) All water, fuel, and refrigerant pressures.

(d) Vane openings, power limits, etc.

b. **Inspection**

(1) Equipment to be inspected.

(2) Points to be inspected.

(3) Frequency of inspection.

(4) Inspection methods and procedure.

(5) Evaluation of observations.

(6) Recording and reporting.

c. **Service and Repair**

(1) Frequency of scheduled service.

(2) Scheduled service procedures.

(3) Repair procedures.

(4) Recording and reporting.

4. **Monitoring of data** (whether computer generated or manually taken) to predict trends and uncover "temporary" system service adjustments, which require more permanent repairs, replacements, adjustments, or other modifications. Over the long term, they may predict the ultimate failure of a bearing or some other vital component. Alternatively, they may uncover neglect of system leaks; adjustments to valves, dampers, or linkages; cleaning of coils or fan wheels; or the treatment of water.

5. **Operation and maintenance manuals** are the central reference of organized information and instructions. Preferably, these manuals are prepared by the design engineer, but they may be prepared by other agents, as previously indicated. Equipment requiring preventive maintenance for efficient operation should come with complete maintenance information. Required routine maintenance actions should be clearly printed on a permanent label and affixed in an accessible location on the equipment. The label can be limited to identifying required actions that are explained in greater detail in an operation and maintenance manual.

When the label refers to a manual, it should identify by title and/or publication number the operation and maintenance manual for that particular model and type of product. The manufacturer should furnish at least one copy of the manual to the original owner.

SUGGESTED OUTLINE FOR OPERATION AND MAINTENANCE MANUALS

In installations with more than one piece of equipment, efficient operation of one device may depend on proper maintenance of one or more of the other system components. In these systems, the design engineer is responsible for providing the original owner with the necessary maintenance information. This section gives suggestions on preparing these manuals.

Organization

A manual may be arranged in two parts; Part I contains information on systems; Part II covers equipment. These can be bound in as many volumes as required for convenient use and reference.

Part I - Systems

1. The systems volumes can be organized into divisions of generic functions. Systems can then be classified under appropriate divisions.

2. The material for each system can then be organized in sections covering the following areas:

a. Descriptive information

b. Operating instructions

c. Inspection and maintenance instructions

d. Area served

3. Sections may be organized to include the following categories:

a. **Descriptive Information**

(1) Function or service

(2) Classification

(3) Design capability
(4) Performance characteristics
(5) Principal components
(6) Distribution arrangement
(7) Schematic diagram
(8) Control diagram
(9) Equipment data
  (a) Inventory designation
  (b) Manufacturer and model
  (c) Size and rating
  (d) Pressure, speed, and temperature limitations
  (e) Spare parts list

b. **Operating Instructions**
(1) Starting and stopping procedures
(2) Adjustment and regulation
(3) Seasonal changeover
(4) Seasonal start-up
(5) Seasonal shutdown
(6) Logs and records
(7) Part load performance

c. **Inspection and Maintenance**
(1) Inspection schedule and checklist
(2) Schedules and procedures for lubrication, replacements, adjustment, calibrating, cleaning, painting, protection, and testing.
(3) Inspection and maintenance records

4. Reference documents could include the following:
a. Construction drawings list
b. Construction specifications
c. As-built record drawings
d. Test and balance records
e. Commissioning Reports
f. Design Intent

Part II - Equipment

1. This part of the manual is composed of manufacturers' and fabricators' data on equipment and materials organized into divisions of generic classifications of equipment, *e.g.*:

Division Title	Division No.
Air conditioning & ventilating	1
Boiler plant	2
Controls	3
Instruments & accessories	4
Motors	5
Pumps	6
Refrigeration	7
Starters	8
Valves	9

2. Each division is organized in sections of specific types of equipment. For example, for Division 1, the sections could include the following:

Air conditioning & ventilating		1.0
Coils-	cooling	1.1
	preheat	1.2
	reheat	1.3
Fans-	axial	1.4
	centrifugal	1.5
	propeller	1.6
Filters-	roughing	1.7
	intermediate	1.8
	terminal	1.9
Humidifiers-central		1.10
	duct	1.11

3. **Section coverage.** Each section would include the following information:
a. **Descriptive Literature**
(1) Catalog cuts, brochures, or shop drawings
(2) Dimensional drawings
(3) Materials of construction
(4) Parts designations

b. **Operating Characteristics**
(1) Performance tables and charts
(2) Performance curves
(3) Pressure, temperature, and speed limitations
(4) Safety devices

c. **Operating Instructions**
(1) Pre-start checklist
(2) Start-up procedures
(3) Inspection during operation
(4) Adjustment and regulation
(5) Testing
(6) Detection of malfunction
(7) Precautions

d. **Inspection Instructions and Procedures**
(1) Normal and abnormal operating temperature, pressure, and speed limits
(2) Schedule and manner of operation
(3) Detection signals

e. **Maintenance Instructions and Procedures**
(1) Schedule of routine maintenance
(2) Procedures
(3) Troubleshooting chart

f. **Parts List**

g. **Spare Parts**
(1) Essential inventory
(2) Distributor directory

h. **Service and Dealer Directory**

i. **Service Contracts**

REFERENCES

Kempf, V. 1967. The end of the low bid. *Plant Engineering,* August, p. 101.

Loveley, J.D. 1973. Durability, reliability and serviceability. ASHRAE *Journal,* Vol. 15, No. 1, January, p. 67.

Parker, C.Z.; and Skidmore, W.B. 1968. Refrigeration and air conditioning logs. *The Locomotive,* Hartford Steam Boiler Inspection and Insurance Co., Vol. 57, No. 4, Winter.

Preventive Maintenance and Service Agreement for Unitary Equipment Inspection Check. ARI Form 260.

Scruggs, J.A. 1969. Preventive or breakdown maintenance. *Buildings,* February.

BIBLIOGRAPHY

Kendrick, G.L. 1969. The engineer's responsibilities in the provision of maintenance. ASHRAE *Journal,* Vol. 11, No. 9, September.

MacPhee, C.W. 1968. Is preventive maintenance the responsibility of ASHRAE engineers? ASHRAE *Journal,* Vol. 10, No. 11, November.

Reefer, M.C. 1968. Design for minimum maintenance. *Air Conditioning, Heating and Ventilating,* November.

Ringquist, C.L. 1969. First cost vs. owning and operating cost. *Air Conditioning, Heating and Ventilating,* May.

Standard Handbook of Plant Engineering. McGraw-Hill, New York.

CHAPTER 60

COMPUTER APPLICATIONS

THE use of digital computers in the heating, refrigeration, and air-conditioning industry has increased rapidly. It has come about because of the wide variety of easily used engineering analysis programs for the HVAC industry, an even larger number and range of programs for business use, and the low cost of powerful computers on which to run them. The ordinary calculations required in the HVAC industry such as heating and cooling loads can be accomplished easily and inexpensively on the computer. In addition, computers sometimes allow the solution of more complicated problems, which otherwise would be impractical to solve. This chapter introduces a number of applications for computers in the HVAC area; a discussion of computer hardware and various alternatives for obtaining computing capabilities precedes it. Howell and Sauer (1981) describe many commercially available programs in the field.

Throughout any discussion of computers, the terms hardware and software are used. They refer to the distinction between the physical equipment (hardware) and the programs or sets of instructions that direct the equipment to perform the desired tasks (software). Chapter 51, "Automatic Control," covers the control aspect of computers in further detail.

HARDWARE OPTIONS

Options in computing may be examined by considering the classes of equipment that can be used: large (mainframes), intermediate (minicomputers), small (microcomputers and personal computers), and programmable calculators. These categories roughly indicate relative rankings in computing speed, number of simultaneous users, and cost.

The support organizations required for large computers require a large commitment to dedicated personnel who direct the use of the computers. Therefore, any organization with plans to use such equipment needs more expertise and guidance than is given here. On the other hand, a computer that someone else owns and maintains may be rented. The two following approaches can be considered:

1. Contract the work to a computer service bureau.
2. Work with a time-sharing service company.

The first method, contracting the work out-of-house, may be the easiest approach and the fastest to implement. The responsibilities and worries are placed on the computer bureau, there

The preparation of this chapter is assigned to TC 1.5, Computer Applications.

is no need to purchase expensive hardware and software packages, no need to establish training programs for in-house personnel, nor to acquire experienced computer staff. In most cases, costs are a little high but can be included in the total project cost.

There are some disadvantages. In-house personnel gain no experience for future projects. The money spent is not recoverable for the next job, and the availability and time span of job turn-around is not readily controllable. A firm that does little work requiring computers and plans to perform only short-term projects finds this approach reasonable, but a firm performing medium to large projects and requiring skilled personnel to handle a large variety of tasks in a relatively short time is limited by this approach.

The second method, working with a time-sharing service, requires the purchase or lease of a minimum amount of hardware (a terminal and telephone coupler) and the use of a telephone-linked time-sharing network. As with the first approach, there is little or no first-cost expense involved. However, the responsibilities and worries are not transferred as with the computer bureau; the firm using the service does the greater part of the work. Most computer service firms supply some technical support in varying degrees. A total service provides consulting, programming, training, and documentation. In addition, interactive and batch processing are available, providing quick response and versatility, as well as economy and computer power. Probably, the biggest advantages to this approach are the accessibility of a large software library and the enormous computing power of a large mainframe computer at relatively low cost. There is no need to acquire computer specialists, update equipment and software, nor contract the work to another firm.

There are some disadvantages, however. Training for in-house personnel to use the service efficiently is essential. It is necessary to allow enough time to become familiar with the services, as well as with the specific program(s), before actual use. In addition, keeping track of operating and storage charges is required to reduce hidden costs.

Operation with a time-sharing service company, which has several large mainframe computers, involves several users simultaneously processing data. Because of the tremendous operating power and scheduling of large computers, an hour that a typical user spends at a terminal may result in less than five seconds of computer time (central processing unit or CPU time). Individual users are protected by passwords and account numbers associated with specific projects to ensure privacy. In addition, technical assistance with software programs and computer processing is available, either locally or by telephone.

The costs involved in using a time-sharing service are related to the computer time used, plus any royalty fees for third-party programs and access fees to enhanced programs. The computer time is often taken as a function of time spent on the computer, type of computing done, size of memory space used, and operating expense of personnel and equipment. Other surcharges encountered are telephone connect time, printing charges for hardcopy output results, and storage charges for retaining information on disks or tapes. Because most time-sharing services charge separately for each resource used, careful oversight can reduce costs substantially. Unnecessary connect time, on-line storage of unneeded files, interactive processing of large programs, and output to slow terminals can all escalate costs dramatically.

Support services, such as consulting, training, and programming, are often considered part of the total service included in the computer time that is used, usually referred to as time and maintenance. However, in some cases, support services can result in additional cost, normally depending on the type or level of support. Such examples would include in-depth training sessions, specific modifications to software, and technical consulting on a specific program application or project. Normally, before those additional charges are assessed, an overall cost or stated rate is presented to the user.

The time-sharing service approach is often the most promising for a first-time user. The experience and knowledge gained from using these computers can later be applied to an in-house computer system. An in-house computer system can also interface with the large mainframe computer of the time-sharing service. The in-house computer system can operate at lower costs to provide interactive usage and storage; data can then be transferred for processing by a specific program available on the time-shared computer. This combination can increase the capabilities of a firm to handle a larger number and variety of projects than would be possible with time-sharing or in-house computing alone.

One use of time-sharing for which there is no substitute is the accessing of specialty databases. The amount and diversity of information available on systems that now exist is vast: databases that contain information on corporate, financial, legal, medical, scientific, cultural, bibliographic, and many other types of data are readily available, although the cost of using the more specialized databases is significant.

The user connects to the database with a terminal or a microcomputer with a modem and terminal program, initiates a search for the information desired, and receives the result of the query. In many instances, the considerable cost of a specialized database system (to search for legal precedents, for example) is offset by the hours of expensive professional effort that is otherwise required.

In-House Mini and Microcomputers

The availability of mini- and microcomputers at prices within the range of any company has made in-house computing an attractive option for even the smallest firm. The obvious advantages of rapid turnaround and unlimited computing for a fixed investment are compelling. Time-sharing and service bureau costs appear to be sufficiently high so that an in-house system could be paid for out of savings.

What cannot be overlooked are additional costs incurred by having the computer in-house, such as maintenance, software, and personnel. Software must either be bought or developed, and as expensive as it may seem to buy, it is almost always more expensive to develop. Also, a firm should have at least one person knowledgeable about the system. Only if a firm can buy all the software that will ever be needed and has someone to call for training and explanations can the computer be treated as just another piece of office equipment. Even though a microcomputer system may not need a full-time data processing professional, there should be at least someone having a computer hobbyist mentality in the company for equipment to be used properly.

The cost of a large computer system can be a burden on a small firm, which is impossible to write off on the first few pro-

Table 1 Ways of Using Computers

	Computer Bureau	In-House Computer	Micro- or Personal Computer	Timesharing Service
Equipment required	—None—	Computer, terminal, printer, hardcopier, storage devices	Computer, monitor, printer, storage (floppy or hard disk)	Terminal, modem
Personnel	—None—	Computer specialists, systems analysts, trained users	Trained users	Trained users
Program types	Usually specializing in a few programs	Dependent on availability of public domain programs or leased arrangements from private companies or locally developed programs	Wide variety for technical and business applications from software vendors, manufacturers and user's groups	Public domain programs, third-party programs w/royalty fee, company program w/access fees, locally developed programs
Charges and costs	Large costs for entire work, man-time costs, computer charges, etc.	Low operating costs, high first cost, cost of maintenance and update to avoid obsolescence	Low operating cost, modest first cost and maintenance cost, cost of initial training, obsolescence occurs only when applications required cannot be accomplished on computer	Computer time costs, printing charges, telephone connect costs, storage charges
Type of user	Small firms seldom requiring projects with large amounts of data to be analyzed	Frequent users, large to medium size firms with several uses for computer system besides outside projects	Small to large firms	Frequent to nonfrequent users requiring access to large computing power of a mainframe or to extensive library of software programs
Advantages	Easiest approach for not being involved with computer technology	Variety of in-house uses, lowest operating costs	Low cost, fast turnaround time, can be used for many functions besides technical	Accessibility, support services

jects. In addition to hardware and maintenance costs, software purchases and maintenance add substantially to the total operating cost of a computer system. Replacement and updating hardware and software also must be accounted for in the overall costs. To justify an in-house computer system, a firm must use it frequently. An infrequent user would find that having a computer in-house is no more rewarding than using a computer bureau.

Microcomputers offer the small office enormous power at low cost. These machines should be considered in the class of business machines, in that they offer possibilities far beyond technical analysis; see sections following on "Microcomputer Productivity Tools" and "Administrative Uses Of Computers."

Table 1 summarizes benefits of the four computing approaches.

Programmable Calculators

Calculators have grown enormously in capability until they can be programmed to perform programs of hundreds of steps and can be outfitted with printers and readers. Because of the attractive price and great capabilities, software firms are creating a wide range of programs for these machines. Several engineering magazines print articles containing program listings. The manufacturers also are making programs available. Top-of-the-line programmable calculators have magnetic card readers; these machines can store user-created programs on cards and can read-in programs created by the user or by a vendor in machine readable form. Long programs can be chained; that is, the program may be on several cards, which are read in succession as each program segment is completed. Some manufacturers also have program modules that plug into the calculator, and others have optical bar code readers that can read printed programs.

Primary advantages of the programmable calculator are low cost and portability, although with printer attached, the calculators are not nearly so portable. For field calculations, they are unexcelled, although they are being challenged by battery-powered, notebook-size "laptop" computers.

Disadvantages of some include the awkwardness of creating programs (they must be programmed in their own machine language) and the fact that they simply cannot handle the size programs a computer does; nor do they work as fast as a computer. Thus, they represent an entirely new tool that encroaches little on the areas in which a computer has its strengths.

DESIGN CALCULATIONS

Although computers are now widely used in the design process, most programs do not perform design, but simulation. That is, the engineer proposes a design and the computer program calculates the consequences of that design. When alternatives are easily catalogued, a program may design by simulating a range of alternatives and then selecting the best according to predetermined criteria. Thus, a program to calculate annual energy usage of a building requires a definition of the building and its systems; it then simulates the performances of that building under certain conditions of weather, occupancy, and scheduling. A duct-design program may actually size ductwork, but an engineer must still decide air quantities, duct routing, etc.

Because computers do repetitive calculations rapidly, accurately, and tirelessly, it is possible for the design engineer to explore a wider range of alternatives and to use selection criteria based on annual energy costs or life-cycle costs, procedures much too tedious for wide usage without a computer.

Heating and Cooling Loads

The calculation of design thermal loads in a building is a necessary step in the selection of HVAC equipment. The calculation procedure is typically performed for weather conditions exceeded only a few hours a year and for worst-case conditions of occupancy and internal loads. Heating loads are usually calculated at steady-state conditions without solar or internal heat gains to ensure that heating equipment can maintain satisfactory building temperature under all conditions.

Cooling loads are more transient than heating loads. Thermal gains and losses by conduction through walls and roofs, solar gains, and gains from internal loads such as people, lights, appliances, and equipment are not identical to cooling loads: radiative heat transfer within a space and thermal storage cause the thermal loads seen by heating and cooling equipment to lag behind gains and losses. This lag can be quite important, especially with cooling loads, in that the peak is both reduced in magnitude and delayed in time compared to the heat gains that cause it. Early methods of calculating cooling loads tended to overestimate loads, resulting in oversized cooling equipment with penalties of both first cost and operating expense. Some widely used methods of performing load analysis for building elements include the following:

1. The steady-state heat transfer method
2. The Total Equivalent Temperature Differential/Time Averaging (TETD/TA) method
3. The response factor method
4. The transfer function method
5. The finite difference method

Because the calculation of many components of cooling load requires carrying history of gains and loads, computers are well-suited for this type of work. In fact, since histories are not initially known, they are assumed zero, and the building under analysis is taken through as many as six daily cycles of weather and occupancy inputs to establish a proper 24-hour load profile. Thus, the calculation procedure requires such a large number of individual calculations of hourly components of gain and load that non-computerized calculations are almost ruled out.

As an alternative to the use of loads programs, templates may be created for spreadsheet programs to implement the tabular methods in Chapters 22 through 27 of the 1985 FUNDAMENTALS Volume and the ASHRAE Cooling and Heating Load Calculation Manual (ASHRAE 1979). Chapters 22 through 27 of 1985 FUNDAMENTALS contain detailed discussions of load calculation procedures, along with equations and algorithms suitable for computer calculation.

Energy and System Simulation

Energy programs differ from loads programs in that loads are integrated over time, the systems that serve the loads are considered, and the energy required by the equipment to support the system is usually the end result. Most energy programs simulate the performance of systems that have already been designed, although programs are now available that make selections formerly left to the designer—such as equipment sizes, system air volume, and fan power. Energy analysis programs have become fundamental tools in making decisions regarding building energy use. Energy programs, along with life-cycle costing routines, quantify the impact of proposed energy conservation measures in existing buildings. In new building design, energy programs aid in determining the type and size of building systems and components, as well as explore the effects of design tradeoffs.

Energy programs that track building energy use accurately have been demonstrated and are now used to determine whether a building is operating efficiently or wastefully. They have also been used to allocate costs from a central heating/cooling plant among customers of the plant.

Characteristics of Energy Programs. Capabilities of energy programs vary widely, although most programs simulate a wide range of building, mechanical equipment, and control options. Among energy programs, many techniques for calculating loads are employed, in part because the time-integrated loads are much less dependent on instantaneous occurrences than are design loads.

While the importance of approximating solar loads on cloudy days is widely recognized, computational results differ substantially from program to program. The shading effect from overhangs, side projections, and adjacent buildings is frequently a factor in energy consumption of buildings; however, the diversity of approaches to the problem results in a wide range of answers.

Depending on the requirements of each program, various weather data are used. These can be broken down into four groups:

1. Hourly data for the year, as well as design conditions for typical design days
2. Hourly data for the year only
3. Reduced weather, commonly a typical day or days per month for the year
4. Reduced weather, non-serial or bin format

Space temperature variations can also be taken into account. When the space temperature is not constant, the rates of heat extraction and space temperatures are calculated, rather than cooling and heating loads. Temperature variations occur due to response requirements of temperature control systems when building systems are shut off and when loads are greater than system capacity.

Heat extraction is the rate at which the HVAC system removes heat from the conditioned space. This rate equals the cooling load when space temperature is kept constant, but this rarely happens, so heat extraction is generally either smaller or larger than the cooling load. This concept is important for the analysis of intermittently operated HVAC systems; it provides information on the relationship between load and space temperature and leads to the calculation of pre-heat/cool load for various combinations of equipment capacity and pre-heat/cool periods.

Both air side and energy conversion simulations are required to handle the wide variations among central heating, ventilation, and air-conditioning systems. System simulations are performed independently for each combination of system design, operating scheme, and control sequence for proper estimation of energy use.

System Simulation Techniques. Two basic approaches currently used in computer simulation of energy systems are the fixed schematic technique and the component relation technique.

The *fixed-schematic-with-options technique* is by far the most prevalent of the two types of program organization. This method was used in developing the first generally available energy analysis programs. The technique consists of writing a calculation procedure that defines a given set of systems. The system schematic then is fixed (inherent in the source code), with the user having some options, usually limited to equipment performance characteristics, fuel types, and the choice of certain components. Generally, not all of a program's capabilities are used in one run. In modeling a system, the user defines only those parts required; the other components and subsystems are then deactivated and not included in the analysis.

The fixed schematic programs have been popular for two reasons: (1) they were less expensive to develop and faster to execute than their more generalized counterparts and (2) at the time they were written, the goal was to provide simulation tools for generally available systems. The drawback of this approach is that distinct system schematics must be programmed separately. As additional systems are incorporated, the program's size increases and it costs more to run. This extra code must be maintained, thereby furthering the expense of the program. The fixed schematic technique restricts the evaluation of innovative system configurations. (Chapter 28 of the 1985 FUNDAMENTALS Volume).

Component Relation Technique. Advances in system simulation and increased interest in special and innovative systems have caused interest in the component approach to system simulation. The component relation technique differs from fixed schematic organization in that it is organized around components rather than systems. Each of the components is described mathematically and placed in a library for use in constructing systems. The user input includes the definition of the system schematic in addition to equipment characteristics and capacities. Once all of the components of a system have been identified and a mathematical model for each has been formulated, the components may be connected together in the desired manner and information transferred between them. There are certain inefficiencies built into this approach, because of its more general organization. This technique does, however, offer much versatility in defining system configurations.

Selecting an Energy Program. In selecting an energy analysis program, such things as cost, availability, ease of use, technical support, and accuracy are very important considerations. There is, however, another fundamental question to pose: Will the program do what is required of it? It should be sensitive to the parameters of concern, and its output should include the necessary data. For other considerations, see Chapter 28 of the 1985 FUNDAMENTALS Volume.

Computer simulation technology in the past two decades has concentrated on thermal load calculation techniques. System simulation was limited to a number of commonly found systems. With increasing interest in energy conservation, simulation development work in the next decade will likely focus on system assimilation techniques—the means by which any system can be configured, given the mathematical models of its components.

Comparisons of Energy Programs. Since most energy analysis computer programs take different approaches in their method of calculation, it is not surprising that significant differences in the results are found. Several comparisons have been made and reported (Spielvogel 1977, Jones 1979). The conclusions resulting from those comparisons are as follows:

1. The results obtained by using several computer programs on the same building range from good agreement to no agreement at all. The degree of agreement is dependent on the interpretations made by the program user and by the ability of the computer programs to model the building.
2. Several people using several programs on the same building will probably not agree on the results of an energy analysis.
3. The same person using several programs on the same building may or may not get good agreement, depending on the complexity of the building and its systems and the ability of the computer programs to handle the specific conditions in that building.
4. Several people using the same program on the same building will probably not produce similar results.

Use of Energy Programs for Modeling Existing Buildings. Computer energy analysis for existing buildings can perform the following:

1. handle complex situations
2. evaluate many alternatives
3. evaluate concepts that could have positive and/or negative energy impacts
4. predict the relative magnitude of energy use

Once simulation of a building has been performed, several alternatives may be evaluated such as changes in control settings, occupancy, equipment performance, etc. There are many programs available with widely varying costs, degrees of complexity, and ease of use (Howell and Sauer 1981).

Some general procedure should be followed in using computer programs for existing buildings (Spielvogel 1975). First, energy consumption data must be obtained for a one- to two-year period. These data usually consist of metered electrical energy consumption and demand on a month-by-month basis, as a minimum. For natural gas, the data are in a form similar to those for electricity and are almost always on a monthly basis. For other types of fuel, such as oil and coal, the data are available by the delivery.

Unless fuel use is metered or measured daily or monthly, consumption for any specific period less than one season or year is difficult to determine. The data should be converted to a per-day usage or adjusted in some other manner to account for differences in the length of metering periods. The data tell how much energy went into the building on a gross basis. It is nearly impossible to determine when and how that energy was used and what it was used for, unless there is extensive submetering. It may be necessary and desirable to install such meters, even if for a few days, to determine when and where the energy is going (May and Spielvogel 1981).

The thermal and electrical characteristics of the building and its energy-consuming systems as a function of ambient conditions, time, and occupancy must also be determined. Most computer programs can use as much detailed information as is available on the building and its mechanical and electrical system. Where the energy implications of these details are or can be significant, it is worth the effort to obtain them. If time and resources permit, testing of fan systems for air quantities, pressures, control setpoints, and actions can provide valuable information on deviations from design conditions. Also, test information on pumps can be useful.

Among the most difficult information to obtain is the building occupancy. Since most energy analysis computer programs simulate the building on an hourly basis for a one-year period, it is necessary to know how the building is used for each of those hours. Making frequent observations of the building during days, nights, and weekends shows what energy consuming systems are being used and to what degree.

Weather data, usually one year of actual hour-by-hour weather data, is necessary for simulation. ASHRAE has summarized weather data for 51 cities in the United States and Canada on a Weather Year for Energy Calculations (WYEC), as described in Chapter 24 of the 1985 FUNDAMENTALS Volume (ASHRAE 1986). Also, the actual weather data for the year for that energy consumption data are available may be chosen, if available. Where the energy consuming nature of the building is related more to internal than to external loads, the selection of weather data is relatively unimportant; however, with residential buildings or those with large outside air loads, the selection of weather data can noticeably affect results. The purpose of making the simulation should also be considered when choosing weather data, i.e., either specific year data, data representative of long-term averages, or data having temperature extremes may be needed, depending on the end use of the simulation.

It is likely that the results of the first computer runs will not agree with the actual metered energy consumption data. Possible reasons for this are as follows:

1. There is insufficient detail for those energy-consuming systems that create the greatest use.
2. Information on the occupancy and time of building use is not accurate.
3. Design information on air quantities, setpoints, and control sequences is not appropriate.

The input data must be adjusted and trial runs continued to match the actual energy use. It is usually difficult to match the metered energy consumption precisely. Results within 10% to 20% in any month are considered adequate. It is more important to match the character of the energy consumption on an hourly and monthly basis than it is to match the annual total precisely.

Having a simulation of the building as it is being used permits subsequent computer runs to evaluate the energy impact of various alternatives or modifications. The evaluation may be accomplished simply by changing the input parameters and rerunning the program. An evaluation may then be made of the various alternatives, and an appropriate one may be selected.

Duct Design

Two major needs exist in duct design: sizing and flow distribution. Duct sizing and equipment selection is required for a new duct system design. Flow distribution is a problem of calculating flows through the duct sections and terminals for an existing system with known cross-sections and fan characteristics.

Duct Sizing. There are two major approaches for computerized duct sizing: (1) application of manual procedures, which, though computerized, are still limited in capability and (2) optimization. No available commercial programs use optimization techniques.

Selecting and Using a Program. Duct design involves laying out ductwork, selecting fittings, and sizing the ducts. Computer programs comply with many duct system constraints that require recomputation of the duct size. Computer printouts provide detailed documentation. Any calculation requires preparing accurate estimates of pressure losses in duct sections and defining these interrelations of velocity heads, static pressures, total pressures, and fitting losses.

The general computer procedure is to designate nodes (the beginning and end of duct sections) by number. Details about each node (divided flow fitting, terminal, etc.) and each section of duct between nodes (maximum velocity, flow rate, length, fitting codes, size limitation, insulation, acoustic liner) are used as input data. An example of these details is shown in Figure 1.

Some characteristics of a duct design program include the following:

1. Calculations for supply, return, and exhaust systems
2. Sizing by constant friction, velocity reduction, static regain, and constant velocity methods
3. Analysis of existing duct systems
4. Inclusion of fitting codes for a variety of common fittings
5. Selection of duct run with the highest pressure loss, and tabulation of all individual losses in each run
6. Printout of all input data for verification
7. Provision for error messages
8. Calculation and printout of airflow for each duct section
9. Printout of velocity, fitting pressure loss, duct pressure loss, and total static pressure change for each duct section
10. Printout of a schematic or line diagram indicating duct size, shape, flow rate, and temperature in the duct system

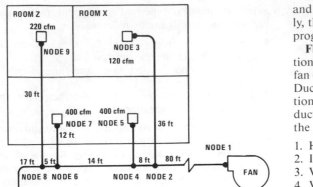

Fig. 1   Example of Duct System Node Designation

11. Calculation of heat gain/loss in the system and correction of temperatures and flow rates, including possible resizing of the system
12. Specification of maximum velocities, size constraints, and insulation thicknesses
13. Consideration of insulated or acoustically lined duct
14. Bill of materials for sheet metal, insulation, and acoustic liner
15. Acoustic calculations for each section of the system

Since many duct design programs are available, the following factors should be considered in program selection:

1. The maximum number of branches that can be calculated
2. The maximum number of terminals that can be calculated
3. The types of fittings that can be selected
4. The number of types of fittings that can be accommodated in each branch
5. The ability of the program to balance pressure losses in branches
6. The ability to size a double-duct system
7. The ability to handle draw-through and blow-through systems
8. The ability to prepare cost estimates
9. The ability to calculate fan motor horsepower
10. Provision for determining acoustical requirements at each terminal
11. The ability to update the fitting library

Optimization Techniques for Duct Sizing. Optimized duct design selects fan pressure and duct cross-sections by minimizing an objective function. This function is the life cycle cost of the system, which includes the initial cost and energy cost. A large number of constraints, including constant pressure balancing, acoustic restrictions, and size limitations, must be satisfied. Duct optimization is a mathematical programming problem with a nonlinear objective function and many nonlinear constraints. The solution must be taken from a set of standard diameters and standard equipment. Several numerical methods for duct optimization exist, such as Coordinate Descent (Tsal and Chechick 1968), Lagrange Multipliers (Stoecker et al. 1971, Kovarik 1971) Dynamic Programming (Tsal and Chechick 1968),

and Reduced Gradient (Arklin and Shitzer 1979). Unfortunately, these methods have not been incorporated into commercial programs.

Flow Distribution. Another important problem is the prediction of airflows in each section of a presized system with known fan characteristics. This is called the "Flow Distribution" or "Air Duct Simulation" problem. The need to calculate flow distribution in a duct system occurs whenever a retrofit to an existing duct system is considered. The HVAC engineer may then ask the following questions:

1. How will this influence the flow at existing terminals?
2. Is it possible to change only the motor and leave the same fan?
3. What is the new working point on the fan characteristic?
4. Which ducts should have their size changed?
5. What are the new sizes of ducts and what are the flows in the system with fully opened dampers?
6. What is the best way to connect additional diffusers to an existing system?

A simulation program can help answer these questions. In addition, a simulation program can analyze the efficiency of a control system effectively, check the effect of the performance of a number of parallel fans if one is not running, predict the flows during field air balancing, etc. The Gradient Steepest Descent method has been used for simulating a duct system (Tsal and Chechik 1968). There are no simulation methods covered in Chapter 33 of 1985 FUNDAMENTALS Volume for solving airflow distribution problems.

Piping Design

A large number of computer programs exist to size piping systems or calculate the flexibility of piping systems. The sizing programs normally size piping and estimate pump head for systems based on velocity and pressure drop limits, and some consider heat gain or loss from piping sections. Several programs produce bill of materials or cost estimates for the piping system. Piping flexibility programs assist in a stress and deflection analysis of piping systems. Many of the piping-design programs can handle thermal effects in pipe sizing, as well as deflections, stresses, and moments.

The general technique for computerizing piping design problems is to represent the three-dimensional system as a set of nodes and links. Each takeoff tee or terminal is a node; each set of nodes is linked by pipe and fittings. (A typical piping problem is shown in Figure 2 in its nodal representation.)

Useful piping programs provide sufficient design information and the following:

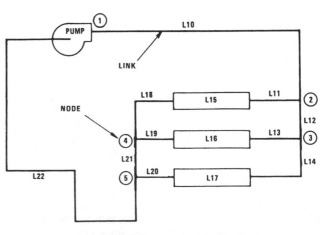

Fig. 2   Nodal System for Piping System

1. Perform calculations for both open and closed systems.
2. Calculate the flow, pipe size, and pressure drop in each section of the system.
3. Handle three-dimensional piping systems.
4. Provide a wide selection of commonly used valves and fitting types, including such specialized types as solenoid and pressure-regulating valves
5. Consider different piping materials such as steel, copper, and plastic by including generalized friction factor routines.
6. Accommodate liquids, gases, and steam by providing property information for a multiplicity of fluids.
7. Calculate pump capacity and head required for liquids.
8. Calculate the available terminal pressure for nonreturn pipe systems.
9. Calculate the required expansion tank size.
10. Estimate heat gain/loss for each portion of the system.
11. Prepare a system cost estimate, including costs of pipe and insulation materials and associated labor.
12. Print out a bill of material for the complete system.
13. Calculate balance valve requirements.
14. Perform a pipe flexibility analysis.
15. Perform a stress analysis for the pipe system.
16. Print out a graphic display of the system.
17. Allow customization of specific design parameters such as maximum and minimum velocities, maximum pressure drops, and design conditions such as condensing temperature, superheat temperature, and subcooling temperature.
18. Allow evaluation of piping systems for off-design conditions.
19. Provide links for calling by other programs, such as equipment simulation programs.

Some limiting factors to consider in piping program selection include the following:

1. The maximum number of terminals the program can accommodate.
2. The maximum number of circuits the program can handle.
3. The maximum number of nodes each circuit can have.
4. The maximum number of nodes the program can handle.
5. Compressibility effects for gases and steam.
6. Provision for two-phase fluids.

Acoustic Calculations

A good system design has proper control of HVAC-related sound in the occupied space. Sound produced by the HVAC equipment should be part of the background and not interfere with communication. To control sound, the system designer can make sound projections from the source (generally a fan or chiller) through various sound paths to the receiver. If the projections are potentially objectionable, the design can be changed to reduce the space sound level. However, HVAC sound projections are difficult and time consuming. For example, sound from the fan of a single system travels down at least four paths (Figure 3):

1. Fan discharge sound travels down the supply duct through the diffusers into the space (path A).
2. Fan discharge sound can "break out" of the supply duct. This path is significant for occupants within 50 feet of the fan discharge (path B).
3. Fan inlet sound travels down the return duct, through the return grilles or ceiling and into the occupied space (path C)
4. Finally, radiated fan sound can penetrate the unit casing, mechanical room wall, and enter the occupied space (path D).

Adding further complexity to a sound study is that each sound path has 6 to 10 octave bands that need to be considered, and each path can have 2 to 30 acoustic components. Pumps, chillers,

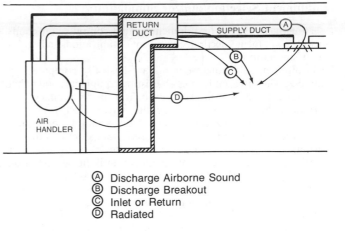

Ⓐ Discharge Airborne Sound
Ⓑ Discharge Breakout
Ⓒ Inlet or Return
Ⓓ Radiated

Fig. 3 Significant Indoor Air Handler Sound Paths

inverters, VAV units, cooling towers, and boilers also generate significant levels of sound. Each significant sound path from each piece of equipment to the space should be checked. The task of HVAC acoustic simulations is well suited to computer and predictive acoustics programs.

Several acoustics programs now available are generally easy to use and less detailed than the custom programs used by acoustic consultants. Acoustics programs are designed for comparative sound studies and allow the system designer to design a comparatively quiet system. Acoustic programs should address the following six key areas of the HVAC system:

1. Equipment sound source
2. Duct element attenuation and regeneration
3. Wall and floor attenuation
4. Ceiling attenuation
5. Sound break out or break in of ducts or casings
6. Room effect (conversion of sound power to sound pressure)

Algorithm-based programs are preferred because they cover more situations. Basic HVAC sound algorithms are covered in Chapter 52. These basic algorithms plus sound data from acoustics laboratories of equipment manufacturers are used in acoustics programs. HVAC equipment sound levels entered into an acoustics program should come from the manufacturer, since there is a wide variation in sound from similar equipment. Whenever possible, equipment sound power, by octave band, should be obtained for the path under study. A good sound predictive program relates all performance data such that it creates reasonably accurate NC prediction.

Many other non-generic acoustics programs are available. These programs relate to a specific application or item of equipment and can help design a specific aspect of a job. For example, duct design programs may contain sound predictions for discharge airborne sound based on the discharge sound power of the fans, noise generation/attenuation of duct fittings, attenuation and end reflections of VAV terminals, attenuation of ceiling tile, and room effect. VAV terminal selection programs generally contain sub-programs that estimate space NC level near the VAV unit in the occupied space.

Acoustic predictive software allows system designers to look at HVAC-generated sound in a realistic, affordable time frame, thus making it part of the services offered to building owners. HVAC-oriented acoustic consultants generally assist designers by providing cost-effective sound control ideas and by handling sound-critical applications like concert halls. Chapter 52 and the Trane Acoustic Seminar Material (1986) contain additional information.

Equipment Selection and/or Simulation

Three basic types of equipment-related computer programs include equipment selection, equipment optimization, and equipment simulation.

Equipment selection programs are basically computerized catalogs. The program locates an existing equipment model that satisfies entered criteria. The output is a model number, performance data, and may include alternative selections.

Equipment optimization programs select all possible equipment alternatives and then let the user establish ranges of performance data or first cost to narrow the selection. The user keeps narrowing the performance ranges until the best selection is found. Performance data used for optimizing selections varies by product family.

Equipment simulation programs select specific equipment and calculate full and part-load performance over time, generally one year. The equipment performance is matched against an equipment load profile to determine energy requirements per hour. Utility rate structures and related economic data are then used to project equipment operating cost, life cycle cost, and comparative payback.

Some advantages of equipment programs include the following:

1. High speed and accuracy of the selection procedure
2. Pertinent data presented in an orderly fashion
3. More consistent selections than with manual procedures
4. More extensive selection capability
5. Multiple or alternate solutions
6. Small changes in specifications or operating parameters easily and quickly evaluated

Simulation programs have the advantage of (1) projecting part-load performance quickly and accurately, (2) establishing minimum part-load performance, and (3) projecting operating costs and payback associated higher performance product options.

Programs have been written for nearly every type of HVAC equipment. Some of the more common ones and their optimization parameters include the following:

Air Distribution Units	Pressure Drop, First Cost, Sound, Throw
Air Handling Units, Rooftop Units	Power, First Cost, Sound, Filtration, Heating and Cooling Capacity
Boilers	First Cost, Efficiency, Stack Losses
Cooling Towers	First Cost, Design Capacity, Power, Flow Rate, Air Temperatures
Chillers	Condenser Head, Evaporator Head, Capacity, Power Input, First Cost, Compressor Size, Evaporator Size, Condenser Size
Coils	Capacity, First Cost, Water Pressure Drop, Air Pressure Drop, Rows, Fin Spacing
Fan Coils	Capacity, First Cost, Sound, Power
Fans	Volume Flow, Power, Sound, First Cost, Minimum Volume Flow
Heat-Recovery Equipment	Capacity, First Cost, Air Pressure Drop, Water Pressure Drop (if used), Effectiveness
Pumps	Capacity, Head, Impeller Size, First Cost, Power
Air Terminal Units (Variable and Constant Volume Flow)	Volume Flow Rate, Air Pressure Drop, Sound, First Cost

Some extensive selection programs have evolved. For example, coil selection programs can select steam, hot water, chilled water, and refrigerant (direct expansion) coils. Generally, they select coils according to procedures in ARI Standards 410 and 430 (ARI 1981, 1985).

Chiller and refrigeration equipment selection programs can choose optimal equipment based on such factors as lowest first cost, highest efficiency, best load factor, and best life cycle performance. In addition, some manufacturers have modular equipment that is arranged for customization of their product. This type of equipment is ideal for computer selection.

However equipment selection programs have limitations. The logic of most of the programs is proprietary and not available to the user. All programs have built-in approximations or assumptions, some of which may not be known to the user. Qualify equipment selection programs before using them.

CAPABILITIES OF CAD FOR HVAC DESIGN

Computer-aided design and drafting (CAD or CADD) systems have been developed that not only give designers computerized tools for the basic drafting of HVAC contract and shop drawings, but that also simplify HVAC analytical and design tasks. Further, CAD systems help coordinate interdisciplinary design of buildings, their mechanical systems and other systems and ease the task of modifying designs.

All systems display a drawing or a part of a drawing on a screen and provide a means of constructing straight lines, circles, polygons, arcs, section crosshatching, dimensioning, and lettering. Pre-defined elements can be added at any scale and in any orientation. Elements can be copied or deleted. Zoom and pan capabilities allow close-up views of areas of the drawing. Options such as a background grid, forcing of orthogonality of lines, snap-to-grid, snap-to-tangent, and filleting can speed-up the drafter's work.

CAD systems usually have layering capabilities, so different parts of a drawing can be displayed or modified separately or together. For example, in a duct drawing, supply ducts may be put on one layer and return ducts on another so either or both can be seen, changed, or removed. Layering can also help an HVAC designer coordinate designs with other disciplines. For example, an HVAC designer working on a duct drawing can have the CAD system display the building's architecture, structure, piping, and electrical systems in the background to check for space conflicts.

Scale drawings express not only physical size, but also how different parts are connected and where they are located within an area. As an example, an architectural designer can draw a building's walls, partitions, and windows and have the computer automatically extract the number and size of windows, the areas and lengths of walls, and the areas and volumes of rooms and zones.

Some CAD systems can link the graphic elements to the nongraphic characteristics of those elements. With these systems, an operator can store information from a drawing for later use in reports, schedules, design procedures, or notes. A fan, for example, can be displayed accurately on a drawing and its air flow, voltage, weight, manufacturer, model number, cost, and other data can be stored in a file or database. The link between graphics and attributes makes it possible to review the characteristics of an item simply by pointing to the graphics on the drawing or to generate schedules of items located in a certain area on a drawing. Conversely, the graphics-to-data links allow the designer to see the graphic items on a drawing that have a certain characteristic by searching for those characteristics in the data files and then making the associated graphics stand out as brighter, flashing, bolder, or different color displays.

Computer-aided design also makes building design drawings and information more useful than manually generated drawings. CAD HVAC drawings and their associated data can be used by building owners and maintenance personnel for ongoing facilities management, strategic planning, and maintenance. They are useful for computer-aided manufacturing such as duct construction, where duct design drawings serve as the basis for flat patterning, nesting, and automatic cutting of ductwork and fittings. Two dimensional CAD drawings can be used to create a three-dimensional model of the building and its components. This 3-D model can then help to visualize all or part of the building; to check for interferences between building parts; and to perform lighting, shading, daylighting, acoustic, or energy analysis of the building and its spaces. The 3-D building model can also aid in developing sections and details for building drawings.

Further, CAD drawings and data can aid in specification preparation by allowing automated cross referencing of drawings, drawing notation, and building documents. CAD drawings of HVAC systems also serve as a basis for extracting quantity and size information of HVAC components that can be used for drawing equipment schedules and cost estimating.

System Selection

The selection of software cannot be made without considering hardware (and vice versa): few software suppliers support more than one type of computer, although some computers may have several potential software suppliers. Graphic displays, input devices, and plotters all need software support and must be selected for compatibility of the computer and the software. The nature of the work, such as the size and type of building, as well as budget considerations, will influence the CAD system selection.

Small microcomputer-based systems have basic CAD capabilities but are limited in the size, number, and coordination of drawings that they can work with. Microcomputer systems are also inherently single-user systems, so other designers generally cannot share drawings while the single user is working on them. On the other hand, minicomputer and mainframe computer-based CAD systems are inherently multiuser, multitasking systems that are designed for sharing drawings and data, as well as managing a large inventory of drawings of almost unlimited size and complexity. Other hardware considerations include system speed, cost, memory, and storage capability.

Software that lets a user perform design and drawing tasks with the least effort is perhaps the most critical consideration. CAD software that is tailored to HVAC design and drafting functions is preferred to software that has only basic graphics and data management capabilities. Further CAD software that has flexible, user-definable features is advantageous to those who need to customize or enhance the CAD HVAC task to suit special needs. Also, built-in error checking and error reporting features of CAD software are important when problems occur. Software support, checkout, training, and enhancement are also important and can make the difference between needing an in-house computer programmer or not. Turnkey CAD systems, in which hardware and software are integrated by the supplier, are generally more customized to particular applications (such as HVAC design) and offer more substantial software checkout, support, enhancements, and training.

Another software consideration is transferability of drawings and data between different CAD systems, because the building owner, architect, and other engineers may have different CAD systems. Several graphic exchange standards used by the CAD industry make this exchange possible. The Initial Graphics Exchange Specification (IGES) and Standard Interchange Format (SIF) are two prominent formats, and software interfaces to these formats are important.

Many issues must be weighed in deciding which approach system and scale is appropriate for the use of CAD for HVAC design (ACEC 1984, Schley 1984). Each CAD use decision should consider the current design tasks, as well as multidisciplinary cooperation, hardware expansion, and using the CAD system throughout more of the design project stages into the future.

COMMUNICATIONS

Computer communications can be defined as the passing of information between two electronic components. In the traditional computer sense, this includes the connection of computer terminals to time-sharing systems, word processing work stations to a central time-shared processor, one computer to another, and the connection of a computer to various peripherals such as plotters, printers, or mass storage units. In the building services industry, this includes the connection of sensors to controllers and of controllers to supervisors in direct digital control (DDC) systems, as well as the connection of HVAC systems to personal computers or to fire, security/alarm, or elevator systems.

Beyond the simplest form, in which a terminal, keyboard, or screen is connected to an adjacent computer, there is a wide range of interconnections, made possible by the growth in numbers of computers and computer networks:

1. Several computers may share peripheral resources that would be under-used by one computer. This includes printers, plotters, laser printers, and disk storage units.
2. One computer may pass information to another for further processing.
3. Small computers may access a central time-sharing system when heavy computing needs to be done. Data may be preprocessed on the local computer, sent to the mainframe for special processing, and returned for final analysis.
4. Computers may access a central software system or database such as a company administrative or accounting system or database containing product, software, bibliographic, or other information.
5. Electronic mail may be transmitted among linked computers within a company or may be sent through a commercial network in which a user may access a "mailbox" by telephone link to the computer. Similarly, electronic bulletin boards and computer conferencing may share information on a central computer with interested persons.
6. Previously independent tasks may be integrated to coordinate the operation of an overall system. For example, a complex HVAC control system may be integrated with other services for energy conservation or fire control.

All forms of computer communication have the following in common: hardware transmitters and receivers, a medium to couple a transmitter to a receiver, and software to activate the transmitters and interpret the output of the receivers.

A wide range hardware transmitters and receivers ("ports") is available for different transmission media (such as twisted wires, coaxial cables, and fiber optic cables).

The fundamental unit of information in a computer is the binary digit or "bit," usually represented as a "0" or a "1." At the next level of organization, eight bits are grouped together and called a "byte." Most computers represent single characters in a message with a byte. There are 256 possible combinations of bits in a byte, and so a byte can represent one of 256 different characters.

A so-called "parallel" port uses eight signal lines in each direction plus a common, plus a few other lines for establishing and maintaining the connections ("handshaking"). The transmitter uses one handshake line to tell the receiver to start reading. All eight bits of the byte are sent at one time, in parallel. The receiver can signal the transmitter through other handshake lines that it has either received the byte or that it is busy and cannot accept the information. The communication proceeds, character-by-character, at a pace set by the slower device. The limitation of this method of transmission is that many wires (a minimum of 12 for one-way communication) are required. This is not practical over large distances or with normal telephones.

An alternative form of communication uses a "serial" port: the eight bits in a character are sent one after the other or serially; this requires no more than two signal lines and a common line for two-way communication and can be adapted easily to telephone link, coaxial cable, fiber optic cable, or even radio. The difficulty with this form of communication is that both the transmitter and receiver must know how long each bit takes; this information is contained in the bit rate, frequently called the "baud rate." In addition, the transmitter and receiver must be synchronized in some manner so that each knows when the eight bits in a byte begin and end.

Serial communications are done either "asynchronously" or "synchronously." With asynchronous or "ASYNC" communications, idling bits (when no characters are being sent) are followed by a start bit, seven or eight information bits, and one or two stop bits. The receiver resynchronizes with the transmitter each time it receives the start bit for each character. This means that at least 10 bits are needed to transmit eight information bits, a 25% time penalty. With synchronous or "SYNC" communications, the transmitter sends a series of bytes with a predetermined bit pattern to allow the receiver to synchronize with it. It then sends a string of bytes, one after the other. Thus once the receiver is synchronized, no extra (start or stop) bits are needed. The transmission ends after a prearranged count of bytes or after a byte or group of bytes recognized as marking the end of transmission. Most microcomputer serial communication is done asynchronously because both the hardware and software are simpler.

When communication takes place over short wires free from noise, it may be regarded as error-free. Over long distances or on telephone lines, interference may disrupt a transmission. For error checking, typically both transmitter and receiver are controlled by software using a protocol, an agreed-upon procedure for sending a block of data, along with a check character or characters obtained by summing or otherwise manipulating the bytes in the data block. The receiver independently determines the check character from the information it has received and compares its check with the transmitter's. If they are not the same, the message has been incorrectly received; the transmitter is told to retransmit that block. Protocols can be used with both asynchronous and synchronous communication.

Communications software manages the movement of data into and out of a computer. With keyboard commands, a user can dial a number; establish connection, possibly with a password for security; initiate a file transfer to the remote computer; or cause the remote computer to send a file to the local computer, store the file, and ensure that the transfer is done without error. When using switched telephone lines, coaxial cables, or fiber optic cables, the voltage level signals used for short distance communications cannot be used. A device called a modem (modulator/demodulator) at each end of the transmission medium converts the signal from voltages to tones or light. A telephone modem often has the ability to dial and store telephone numbers and to answer the telephone when it rings. Thus, with proper software, it is possible to communicate to or from an unattended computer.

The current generation of high speed modems is limited to 2400 bits per second over normal telephone lines, although a new generation is coming on the market at 9600 bits per second; 9600 to 19 200 bits per second have been possible for a number of years using premium data lines. Most standard serial ports on microcomputers are limited to 9600 bits per second, although 19 200 and even 38 400 are occasionally found. Fiber optic and coaxial cable networks are capable of transmitting from 1 to 10 million bits per second; however, special interfaces are required.

Networks dedicated to computer communications are quite common and vary in size from one or two computers to ones of worldwide scope. If they are limited to an office, a building, or to several buildings close together, they are referred to as Local Area Networks (LANs). A number of network designs and standards are available, but they are not all compatible. Work is being done to interconnect these dissimilar systems via a device known as a gateway. This allows two networks to communicate, but they are often not fully integrated to the extent that the users are able to ignore the differences.

Some networks can support a combination of different uses at the same time such as voice, computer communications, building services data (as with a Direct Digital Control System), and closed-circuit television. This makes possible savings in the amount of wire installed in a building and consequently in the time and effort involved in changing and maintaining the network.

Additional information on communications can be found in Chapter 51.

SOFTWARE—WHERE TO GET PROGRAMS AND AT WHAT COST

Computer software consists of instructions given a computer to perform useful tasks. Without software, the computer is powerless as a tool to provide design solutions.

Software can be categorized as systems, utilities, and applications programs. System software (operating system) is the program that runs other programs: it interprets commands from the user and initiates proper responses; it handles the tasks of communicating with all input/output (I/O) devices (keyboard, video terminal, printer); it does file transfer operations, getting files from disk memory and putting them back to disk; and in multiple-user systems, it keeps track of each user, allowing small amounts of time for each and keeping the tasks from interfering, either with each other or with the operating system. Operating systems are frequently supplied by the computer manufacturer, although some software firms create them. These programs are very specific to a machine.

Utilities are programs that do standard housekeeping or data-handling tasks for a specific machine, such as copying files from one disk to another, printing directories of files on a disk, printing files (listing), creating files, merging files (putting two or more files together in some specified order). Data base management systems might also be considered utilities. These latter are programs for managing large files of diverse information such that entries can be made easily and information can be retrieved quickly.

Applications programs have a specific purpose unrelated to the functions of a machine; e.g., programs such as loads, energy, piping design, accounting, and word processing. The previous section covered many areas of applications software related to the HVAC industry.

Computer manufacturers in the past packaged hardware and systems software in a bundled offering. The software costs were nominal and were not indentifiable in the package. More recently, advances in computer and electronic technology have resulted in a dramatic reduction of hardware cost. The software, however, is labor intensive in its creation, and its development cost has risen dramatically. Many suppliers of computer equipment have chosen to unbundle their offering and identify the true cost of software. Many organizations now specialize in software alone, with little or no association with hardware manufacturers.

Computer services companies have also emerged offering software, support services, and computer hardware on a time-sharing basis. Because choices of systems and utility software are limited and are usually made only once, the following discussion is limited to applications software.

Purchased Software

Virtually all manufacturers of computer equipment also offer software. They are also aware of or are distributors for independent groups developing software compatible with their equipment.

Software can be purchased in several ways. The supplier may provide a machine-readable version of the software (usually on magnetic tape or diskette). The machine-readable version is prepared for a specific computer and is not easily moved to other machines without modifications. The contents of the software cannot be practically interpreted by humans when in machine-readable form. The machine-readable version is distributed by those who wish to keep the algorithms proprietary. Those distributing this software generally offer periodic updates and/or maintenance, since in-house modification of the program is virtually impossible.

Some suppliers offer the program source. The source is a set of instructions presented in a widely-used computer language (i.e., FORTRAN, BASIC, COBOL, Pascal). Anyone familiar with the languages can identify the step-by-step computational procedure in source software. The source may be on magnetic tape, or diskette, or punched cards, or simply a printed list of the program statements. Before the program is used, it must be entered into the computer and then converted into machine language form, a process called compilation. Source programs are more easily transported from one computer to another. Source programs offer the option of in-house updates and modifications without the assistance of the original supplier.

First costs for programs related to the HVAC industry vary from several hundred to hundreds of thousands of dollars, depending on program complexity, perceived market value, and contingency support sources. Source programs are usually more expensive than machine-readable. Suppliers of time-sharing software can also make provision for pricing based on usage. By programming a counter or a measure of computer resources used, their programs on third-party computers can be priced as a function of software activity.

Royalty Software in Time-sharing

Unused computers cost almost as much to own as heavily-used computers. This fact created a large industry—computer time-sharing. Computer time-sharing consists of more than one user using a computer or family of computers simultaneously. Most major time-sharing services organizations have networks of computers and communications equipment capable of serving thousands of customers on an international basis. Frequently, telephone communications are used between customers and the computer centers, allowing a customer to access to a computer across the country simply by dialing a local number.

Time-sharing organizations sell computer resources. Purchased software can be installed on the networks for the private use of individual customers. Under this arrangement, raw computer resources are used and the cost varies with the activity level. But, like hardware manufacturers, time-sharing organizations offer software to provide a desired solution rather than just access to the computer.

This software is either developed by the time-sharing company or by third-party authors who license the time-sharing company to sell network time or the software itself. In either case, the cost to the user is generally higher than the actual cost of the resources consumed.

The difference is a royalty charge to support the cost of maintaining the software and to repay the author's cost in developing it. The royalty can be a fixed charge per access or can be computed as a fraction of the total resources used. In some cases, it is an initiation charge, paid once, for the privilege of using the program. The services vary considerably in the time-sharing field. Some offer user support, training, consulting, and money-back guarantees, while others offer access to the computer only.

Custom Programming

Outside Services. Most equipment manufacturers and time-sharing service companies offer expertise for creation of customer programs. A host of software specialty organizations also exist. Hourly fees vary considerably, but tend to be in line with fees charged by senior HVAC consultants.

The cost to create a specific program depends on its intended use. A program to solve a specific, nonrecurring problem does not take the design forethought of a program to be widely used by many people. For recurring problems and usage, the solution technique (algorithms) must be identified, the human input interface designed, the output reports designed, the source code written and thoroughly tested, the source code documented so others can understand and maintain it, and user documentation and instructions created. Developing a good computer program requires both a thorough understanding of the subject matter and a good knowledge of computer science.

Costs of creating quality software are greatly diminished if the customer can provide a detailed functional design. The customer is usually intimately familiar with the problem and the desired format of the solution. The end use affects the structure of the program dramatically. Software can be made portable to different machines or highly machine dependent. It can be structured to facilitate future maintenance and/or additions or enhancements. It can be broken into segments to allow independent solution of subtasks.

In-House Programming. Almost all that applies to seeking outside services for custom software applies to in-house creation of software. One significant distinction is that all hidden costs will be apparent in an in-house activity.

Documentation and ongoing maintenance are two cost areas most often overlooked. These two task areas generally distinguish high quality software from low quality. Good documentation saves labor on the part of the end user and facilitates portability. Portability is the ease with which the program can be installed on computers other than that for which the software was designed. It affects every user who upgrades equipment periodically. It also applies to the ease with which other people can maintain the program. Often, when the creator of a computer program leaves an organization, the program dies because inadequate documentation prevents proper updating and maintenance.

Computer programs are designed to perform specific tasks. Good programs are based on generalized algorithms that provide accurate or appropriate results over a wide range of input values. Users often go beyond the limits of an algorithm through new or unique input values or combinations of input values. Some programs also have mistakes—either typographical entries or fundamental flaws in the algorithms. The net result of both of these areas of failure is the need for ongoing maintenance. This is particularly true of large programs or those used by a wider range of people. Maintenance costs can easily exceed original creation costs, particularly if tight design standards are not followed at the outset.

The cost of using the software, once created, is the cost of the user's labor, the cost of the computer resource, and the cost of software support. All three cost components can be minimized through emphasis on initial design of the software.

A quality program with good documentation usually also contains some error checking capability to prevent unreasonable combinations of data and individual data errors from entering the program or, at the least, helps the user identify faulty data that causes a program to terminate. Some programs have interactive user interfaces through which a user creates the input model while on-line with a computer. The computer interrogates the user and checks the validity of the response. A friendly interface can save hours of training and troubleshooting on the part of the user.

Where to Get the Programs

ASHRAE-sponsored research has produced a document entitled "A Bibliography on Available Computer Programs in the General Area of Heating, Refrigerating, Air Conditioning and Ventilating." This document is one of the most comprehensive listings of HVAC-related software available today. A brief description of each program is given, along with information on availability.

MICROCOMPUTER PRODUCTIVITY TOOLS

Spreadsheets

To the typical business manager, the most important microcomputer programs are "spreadsheets" or electronic ledger sheets. They are not currently being used as widely for engineering tasks. Spreadsheets are electronic tables in which the user may enter labeling text, numbers, or formulas in each cell (location identified by row and column indices). The most important advantage of a spreadsheet is that when a parameter within the table is changed (e.g., a unit cost rises, labor rate changes, etc.), the associated computations are recalculated by the program almost instantaneously. This feature is as important to the engineer as to the accountant, manager, or planner.

All spreadsheets have some built-in functions, such as sum, average, count, exponential, logarithmic, and trigonometric functions. Some also provide financial functions, matrix inversion, and multivariable linear equation solution, and multivariate linear regression. Many spreadsheets also include some additional capabilities, such as for graphics and data base functions.

Presentation Graphics Software

Creating computer-generated graphics has historically been time-consuming, frustrating, and expensive, especially the latter. The convenience, power, and speed of currently available graphics software and hardware have improved enormously, while the cost has dropped precipitously. It is now possible, for example, to purchase an excellent plotter with multicolor capability and powerful graphics software for under $2000. With such a system (and a compatible microcomputer), engineering and business plots of presentation quality can be prepared in a few minutes. Multicolor X-Y graphs, bar and pie charts, etc.,

are typically provided by the better software packages. Recent "integrated" spreadsheet programs include extremely convenient, although rather inflexible, graphics capability.

Communications

One rapidly expanding and changing area is that of electronic communication between computers, especially using telephone lines. Although telephone systems are being upgraded to provide digital capabilities, it will take many years before it is completed. Thus, for the present and near-term future, such communication will continue to require both appropriate software and a modem, which performs the translation of the digital computer signals to analog signals capable of being transferred by current telephone lines. The modems most commonly used at present transfer data at about 30 to 120 characters per second, but greatly increased speeds promise to become widely available in the near future.

Communications programs, at the least, allow messages typed at the keyboard to be sent to a remote computer; allow the user to specify a file in local storage to be sent to the remote computer; and allow the user to receive a file from the remote computer and save it locally. Other possible capabilities include executing error-checking protocols with the remote computer to eliminate transmission errors and allowing the remote computer to take control of the local one.

Microcomputer Data Bases

Microcomputer data base systems allow the user to record and organize information. One application could be a client list, containing the following for each client: firm name, street address, city, state, zip code, telephone number, and contact person; each "record" in the data base file would contain the above information for one client.

With the information retrieval capabilities of the data base program, it is possible to alphabetize the list; select all clients in a given city, state, or zip code, or range of zip codes; find the client with a given contact person; and print envelopes or mailing labels to everyone on the list.

Some data base programs include a programming language, which can be used to construct complex applications such as payroll, job cost accounting, cost estimating, equipment selection, schedule generation, or cross-referencing.

Desk Top Organizers

These useful programs, which coexist with other programs in the computer memory available, provide one or more of the following:

1. A note pad editor
2. An appointment calendar
3. A name and address file
4. An alarm clock
5. A calculator for decimal, octal, or hexadecimal integer arithmetic
6. A scientific calculator
7. A telephone dialer
8. A keyboard translation program
9. An ASCII table (numeric codes for the characters on a keyboard)

When the microcomputer is turned on, the user selects desired functions; a disadvantage of activating all available functions is that an unacceptable amount of memory may be consumed.

The selected functions remain in memory until the user turns the machine off or intentionally deactivates the functions. While resident, the functions remain immediately available while the user works with virtually any other software (word processing, communication, programming language, etc.). For example, the user, while working on a data base, might receive notification of an appointment. Without interrupting the data base session, the user could call the appointment calendar and alarm clock functions onto the screen, enter notations of the appointment in both, and then dismiss both functions from the screen to resume the data base work. If a long series of commands must be issued to the data base during each use, the keyboard translation function may be directed to issue this series of commands when a selected key combination is pressed.

Programming Languages

In the early days of computing, every user was a programmer. In the engineering community, FORTRAN was the language principally used. With microcomputers, however, the language to gain early prominence was BASIC. Some time passed before fully capable FORTRAN compilers for microcomputers appeared. Today, a wide variety of capable languages, including BASIC, FORTRAN, COBOL, Pascal, Modula-2, C, APL, PL/I, Forth, Lisp, Prolog, as well as assembly languages and many others, is available for the more popular microcomputers. But, unlike the early days of computing, few microcomputer users today are capable programmers.

The large amount of high quality application software such as that described above provides the user tremendous capability at relatively low cost. There is little that most users want to do that cannot be accomplished effectively with application software. However, the HVAC engineer is more likely than the typical business manager to need a unique computational capability; when such need arises, the available programming languages provide a full capability.

Integrated Software

Integrated software typically combine many of the following functions into a single program: spreadsheet, data base, word processing, spelling checking, communications, and graphics. Several major advantages are claimed for such integrated packages:

1. The cost may be considerably less than the total cost of individual programs, each of which only provide one of the above functions.
2. The syntax of the commands of all functions is similar— thus, the user only needs to learn a single set of commands instead of having to learn a number of dissimilar programs.
3. Data transfer between the various functions is easy; for example, the user may extract a portion of a spreadsheet and insert it into a document in the word processor. This type of capability is not always routine.

Many users have not been willing to abandon their favorite applications software, such as word processing, spreadsheet, etc., in which they have invested considerable effort in becoming expert users, to gain the advantages claimed for the integrated packages. Furthermore, users often find one or more of the major capabilities of any given integrated package to be unsatisfactory for their needs, and thus the desirability of the entire package is greatly diminished. Also the major integrated packages typically require a large amount of memory (RAM) to operate effectively.

The popularity of some data base and spreadsheet programs has caused other suppliers to provide the ability to read and write data in the format of the "best sellers." Thus it is possible to gain some of the advantages of integration with software from different suppliers: while it may not be possible to go from one function to another without loading a new program, data do not have to be reentered.

Other Programs

Mainframe statistical analysis packages have existed for many years and are now available for micros. Similarly, multiple linear equation solvers and differential equation solvers, originally on mainframes, can now be found for micros.

More recent developments include symbolic equation manipulators and solvers, which can factor, integrate, and differentiate algebraic expressions symbolically; and a numerical equation solver, which will aid in solving multiple nonlinear equations and implicit equations.

ADMINISTRATIVE USES OF COMPUTERS

Surveys indicate that the major uses of computers by engineers are administrative, rather than technical. The following categories of engineering administrative computer usage are discussed in this section:

Word Processing & Specification Writing
Management Information
Accounting and Personnel
Project Scheduling and Job Costing
Data Security and Integrity

Word Processing and Specification Writing

Almost invariably, the first use to which a system is put, be it micro or mainframe, is word processing. Word processing creates documents electronically rather than physically, as in typing. As such, editing text is easier and less expensive, since the entire document does not have to retyped with each draft. The documents are usually stored on magnetic tape or disk.

Text can be entered continuously without the need to type carriage returns ("word wrap"); it can be corrected or reformatted; it can be moved, copied, and deleted in blocks. Heading and footing text can be specified for all pages in a report. Global search and replace functions locate and replace words or phrases wherever desired in a document, sometimes even reformatting paragraphs where the changes took place.

A few word processors can do arithmetic with columns of figures, renumber paragraphs to match an outline, and organize footnotes, either on the page of the reference or at the end of the document.

Commonly found additional functions are as follows:

Mail-merging, the ability to insert text such as names and addresses from one file into a form letter being printed; thus, everyone on the list receives an individualized copy of the form letter.

Spelling checking, in which words in the text are compared with a master dictionary and "mistakes" are flagged; this may be done either after completing a document or as the text is entered, depending on the program. Similarly, on-line thesaurus programs allow the user to ask for a list of equivalent words. Most spelling checkers allow adding of specialty words to the main standard dictionary or to an auxiliary dictionary for future reference.

Grammar and style checking.

Indexing, in which programs can create a table of contents from specially marked section and paragraph headings in the text.

Word processing software is available for almost all computers. In addition, many companies offer dedicated word processors: computer-like machines that are optimized for word processing functions. The distinctions between general purpose computers and dedicated word processors are becoming less clear as word processing programs are written as "look-alikes" to dedicated word processors and the dedicated word processors are supplied with arithmetic and accounting capabilities.

Word processing can be used to generate specifications. A master specification, from which individual project specifications are created, permits technical personnel to spend more time in research and design, assures consistency of language and appearance, and, if kept up to date, lessens the possibility of including inaccurate or incomplete information. By storing the master specification in a computer, it is possible to retrieve any or all the sections, edit them, and have an error-free copy of the project specification within a few days.

The following options are available to the firm desiring to use a computerized master specification:

1. Buy a computer and software necessary to process and print the text onsite.
2. Subscribe to a master specification service commercially available to design firms. The service company providing the master specification bears the responsibility for periodically updating the text and furnishing the user with updated copy. The editing is done by the users on a paper copy provided by the service company. Then, the edited copy is sent to the service company, and a typed copy of a rough or final draft is returned by mail. This process is potentially cumbersome and time consuming.
3. Invest in a terminal unit for use with a time-sharing service. With this arrangement, clerical personnel are trained to operate the terminal and make the corrections. The corrected text can be printed at the terminal or transmitted to the location of the time-sharing service, where the finished document is printed and returned through the mail. Most time-sharing services provide either a standardized master specification or allow the user to create a master, to be stored in the computer of the time-sharing service. It is essential that the requirements of the particular firm be carefully analyzed before its master specification is typed and stored. The service representative can aid in making decisions about text arrangement so that a flexible, easily edited document is prepared.

The efficiency and flexibility of a computerized master specification make it a valuable tool for preparing project specifications. Those who use the master specification should agree on the standardization of computer language and products to avoid repetitive editing of text. Attempting to rewrite the master for every project increases the risk of inaccuracy and may hurt the uniformity of style. These defects, inherent in the traditional cut and paste method of specification preparation, are undesirable in documents that must convey information clearly and directly. The need to minimize extensive rewriting and the insertion of new material will make the use of a master specification most beneficial to firms that do not specialize in unique, one-of-a-kind designs. Unless the master can be used with only minor revisions for the majority of specifications, the cost and time spent in editing may not be justifiable. Generally, the larger the size and the greater the number of documents produced, the greater the savings in time and money in comparison to traditional preparation and typing.

Even without a master specification, however, it is possible for the writer and the typist to save considerable time by "cutting and pasting" from previous specifications with minor revisions.

Management Planning and Decision-Making

Computers are ideal for such repetitive operations as inventory control, accounting, purchasing, and project control, providing managers with up-to-date facts and figures. The ability to store and manipulate large amounts of data provides a powerful technique for forecasting. With sufficient historical data, such concerns as sales, inventory needs, production capability, manpower needs, and capital requirements may be forecast using statistical methods. Econometric modeling may be included to help forecast such things as the effects of varying inflation rates.

Much of the data required to implement some of the techniques above may not be in the company's files and must be found elsewhere. Technical papers, market trends, industry reports, financial forecasts, codes, standards, regulatory data, and demographic or geographic information are all examples of the information needed for engineering management that can be searched electronically by computer. In most cases, only a local phone call must be made, and the company is charged a time-sharing fee for time spent on the system. Management information systems should also have capabilities that provide special or supporting information should it become necessary to delve deeper into an operation.

Employee Records and Accounting

All corporate accounting functions from payroll, aging accounts receivable, and taxes can be automated on even the smallest microcomputers with a wide choice of engineering-specific accounting software. In addition, a firm that has unique accounting requirements may often meet them by developing specific applications called templates or overlays for common spreadsheet programs. Continuously updated financial reports needed for project evaluation and government use can be handled more readily than through manual methods or off-site accounting services. Labor expense for various projects or departments can easily be separated and monitored on a regular basis. Personnel records for each employee can also be maintained on a computer.

Project Scheduling and Job Costing

The success of any project, no matter its size, depends on good scheduling and control, so that manpower and materials will be where they are supposed to be at the proper time. Whenever portions of a project can be done simultaneously, are dependent on the completion of one or more prior parts, or must share a limited amount of manpower and equipment, a project scheduling technique such as CPM (Critical Path Method) or PERT (Program Evaluation and Review Technique) can determine which portions are of critical importance. These techniques are well-implemented on microcomputers. The current microcomputer programs can also perform manpower leveling to make the best use of available resources, and some may provide graphics suitable for client presentations.

Computerized scheduling techniques commercially available quickly provide updated schedules and critical items, even if the critical path does change due to a delay in one part of the job. This capability is valuable for determining if scheduled completion dates and costs can be met and for determining possible alternatives. Once a computerized system of personnel, payroll, and accounting functions has been established, a history of past project costs, manpower requirements, and material requirements can be obtained. A computer system can catagorize and tabulate them for future reference, permitting more accurate estimates of future projects.

Security and Integrity

While computers are generally reliable, provision must be made for potential loss of important data in the event of equipment failure, theft, sabotage, natural catastrophe, or a previously undiscovered problem in the software. The most common method of protection is periodic duplication of master tape or disk files. For the most important data files, such as the firm's accounts, this duplication should take place with every posting. These duplicate files should be kept in a secure area, such as a fireproof vault on the premises or totally off-site storage.

Unauthorized access to particular data is another security concern. Implementing a formal, written policy of data security, no matter how minimal it is initially, is a critical step in the computerization of any firm. Making certain that only authorized personnel have access to confidential files requires careful planning. Most major accounting packages, as well as many popular spreadsheet and data base management programs, contain built-in safeguards such as multilevel password protection to avoid this problem.

MONITORING AND CONTROL

Microprocessors significantly contribute to HVAC controls equipment, as described in Chapter 51. This section reviews recent advances, suggests future applications, and describes the use of computers in monitoring equipment performance.

Direct digital control (DDC) of HVAC components gives more accurate control than the proportional control commonly used in pneumatics and also greatly increases flexibility. Such flexibility permits controllers to be tuned or allows control algorithms to be replaced or extended. For example, DDC can control temperature in a variable air volume terminal box, with control based only on a dry-bulb temperature sensor. The same microprocessor can be modified to monitor relative humidity and mean radiant temperature and change the dry-bulb setpoint to maintain comfort conditions better (Int-Hout 1986). The microprocessor could also adjust airflows based on occupancy indicators or occupant preferences.

Microprocessor-based devices are currently used to turn on chillers and boilers at an optimal time to recover from a period when a building is unconditioned. The required programs measure the building's thermal behavior to adjust the equipment start time; such programs are examples of parameter estimation routines and give the controller an adaptive capability. Parameter estimation and optimal control algorithms have many potential applications. Fan and chiller part-load performance could be measured, and such setpoints as chilled water and supply air temperature, as well as scheduling multiple units, could be optimized. This kind of optimization is currently performed off line by researchers and only for the systems under investigation (Hackner et al., 1985); microprocessors could implement optimal control in all buildings. The control could be extended to include weather forecasting algorithms, which could improve control of thermal storage or schedule precooling by night ventilation, for example.

Linking local, dedicated microprocessor controllers together with a central, supervisory computer makes it possible to integrate HVAC control with such services as security, life safety monitoring, and lighting. The network can be extended to the electric utility, with the utility providing spot pricing information as input to load-shedding programs and even dropping specified equipment in the event of power shortages; this technology has been demonstrated in pilot projects (Peddie and Bulleit).

Central computers are already used to collect data from individual controllers or meters, but perform a minimal amount of data analysis. Analysis performed off-site by consultants identifies long-term trends in energy consumption, isolates beneficial or harmful changes in equipment operation, and normalizes energy consumption for changes in weather. These analysis programs could be incorporated into on-site computers, providing operators and management with up-to-date, readily available information.

Hardware is available in a wide range of sizes and capabilities; from specialized packaged units such as individual air handler controls, through intelligent field panels or programmable controllers that gather information from several inputs and control multiple outputs, to standalone computers, which not only monitor and control but are also suitable for program development.

ARTIFICIAL INTELLIGENCE

In 1956 the term "Artificial Intelligence" (AI) was coined for the area of computer science that deals with human-like computer activity. This has come to include the following:

Natural language systems, in which a computer "understands" and can act on ordinary language commands. This may also include speech recognition.
Visualization systems, including pattern recognition.
Robotics systems, which move and "feel."
Expert or knowledge-based systems, which make decisions based on accumulated knowledge from one or more human experts.

Of these, expert systems have the most immediate potential in the HVAC field, although broad applications are still years away.

Expert systems differ from computer programs (which use algorithms or mathematical rules for calculation) in that expert systems have less clear rules and may include probabilities for various outcomes. Creating an expert system is done by a "knowledge engineer," who interviews the human expert(s) experts) in depth to extract rules for decision making. The rules are programmed into a knowledge data base, and the system is tested and refined with feedback from the expert.

Developing new applications is tedious and expensive, so few applications are available. Some powerful expert systems have been created for medical diagnosis, aircraft design, computer system configuration, locomotive engine failure analysis, and chemical structure prediction. However, most applications will be in the realm of research for many years.

REFERENCES

ARI. 1981. Forced-Circulation Air-Cooling and Air-Heating Coils, ARI Standard 410-81. Air-Conditioning and Refrigeration Institute, Arlington, VA.

ARI. 1985. Central Station Air-Handling Units. ARI Standard 430-85.

ASHRAE. 1979. Cooling and Heating Load Calculation Manual, ASHRAE GRP 158.

American Consulting Engineers Council. 1984. CADD for Design Professional. Washington, DC.

Arklin, H. and Shitzer, A. 1979. Computer Aided Optimal Life-Cycle Design of Rectangular Air Supply Duct Systems. ASHRAE Transactions, Vol. 85, Part 1.

Hackner, R. J.; Mitchell, J. W.; and Beckman, W. A. 1985. System Dynamics and Energy Use. ASHRAE Journal, June.

Howell, R. H. and Sauer, H. J. 1981. Bibliography on Available Computer Programs in the General Area of Heating, Refrigerating, Air Conditioning and Ventilating. ASHRAE, Atlanta, GA.

Int-Hout, D., III 1986. Microprocessor Control of Zone Comfort. ASHRAE Transactions, Vol. 92, Part 1.

Jones, L. 1979. The Analyst as a Factor in the Prediction of Energy Consumption. Proceedings of the Second International CIB Symposium on Energy Conservation in the Build Environment, Session 4, Copenhagen, Denmark.

Kovarik, M. 1971. Automatic Design of Optimal Duct Systems. Use of Computers for Environmental Engineering Related to Buildings, National Bureau of Standards, Building Science Series 39, October.

May, W. B. Jr.; and Spielvogel, L. G. 1981. Analysis of Computer Simulated Thermal-Performance of the Norris Cotton Federal Building. ASHRAE Transactions, Vol. 87, Part 1.

Peddie, R. A. and Bulleit, D. A. Managing Electricity Demand Through Dynamic Pricing. Chapter 20 in Energy Sources: Conservation and Renewables, American Institute of Physics Conference Proceeding 135, American Institute of Physics, New York, NY.

Schley, M. 1984. CAD Buyers Checklist. Architectural Technology, Summer, Washington, DC.

Spielvogel, L. G. 1975. Computer Energy Analysis for Existing Buildings. ASHRAE Journal, August, p. 40.

Spielvogel, L. G. 1977. Comparisons of Energy Analysis Computer Programs. ASHRAE Transactions, Vol. 83, Part 2.

Stoecker, W. F.; et al., 1971. Optimization of an Air-Supply Duct System. Use of Computers for Environmental Engineering Related to Buildings, National Bureau of Standards, Building Science Series 39, October.

Trane Company. 1986. Trane Acoustics Seminar. La Crosse, WI.

Tsal, R. J. and Chechik, E. I. 1968. Use of Computers in HVAC Systems. Budivelnick Publishing House, Kiev. Available from the Library of Congress, Service #TD153.T77) (Russian language).

CHAPTER 61

CODES AND STANDARDS

THE Codes and Standards listed in Table 1 represent practices, methods, or standards sponsored by the organizations indicated. They are valuable guides for the practicing engineer in determining test methods, ratings, performance requirements, and limits applying to the equipment used in heating, refrigerating, ventilating, and air conditioning. *Copies can usually be obtained from the organization listed in the Reference column.* These listings represent the most recent information available at the time of publication.

Table 1   Codes and Standards Sponsored by Various Societies and Associations

Subject	Title	Sponsor	Reference
Acoustics	Standard Acoustical Terminology (reaffirmed 1976)	ASA	ANSI S1.1-1960
Air Conditioners			
Room	Method of Testing for Rating Room Air Conditioners and Packaged Terminal Air Conditioners	ASHRAE	ANSI/ASHRAE 16-1983
	Methods of Testing for Rating Room Fan Coil Air Conditioners	ASHRAE	ASHRAE 79-1984
	Room Air Conditioners (1982)	UL	ANSI/UL 484-1986
	Room Air Conditioners	AHAM	ANSI/AHAM RAC 1-1982
	Method of Testing Room Air Conditioner Heating Capacity	ASHRAE	ANSI/ASHRAE 58-74
	Performance Standard for Room Air Conditioners	CSA	C368.1-M1980
	Central Commercial and Residential Air Conditioners	CSA	C22.2 No. 119-M1985
Packaged Terminal	Packaged Terminal Air Conditioners	ARI	ARI 310-85
	Packaged Terminal Heat Pumps	ARI	ARI 380-85
Transport	Air Conditioning of Aircraft Cargo	SAE	SAE AIR 806A
	Nomenclature, Aircraft Air-Conditioning Equipment (1978)	SAE	SAE ARP 147C
Unitary	Air Conditioners, Central Cooling (1982)	UL	ANSI/UL 465-1984
	Load Calculation for Commercial Summer and Winter Air Conditioning (Using Unitary Equipment), 2nd ed. (1983)	ACCA	ACCA Manual N
	Methods of Testing for Rating Heat Operated Unitary Air Conditioning Equipment for Cooling	ASHRAE	ASHRAE 40-1980
	Methods of Testing for Rating Unitary Air-Conditioning and Heat Pump Equipment	ASHRAE	ANSI/ASHRAE 37-1978
	Methods of Testing for Seasonal Efficiency of Unitary Air-Conditioners and Heat Pumps	ASHRAE	ANSI/ASHRAE 116-1983
	Sound Rating of Outdoor Unitary Equipment	ARI	ARI 270-84
	Application of Sound Rated Outdoor Unitary Equipment	ARI	ARI 275-84
	Unitary Air-Conditioning Equipment	ARI	ARI 210-81
	Unitary Air-Conditioning and Air-Source Heat Pump Equipment	ARI	ARI 210/240-84
	Commercial and Industrial Unitary Air-Conditioning Equipment	ARI	ARI 360-86
Air Conditioning	Automotive Air Conditioning Hose (1971)	SAE	SAE J 51-1985
	Environmental System Technology (1984)	NEBB	NEBB
	Equipment Selection and System Design Procedures for Commercial Summer and Winter Air Conditioning, First ed. (1977)	ACCA	Manual Q

Table 1   Codes and Standards Sponsored by Various Societies and Associations (*continued*)

Subject	Title	Sponsor	Reference
	Gas-Fired Absorption Summer Air Conditioning Appliances (with 1982 addenda)	AGA	ANSI Z21.40.1-1981
	Load Calculation for Residential Winter and Summer Air Conditioning, 7th ed. (1986)	ACCA	ACCA Manual J
	Equipment Selection and System Design Procedures, 2nd ed. (1984)	ACCA	ACCA Manual D
	Installation Standards for Heating and Air-Conditioning Systems, 6th ed. (1986)	SMACNA	SMACNA
Transport	HVAC Systems and Applications, First ed. (1986)	SMACNA	SMACNA
	Air Conditioning Equipment, General Requirements for Subsonic Airplanes (1961)	SAE	SAE ARP 85D
	General Requirements for Helicopter Air Conditioning (1970)	SAE	SAE ARP 292B
	Testing of Commercial Airplane Environmental Control Systems (1973)	SAE	SAE ARP 217B
Air Curtains	Test Methods for Air Curtain Units	AMCA	AMCA 220-82
	Air Outlets and Inlets	ARI	ARI 650-80
	Air Volume Terminals	ARI/ADC	ARI/ADC 880-83
	Selection of Distribution Systems First ed. (1963)	ACCA	ACCA Manual G
	Room Air Distribution Considerations First ed. (1963)	ACCA	ACCA Manual E
	Methods of Testing for Rating the Air Flow Performance of Outlets and Inlets	ASHRAE	ASHRAE 70-72
	High Temperature Pneumatic Duct Systems for Aircraft (1981)	SAE	SAE ARP 699D
	Metric Units and Conversion Factors	AMCA	AMCA 99-0100-76
	Installation Code for Residential Mechanical Exhaust Systems	CSA	C260.1-1975
	Laboratory Certification Manual	ADC	ADC 1062:LCM-83
	Residential Air Exhaust Equipment (1e)	CSA	C260.2-1976
	Test Code for Grilles, Registers and Diffusers	ADC	ADC 1062:GRD-84
Air Ducts and Fittings	Flexible Air Duct Test Code	ADC	ADC FD-72 R1-1979
	Installation of Air Conditioning and Ventilating Systems (1981)	NFPA	ANSI/NFPA 90A-1985
	Installation of Warm Air Heating and Air-Conditioning Systems (1980)	NFPA	ANSI/NFPA 90B-1984
	HVAC Duct Construction Standards—Metal and Flexible, First ed. (1985)	SMACNA	SMACNA
	HVAC Systems—Duct Design, 2nd ed. (1981)	SMACNA	SMACNA
	Round Industrial Duct Construction (1977)	SMACNA	SMACNA
	Rectangular Industrial Duct Construction (1980)	SMACNA	SMACNA
	Ducted Electric Heat Guide for Air Handling Systems (1971)	SMACNA	SMACNA
	Thermoplastic Duct (PVC) Construction Manual (1974)	SMACNA	SMACNA
	Pipes, Ducts, and Fittings for Residential-Type Air-Conditioning Systems	CSA	B228.1-1968
	Factory-Made Air Ducts and Connectors (1981)	UL	UL 181
Air Filters	Test Performance of Air Filter Units (1977)	UL	ANSI/UL 900-1982
	Methods of Testing Air-Cleaning Devices Used in General Ventiltion for Removing Particulate Matter	ASHRAE	ASHRAE 52-76
	Commercial and Industrial Air Filter Equipment	ARI	ARI 850-84
	Air Filter Equipment	ARI	ARI 680-86
	Test Performance of High Efficiency, Particulate, Air Filter Units (1985)	UL	ANSI/UL 586-1985
	Methods of Test for Air Filters Used in Air Conditioning and General Ventilation	BSI	BS 6540 Part 1
	Method for Sodium Flame Test for Air Filters	BSI	BS 3928
	Electrostatic Air Cleaners (1980)	UL	ANSI/UL 867-1981
Air-Handling Units	Central Station Air-Handling Units	ARI	ARI 430-86
	Application of Central Station Air-Handling Unit	ARI	ARI 435-81
Boilers	Recommended Design Guidelines for Stoker Firing of Bituminous Coals (1983)	ABMA	ABMA
	Boiler Water Limits and Steam Purity Recommendations for Watertube Boilers (3rd ed., 1982)	ABMA	ABMA
	Boiler Water Requirements and Associated Steam Purity— Commercial Boilers (1981)	ABMA	ABMA
	Boiler and Pressure Vessel Code (eleven sections) (1983)	ASME	ASME
	Code for the Construction and Inspection of Boilers and Pressure Vessels	CSA	B51-M1981
Cast-Iron	Testing and Rating Heating Boilers (1982) (amended 1984)	HYD I	IBR/SBI
	Ratings for Cast-Iron and Steel Boilers (1985)	HYD I	IBR/SBI
Gas or Oil	Explosion Prevention of Fuel Oil and Natural Gas-Fired Single-Burner Boiler-Furnaces (1984)	NFPA	NFPA 85A
	Explosion Prevention of Natural Gas-Fired Multiple-Burner Boiler-Furnaces (1978)	NFPA	ANSI/NFPA 85B-1984

Table 1 Codes and Standards Sponsored by Various Societies and Associations (*continued*)

Subject	Title	Sponsor	Reference
	Gas-Fired Low-Pressure Steam and Hot Water Boilers (with 1983 addenda)	AGA	ANSI Z21.13-1982
	Gas Utilization Equipment in Large Boilers (with 1972 and 1976 addenda; R-1983)	AGA	ANSI Z83.3-1971
	Oil Fired Boiler Assemblies (1975)	UL	ANSI/UL 726-1975
	Prevention of Furnace Explosions in Fuel Oil-Fired Multiple-Burner Boiler-Furnaces (1984)	NFPA	ANSI/NFPA 85D-1984
	Control and Safety Devices for Automatically Fired Boilers (CSD.1a is an addenda to 1982 ed.)	ASME	ANSI/ASME CSD.1-1982 CSD.1a-1984
	Oil-Fired Steam and Hot-Water Boilers for Residential Use (3a)	CSA	B140.7.1-1976
	Oil-Fired Steam and Hot-Water Boilers for Commercial and Industrial Use (1a)	CSA	B140.7.2-1967
Watertube	Recommended Standard Instrument Connections Manual (1982)	SAMA ABMA	ABMA
Building Codes	BOCA/National Building Code, 10th ed. (1987)	BOCA	BOCA
	CABO One- and Two-Family Dwelling Code (1986)	CABO	CABO
	Standard Building Code (1985) (with 1986 revisions)	SBCCI	SBCCI
	Uniform Building Code (1985)	ICBO	ICBO
	Uniform Building Code Standards (1985)	ICBO	ICBO
	BOCA/National Existing Structures Code, 2nd ed. (1987)	BOCA	BOCA
	Model Energy Code (1986)	CABO	CABO
Mechanical	BOCA/National Mechanical Code, 6th ed. (1987)	BOCA	BOCA
	Safety Code for Elevators and Escalators	ASME	ANSI/ASME A17.1-1984
	Uniform Mechanical Code (1985)	ICBO/ IAPMO	ICBO/IAPMO
	Uniform Mechanical Code Standards (1985)	ICBO/ IAPMO	ICBO/IAPMO
	Standard Mechanical Code (1985) (with 1986 revisions)	SBCCI	SBCCI
Burners	Installation of Domestic Gas Conversion Burners	AGA	ANSI Z21.8-1984
	Domestic Gas Conversion Burners	AGA	ANSI Z21.17-1984
	Oil Burners (1980)	UL	ANSI/UL 296-1980
	Installation Code for Oil Burning Equipment	CSA	B139-1976
	General Requirements for Oil Burning Equipment	CSA	B140.0-1972
	Vaporizing Type Oil Burners	CSA	B140.1-1966 (R1980)
	Oil Burners, Atomizing Type	CSA	B140.2.1-1973
	Pressure Atomizing Oil Burner Nozzles	CSA	B140.2.2-1971 (R1980)
	Replacement Burners and Replacement Combustion Heads for Residential Oil Burners	CSA	B140.2.3-M1981
Capillary Tubes	Method of Testing Flow Capacity of Refrigerant Capillary Tubes	ASHRAE	ASHRAE 28-78
Chillers	Methods of Testing Liquid Chilling Packages	ASHRAE	ASHRAE 30-78
	Absorption Water-Chilling Packages	ARI	ARI 560-82
	Centrifugal Water-Chilling Packages	ARI	ARI 550-86
	Reciprocating Water-Chilling Packages	ARI	ANSI/ARI 590-86
Chimneys	Chimneys, Fireplaces, and Vents (1977)	NFPA	ANSI/NFPA 211-1984
	Chimneys, Factory-Built, Residential Type and Building Heating Appliance (1983)	UL	ANSI/UL 103-1977
	Chimneys, Factory-Built, Medium Heat Appliance (1986)	UL	ANSI/UL 959-1985
	Glossary of Terms Relating to Chimneys, Vents, and Heat Producing Appliances (1984)	NFPA	NFPA 97M
Coils	Forced-Circulation Air-Cooling and Air-Heating Coils	ARI	ANSI/ARI 410-81
	Methods of Testing Forced Circulation Air Cooling and Air Heating Coils	ASHRAE	ASHRAE 33-78
Comfort Conditions	Thermal Environmental Conditions for Human Occupancy	ASHRAE	ANSI/ASHRAE 55-1981
Compressors	Compressors and Exhausters (reaffirmed 1979)	ASME	ANSI/ASME PTC 10-74
	Compressed Air and Gas Handbook, 4th ed. (1973)	CAGI	CAGI
	Safety Standard for Compressors for Process Industries	ASME	ANSI/ASME B19.3-1981
Refrigeration	Methods of Testing for Rating Positive Displacement Refrigerant Compressors	ASHRAE	ASHRAE 23-78
	Ammonia Compressor Units	ARI	ANSI/ARI 510-83
	Hermetic Refrigerant Motor-Compressors (1984)	UL	ANSI/UL 984-1984
	Positive Displacement Refrigerant Compressors and Condensing Units	ARI	ARI 520-85
Computers	Protection of Electronic Computer/Data Processing Equipment (1981)	NFPA	ANSI/NFPA 75-1981
Condensers	Water-Cooled Refrigerant Condensers, Remote Type	ARI	ANSI/ARI 450-79
	Methods of Testing for Rating Remote Mechanical Draft Air-Cooled Refrigerant Condensers	ASHRAE	ASHRAE 20-70

Table 1   Codes and Standards Sponsored by Various Societies and Associations (*continued*)

Subject	Title	Sponsor	Reference
	Method of Testing for Rating Water-Cooled Refrigerant Condensers	ASHRAE	ASHRAE 22-78
	Methods of Testing Remote Mechanical Draft Evaporative Refrigerant Condensers	ASHRAE	ASHRAE 64-74
	Remote Mechanical Draft Air-Cooled Refrigerant Condensers	ARI	ANSI/ARI 460-80
	Standards for Steam Surface Condensers, 8th ed. (1984)	HEI	HEI
Condensing Units	Methods of Testing for Rating Positive Displacement Condensing Units	ASHRAE	ASHRAE 14-80
	Refrigeration and Air-Conditioning Condensing and Compressor Units (1980)	UL	ANSI/UL 303-1979
	Commercial and Industrial Unitary Air-Conditioning Condensing Units	ARI	ARI 365-85
Contractors	Definite Purpose Magnetic Contactors	ARI	ARI 780-86
	Definite Purpose Contactors for Limited Duty	ARI	ARI 790-86
Controls	Limit Controls (1974)	UL	ANSI/UL 353-1974
	Automatic Control Terminology for Heating, Ventilating, Air Conditioning and Refrigeration Equipment	ASHRAE	ASHRAE 85-78
	Primary Safety Controls for Gas- and Oil-Fired Appliances (1985)	UL	ANSI/UL 372-1985
	Temperature-Indicating and Regulating Equipment (1979)	UL	ANSI/UL 873-1981
	Industrial Control Equipment (1984)	UL	ANSI/UL 508-1983
Residential	Temperature-Indicating and Regulating Equipment	CSA	C22.2 No. 24-1981
	Automatic Gas Ignition Systems and Components	AGA	ANSI Z21.20-1985
	Temperature Limit Controls for Electric Baseboard Heaters	NEMA	NEMA DC 10-1983
	Load Control for Use on Central Electric Heating Systems	NEMA	NEMA DC 22-1977 (R1982)
	Quick Connect Terminals	NEMA	ANSI/NEMA DC 2-1982
	Line-Voltage Integrally Mounted Thermostats for Electric Heaters	NEMA	NEMA DC 13-1985
	Low-Voltage Room Thermostats	NEMA	NEMA DC3-1984
	Hot Water Immersion Controls	NEMA	NEMA DC 12-1985
	Warm Air Limit and Fan Controls	NEMA	NEMA DC 4-1975 (R1980)
	Gas Appliance Thermostats (with 1985 addenda)	AGA	ANSI Z21.23-1980
	Gas Appliance Pressure Regulators (with 1982 and 1984 addenda)	AGA	ANSI Z21.18-1981
Coolers			
Air	Methods of Testing Forced Convection and Natural Convection Air Coolers for Refrigeration	ASHRAE	ASHRAE 25-77
	Unit Coolers for Refrigeration	ARI	ARI 420-84
Bottled Beverage	Methods of Testing and Rating Bottled and Canned Beverage Vendors and Coolers	ASHRAE	ASHRAE 32-1982
Drinking Water	Methods of Testing for Rating Drinking Water Coolers with Self-Contained Mechanical Refrigeration Systems	ASHRAE	ASHRAE 18-79
	Drinking Water Coolers (1978)	UL	ANSI/UL 399-1986
	Drinking Fountains and Self-Contained, Mechanically Refrigerated Drinking Water Coolers	ARI ANSI	ARI 1010-84
	Application and Installation of Drinking Water Coolers	ARI	ARI 1020-84
	Drinking Water Coolers and Beverage Dispensers	CSA	C22.2 No. 91-1971
Liquid	Methods of Testing for Rating Liquid Coolers	ASHRAE	ASHRAE 24-78
	Refrigerant-Cooled Liquid Coolers, Remote Type	ARI	ANSI/ARI 480-80
Cooling Towers	Water Cooling Towers (1983)	NFPA	ANSI/NFPA 214-1983
	Atmospheric Water Cooling Equipment Test Code	ASME	ANSI/ASME PTC 23-1986
	Acceptance Test Code for Water Cooling Towers: Mechanical Draft, Natural Draft Fan Assisted Types, and Evaluation of Results. Addendum-1, For Thermal Testing of Wet/Dry Cooling Towers (1986)	CTI	CTI ATC-105
	Acceptance Test Code for Spray Cooling Systems (1985)	CTI	ATC-133
	Certification Standard for Commercial Water Cooling Towers (1986)	CTI	STD-201
	Code for Measurement of Sound from Water Cooling Towers	CTI	ATC-128 (1981)
	Fiberglass-Reinforced Plastic Panels for Application on Industrial Water Cooling Towers	CTI	STD-131 (1983)
Dehumidifiers	Dehumidifiers	AHAM	ANSI/AHAM DH 1-1980
	Dehumidifiers (3r)	CSA	C22.2 No. 92-1971
	Dehumidifiers (1981)	UL	ANSI/UL 474-1982
Desiccants	Method of Testing Desiccants for Refrigerant Drying	ASHRAE	ASHRAE 35-1983
Driers	Liquid-Line Driers	ARI	ARI 710-86
	Methods of Testing Liquid-Line Refrigerant Driers	ASHRAE	ASHRAE 63-86
Electrical	National Electric Code (1984)	ANSI/ NFPA	ANSI/NFPA 70-1987
	Canadian Electrical Code	CSA	C22.1-1982
	Essential Electrical Systems for Health Care Facilities (1977)	NFPA	NFPA 76A

Table 1 Codes and Standards Sponsored by Various Societies and Associations (*continued*)

Subject	Title	Sponsor	Reference
Energy	Compatibility of Electrical Connectors and Wiring (1975)	SAE	SAE AIR 1329
	Manufacturers' Identification of Electrical Connector Contacts, Terminals and Splices (1982)	SAE	SAE AIR 1351 A
	Voltage Ratings for Electrical Power Systems and Equipment	ANSI	ANSI C84.1-1982
	Air Conditioning and Refrigerating Equipment Nameplate Voltages	ARI	ARI 110-80
	Energy Conservation in New Building Design	ASHRAE	ANSI/ASHRAE/IES 90A-1980
	Energy Conservation in Existing Buildings—High-Rise Residential	ASHRAE	ANSI/ASHRAE/IES 100.2-1981
	Energy Conservation in Existing Buildings—Institutional	ASHRAE	ANSI/ASHRAE/IES 100.5-1981
	Energy Conservation in Existing Buildings—Public Assembly	ASHRAE	ANSI/ASHRAE/IES 100.6-1981
	Energy Recovery Equipment and Systems, Air-to-Air (1978)	SMACNA	SMACNA
	Energy Conservation Guidelines (1984)	SMACNA	SMACNA
	Model Energy Code (MEC) (1986)	CABO	BOCA/ICBO/NCSBCS/ SBCCI
	Retrofit of Building Energy Systems and Processes (1982)	SMACNA	SMACNA
Exhaust Systems	Installation of Blower and Exhaust Systems for Dust, Stock, Vapor Removal or Conveying (1983)	NFPA	ANSI/NFPA 91-1983
	Fundamentals Governing the Design and Operation of Local Exhaust Systems	AIHA	ANSI Z9.2-1979
	Practices for Ventilation and Operation of Open Surface Tanks	AIHA	ANSI Z9.1 1977
	Safety Code for Design, Construction, and Ventilation of Spray Finishing Operations (reaffirmed 1971)	ANSI	ANSI Z9.3-1985
	Ventilation and Safe Practices of Abrasives Blasting Operations	ANSI	ANSI Z9.4-1985
	Mechanical Flue-Gas Exhausters	CSA	B255-M81
Expansion Valves	Method of Testing for Capacity Rating of Thermostatic Refrigerant Expansion Valves	ASHRAE	ANSI/ASHRAE 17-1982
	Thermostatic Refrigerant Expansion Valves	ARI	ARI 750-81
Fan Coil Units	Room Fan-Coil Air Conditioners	ARI	ARI 440-84
	Safety Standards for Fan Coil Units and Room Fan Heater Units (1980)	UL	ANSI/UL 883-1986
	Methods of Testing for Rating Room Fan-Coil Air Conditioners	ASHRAE	ASHRAE 79 1984
Fans	Standards Handbook	AMCA	AMCA 99-83
	Electric Fans (1977)	UL	ANSI/UL 507-1976
	Laboratory Methods of Testing Fans for Rating	ASHRAE	ANSI/ASHRAE 51-85 ANSI/AMCA 210-85
	Methods of Testing Dynamic Characteristics of Propeller Fans— Aerodynamically Excited Fan Vibrations and Critical Speeds	ASHRAE	ANSI/ASHRAE 87.1-1983
	Laboratory Methods of Testing Fans for Rating	AMCA	ANSI/AMCA 210-85
	Drive Arrangements for Centrifugal Fans	AMCA	AMCA 99-2404-78
	Designation for Rotation and Discharge of Centrifugal Fans	AMCA	AMCA 99-2406-83
	Motor Positions for Belt or Chain Drive Centrifugal Fans	AMCA	AMCA 99-2407-66
	Drive Arrangements for Tubular Centrifugal Fans	AMCA	AMCA 99-2410-82
	Fans and Blowers	ARI	ARI 670-85
	Inlet Box Positions for Centrifugal Fans	AMCA	AMCA 99-2405-83
	Fans and Ventilators	CSA	C22.2 No. 113-M1984
Ceiling	AC Electric Fans and Regulators	AMCA	ANSI-IEC Pub. 385
Filters	Flow-Capacity Rating and Application of Suction-Line Filters and Filter Driers	ARI	ANSI/ARI 730-86
Fire Dampers	Fire Dampers and Ceiling Dampers (1979)	UL	ANSI/UL 555-1972
Fire Protection	Fire Prevention Code (1976, with 1982 amendments)	AIA	AIA
	Basic/National Fire Prevention Code, 6th ed. (1984, with 1986 amendments)	BOCA	BOCA
	National Fire Codes (8 Volumes, issued annually)	NFPA	NFPA
	Fire Prevention Code (1982)	NFPA	NFPA 1
	Fire Protection Handbook, 15th ed. (1981)	NFPA	NFPA
	Flammable and Combustible Liquids Code (1981)	NFPA	ANSI/NFPA 30-1982
	Heat Responsive Links for Fire Protection Service (1982)	UL	ANSI/UL 33-1982
	Method of Test for Surface Burning Characteristics of Building Materials (1984)	ASTM/ NFPA	ASTM (E 84a)/NFPA 255
	Fire Doors and Windows	NFPA	ANSI/NFPA 80-1986
	Life Safety	NFPA	ANSI/NFPA 101-85
	Standard Fire Prevention Code (1985) with 1986 revisions	SBCCI	SBCCI
	Standard Method of Fire Tests of Door Assemblies	NFPA	NFPA 252
	Uniform Fire Code (1985)	ICBO/ WFCA	ICBO/WFCA

Table 1   Codes and Standards Sponsored by Various Societies and Associations (*continued*)

Subject	Title	Sponsor	Reference
	Uniform Fire Code Standards (1985)	ICBO/ WFCA	ICBO/WFCA
Fireplace Stoves	Fireplace Stoves (1982)	UL	ANSI/UL 737-1978
Flow Capacity	Method of Testing Flow Capacity of Suction Line Filters and Filter Driers	ASHRAE	ASHRAE 78-1985
Freezers			
Household	Household Refrigerators, Combination Refrigerator-Freezers, and Household Freezers	AHAM	ANSI/AHAM HRF 1-1979
	Capacity Measurement and Energy Consumption Test Methods for Household Refrigerators and Combination Refrigerator-Freezers (4a)	CSA	C300 M1984
	Energy Consumption, Freezing Capability, and Capacity Measurement Test Methods for Household Freezers	CSA	C359 M1979
Commercial	Ice Cream Makers (1977)	UL	ANSI/UL 621-1985
	Soda Fountain and Luncheonette Equipment	NSF	NSF-1
	Dispensing Freezers	NSF	NSF-6
	Food Service Refrigerators and Storage Freezers	NSF	NSF-7
Furnaces	Gas-Fired Gravity and Fan Type Direct Vent Wall Furnaces	AGA	ANSI Z21.44-1985
	Gas-Fired Central Furnaces (except Direct Vent Central Furnaces) (with 1985 addenda)	AGA	ANSI Z21.47-1983
	Direct Vent Central Furnaces (with 1980 and 1982 addenda)	AGA	ANSI Z21.64-1985
	Gas-Fired Gravity and Fan Type Floor Furnaces (with 1982 and 1985 addenda)	AGA	ANSI Z21.48-1982
	Gas-Fired Gravity and Fan Type Vented Wall Furnaces (with 1982 and 1985 addenda)	AGA	ANSI Z21.49-1982
	Methods of Testing for Rating Non-Residential Warm Air Heaters	ASHRAE	ASHRAE 45-78
	Methods of Testing for Heating Seasonal Efficiency of Central Furnaces and Boilers	ASHRAE	ANSI/ASHRAE 103-1982
	Installation of Oil Burning Equipment	NFPA	NFPA 31-1983
	Oil-Fired Central Furnaces (1980)	UL	ANSI/UL 727-1986
	Gas-Fired Duct Furnaces (with 1983 and 1985 addenda)	AGA	ANSI Z83.9-1986
	Oil-Fired Floor Furnaces (1976)	UL	ANSI/UL 729-1975
	Oil-Fired Wall Furnaces (1974)	UL	ANSI/UL 730-1986
	Standard Gas Code (1985) with 1986 revisions	SBCCI	SBCCI
	Oil Burning Stoves and Water Heaters (2a)	CSA	B140.3-1962 (R1980)
	Oil-Fired Warm Air Furnaces (8a)	CSA	B140.4-1974
	Oil-Fired Floor Furnaces (4a)	CSA	B140.5-1963 (R1981)
	Installation Code for Solid-Fuel Burning Appliances and Equipment	CSA	CAN3-B365-M84
	Solid Fuel-Fired Appliances for Residential Use	CSA	CAN3-B366.1-M81
	Electric Central Warm-Air Furnaces	CSA	C22.2 No. 23-1980
Heat Exchangers	Standard Methods of Test for Rating the Performance of Heat Recovery Ventilators	CSA	C439-M1985
	Standards of Tubular Exchanger Manufacturers Association, 6th ed. (with 1982 addenda)	TEMA	TEMA
	Sample Problem Book Supplement (1980)	TEMA	TEMA
	Liquid Suction Heat Exchangers	ARI	ANSI/ARI 490-79
	Method of Testing Air-to-Air Heat Exchangers	ASHRAE	ASHRAE 84-78
Heat Pumps	Heat Pumps (1985)	UL	ANSI/UL 559-1985
	Air-Source Unitary Heat Pump Equipment	ARI	ARI 240-81
	Water-Source Heat Pumps	ARI	ARI 320-86
	Ground Water-Source Heat Pumps	ARI	ARI 325-85
	Commercial and Industrial Heat Pump Equipment	ARI	ARI 340-86
	Central Forced-Air Unitary Heat Pumps with or without Electric Resistance Heat	CSA	C22.2 No. 186.1 M1980
	Add-on Heat Pumps	CSA	C22.2 No. 186.2-M1980
	Performance Standard for Unitary Heat Pumps (1a)	CSA	C273.3-M1977
	Installation Requirements for Air-to-Air Heat Pumps (2a)	CSA	C273.5-1980
Heat Recovery	Energy Recovery Equipment and Systems, Air-to-Air (1978)	SMACNA	SMACNA
Heaters	Infrared Application Manual	NEMA	NEMA HE 3-1983
	Desuperheater/Water Heaters	ARI	ANSI/ARI 470-80
	Electric Heaters for Use in Hazardous Locations, Class I, Groups A, B, C, and D, and Class II, Groups E, F, and G (1985)	UL	ANSI/UL 823-1985
	Standards for Closed Feed Water Heaters, 4th ed. (1984)	HEI	HEI
	Oil-Fired Air Heaters and Direct-Fired Heaters (1975)	UL	UL 733
	Oil-Fired Room Heaters (1973)	UL	UL 896
	Solid Fuel-Type Room Heaters (1983)	UL	ANSI/UL 1482-1981
	Gas-Fired Room Heaters, Vol. I, Vented Room Heaters	AGA	ANSI Z21.11.1-1983

Table 1 Codes and Standards Sponsored by Various Societies and Associations (*continued*)

Subject	Title	Sponsor	Reference
	Gas-Fired Room Heaters, Vol. II, Unvented Room Heaters (with 1984 addenda)	AGA	ANSI Z21.11.2-1983
	Gas-Fired Infrared Heaters (with 1984 and 1985 addenda)	AGA	ANSI Z83.6-1982
	Gas-Fired Construction Heaters (with 1981 and 1984 addenda)	AGA	ANSI Z83.7-1974
	Direct Gas-Fired Make-Up Air Heaters	AGA	ANSI Z83.4-1985
	Gas-Fired Unvented Commercial and Industrial Heaters (with 1984 addenda)	AGA	ANSI Z83.16-1982
	Gas-Fired Pool and Spa Heaters (with 1984 and 1985 addenda)	AGA	ANSI Z21.56-1983
	Motor Vehicle Heater Test Procedure (1982)	SAE	SAE J638 June 1982
	Electric Heating Appliances (1978)	UL	ANSI/UL 499-1978
	Gas-Fired Heating Equipment, Commercial-Industrial (1973)	UL	UL 795
	Fuel-Fired Heaters—Air Heating—for Construction and Industrial Machinery (1980)	SAE	SAE J1024 April 1980
	Electric Air Heaters (1980)	UL	ANSI/UL 1025-1980
	Space Heaters for Use with Solid Fuels	CSA	B366.2 M1984
	Unvented Kerosene-Fired Room Heaters and Portable Heaters (1982)	UL	UL 647
Heating	Aircraft Electrical Heating Systems (1965) (reaffirmed 1983)	SAE	SAE AIR 860
	Environmental System Technology (1984)	NEBB	NEBB
	Installation and Operation of Pulverized Fuel Systems	NFPA	ANSI/NFPA 85F-1982
	Manual for Calculating Heat Loss and Heat Gain for Electric Comfort Conditioning	NEMA	NEMA HE 1-1980
	Heat Loss Calculation Guide (1984)	HYD I	IBR H-21
	Installation Guide for Residential Hydronic Heating Systems, 6th ed. (1986)	HYD I	IBR 200
	Advanced Installation Guide for Hydronic Heating Systems, 2nd ed.	HYD I	IBR 250
	Installation Standards for Heating and Air-Conditioning Systems (1984)	SMACNA	SMACNA
	HVAC Systems—Applications, First ed. (1986)	SMACNA	SMACNA
	Electric Baseboard Heating Equipment (1979)	UL	ANSI/UL 1042-1986
	Electric Central Air Heating Equipment (1986)	UL	ANSI/UL 1096-1985
	Portable Industrial Oil-Fired Heaters	CSA	B140.8-1967 (R1980)
	Portable Kerosene-Fired Heaters (15a)	CSA	B140.9.3 M1979
	Oil-Fired Service Water Heaters and Swimming Pool Heaters (7a)	CSA	B140.12-1976
	Automatic Flue-Pipe Dampers for Use with Oil-Fired Appliances	CSA	B140.14-M1979
	Residential Electric Heating	CSA	C273.1-M1980
	Performance Standard for Residential Electric Baseboard Heaters	CSA	C273.2-1971
	Performance Requirements for Electric Heating Line-Voltage Wall Thermostats	CSA	C273.4-M1978
	Electric Air Heaters	CSA	C22.2 No. 46-1981
	Heating and Heater Elements (Replacement Types)	CSA	C22.2 No. 72-M1984 (R1965)
Humidifiers	Humidifiers (1980)	UL	ANSI/UL 998-1985
	Central System Humidifiers	ARI	ARI 610-82
	Self-Contained Humidifiers	ARI	ARI 620-80
	Selection, Installation, and Servicing of Humidifiers	ARI	ARI 630-82
	Appliance Humidifiers	AHAM	ANSI/AHAM HU 1-1980
Ice Makers	Ice Makers (1984)	UL	ANSI/UL 563-1985
	Methods of Testing Automatic Ice Makers	ASHRAE	ASHRAE 29-78
	Automatic Commercial Ice Makers	ARI	ANSI/ARI 810-79
	Split System Automatic Commercial Ice Makers	ARI	ANSI/ARI 815-79
	Ice Storage Bins	ARI	ANSI/ARI 820-79
	Automatic Ice-Making Equipment	NSF	NSF-12
Incinerators	Residential Incinerators (1973)	UL	UL 791
	Incinerators, Waste and Linen Handling Systems	NFPA	ANSI/NFPA 82-1982
	Incinerator Performance	CSA	Z103-1976
Induction Units	Room Air-Induction Units	ARI	ARI 445-81
Industrial Duct	Round Industrial Duct Construction (1977)	SMACNA	SMACNA
	Rectangular Industrial Duct Construction (1980)	SMACNA	SMACNA
Infrared Sensing Devices	Application of Infrared Sensing Devices to the Assessment of Building Heat Loss Characteristics	ASHRAE	ANSI/ASHRAE 101-1981
Insulation	Test Method for Steady-State Thermal Performance of Building Assemblies by Means of a Guarded Hot Box	ASTM	ASTM C236-80
	Test Method for Steady-State Thermal Transmission Properties by Means of the Guarded Hot Plate	ASTM	ASTM C177-85
	Test Method for Steady-State Heat Transfer Properties of Horizontal Pipe Insulations	ASTM	ASTM C335-85
	Test Method for Steady-State Thermal Transmission Properties by Means of the Heat Flow Meter	ASTM	ASTM C518-85

Table 1   Codes and Standards Sponsored by Various Societies and Associations (*continued*)

Subject	Title	Sponsor	Reference
	Mineral Fiber Thermal Building Insulation	CSA	A101 M-1977
Louvers	Test Method for Louvers, Dampers, and Shutters	AMCA	AMCA 500-83
Lubricants	Test Methods for Carbon-Type Composition of Insulating Oils of Petroleum Origin	ASTM	ASTM D2140-86
	Method for Conversion of Kinematic Viscosity to Saybolt Universal Viscosity or to Saybolt Furol Viscosity	ASTM	ASTM D2161-82
	Method for Calculating Viscosity Index from Kinematic Viscosity at 40 and 100 °C	ASTM	ASTM D2270-79
	Method for Estimation of Molecular Weight of Petroleum Oils from Viscosity Measurements	ASTM	ASTM D2502-82
	Test Method for Molecular Weight of Hydrocarbons by Thermoelectric Measurement of Vapor Pressure	ASTM	ASTM D2503-82
	Test Method for Mean Molecular Weight of Mineral Insulating Oils by the Cryoscopic Method	ASTM	ASTM D2224-78 (1983)
	Tests Methods for Pour Point of Petroleum Oils	ASTM	ASTM D97-66 (1985)
	Recommended Practice for Viscosity System for Industrial Fluid Lubricants	ASTM	ASTM D2422-75 (1980)
	Test Method for Dielectric Breakdown Voltage of Insulating Liquids Using Disk Electrodes	ASTM	ASTM D877-84a
	Test Method for Dielectric Breakdown Voltage of Insulating Oils of Petroleum Origin Using VDE Electrodes	ASTM	ASTM D1816-84a
	Method for Separation of Representative Aromatics and Nonaromatics Fractions of High-Boiling Oils by Elution Chromatography	ASTM	ASTM D2549-85
	Method of Testing for Floc Point of Refrigeration Grade Oils	ASHRAE	ANSI/ASHRAE 86-1983
Measurements	Standard Measurements Guide: Section on Temperature Measurements	ASHRAE	ASHRAE 41.1-74
	Standard Measurement Guide: Measurement of Proportion of Oil in Liquid Refrigerants	ASHRAE	ANSI/ASHRAE 41.4-1984
	Standard Measurement Guide: Engineering Analysis of Experimental Data	ASHRAE	ASHRAE 41.5-75
	Standard Method for Measurement of Moist Air Properties	ASHRAE	ANSI/ASHRAE 41.6-1982
	Standard Method for Measurement of Flow of Gas	ASHRAE	ASHRAE 41.7-1984
	Standard Methods of Measurement of Flow of Fluid-Liquids	ASHRAE	ASHRAE 41.8-78
Mobile Homes and Recreational Vehicles	Plumbing System Components for Mobile Homes and Recreational Vehicles	NSF	NSF-24
	Recreational Vehicle Parks	NFPA	NFPA 501C-1983
	Shear Resistance Tests for Ceiling Boards for Mobile Homes (1980)	UL	UL 1296
	Roof Trusses for Mobile Homes (1979)	UL	UL 1298
	Gas Burning Heating Appliances for Mobile Homes and Recreational Vehicles (1965)	UL	UL 307B
	Gas Supply Connectors for Mobile Homes	IAPMO	IAPMO TSC 9-1985
	Liquid-Fuel-Burning Heating Appliances for Mobile Homes and Recreational Vehicles (1978)	UL	ANSI/UL 307A-1978
	Recreational Vehicle Cooking Gas Appliances (with 1982 and 1984 addenda)	AGA	ANSI Z21.57-1982
	Gas-Fired Cooking Appliances for Recreational Vehicles (1976)	UL	UL 1075
	Oil-Fired Warm-Air Heating Appliances for Mobile Housing and Recreational Vehicles (2a)	CSA	B140.10-1974 (R1981)
	Definitions and General Requirements for Mobile Homes	CSA	Z240.0.1-1981
	Definitions and General Safety Requirements for Recreational Vehicles	CSA	Z240.0.2-M1981
	Vehicular Requirements for Mobile Homes	CSA	Z240.1.1-M1982
	Vehicular Requirements for Recreational Vehicles	CSA	Z240.1.2-M1981
	Structural Requirements for Mobile Homes	CSA	Z240.2.1-1979
	Plumbing Requirements for Mobile Homes	CSA	Z240.3.1-M1980
	Plumbing Requirements for Recreational Vehicles	CSA	Z240.3.2-M1980
	Installation Requirements for Gas Burning Appliances in Mobile Homes	CSA	Z240.4.1-M1983
	Installation Requirements for Propane Appliances and Equipment in Recreational Vehicles	CSA	Z240.4.2-M1981
	Oil Requirements for Mobile Housing and Recreational Vehicles	CSA	Z240.5-1971
	Electrical Requirements for Recreational Vehicles	CSA	Z240.6.2/C22.2 No. 148-1982
	Mobile Home Parks	CSA	Z240.7.1-1972
	Recreational Vehicle Parks	CSA	Z240.7.2-1972
	Light Duty Windows	CSA	pZ240.8.1-1979
	Requirements for Load Calculations and Duct Design for Heating and Cooling of Mobile Homes	CSA	pZ240.9.1-1979

Table 1 Codes and Standards Sponsored by Various Societies and Associations (*continued*)

Subject	Title	Sponsor	Reference
Motors and Generators	Motors and Generators	NEMA	ANSI/NEMA MG 1-1978 (R1981)
	Electric Motors (1984)	UL	ANSI/UL 1004-1983
	Energy Efficiency Test Methods for Three-Phase Induction Motors/ Sampling Methods and Marketing Requirements for Energy Efficiency of Three-Phase Induction Motors	CSA	C390.1/C390.2-M1982
Outlets and Inlets	Method of Testing for Rating the Air Flow Performance of Outlets and Inlets	ASHRAE	ASHRAE 70-72
Pipe, Tubing, and Fittings	Power Piping	ASME	ANSI/ASME B31.1-1986
	Plastics Piping Components and Related Materials	NSF	NSF-14
	Scheme for the Identification of Piping Systems	ASME	ANSI A13.1-1981
	National Fuel Gas Code (1984)	NFPA	ANSI/NFPA 54-1984
		AGA	ANSI Z223.1-1984
	Refrigeration Piping	ASME	ANSI B31.5-1983
	Refrigeration Tube Fittings (1977)	SAE	ANSI/SAE J513F
	Specification for Seamless Copper Pipe, Standard Sizes	ASTM	ASTM B42-85
	Specifications for Acrylonitrile-Butadiene-Styrene (ABS) Plastic Pipe, Schedules 40 and 80	ASTM	ASTM D1527-77 (1982)
	Specifications for Poly (Vinyl Chloride) (PVC) Plastic Pipe, Schedules 40, 80, and 120	ASTM	ASTM D1785-83
	Specifications for Polyethylene (PE) Plastic Pipe, Schedule 40	ASTM	ASTM D2104-85
	Standards of the Expansion Joint Manufacturers Association, Inc., 5th ed. (1980 with 1985 addenda)	EJMA	EJMA
	Tube Fittings for Flammable and Combustible Fluids, Refrigeration Service and Marine Use (1978)	UL	UL 109
Plumbing	BOCA/National Plumbing Code, 7th ed. (1987)	BOCA	BOCA
	Standard Plumbing Code (1985) with 1986 revisions	SBCCI	SBCCI
	Uniform Plumbing Code (1985)	IAPMO	IAPMO
Pumps	Circulation System Components for Swimming Pools, Spas, or Hot Tubs	NSF	NSF-50
	Hydraulic Institute Standards, 14th ed. (1983)	HI	HI
	Hydraulic Institute Engineering Data Book, First ed. (1979)	HI	HI
Radiation	Testing and Rating Code for Baseboard Radiation, 6th ed. (1981)	HYD I	IBR
	Testing and Rating Code for Finned-Tube Commercial Radiation (1966)	HYD I	IBR
	Ratings for Baseboard and Fin-tube Radiation	HYD I	IBR
Receivers	Refrigerant Liquid Receivers	ARI	ANSI/ARI 495-85
Refrigerant Containing Components	Refrigerant-Containing Components and Acessories, Non-electrical (1982)	UL	ANSI/UL 207-1986
Refrigerants	Number Designation of Refrigerants	ASHRAE	ANSI/ASHRAE 34-1978
	Refrigeration Oil Description	ASHRAE	ANSI/ASHRAE 99-1981
	Methods of Testing Discharge Line Refrigerant-Oil Separators	ASHRAE	ASHRAE 69-71
	Sealed Glass Tube Method to Test the Chemical Stability of Material for Use Within Refrigerant Systems	ASHRAE	ANSI/ASHRAE 97-1983
Refrigeration	Refrigeration Terms and Definitions	ASHRAE	ANSI/ASHRAE 12-75
	Safety Code for Mechanical Refrigeration	ASHRAE	ANSI/ASHRAE 15-1978
	Refrigerated Medical Equipment (1978)	UL	UL 416
	Commercial Refrigerated Equipment	CSA	C22.2 No. 120-1974 (R1981)
	Equipment, Design and Installation of Ammonia Mechanical Refrigeration Systems	ANSI	ANSI/IIAR2-1984
Steam Jet	Standards for Steam Jet Ejectors, 3rd ed. (1956, 3rd printing, 1980)	HEI	HEI
	Ejectors	ASME	ASME PTC 24-76
Symbols	Graphic Electrical Symbols for Air-Conditioning and Refrigeration Equipment	ARI	ARI 130-82
Transport	Safety Practices for Mechanical Vapor Compression Refrigeration Equipment or Systems Used to Cool Passenger Compartment of Motor Vehicles (1981)	SAE	SAE J639 Oct. 1981
	Mechanical Refrigeration Installations on Shipboard	ASHRAE	ANSI/ASHRAE 26-1985
	Mechanical Transport Refrigeration Units	ARI	ARI 1110-83
	General Requirements for Application of Vapor Cycle Refrigeration Systems for Aircraft (1973) (reaffirmed 1983)	SAE	SAE ARP 731A
Refrigerators	Methods of Testing Open Refrigerators for Food Stores	ASHRAE	ANSI/ASHRAE 72-1983
Commercial	Commercial Refrigerators and Freezers (1985)	UL	ANSI/UL 471-1984
	Food Service Refrigerators and Storage Freezers	NSF	NSF 7
	Food Carts	NSF	NSF 59
	Refrigerating Units (1976)	UL	UL 427
	Refrigeration Unit Coolers (1980)	UL	ANSI/UL 412-1984
	Soda Fountain and Luncheonette Equipment	NSF	NSF 1

Table 1   Codes and Standards Sponsored by Various Societies and Associations (*continued*)

Subject	Title	Sponsor	Reference
Household	Food Service Equipment	NSF	NSF-2
	Refrigerators Using Gas Fuel (with 1984 addenda)	AGA	ANSI Z21.19-1983
	Household Refrigerators, Combination Refrigerator Freezers and Household Freezers	AHAM	ANSI/AHAM HRF 1-1979
Refrigerators and Freezers, Household	Household Refrigerators and Freezers (1983)	UL	ANSI/UL 250-1984
	Household Refrigerators, Combination Refrigerator-Freezers, and Household Freezers	AHAM	ANSI/AHAM HRF 1-1979
Roof Ventilators	Power Ventilators (1984)	UL	ANSI/UL 705-1984
Solar Collectors	Methods of Testing to Determine the Thermal Performance of Solar Collectors	ASHRAE	ANSI/ASHRAE 93-77
	Methods of Testing to Determine the Thermal Performance of Unglazed Flat-Plate Liquid-Type Solar Collectors	ASHRAE	ANSI/ASHRAE 96-1980
Solar-Optical Properties	Method of Measuring Solar-Optical Properties of Materials	ASHRAE	ASHRAE 74-73
Solenoid Valves	Solenoid Valves for Liquid Flow Use with Volatile Refrigerants and Water	ARI	ARI 760-80
Sound Measurement	Measurement of Sound from Boiler Units, Bottom-Supported Shop or Field Erected, 3rd ed.	ABMA	ABMA-1973
	Sound Rating of Outdoor Unitary Equipment	ARI	ARI 270-84
	Sound Rating of Non-Ducted Indoor Air-Conditioning Equipment	ARI	ARI 350-86
	Sound Rating of Large Outdoor Refrigerating and Air-Conditioning Equipment	ARI	ARI 370-86
	Procedural Standards for Measuring Sound and Vibration	NEBB	NEBB-1977
	Sound and Vibration in Environmental Systems	NEBB	NEBB-1977
	Application of Sound Rated Outdoor Unitary Equipment	ARI	ARI 275-84
	Method of Measuring Machinery Sound within Equipment Rooms	ARI	ARI 575-79
	Method of Testing In-Duct Sound Power Measurement Procedure for Fans	ASHRAE	ASHRAE 68-78
	Specification for Sound Level Meters (reaffirmed 1976)	ASA	ANSI S1.4-1983 ANSI S1.4A-1985
	Method for the Calibration of Microphones (reaffirmed 1976)	ASA	ANSI S1.10-1966 (R1986)
	Reverberant Room Method for Sound Testing of Fans	AMCA	AMCA 300-85
	Sound Rating of Room Air Conditioners	AHAM	AHAM RAC-2SR
	Guidelines for the Use of Sound Power Standards and for the Preparation of Noise Test Codes (reaffirmed 1985)	ASA	ASA 10 ANSI S1.30-1979 (R1985)
Space Heaters	Electric Air Heaters (1980)	UL	ANSI/UL 1025-1980
Testing and Balancing	Procedural Standards for Testing, Adjusting, Balancing of Environmental Systems, 4th ed. (1983)	NEBB	NEBB-1983
	HVAC Systems—Testing, Adjusting and Balancing (1983)	SMACNA	SMACNA
Terminals, Wiring	Equipment Wiring Terminals for Use with Aluminum and/or Copper Conductors	UL	UL 486E
Thermal Storage	Methods of Testing Thermal Storage Devices Based on Thermal Performance	ASHRAE	ANSI/ASHRAE 94-77
	Methods of Testing Thermal Storage Devices with Electric Input and Thermal Output Based on Thermal Performance	ASHRAE	ANSI/ASHRAE 94.2-1981
Turbines	Steam Turbines for Mechanical Drive Service	NEMA	NEMA SM 23-1979
Unit Heaters	Oil-Fired Unit Heaters (1975)	UL	ANSI/UL 731-1974
	Gas Unit Heaters	AGA	ANSI Z83.8-1985
Valves	Methods of Testing Nonelectric, Nonpneumatic Thermostatic Radiator Valves	ASHRAE	ASHRAE 102-1983
	Automatic Gas Valves for Gas Appliances (with 1977 and 1981 addenda)	AGA	ANSI Z21.21-1974
	Manually Operated Gas Valves (with 1981 and 1984 addenda)	AGA	ANSI Z21.15-1979
	Relief Valves and Automatic Gas Shutoff Devices for Hot Water Supply Systems (with 1983 and 1984 addenda)	AGA	ANSI Z21.22-1979
	Refrigerant Access Valves and Hose Connectors	ARI	ARI 720-81
	Refrigerant Pressure Regulating Valves	ARI	ARI 770-84
	Solenoid Valves for Use with Volatile Refrigerants	ARI	ARI 760-80
Vending Machines	Refrigerated Vending Machines (1979)	UL	ANSI/UL 541-1979
	Methods of Testing Pre-Mix and Post-Mix Soft Drink Vending and Dispensing Equipment	ASHRAE	ASHRAE 91-76
	Sanitation Ordinance and Code for Vending of Foods and Beverages (1965)	USDA	USDA 546
	Vending Machines for Food and Beverages	NSF	NSF-25
Vent Dampers	Electrically Operated Automatic Vent Damper Devices for Use with Gas-Fired Appliances	AGA	ANSI Z21.66-1985
	Mechanically Actuated Automatic Vent Damper Devices for Use with Gas-Fired Appliances	AGA	ANSI Z21.67-1985

Table 1   Codes and Standards Sponsored by Various Societies and Associations (*continued*)

Subject	Title	Sponsor	Reference
	Thermally Actuated Automatic Vent Damper Devices for Use with Gas-Fired Appliances	AGA	ANSI Z21.68-1985
Venting	Vent or Chimney Connector Dampers for Oil-Fired Appliances (1982)	UL	ANSI/UL 17-1983
	Guide for Explosion Venting (1978)	NFPA	ANSI/NFPA 68-1978
	Guide for Smoke and Heat Venting (1982)	NFPA	ANSI/NFPA 204M-1985
	Type L Low-Temperature Venting Systems (1986)	UL	ANSI/UL 641-1985
	Draft Hoods (with 1983 addenda)	AGA	ANSI Z21.12-1981
	Draft Equipment (1973)	UL	UL 378
	Gas Vents (1986)	UL	ANSI/UL 441-1985
	National Fuel Gas Code	AGA	ANSI Z223.1-1984
	Guide for Steel Stack Design and Construction (1983)	SMACNA	SMACNA
Ventilation	Vapor Removal from Cooking Equipment (1984)	NFPA	ANSI/NFPA 96
	Parking Structures (1979); Repair Garages (1979)	NFPA	ANSI/NFPA 88A; 88B
	Ventilation for Acceptable Indoor Air Quality	ASHRAE	ASHRAE 62-1981
	Industrial Ventilation	ACGIH	ACHIH
Water Heaters	Gas Water Heaters, Vol. I, Automatic Storage Water Heaters with Inputs of 75,000 Btu per Hour or Less (with 1985 addenda)	AGA	ANSI Z21.10.1-1984
	Gas Water Heaters, Vol. III, Circulating Tank, Instantaneous and Large Automatic Storage Water Heaters (with 1985 addenda)	AGA	ANSI Z21.10.3-1984
	Household Electric Storage Tank Water Heaters (1983)	UL	ANSI/UL 174-1982
	Oil-Fired Storage Tank Water Heaters (1974)	UL	ANSI/UL 732-1975
	Electric Booster and Commercial Storage Tank Water Heaters (1982)	UL	ANSI/UL 1453-1982
	Hot Water Generating and Heat Recovery Equipment	NSF	NSF-5
	Construction and Test of Electric Storage Tank Water Heaters	CSA	C22.2 No. 110 M-1981
	Oil Burning Stoves and Water Heaters	CSA	B140.3-1962 (R1980)
	Oil-Fired Service Water Heaters and Swimming Pool Heaters	CSA	B140.12-1976
	Standards on Performance of Electric Storage Tank Water Heaters	CSA	C191-series-M1983
	Methods of Testing to Determine the Thermal Performance of Solar Domestic Water Heating Systems	ASHRAE	ANSI/ASHRAE 95-1981
Woodburning Appliances	Installation Code for Solid Fuel Burning Appliances and Equipment	CSA	CAN3-B365-M84
	Method of Testing for Performance Rating of Woodburning Appliances	ASHRAE	ANSI/ASHRAE 106-1984
	Solid Fuel-Fired Appliances for Residential Use	CSA	CAN3-B366.1-M81
	Space Heaters for Use with Solid Fuels	CSA	B366.2-M1984

ABBREVIATION AND ADDRESSES
The Codes and Standards Listed in Table 1 Can Be Obtained from the Organizations Listed in the *Sponsor* Column.

ABMA   American Boiler Manufacturers Association, Ste. 160, 950 N. Glebe Rd., Arlington, VA 22203
ACCA   Air Conditioning Contractors of America, 1228 17th St., NW, Washington, DC 20036 (formerly the National Environmental Systems Contractors Association)
ACGIH   American Conference of Governmental Industrial Hygienists, 6500 Glenway Ave., Bldg. D-7, Cincinnati, OH 45211
ADC   Air Diffusion Council, 230 N. Michigan Ave., Suite 1200, Chicago, IL 60601
AFS   American Foundrymen's Society, Golf and Wolf Rds., Des Plaines, IL 60016
AGA   American Gas Association, 1515 Wilson Blvd., Arlington, VA 22209
AHAM   Association of Home Appliance Manufacturers, 20 N. Wacker Dr., Chicago, IL 60606
AIA   American Insurance Association, 85 John St., New York, NY 10038
AIHA   American Industrial Hygiene Association, 475 Wolf Ledges Pkwy., Akron, OH 44311-1087
AMCA   Air Movement and Control Association, 30 W. University Dr., Arlington Heights, IL 60004
ANSI   American National Standards Institute, 1430 Broadway, New York, NY 10018
ARI   Air-Conditioning and Refrigeration Institute, 1501 Wilson Blvd., 6th Fl., Arlington, VA 22209
ASA   Acoustical Society of America, 335 E. 45 St., New York, NY 10017
ASHRAE   American Society of Heating, Refrigerating and Air-Conditioning Engineers, Inc. 1791 Tullie Circle, N.E., Atlanta, GA 30329
ASME   American Society of Mechanical Engineers, 345 E. 47th St., New York, NY 10017
ASTM   American Society for Testing and Materials, 1916 Race St., Philadelphia, PA 19103
BOCA   Building Officials and Code Administrators International, Inc., 4501 W. Flossmoor Rd., Country Club Hills, IL 60477-5795
BSI   British Standards Institution, 2 Park St., London, W1A 2BS, England
CABO   Council of American Building Officials, 5203 Leesburg Pike, Ste. 708, Falls Church, VA 22041
CAGI   Compressed Air and Gas Institute, Ste. 1230, Keith Bldg., 1621 Euclid Ave., Cleveland, OH 44115
CSA   Canadian Standards Association, 178 Rexdale Blvd., Rexdale, Ont. M9W 1R3, Canada
CTI   Cooling Tower Institute, P.O. Box 73383, Houston, TX 77273
EJMA   Expansion Joint Manufacturers Association, Inc., 25 N. Broadway, Tarrytown, NY 10591
HEI   Heat Exchange Institute, Ste. 1230, Keith Bldg., 1621 Euclid Ave., Cleveland, OH 44115
HI   Hydraulic Institute, 712 Lakewood Ctr. N., 14600 Detroit Ave., Cleveland, OH 44107
HYD I   Hydronics Institute, 35 Russo Pl., Berkeley Heights, NJ 07922
IAPMO   International Association of Plumbing and Mechanical Officials, 5032 Alhambra Ave., Los Angeles, CA 90032-3490

ABBREVIATION AND ADDRESSES (*continued*)

IBR   Institute of Boiler and Radiator Manufacturers, superseded by Hydronics Institute
ICBO   International Conference of Building Officials, 5360 S. Workman Mill Rd., Whittier, CA 90601
MCAA   Mechanical Contractors Association of America, 5530 Wisconsin Ave., Chevy Chase, MD 20815
NCSBCS   National Conference of States on Building Codes and Standards, 481 Carlisle Dr., Herndon, VA 22070
NEBB   National Environmental Balancing Bureau, 8224 Old Courthouse Rd., Vienna, VA 22180
NEMA   National Electrical Manufacturers Association, 2101 L St., N.W., Ste. 300, Washington, DC 20037
NFPA   National Fire Protection Association, Batterymarch Park, Quincy, MA 02269
NSF   National Sanitation Foundation, Box 1468, Ann Arbor, MI 48106
SAE   Society of Automotive Engineers, 400 Commonwealth Dr., Warrendale, PA 15096
SBCCI   Southern Building Code Congress International, Inc., 900 Montclair Rd., Birmingham, AL 35213
SMACNA   Sheet Metal and Air Conditioning Contractors' National Association, 8224 Old Courthouse Rd., Vienna, VA 22180
TEMA   Tubular Exchanger Manufacturers Association, Inc., 25 N. Broadway, Tarrytown, NY 10591
UL   Underwriters Laboratories Inc., 333 Pfingsten Rd., Northbrook, IL 60062
WFCA   Western Fire Chiefs Association, Inc., 5360 S. Workman Mill Rd., Whittier, CA 90601

ASHRAE HANDBOOK
ERRATA

The errata section mainly includes technical errors. Occasional typographical errors and nonstandard symbol labels will be corrected in future volumes.

The authors and editor will be grateful to readers who notify them of other technical errors. Please send corrections to:

Handbook Editor
ASHRAE
1791 Tullie Circle, NE
Atlanta, GA 30329

1983 EQUIPMENT

p. 3.1, RH column. The definition of η_t and η_s should read:

η_t = mechanical efficiency of a fan (or fan total efficiency): the ratio of power output to power input ($\eta_t = W_o/W_i$).

η_s = static efficiency of a fan: the mechanical efficiency multiplied by the ratio of static pressure to fan total pressure ($\eta_s = P_s/P_t$) η_t. Point of rating may be any point on the fan performance curve; for each case, the particular point on the curve must be specifically defined.

p. 3.5, Table 2.

H_1 and H_2 in equations (1c), (2c), and (3c) should be changed to W_1 and W_2, respectively.

p. 3.6, Eq. (1) should read:

$$\Delta P_2 = \Delta P_1 = (Q_2/Q_1)^2$$

p. 3.7, Example in paragraph 3, LH column should read:

For 12,712 cfm

$$\Delta P_2 = 1.2 \left(\frac{12,712}{21,186}\right)^2 = 0.43 \text{ in. water gauge}$$

p. 3.7, Figure 10. Volume flow rate is in L/s × 1000.

p. 12.3, RH column. The paragraph after paragraph number 4 should read:

Chapter 32 of this volume has further information on motors and motor protection.

p. 12.21, Eq. (14) should read:

$$W_i = \mu_i c_\mu/g \tag{14}$$

where g = gravitational constant

p. 12.21, second line of text above Figure 22 should read:

the impeller with magnitude $c^2/2g$.

p. 32.2, First sentence, second paragraph, RH column should read:

The *National Electrical Code,* developed by the National Fire Protection Association, contains the minimum requirements to make electrical installations and equipment safe.

p. 34.1, Table 1.

Change the coefficient, y, in the equation to c.

p. 44.3, Eq. (1) should be:

$$\text{COP}_{\text{cooling}} = \frac{T_L}{T_H - T_L} \tag{1}$$

1985 FUNDAMENTALS
(I-P Edition)

p. 1.4, First paragraph. Value for R should be 1545.3 ft · lb/lb mol · °R.

p. 1.10, RH column. Line 6 of the paragraph below *Example 1* should read:

is $\Delta S_o = -250/500 = -0.5$ Btu/°R, giving a change in entropy

p. 3.13, Table 5. Equation below heading, **IV. With Air,** should read:

Gr · Pr = 1.6 · 10⁶ L³ ΔT

p. 3.15, Table 6. Values for c in Eqs. (9), (10), and (14) are listed in I-P units in Table 7, p. 2.16, of the 1981 FUNDAMENTALS Volume.

p. 12.1, LH column, change second sentence to read:

Malodors can signal poor or unsafe conditions (i.e. spoiled food or other toxic substances).

p. 15.8, Table 9. Delete raised dots on the left of the numerical values.

p. 18.9, Figures 19 and 20. Add 0.05 to the Thermal Conductivity values shown on the vertical axis of the graph.

p. 23.3, Eq. (9). The variable R_s should be added to the denominator.

p. 23.15, Table 5A. U-values for 1-¾ in. solid core flush door with wood and metal storm doors should be reversed.

p. 24.24. T. Kusuda is the author for references 16 and 17. C.C. Boughner is the author for reference 18.

p. 25.2, Table 12. Equations in the section titled, **Infiltration and ventilation air,** should read:

Sensible $q_s = 0.019 \, \dot{V} \cdot \Delta t$

Latent $q_l = 79.5 \, \dot{V} \cdot \Delta W$

p. 25.8. Example 6 does not follow the calculation method shown in Chapter 22 and will be reworked for the 1989 Volume.

p. 26.5, Table 1. References in the section titled "Solar" should list Tables 29, 34, and 37 from Chapter 37 instead of those listed.

p. 26.7, RH column. Example 3 correction factors should read:

The correction factors to be applied to the tabulated CLTDs are:

1. Correction factor for outside conditions:

   Average temperature $= 90 - \dfrac{20}{2} = 80$ F.

   Correction $= -5$ deg F.

2. Correction factor for inside design dry-bulb temperature:

   Correction $= 0$ deg F.

3. Latitude-month correction (Table 9):

   Roof $= -1$
   S. Wall $= +1$
   W. Wall $= 0.0$

4. Color correction:

   Dark rook K $= 1.0$
   Medium walls K $= 0.83$

5. Total correction

   Roof CLTD $= 1.0 \, (\text{CLTD} -1) + (0) + (-5)$
                 $= \text{CLTD} -6$

   S. Wall CLTD $= 0.83 \, (\text{CLTD} + 1) + (0) + (-5)$
                 $= 0.83 \, (\text{CLTD} + 1) - 5$

   W. Wall CLTD $= 0.83 \, (\text{CLTD} - 0) + (0) + (-5)$
                 $= 0.83 \, (\text{CLTD}) - 5$

p. 26.11, Table 8. Some corrections are shown on page E.5 of the 1986 REFRIGERATION Volume. The following are additional corrections:

The R-value for 1-in. insulation should be 3.32.

The thickness, L, of 2-in. heavyweight concrete (Code No. B2 and shown as l.w. in the 1985 Volume) should be 0.167 and the R-value should be 0.167.

The R-value of 6-in. heavyweight concrete (Code No. C13) should be 0.5.

p. 26.13, RH column. Summary of *Example 3* should read:

Roof

Time	Table 5 CLTD	CLTD Corrected	$q = U \cdot A \cdot \text{CLTD}$ Btu/h
1200	25	19	6954
1400	35	29	10,614
1600	43	37	13,542

South Wall

Time	Table 7 CLTD	CLTD Corrected	$q = U \cdot A \cdot \text{CLTD}$ Btu/h
1200	11	5.0	570
1400	12	5.8	666
1600	15	8.3	952

West Wall

Time			
1200	11	4.1	198
1400	20	11.5	564
1600	39	27.4	1330

p. 26.14, RH column. First sentence should read:

The total load through fenestration is the sum of the conduction heat gain, Eq. (9), and the solar heat gain, Eq. (12).

p. 26.34, Eq. (36) should read:

$$F_c = 1 - 0.02 \, K_T$$

p. 27.2, Table 1. Replace with the table shown in the 1981 Volume as follows:

Table 1   Extraterrestrial Solar Radiation Intensity and Related Data for Twenty-First Day of Each Month, Base Year 1964

	I_0 Btu/h·ft²	Equation of Time, min.	Declination, deg	A Btu/h·ft²	B (Dimensionless Ratios)	C
Jan	442.7	−11.2	−20.0	390	0.142	0.058
Feb	439.1	−13.9	−10.8	385	0.144	0.060
Mar	432.5	−7.5	0.0	376	0.156	0.071
Apr	425.3	+1.1	+11.6	360	0.180	0.097
May	418.9	+3.3	+20.0	350	0.196	0.121
June	415.5	−1.4	+23.45	345	0.205	0.134
July	415.9	−6.2	+20.6	344	0.207	0.136
Aug	420.0	−2.4	+12.3	351	0.201	0.122
Sep	426.5	+7.5	0.0	365	0.177	0.092
Oct	433.6	+15.4	−10.5	378	0.160	0.073
Nov	440.2	+13.8	−19.8	387	0.149	0.063
Dec	443.6	+1.6	−23.45	391	0.142	0.057

p. 27.3, LH column, third paragraph. Delete sentence referring to *Hydrographic Office Bulletin No. 214.*

p. 28.6, RH column. Change reference 46 to reference 48 in paragraph under Seasonal Efficiency.

p. 28.11, Table 6. Column **K** heading should read **Resist. Heat Input (J/3413).**

p. 33.10, Table 3. Duct leakage is given in cfm/100 ft² surface area.

p. 33.31, Table B-2-4. Values are given for $\theta = 8, 10, 14, 20, 30, 45,$ and $\geqslant 60°$, not 34°.

p. 33.39, Table B-5-2. Add the following K-values:

A/A	K	A/A	K
0	1.0	0.8	0.30
0.2	0.85	0.9	0.18
0.4	0.68	1.0	0
0.6	0.50		

p. 33.44, Table B-6-23. Replace figure with the following:

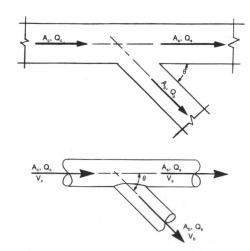

1985 FUNDAMENTALS

(SI Edition)

p. 3.15, Table 6. Values for c in Eqs. (9), (10), and (14) are listed in I-P units in Table 7, p. 2.16, of the 1981 FUNDAMENTALS Volume.

p. 4.6, Table 2. Delete 0.102 from Eq. (1).

p. 6.9, RH column. Text from Eq. (35) should read:

$$t_d = -35.957 - 1.8726\alpha + 1.1689\alpha^2 \qquad (35)$$

and for temperatures from -60 to $0\,°C$:

$$t_d = -60.45 + 7.0322\alpha + 0.3700\alpha^2 \qquad (36)$$

In both Eq. (35) and (36), t_d is the dew point temperature in °C, and $\alpha = \log_e(p_w)$, where p_w is the water vapor partial pressure in Pa.

p. 12.1, LH column, change second sentence to read:
Malodors can signal poor or unsafe conditions (i.e. spoiled food or other toxic substances).

p. 15.8, Table 9. Delete raised dots on the left of the numerical values.

p. 22.11, LH column. First sentence in paragraph for **Commercial Building Components** should read:

Standards of the National Association of Architectural Metal Manufacturers call for maximum leakage per unit area of 0.3 $L/(s \cdot m^2)$ at a pressure difference of 75 Pa through curtain wall specimens, exclusive of leakage through operable windows.

p. 22.15, Eq. (25). The exponent is -1 for K in the variable, A.

p. 23.3, Eq. (9). The variable R_s should be added to the denominator.

p. 23.15, Table 5A. U-values for 44 mm solid core flush door with wood and metal storm doors should be reversed. Also **Door Thickness** heading should include a superscript, d.

p. 24.19, Table 2. The elevations shown in column 4 are in metres.

p. 24.24. T. Kusuda is the author for references 16 and 17. C.C. Boughner is the author for reference 18.

p. 25.9, Table 5. Degree day values should be 4129, 2972, and 1639, respectively.

p. 26.5, Table 1. References in the section titled "Solar" should list Tables 29, 34, and 37 from Chapter 37 instead of those listed.

p. 26.14, RH column. First sentence should read:

The total load through fenestration is the sum of the conduction heat gain, Eq. (9), and the solar heat gain, Eq. (12).

p. 27.3, LH column, third paragraph. Delete sentence referring to *Hydrographic Office Bulletin No. 214*.

p. 27.14, Table 16. First Glass Temperature value is 17°C.

p. 28.6, RH column. Change reference 46 to reference 48 in paragraph under Seasonal Efficiency.

p. 32.15, Table 5. Velocity over Gross Area is in m/s.

p. 33.10, Table 3. Duct leakage is given in L/s per 100 m^2 surface area.

p. 33.22, RH column, unnumbered table. Value shown for Design No. 2 unbalance should be 1271, not 271.

p. 33.22, Table 9. Heading of the third column from left of table should be **Pressure Drop, Pa/m.**

p. 33.31, Table B-2-4. Values are given for $\theta = 8$, 10, 14, 20, 30, 45, and $\geq 60°$, not 34°.

p. 33.39, Table B-5-2. Add the following K-values:

A/A	K	A/A	K
0	1.0	0.8	0.30
0.2	0.85	0.9	0.18
0.4	0.68	1.0	0
0.6	0.50		

p. 33.44, Table B-6-23. Replace figure with the following:

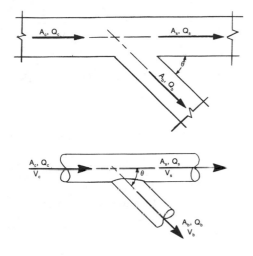

1986 REFRIGERATION

(I-P Edition)

p. 3.7, Table 7.
Last two columns for Steel Lines are reversed and should be switched.

p. 5.2, Table 2 should read:

Table 2   Comparative Ranking of Heat Transfer Factors at 7 fps[a]

Brine	Heat Transfer Factor	Brine	Heat Transfer Factor
Propylene Glycol	1.000	Methanol	2.307
Ethylene Glycol	1.981	Sodium Chloride	2.722
R-11	2.088	Calcium Chloride	2.761
Trichlorethylene	2.107	Methylene Chloride	2.854

p. 38.20, Text starting with Eq. (13) should read:

$$W_{gc} = \frac{\gamma + 1}{\gamma - 1}\,\alpha\left(\frac{R}{8\pi MT}\right)^{0.5} P\,(T_2 - T_1) \qquad (13)$$

where

$$\alpha = (\alpha_1\alpha_2)/[\alpha_2 + \alpha_1(1 - \alpha_2)(A_1/A_2)] \qquad (14)$$

W_{gc} = net energy transfer, Btu/h per ft^2 of inner surface
γ = c_p/c_v, the specific heat ratio of the gas, assumed constant
R = molar gas constant
P = pressure, mm Hg
M = molecular weight of the gas
T = absolute temperature at the point where P is measured, °R
α = overall accommodation coefficient
A = area, where subscripts 1 and 2 refer to the inner and outer surfaces, respectively

This expression reduces to

$$W_{gc} = C\alpha P\,(T_2 - T_1) \qquad (15)$$

where

$$C = (\gamma + 1)R^{0.5}/[(\gamma - 1)(8\pi MT)^{0.5}] \qquad (16)$$

Table 4 gives the value of C when the assumed temperature at the pressure gauge is 80 F.

Table 4   Gas Conduction Equation Constant, C
(Derived from Ref. 35)

Gas	T_2 and T_1, °R	C
N_2	$\leqslant$ 720	28.0
O_2	$\leqslant$ 540	26.0
H_2	540 and 139 or 540 and 162	93.0
H_2	139 and 36	70.1
He	any	49.3

1986 REFRIGERATION
(SI Edition)

p. 3.1, LH column, line 1 of the second item in the second paragraph should read:

2. The next column in each table is headed T = 2 °C. This

p. 5.2, Table 2 should read:

Table 2   Comparative Ranking of Heat Transfer Factors at 2.1 m/s[a]

Brine	Heat Transfer Factor	Brine	Heat Transfer Factor
Propylene Glycol	1.000	Methanol	2.307
Ethylene Glycol	1.981	Sodium Chloride	2.722
R-11	2.088	Calcium Chloride	2.761
Trichlorethylene	2.107	Methylene Chloride	2.854

p. 38.20, Text starting with Eq. (13) should read:

$$W_{gc} = \frac{\gamma + 1}{\gamma - 1} \alpha \left(\frac{R}{8\pi MT}\right)^{0.5} P \, (T_2 - T_1) \quad (13)$$

where

$$\alpha = (\alpha_1 \alpha_2)/[\alpha_2 + \alpha_1 \, (1 - \alpha_2)(A_1/A_2)] \quad (14)$$

W_{gc} = net energy transfer, W/m^2 of inner surface
γ = c_p/c_v, the specific heat ratio of the gas, assumed constant
R = molar gas constant
P = pressure, Pa
M = molecular weight of the gas
T = absolute temperature at the point where P is measured, K
α = overall accommodation coefficient
A = area, where subscripts 1 and 2 refer to the inner and outer surfaces, respectively

This expression reduces to

$$W_{gc} = C\alpha P \, (T_2 - T_1) \quad (15)$$

where

$$C = (\gamma + 1)R^{0.5}/[(\gamma - 1)(8\pi MT)^{0.5}] \quad (16)$$

Table 4 gives the value of C when the assumed temperature at the pressure gauge is 300 K.

Table 4   Gas Conduction Equation Constant, C
(Derived from Ref. 35)

Gas	T_2 and T_1, °R	C
N_2	$\leqslant$ 400	1.1925
O_2	$\leqslant$ 300	1.1074
H_2	300 and 77 or 300 and 90	3.9605
H_2	77 and 20	2.9854
He	any	2.1003

COMPOSITE INDEX TO TECHNICAL DATA
ASHRAE HANDBOOK SERIES

This index covers the technical data sections of *the four current* HANDBOOK volumes published by ASHRAE. Listings from each volume are identified by a code letter preceding the page number:

H = 1987 HVAC
R = 1986 Refrigeration
F = 1985 Fundamentals
E = 1983 Equipment

For example, the first listing, **"Abbreviations,"** is followed by secondary listings, "symbols," "graphical, F36.5-11" and so forth. This indicates that abbreviations for graphical symbols can be found on pages 5 through 11 of Chapter 36 in the 1985 FUNDAMENTALS Volume. Note that the code numbers include the chapter number followed by a decimal point and the page number(s) within the chapter. This index is updated in each Handbook volume.

Practical Applications
for Cooling Load Calculations

Six experienced engineers—each a specialist in his field—present *application-oriented information* for the common problems encountered by designers, contractors and architects.

Each expert panelist in the round table design conference discusses the source and limitations of the cooling load estimate he's presenting for a six story office building with a center atrium. In order to make the discussions applicable to many areas, the building is located in several geographic locations.

Practical information is presented on **cooling load calculations, the effect of field construction practices on thermal performance, insulation requirements, weather data considerations, solar load, window mullion heat gain** and **the effect of system design on indoor air quality.**

The video package includes a booklet containing an introduction; presenter biographies; an abstract for each presentation, including artwork; and the most frequently asked questions and answers.

Produced: 1987   **Length:** 1 hr, 50 min
Code: VDOTP2
Format:
VHS or Beta
List: $210.00   **Member:** $140.00
PAL
List: $250.00   **Member:** $155.00

Videotape may be rented (purchase option available) for 10 business days. Prepaid rental fee is $50.00 plus $4.00 shipping and handling. Distribution on rentals is limited to the U.S. Call (404) 636-8400 for rental details.

------------------------------------ If you do not wish to cut page, photocopy form below and mail to ASHRAE. ------------------------------------

Yes, send me the Cooling Load Calculations videotape.

( ) VHS   ( ) Beta

( ) List: $210.00   ( ) Member: $140.00

Name _____

Street _____
(do not use a post office box)

City _____

State/Prov. _____ Zip _____

Country _____ Phone (   ) _____

Mail to: **ASHRAE Publication Sales**
1791 Tullie Circle, NE
Atlanta, GA 30329

Phone credit card orders to: ASHRAE Publication Sales
404-636-8400.

( ) PAL

( ) List: $250.00   ( ) Member: $155.00

Member No. [ ][ ][ ][ ][ ][ ][ ][ ]

Payment Options:

( ) Check enclosed (U.S. funds)

Charge: ( ) VISA   ( ) AMEX
( ) MasterCard

Card No.
[ ][ ][ ][ ][ ][ ][ ][ ][ ][ ][ ][ ][ ][ ][ ][ ]

Signature (required) _____

Purchase order does not constitute prepayment.
Money back guarantee if not satisfied.
All prices subject to change without notice.

Prices effective April 1, 1987. Subject to change without notice.